INTERNATIONAL DICTIONARY
of
METALLURGY - MINERALOGY
GEOLOGY

Al Dott. Ing. ORONZIO DE NORA

con grande stima

To ORONZIO DE NORA

With great esteem

INTERNATIONAL DICTIONARY
of
METALLURGY - MINERALOGY
GEOLOGY

Mining and Oil Industries

in four languages
ENGLISH - FRENCH
GERMAN - ITALIAN

compiled by
Angelo Cagnacci Schwicker

TECHNOPRINT INTERNATIONAL
MILANO

In association with
McGRAW-HILL BOOK CO.
New York   Toronto   London   Sydney

THE McGRAW-HILL
LIBRARY OF
INTERNATIONAL
DICTIONARIES

With the special collaboration of:

Mr. Tito CACCIATORE, *Engineer,* E. N. I., Scuola « E. Mattei » di Studi Superiori

Sugli Idrocarburi - Milan

Mr. J. A. CHRISTENSEN, *Engineer,* Consultant in Oil and Mining Industries - Rome

Mr. Louis GIRAUD, *Engineer,* Consultant in Oil and Mining Industries TOTAL - Milan

Mr. Antoine LE DUC, *Engineer,* Consultant in Metallurgy - Paris

Mr. Guido LOMBARDO, *Professor of Geology,* Istituto Tecnico - Ceccano (Roma)

Mr. Giuseppe MARCHETTI, *Engineer,* Consultant in Metallurgy - Düsseldorf

Mrs. Irène MONLEONE, *Director,* UTA (Unione Traduttori Associati) - Milan

Mrs. Hélène SABATINI, *Professor,* Centre Français d'Etudes et d'Information - Milan

Mr. Friedrich SCHWARZ, *Engineer,* Consultant in Metallurgy - Frankfurt a/M

Chief editor: Albertina MALISANI, *Journalist,* Milan

INTRODUCTION

In an age in which technology, the study of languages and business relations have developed rapidly, this specialized technical dictionary in the four main E.C.M. (European Common Market) languages has been conceived in the hope of contributing to the improvement of relationships among men and to the cause of peace, progress and culture. The work includes terms inherent to sciences, techniques and industries closely related to each other, such as metallurgy, mineralogy, geology, mining and oil industries and their products.

It is dedicated to technicians, scholars and particularly to translators, who, in the course of their work, are compelled to consult various dictionaries at times too general or too specific even though of indisputable value.

The concept of grouping together similar sciences and technologies allows for rapid, precise and concise consultation, avoiding the loss of time and the considerable expense of purchasing texts which are either sold out or no longer up-to-date.

English has been adopted as the basic language since it is commonly used by scholars and technicians the world over in their meetings and reports. French, German and Italian follow. The most common terms, easily traceable in any good general dictionary, have been omitted to reduce the size and the cost of the publication.

Works of famous lexicographers have been studied, including more than fifty dictionaries and glossaries on each single subject, and new terms have been taken from catalogues, price lists and monographs of the main Italian and foreign industries in the hope of making this book as complete as possible. The terms are listed in English alphabetical order and are numbered in the correct sequence. The second part contains an index in each language for simple and rapid consultation.

To facilitate the task for translators, more than two thousand synonyms have been inserted. When the same term in English has different meanings, it is repeated under a different number.

The spelling and translation of each term have been carefully checked by mother-tongue translators and technicians specialized in the various fields contained herein.

Thanks are extended to the more than one hundred collaborators, whose names are too many to list, for their valuable contributions to the achievement of this work.

THE AUTHOR

CONTENTS

METALLURGY, FOUNDRY, IRON-WORKING

Metals and alloys; crystalline structure, constitution and properties, intermetallic phases; extraction from ores, refining, alloying, shaping; iron and steel products; pipes and pipings; raw materials, flux coverings, sands and refractories; metal castings, moulds, casting methods and practices; melting, melting material, furnaces and converters, cupolas; metal patterns, pattern making and plates, core boxes, prints, dies, pressure die casting; moulding, stoving, baking and assembly; cores and core making; finishing, electroplating, dipping, heat and surface treatments; cold and hot working, annealing, hammering, forging, extrusion, rolling, piercing, drawing, power pressing, foundry defects and metal failures, inspection, testing and handling, metallurgical analysis, powder metallurgy; structural steel frameworks, steel constructions, steel utilization, prefabrication; x-rays in metallurgy, metallography.

MINING AND OIL INDUSTRIES

Drilling methods and practice, drilling equipment, installations and tools; mine techniques, bore holes, preparations for drilling, coring and fishing, hand and directional drilling, rotary and cable drilling; surface and underground mining, ventilation, prospecting, exploration and surveying, examination of minerals; drifting, tamping, priming; well servicing, hauling and conveying, pipelines, casings and tubings, well heads; oil fields and wells, exploitation and reservoir engineering, flush drillings, and muds, cementing, flowing and gas lifting, drilling bits and drill pipes; waters, sands and emulsions; well pumps and pumping, tanks and separators, oil and mineral production, hydrocarbon compounds, distillation, cracking, reforming, polymerization, special treatments; petroleum products, distillates and residues, natural and refinery gas; safety appliances and regulations.

GEOLOGY-MINERALOGY

Physical geology, petrology, stratigraphy, palaeontology, endodynamic-esodynamic-tectonic geology, hydrogeology, mining geology, hydrocarbon geology; geological cycles, facies, metallomorphism, orogenesis, petrotectonics, foldings, faults, layers, profiles; surveying, sedimentalogy.

PREFACE

A une époque où la technique, l'étude des langues et les rapports commerciaux se sont développés vertingineusement, ce dictionnaire technique spécialisé, dans les quatre langues principales du M.E.C., a été conçu dans l'espoir de contribuer à améliorer les relations entre les hommes, pour la cause de la paix, du progrés et de la culture.

L'ouvrage conprend les termes se rapportant aux secteurs de la science, de la technique et des industries, étroitement liés entre eux comme la métallurgie, la minéralogie, la géologie et les industries extractives avec les produits qui s'y rapportent.

Cet ouvrage est adressé aux techniciens, aux chercheurs et en particulier aux traducteurs qui pour leur travail, sont souvent obligés de consulter plusieurs dictionnaires, parfois trop généraux ou trop spécifiques, même s'ils sont bien conçus.

Le groupement des sciences et des techniques similaires permet donc, dans les limites du possible, une consultation rapide, précise, évitant d'inutiles pertes de temps et l'engagement de frais importants pour l'achat de textes parfois épuisés ou non mis à jour.

L'anglais, communément employé par les chercheurs et les techniciens du monde entier dans leurs congrès et leurs rapports, a été adopté comme langue de base. Suivent le français, l'allemand et l'italien, selon l'ordre alphabétique anglais.

Les termes les plus communs, que l'on peut trouver facilement dans n'importe quel dictionnaire générique ont été évités pour ne pas surcharger la publication.

Les oeuvres de remarquables auteurs de dictionnaires ont été étudiées, examinant plus de 50 vocabulaires et glossaires de chaque matière, trouvant des termes nouveaux dans des catalogues, bordereaux et monographies des principales industries italiennes et étrangères du secteur, afin de rendre la publication la plus actuelle possible.

Les termes sont énumérés par ordre alphabétique anglais et numérotés: à la fin de l'ouvrage, dans le deuxième volume, et pour chaque langue, existe un index que l'on peut consulter facilement et rapidement.

Pour faciliter le travail des traducteurs plus de 2000 synonymes ont été insérés. Quand un même terme anglais a différentes significations, il est répété aux numéros suivants.

L'orthographe et la traduction de chaque terme ont été scrupuleusement soignées par des techniciens des différentes branches et des experts traducteurs.

Mes remerciements vont aux cent et plus collaborateurs, dont il serait trop long d'énumérer les noms, qui ont donné leur apport précieux et désintéressé à la réalisation de cet ouvrage.

L'AUTEUR

TABLE DES MATIERES

METALLURGIE, FONDERIE, SIDERURGIE

Métaux et alliages, structure cristalline, constitution et propriétés, phases intermétalliques, extraction des métaux; finissage, préparation des alliages, façonnage; produits sidérurgiques, tuyaux et tubages; matières premières, flux-fondants-couvertes, sables et réfractaires; moulages, moules, systèmes et techniques de coulée; fusion, matériels de fusion, fours et convertisseurs, cubilots; moulage, étuvage, cuisson et remmoulage; noyaux, exécution des noyaux, finition, galvanostégie, traitements superficiels, thermiques, par immersion; façonnage à froid et à chaud, recuit, martelage, forgeage, extrudage, laminage, poinçonnage, emboutissage; anomalies et défauts de fonderie, contrôles, essais, manutention, analyses métallurgiques, métallurgie des poudres; ossatures et constructions en acier, utilisation de l'acier, préfabrication, rayons Röntigen en métallurgie.

GEOLOGIE-MINERALOGIE

Géologie physique, pétrologie, stratigraphie, paléontologie, géologie endodynamique-exodynamique et tectonique, hydrogéologie, géologie minière, géologie des hydrocarbures, cycles géologiques, faciès, métallomorphisme, orogénèse, pétrotectonique, plissements, failles, coupes, couches, sédimentalogie, levés.

INDUSTRIES EXTRACTIVES

Systèmes et techniques de forage, équipement et installation de forage, sondages et préparation des sondages, carottage et repêchage, forages normaux et dirigés, forage à la corde et rotatif; exploitation à ciel ouvert et en souterain, ventilation, prospection, exploration et relèvements, examen des minerais; extraction, bourrage, amorçage et entretien des puits, roulage et transport; oléoducs, tubages et colonnes d'extraction, têtes de tubage, d'injection et d'éruption, brides et raccords; champs et puits de pétrole, technique d'exploitation, forages avec circulation et boues, éruption, exploitation à gaz comprimé, trépans, outils et tiges de forage; eaux, sables et émulsions; pompes et pompage de puits, réservoirs et séparateurs, production d'huiles et de minerais, hydrocarbures et leurs composés, distillation, cracking, réformation, polymérisation, traitements spéciaux; produits pétrolifères, distillats et résidus, gaz naturels et de raffinerie; dispositifs et mesures de sécurité.

VORWORT

In einer Zeit, wo die Technik, das Sprachenstudium und die Handelsbeziehungen sich überaus schnell entwickelt haben, ist dieses technische Speziallexikon in den vier Sprachen der E.W.G. in der Hoffnung entstanden, zur Verbesserung der menschlichen Beziehungen, zur Sache des Friedens, des Fortscritts und der Kultur beizutragen.

Das Werk umfasst die Fachausdrücke für die eng miteinander verbundenen Gebiete der Wissenschaft und Technik, wie die Metallurgie, Mineralogie, Geologie und die Erdölindustrie und den Bergbau mit den entsprechenden Erzeugnissen.

Es richtet sich an die Techniker, Wissenschaftler und besonders an die Übersetzer, die bei ihrer Arbeit oft dazu gezwungen sind, verschiedene technische Lexika zu benutzen, die, wenn auch wertvoll, oft zu allgemein oder zu spezialisiert sind. Das Prinzip, die Naturwissenschaften und die angrenzenden technischen Sachgebiete gemeinsam zu behandeln, gestattet ein rasches und im Rahmen des Möglichen auch zuverlässiges Nachschlagen; unnötige Zeitverluste und nicht unbeträchtliche Kosten für den Kauf manchmal vergriffener oder veralteter Texte werden so vermieden.

Das Englische wurde zur sprachlichen Grundlage gemacht, da es allgemein von Wissenschaftlern und Technikern bei ihren Kongressen und Berichten benutzt wird. Es folgen, das Französische, das Deutsche und das Italienische, gemäss der Reihenfolge des englischen Alphabets.

Es wurde versucht, die gebräuchlichsten Ausdrücke zu vermeiden, die in jedem allgemeinen Lexikon leicht aufzufinden sind, um das Werk nicht aufzuschwellen.

Es wurden die Werke berühmter Lexika-Autoren studiert, über 50 Lexika und Glossare der einzelnen Sachgebiete durchgesehen und neue Ausdrücke aus Katalogen. Listen und Monographien der wichtigsten italienischen und ausländischen Industrien entnommen, um das Werk so zeitnahe und modern wie möglich zu machen.

Die Fachausdrücke sind in der Reihenfolge des englischen Alphabets aufgeführt und der Reihenfolge nach numeriert. Am Schluss, im zweiten Bande, folgt für jede Sprache ein Index zum leichten und schnellen Nachschlagen.

Um die Arbeit der Übersetzer zu erleichtern, wurden über 2000 Synonyme eingefügt. Hat ein englischer Ausdruck verschiedene Bedeutungen, wird er in den folgenden Nummern wiederholt.

Mit Hilfe von Fachleuten auf den einzelnen Gebieten und von technischen Übersetzern der jeweiligen Muttersprache wurden Orthographie und Übersetzung jedes einzelnen Fachausdrucks gewissenhaft ermittelt.

Herzlich danke ich den über hundert Mitarbeitern, deren sämtliche Namen aufzuzählen zu weit führen wurde, für ihrer uneigennützigen und wertvollen Beitrag zur Verwirklichung dieses Werkes.

DER VERFASSER

INHALTSÜBERSICHT

METALLURGIE, GIESSEREI, EISENHÜTTENKUNDE

Metalle und Legierungen, Kristallstruktur, Gefüge und Eigenschaften, intermetallische Phasen, Metallgewinnung aus Mineralien, Weiterverarbeitung, Legierung, Formerei; Eisen-und Stahlerzeugnisse; Röhren und Rohrleitungen, Rohstoffe, Schmelz-Fluss-und Abdeckmittel, Sande, feuerfeste Stoffe; Metallgiessen, Formen, Formverfahren; Schmelzen und Schmelzeinrichtungen, Ofen und Konverter, Kupolöfen; Modelle und Modellbau, Modellplatten, Kernkästen, Kernmarken, Formen, Kokillenguss, Schleuderguss, Druckguss; Formerei, Trocknen, Brennen und Zulegen; Kerne und Herstellung der Kerne, Elektroplattierung, Tauchverfahren, Wärme-und Oberflächenbehandlung, Kalt-und Warmbearbeitung, Glühen, Hammerschmieden, Schmieden, Strangpressen, Walzen, Stanzen, Recken, Spritzgiessen; Gussfehler, Werkstoffprüfung, Kontrollen und Materialbewegung, metallurgische Analysen, Pulvermetallurgie, Stahlskelettbau, Stahlbau, Stahlverwendung, Vorfertigung, Röntgenstrahlen in der Metallurgie.

GEOLOGIE-MINERALOGIE

Physikalische Geologie, Gesteinskunde, Stratigraphie, Paläontologie, endodynamishe-exodynamische-tektonische Geologie, Hydrogeologie, Bergbaugeologie, Kohlenwasserstoff-Geologie, geologische Zeitalter, Fazies, Metallomorphismus, Orogenese, Petrotektonik, Faltungen, Verwerfung, Flöze und Schichtung, Aufnahmen, Sedimentalogie.

FÖRDERINDUSTRIEN UND ÖLFELDER

Bohrverfahren und Bohrpraktik, Bohreinrichtungen, Bohranlagen und Bohrwerkzeuge, Bohrungen und Bohrlöcher, Bohrvorbereitungen, Kernen und Fangen, Handbohren, Richtbohren, Rotarybohren, Seilbohren, Tagebau und Tiefbau, Grubenlüftung, Schürfen, Untersuchungen von Mineralien, Grubenförderung, Feststampfung; Auffahren, Wartung und Behandlung der Bohrungen, Fahrzeuge, Ölleitungen, Verrohrung und Zubehör, Bohrstangen und Zubehör, Leitungsroher und Verbindungsstücke; Ölfelder und Ölbrunnen, Abbau-und Lagerstätten-Technik, Ölförderung, Zementierung, Eruptiv-Produktion, Gaslift; Bohrmeissel und Gestängerohre; Wasser, Sande und Emulsionen; Pumpen, Behälter und Abscheider; Öl-und Erzproduktion; Kohlenstoffe und Kohlenstoffverbindungen, Destillation, Crackverfahren, Reforming, Polymerisation, besondere Behandlungen, Benzin und Ölprodukte, Destillate und Rückstände, Erdgas, Raffinerie-Produkte, Sicherheitsvorrichtungen und Vorschriften.

INTRODUZIONE

In un'epoca in cui la tecnica, lo studio delle lingue e i rapporti commerciali si sono vertiginosamente sviluppati, questo dizionario tecnico specializzato nelle quattro lingue del M.E.C., é stato concepito nella speranza de contribuire al miglioramento delle relazioni fra gli uomini, alla causa della pace, del progresso e della cultura.

L'opera comprende i termini riguardanti scienze, technice e industrie strettamente connesse fra loro, come la metallurgia, la mineralogia, la geologia e le industrie estrattive e petrolifere con i relativi prodotti.

Essa é diretta ai tecnici, agli studiosi ed in particolare ai traduttori, che nel loro lavoro sono spesso costretti a consultare diversi dizionari, talvolta troppo generici o troppo specifici, anche se pregevoli. Il criterio de raggruppare scienze e tecniche affini, permette quindi una consultazione rapida e, nei limiti del possibile, precisa, evitando inutili perdite de tempo e spese non indifferenti per l'acquisto di testi spesso esauriti o non aggiornati.

Come lingua base é stato adottato l'inglese, comunemente usato dagli studiosi e dai tecnici di tutto il mondo nei loro congressi e rapporti; seguono quindi il francese, il tedesco e l'italiano nell'ordine alfabetico inglese.

Si é cercato di evitare i termini più comuni, facilmente reperibili in qualsiasi dizionario generico, per non inflazionare la pubblicazione.

Sono state studiate le opere d'insigni dizionaristi, esaminando oltre cinquanta dizionari e glossari delle singole materie, attingendo nuovi termini dai cataloghi, listini e monografie delle principali industrie italiane e straniere del settore, per rendere la pubblicazione il più possiblile completa.

I termini sono elencati in ordine alfabetico inglese e numerati successivamente; alla fine del testo, nel secondo volume, segue un indice di facile e rapida consultazione, per ogni singola lingua.

Per agevolare il compito dei traduttori sono stati inseriti oltre duemila sinonimi. Quando lo stesso termine inglese ha diversi significati, viene ripetuto sotto i numeri successivi.

L'ortografia e la traduzione di ogni termine sono state scrupolosamente curate dai tecnici delle singole materie e da esperti traduttori di madre-lingua.

Si ringraziano vivamente gli oltre cento collaboratori, i cui nomi sarebbe troppo lungo elencare, per il loro disinteressato e prezioso contributo alla realizzazione dell'opera.

L'AUTORE

INDICE DELLE MATERIE

METALLURGIA, FONDERIA, SIDERURGIA

Metalli e leghe; struttura cristallina, costituzione e proprietà dei metalli, fasi intermetalliche, estrazioni di metalli dai minerali, finitura, preparazione delle leghe, formatura; prodotti siderurgici, tubi e tubazioni; materie prime, fondenti, terre e sabbie, refrattari; getti e forme, sistemi e tecniche di colata; fusione, materiale per fusioni, altiforni e convertitori, cubilotti; modelli, preparazione dei modelli, placche-modello, casse d'anima, portate, conchiglie, pressofusione; formatura, essiccazione, cottura, ramolaggio; anime e loro preparazione; finitura, galvanostegia, trattamenti termici, superficiali e per immersione; lavorazione a freddo e a caldo, ricottura, martellatura e stiratura, forgiatura, estrusione, laminazione, punzonatura, imbutitura, stampaggio; difetti di fonderia, controlli, trasporto dei materiali, analisi metallurgica, metallurgia delle polveri; ossature metalliche, costruzioni in acciaio, utilizzazione dell'acciaio, prefabbricazione, raggi X in metallurgia, metallografia.

GEOLOGIA-MINERALOGIA

Geologia fisica, petrologia, stratigrafia, paleontologia; geologia endodinamica, esodinamica e tettonica, idrologia, geologia mineraria, geologia degli idrocarburi; cicli geologici, facies, metallomorfismo, orogenesi, petrotettonica, pieghe, faglie, strati, profili, rilevamenti, sedimentalogia.

INDUSTRIE ESTRATTIVE

Sistemi e tecniche di perforazione, impianti e utensili di perforazione, fori e preparativi di trivellazione, carotaggio e recupero, perforazioni normali e direzionali, perforazioni alla corda e rotative; scavi a cielo aperto e in galleria, ventilazione, prospezione, esplorazione e rilevamenti, esame dei minerali; estrazione, costipamento, avvimento e manutenzione dei pozzi, trasporti; oleodotti, colonne d'estrazione e intubaggi, teste di tubaggio, d'iniezione e d'eruzione, flangie e manicotti; campi e pozzi petroliferi; ingegneria e tecnica d'estrazione, perforazione a circolazione e fanghi, cementazione, eruzione spontanea, estrazione a gas compresso, trivelle e tubi di perforazione; acque, sabbie ed emulsioni; pompe e pompaggio di pozzi, serbatoi e separatori, produzione di oli minerali, composti degli idrocarburi; distillazione, piroscissione, «reforming», polimerizzazione, trattamenti speciali, prodotti petroliferi, distillati e residui, gas naturali e di raffineria, dispositivi e misure di sicurezza.

LIST OF ABBREVIATIONS

	ENGLISH	FRENCH	GERMAN	ITALIAN
m	masculine	masculin	Maskulinum	maschile
f	feminine	féminin	Femininum	femminile
n	neuter	neutre	Neutrum	neutro
pl	plural	pluriel	Plural	plurale
s	see	voir	siehe	vedi
S	synonym	synonyme	Synonym	sinonimo
o	metallurgy	métallurgie	Metallurgie	metallurgia
—	{ geol. miner. { mining	géol. minér. ind. minière	Geol. Miner. Bergbau	geol. miner. ind. miner.
∧	oil industry	ind. pétrolifère	Erdölindustrie	ind. petrolifera

	English	French	German	Italian
− 1	**abacus**	batée *f*	Waschschüssel *f*, Waschtrog *m*	batea *f* (per lavaggio minerali)
° 1a	**abating**	réduction *f* de trempe	Härtungsminderung *f*	riduzione *f* di tempera
− 2	**abichite**	abichite *f*	Abicht(e) *m*	abichite *f*
− 3	**ablation**	ablation *f*	Ablation *f*	ablazione *f*
− 4	**abnormal contact**	contact *m* anormal	abnormaler Kontakt *m*	contatto *m* anormale
° 4a	**abnormal steel**	acier *m* anormal	abnormaler Stahl *m*	acciaio *m* anormale
− 5	**above ground, in open cut**	à ciel ouvert, au jour	am Tage, im Tagebau oberirdisch	a ciel aperto, a giorno
° 5a	**to abrade**	ronger par frottement	abreiben, abschleifen	abradere, molare
° 6	**abrasion**	abrasion *f*, meulage	Abrieb *m*, Abrasion, Schleifen	abrasione *f*
° 7	**abrasive, abrading agent**	abrasif *m*	Schärfmittel *n*, Schleifmittel *n*	abrasivo *m*
° 8	**abrasive, abrading**	abrasif	abrasiv	abrasivo
° 9	**abrasive belt**	bande *f* abrasive	Reibband *n*	nastro *m* abrasivo
° 9a	**abrasive hardness**	dureté *f* d'abrasion	Abschleifhärte *f*	durezza *f* di abrasione
− 10	**absarokite**	absarokite *f*	Absarokit *m*	absarochite *f*, absarokite *f*
° 11	**to absorb the moisture**	absorber l'humidité	die Feuchtigkeit aufsaugen	assorbire l'umidità
− 12	**absorber**	absorbeur *m*	Absorptionsgefäss *n*	assorbitore *m*
˄ 13	**absorber**	colonne *f* d'absorption	Absorptionsturm *m*	colonna *f* d'assorbimento
° 14	**absorption**	absorption *f*	Absorption *f*, Aufnahmefähigkeit *f*	assorbimento *m*
° 15	**absorption apparatus**	appareil *m* d'absorption	Absorptionsapparat *m*	assorbitore *m*
° 16	**absorption bottle**	flacon *m* d'absorption	Absorptionsflasche *f*	bottiglia *f* d'assorbimento
° 17	**absorption coil**	serpentin *m* pour l'absorption	Absorptionsschlange *f*	serpentino *m* d'assorbimento

absorption flask, *s. absorption bottle*

		English	French	German	Italian
°	18	**absorption of gases**	absorption *f* des gaz	Gasaufnahme *f*	assorbimento *m* di gas
°	19	**absorption of heat by evaporation**	absorption *f* de chaleur par vaporisation	Bindung *f* von Wärme durch Verdampfung	assorbimento *m* di calore per vaporizzazione
°	20	**absorption of hydrogen by metals**	absorption *f* de l'hydrogène par les métaux	Absorption *f* des Wasserstoffes durch Metalle	assorbimento *m* dell'idrogeno nei metalli
°	21	**absorption of oxygen**	absorption *f* d'oxygène	Sauerstoff-absorption *f*	assorbimento *m* d'ossigeno
—	22	**absorption of oxygen by coal**	absorption d'oxygène par la houille	Sauerstoff-aufnahme *f* durch Kohle	assorbimento di ossigeno nel carbone
°	23	**absorption pipette**	pipette *f* d'absorption	Absorptionspi-pette *f*	pipetta *f* d'assor-bimento (o gaso-metrica)
^	24	**absorption plant**	installation *f* de récupération des gaz	Absorptionsanla-ge *f*	impianto di recupe-ro dei gas
°	25	**absorption tube**	tube *m* à dessécher	Absorptionsröhre *f*	tubo *m* d'assorbi-mento
^	26	**to abstract**	distiller, extraire	destillieren, absondern	distillare, estrarre togliere, eliminare
—	27	**to abut**	abouter	stumpf aneinanderfügen	appoggiarsi, attestarsi
—	28	**abut against**	disparition *f* brusque d'une couche	Absetzen *n* einer Schicht	sparizione *f* improvvi-sa d'uno strato
—	29	**abutment**	aboutement *m*, contrefort *m*	Strebe *f*, Strebepfeiler *m*	attestatura, con-trafforte, trave di sostegno, puntello
—	30	**abyssal area**	région *f* abyssale	abyssische Region *f*	regione *f* abissale
—	31	**abyssal deposits** *pl.*	dépôts *m pl.* abyssaux	abyssische Ablagerungen *f pl.*	depositi *m pl.* abissali
—	32	**abyssal rocks, deep-seated rocks**	roches *f pl.* abyssales	abyssische Gesteine *n pl.*	rocce *f pl.* abissali rocce *f pl.* plutoniche
—	33	**acadialite**	accadialite *f*	Acadialith *n*	acadialite *f*
—	34	**acadian**	acadien *m*	Akadisches *n*	acadiano *m*

	English	French	German	Italian
— 35	acanthicone	acanthicone	grüner Schörl *m*	acanticonite *f*
— 36	acanthite	acanthite *f*	Akanthit *m*	acantite *f*
° 37	accelerated aging test	essai *m* de vieillissement rapide	Schnellaushärtungsversuch *m*	prova di invecchiamento rapido
° 38	acceleration	accélération *f*	Beschleunigung *f*	accelerazione *f*
° 39	acceleration of draught	accélération *f* de tirage	Zugbeschleunigung *f*	accelerazione *f* del tiraggio
° 40	accelerometer	accéléromètre *m*	Beschleunigungsmesser *m*	accelerometro *m*
° 41	acceptance test (or trial)	essai *m* d'acceptation	Abnahmeprüfung *f*	prova *f* di collaudo
° 42	accessible hearth	sole *f* accessible	zugängliche Sohle *f*	suola *f* accessibile
° 43	accessible shaft	cuve *f* accessible	zugänglicher Schacht *m*	tino *m* accessibile
— 44	accessory minerals	minerais *m. pl.* accessoires	zusätzliche Gemengeteile *n pl.*	minerali *m pl.* accessori

accidental by-products, *s. occasional by-products*

	English	French	German	Italian
— 44a	accidental xenolith	enclave *f* énallogène *m*	exogener Einschluss *m*	inclusione *f* esogena
— 45	acclivity, acclivous	acclivité *f*, montée *f*, montant, en talus	Abhang *m*, Steigung *f*, abschüssig	declivio *m*, pendio *m*, china *f*, erto, ripido, scosceso
° 46	accommodation	adaptation *f*	Anpassung *f*	adattamento *m*
— 47	accompanying mineral	minerai *m* associé	Begleitmineral *n*	minerale *m* associato
— 48	accordant unconformity	transgressivité *f* concordante	unterbrochene gleichförmige Auflagerung *f*	trasgressione *f* concordante
° 49	according to calculation	conforme aux calculs	rechnungsmässig	secondo i calcoli, conforme ai calcoli
° 50	according to UNI specifications	conforme aux normes UNI	nach UNI-Normen	secondo le norme UNI
° 51	accordion doors, folding doors	portes *f pl.* repliantes	Falttüren *f pl.*	porte *f pl.* a libro

		English	French	German	Italian
	52	to accumulate, to store	accumuler	stapeln	ammucchiare, immagazzinare
o	53	accumulated heat, stored heat	chaleur f accumulée	aufgespeicherte Wärme f	calore m immagazzinato
o	54	accumulator, storage battery	accumulateur m	Sammler m, Akkumulator m	accumulatore m, batteria f
o	55	accumulator building battery house	bâtiment m des accumulateurs	Sammlergebäude n	edificio m degli accumulatori
o	56	accumulator metal	métal m pour accumulateurs	Akkumulatorenmetall n	metallo m per accumulatori
^	57	accumulator still	réservoir m de décantation	Klärbehälter m	serbatoio m di decantazione
o	58	aceration, steeling	aciérage, aciération f	Verstählung f	acciaiatura f
—	59	acerdese, manganite	acerdèse f, manganite f	Braunmanganerz n, Manganit n	acerdese, manganite f
o	60	acetate of barium	acétate m de baryte	Bariumacetat n	acetato m di bario
o	61	acetate of potassium	acétate m de potasse	essigsaures Kali n Kaliumacetat n	acetato m potassico
o	62	acetic acid	acide m acétique	Essigsäure f	acido m acetico
o	63	acetylene Bunsen burner	brûleur m de Bunsen à l'acétylène	Azetylen-Bunsenbrenner m	becco m Bunsen ad acetilene
o	64	acetylene flame	flamme f acétylénique	Azetylenflamme f	fiamma f acetilenica
o	65	acetylene gas	gaz f d'acétylène	Azetylengas n	gas m d'acetilene
o	66	acetylene lamp	lampe f à acétylène	Karbidlampe f	lampada f ad acetilene
o	67	acetylene welding, oxy-acetylene welding	soudure f oxyacétylénique	autogenes Schweissen n	saldatura f ossiacetilenica
—	68	achroite	achroïte f	Achroit m	acroite f
o	69	achromatic	achromatique	achromatisch	acromatico
o	70	acicular	aciculaire	nadelförmig	aciculare
o	71	acicular cast iron	fonte f bainitique , fonte f aciculaire	Gusseisen n mit Zwischenstufengefüge, Nadelgusseisen n	ghisa f aciculare

	English	French	German	Italian
— 72	acicular habitus	faciès *m* aciculaire	stengeliger Habitus *m*	facies *f* aciculare
° 72a	acicular iron	fonte *f* aciculaire	Nadelgusseisen *n*	ghisa *f* aciculare
— 73	aciculite	aciculite *f*	Nadelerz *n*	aciculite *f*
74	acid	acide *m*	Säure *f*	acido *m*
° 75	acid bath, pickle	bain *m* acide	Säurebad *n*	bagno *m* acido
° 76	acid Bessemer steel	acier *m* Bessemer	Bessemerstahl *m*	acciaio *m* Bessemer
° 77	acid blowcase, acid egg	monte-jus *m*	Druckbirne *f*	contenitore *m* d'acido
° 78	acid bottom	sole *f* acide	Säureherd *m*	suola *f* acida
° 79	acid brittleness, acid embrittlement	fragilité *f* de décapage	Beizsprödigkeit *f*	fragilità *f* di/da decapaggio
° 80	acid-heat test	essai *m* de réchauffement par acides	Säureerhitzungsprobe *f*	prova di riscaldimento con acido
° 81	acid ion	ion *m* acide	saures Ion *n*	ione *m* acido
° 82	acid lining	garnissage *m* acide	saure Verkleidung *f*	rivestimento acido
° 83	acid openhearth furnace	four Martin acide	saurer Martinofen *m*	forno *m* Martin acido
° 84	acid open-hearth steel acid Siemens-Martin steel	acier Martin (par le procédé) acide, acier sur sole acide	saurer Siemens-Martinstahl *m*	acciaio Martin acido, acciaio *m* di suola acida
° 85	acid process	procédé *m* acide	saures Verfahren *n*	procedimento *m* acido
° 86	acidproof	résistant aux acides	säurebeständig	resistente all'acido
° 87	acid proof box	boîte *f* à l'épreuve des acides	säurefester Kasten *m*	scatola *f* (o cassa *f*) a prova d'acido
° 88	acid-proof steel	acier *m* inattaquable aux acides, acier résistant aux acides	säurebeständiger Stahl *m*	acciaio *m* inattaccabile agli acidi
° 89	acid-proof sulphuric putty	mastic *m* sulfo-asphaltique résistant aux acides	Schwefelzement *m*	mastice *m* solfo-asfaltico
° 90	acid refractory	réfractaire *m* acide	saurer feuerfester Stein *m*	refrattario *m* acido

		English	French	German	Italian
°	90a	acid-resisting steel	acier *m* résistant aux acides	säurebeständiger Stahl *m*	acciaio *n* inattacabile agli acidi
—	91	acid rocks *pl.* acidic rocks *pl.*	roches *f pl.* acides	saure Gesteine *n pl.*	rocce *f pl.* acide (o persiliciche)
°	92	acid room	dépôt *m* des acides	Säureraum *m*	deposito *m* degli acidi
°	92a	acid Siemens-Martin steel	acier *m* Martin	saurer Siemens-Martinstahl *m*	acciaio *m* Martin acido
°	93	acid slag	laitier *m* acide	saure Schlacke *f*	scoria *f* acida, loppa *f* acida, loppa *f* filante
—	94	acid sludge	boues *f pl.* acides	saurer Schlamm *m*	fango acido, melma acida
°	95	acid steel	acier *m* acide, acier *m* Bessemer	saurer Stahl *m*	acciaio *m* acido, acciaio *m* Bessemer
°	96	acidic oxide	oxyde *m* acide	saures Oxyd *n*	ossido *m* acido
		acidic rocks, *s. acid rocks*			
—	97	acidiferous	acidifère	säurehaltig	acidifero
—	98	acidifiable	acidifiable	säurefähig	acidificabile
—	99	acidifier	acidifiant *m*	Säurebildner *m*	acidificante *m*
—	100	acidizing (of wells)	traitement *m* à l'acide	Säurebehandlung *f*	acidificazione *f* dei pozzi
°	101	acidulated water	eau *f* acidulée	angesäuertes Wasser *n*	acqua *f* acidula
°	102	acierable	aciérable	verstählbar	acciaiabile
°	103	acierage, steeling	aciération *f*, aciérage	Verstählung *f*, Ausstählung *f*	acciaiatura *f*
°	104	to acierate, to steel	aciérer	verstählen	acciaiare, trasformare in acciaio
—	105	acinose	granuleux	körnig	granuloso
—	106	aclinal	aclinique	aklinisch	aclinale, aclinico
—	107	acmite, aegirite	acmite *f*, aegyrite *f*	Akmit *m*, Aegirit *m*	acmite *f*, egirina *f*
		acorn nut, *s. cap nut*			
°	108	acoustic insulation of rockwool	isolation *f* phonique en laine de roche	Schallisolierung *f* aus Steinwolle	isolamento *m* acustico in lana di roccia

	English	French	German	Italian
− 109	actinium	actinium *m*	Actinium *n*	attinio *m*
− 110	actinolite	actinolite *f*	Aktinolith *m*	attinolite *f*
	actinote, *s. actinolite*			
− 111	action of ice	action *f* des glaces	(Ein)wirkung *f* des Eises	azione *f* dei ghiacci
− 112	action of running water	action *f* des eaux courantes	(Ein)wirkung *f* des strömenden Wassers	azione *f* delle acque correnti
− 113	action of snow	action *f* de la neige	Schnee(ein)wirkung *f*	azione *f* della neve
− 114	action of the blast	allure *f* de la soufflerie	Spiel *n* des Gebläses	andamento *m* (o funzionamento) della soffieria
° 115	activated carbon	charbon *m* activé	aktivierte Kohle *f*	carbone attivato (o attivo)
° 115a	activator	substance *f* activatrice	aktivierende Substanz *f*	attivatore *m*
° 116	active iron	fer *m* actif	wirksames Eisen *n*	ferro *m* attivo
^ 117	active mud	boue *f* active	Aktivschlamm *m*	fango *m* in circolazione, fango *m* attivo
° 118	activator	activant *m*	Anreger *m*	attivante *m*
− 119	activism	activisme *m*	Aktivismus *m*	attivismo *m*
° 120	actual breaking load	charge *f* ultime, charge *f* de rupture	Bruchlast *f*, Bruchbelastung *f*	carico *m* di rottura
− 121	adamantin(e)	adamantin	diamantartig	adamantino
− 122	adamantine drill	couronne *f* à grenaille d'acier, sondeuse *f* à grenaille	Schrotbohrer *m*	perforatrice *f* con corona a graniglia
° 123	adamantine lustre	éclat adamantin	Diamantglanz *m*	splendore adamantino
− 124	adamite	adamine *f*	Adamin *m*	adamina *f*
^ 125	adapter	allonge *f*	Vorstoss *m*, Allonge *f*	prolunga *f*, raccordo *m*
^ 126	adapter flange	bride *f* de réduction	Reduktionsflansch *m*	flangia *f* di riduzione
° 127	adapter for milling machines	manchon réducteur *m* à doigts d'entraînement	Reduktionshülse *f* mit Mitnehmer	manicotto *m* riduttore per fresatrice
	adaptive metallurgy, *s. physical metallurgy*			

	English	French	German	Italian
− 128	adarce	croûte f calcaire déposée par les eaux de source	Kalkablagerungen f pl. von Mineralquellen	crosta f calcarea deposita dalle acque sorgive
° 129	to add binder	agglomérer	Trockenbinder m zusetzen, Zusammenbacken n	agglomerare
° 130	to add bond	agglutiner	Bindemittel n zusetzen, agglutinieren	agglutinare
° 131	added iron	fer m à ajouter, addition f de fer	Zusatzeisen n	ferro m addizionale, aggiunta f di ferro
° 132	adding of ore	addition f de minerai	Erzzusatz m	addizione f di minerale
° 133	adding of sand	addition f de sable	Sandzusatz m	addizione f di sabbia
° 134	addition	addition f	Zusatz m	aggiunta f, addizione f
° 135	addition drop by drop	addition f par gouttes	tropfenweiser Zusatz m	aggiunta f a goccie
° 136	addition of colour	addition f de matière colorante	Farbzusatz m, Farbzugabe f	addizione f di colore
° 137	addition of ferromanganese	addition f de ferromanganèse	Zusatz m von Ferromangan	addizione f (o aggiunta) di ferro manganese
° 138	addition of magmatic material	apport m de matière magmatique	magmatische Stoffzufuhr f	apporto m di materia magmatica
° 139	addition of nickel	addition f de nickel	Nickelzusatz m	addizione f (aggiunta f) di nickel
° 140	addition of ores (or slags)	addition f de minérais (ou de scories)	Zusetzen n von Erzen (oder Schlacken)	aggiunta f di minerali (o di scorie)
° 141	addition of sand	addition f de sable	Sandzusatz m, Sandbeigabe f	addizione f di sabbia
^ 142	additional tank	réservoir m supplémentaire	Zusatzbehälter m	serbatoio supplementare, serbatoio di riserva
° 143	additive	additif m	Zusatzmittel n	additivo m
° 144	additive	additif	additiv	aggregativo, additivo
− 145	adelfotype	adelfotype m	Adelfotypus m	adelfotipo m
− 146	adelite	adélite f	Adelit m	adelite f

	English	French	German	Italian
° 147	to adhere	adhérer	haften	aderire
° 148	adhering moulding sand	sable m de moulage adhérent	anhaftender Formstoff m	sabbia f da formare aderente
° 149	adhesion of the slag	garnissage m de scories	Schlackenansatz m	rivestimento m di scorie
° 150	adhesive	adhésif m	Haftvermittler m	adesivo m
— 151	adipocere	adipocire f, adipocérite f	Leichenwachs n	adipocerite f
— 152	adit, side drift	entrée de fendue	Tagesstollen m	imboccatura f, galleria f di accesso
— 153	adit cut mining	exploitation f à flanc de coteau	Stollenbetrieb m	coltivazione f con accesso a pozzo
— 154	adit end	fond m de fendue	Stollenstoss m	fondo m della galleria
— 155	adit entrance	entrée f de fendue	Stolleneingang m	entrata f della galleria, accesso m della galleria
— 156	adit level	miveau m de la fendue	Stollensohle f	fondo m della galleria, livello m della galleria
— 157	adit rock	roche f encaissante	Nebengestein n	roccia f incassante
— 157a	adjoining rock	roche f encaissante	Nebengestein n	roccia f incassante
° 158	to adjust, to straighten	dresser, ajuster	richten	radrizzare, aggiustare
° 159	adjustable discharger	déchargeur m mobile	verstellbarer Ablader m	scaricatore m mobile
— 160	adjustable prop	étançon m métallique flexible	nachgiebiger Stempel m	puntello metallico regolabile
° 161	adjustable vent flap	fermeture f de ventilation	Lüftungsverschluss m	apertura f di ventilazione
° 162	adjuster	régulateur m	Regulator m, Regler m	regolatore m
° 163	adjusting	ajustage m	Adjustieren n	aggiustaggio, regolazione, registrazione
° 164	adjusting operation	ajustage m	Adjustage f	lavorazione f d'aggiustaggio

		English	French	German	Italian
−	165	**adjusting rod**	tige-rallonge f	Aufsatzstange f	asta f di regolazione
o	166	**adjusting screw**	vis f de serrage	Druckschraube f	regolazione f di chiusura, vite f di regolazione
o	167	**adjustment**	réglage m, mise f au point	Einstellung f	regolazione f, registrazione f
o	168	**adjustment by means of length bars**	ajustage m au moyen d'intercalaires	Einrichten n mit Hilfe von Führungsstangen	aggiustaggio m per mezzo di barre spaziatrici
o	169	**adjustment of electrodes**	réglage m des électrodes	Elektrodenreglung f	regolazione f degli elettrodi
o	170	**admiralty metal**	métal m amirauté	Admiralitätsmetall n	ottone m per imbutitura (o stampaggio) a freddo
o	171	**admission of air**	admission f d'air	Luftzufuhr f	ammissione f d'aria
o	172	**admission valve, slide valve**	soupape f d'admission	Dampfeinlassventil n	valvola f d'ammissione
o	173	**admitting port**	orifice m d'admission	Eintrittsöffnung f	luce f di foro
o	174	**admixture**	addition f	Beimengung f	aggiunta f
o	175	**admixture of clay**	addition f d'argile	Tonbeimengung f	aggiunta f di argilla
	176	**adobe**	brique f crue	Luftziegel m, ungebrannter Ziegel m	mattone m crudo, mattone m seccato all'aria
o	177	**adsorption**	adsorption f	Adsorption f	adsorbimento m
−	177a	**adularescence**	adularescence f	Blauschimmer m	adularescenza f
−	178	**adularia**	adular, adulaire f	edler Feldspat m	adularia f
−	179	**advance borehole**	trou m d'avancement	Vorbohrloch n	foro m d'avanzamento
−	180	**advance heading**	galerie f d'avancement, avancement m	Richtstrecke f Vortrieb m	galleria f d'avanzamento, avanzamento m
−	181	**adventive crater**	cratère m adventif	Adventivkrater m	cratere m avventizio
−	182	**aegirite, aegirine**	aegyrine f, acmite f	Ägirin n	acmite f, egirina f
−	183	**aenigmatite**	aenigmatite f	Aenigmatit m	aenigmatite f
−	184	**aeolation**	érosion f éolienne	Winderosion f	erosione f eolica
−	185	**aeolian deposits** pl.	dépôts m pl. éoliens	aeolische Ablagerung f	depositi m pl. eolici

11

		English	French	German	Italian
°	186	**to aerate the sand**	aérer le sable, ventiler le sable	den Sand *m* auflockern	ventilare la sabbia
^	187	**aerated mud**	boue *f* aérée	lufterleichterte Spülung *f*	fango aerato
°	187a	**aerating apparatus**	diviseur-aérateur *m*	Sandschleuder *m*	disintegratore-aereatore *m*
°	188	**aeration, ventilation aerating**	aération *f*, ventilation *f*	Wetterführung *f*, Wetterleitung *f*	aer(e)azione *f*, ventilazione *f*
°	188a	**aeration fold**	selle *f* aérienne	Luftsattel *m*	sella *f* aerea
°	189	**aerator, aerating apparatus**	diviseur-aérateur *m*, appareil-diviseur *m* du sable	Sandschleuder *f* Sandschleuderma-schine *f*	disintegratore-aeratore *m*, ventilatore-separatore *m* di sabbia
–	190	**aerial arch, aeration fold**	voûte *f* anticlinale dénudée, pli *m* dénudé, selle *f* aérienne	Luftsattel *m*	volta *f* anticlinale, sella *f* aerea
°	191	**aerial line, overhead line**	canalisation *f* aérienne, ligne *f* aérienne	oberirdische Stromleitung *f*	conduttura *f* aerea, cana-lizzazione *f* aerea, li-nea *f* aerea
°	192	**aerial railway**	câble *m* aérien	Seilbahn *f*	teleferica *f*, funivia *f*
	193	**aerial railway charging**	chargement *m* par câble aérien	Seilbahnbegich-tung *f*	caricamento *m* per cavo aereo
		aerial ropeway, s. *overhead rope railway*			
^	194	**aerification**	aérification *f*	Verdunstung *f*	nebulizzazione *f*
	195	**aeripherous, conduc-ting air**	aériphère	luftleitend	aerifero
–	196	**aerolite**	aérolite *f*	Aerolith *m*	aerolite *f*
°	196a	**aerose**	de bronze	aus Bronze *f*	in bronzo
–	197	**aeschynite**	aeschynite *f*	Aschynit *m*	aeschynite *f*
–	198	**aetites, eagle-stone**	aétite *f*, pierre *f* d'aigle	Aetit *m*, Adlerstein *m*	aetite *f*, etite *f*
°	199	**after blow**	sursoufflage *m*	Nachblasen *n*	iniezione *f* d'aria finale, postsoffiamira *f*
°	199a	**after contraction**	post-contraction *f*	Nachschrumpfen *n*	postcontrazione *f*
–	200	**after damp**	fumée *f*, grisou *m*	Explosions-schwaden *m*	gas *m* d'esplosione, grisou *m*
^	200a	**after flow**	fluage *m* postérieur	Nachfliessen *n*	scorrimento *m* posteriore

	English	French	German	Italian
^ 201	**after fractionnating tower**	tour *f* de fraction- nement secondaire	Nachfraktionïer- turm *m*	torre *f* di frazionamen- to secondaria
− 202	**aftergases, afterdamp**	produits gazeux d'explosion	Explosionsschwa- den *m*	gas *m* d'esplosione
° 203	**aftershock**	secousse *f* consé- cutive	Nachbeben *n*	scossa *f* di replica, replica
− 204	**afwillite**	afwillite *f*	Afwillit *m*	afwillite *f*
− 205	**agalite**	agalite *f*	Agalit *m*	agalite *f*
− 206	**agalmatolite**	agalmatolite *f*	Agalmatolith *m*, Koreit *m*	agalmatolite *f*, steatite *f* cinese
− 207	**agaphite**	agaphite *f*	Agaphite *m*	agafite *f*
− 207a	**agaric mineral**	agarice *f*	Bergmilch *f*	agarico *m* minerale
− 208	**agate**	agate *f*	Achat *m*	agata *f*
° 208a	**agate fur burnishing**	agate *f* à brunir	Polierstein *m*	agata *f* da brunire
° 209	**agate knife**	couteau *m* en agate	Achatschneide *f*	coltello *m* d'agata
° 210	**agate mortar**	mortier *m* en agate	Achatmörser *m*, Achatschale *f*	mortaio *m* d'agata
° 210a	**agated**	agaté	mit eingesprengtem Achat *m*	agatato
− 211	**agatiferous**	agatifère	achathaltig	agatifero
− 212	**agatoide**	agatoïde	achatähnlich, achatartig	agatoide
− 213	**agaty**	agaté	mit eingesprengtem Achat	agatato
° 214	**to age-harden**	vieillir	härten, aushärten	invecchiare
° 215	**age hardening, preci- pitation hardening**	durcissement *m* par précipitation (ou par vieillissement)	Ausscheidungs- härtung *f*, Alter- ungszähigkeit Aushärten *n*	incrudimento *m* per in- vecchiamento, invecchia- mento *m* con aumento di durezza
° 216	**aged**	vieilli	ausgehärtet, gealtert	invecchiato
° 217	**aged steel**	acier *m* vieilli	gealterter Stahl *m*	acciaio *m* invecchiato
° 218	**ageing, aging**	vieillissement *m*	Alterung *f*	invecchiamento *m*

		English	French	German	Italian
°	219	ageing (artificial)	vieillissement *m* accéléré	künstliche Alterung *f*	invecchiamento *m* artificiale
°	220	ageing crack	fissure *f* de vieillissement ·	Alterungsriss *m*	incrinatura *f* di invecchiamento
—	220a	agency of snow	action *f* de la neige	Schneewirkung *f*	azione *f* della neve
	221	agent of transportation	agent *m* de transports	Transportmittel *n*	agente *m* di trasporto
°	221a	agglomerate	agglomérat *m*	Agglomerat *n*	agglomerato *m*
°	222	agglomerated cake	gâteau *m* aggloméré	Agglomeratkuchen *m*	impasto *m* d'agglomerati
°	223	to agglomerate, to conglomerate, to ball	agglomérer, conglomérer	anhäufen, agglomerieren	agglomerare, conglomerare
—	224	agglomerated coal	charbon *m* aggloméré	Homogenkohle *f*	carbone *m* agglomerato
—	225	agglomerating plant	installation *f* d'agglomération	Agglomerieranlage *f*	impianto *m* d'agglomerazione
—	226	agglomerating power	pouvoir *m* agglomérant	Klebekraft *f*	potere *m* agglomerante
°	226a	agglomeration	agglomération *f*	Agglomeration *f*	agglomerazione *f*
°	227	agglutinant	agglutinant	anklebend	agglutinante
°	228	agglutinated	agglutiné	zusammengeklebt	agglutinato
°	229	agglutinogen	agglutinogène	agglutinogen	agglutinogeno
—	230	aggradation	alluvionnement	Anschwemmung *f*	alluvionamento *m*
—	231	aggradational deposit	dépôt *m* alluvionnaire	Flussablagerung *f*	deposito *m* alluvionale
—	232	to aggrade	alluvionner	ablagern, (im Flussbett *n*)	alluvionare
—	233	aggregates	matériaux *m pl.* pierreux	Zuschläge *m pl.*	componenti *m pl.* litoidi
°	234	aggregates	agrégats *m pl*,	Zusatzstoffe *m pl.* Aggregate *n pl.*	inerti *m pl.*, aggregati *m pl.*

agitated molten pool, *s. boiling molten pool*

		English	French	German	Italian
°	235	agitating tank	cuve *f* d'agitation	Rührtank *m*	vasca *f* d'agitazione
°	236	agitation	agitation *f*	Umrühren *n*	agitazione *f*
°	237	agitator	agitateur *m*	Rührwerk *n*	agitatore *m*

		English	French	German	Italian
−	238	**agricolite**	agricolite *f*	Agricolit *m*	agricolite *f*
−	239	**aguilarite**	aguilarite *f*	Aguilarit *m*	aguilarite *f*
°	240	**air bath**	bain *m* d'air	Luftbad *n*	bagno *m* d'aria
°	241	**air blast, jet**	jet *m* d'air	Luftstrahl *m*	getto *m* d'aria
°	241a	**air blasting**	nettoyage *m* à jets d'air	Luftstrahlreinigung *f*	pulizia *f* a getti d'aria
°	241b	**air bell**	cloque *f*	Blase *f*	bolla d'aria
°	242	**air belt, air box**	boîte à vent (cubilot)	Windkasten *m*	cintura *f* d'aria, camera *f* (o collettore) del vento
°	243	**air blower**	soufflerie *f*	Gebläse *n*	soffieria *f*
°	244	**air blowing**	soufflage *m*	Einblasen *n*, Verblasen *n*	soffiaggio *m*
	245	**airborne magnetometre**	aéromagnétomètre *m*	Aeromagnetometer *n*	aeromagnetometro *m*
−	246	**air box**	caisson *m* d'aérage	Holzlutte *f*	cassa *f* d'aerazione
−	247	**air brattice**	cloison *f* d'aérage	Wetterscheider *m*	diaframma *f* d'aerazione
−	248	**air bridge**	crossing *m* d'aérage	Wetterbrücke *f*	ponte *m* d'aerazione
°	249	**air bubble, blister, air bell**	cloque *f*, bulle d'air	Blase *f*, Gussblase	bolla *f* d'aria
°	250	**air chamber (or reservoir)**	chambre *f* ou réservoir *m* à air	Windkammer *f*	camera *f* d'aria
^	251	**air chamber**	chambre *f* de la pompe à schlamms	Schlammpumpenflasche *f*	bottiglia *f* della pompa per fanghi
°	251a	**air channel**	canal *m* du vent	Windkanal *m*	canale *m* del vento
°	252	**air chill**	trempe *f* à l'air, durcissement à l'air	Lufthärtung *f*, Luftverhärtung *f*	tempra *f* all'aria, indurimento *m* all'aria
−	253	**air chisel**	burin *m* pneumatique	Pressluftmeissel *m*	scalpello *m* pneumatico
		air classification, *s. elutration*			
−	254	**air cleaner**	filtre *m* à air	Luftfilter *m*	filtro d'aria
°	255	**air-clutch forging machine**	machine *f* à forger à embrayage pneumatique	Schmiedemaschine *f* mit pneumatischer Kupplung	fucinatrice *f* a frizione pneumatica
−	256	**air compartment**	compartiment *m* de ventilation	Wetterraum *m*	scompartimento *m* di ventilazione
°	257	**air conduit**	buse *f* d'aérage	Wetterlutte *f*	condotto *m* (o ugello) d'aerazione

		English	French	German	Italian
o	258	**air-cooled**	refroidi par l'air	luftgekühlt	raffreddato ad aria
o	259	**air cooling**	refroidissement *m* par l'air	Luftkühlung *f*	raffredamento *m* ad aria
o	260	**air core barrel**	lanterne *f*	Luftspindel *f*	lanterna *f* per anime
—	261	**air crossing**	crossing *m* d'aérage	Wetterkreuz *n*	incrocio *m* di ventilazione
o	262	**air or blast distribution**	répartition *f* du vent	Windverteilung *f*	distribuzione *f* del vento, ripartizione del vento
—	263	**air cushion**	amortisseur *m* à air	Luftdämpfer *m*	ammortizzatore *m* ad aria
—	264	**air door**	porte *f* d'aérage	Wettertür *f*	porta *f* di ventilazione
o	265	**air draught**	tirage *m*	Luftzug *m*	tiraggio *m*
o	266	**air dried brick**	brique *f* séchée à l'air	Luftstein *m*	mattone *m* seccato all'aria
—	267	**air-dried coal**	charbon *m* séché à l'air	luftgetrocknete Kohle *f*	carbone *m* essicato all'aria
—	268	**air drifter drill**	perforateur *m* pneumatique à colonne	Presslufthammer *m* mit Bohrsäule *f*	perforatore *m* pneumatico a colonna
—	269	**air drill**	marteau *m* perforateur, marteau *m* pneumatique	Pressluftbohrhammer *m*	martello *m* perforatore
^	270	**air drilling, air drive**	puisage *m* à l'air comprimé, forage *m* à l'air	Luftbohren *n*	perforazione *f* (o estrazione) ad aria compressa
o	271	**to air dry**	essuyer, essorer à l'air	an der Luft trocknen	asciugare all'aria
o	272	**air dry, air dried**	séché à l'air	lufttrocken	asciugato all'aria
—	273	**air end way**	voie *f* jumelle	Begleitort *m*	galleria *f* gemella
—	274	**air exhaust**	sortie *f* de l'air	Luftauslass *m*	scarico *m* d'aria
—	275	**air-exhauster**	ventilateur *m*	Luftabsauger *m*	aspiratore *m* d'aria
—	276	**air feed**	avancement *m* (ou alimentation) à air comprimé	Pressluftvorschub *m*	alimentazione *f* (o avanzamento) ad aria compressa

		English	French	German	Italian
—	277	**air feed stoper**	perforatrice f télescopique	Teleskop-Hammer m	perforatrice f telescopica
—	278	**air fin cooler**	refrodisseur m d'air à ailettes	Flügelluftkühler m	raffreddatore m a alette
—	278a	**air flooding**	forage m à l'air	Pressluftbohren n	perforazione f ad aria compressa
°	279	**air flow**	courant m d'air	Wetterstrom m	corrente f d'aria
°	280	**air furnace (by natural draft)**	four m à air, four m à réverbère	Luftofen m, Flammofen n	forno m ad aria non soffiata, forno m a riverbero
—	281	**air gallery**	galerie f de ventilation	Wetterstrecke f	galleria f di ventilazione, galleria f d'aerazione
°	282	**air gas**	gaz m pauvre	Luftgas n	gas m povero. gas m d'aria
		air gate, s. air vent			
°	283	**air gun, blow gun**	soufflette f	Abblashahn m, Zerstäuber m	soffiatore m, soffietto m a pulsante
—	283a	**air hammer**	marteau m pneumatique	Pressluftbohrhammer m	martello m pneumatico
°	284	**air-hardened steel, self-hardening steel**	acier m auto-trempant	Lufthärtungsstahl m, Lufthärter m	acciaio m temprante in aria, acciaio auto-temprante
°	285	**air hardening**	trempe f à l'air	Lufthärtung f	tempra f all'aria
	286	**air hardening**	prise f ou durcissement m à l'air	Lufterhärtung f	presa f (o indurimento) all'aria
		air hardening steel, s. air-hardened steel			
—	286a	**air heading**	galerie f de ventilation	Wetterstrecke f	galleria f d'aereazione
°	287	**air heater**	appareil m à air chaud	Winderhitzer m	apparecchio m ad aria calda
°	288	**air heater with suspended pipes**	appareil m à air chaud à tuyaux suspendus	Winderhitzer m mit hängenden Röhren	apparecchio m ad aria calda a tubi sospesi
°	289	**air hole, vent**	orifice m de sortie des gaz	Windpfeife f	respiro m, sfiatatoio
°	289a	**air hose**	tuyau m à air comprimé	Luftschlauch m	manica f per aria
—	290	**air in a mine,**	air m de mine(s)	Grubenwetter m.pl.	aria f di miniera
°	291	**air in the core**	air m du noyau	Kernluft f	aria f dell'anima

AIR INLET

		English	French	German	Italian
°	292	air inlet, air hole	ouverture *f* d'entrée d'air, arrivée *f* d'air	Lufteinströmöffnung *f*, Luftschlitz *m*	apertura *f* d'entrata dell'aria, entrata *f* dell'aria, foro *m* di tiraggio
°	293	air inlet valve	clapet *m* d'entrée d'air	Lufteinströmklappe *f*, Windklappe *f*	valvola *f* per l'entrata dell'aria
°	294	air intake	entrée *f* d'air	Lufteinlass *m*	aspirazione *f* dell'aria, entrata *f* dell'aria
—	295	air jig	crible-classeur *m* à air *m* comprimé	Luftsetzmaschine *f*	vaglio *m* (o crivello) ad aria compressa
°	295a	air knock out	éjecteur *m* pneumatique	pneumatischer Auswerfer *m*	eiettore *m* pneumatico
—	296	air leg	support *m* à air comprimé	Bohrknecht *m*	supporto *m* ad aria compressa
—	297	air level	galerie *f* d'aérage	Wetterstrecke *f*	galleria *f* di ventilazione
—	298	air level	niveau *m* à bulle	Wasserwaage *f*	livella *f* a bolla d'aria
—	299	air lift	extraction *f* par air comprimé	Gewinnung *f* durch Pressslufteinsatz	estrazione *f* ad aria compressa
—	300	air line	tuyauterie *f* d'air, canard *m*	Windleitung *f*	condotta *f* d'aria
—	301	air lock	porte *f* d'aérage	Wetterloch *n*	porta *f* di ventilazione
°	302	air lock	poche *f* à air	Luftsack *m*	sacca *f* d'aria
°	303	air machine (die casting machine)	machine *f* à fondre à air comprimé	Spritzgussmaschine *f*	macchina *f* per pressofusione ad aria compressa
°	304	air main, blast main	conduite *f* de vent principale	Hauptwindleitung *f*	condotto *m* principale del vento
°	304a	air orifice	arrivée *f* d'air	Luftschlitz *m*	foro *m* di tiraggio
°	305	air pipe, blast pipe	conduite *f* de vent	Windleitung *f*	condotto *m* del vento, sfiatatoio *m*
—	306	air pit	puits *m* d'aérage, puits de ventilation	Wetterschacht *m*, Luftschacht *m*	pozzo *m* d'aerazione (o di ventilazione)
°	307	air pocket	retassure *f*, soufflure, poche d'air	Lunker *m*, Gussblase *f*, Luftsack *m*	risucchio *m*, soffiatura, sacca *f* d'aria
°	308	air port	parcours *m* de l'air	Luftweg *m*	direzione *f* dell'aria

		English	French	German	Italian
°	309	**air pump**	pompe *f* à air	Luftpumpe *f*	pompa *f* pneumatica
°	310	**air pump bell**	cloche *f* de la pompe à air	Luftpumpenglocke *f*	campana *f* di pompa pneumatica
°	311	**air pump cylinder**	cylindre *m* à air	Luftpumpenzylinder *m*	cilindro *m* della pompa d'aria
°	311a	**air pump disc**	plateau *m* de la pompe à air	Luftpumpenteller *m*	piatto *m* della pompa pneumatica
°	312	**air pump piston**	piston *m* pneumatique	Luftpumpenkolben *m*	stantuffo *m* della pompa d'aria
°	313	**air pump plate or disc**	plateau *m* de pompe à air	Luftpumpenteller *m*	piatto *m* della pompa pneumatica
°	313a	**air pump receiver**	cloche *f* de la pompe à air	Luftpumpenglocke *f*	campana *f* di pompa pneumatica
—	314	**air pumping**	pompage *m* pneumatique (ou à air comprimé)	Pressluftpumpen *n*	pompaggio *m* pneumatico
°	315	**air pyrometer**	pyromètre *m* à air	Luftpyrometer *n*	pirometro *m* ad aria
		air quenched steel, *s. air-hardening steel*			
—	316	**air rammer**	dame *f* pneumatique	Pressluftstampfer *m*	calcatoio *m* pneumatico, pestello *m* pneumatico
°	317	**air-refined steel**	acier *m* affiné par le vent	Windfrischstahl *m*	acciaio *m* affinato al vento
°	318	**air release valve**	soupape *f* d'échappement d'air	Entlüftungsventil *n*	valvola *f* di scappamento dell'aria
—	319	**air removal**	désaérage *m*	Entlüftung *f*	deaerazione
—	320	**air saddle**	voûte *f* anticlinale dénudée	Luftsattel *m*	volta *f* anticlinale, sella *f* aerea
—	321	**air separator**	séparateur *m* pneumatique	Druckluft-Abscheider *m*	separatore *m* ad aria compressa
—	322	**air shaft, airshaft**	puits *m* d'aérage	Wetterschacht *m*	pozzo *m* di ventilazione, pozzo *m* d'aerazione
—	323	**air sifting**	épuration pneumatique, épuration *f* à air comprimé	Windsichtung *f*	depurazione *f* pneumatica
—	324	**air slit**	recoupe *m* de ventilation	Wetterdurchhieb *m*	galleria *f* di collegamento di ventilazione

	English	French	German	Italian
− 325	air sluice	sas *m* à air, sas *m* d'aérage	Luftschleuse *f*	paratoia *f* di ventilazione
° 326	air space, gap	vide *m* d'air	Luftraum *m*	intercapedine *f* d'aria
− 327	air split	division *f* du courant d'air, cloison *f* d'aérage	Wetterteilung *f*, Wetterscheider *m*	ripartizione *f* della corrente *f* d'aria, diaframma *f* di ventilazione
° 328	air supply	déplacement *m* d'air	Luftförderung *f*	quantità *f* d'aria, flusso d'aria
− 328a	air test	épreuvre *f* d'étanchéité	Luftdichtigkeitsprobe *f*	prova *f* pneumatica
− 329	air tight	étanche à l'air	luftdicht	a tenuta dell'aria
° 330	air valve	valve *f* à air	Luftventil *n*	valvola *f* ad aria
° 331	air vent	trainée *f* d'air	Entlüftungsrille *f*	canale *m* d'aria
− 332	air way, airway	voie *f* d'aérage	Wetterstrecke *f*	galleria *f* di ventilazione
− 333	air well	puits *m* de ventilation	Wetterschacht *m*, Luftschacht *m*	pozzo *m* di ventilazione
− 334	airless end	taille *f* en cul-de-sac	Blindort *m*	galleria *f* cieca
	airtight fitting, *s. airtight joint*			
° 335	airtight joint	fermeture *f* hermétique (ou imperméable) au vent	luftdichter, winddichter Abschluss *m*	chiusura *f* ermetica (o a tenuta d'aria)
− 336	akaustobiolite	acaustobiolite *f*	Akaustobiolith *m*	acaustobiolite *f*
− 337	akerite	akérite *f*	Akerit *m*	acherite *f*
− 338	akermanite	akermanite *f*	Akermanit *m*	akermanite *f*
− 339	akrochordite	akrochordite *f*	Akrochordit *m*	acrocordite *f*
− 340	alabandin(e), alabandite	alabandine *f*, alabandite *f*	Alabandin *m*, Alabandit *m*	alabandina *f*, alabandite *f*
− 341	alabaster	albâtre *m*	Alabaster *m*	alabastro *m*
− 342	alabastrite	alabastrite *f*	Alabastergips *m*	alabastrite *f*
− 343	alaite	alaïte *f*	Alait *m*	alaite *f*
− 344	alamosite	alamosite *f*	Alamosit *m*	alamosite *f*

	English	French	German	Italian
— 345	**alaskaite**	alaskaïte *f*	Alaskait *m*	alascaite *f*
— 346	**albertite**	albertite *f*	Albertit *m*	albertite *f*
· — 347	**albian stage**	albien *m*	Alb *n*	albiano *m*
— 348	**albite, clevelandite**	albite *f*	Albit *m*, Natronfeld-spat, Kieselspat *m*	albite *f*
° 348a	**albion metal**	feuille *f* de plomb étamée	verzinnte Bleifolie *f*	foglio *m* di piombo stagnato
— 349	**albitophyre**	albitophyre *m*	Albitophyr *m*	albitofiro *m*
° 350	**albumen paper**	papier *m* à l'albu-mine (ou albuminé)	Eiweisspapier *n*	carta *f* all'albumina (o albuminata)
° 351	**alclad**	tôle *f* d'alclad	Alkladblech *n*	alclad *m*, lamiera *f* di alclad
352	**alcohol**	alcool *m*	Alkohol *m*	alcool *m*
· — 353	**alexandrite**	alexandrite *f*	Alexandrit *m*	alessandrite *f*
— 354	**algonkian period**	algonkien *m*	Algonkium *n*	algonkiano *m*
— 355	**alkali**	alcali *m*	Alkali *n*	alcale *m*
— 356	**alkali rock**	roche *f* alcaline	Alkaligestein *n*	roccia *f* alcalina
— 357	**alkaline chlorids**	chlorures *m pl.* alcalins	Chloralkalien *n pl.*	cloruri *m pl.* alcalini
— 358	**alkaline earths**	terres *f pl.* alcalines	alkalische Erden *f pl.*	terre *f pl.* alcaline
° 359	**alkaline metals**	métaux *m pl.* alcalins	Alkalimetalle *n pl.*	metalli *f pl.* alcalini
— 360	**alkaline salts**	sels *m pl.* alcalins	alkalische Salze *n pl.*	sali *m pl.* alcalini
— 361	**alkali(ne) water**	eau *f* alcaline	alkalisches Wasser *n*	acqua *f* alcalina
^ 362	**to alkalize**	alcaliser	alkalisieren	alcalizzare
^ 363	**alkalizing**	alcalinisation *f*	Alkalisierung *f*	alcalinizzazione
^ 364	**alkylate bottom**	résidu *m* d'alkyla-tion	Alkylatrückstand *m*	residuo *m* alchilato
^ 365	**alkylation acid**	acide *m* pour alkylation	Alkylationssäure *f*	acido *m* per alchilazione
° 365a	**all-mine iron**	fer *m* virginal	Frischeisen *n*	ferro *m* vergine

allen head cap screw, *s. hexagonal socket head cap screw*

	English	French	German	Italian
— 366	**all level sample**	échantillon *m* moyen	Durchschnittsmuster *n*	campione *m* medio
— 367	**all sliming**	broyage fin	Total-Feinmahlung *f*	macinazione *f* fine, triturazione *f* fine
— 368	**allactite**	allactite *f*	Allaktit *m*	allactite *f*
— 369	**allalinite**	allalinite *f*	Saussuritgabbro *m*	allalinite *f*
— 370	**allanite**	allanite *f*, orthite *f*	Allanit *m*, Orthit *m*	allanite *f*, ortite *f*
— 371	**alleghanyte**	alléghanyte *f*	Alleghanyt *m*	alleganite *f*
— 372	**allemontite**	allémontite *f*	Allemontit *m*	allemontite *f*
^ 373	**alleviator**	équilibreur *m* de pression	Druckausgleicher *m*	compensatore *m* di pressione
° 374	**alligator**	presse *f* à cingler, presse *f* à former	Alligatorquetsche *f*	pressa *f* per forgiare, formatrice
° 375	**alligator shears**	cisaille *f* à balance	Alligatorschere *f*	cesoie *f pl.* ad alligatore
^ 375a	**alligator skin**	effet *m* de pelure d'orange	Apfelsinenschaleneffekt *m*	effetto *m* di buccia d'arancia
° 376	**alligator squeezer**	macque, presse *f* à cingler	Alligatorquetsche *f*, Luppenquetsche	formatrice *f* a leva (a compressione)
° 376a	**alligatoring**	affeuillement *m* longitudinal	Längsabblätterung *f*	screpolatura *f* longitudinale
— 377	**allochroite**	allochroïte *f*	Allochroit *m*	allocroite *f*
— 378	**allochromatic**	coloré	allochromatisch	allocromatico
— 379	**allochthonous**	allochthone	allochthon	alloctono
— 380	**allochthonous deposit**	dépôt *m* allochthone	allochthone Ablagerung *f*	deposito *m* alloctono
— 381	**allochthonous fold**	pli *m* allochthone	allochthone Falte *f*	piega *f* alloctona
— 382	**allochthonous rock**	roche *f* allochthone	allochthones Gestein *n*	roccia *f* alloctona
— 383	**alloclasite**	alloclasite *f*	Alloklas *n*	alloclasite *f*
— 384	**allodelphite**	allodelphite *f*	Allodelphit *m*	allodelfite *f*
— 385	**allogene**	allogène	allothigen	allogeno
— 385a	**allogenic**	allogène	allothigen	allogeno
— 386	**allomerism**	allomérisme *m*, allomérïe *f*,	Allomerismus *m*	allomerismo *m*, allomeria *f*

	English	French	German	Italian
— 387	allomorph	allomorphe	allomorph	allomorfo
— 387a	allophane	allophane *m*	Allophan *m*	allofane *m*
— 388	allotment	concession *f* minière	Grubenfeld *n*	concessione *f* mineraria
— 389	allotriomorphic	allotriomorphe	allotriomorph	allotriomorfo
— 390	allotriomorphic structure	structure *f* allotriomorphe	allotriomorphe Struktur *f*	struttura *f* allotriomorfica
— 391	allotropic form	forme *f* allotropique	allotropische Form *f*	forma *f* allotropica

allotropic modification, *s. allotropic form*

— 392	allotropy	allotropie *f*	Allotropie *f*	allotropia *f*
— 393	allowable production, allowable	production consentie	zulässige Produktion *f*	produzione autorizzata (o permessa)
° 394	allowance, upsetting allowance, push up	surépaisseur *m* pour l'usinage	Bearbeitungszugabe *f*	sovrametallo *m* per ricalcatura
° 394a	allowance, clearance	jeu *m* de coiffage	Spielraum *m* der Kernmarke	giuoco *m* delle portate
° 396	alloy	alliage *m*	Legierung *f*	lega *f*
° 397	alloy cast iron	fonte *f* spéciale	legiertes Gusseisen *n* Legierungseisen *n*	ghisa *f* legata
° 398	alloy constituent	constituant *m* d'un alliage	Verschmelzungskörper *m*	costituente *m* della lega
° 399	alloy of high percentage	alliage *m* à haute teneur	hochprozentige Legierung *f*	lega *f* ad alto tenore
° 400	alloy of low percentage	alliage *m* à faible teneur	niedrigprozentige Legierung *f*	lega *f* a basso tenore
° 401	alloy steel	acier *m* allié	legierter Stahl *m*, Legierungsstahl *m*	acciaio *m* legato
° 402	alloy structure	structure *f* des alliages	Gefüge *n* der Legierungen	struttura *f* delle leghe

alloyage, *s. alloy*

° 403	alloyed	allié	legiert	legato
° 403a	alloyed steel	acier *m* spécial	legierter Stahl *m*	acciaio *m* legato

		English	French	German	Italian
°	404	alloyed super-refined steel	acier *m* spécial allié	legierter Edelstahl *m*	acciaio *m* speciale alligato
°	405	alloying element	élément *m* d'addition, liant *m*	Zusatzelement *n*, Legierungselement *n*	additivo *m*, legante *m*
—	405a	alluvial cone	cône *m* de déjection	Schuttkegel *m*	cono *m* di deiezione
—	406	alluvial deposit, placer	gisement *m* alluvionnaire	Alluviallagerstätte *f* Alluvialrevier *n*	giacimento *m* alluvionale
—	407	alluvial fan, alluvial cone	cône *m* de déjection	Schuttkegel *m*	conoide *m* o cono *m* di deiezione
—	408	alluvial plain	plaine *f* alluvionnaire	Schwemmebene *f*	piana *f* alluvionale
—	409	alluvial terrace, drift terrace	terrasse *f* alluviale, terrasse *f* d'accumulation	Aufschüttungsterrasse *f*	terrazzo *m* alluviale
—	410	alluviation	alluvionnement *m*	Anschwemmung *f*	alluvionamento *m*
—	411	alluvium	dépôts *m pl.* alluviaux, alluvion *m*	Geschiebebänke *f pl.* angeschwemmter Boden, Alluvium *n*	detriti *m pl.* alluvionali, materiale *m* alluvionale, alluvione *f*
—	412	alluvium period	période *f* alluvienne	Alluvialepoche *f*	periodo *m* alluvionale
—	412a	almandine, spinel	spinel *m* violet de magnésium	Almandinspinel *m*	spinello *m* di magnese violetto
—	413	almandite	almandin *m*	Almandin *m*	almandino *m*
°	414	almond section iron	fer *m* à feuille de saule	Mandeleisen *n*	ferro *m* a mandorla
—	415	alnico	alnique	Alnik *m*	alnico *m*
—	416	alnoite	alnöite *f*	Alnöit *m*	alnoite *f*
°	417	alpax	alpax *m*	Silinium, Wilmil	alpax *m*, silumina *f*
°	418	alpha bronze	bronze *m* alpha	Alphabronze *f*	bronzo *m* alfa
°	419	alpha iron	fer *m* alpha	Alpha Eisen *n*	ferro alfa *m*
°	420	alquifou	alquifoux *m*	Alquifoux *m*	alquifoux *m*
—	421	alsbachite	alsbachite *f*	Alsbachit *m*	alsbachite *f*
—	422	alshedite	alshedite *f*	Alshedit *m*	alshedite *f*

	English	French	German	Italian
— 424	alstonite	alstonite *f*	Alstonit *m*	alstonite *f*
— 425	altaite	altaïte *f*	Altait *m*, Tellurblei *m*	altaite *f*
° 426	alteration of angle, angular slip	déformation *f* angulaire	Winkelveränderung *f*	deformazione *f* angolare
° 427	alteration of concentration of the electrolyte	variation *f* de concentration de l'électrolyte	Dichteänderung *f* des Elektrolyten	variazione *f* di concentrazione dell'elettrolito
° 428	alternate coke charge, coke charge	charge *f* de coke	Koksgicht *f*	carica *f* di coke, coke di esercizio
° 429	alternate working kiln	four *m* discontinu, four *m* intermitent	Ofen *m* mit unterbrochenem Betrieb	forno *m* con funzionamento discontinuo
° 430	alternating bending test	essai *m* de pliage alterné	Hin-und-Herbiegeprobe *f*	prova *f* di piegamento alterno
° 431	alternating current furnace	four *m* à courant alternatif	Drehstromofen *m*	forno *m* a corrente alternata
° 432	alternating current plant	installation *f* à courant alternatif	Wechselstromanlage *f*	impianto *m* a corrente alternata
° 433	alternating load	charge *f* alternée	wechselnde Belastung *f*	carico *m* alternato
° 434	alternating stress	contraintes *f pl.* alternées	Wechselspannungen *f pl.*, Wechselsbeanspruchungen *f pl.*	sollecitazioni *f pl.* alternate
— 435	alternation of beds	alternance *f* des couches	Schichtenwechsel *m*	strati *m pl.* alternati
° 436	alternation of stress	alternance *f* de charge	wechselnde Beanspruchung *f*	sollecitazioni *f pl.* alternate
— 437	altogether coal	charbon *m* tout venant	Förderkohle *f*	carbone *m* grezzo di miniera
— 438	alum	alun *m*	Alaun *m*	allume *m*
— 439	alum earth	terre *f* alumineuse	Alaunerde *f*	terra *f* alluminosa
— 440	alum mine	aluminière *f*	Alaungrube *f*	miniera *f* d'allume
— 440a	alum pit	aluminière *f*	Alaungrube *f*	miniera *f* d'allume

	English	French	German	Italian
— 441	**alum slate**	schiste *m* alumineux	Alaunschiefer *m*	scisto *m* alluminoso
— 442	**alumel**	alumel *m*	Alumel *n*	alumel *m*
— 443	**alumina**	alumine *f*, oxyde *m* d'aluminium	Tonerde *f*	ossido *m* d'alluminio, allumina *f*
— 443a	**alumina brick**	brique *f* réfrectaire	Schamottestein *m*	mattone *m* refrattario
— 444	**aluminate**	aluminate *m*	Aluminat *n*	alluminato *m*
— 445	**aluminite, websterite**	alumnite *f*	Aluminit *m*	alluminite *f*, websterite *f*
° 446	**aluminium, aluminum**	aluminium *m*	Aluminium *n*	alluminio *m*
° 447	**aluminium alloy**	alliage d'aluminium	Aluminiumlegierung *f*	lega *f* di alluminio
° 448	**aluminium alloy (with more than 14% silicon)**	alliage *m* d'aluminium hypersilicié	übereutektische Aluminium-Silizium-Legierung *f*	lega *f* d'alluminio ad alto contenuto silicico
° 449	**aluminium brass**	laiton *m* d'aluminium	Aluminiummessing *n*	ottone *m* all'alluminio
° 450	**aluminium bronze, al.br.**	cupro-aluminium *m*, bronze *m* d'aluminium	Aluminiumbronze *f*, Kupferaluminium *n*	cupralluminio *m*, bronzo *m* d'alluminio
° 451	**aluminium filings**	limaille *f* d'aluminium	Aluminiumfeilspan *m*	limatura *f* d'alluminio
° 452	**aluminium foam**	mousse *f* d'aluminium, écume *f* d'aluminium	Aluminiumluppe *f*, Aluminiumschaum *m*	schiuma *f* di alluminio
° 453	**aluminium foundry**	fonderie *f* d'aluminium	Aluminiumgiesserei *f*	fonderia *f* d'alluminio
° 454	**aluminium iron, ferro-aluminium**	ferroaluminium *m*	Aluminiumeisen *n*	ferro-alluminio *m*
° 455	**aluminium magnesium alloy**	magnalium *m*	Magnalium *n*	magnalio *m*
— 456	**aluminium ore**	minerai *m* d'aluminium	Aluminiumerz *n*	minerale *m* d'alluminio
° 457	**aluminium plate**	tôle *f* d'aluminium	Aluminiumblech *n*	lamiera *f* d'alluminio
° 458	**aluminium powder**	poudre *f* d'aluminium	Aluminiumpulver *n*	polvere *f* d'alluminio
° 459	**aluminium removal**	désaluminage *m*	Entfernung *f* von Aluminium, Enteloxieren *n*	rimozione *f* dell'alluminio, disalluminiatura *f*

		English	French	German	Italian
°	460	aluminium rolling mill	laminoir *m* à aluminium	Aluminiumwalzwerk *n*	laminatoio *m* per alluminio
°	461	aluminium sheet	feuille *f* d'aluminium	Aluminiumblech *n*	lamiera *f* d'alluminio
°	462	aluminium steel	acier *m* à l'aluminium	Aluminiumstahl *m*	acciaio *m* all'alluminio
°	463	aluminium weighing boat	capsule *f* de pesée en aluminium	Wägeschiffchen *n* aus Aluminium	navicella *f* d'alluminio per pesare
°	464	aluminium welding	soudure *f* à l'aluminium	Aluminiumschweissung *f*	saldatura *f* all'alluminio
°	465	aluminium wire	fil *m* d'aluminium	Aluminiumdraht *m*	filo *m* d'alluminio
°	466	aluminizing	aluminage *m*	Eloxieren *n*, Aluminisieren *n*	alluminiatura
°	467	alumino-silicate brick	brique *f* alumineuse, brique *f* réfractaire	Schamottestein *m*	mattone *m* refrattario (silico-aluminoso)

aluminothermic welding, *s. thermit welding*

		English	French	German	Italian
°	468	aluminous cement	ciment *m* alumineux	Tonerdezement *m*	cemento *m* alluminoso
°	468a	aluminium	aluminium *m*	Aluminium *n*	alluminio *m*
—	469	alumogel	alumogel *m*	Alumogel *n*	allumogelo *m*
—	470	alumosilicate	aluminosilicate *m*	Alumimiumsilikat *n*	alluminosilicato *m*, silicato *m* d'alluminio
—	470a	alumshale	schiste *m* alumineux	Alaunschiefer *m*	scisto *m* alluminoso
—	471	alumstone	alunite *f*	Alunit *m*	alunite *f*
—	472	alundum	corindon *m*, oxide *m* d'aluminium	Alundum *n*, Aluminiumoxid *n*	alundum *m*, corindone *m*
—	473	alunite	alunite *f*	Alunit *m*, Alaunstein *m*	alunite *f*.
—	474	alunitization	alunitisation *f*	Alunitisation *f*	alunitizzazione *f*
—	475	alunitized	alunitisé	alunitisiert	alunitizzato
—	476	alunogen	alunogène *m*	Alunogen *n*	alunogeno *m*

alvan, *s. apophyse*

		English	French	German	Italian
°	477	to amalgam	amalgamer	amalgamieren	amalgamare
°	478	amalgam	amalgame *m*	Amalgam *n*	amalgama *f*

		English	French	German	Italian
○	479	**amalgam catcher**	collecteur *m* de mer-cure	Amalgamfänger *m*	collettore *m* di amalgama
○	480	**amalgam distilling furnace**	four *m* pour distiller l'amalgame	Amalgamdestilla-tionsofen *m*	forno *m* per distilla-re l'amalgama
○	481	**amalgam drum**	tambour *m* à amalga-mer	Amalgamtrommel *f*	tamburo *m* per l'amal-gama
○	482	**amalgam filter**	filtre *m* pour amalgame	Amalgamfilter *m*	filtro *m* per amalgama
○	483	**amalgam of gold**	amalgame *m* d'or	Goldamalgam *n*	amalgama *f* d'oro
○	484	**amalgam of mercury**	amalgame *m* de mercure	Amalgam *n*	amalgama *f* di mer-curio
○	485	**amalgam pot retort**	cornue *f* pour distiller l'amalgame	Amalgamausbrenn-topf *m*	storta *f* per la distil-lazione dell'amalgama
○	486	**amalgam press**	presse *f* à amalgame	Amalgampresse *f*	pressa *f* per amalgama
○	487	**amalgam process**	procédé *m* par amalga-mation	Amalgamations-verfahren *n*	processo *m* d'amalgama-zione
○	488	**amalgam retort**	cornue pour distiller les amalgames	Amalgamretorte *f*	storta *f* per la di-stillazione dell'amal-gama
○	489	**amalgamable**	amalgamable	amalgamierbar	amalgamabile
○	489a	**to amalgamate**	amalgamer	amalgamieren	amalgamare
○	490	**amalgamating**	amalgamation *f*	Amalgamation *f*	amalgamazione *f*
○	491	**amalgamating**	amalgamé	amalgamiert	amalgamato
○	492	**amalgamating barrel**	amalgamateur *m*	Amalgamator *m*, Amalgamierer *m*	amalgamatore *m*, tam-buro *m* d'amalgamazione
○	493	**amalgamating bath**	bain *m* d'amalgama-tion	Amalgambad *n*	bagno *m* d'amalga-mazione
○	493a	**amalgamatting cask**	almalgamateur *m*	Amalgamator *m*	amalgamatore *m*
○	494	**amalgamating mill**	moulin *m* à amalgamer	Quickmühle *f*	mulino *m* per amalgama

		English	French	German	Italian
o	495	amalgamating pan	cuve f d'amalgamation	Amalgamierpfanne f	vasca f d'amalgazione
o	496	amalgamating plant	installation f d'amalgamation	Amalgamationsanlage f	impianto m d'amalgamazione
o	497	amalgamating table	table f d'amalgamation	Amalgamiertisch m	tavola f d'amalgamazione
o	498	amalgamation	amalgamation f	Amalgamation f, Amalgamierung f	amalgamazione f
o	499	amalgamation apparatus	appareil m d'amalgamation	Amalgamiervorrichtung f	apparecchio m d'amalgamazione
		amalgamation barrel, *s. amalgamating barrel*			
o	500	amalgamation in barrels	amalgamation f aux tambours tournants	Trommelamalgamation f, Amalgation f in rotierenden Fässern	amalgamazione f a mezzo tamburi rotanti
o	501	amalgamation in pans	amalgamation f aux cuves	Amalgamation f in Pfannen	amalgamazione f in vasche
o	501a	amalgamator	amalgamateur m	Amalgamator m	amalgamatore m
		to amalgamize, *s. to amalgam*			
—	502	amarantite	amarantite f	Amarantit m	amarantite f
—	503	amatol	amatol m	Amatol n	amatolo m
		amazonite, *s. amazonstone*			
—	504	amazonstone	amazonite f	Amazonit m	amazonite f
—	505	ambatoarinite	ambatoarinite f	Ambatoarinit m	ambatoarinite f
—	506	amber	ambre m	Bernstein m	ambra f
—	507	amber mica	mica m magnésien	Magnesiaglimmer m	mica f d'ambra, flogopite f
—	508	amblygonite	amblygonite f	Amblygonit m	ambligonite f
—	509	ambrite	ambrite f	Ambrit m	ambrite f
—	509a	ambroid	ambroïde m	Ambroid n	ambroide m

		English	French	German	Italian
°	509a	**American box**	châssis *m* américain	amerikanischer Formkasten *m*	staffa *f* americana
°	510	**American frame box**	châssis *m* américain	amerikanischer Formkasten *m*	staffa *f* americana
		American process iron, *s. blackheart iron*			
—	511	**American system of drilling**	sondage *m* à la corde	Seilbohren *n*	perforazione *f* a percussione alla fune
°	512	**American throat stopper**	système *m* de fermeture américain du gueulard	amerikanischer Gichtverschluss *m*	chiusura *f* americana (della bocca dell'alto forno)
°	513	**americium**	américium *m*	Americium *n*	americio *m*
—	514	**amesite**	amésite *f*	Amesit *m*	amesite *f*
—	515	**amethyst**	amétyste *f*	Amethyst *m*	ametista *f*
—	516	**amianthus**	amiante *m*, asbeste *m*	Amiant *m*, Asbest *n*	amianto *m*, asbesto *m*, bissolite *f*
°	517	**ammeter**	ampèremètre *m*	Amperemesser *m*	amperometro *m*
	518	**ammonia**	ammoniaque *f*	Ammoniak *n*	ammoniaca *f*
°	519	**ammonia hardening**	nitruration *f*	Nitrierhärtung *f*	nitrurazione
°	520	**ammonia water**	eau *f* ammoniacale	wässeriges Ammoniak *n*	acqua *f* ammoniacale
—	521	**ammonioborite**	ammonioborite *f*	Ammonioborit *m*	ammonioborite *f*
—	522	**ammoniojarosite**	ammoniojarosite *f*	Ammoniojarosit *m*	ammoniojarosite *f*
—	523	**ammonite**	ammonite *f*	Ammonit *n*	ammonite *f*
°	524	**ammonium acetate**	acétate *m* d'ammonium	essigsaures Ammoniak *n*, Ammoniumacetat *n*	acetato *m* di ammonio (o ammonico)
		ammonium chloride, *s. sel ammoniac*			
°	525	**ammonium fluoride**	fluorure *m* d'ammonium	Fluorammonium *n*	fluoruro *m* ammonico

	English	French	German	Italian
— 526	ammonium molybdate	molybdate *m* d'ammonium	Ammoniummolyb- dat *n*	molibdato *m* d'ammonio
— 527	ammonium nitrate explosive	explosif *m* au nitrate d'ammonium	Ammonsalpeter- sprengstoff *m*	esplosivo *m* al nitrato ammonico
° 528	ammonium-sodium phosphate	phosphate *m* de soude ammoniacal	Natriumammonium- phosphat *n*	fosfato *m* sodico ammoniacale
° 529	ammonium sulphate	sulfate *m* d'ammonium	schwefelsaures Ammoniak *n*	solfato *m* d'ammonio
° 530	ammonium sulphide	sulfure *m* d'ammonium	Schwefelammonium *n*	solfuro *m* ammonico
— 531	amorphus carbon	carbone *m* amorphe	gestaltloser Kohlenstoff *m*	carbonio *m* amorfo
— 531a	amorphousness	amorphie *f*	Amorphie *f*	amorfia *f*
— 532	amosite	amosite *f*	Amosit *m*	amosite *f*
° 533	amount of contraction (or shrinkage)	mesure *f* du retrait	Schwindmass *n*	misura *f* del ritiro
° 533a	amount of load	agent *m* de transports	Transportmittel *n*	agente *m* di trasporto
° 533b	amount of shrinkage	mesure *f* de retrait	Schwindmass *n*	misura *f* del ritiro
534	amount of water required	besoin *m* en eau	Wasserbedarf *m*	fabbisogno *m* d'acqua
— 535	ampelite	ampélite *f*	Ampelit *m*	ampelite *f*
— 536	amphibole	amphibole *f*	Amphibol *m*, Hornblendeasbest *n*	anfibolo *m*
— 537	amphibolite	amphibolite *f*	Amphibolith *m*, Hornblende *f*	anfibolite *f*
— 538	amphibolization	amphibolisation *f*	Amphibolitbildung *f*	anfibolizzazione *f*
— 539	amphigene	amphigène *m*	Leucit *m*	anfigeno *m*, leucite *f*
° 540	amphoteric electrolyte	électrolyte *m* amphotère	amphoterer Elektrolyt *m*	elettrolito *m* anfoterico
° 541	ample supply of air	admission *f* d'air amplement suffisante	reichliche Luftzu- führung *f*	introduzione *f* d'aria abbondante

	English	French	German	Italian
— 542	amygdale	amygdale f	Mandel f	amigdulo m
— 543	amygdaloidal rock	roche f amygdaloïde	Mandelstein m	roccia f amigdaloide
— 544	amygdaloidal struc-ture	structure f à noyaux, structure f à amygdales	Mandelsteintextur f	struttura f amigdaloi-de
— 544a	amygdule	amygdale f	Mandel f	amigdulo m
— 545	anaerobic	anaérobique	anaerob	anaerobico
— 546	anagenesis	anagénèse f	Anagenese f	anagenesi f
— 547	analcite	analcime f	Analzìm m	analcite f
548	analysis	analyse f	Analyse f	analisi f
549	analysis certificate	certificat m d'analyse	Analysenbericht m	certificato m d'analisi
° 550	analytical balance	balance f de labora-toire	chemische Analy-senwaage f	bilancia f per analisi chimiche
— 551	anamesite	anamésite f	Anamesit m	anamesite f
— 552	anamorphism	anamorphisme m	Anamorphose f	anamorfismo m
— 553	anapaite	anapaïte f	Anapait m	anapaite f
— 554	anatase	anatase m	Anatas m	anatasio m
— 555	anatexis	anatexis f	Anatexis f	anatessi f
— 556	anauxite	anauxite f	Anauxit m	anauxite f
° 556a	anchor bolt	boulon m d'ancrage	Ankerschraube f	bullone m d'ancoraggio
	anchor pin, s: anchor screw			
^ 557	anchor pipe	tube m d'ancrage	Ankerrohrtour m	tubo m d'ancoraggio
° 558	anchor screw, anchor pin (or bolt)	boulon m d'ancrage	Ankerschraube f	bullone m d'ancoraggio
° 559	anchor steel	acier m pour ancres	Ankerstahl m	acciaio m per ancore
° 560	anchoring fitting	pièce f d'ancrage	Verankerungsstück n	pezzo m d'ancoraggio
—561	andalusite	andalousite f	Andalusit m	andalusite f
—562	andesine	andésine f	Andesin m	andesina f

		English	French	German	Italian
—	563	**andesite**	andésite f	Andesit m	andesite f
—	564	**andesitic**	andésitique	andesitisch	andesitico
—	565	**andorite**	andorite f	Andorit m	andorite f
—	566	**andradite**	andradite f	Andradit m	andradite f
—	567	**andrewsite**	andrewsite f	Andrewsit m	andrewsite f
°	567a	**anelasticity**	friction f interne	innere Reibung f	frizione f interna
°	568	**anemometer**	anémomètre m	Windmesser m	anemometro m
°	568a	**angle**	fer m cornière	Winkeleisen n	ferro m angolare
		angle bar, s. angle iron			
—	569	**angle build up**	accroissement m d'angle	Ansteigung f der Bohrlochneigung	aumento m d'angolo (di scavo)
—	570	**angle drop off**	réduction f d'angle	Abnahme f der Bohrlochneigung	riduzione f d'angolo (di scavo)
°	571	**angle fishplate,**	éclisse f à cornière, ou d'équerre	Winkellasche f, Kremplasche f	stecca f angolare (o a squadra)
°	572	**angle-iron, angular iron. angle bar**	fer cornière, fer d'angle, fer L, équerre f en fer, cornière f	Winkeleisen n Eckeisen n	ferro angolare, ferro a L, cantonale, ferro a squadra, angolari m pl.
—	573	**angle of bedding**	angle m de stratification	Schichtungswinkel m	angolo m di stratificazione
°	574	**angle of bosh**	angle m des étalages	Rastwinkel m	angolo m della sacca (d'altoforno)
—	574a	**angle of contact**	angle m de contact	Greifwinkel m	angolo m di contatto
—	575	**angle of dip**	angle m d'inclinaison	Neigungswinkel m	angolo m di declinazione magnetica
—	576	**angle of hade**	angle m d'incidence	Verwurfswinkel m	angolo m d'incidenza
°	576a	**angle of rotation**	angle m de rotation	Drehungswinkel m	angolo m di rotazione
		angle of slope, s. weld slope			
°	577	**angle of torsion, torsion angle**	angle m de torsion	Drehwinkel m	angolo m di torsione
—	578	**angle of unconformity**	angle m de discordance	Diskordanzwinkel m	angolo m di discordanza
°	579	**angle sleeker**	équerre f à lisser	Winkelknopf m	squadra f per lisciare, lisciatoio m d'angolo

	English	French	German	Italian
° 579a	angle splice bar	éclisse à cornière	Winkellasche f	stecca f angolare
° 580	angle steel	cornière f d'acier	Winkelstahl m	angolare m d'acciaio
° 581	angle steel with round edges, L-beams with round edges	cornière f à bords rondis, cornière f à ailes égales	gleichschenkliger Winkelstahl m	angolare m ad L a lati uguali (o a spigoli arrotondati)
° 582	angle steel with sharp edges	cornières f pl. à arêtes vives	scharfkantiger Winkelstahl m	angolari a spigoli vivi
^ 583	angle valve	robinet m d'équerre	Eckventil n	valvola f ad angolo
	angle with equal sides, s. equal angle			
° 584	angle with round corners	cornière f à coins arrondis	rundkantiges Winkeleisen n	cantonale m ad angolo tondo
° 585	angle with sharp corners	cornière f à arêtes vives	scharfkantiges Winkeleisen n	cantonale m ad angolo vivo
− 586	anglesite	anglésite f	Anglesit m	anglesite f
587	angular	angulaire	winklig	angolare m
− 588	annular auger	tarière f (ou sondeuse) à couronne	Kronenbohrer m	trivella f a corona
° 589	angular core	noyau m carré	Kernstück n	anima f quadrata
° 589a	angular iron	fer m cornière	Winkeleisen n	angolare m a spigoli
− 590	angular sand	sable à grains pointus	Spitzsand m	sabbia f a spigoli vivi
° 590a	angular slip	déformation f angulaire	Winkelveränderung f	deformazione f angolare
− 591	angular unconformity	discordance f angulaire	Winkeldiskordanz f	discordanza f angolare
− 592	anhedral	allotriomorphe	allotriomorph	allotriomorfo
− 593	anhydrite	anhydrite m	Anhydrit m, Würfelspat m	anidrite f
− 594	animal substance	matière f animale	tierischer Stoff m	sostanza f (o prodotto) animale
° 595	anion	anion m	Anion n	anione m
− 596	anisotropic	anisotropique	anisotrop	anisotropico

		English	French	German	Italian
—	597	**anisotropic crystal**	cristal *m* anisotrope	anisotroper Kristall *m*	cristallo *m* anisotropico
—	597a	**anisitropism**	anisotropie *f*	Anisotropie *f*	anisotropia *f*
—	598	**anisotropy**	anisotropie *f*	Anisotropie *f*	anisotropia *f*
—	599	**ankerite**	ankérite *f*	Ankerit *m*	ancherite *f*
—	600	**ankylostomiasis**	ankylostomiase *f*	Wurmkrankheit *f*	anchilostomiasi *f*
—	601	**annabergite**	annabergite *f*	Annabergit *m*	annabergite *f*
°	602	**to anneal**	recuire	ausglühen	ricuocere
°	603	**to anneal the steel**	recuire l'acier	Stahl ausglühen	ricuocere l'acciaio
°	604	**annealed**	recuit	geglüht	ricotto
		annealed cast iron, *s. malleable cast iron*			
°	605	**annealed sheet iron**	tôle recuite	ausgeglühtes Eisenblech *n*	lamiera *f* ricotta
°	~606	**annealed stell**	acier *m* recuit	ausgeglühter Stahl *m*, angelassener Stahl. *m*	acciaio *m* ricotto
°	607	**annealed wire**	fil *m* recuit	ausgeglühter Draht	filo *m* ricotto
°	608	**annealing, anneal**	recuit *m*	Glühen *n*, Tempern *n*	ricottura *f*
°	609	**annealing black**	recuit *m* en noir	Schwarzglühen *n*	ricottura *f* nera
°	610	**annealing box**	pot *m* de recuit, caisse *f* de recuit	Tempertopf *m* Glühtopf *m*	cassa *f* di cementazìone o di ricottura
°	611	**annealing chamber**	chambre *f* à recuire (ou de recuit)	Glühfrischkammer *f*	camera *f* di ricottura
°	612	**annealing colours**	couleurs *f pl.* de recuit	Anlauffarben *f pl.*	colori *m pl.* d'incandescenza
°	613	**annealing for workability, machinability annealing**	recuit *m* pour usinage	Glühen *n* für Bearbeitbarkeit	ricottura *f* di lavorabilità
°	614	**annealing furnace**	four *m* de recuit	Glühofen *m*	forno *m* di ricottura, forno *m* d'arroventamento

		English	French	German	Italian
	615	annealing furnace (for glass)	carquaise f, four m de recuisson	Glastemperofen m, Kühlofen m	fomo m di ricottura (per vetro)
—	615a	annealing ore	minerai m de fer	Eisenerz n	minerale m di ferro
°	616	annealing period	durée f de recuit	Glühdauer f	durata f di ricottura
°	617	annealing-pot	pot m à recuire	Glühtopf m	cassetta f di ricottura
°	618	annealing process	procédé m de recuit	Ausglühverfahren n, Glühprozess m	processo m di ricottura
°	619	annealing the steel	recuit de l'acier (ou de trempe)	Ausglühen n des Stahls	ricottura f dell'acciaio
°	620	annular furnace for roasting limestone	four m annulaire à griller le calcaire	Ringofen m zum Brennen des Kalk-steins	fomo m anulare per arrostire il calcare
°	621	annular groove or hearth	chenal m de fusion	Schmelzrinne f	canale m di fusione
°	622	annular melting trough	chenal m de fusion annulaire	ringförmige Schmelz-rinne f	canale m anulare di fusione
˄	623	annular return velocity	vitesse f de retour des boues de forage	Schlammrücklauf-geschwindigkeit	velocità f del fango d'intercapedine
		annular ring, s. circular ring			
˄	624	annular space	espace m annulaire	Ringraum m	spazio m anulare
°	625	annular spring	ressort m annulaire	Ringfeder f	molla f ad anello
°	626	anode	anode f	Anode f	anodo m
°	627	anode copper	cuivre m anodique	Anodenkupfer n	rame m anodico
°	628	anode mold	moule m pour anodes	Anodenform f	forma f per anodi
°	629	anode mud, anode slime	boue f anodique	Anodenschlamm m	fango m anodico
°	630	anode potential	potentiel m anodique	Anodenpotential n	potenziale m anodico
°	631	anodic coating	revêtement m anodique	anodischer Ober-flächenschutz m	rivestimento m anodico
°	632	anodic oxidation	oxydation f anodique	anodische Oxyda-tion f, Anodenoxy-dation f	ossidazione f anodica, anodizzazione f
°	632a	anodic protection	protection f anodique	anodischer Schutz m	protezione f anodica
°	633	anodic treatment	traitement m anodique	Eloxieren n	ossidazione f anodica

	English	French	German	Italian
	to anoint ⟨ ⟩, s. to oil			
° 634	to anodize	anodizer	eloxieren	anodizzare
° 634a	anodizing	oxydation f anodique	anodische Oxydation f	anodizzazione f
— 634b	anorthic system	système m triclinique	triklines System n	sistema m triclinico
— 635	anorthite	anorthite f	Anorthit m	anortite f
— 636	anorthoclase	anorthose f	Anorthoklas m	anortoclasio m
— 637	anorthosite	anorthosite f	Anorthosit m	anortosite f
— 638	antediluvian	antédiluvien	vorsündflutlich	antidiluviano
— 639	anthophyllite	anthophyllite f	Anthophyllit m	antofillite f
— 640	anthosiderite	anthosidérite f	Anthosiderit m	antosiderite f
^ 641	anthracene oils	anthracéniques m pl. (huiles)	Anthrazenöl n	oli m pl. antracenici
— 642	anthracite, hard coal, stonecoal	anthracite f	Anthrazit m, Glanzkohle f	antracite f
° 643	anthracite blast furnace	haut-fourneau m à l'anthracite	Anthrazithochofen m	alto forno m ad antracite
° 644	anthracite pig iron	fonte f à l'anthracite	Anthrazitroheisen n	ghisa f all'antracite
— 645	anthracitization	anthracitisation f	Anthrazitbildung f	antracitizzazione f
— 646	anthracmite	anthracmite f	Stinkkalk m	antracmite f
— 647	anthraco-silicosis	anthraco-silicose f	Silikose f	antraco silicosi f
— 648	anthracolithic system	système m anthracolithique	Permokarbon n	sistema f antracolitico
— 649	anthraconite	anthraconite f	Kohlenspat m	antraconite f
— 650	anthracosis	anthracose f	Anthrakose f	antracosi f
— 651	anthraxylon	houille f brillante	Glanzkohle f	antraxilone m, antracite
° 652	anti-acid coat	couche f anti-acide	säurefester Anstrich m	strato anti-acido
° 653	anti-chamber, lock	antichambre f, sas	Vorraum m, Schleuse f	anticamera f
— 653a	anticlastic	anticlastique	antiklastisch	anticlastico
— 654	anticlinal, anticline	anticlinal m	Antiklinale f	anticlinale f

		English	French	German	Italian
−	655	anticlinal crest	charnière anticlinale	Sattellinie f	cresta f anticlinale
−	656	anticlinal fault	faille f anticlinale	Schenkelbruch m, Gewölbescheitelbruch m	faglia f anticlinale
−	657	anticlinal flexure	flexure f anticlinale	Flexur f	piega f anticlinale
−	657a	anticlinal fold	anticlinale m	Antiklinale f	anticlinale f
−	658	anticlinal limb	flanc m anticlinal	Sattelflügel m	sella f anticlinale
−	659	anticlinal ridge	crête f anticlinale	Antiklinalkamm m	cresta f anticlinale
		anticline, s. anticlinal			
−	660	anticline crest	charnière f anticlinale	Neigungslinie f, Sattellinie f	cresta f anticlinale
o	661	anti-dazzle device	protection f contre l'éblouissement	Blendschutz m	schermi m pl. anabbaglianti
o	661a	antiferromagnetic	antiferromagnétique	antiferromagnetisch	antiferromagnetico
⌃	662	anti-foam agent	antimousse m	Schaumdämpfer m	sostanza f antischiuma
o	663	anti-friction metal	métal m antifriction	Lagermetall n	metallo m antifrizione
−	664	antigorite	antigorite f	Antigorit m	antigorite f
o	665	anti-incrustator	anti-incrustant m	Kesselsteinschutz m	antincrostante m, disincrostante
⌃	666	anti-knock agent	antidétonant m	Antiklopfmittel n	antidetonante m
⌃	667	anti-knock fuel	combustible m antidétonant	Antiklopfbrennstoff m	combustibile m antidetonante
o	667a	antimonial alloy	alliage m d'antimoine	Antimonlegierung f	lega f d'antimonio
−	668	antimonite, stibnite	antimonite f, stibine f, stibnite f	Antimonglanz m, Antimonit m, Stibinit m	antimonite f stibina f, stibite f
.o	669	antimony	antimoine m	Antimon n	antimonio m
		antimony glance, s. antimonite antimony ochre, s. cervantite			
o	670	antimony trichloride	chlorure m d'antimoine	Chlorantimon n	cloruro m d'antimonio
o	670a	anti-piping compound	couverte f	Abdeckmittel n	copertura f
−	671	antipode	antipode m	Antipode m	antipode m
o	672	anti-rust coat	couche f anti-rouille	Rostschutz m	strato m antiruggine, rivestimento m antiruggine

		English	French	German	Italian
°	673	**anti-skid (surface iron plate)**	tôle *f* striée	Riffelblech *n*	lamiera *f* di ferro striata
^	674	**anti-vortex baffle**	déflecteur *m* anti-tourbillon	Wirbelablenker *m*	deflettore *m* antivortice
—	675	**antlerite**	antlérite *f*	Antlerit *m*	antlerite *f*
—	676	**antozonite**	antozonite *f*	Antozonit *m*	antozonite *f*
°	677	**anvil**	enclume *f*	Amboss *m*	incudine *f*
°	678	**anvil (of a power hammer)**	plaque *f* d'appui	Widerlager *n*	piastra *f* d'appoggio, basamento *m*, incudine *m*
—	679	**apachite**	apachite *f* .	Amphibolphonolith *m*	apachite *f*
—	680	**apatite**	apatite *f*, phosphorite *f*	Apatit *m*	apatite *f*
—	681	**apex**	apex *m*	Apex *m*	apice *m*, cima *f* (di una piega)
—	682	**apex**	recette *f* supérieure	obere Auschlagbühne *f*	parte *f* superiore (d'un filone)
—	683	**aphanesite**	aphanèse *f*, clinoclasite *f*	Klinoklas *n*, Abichit *m*	afanesite *f*, clinoclasite *f*
—	684	**aphanite**	aphanite *f*	Aphanit *m*	afanite *f*
—	685	**aphanitic**	aphanitique	aphanitisch	afanitico
—	686	**aphotic region**	région *f* aphotique	aphotische Region *f*	regione *f* afotica
—	687	**aphrite**	aphrite *f*	Aphrit *m*	afrite *f*, argentina *f*
—	688	**aphrosiderite**	aphrosidérite *f*	Aphrosiderit *m*	afrosiderite *f*
—	689	**aphthalose, arcanite**	aphtalose *f* ou arcanite *f*	Aphtalos *m*, Arkanit *m*	aftalose *f*, aftalite *f*
—	690	**aphthonite**	aphthonite *f*	Aphthonit *m*	aftonite *f*
—	691	**apjohnite**	apjohnite *f*	Apjohnit *m*	apjohnite *f*
—	692	**aplanatic**	aplanétique	aplanatisch	aplanatico
—	693	**aplite**	aplite *f*	Aplit *m*	aplite *f*
—	694	**aplic rocks** *pl.*	aplites *f pl.*	aplistische Ganggesteine *n pl.*	apliti *f pl.*

		English	French	German	Italian

	English	French	German	Italian
– 695	**aplome**	aplome *m*, andradite *f*	Aplom *m*, Andradit *m*	andradite *f*
– 696	**apochromatic**	apochromatique	apochromatisch	apocromatico
– 697	**apomagmatic**	apomagmatique	apomagmatisch	apomagmatico
– 698	**apophyllite**	apophyllite *f*	Fischaugenstein *m*	apofillite *f*
– 699	**apophyse, tongue**	apophyse *f*	Apophyse *f*	apofisi *f*
° 700	**apparatus for non-destructive test**	appareil *m* pour les essais non destruc-tifs	Apparat *m* für nichtzerstörende Untersuchungen	apparecchio *m* per i controlli non distrut-tivi
° 701	**apparatus for producing hydrofluoric acid**	appareil *m* pour la production de l'acide fluorhydrique	Flussäureapparat *m*	generatore *m* di acido fluoridrico
° 702	**apparatus for producing sulphuretted hydrogen**	appareil *m* pour la préparation de l'hy-drogène sulfuré	Schwefelwasserstoff-apparat *m*	apparecchio *m* per l'idrogeno solforato
° 703	**apparatus for the determination of arsenic**	appareil *m* pour la recherche de l'arse-nic	Arsenbestimmungs-apparat *m*	apparecchio *m* per determinare il conte-nuto d'arsenico
° 704	**apparatus for the determination of carbon in iron**	appareil *m* pour le dosage du carbone dans le fer	Eisen-Kohlenstoff-bestimmer *m*	apparecchio *m* per de-terminare il tenore di ferro e carbonio
° 705	**apparatus for the determination of carbonic acid**	appareil *m* pour le dosage de l'acide carbonique	Kohlensäurebestim-mer *m*	apparecchio *m* per de-terminare il tenore in acido carbonico
° 706	**apparatus for the determination of melting points**	appareil *m* pour la détermination du point de fusion	Schmelzpunktbestim-mungsapparat *m*	apparecchio *m* per de-terminare il punto di fusione
° 707	**apparatus for the determination of nitrogen**	appareil *m* pour le dosage de l'azote	Stickstoffbestim-mungsapparat *m*	apparecchio *m* per la determinazione dello azoto
– 708	**apparent dip**	pendage *m* apparent	scheinbares Einfal-len *n*	inclinazione *f* appa-rente

apparent gap in plane of bedding, *s. apparent stratigraphical gap*

| – 709 | **apparent heave** | rejet *m* horizontal transversal apparent | scheinbare sohlige Sprungbreite *f* | rigetto *m* orizzontale trasversale apparente |
| – 710 | **apparent slip, throw, total throw** | rejet *m* incliné, glis-sement | schräge Sprunghöhe *f* | rigetto *m* inclinato |

	English	French	German	Italian
— 711	apparent stratigraphical gap	rejet *m* apparent parallèle aux couches	scheinbare Sprungbreite in der Schichtebene	rigetto *m* apparente parallelo agli strati
— 712	apparent stratigraphical overlap	recouvrement *m* stratigraphique apparent	scheinbare stratigraphische Wechselbreite *f*	ricoprimento *m* tettonico apparente
° 713	apparent temperature with colour pyrometer	température *f* de couleur	Farbtemperatur *f*	temperatura *f* di colore
° 714	apparent temperature with optical pyrometer	température *f* de brillance	Teilstrahlungstemperatur *f*	temperatura *f* di brillanza
° 715	apparent temperature with radiation pyrometer	température *f* de radiation	Strahlungstemperatur *f*	temperatura *f* di radiazione
— 716	apparent throw	rejet *m* vertical	saigere Sprunghöhe *f*	rigetto *m* verticale, lacuna *f* stratigrafica verticale
° 717	appearance of flame	aspect *m* de la flamme	Aussehen *n* der Flamme	aspetto *m* della fiamma
° 718	appearance of fracture	aspect *m* de la cassure	Bruchaussehen *n*	aspetto *m* della frattura o della rottura
° 719	appearance of slag	aspect *m* de la scorie	Aussehen *n* der Schlacke	aspetto *m* della scoria
° 720	applied load	charge *f* appliquée	Lastdruck *m*	carico *m* applicato
° 720a	applied stress	effort *m* appliqué	angelegte Belastung *f*	forza *f* applicata
° 721	apply stress relieving groove	décriquer	ausmeisseln	scriccare
— 722	apron conveyor	transporteur *m* à bande articulée	Gliedertransportband *n*	trasportatore *m* a nastro
— 723	apron feeder	alimentateur *m* à courroie	gegliederter Telleraufgebeapparat *m*	alimentatore *m* a piastre snodate
^ 724	appraisal well	puits *m* d'essai	Untersuchungsbohrung *f*	pozzo *m* di prova
— 725	aquamarine	aigue-marine *f*	Aquamarin *n*	acquamarina *f*
— 726	aqua regia	eau *f* régale	Königswasser *n*	acqua *f* regia
— 727	aquifer	nappe *f* aquifère	Aquifer	falda *f* idrica

		English	French	German	Italian
—	728	arable earth	sol *m* arable, sol *m* actif	Ackererde *f*	suolo *m* arabile, suo-lo *m* attivo
—	729	aragonite	aragonite *f*	Aragonit *m*	aragonite *f*
—	730	arakawaite	arakawaite *f*	Arakawait *m*	arakawaite *f*
—	731	aramayoite	aramoyoite *f*	Aramayoit *m*	aramoyoite *f*
—	732	arandisite	arandisite *f*	Arandisit *m*	arandisite *f*
—	733	arapahite	arapahite *f*	Arapahit *m*	arapaite *f*
	734	arbitration analysis	analyse *f* d'arbitrage	Schiedsanalyse *f*	analisi *f* arbitrale
	735	arbritation chemist	chimiste *m* arbitre	Schiedschemiker *m*	chimico *m* arbitro
—	735a	arbor	mandrin*m*	Dorn *m*	mandrino *m*
°	736	arbor (of a core)	châssis *m* (d'un noyau)	Kernformkasten *m*	armatura *f* (di anima)
°	737	arbor for shell-end mill	arbre *m* porte-fraise ou porte-taille	Mitnehmer *m* fuer Stirnfraeser	albero *m* porta-fresa
—	738	arborescent, dendritic	arborescent	baumförmig, dendritisch	arborescente, dendritico
—	739	arborescent crystals	cristal *m* en forme de sapin	Tannenbaumkristall *m*	cristallo *m* aghiforme
—	740	arborescent structure	structure *f* arborescente (ou dendritique)	dendritische Struktur *f*	struttura *f* dendritica, struttura *f* arborescente
—	741	arborized agate, dendritic agate, tree-agate	agate *f* arborisée (ou dendritique), quartz arborisé	Baumachat *m*, Dendritenachat *m*	agata *f* arborizzata, agata *f* dendritica
°	742	arc and resistance furnace	four *m* à arc et à résistance	Lichtbogen-und Widerstandsofen *m*	forno *m* ad arco ed a resistenza
		arc blow, s. *magnetic blow-out*			
°	743	arc cutting	découpage *m* à l'arc	Bogenschnitt *m*	taglio *m* con arco
°	744	arc cutting machine	coupeur *m* à l'arc	Bogenschneidemaschine *f*	tagliatrice *f* ad arco
°	745	arc furnace, electric arc furnace	four *m* à arc (électrique)	Lichtbogenofen *m*	forno *m* ad arco (voltaico)
°	746	arc heating	chauffage *m* par arc électrique	Lichtbogenerhitzung *f*	riscaldamento *m* ad arco voltaico
°	746a	arc image furnace	four *m* à arc indirect	indirekter Lichtbogenofen *m*	forno *m* ad arco indiretto

	English	French	German	Italian
° 747	**arc lamp**	lampe f à arc	Bogenlampe f	lampada f ad arco
° 748	**arc-lamp accesso-ries** pl.	accessoires m pl. pour lampes à arc	Bogenlampenzu-behör n	accessori m pl. per lam-pade ad arco
° 749	**(arc-lamp) carbon**	charbon m d'arc, charbon m de lampe à arc	(Lichtbogen)-Kohle f	carbone m (per arco)
— 750	**arc of folding**	arc m de plissement	Stauungsbogen m	arco m di piegamento, arco m di compressione
° 751	**arc resistance furna-ce**	four m à résistance de l'arc	Lichtbogenwider-standsofen m	forno m a resistenza d'arco
° 752	**arc welding**	soudure f à l'arc	Lichtbogenschweis-sung f	saldatura f ad arco
	arcanite, s. *aphthalmose*			
° 753	**arcatomic welding**	soudure f arcato-mique	Arcatomschweis-sung f	saldatura f arcatomica (o all'idrogeno atomico)
— 754	**arch bend**	charnière f anticli-nale	Sattelscharnier n	cresta f anticlinale
— 755	**arch core**	noyau m du pli	Sattelkern m	nucleo m della sella anticlinale
— 756	**arch girder**	cintre m en I	Streckengestell n	trave f ad arco
° 757	**arch lid**	couvercle m de la voûte	Gewölbedeckel m	coperchio m della volta
— 758	**arch limb**	flanc m supérieur (d'un pli couché)	hängender Schenkel m (einer liegenden Fal-te m)	fianco m superiore (d'una piega f coricata)
	arch of furnace, s. *roof of furnace*			
— 759	**arch set**	cadre m complexe	Polygonzimmerung f	quadro m complesso
— 760	**archean**	archéen	archäozoisch	archeano m
— 761	**archeozoic era**	ère f archéenne	archäozoische Ära f	era f archeozoica
	arcing time, s. *burning time*			
— 762	**arcose**	arkose f	Arkose f	arcose f
— 763	**ardennite**	ardennite f, dewal-quite	Ardennit m	ardennite f

	English	French	German	Italian
− 764	area in advance	région *f* frontale	Vorland *n*	regione *f* frontale
° 765	area of counter pressure	surface *f* de contre-pression	Gegendruckfläche *f*	superficie *f* di contro-pressione
− 766	area of sedimentation	zone *f* de sédimen-tation	Sedimentorium *n*	zona *f* di sedimenta-zione
− 767	area of subsidence	zone *f* d'affaisse-ment	Senkzone *f*	zona *f* di subsidenza
− 768	areal geology	géologie *f* régionale	Regionalgeologie *f*	geologia *f* regionale
− 769	arenaceous texture	structure *f* psam-mitique	psammitische Struk-tur *f*	struttura *f* psammitica
° 770	argental	argental *m*	Argental *n*	argentale *m*
° 771	argentan, German silver	argentan *m*	Neusilber *n*, Argentan *m*	argentana *f* (lega), argentone *m* (lega)
° 772	argentiferous	argentifère	silberhaltig	argentifero
− 773	argentine	argentine *f*	Schaumkalk *m*	argentina *f*, afrite *f*
− 774	argentite, argyrose	argentite *f*, argyro-se *f*	Argentit *n*, Glanzerz *n*	argentite *f*. argirose *f*, argirite *f*
− 775	argentojarosite	argentojarosite *f*	Argentojarosit *m*	argentojarosite *f*
− 776	argentopyrite	argentopyrite *f*	Argentopyrit *m*	argentopirite *f*
− 777	argil	argile *f*	Ton *m*	argilla *f*
	argillaceous earth, *s. clay*			
− 778	argillaceous facies	faciès argileux	tonhaltende Fazies *f*, tonreiche Fazies *f*	facies *f* argillosa
	argillaceous iron ore, *s. clay ironstone*			
− 779	argillaceous sand-stone	grès *m* argileux	Tonsandstein *m*	arenaria *f* argillosa
	argillaceous schist, *s. argillaceous slate*			
− 780	argillaceous slate	schiste *m* argileux	Tonschiefer *m*	argilloscisto *m*
− 781	argillaceous texture, pelitic texture	texture *f* argileuse	pelitische Struktur *f*	struttura *f* argillosa (o pelitica)
− 782	argillaceous veined agate	agate *f* jaspée argi-leuse	Schichtling *m*	agata-diasporo *f* argillosa

		English	French	German	Italian
—	783	**argillite, clay slate**	argil(l)ite f, argile f schisteuse f	Argillit m, Schiefer- ton m	argillite f, argilla f schistosa
—	784	**argillization**	argilisation f	Tonbildung f	argillizzazione f
—	784a	**argyrite**	argentite f	Argentit m	argentite f
—	785	**argyrodite**	argyrodite f	Argyrodit m	argyrodite f
—	786	**argyropyrite**	argyropyrite f	Argyropyrit m	argiropirite f
—	786a	**argyrose**	argentite f	Argentit m	argentite f
—	787	**argon**	argon m	Argon n	argo m
—	788	**arite**	arite f	Arit m	arite f
—	789	**arizonite**	arizonite f	Arizonit m	arizonite f
—	790	**arkansite**	arkansite f	Arkansit m	arkansite f
—	791	**arkose**	arkose f	Arkose f	arcosi f
—	792	**arkosic**	d'arkose	arkosehaltig	arcosico
—	793	**arm coal cutter**	haveuse f à barre	Stangenschrämma- schine f	tagliatrice f a barra
°	794	**arm steel**	acier m pour armes	Waffenstahl m	acciaio m per armi
—	795	**armangite**	armangite f	Armangit m	armangite f
°	796	**arm support of template**	support m de la trousse	Schablonenhalter m	sopporto m della sagoma
°	797	**Armco iron**	fer m Armco	Armco Eisen n	ferro m Armco
°	798	**to armor, to ironclad**	cuirasser	bepanzern	corazzare
		armour of the furnace, s. iron fitting of the furnace			
°	799	**armour plate**	plaque f de blindage, tôle f de blindage	Panzerplatte f	piastra f di corazza, lamiera f di corazzatura
		armour plate mill, s. armour plate rolling mill			
°	800	**armour plate rolling mill**	laminoir m à blin- dages	Panzerstrecke f	laminatoio m per co- razze
°	801	**armour plate steel**	acier m à plaques de blindages	Panzerplattenstahl m	acciaio m per piastre di corazza

		English	French	German	Italian
°	802	armour plating	blindage *m* en tôle	Blechpanzerung *f*	rivestimento *m* di lamiera, armatura *f* in lamiera
°	803	armour steel	acier *m* à blindages	Panzerstahl *m*	acciaio *m* da corazze
°	804	armoured cable	câble *m* armé	Panzerkabel *n*	cavo *m* armato, cavo *m* protetto
°	805	armouring with inter-locking wires	armure *f* en fer profilé	Profildrahtbewehrung *f*	armatura *f* in ferro profilato
^	806	aromatic tar	résidu *m* aromatique	aromatischer Rückstand *m*	residuo *m* aromatico
—	807	arrangement in layers	arrangement *m* en couches	Aufschichtung *f*	disposizione *f* in strati, stratificazione
°	808	arrangement of the converters	disposition *f* des convertisseurs	Anordnung *f* der Birnen	disposizione *f* dei convertitori
—	808a	arrastre	bocard *m* à pilons	Pochmühle *f*	mulino *m* a piloni
—	809	arrested anticline	anticlinal *m* non développé	nicht entwickelte Antiklinale *f*	anticlinale *f* non sviluppata
—	810	arrester	séparateur *m*	Abscheider *m*	separatore *m*
—	811	arrow	flèche *f*	Pfeil *m*	freccia *f*
—	812	arrow headed drill	mèche *f* plate, foret à langue d'aspic	Spitzbohrer *m*, Flachbohrer *m*	trapano *m* piatto, trapano *m* a punta di lancia
°	813	arsenic	arsenic *m*	Arsen *n*	arsenico *m*
°	814	arsenic anhydride	anhydride *m* arsénique	Arsensäureanhydrid *n*	anidride arseniosa
—	815	arsenic silverblende	proustite *f*	Arsenblende *f*, Proustit *m*	proustite *f*
—	816	arsenic trisulphide, orpiment	orpiment *m*	Schwefelarsen *n*, Auripigment *n*	trisolfuro *m* d'arsenico, orpimento
—	817	arsenical iron ore	minerai *m* de fer arsénieux	arsenhaltiges Eisenerz *n*	minerale *m* di ferro arsenicale
—	818	arsenical pyrites	pyrite *f* arsenicale	Arsenkies *m*	arsenopirite *f*
—	819	arseniferous	arsénifère	arsenführend	arsenifero
—	820	arseniolite	arsénite *f*, arsénolite *f*	Arsenblüte *f*	arsenolite *f*

		English	French	German	Italian
–	821	arseniopleite	arséniopléite *f*	Arseniopleit *m*	arsenicopleite *f*
–	822	arseniosiderite	arséniosidérite *f*	Arseniosiderit *m*	arsenicosiderite *f*
–	823	arsenious acid	anhydride *m* arsénieux	arsenige Säure *f*	acido *m* arsenico, anidride *f* arseniosa
–	823a	arsenkies	arsénopyrite *f*	Arsenkies *m*	arsenopirite *f*
–	824	arsenobismite	arsénobismite *f*	Arsenobismit *m*	arsenobismite *f*
–	825	arsenoclasite	arsénoclasite *f*	Arsenoklasit *m*	arsenoclasite *f*
–	826	arsenoferrite	arsénoferrite *f*	Arsenoferrit *m*	arsenoferrite *f*
–	827	arsenolamprite	arsénolamprite *f*	Arsenolamprit *m*	arsenolamprite *f*
–	828	arsenolite	arsénolite *f*	Arsenolith *m*	arsenolite *f*
–	829	arsenopyrite, mispickel, arsenical pyrites	arsénopyrite *f*, mispickel, arsénosidérite *f*	Arsenkies *m*, Arsenopyrit *m*	arsenopirite *f*, pirite *f* arsenicale
°	829a	art bronze	bronze *m* statuaire	Kunstbronze *f*	bronzo *m* d'arte
–	830	artesian well	puits *m* artésien	artesischer Brunnen *m*	pozzo *m* artesiano
°	831	artificial ageing	vieillissement *m* accéléré(ou artificiel)	künstliche Alterung *f*	invecchiamento *m* artificiale (o accellerato)
°	832	artificial coal	charbon *m* artificiel	Kunstkohle *f*	carbone *m* artificiale
°	833	artificial cooling	refroidissement *m* artificiel	künstliche Kühlung *f*	raffreddamento *m* artificiale
°	834	artificial fuel	combustible *m* artificiel	künstlicher Brennstoff *m*	combustibile *m* artificiale
–	835	artificial magnetite	magnétite *f* artificielle	künstlicher Magnetit *m*	magnetite *f* artificiale
°	836	artificial resin moulding press	moule *m* à presser la matière synthétique	Kunstharzpressform *f*	matrice *f* per materie plastiche
–	837	artinite	artinite *f*	Artinit *m*	artinite *f*
°	838	as-cast	brut de fonderie	Rohguss *m*	grezzo di colata
°	839	as-rolled	brut *m* de laminage	nur gewalzt	grezzo di laminazione₁
–	840	asbestos	amiante *m*, asbeste *m*	Asbest *m*	asbesto *m*, amianto *m*

		English	French	German	Italian
o	841	**asbestos cord**	corde f en amiante	Asbestschnur f	corda f d'amianto
o	842	**asbestos dish**	capsule f d'amiante	Asbestschale f	disco m d'amianto
o	843	**asbestos fabric**	tissu m d'asbeste	Asbestgewebe n, Asbesttuch n	tessuto m d'amianto
o	844	**asbestos glove**	gant m en amiante	Asbesthandschuh m	guanto m d'amianto
o	845	**asbestos packing**	garniture f en amiante, joint m en amiante	Asbestdichtung f	guarnizione f d'amianto
o	846	**asbestos paper**	papier m d'amiante, carton m d'asbeste	Asbestpapier n	carta d'amianto
o	847	**asbestos sheet**	plaque f d'amiante	Asbestplatte f	foglio m (o strato m) d'asbesto
o	848	**asbestos wire net**	toile f d'amiante	Asbestdrahtnetz n	rete f di fili d'amianto
o	849	**asbestos wool**	laine f d'amiante	Asbestwolle f	lana f d'amianto
—	850	**asbolite, asbolan(e)**	asbolane f, asbolite f	Kobaltschwärze f, Kobaltmanganerz n	asbolano m, asbolite f
o	851	**ascending flue, uptake**	rampant m ascendant	fliegender Fuchs m	condotto m montante od ascendente
—	852	**ascending horizontal slicing**	exploitation f par tranches horizontales ascendantes	horizontaler aufsteigender Scheibenbau m	coltivazione f a trance orizzontali ascendenti
—	853	**ascending velocity**	vitesse f ascendante	aufsteigende Geschwindigkeit f	velocità f ascendente
—	854	**ascending water**	eau f ascendante, eau f hypogène	aufsteigendes Wasser n, hypogenes Wasser n	acqua f ascendente, acqua f ipogena
—	855	**ascensional ventilation**	aérage m ascendant	steigende Bewetterung f	ventilazione f ascendente
—	856	**ascent**	montée f, remonte f	Ausfahrt f	rimonta f
—	857	**ascharite**	ascharite f	Ascharit m	ascarite f
—	858	**aschistic**	aschiste	aschistisch	ascistico
—	859	**aschistic rock**	roche f aschiste	ungespaltenes Gestein n	roccia f ascistica

		English	French	German	Italian
°	860	**ascoloy**	ascoloy *f*	Ascoloy *f*	ascoloy *m* (acciaio americano al cromo)
°	861	**ash cellar**	cave *f* (ou soute *f*) aux cendres	Aschenkeller *m*	deposito *m* di cenere, cenerario *m*
—	862	**ash coal**	charbon *m* riche en cendres	Aschenkohle *f*	carbone *m* con alto tenore in cenere
—	863	**ash cone**	cône *m* de cendres	Aschenkegel *m*	cono *m* di ceneri
—	864	**ash content**	teneur *f* en cendres	Aschengehalt *m*	tenore *m* in ceneri
—	865	**ash free**	exempt de cendres	aschenfrei	esente da ceneri, privo di ceneri
—	866	**ash hopper**	trémie *f* à cendres	Aschenrumpf *m*	tramoggia *f* per ceneri
		ash inclusion, *s. fly ash*			
—	867	**ash pan**	cendrier *m*, bac *m* à cendres	Aschenkasten *m*	cassa *f* per la cenere
—	868	**ash pit**	cendrier *m*	Aschenteller *m*	cenerario *m*
—	869	**ash pocket**	poche *f* de dépôt des cendres	Aschensack *m*	pozzetto *m* per la cenere
—	870	**asiderite**	asidérite *f*	Asiderit *m*	asiderite *f*
—	871	**asmanite**	asmanite *f*	Asmanit *m*	asmanite *f*
—	872	**aspasiolite**	aspasiolite *f*	Aspasiolith *m*	aspasiolite *f*
—	873	**asphalt base course**	formation *f* asphaltique	Asphaltbildung *f*	formazione *f* asfaltica
—	874	**asphalt base crude**	huile *f* brute asphaltique	Asphaltrohöl *n*	greggio *m* asfaltico
—	875	**asphalt deposits**	gisements *m pl.* asphaltiques	Asphaltlager *n*	giacimenti *m pl.* asfaltici
—	876	**asphalt furnace**	four *m* à asphalte	Asphaltofen *m*	forno *m* di asfalto
—	877	**asphalt powder**	poudre *f* d'asphalte	Asphaltmehl *n*	polvere *f* di asfalto
—	879	**asphalt prime work**	préparation *f* au goudron	Asphaltbearbeitung *f*	preparazione *f* con asfalto
—	880	**asphalt primer**	goudron *m* de préparation	Bearbeitungs-asphalt *n*	asfalto *m* di preparazione

		English	French	German	Italian
—	881	asphaltic	asphaltique	asphalthaltig	asfaltico
—	882	asphaltic hydro-carbon	hydrocarbure *m* asphaltique	asphaltischer Kohlenwasserstoff *m*	idrocarburo *m* asfaltico
—	883	asphaltic limesto-ne	calcaire *m* bitumi-neux	Asphaltkalkstein *m*	calcare *m* bituminoso
—	884	asphaltic pyrobi-tumen	pyrobitume *m* asphal-tique	asphaltisches Pyro-bitumen *n*	pirobitume *m* asfaltico
—	885	asphaltite	asphaltite *f*	Asphalthit *m*	asfaltite *f*
°	886	aspirail	ouverture *f* de venti-lation	Wetterloch *n*	apertura *f* di ventila-zione, foro *m* di ventilazione
°	887	aspirated volume	volume *m* d'air aspiré	Ansaugvolumen *n*	volume *m* d'aspirazione
—	888	aspirator	aspirateur *m*	Luftsauger *m*	aspiratore *m*
°	889	assay balance	balance *f* d'essai	Versuchswaage *f*	bilancia *f* d'assaggio
°	890	assay button	bouton *m* d'essai	Metallkorn *n*	grano *m* di prova (o di saggio)
°	891	assay crucible	creuset *m* d'essai	Probiertiegel *m*	crogiolo *m* di prova (o di saggio)
°	892	assaying	docimasie *f*	Versuchsverfahren *n*	sistema *m* delle prove
°	893	assaying furnace	four *m* à coupellation	Kapellenofen *m*	forno *m* a coppella
°	894	assemblage of heavy minerals	association *f* de mi-nerais lourds	Schwererzverbin-dung *f*	associazione *f* di minerali pesanti
°	895	to assemble and to close a mould	remmouler	die Form *f* giessfer-tig machen	ramolare, preparare la forma per la fusione
°	896	assembling (of cores)	remmoulage *m*	(die Formen) Zusam-menlegen *n*	ramolaggio *m*
°	897	assembly	bâti *m*	Maschinenrahmen *m*	telaio *m*, incastellatu-ra *f*, intelaiatura *f*
°	898	assembly mark	repère *m* de remmoulage	Führungskegel *m*	riferimento *m* di ramo-laggio
—	899	assistant driller	aide-sondeur *m*	Bohrmeistergehilfe *m*	aiuto perforatore *m*

		English	French	German	Italian
—	900	**assize**	assise *f*	Zone *f*	zona *f*
—	901	**associated sheets**	couches *f pl.* asso- ciées	vereinigte Flöze *n pl.*	strati *m pl.* associati
—	902	**astatine**	astate *m*	Astatin *n*	astato *m*
—	903	**astel**	bois *m* de garnissage	Firstbrett *n*	armatura *f* in legno
—	904	**asteriated sapphire**	saphir *m* astérique	Sternsaphir *m*	zaffiro *m* asterico
—	905	**asterism**	astérisme *m*	Asterismus *m*	asterismo *m*
—	906	**astian stage**	astien *m*	Astian *n*	astiano *m*
—	907	**astillen**	salbande *f*	Salband *n*	parete *f* laterale di galleria, salbanda *f*
—	908	**astillen**	cloison *f*	Wetterscheider *m*	diaframma *f* (di ventila-zione)
—	909	**astrakanite**	astrakanite *f*	Astrakanit *m*	astrakanite *f*
—	910	**astrolite**	astrolite	Astrolith *m*	astrolito *m*
—	911	**asymmetric anti-cline**	anticlinal *m* asymé-trique	asymmetrische Antiklinale *f*	anticlinale *f* asimme-trica
—	912	**asymmetrical fold**	pli *m* dissymétri-que	asymmetrische Falte *f*	piega *f* asimmetrica
—	913	**at grass**	au jour	über Tage	a giorno, alla superfice
—	914	**at the pit's mouth**	sur le carreau *m* de la mine	an der Schachtmün-dung *f*	all'imboccatura della miniera
°	914a	**at white heat**	au rouge blanc	zur Weissglut	al (calore) bianco
—	915	**atacamite**	atacamite *f*	Atakamit *m*	atacamite *f*
—	916	**atlasite**	atlasite *f*	Atlasit *m*	atlasite *f*
—	917	**ataxic**	ataxique	ungeschichtet	ataxico
—	918	**atelestite**	atélestite *f*	Atelestit *m*	atelestite *f*
°	918a	**athermal**	athermique	athermal	atermico
—	919	**atlantic suite**	série *f* atlantique	atlantische Sippe *f*	serie *f* atlantica
—	920	**atmoclastic rock**	roche *f* clastique in situ	atmoklastisches Gestein *n*	roccia *f* clastica «in situ», roccia *f* atmoclastica

English	French	German	Italian
– 921 atmogenic	éolien	äolisch	eoliano
– 922 atmophylic element	élément *m* atmophile	atmophiles Element *n*	elemento *m* atmofilo
– 923 atmosphere	atmosphère *f*	Atmosphäre *f*	atmosfera *f*
– 924 atmospheric feeder	masselotte *f* atmosphérique	atmosphärischer Speiser *m*	materozza *f* atmosferica
– 925 atmospheric influence	influence *f* atmosphérique	- atmosphärischer Einfluss *m*	influenza *m* atmosferica
– 926 atmospheric oxygen	oxygène *m* atmosphérique	atmosphärischer Sauerstoff *m*	ossigeno *m* atmosferico
– 927 atmospheric pressure	pression *f* atmosphérique	Luftdruck *m*	pressione *f* atmosferica
– 928 atmospheric rock	roche *f* éolienne	äolisches Gestein *n*	roccia *f* eolica
^ 929 atmospheric topping	distillation *f* atmosphérique	atmosphärische Destillation *f*	distillazione *f* atmosferica

atmospheric riser, *s. atmospheric feeder*

o 930 atom	atome *m*	Atom *n*	atomo *m*

atomic arc welding, *s. atomic hydrogen welding*

o 931 atomic hydrogen welding, arc welding	soudure *f* par l'hydrogène atomique	Arcatomschweissung *f*, atomische H-Schweissung *f*	saldatura *f* a idrogeno atomico
o 932 atomic number	index *m* d'un atome	Atomzahl *f*	numero atomico
o 933 atomic weight	poids *m* atomique	Atomgewicht *n*	peso *m* atomico
o 934 atomiser, sprayer	atomiseur *m*	Zerstäuber *m*	polverizzatore *m*
o 934a atomizing	atomisation *f*	Zerstäubung *f*	atomizzazione *f*
– 935 atopite	atopite *f*	Atopit *m*, Romeit *m*	atopite *f*, romeite *f*
o 935a attached foundry	fonderie *f* intégrée	Giesserei *f* für Eigenbedarf	fonderia *f* dipendente

attached test coupon, *s. cast-on bar*

o 935b to attack	attaquer à l'acide	ätzen	mordere, corrodere
o 936 attack	attaque *f*	Aufschliessung *f*	attacco *m*
o 937 attack by uniform corrosion	attaque *f* de la corrosion uniforme	Angriff *m* durch ebenmässige Korrosion *f*	attacco *m* della corrosione uniforme

		English	French	German	Italian
°	938	**attemperator**	régulateur *m* de température	Temperaturregler *m*	attemperatore *m*
°	939	**attendance**	surveillance *f*, service *m*	Wartung *f*	servizio *m*, sorveglianza
—	940	**attle**	déchets *m pl.*, rebuts *m pl.*, remplai *m*	Gangmasse *f*, Versatzberge *m pl.*	rifiuti *m pl.*, scarti *m pl.* di miniera
°	940a	**attrition**	usure *f* par frottement	Reibungsverschleiss *m*	logorio *m*, sfregamento *m*
—	941	**aturian stage**	aturien *m*	Aturian *n*	aturiano *m*
—	942	**auerlite**	auerlite *f*	Auerlith *m*	auerlite *f*
—	943	**augelite**	augélite *f*	Augelith *m*	augelite *f*
—	944	**augen-gneiss**	gneiss oeillé	Augengneis *m*	gneiss *m* occhiadino
^	945	**auger stem, drill stem, kelly**	barre *f* de battage	Schwerstange *f*	asta motrice di sonda
—	946	**auger**	tarière *f*, tourniquet	Spiralbohrer *m*,	verrina *f*, trivella *f*,
—	947	**auger**	cuiller, tarière *f* à cuiller	Bohrschappe *f*	trivella *f* a cucchiaio
—	948	**augite**	augite *f*	Augit *m*	augite *f*, pirosseno *m*
—	949	**augite syenite**	augite syénite *f*	Augitsyenit *m*	augite sienite *f*
—	950	**augitic**	augitique	augitartig	augitico
—	951	**augitophyre**	augitophyre *m*	Augitporphyr *m*	augitofiro *m*
—	952	**aurichalcite**	aurichalcite *f*	Aurichalcit *m*	auricalcite *f*
—	953	**auriferous**	aurifère	goldhaltig	aurifero
°	954	**austempering**	trempe *f* étagée bainitique	Zwischenstufenvergütung *f*	trattamento *m* isotermico, bonifica *f* isotermica
°	955	**austenising**	austénitisation *f*, traitement *m* austénitique	Austenitisierung *f*	austenitizzazione *f*, trattamento *m* austenitico
—	956	**austenite**	austénite *f*	Austenit *m*	austenite *f*
—	956a	**austenite grain**	grain *m* austénitique	austenitisches Korn *n*	grano *m* austenitico
		austenite steel, *s. austenitic steel*			
—	957	**austenitic**	austénitique	austenitisch	austenitico

		English	French	German	Italian
°	958	**austenitic cast iron**, **austenite cast iron**	fonte *f* austénitique	austenitisches Gusseisen *n*	ghisa *f* austenitica o poliedrica
°	959	**austenitic steel**	acier *m* austénitique	austenitischer Stahl *m*	acciaio *m* austenitico
°	959a	**austenitizing**	austénitisation *f*	Austenetisierung *f*	austenizzazione *f*
—	960	**authigene** **authigenic**, *s. authigène*	authigène	authigen	autigeno
—	961	**authigenic rock**	roche *f* authigène	authigenes Gestein *n*	roccia *f* autigena
—	961a	**authigenous**	authigène	authigen	autigeno
°	962	**auto lathe**	tour *m* revolver, tour *m* automatique	automatische Futterdrehbank *f*	tornio *m* automatico
—	963	**autochthonous**	autochtone	autochthon	autoctono
—	964	**autochthonous rocks** *pl.*	roches *f pl.* autochtones	autochthone Gesteine *n pl.*	rocce *f pl.* autoctone
—	965	**autoclave**	autoclave *m*	Autoklav *m*	autoclave *f*
°	965a	**autofrettage**	autofrettage *m*	Vorspannung *f*	pretensione *f*
°	966	**autogenous**	autogène	autogen	autogeno
°	967	**autogenous ignition temperature**	température *f* d'autoallumage	Selbstentzündungstemperatur *f*	temperatura *f* di autoaccensione
		autogenous soldering, *s. autogenous welding*			
°	968	**autogenous welding**, **oxyacetylene welding**	soudure *f* oxyacétylénique	Autogen-Schweissung *f*, Gasschmelzschweissung *f*	saldatura *f* ossiacetilenica (o autogena)
°	969	**autogenous welding by fusion**	soudure *f* autogène par fusion	Schmelzschweissung *f*	saldatura *f* autogena per fusione
°	970	**(autogenous) welding by pressure**	soudure *f* par pression	Pressschweissung *f*	saldatura *f* per pressione
°	971	**autogenous welding joints**	joints *m pl.* pour soudure autogène	Schweissmuffenverbindungen *f pl.*	giunti *m pl.* per saldatura autogena
°	972	**autogenously welded**	soudé à l'autogène	autogen geschweisst	saldato all'autogeno
°	973	**automatic balance**	balance *f* automatique	selbsttätige Waage *f*	bilancia *f* automatica
—	974	**automatic cager**	encageur *m* automatique	automatischer Aufschiebvorrichtung *f*	ingabbiatore *m* automatico

	English	French	German	Italian
— 975	automatic cat head	poulie f automatique du câble de cabestan	automatïsches Spill n	cabestano m automatico
— 976	automatic charging	chargement m automatique	selbsttätige Aufgabevorrichtung f	-caricamento m automatico
— 977	automatic charging equipment	appareil de chargement automatique	automatische Beschickungseinrichtung f	apparecchiatura f per il caricamento automatico
— 978	automatic coal tipple (or tippler)	basculeur m automatique à charbon	selbsttätiger Kohlenkipper m	scaricatore m a bilico automatico per carbone
	automatic device to prevent acetylene pressure, $s.$ $flow$ $control$			
— 979	automatic discharge	déchargement m automatique	Selbstentleerung f	scarico m automatico
° 979a	automatic doser	distributeur-doseur m	Zuteiler m	distributore-dosatore m
° 980	automatic feed	avance f automatique	selbsttätiger Vorschub m	avanzamento m automatico
° 981	automatic feeding	alimentation f automatique	automatische Zufuhr f	alimentazione f automatica, caricamento m automatico
° 982	automatic forger	machine f à forger automatique	automatische Schmiedemaschine f	fucinatrice f automatica
— 983	automatic grab	griffe f automatique, cuiller f, benne-drague f	(Selbst) Greifer m, Drehschaufelbagger m, Greifbagger m	benna f (o mascella) automatica, cucchiaia f automatica
— 984	automatic grabbing	fonctionnement m par cuiller automatique	(Selbst) Greiferbetrieb m	funzionamento m a scavo automatico
° 985	automatic lathe	tour m automatique	selbsttätige Drehbank f	tornio m automatico
° 986	automatic plain pipette	pipette f jaugée automatique	selbsttätige Vollpipette f	pipetta f tarata automatica
° 987	automatic (or self) regulation	distribution f automatique	Selbststeuerung f	distribuzione f automatica
° 988	automatic sand plant	sablerie f automatique	automatische Sandaufbereitung f	impianto m automatico per lavorare le terre (o le sabbie)
° 989	automatic steel	acier m à décolletage rapide	Automatenstahl m	acciaio m automatico, acciaio m da taglio

	English	French	German	Italian
— 990	automatic tipper	culbuteur *m* automatique	selbsttätiger Kipper *m*, Automatenkipper *m*	meccanismo *m* di ribaltamento automatico
— 991	automatic uncoupling	décrochage *m* automatique	selbsttätiges Abschlagen *n*	distacco *m* automatico
— 992	automatic uncoupling device	décrocheur *m* automatique	selbsttätige Abschlag(e)vorrichtung *f*	apparecchio *m* automatico di distacco
° 993	automatically controlled boiler	chaudière *f* à réglage automatique	selbsttätig geregelter Kessel *m*	caldaia *f* a regolazione automatica
— 994	automolite	automolite *f*	Automolit *m*	automolite *f*
— 995	automorphic	automorphe	automorph	automorfo
— 996	autoneomorphic	autonéomorphique	autoneomorph	autoneomorfo
— 997	autopneumatolysis	auto-pneumatolyse *f*	Autopneumatolyse *f*	autopneumatolisi *f*
— 998	autunit	autunite *f*	Autunit *m*	autunite *f*
— 999	auversian stage	auversien *m*	Auversian *n*	auversiano *m*
—1000	auxiliary appliances	appareils *m pl.* auxiliaires	Hilfsgeräte *n pl.*	apparecchi *m pl.* ausiliari
—1001	auxiliary boiler	chaudière *f* auxiliaire	Hilfskessel *m*	caldaia *f* ausiliare (o supplementare)
—1002	auxillary tool	outil *m* auxiliaire	Hilfswerkzeug *n*	utensile *m* ausiliario
—1003	auxiliary units	ensemble *m* auxiliare	Hilfsgruppe *f*	complessi *m pl.* ausiliari
° 1004	available magnification	grossissement *m* utile	förderliche Vergrösserung *f*	ingrandimento *m* utile
—1005	aventurin, gold stone	aventurine *f*, aventurin *m*	Aventurin *m*	(a)venturina *f*
—1006	aventurism	schillérisation *f*	Aventurisieren *n*	aventurismo *m*, schillerizzazione *f*
—1007	average analysis percent value	pourcentage *m* moyen d'analyses	prozentiger Analyse-Mittelwert *m*	analisi *f* media percentuale
—1008	average hade	pendage *m* général	allgemeines Einfallen *n*	pendenza *f* media (o generale)

		English	French	German	Italian
°	1009	**average of test results**	moyenne *f* des résultats d'essai	Mittelwert *m* der Versuchsergebnisse	risultato *m* medio delle prove
	1010	**average output**	production *f* moyenne	durchschnittliche Leistung *f*	produzione *f* media, rendimento *m* medio
	1011	**average sample**	échantillon *m* moyen	Durchschnittsprobe *f*	campione *m* medio
—	1012	**average trend**	direction *f* moyenne	durchschnittliches Streichen *n*	direzione *f* media
	1013	**average weight**	poids *m* moyen	Durchschnittsgewicht *n*	peso *m* medio
—	1014	**avogadrite**	avogadrite *f*	Avogadrit *m*	avogadrite *f*
—	1015	**awaruite**	awaruite *f*	Awaruit *m*	awaruite *f*
	1016	**awl steel**	acier à alêne	Ahlenstahl *m*	acciaio per lesine
—	1017	**axial angle**	angle *m* axial	Axialwinkel *m*	angolo *m* assiale
—	1018	**axial direction**	direction *f* axiale	achsiale Richtung *f*	direzione *f* assiale
—	1019	**axinite**	axinite *f*	Axinit *m*	axinite *f*
—	1020	**axiolite**	axiolite *f*	Axiolith *m*	axiolite *f*
°	1021	**axis**	axe *m*	Achse *f*	asse *m*
°	1022	**axis of a weld**	axe *m* du cordon de soudure	Achse *f* der Schweissraupe	asse *m* del cordone di saldatura
°	1023	**axis of grooves**	ligne *f* médiane des cannelures	Walzlinie *f*	linea *f* di rotolamento (o delle scanalature)
°	1024	**axis of rotation**	axe *f* de rotation	Drehachse *f*	asse *m* di rotazione
°	1025	**axle, axletree**	essieu *m*	Wagenachse *f*	asse *m*, assale *m*, sala *f*
°	1026	**axle arm**	fusée *f* d'essieu	Achsschenkel *m*	perno *m* dell'asse
°	1027	**axle box, journal box**	boîte *f* d'essieu, boîte *f* à huile	Achsbüchse *f*, Achslager *m*	boccola *f* della sala
°	1027a	**axle guide**	plaque *f* de garde	Achsbüchse *f*	parasala *f*
°	1028	**axle pressure**	pression *f* par essieu	Achsdruck *m*	carico *m* sull'asse
^	1029	**azeotrope, azeotropic mixture**	mélange *m* azéotropique, azéotrope *m*	Azeotrop *n*	miscela *f* azeotropica

	English	French	German	Italian
^ 1030	**azeotropic column**	tour *f* azéotropique	Azeotropturm *m*	torre *f* azeotropica
— 1031	**azoic**	azoique	azoisch	azoico
— 1032	**azotic acid**	acide *m* azotique	Salpetersäure *f*	acido *m* azotico
— 1033	**azotized waters** *pl.*	eaux *f pl.* azotées	stickstoffhaltige Wässer *n pl.*	acque *f pl.* nitrogenate
— 1034	**azotometer**	azotomètre *m*	Azotometer *n*	azotometro *m*
— 1034a	**azure copper ore** **azure quartz,** s. *siderite*	azurite *f*	Bergblau *n*	azzurrite *f*
— 1035	**azure stone**	lapis-lazuli *m*	Lapislazuli *m*	lapislazuli *m*
— 1036	**azurite, chessy copper, azure copper-ore, chessylite**	azurite *f*, bleu *m* de montagne, chessylite	Kupferlasur *f*, Berglasur *f*	azzurrite *f*, carbonato *m* basico di rame

		English	French	German	Italian
^	1037	to babbit	épisser un câble dans le «rope socket»		impiombare un cavo entro il «rope socket»
○	1038	babbitt, babbitt metal, antifriction metal, antifriction alloy	métal *m* antifriction	Lagerweissmetall *n*	babbit *m*, lega antifrizione
—	1039	babingtonite	babingtonite *f*	Babingtonit *m*	babingtonite *f*
○	1040	babo's boiling sheet	tôle *f* de Babo	babosches Siedeblech *n*	rete *f* di Babo
○	1041	baby Bessemer steel	acier Bessemer de petit convertisseur	Kleinbessemerstahl *m*	acciaio *m* Bessemer di piccolo convertitore
—	1042	to back	boiser	zimmern	armare (o rivestire un pozzo)
^	1043	to back off	décrocher dans le puits	abkuppeln (im Schachte)	svitare in pozzo
○	1044	back	dos *m*	Rückseite *f*	dorso *m*
—	1045	back	diaclase *f* longitudinale, fissure *f*	Längsspalte *f*, Hauptschlechte *f*	diaclasi *f* longitudinale, crepaccio *m*
—	1046	back	plafond *m* de mine	Ulm *m*, Grubenkranz *m*	corona *f*, tetto di miniera
○	1047	back axle	essieu *m* arrière	Hinterachse *f*	asse *m* posteriore
—	1048	back balance	plat *m* incliné à une voie et contrepoids	eintrümmiger Bremsberg *m* mit Gegengewicht	piano *m* inclinato a via unica con contrappeso
○	1049	back bead	cordon à revers	Rückraupe *f*	cordone *m* a rovescio
—	1050	back coming	exploitation *f* en rabattant	Rückbau *m*	coltivazione *f* in ritirata
^	1051	back crank	pompage *m* combiné	kombiniertes Pumpen *n*	pompaggio *m* combinato
○	1052	back draft, undercut	contredépouille *f*	Hinterschneidung *f*, Unterschneidung *f*	controsformo *m*, sottoquadro *m*, controspoglia *f*
○	1053	back end plate	fond *m* (ou paroi *f*) postérieur	Rückenwand *f*	piastra *f* posteriore (o di fondo), fondo *m* posteriore
—	1054	back entry	passage *m* d'aérage	Begleitort *m*	passaggio *m* (o galleria *f*) di ventilazione
—	1055	back fill	terre *f* de remblayage	Rückfüllung *f*	materiale per ripiena

	English	French	German	Italian
– 1056	**back-fill stoping, cut and fill stoping**	exploitation *f* par remblayage	Versatzabbau *m*	coltivazione *f* a ripiena
– 1057	**back filling**	remblayage *m*, rebouchage *m*	Versetzen *n*, Verfüllen *n*	ripiena *f*, materiale *m* di riempimento, tamponatura *f*
– 1058	**back filling machine**	machine *f* à remblayer, remblayeuse *f*	Versatzmaschine *f*	macchina *f* per ripiena
° 1059	**back flash, back-flash**	cannelure *f* à ébarbures	Entgratrille *f*	scanalatura per sfogo bavatura
° 1059a	**back gears**	démultiplicateurs *m. pl.*	Spindelvorgelege *n*	ingranaggi *m.pl.* riduttori
° 1060	**back-hand welding**	soudure *f* à gaz en arrière	Rückgassschweissung *f*	saldatura *f* a gas all'indietro
° 1061	**back hole**	trou *m* de décharge	Rolloch *n*, Schüttloch *n*	foro *m* di scoronamento, foro *m* di scarico
° 1062	**back iron, top iron, plane back iron**	contre-fer *m*, fer *m* de dessous	Deckplatte *f*, Doppeleisen *n*, Überlageisen *n*	controlama *f*, ferro *m* a registro
– 1063	**back joint**	limet *m*	Schlechte *f*	piano *m* di stratificazione
– 1064	**back lash**	contre-coup *m*	Rückschlag *m*	contraccolpo *m*
° 1065	**back lash**	jeu *m*, marche *f* à vide	Spielraum *m*, toter Gang	giuoco *m*, marcia *f* a vuoto
– 1066	**back lath**	palplanche *f*	Getriebepfahl *m*	armatura *f* in legno, tavolone *m*
– 1067	**back of gallery**	toit *m* de galerie	Firste einer Strecke	tetto *m* di galleria
° 1068	**back off**	dévisser	gewindebrechen	svitare
– 1069	**back off tool**	outil-exploseur *m* pour mine (dans la batterie en puits)		attrezzo *m* per brillare una carica (nella batteria presa in pozzo)
° 1070	**back plate**	plaque *f* de rustine	Hinterzacken *m*	lamiera *f* di fondo
° 1071	**back pressure, back lash**	contre-pression *f*	Gegendruck *m*	contropressione *f*
° 1072	**back pressure valve**	soupape *f* de contre-pression	Gegendruckventil *n*	valvola *f* di ritorno

		English	French	German	Italian
−	1073	**back saddle**	cloche *f* du toit	Auskesselung *f* in der Firste	campana *f* del tetto
⌃	1074	**back side pumping**	pompage *m* latéral	Seitenpumpen *n*	pompaggio *m* laterale (di un pozzo)
°	1075	**back steam**	contre-vapeur *f*	Gegendampf *m*	controvapore *m*
°	1076	**back step sequence (welding)**	soudure *f* en arrière (ou à droite)	Rückschweissung *f*	saldatura *f* a ritroso
−	1077	**back stone**	pierre *f* faisant vis-à-vis à la dame, rustine *f*	Rückstein *m*	pietra *f* posteriore, rustico *m*
− −	1078	**back stoping**	abattage en gradins	Firstenbau *m*	coltivazione *f* a gradini
−	1079	**back timber**	boisage *m* du toit	Firstenstempel *m*	armatura *f* del tetto
°	1080	**back titration, restandardize**	retitrer	Rücktitrieren *n*	analisi *f* volumetrica ripetuta
°	1081	**back twist**	contre-torsion *f*	Gegendrall *m*	controtorsione *f*
°	1082	**back up roll**	cylindre de soutien	Stützwalze *f*	cilindro *m* di rinforzo
°	1083	**back weld**	soudure *f* de renforcement	Verstärkungs-schweissung *f*	saldatura *f* di rinforzo
°	1084	**background**	fond *m*	Hintergrund *m*	fondo *m*
°	1084a	**backhand welding**	soudage *f* à droite	Rückschweissung *f*	saldatura *f* all'indietro
−	1085	**backing deal**	bois *m* de garnissage	Verzugsholz *n*	legname *m* per rivestimento, armatura *f*
°	1085a	**backing electrode**	contre-électrode *m*	Gegenelektrode *f*	contro-elettrodo *m*
⌃	1086	**backing-off lathe**	tour *m* à dépouiller	Hinterdrehbank *f*	tornio *m* per spogliare
°	1087	**backing up ring**	support *m* à anneau	Ringstütze *f*	sostegno *m* ad anello
°	1088	**backing sand, backing earth**	sable *m* de remplissage	Füllsand *m*	terra *f* (o sabbia) di riempimento
−	1089	**backstay**	chambrière *f*	Fanghaken *m*	gancio *m* d'arresto, dispositivo *m* di blocco
°	1089a	**backward welding**	soudure *f* à gaz à droite	Rückgasschweissung *f*	saldatura *f* a gas all'indietro
−	1090	**backwashing**	lavage *m* contre-courant	Gegenstromwaschen *n*	lavaggio *m* controcorrente
−	1091	**backwater**	eaux *f pl.* dormantes	Stauwasser *n*, stilles Wasser *n*	acque *f pl.* stagnanti

English	French	German	Italian
1092 **baddeleyte**	baddeleyite *f*	Baddeleyit *m*	baddeleite *f*
1093 **badly faulted**	très faillé	stark verworfen	molto fagliato
1094 **baffle**	chicane *f*	Umlenkung *f*	labirinto *m* a diaframmi
1095 **baffle board**	plancher *m* de protection	Schutzbrett *n*	tavola *f* di protezione
1096 **baffle plate**	plaque *f* de contrevent *m*	Windzacken *m*, Gichtzacken *m*	placca *f* di controvento, parafiamma
1097 **baffle plate**	plaque *f* de retenue.	Fussplatte *f.*	piastra *f* di sostegno
1097a **bag filtration**	filtration *f* en sacs	Staubfang mit Sackfilter	filtrazione *f* in sacchi
1099 **to bail**	puiser par cuiller, curer	mit dem Schöpflöffel gewinnen, löffeln	estrarre con cucchiaia (o con secchie)
1100 **bail**	anse *f*	Tragbügel *m*	staffone *m* della testa d'iniezione
1101 **bailer**	cuiller *f*	Schöpflöffel *m*	cucchiaia *f*, estrattore *m* a tazze
1102 **bailer and tubing clamp**	collier *m* de cuiller et tubing	Löffel-und Rohrgreifhaken *m*	cravatta *f* per cucchiaia e tubing
1103 **bailing**	extraction *f* par skip	Schachtförderung *f* mit Greiferkübel	estrazione *f* con secchie (o a cucchiaia)
1104 **bailing crusher**	broyeur *m* à boulets	Kugelmühle *f*	mulino *m* a palle
1105 **bailing iron**	fer *m* en loupe	Luppeneisen *n*	ferro *m* in blumi
1106 **bailing iron**	minerai *m* de fer argileux	tonhaltiges Eisenerz *n*	minerale *m* di ferro argilloso
1107 **bailing test**	essai *m* par curage	Schöpfversuch *m*	prova *f* d'estrazione con cucchiaia
1108 **bailing well**	puits *m* en puisage	Schöpfsonde *f*	pozzo *m* in fase di estrazione
1109 **bailing production**	production *f* par puisage	Schöpfproduktion *f*	produzione con estrazione a secchie
1110 **bainite**	bainite *f*	Bainit *m*	bainite *f*
1111 **bainitic hardening**	trempe *f* bainitique	Zwischenstufenhärtung *f*	tempra *f* isotermica

	English	French	German	Italian
— 1112	to bake	cuire	backen, brennen	trattare (o cuocere) al forno
— 1113	baked clay	argile f cuite, terre-cuite f	Steingut n	argilla f cotta, cotto, terracotta f
— 1114	baked coal	charbon m cuit	zusammengebackene Kohle f	carbone m cotto
° 1115	baked mass	masse f agglutinée	zusammengebackene Masse f	massa f agglutinata
— 1115a	baked permeability	perméabilité f à sec	trockene Gasdurch-lässigkeit	permeabilità f a secco
° 1116	baking	cuisson f	Brennen n	cottura f (al forno)
° 1117	baking (to remove hydrogen embrit-tlement)	déhydrogénation f	Dehydrierung f	deidrogenazione f
— 1118	baking cherry coal	houille f maigre col-lante	backende Sinterkohle f	carbone m agglutinante a fiamma lunga
— 1119	baking coal	charbon m collant	Backkohle f	carbone m agglutinante o bituminoso
— 1119a	baking of coke	cuisson f du coke	Koksbacken n	agglutinamento m del coke
— 1120	bal	mine f, entreprise f minière	Grube f, Bergwerks-gesellschaft f	miniera f, società mine-raria, impresa estrattiva
1121	to balance	équilibrer	ausgleichen	equilibrare
1122	balance, scales	balance f	Waage f	bilancia f
— 1123	balance bob	contre-balancier m	Schwengel m mit Gegengewicht	contrappeso m, bilanciere m a contrappeso
— 1124	balance brow	plan m à chariot-por-teur	Gestellbremsberg m	piano m a carrello tra-sportatore
1125	balance case	caisse f de la balan-ce	Waagekasten m	cassetta f della bilancia
— 1126	balance car	chariot m contre-poids	Spannwagen m	carello m a contrappeso
° 1127	balance desiccator	récipient m à chloru-re de calcium	Waageeinsatz m für Chlorcalcium	piattello m di bilancia per cloruro di calcio
° 1128	balance of pressure	compensation f de la pression	Druckausgleich m	compensazione f della pressione
° 1129	balance pan	plateau m de balance	Waagschale f	piattello m della bilancia

	English	French	German	Italian
1130	balance pit	puits *m* pour contre-poids	Schächtchen *n* für Spannvorrichtung	pozzetto *m* per contrappeso
1131	balance plate	plateau compensateur, contre-plaque	Gegenplatte *f*, Schieberteller *m*	piastra *f* di equilibrio, contropiastra *f*
1132	balance print	portée *f* (de modèle) à renflement	verstärkte einseitige Kernmarke *f* mit Sicherung	portata *f* (di modello) a padella
1133	balance room	salle *f* de pesée	Wägezimmer *n*	sala *f* delle bilancie
1134	balance rope	câble *m* d'équilibre	Unterseil *n*	fune *f* di ritorno
1134a	balance weight	contrepoids *m* de la porte	Türverschluss *m*	fermaporta *m*
1135	balanced blast cupola	cubilot *m* à air soufflé équilbré	entlasteter Blaukupolofen *m*	cubilotto *m* equilibrato ad aria soffiata
1136	balanced hoisting	extraction *f* équilibrée	Förderung *f* mit Seilgewichtsausgleich	estrazione *f* equilibrata
	balanced housing, *s. balanced stand*			
1136a	balanced pressure	pression *f* équilibrée	Ausgleichdruck *m*	pressione *f* equilibrata
1137	balanced stand	cage *f* à cylindres équilibrés	Fahrkorb *m* mit entlasteter Oberwalze	gabbia *f* a cilindri equilibrati
1138	balanced top roll	cylindre *m* supérieur suspendu ou équilibré	entlastete Oberwalze *f*	cilindro *m* superiore sospeso od equilibrato
1139	balancing	équilibrage *m*	Gewichtsausgleichung *f*	bilanciamento *m*, equilibratura *f*
1140	balancing by weights	équilibrage *m* par contrepoids	Gewichtausgleichung *f* durch Gewichte	equilibratura *f* o bilanciamento *m* con contrappesi
1141	balas-ruby, ballas	rubis *m* balais	Rubinbalais *m*, roter Spinell *m*	rubino *m* «balais», spinello *m* rosso
1142	baldaufite	baldaufite *f*	Baldaufit *m*	baldaufite *f*
1143	bale-out furnace	four *m* fixe	ortfester Ofen *m*	forno *m* fisso
	baled scrap, *s. bundled scrap*			
1144	baling band	feuillard d'emballage	Packband *n*	reggetta *f* da imballaggio
1145	baling wire	fil de fer *m* pour emballage	Verpackungsdraht *m*	filo *m* di ferro per imballaggio

English	French	German	Italian
— 1145a **to ball**	tasser	in Haufen setzen	ammucchiare
° 1145b **to ball**	agglomérer	agglomerieren	agglomerare
1146 **to ball up**	former des capuchons	Klumpen bilden	agglomerarsi, impastarsi
— 1147 **ball**	tas *m*	Haufen *m*	mucchio, agglomerato
° 1148 **ball, lump**	loupe *f*	Massel *f*	massello *m*
° 1149 **ball-and ring method**	méthode *f* à boule et anneau	Kugel-und Ringverfahren *n*	metodo *m* a palla e anello
° 1150 **ball bearing**	coussinet *m* à billes	Kugellager *n*	cuscinetto *m* a sfere
° 1151 **ball-bearing centre**	pointe *f* à roulements à billes	Koernerspitze *f* mit Kugellager	contropunta *f* girevole a cuscinetto
° 1152 **ball bearing steel**	acier *m* pour roulements à billes	Kugellagerstahl *m*	acciaio *m* per cuscinetti a sfere
° 1152a **ball burnishing**	brunissage *m* à billes	Kugelpolieren *n*	brunitura *f* a palle
— 1153 **ball clay**	argile *f* pour revêtement ou figuline	Keramikerton *m*	argilla *f* da ceramica, argilla *f* grassa
^ 1154 **ball cock**	robinet-flotteur *m*	Schwimmerhahn *m*	valvola *f* (o rubinetto) galleggiante
° 1154a **ball gate**	jet *m* de coulée rond	runder Einguss *m*	colata *f* rotonda
° 1155 **ball hardness test**	essai *m* de pression à bille	Kugeldruckprobe *f*	prova *f* Brinell
° 1156 **ball hardness testing machine**	presse *f* à bille pour l'essai de dureté	Kugelhärteprüfer *m*	sclerometro *m* a sfera, scleroscopio *m* a sfera
ball jasper, s. *banded jasper*			
° 1157 **ball joint**	joint *m* sphérique	Kugelgelenk *n*	giunto *m* sferico
— 1158 **ball mill**	broyeur *m* à boulets	Kugelmühle *f*	mulino *m* (o macina *f*) a palle
— 1159 **ball shaker conveyor**	goulotte *f* oscillante à billes	Kegelrutsche *f*	scivolo *m* a scosse a sfere
° 1160 **ball shape**	forme *f* sphérique	Kugelform *f*	forma *f* sferica
° 1161 **ball shaped**	en forme de loupe	ballenförmig	a forma di palla
^ 1162 **ball shaped head**	allonge *f* bombée	kugelförmiger Kopf *m*	testa *f* arrotondata
° 1163 **ball squeezer**	presse *f* à cingler	Luppenquetsche *f*	pressa *f* per fucinare, fucinatrice *f*

	English	French	German	Italian
1164	ball structure	structure f orbiculaire ou sphéroïdale	sphäroidische Absonderung f	struttura f sferoidale
1165	ball structure parting	division f en boules	kugelige Absonderung f	divisione f in palle
1166	ball test, Brinell's method	procédé m d'empreinte par pression, procédé m Brinell	Eindruckverfahren n Kugelhärteprobe f	processo m di stampo a pressione (o di Brinell)
1167	ball thrust test	billage m	Kugeldruckversuch m	brinellatura f, collaudo delle sfere
1168	ball tube mill	broyeur m à boulets tubulaires	Rohrkugelmühle f	mulino m a palle tubolari
1169	ballasting	ballast m	Schotterbett n, Bettung f	acciottolato m, massicciata f
1170	balling	ballage m	Luppenmachen n	produzione di blumi, puddellaggio m
1171	balling-furnace,	four m à loupes	Stückofen m, Luppenofen m	forno m da blumi
1172	balloon	bouteille f	Flasche f	bombola f
1173	Banca tin	étain m de Banca	Bankazinn n	stagno m di Banca
1174	band	filon m mince	Flöz n	filone m sottile
1175	band, strap	feuillard m	Band n	piattina f, moietta f
1176	band conveyor	transporteur m à ruban	Bandförderer m, Förderband n	trasportatrice f a nastro
1177	band iron. hoop	(fer) feuillard m	Bandeisen n	ferro m a nastro, nastro m di ferro, reggetta f
1178	band saw	scie f alternative	Blattsäge f	sega f alternativa
1179	band steel for pens	acier m pour plumes	Schreibfederbandstahl m	acciaio m per pennini
1180	banded	rubané	gebändert	striato, a strisce, nastriforme
1181	banded agate, ribbed agate	agate f rubanée	Bandachat m	agata f nastriforme
1182	banded clay	argile f rubanée	Bänderton m	argilla f nastriforme (o laminare)

	English	French	German	Italian
— 1183	banded coal	charbon *m* barré	Schieferkohle *f*	carbone *m* scistoso
— 1183a	banded jasper	jaspe *m* rubané	Bandjaspis *m*	diaspro *m* a bande
— 1184	banded vein	filon *m* zoné	Gang *m* mit Lagen-struktur	filone *m* laminato o stratificato
— 1185	banding	rubanement *m*	Bänderung *f*	rigatura *f*
— 1186	banding	structure *f* de bande	Zellenbildung *f*	stratificazione *f*
— 1187	banding structure	structure *f* en bandes	Zeilengefüge *n*	struttura *f* in forma di strisce
° 1188	band-saw steel	acier *m* à scies à ruban	Bandsägestahl *m*	acciaio *m* per seghe a nastro
— 1189	bands	banc *m* de schiste	Schieferbank *f*	banco *m* scistoso
° 1190	banister iron	fer *m* pour garde-corps	Geländereisen *n*, Handleisteneisen *n*	ferro *m* da parapetto, ferro *m* corrimano
° 1190a	to bank the fire	coucher les feux	das Feuer auf-dämmen	coprire il fuoco
— 1191	bank	batterie *f*	Batterie *f*	batteria *f*
— 1192	bank engine	machine *f* d'extrac-tion	Schachtfördermaschi-ne *f*	macchina *f* d'estrazione
— 1193	bank head	recette *f* supérieure du plan incliné	obere Auschlag-bühne *f* eines Brems-berges	stazione *f* superiore del piano inclinato
— 1194	bank of gravel	banc *m* de gravier	Schotterbank *f*	banco *m* di ghiaia
— 1195	bank out	empiler	verkippen	accatastare
— 1196	bank rider	freineur *m*	Bremser *m*	frenatore *m*
— 1197	bank to bank	durée *f* de poste	Schichtdauer *f*	durata *f* del turno
— 1198	banket	conglomérat *m* auri-fère	goldführendes Konglomerat *n*	conglomerato *m* aurifero
— 1199	banket structure	structure *f* en pla-quettes	plattenförmige Struktur *f*	struttura *f* lastriforme
— 1200	banking	atterrissage *m* de la cage	Ankunft *f* des Förderkorbes	arrivo *m* della gab-bia
— 1201	banking out	décagement *m*	Wegziehen *n* der Förderwagen	distacco *m* delle gabbie
— 1202	banking up	étouffement *m*	Erstickung *f*	soffocamento *m*

		English	French	German	Italian
—	1203	banksman	décageteur *m*	Anschläger *m*, Steiger *m*	sorvegliante *m* (di miniera)
—	1204	bannocking	saignée *f*	Schram *m*	taglio *m*, intaglio, tacca *f*
o	1205	bar	barre *f*, barreau *m*	Stange *f*, Stab *m*	barra *f*
o	1206	bar, plate, bloom	bloom *m*, fer *m*, lingot *m*	· Barren *m*, Platte *f*, Bramme *f*	barra *f*, lingotto, verga, ferro *m*
—	1207	bar	barre *f*	Brechstange *f*	barra *f*, palanchino *m*
o	1208	bar, arbor (of a core)	châssis *m* (d'un noyau)	(Kern) Kasten *m*	armatura *f* (di un'anima)
o	1209	bar and tube turning machine	tour *m* à tubes et à barres	Rohr-und-Barren-drehbank *f*	tornio *m* per tubi e barre
o	1210	bar bender	cintreuse *f* à ronds	Rundeisenbiege-maschine *f*	curvatrice *f* per tondini
o	1211	bar bending	cintrage *m* de ronds	Rundeisenbiegung *f*	curvatura *f* di tondini
—	1212	bar coalcutter	haveuse *f* à barre	Stangenschraemma-schine *f*	tagliatrice *f* di carbone a barra
—	1213	to bar down	abattre par des pin-ces	mit Brechstange *f* abreissen, abbrechen	abbattere con palanchino
o	1214	bar drawing	étirage *m* de tube à mandrin	Rohrziehen *n* mit Dorn	trafilatura *f* di tubi a mandrino
o	1214a	bar hold, tong hold	queue *f*	Stiel *m*	codulo (fucinatura)
	1215	bar iron, iron bar, rounds *pl.*	fer *m* en barre(s)	Stabeisen *n*, Stangeneisen	ferro *m* in barre
	1216	bar joint	attaque *f* des tiges	Stangenschuss *m*	attacco *m* delle aste
		bar K/O, *s. bar knockout*			
	1217	bar knockout, bar K/O	décochage *m* par barre de piquage	Ausleeren *n* durch Brechstange	espulsione *f* a cande-la
—	1218	bar mill	broyeur *m* à barres	Stabmühle *f*	molazza *f* a barre, frantoio *m* a barre
	1219	bar rolling mill, bar mill	laminoir *m* à barres	Barrenwalzwerk *n*	laminatoio *m* per barre
	1220	bar steel, steel bar	acier en barres	Stabstahl *m*, Stangenstahl *m*	acciaio in barre o in verghe
	1221	barbed (in foundry)	avec bavures	grathältig	con bavatura
	1222	barbed wire	ronce *f* artificielle, fil à ronces, fil barbelé	Stacheldraht *m*	filo *m* spinato, corda *f* spinosa, filo *m* spinoso

		English	French	German	Italian
°	1223	barbed wire 2 or 3 ply, 2-4 points	ronce f artificielle à 2 et 3 fils, 2-4 picots	Stacheldraht m 2 oder 3 fach, 2-4 Spitzen	corda f spinosa a 2 e 3 fili, corda f spinosa a 2 e 4 punte
—	1224	bardiglio	bardiglio m	Bardiglio m	bardiglio m
—	1225	bardolite	bardolite f	Bardolith m	bardolite f
—	1226	bare measures	couches f pl. stériles	taube Schichten f pl.	strati m pl. (o filoni m pl sterili
°	1227	bare metal arc welding	soudure f à l'arc par électrode nue	Bogenschweissung f mit nackter Elektrode	saldatura f ad arco con elettrodo metallico nudo
°	1228	bare wire	fil nu, conducteur nu	nackter Draht m	filo nudo, conduttore nudo
°	1229	bare wire	fil m de fer clair	blanker Draht m	filo m di ferro lucido
—	1230	barefoot completion	nu-pied m	nacktes Loch n	foro m non tubato
°	1230a	barffing	procédé m de Barff	Barffsches Verfahren n	processo m di Barff
—	1231	baring	déblaiement m de terrains de recouvrement	Freilegen n der Deckgebirgeschicht	sgombero m del terreno di copertura
—	1232	barings	havrit m	Schrämklein n	detriti m pl.
—	1233	barite, barytes, heavy spar	barytine f	Barytsulfat n, Schwerspat m	baritina f, spato m pesante
—	1234	barium	baryum m	Barium n	bario m
—	1234a	barium monoxyde	baryte f	Baryt m	barite f
°	1234b	bark	couche f intermédiaire décarburée	entkohlte Zwischenschicht f	strato m intermedio decarburato
—	1235	barkevikite	barkévicite f	Barkevikit m	barkevichite f
—	1236	barney	chariot m contrepoids d'un plan incliné	Gegengewichtswagen m im eintrümmigen Bremsberg	carrello contrappeso m d un piano inclinato
—	1237	barometrical levelling	nivellement m barométrique	barometrische Höhenmessung f	livellamento m barometrico
—	1238	barranco	barranco m	Barranco n	barranco m
°	1239	barred box	châssis m à barres	Formkasten m mit Schoren	staffa f a traverse
—	1240	barrel amalgamation	amalgamation f au tonneau	Trommelamalgamation f	amalgamazione f al tamburo

English	French	German	Italian
1241 barrel converter	convertisseur *m* horizontal	Trommelkonverter *m*	convertitore *m* orizzontale
1242 barrel of a capstan	cloche *f* de treuil	Spilltrommel *f*	tamburo *m* del cabestano
barrel rolling, *s. tumbling*			
1243 barrel plating	rotogalvanostégie *f*	Rotogalvanostegie *f*	rotogalvanostegia *f*
1244 barrel shaped cutters	rouleaux d'alésoir non parallèles à l'axe de l'outil		rulli *m pl.* d'alesatore non paralleli all'asse dell'attrezzo
1245 barren spots	zone *f* stérile	taube Zone *f*	zona *f* sterile
1246 barren well	sondage *m* stérile	unergiebige Bohrung *f*	sondaggio *m* sterile
1247 barrier	barrière *f*	Schranke *f*	barriera *f*, chiusura *f*
1248 barrier	pilier *m*	Pfeiler *m*	pilastro *m*
1249 barrier pillar	pilier *m* de limite	Grenzpfeiler *m*	pilastro *m* di limite
1250 barrier reef	récif-barrière *m*	Barrierriff *n*	scogliera *f* di sbarramento
1251 barrier system	exploitation *f* par chambres et piliers	Kammerpfeilerbau *m*	coltivazione *f* a camere e pilastri
1252 barring	boisage *m* du toit	Verzimmerung *f* der Firste	armatura *f* del tetto, rivestimento *m* del tetto
1253 barring down	abattage *m* au moyen de pinces	Abreissen *n* durch Brechstangen	abbattimento *m* a mezzo palanchini
1254 bars and sections	fers *m pl.* marchands et profilés	Stab-und Formstahl *m*	ferri *m pl.* commerciali e profilati, ferri *m pl.* mercantili e profilati
1255 bartonian stage	bartonien *m*	Bartonian *n*	bartoniano *m*
1256 bar-type induction heater	four *m* à induction pour barres	Induktionsofen *m* für Bundeisen	forno *m* a induzione per barre
1257 barylite	barylite *f*	Barylith *m*	barilite *f*
1258 barysilite	barysilite *f*	Barysilit *m*	barsilite *f*
1259 barysphere	barysphère *f*	Barysphäre *f*	barisfera *f*
1260 baryta, barium (mon) oxide	baryte *f*, (prot)oxyde de baryum	Baryt *m*	barite *f*, (prot)ossido di bario
1261 baryta water	eau *f* de baryte	Barytwasser *n*	acqua *f* di barite

	English	French	German	Italian
— 1262	**barytocalcite**	barytocalcite *f*	Barytocalcit *m*	baritocalcite *f*
— 1263	**barytocelestite**	barytocélestite *f*	Barytocölestin *m*	baritocelestite *f*
— 1264	**basal cleavage**	clivage *m* de base	Basis-Spaltbarkeit *f*	sfaldatura *f* di base
° 1265	**basal crack**	crique *f* de fond, cra-quelure du fond	unterer Riss *m*	cricca *f* di fondo
— 1266	**basal moraine**	moraine *f* de fond	Grundmoräne *f*	morena *f* di fondo
— 1267	**basalt**	basalte *m*	Basalt *m*	basalto *m*
— 1268	**basaltic**	basaltique	basalthaltig	basaltico
— 1269	**basaltic shape**	forme *f* basaltique	basaltartige Form *f*	forma *m* basaltica
— 1270	**basalt(ic) tuff**	tuf *m* basaltique	Basalttuff *m*	tufo *m* basaltico
— 1271	**basanite**	basanite *f*	Basanit *m*	basanite *f*
° 1272	**bascule-type set-tling cone**	cône *m* décanteur basculant	Kippkegeldekan-tator *m*	cono *m* decantatore a bilico
° 1273	**base, basis**	base *f*	Grundlage *f*, Basis *f*	base *f*, basamento *m*
— 1274	**base, sole**	lit ou mur (d'un gi-sement)	Liegendes *n*	letto *m* (di un giaci-mento
ˆ 1275	**base of the derrick**	base *f* du chevale-ment de sondage	Grundfläche *f* des Bohrturmes	base *f* della torre di trivellazione
° 1276	**base block, hearth block**	fond *m* du creuset	Boden *m*, Boden-stein *m*	fondo *m* del crogiuolo
— 1277	**base box with flan-ge**	boîte *f* de pied avec manchon	Fusskasten *m* mit Muffe	cassa *f* di fondo con manicotto
— 1278	**base conglomerate**	conglomérat *m* de base	Basalkonglomerat *n*	conglomerato *m* di base
° 1279	**base iron**	fonte *f* de base	Ausgangseisen *n*	ghisa *f* di partenza
° 1280	**base metal**	métal non précieux	unedles Metall *n*	metallo *m* comune, me-tallo *m* vile
° 1281	**base metal (in wel-ding)**	métal *m* base	Grundmetall *n*	metallo *m* base (nella saldatura)
ˆ 1282	**base of petroleum**	base *f* de pétrole	Erdölbasis *f*	base *f* di petrolio

	English	French	German	Italian
1283	base oil	pétrole *m* brut	Rohöl *n*	petrolio *m* grezzo, olio *m* minerale grezzo
1284	base ore	minerai *m* pauvre	armes Erz *n*	minerale *m* povero
1285	base plate	plateau *m* de fond	Grundplatte *f*	piastra *f* di fondo, piastra *f* di base
1286	base-plate, bed-plate	plaque *f* de fond, plaque d'assise, plaque de base	Grundplatte *f*	piastra *f* di fondazione
1287	base size, common draw size	dimension *f* intermédiaire	durchschnittliche Zuggrösse *f*	dimensione *f* intermedia
1288	base surface	surface *f* de base	untere Sohle *f*	superfice *f* di base
1289	baselevelling	pénéplaination *f*	Bildung *f* der Feststehenden	livellamento *m* del piano
1290	basement rock	roche *f* de base	Liegendgestein *n*	roccia *f* di base, basamento *m*
1291	to bash	remblayer	versetzen	eseguire una ripiena, riempire
1292	basic Bessemer process	procédé Thomas	Thomasverfahren *n*	procedimento *m* Thomas, processo *m* Thomas
1293	basic Bessemer steel	acier *m* Thomas	Thomasstahl *m*	acciaio *m* (al procedimento) Thomas
1293a	basic bottom	sole *f* basique	basischer Bodenstein	suola *f* basica
1294	basic brick	brique *f* basique	basischer Stein *m*	mattone *m* basico
1295	basic converter	convertisseur basique	basischer Konverter *m*	convertitore *m* basico, convertitore *m* a suola basica
1296	basic ion	ion *m* basique	Basision *n*	ione *m* basico
1297	basic iron, Thomas iron	fonte *f* Thomas, fer *m* Thomas	Thomaseisen *n*, basisches Roheisen *n*	ferro *m* Thomas, ghisa Thomas
	basic lead carbonate, s. *white lead*			
1297a	basic material	matière *f* première	Rohstoff *m*	materia *f* prima
1298	basic nitrate of mercury	nitrate *m* de mercure basique	Quecksilberoxydulnitrat *n*	nitrato *m* di mercurio basico
1299	basic openhearth furnace	four *m* Martin basique	basischer Martinofen *m*	forno *m* Martin basico
1300	basic open hearth steel	acier *m* Siemens-Martin (par le procédé basique)	basischer Siemens-Martinstahl *m*	acciaio *m* Siemens-Martin (al processo basico)

		English	French	German	Italian
°	1301	**basic oxide**	oxyde *m* basique	basisches Oxyd *n*	ossido *m* basico
°	1301a	**basic pig iron**	fonte *f* Thomas	Thomaseisen *n*	ferro *m* Thomas
°	1302	**basic process**	procédé *m* Thomas-Gilchrist, procédé *m* basique	Thomas-Gilchrist-Verfahren *n*, basisches Verfahren *n*	processo *m* Thomas o basico
°	1303	**basic refractory**	réfractaire *m* basique	basischer feuerfester Stoff *m*	refrattario *m* basico
—	1304	**basic rocks** *pl.*	roches *f pl.* basiques	basische Gesteine *n pl.*	rocce *f pl.* basiche
°	1305	**basic slag, Thomas slag**	laitier *m* basique, scories *f pl.* basiques	Thomas Schlacke *f*, basische Schlacke *f*	scoria *f* basica, scoria *f* (o loppa) - Thomas
°	1306	**basic steel**	acier *m* basique	basischer Stahl *m*	acciaio *m* basico
°	1307	**basic steel works**	aciérie *f* Thomas	Thomasstahlwerk *n*	acciaieria *f* Thomas
°	1308	**basicity**	basicité *f*	Basizität *f*	basicità *f*
°	1309	**basin**	bassin *m*	Becken *n*	bacino *m*
°	1310	**basin, pouring basin**	bassin *m* de coulée	Eingusstrichter *m*	pozzetto *f* di colata
°	1311	**basin and gate**	entonnoir *m* de coulée, bassin *m* de coulée	Einguss *m*	bacino *m* di colata
°	1312	**basin with handle**	casserole *f*	Kasserolle *f*	casseruola *f*
°	1313	**basin with mouthpiece, pouring head with sunk basin**	entonnoir *m* de coulée, cuvette *f*	Einguss *m* mit Vormulde	imbuto *m* di colata, bacino *m* di colata a vasca
°	1313a	**basis brass**	alliage *m* de Bobierre	Bobierrelegierung *f*	lega *f* di Bobierre
—	1314	**basket**	panier *m*	Korb *m*	paniere *m*, cesta *f*
—	1315	**basket-type core barrel**	tube-carottier *m* avec arrache-carotte	Kernrohr *n* mit Kernzieher	tubo carotiere *m* con anello strappa carote
°	1316	**basque**	revêtement *m* d'un four	Ofenfutter *n*	rivestimento *m* d'un forno
—	1317	**bass**	argile *f* compacte	dichter Ton *m*	argilla *f* compatta
—	1318	**bass**	charbon *m* schisteux	schieferige Kohle *f*	carbone *m* scistoso
—	1319	**bassanite**	bassanite *f*	Bassanit *m*	bassanite *f*

English	French	German	Italian
— 1320 basset, crop, blossoming, blow, outburst	affleurement, sopement ou sope	Ausgehende *n*, Ausbeissen *n*	affioramento *m*
— 1321 bastard	roche *f* massive	hartes Gestein *n*	roccia *f* dura
— 1322 bastard coal	charbon *m* dur	feste Kohle *f*	carbone *m* duro
— 1323 bastite	bastite *f*	Bastit *m*	bastite *f*
— 1324 bastnasite	bastnaesite *f*	Bastnäsit *m*	bastnaesite *f*
— 1325 bat	schiste *m* bitumineux compact	harter Bitumenschiefer *m*	scisto *m* bituminoso compatto
— 1326 to bate	couper le mur *m*	das Liegende *n* nachreissen	abbassare il piano di scavo
— 1327 batea	batée *f*	Waschschüssel *f*	bacinella *f* (per lavare minerali)
1327a batch	charge *f*	Einsatz *m*	carica *f*
1328 batch by batch	à tas, par lots	haufenweise	a strati, a mucchi
1329 batch agitator, batch mixer	mélangeur *m* en discontinu	Satzmischer *m*	agitatore *m* discontinuo
1330 batch coke steel	four *m* de coke intermittant	Kokingstapelofen *m*	forno *m* di coking discontinuo
1331 batch distillation	distillation *f* intermittante	Postendestillation *f*	distillazione *f* discontinua
1331a batch furnace	four *m* à charges	Chargenofen *m*	forno *m* a lotti
— 1332 batch mill	broyeur-frotteur *m* discontinu	diskontinuierlich arbeitender Kollergang *m*	molazza miscelatrice *f* intermittente (o discontinua)
— 1333 batch oil	huile *f* à cordes	Seilöl *n*	olio *m* per corde
1334 batch process (or processing)	procédé *m* discontinu	Postenverfahren *n*	processo *m* discontinuo
— 1335 batch still	distillateur *m* discontinu	Aussetzdestillierapparat *m*	distillatore *m* discontinuo
1336 batching (of machinery)	graissage *m*	Schmierung *f*	ingrassaggio *m*, oleaggio *m*
1337 batching plant	dispositif *m* doseur	Dosiervorrichtung *f*	dispositivo *m* di dosaggio

		English	French	German	Italian
°	1338	**bath**	bain *m*	Bad *n*	bagno *m*
°	1338a	**bath sample**	échantillon *m* du four	Ofenmuster *n*	campione *m* dal forno
—	1339	**batholith**	batholithe *f*	Batholith *m*	batolite *f*
—	1340	**bathyal deposits**	dépôts *m pl.* bathyaux	bathyale Ablagerungen *f pl.*	depositi *m pl.* batiali
—	1341	**bathyal facies**	faciès *m* bathyal	bathyale Fazies *f*	facies *f* batiale
—	1341a	**bathylith**	batholite *f*	Batholith *m*	batolite *f*
—	1342	**bating**	abaissement *m* du plan d'excavation	Grubenrissenkung *f*	abbassamento *m* del piano di scavo
—	1343	**batrachite**	batrachite *f*	Batrachit *m*	batrachite *f*
—	1343a	**batt**	schiste *m* bitumineux compact	härter Bitumenschiefer	scisto *m* bituminoso compatto
—	1344	**batter**	talus *m*, escarpe *f*	Böschung *f*	scarpa *f*, scarpata
°	1345	**batter for freeing castings**	tambour *m* à nettoyer la fonte	Putztrommel *f*	tamburo *m* sbavatore
°	1346	**battery**	batterie *f*	Batterie *f*	batteria *f*
°	1347	**battery boiler**	chaudière à multi-bouilleurs	Batterienkessel *m*	caldaia *f* a batterie
		battery house, *s. accumulator building*			
°	1348	**battery jar**	récipient *m* en verre pour piles	Batterienglas *n*	vaso *m* di vetro per batterie
°	1349	**battery of boilers**	batterie *f* de chaudières	Kesselbatterie *f*	batteria *f* di caldaie
°	1350	**battery of coke ovens**	batterie *f* de fours à coke	Koksofengruppe *f*, Koksofenbatterie *f*	batteria *f* di forni a coke
—	1351	**battery stulls**	rangée *f* de buttes serrées	Orgel *f*	batteria *f* di puntelli ravvicinati
—	1352	**baulk**	étranglement d'une couche	Auskeilen *n*	strozzamento *m* di uno strato, riduzione a cuneo del filone
°	1353	**Baumann test, sulphur print**	essai Baumann	Baumann-Abdruck *m*	prova *f* Baumann
	1354	**Baume gravity**	densité *f* Baume	Baume-Dichte *f*	densità *f* Baume

English	French	German	Italian
– 1355 **baumhauerite**	baumhauérite *f*	Baumhauerit *m*	baumhauerite *f*
– 1356 **bauxite**	bauxite *f*	Bauxit *m*	bauxite *f*
– 1357 **bauxite kiln**	four *m* pour bauxite	Bauxitofen *m*	forno *m* per bauxite
– 1358 **bavenite**	bavénite *f*	Bavenit *m*	bavenite *f*
– 1359 **bawke**	benne *f*	Kübel *m*	benna *f*, draga *f*
– 1360 **bayldonite**	bayldonite *f*	Bayldonit *m* ·	bayldonite *f*
– 1361 **bayshon**	cloison *f* d'aérage	Wetterscheider *m*	diaframma *f* di ventilazione
– 1362 **bazzite**	bazzite *f*	Bazzit *m*	bazzite *f*
B.C.S., *s. best cast steel*			
Bbl, *s. barrels*			
1363 **beacon pole**	pylône *m* portephares	Rohrmast *m* für Scheinwerfer	palo *m* portafari
1364 **bead, welding seam**	cordon *m*	Raupe *f*	cordone *m* (di saldatura)
1365 **bead**	perle *f*	Perle *f*	perla *f*
1365a **bead**	nervure *f*	Rippe *f*	nervatura *f*
1366 **bead test**	essai *m* à la perle	Verhalten *n* in der Perle	prova *f* alla perla
1367 **bead weld**	soudure *f* à cordon	Raupenschweissung *f*	saldatura *f* a cordone
1368 **beaded end of a fire-tube, flange of a fire-tube**	bord *m* de tube de fumée	Heizrohrbord *m*, Heizrohrflansch *m*	bordino *m* del tubo del fumo
1369 **beaded fittings** *pl.*	accessoires *m pl.* à rebord	umbördeltes Zubehör *n*	accessori *m pl.* a risvolta
1370 **beaded iron**	fer *m* pour clôtures	Geländer-Eisen *n*	cordonato *m* doppio
1371 **beaded texture**	structure *f* en chapelet	Linsenstruktur *f*	struttura *f* lenticolare
1372 **beaded vein**	filon *m* en chapelet	Linsengang *m*	filone *m* lenticolare
1373 **beading, deposition of beads**	disposition *f* des cordons de soudure	Schweissnahtvorrichtung *f*	disposizione *f* dei cordoni (di saldatura)
1373a **beading**	bordelage *m*	Umbördelung *f*	bordatura *f*
1374 **beak**	cap *m*, éperon	Kap *n*	capo *m*, punta *f*, sperone *m*

		English	French	German	Italian
o	1375	**beak iron**	bigorne f	Hörneramboss m	bicornia f
o	1376	**beak of tin**	bec d'étain	Visiergraupe f	becco m di stagno
o	1377	**beaker**	becher m	Becherglas n	bicchiere m
		beam, s. girder			
o	1378	**beam engine**	machine f à balancier	Schwinghebelmaschine f	macchina f a bilanciere
^	1379	**beam well**	puits m pompé par balancier	Grube f mit Schwinghebelvorrichtung ausgepumpt	pozzo m pompato per mezzo di bilanciere
o	1380	**beams and rafters**	poutrages m pl.	Balkenwerk n	travate f pl.
o	1381	**beams with round edges, angle steel with round edges**	cornière à ailes égales (ou à coins arrondis)	gleichschenkliger Winkelstahl m	angolare ad L a lati uguali (o a spigoli arrotondati)
—	1381a	**beam ore**	limonite f pisolitique	Bohnerz n	limonite f pisolitica
o	1382	**bear, build up, salamander**	loupe f	Ofenbär m, Bodensatz m, Ofensau f	culaccio m
o	1382a	**bear**	loup m	Sau f	blocco m di ferro
^	1383	**bear cat**	puits m à haute production	Grube f mit hoher Produktion	pozzo m di alta produzione
—	1384	**bear frame**	cadre m à col d'oie	Kröpfungsgeviert n	incastellatura f a collo d'oca
o	1384a	**bear punch**	poinçonneuse f portative	Handlochmaschine f	punzonatrice f portatile
—	1385	**beard**	travers-bancs m	Querschlag m	traverso banco m
—	1386	**bearer**	cadre-porteur m	Traggeviert n	quadro m portante
o	1387	**bearing, bush, brass, pillow**	couche f, coussinet, partie f inférieure d'un coussinet	Lagerschale f	cuscinetto m, bronzina f
		bearing, s. strike			
o	1388	**bearing or carrying axle**	essieu m portant	Tragachse f, Laufachse f	asse m portante
o	1389	**bearing bush**	palier m d'appui	Lagerbüchse f	boccola f del supporto, cuscinetto m d'appoggio
o	1390	**bearing capacity**	force f portante	Tragfähigkeit f	capacità f di portanza

	English	French	German	Italian
1391	bearing crib	cadre-porteur *m*, rouet *m*	Traggeviert *n*	trave *f* portante. quadro *m* portante
	bearing curb, *s. bearing-crib*			
1392	bearing door	porte *f* d'aérage	Wettertür *f*	porta *f* di ventilazione
1393	bearing-in	profondeur *f* de la saignée	Schrämtiefe *f*	profondita *f* del taglio (o dell'intaglio)
1394	bearing length	longueur *f* du coussinet	Lagerlänge *f*	lunghezza *f* del cuscinetto
1395	bearing load	charge *f*	Traglast *f*	carico *m*
1396	bearing metal, box metal	métal *m* pour coussinets	Lagermetall *n*	metallo *m* per cuscinetti
1397	bearing plate	plate-forme *f* de support	Tragplatte *f*	piattaforma *f* di supporto
1397a	bearing ring	cadre-porteur *m*	Traggeviert *n*	quadro *m* portante
1398	bearing rod	support *m* du balancier, bielle *f* de suspension	Tragstange *f*	supporto *m* del bilanciere
1399	bearing or suspension spring	ressort *m* de suspension	Tragfeder *f*	molla *f* di sospensione
1400	bearing stop	cloison *f* d'aérage	Wetterscheider *m*	diaframma *f* di ventilazione
1401	bearing surface	face *f* portante	Führungsfläche *f*	faccia *f* portante, superficie *f* d'appoggio
1401a	bearing timber	cadre-porteur *m*	Traggeviert *n*	quadro *m* portante
1402	to beat	battre, frapper	schlagen, klopfen	battere, colpire
1403	beat	affleurement *m*	Ausgehende *n*	affioramento *m*, cappello *m*
1404	beater	bourroir *m*	Ladestock *m*	mazza *f* a rincalzare
1404a	beating	battement *m*	Metallhämmern *n*	battitura *f* dei metalli
1405	beating iron	sabot *m* de bocard	Pochschuh *m*, Pocheisen *n*	zoccolo *m* del mulino
	beating shoe, *s. beating iron*			
1405a	beauxite	bauxite *f*	Bauxit *m*	bauxite *f*

	English	French	German	Italian
— 1406	beaverite	beavérite *f*	Beaverit *m*	beaverite *f*
— 1407	beckelite	beckélite *f*	Beckelith *m*	becchelite *f*
° 1408	becking (forging operation)	élargissement *m*, dégorgement *m* à choc	Ausdehnung *f*, Stossräumen *n*	allargatura *f* ad urto
° 1408a	becking bar	dégorgeoir *m*	Räumnadel *f*	barra *f* di alesatrice
— 1408b	becking stand	chevalet *m*	Bock *m*	cavalletto *m*, sella *f*
^ 1409	to become reemulsioned	se réémulsionner	Reemulgieren *n*	riemulsionarsi
° 1410	to become vitreous	se vitrifier	glasig werden	vetrificarsi
— 1411	becquerelite	becquérélite *f*	Becquerelit *m*	bequerellite *f*
° 1412	bed, to bed in	mettre sur couche	auf das Sandbett stellen	piazzare sul letto di terra, affondare
— 1413	bed, seam	gisement *m*	Lagerstätte *f*	giacimento *m*
° 1414	bed	couche *f* de coulée	Herd *m*, Formherd *m*	piano *m* di colata
° 1415	bed charge	fausse charge *f*, charge *f* de base	Kokssatz *m*	prima *f* carica, carica *f* di base
° 1416	bed-coke	coke *m* d'allumage	Anheizkoks *m*	coke *m* d'accensione, coke *m* di riscaldo, dote *f*
° 1416a	bed die	matrice *f*, forme *f*	Matrize *f*, Form *f*	matrice *f*, forma *f*
° 1417	bed fuel	couche *f* inférieure de combustible	Unterschicht *f* des Brennmaterials *m*	strato *m* inferiore di combustibile
° 1418	bed joint	joint *m* horizontal, fracture ou cassure parallèle à la surface	Horizontalspalte *f*, Spalte parallel zur Oberfläche	giunto *m* orizzontale, incrinatura *f* orizzontale
° 1419	bed plate, base plate	plaque *f* ou taque *f* de fond	Zacken *m*	placca *f* di fondo
° 1420	bed plate, switch plate	plaque *f* d'assise (d'aiguille)	Grundplatte *f*, Tragplatte *f*, Weichenplatte *f*	piastrone *m* (di scambio)
— 1421	bed succession	suite *f* des couches	Schichtenfolge *f*	serie *f* di strati
— 1422	bed vein	filon-couche *m*	Lagergang *m*	vena *f* parallela al piano di stratificazione
_ 1423	bedded	stratifié	geschichtet	stratificato

	English	French	German	Italian
1424	**bedded-in moulding**	troussage *m*	Schablonieren *n*	tornitura *f* a sagoma
1425	**bedded ore deposits**	formations *f pl.* métallifères stratiformes	geschichtete Erzlagerstätten	formazioni *f pl.* metallifere stratificate
1426	**bedded rock. sedimentary rock**	roche *f* stratifiée	geschichtetes Gestein *n*	roccia *f* stratificata
1427	**bedded structure**	structure *f* stratifiée	geschichtete Textur *f*, Lagen-Textur *f*	struttura *f* stratificata
1428	**bedding (in foundry)**	lit *m* de fusion, paillasse *f*	Möllerbett *n*, Schicht *f*	letto *m* di fusione, miscela *f* di carica
1429	**bedding**	mise *f* sur couche	Setzen *n* auf das Sandbett	mettere a placca, placcare
1430	**bedding**	stratification *f*	Schichtung *f*, Lagerung *f*	giacimento *m*, stratificazione *f*
1431	**bedding angle**	angle *m* de stratification	Schichtfallwinkel *m*	angolo *m* di stratificazione
1432	**bedding fault**	glissement *m* dans le plan des couches	Lagersprung *m*, schichtenparallele Verwerfung *f*	slittamento *m* del piano di stratificazione
1433	**bedding of a unit**	soubassement *m*	Lagerung *f*	basamento *m*
1434	**bedding plane**	plan *m* de stratification	Schichtfläche *f*	piano *m* di stratificazione
1435	**bedrock**	roche *f* de lit	Bettgestein *n*	roccia *f* di letto
1436	**beds of passage**	couches *f pl.* de transition	Übergangsschichten *f pl.*	strati *m pl.* di transizione
1437	**beech coal**	charbon de hêtre	Buchenholzkohle *f*	carbone *m* di faggio
1438	**beegerite**	beegérite *f*	Beegerit *m*	beegerite *f*
1439	**beehive oven**	four à ruche	Bienenkorbofen *m*	forno ad alveare
1440	**beele**	pic *m* à deux pointes	Doppelhacke *f*	piccone *m* a due punte
1441	**behaviour in the blast furnace**	comportement *m* dans le haut-fourneau	Verhalten *n* im Hochofen	comportamento dell'alto forno
1442	**beidellite**	beidellite *f*	Beidellit *m*	beidellite *f*

	English	French	German	Italian
— 1443	belemnite	bélemnite *f*	Belemnit *m*	belemnite *f*
° 1444	**Belgian rod mill**	laminoir *m* belge	belgische Drahtstrasse *f*	laminatoio *m* belga
° 1445	**to bell, to flare**	claquer	schlagen	scampanare, accampanare
° 1446	**bell**	cône *m* de fermeture	Verschlusskegel *m*	cono *m* di chiusura
° 1447	**bell**	cloche *f*	Tauchglocke *f*	campana *f* di immersione
° 1448	**bell and hopper arrangement**	dispositif *m* coupe et cône	Gichtverschluss *m*	dispositivo *m* di coperchic e cono
^ 1449	**bell cap**	capuchon *m*	Deckel *m*, Kopf *m*	campanella *f*. cappellotto *m*
— 1450	**bell crusher**	broyeur *m* à cloche	Glockenmühle *f*	macina *f* a campana
° 1451	**bell founding**	fusion *f* de cloches	Glockenguss *m*	fusione *f* di campane
° 1451a	**bell furnace**	four *m* à cloche	Haubenofen *m*	forno *m* a campana
° 1452	**bell hoist**	treuil *m* de cône	Gichtwinde *f*	argano *m* a campana
	bell jar, *s. glass bell*			
° 1452a	**bell-krupp metal**	fonte *f* épurée	Bell-Kruppmetal *n*	ghisa *f* depurata
° 1453	**bell line rope**	câble *m* de signalisation ’	Signalseil *n*	cavo *m* di segnalazione
1454	**bell lifting rod**	tige *f* de suspension (du cône)	Zugstange *f*	barra *f* di sospensione (del cono)
° 1455	**bell lifting rod**	tige *f* du piston	Hubstange *f*	gambo *m* del pistone
° 1456	**bell-metal**	bronze *m* à (ou des) cloches	Glockenmetall *n*, Glockenbronze *f*	bronzo *m* da campane
— 1457	**bell safety rod**	tige *f* de sûreté	Sicherheitsstange *f*	barra *f* di sicurezza (della campana)
° 1458	**bell shaped**	en forme de cloche (de la cloche)	glockenförmig	a forma di campana, accampanato
— 1459	**belt shifter**	passe-courroie *m*	Riemenschieber *m*	sposta-cinghia *m*
— 1460	**bell socket, casing bowl**	arrache-tube *m*, cloche	Rohrfänger *m*	corona *f*, pescatore *m* a campana (per tubi)
— 1461	**bell winch**	treuil *m* de manoeuvre de la cloche	Winde *f* für die Glocke	arganó *m* per la manovra della campana

	English	French	German	Italian
− 1462	**belland**	minerai *m* de plomb pulvérulent	staubiges Bleierz *n*	minerale *m* di piombo pulverulento. piombaggine *f* polverosa
° 1463	**Belleville boiler**	chaudière *f* Belleville	Bellevillekessel *m*	caldaia *f* Belleville
− 1464	**bellite**	bellite *f*	Bellit *m*	bellite *f*
− 1465	**bellman**	encageur *m*	Anschläger *m*	ingabbiatore *m*
° 1466	**bellows**	soufflet *m* de forge	Blasebalg *m*	soffietto *m*, mantice
° 1467	**to belly**	enfler	aufblasen	gonfiare, spanciare
° 1468	**belly**	calotte *f*	Haube *f*, Hals *m*	cupola *f*, collo *m*
° 1469	**belly of the crucible**	ventre *m* du creuset	Tiegelbauch *m*	ventre *m* del crogiuolo
° 1469a	**belly pipe**	conduit *m* du vent	Windleitung *f*	canale *m* del vento
° 1470	**bellying**	bombement *m*, ventre *m*	Ausbauchung *f*	allargamento *m*, accampanatura *f*, scampanatura *f*
− 1471	**belonite**	bélonite *f*	nadelförmiger Kristallit *m*	belonite *f*. cristallite *f* aghiforme
− 1472	**belt conveyance**	transport *m* par bande ou par ruban	Bandförderung *f*	trasporto *m* a nastro
− 1473	**belt conveyor**	transporteur *m* à bande	Transportband *n*	trasportatore *m* a nastro, convogliatore *m* a nastro
− 1474	**belt conveyor for coal**	bande *f* transporteuse (sans fin)	Kohlenbeförderungsband *n*	trasportatore *m* a nastro per carbone
− 1475	**belt driven hammer**	marteau *m* à transmission	Transmissionshammer *m*	maglio *m* con trasmissione a cinghia
° 1476	**belt driven machine**	machine *f* à commande par courroie	Maschine *f* für Riemenbetrieb	macchina *f* con trasmissione a cinghia
^ 1477	**belt driven pump**	pompe *f* commandée par courroie	Riemenpumpe *f*	pompa *f* con trasmissione a cinghia
° 1477a	**belt furnace**	four *m* à tapis	Förderbandofen *m*	forno *m* a nastro trasportatore
° 1478	**belt of cementation**	zone *f* de cémentation	Zementationszone *f*	zona *f* di cementazione
− 1479	**belt of folded strata**	zone *f* plissée	Faltengürtel *m*	zona *f* ripiegata
− 1480	**belt of weathering**	zone *f* d'érosion	Verwitterungszone *f*	zona *f* d'erosione

	English	French	German	Italian
— 1481	belt shifter	mécanisme de débray-age de la courroie	Riemenschalter *m*	spostacinghia *m*
	belt surfacer, *s. finisher*			
— 1482	bementite	bémentite *f*	Bementit *m*	bementite *f*
— 1483	bench	gradin *m*	Absatz *m*	gradino *m*, scalino *m*
— 1484	bench and bench	exploitation *f* par tranches	Scheibenbau *m*	coltivazione *f* a trance
— 1485	bench drill	perceuse *f* d'établi	Tischbohrer *m*	trapano *m* da banco
° 1486	bench drilling machine	perceuse *f* sensitive, foreuse *f* d' établi	Tischbohrmaschine *f*	trapanatrice *f* da banco
° 1486a	bench engine lathe	tour *m* d'établi	Tisch-Leitspindel-drehbank *f*	filettatrice *f* da banco
° 1487	bench horizontal milling machine	fraiseuse *f* horizontale	horizontale Tisch-fraesmaschine *f*	fresatrice *f* orizzontale da banco
° 1488	bench mark	repère *m*	Anhaltspunkt *m*	punto *m* di riferimento (del banco)
— 1489	bench placer	placer *m* de terrasse	Terrassenseife *f*	deposito *m* alluvionale di terrazza
— 1490	bench stoping, stoping	exploitation *f* par gradins, abatage *m* en gradins	Strossenbau *m*, Firstenbau *m*, Stufenbau *m*	coltivazione *f* a gradini, gradinatura
° 1491	bench mould	mouler à la table	auf dem Tisch formen	formare al banco
° 1492	bench moulder	mouleuse *f* d'établi	Tischformpresse *f*	formatrice *f* da banco
° 1493	bench screw cutting lathe, bench engine lathe	tour *m* de filetage, tour *m* d'établi	Tisch-Leitspindel-drehbank *f*	filettatrice *f* da banco
° 1494	bench shaping machine	étau-limeur *m*, limeuse *f*	Tischhobelmaschine *f*	limatrice *f* da banco
° 1495	bench vice	étau *m* (d'établi)	Schraubstock *m*	morsa *f*
— 1496	benching	exploitation *f* par gradins, abattage *m* en gradins	Strossenbau *m*, Firstenbau *m*, Stufenbau *m*	gradinatura *f*, coltivazione *f* a gradini
— 1497	benching	banquette *f*	Seitenstreifen *m*	banchina *f*, spalletta *f*

		English	French	German	Italian
°	1498	**to bend**	plier, courber	biegen	piegare, curvare
°	1499	**to bend round a mandrel**	plier autour d'un mandrin	um einen Dorn biegen	piegare intorno a un mandrino
°	1500	**to bend the rivet iron into a loop**	plier en boucle le fer à rivets	das Nieteisen zu einer Schleife biegen	piegare a nodo il ferro da chiodi
^	1501	**bend**	coude *m*	Krümmling *m*, Rohrkrümmer *m*	gomito *m*
°	1501a	**bend**	charnière *f*	Scharnier *n*	cerniera *f*
—	1502	**bend of ground**	pli *m* de terrain	Bodenfalte *f*	piega *f* del terreno
°	1503	**bend test, bending test**	essai *m* de pliage	Biegeversuch *m*, Biegeprobe *f*	prova *f* di piegamento
°	1504	**bender**	cintreuse *f*	Biegemaschine *f*	piegatrice *f*, curvatrice
°	1505	**bending**	courbage, flexion *f*	Biegung *f*	curvatura *f*, flessione *f*
°	1506	**bending**	retroussement *m*	Umbiegung *f*	incurvamento *m*, (o piega) del terreno
°	1507	**bending angle**	angle *m* de flexion	Biegungswinkel *m*	angolo di curvatura
°	1508	**bending coefficient**	coefficient *m* de pliage	Biegegrösse *f*	coefficente *m* di curvatura (o di piegatura)
°	1509	**bending jaws**	mâchoires *f pl.* de pliage	Biegebacken *f pl.*	mascelle *f pl.* di piegatura
°	1510	**bending line**	ligne *f* de flexion	Biegungslinie *f*	linea *f* di flessione
°	1511	**bending machine**	cintreuse *f*	Biegemaschine *f*	piegatrice *f*, curvatrice *f*
°	1512	**bending moment**	moment *m* fléchissant	Biegungsmoment *n*	momento *m* flettente
°	1513	**bending-off press**	presse *f* à chanfreiner	Abkantpresse *f*	pressa *f* da smussare, piegatrice *f*, profilatrice
°	1514	**bending point**	point *m* de pliage	Biegestelle *f*	punto *m* di piegatura (o di flessione)
°	1515	**bending press**	presse *f* à plier ou à cintrer	Biegepresse *f*	piegatrice, curvatrice
°	1516	**bending radius**	rayon *m* de pliage	Biegehalbmesser *m*	raggio *m* di piegatura o di curvatura

		English	French	German	Italian
°	1517	**bending roll**	cylindre *m* de flexion (ou à cintrer)	Biegewalze *f*	cilindro *m* di flessione, rullo *m* curvatore
°	1518	**bending strain**	effort de flexion, effort transversal, travail à la flexion	Biegebeanspruchung *f*, Biegespannung *f*	sollecitazione *f* a flessione, sforzo di flessione
°	1519	**bending strength**	résistance *f* à la flexion	Biegungsfestigkeit *f*	resistenza *f* a flessione
°	1520	**bending stress**	tension *f* de pliage, effort *m* de flexion	Biegespannung *f*	carico *m* di flessione, sollecitazione *f* a flessione
°	1521	**bending test**	essai *m* de flexion	Biegeprobe *f*	prova *f* di flessione (o di piegatura)

bending test in a cold state, *s. cold bending test*

		English	French	German	Italian
°	1522	**bending test in tempered state**	essai *m* de flexion après trempe	Abschreckbiegeprobe *f*, Härtungsbiegeprobe *f*	prova *f* di piegatura dopo la tempra
°	1523	**bending through 180°, doubling on itself**	pliage à 180°	Biegung *f* um 180°	piegamento *m* a fondo, piegamento *m* a 180°
—	1524	**to beneficiate**	enrichir	aufbereiten	arricchire
—	1525	**benitoite**	bénitoïte *f*	Benitoit *m*	benitoite *f*
—	1526	**benjaminite**	benjaminite *f*	Benjaminit *m*	benjaminite *f*
°	1527	**bent**	tordu, courbé	krumm, gebogen	storto, curvo, curvato
—	1528	**bent**	affaissement *m* du toit	Absenkung *f* der Firste	cedimento *m* del tetto
—	1529	**benthos**	benthos *m*	Benthos *n*	benthos *m*
—	1530	**bentonite**	bentonite *f*	Bentonit *m*	bentonite *f*
^	1530a	**benzene**	benzol *m*	Benzol *n*	benzolo *m*
°	1531	**benzine burner**	brûleur *m* à benzine	Benzinbrenner *m*	bruciatore *m* a benzina
^	1532	**benzol, benzene**	benzol *m*	Benzol *n*	benzolo *m*
—	1533	**beraunite**	beraunite *f*	Beraunit *m*	beraunite *f*
—	1534	**beresite**	bérésite *f*	Beresit *m*	beresite *f*

85

	English	French	German	Italian
— 1535	berg crystal	cristal *m* de roche	Bergkrystall *m*, Bergglas *n*	cristallo *m* di rocca
— 1536	berkelium	berkélium *m*	Berkelium *n*	berchelio *m*
— 1537	berlinite	berlinite *f*	Berlinit *m*	berlinite *f*
— 1537a	berm	banquette *f*	Berme *f*	banchina *f*
— 1538	berme	berme *f*	Böschungsabsatz *m*	berma *f*, banchina *f*
— 1539	berthierite	berthiérite *f*	Berthierit *m*	berthierite *f*
— 1540	Bertrand lens	lentille *f* de Bertrand	Bertrand'sche Linse *f*	lente *f* di Bertrand
— 1541	bertrandite	bertrandite *f*	Bertrandit *m*	Bertrandite *f*
— 1542	beryl	beryl *m*	Beryll *m*	berillo *m*
— 1543	beryllia	oxyde *m* de béryllium	Berylliumoxyd *n*	ossido di berillio
— 1544	beryllium	béryllium *m*	Beryllium *n*	berillio
— 1545	beryllium copper	cupro-béryllium *m*	Berylliumbronze *f*, Kupferberyllium *n*	cuproberillio *m*
— 1546	beryllonite	béryllonite *f*	Beryllonit *m*	berillonite *f*
— 1547	berzelianite	berzélianite *f*	Berzelianit *m*	berzelianite *f*
— 1548	berzeliite	berzéliite *f*	Berzeliit *m*	berzeliite *f*
° 1549	Bessemer basic steel	acier *m* Thomas	Thomasstahl *m*	acciaio *m* Thomas
° 1550	Bessemer converter	convertisseur *m* Bessemer	Bessemerbirne *f*, Bessemerkonverter *m*	convertitore *m* Bessemer
° 1551	Bessemer iron	fer *m* Bessemer	Bessemer Eisen *n*	ferro *m* Bessemer
° 1552	Bessemer pig	fonte *f* Bessemer	Bessemerroheisen *n*	ghisa *f* Bessemer
	Bessemer pig iron, *s. Bessemer pig*			
° 1553	Bessemer process, Bessemerization	procédé *m* Bessemer	Bessemerverfahren *n*, saures Verfahren *n*	processo *m* Bessemer, processo *m* acido
° 1554	Bessemer converter refining process	affinage *m* au convertisseur Bessemer	Bessemerverfahren *n*	affinamento *m* al convertitore Bessemer

		English	French	German	Italian
°	1555	**Bessemer slag**	scorie *f* Bessemer	Bessemerschlacke *f*	scoria *f* Bessemer
°	1556	**Bessemer-steel**	fer *m* homogène (ou acier) Bessemer	Bessemerflusstahl *m* Bessemerstahl *m*	ferro *m* fuso Bessemer, acciaio *m* acido
°	1557	**Bessemer steel and Thomas Works**	aciéries *f.pl.* Bessemer et Thomas	Bessemer-und Thomasanlage *f pl.*	acciaierie Bessemer e Thomas
°	1558	**Bessemer steel works**	acièrie *f* Bessemer	Bessemerstahlwerk *n*	acciaieria *f* Bessemer
°	1559	**bessemerization**	procédé *m* Bessemer, procédé acide	Bessemerverfahren *n*	procedimento Bessemer, trattamento Bessemer
°	1560	**to bessemerize**	traiter la fonte par le procédé Bessemer	bessemern	trattare la ghisa col procedimento Bessemer
		bessemerizing, *s. Bessemer process*			
°	1560a	**best bar**	fer *m* ébauché ·	Rohschiene *f*	billetta *f* di ferro grezzo
		best coal, *s. large coal*			
°	1561	**best foundry pig iron**	fonte *f* spéciale pour pièces de machines	Bestmaschinenguss-eisen *n*	ghisa *f* buona per pezzi di macchine
°	1561a	**best iron**	fer *m* doux	Schmiedeeisen *n*	ferro *m* dolce
°	1562	**best plate iron**	fer *m* pour tôles de qualité supérieure	Platteneisen *n* bester Qualität	ferro *m* per lamiere di qualità superiore
—	1563	**best-quality coal**	charbon *m* de la meilleure qualité	Kohle *f* bester Qualität	carbone *m* in pezzi grossi
°	1564	**best selected copper**	cuivre *m* au 99,75	Bestkupfer *n* (99,75%)	rame al 99,75%
°	1564a	**best tap**	oxyde *m* magnétique pur de fer	reines magnetisches Eisenoxyd *n*	ossido *m* magnetico di ferro puro
°	1565	**beta iron**	fer *m* bêta	Beta-Eisen *n*	ferro beta *m*
—	1566	**betafite**	béton *m*	Beton *m*	calcestruzzo *m*
°	1567	**bevel**	biseau *m*, chanfrein *m*	Abschrägung *f*	bisello *m*, taglio a sbiego
°	1567a	**bevel coupling**	embrayage *m* à cônes	Kegelkupplung *f*	innesto *m* a cono
°	1568	**bevel head**	cordon conique	Kegelnaht *f*	codolo *m* conico
°	1569	**bevel gear**	engrenage *m* conique	Kegelräder *f*	ingranaggio *m* conico
°	1570	**bevel protractor**	sauterelle *f*, fausse équerre *f*	Stellwinkel *m* Schmiege *f*	squadra *f* zoppa (o falsa)
°	1571	**bevel scale with knob**	règle *f* divisée,dou-ble décimètre *m*	Anleg(e)massstab *m*	doppio decimetro *m*

		English	French	German	Italian
°	1572	**bevelled, chamfered**	biseauté, chanfreiné	abgeschrägt	tagliato in sbieco, smussato
°	1572a	**bevelling**	conique	konisch	conico
		bevel s. *shank or ladle shank*			
—	1573	**Bian's washer**	laveur *m* Bian	Bianscher Wascher *m*	deputatore *m* Bian
		Bibus'blower, s. *rotary blower*			
—	1574	**biche**	cloche *f* à écrou, cloche *f* de repêchage	Fangglocke *f*	pescatore *m* a campana, corona *f*
°	1575	**bichromate of potassium**	bichromate *m* de potasse	Kaliumbichromat *n*	bicromato *m* potassico
—	1576	**bieberite**	biebérite *f*	Bieberit *m*	bieberite *f*
°	1577	**bifurcated or forked pipe**	tuyau *m* bifurqué	gabelförmiges Rohr *n*, Gabelrohr *n*	tubo *m* biforcato
°	1578	**big mill, breaking down mill**	train *m* ébaucheur, train *m* de puddlage	Grobstrecke *f*, Grobeisenstrasse *f*	treno *m* sbozzatore
—	1579	**bilinite**	bilinite *f*	Bilinit *m*	bilinite *f*
	1580	**bill of quantities**	avant-métré *m*	Leistungsverzeichnis	computo *m* metrico
°	1581	**billet**	billette *f*	Knüppel *m*	billetta *f*
°	1582	**billet iron**	fer *m* en billette	Knüppeleisen *n*	ferro *m* in billette
		billet mill, s. *billet rolling mill*			
°	1582a	**billet roll**	cylindre *m* ébaucheur	Vorwalze *f*	cilindro *m* sbozzatore
°	1583	**billet rolling mill, billet mill**	laminoir *m* à billettes	Knüppelwalzwerk *n*	laminatoio *m* per billette
°	1584	**billet shears**	cisaille *f* à billettes	Knüppelschere *f*	cesoia *f* per billette
°	1585	**billet or bloom trolley**	wagonnet *m* à lingots	Blockwagen *m*	carro *m* per lingotti
°	1586	**billet steel, new-billet steel**	acier *m* en billette	Knüppelstahl *m*	acciaio *m* in billette
		billets, s. *small iron bars*			
—	1587	**billy playfair**	balance *f* automatique pour fines	automatische Waage *f* für Kohlenklein	bilancia *f* automatica per fini da coke

		English	French	German	Italian
°	1588	**bimetal tube**	tube *m* bimétallique	metallplattiertes Rohr *n* (mit Ausplattierung oder Innenfutterung)	tubo *m* bimetallico
°	1589	**bimetallic**	bimétallique	bimetallisch	bimetallico
—	1589a	**bin**	soute *f* à charbon	Bunker *m*	carbonile *m*
°	1590	**binary alloy**	alliage *m* binaire	binäre Legierung *f*	lega *f* binaria
—	1591	**binary granite**	granit *m* à deux micas	Zweiglimmergranit *m*	granito *m* a due miche (o binario)
°	1592	**binary steel**	acier *m* binaire	Binärstahl *m*	acciaio *m* binario
°	1593	**to bind (or wind) the core spindle**	envelopper la tige du noyau	die Kernspindel umwickeln	avvolgere l'armatura dell'anima o (la lanterna per anime)
—	1594	**bind**	schiste *m* bitumineux	bituminöser Tonschiefer *m*	scisto *m* bituminoso
—	1595	**bind**	amincissement *m* en coin	Auskeilen *n*	restringimento *m* a cuneo, appuntimento *m*
—	1596	**bindheimite**	bindheimite *f*	Bindheimit *m*	bindheimite *f*
°	1597	**binder**	liant *m*	Bindemittel *n*	legante *m*, sostanza *f* legante
°	1598	**binder**	déchet *m*	Abfall *m*	cartella *f* (sfrido di lamiera)
°	1598a	**binder**	châssis *m* à démotter	Abschlagrahmen *m*	staffa *f* a cerniera
°	1599	**binder core**	portée *f*	Schloss *n*	portata *f* (dell'anima)
°	1599a	**binder phase**	phase *f* liante	Bindephase *f*	fase *f* legante
°	1600	**binding, winding**	enroulement *m*	Umwicklung *f*	avvolgimento *m*
°	1601	**binding core**	portée *f* du noyau	Schloss *n*	portata *f* dell'anima
		binding power, *s. cementing power*			
°	1602	**binding material, binding agent**	liant *m*, matière *f* agglomérante	Bindemittel *n*	agglutinante *m*, materiale legante
°	1603	**binding rig**	anneau *m* de serrage	Stellring *m*	vite *f* di pressione, serrafilo *m*
—	1604	**bing**	minerai *m* riche de plomb	reiches Bleierz *n*	minerale *m* ricco di piombo

		English	French	German	Italian
—	1605	**bing**	terril, halde	Halde *f*	ammasso *m* di materiale sterile
—	1606	**bingstead**	installation *f* de traitement de minerai de plomb	Aufbereitungsanlage *f* für Bleierze	impianto *m* per il trattamento di minerale di piombo
—	1607	**binnite**	binnite *f*	Binnit *n*	binnite *f*
		biolite, *s. biolith*			
—	1608	**biolith**	biolite *f*	Biolith *m*	biolite *f*
—	1609	**biotite**	biotite *f*	Biotit *m*	biotite *f*
—	1610	**biotite gneiss**	gneiss *m* à biotite	Biotigneis *m*	gneiss *m* a biotite
—	1611	**birch coal**	charbon *m* de bouleau	Birkenkohle *f*	carbone *m* di betulla
		bird shot, *s. tare shot*			
—	1612	**bisbeeite**	bisbéeite *f*	Bisbeeit *m*	bisbeeite *f*
—	1613	**bischofite**	bischofite *f*	Bischofit *m*	bischofite *f*
—	1614	**bismite**	bismite *f*	Bismit, Wismutocker *m*	bismite *f*
—	1615	**bismuth**	bismuth *m*	Wismut *n*	bismuto *m*
—	1616	**bismuth glance.**	bismuthine *f*	Wismutglanz *m*	bismutina *f*
°	1617	**bismuth solder**	soudure *f* au bismuth	Wismutlot *n*	saldatura *f* al bismuto
—	1618	**bismuth telluride**	tétradymite *f*	Tetradymit *m*	tetradimite *f*
		bismuthinite, *s. bismuth glance*			
—	1619	**bismutoplagionite**	bismutoplagionite *f*	Bismutoplagionit *m*	bismutoplagionite *f*
—	1620	**bismutosphaerite**	bismuthosphérite *f*	Bismutosphärit *m*	bismutosferite *f*
—	1621	**bismutotantalite**	bismutotantalite *f*	Bismutotantalit *m*	bismutotantalite *f*
—	1622	**bit**	bit *m*, taillant *m* fleuret *m*, trépan	Schneide *f*, Meissel Bohrer *m*	punta *f*, taglio *m*, saetta *f*, mecchia *f*,
—	1623	**bit**	fragment *m*, morceau	Stück *n*	frammento *m*, pezzo *m*
—	1624	**bit blade**	lame *f* du trépan	Meisselblatt *n*	lama *f* del trapano

		English	French	German	Italian
—	1625	bit breaker	débloqueur de trépan	Meisselbrecher *m*	piastra *f* sagomata (per svitare lo scalpello)
—	1626	bit hook	caracole à trépan	Meisselfanghaken *m*	pescatore *m* per trapano
—	1627	bit neck	col *m* du trépan	Meisselhals *m*	collo *m* del trapano
—	1628	bit pin	tenon *m* du trépan	Meisselzapfen *m*	tenone *m* del trapano
—	1629	bit sample	échantillon *m* de trépan	Meisselprobe *f*	campione *m* di trapano
—	1630	bit wings	ailes *f pl.* du trépan	Meisselflügel *m pl.*	ali *f pl.* del trapano
°	1630a	to bite	attaquer à l'acide	ätzen	attaccare con l'acido
		to bite the piece, *s. to grip the piece*			
—	1631	bitter earth	magnésie *f*	Magnesia *f*	magnesia *f*
—	1632	bitter salt	epsomite *f*	Bittersalz *n*	solfato *m* di magnesio
—	1633	bitter spar	dolomite *f*	Bitterspat *m*, Dolomit *m*	dolomite *f*
—	1634	bituminous coal, fat coal, soft coal	charbon *m* bitumineux, houille *f* grasse, charbon gras, charbon mou	bituminöse Kohle *f*, Fettkohle *f*, Weichkohle *f*	carbone *m* bituminoso, carbone *m* grasso
—	1635	bituminous peat	tourbe *f* grasse	fetter Torf *m*	torba *f* grassa
—	1636	bituminous pitch	poix *f* (ou brai *m)* d'asphalte	Asphaltpech *n*	pece *f* d'asfalto o di catrame di lignite
—	1637	bituminous rock	roche *f* bitumineuse	bituminöses Gestein *n*	roccia *f* bituminosa
—	1638	bitusol	asphalte *m* de Trinité	Trinidadasphalt *m*	asfalto *m* di Trinidad
—	1639	bityite	bityite *f*	Bityit *m*	bityite *f*
°	1640	to black (a mold)	noircir	nass schwärzen, schlichten	dare la tinta, applicare il nero
°	1641	to black	noircir	trocken schwärzen	dare (o applicare) il nero in polvere
c	1641a	black annealing	recuit *m* en noir	Schwarzglühen *n*	ricottura *f* in nero
°	1642	black annealed wire	fil *m* de fer recuit noir	schwarzer Weichdraht *m*	filo *m* ricotto nero
°	1643	black band	black-band *m*	Blackband *n*	black-band *m*, ferro *m* carbonato

		English	French	German	Italian
°	1644	black-band ironstone	black-band *m*	Blackband *n*	ferro *m* carbonato
—	1645	black bat	schiste houiller ou pyroschiste	Brandschiefer *m*,	scisto *m* carbonifero o bituminoso, piroscisto *m*
		black bog, *s. low level bog*			
—	1646	black chalk	craie *f* noire	Schwarzkreide *f*	gesso *m* nero
		black charcoal, *s. common charcoal*			
—	1647	black copper, raw copper	cuivre noir	Schwarzkupfer *n*, Rohkupfer *n*	rame nero, rame greggio
—	1648	black damp	air *m* vicié	mattes Wetter *n* Stickluft *f*, Stickwetter *n*	aria *f* viziata, aria *f* con grisou
°	1648a	black diamond	bort *m*	Bort *m*	diamante *m* Bort
—	1649	black iron ore	psilomélane *m*	Psilomelan *m*	psilomelano *m*
°	1650	black iron pipe	tube *m* noir en fer	Eisenschwarzrohr *n*	tubo *m* nero in ferro
—	1651	black jack	blende *f* obscure	dunkle Zinkblende *f*	blenda *f* scura
—	1652	black jack	intercalation *f* de charbon schisteux	Zwischenlage von schieferiger Kohle *f*	intercalazione *f* di carbone scistoso
—	1653	black Jura	Jura *m* noir	schwarzer Jura *m*	Jura *m* nero, Lias *m*
—	1654	black lead, graphite	graphite *m*	Graphit *m*	grafite *f*, piombaggine *f*
—	1655	black lignite	charbon *m* subbitumineux	schwarzer Lignit *m*	carbone *m* subbituminoso, lignite *f*
—	1656	black mica	biotite *f*	Biotit *m*	biotite *f*
°	1657	black needles	aiguilles *f pl.* noires	schwarze Nadeln *f pl.*	aghi *m pl.* neri
—	1657a	black oxide of iron	magnétite *f*	Magnetit *m*	magnetite *f*
^	1658	black oil	mazout *m*	Mazut *m*	petrolio *m* grezzo
—	1659	black ore	pyrite *f* cuivreuse oxydée	teilweise zersetzter Kupferpyrit *m*	pirite *f* rameosa ossidata
°	1660	black pig iron	fonte *f* graphiteuse	schwarzes Roheisen *n*	ghisa *f* grafitosa *f*, ghisa *f* nera
°	1661	black plate, black sheet	tôle *f* noire	Schwarzblech *n*	lamiera *f* nera

	English	French	German	Italian
° 1662	**black red heat**	porté au rouge naissant	schwarzrotglühend	portato al calor rosso scuro
° 1663	**black sand**	terre f noire, sable m vieux	Schwarzsand m, Altsand m	terra f mista a nero di fonderia, terra f vecchia
° 1664	**black-sheet, sheet iron**	tôle f noire, tôle f en fer (noire)	Schwarzblech n, Eisenblech n	lamiera f nera, lamierino m
— 1665	**black silver**	stéphanite f	Stephanit m	stefanite f, argento m nero
— 1666	**black stone**	schiste m charbonneux	Kohlenschiefer m	scisto m carbonifero
° 1667	**black strips**	bandes noires	Schwarzstreifen m pl.	bande f pl. nere
— 1668	**blackband**	fer carbonaté lithoïde, mineral houillé	Kohleneisenstein m, Weisserz n	sferosiderite f carboniosa
° 1668a	**blackwash**	noir m de fonderie	Kohlenstaub m	nero m di fonderia
	to blacken, s. *to paint black, or to black*			
° 1668b	**blackening**	noircissage m	Schwärzen n	annerimento m
° 1669	**blackheart iron**	fonte f à coeur noir	schwarzer Temperguss m	ghisa f a cuore nero
° 1670	**blackheart malleable cast iron**	fonte f malléable à coeur noir, fonte f malléable américaine	schwarzer Temperguss m	ghisa f malleabile a cuore nero, ghisa f malleabile americana
° 1671	**black-hot short iron**	fer cassant à chaud noir	schwarzbrüchiges Eisen n	ferro vetrino a caldo nero
° 1672	**blacking, blackening**	noircissage m	Schwärzen n	rivestimento m con nero di fonderia
	blacking, s. *dressing*			
° 1673	**blacking holes**	soufflures f pl. (ou retassures) internes	Gussloch n mit Kohlenstoffen, Innenlunker m	cavità contenenti materie carboniose, risucchio m interno
° 1674	**blacking scab**	dartre f franche	festsitzende Schwärzeschülpe f	sfoglia f di tinta aperta
° 1675	**blacking scab**	dartre f volante	abgespülte Schwärzeschülpe f	sfoglia f di tinta libera
— 1676	**blacks**	schiste m argileux tendre	weicher Tonschiefer m	scisto m argilloso tenero, argilla f scistosa

English	French	German	Italian
○ 1677 **blackwork**	pièces *f pl.* forgées brutes	Rohling *m*	pezzi *m pl.* fucinati grezzi
— 1677a**bland coal**	charbon *m* maigre	Magerkohle *f*	carbone *m* magro
○ 1678 **blank**	fromage *m*	Bodenstein *m*, Tiegeluntersatz *m*	formaggella *f* rullata
○ 1679 **blank**	ébauche *m*, lopin *m*	Rohling *m*, Blankett *m*	sbozzato *m*, sbozzo *m*, scapolato *m*
○ 1680 **blank**	brut	roh	greggio
blank anneal, s. *close annealing*			
— 1681 **blank bit**	couronne *f*	Bohrkrone *f*	corona *f* (di trivellazione)
○ 1681a**blank carburizing**	pseudocémentation *f*	Pseudozementieren *n*	pseudocementazione *f*
blank cutting, s. *blanking*			
— 1682 **blank flange**	bride *f* fausse	Blindflansch *m*, Deckelflansch *m*	flangia *f* cieca
○ 1683 **blank holder**	presse-tôle *m*. support *m* de pièce	Blechhalter *m*, Gegenhalter *m*	premilamiera *m*, portapezzo *m*
○ 1684 **blank pipe**	tube *m* à paroi pleine	blindes Rohr *n*	tubo *m* a parete piena
○ 1685 **blank test**	essai *m* à blanc	Leerversuch *m*	prova *f* a vuoto
— 1686 **blanket**	couche *f*, filon-couche *m* horizontal	Schicht *f*, Flöz *n*, Decke *f*	strato *m*, filone *m*, filone *m* parallelo al piano di stratificazione
○ 1687 **blanket**	couverture *f*	Überzug *m*	rivestimento *m*, copertura *f*
— 1688 **blanket**	couverture *f*	Decke *f*	setto di stoffa
— 1689 **blanket basalt**	basalte *m* en nappes	Deckbasalt *m*	basalto *m* di copertura
^ 1690 **blanket lease**	adjudication *f* pour gros travaux de sondage	Grossbohrenakkord *m*	appalto *m* per grandi lavori di perforazione
— 1691 **blanket sand**	dépôt *m* de sable alluvionnaire	Schwemmsand *m*	deposito *m* di sabbia alluvionale
1692 **blanket steam**	vapeur *f* de tête	Kopfdampf *m*	vapore *m* di testa
— 1693 **blanket table**	table *f* à toile	Tuchtisch *m*	tavola *f* di tela
^ 1694 **blanket term**	condition *f* générale	allgemeine Bedingung *f*	condizione *f* generale

	English	French	German	Italian
− 1695	blanket vein	filon-couche *m* horizontal	horizontaler Lagergang *m*	filone *m* parallelo al piano di stratificazione
° 1695a	blanking	découpage *m* d'un flanc	Ausschneiden *n*	tranciatura *f*
° 1696	to blast	dessabler	entsanden	sabbiare, togliere la sabbia
− 1697	to blast	tirer	sprengen	far saltare, far brillare
° 1698	blast, wind	air, vent *m*	Gebläseluft *f*, Wind *m*	aria *f*, vento *m*
− 1698a	blast	explosion *f*	Sprengung *f*	esplosione *f*
− 1698b	blast air	air *m*, vent *m*	Wind *m*	vento *m*, aria *f*
° 1699	blast box	boîte *f* à vent	Windkasten *m*	cassa *f* del vento, camera *f* d'aria
° 1700	blast burner	brûleur *m* pour soufflerie	Gebläsebrenner *m*	bruciatore *m* per soffieria
° 1701	blast capacity	quantité *f* de vent	Windmenge *f*	quantità *f* d'aria o del vento
° 1702	blast connection	porte-vent *m*	Düsenstock *m*, Windstock *m*	portavento *m*
° 1703	blast control blast regulator	régulateur *m* de débit de vent	Windschieber *m*	regolatore *m* di portata
	blast distribution, *s. air distribution*			
° 1704	blast engine	machine *f* soufflante	Gebläsemaschine *f*	soffiante *f*
− 1705	blast firing	sautage *m*	Sprengen *n*	abbattimento *m* con esplosivo
° 1706	blast furnace, wind furnace	haut fourneau *m*	Hochofen *m* Blasofen *m*, Blaseofen *m*	alto-forno *m*
° 1707	blast furnace blower	soufflante *f* de haut fourneau	Hochofen-Gebläse *n*	soffiante di altoforno
° 1708	blast furnace cone	cloche *f* de haut fourneau	Gichtglocke *f*	campana *f* di altoforno
° 1709	blast furnace coke	coke *m* de haut-fourneau	Hochofenkoks *m*	coke *m* d'alto forno
° 1710	blast furnace construction	construction *f* du haut-fourneau	Hochofenbau *m*, Aufbau *m*	costruzione d'altoforno

		English	French	German	Italian
°	1711	**blast furnace drawing**	plan *m* de haut-fourneau	Hochofenzeichnung *f*	disegno *m* d'altoforno
°	1712	**blast furnace gas**	gaz *m* du gueulard	Gichtgas *n*	gas *m* d'altoforno
°	1713	**blast furnace plant**	installation *f* de hauts fourneaux	Hochofenwerk *n*, Hochofenanlage *f*	stabilimento *m* di alti-forni
°	1714	**blast furnace process**	allure *f* du haut-fourneau	Verlauf *m* des Hochofenganges	andamento o marcia dell'altoforno
°	1715	**blast furnace section**	profil *m* de haut-fourneau	Hochofenriss *m*	profilo *m* d'un altoforno
°	1716	**blast furnace sinter**	aggloméré *m* pour haut-fourneau	Hochofensinter *m*	agglomerato *m* per altoforno
°	1717	**blast furnace slag**	laitier *m* du haut-fourneau	Hochofenschlacke *f*	scoria o loppa *f* di altoforno
°	1718	**blast-furnace slag cement**	ciment *m* de haut fourneau	Hochofen-Zement *m*, Hüttenzement *m*	cemento *m* d'altoforno, cemento *m* di scorie
°	1719	**blast furnace slag treated with steam**	laitier *m* de haut-fourneau traité à la vapeur	mit Dampf behandel-te Hochofenschlak-ke *f*	scoria *f* d'altoforno trattata al vapore
°	1720	**blast furnace smelting**	fusion *f* au haut-fourneau	Hochofenschmelze *f*	fusione *f* nell'alto-forno
		blast furnace stove, s. *cowper stove*			
°	1721	**blast furnace with chamber hearth**	haut-fourneau *m* en-veloppé	Hochofen *m* mit ein-gebautem Gestell	altoforno *m* rivestito
°	1722	**blast furnace with closed hearth**	haut-fourneau *m* à poitrine fermée	Hochofen *m* mit ge-schlossener Brust	altoforno *m* a crogiolo chiuso
°	1723	**blast furnace with open hearth**	haut-fourneau *m* à poitrine ouverte	Hochofen *m* mit offe-ner Brust	altoforno *m* con crogiuo-lo aperto
°	1724	**blast furnace with oval hearth**	haut-fourneau *m* à creuset ovale	Hochofen *m* mit ova-lem Gestell	altoforno *m* con crogiuo-lo ovale
°	1725	**blast furnace with rough brickwork**	haut-fourneau *m* avec massif en maçonnerie	Hochofen *m* mit Rauhgemäuer	altoforno *m* in muratura massiccia
°	1726	**blast furnace with sheet iron shell**	haut-fourneau *m* à enveloppe en tôle	Hochofen *m* mit Blechmantel	altoforno *m* blindato
°	1727	**blast gate**	registre *m* du vent, régulateur *m* du vent	Windschieber *m*	regolatore *m* del vento

		English	French	German	Italian
o	1728	**blast gauge**	indicateur *m* de tirage	Windmesser *m*	misuratore *m* del tiraggio
—	1729	**blast hole**	trou *m* de mine	Schuss *m*, Sprengschuss *m*	foro *m* da mina, pozzetto *m* di scoppio
o	1730	**blast inlet**	admission *f* du vent	Windzuführung *f*	entrata *f* dell'aria
o	1731	**blast inlet**	orifice *m* d'admission du vent	Windloch *n*	foro *m* del vento
o	1731a	**blast main**	conduite *f* de vent principale	Hauptwindleitung *f*	condotto *m* principale del vento
o	1731b	**blast pipe**	conduite *f* du vent	Windleitung *f*	condotto *m* del vento
o	1732	**blast pressure**	pression *f* du vent	Windpressung *f*, Pressung *f* des Windes	pressione *f* dell'aria o del vento
		blast regulator, s. *blast control*			
o	1732a	**blast roasting**	grillage *m* forcé	Schnellröstung *f*	arrostimento *m* forzato
		blast tank, s. *blast box*			
o	1733	**blast tube**	tubulure *f* (du porte-vent)	Anschlussstutzen *m* (an den Windkranz)	bocchettone *m*
o	1734	**blast valve**	soupape *f* à vent	Windventil *n*	valvola *f* del vento
—	1735	**blasted ore**	minerai *m* abattu	herausgesprengtes Erz *n*	minerale *m* abbattuto
—	1736	**blaster**	boutefeu *m*	Sprengmeister *m*	artificere *m*
o	1737	**blaster**	sableuse *f*	Sandstrahler *m*	sabbiatrice *f*, pulitrice *f* a getto di sabbia
—	1738	**blaster cap**	détonateur *m*	Sprengkapsel *f*	detonatore *m*, capsula *f*
—	1739	**blaster fuse**	mèche *f* de Bickford	Zündschnur *f*	miccia *f* di Bickford
—	1740	**blaster oil**	nitroglycérine *f*	Nitroglyzerin *n*	nitroglicerina *f*
—	1741	**blasthole**	chambre *f* de mine	Bohrloch *n*, Schiessloch *n*	foro *m* da mina
o	1742	**blasting**	dessablage *m*	Entsanden *n*	sabbiatura *f*, pulitura della sabbia
—	1743	**blasting**	tir *m*, sautage *m*	Sprengen *n*, Schiessarbeit *f*	brillamento *m*, abbattimento *m* con esplosivi
—	1744	**blasting agent, explosive**	(agent) explosif	Sprengmittel *n*, Sprengstoff *m*	(agente) esplosivo, sostanza *f* esplosiva

		English	French	German	Italian
−	1745	blasting cap	détonateur m, capsule f	Sprengkapsel f	detonatore m, capsula f fulminante
−	1746	blasting cap crimper	pince f à sertir	Sprengkapselzange f	pinze f pl. per capsule
−	1747	blasting charge	charge f de mine	Sprengladung f	carica f esplosiva
−	1747a	blasting fuse	mèche f de Bickford	Zündschnur f von Bickford	miccia f di Bickford
−	1748	blasting gelatine	gélatine f explosive	Sprenggelatine f	gelatina f esplosiva, dinamite f
−	1748a	blasting hole	trou m de mine	Sprengschuss m	foro m da mina
▸−	1749	blasting machine	exploseur m	Zündmaschine f	esploditore m elettrico
		blasting oil, s. blaster oil			
−	1750	blasting powder	poudre f de mine	Sprengpulver n	polvere f esplosiva. polvere f nera
−	1751	blastogranitic	blastogranitique	blastogranitisch	blastogranitico
−	1752	blastoporphyric texture	texture f blastoporphyrique	blastoporphyrische Struktur f	struttura f blastoporfirica
°	1753	to blaze off	recuire (l'acier) par le flambage	abbrennen	ricuocere (l'acciaio) alla fiamma, rinvenire in olio
°	1753a	blazed iron	fonte f au vent	erblasenes Roheisen	ghisa f grigio-siliciosa
°	1754	bleb	soufflure f	Blase f, Gussblase f	soffiatura f
°	1755	to bleed pressure, to blow down pressure	faire une décompression, purger	Druck ablassen, ablassen	diminuire la pressione
^	1756	bleeder	soupape f de décharge	Auslasshahn m	scarico m, valvola f (o rubinetto) di scarico
−	1757	bleeding	éruption f	Ausbruch m	eruzione f
		bleeding (casting defect), s. runout			
^	1758	bleeding	séparation f	Scheidung f	separazione f
−	1759	bleeding core, weeping core	carotte f exsudante	schweisstreibender Bohrkern m	carota f trasudante
−	1760	bleischweif	bleischweif	Bleischweif m	bleischweif m
−	1761	blende, sphalerite, mock lead	blende f, sphalérite f	(Zink)Blende f, Sphalerit m	blenda f, sfalerite f

		English	French	German	Italian
°	1762	blende concentrate	concentré m de blende	Blendenkonzentrat n	concentrato di blenda
°	1763	blende roasting furnace	four m à calciner la blende	Blenderöstofen m	forno m di arrostimento della blenda
^	1764	blended fuel	combustible composé	Verbundbrennstoff m	combustibile composto
°	1765	to blind	blinder	panzern	blindare, proteggere
—	1766	blind	aveugle	blind	cieco, senza affioramento
—	1767	blind	fumée f pl, gaz m pl. délétères	Nachschwaden n	gas m pl. deleteri, esalazioni f pl. di grisou
—	1767a	blind bore	trou m borgne	Sackloch n	foro m cieco
—	1768	blind coal, anthracite	charbon m sec	magere Steinkohle f, Magerkohle f	antracite f, carbone m a fiamma corta
—	1769	blind copper	cuivre m ampoulé	Rohkupfer n	rame m grezzo
°	1770	blind core	noyau m borgne	blinder Kern m	anima f cieca, cuore m cieco
—	1771	blind drift	galerie f en cul-de-sac	Blindstrecke f	galleria f cieca, cunicolo m cieco
°	1772	blind feeder	masselotte f borgne	geschlossener Spreizer m	materozza f cieca
—	1773	blind flange	bride f pleine	Blindflansch m	flangia f piena
—	1774	blind hole	trou m borgne	Blindort m	foro m cieco
—	1775	blind joint	schistosité f confuse	versteckte Spalte f	scistosità f confusa, giunto virtuale
—	1776	blind level	niveau m intermédiaire	Zwischensohle f, Teilsohle f	livello m intermedio
—	1777	blind level	galerie d'exhaure	Wasserstrecke f	galleria f di scolo
—	1778	blind lode	filon m sans affleurement	verdeckter Gang m	filone m senza affioramento
		blind nut, s. cap nut			
		blind pass, s. false pass			
—	1779	blind pit	puits m intérieur, bure f	Blindschacht m, Gesenk n	pozzo m interno (o cieco), falso pozzo m
		blind roaster, s. muffle-furnace			

		English	French	German	Italian
o	1780	**blister, air bubble**	cloque *f*	Blase *f*	bolla *f* d'aria
o	1780a	**blister**	poquette *f*	Wanze *f*	ruvidezza *f*
o	1781	**blister**	soufflure *f*	Blase *f*, Gasblase *f*	soffiatura *f*, bolla *f*
o	1781a	**to blister**	s'écailler	abblättern	screpolarsi, sfaldarsi
o	1782	**blister bar, cemented bar, converted bar**	barre *f* cimentée	zementierter Stab *m* Zementstahlstab *m*	barra *f* cementata
o	1783	**blister copper**	cuivre *m* noir, cuivre à soufflures	Schwarzkupfer *n*, Rohkupfer *n*	rame *m* nero, rame *m* a soffiature
o	1784	**blister steel**	acier *m* boursouflé	Blasenstahl *m*, Zementstahl *m*	acciaio *m* da cementazione, acciaio *m* cementato, acciaio *m* vescicolare
o	1785	**blistered**	crépelé	krispelig, gekräuselt	increspato
o	1786	**blister-free steel**	acier *m* sans soufflures	blasenfreier Stahl *m*	acciaio *m* senza soffiature
o	1787	**blistering**	écaillage *m*	Abblättern *n*	vescicatura *f*, scagliatura *f*
ɔ	1788	**blistering**	traitement *m* par soufflage au convertisseur	Verblasen *n*	trattamento *m* a mezzo soffiaggio al convertitore
ɔ	1789	**blisters** *pl.*	pustule *f*, poquette *f*	Wanze *f*	ruvidezza *f*
–	1790	**to block hole**	fragmenter par explosif	nachsprengen	frantumare con esplosivi
–	1791	**to block out**	sous-caver	unterhöhlen	tagliare al di sotto
–	1792	**to block up**	caler, étançonner	verkeilen, festmachen	inchiavettare, bloccare, puntellare
–	1793	**block**	bloc *m*	Block *m*, Klotz *m*	blocco *m*
o	1794	**block**	paquet *m*	Puddelpaket *n*	pacchetto *m* di ferro (da puddellare)
–	1795	**block and falls**	palan *m*	Flaschenzug *m*	paranco *m*, taglia *f* mobile
–	1796	**block and tackle**	moufle *m*	Flaschenzug *m*	paranco *m* a puleggia doppia, taglia *f*
–	1797	**block caving**	foudroyage *m* en masse du minerai	Blockbruchbau *m*	coltivazione *f* per franamento a blocchi

		English	French	German	Italian
−	1798	block coal	gailleterie *f*	Stückkohle *f*	carbone *m* a cubetti
−	1799	block disintegration	désintégration *f* en blocs	Blockzerfall *m*	disintegrazione *f* a blocchi
−	1800	block-fault	faille *f* tabulaire	Tafelbruch *m*	faglia *f* tabulare
−	1801	block faulting	morcellement *m* par failles	Tafelbruchbildung *f*	suddividere *f* in faglie
−	1802	block holing	tir *m* par pétards	Knäppersprengung *f*	minaggio *m* di blocchi
°	1802a	block iron	paquet *m*	Puddelpaket *n*	pacchetto *m* di ferro
−	1803	block mountain	terrain *m* faillé	Schollengebirge *n*	terreno *m* fagliato
°	1803a	block pattern	modèle *m* complet	komplettes Modell	modello *m* completo
−	1804	block pulley	moufles *f. pl.*	Flaschenzug *m*	paranco *m*
		block sequence, *s. block welding*			
°	1805	block-tin	étain en saumons	Blockzinn *n*	stagno *m* in pani
^	1806	blocked operations	opérations *f pl.* alternatives	wechselweise Arbeiten *f pl.*	operazioni *f pl.* alternate
−	1807	blocking	calage *m*	Verkeilen *n*	inchiavettatura *f*, puntellamento *m*
		blocking, *s. pigging up*			
°	1808	blocking	ébauchage *m*	Vorwalzen *n*	sbozzatura *f*
		blocking die, *s. blocker*			
°	1809	blocking impression	empreinte *f* d'ébauchage	Vorwalzabdruck *m*	impronta *f* di sbozzatura
°	1810	blocking of the hearth	engorgement *m* du creuset	Verstopfung *f* des Gestells	crogiuolo *m* bloccato o intasato
°	1811	blocking plate	plaque de réduction	Reduktionsplatte *f*	piastra *f* di riduzione
−	1812	blocking out	découpage *m* en massif d'abattage	Abbauvortrieb *m*	taglio *m* con franameto a blocchi
−	1813	blödite	bloedite *f*	Blödit *m*	blodite *f*
		bloedite, *s. blödite*			
−	1814	blomstrandine	blomstrandine *f*	Blomstrandin *m*	betafite *f*
−	1815	blood rain	pluie *f* de poussière	Blutregen *m*	pioggia *f* di polvere
−	1816	blood stone	sanguine *f*	Heliotrop *n*	eliotropio *m*

		English	French	German	Italian
—	1817	**bloody agate**	agate f sanguine	Blutachat m	agata f sanguigna
°	1818	**to bloom**	battre, marteler	vorhämmern, blocken	battere, martellare
˄	1819	**bloom**	fluorescence f	Fluoreszenz f	fluorescenza f (del petrolio)
°	1820	**bloom, lump**	loupe f, brame f	Luppe f, Bramme f, Block m	bramma f, blumo m, lingotto m sgrossato al laminatoio, massello m
°	1821	**bloom iron**	fer m obtenu au bas-foyer	Herdfrischeisen n	ferro m in blumi
°	1821a	**bloom mill**	laminoir m à blooms	Blockwalzwerk n	laminatoio m per blumi
°	1822	**bloom (or cogging) pass**	cannelures $f\,pl.$ de blooming	Blockwalzkaliber n	tracciato m per blooming
		bloom pressing, $s.$ *squeezing*			
°	1823	**bloom roll, billet roll**	cylindre m ébaucheur	Vorwalze f	cilindro m sbozzatore
°	1824	**bloom shears**	cisailles $f\,pl.$ à blooms	Blockschere f	cesoie $f\,pl.$ per blumi
°	1825	**bloom steel**	acier en loupes	Luppenstahl m	acciaio m in pani
		bloom trolley, $s.$ *billet trolley*			
°	1826	**bloomery**	laminoir m à blooms	Luppenwalzwerk n	fucina f per la produzione di blumi sgrossati al laminatoio
°	1827	**bloomery fire, Catalan hearth**	bas-foyer m, forge f catalane	Rennfeuer n, Luppenfrischfeuer n	fucina catalana
°	1828	**bloomery furnace, balling furnace**	four m à loupes	Stückofen m	forno m per blumi
°	1829	**bloomery iron**	fer au bois	Herdfrischeisen n	ferro m al basso fuoco
°	1830	**blooming**	ébauchage m	Vorwalzen n	sbozzatura f
°	1830a	**blooming mill**	train m dégrossisseur	Vorstrasse f	treno m sbozzatore
°	1831	**blooming mill stand**	cage f de blooming	Blockwalzgerüst n	gabbia f del treno sbozzatore
°	1832	**blooming mill train**	train m à blooms ou blooming	Blockstrasse f	treno m blooming

		English	French	German	Italian
o	1833	**blooming mill pass**	cylindre *m* ébaucheur	Vorwalze *f*	cilindro *m* sbozzatore
o	1834	**blooming rolling mill**	laminoir *m* à blooms	Blockwalzwerk *n*	laminatoio *m* per blumi
		blooming shears, *s. bloom shears*			
o	1835	**blooms**	blooms carrés	Blöcke *m pl.*, Vorblöcke *m pl.*	blumi *m pl.* quadri
—	1836	**blossom**	affleurement *m* oxydé	verwitterter Ausbiss *m*	affioramento *m* ossidato
—	1837	**blossom rock**	minerai *m* oxydé	oxydiertes Erz *n* vom Ausbiss	minerale *m* ossidato (proveniente dall'affioramento)
^	1838	**blotter press**	filtre-presse *m*	Pressfilter *m*	filtropressa *m*
o	1839	**to blow**	souffler, donner le vent	blasen	soffiare
—	1840	**to blow**	faire sauter	sprengen	far saltare
o	1841	**to blow a core**	souffler un noyau	einen Kern *m* blasen	soffiare un'anima
o	1842	**to blow a furnace**	souffler le vent	den Wind blasen	soffiare il vento, accendere il forno
o	1843	**to blow down the furnace**	mettre le fourneau hors de feu	den Hochofen *m* ausgehen lassen	spengere il forno
o	1844	**to blow hot**	souffler au vent chaud	heissblasen	soffiare con aria calda
o	1845	**to blow in**	mettre à feu le haut fourneau	den Hochofen *m* anblasen	accendere l'altoforno, regolare l'altoforno
o	1846	**to blow out**	mettre hors feu, éteindre	ausblasen, niederblasen	arrestare la marcia, spengere
o	1847	**to blow out (a core)**	souffler (un noyau)	einen Kern *m* abblasen	soffiare un'anima, pulire un'anima
o	1848	**blow, shock, impact**	choc *m*	Schlag *m*	urto *m*
o	1849	**blow, stroke**	coup *m*	Schlag *m*	colpo *m*
o	1850	**blow (casting defect)**	creux *m*	Gussloch *n*	avvallamento *m*

	English	French	German	Italian
°	1851 blow (in the Bessemer process)	soufflage *m*	Blasen *n*	soffiaggio *m*
°	1852 blow	soufflure *f*	Blase *f*	soffiatura *f*
—	1853 blow basset	bombement *m* d'un filon	Gangausbauchung *f*	rigonfiamento *m* del filone, allargamento *m* del filone
—	1854 blow	passage *m* de grisou à travers une cloison		passaggio *m* di grisou attraverso il diaframma
°	1855 blow-by	perte *f* de compression	Druckverlust *m*	perdita *f* di compressione
°	1856 blow casing	corps *m* de soufflante	Gebläsegehäuse *n*	corpo *m* della soffiante, camicia *f* della soffiante
^	1857 blow down valve	soupape *f* de décharge	Ablassventil *n*, Auslassventil *n*	valvola *f* di scarico
°	1858 blow engine	machine soufflante	Gebläsemaschine *f*	macchina *f* soffiante, soffiante *f*
	blow hole, *s. space cavity*			
°	1859 blow of hammer	coup *m* de marteau pilon *m*	Hammerschlag *m*	colpo *m* di maglio
^	1860 blow-out	éruption *f*	Ausbruch *m*	eruzione *f*
°	1861 blow out pipe	bouffoir *m*	Lötrohr *n*, Blasrohr *n*	cannello *m* ferruminatorio
^	1862 blow out preventer, out valve	vanne *f* d'éruption	Ausbruchventil *n*	valvola *f* d'eruzione, valvola *f* di scarico
°	1863 blow pipe	chalumeau *m*	Lötrohr *n*	cannello *m*
	blow stress, *s. shock stress*			
°	1864 blower, blowing machine	soufflante *f*	Gebläse *n*	soffiante *f*
°	1865 blower	soufflerie *f*	Gebläseanlage *f*	soffieria *f*
°	1866 blower, ventilator	ventilateur *m*	Ventilator *m*	ventilatore *m*, aereatore
°	1867 blower with electric drive	soufflerie *f* avec moteur électrique	Gebläse *n* mit elektrischem Antrieb	soffiante *f* o soffieria *f* elettrica
°	1868 blowhole	soufflure *f*	Blase *f*	soffiatura *f*

		English	French	German	Italian
°	1869	**blowing**	soufflage *m*	Blasen *n*	soffiaggio *m*
°	1870	**blowing (a core)**	soufflage *m* (d'un noyau)	Abblasen *n* (eines Kerns)	soffiaggio *m* (di un'anima)
—	1871	**blowing cone**	hornito *m*	Hornito *n*	getto *m* di lava
°	1872	**blowing down device**	dispositif *m* pour la mise hors feu	Ausblasevorrichtung *f*	dispositivo *m* per spengere l'altoforno
°	1872a	**blowing in**	mise *f* en feu	Anblasen *n*	messa *f* in marcia (dell'altoforno)
		blowing engine, *s. blower engine*			
°	1873	**blowing fan**	ventilateur *m* soufflant	Gebläse *n*	ventilatore *m* soffiante
		blowing furnace, *s. glory hole*			
		blowing in, *s. starting or restarting*			
°	1874	**blowing-in practice**	procédé *m* de mise en marche	Anblaseverfahren *n*	sistema *f* di messa in moto, sistema *f* di accensione
°	1875	**blowing machine**	machine *f* soufflante, soufflante *f*	Gebläsemaschine *f*	macchina *f* soffiante, soffiante *f*
°	1876	**blowing off a boiler**	vidange *f* d'une chaudière	Abblasen *n* eines Kessels	spurgo o scarico di una caldaia
°	1877	**blowing out**	mise *f* hors feu	Ausblasen *n*, Niederblasen *n*	messa *f* fuori esercizio, spegnimento
°	1878	**blowing plate**	plaque *f* de soufflage	Schiesskopfplatte *f*	piastra *f* per soffiare
		blowing through, *s. bubbling through*			
°	1879	**blowing under full pressure**	soufflage *m* à pleine pression	Blasen *n* unter vollem Druck	soffiatura *f* (o soffiaggio) a tutta pressione
°	1880	**blown casting, honeycomb casting**	moulage *m* soufflé	Blasenguss *m*, blasiger Guss *m*	getto *m* soffiato
°	1881	**blown core**	noyau *m* soufflé	geblasener Kern *m*	anima *f* soffiata
°	1882	**blown ingot**	lingot *m* soufflé, lingot *m* à soufflures	geblasene Massel *f*	lingotto *m* con soffiature pronunciate
°	1883	**blown metal (in the Bessemer process)**	métal *m* après le soufflage	Metall *n* nach dem Blasen	metallo *m* dopo il soffiaggio

		English	French	German	Italian
°	1884	**blown point**	joint soudé au chalumeau	Lötstelle *f*	giunto *m* saldato al cannello
		blown sand, *s. drift-sand*			
^	1885	**blowout**	jaillissement *m* de gaz	Gasausbruch *m*	eruzione *f* (di gas)
^	1886	**blowout preventer**	soupape *f* de sûreté	Sicherheitsventil *n*	valvola *f* di emergenza
°	1887	**blow pipe burner**	brûleur *m* à vent	Gebläsebrenner *m*	bruciatore *m* ad aria
		blowpipe, *s. air pipe or torch*			
°	1888	**blowpipe essay**	essai *m* au chalumeau	Loetrohrprobe *f*, Brennerprobe *f*	prova *f* al cannello
°	1889	**blowpipe lamp**	lampe *f* pour chalumeau	Lötrohrlampe *f*	lampada *f* da saldatore
		blowpipe nozzle connection, *s. head tube nipple*			
°	1890	**blowpipe table**	table *f* de soufflage	Blasetisch *m*	tavolo *m* di soffieria
°	1891	**blowpipe test**	essai *m* au chalumeau	Lötrohrprobe *f*	analisi al cannello ferruminatorio
°	1892	**blowpipe testing outfit**	appareils *m pl.* pour l'essai au chalumeau	Lötrohrprüfgeräte *n pl.*	apparecchi *m pl.* per l'analisi al cannello
°	1893	**blowtorch**	chalumeau *m*	Lötrohr *n*	fiaccola *f* (per saldare lo stagno)
°	1894	**to blue**	bleuir	blau anlaufen lassen	brunire
°	1895	**blue annealed**	recuit (au) bleu	ausgeglüht	ricotto blu (o al blu)
°	1896	**blue annealed wire**	fil *m* recuit bleu	ausgeglühter Draht *m*	filo *m* ricotto blu
°	1897	**blue annealing**	recuit bleu	Blauglühen *n*	ricottura *f* al blu
—	1898	**blue billy**	briquette *f* de pyrite grillée	Brikett *n* aus geröstetem Schwefelkies	mattonella *f* di pirite arrostita, mattonella *f* di minerale di rame arrostita
°	1899	**blue brittle**	fragile au bleu	blaubrüchig	fragile al colore blu
°	1900	**blue brittleness**	cassure *f* au bleu, rupture *f* au bleu, fragilité *f* au bleu	Blaubruch *m*, Blausprödigkeit *f*	fragilità *f* al blu, rottura *f* azzurra
—	1901	**blue cap**	auréole *f* de lampe de sûreté	blauer Flammensaum *m*	aureola *f* della lampada di sicurezza

	English	French	German	Italian
	blue carbonate of copper, s. *azurite*			
— 1902	blue clay	argile *f* bleue	blauer Ton *m*	argilla *f* azzurra
	blue copper ore, s. *azurite*			
	blue copperas, s. *sulphate of copper*			
° 1902a	blue dip	bain *m* bleu	blau Brenne *f*	bagno *m* azzurro
	blue flame, s. *Bunsen flame*			
° 1903	blue hot	chauffé au bleu, porté au bleu	blauglühend, blauwarm	scaldato al colore blu, scaldato al blu
— 1903a	blue ground	gîte *m* de diamants	Diamantablagerung *f*	giacimento *m* diamantifero
— 1904	blue iron earth	vivianite *f*	Vivianit *m*, Blaustein *m*	vivianite *f*
— 1905	blue-John	fluorine *f*	Flussspat *m*	fluorite *f*
— 1906	blue malachite	azurite *f*	Azurit *m*	azzurrite *f*
— 1907	blue metal	schiste argileux bleu	blauer kupferhaltiger Tonschiefer *m*	scisto *m* argilloso blu (colorato dal rame)
— 1908	blue metal	matte *f* de cuivre ou cuivreuse	Kupferstein *m*	matta *f* di rame
— 1909	blue peach	tourmaline *f* à grain fin	feinkörniger blauer Turmalin *m*	tormalina *f* a grana fine
1910	blue pencil, pencil for marking glass	crayon *m* bleu. crayon *m* gras	Blaustift *m*, Farbstift *m*	matita *f* bleu, matita *f* colorata, matita *f* grassa
° 1911	blue sheet steel	tôle *f* en acier bleu	blaues Stahlblech *n*	lamiera *f* di acciaio azzurrata
	blue short, s. *blue-brittle*			
	blue shortness, s. *blue-brittleness*			
° 1912	blue steel, blued steel	acier *m* bleui	angelaufener Stahl *m*	acciaio *m* azzurro, acciaio *m* sbozzato
	blue stone, s. *sulphate of copper*			
° 1913	blue stripe	raie *f* bleue	blauer Streifen *m*	striscia *f* bleu o turchina
— 1913a	blue tourmalin	indicolite *f*	Indigolit *m*	indicolite *f*
	blue vitriol, s. *sulphate of copper*			
° 1914	blued	bleui	angelaufen	brunito
	blued steel, s. *blue steel*			

		English	French	German	Italian
°	1915	blueing	bleuissage *m*, brunissage *m*	Anlaufen *n*, Brünieren *n*	brunitura *f*
—	1916	bluff	rocher *m*	Felsen *m*	promontorio *m* a picco, scarpata *f*
—	1917	to board	planchéier	verschalen, dielen	rivestire, armare
—	1918	board	planche *f*	Brett *n*, Platte *f*, Tafel *f*	tavola *f*, tabella *f*, tavolame *m*
—	1919	board	chambre *f*	Streb *n*	camera *f*, taglio *m*
°	1920	board	batte *f*	Schlagholz *n*	battola *f*, mazzarenga *f*
—	1921	board-and-pillar method	exploitation *f* par chambres et piliers	Kammerpfeilerbau *m*	coltivazione *f* a camere e pilastri
—	1922	board coal	charbon *m* fibreux	faserige Kohle *f*	carbone *m* fibroso
°	1923	board drop hammer	marteau-pilon *m* à table	Brettfallhammer *m*	berta *f* a tavola (maglio *m* a tavola)
—	1924	boarding	planchéiage *m*	Verschalung *f*, Verschlag *m*	armatura *f* (di pozzi), assito *m*, tavolato *m*
—	1925	boards	voies d'exploitation	Abbaustrecken *fpl.*	gallerie *f pl.* di sfruttamento
—	1926	to boast	dégrossir	behauen	sgrossare, formare
—	1927	boaster	burin *m* de carrier	Stemmeisen *n*	scalpello *m* di cavapietre
—	1928	boasting	taille *f* de pierres	Steinklopfen *n*	taglio *m* di pietre
°	1929	bob	balancier *m*	Schwengel *m*	contrappeso *m*
	1930	bob	fil *m* à plomb	Senkblei *n*	filo *m* a piombo
°	1930a	bob, polishing bob	touffe *f* polisseuse	Schwabbel *m*	brunitoio *m*
		bob, *s. feederhead*			
		bobbin, *s. spool*			
—	1931	bobierrite	bobierrite *f*	Bobbierrit *m*	bobierrite *f*
^	1932	bob-tail			rimorchiatore *m* leggero per millepiedi
—	1933	bocca	bocca *f*	Bocca *f*	bocca *f*
°	1934	bod, bot	tampon *m*, bouchon *m*	Stopfen *m*	tampone *m* tappo *m*

	English	French	German	Italian
− 1935	bodenbenderite	bodenbenderite *f*	Bodenbenderit *m*	bodenbenderite *f*
° 1936	body	corps *m*, caisse *f*	Körper *m*, Kasten *m*	corpo *m*, cassa *f*
^ 1937	body	consistance *f*, viscosité *f*	Dichtigkeit *f*, Viskosität *f*	consistenza *f*, viscosità *f*
− 1938	body, ore body body casting deposit	gisement *m*	Vorkommen *n*, Lagerstätte *f*	giacimento *m*, corpo *m* in ferro fuso
° 1939	body of revolution	solide *m* de révolution	Rotationskörper *m*	solido *m* di rotazione
° 1940	body of roll	table *f* du cylindre	Walzenbund *m*, Ballen *m* der Walze	tavola *f* del cilindro
° 1941	body plan	section *f* transversale	Querschnitt *m*	sezione *f* trasversale
° 1942	Boecker's valve	robinet *m* sphérique de Boecker	Böckerscher Hahnverschluss *m*	valvola *f* di Boecker
− 1943	bog	tourbière *f*	Moor *n*	torbiera *f*
− 1944	bog body	gîte *m* de minerai des prés	Sumpferzlagerstätte *f*	giacimento *m* di limonite
− 1945	bog iron ore	minerai *m* des prés	Limonit *m* Sumpferz *n*, Rasenerz *n*	limonite *f*
− 1946	bog manganese	wad *m*	Wad *n*	vad *m*
	bog ore, *s. limonite*			
− 1947	bogen structure	structure *f* plissée	Bogenstruktur *f*	struttura *f* pieghettata
° 1948	bogie hearth furnace	four *m* à chariot	Auszugofen *m*, Ofen mit ausziehbarem Herd *m*	forno *m* a carrello
° 1949	bogie of moving hearth furnace	chariot *m* de four à sole mobile	Beschickungswagen *m*	carrello *m* del forno a suola mobile
− 1950	boggy	marécageux	sumpfig	paludoso
− 1951	boggy soil	sol *m* tourbeux	Torfboden *m*	suolo *m* paludoso
− 1952	boghead	boghead *m*	Bogheadkohle *f*	carbone *m* boghead
° 1953	boil	agitation *f* du bain, bouillonnement *m*	Badbewegung *f*, Kochen *n*	agitazione *f* del bagno, ebollizione *f*, ribollimento *m*, sobbollimento *m*

		English	French	German	Italian
°	1954	**boil eruption period**	période *f* de bouil-lonnement et de projections	Koch-Eruptions-periode *f*	periodo *m* d'eruzione e d'ebollizione
°	1955	**boiler, copper**	chaudière *f*, chaudron *m*	Kessel *m*, Pfanne *f*, Blase *f*	caldaia *f*, calderone *m*
°	1956	**boiler-coal, steam-coal**	charbon *m* à chau-dières, houille *f* de chaudière	Kesselkohle *f*, Dampfkohle *f*	carbone *m* per caldaie
°	1957	**boiler-coating**	matériel calorifuge pour chaudières	Kesselauskleidungs-material *n*	materiale di rivestimen-to per caldaie
°	1958	**boiler explosion, bursting of a boiler**	'explosion *f* d'une chaudière	Kesselexplosion *f*, Dampfkesselexplo-sion *f*	scoppio *m* di una caldaia
°	1959	**boiler fired with coal, coal fired boi-ler**	chaudière *f* chauf-fée au charbon	Kohlenfeuerungs-kessel *m*	caldaia *f* a carbone
°	1960	**boiler fired with peat**	chaudière *f* chauffée (ou se chauffant) à tourbe	Torfkessel *m*	caldaia *f* a torba
°	1961	**boiler fired with straw**	chaudière *f* chauffée à paille	Kessel *m* mit Strohfeuerung	caldaia *f* alimentata a paglia
°	1962	**boiler flue**	carneau *m*	Schornstein *m*	canna fumaria *f*
°	1963	**boiler fired with wood, wood-fired boiler**	chaudière *f* chauffée au bois	Holzfeuerungs-kessel *m*	caldaia *f* a legna
°	1964	**boiler for a pressure of 12 atmospheres**	chaudière *f* timbrée à 12 atmosphères	Dampfkessel *m* für einen betriebsmässi-gen Überdruck von 12 Atm.	caldaia *f* registrata a 12 atmosfere
°	1965	**boiler for central-heating**	chaudière *f* pour le chauffage central	Zentralheizungs-kessel *m*	caldaia *f* per riscalda-mento centrale
°	1966	**boiler for coal-dust combustion**	chaudière *f* à pous-sier de charbon	Kohlenstaubkessel *m*	caldaia *f* a carbone polverizzato
°	1967	**boiler furnace, furna-ce (of a boiler)**	foyer *m*, four de chaufferie, fourneau (de chaudière)	Kesselfeuerung *f*	focolare *m* o forno *m* (di caldaia)
°	1968	**boiler header**	collecteur *m* de chau-dière	Endkammer *f*	collettore *m* di caldaia

	English	French	German	Italian
° 1969	boiler house	bâtiment *m* des chaudières	Kesselhaus *n*	locale *m* delle caldaie
° 1970	boiler inspection	inspection *f* des chaudières	Kesselrevision *f*	ispezione *f* delle caldaie
° 1971	boiler lagging	enveloppe *f* d'une chaudière	Kesselbekleidung *f*	rivestimento *m* (o mantello *m)* di una caldaia
° 1972	boiler-maker	chaudronnier *m*	Kesselschmied *m*	calderaio *m*
° 1973	boiler plant	installation *f* de chaudières	Kesselanlage *f*	impianto *m* di caldaie
° 1974	boiler plate	tôle *f* de chaudière	Kesselblech *n*	lamiera *f* da caldaie, piastra *f* di caldaie. lamiera *f* grossa (¼" ½" di spessore)
° 1975	boiler setting	assise *f* de la chaudière	Kessellagerung *f*	sostegno *m* o base della caldaia
° 1976	boiler shell	corps *m* de la chaudière	Kesselmantel *m*, Kesselkörper *m*	corpo *m* della caldaia
° 1977	boiler-shop, boiler -forge	atelier *m* de chaudronnerie en fer	Kesselschmiede *f*	fabbrica *f* di caldaie

boiler smith, *s. boiler maker*

	English	French	German	Italian
° 1978	(boiler)-smith's work	grosse chaudronnerie *f*	Schmiedearbeit *f*	lavoro *m* di calderaio
° 1979	boiler steel	acier *m* à chaudières	Kesselstahl *m*	acciaio *m* da caldaie
° 1980	boiler under pressure	chaudière *f* sous pression	unter Druck stehender Kessel *m*	caldaia *f* sotto pressione
° 1981	boiled water	eau *f* bouillie	gekochtes Wasser *n*	acqua *f* bollita

boiler with boiler tubes, *s. French boiler*

	English	French	German	Italian
° 1982	boiler with copper fire box	chaudière *f* avec foyer en cuivre	Kessel *m* mit kupferner Feuerbüchse	caldaia *f* con focolare di rame
° 1983	boiler with corrugated flues	chaudière *f* à tubes-foyers ondulés, chaudière à foyer	Wellrohrkessel *m*	caldaia *f* a focolare ondulato
° 1984	boiler with double steam space	chaudière *f* à double chambre de vapeur	Doppeldampf-raumkessel *m*	caldaia *f* a doppia camera di vapore

	English	French	German	Italian
° 1985	boiler with eccentric flue	chaudière *f* à tube-foyer excentrique	Seitenrohrkessel *m*	caldaia *f* a tubo di fiamma eccentrico
° 1986	boiler with fire (or smoke) tubes	chaudière *f* à tubes de fumée	Rauchrohrkessel *m*, Siederohrkessel *m*	caldaia *f* a tubi di fumo
° 1987	boiler with forced circulation	chaudière *f* à circulation forcée	Kessel *m* mit Zwangsumlauf, Kessel *m* mit Umwälzpumpe	caldaia *f* a circolazione forzata
° 1988	boiler with large water space	chaudière *f* à grand volume d'eau	Grosswasserraumkessel *m*	caldaia *f* a gran volume d'acqua
° 1989	boiler with partly corrugated flue	chaudière *f* à tube-foyer demi-ondulé	Halbwellrohrkessel *m*	caldaia *f* a tubo-focolare semiondulato
° 1990	boiler with plain flue	chaudière *f* à tube-foyer lisse	Kessel *m* mit glatten Flammrohren	caldaia *f* a focolare interno liscio
° 1991	boiler with removable nest of tubes	chaudière *f* à tubes démontables	Teilkammerrohrkessel *m*	caldaia *f* a tubi smontabili
° 1992	boiler with ribbed flue-tube	chaudière *f* avec tube-foyer à ailettes	Rippenrohrkessel *m*	caldaia *f* con focolare a nervature
° 1993	boiler with single steam space	chaudière *f* à chambre de vapeur unique	Einfachdampfraumkessel *m*	caldaia *f* ad unica camera di vapore
° 1994	boiler with small water space	chaudière *f* à faible volume d'eau	Kleinwasserraumkessel *m*	caldaia *f* a piccolo volume d'acqua
	boiler with smoke tubes, *s. boiler with fire*			
° 1995	boiler with stepped flue	chaudière *f* à tube-foyer échelonné	Stufenrohrkessel *m*	caldaia *f* con tubo da fiamma a gradini
° 1996	boiler with rapid circulation	chaudière *f* à circulation rapide	Schnellumlaufkessel *m*	caldaia *f* a circolazione rapida
° 1997	boiler without water circulation	chaudière *f* sans circulation d'eau	Kessel *m* ohne Wasserumlauf	caldaia *f* senza circolazione d'acqua
° 1998	boiling	ébullition *f*	Aufkochen *n*, Aufwallen *n*	ebollizione *f*
° 1998a	boiling	scorie *f* de puddlage	Puddelschlacke *f*	scoria *f* di puddellaggio
° 1999	boiling on an open fire	chauffage *m* à feu nu	Heizung mit offenem Feuer	riscaldamento *m* a fuoco scoperto o libero
° 2000	boiling period	période *f* d'ébullition	Kochzeit *f*	periodo *m* d'ebollizione
° 2001	boiling water	eau *f* bouillante	kochendes Wasser *n*	acqua *f* bollente

BOLE **112**

		English	French	German	Italian
−	2002	bole, bolus	bol *m*	Siegelerde *f*	bolo *m*, terra bolare
−	2003	bolivarite	bolivarite *f*	Bolivarit *m*	bolivarite *f*
−	2004	bolivianite	bolivianite *f*	Bolivian *m*	bolivianite *f*
ˆ	2005	boll weevil	coin *m* spécial pour bridage de colonnes	Keil *m* für Rohr-flanschverbindung *f*	«baco del cotone», cuneo speciale per inflangiatura di colonne
ˆ	2006	boll weevil hangers	bridage *m* à «boll weevil»	Sonderkeil *m* für Rohrflanschverbindung *f*	inflangiatura *f* a «boll weevil»

bolster, *s. botton die*

		English	French	German	Italian
	2007	bolster plate	plateau *m* porte-moule	Matrizenhalter *m*	piastra *f* portastampo
°	2008	bolt, latch	verrou *m*	Riegel *m*	chiavistello *m*
°	2009	bolt and nut	boulon à écrou	Schraubenbolzen *m* mit Mutter	bullone *m* con dado
−	2010	bolt hole	galerie *f* de contournement	Umfahrungsstrecke *f*	galleria *f* di contorno
−	2011	bolt hole	passage *m* de ventilation	Wetterloch *n*	passaggio *m* di ventilazione
°	2012	bolt rod	fil *m* machine	Maschinendraht *m*	bordione *m*

bolt steel, *s. screw-steel*

		English	French	German	Italian
°	2013	bolt with machined head	boulon *m* avec tête usinée	Bolzen *m* mit bearbeitetem Kopf	bullone *m* con testa lavorata

bolted cover (A), *s. screwed-on cover*

bolting together, *s. screwing*

bolting of edges, *s. clamping of edges*

		English	French	German	Italian
°	2014	bolts and nuts, bolt products	produits *m pl.* de boulonnerie	Schraubenerzeugnisse *n pl.*	bulloneria *f*

bolus, *s. bole*

		English	French	German	Italian
−	2015	bomb	mesureur de la pression de couche	Schichtdruckmessgerät *n*	- misuratore *m* di pressione di strato
°	2016	to bond	unir, connecter	verbinden	unire, congiungere

		English	French	German	Italian
°	2017	**bond**	agglutinant *m*, agglomérat *m*	Grünsandbinder *m*	agglutinante *m*
°	2018	**bond**	joint *m*, agglomérat *m*	Fuge *f*, Sinter *m*, Agglomerat *n*	giunto *m*, legante *m*, agglomerato *m*
—	2019	**bond**	révolution de machine d'extraction	Umdrehung *f* der Fördermaschine	rivoluzione *f* di macchina da estrazione
°	2020	**bonderising**	bondérisation *f*	Bondern *n*	bonderizzazione *f*
°	2021	**bonding**	enture *f*, liaison *f*	Zusammenfügung *f*	giunto *m*, giunzione *f*, connessione *f*
—	2022	**bonding**	boisage *m*	Zimmerung *f*	armatura *f* (a cassetto)
°	2023	**bonding agent**	liant *m*, agglutinant	Bindemittel *n*	legante *m*, agglutinante
°	2024	**bonding property**	propriété *f* liante	Bindeeigenschaft *f*	proprietà *f* legante
—	2025	**bone**	charbon *m* schisteux	schieferige Kohle *f*	carbone *m* scistoso
—	2026	**bone bed**	bone-bed	Knochenbrekzie *f*	bone-bed *m*
—	2027	**bone black, bone charcoal**	charbon *m* (ou noir) d'os	Knochenkohle *f*	carbone *m* di ossa, nero *m* di ossa

bone charcoal, *s. bone black*

		English	French	German	Italian
—	2028	**bone coal**	charbon *m* barré, schiste *m* houiller	Schieferkohle *f*, Kohlenschiefer *m*	carbone *m* terroso, scisto *m* carbonifero
—	2029	**boning**	nivellement *m*	Nivellement *n*, Nivellieren *n*	livellamento *m*
—	2030	**boning board**	nivelette *f*	Fluchtstab *m*	livelletta *f*
—	2031	**bonnet**	chapeau *m*	Kappe *f*	cappello *m*
°	2032	**bonnet**	couvercle *m*	Deckel *m*, Haube *f*	coperchio *m*
—	2033	**bonnet**	toit *m* protecteur d'une cage d'extraction	Schutzdach *n* der Fördersteige	tetto *m* protettore della gabbia d'estrazione
°	2034	**bonnet**	chapeau *m*	Kappe *f*	cappello *m*, coperchio *m*
°	2035	**bonnet, hood**	calotte *f*, coupole *f*	Kuppel *f*, Haube *f*	cupola *f*, calotta *f*
—	2036	**bonney**	nid *m* de minerais	Erznest *n*	nido *m* di minerali

bonny, *s. bonney*

	English	French	German	Italian
— 2037	**bonsdorffite**	bonsdorffite *f*	Bonsdorffit *m*	bonsdorffite *f*
— 2038	**bont**	câble *m* et cage *f* d'extraction	Förderseil *n* und Fördergestell *n*	fune *f* e gabbia *f* d'estrazione
— 2039	**bont**	rétrécissement *m* d'un filon	Gangverdrückung *f*	ritiro *m* d'un filone
— 2040	**bony coal**	charbon *m* schisteux, schiste *m*	Kohle *f*, Kohlen- schiefer *m*	carbone *m* scistoso, scisto *m* carbonifero
° 2040a	**bony ingot**	lingot *m* brûlé	verbrannter Block *m*	lingotto *m* bruciato
° 2041	**booked type core box**	cage *f* de noyau à charnière	Scharnierkernkasten *m*	cassa *f* d'anima a li- bro (o a cerniera)
° 2042	**boom**	flèche *f*, volée *f* (d'une pelle)	Kranausleger *m*	braccio *m* (di gru), tra- ve *f* lunga
^ 2043	**boom cat**	tracteur *m* porte- tubes	Rohrträgertraktor *m*	trattore *m* portatubi
^ 2044	**boom hoist**	treuil *m* à antenne	Antennenwinde *f*	arganello *m* ad antenna
^ 2045	**boom telescope**	tige *f* télescopique	Teleskopantenne *f*	asta *f* (o antenna *f*) telescopica
— 2046	**booming**	poussage *m* (par palplanches)	Vortrieb *m* mit Ge- triebezimmerung	avanzamento *m*, avanza- mento *m* a tavoloni
— 2047	**boort**	bort *m*	Bort *m*	diamante *m* bort
— 2048	**boose**	stérile *m* mélangé avec du minerai	Haufwerk *n*	sterile *m* misto a mi- nerale
^ 2049	**boost feed**	alimentation *f* forcée	Druckzufuhr *f*	alimentazione *f* forzata
— 2050	**booster**	ventilateur *m* secon- daire, machine *f* auxiliaire	Hilfsventilator *m*, Zusatzmaschine *f*	ventilatore *m* secunda- rio, macchina *f* ausi- liare
^ 2051	**booster compressor**	surpresseur *m*	Zusatzgerät *n*	reintegratore *m* di pressione, compresso- re *m*
— 2052	**booster fan**	ventilateur *m* se- condaire	Hilfsventilator *m*	ventilatore *m* secon- dario
^ 2053	**booster station**	station *f* de relais	Zwischenpumpsta- tion *f*	stazione *f* di **pompag**- gio secondaria, cen- trale *f* di spinta
° 2054	**boot, forehearth**	avant-creuset *m*	Vorofen *m*	avancrogiolo *m*

		English	French	German	Italian
−	2055	**boot jack**	fourche *f* à cliquet	Klinkenfanggabel *f*	forcella *f* a nottolino
⌐	2056	**boothite**	boothite *f*	Boothit *m*	boothite *f*
−	2057	**bootleg**	culot *m* de mine	Pfeife *f*	fondello *m* di mina
−	2058	**bootleg packer**	presse-étoupe *m*	Stopfbüchse *f*	premistoppa *m*
−	2059	**booze**	minerai *m* de plomb	Bleierz *n*	minerale *m* di piombo

bop, *s. blow-out preventer*

B.O.P.D., *s. barrels of oil per doy*

		English	French	German	Italian
−	2060	**boracit**	boracite *f*	Borazit *m*	boracite *f*
−	2061	**borax, sodium borate**	borax *m*, borate *m* de soude	Borax *m*, borsaures Natron *n*	borato *m* sodico, borace *m*
−	2062	**Borcher furnace**	four *m* Borcher	Borcherscher Ofen *m*	forno *m* Borcher
−	2063	**bord**	chambre *f*, recoupe *f*	Kammer *f*, Strecke *f*	camera *f*, galleria *f*, cunicolo *m*
−	2064	**bord-and-pillar method**	exploitation *f* par chambres et piliers	Kammerpfeilerbau *m*	coltivazione *f* a camere e pilastri
−	2065	**bord gate**	chantier *m* montant, chantier en montant	schwebender Bau *m*	cantiere *m* in rimonta
−	2066	**bord ways course**	direction *f* du front de taille normale au clivage	Stosstellung *f* senkrecht zur Spaltfläche *f*	direzione *f* del fronte di taglio normale al piano di sfaldatura
°	2067	**(Bordeaux) mixture**	bouillie *f* (bordelaise)	Bordeauxbrühe *f*	poltiglia *f* (bordolese)
°	2068	**to border, knurl**	border, marger,	rändeln	orlare, zigrinare, mollettare, godronare
°	2069	**border hardening**	tremper les bords	randhärten	temprare i bordi
˄	2070	**border rim**	auréole *f* kélyphitique	Kelyphitrinde *f*	aureola o corona kelyfitica
°	2071	**border zone**	zone marginale	Randzone *f*	zona *f* marginale
−	2072	**bordering**	bourrage *m*	Besatzeinbringen *n*	rincalzamento *m*
−	2073	**to bore**	forer, sonder, creuser	bohren, durchbohren	scavare, perforare, forare

	English	French	German	Italian
° 2074	**to bore a hole**	forer un trou de mine	ein Bohrloch *n* herstellen	perforare un foro da mina
° 2075	**to bore a well**	percer un puits	einen Schacht bohren	scavare un pozzo
	to bore the earth, *s. to sound the soil*			
	to bore through, *s. to punch (holes)*			
° 2076	**bore**	sondage *m*, trou *m* de sonde, alésage *m*, diamètre intérieur	Bohrung *f*, Innen-durchmesser *m*	sondaggio *m*, trivella-zione *f*, foro di sonda, alesaggio *m*, diametro *m* interno
— 2077	**bore-bit**	tranchant, fleuret *m*	Bohrschneide *f*, Bohreinsatz *m*, Bohrer *m*	punta *f* di trapano, fioret-to *m*
— 2078	**bore-bit**	trépan *m*	Meissel *m*	trapano *m*, sonda *f*
— 2079	**bore frame**	chevalet *m* de forage	Bohrgerüst *n*	incastellatura *f* di trivellazione
— 2080	**bore hole**	sondage *m*	Bohrung *f*	sondaggio *m*
— 2081	**bore hole**	trou *m* de mine (ou de sondage)	Sprengloch *n*	foro *m* di trivellazione, pozzetto *m* di scoppio
— 2082	**bore-hole bottom**	fond d'un trou de mine	Bohrlochtiefe *f*	fondo *m* di un foro da mina
— 2083	**bore-hole pump**	pompe *f* de forage	Bohrlochpumpe *f*, Spülpumpe *f*	pompa *f* di trivellazio-ne
— 2084	**bore hole wall**	paroi *f* du puits	Bohrlochwand *f*	parete *f* del pozzo
— 2085	**bore meal**	farine *f* de sondage	Bohrmehl *n*	polvere *f* di sondaggio
° 2086	**bore of a pipe, bore of a cylinder**	alésage du cylindre	Zylinderausbohrung *f*	diametro interno d'un tubo, alesaggio di un cilindro
— 2087	**bore pit**	puits *m* de recherche	Schurf *m*	pozzo *m* di ricerca (o d'assaggio)
— 2088	**bore rod**	tige *f* de sonde	Bohrgestänge *n*	asta *f* di sonda
— 2089	**bore specimen**	échantillon *m* de trépan	Meisselprobe *f*	campione *m* di trapano
— 2090	**bore well**	puits *m* artésien, sondage	artesischer Brunnen *m*, Bohrung *f*	pozzo *m* artesiano, sondaggio *m*

	English	French	German	Italian
— 2091	**borer**	sondeur *m*, fleuret *m*, mèche *f*	Bohrarbeiter *m*, Bohrer *m*	trivellatore *m*, perforatore *m*, fioretto *m*, sonda *f*, trivella *f*
— 2092	**borer bit**	trépan *m* pour sondage percutant	Schlagbohrer *m*	trapano *m* per sondaggio a percussione
— 2093	**borgströmite**	borgströmite *f*	Borgströmit *m*	borgstromite *f*
° 2094	**boring**	alésage *m*	Ausbohren *n*	alesatura *f*
— 2095	**boring**	forage, sondage *m*	Bohrung *f*	perforazione *f*, sondaggio *m*, trivellazione *f*
° 2096	**boring and mortising machine**	mortaiseuse *f* combinée	Verbundstossmaschine *f*	mortesatrice *f* combinata
° 2097	**boring and surfacing lathe**	tour *m* vertical	Vertikaldrehbank *f*	tornio *m* verticale
° 2098	**boring and turning mill**	tour *m* à plateau horizontal	Karusseldrehbank *f*	tornio *m* orizontale
— 2099	**boring bar, boring rod**	tige *f* de sonde	Bohrgestänge *n*	asta *f* di sonda
— 2100	**boring by percussion with rods**	sondage *m* par battage rapide	Schnellstossbohrung *f*	sondaggio *m* a percussione rapida
— 2101	**boring by rotation**	sondage *m* rotatif	Drehbohrung *f*	sondaggio *m* a rotazione
— 2102	**boring head**	tête *f* de sondage	Bohrkopf *m*	testa *f* per trivelle
— 2103	**boring journal**	rapport de sondage	Bohrbericht *m*	rapporto *m* di perforazione

boring machine for iron and steel, *s. drilling machine for iron and steel*

	English	French	German	Italian
— 2104	**boring rig**	appareil *m* de sondage, derrick de sondage	Bohrkran *m*, Bohrturm *m*	apparecchio *m* di sondaggio, torre *f* di trivellazione
— 2105	**boring rod**	canne *f* de sondage	Bohrstab *m*	asta *f* di perforazione, asta *f* di sonda
— 2106	**boring shoe**	sabot *m*	Bohrschuh *m*	scarpa *f*
— 2107	**boring test**	essai *m* de forage	Bohrversuch *m*	prova *f* di sondaggio
— 2108	**boring (test) sample**	échantillon *m* de sondage	Bohrungsprobe *f*	campione *m* d'assaggio (trivellazione)

	English	French	German	Italian
— 2109	**boring tripod**	trépied *m* de sonda-ge	Dreibein *n*	treppiede *m* della son-da
— 2110	**boring tool**	outil *m* de forage	Bohrwerkzeug *n*	utensile *m* di trivella-zione
— 2111	**boring tower**	tour *f* de sondage	Bohrturm *m*	torre *f* o derrick di trivellazione
— 2112	**boring wells,** **well-drilling**	ouverture *f* (ou perçage ou forage) des puits	Brunnenbohren *n*	apertura *f* (o trivella-zione *f)* di pozzi
° 2113	**borings** *pl.,* **turnings** *pl.*	tournure *f* ou tournu-res *f pl.*	Drehspäne *m pl.*	trucioli *m pl.*
— 2114	**borings**	⸜farine *f* de sondage	Bohrmehl *n*	polvere *f* di trivellazione
— 2115	**bornite**	bornite *f*	Bornit *m*	bornite *f,* erubescite *f*
° 2116	**boron iron**	ferrobore *m*	Ferrobor *n*	ferroboro *m*
° 2117	**boron steel**	acier *m* au bore	Borstahl *m*	acciaio *m* al boro
— 2118	**bort**	bort *m*	Bort *m*	diamante *m* industriale, diamante bort
° 2118a	**bosh of a blast** **furnace**	étalage *m* du haut-fourneau	Rast *f*	sacca *f* (d'altoforno)
	bosh (foundry tool), *s. swab*			
° 2119	**bosh brickwork**	parois *f pl.* des éta-lages, maçonnerie *f* des étalages	Rastmauerung *f*	parete *f* della sacca
° 2120	**bosh in a blast**	ventre *m* (ou étalage) du haut fourneau	Rast *f* eines Hochofens	sacca *f* dell'alto forno
° 2121	**bosh jacket**	blindage *m* des étalages	Rastpanzer *m*	armatura *f* della sacca (di altoforno)
° 2122	**bosh plate**	plaque *f* des étala-ges	Rastplatte *f*	piastra *f* della sacca d'altoforno
° 2123	**bosh stones**	briques *f pl.* d'étalages	Raststeine *m pl.*	mattoni *m pl.* della sacca
° 2124	**boss**	saillie *f*	Ansatz *m,* Nase *f*	formaggella *f,* bor-chia *f,* risalto *m,* aggetto
— 2125	**boss**	massif *m* intrusif	Stock *m,* Intrusiv-körper *m*	blocco *m* intrusivo

	English	French	German	Italian
2126	boss	contre-maître *m*	Aufseher *m*	capo *m*, capo *m* servizio
° 2127	boss	matrice *f*	Gesenk *n*	matrice *f*, stampo *m*
− 2128	bossing	havage *m*	Unterschrämen *n* eines Flözes	taglio *m* orizzontale sotto il filone
° 2128a	bossing	battre en forme	in die Form klopfen	battere in forma
− 2129	botryogen	botryogène *m*	Botryogen *n*	botriogeno *m*
− 2130	botryoidal structure	structure *f* botryoïde	traubige Struktur *f*	struttura *f* botrioidale
− 2131	botryoidal blende	blende *f* concrétionnée	Schalenblende *f*	blenda *f* botrioidale
− 2132	botryoidal iron ore	minerai *m* de fer en rognons	Schaleneisenstein *m*	minerale *m* di ferro in arnioni
° 2133	bott (plug of clay)	bouchon *m* de coulée en argile	Verschlussstopfen *m*, Gussverschlussstopfen *m*	tappo *m* di argilla, tappo *m* di colata
° 2134	bott stick	porte-tampon *m*	Stopfenstange *f*	portatampone *m*
° 2135	botting, plugging	bouchage *m*	Schliessen *n* des Stichlochs	tamponatura *f*
	bottle, *s. flask*			
° 2136	bottle cap	capuchon *m* de flacon	Flaschenkappe *f*	cappelletto *m* di bottiglia
^ 2137	bottle necking	déformation *f* à col de bouteille	flaschenhalsartige Verformung *f*	deformazione *f* a collo di bottiglia
− 2138	bottleneck removal	abolition *f* de limitation	Beschränkungsaufhebung *f*	abolizione *f* di limitazione
− 2139	bottling	effilement *m*	Verjüngung *f*	rastrematura, rastremazione
° 2140	bottling clay	argile *f* à aveugler	Stopflehm *m*	argilla *f* da stagnare
^ 2141	to bottom	épuiser	gänzlich ausbeuten	esaurire
− 2142	bottom	mur, sol, fond, substratum, couche-limite *f*	Sohle *f*, Basis *f*, Sohlfläche *f*, Grenzschicht *f*	suola *f*, fondo *m*, muro *m*, base *f*, zoccolo *m*, substrato *m*, livello *m* inferiore

	English	French	German	Italian
— 2143	bottom	recette inférieure du puits	Füllort *m*	stazione *f* inferiore del pozzo
^ 2144	bottom	résidu *m*	Rückstand *m*	fondame *m*
° 2145	bottom (of a furnace)	sole *f*	Herd *m*	suola *f*
° 2146	bottom bed	couche *f* de fond	Formbett *n* in der Formgrube	letto *m* di formatura
° 2147	bottom board	plaque *f* de fond	Grundplatte *f*	placca *f* di fondo, banco *m*
	bottom box, *s. lower box*			
° 2148	bottom-brass	coquille *f* inférieure	Unterschale *f*	cuscinetto *m* inferiore
— 2149	bottom cager	encageur *m*	Anschläger *m*	ingabbiatore *m*
° 2150	bottom-cast	couler en source	steigend giessen	colare in sorgente
° 2151	bottom casting	coulée *f* en source	steigendes Giessen *n*	colata *f* in sorgente (dal fondo)
	bottom cementing plug, *s. bottom plug*			
— 2152	bottom cut	havée *f* inférieure	unterer Schram *m*	taglio *m* inferiore (o dal disotto)
° 2153	bottom die	matrice *f* (inférieure)	Stanzboden *m*	matrice *f* (inferiore), dado, piastra *f* portastampi
° 2154	bottom door, drop-bottom	fond *m* ouvrant	Bodenklappe *f*	fondo *m* apribile, sportello *m* di fondo
	bottom drag, *s. bottom part*			
° 2155	bottom ejector plate	contre-plaque *f* d'éjection	Auswerferdeck-platte *f*	piastra *f* d'espulsione, contropiastra *f* d'eiezione
	bottom electrode, *s. lower electrode*			
^ 2156	bottom flange	bride *f* de fond	Grundflansch *m*, Unterflansch *m*	flangia *f* di fondo
° 2157	bottom flash	ébarbure *f* inférieure (d'un lingot)	unterer Grat *m*	bava *f* inferiore (di un lingotto)
° 2158	bottom flue	canal *m* de la sole	Sohlenkanal *m*	canale *m* della suola o del fondo
	bottom gate, *s. sprue*			

	English	French	German	Italian
− 2159	bottom heading	galerie _f_ d'avance-ment de fond	untere Richtstrecke _f_	galleria _f_ d'avanzamen-to di fondo
° 2160	bottom heating	chauffage _m_ par le fond	Bodenheizung _f_	riscaldamento _m_ del forno dal basso
^ 2161	bottom hold down	butée d'ancrage inférieur	Fusshaltestück _n_	piastrina _f_ d'ancorag-gio inferiore
− 2162	bottom hole	coup _m_ de fond, mine de relevage	Sohlenschuss-bohrloch _n_	foro _m_ di fondo, mina _f_ di rottura
− 2163	bottom hole packer	presse-étoupe _m_ de fond	Sohlenstopfbüchse _f_	premistoppa _m_ di fon-do
− 2164	bottom hole pressure	pression _f_ de fond	Sohlendruck _m_	pressione _f_ di fondo
^ 2165	bottom hole scraper	curette _f_ de fond pour «bottlenecking»	Bodenschrapper _m_ für «bottlenecking»	attrezzo _m_ con lame al fondo per «bottlenecking»
− 2166	bottom hole sample	échantillon _m_ de fond	Bodenprobe _f_	campione _m_ di fondo
^ 2167	bottom hole test adapters	allonge _f_ de fond fixée sur la tête d'éruption	Bodenvorstoss _m_ auf dem Eruptions-kreuz	adapters per lavorare al fondo pozzo fissati sul «Christmass tree»
^ 2168	bottom hole test wash nipple adapter	robinet _m_ d'allonge de fond fixé sur la tête d'eruption	Bodenvorstosshahn _m_ auf dem Eruptions-kreuz	attrezzo _m_ da avvitare sul «bottom hole test adapters»
− 2169	bottom joint	bathroclase _f_	Bathroklas _m_	batroclasi _f_, diaclasi _f_ orizzontale
− 2170	bottom landing	accrochage _m_ du fond	Füllort _m_	stazione _f_ di fondo
− 2171	bottom level	niveau de fond	Grundsohle _f_, Grundstrecke _f_	livello _m_ di fondo, galleria _f_ inferiore
^ 2172	bottom liquid level controller	régulateur _m_ du niveau de fond	Grundniveauregler _m_	regolatore _m_ di livel-lo di fondo
	bottom of hearth, _s. crucible_			
− 2173	bottom of the bore hole	fond _m_ du trou, fond du sondage	Bohrlochsohle _f_	fondo _m_ del foro (o del sondaggio)
° 2174	bottom part	partie _f_ de dessous, demi-moule _m_ infé-rieur, corps _m_ de châs-sis, châssis _m_ de dessous	Formunterteil _n_	mezza forma _f_ infe-riore, staffa _f_ inferiore, mezza _f_ di sotto

		English	French	German	Italian
−	2175	bottom pillar	massif *m* de pro-tection du puits	Schachtpfeiler, *m*	pilastro *m* di protezio-ne del pozzo
−	2176	bottom plat	accrochage *m* du fond	Füllort *m*	stazione *f* di fondo
°	2177	bottom plate	patin *m* d'ancrage, plaque *f* d'ancrage	Ankerplatte *f*,	piastra *f* d'ancoraggio, piastra *f* di fondo
°	2178	bottom plate	plaque *f* de fermetu-re du fond	Bodenplatte *f*	placca *f* di fondo
°	2179	bottom plate, base plate	plaque *f* de la sole	Sohlplatte *f*	placca *f* della suola
	2180	bottom plug	tampon *m* d'avance	Vorstopfen *m*	tampone *m* d'avanza-mento
		bottom pouring, *s. bottom casting*			
°	2181	bottom pouring ladle	poche *f* à quenouille	Stopfenpfanne *f*, Stopfengiesspfanne *f*	siviera *f* di colata a tampone, secchia *f* di colata a tampone
−	2182	bottom ring	trousse *f* coupante	Schneidschuh *m*	anello *m* tagliente
°	2183	bottom roll	cylindre *m* inférieur	Unterwalze *f*	cilindro *m* inferiore
^	2184	bottom sediments, B.S.	fonds *m* *pl.* de réser-voir	Bodensatz *m*	fanghiglia *f*, fondi *m* *pl.* del serbatoio
°	2185	bottom side of a tube	génératrice *f* infé-rieure d'un tube	Unterseite *f* eines Rohres	generatrice *f* inferio-re di un tubo
		bottom shot, *s. bottom hole*			
−	2186	bottom spreader	poussard de pied	Sohlenspreize *f*	puntello *m* di base
°	2187	bottom stamp	étampe *f* inférieure ou de dessous	Unterstempel *m*	stampo *m* inferiore
°	2188	bottom stone	argile *f* réfractaire	feuerfester Ton *m*	argilla *f* refrattaria
−	2189	bottom-stoping	abattage *m* descendant	Strossenbau *m*	abbattimento *m* di-scendente (o a gradi-ni dritti)
−	2190	bottom workings	chantiers *m* *pl.* du fond	untere Abbaugruben *f* *pl.*	cantieri *m* *pl.* di sca-vo del fondo
−	2191	bottomer	encageur *m* (à la recette du fond)	Anschläger *m*	ingabbiatore *m* (nella stazione di fondo)

	Eenglish	French	German	Italian
— 2192	**boulder, bowlder**	galet *m*, caillou *m* roulé	Geröll *n*, Gestein *n*	ciottolo *m*, masso *m* erratico
	boulder age, *s. ice age*			
— 2193	**boulder-clay**	argile à blocaux	Geschiebelehm *m*, Geschiebemergel *m*	argilla *f* in blocchi
— 2194	**boulder flint**	silex	Flintstein *m*	silice *f*
— 2195	**boundary-fault**	faille-limite *f*	Randverwerfung *f*	faglia-limite *f*
— 2196	**bournonite**	bournonite *f*	Bournonit *m*	bournonite *f*
— 2197	**boussingaultite**	boussingaultite *f*	Boussingaultit *m*	boussingaultite *f*
2198	**bow**	courbe *f*, cintre *m*	Bogen *m*, Bügel *m*	curva *f*, curvatura *f*, arco *m*
° 2199	**bow, bewel**	brancard *m*	Tragschere *f*	portante *m*
— 2200	**bow area**	zone *f* plissée	Faltungszone *f*	zona *f* corrugata
— 2201	**bowenite**	bowénite *f*	Bowenit *m*	bowenite *f*
— 2202	**bowk**	tonneau *m*, cuffat *m*	Förderkübel *m*	botte *f* (o draga *f*) d'estrazione
— 2203	**bowl classifier**	classificateur *m* à coupe	Schüsselklassierer *m*	classificatore *m* a coppa
— 2204	**bowmanite**	bowmanite *f*	Bowmanit *m*	bowmanite *f*, hamlinite *f*
— 2205	**bowse**	minerai *m* de plomb	Bleierz *n*	minerale *m* di piombo
— 2206	**box**	berline *f*	Förderwagen *m*	vagoncino *m*, vagonetto *m*
° 2206a	**box, staff**	porte-lingot *m*	Blockhalter *m*	portalingotto *m*
2207	**box**	boîte *f*	Dose *f*	scatola *f*
° 2208	**box (of a mould)**	caisse *f*, châssis *m*	Formrahmen *m*, Kasten *m*, Form, Lade *f* für die Sandformerei	cassa *f*, staffa *f*
° 2209	**box-annealing**	cémentation *f* en pots, recuit en caisse	Kastenglühung *f*	ricottura *f* in cassetta, cementazione *f* in staffe
— 2210	**box auger**	tarière *f* à caisson	Hohlbohrer *m*	trivella *f* cava
° 2211	**box bar**	barre *f* d'ancrage	obere Verankerungsschiene *f*	traversa *f* d'ancoraggio, barra *f* d'ancoraggio

		English	French	German	Italian
—	2212	box bill, fishing tool	instrument *m* de re-pêchage des tiges de sonde	Gestängefangvor-richtung *f*	pescatore *m* delle aste di sonda
°	2213	box blower	soufflerie *f* à caisse	Kastengebläse *n*	soffieria *f* a cassa
—	2214	box bottoms	charbon *m* fin, menu	Kohlenklein *n*	carbone *m* fino, minuto
		box carburizing, *S. box annealing*			
°	2215	box-casting	. moulage en châssis	Kastenguss *m*	getto *m* in staffe, forma-tura *f* in staffe, staffatura
—	2216	box fold	pli *m* en éventail	Kastenfalte *f*	piega *f* a ventaglio
°	2217	box for casting'	châssis de moulage	Formkasten *m*	staffa *f*
°	2218	box for columns	châssis *m* pour colonnes	Formkasten *m* für Säulen	staffa *f* da colonne
	2219	box drain, culvert	dallot *m*	Abzugkanal *m*	tombino *m*
		box furnace, s. *muffle furnace*			
°	2220	box hardening	cémentation *f* en châssis	Kastenzementation *f*	cementazione *f* in cassetta
—	2221	box head	tourne-à-gauche *m*	Bohrrückel *m*	barra *f* di manovra
		box metal, *s. bearing metal*			
°	2222	box mold	châssis *m* de moulage	Kastenform *f*	staffa *f*, matrice *f*
°	2223	box part	barre *f* de châssis	Schore *f*, Kasten-schore *f*	traversa *f* (di staffa)
°	2224	box pass, box groove	cannelure *f* fermée	Flachkaliber *n*	canale *m* per ferro piatto, canale chiuso
°	2225	box regulator	porte *f* à guichet	Stromverteilungs-tür *f*	porta *f* dosatrice dell'aria
°	2226	box section frame construction	construction *f* en ossature de poutres creuses rectangulai-res	Hohlkastenrahmen-konstruktion *f*	incastellatura *f* di travi a scatola
°	2227	box with movable part	châssis *m* à pièces rapportées	geschnittener Form-kasten *m*, Abzieh-formkasten *m*	staffa *f* con pezzi riportati
—	2228	boxing	boisage à cadres espacés	Kastenzimmerung *f*	armatura *f* (di pozzi) a quadri spaziati

		English	French	German	Italian
o	2229	**boxless molding**	moulage *m* en motte	Kastenformen *n*	formatura a motta
ˆ	2230	**to brace**	étayer	unterstützen	controventare, irrigidire, puntellare
		brace, *s. shaft mouth*			
		brace plate, *s. cover plate*			
—	2231	**braced timbering**	boisage contrefiché	verstrebte Zimmerung *f*	rivestimento con rinforzi
ˆ	2232	**braces**	croisillons *m pl.* de la tour	Turmverstrebung *f*	diagonali *f pl.* della torre
—	2233	**brachy-anticline**	brachyanticlinal *m*	Brachyantiklinale *f*	brachianticlinale *f*
—	2234	**brachydome**	brachydôme *m*	Brachydoma *n*	brachidoma *m*
—	2235	**brachypinacoid**	brachypinacoïde *m*	Brachypinakoid *n*	brachipinacoide *m*
ˆ	2236	**bracings**	croisillons *m. pl.* de la tour	Turmverstrebung *f*	diagonali *f pl.* della torre
o	2237	**bracket**	support *m*	Auflage *f*	traversa *f*
o	2238	**bracket**	console *f*	Traglappen *m*	mensola *f*, staffa *f*
o	2239	**bracket**	chevalet des rouleaux	Rollenbock *m*	supporto *m* dei rulli, staffa *f* della puleggia
—	2240	**bracket**	moulinage *m*	Schachthalle *f*	camera *f* del pozzo
o	2241	**bracket carrying the front plate**	console *f* de la plaque antérieure	Träger *m* der Vorderplatte	sostegno *m* della placca frontale
o	2242	**bracket crane**	grue *f* à console	Konsolkran *m*	gru *f* a mensola
	2243	**bracket elevator**	élévateur *m* à console	Bauwinde *f* mit Konsole	elevatore *m* a mensola
o	2244	**bracket for bearing bush, journal**	montant *m* du marteau	Büchsensäule *f*	ritto *m* del supporto
o	2245	**bracket for the cooling water pipe**	console *f* de support du tuyau d'eau de refroidissement	Träger *m* des Kühlwasserrohres	mensola *f* o supporto *m* per il tubo dell'acqua di refrigerazione
		brackets of a boiler, *s. boiler-holders*			
o	2246	**bracket rim**	couronne *f* de support, marâtre *f*	Tragkranz *m*	marada *f*, corona *f* del supporto

		English	French	German	Italian
°	2247	**brackets** *pl.* **of a boiler, boiler-holders** *pl.*	supports *m pl.* de la chaudière	Kesselträger *m pl.*	supporti *m pl.* della caldaia
—	2248	**brackish water facies**	faciès saumâtre	Brackwasser-Fazies *f*	«facies» *f* d'acqua salmastra
		brad, *s. sprig*			
—	2249	**bradenhead, landing head**	tête *f* de tubage	Rohrkopf *m*	testa *f* di tubaggio
—	2250	**bradygenesis**	bradygénèse *f*	Bradygenese *f*	bradigenesi *f*
—	2251	**bragite**	bragite *f*	Bragit *m*	bragite *f*, fergusonite *f*
		braided wire, *s. wire with braided wrapping*			
		braise, *s. braize*			
—	2252	**braize**	poussière *f* de charbon	Kohlenstaub *m*	polvere *f* di carbone (o di coke)
		brake, *s. bending jaw or solder bar*			
°	2253	**brake cylinder**	cylindre *m* du frein	Bremszylinder *m*	cilindro *m* del freno
°	2254	**braking friction**	frottement *m* de freinage	Bremsreibung *f*	attrito *m* di frenatura
—	2255	**braking incline**	plan *m* incliné automoteur	Bremsberg *m*	piano *m* inclinato automotore
°	2255a	**brale**	presse *f* Brinell	Brinell-Presse *f*	pressa *f* Brinell
°	2256	**branch, fork junction**	embranchement *m*	Abzweigung *f*	diramazione *f*
		branch, *s. side leg*			
°	2257	**branch gate, multiple gate**	attaque *f* de coulée multiple	Vielfachanschnitt *m*	attacco *m* di colata multiplo
°	2258	**branch pipe**	tuyau *m* branché	Abzweigrohr *n*	tubo *m* di diramazione
^	2259	**branched (or chained) hydro-carbons**	hydrocarbures *m pl.* ramifiés	verzweigte Kohlenwasserstoffe *m pl.*	idrocarburi *m pl.* a catena
—	2260	**branched vein**	filon *m* ramifié	zerschlagener Gang *m* verzweigter Gang *m*	filone *m* ramificato
—	2261	**branching fault, subsidiary-fault**	faille *f* ramifiée, éclatement	verzweigte Verwerfung *f*	faglia *f* ramificata
		branching, *s. arborescent*			

		English	French	German	Italian
		brand, *s. trade mark*			
o	2262	**branding iron, brand iron**	fer à marquer	Brandeisen *n*	marchio *m*
–	2263	**brandisite**	brandisite *f*	Brandisit *m*	brandisite *f*
–	2264	**brannerite**	brannerite *f*	Brannerit *m*	brannerite *f*
o	2265	**brasque**	brasque *f*	Kohlengestübbe *n*	rivestimento *m* refrattario per forni
o	2266	**brass**	laiton *m*	Messing *n*	ottone *m*
		brass, *s. bearing*			
		brass bearings, *s. brasses*			
o	2267	**brass column**	colonne *f* de laiton	Messingsäule *f*	colonna *f* d'ottone
⊃	2268	**brass curves** *pl.*	réglettes *f pl.* courbées en laiton	Messingbogenregletten *f pl.*	lingotti *m pl.* d'ottone incurvati
o	2269	**brass fittings** *pl.*	accessoires *m pl.* en laiton, laitonnerie *f*	Messingteile *m pl.*	attrezzature *f pl.* d'ottone
⊃	2270	**brass-founder**	fondeur de bronze	Erzgiesser *m*	fonditore in bronzo
⊃	2271	**brass-foundry**	fonderie *f* de bronze	Gelbgiesserei *f*	fonderia *f* di ottone
⊃	2272	**brass mould**	moule *m* en laiton	Messingform *f*	forma *f* d'ottone
⊃	2273	**brass pan**	chaudière *f* de laiton	Messingpfanne *f*	caldaia *f* di ottone
⊃	2274	**brass-plate, sheet-brass**	tôle *f* (ou plaque *f*) de laiton	Messingblech *n*	lamiera *f* di ottone
⊃	2275	**brass plating**	laitonnage *m*, placage au laiton	Vermessingung *f*	ottonatura *f* elettrolitica
		brass-solder, *s. spelter solder*			
⊃	2276	**brass soldering**	soudure *f* au laiton	Messinglötung *f*	saldatura *f* all'ottone
⊃	2277	**brass wire**	fil *m* de laiton	Messingdraht *m*	filo *m* di ottone
⊃	2278	**brass works**	fonderie *f* de cuivre	Kupfergiesserei *f*	fonderia *f* di rame
⊃	2279	**brasses** *pl.*	coussinets *m pl.*, portées *f pl.*	Lagerschalen *f pl.*	cuscinetti *m pl.*, bronzine *f pl.*
–	2280	**brassil**	pyrite *f*	Schwefelkies *m*	pirite *f*

		English	French	German	Italian
—	2281	brassil	charbon *m* pyriteux	schwefelkieshaltige Kohle *f*	carbone *m* piritico

brassing, *s. brass plating*

		English	French	German	Italian
—	2282	brassy	houille *f* pyriteuse	pyrithaltige Kohle *f*	carbone *m* piritico
°	2283	brassy	de laiton *f*	messingartig	di ottone
—	2284	brat	intercalation *f* de charbon pyriteux, charbon *m* terreux	Zwischenlage *f* von pyrithaltiger Kohle *f*, erdige Kohle *f*	intercalazione *f* da carbone piritico, carbone *m* terroso
—	2285	brattice	cloison *f* d'aérage, pile de bois	Wetterscheider *m*, Holzpfeiler *m*	diaframma *f* (di ventilazione), pilastro *m* di legno
—	2286	brattice cloth	toile *f* d'aérage	Wettertuch *n*	sbarramento *m* di ventilazione
—	2287	braunite	braunite *f*	Braunit *m*	braunite *f*
°	2288	to braze	souder fort, braser	hart löten	saldare a ottone
°	2289	braze welding	soudure *f* forte	Hartlöten *n*	saldobrasatura *f*
°	2290	brazer	brasure *f*	Hartlot *n*	brasatura *f*, saldatura *f* forte
—	2291	brazillite	brazilite *f*	Brazilit *m*	brasilite *f*, baddeleyite *f*
°	2292	brazing, hard solder	brasage, brasement, soudure *f* forte	Hartlöten *n*	brasatura *f* capillare, brasatura *f*
°	2293	brazing seam	cordon *m* de brasage	Hartlotnaht *f*	cordolo *m* (o linea) di brasatura
°	2293a	brazing solder	soudure *f* forte	Hartlot *n*	lega *f* da brasatura
—	2294	brea bed	couche *f* de brai	Teerschicht *f*	strato *m* di pece
°	2295	to break	casser	brechen	rompere
°	2296	to break a joint	dédoubler un moule	eine Form *f* öffnen	scomporre (o aprire) una forma

to break and separate out, *s. to cob*

		English	French	German	Italian
—	2297	break coal	haver le charbon	Kohle *f* unterschrämen	tagliare o intagliare il carbone
—	2298	to break down the ore	abattre le minerai	Erz *n* hereingewinnen	abbattere il minerale

	English	French	German	Italian
2299	to break the circulation	rompre la circulation	Zirkulation beginnen	iniziare la circolazione
2300	to break off	abattre	hereingewinnen	abbattere, scavare
2301	to break out	décrocher, dégager.	losbrechen	aprire, staccare
2302	to break up	arracher, briser, ouvrir	aufbrechen, aufstechen	spaccare, fendere
2303	to break up	creuser en montant	aufbrechen	scavare in rimonta
2304	to break up	soulever	aufbrechen	sollevare, staccare
2305	to break up the sand	diviser le sable	den Sand m schleudern, den Sand m brechen	dividere la sabbia
2306	break	fleurage m	Oberflächenspiel n	giuoco m di colori
2307	break	cassure f, fracture f	Spalte f, Verwerfung f	frattura f, rottura f, faglia f
2307a	breakdown	larget m	Platine f	piatto m, bidone m
2308	breakdown (forging die)	déplacement m (de moule)	(Form) Versetzung f	scapolatura f
2309	break-down test	essai m de rupture	Bruchprobe f	prova f di rottura
2310	breakdown time	temps m de résistance	Widerstandszeit f	tempo m di resistenza
2311	breakdown viscosity	viscosité f de rupture	Viskositätsbruch m	viscosita f di rottura
2312	break in	rodage m du train de tige	Einbrechen n, Einreissen n	rodaggio m del treno dell'asta
2313	break in the succession	lacune stratigraphique	Schichtenunterbrechung f	lacuna f stratigrafica
2314	break-out cathead	cabestan m automatique de premier vissage	selbsttätiges Bruchspill n	cabestano m automatico di primo avvitamento
2315	break-thrust	chevauchement m anticlinal	Scheitelbruch m	sovrapposizione f anticlinale
2316	breaker	interrupteur m	Ausschalter m, Unterbrecher m	interruttore m
2317	breaker	concasseur m	Brecher m	macina f, mulino m, frantumatore m
2318	breaker	abatteur m	Hauer m	picconiere m

		English	French	German	Italian
°	2319	breaker core, washburn core	noyau *m* de liaison noyau *m* d'étrangle-ment	Einschnürkern *m*	anima *f* a segmentazio-ne
°	2320	breaker mouth	mâchoire *f* du con-casseur	Brechmaul *n*	bocca *f* dello spezza-masselli
—	2321	breaking	cassage *m*	Brechen *n*	frantumazione *f*
—	2322	breaking, disintegration	désagrégation *f*	Auflockerung *f*	disgregazione *f*
°	2323	breaking chamfer	chanfrein *m* de rupture	Bruchanschnitt *m*	invito *m* di rottura
—	2324	breaking down	abattage *m*, éboulement *m*	Gewinnung *f* Erdrutsch *m*	abbattimento *m*, franamento *m*
—	2325	breaking down	broyage *m*	Zerkleinerung *f*	macinazione *f*, tritura-zione *f*
		breaking down mill, *s. big mill*			
°	2326	breaking-down pass	cylindre *m* dégrossisseur	Streckwalze *f*	cilindro *m* sgrossatore
°	2327	breaking in	jet *m* cassé dans la pièce	am Stück ausgebro-chener Anschnitt *m*	getto *m* sbarbato, get-to *m* rotto nel pezzo
—	2328	breaking into small pieces	casser en morceaux	Zerstückelung *f*	sminuzzare
°	2329	breaking limit. breaking point	limite *f* de rupture	Bruchgrenze *f*	limite *m* di rottura
°	2330	breaking load	contrainte *f* de rupture	Zerreiss·spannung *f*	tensione *f* di rottura :
°	2331	breaking of the core	démolition *f* du noyau	Zertrümmerung *f* des Kernes	rottura *f* dell'anima
—	2332	breaking off the ore	décrochage *m* du mi-nerai	Losbrechen *n* des Erzes	distacco *m* del mine-rale
°	2333	breaking out	cassure *f*, rupture *f*	Durchbruch *m*	rottura *f*
		breaking point, *s. breaking limit*			
—	2335	breaking prop	étançon *m* de cassage	Bruchstempel *m*	puntello *m* di rottura
—	2336	breaking shot	mine *f* d'empiétage	Einbruchbohrloch *n*	mina *f* di rottura

English	French	German	Italian
2336 breaking test	essai *m* de rupture	Brechprobe *f*, Bruchprobe *f*	prova *f* alla frattura, prova *f* di rottura
2337 breaking up	abattage *m* en montant	Aufbrechen *n*	abbattimento *m* in rimonta. scavo *m* in rimonta
2337a breaking up the sand	division *f* du sable	Sandschleudern *n*	divisione *f* della terra
2338 breakoff	recoupe, galerie *f* de ventilation	Querstrecke *f*	galleria *f* di collegamento, galleria *f* di ventilazione
2339 break-out	ébarbure *f*	Grat *m*	bavatura *f*, bava *f*
2340 breakthrough	boyau *m*, recoupe *f*, recoupe *f* d'aérage	Durchbruch *m*, Wetterdurchhieb *m*, Querstrecke *f*	cunicolo *m*, galleria *f* di ventilazione
2341 breast	ventre *m*	Bauch *m*	ventre *m*
2342 breast	front *m* de taille, taille *f*, chambre *f*	Stoss *m*, Ort *m*, Kammer *f*	fronte *m* di avanzamento, fronte *m* di scavo
2343 breast-and-pillar	exploitation *f* par poche et pilier	Kammerpfeilerbau *m*	sistema *m* di coltivazione a camere e pilastri
2344 breast-boards	bouclier *m*	Bretterschild *n*	scudo *m* d'avanzamento, gabbia *f* protettiva (d'avanzamento)
2345 breast door	porte *f* de préchauffage	Vorwärmöffnung *f*, Vorwärmtür *f*	porta *f* di preriscaldamento, orifizio di preriscaldamento
2346 breast drill	vilebrequin *m*	Brustleier *f*	trapano *m* a petto, girabecchino *m*
2347 breast hole	trou *m* à crasse	Schlackenloch *n*	foro *m* per scaricare le scorie
2348 breast hole (in a mine gallery)	coup *m* de mine vers le toit	Firstloch *n*	foro *m* in corona
2349 breast stope	chantier *m* d'avancement frontal	Bruststoss *m*	cantiere *m* ad avanzamento frontale
2350 breast stoping	abattage *m* de front	Strebbau *m*	coltivazione *f* a gradini dritti
2351 breather	soupape *f* de respiration	Atmungsventil *n*	valvola *f* di respirazione .
2352 breather cap	goulotte *f* de décharge	Abzugsstutzen *m*	bocchettone *m* di sfiato

	English	French	German	Italian
− 2353	**breccia**	brèche *f*	Breccie *f*	breccia *f*
− 2354	**brecciated**	bréchiforme	breccienartig	breccioso, brecciato
− 2355	**brecciated agate**	agate-brèche *f*	Trümmerachat *m*	agata-breccia
− 2356	**brecciated vein**	filon *m* bréchiforme	Brecciegang *m*	filone *m* brecciforme, filone *m* a coccarda
° 2357	**breeching**	carneau *m*	Schornstein *m*	canna *f* fumaria, condotto *m* dei fumi
− 2358	**breeze, small coke**	poussière *f* de charbon	Kohlenklein *n*, Grus *m*	polvere *f* di carbone, polverino *m*
− 2359	**breislakite**	breislakite *f*	Breislakit *m*	breislakite *f*
− 2360	**breithauptite**	breithauptite *f*	Breithauptit *m*	breithauptite *f*
° 2361	**Brescian steel**	acier *m* de Brescia	Münzstahl *m*, Brescianerstahl *m*	acciaio *m* di Brescia
− 2362	**brettis**	pile *f* de bois, cloison *f* d'aérage	Holzpfeiler *m*, Wetterscheider *m*	pilastro *m* di legno, diaframma *m* d'aereazione
− 2363	**breunnerite**	breunnérite *f*	Breunnerit *m*	breunnerite *f*
− 2364	**brevicite**	brévicite *f*	Brevicit *m*	brevicite *f*
− 2365	**brewsterite**	brewstérite *f*	Brewsterit *m*	brewsterite *f*
° 2366	**to brick**	maçonner	einmauern	murare
° 2367	**brick**	brique *f*	Formstein *m*, Ziegel *m*	mattone *m*
° 2368	**brick arch, furnace arch**	écran *m*, voûte *f* en briques	Feuerschirm *m*	parafuoco *m*, arco *m* di mattoni
° 2369	**brick clay**	argile *f* à brique(s)	Ziegelton *m*	argilla *f* da mattoni
° 2370	**brick foundation**	fondation *f* en briques	Fundament *n* aus Ziegelmauerwerk	fondazione *f* in mattoni
° 2371	**brick-kiln, tilery**	four *m* à briques, briqueterie *f*	Ziegelhütte *f*, Ziegelofen *m*	fabbrica *f* di mattoni, fornace *f* per mattoni
	brick rim, *s. wall rim*			
2372	**brick roasting furnace, bricked calciner, kiln**	four *m* de grillage en maçonnerie	gemauerter Röstofen *m*	forno *m* di torrefazione in muratura

English	French	German	Italian
2373 **brick shape**	forme *f* de brique	Ziegelform *f*	forma *f* di mattone
2374 **brick standing on edge**	brique *f* sur champ	hochkantig stehender Ziegel *m*	mattone *m* a coltello o per ritto
2375 **brick or wall**	socle *m* en maçonnerie, socle *m* en pierre	Mauersockel *m*, Steinsockel *m*	zoccolo *m* in muratura
bricked calciner, *s. brick roasting furnace*			
2376 **bricked fire place**	foyer *m* maçonné	ausgemauerte Feuergrube *f*	focolare *m* in muratura
2377 **brickwork**	massif *m* de maçonnerie	Gemäuer *n*	muratura *f* in mattoni
2378 **to bridge**	coffrer le toit *m*	die Firste *f* verschalen	rivestire (o armare) il tetto
2379 **bridge**	pont *m*	Brücke *f*	ponte *m*
2380 **bridge**	croisement *m* de courants d'air	Wetterbrücke *f*, Wetterkreuz *n*	incrocio *m* di correnti *f pl.* d'aria
2381 **bridge, fire bridge**	autel *m*	Feuerbrücke *f*	altare *m* (di focolare di caldaia)
2382 **bridge**	couronne *f*	Schlackenkranz *m*, Ofenansatz *m*	corona *f*, ponte *m*
2383 **bridge, viaduct**	viaduc *m* supérieur, pont *m*	Überführung *f*	cavalcavia *m*, ponte *m*
2384 **bridge crane**	pont-grue *m*	Brückenkran *m*	gru *f* mobile a cavalletto
2385 **bridge guide**	pont *m*	Haltebügel *m*	ponte *m*
2386 **bridge plug**	bouchon-pont *m* en puits	Kranz-Propfen *m* im Schachte	tappo-ponte *m* in pozzo
bridge wall, *s. fire bridge*			
2387 **bridged**	couronné	hängend	ostruito (da una corona di scorie)
2388 **bridging**	couronnement *m*	Schlackenkranzbildung *f*	ostruzione *f* periferica
2389 **bridging**	formation *f* du pont	Brückenbildung *f*	formazione *f* del ponte

		English	French	German	Italian
°	2390	bridging (in the cupola)	accrochage *m* (du cubilot)	Hängen *n* (der Gicht)	formazione *f* del ponte (o della volta)
		bridle rolls, *s. pinch rolls*			
		bright annealed wire, *s. white annealed wire*			
°	2391	bright annealing	recuit *m* blanc	Blankglühen *n*	ricottura *f* in bianco (o antiossidante)
—	2392	bright coal	charbon *m* brillant	Glanzkohle *f*	carbone *m* lucido
°	2393	bright cold-rolled	laminé au blanc	blankgewalzt	laminato bianco
°	2394	bright drawn	étiré brillant	blankgezogen	trafilato bianco
°	2395	bright-drawn steel	acier *m* étiré bruni	blank gezogener Stahl *m*	acciaio *m* stirato brunito, acciaio *m* trafilato bianco
°	2396	bright drawing	étirer brillant	blankziehen	trafilare bianco
°	2397	bright ground	meulé brillant	blankgeschliffen	rettificato bianco
°	2398	bright hardening	trempe *f* brillante	Blankhärtung *f*	temperatura *f* brillante
°	2399	bright plate	tôle *f* brillante	Hochglanzblech *n*	lamiera *f* lucida
°	2400	(to a) bright red-heat	au rouge clair	auf helle Rotglut *f*	al calor rosso chiaro
°	2401	bright steel, polished steel	acier *m* bruni	Weissglühstahl *m*	acciaio *m* ricotto in bianco
°	2402	bright steel bars	barres *f pl.* d'acier poli	polierter Stabstahl *m*	barre *f pl.* di acciaio levigato
		brightly-finished steel, *s. polished steel*			
		bright wire, *s. un-annealed wire*			
°	2402a	brightener	agent *m* de brillantage	Glanzmittel *n*	sostanza *f* per brillantatura
°	2403	brightening	polissage *m*	Blankschleifen *n*, Polieren *n*	brillantatura *f*
°	2404	brightness of a surface	brillance *f* d'une surface	Leuchtdichte *f*	splendore di una superficie
°	2405	brightness of the flame	clarté *f* de la flamme	Helligkeit *f* der Flamme, Lauch *m*	luminosità *f* o splendore della fiamma
°	2406	brillant finish, glossy finish	fini *m* brillant	schöne Politur *f*, glänzende Oberflächen *f pl.*	finitura *f* brillante
^	2407	brine	saumure *f*	Salzlösung *f*	salamoia *f*, soluzione *f* salina

	Eneglish	French	German	Italian
2408	**Brinnell hardness (number)**	dureté *f* Brinell, nombre de dureté (Brinell)	Brinellhärte *f*	durezza *f* Brinell, numero di durezza Brinell
2409	**Brinell hardness test**	essai *m* de dureté Brinell	Brinellhärteprobe *f*, Brinellprobe *f*	prova *f* di durezza Brinell
	Brinell's method, *s. ball test*			
2410	**to bring the well**	commencer l'exploitation d'un puits	einen Schacht in Produktion setzen	incominciare lo sfruttamento d'un pozzo
2411	**to bring-back**	exploiter en rabattant	gewinnen im Rückbau *m*	coltivare a riporto
2412	**to bring in, to bring into production**	mettre en production	zur Produktion bringen, in Produktion setzen	iniziare la produzione
2413	**bringing out the depths**	développement *m* en profondeur	Tiefenentwicklung *f*	sviluppo *m* in profondità
2414	**to bringing red heat**	chauffage au rouge	auf Rotwärme bringen	arroventamento *m*
2415	**briquet(te), patent-fuel**	aggloméré *m*, briquette *f*	Brikett *n*, Ziegel *m*, Pressling *m*	agglomerato *m*, formella *f* o mattonella *f*, bricchetta *f*
2416	**briquetting method**	procédé *m* de briquettage	Brikettierverfahren *n*	processo *m* per la fabbricazione di mattonelle, brichettatura *f*
2417	**briquetting plant**	installation *f* de briquettage	Brikettierungsanlage *f*	impianto *m* per la fabbricazione di mattonelle
2418	**brisk combustion, lively combustion**	combustion *f* rapide	Schnellverbrennung *f*	combustione *f* rapida
2419	**britholite**	britholite *f*	Britholit *m*	britholite *f*
2420	**brittle**	sec, fragile, cassant	spröde	fragile
2421	**brittle core**	noyau *m* fragile	zerbrechlicher Kern *m*	anima *f* fragile
2422	**brittle fracture**	rupture *f* fragile	Sproedigkeitsbruch *m*	rottura *f* fragile
2423	**brittle iron**	fer *m* aigre	sprödes Eisen *n*	ferro *m* friabile, ferro *m* fragile
2424	**brittle iron ore**	minerai *m* de fer dur et cassant	sprödes Eisenerz *n*	minerale *m* di ferro fragile

		English	French	German	Italian
°	2425	**brittle point (Fraass)**	point m de Fraass	Brechpunkt m nach Fraass	punto m di rottura (secondo Fraass)
—	2426	**brittle silver ore**	stéphanite f	Stephanit m, Sprödglaserz n	stefanite, argento m nero
°	2427	**brittleness, fragility**	fragilité f	Sprödigkeit f	fragilità f
°	2428	**brittleness of iron**	fragilité f du fer	Sprödigkeit f des Eisens	fragilità f del ferro
		brittlerer, $s.$ *short-iron*			
°	2429	**broach**	broche f	Aufreiber m	broccia f
°	2430	**broach, reamer**	alésoir m	Reibahle f	alesatore m
°	2430a	**broaching**	brochage m	Räumen n	brocciatura f
°	2431	**broaching machine**	machine m à	Räummaschine f	macchina f alesatrice, brocciatrice f, spinatrice
°	2432	**broad-flange I-section props**	béquilles f $pl.$ en fers H	Stuetzen f $pl.$ aus Doppel-T-Profilen	appoggi m $pl.$ ricavati da putrelle ad ali larghe
°	2433	**broad-flanged beams**	poutrelles f $pl.$ à larges ailes	Breitflanschträger m $pl.$	profilati m $pl.$ ad ali larghe
		broad-flanged rolled girder, $s.$ *differdinger rolled section*			
°	2434	**broad flange(d)**	fer T à larges ailes, fer à T à large semelle	breitfüssiges T-Eisen n	ferro m a T ad ali larghe ferro m a T a larga base
—	2435	**broadwall**	exploitation f par longue taille	Strebbau m mit breitem Blick	coltivazione f a lunghe trance
—	2436	**brochantite**	brochantite f	Brochantit m	brochantite f
—	2437	**broggerite**	broggérite f	Bröggerit m	broggerite f
°	2438	**broken back, cracked back**	criques f $pl.$ transversales	Querrisse m $pl.$	incrinature trasversali
°	2439	**broken bricks**	briques f $pl.$ concassées	Ziegelsteinbrocken m	frammento m di mattoni
—	2440	**broken coal**	anthracite f de 60 à 100 mm.	Anthrazit m von 60 bis 100 mm.	antracite f da 60 a 100 mm.
—	2441	**broken coke**	déchet m de coke	Bruchkoks m	coke m a pezzi

	English	French	German	Italian
2442	broken core	noyau *m* cassé	abgebrochener Kern *m*	rottura *f* dell'anima, anima *f* rotta
2443	broken fold	pli *m* faillé	Bruchfalte *f*	piega *f* fagliata
	broken iron, *s. scrap iron*			
2444	broken mould	dèche *f*	abgebrochenes Formteil *n*	rottura *f* della forma, forma *f* rotta
2445	broken ore	minerai *m* abattu	abgebautes Erz *n*	minerale *m* abbattuto
2446	broken stone	cailloutis *m*	Steinschlag *m*,	pietrisco *m*, breccia *f*
2447	broken stone foundation	fondation *f* en moellons	Fundament *n* aus Bruchsteinen	fondazione *f* in pietrame di cava
2448	broken up	fissuré	gespaltet	fessurato, crepato
2449	broken working	abattage *m*, dépilage *m*	Hereingewinnung *f*, Abbau *m*	abbattimento *m*. taglio *m*, demolizione *f* dei pilastri
2450	bromargyrite	bromargyrite *f*, bromite *f*	Bromargyrit *m*, Bromit *m*	bromargirite *f*, bromirite *f*, bromite *f*
2451	bromification apparatus	appareil *m* à brome	Bromierungsapparat *m*	apparecchio *m* per bromurazione
2452	bromite	brome *m*	Brom *n*	bromo *m*
2453	bromite wash bottle	ballon *m* de lavage du brome	Bromwaschflasche *f*	bottiglia *f* di lavaggio per bromo
	bromyrite, *s. bromargyrite*			
2454	to bronze	bronzer	bronzieren	bronzare
2455	bronze	bronze	Bronze *f*	bronzo *m*
	bronze for coins, *s. metal for medals*			
2456	bronze lustre	éclat *m* bronzé	bronzeartiger Glanz *m*	bagliore *m* bronzeo
2457	bronze tube	tube *m* en bronze	Bronzerohr *n*	tubo *m* di bronzo
2458	bronze tuyere	tuyère *f* en bronze	Bronzeform *f*	ugello *m* o tubiera *f* di bronzo
2459	bronze wire	fil *m* de bronze	Bronzedraht *m*	filo *m* di bronzo
2460	bronzer	bronzeur	Bronzierer *m*	brunitore *m*

		English	French	German	Italian
°	2461	**bronzing**	bronzage *m*	Bronzierung *f*	bronzatura *f*, brunitura *f*
°	2462	**bronzing by means of rolls**	brunissage *m* au gallet	Brünieren *n* mit Hilfe von Rollen	brunitura *f* a rullo
°	2463	**bronzing machine**	machine *f* à bronzer	Bronzierapparat *m*, Bronziermaschine *f*	bronzatrice *f*
—	2464	**bronzite**	bronzite *f*	Bronzit *m*	bronzite *f*
—	2465	**brood**	gangue *f*	Gang *m*	ganga *f*
—	2466	**brookite**	brookite *f*	Brookit *m*	brookite *f*
—	2467	**brotocrystal, corroded crystal**	cristal *m* corrodé	korrodierter Kristall *m*	cristallo *m* corroso
—	2468	**brow**	front *m* de charriage	Faltenstirn *f*	fronte *m* di faglia
—	2469	**brow**	galerie *f* inclinée, descenderie *f*	schwebende Strecke *f*, Bremsberg *m*	galleria *f* inclinata, piano *m* inclinato, discenderia *f*
	2470	**brown**	brun	braun	bruno, marrone
	2471	**brown acid**	acide *m* brun	Braunsäure *f*	acido *m* scuro
—	2472	**brown coal, lignite**	lignite *m*	Braunkohle *f*	lignite *f*
°	2473	**brown coal ash binder**	liant *m* aux cendres de lignite	Braunkohlen-aschenbinder *m*	legante *m* di cenere di lignite

brown hematite, *s. limonite*

—	2474	**brown iron-ore, ochry-brown iron ore**	fer *m* oxydé brun terreux	Braun-Toneisenstein *m*, Brauneisenocker *m*	limonite *f*
—	2475	**brown iron ore nodules**	grumeaux *m pl.* d'hématite brune	Brauneisenstein-knollen *m pl.*	noduli di ematite *f* bruna
°	2475a	**brown metal**	alliage *m* brun	braune Legierung *f*	lega *f* bruna

brown ore, *s. vivianite*

°	2476	**brown smoke**	fumée *f* brune	brauner Rauch *m*	fumo *m* scuro
—	2477	**brown spar**	ankérite *f*	Braunspat *m*, Ankerit *m*	ancherite *f*, braunite *f*
°	2478	**brown with purple spots**	brun avec taches pourpres	braun mit Purpurflecken	bruno a macchie porporine
°	2478a	**browning**	brunissage *m*	Brünieren *n*	brunitura *f*

	English	French	German	Italian
2479	brush	queue f de morue	Flachpinsel m	pennellessa f
2480	brush	brosse f à nettoyer	Gussputzbürste f	spazzola f per sbavare
2481	brush ore	minerai m de fer en forme de stalactites	stalaktitförmiges Eisenerz n	minerale m di ferro a stalattiti
2482	brusher	abatteur m	Abkohler m, Häuer m	minatore m di carbone, picconiere m
2483	brushing the roof	recoupage m du toit	Nachreissen n des Daches	ritaglio m del tetto
2484	brushite	brushite f	Brushit m	bruscite f
2485	bryle	filon m conducteur, indices m pl. du filon	Ganganzeichen n	indici del filone, filone m conduttore

BRZ = *bronze*

BSB = *British standard beam*

BSBP = *British standard bulb plate*

BSC = *British standard channel*

BSEA = *British standard equal angle*

BSF thread = *British standard fine thread*

BSP thread = *British standard pipe thread*

BST = *British standard tee*

BSUA = *British standard unequal angle*

BS and W = *bottom sediment and water*

BSW thread = *British standard Whitworth thread*

BTU = *British thermal unit*

	English	French	German	Italian
2486	bubble	bulle f de gaz m	Gasblase f	bolla f (di gas)
2487	bubble bucket	seau m à pierres	Kübel für Probeentnahme	secchio m per prelevare sassi (durante il sondaggio)
2488	bubble cap	cloche f de barbotage	Schrubberglocke f	cappellotto m (o campanella) di gorgogliamento
2489	bubble cap tray	plat m à coupelles	Kupellenplatte f	piatto m a coppelle
2490	bubble plate	plat m de barbotage	Schrubberplatte f	piatto m a gorgogliamento

	English	French	German	Italian
^ 2491	**bubble point**	pression *f* de bulle	Gasentlösungspunkt *m*	punto *m* di gorgogliamento
^ 2491a	**bubble raft**	modèle à bulles de savon	Seifenblasenmodell *n*	modello *m* a bolle di sapone
^ 2492	**bubble tower**	tour *f* de fractionnement	Fraktionierturm *m*	torre *f* di frazionamento
^ 2493	**bubble tray**	plateau *m* de barbotage	Glockenboden *m*	piatto *m* di gorgogliamento
∘ 2494	**bubbling, bubbling through**	barbotage *m*	Durchspülung *f* .	gorgogliamento *m*, ribollimento *m*.
∘ 2494a	**buck plate**	plaque *f* de support	Stützplatte *f*	piastra *f* di sostegno
— 2495	**buck stone**	roche *f* stérile	goldfreies Gestein *n*	roccia *f* sterile
— 2496	**bucked ore**	minerai riche	Scheiderz *n*	minerale *m* ricco
— 2497	**bucket**	benne *f*	Kübel *m*	benna *f*
— 2498	**bucket chain**	chaîne *f* à godets	Eimerkette *f*	catena *f* a tazze, noria
— 2499	**bucket chain dredger**	excavateur *m* à godets	Eimerkettenbagger *m*	escavatore *m* a tazze (o a catena di tazze), draga *f* a noria
— 2500	**bucket conveyor**	transporteur *m* à godets	Becherwerk *n*	trasportatore *m* a tazze
— 2501	**bucket dredge(r)**	drague *f* ou excavateur à godets	Eimerbagger *m*	draga *f* (o escavatore *m*) a tazze
— 2502	**bucket elevator**	élévateur *m* à godets	Becherwerk *n*, Becherkettenförderer *m*	elevatore *m* a tazze, elevatore *m* a noria

bucket grab, *s. coal grab*

bucket line, *s. bucket chain*

— 2503	**bucket loader, loading shovel**	chargeuse *f* à godets	Eimerlademaschine *f*	caricatrice *f* a tazze
— 2504	**buckeying**	exploitation *f* irrationnelle	Raubbau *m*	sfruttamento *m* irrazionale, coltivazione *f* irrazionale
— 2505	**bucking**	scheidage *m*	Scheidung *f* der Erze	cernita *f* a mano del minerale
— 2506	**bucking board**	plaque *f* de scheidage	Klaubplatte *f*	piastra *f* per la cernita a mano
— 2507	**bucklandite**	bucklandite *f*	Bucklandit *m*	bucklandite *f*
∘ 2507a	**buckle**	pli *m*	Falte *f*	rigonfiamento *m*

	English	French	German	Italian
	buckle, *s. expansion scab*			
2508	buckle sand, buckle scab	gale *f* fausse	falsche Sandschülpe *f*	falso taccone *m*, falsa sfoglia *f*, scatola *f*
2509	buckled plate, pressed steel plate	tôle *f* bombée, tôle emboutie	Buckelplatte *f*	lamiera *f* imbutita, lamiera *f* stampata
	buckling (casting defect), *s. scab*			
2510	buckling	voile *m*, déformation *f* des tensions internes	Verzug *m*	scentratura *f*, deformazione *f* delle tensioni interne
	buckling strain, *s. crippling strain*			
2510a	buckling stress	charge *f* de flambage	Knicklast *f*	carico *m* di schiacciamento
2511	buckling stress	contrainte *f* de flambage	Knickbeanspruchung *f*	sollecitazione *f* a carico di punta
2512	buckling test	essai *m* de flambage	Knickversuch *m*	prova *f* al carico di punta
2513	buddle, sluice-box	abaque *m*, auge *f* à laver (l'or)	Sichertrog *m*	trogolo *m* di lavaggio
2514	buddled ore	minerai *m* lavé	gewaschenes Erz *n*	minerale *m* lavato
2515	buddling	lavage *m* de minerai	Schlämmung *f* der Erze, Erzwaschen *n*	lavaggio *m* del minerale
2515a	buff	disque *m* de cuir	Schwabbelscheibe *f*	cuoio *m* per pulitrici
2516	buffer	tampon *m* de choc	Puffer *m*, Buffer *m*	paraurti *m*, respingente *m*
2517	buffer coke charge	fausse charge *f* (de coke)	Zwischenkoks *m*	falsa carica *f* (di coke)
2518	buffer plate	plaque-butée *f*, plaque *f* de tampon	Druckplatte *f*, Stosspfanne *f*, Pufferbohle *f*	piatto *m* del respingente
2519	buffer spring	ressort *m* de choc	Bufferfeder *f*, Spiralfeder *f*	molla *f* del respingente
2520	buffer tank	bac *m* régulateur	Puffertank *m*	serbatoio *m* regolatore
2521	buffer spring case	boîte *f* à ressort pour tampon	Federgehäuse *n* für Puffer	asta *f* cava per molle di paracolpi
	buffle plate, *s. protecting shield*			
2522	buffling	polissage *m*	Polieren *n*, Glanzschleifen *n*	brillantatura *f*, lucidatura *f*, pulitura *f* dei metalli

	English	French	German	Italian
° 2523	**buffling wheel**	disque *m* polisseur	Polierscheibe *f*	mola *f* per lucidare, disco *m* per pulitrice
— 2524	**bug dust**	havrits *m pl.*	Schrämklein *n*	minuto *m*
— 2525	**bug hole**	cavité *f* de druse	Drusenhöhle *f*	cavità *f* (o foro) di drusa
— 2526	**buggy**	wagonnet *m*	kleiner Grubenwagen *m*	vagoncino *m*, carrello *m*
— 2527	**buggy man**	rouleur *m*	Schlepper *m*	addetto *m* ai carrelli
	bugs, *s. dodlebug*			
— 2528	**buhr**	calcaire *m*	Kalkstein *m*	calcare *m*
— 2529	**buhrstone**	meule *f*	Mühlstein *m*	mola *f*
° 2530	**to build-up or to pack**	s'amonceler, se chevaucher, se tasser	sich anhäufen	accavallarsi o ammuchiarsi
° .2531	**build up**	loupe *f*	Ofenbär *m*, Bodensatz *m*	groppo *m*, scoria *f* metallica, culaccio
— 2532	**build up**	sondage *m* dirigé	gerichtete Bohrung *f*	perforazione *f* direzionata
— 2533	**builder-up**	remblayeur *m*	Versatzarbeiter *m*	addetto *m* alla ripiena
— 2534	**building**	remblai *m*, murette *f*	Versatz *m*, Versatzmauer *f*	ripiena *f*, materiale *m* (o strato) di ripiena, muro *m* per ripiena
	building iron, *s. constructional iron*			
— 2535	**building material**	matériaux *m.pl.* de construction	Baustoff *m*	materiali *m.pl.* da costruzione
° 2535a	**building up**	épaississement *m*	Verstärkung *f*	riporto *m* galvanico
° 2536	**building-up**	tassement *m* (ou amoncellement *m*) ou chevauchement *m*	Anhäufung *f* (von Spänen auf dem Werkzeug)	accavallamento *m* (del metallo sull'utensile da taglio)
° 2537	**building-up of the box**	monter le moule	Zusammenbauen *n* der Form	montare la forma
— 2538	**building up of the bricks**	mode *m* d'empilage des briques	Aufbau *m* der Ziegel	disposizione *f* dei mattoni del riempimento
	built terrace, *s. river terrace*			
° 2539	**built-up crossing with base plate**	croisement *m*, ou coeur *m* en rails assemblés	Schienenherzstück *n*	cuore *m* composto di rotaie

English	French	German	Italian
2540 **built-up mould**	moule *m* monté	zusammengestellte Form *f*	forma *f* montata (o piazzata
2541 **built up moulding box**	châssis *m* universel ou démontable	zerlegbarer Formkasten *m*	staffa *f* scomponibile (o smontabile)
built-up weld, *s. building up by welding*			
2542 **bulb angle**	cornière *f* à bourrelet	Winkelwulsteisen *n*	cantonale *m* a bordino, angolare *m* con bulbo, profilato ad L con bulbo
2543 **bulb angles**	cornières *f pl.* à boudin	Wulstwinkel *m*	angolari *m pl.* a bulbo
bulb bar, *s. bulb iron*			
bulb beam, *s. bulb iron*			
2544 **bulb iron, bulb bar, bulb iron**	fer *m* à boudin	Wulststahl *m*	ferro *m* a bulbo, profilato *m* a bulbo
2545 **bulb plate, bulb rail**	fer *m* plat à bourrelet, fer *m* à boudin, fer *m* à boudin à patin	Flachwulsteisen *n*, Flanschwulsteisen *n*	ferro *m* piatto a bulbo, profilato a T con bulbo, ferro *m* a T a bordino
2546 **bulb tube**	tube *m* à boules	Kugelröhre *f*	tubo *m* a bulbo
bulge, *s. bulging*			
2547 **bulging**	renflement *m*	Ausbauchen *n*	rigonfiamento *m*
2548 **bulging test, drift test**	essai *m* d'élargissement	Aufweitversuch *m*	prova *f* al mandrino
2549 **bulk flotation**	flottation *f* collective	kollektive Schwimmaufbereitung *f*	flottazione collettiva
2550 **bulkhead**	cloison *f*	Scheider *m*	paratia, diaframma
2551 **bull dog**	appareil de repêchage	Fanggerät *n*	pescatore *m*
2552 **bull ladle**	grande poche *f* de coulée	Giesspfanne *f*	grande siviera *f*, secchione *m*
2553 **bull nose**	boulon *m* à haute pression	Hochdruckpfropfen *m*	tappo *m* ad alta pressione
2554 **bull plug adapter**	allonge *m* à haute pression	Hochdruckadapter *m*	adapter a fondo massiccio per alte pressioni

	English	French	German	Italian
— 2555	bull pump	pompe *f* à maîtresse-tige	Gestängepumpe *f*	pompa *f* ad asta
— 2556	bull quartz	quartz *m* enfumé	Rauchquarz *m*	quarzo *m* affumicato
— 2557	bull rod	tige *f* de sondage	Bohrgestänge *n*	asta *f* di trivellazione
— 2558	bull rope	câble *m* de sondage	Bohrseil *n*	cavo *m* di trivellazione
— 2559	bull's eye structure	structure *f* à oeil de boeuf	Graphitkugel *f* mit Ferrithof	struttura *f* a occhio di bue
— 2560	bull wheel	treuil de forage, tambour *m* de forage	Bohrfördertrommel *f*, Förderrad *n*	tamburo *m* di perforazione a corda
— 2561	bull-wheel brake band	fer *m* à bande de la cloche de sondage	Bohrtrommelband-bremse *f*	freno *m* a nastro
— 2562	bull-wheel post brace	croisillon *m* de la cloche de sondage	Bohrtrommelstrebe *f*	diagonale *f* supporto tamburo di manovra
— 2563	bull-wheel spool	treuil pour corde de sondage	Bohrseilwinde *f*	argano *m* per cavo di trivellazioni
° 2564	bulldog	scorie *f* de puddlage	Bulldogschlacke *f*, Puddelschlacke *f*	scoria *f* di puddellaggio

bulldog, *s. tap cinder*

— 2565	to bulldoze	fragmenter	nachsprengen	frantumare

bulldozer, *s. horizontal-type forging machine*

— 2566	bulldozing	fragmentation *f* par explosif, tir par pétards	Nachsprengen *n*	frantumazione a mezzo esplosivo o in blocchi
° 2567	bullet mould	moule *m* à balles	Kugelform *f*	forma *f* per pallottole
— 2568	bulling	bourrage *m* d'un trou de mine	Besetzen *n*	costipamento di un foro da mina
— 2569	bulling bar	bourroir *m*	Ladestock *m* _	costipatore *m*
° 2570	bullion	métal *m* noble en barres	Edelmetallbarre *f*	barra *f* di metallo prezioso
— 2571	bullwheel	tambour *m* de forage	Bohrseiltrommel *f*	tamburo *m* di trivellazione (a corda)
— 2572	bully	marteau *m* perforateur	Bohrhammer *m*	martello *m* perforatore

English	French	German	Italian
2573 **bummer(worker)**	rouleur *m*	Fördermann *m*	addetto *m* ai trasporta-tori
bumper, *s. jolting machine*			
2574 **bumper sub**	coulisse *f* de battage	spezielle Schlagschere *f*	snodo *m* per sondaggi, pescatore *m*
2575 **bumping conveyor**	couloir *m* oscillant	Schüttelförderer *m*	trasportatore *m* a scosse
2576 **bumping table**	table *f* à secousses	Stossherd *m*	tavolo *m* (separatore) a scosse
2577 **bumpy coal**	charbon *m* qui écla-te à cause des gaz contenus	unter Entgasung zersplitterte Kohle *f*	carbone *m* scoppiettante (per i gas contenuti)
2578 **bunch**	nid *m* de minerai, élargissement	Erznest *n*, Ausbau-chung *f*	sacca *f* di minerali, al-largamento *m*
2579 **bundled scrap**	paquet *m* de fer-railles	Schrottpaket *n*	pacchetto *m* di rottami
2580 **bunker, coal-bunker**	réservoir *m* (ou sou-te *f)* à charbon	Bunker *m*, Kohlenbunker *m*	carbonile *m*, tramoggia *f* per carbone
2581 **bunker C fuel oil**	huile *f* épaisse	dickflüssiges Öl *n*	olio *m* combustibile denso
bunny, *s. bunch*			
2582 **Bunsen burner**	brûleur *m* Bunsen	Bunsenbrenner *m*	becco *m* Bunsen
2583 **bunsenite**	bunsénite *f*	Bunsenit *m*	bunsenite *f*
2584 **bunton**	poussard *m*,	Spreize *f*, Schacht-holz *n*	rinforzo *m*, puntello *m*, traversa *f*
2585 **burden**	roches de recouvre-ment, morts-terrains	Deckgebirge *n*	terreno *m* di copertura, copertura *f*, materiale *m* sterile
2586 **burden, charge (of material in a blast furnace**	lit *m* de fusion, charge *f*	Gattierung *f*, Einsatz *m*, Charge *f*, Gicht *f*	letto *m* di fusione, cari-ca metallica, carico *m* (d'altoforno)
2587 **burette**	burette *f*	Messröhre *f*	buretta *f*
2588 **Burger's rotary valve**	valve *f* rotative de Burger	Burgersches Dreh-ventil *n*	valvola *f* rotativa Burger
2589 **Burgundy mixture**	bouillie *f* bourguignonne	Burgunderbrühe *f*	poltiglia *f* borgognona

	English	French	German	Italian
— 2590	**burgy**	charbon *m* fin	Kohlenklein *n*	carbone *m* fine, minuto
— 2591	**buried**	enterré	vergraben	interrato, sepolto
— 2592	**buried outcrop**	affleurement *m* masqué	verstecktes Ausgehende *n*	affioramento *m* mascherato, affioramento *m* seminascosto
— 2593	**buried structure**	structure *f* profonde	verdeckte Struktur *f*	struttura *f* profonda
— 2594	**burk**	partie *f* très dure d'un filon	Knauer *m*	parte *f* molto dura di un filone
° 2595	**to burn through**	percer, brûler	durchbrennen	sfondare bruciando
	burn-off, *s. flashing loss*			
° 2596	**burn on (sand)**	grippure *f*, sable *m* incrusté, sable *m* brûlé	angebrannter Sand *m*	sabbia *f* attaccata, incrostazione *f* di sabbia, sabbia *f* bruciata
° 2597	**burned fire clay**	chamotte *f*	Schamotte *f*	argilla *f* refrattaria
° 2598	**burned iron**	fer *m* rouverin	faulbrüchiges Eisen *n*	ferro *m* fragile a caldo ed a freddo
— 2599	**burned off**	parfaitement cuit	vollständig gar	perfettamente cotto
° 2600	**burner**	brûleur *m*	Brenner *m*	becco *m* a gas, bruciatore
° 2601	**burner for welding**	torche *f* à souder	Schweissbrenner *m*	cannello *m* ferruminatorio
° 2602	**burner port**	porte *f* de préchauffage	Vorwärmtür *f*	porta *f* di preriscaldamento
° 2603	**burning**	brûlure *f*	Verbrennen *n*, Verbrennung *f*	bruciatura *f*
— 2604	**burning**	combustion *f*, brûlure *f*, carbonisation *f*, calcination *f*, cuisson	Brennen *n*, Verbrennen *n*, Rösten *n*	combustione *f*, carbonizzazione *f*, arrostimento *m*, calcinazione
— 2605	**burning**	élargissement *m* du fond de trou de mine	Auskesseln *n* des Bohrloches	allargamento *m* del fondo di un foro da mina
	burning house, *s. roasting furnace*			
° 2606	**burning in, metal penetration**	coquille *f* d'oeuf abreuvante	Schalenbildung *f*	segregazione *f* infiltrata
	burning in (casting defect), *s. metal penetration*			

	English	French	German	Italian
°	2607 **burning period**	durée *f* de marche	Brennzeit *f*	durata *f* d'accensione
°	2608 **burning the filter**	incinération *f* du filtre	Einäschern *n* des Filters	incenerimento *m* del filtro
°	2609 **burning through**	ronger par le feu	Durchbrennen *n*	perforare a fuoco
°	2610 **to burnish**	brunir	bräunen, (brünieren)	brunire, lisciare, lucida-re
°	2610a **burnishing**	brunissage *m*	Brünierung *f*	lucidatura *f*
—	2611 **burnishing agate**	agate *f* à brunir	Polierstein *m*	agata *f* da brunire
	burnt dolomite, *s. calcined dolomite*			
°	2612 **burnt gas**	gaz *m pl.* brûlés	Verbrennungsgase *n pl.*	gas *m pl.* combusti
°	2613 **burnt iron, rusty iron**	fer *m* brûlé	verbranntes Eisen *n*, Brandeisen *n*	ferro *m* bruciato
	burnt limestone, *s. quick lime*			
°	2614 **burnt sand**	sable *m* brûlé	verbrannter Sand *m*	terra *f* bruciata
°	2615 **burnt steel**	acier *m* brûlé	verbrannter Stahl *m*	acciaio *m* bruciato
°	2616 **to burr, to trim**	ébarber	abgraten	sbavare
—	2617 **burr**	roche *f* dure, roche *f* encaissante	hartes Gestein *n*, Nebengestein *n*	roccia *f* dura, roccia *f* adiacente
°	2618 **burr, ridge, tang**	bavure *f*, ébarbure *f*, barbe *f*, barbure *f*	Grat *m*, Bart *m*	bavatura *f*
°	2619 **burr-free product**	produit *m* sans bavures	gratloses Erzeugnis *n*	prodotto *m* senza sba-vatura (o ad orlo regolare)
°	2620 **burring machine**	ébarbeuse *f*	Putzer *m*, Entgratmaschine *f*	sbavatrice *f*
—	2621 **to burrow**	prospecter	schürfen	sondare, esplorare
—	2622 **burrow**	roche *f* stérile, halde	taubes Gestein *n*, Grubenhalde *f*	roccia *f* sterile
	burst test, *s. pillow test*			
	bursting of a boiler, *s. boiler explosion*			
—	2623 **bursting shot**	mine *f* d'empiétage	Einbruchbohrloch *n*	mina *f* di sondaggio (o di rottura)
°	2624 **bustamente furnace**	four *m* à cuve pour minerai de mercure	Bustamenteofen *m*	forno *m* a tino per mi-nerale di mercurio

	English	French	German	Italian
o	2625 **bush, bearing**	bague *f*	Führungsbüchse *f*	boccola *f.*
o	2626 **bush metal**	métal *m* pour boussoles	Kompassmetall *n*	metallo *m* per bussole
o	2627 **busheling**	malaxage *m* des chutes	Schrottmischung *f*	rimpasto *m* di rottame
o	2628 **busheling scrap**	chutes *f pl.* à malaxer	Mischungsschrott *m*	rottame *m* da rimpasto
	bushing, *s. bearing*			
—	2629 **bustamite**	bustamite *f*	Bustamit *m*	bustamite *f*
o	2630 **bustle pipe**	buse *f*, conduite *f* circulaire *f* de vent	Windverteilungsrohr *n*	ugello *m*, condotto *m* circolare dell'aria
—	2631 **buszite**	buszite *f*	Bussit *m*	bussite *f*
^	2632 **butane**	butane *m*	Butan *n*	butano *m*
	butler finish, *s. satin finish*			
—	2633 **butlerit**	butlerite *f*	Butlerit *m*	butlerite *f*
o	2634 **to butt**	abouter	stumpf aneinanderfügen	unire a tenone
—	2635 **butt**	front *m* de taille normal aux limets	normal zur Spaltfläche *f* verlaufender Stoss *m*	fronte *m* di scavo normale al piano di stratificazione
o	2636 **to butt weld**	souder par contact	stumpf schweissen	saldare per contatto
—	2637 **butt entry**	plan incliné, cheminée, recoupe *f*	Bremsberg *m*, Rollloch *n*, Querschlag *m*	piano *m* inclinato, scivolo, galleria *f* di livello
	butt-seam welding, *s. seam welding*			
o	2638 **butt welded casing**	tube *m* soudé par rapprochement	stumpfgeschweisstes Rohr *n*	tubo *m* saldato per avvicinamento
o	2639 **butt-welded joints**	joints soudés bout à bout	stumpf verschweisste Stoesse *m pl.*	giunti *m pl.* saldati di testa (o testa a testa)
o	2640 **butt-welded plate**	planche *f* soudée (en about)	stumpfgeschweisste Platte *f*	piastra *f* saldata testa a testa (o a bordi giustapposti)
o	2641 **butt welded tube**	tube *m* soudé par contact	stumpfgeschweisstes Rohr *n*	tubo *m* saldato testa a testa
o	2642 **butt welder**	machine *f* à souder en bout	elektrische Stumpfschweissmaschine *f*	saldatrice *f* elettrica di testa

English	French	German	Italian
° 2643 **butt-weld(ing), butt weld(ed) joint, jump-weld**	soudure f en about, soudure f bout à bout	Stumpfschweissung f, stumpfe Schweissung f	saldatura f di testa, saldatura f testa a testa
— 2644 **butte**	butte-témoin m	Zeugenberg m	puntello m
butter roch, s. *halotrichite*			
° 2645 **butterfly valve**	papillon m, registre m à papillon	Drosselklappe f	farfalla f, valvola f a farfalla
— 2646 **buttgenbachite**	buttgenbachite f	Buttgenbachit m	buttgenbachite f
button sleeker, s. *spoon tool*			
° 2647 **button**	saillie f	Vorsprung m	sporgenza f, risalto m rotondo
° 2648 **by-product coke (U.S.), gas coke**	coke m de gaz	Gaskoks m	sottoprodotti del gas
— 2649 **by level**	niveau m intermédiaire	Teilsohle f	livello m intermedio, suola intermedia
^ 2650 **by-pass**	branchement m en dérivation	Umführung f, Abzweigung f	diramazione, presa ausiliaria
^ 2651 **by-pass filter**	filtre m de dérivation	Umlauffilter n	filtro m in derivazione
— 2652 **by-pass pit**	puits m d'aérage, voie f de ventilation	Wetterschacht m	pozzo m di ventilazione, falso pozzo m
° 2653 **By-products of the blast Furnace**	produits m pl. accessoires du haut-fourneau	Nebenerzeugnisse n pl. des Hochofens	sottoprodotti m pl. dell'alto forno
° 2654 **by sets, in series**	par série	satzweise	in serie

	English	French	German	Italian
	C-iron, s. *channel iron*			
	C-type gun, s. *C-type spot welding head*			
°	2655 **to cabbage**	empaqueter les chutes	den Schrott *m* verpacken	impacchettare rottami
°	2656 **cabbaging**	empaquetage *m* de chutes	Schrottverpackung *f*	impacchettatura di rottami
°	2657 **cabbaging press**,	machine *f* à empaqueter les chutes	Schrottpresshammer *m*	pressa *f* per impacchettare i rottami, impacchettatrice per rottami
°	2658 **to cable**	couper les barres de fer	Stabeisen *n pl.* schneiden	tagliare (o spezzonare) barre di ferro
°	2659 **cable fittings, cable attachments**	accessoires *m pl.* pour câbles	Kabelgarnitur *f*, Kabelzubehör *n*	accessori *m pl.* per cavi
°	2660 **cable conveyor**	transporteur *m* à câble	Bandförderer *m* mit Zugseil	trasportatore *m* a nastro (o a cavo)
—	2661 **cable drill, cable drilling**	forage *m* à la corde	Seilbohren *n*	perforazione *f* a corda, sondaggio a percussione
—	2662 **cable drum, hoisting drum**	tambour à câble	Seiltrommel *f*, Fördertrommel *f*	tamburo *m* a corda (o a cavo)
°	2662a **cable iron**	fer *m* de câble	Kabeleisen *n*	ferro *m* per cavi (o funi)
	cable railway, s. *rope railway*			
—	2663 **cable rig**	appareil *m* de forage à la corde	Seilbohrkran *m*, Stossbohrer *m*	trivella *f* a percussione
—	2664 **cable subway**	galerie *f* du câble, tunnel	Kabeltunnel *m*, Stollen *m*, Kabelgrube *f*	galleria *f* o letto *m* del cavo
—	2665 **cable system**	sondage *m* à la corde	Seilbohren *n*	perforazione *f* a percussione
—	2666 **cable tools**	outillage *m* de forage au câble	Seilbohrgerät *n*	utensili *m pl.* a corda
—	2667 **cableway excavator**	grue à câble, blondin	Kabelkran *m*	escavatore *m* a cavi, gru *f* a cavi
—	2668 **cabrerite**	cabrérite *f*	Cabrerit *m*	cabrerite *f*
—	2669 **cacoxenite**	cacoxénite *f*	Kakoxen *n*	cacosseno *m*
°	2670 **cadmia**	cadmie *f*	Zink-und Kadmiumstaub *m*	cadmia *f*, residuo *m* d'alto forno

	English	French	German	Italian
°	2671 cadmiferous	cadmifère	kadmiumhaltig	cadmifero
°	2672 to cadmium	cadmier	kadmieren	cadmiare
°	2673 cadmium	cadmium m	Kadmium n	cadmio m
°	2674 cadmium plated	cadmié	kadmiert	cadmiato
°	2675 cadmium plating	cadmiage m	Verkadmung f	cadmiatura f
°	2676 cadmium blend	greenockite f	Greenockit m	blenda f cadmifera
°	2677 cadmium plating	cadmiage m, cadmiumage m	Kadmieren n	cadmiatura f
—	2678 caesium	césium m	Caesium n	cesio m
—	2679 cage bail	attache f de câble à la cage d'extraction	Zwischengeschirr n	attacco m del cavo alla gabbia di estrazione
—	2680 cage box	cage f d'extraction	Fördergestell n	gabbia f d'estrazione
—	2681 cage safety apparatus, parachute	parachute m	Fallschutzvorrich- tung f für Förderkörbe	paracadute m (per gab- bia di miniera)
—	2682 cage seats	clichage m pour cages	Aufsetzvorrichtung f	tacchetti m pl. per gabbia di miniera
—	2683 cage winding	extraction f par cages	Gestellförderung f	estrazione f con gabbie
—	2684 cager	moulineur, encageur	Anschläger m	ingabbiatore m
—	2685 caging	encagement m	Wagenaufschieben n	ingabbiamento m
—	2686 cahnite	cahnite f	Cahnit m	cahnite f
—	2687 cainosite	cénosite f	Kainosit m	cenosite f
—	2688 cainozoic	cénozoïque m	känozoische Ära f	era f cenozoica, ceno- zoico m
—	2689 cairngorm stone	quartz m enfumé	Rauchquarz m	quarzo m affumicato
^	2690 to cake together (of fuels)	se coller, (se) cailler empâter (la grille), se lier, s'agglutiner	backen, festbacken	impastarsi, accagliarsi, rapprendersi
—	2691 cake	tourteau m	Kuchen m	panello m
°	2691a cake	lingot m de départ	Ausgangsblock m	lingotto m di partenza

		English	French	German	Italian
°	2692	cake of cinder	gâteau ou plaque de scories	Schlackenkuchen *m*	blocco *m* di loppa, impasto *m* di scorie
°	2693	cake of coke	tourteau de coke	Kokskuchen *m*	impasto *m* di coke
		caked mass, *s. baked mass*			
°	2694	caking	agglutination *f*, cuisson *m*	Backen *n*	agglutinamento *m*, impasto *m*
		caking, *s. caking coal*			
°	2695	caking capacity	pouvoir *m* collant	Backfähigkeit *f*	carattere *m* agglutinante
—	2696	caking coal, close burning coal	charbon *m* collant (ou agglutinant), houille *f* agglutinante	Backkohle *f*	carbone *m* agglutinante (o collante)
°	2697	caking of the coal, clinkering	agglutination *f* du coke, cuisson *f* du coke	Backen *n* des Kokses	impasto *m* od agglutinamento *m* del coke
—	2698	cal	wolframite *f*	Wolframit *m*	wolframite *f*
		calaite, *s. turquoise*			
—	2699	calamine, smithsonite, zinc-spar	calamine *f*, smithsonite *f*	Zinkspat *m*, Galmei *m*, Kalamin *m*	calamina *f* o giallamina *f*
—	2700	calaverite	calavérite *f*	Calaverit *m*	calaverite *f*
—	2701	calc-sinter, travertin	travertin, tuf calcaire	Kalksinter *m*	travertino *m*, stalattite *f* calcarea
—	2702	calc spar	calcite *f*	Kalzit *m*	calcite *f*
—	2703	calcar	fourneau à calciner	Kalzinierofen *m*	forno *m* di calcinazione
°	2704	calcareous binding	ciment *m* calcaire	kalkiges Bindemittel *n*	cemento *m* calcare,
—	2705	calcareous facies	faciès calcaire	kalkige Fazies *f*	facies *f* calcarea
—	2706	calcareous iron ore	minerai *m* de fer calcareux	kalkiges Eisenerz *n*	minerale *m* di ferro contenente carbonato di calcio
		calcareous rock, *s. limestone-rock*			
—	2707	calcareous sandstone	grès calcaire	kalkiger Sandstein *m*	arenaria *f* calcarea
—	2708	calcareous sinter, travertin	travertin *m*	Kalksinter *m*	travertino *m*, deposito *m* calcareo
		calcareous spar, *s. calcite*			

	English	French	German	Italian
−	2709 calcedonite	calcédoine *f*	Kalzedon *m*	calcedonio *m*
−	2710 calciclase	anorthite *f*	Anorthit *m*	anortite *f*
−	2711 calcimeter	calcimètre *m*	Kalzimeter *n*	calcimetro *m*
−	2712 to calcinate	calciner	kalzinieren, ausglühen	calcinare, arrostire, bruciare
	calcined baryta, *s. baryta*			
o	2713 calcined copper metal	matte *f* de cuivre grillée	gerösteter Kupferstein *m*	matta *f* di rame calcinato
o	2714 calcined dolomite, burnt dolomite	dolomie *f* cuite	gebrannter Dolomit *m*	dolomite *f* cotta
	calcined ore, *s. roasted ore*			
o	2715 calcined pyrites, purple ore	résidu *m* de pyrites grillées, cendres *f pl.* de pyrites	Kiesabbrand *m*	ceneri *f pl.* di pirite, piriti *f pl.* calcinate
	calciner, *s. roasting furnace*			
o	2716 calcining-furnace, calciner	four de (ou à) calcination, fourneau (ou four) à calciner	Kalzinierofen *m*	forno di arrostimento o di calcinazione
o	2717 calcining furnace for converter bottoms	four *m* à cuire les fonds de convertisseurs	Brennofen *m* für die Birnenböden	forno *m* per cuocere i fondi dei convertitori
	calcining installation, *s. roasting plant*			
	calcining plant, *s. roasting plant*			
−	2718 calcite, calcareous spar	calcite *f*, spath calcaire	Kalkspat *m*, Kalzit *m*	calcite *f*, spato *m* calcare, spato *m* d'Islanda
−	2719 calcite cleavage	clivage rhomboédrique	rhomboedrische Spaltbarkeit *f*	sfaldatura *f* romboedrica
−	2720 calcitrant	réfractaire	feuerfest	refrattario
−	2721 calcium	calcium *m*	Kalzium *n*	calcio *m*
o	2722 calcium chloride	chlorure de calcium	Chlorkalcium *n*	cloruro *m* di calcio
o	2723 calcium chloride cylinder or tube	tube *m* à chlorure de calcium	Chlorkalciumzylinder *m*, Trockenturm *m*	cilindro *m* per cloruro di calcio

		English	French	German	Italian
°	2724	calcium chloride tube	tube *m* en U pour chlorure de calcium	Chlorkalciumröhre *f*	tubo *m* a U per cloruro di calcio
—	2725	calcium-chromium garnet	grenat *m* chromo--calcareux , ouwarowite *f*	Chromgranat *m*, Kalkchromgranat *m*	granato *m* cromo-calcareo, uvarovite *f*

calcium fluoride, *s. fluor-spar*

—	2726	calcium -larsenite	calcium-larsénite *f*	Kalziumlarsenit *m*	calcio-larsenite *f*

calcium mica, *s. margarita*

—	2727	calcium silicon	silico-calcium *m*	Kalzium-Silizium *n*	silico calcio *m*

calcouranite, *s. autunite*

—	2728	calcspar, calcite	spath *m* calcaire	Kalkspat *m*	spato *m* calcare, calcite *f*
—	2729	calctuff	tuf *m* calcaire	Kalktuff *m*	tufo calcareo
°	2730	to calculate the burden	préparer le lit de fusion	gattieren	preparare il letto di fusione
°	2731	to calculate the calorific value from the analysis	calculer la puissance calorifique d'après l'analyse	den Heizwert aus der Analyse berechnen	determinare il potere calorifico in base all'analisi
°	2732	calculation of blast	calcul *m* du vent ou de l'air	Windberechnung *f*	calcolo *m* dell'aria e del vento
°	2733	calculation of charge	calcul *m* des charges	Berechnung *f* der Beschickung	calcolo *m* delle cariche
°	2734	calculation of slags	calcul *m* du laitier ou des scories	Berechnung *f* der Schlacken	calcolo *m* della loppa o delle scorie
°	2735	calculation of the analysis	calcul *m* de l'analyse	Berechnung *f* der Analyse	calcolo *m* dell'analisi
°	2736	calculation of the mixture	calcul *m* du lit de fusion	Berechnung *f* des Möllers	calcolo *m* del letto di fusione
°	2737	caldera, chauldron-shaped valley	caldeira *f*	Caldera, Kesseltal *n*	caldera *f*
—	2738	Caledonian folds	plissement *m* calédonien	caledonische Faltung *f*	corrugamento *m* caledoniano
—	2739	caledonite	calédonite *f*	Caledonit *m*	caledonite *f*
—	2740	calf wheel	treuil *m* pour tubage	Verrohrungstrommel *f*	argano *m* per tubi, tamburo *m* di manovra
°	2741	calibrated iron	fer *m* calibré	kalibriertes Eisen *n*	ferro *m* calibrato

English	French	German	Italian
° 2742 **calibration**	calibrage *m*	Eichung *f* ·	taratura *f*
° 2742a **calibration furnace**	four *m* d'étalonnage	Eichofen *m*	forno *m* campione
^ 2743 **calibration tank**	bac *m* étalonné	Messtank *m*	serbatoio *m* tarato
− 2744 **caliche**	caliche *f*	Caliche *f*	nitratina *f*
− 2745 **californium**	californium *m*	Californium *n*	californio *m*
° 2746 **caliper gauge**	calibre *m* à mâchoire	Tasterlehre *f*, Rachenlehre *f*	calibro *m* a forcella
° 2747 **caliper square**	jauge *f* à coulisse	Schublehre *f*, Schieblehre *f*	calibro *m* a corsoio, calibratura *f* del foro
° 2748 **calipers** *pl.*	compas *m* d'épaisseur	Tasterzirkel *m*	compasso *m* di spessore
− 2748a **calk**	barytine *f* de Derbyshire	Derbyshire-Barit *m*	baritina *f* di Derbyshire
calk weld, *s. seal weld*			
calipper, *s. caliper*			
− 2749 **Callovian stage**	Callovien *m*	Callovien *n*	Calloviano, stadio *m* calloviano
− 2750 **callys**	roches *f pl.* stratifiées coupées par filons	Schichtgesteine mit Adern durchsetzt *n pl*	rocce *f pl.* stratificate tagliate a filoni
− 2751 **Calomel**	Calomel *m*	Kalomel *n*	calomelano
° 2752 **calorie**	calorie *f*	Kalorie *f*	caloria *f*
calorific capacity, *s. specific heat*			
° 2753 **calorific effect**	effet *m* calorifique	Heizwirkung *f*	effetto *m* calorifico, effetto *m* termico
° 2754 **calorific value**	pouvoir *m* calorifique	Heizwert *m*	potere *m* calorifico (o calorifero)
° 2755 **calorimeter**	calorimètre *m*	Heizwertmesser *m*	calorimetro *m*
° 2756 **calorimetric bomb**	bombe *f* calorimétrique	Wärmemessbombe *f*	bomba *f* calorimetrica
° 2757 **calorimetric test**	détermination *f* calorimétrique	Heizwertuntersuchung *f*	determinazione *f* calorimetrica
° 2758 **calorimetry**	calorimétrie	Kalorimetrie *f*, Wärmemessung *f*	calorimetria *f*
° 2759 **calorising**	calorisation *f*	Kalorisieren *n*	calorizzazione *f*, cementazione *f* metallica

		English	French	German	Italian
°	2760	**to calorize, to calorise**	caloriser	kalorisieren	calorizzare
°	2761	**calorized, calorised**	calorisé	kalorisiert	calorizzato
°	2762	**calorized steel**	acier *m* calorisé	kalorisierter Stahl *m*	acciaio *m* calorizzato
		calorizing, *s. calorising*			
—	2763	**calyx drill**	sondage *m* à grenaille	Schrotbohren *n*	sondaggio *m* a graniglia
—	2764	**cam**	came *f*, taquet *m*	Nocken *m*, Daumen *m*	cama *f*. tacchetto *m* (per gabbie)
—	2765	**cam**	calcite *f* et fluorine dans la salbande	Kalkspat *m* und Flussspat *m* im Salband	calcite *f* e fluorina *f* nella salbanda
—	2766	**cam-parachute**	parachute *m* à excentriques	Exzentrik-Fangvorrichtung *f*	paracadute *m* a eccentrici
°	2767	**cam shoe**	sabot *m* de la came	Frosch *m*	zoccolo *m* della palmola
		cam drum, *s. tappet drum*			
°	2768	**camber, belly**	ventre *m*	Ausbauchung *f*, Bauch *m*	ventre *m* (d'alto forno)
°	2769	**camber**	cambrage *m* (du modèle)	Durchformen *n* (des Modells)	controcurvatura *f* (del modello)
°	2770	**camber**	bombement *m*, cambrure *f*	Wölbung *f*, Gewölbe *n*, Krümmung *f*	bombatura *f*
—	2771	**Cambrian period**	Cambrien *m*	Kambrium *n*	cambriano *m*
—	2772	**camptonite**	camptonite *f*	Camptonit *m*	camptonite *f*
—	2773	**campylite**	campylite *f*	Kampylit *m*	campilite *f*
—	2774	**camsellite**	camsellite *f*	Camsellit *m*	camsellite *f*
°	2775	**camshaft tube**	tube *m* pour arbre à cames	Exzenterwellenrohr *n*	tubo *m* per albero a camme
		can, *s. casing or jacket*			
—	2776	**canbyite**	canbyite *f*	Canbyit *m*	cambite *f*
—	2777	**canch**	caniveau *m*, entaillement *m*	Rösche *f*, Nachreissen *n*	condotto *m* (per cavi), intaglio
—	2778	**canch hole**	trou *m* de mine horizontal	horizontales Bohrloch *n*	foro *m* da mina orizzontale

English	French	German	Italian
− 2779 **cancrinite**	cancrinite *f*	Cancrinit *m*	cancrinite *f*
− 2780 **cand**	fluorine *f*	Flussspat *m*	fluorina *f*
− 2781 **candelit**	charbon *m* flambant	Flammkohle *f*	carbone *m* a lunga fiamma (o bituminoso)
− 2782 **candle coal**	cannel-coal *m*, houille *f* grasse	Cannelkohle *f*, Fettkohle *f*	carbone *m* a lunga fiamma, carbone *m* grasso
° 2783 **candle power**	pouvoir *m* éclairant, intensité *f* lumineuse	Lichtstärke *f*	potere *m* luminoso, intensità *f* luminosa
° 2784 **canebrake**	paille *f* hachée	Häcksel *n*	paglia *f* tritata
− 2785 **canfieldite**	canfieldite *f*	Canfieldit *m*	canfildite *f*
− 2786 **cannel coal, candle coal, free burning coal**	charbon *m* à longue flamme	langflammige Kohle *f*	carbone *m* a lunga fiamma
^ 2787 **canning plant**	département *m* de remplissage et confection des produits pétrolifères	Füllung-u, Verpakkungshalle *f*	reparto *m* riempimento e confezionatura prodotti petroliferi
− 2788 **cannizzarite**	cannizzarite *f*	Cannizarit *m*	cannizzarite *f*
° 2789 **cantilever**	poutre *f* en encorbellement	Konsolträger *m*	trave a mensola
^ 2790 **cantilever mast**	mât de forage cantilever	Bohrklappmast *m*	torre ad antenna
^ 2791 **to cap**	capter, maîtriser	unter Kontrolle bringen, fassen	captare, imbrigliare, controllare
− 2792 **cap**	amorce *f*, détonateur *m*	Zünder *m*, Sprengkapsel *f*	capsula *f*, detonatore *m*
° 2793 **cap**	couvercle *m*, calotte *f*	Hut *m*, Deckel *m*	coperchio *m*, calotta *f*
^ 2794 **cap**	tête *f* de tubage	Rohrkopf *m*	testa *f* di tubazione
− 2795 **cap**	chapeau *m*, rallonge *f*	Kappe *f*	cappello *m*, prolunga *f*, cappello *m* d'armatura in legno
− 2796 **cap**	terrain *m* de recouvrement, banc supérieur	Deckgebirge *n*	terreno *m* di copertura, banco *m* superiore
− 2797 **cap crimper**	pince *f* à sertir	Sprengkapselzange *f*	pinze *f pl.* per capsule

		English	French	German	Italian
—	2798	**cap of rock, cap rocks**	terrain *m* de recouvrement	Deckgebirge *n*	terreno *m* di copertura
—	2799	**cap-piece (of timbering)**	chapeau, rallonge *f*	Kappe *f*	cappello *m* (di armatura in legno), prolunga
		cap stopper, *s. bottle cap*			
		capacitor foil, *s. condensator foil*			
	2800	**capacity**	capacité *f*	Fassungsvermögen *n*	capacità *f*
°	2801	**capacity (of the furnace)**	capacité *f* du fourneau	Fassungsraum *m*	capacità *f* o volume *m* del forno
°	2802	**capacity of the central station**	puissance *f* de la centrale	Leistungsfähigkeit *f* des Kraftwerkes	capacità *f* della centrale
°	2803	**capacity value**	grandeur *f* de la capacité	Kapazitätsgrösse *f*	grandezza *f* della capacità
°	2804	**cape bolt, set bolt**	boulon *m* à chapeau, boulon *m* à tête	Kopfschraube *f*, Kopfbolzen *m*	bullone *m* a cappello, bullone *m* a testa
		cape ruby, *s. pyrope*			
°	2805	**capillarity**	capillarité *f*	Kapillarität *f*	capillarità *f*
°	2806	**capillary attraction (in welding)**	attraction *f* capillaire	Kapillarwirkung *f*	attrazione *f* capillare (saldatura)
°	2807	**capillary bottle**	petit flacon *m* capillaire	Kapillarfläschchen *n*	boccetta *f* capillare
—	2808	**capillary fringe**	frange *f* capillaire	Kapillarsaum *m*	frangia *f* capillare
°	2809	**capillary power**	tension *f* capillaire	Kapillarkraft *f*	tensione capillare
°	2810	**capillary rise**	ascension *f* capillaire, montée *f* capillaire	Kapillarsteigung *f*	ascesa *f* per capillarità
—	2811	**caporcianite**	caporcianite *f*	Laumontit *m*	laumontite *f*, caporcianite *f*
—	2812	**cappelenite**	cappelénite *f*	Cappelenit *m*	cappelenite *f*
—	2813	**capping**	couche *f* supérieure	Oberschicht *f*	strato sovrastante
—	2814	**capstan**	cabestan *m*	Seilwinde *f*, Winde *f*	argano *m*, cabestano
		capstan lathe, *s. turret lathe*			
°	2814a	**capsule metal**	métal *m* pour capsule	Kapselmetall *n*	metallo *m* per capsule
—	2815	**captain dresser**	maître-bocardeur	Pochsteiger *m*	capo frantumatore
°	2816	**captive foundry, attached foundry**	fonderie *f* intégrée	Giesserei *f* für Eigenbedarf	fonderia *f* dipendente, fonderia *f* per uso proprio

English	French	German	Italian
— 2817 **capwise**	en direction *f* de rallonge	in Richtung *f* der Kappe	in direzione *f* del cappello
— 2818 **car (for mine working, wagonnet)**	wagonnet *m*, benne *f*, berline *f*	Wagen *m*	vagonetto *m*, vagoncino
— 2819 **caracolite**	caracolite *f*	Caracolit *m*	caracolite *f*
— 2820 **Caradoc stage**	Caradocien *m*	Caradoc *n*	caradociano *m*
caravan boiler, *s. wagon (head) boiler*			
∘ 2821 **carbide carbon, cementing carbon**	carbone *m* de cémentation	Karbidkohle *f*, Zementkohle *f*	carbonio *m* di cemen-- tazione
2822 **carbide furnace**	four *m* à carbure	Karbidofen *m*	forno *m* di carburo
carbide of iron, *s. cementite*			
2823 **carbide stringers**	alignement *m* des carbures	Karbidanreihung *f*	allineamento *m* di carburi
carbo-hydrogen, *s. oil gas*			
2824 **carbon**	carbone *m*	Kohlenstoff *m*	carbonio *m*
carbon, *s. carbon diamant*			
∘ 2825 **carbon bisulphide**	bisulfure *m* de carbone	Schwefelkohlenstoff *m*	solfuro *m* di carbonio
2826 **carbon black**	noir *m* de fumée	Erdgasruss *m*	nero *m* di carbone, nero- fumo *m*
— 2827 **carbon borer**	foret *m* à charbon	Kohlenbohrer *m*	trivella (o fioretto *m*) per carbone
∘ 2828 **carbon brick**	brique *f* de carbone	Kohlenstoffziegel *m*	mattone *m* di carbone
∘ 2829 **carbon content, temper**	teneur *f* en carbone	Kohlenstoffgehalt *m*	contenuto *m* di carbonio, tenore *m* in carbonio
∘ 2830 **carbon content analysing apparatus**	appareil *m* à essayer le carbone	Kohlenstoffprüfer *m*	apparecchio *m* per l'analisi del carbonio
— 2831 **carbon diamond**	bort *m*	Bort *m*	diamante *m* di trivel- lazione
∘ 2832 **carbon dioxide**	anhydride *m* carbonique	Kohlendioxyd *n*	anidride *f* carbonica
∘ 2833 **carbon electrode**	électrode *f* en charbon	Kohlenelektrode *f*	elettrodo *m* di carbone
∘ 2834 **carbon equivalent**	carbone *m* équivalent	Kohlenstoffäquiva- lent *n*	carbonio *m* equivalente, equivalente *m* in carbonio

		English	French	German	Italian
−	2835	carbon granules, granulated carbon	fines de charbon, menu de coke	Kohlenklein *n*, Kohlengrus *m*	carbone *m* minuto a granelli, carbonella *f*
°	2836	carbon holder	pince *f* à charbon	Kohlenhalter *m*	portacarbone *m*
−	2837	carbon-manganese steel	acier *m* au manganè-se à forte teneur de carbone	Kohlenstoff- -Mangan-Stahl *m*	acciaio *m* al manganese ad alto contenuto di carbonio
°	2838	carbon monoxide	oxyde *m* de carbone	Kohlen(mon)oxyd *n*	ossido *m* di carbonio
°	2839	carbon monoxide content	teneur *f* en oxyde de carbone	Kohlenoxydgehalt *m*	tenore *m* in ossido di carbonio
		carbon powder, *s. powdered coal*			
°	2840	carbon ratio, carbon content	teneur *f* en carbone fixe	Kohlenstoff- gehaltverhältnis *n*	tenore *m* in carbonio fisso, contenuto di carbonio fisso
		carbon restauration, *s. recarburation*			
−	2841	carbon saw	scie *f* à charbon	Kohlensäge *f*	sega *f* per carbone
°	2842	carbon steel	acier *m* au carbone, acier *m* carboné	Kohlenstoffstahl *m*	acciaio *m* al carbonio
°	2843	0,3-0,35% carbon steel	acier *m* demi-dur	halbharter Stahl *m*	acciaio *m* semiduro, ac-ciaio *m* al 0,3%-0,35 di carbonio
°	2844	0,4-0,5% carbon steel	acier *m* dur	harter Stahl *m*	acciaio *m* duro, acciaio *m* al 0,4%-0,5% di carbonio
°	2845	0,6-0,8% carbon steel	acier *m* extra-dur	extraharter Stahl *m*	acciaio *m* extra duro, ac-ciaio *m* al 0,6-0,8% di carbonio
		carbon temper, *s. carbon content*			
		carbon tool steel, *s. unalloyed tool steel*			
°	2846	carbonaceous inclusion	inclusion *f* de noir, inclusion carboneuse	Schwärzeeinschluss *m*	inclusione *f* di nero (o di tinta)
°	2847	carbonado, black diamond, carbon diamond, bort	bort *m*	Bort *m*	carbonado *m*, bort *m*
−	2848	carbonate of ammo-nium	carbonate *m* d'ammo-niaque	Ammonium- karbonat *n*	carbonato *m* ammonico
−	2849	carbonate of barium	carbonate *m* de ba-ryum	Bariumkarbonat *n*	carbonato *m* di bario
−	2850	carbonate of iron	carbonate *m* de fer, sidérose *f*	Eisenkarbonat *n*	carbonato *m* di ferro

English	French	German	Italian
— 2851 carbonate of lime	carbonate *m* de chaux	Kalziumkarbonat *n*	carbonato *m* di calcio
— 2852 carbonate of magnesia	carbonate *m* de magnésie	kohlensaures Magnesium *n*, Magnesiumkarbonat *n*	carbonato *m* di magnesio, magnesite *f*
carbonate of manganese, *s. manganese spar*			
— 2853 carbonate of potassium	. carbonate *m* de potasse	kohlensaures Kalï *n*, Pottasche *f*	carbonato *m* potassico o di potassa
— 2854 carbonate of sodium	carbonate *m* de soude	kohlensaures Natron *n*, Soda *f*	carbonato *m* sodico o di soda
— 2855 carbonation	métasomatose *f*	Metasomatose *f*	metasomatosi *f*
⁰ 2856 carbonic acid	acide *m* carbonique	Kohlensäure *f*	acido *m* carbonico
⁰ 2857 carbonic acid hardening	trempe *f* à l'acide	Kohlensäurehärtung *f*	tempera *f* all'acido carbonico
carboniferous, *s. carboniferous period*			
— 2858 carboniferous formation, coal-bearing formation, coal--formation	formation *f* carbonifère, terrain houiller carbonifère	Steinkohlen-formation *f*, Kohlen-formation *f*	formazione *f* carbonifera, carbonifero, carbone fossile, roccia *f* organica
carboniferous grit, *s. coal-grit*			
— 2859 carboniferous period	carbonifère *m*	Karbon *n*	carbonifero *m*, epoca *f* carbonifera
— 2860 carboniferous limestone	calcaire *m* carbonifère	Kohlenkalk *m*	calcare *m* carbonifero
— 2861 carboniferous series	série *f* carbonifère	Karbonformation *f*	serie *f* carbonifera
⁾ 2862 carbonised fuel	combustible *m* carbonisé	verkohlter Brennstoff *m*	combustibile *m* carbonizzato
⁾ 2863 carbonising flame	flamme *f* réductrice	Reduktionsflamme *f*	fiamma *f* riduttrice
⁾ 2864 carbonising period	durée *f* de la distillation, periode *f* de carbonisation	Destillationsdauer *f*, Periode *f* der Karbonisation	durata *f* di distillazione, periodo *m* di carbonizzazione
carbonising zone, *s. carbonisation zone*			
— 2865 carbonite	carbonite *f*	Karbonit *m*	carbonite *f*
⁾ 2866 carbonitriding	carbonitruration *f*	Karbonitrierung *f* Nitrozementierung *f*	nitro-carburazione *f*, carbonitrurazione *f*

	English	French	German	Italian
° 2867	carbonization, carburization	carburation f, cémentation f	Aufkohlung f	carburazione, carbo-cementazione f
— 2868	carbonization of coal	distillation f lente du charbon	Kohlenschwelung f	distillazione lenta del carbone
° 2869	to carbonize	carboniser	verkohlen	carbonizzare
° 2870	carbonized steel	acier m cémenté	Einsatzstahl m	acciaio m cementato
	carbonizing time, s. distillation time			
° 2871	carbons pl. for arc lamp	charbons m pl. d'arc	Bogenlampenkohlen f pl.	carboni m pl. per lampade ad arco
° 2872	carborundum	carborundum m	Karborundum n	carborundum m, carburo m al silicio
° 2873	carboy	bonbonne f, ballon m	Ballon m	damigiana f, bottiglia f per acidi corrosivi
° 2874	carboy filling apparatus	appareil m pour le remplissage des bonbonnes	Ballonabfüller m	apparecchio m per riempire le damigiane
2875	carboy filter	filtre m pour bonbonne	Ballonfilter n	filtro m da damigiana
› 2876	carboy tipper	bascule f à bombonnes	Ballonkipper m	apparecchio m per inclinare le damigiane
2876a	carbonyl	carbonyle m	Karbonyl n	carbonile m
2877	carburated water gas	gaz m à l'eau enrichi	gekohltes Wassergas n	gas m d'acqua arricchito
° 2878	carburetted iron, carburated iron	fer m carburé	gekohltes Eisen n	ferro m carburato
° 2879	carburisation, carbonisation, carburizing	carburation f	Kohlung f, Aufkohlung f	carburazione f
° 2880	carburisation by means of solid carbon	carburation f par le carbone solide	Kohlung f durch festen Kohlenstoff	carburazione f col carbonio solido
° 2881	carburisation material	addition f carburante	Kohlungsstoff m	addizione f riducente o carburante, (materiale m) carburante m
° 2882	carburisation zone	zone f de carburation	Kohlungszone f	zona f di carburazione
	carburised steel, s. casehardening steel			
	carburization, s. also carburisation			

	English	French	German	Italian
°	2883 **carburization**	carburation f	Aufkohlung f, Kohlung f	carburazione f, cementazione f carburante
°	2884 **to carburize, to carburet**	carburer	aufkohlen	carburare, cementare
°	2885 **carburizing, carburization**	cémentation f, carburation f	Aufkohlung f, Zementation f	carburazione f, cementazione f, carbocementazione f
°	2886 **carburizing furnace**	four m à cémenter	Einsatzofen m	forno m di cementazione, forno m di carburazione
°	2886a **carburizing material**	addition f carburante	Kohlungsstoff m	addizione f carburante
°	2887 **cardan joint**	joint m de cardan	Kardangelenk n	giunto m cardanico
−	2888 **Cardiff coal**	charbon m Cardiff	Cardiffkohle f	carbone m Cardiff
°	2889 **care of the furnace lining**	ménagement m du revêtement du cubilot	Schonung f des Ofenfutters	cura f del rivestimento del forno
−	2890 **carinate anticline**	anticlinal caréné	Spitz-Antiklinale f	anticlinale f carenata
°	2891 **carmine paper**	papier m carmin	Karminpapier n	carta f al carminio
−	2892 **carminite**	carminite f	Karminit m	carminite f
−	2893 **carnallite**	carnallite f	Carnallit m	carnallite f
−	2894 **carnegieite**	carnegiéite f	Carnegieit m	carnegieite f
	camelian, s. *cornelian*			
−	2895 **carneol**	carnaline f	Karneolstein m	cornalina f
−	2896 **carnotite**	carnotite f	Carnotit m	carnotite f
	carpenter's gauge, s. *marking gauge*			
°	2897 **carriage fittings**	ferrures f pl. de wagons	Wagenbeschlag m	armatura f in ferro dei vagoni
°	2898 **carriage frame**	châssis m de truck	Wagengestell n	telaio m del vagone (o carro)
−	2899 **carriage gangway**	galerie f principale de roulage	Hauptförderstrecke f	galleria f principale di carreggio
°	2900 **carrier, driving dog**	toc m d'èntrainement	Drehbankherz n	cuore m del tornio
−	2901 **carrollite**	carollite f	Carrollit m	carrollite f
	2902 **to carry**	porter, transporter	tragen, übertragen	portare, trasportare
−	2903 **carry**	portage m	Tragstrecke f	filone m portante

	English	French	German	Italian
2904	**carrying capacity, load**	charge f utile	Tragfähigkeit f	portata f massima, portata f, carico m
2905	**cartage**	frais m pl, de transport	Transportkosten fpl.	spese di trasporto
— 2906	**cart**	tombereau m	Kippkarren m	carretta a due ruote a scarico posteriore
^ 2907	**to case, to set casing**	tuber, entuber	verrohren, auskleiden	tubare, rivestire
^ 2908	**to case a pipe**	revêtir un tuyau	ein Rohr n auskleiden	rivestire un tubo
° 2909	**to case harden**	cémenter	einsatzhärten	cementare, indurire per cementazione

to case with lead, $s.$ to $lead$

2910	**case**	boîte f, caisse f	Behälter m, Kiste f	scatola f, cassa f
— 2911	**case**	fissure f aquifère	wasserführende Spalte f	fessura f acquifera
° 2911a	**case**	surface f	Oberfläche f	superficie f
° 2912	**case chilled**	coulée en coquille	hart gegossen	colato in superficie
° 2913	**case-hardened**	aciéré à la surface	durch Einsetzen (od. Einsatz) gehärtet, einsatzgehärtet	cementato in superficie

case-hardened castings, $s.$ $chilled$ $iron$

case-hardened iron, $s.$ $chilled$ $iron$

° 2914	**case-hardened steel, cement steel**	acier m cémenté	Zementstahl m, Einsatzstahl m	acciaio m cementato
° 2915	**case-hardened, steel system**	système m de cémentation de l'acier	Zementstahldarstellung f	cementazione f dell'acciaio
° 2916	**case-hardened surface**	surface f cémentée	gehärtete Oberfläche f	strato m superficiale m indurito
° 2917	**case hardening, aceration**	cémentation f, trempe f de surface	Einsatzhärten n	cementazione f, indurimento m superficiale
° 2918	**case-hardening, half converting**	trempe f en paquet, hypertrempe f	Einsatzhärtung f, Oberflächenhärtung f Zementation f	tempera f a cartoccio, cementazione f, sovratempera f
° 2919	**case-hardening pot, case-hardening box**	caisse f de cémentation	Einsatztopf m	cassa f di cementazione
° 2920	**case-hardening powder**	poudre f de cémentation	Einsatzpulver n	polvere f di cementazione

English	French	German	Italian
° 2921 **case-hardening steel**	acier *m* à cémenter	Einsatzstahl *m*	acciaio *m* cementato
° 2922 **case-hardening temperature**	température *f* de cémentation	Einsatztemperatur *f*	temperatura *f* di cementazione
° 2923 **case hardness**	dureté *f* de cémentation	Verstählungshärte *f*	durezza *f* di cementazione
^ 2924 **cased hole**	trou *m* entubé	verrohrtes Loch *n*	foro *m* tubato
° 2925 **cased-in blower, Lehmann's blower**	ventilateur *m* enveloppé ou blindé	Kapselwerk *n*, Lehmannsches Gebläse *n*	ventilatore *m* blindato
cased with lead, *s. lead-cased*			
° 2926 **casehardening furnace**	four *m* de cémentation	Einsatzhärtungsofen *m*, Zementierofen *m*	forno *m* da cementazione
— 2927 **cash**	schiste *m* tendre	weicher Schiefer *m*	scisto *m* tenero
° 2928 **casing, cased joists**	revêtement *m*	Verkleidung *f*	rivestimento *m*
— 2929 **casing**	revêtement *m* du puits	Schachtausbau *m*	rivestimento *m* (o armatura *f*) del pozzo
° 2930 **casing, shell**	carcasse *f*, chemise *f*, enveloppe *f*, corps	Blechmantel *m*, Mantel *m*, Gehäuse *n*	carcassa *f*, mantello *m*, armatura *f*, ossatura *f*
° 2931 **casing**	chemise *f* de revêtement, plaque *f* de revêtement	Umkleidungsplatte *f*	placca *f* o piastra di rivestimento
^ 2932 **casing**	tubage *m*	Verrbohrung *f*, Röhrentour *f*	tubaggio *m*, tubo di rivestimento
— 2933 **casing bowl**	cloche *f* de repêchage à coins	Rohrfangglocke *f*	manicotti *m pl.* a cunei interni e anelli di tenuta
^ 2934 **casing centralizer**	centreur *m*	Rohrzentrierkorb *m*	centratore *m* per tubi
^ 2935 **casing clamp**	crampe *f* à tubes, colliers *m pl.* de serrage	Röhrengreifhaken *m*, Bohrrohrschelle *f*	clampa *f* per tubi
— 2936 **casing collar**	manchon *m* de tube	Rohrmuffe *f*	manicotto *m* per tubi
— 2937 **casing cutter**	coupe-tube *m*	Rohrschneider *m*	tagliatubi *m.*
— 2938 **casing elevator**	élévateur *m* de tubage	Rohrheber *m*	elevatore *m* per tubi
— 2939 **casing fitting**	raccord *m*	Verbindungsstück *n*	raccordo *m*

	English	French	German	Italian
— 2940	**casing-grab**	accroche-tube *m*	Rohrfänger *m*	pescatore *m* per tubi
— 2941	**casing groove**	attaque *f* de tubage	Rohrverbindung *f*	attacco *m* per tubi
— 2942	**casing-gun**	perforateur *m* de tubage	Rohrlocher *m*	perforatore *m* per tubazioni
— 2943	**casing head**	tête *f* de tubage	Rohrkopf *m*	testa *f* ermetica dei tubi
^ 2944	**casing hanger**	support *m* de suspension pour tuyaux	Rohraufhänger *m*	elemento *m* costituente inflangiatura per casing
^ 2945	**casing head adapters**	raccords *m pl.* pour tête de tubage	Kopfrohrverschraubungen *f pl.*	rocchetti *m pl.* vari d'inflangiatura per casing
^ 2946	**casing head gas**	produit *m* de tête gazeux	Kopfabgas *n*	prodotto *m* di testa gassoso, gas contenenti idrocarburi superiori
^ 2947	**casing head gasoline**	essence *f* naturelle	Naturbenzin *n*	gasolina *f* naturale
^ 2948	**casing head with braden head**	tête *f* de tubage avec presse-étoupe	Verrohrungskopf *m* mit Stopfbüchse	testa *f* di tubaggio con premistoppa
^ 2949	**casing hook, rotary hook**	crochet *m* à émerillon	Bohrhaken *m*, Förderhaken *m*	gancio *m* per perforazioni rotary
^ 2950	**casing line**	câble *m* de tubage	Verrohrungsseil *n*	cavo *m* di tubaggio
^ 2951	**casing perforator**	perforateur *m* de tubage	Rohrperforator *m*	perforatore *m* di tubaggio
^ 2952	**casing pressure**	pression *f* de tubage	Ringraumdruck *m*, Casingdruck *m*	pressione *f* di tubaggio
^ 2953	**casing protector**	manchon *m* de protection	Bohrrohrschutzring *m*	manicotto *m* di protezione
^ 2954	**casing reamer, casing roller**	alésoir pour tubes	Rohrbohrer *m*	attrezzo *m* per riportare a calibro l'interno d'un tubo deformato o irregolare
^ 2955	**casing ripper**	incise-tube *m*	Rohrschlitzer *m*	intagliatubi *m*
	casing roller, *s. casing reamer*			
^ 2956	**casing scraper**	grattoir *m* de tubes	Rohrkrätzer *m*	raschiatore *m* di tubi
^ 2957	**casing shoe**	sabot *m* de cuvelage	Rohrschuh *m*	scarpa per tubi (o per colonna)
— 2958	**casing spear**	mandrin *m* relève-tubes	Backenfänger *m*, Rohrkrebs *m*	mandrino *m* sollevatubi

	English	French	German	Italian
−	2959 **casing spider**	support *m* de tubage à coins	Rohrkeilkranz *m*	supporto *m* per tubi a cuneo
ˆ	2960 **casing splitter**	déchire-tube *m*	Rohrschlitzer *m*	attrezzo *m* per raschiare l'interno di una colonna
ˆ	2961 **casing string**	colonne *f* de tubage	Rohrbatterie *f*	colonna *f* di tubi di pozzo
ˆ	2962 **casing spring design**	profils *m pl.* de tubage	Rohrprofile *n pl.*	profili *m pl.* di tubaggio
ˆ	2963 **casing swage**	emboutissoir *m*	Rohrbirne *f*, Treibbirne *f*	allargatore *m* per tubi
−	2964 **casing tongs**	pinces *f pl.* à tubes	Rohrzange *f*	tenaglie *f pl.* per tubi; chiave *f* stringitubi
°	2965 **to cast, to found**	couler	giessen	colare, fondere, gettare
°	2966 **to cast centrifugally**	centrifuger	schleudern	centrifugare
°	2967 **to cast cold**	couler à froid	kalt giessen	colare a freddo
°	2968 **to cast from two sides**	couler de deux côtés	von zwei Seiten giessen	colare o gettare da due lati
°	2969 **to cast green**	mouler à vert	grün giessen	colare in verde
°	2970 **to cast hollow**	couler à noyau	hohl giessen	colare in getti cavi
°	2971 **to cast horizontally**	couler à plat	liegend giessen	colare in piano, colare orizzontale
°	2972 **to cast in mould**	couler en moule	in Form *f* giessen	colare in forme
°	2973 **to cast in open sand**	couler à découvert	im Herd *m* giessen	colare allo scoperto
°	2974 **to cast in vertical clamped moulds**	couler en presse	in der Presse giessen	colare in pressa, colare in strettoio
°	2975 **to cast into ingots**	lingoter	blockgiessen	lingottare, fondere in lingotti
°	2976 **to cast on**	venir de fonte	angiessen	gettato, prodotto in getto, fuso in un sol pezzo
°	2977 **to cast on end**	couler en source	stehend giessen	colare in sorgente
°	2978 **to cast over the lip by tipping**	faire basculer pour couler le métal par le bec	durch Kippen aus der Schnauze giessen	far colare dal becco rovesciando

	English	French	German	Italian
° 2979	**to cast soft**	couler la fonte à faible teneur de carbone	Weichguss *m* giessen	produrre ghisa a basso tenore di carbonio
° 2980	**to cast the iron**	couler le fer en moules	das Eisen vergiessen	colare o gettare o fondere il ferro nelle forme
° 2981	**to cast through the plug hole**	couler par la quenouille	durch den Stopfen giessen	colare dal tappo
° 2982	**to cast white**	couler de la fonte blanche	Weisseisen giessen	fondere nella qualità bianca, fondere ghisa bianca
° 2983	**cast, mould**	moule *m*	Form *f*, Modellform *f*	modello *m*, calco *m*
° 2984	**cast, tap**	coulée *f*	Guss *m*	colata *f*, getto *m*
	cast, *s. bloom*			
° 2985	**cast-brass**	laiton *m* coulé	Gussmessing *n*	ottone *m* per getti
° 2986	**cast furnace**	fourneau *m* de fonderie	Giessofen *m*	forno *m* di fonderia, forno *m* di fusione
° 2987	**cast horizontally**	coulé à plat	liegend gegossen	colato orizzontalmente
° 2988	**cast house**	halle *f* de coulée	Giesshalle *f*	reparto *m* colate
	cast-in, *s. moulded in place*			
° 2989	**cast-in insert**	pièce *f* noyée	eingegossener Teil *m*	pezzo *m* inserito, pezzo *m* annegato, pezzo *m* preso in fondità
° 2990	**cast in one piece**	coulé en bloc, coulé monobloc	voll gegossen	colato in un sol pezzo
° 2991	**cast iron, gray iron**	fonte *f*	Gusseisen *n*	ghisa *f*, ferro *m* fuso
° 2992	**cast iron, pig iron**	fonte *f* de première fusion	Gusseisen *n* erster Schmelzung	ghisa *f* di prima fusione
° 2993	**cast iron**	fonte *f* de deuxième fusion	Gusseisen *n*, zweiter Schmelzung	ghisa *f* di seconda fusione
° 2994	**cast iron, foundry pig iron**	fonte *f* de moulage	Giessereiroheisen *n*	ghisa *f* da fonderia
° 2995	**cast iron castings**	pièce *f* de fonte, fonte *f* moulée	Roheisenguss *m*, Eisenguss *m*, Grauguss *m*	ghisa *f*, ghisa *f* grigia di fonderia
2996	**cast iron chip**	éclat *m* de fonte	Gusseisensplitter *m*	scheggia *f* di ghisa

		English	French	German	Italian
°	2997	cast iron column	colonne *f* en fonte	Gusseisensäule *f*	colonna *f* di ghisa
°	2998	cast iron crown	couronne *f* en fonte	Gusseisenkranz *m*	corona *f* di ghisa
°	2999	cast iron cylinder	cylindre *m* en fonte	gusseiserner Zylinder *m*	cilindro *m* di ghisa
°	3000	cast iron disc	disque *m* de fonte	Gusseisenscheibe *f*	disco *m* di ghisa
		cast iron flange, *s. cast iron rim*			
°	3001	cast iron foot	pilier *m* en fonte	gusseiserner Fuss *m*	piede *m* di ghisa
°	3002	cast iron furnace (cupola)	cubilot *m*	Kupolofen *m*, Kuppelofen *m*, Schachtofen *m*	cubilotto *m*
°	3003	cast iron grid	grille *f* en fonte	Gusseisengitter *n*	griglia *f* di ghisa
°	3004	cast iron grinder	triturateur *m* en fonte	gusseiserner Reiber *m*	trituratore *m* di ghisa
°	3005	cast iron grinding plate	plaque *f* de trituration en fonte	gusseiserne Reibeplatte *f*	piastra *f* di triturazione di ghisa
°	3006	cast iron in ingots for melting	fonte *f* en saumons pour fusion	Blockguss *m*	ghisa *f* in pani di fusione
°	3007	cast iron mould, chill	moule *m* en fonte, coquille *f*, lingotière *f*	gusseiserne Form *f*, Gussschale *f*, Kokille *f*	conchiglia *f*
		cast iron muffle, *s. iron muffle*			
°	3008	cast iron pipe	tuyau *m* en fonte	Gusseisenrohr *n*	tubo *m* in ghisa
°	3009	cast iron rim	couronne *f* en fonte	Gusseisenkranz *m*	corona *f* di ghisa
°	3010	cast iron ring	anneau *m* en fonte	gusseiserner Ring *m*	anello *m* di ghisa
		cast iron splinter, *s. cast iron chip*			
°	3011	cast on bar	barreau *m* attenant	angegossene Probeleiste *f*	provetta *f* fusa col getto
°	3012	cast-on flange	manchon *m* venu de fonte, tubulure *f* venue de fonte	angegossene Muffe *f*	manicotto *m* fuso in un sol pezzo
°	3013	cast-on guide bar	guidage *m* venu de fonte	angegossene Führungsleiste *f*	guida *f* fusa in un sol pezzo
°	3014	cast-on pin	tenon *m* venu de fonte	angegossener Zapfen *m*	manico *m* fuso in un sol pezzo

English	French	German	Italian
○ 3015 **cast-on test bar**	éprouvette *f* attenante	angegossener Probestab *m*.	provetta *f* fusa attaccata al pezzo
○ 3015a **cast shell process (of pipes)** **cast scrap**, *s. iron scrap*	étirage à froid de tubes coulés	Kaltziehen von nahtlos gegossenen Röhren	trafilatura a freddo di tubi colati
○ 3016 **cast solid, cast whole**	venu de fonte, venu à la coulée	zusammengegossen	fuso in un sol pezzo
○ 3017 **cast speed**	vitesse *f* de coulée	Giessgeschwindigkeit *f*	velocità *f* di colata
○ 3018 **cast steel**	acier *m* moulé	Stahlguss *m*, Gussstahl *m*	acciaio *m* in getti, acciaio *m* fuso
○ 3019 **cast steel crucible**	creuset *m* en acier coulé	Gussstahltiegel *m*	crogiolo *m* in acciaio fuso
○ 3020 **cast steel grating**	grille *f* en acier fondu	Gussstahlrost *m*	griglia *f* in acciaio fuso
○ 3021 **cast steel plate**	plaque *f* en acier coulé	Gussstahlblech *n*	piastra *f* di acciaio fuso
cast steel products, *s. steel casting*			
○ 3022 **cast steel valve**	vanne *f* en acier coulé	Stahlgussschieber *m*	valvola *f* in acciaio fuso
○ 3023 **cast-steel wheel centre**	centre *m* (de roue) en acier fondu	Radstern *m* aus Stahlguss *m*, Stahlgussradstern *m*	centro *m* di ruota in acciaio fuso
○ 3024 **cast steel wire brush with handle**	brosse *f* à main en fils d'acier	Gussstahldrahtbürste *f* mit Handgriff	spazzola *f* a mano in fili d'acciaio
○ 3025 **cast-steel works**	aciérie *f*	Gussstahlwerk *n*	acciaieria *f*
○ 3026 **cast structure** **cast structure**, *s. alloy structure*	structure *f* de coulée	Gussgefüge *n*	struttura *f* di colata
○ 3027 **cast temperature**	température *f* de coulée	Giesstemperatur *f*	temperatura *f* di colata
○ 3028 **cast-to-size**	coulé à mesure	nach Massgabe *f* gegossen	fuso *m* a misura
○ 3029 **cast tooth**	dent *f* brute (de fonte)	unbearbeiteter Zahn *m*	dente *m* greggio (di fusione)
○ 3030 **cast tube**	tuyau *m* moulé	Gussrohr *n*	tubo *m* fuso

English	French	German	Italian
cast whole, *s. cast solid*			
– 3031 castanite	castanite *f*	Castanit *m*	castanite *f*
° 3032 castable	coulable	vergiessbar	colabile
° 3033 castability, flowability	coulabilité *f*	Vergiessbarkeit *f*	colabilità *f*
° 3034 castability test	essai *m* de coulabilité	Fliessvermögenversuch *m*	prova *f* di colabilità
° 3035 caster	couleur *m*	Giesser *m*	colatore *m*
° 3036 casting	moulage *m*, pièce *f* de fonte	Abguss *m*, Gussstück *n*	pezzo *m* fuso, getto *m*
° 3037 casting (operation), pouring	coulée *f*	Giessen *n*, Guss *m*, Vergiessen *n*	colata *f*
° 3038 casting a spray	coulée *f* en grappe	Stapelguss *m*	colata *f* a grappolo
° 3039 casting area	aire *f* de coulée	Giessbett *n*	area *f* di colata, letto *m* di colata
° 3040 casting bay	chantier *m* de coulée	Giessplatz *m*, Giessstelle *f*	posto *m* di colata, piazza (o stazione *f*) di colata
° 3041 casting bed	lit *m* de coulée	Giessbett *n*	letto *m* di colata
° 3042 casting block	lingot *m*	Block *m*	lingotto *m*
casting box, *s. flask*			
° 3043 casting brush	brosse *f* pour fontes brutes	Gussputzbürste *f*	spazzola *f* per ghisa grezza
° 3044 casting by hand	fonte *f* à main	Handguss *m*	fusione *f* a mano
° 3045 casting carriage	chariot *m* de coulée	Giesswagen *m*	carro *m* di colata
° 3046 casting cleaning machine	ébarbeuse *f*, machine *f* à ébarber	Putzer *m*, Putzmaschine *f*, Entgratmaschine *f*	sbavatrice *f* per getti
° 3047 casting conduit	orifice *m* de coulée	Gussrinne *f*	bocca *f* di colata, foro *m* di colata
° 3048 casting copper	cuivre *m* pour jets	Gusskupfer *n*	rame *m* per getti
° 3049 casting crane	grue *f* de fonderie	Giesskran *m*	gru *f* di colata (o da fonderia)

		English	French	German	Italian
○	3050	casting form	moule *m*	Giessform *f*	forma *f*, staffa *f*
○	3051	casting free from internal stress	fonte *f* sans tensions internes	spannungsfreier Guss *m*	getto *m* senza tensioni interne
○	3052	casting free from blowholes	fonte *f* sans retassures	lunkerfreier Guss *m*	getto *m* senza soffiature
○	3053	casting head	masselotte *f*, tête *f* de lingotière	Haupteinguss *m*, Steiger *m*	materozza *f*
○	3054	casting house	halle *f* de coulée	Giesshalle *f*	campo *m* di colata
○	3055	casting in chills	moule *m* pour moulage en coquille	Hartgussform *f*	staffa *f* per getto in conchiglia
○	3056	casting in flasks	moulage *m* en châssis	Kokillenguss *m*	fusione in staffe, getto *m* in staffe, colata *f* in staffe
○	3057	casting in open	coulée *f* à découvert	offener Guss *m*	fusione *f* in forma aperta, colata *f* allo scoperto
○	3058	casting ladle, foundry ladle, moulder scoop	poche *f* à couler, cuiller *f*	Giesspfanne *f*, Giesslöffel *m*	cucchiaia *f*, siviera *f* per getto

casting loom, *s. molding clay*

		English	French	German	Italian
○	3059	casting machine	machine *f* à couler	Giessmaschine *f*	macchina *f* per colare o per fondere
○	3060	casting matrix	matrice *f* de coulée	Gussmatrize *f*	matrice *f* per fusione
○	3061	casting mould	moule *m*	Giessform *f*, Giesskasten *m*	forma *f*, staffa *f*

casting mould in the flask, *s. casting in flasks*

		English	French	German	Italian
○	3062	casting of the iron	coulée *f* de la fonte	Giessen *n* des Eisens	colata *f* della ghisa
○	3063	casting on an inclined bank	coulée *f* rampée	Giessen *n* in schrägliegende Form	colata *f* inclinata, colata *f* in discesa
○	3064	casting on flat	coulée *f* à plat	liegender Guss *m*	colata *f* orizzontale

casting pig, *s. pig*

casting pig-iron, *s. foundry pig-iron*

		English	French	German	Italian
○	3065	casting pit crane	grue *f* de fosse de coulée	Giessgrubenkran *m*	gru *f* della fossa di colata

	English	French	German	Italian
° 3066	casting pit, moulding-hole	fosse f de coulée, moule m	Giessgrube f, Dammgrube f	fossa f di colata, forma f
° 3067	casting shop	fonderie f	Giesserei f	fonderia f
	casting scrap, s. iron shot			
° 3068	casting skin	peau f de coulée	Gusshaut f	crosta f di fusione
° 3069	casting steel	acier m de moulage, acier m fondu	Gussstahl m	acciaio m fuso, acciaio m da fucina
° 3070	casting strains, distorsion by relieve of internal stresses	déformation f par libération des tensions internes	Verzug m durch Auslösung innerer Spannungen	deformazioni f pl. dovute a tensioni interne (di fusione)
° 3071	casting strand	convoyeur m de coulée	Giessband n	convogliatore m di colata
° 3072	casting stress	tension f de coulée	Gussspannung f	tensione f di colata
° 3073	casting temperature	température f de coulée	Giesstemperatur f	temperatura f di fusione
° 3074	casting wax	cire f à mouler	Gusswachs n	cera f per fusioni
° 3075	casting wheel	roue f de coulée	Giessrad n	ruota f per colare
° 3076	castings breaker	casse-fonte m	Gussbrechmaschine f	spezza-ghisa m
° 3077	castor, castorite	castor m	Kastor n, Petalit m	castorite f, petalite f
	CAT = caterpillar.			
	CAT cracker, s. catalytic cracking plant			
	CAT cracking, s. catalytic cracking			
– 3078	cat dirt	charbon m pyriteux	schwefelkieshaltige Kohle f	carbone m piritico
^ 3079	cat line, spinning rope	câble m de cabestan	Spillseil n	cavo m del cabestano
– 3080	cat's eye	oeil-de-chat m	Katzenauge n	occhio m di gatto
3080a	cat sapphire	saphir glauque	blaugrüner Saphir	zaffiro m glauco
– 3081	cataclastic	cataclastique	kataklastisch	cataclastico
– 3082	cataclastic structure	texture f cataclastique	Kataklasstruktur f	struttura f cataclastica
° 3083	catalan furnace	four m catalan, bas-foyer	Rennenofen m, Rennfeuer n	forno m catalano, crogiolo m catalano, basso fuoco m

	English	French	German	Italian
° 3084	catalan furnace slag, tap cinder	scorie _f_ catalane ou de forge catalane	Rennfeuerschlacke _f_	scoria _f_ di basso fuoco
— 3084a	cataphoresis	cataphorèse	Kataphorese _f_	cataforesi _f_
— 3085	catapleiite	catapléite _f_	Katapleit _m_	catapleite _f_
° 3086	catch basin	bassin _m_ épurateur	Sammelgrube _f_	bacino _m_ di raccolta (impurità)
— 3087	catch device, safety catch	palier _m_ d'arrêt de la cage	Aufsetzvorrichtung _f_	congegno d'arresto _m_ (della gabbia)
° 3088	catch drain	caniveau _m_ de drainage	Entwässerungs-graben _m_	fossetta _f_ di scolo
— 3089	catch hook	crochet _m_ de sauvetage	Fanghaken _m_	gancio _m_ di salvataggio, pescatore
° 3090	catch member	chaînon _m_ entraîneur	Mitnehmerglied _n_	maglia _f_ d'attacco
— 3091	catcher	parachute _m_ pour tubes	Rohrfang-vorrichtung _f_	paracadute _m_ per tubi
— 3092	catches	taquets _m pl._ de calage pour berline dans la cage	Klinken _f pl._ für das Festhalten der Wagen auf dem Gestell	tacchette _f pl._ per le gabbie
^ 3093	cathead, break-out	cabestan _m_ (à dévisser)	Spill zum Brechen	cabestano (per svitare)
^ 3094	cathead, make-up	cabestan _m_ (à visser)	Spill _n_ zum Kontern	cabestano _m_ (o argano) per avvitare
° 3095	catching of the sparks	recueillir les étincelles	Auffangen _n_ der Funken	raccolta _f_ delle scintille
° 3096	cathetometer	cathétomètre _m_	Kathetometer _n_	catetometro _m_
— 3097	cathkinite	cathkinite _f_	Cathkinit _m_	cathkinite _f_, saponite _f_
— 3098	catline	câble _m_ de cabestan	Spillseil _n_	cavo _m_ del cabestano
	cat forming, _s. catalytic reforming_			
^ 3099	catline rope-guard	rouleau-guide _m_ du câble du cabestan	Führungsrolle _f_ für Spillseil	rullo _m_ di guida della fune del cabestano
^ 3100	cat-plant	unité _f_ de traitement catalytique	Katalytraffinerie _f_	stabilimento _m_ di raffineria catalitica
^ 3101	cat wagon	autocar _m_ chenillé	Raupenkettenwagen _m_	automezzo cingolato

English	French	German	Italian
^ 3102 **cat-walk**	passerelle f	Laufsteg m	passarella f, cavalletti per tubi a aste, piattaforma f del pontista
° 3103 **cathodic protection**	protection f cathodique	kathodischer Schutz m	protezione f catodica
— 3104 **catoptrite**	catoptrite	Katoptrit m	catoptrite f
— 3105 **cauf**	berline f	Förderwagen m	vagoncino m
— 3106 **cauk**	barytine	Schwerspat m	baritina f
— 3107 **cauldron**	effondrement circulaire	Kesselbruch m	cedimento m circolare
° 3108 **cauliflower head (of feedhead)**	boursouflement m (de masselotte)	Aufblähung (des Steigers)	rigonfiamento m (di materozza)
° 3109 **cauliflower head**	champignon m	pilzförmig aufgetriebener Speiser m	rigonfiamento m, fungo m

caulk weld, s. *seal weld*

English	French	German	Italian
° 3110 **caulked seam**	couture f moulée	Stemmnaht f	aggraffatura f ribadida (o cianfrinata)
° 3110a **caulking**	montage m	Verstemmen n	cianfrinatura f
° 3111 **caulking iron**	ciseau de calfat, fer de calfat	Kalfateisen n Dichteisen n	scalpello per presellare (o per cianfrinare)
° 3111a **caulking ring**	anneau m de matage	Abdichtring n	anello m di presellatura
° 3112 **caulking tool**	matoir m	Stopfgerät n, Streckeisen n	presello m da idraulico per calafatare
° 3113 **caustic cracking, caustic embrittlement**	fragilité f caustique	Laugensprödigkeit Beizsprödigkeit f	fragilità f intercristallina (o per corrosione)
° 3114 **caustic dip**	bain m caustique	Natriumhydroxyd-Bad m	bagno m caustico

caustic potash, s. *hydrate of potash*

English	French	German	Italian
° 3115 **caustic potash solution**	solution f de potasse caustique	Kalilauge f	soluzione f di potassa caustica
° 3116 **caustic soda**	soude f caustique	Natronhydrat n	soda f caustica
° 3117 **caustic soda solution**	solution f de soude caustique	Natronlauge f	soluzione f di soda caustica
— 3118 **caustobiolith**	caustobiolite f	Kaustobiolith m	caustobiolite f
— 3119 **to cave, to cave in, to fall in**	s'ébouler, s'écrouler	einfallen, einstürzen	franare, smottarsi

	English	French	German	Italian
— 3120	caved	foudroyé, éboulé	eingestürzt	franato, smottato
— 3121	caving	foudroyage *m*, exploitation *f* par écroulement	Einsturzbau *m*	coltivazione *f* per franamento
— 3122	caving, caving in, falling in	écroulement *m*, éboulement *m*	Zusammensturz *m*, Einsturz *m*, Rutschung *f*	franamento *m*, frana
— 3123	caving formation	terrain *m* boulant	zusammenstürzendes Gebirge *n*	formazione *f* franosa
— 3123a	cavitation corrosion	attaque *f* par cavitation	Kavitationskorrosion *f*	attacco *m* per cavitazione
° 3124	cavity	cavité *f*, retassement *m*	Hohlraum *m*, Lunker *m*	cavità *f*, vuoto *m*, incavo *m*, risucchio *m*
— 3125	cavity-filled ore deposits	gîtes *m pl.* de remplissage des fissures et des cavités	Lagerstätten *f pl.* von Hohlraumausfüllung	giacimenti *m pl.* di riempimento delle cavità e delle fessure
— 3126	cavity filling	remplissage *m* de fissures ou des cavités	Höhlenfüllung *f*	riempimento *m* di cavità e di fessure
— 3127	cawk	barytine *f*	Schwerspat *m*	baritina *f*
° 3128	to cease charging	cesser le chargement	mit dem Aufgichten aufhören	cessare le cariche, smettere di caricare
— 3129	cebollite	cebollite *f*	Cebollit *m*	cebollite *f*
° 3130	ceiling convector	convecteur *m* en plafond	Deckenheizkoerper *m*	termoconvettore *m* a soffitto
— 3131	celestine, celestite	célestine *f*	der schwefelsaurer Strontian *m*, Cölestin *m*	celestina *f*, celestite *f*
	celestite; *s. celestine*			
3132	cell	élément *m* de pile	Element *n*	cella, elemento di pila
3133	cellar	cave *f*	Keller *m*	cantina *f*
— 3134	cellar	avant-puits *m*	Vorschacht *m*	avanpozzo *m*
— 3135	cellular	cellulaire	zellig	cellulare
	cellular texture, *s. mosaic texture*			
— 3136	celsian	celsian *m*	Celsian *m*, Baryumfeldspat *m*	celsiano *m*
— 3137	celtium	hafnium *m*	Hafnium *n*	afnio *m*

	English	French	German	Italian
3138	to cement	cimenter	zementieren, verstählen	cementare
3139	to cement-up	cimenter à haut niveau	hochzementieren	cementare ad alto livello
3140	cement	ciment *m*	Zement *m*	cemento *m*
3141	cement	matériel *f* à cémenter, cément	Zement *m*	materiale *m* da cementazione, cemento *m*
3142	cement, binding material	matière *f* agglutinante, liant *m*	Bindemittel *n*	materia *f* agglomerante (o agglutinante)
3143	cement bond	adhérence *f* du ciment	Zementabbindung *f*	aderenza *f* del cemento
3144	cement clinker	clinker *m*	Zementklinker *m*	clinker *m* di cemento
3145	cement column	colonne *f* de ciment	Zementhöhe *f*	colonna *f* di cemento
3146	cement copper	cuivre *m* cémenté	Zementkupfer *n*	rame *m* di cementazione
3147	cement cut mud	boue *f* contaminée de ciment	durch Zement *m* verunreinigte Spülung	fango *m* contaminato dal cemento

cement furnace, *s. cement-kiln*

	English	French	German	Italian
3148	cement gold	or *m* cémentatoire	Zementgold *n*	oro *m* raffinato
3148a	cement gun	guniteuse *f*	Zementkanone *f*	iniettore *m* spruzza-cemento
3149	cement head	tête *f* de cimentage	Zementierkopf *m*	testa *f* di cementazione
3150	cement hopper	malaxeur de ciment	Zementmischmaschine *f*	betoniera *f* per cemento
3151	cement-kiln	four *m* à ciment	Zementbrennofen *m*	forno *m* da cemento
3152	cement moulding	moulage *m* en sable au ciment	Zementsand-Formverfahren *n*	formatura *f* in sabbia cemento
3153	cement retainer	presse-étoupe *m* de cimentation	Zementierpackung *f*	premistoppa *m* di cementazione
3154	cement sand	sable *m* au ciment, sable-ciment *m*	Zementsand *m*	sabbia *f* al cemento
3155	cement slurry	pâte *f* de ciment, lait *m* de ciment	Zementschlamm *m*	pasta *f* di cemento, latte *m* di cemento
3156	cement steel, case--hardened steel	acier *m* cémenté	Zementstahl *m*, Einsatzstahl *m*	acciaio *m* cementato (od ottenuto per cementazione)

	English	French	German	Italian
	cement testing sand, *s. standard sand*			
^ 3157	cement unit	groupe *m* de cimentation	Zementieraggregate *n pl.*	unità *f* di cementazione
° 3158	cementation (as of steel)	cémentation *f*	Zementieren *n*	cementazione *f*
° 3159	cementation carbon	carbone *m* de cémentation	Zementkohle *f*	carbonio *m* di cementazione
° 3160	cementation furnace, cementing furnace	four *m* à cémenter	Zementierofen *m*	forno *m* di cementazione
	cementation powder, *s. cementing powder*			
° 3161	cementation process, converting process, manufacture of cement steel	fabrication *f* d'acier cémenté, cémentation	Zementieren *n*, Zementstahl-herstellung *f*	fabbricazione dell'acciaio cementato, metodo di cementazione, cementazione
° 3162	cementation steel	acier de cémentation	Einsatzstahl *m*, Zementstahl *m*	acciaio *m* da cementazione
— 3163	cementation zone	zone de cémentation	Zementationszone *f*	zona *f* di cementazione
° 3164	cemented	cémenté	zementiert	cementato
	cemented bar, *s. blister bar*			
° 3165	cemented coat	couche *f* cémentée	zementierte Schicht *f*	strato *m* cementato
° 3166	cemented steel	acier *m* de cémentation, acier *m* ferritique	Zementstahl *m*, ferritischer Stahl *m*	acciaio *m* cementato
3167	cemented superficially	aciéré à la surface	einsatzgehärtet	acciaiato in superficie
— 3168	cementing	cimentation *f*	Zementierung *f*	cementazione *f*
° 3169	cementing	cémentation *f*	Zementation *f*	cementazione *f*
^ 3170	cementing basket	panier *m* de cimentation	Zementierungskorb *m*	ombrello *m* per cementazioni
° 3171	cementing box	caisse *f* de cémentation	Zementierkiste *f* Einsatztopf *m*	cassa *f* di cementazione
	cementing carbon, *s. carbide carbon*			
^ 3172	cementing float collar	soupape *f* flottante pour tubes	Rohrschwimmer-ventil *n*	valvola *f* di galleggiamento per tubi

	English	French	German	Italian
3173	cementing-furnace, converting furnace	four *m* de cémentation, four à cémenter	Zementierofen *m*	forno *m* di (o per) cementazione
3174	cementing head	tête *f* de cémentation	Zementierkopf *m*	testa *f* di cementazione
3175	cementing material	matière *f* de cémentation	Glühmittel *n*	sostanza *f* per la cementazione
3176	cementing plug	tampon *m* de cimentation	Zementierpfropfen *m*	tappo *m* di cementazione
3177	cementing powder	poudre *f* à cémenter	Zementierpulver *n*, Härtepulver *n*	polvere *f* di cementazione
3178	cementing or binding power	pouvoir *m* agglutinant	Bindevermögen *n*	potere *f* agglomerante (o agglutinante)
3179	cementite	cémentite *f*	Zementit *m*	cementite *f*
3180	cementitious	cimentant	zementierend	cementante
3181	qenogenesis	coenogénèse *f*	Coenogenese *f*	cenogenesi *f*
3182	cenosite	cénosite *f*	Kainosit *m*	cenosite *f*
3183	cenotypal	néovolcanique	jungvulkanisch	neovulcanico, cenotipo
3184	Cenozoic era, cenozoic	ère *f* cénozoïque	känozoische Formation *f*	era *f* cenozoica, cenozoico *m*
3185	center bit	alésoir *m* de centrage	Zentrierbohrer *m*	scalpello *m* di guida
3185a	center line shrinkage	retassure au centre	Zentrallunker *m*	risucchio *m* centrale
3186	center shots	mines *f pl.* d'empiétage	Einbruchbohrlöcher *n pl.*	mine di rottura
3187	center spear	harpon *m*	Fanghaken *m*	pescatore *m* ad arpione
3188	centering, centring	centrage *m*	Zentrierung *f*	centratura *f*
3189	centering borer	alésoir *m* de centrage	Zentrierbohrer *m*	alesatore *m* di centratura *f* (o di centraggio *m*)
3190	centesimal balance	bascule *f* centésimale	Hunderterwaage *f*	bilancia *f* centesimale

centesimal weighing machine, *s. centesimal balance*

centipoise, *s. unit of absolute dynamic viscosity*

| 3191 | central jack plant | station *f* centrale de pompage | Pumphauptanlage *f* | stazione *f* centrale di pompaggio |

	English	French	German	Italian
○ 3192	central tube	tuyau *m* central	Zentralrohr *n*	tubo *m* centrale
^ 3193	centraliser	outil *m* à centrer	Zentriervorrichtung *f*	centratore *m*
— 3194	centrallasite	centrallasite *f*	Centrallasit *m*	centrallasite *f*
○ 3195	centre bit	foret *m* à centre, foret *m* à téton, mèche *f* à centre	Zentrumbohrer *m*	punta *f* da trapano a a centro, punta *f* inglese
○ 3196	centre drill	mèche *f* de centrage	Zentrumbohrer *m*	trapano *m* autocentrante
○ 3197	centre lathe	tour *m* à pointes, tour *m* parallèle	Spitzendrehbank *f*	tornio *m* a punte, tornio *m* parallelo
○ 3198	centre plate	crapaudine *f* de trousseau	Spurlager *n*	base *f*, rallino *m*
○ 3199	centreless grinding machine	machine *f* à rectifier sans pointes	spitzenlose Schleifmaschine *f*	rettificatrice *f* senza punte

centricast, *s. centrifugal casting*

| ○ 3200 | centrifugal apparatus | essoreuse *f* | Schleuderabscheider *m*, Zentrifuge *f* | centrifuga *f* |

centrifugal atomiser, *s. centrifugal sprayer*

○ 3201	centrifugal blower	ventilateur *m* centrifuge	Schleudergebläse *n*, Ventilator *m*	ventilatore *m* centrifugo
○ 3202	centrifugal casting, centricast	moulage *m* centrifuge	Schleuderguss *m*	getto *m* centrifugato
○ 3203	centrifugal casting	coulée *f* (par la force) centrifuge	Zentrifugalguss *m*, Schleuderguss *m*	colata *f* a forza centrifuga, fusione *f* per centrifugazione
○ 3204	centrifugal casting die	coquille *f* de centrifugation	Schleudergiesskokille *f*	conchiglia *f* per centrifugazione
○ 3205	centrifugal casting machine	machine *f* à couler par centrifugation	Schleudergiessmaschine *f*	macchina *f* per colata centrifuga
○ 3206	centrifugal casting pipe	tuyau *m* centrifuge	Schleudergussrohr *n*	tubo *m* centrifugato

centrifugal cutter, *s. centrifuge cutter*

centrifugal mill, *s. disintegrator*

| ○ 3207 | centrifugal pressure casting | coulée *f* sous pression centrifuge | Schleuderformguss *m* | colata *f* o fusione centrifugata |

English	French	German	Italian
3208 centrifugal pump	pompe *f* centrifuge	Schleuderpumpe *f*	pompa *f* centrifuga
3209 centrifugal separation	séparation *f* par centrifugation (ou centrifuge)	Schleuderab- scheidung *f*	separazione *f* centrifuga
3210 centrifugal sprayer	pulvérisateur *m* centrifuge	Schleuderzerstäuber *m*, Zentrifugal- zerstäuber *m*	polverizzatore *m* centrifugo
to centrifugate, *s. to centrifuge*			
3211 centrifugation	centrifugation *f*	Schleudern *n*	centrifugazione *f*
3212 to centrifuge, to centrifugate	centrifuger	schleudern	centrifugare
3213 centrifuge	diviseur *m* centrifuge	Radschleuder *m*, Zentrifuge *f*	disintegratore *m* centrifugo, centrifuga *f*
3214 centrifuged steel	acier *m* centrifugé	Schleuderstahl *m*	acciaio *m* centrifugato
centring, *s. centering*			
3215 centring boss	bossage *m* de centrage d'usinage	Zentrierauge *n*	centro *m* posticcio per tornìtura
3216 centring frame	cadre *m* de presse à centrer les châssis	Ausrichtrahmen *m*, Zentrierrahmen *m*	telaio *m* per centrare le staffe
3217 centring frame or ring	couronne *f* à mouler, centreuse	Durchzugring *m*	portamodello *m*
3218 centring moulding machine	presse *f* de précision ou à centrer les châssis	Ausrichtmaschine *f*, Zentriermaschine *f*	macchina *f* per precisare la posizione delle staffe
3219 centring pin	goujon *m* de centrage	Zentrierstift *m*	pernio *m* di centratura
3220 centripetal fault	faille *f* normale	normale Verwerfung *f*	faglia *f* normale
3221 centroclinal	cuvette *f*, périsynclinal *m*	Schüssel *f*	centroclinale , perisinclinale *f*
3222 centroclinal dip	pendage *m* périclinal	periklinales Einfallen *n*	inclinazione *f* periclinale
3223 cephalopods	céphalopodes *m pl.*	Cephalopoden *m pl.*	cefalopodi *m pl.*
3224 cerametallic	métalcéramique	metallkeramisch	metalceramico
3225 ceramic coating	revêtement *m* céramique	keramische Bekleidung *f*	rivestimento *m* ceramico

	English	French	German	Italian
° 3226	ceramic kiln	four *m* céramique, four *m* de céramique	keramischer Brennofen *m*	forno *m* ceramico
— 3227	cerargyrite	cérargyrite *f*	Chlorsilber *n*, Silberhornerz *n*	cerargirite *f*, clorargirite *f*
— 3228	ceresin wax	cérésine *f*	Zeresin *m*	ceresina *f*, cera fossile
° 3229	cerium	cérium *m*	Zer *n*, Cer *n*	cerio *m*
° 3230	cermet	métal céramique	keramisches Metall *n*	metallo *m* ceramico
— 3231	cerussite	cérusite *f*	Zerussit *m*	cerussite *f*
— 3232	cervantite	cervantite *f*	Cervantit *m*	cervantite *f*
— 3233	cesarolite	césarolite *f*	Cesarolith *m*	cesarolite *f*
— 3234	ceylanite	ceylanite *f*	Ceylanit *m*	ceilanite
	ceylonite, *s. ceylanite*			
— 3235	chabazite	chabasite *f*	Chabasit *m*	chabasite *f*
° 3236	chafery, furnace for blooms	four *m* de réchauffage four *m* à réchauffer	Heizungsofen *m*	forno *m* di riscaldo
° 3237	chafing	chauffage *m* par frottement	Reibungsheizung *f*	riscaldamento *m* per attrito
° 3238	chain	chaîne *f*	Kette *f*	catena *f*
— 3239	chain coalcutter	haveuse *f* à chaîne	Kettenschraemmaschine *f*	tagliatrice *f* da carbone a catena
° 3240	chain cogwheel	pignon *m* de chaîne	Kettenrad *n*	pignone *m* per catena
^ 3241	chain compound	composé *m* en chaîne	Kettenverbindung *f*	composto *m* a catena
° 3242	chain drive	transmission *f* par chaîne	Kettentrieb *m*, Kettenantrieb *m*	trasmissione *f* a catena
° 3243	chain grate	grille *f* à chaîne	Kettenrost *m*	griglia *f* a catena
° 3244	chain grate stoker	foyer *m* avec grille à chaîne	Kettenrostfeuerung *f*	focolare *m* con griglia a catena, focolare *m* a grata mobile
° 3245	chain hoist	palan *m*	Flaschenzug *m*	paranco *m*
° 3246	chain iron	fer *m* de chaîne	Ketteneisen *n*	ferro *m* per catene

English	French	German	Italian
chain-pipe vice, *s. chain-vice*			
3247 **chain railway**	transporteur *m* à chaîne	Kettenbahn *f*	trasportatore *m* a catena
3248 **chain steel**	acier *m* à chaînes	Kettenstahl *m*	acciaio *m* da catene
3249 **chain-vice**	étau *m* à chaîne (pour tubes)	Kettenrohr-schraubstock *m*	morsa *f* a catena (per tubi)
3250 **chair pass**	cannelures *f pl.* pour plaques ou selles	Unterlagplatten-kaliber *n*	tracciato *m* per piastre
3251 **chair-plate, saddle-plate**	coussinet-selle. selle *f*	Stuhlplatte *f*	lastra *f* a cuscinetto, scarpa *f*
3252 **chalcanthite**	chalcanthite *f*	Chalkanthit *m*	calcantite *f*, cianosio *m*
3253 **chalcedony**	calcédoine *f*	Kalzedon *m*	calcedonio *m*
3254 **chalcocite, redruthite, chalcosine**	chalcosine *f*, cuivre *m* vitreux, cuivre sulfuré gris	Kupferglanz *m*, Chalkosin *m*, Redouthit *n*	calcosina *f*, rame *m* vetroso
3255 **chalcodite**	chalcodite *f*	Chalkodit *m*	calcodite *f*
3256 **chalcography, copperplate printing**	calcographie *f*, impression en taille-douce *f*	Kupferstecherei *f*, Kupferstechkunst *f*	calcografia *f*
3257 **chalcophyllite**	chalcophyllite *f*	Chalkophyllit *m*	calcofillite *f*
3258 **chalcolamprite**	chalcolamprite *f*	Chalkolamprit *m*	calcolamprite *f*
3259 **chalcomenite**	chalcoménite *f*	Chalkomenit *m*	calcomenite *f*
3260 **chalcophanite**	chalcophanite *f*	Chalkophanit *m*	calcofanite *f*
3261 **chalcopyrite**	chalcopyrite *f*	Kupferkies *m*	calcopirite *f*
3262 **chalcosine**	chalcosine *f*	Chalkosin *m*	calcosina *f*
3263 **chalcostibite**	chalcostibine *f*	Chalkostibit *m*	calcostibite *f*
3264 **chalcotrichite**	chalcotrichite *f*	Chalkotrichit *m*, Kupferblüte *f*	calcotrichite *f*
3265 **chalk, limestone**	pierre *f* calcaire, castine *f*	Kalkstein *m*	calcare *m*, creta *f*
3265a **chalk test**	essai *m* à la craie	Kreideprobe *f*	prova *f* con creta
3266 **chalking (the wire)**	chauler le fil	Kalken *n* des Drahtes	calcinatura *f* del filo
3266a **chalking**	pulvérisation *f*	Verpulverung *f*	polverizzazione *f*

	English	French	German	Italian
— 3267	chalky sandstone, calcareous sandstone	grès m calcaire	kalkiger Sandstein m	arenaria f calcarea
— 3268	chalibeate water, iron water	eau f ferrugineuse, eau f martiale	Eisenwasser n	acqua f marziale, acqua f ferruginosa
	chalybite, s. siderite			
— 3269	chamber-and-pillar	exploitation f par chambres et piliers	Kammerpfeilerbau m	coltivazione f a camere e pilastri
— 3270	chamber blast	sautage m par chambres	Kammerschiessen n	abbattimento m a camere
	chamber-furnace, s. muffle-furnace			
^ 3271	chamber lift	gaz lift par chambre	Kammer-Gasliften	gas «lift» per camera
º 3272	chambered core	noyau m chambré	hohler Gusskern m	anima f cava (o a caverne)
— 3273	chambered vein	filon m en forme de chambres	Kammergang m	filone m a camere (o a caverne)
— 3274	chambering	agrandissement m du fond d'un trou de mine	Auskesselung f des Bohrloches	allargamento m del fondo di un foro da mina
º 3274a	chamfer	biseau m	Fase f	modanatura f
	chamfering of the edge, s. bevelling of the edge			
º 3275	chamois leather	peau f de chamois	Putzleder n	pelle f di camoscio
— 3276	chamoisite	chamoisite f	Chamosit m	chamosite f
º 3277	chamotte	chamotte f	Schamotte f	«chamotte» f, terra f refrattaria
º 3278	chamotte brick	brique f de chamotte	Schamottestein m	mattone m refrattario
º 3279	chamotte molding	moulage m en chamotte	Schamotteguss m	formatura f in «chamotte»
º 3280	chamotte sand, campo	sable m à la chamotte	Schamottesand m	terra f di chamotte
^ 3281	chain tong	clef f à chaîne	Kettenzange f	chiave f a catena
	change, s. variation			
º 3282	changeability of phases	possibilité f de modification des phases	Veränderungsmöglichkeit f der Phasen	possibilità f di modifica delle fasi
— 3283	to channel	haver	schrämen	tagliare (carbone), intagliare

English	French	German	Italian
3284 **channel, conduit**	canal *m*, carneau *m*	Kanal *m*	canale *m*, condotto *m*
3285 **channel**	saignée *f*	Einschnitt *m*	taglio *m*, tacca *f*, intaglio *m*
3286 **channel**	filon *m* de roche	Gesteinsgang *m*	filone *m* di roccia
channel bar, *s. U-iron*			
channel-beam, *s. channel-iron*			
3287 **channel bed**	couche *f* de gravier	Schotterbett *n*	strato *m* ghiaioso
3288 **channel black**	noir *m* de fumée	Kienruss *m*	nerofumo *m*
3289 **channel(-iron), U-iron, channel-beam, channel-bar, C-iron**	fer *m* à U, fer *m* E, fer *m* à côtés, fer *m* à brancards, fer *m* à C	U-Eisen *n*, U-Träger, Hohlschiene *f*	ferro *m* a E o ad U, ferro *m* a C, profilati *m pl.* (o sagomati *m pl.*) ad U
3290 **channel lode**	canal *m* filonien	Flözkanal *m*	canale *m* filoniano
channel plate, *s. riffled (or checker) plate*			
channel steel, *s. U-Steel*			
channel type furnace, *s. slot furnace*			
3291 **channel type induction furnace**	four-tunnel électrique à induction à canal	Rinnen-Induktionsofen *m*	forno *m* elettrico a induzione a canale
3292 **channels**	fers *m pl.* U	U-Eisen *n*	profilati *m pl.* ad U
3293 **channels for running lead**	canaux *m pl.* pour recueillir le plomb	Kanäle *m pl.* zur Bleigewinnung	canali *m pl.* per raccogliere il piombo
3294 **channeling**	canalisation *f*	Kanalbildung *f*	canalizzazione *f*
3295 **chaplet**	support *m* de noyau	Kernstütze *f*	sopporto *m* per anima
3296 **chapmanite**	chapmanite *f*	Chapmanit *m*	chapmanite *f*
3297 **characteristics of the ore**	caractère *m* du minerai	Eigenart *f* oder Charakter *m* des Erzes	caratteristica *f* del minerale
3298 **charcoal, wood-charcoal, wood coal**	charbon de bois, charbon végétal	Holzkohle *f* Pflanzenkohle *f*	carbone *m* di legna, carbone *m* vegetale
3299 **charcoal ashes** *pl.*, **pearlash**	fraisil *m* de charbon de bois	Holzkohlenasche *f*	ceneri *f pl.* di carbone di legna
3300 **charcoal blacking**	poudre *f* de charbon de bois	Holzkohlenpulver *n*	polverino *m* di carbone dolce
3301 **charcoal blast furnace**	haut-fourneau *m* au charbon de bois	Holzkohlenhochofen *m*	alto forno *m* a carbone di legna

English	French	German	Italian

charcoal block, s. *soldering carbon*

		English	French	German	Italian
°	3302	**charcoal briquette**	aggloméré m de charbon de bois	Holzkohlenbrikett n	agglomerato m di carbone di legna
°	3303	**charcoal dust (or powder)**	charbon de bois en poudre, poussier de charbon de bois	Holzkohlenstaub m	carbone m di legna in polvre, polvere di carbone in le
°	3303a	**charcoal grade**	fer m au bois	Frischfeuereisen n	ferro m affinato
°	3304	**charcoal heap, charcoal pile**	meule f en charbon de bois	Holzkohlenmeiler m	carbonaia f
°	3305	**charcoal hearth**	feu m brasqué	Löschfeuer n	basso-fuoco m
°	3306	**charcoal hearth steel**	acier m (d'affinage) au bas-foyer, acier de finerie	Löschfeuerstahl m, Holzkohlenstahl m	acciaio m al basso fuoco
°	3307	**charcoal hearth cast iron**	fonte f mazée, fonte de finage	Herdfrischroheisen n, Frischereiroheisen n	ghisa f di primo affinaggio, ghisa al carbone di legna
°	3308	**charcoal iron, fined iron**	fer m au bois, fer affiné	Holzkohleneisen n, Frischfeuereisen n	ferro m al carbone di legna, ferro affinato

charcoal kiln, s. *oven for carbonizing*

		English	French	German	Italian
°	3309	**charcoal lump**	charbon m de bois en morceaux	Holzkohle f in Stücken	carbone m di legna in pezzi

charcoal pig iron, s. *charcoal hearth cast iron*

		English	French	German	Italian
°	3310	**charcoal oven for peat**	four m de carbonisation de la tourbe	Torfkohlenofen m	forno m per carbonizzare la torba
°	3311	**charcoal powder or dust**	noir m végétal	Holzkohlenstaub m	nero m vegetale, polvere f di carbone vegetale
°	3312	**charcoal sheet iron**	tôle f au charbon de bois	Holzkohlenblech n	lamiera f al carbone di legna
	3313	**to charge**	charger	beschicken	caricare
°	3314	**to charge the boxes**	charger les caisses	die Kisten laden	caricare le casse
°	3315	**charge**	matières f pl. à fondre, charge f	Schmelzstoff m, Einsatz m	carica f
°	3316	**charge, batch, burden**	fournée f, charge f (de fourneau)	Satz m, Gicht f, Schicht f	infornata f, carica f (di forno)

charge bogie, s. *charge wagon*

English	French	German	Italian
3317 charge book	livre *m* des charges, livre *m* des coulées	Schmelzbuch *n*	registro *m* delle cariche, libro *m* delle colate
3318 charge bridge	pont *m* de chargement	Gichtbrücke *f*	passerella *f*, ponte *m* di carico
3319 charge coke	coke *m* de fusion	Satzkoks *m*	carica *f* di coke
3320 charge gauge	tige *f* de jaugeage, bécasse *f*	Satzanzeiger *m*	indicatore *m* di carica
3321 charge labourer	chargeur *m* de minerai	Erzverlader *m*	operaio *m* addetto a caricare il minerale
3322 charge level or platform	niveau *m* de chargement	Setzboden *m*	piano *m* di caricamento, piattaforma *f* di carico
3323 charge of coke without ore	fausse charge *f*, coke *m* sans minerai	leere Koksgicht *f*	carica *f* bianca
3324 charge of fuel	charge *f* de combustible	Brennstoffgicht *f*	carica *f* di combustibile
3325 charge of ores and fluxes	charge *m* de minerai et du fondant	Möller *m*, Erzsatz *m*	carica *f* del minerale e del fondente
3326 charge of pig	charge *f* de fonte	Heissen *m*, kleine Einsatzmenge *f*	carica *f* di ghisa
charge shovel, *s. peel*			
3327 charge stock	pétrole *m* à traiter	Beschickungsöl *n*	petrolio *m* di carica (o da trattare)
3328 charge wagon, charge bogie	wagon *m* de chargement	Beschickwagen *m*, Beschickungswagen *m*	caricatrice *f* a vagone
3329 chargeman	boutefeu *m*	Sprengmeister *m* Schiessmeister *m*	artificiere *m*
3330 charger	chargeur *m*	Begichter *m*	caricatore *m*
3331 charging	chargement *m*	Beschicken *n*	caricamento *m*, carico *m*
3332 charging apparatus	appareil de chargement	Füllvorrichtung *f*, Ladevorrichtung *f*	apparecchio *m* di carica, meccanismo *m* di caricamento
3333 charging bar	flèche *f* mobile horizontale	bewegliche Stange *f*	braccio *m* mobile
3334 charging bin or hopper	trémie *f* de chargement	Füllrumpf *m*	tramoggia *f* di caricamento

	English	French	German	Italian
° 3335	charging box	récipient *m* de chargement, cuiller *f* de chargement	Beschickmulde *f*, Chargiermulde *f*, Lademulde *f*	lingottiera *f* di caricamento
° 3336	charging capacity	poids *m* maximum	Tragkraft *f*, Ladefähigkeit *f*	capacità *f* di carico, potenziale di carica
° 3337	charging cone	cône *m* de glissement	Abrutschkegel *m*	imbuto *m* di carica
° 3338	charging crane	grue *f* de chargement	Beschickkran *m*, Einsetzkran *m*, Chargierkran *m*	caricatrice *f* a gru
° 3339	charging device	dispositif *m* de chargement du gueulard	Aufgichtvorrichtung *f*	meccánismo *m* o sistema *m* di caricamento
° 3340	charging device, charging machine	machine *f* à charger, chargeur *m* mécanique, enfourneuse *f*	Einsetzmaschine *f*, Beschickmaschine *f*	caricatrice od infornatrice *f*
° 3341	charging door	gueulard *m*, orifice *m* de chargement	Beschickungsöffnung *f*, Gichtöffnung *f*, Füllöffnung *f*	bocca *f* o porta *f* o apertura *f* di caricamento
° 3342	charging end	bande *f* collectrice, brin *m* collecteur	Sammeltrumm *n*	estremità *f* di nastro collettore
° 3343	charging gallery foot plates, charging platform	plancher *m* de la plate-forme du gueulard	Gichtbelag *m*	pavimento *m* della piattaforma di caricamento
° 3344	charred hartshorn	corne *f* de cerf calcinée	gebranntes Hirschhorn *n*	corno *m* calcinato di cervo
° 3345	charging hole	gueulard *m*	Gichtöffnung *f*	bocca *f* di caricamento
° 3346	charging hopper	dispositif *m* de chargement	Füllvorrichtung *f*	apparecchio *m* di caricamento
° 3347	charging ladle	poche *f* à couler	Gabelpfanne *f*	siviera *f* di colata
° 3348	charging level	niveau *m* de chargement	Setzboden *n*	piattaforma *f* di caricamento
° 3349	charging machine	enfourneuse *f*	Aufgichtvorrichtung *f*	infornatrice *f*
° 3350	charging man	chargeur *m*	Gichtmann *m*	addetto *m* alle cariche
° 3351	charging of ores	chargement *m* des minerais	Einfüllen *n* der Erze, Aufgeben *n*, Beschicken *n*	carica *f* dei minerali
° 3351a	charging pan	benne *f* de chargement	Gichtkübel *m*	benna *f* di caricamento

English	French	German	Italian
3352 **Charpy shock test on notched bar**	essai *m* de résilience Charpy pour l'acier	Charpy-Kerbschlag-probe *f* für Stahl	prova di resistenza col pendolo di Charpy per l'acciaio
3353 **charring**	carbonisation *f*	Verkohlung *f*	carbonizzazione *f*, cokificazione
to chase a thread on a lathe, *s. to turn a thread*			
3354 **to chase to bottom**	mettre hors feu un haut fourneau	den Hochofen *m* ausblasen	spengere il forno
3355 **chaser**	moulin *m* chilien	chilenische Mühle *f*	mulino *m* a rulli, macina *f* cilena
3356 **chasing**	exploration *f* du filon en direction	Verfolgung *f* eines Ganges im Streichen	esplorazione *f* del filone in direzione
3357 **chat-rollers**	broyeur *m* à cylindres	Quetschwerk *n*	mulino *m* a cilindri
3357a **chatoyancy**	chatoiement *m*	Schillern *n*	a colore cangiante
3358 **chats**	produits *m pl.* intermédiaires	Mittelprodukte *n pl.*	prodotti *m pl.* intermedi
3358a **chatter mark**	marque *f* de vibration	Rattermarke *f*	traccia *f* di vibrazione
3359 **Chattian stage**	Chattien *m*	Chattian *n*	Chattiano *m*
3360 **chatty ore**	minerai *m* finement disséminé	fein eingesprengtes Erz *n*	minerale *m* finemente disseminato
3361 **check**	vérifier, contrôler, contrôle	nachprüfen *n*, Kontrolle *f*	verificare, controllare, controllo *m*, verifica *f*
3362 **check**	plaque *f* de contrôle	Kontrollmarke *f*	piastra *f* di controllo
3363 **check**	crique *f*, tapure *f*	Riss *m*, Sprung *m*	screpolatura *f*, incrinatura *f*
3364 **check battery**	panneau *m* de fermeture de cheminée	Brettscheider *m* am Fusse der Stürzrolle zwecks Aufhalten der Kohle	pannello *m* di chiusura dello scivolo
check mark, *s. crowfeet*			
3365 **check plate**	plaque *f* de butée	Anlaufscheibe *f*	piattello *m* reggispinta, disco *m* di ritegno
3366 **check valve**	clapet *m* de retenue	Rückschlagventil *n*, Sperrventil *n*	valvola *f* di contropressione
3367 **checker**	chambre *f* de régénération	Regenerierungs-kammer *f*	camera *f* di recupero (o di rigenerazione)
3368 **checker coal**	anthracite *f* en morceaux	Stückanthrazit *m*	antracite *f* in pezzi

		English	French	German	Italian
o	3369	checker plate, rifled plate	tôle f rainurée (ou striée)	Riffelblech n	lamiera f striata
o	3370	checkered, chequered	rainuré, strié	geriffelt	striato
o	3371	checkered plate	tôle f striée	Riffelblech n	lamiera f striata
o	3372	checker	chambre f de régénération	Regenerierungs- kammer f	camera f di rigenera- zione
o	3373	checking	contrôle m	Kontrolle f	controllo m
o	3374	checking	craquelure (du moule)	Haarriss (der Form), Rissbildung f	criccatura f (dello stampo)
o	3375	checking with thickness pieces	mouchetage m	Prüfen n der Wand- dicke mit Lehm- pfropfen	verifica f degli spesso- ri (con mosche di argilla) applicazione f delle mos
—	3376	checks	parois f pl.	Ulmen f pl.	pareti f pl.
o	3377	checks	fissures f pl. longitudinales	Längsspalten f pl.	fessure f pl. (o cricche f pl.) longitudinali
o	3378	checkwork	chambre f de ré- génération	Regenierungs- kammer f	camera f di rigenerazio
—	3379	cheek	paroi f, éponte	Ulmen f pl.	parete f, tetto m
o	3380	cheek (foundry)	châssis m de milieu, part f centrale	Zwischengussform f zentraler Teil	fascia f, parte centrale
o	3381	cheese, stool, stand	fromage m, tourte f	Bodenstein m, Käse m Tiegeluntersatz m	formaggella f, pa- nello m
^	3382	cheese box	cornue f cylindrique	Zylinderretorte f	storta f cilindrica
o	3383	chemical analysis	analyse f chimique	chemische Analyse f	analisi f chimica
o	3384	chemical affinity	affinité f chimique	chemische Verwandtschaft f	affinità f chimica
o	3385	chemical combination	combinaison f chi- mique	chemische Bindung f	combinazione f chimi- ca
o	3386	chemical composition	composition f chi- mique	chemische Zusammensetzung f	composizione f chimi- ca
o	3387	chemical constitution	constitution f chi- mique	chemischer Aufbau m	costituzione f chimica
o	3388	chemical deposition	déposition f chi- mique	chemisches Verfahren n	deposizione f chimica

English	French	German	Italian
3389 chemical determination of the calorific value	détermination *f* chimique de la puissance calorifique	chemische Heizwertbestimmung *f*	determinazione *f* chimica del potere calorifico
3390 chemical impurity	souillure *f* par des substances chimiques	chemische Verunreinigung *f*	impurità *f* chimica
3391 chemical reaction	réaction *f* chimique	chemische Einwirkung *f*	reazione *f* chimica
3392 chemical resistant steel	acier *m* résistant aux produits chimiques	chemisch beständiger Stahl *m*	acciaio *m* resistente alla corrosione chimica
3392a chemical stripping	dépouillage chimique	chemische Entplattierung	strappamento *m* chimico
3393 chemical symbol	symbole *m* chimique	chemisches Zeichen *n*	simbolo *m* chimico
3394 chemical weight equivalent	équivalent *m* chimique	chemisches Äquivalent *n*	peso *m* equivalente chimico
3395 chemicals	correctifs *m pl.*	Verbesserungsmittel *n*	correttivi *m pl.* chimici (del fango)
3396 chemically combined oxygen	oxygène *m* chimiquement combiné	chemisch gebundener Sauerstoff *m*	ossigeno combinato chimicamente
3397 chemically equivalent quantities	quantités *f pl.* chimiquement équivalentes	chemisch gleichwertige Mengen *f pl.*	quantità *f pl.* chimicamente equivalenti
3398 chemically pure iron	fer *m* chimiquement pur	chemisch reines Eisen *n*	ferro *m* chimicamente puro
3399 chemically pure sulphuric acid	acide *m* sulfurique chimiquement pur	chemisch reine Schwefelsäure *f*	acido *m* solforico chimicamente puro
3400 chemistry of iron	étude *m* chimique du fer	Chemie *f* des Eisens	studio *m* chimico del ferro
3401 chemistry of the blast furnace process	chimie *f* du haut-fourneau	Chemie *f* des Hochofenganges	chimica *f* dell'alto forno
3402 chenevixite	chenevixite *f*	Chenevixit *m*	Chenevixite *f*
3403 chequered head milled nail	pointe *f* fraisée rayée	gefräster und gestreifter Stift *m*	punta *f* fresata rigata
3404 chequered plate	tôle *f* rainurée	Riffelblech *n*	lamiera *f* striata
3405 chequerwork	chambre *f* de régénération	Regenierungskammer *f*	camera *f* di rigenerazione
3406 cherry coal	houille *f* grasse à longue flamme	Sinterkohle *f*	carbone *m* grasso a fiamma lunga

		English	French	German	Italian
—	3407	cherry picker	tube *m* de repêchage fendu	geschlitzte Fangbüchse *f*	tubo *m* del pescatore tagliato
o	3408	to a cherry red-heat	au rouge cerise	auf Kirschrotglut	al rosso ciliegia
o	3409	cherry red(-hot)	chauffé au rouge cerise	kirschrotglühend	scaldato al rosso ciliegia
—	3410	chert	roche *f* cornéenne	Hornstein *m*	selce *f* cornea
—	3411	chess-board structure	structure *f* en damier	Schachbrettfigur *f*	struttura *f* a scacchiera
—	3412	chessom	terre *f* noire	Schwarzerde *f*	terra *f* nera
		chessy copper, *s. azurite*			
—	3413	chessylite, azurite	chessylite *f*, azurite *f*	Chessylith *m*, Azurit *m*	azzurrite *f*
—	3414	chestnut coal, nuts *pl.* egg coal	gailletins *m pl.*, têtes *f pl.* de moineau, noisettes *f pl.*	Nusskohle *f*	carbone *m* di pezzatura noce
—	3415	chiastolite	chiastolite *f*	Chiastolith *m*, Hohlspat *m*	chiastolite *f*, andalusite *f*
	3416	chief laboratory	laboratoire *m* principal	Hauptlaboratorium *n*	laboratorio *m* principale
	3417	chief of laboratory	chef *m* du laboratoire	Laboratoriumsvorstand *m*	responsabile *m* del laboratorio
—	3418	childrenite	childrénite *f*	Childrenit *m*	childrenite *f*
o	3418a	chile bar	barre *f* de cuivre impur	Rohkupferstab *m*	barra *f* di rame impuro
—	3419	chileite	chiléite *f*	Chileit *m*	cileite *f*
—	3420	chilenite	chilénite *f*	Chilenit *m*	cilenite *f*
o	3421	to chill, to chill-harden	coquiller	Schreckplatten *f pl.* anlegen	conchigliare, fondere in conchiglia, temprare
o	3422	chill	solidification *f* blanche, trempe *f*	Weisserstarrung *f*	solidificazione *f* bianca, fusione *f* bianca
		chill, *s. chill cast*			
o	3423	chill (of a sand mold)	coquille *f*	Schreckschale *f*	raffreddatore *m*
o	3424	chill anomaly	anomalie *f* de trempe	Abschreckanomalie *f*	anomalia *f* di tempra
o	3425	chill block chill test-piece	éprouvette *f* de trempe	Abschreckprobe *f*	provetta *f* di tempra

English	French	German	Italian
3426 chill cast	fondu en coquille	in Kokillen f $pl.$ gegossen	fuso in conchiglia
3427 chill cast ingot	gueuset m (moulé, en coquille)	Roheisenmassel f	pane m di ghisa grezzo, lingotto m fuso in conchiglia
3428 chill casting	moulage m en coquille	Schalenguss m	getto m in conchiglia, fusione f in conchiglia
3429 chill cracks, fire cracks	tapures à froid (ou de récristallisation)	Kaltriss m, Rekristallisations-riss m	cricche f $pl.$ di laminazione (o intercristalline)
3430 chill crystals	cristaux m $pl.$ de trempe	Abschreckkristalle m $pl.$	cristalli di conchigliatura
3431 chill depth	profondeur f de trempe	Einstrahlung f	profondità f di tempera
3432 chill foundry pig iron, chilled iron	fonte f pour moulage en coquille	Hartgussroheisen n	ghisa f per fusione in conchiglia
3433 chill mould	coquille f (de fonderie)	Kokille f, Hartguss, Kokillenform f	conchiglia f (di fonderia)
3434 chill molding	moulage m en coquille	Kokillenguss m	fusione f in conchiglia
3435 chill nail	clou m refroidisseur	Kühlnagel m	chiodo m raffreddatore
3436 chill shot drilling	sondage m à la grenaille	Schrotbohren n	perforazione f alla graniglia
3436a chill test	essai m de trempe	Abschreckprobe f	prova f di tempera
3437 chill test piece	éprouvette f de trempe	Abschreckprobe f	provetta f di tempera
3438 chill value	valeur f de refroidissement	Abschreckwert m	valore m di raffreddamento (o di conchigliatura)
3439 chill zone	trempe f primaire partielle normale	normal ausgebildete weisserstarrte Zone f	tempra f primaria parziale normale
3440 chill zone without mottle	trempe f primaire partielle sans transition	weisserstarrte Zone f ohne Übergang	tempra f primaria parziale senza transizione
3441 chillagite	chillagite f	Chillagit m	chillagite f
3442 chilled-casting	fonte f en coquille	Hartguss m, Schalenguss m	ghisa f fusa in conchiglia
3443 chilled iron, case--hardened iron, chill casting	fer m fondu en coquille(s), fonte f durcie	Hartguss m, Kokillenguss m, Schalenguss m	ghisa f indurita (in conchiglia), ghisa f temperata

		English	French	German	Italian
°	3444	chilled iron wheel	roue *f* coquillée	Hartgussrad *n*	ruota *f* conchigliata
—	3445	chilled margin	auréole *f* de contact	Kontakthof *m*	aureola *f* di contatto
°	3446	chilled roll	rouleau *m* coquillé	Hartgusswalze *f*	rullo *m* conchigliato
—	3447	chilled shot bit. shot bit	couronne *f* à grenailles	Schrotkrone *f*	corona *f* a graniglia
—	3448	chilled steel shot	grenaille *f* d'acier	Stahlschrot *m*	graniglia *f* d'acciaio
°	3449	chilled steel	acier *m* à trempe glacée	abgeschreckter Stahl *m*	acciaio *m* a tempra vitrea, acciaio fuso in conchiglia
°	3450	chiller	coquille *f*	Schreckschale *f*	raffreddatore *m*
°	3451	chilling	fonte en coquille, trempe	Hartguss *m*, Abschreckung *f*	ghisa *f* in conchiglia, tempra *f*
		chilling, *s. cooling*			
°	3452	chilling effect	effet *m* trempant	Hartgusseffekt *m*	effetto *m* temprante
°	3453	chimney	cheminée *f*	Schornstein *m*	camino *m*
—	3454	chimney	évent, cheminée (d'éruption)	Eruptionskanal *m*, Schlot *m*	canale *m* (d'eruzione)
—	3455	chimney	colonne de minerai	Erzfall *m*	colonna di minerale
°	3456	chimney cap	lanterne de cheminée	Schornsteinhaube *f*	comignolo *m*
°	3457	chimney cooler	réfrigérant *m* à cheminée	Kaminkühler *m*	refrigeratore *m* a camino
°	3458	chimney draught	tirage *m* de cheminée	Schornsteinzug *m*	tiraggio *m* del camino
°	3459	chimney flue	canal *m* ou conduit de fumée	Rauchkanal *m*, Essenkanal *m*	condotto *m* del fumo
°	3460	chimney hole	orifice *m* du canal de fumée	Rauchabzugöffnung *f*	apertura *f* del condotto del fumo
°	3461	chimney hood	hotte *f* de la cheminée	Rauchfang *m*	cappa *f* del camino
°	3462	chimney lid	clapet *m* de cheminée	Temper *m*	coperchio *m* (o valvola *f* di chiusura del camino
°	3463	chimney platform	plate-forme *f* des cheminées	Kaminbühne *f*	piano *m* dei camini

	English	French	German	Italian
3464	chimney rock	pyramide *f* coiffée	Erdpyramide *f*	piramide *f* rocciosa
3465	chimney ventilator	ventilateur *m* de cheminée	Schornsteinlüfter *m*, Schornsteinventilator	ventilatore *m* del camino
3466	chimneying	accrochage *m* des charges, formation de voûtes	Hängen *n* der Gicht, Gewölbebildung *f*	attacco *m* delle cariche, formazione *f* di volte
	china clay, *s. kaolin*			
3467	chinese soapstone	agalmatolite *f*	Agalmatolith *m*	Agalmatolite *f*
	chinese white, *s. flowers of zinc*			
3468	to chink	se fendre, se crevasser	aufreissen	fessurarsi, creparsi
3469	chink	fissure *f*	Spalte *f*	fessura *f*, crepa *f*
3470	chinley coal	gailleterie *f*	Stückkohle *f*	carbone *m* minuto, carbone a cubetti
	chinsing, *s. caulting*			
3471	chiolite	chiolite *f*	Chiolith *m*	chiolite *f*
3472	to chip	ébarber	abgraten	sbavare
3473	to chip	décriquer	meisseln	scriccare
	to chip, to chip out, *s. to cut*			
3474	chip	copeau, éclat *m*, morceau *m*	Span *m*, Splitter *m*	truciolo *m*, scheggia *f*, pezzo *m*
3474a	chip test	analyse *f* des copeaux	Spananalyse *f*	analisi *f* delle scaglie
3475	chipless shaping	formage *m* sans enlèvement de copeaux	spanlose Verformung *f*	formatura *f* senza asportazione di trucioli
3476	chipper	machine à décriquer	Ausmeissel- maschine *f*	scriccatore *m*
3477	chipping	décriquage *m*	Meisseln *n*	scalpellatura *f*, scriccatura *f*
3477a	chipping	burinage *m*	Aushauen *n*	scheggiatura *f*, scagliatura *f*
3478	chipping	ébarbage *m*	Abgraten *n*	sbavatura *f*
3479	chipping, scaling off	décalaminage *m*	Entzünderung *f*	sfaldamento *m*
3480	chipping hammer	marteau *m* à ébarber, marteau à buriner	Abputzhammer *m* Abklopfhammer *m*	martello *m* per sbavare martello *m* per picchiettare

	English	French	German	Italian
— 3481	chippings	gros gravier *m*, pierres *f pl.* concassées	Steinschlag *m*	ghiaia *f* grossa, pietre *f pl.* frantumate
° 3482	chips *pl.* of metal, shavings *pl.*	copeaux *m pl.* métalliques, copeaux *m pl.* de métal	Metallspäne, Drehspäne *m pl.*	trucioli *m pl.* metallici
° 3483	to chisel	buriner	meisseln	scalpellare
° 3484	to chisel off	découper au ciseau	wegmeisseln	scalpellare
° 3485	chisel	burin *m*, tranche *f*	Schrotmeissel *m*	tagliolo *m*, scalpello *m*
^ 3486	chisel auger	tarière *f* à tranchant	Flachmeissel *m*	trivella *f* a tranciante
° 3487	chisel steel	acier *m* à burins, acier *m* à ciseau	Meisselstahl *m*	acciaio *m* da scalpelli, acciaio per bulino
° 3488	chisel-shaped soldering-iron	fer *m* à souder à tête carrée	Hammerlötkolben *m*	saldatoio *m* a testa di martello
	chisel temper, *s. chisel steel*			
	chisel-temper steel, *s. chisel steel*			
— 3489	chisley	pierreux, à gros grain	steinig, grobkörnig	pietroso, a grana grossa
— 3490	chloanthite	chloanthite *f*	Chloanthit *m*	cloantite *f*
— 3491	chloralluminite	chloroaluminite *f*	Chloraluminit *m*	cloraluminite *f*
— 3492	chlorapatite	chlorapatite *f*	Chlorapatit *m*	cloropatite *f*
— 3493	chlorargyrite	chlorargyrite *f*	Chlorargyrit *m*, Chlorsilber *n*	clorargirite *f*, cerargirite *f*
° 3494	chloride of barium	chlorure *m* de barium	Bariumchlorid *n*	cloruro *m* di bario
° 3495	chloride of calcium free of water	chlorure *m* de calcium anhydre	wasserfreies Chlorkalzium *n*	cloruro *m* di calcio secco od anidro
° 3496	chloride of iron	chlorure *m* de fer	Eisenchlorid *n*	cloruro *m* di ferro
° 3497	chloride of lime	chlorure *m* de calcium	Chlorkalk *m*	cloruro *m* di calce
° 3498	chloride of magnesium	chlorure *m* de magnésium	Chlormagnesium *n*, Magnesiumchlorid *n*	cloruro *m* di magnesio

English	French	German	Italian
3499 chloride of potassium	chlorure *m* de potassium	Chlorkalium *n*, Kaliumchlorid *n*	cloruro *m* potassico
3500 chlorine	chlore *m*	Chlor *n*	cloro *m*
3501 chlorine developing apparatus	appareil *m* pour la fabrication du chlore	Chlorentwicklungsflasche *f*	generatore *m* di cloro
3502 chlorine developing flask	ballon *m* pour la fabrication du chlore	Chlorentwicklungskolben *m*	pallone *m* per fabbricare cloro
3503 chlorite	chlorite *f*	Chlorit *n*	clorite *f*
3504 chloritic	chloriteux	chlorithaltig	cloritico
3505 chloritic schist	chloritoschiste *m*	Chloritschiefer *m*	cloritoscisto *m*
3506 chloritization	chloritisation *f*	Chloritbildung *f*	cloritizzazione *f*
3507 chloritoid	chloritoïde *m*	Chloritoid *n*	cloritoide *m*
3508 chlormanganokalite	chlormanganokalite	Chloromanganokalit	cloromanganocalite *f*
3509 chlorocalcite	chlorocalcite *f*	Chlorocalcit *m*	clorocalcite *f*
3510 chloromelanite	chloromélanite *f*	Chloromelanit *m*	cloromelanite *f*
3511 chloropal	chloropal *m*	Chloropal *m*	cloropale *m*
3512 chlorophane	chlorophane *m*	Chlorophan *m*	clorofano *m*
3513 chock (supporting a mine roof)		Bretterschloss *n*	catasta *f*
3514 choke (runners)	engorger la coulée	den Einguss vollhalten	colare a getto pieno, strozzare le colate
3515 to choke, to bean	étrangler	drosseln	soffocare
3516 to choke tuyeres	fermer les tuyères	die Düsen *f pl.* schliessen	parzializzare gli ugelli
3517 choke bean	buse *f* réglable	einstellbare Düse *f*	ugello *m* regolabile a spillo
3518 choked runner system	coulée *f* en dépression	Giessen *n* mit Entspannung	colata *f* in depressione
chokedamp, *s. blackdamp*			
3519 choking or clogging the blast furnace scaffolding	engorgement *m* du haut-fourneau	Ersticken *n* des Hochofens	strozzamento *m* del passaggio del gas

	English	French	German	Italian
° 3520	chocks	chaise *f*, empoise *f*, coussinet *m* de tourillon	Zapfenlager *n*	sedia *f*, cuscinetto *m* d'alberino portante
° 3521	chop	impureté *f* enfoncée	eingehämmerter Fremdkörper *m*	impurità *f* affondata
° 3521a	chop	marque *f* de fabrique	Schutzmarke *f*	marchio *m* di fabbrica
^ 3522	Christmas tree, Xmas tree	tête *f* d'éruption	Eruptionskreuz *n*	croce *f* di eruzione
^ 3523	Christmas tree assemblies	outillage *m* de la tête d'éruption	Eruptionskreuz-vorrichtung *f*	attrezzature *f pl.* di captazione
° 3524	chromallizing	chromage *m*	Verchromung *f*	cromatura *f*
° 3525	chromate	chromate *m*	Chromat *m*	cromato *m*
° 3526	chromatic	chromatique	chromatisch	cromatico
° 3527	chromating, chromate treatment	mordançage *m*, chromage *m*	Bichromatbeize *f*, Verchromung *f*	mordenzatura *f*, cromatazione *f*
° 3528	chromatography	chromatographie *f*	Chromatographie *f*	cromatografia *f*
° 3528a	chrome alum	alun chromo-potassique	Chromalaun *m*	allume *m* cromico
	chrome, *s. chromium*			
° 3529	chrome iron, chromite, chromite of iron	fer *m* chromé, fer *m* chromaté, chromite *f*	Chromeisen *n*, Chromit *m*	ferro *m* cromato, cromite *f*
° 3529a	chrome check	craquelure *f*	Haarriss *m*	criccatura *f*, crepa *f*
° 3530	chrome-magnesite	chrome magnésie *m*	Chromomagnesit *m*	cromo-magnesite *m*
° 3531	chromemoly(bdenum) steel	acier au chrome--molybdène	Chrommolyb-dänstahl *m*	acciaio *m* al cromo-molibdeno
° 3532	chrome-nickel--molybdenum steel	acier *m* (au) nickel--chrome-molybdène	Chromnickel--Molybdänstahl *m*	acciaio *m* al nichel-crom -molibdeno
° 3533	chrome-nickel steel, nickel-crome steel	acier (au) chrome--nickel, acier (au) nickel-chrome	Chromnickelstahl *m*	acciaio *m* al cromo--nichel, acciaio al nichel-cromo
° 3534	chrome plating	chromage *m*	Verchromung *f*	cromatura *f*
	chrome red, *s. phoenicite*			
° 3535	chrome-silicon steel	acier *m* au chrome--silicium *m*	chromsiliziumlegier-ter Stahl *m*	acciaio *m* al cromo-silicio
− 3536	chrome spinel	spinelle *m* de chrome, picotite *f*	Chromspinell *m*, Pikotit *m*	spinello *m* di cromo, (minerale) picotite *f*
° 3537	chrome-tungsten steel	acier *m* au chrome--tungstène	Chrom-Wolframstahl *m*	acciaio *m* al cromo--tungsteno
° 3538	chrome-vanadium steel	acier *m* au chrome--vanadium	Chromvanadium--Stahl *m*	acciaio *m* al cromo--vanadio

English	French	German	Italian
3539 chromic acid	acide *m* chromique	Chromsäureanhydrid *n*	acido *m* cromico
3540 chromic iron	fer *m* chromé	Chromeisen *n*	sidercromo *m*
3541 chromise	chromiser par diffusion	Inchromieren *n*	cromare l'acciaio
3542 chromising, chromizing	chromisation *f*	Inkromieren *n*	cromizzazione *f*, cromatura *f* dell'acciaio
3543 chromite	chromite *f*	Chromit m	cromite *f*
3544 chromium	chrome *m*	Chrom *n*	cromo *m*
3545 chromium-nickel--steel	acier *m* au chrome et nickel	Chromnickelstahl *m*	acciaio *m* al cromo nickel
3546 to chromium-plate	chromiser	verchromen	cromare
3547 chromium plating	chromage *m*	Verchromung *f*	cromatura *f*
3548 chromium steel, chrome steel	acier *m* au chrome, acier *m* chromé, acier-chrome	Chromstahl *m*, chromlegierter Stahl *m*	acciaio *m* al cromo, acciaio *m* cromato

chromium-tungsten, *s. chrome tungsten*

English	French	German	Italian
3549 chromometer	colorimètre *m*	Kolorimeter *n*	colorimetro *m*
3550 chrysoberyl	chrisobéryl *m*	Crysoberyll *m*	crisoberillo *m*
3551 chrysolite	chrysolite *f*, olivine *f*	Chrysolith *m*, Olivin *m*	crisolite *f*, olivina *f*
3552 chrysoprase	chrysoprase *f*	Chrysopras	crisoprase *m*
3553 chrysotile	chrysotile *m*	Chrysotil *m*	crisotilo *m*
3554 chubutite	chubutite *f*	Chubuttit *m*	chubutite *f*
3555 chuck	porte-fleuret *m*	Bohrerträger *m*	portafioretto *m*
3556 chucking operations	travaux *m pl.* sur plate-forme	Bühnenarbeiten *fpl.*	lavori su piattaforma
3557 chunk	morceau *m*	Klumpen *m*	pezzo di minerale granuloso
3558 churchite	churchite *f*	Churchit *m*	churchite *f*
3559 to churn	agiter	rühren	agitare, scuotere

	English	French	German	Italian
— 3560	churn	trépan *m* pour sondage au câble	Seilschlagbohrer *m*	sonda *f* a percussione alla fune
— 3561	churn drilling	sondage *m* à la corde	Seilbohren *n*	perforazione *f* a percussione alla fune
— 3562	chusca	gypse *m* ferreux	Chusca	gesso *m* terroso
— 3563	chute	cheminée *f*, couloir, goulotte	Stürzrolle *f*, Rolle *f*	scivolo *m*, piano inclinato, trasportatore
— 3564	chute and pillar system	exploitation *f* par piliers	Pfeilerbau *m*	coltivazione a pilastri
— 3565	chute door	porte de cheminée	Stürzrollentür *f*	porta di scarico dello scivolo
— 3566	chute mouth	bouche *f* de cheminée	Stürzrollenöffnung *f*	foro di scarico
— 3567	chute set	cadre *m* base de cheminée	Grundstock *m* einer Rutsche	quadro base dello scivolo
	C.I., *s. cast iron*			
— 3568	ciminite	ciminite *f*	Ciminit *m*	ciminite *f*
— 3569	cimolite	cimolite *f*	Cimolit *m*	cimolite *f*
° 3570	cinder, slag	laitier *m*	Schlacke *f*	scoria, loppa, scaglia
° 3571	cinder charging	addition *f* de scories	Schlackenzusatz *m*	aggiunta *f* di scoria
° 3572	cinder dump	crassier *m*	Schlackenhalde *f*	mucchio *m* di scorie
° 3573	cinder frame	capteur *m* de cendres	Aschenfänger *m*	parascorie *m*
° 3574	cinder hole	trou *m* de laitier	Schlackenloch *n*	foro *m* delle scorie
° 3575	cinder notch, cinder tap	bec *m* de passage du laitier	Schlackenspur *f*, Schlackenloch *n*	foro *m* d'uscita delle scorie fuse (o della loppa)
° 3576	cinder pig iron	fonte *f* contenant des scories	schlackenhaltiges Roheisen *n*	ghisa *f* con scorie
	cinder pot, *s. slag ladle or thimble*			
	cinder tap, *s. cinder notch*			
° 3577	cinderman	décrasseur *m*	Schlackenmann *m*	addetto *m* alle scorie
— 3578	cinnabar	cinabre *m*	Zinnober *m*	cinabro *m*

English	French	German	Italian
3579 **cinnamon-stone**	cinnamonstone *f*	Hessonit *m*	essonite *f*
cinoclasite, *s. abichite*			
3580 **circle cutting attachment**	appareil *m* auxiliaire pour coupe circulaire	Einrichtung *f* fuer Kreisbrennen	attacco per taglio a circolo
3581 **circlip**	anneau *m* de butée (ou de rappel)	Anschlagring *m*	anello *m* di arresto di sicurezza
circular ring, *s. annular ring*			
3582 **circulating head**	tête *f* d'injection	Spülwirbel, Spülkopf	testa d'iniezione
3583 **circulating pump**	pompe *f* de circulation	Zirkulationspumpe *f*, Umwälzpumpe *f*	pompa *f* di circolazione
3584 **circulating reflux**	reflux *m* de circulation	Umlaufrückfluss *m*	riflusso *m* di circolazione
3585 **circumferentor**	poche de mineur	Hängekompass *m*	bussola *f* (da minatore)
3586 **circus**	cirque *m*	Kar *n*	circo *m*
3587 **circular beam**	fléau *m* circulaire	kreisförmiger Balken *m*	gioco *m* circolare
3588 **circular brush**	queue *f* de rat pour fontes	runde Gussputzbürste *f*	spazzola *f* circolare
3589 **circular channel**	canal *m* annulaire	ringförmiger Kanal *m*	canale *m* circolare
3590 **circular gas outlet tube**	prise *f* de gaz annulaire, prise *f* de gaz belge	ringförmiger Gasfang *m*, belgischer Gasfang *m*	presa *f* di gas anulare o belga
3591 **circular gate**	entonnoir *m* de coulée à tuyau	Rohrtrichter *m*	canale *m* di colata circolare
3592 **circular gate runner**	jet *m* de coulée annulaire	Ring- oder Grateinguss *m*	colata *f* anulare
3593 **circular kiln**	four circulaire	Ringofen *m*	forno *m* circolare
3594 **circular knife**	molette *f*	Kreismesser *n*	cesoia *f* circolare
3595 **circular plate, circle**	tôle circulaire, plaque circulaire	Rundblech *n*. runde Platte *f*	lamiera *f* circolare, piastra *f* rotonda
3596 **circular rim**	bordure *f* périphérique ou circulaire	herumlaufender Bord *m*	bordo *m* periferico

	English	French	German	Italian
o	3597 circular saw	scie circulaire	Kreissäge f	sega f circolare
o	3598 circular seam welding	soudure f continue circulaire	Rundnaht- schweissung f	saldatura f continua circolare
o	3599 circular section	section f circulaire	runder Querschnitt m	sezione f circolare
o	3600 circular shape	forme f circulaire	Kreisform f	forma f circolare
o	3601 circular slot burner	brûleur m à orifice circulaire	Rundlochbrenner m	bruciatore m a sca- nalatura circolare
o	3602 circular T-bearers	poutrelles f $pl.$ cin- trées	zum Ring gebogene T-Träger m $pl.$	travi f $pl.$ a curvatura circolare
o	3603 circulating boiler, circulation boiler	chaudière f à circulation	Zirkulationskessel m	caldaia f a circolazio- ne
o	3604 circulation channel or passage, air way	canal m de retour	Umströmkanal m	canale m di circolazione o di ritorno
o	3605 circulation pump	pompe f à circulation	Umlaufpumpe f	pompa f di circolazione
o	3606 circumferential velocity	vitesse f tangentielle	Umfangsgesch- windigkeit f	velocità f tangenziale
—	3607 cirque	cirque m	Kar n	circo m
—	3608 cirque cutting	formation f des cirques	Karbildung f	formazione f di circhi
—	3608a citrine	citrine f	Zitrin m	citrina f
^	3609 to clabber	coaguler	gerinnen, koagulieren	coagulare
	clad, $s.$ plated			
o	3610 clad metal	métal m de couverture, laminé m à froid	Abdeckmetall n, Kaltwalzgut n	metallo m di copertura, laminato m a freddo
o	3611 clad steel	acier m plaqué	plattierter Stahl m	acciaio m placcato
o	3611a cladding, plating	doublage m	Plattierung f	placcatura f
	clagging, $s.$ sticking to pattern			
—	3612 claggy	faux-toit schisteux	Nachfalldach n	falso tetto m scistoso
—	3613 claim	concession f de mine	Mutung f	concessione f di una miniera
—	3614 claimholder	concessionnaire m	Muter m	concessionario m

	English	French	German	Italian
3615	clam	coquille *f*	Muschel *f*	conchiglia *f*
3616	to clamp	attacher, fixer, fermer	klemmen, schliessen, festklemmen	attaccare, chiudere, bloccare
3617	to clamp	cramper	Verklammern	mettere le graffe (o grappe), aggraffare
3618	to clamp	claveter	verkeilen	inchiavettare, fissare
3619	clamp	collier *m*, carcan *m*, bride *f* de serrage	Klemme *f*, Schelle *f*, Krampe *f*	clampa, morsetto, morsa, cravatta *f*
3620	clamp	tas *m* de minerai à griller, tas *m* de charbon à cokéfier	Erzhaufen *m* zum Rösten, Kohlenhaufen *m* zur Verkokung	mucchio *m* di minerale pronto per l'arrostimento, minerale di carbone da cokificare
3621	clamp	presse *f* de coulée	Spannvorrichtung *f*	torchio *m* di colata
3622	clamp	crampe *f*	Klammer *f*	grappa *f*, clampa *f*
3623	clamp for stand	pince *f* de support	Ständerklemme *f*	morsetto *m* per treppiede, pinza *f*
3624	clamp plate, clip plate, clip	griffe *f* de serrage, plaque *f* de serrage	Klemmplatte *f*	piastrina *f* di serraggio
3625	clamping	clavetage *m* (du moule)	Verkeilen *n*	inchiavettatura *f* della forma
3626	clamping	crampage *m*	Verklammern *n*	aggraffatura *f*, serraggio *m*, bloccaggio *m*
3627	clamping bar	traverse *f* de serrage	obere Verankerungsschiene *f*	traversa *f* di bloccaggio (o di chiusura)
3628	clamping plate	plaque *f* de serrage	Klemmplatte *f*	piastra *f* di serraggio
3629	clamshell, clam	coquille *f* (benne preneuse)	Greifer *m* .	benna *f* (a 2 pezzi), draga *f* a mascelle
3630	clamshell bucket	benne *f* preneuse (ou à deux mâchoires)	Greifer *m*	benna *f* (a 2 pezzi)
3631	clamshell excavator	excavateur *m* à benne preneuse (ou à deux mâchoires)	Greiferbagger *m*	scavatrice *f* a benna a mascella
	clarain, *s. banded coal*			
3632	claret	rouge *m* Bordeaux	Bordeaux-rot *n*	rosso *m* Bordeaux

		English	French	German	Italian
o	3633	clarifier	chaudière.f à clarification	Klärpfanne f	caldaia f di chiarificazione
o	3634	to clarify	clarifier	abklären	chiarificare
—	3635	clarite	clarite f	Clarit m	clarite f
—	3636	clarkeite	clarkeite f	Clarkeit m	clarkeite f
o	3637	clasp	agrafe f	Agraffe f, Klammer f	graffetta f, punto metallico
o	3638	clasp	arrêt m	Verschluss m	arresto, fermo
—	3639	classification of ore	désignation f du minerai	Bezeichnung f des Erzes	classificazione f del minerale
—	3640	classifier, classificator	appareil m classeur	Klassiervorrichtung f, Klassierapparat m	classificatore m
—	3641	classify	classifier, trier, séparer	klassifizieren, scheiden	classificare, cernere, selezionare, separare
—	3642	to classify the coal	classer le charbon	die Kohle klassieren	pezzare il carbone, classificare il carbone
—	3643	classifying and dewatering machine	clasificateur m débourbeur	Dekantierklassifikator m	classificatore m slimatore
—	3644	classifying screen	crible-classeur m	Klassiersieb n	vaglio m classificatore
—	3645	clastate	fragmenter, broyer	zerkleinern	frantumare, macinare
—	3646	clastic	clastique	klastisch	clastico
—	3647	clasto-crystalline	clasto-cristallin	klasto-kristallin	clasto-cristallino
—	3648	clastogene	clastogène	klastogen	clastogeno
—	3649	clastogene	brèche f, conglomérat m	Breccie f, Konglomerat n	breccia f, conglomerato m
—	3650	clastomorphic	clastomorphique	klastomorphisch	clastomorfico
—	3651	claudetite	claudétite f	Claudetit m	claudetite f
—	3652	clausthalite	clausthalite f	Clausthalit m	claustalite f
—	3653	clay, potter's clay	glaise f	Letten m, Ton m	argilla f, creta f
—	3654	clay auger	sonde f	offener Bohrlöffel m	trivella f per terreni argillosi

clay band, s. *clay ironstone*

	English	French	German	Italian
	clay-band mixed with coal, s. *blackband*			
3655	**clay base mud**	boue f à base d'argile	Tonspülung f	fango m a base d'argilla
3656	**clay containing iron**	argile f ferrugineuse	eisenschüssiger Ton m	argilla f ferruginosa
3657	**clay course**	salbande f	Salband n	salbanda f, bordo di argilla
	clay crucible, s. *fire clay crucible*			
3658	**clay cutter**	malaxeur m à argile	Tonschneider m	mescolatore m (o separatore) d'argilla
3659	**clay disc**	plaque f en terre réfractaire	Tonplatte f	piastra f di terracotta
3660	**clay furnace**	petit four m en terre réfractaire	Tonöfchen n	fornello m in refrattari
3661	**clay gall**	tache f d'argile	Tongalle f	macchia f d'argilla
3662	**clay gouge**	salbande	Salband n, Lettenbesteg m	salbanda f, intercalazione argillosa
	clay gun, s. *tap hole stopping machine*			
	clay iron ore, s. *clay ironstone*			
3663	**clay ironstone, clay--band, argillaceous iron ore**	minerai de fer argileux, fer oxydé argilifère	Toneisenstein m, Roteisenstein m, Sphärosiderit m	sferosiderite f argillosa, argilla f ferruginosa
	clay mixer, s. *clay cutter*			
	clay parting, s. *clay gouge*			
3664	**clay plate**	plaque f d'argile	Lehmplatte f	placca f d'argilla
3665	**clay-revivifying system**	régénérateur m de sable	Erdregenerator m	rigeneratore m per terre
	clay slate, s. *argillite*			
	clay stone, s. *argillite*			
3666	**to clay wash a moulding box**	glaiser un châssis	einen Formkasten m verletten	applicare la creta
3667	**clay work**	construction f en pisé réfractaire	Massenzustellung f	pigiata f

		English	French	German	Italian
○	3668	clayey sand	sable *m* argileux	tonhaltiger Formsand *m*	sabbia *f* o terra *f* argillosa
○	3669	claying	glaisage *m*	Verletten *n*,	applicare l'argilla (o la creta)
—	3670	claying bar	tarière *f* à argile	Lettenbohrer *m*	trap'ano *m* a secco, sonda *f* per argilla
—	3671	to clean, to clean out	curer	reinigen	pulire
○	3672	to clean the casting	nettoyer les moules, ébarber	den Guss putzen	pulire il getto, sbavare
○	3673	clean, clean-out	nettoyage *m*	Behandlung *f*, Reinigung *f*	pulizia, manutenzione *f*
	3674	clean	propre, net	sauber	pulito, puro
—	3675	clean coal	charbon *m* pur	reine Kohle *f*	carbone *m* puro
○	3676	clean fresh sand	sable *m* neuf	reiner, frischer Sand *m*	sabbia *f* o terra *f* fresca
		clean gas, *s. purified gas*			
○	3677	clean grinding surface	surface *f* polie propre	reine Schleifffläche *f*	superficie *f* levigata pulita
○	3678	clean hardening	trempe *f* brillante	Glanzhärtung *f*	tempera *f* brillante
^	3679	clean oil	huile *f* anhydre	reines Öl *n*	olio *m* anidro
^	3680	clean-out crew	équipe *f* de nettoyage	Behandlungs- mannschaft *f*	squadra *f* pulitori
	3681	clean suction strainer	crépine *f*	Saugkorb *m*	succhierola *f*
○	3682	cleaned, deburred	ébarbé	entgraten. geputzt	sbavato
○	3683	cleaned, trimmed	fini	fertiggeputzt	rifinito
○	3684	cleaner	crochet *m* à ramasser	Sandhaken *m*	cavasabbia *m*
○	3685	cleaner	finisseuse *f*	Reiniger *m*	finitore *m*
○	3686	cleaner	curette *f*	Bohrlöffel *m*	raschietto *m*, rastrello *m*
○	3687	cleaner	décapeur *m*	Beizer *m*	operaio *m* addetto al decapaggio
○	3688	cleaner	crochet *m* à talon	Sandhaken *m*	battisabbia *m*
^	3689	cleaners	gratteurs *m pl.* de tubage rotatifs	rotierende Rohr- krätzer *m pl.*	baffi *m pl.* di gatto rotativi

	English	French	German	Italian
3690	cleaning casting	ébarbage *m*	Fertigputzen *n*	sbavatura *f*
3691	cleaning, pickling (of steel wire)	décapage *m*	Beizung *f*	decapaggio *m*
3692	cleaning, sandblasting	sablage *m*	Strahlen *n*, Strahlputzen *n*	pulitura *f* (con sabbia), sabbiatura *f*
3693	cleaning door	porte *f* de nettoyage	Reinigungstür *f*	porta *f* di pulizia
3694	cleaning hole, man hole	orifice *m* de nettoyage	Reinigungsöffnung *f*	foro *m* di visita, porta di pulizia
3695	cleaning of ore	débourbage *m*	Läuterung *f*	lavaggio *m* del minerale
3696	cleaning shop	atelier *m* d'ébarbage	Putzerei *f*	officina *f* di sbavatura
3697	cleaning table	table *f* de dessablage	Putzbank *f*	tavola *f* di sbavatura
3698	cleanliness of surface	netteté *f* de la surface	Oberflächenreinheit	purezza *f* della superficie
3699	cleanout bailer	godet *m* à nettoyer	Putzlöffel *m*	cucchiaia *f* da pulizia
3700	cleanout gate	porte *f* de nettoyage des caissons à boue	Schlammereinigungsöffnung *f*	portello *m* di scarico dei cassoni per fango
3701	cleanout rig	installation *f* de nettoyage d'un puits	Schachtputzanlage *f*	impianto *m* per pulire un pozzo
3702	cleanser	ébarbeur *m*	Putzer *m*	sbavatore *m*, sbavatrice *f*
3703	cleansing drum	tambour *m* de nettoyage	Putzscheuertrommel *f*	tamburo *m* per togliere la sabbia
3704	cleansing machine	machine *f* d'ébarbage	Putzmaschine *f*	macchina *f* per sbavare, sbavatrice
3705	cleansing material	matières *f pl.* pour l'ébarbage	Putzmittel *n*	materiale *m* per sbavare
3706	cleansing tool	outil *m* d'ébarbage	Putzwerkzeug *n*	attrezzo *m* per sbavare
3707	clear filtrate	solution *f* filtrée claire	klares, helles Filtrat *n*	soluzione *f* filtrata chiara o limpida
3708	clear solution	solution *f* claire	klare Lösung *f*	soluzione *f* limpida o chiara
3709	clearance	jeu *m* de coiffage	Spielraum *m* der Kernmarke	gioco *m* delle portate (d'anima)

	English	French	German	Italian
° 3710	clearance diagram	gabarit *m*	Formbrett *n*	sagoma *f*
° 3711	clearance print	fausse portée *f* (du noyau)	verlängerte Kernmarke *f*	portata *f* (d'anima) falsa
° 3712	clearance taper coreprint	portée *f* tirée à l'anglaise	Ziehmarke *f*, Schleifmarke *f*	portata *f* a strascico
° 3713	clearing	dégarnissage *m*	Ausräumen *n*	sguarnitura *f*
	clearing pan, *s. clarifier*			
— 3714	cleavability	clivage *m*	Spaltbarkeit *f*, Spalten *n*	fenditura *f*, frattura, fessurazione, clivaggio
— 3715	cleavable rock	roche *f* clivable	spaltbares Gestein *n*	pietra *f* sfaldabile
— 3716	cleavage	clivage *m*	Spaltbarkeit *f*, Spalten *n*	clivaggio *m*, sfaldamento *m*, sfaldatura *f*
	cleavage fracture, *s. brittle fracture*			
— 3717	cleavage plane	plan *m* de clivage	Spaltungsrichtung *f*	piano di frattura, piano di fenditura o di sfaldatura
— 3718	cleavage structure	schistosité *f*	Schieferung *f*	scistosità *f*, struttura *f* scistosa
— 3719	to cleave	fendre, cliver	ketzen, spalten	fendersi, sfaldarsi
° 3720	Cleveland blower with one connecting rod	machine *f* soufflante de Cleveland à une bielle	Clevelandsches Gebläse *n* mit einer Kurbelstange	soffieria *f* di Cleveland ad una biella
° 3721	Cleveland flash test	essai *m* d'inflammabilité	Flammpunktprüfung *f*	prova *f* d'infiammabilità
° 3722	Cleveland open-cup tester	appareil *m* Cleveland	Cleveland-Apparat *m*	apparecchio *m* Cleveland
° 3723	Cleveland roasting furnace	four *m* de grillage de Cleveland	Clevelander Röstofen *m*	forno *m* di torrefazione Cleveland
	clevelandite, *s. albite*			
° 3724	clevis	étrier *m*	Bügel *m*	gambetto *m*, staffa *f*
— 3725	cliff, seacliff	falaise *f*	Kliff *n*	falesia *f*
— 3726	cliftonite	cliftonite *f*	Cliftonit *m*	cliftonite *f*
° 3726a	clink	crique *f* interne, fracture *f* interne	Innenriss *m*	crepa *f* (o fessura) interna
	to clinker, *s. to sinter*			

	English	French	German	Italian
3727	clinker,(iron-)slag	mâchefer, scorie f de fer	Kohlenschlacke f, Herdschlacke f	scorie f $pl.$ del ferro
	clinker grate, $s.$ $dumping$ $grate$			
	clinkering, $s.$ $caking$ of the $coal$			
3728	clinkering coal	charbon m très scorifère	stark schlackende Kohle f	carbone m con molte scorie
3729	clinkstone	phonolithe f	Phonolith m	fonolitite f
3730	clino-unconformity	discordance f angulaire	Klinodiskordanz f	discordanza f angolare
3731	clinochlore	clinochlore m	Klinochlor n	clorite f
3732	clinoclase	clinoclase f	Klinoklas n, Abichit	clinoclasite f, abichite f
3733	clinoenstatite	clinoenstatite f	Klinoenstatit m	clinoenstatite f
3734	clinograph	clinographe m	Klinograph m	clinografo m
3735	clinohumite	clinohumite f	Klinohumit m	clinohumi te f
3736	clinometer	clinomètre m	Neigungsmesser m	clinometro m
3737	clinopinacoid	clinopinacoïde m	Klinopinakoid m	clinopinacoide m
3738	clinoprism	clinoprisme m	Klinoprisma n	clinoprisma m
	clinorhombic system, $s.$ $monoclinic$ $system$			
	clinorhomboidal system, $s.$ $triclinic$ $system$			
3739	clinozoisite	clinozoïsite f	Klinozoisit m	clinozoisite f
3740	clintonite	clintonite f	Clintonit m	clintonite f
3741	to clip, to trim	ébarber	entgräten	sbavare
	to clip, $s.$ to $finish$			
	clipping, $s.$ $trimming$			
3742	clip, Mohr's clip	pince f de Mohr	Quetschhahn m	serratubi m a morsetto
3743	clipping base	plaque d'ébarbage	Putzplatte f	base per attrezzo di sbavatura
	clipping tool, $s.$ $trimmer$			
3744	clips and fixing brackets	crampons et pattes de fixation	Krampen und Bauklammern	graffe e graffette di fissaggio

	English	French	German	Italian
—	3745 **clod**	motte *f*	Erdballen *m*	zolla, motta *f*
—	3746 **clod**	faux-toit *m* schisteux	Nachfalldach *n*	falso-tetto *m* scistoso
—	3747 **clod coal**	charbon en morceaux	Grobkohle *f*	carbone *m* in pezzi
—	3748 **cloddy**	terreux, plein de mottes	erdig, klumpig	terroso, granuloso
^	3749 **to clog**	boucher, s'obstruer	sich verstopfen, verschlämmen	otturasi, ostruirsi, tapparsi
—	3750 **clog pack**	pile *f* de bois	Holzschrank *m*	catasta *f* di legno
^	3751 **clogged**	bouché	verstopft	intasato, ostruito
o	3752 **clogging up of the roasting furnace**	engorgement *m* du four de grillage	Verstopfung *f* des Röstofens	ingorgo *m* (od ostrusione) del forno di torrefazion
	to close, *s. to cover*			
o	3753 **to close**	fermer	(ab)schliessen	chiudere, racchiudere
o	3754 **to close the openings**	luter les ouvertures	die Öffnungen verstreichen	tappare o chiudere le aperture
o	3755 **close annealing**	recuit *m* en creuset clos (ou en caisse)	Kastenglühen *n*	tempera (o rinvenimento) in crogiuolo chiuso (o casetta)
o	3756 **close boiling cut**	coupe *f* courte	kurzer Schnitt *m*	taglio *m* corto
—	3757 **close burning coal, hard coal, short flaming coal**	houille *f* à courte flamme	magere Steinkohle *f*, Magerkohle *f*	carbone a corta fiamma
—	3758 **close cribbing**	boisage *m* jointif	Schrotzimmerung *f*	armatura *f* in legno compatta
—	3759 **close fault**	faille *f* fermée	geschlossene Verwerfung *f*	faglia *f* chiusa
—	3760 **close fold**	pli *m* resserré	steile Falte *f*	piega *f* ripida
o	3761 **close-grained, dense**	à texture *f* serrée, à grain *m* serré	feinkörnig, kleinlückig	a grana chiusa (o fitta)
o	3762 **close grained iron**	fer *m* à grain fin, fer *m* dur *f*	Feinkorneisen *n*, kleinlückiges Eisen *n*	ferro *m* a grana fine
o	3763 **close grained pig iron**	fonte *f* à grain fin (ou serré)	kleinlückiges Eisen *n*	ghisa *f* a piccole caverne (o a grana compatta)

English	French	German	Italian
3764 **close packed metal**	métal *m* à structure serrée	feinkörniges Metall *n*	metallo *m* a struttura compatta
close shaft, *s. blind shaft*			
3765 **close timbering**	boisage *m* jointif	Schrotzimmerung *f*	armamento *m* in legno con puntelli serrati
closed ashpit furnace, *s. forced-draught furnace*			
3766 **closed circulation**	circulation *f* en circuit fermé	geschlossener Kreislauf *m*	ciclo *m* (o circuito) chiuso
3767 **closed circuit**	circuit *m* fermé	Ruhestromkreis *m*	circuito *m* chiuso
3768 **closed coke oven**	four *m* à coke à cycle fermé	geschlossener Koksofen *m*	forno *m* a coke a ciclo chiuso
3769 **closed-cycle furnace**	four *m* à cycle fermé	Kreisprozessofen *m*	forno *m* a ciclo chiuso
3769a **closed die**	moule *m* fermé	geschlossener Stempel *m*	stampo *m* chiuso
3770 **closed-die forging**	forgeage *m* à moule fermé	Schmieden *n* mit geschlossenem Gesenk	fucinatura *f* a stampo chiuso
3771 **closed-in pressure**	pression *f* statique	statischer Druck *m*	pressione *f* statica
3772 **closed-in production**	production *f* latente	eingeschlossene Produktion *f*	produzione *f* latente
3773 **closed mould**	moule *m* fermé	geschlossene Form *f*	forma *f* in staffa
closed moulding, *s. moulding in flask*			
3774 **closed pass, box pass**	cannelure *f* fermée	geschlossenes Kaliber *n*	canale *m* chiuso
3775 **closed pressure**	pression *f* de gisement	Lagerdruck *m*	pressione *f* del giacimento
3776 **closed stope**	taille *f* remblayée	versetzter Stoss *m*	taglio *m* con ripiena
3777 **closed top**	gueulard *m* fermé	geschlossene Gicht *f*	bocca *f* di caricamento chiusa, cono *m* chiuso
3778 **closed wagon**	wagon *m* fermé	geschlossener Wagen	carro *m* chiuso
3779 **closed work**	ouvrage *m* souterrain	unterirdischer Grubenbau *m*	opera *f* sotterranea
3780 **closing cover**	couvercle *m* obturateur	Verschlussdeckel *m*	coperchio *m* (o cappello *m*) di chiusura
3781 **closing device**	vanne *f* d'isolement	Absperrvorrichtung *f*	valvola *f* di chiusura

		English	French	German	Italian
o	3782	closing pin	goujon *m* de remmoulage	Zulegestift *m*	pernio *m* (o spina, o pirone) di accoppiamento
o	3783	closing screw	boulon *m* de fermeture	Verschlussschraube *f*	bullone *m* di chiusura
—	3784	clotting	consolidation *f*	Erstarren *n*	consolidamento *m* (di minerale)
		cloud-bursting, *s. steel ball peening*			
^	3785	cloud point	point *m* de trouble	Trübpunkt *m*	punto *m* di nebbia
^	3786	cloudiness	aspect *m* trouble	Trübheit *f*	aspetto *m* torbido
—	3787	clouded agate, mottled agate	agate *f* tachetée	Wolkenachat *m*	agata *f* macchiata
^	3788	clove hitch	noeud *m* simple	ebener Knoten *m*	nodo *m* piano
		clowhole, *s. shrinkhole*			
—	3789	clumpy	en mottes	klumpig	granuloso
—	3790	clunch	argile *f*, roche *f* argileuse	Ton *m*, tonhaltiges Gestein *n*	argilla *f*, roccia *f* argillosa
—	3791	**Clunian stage**	Clunien *m*	Clunian *n*	Cluniano *m*
o	3792	cluster	grappe *f*	Giesstraube *f*, Stapelabguss *m*	grappolo *m*
o	3793	cluster gate	attaque *f* de coulée en grappe	Stapelgussanschnitt *m*	attacco *m* di colata a grappolo
o	3793a	cluster mill	laminoir *m* à six cylindres	Sechsrollenwalzwerk *n*	laminatoio *m* a sei cilindri
o	3794	clutch	embrayage *m*	Klemmvorrichtung *f*	attacco *m*, innesto *m*
o	3795	clutch for shunting railways	embrayage *m* de serrage pour voies de manoeuvre	Klemmvorrichtung *f* für Verschiebebahnen	attacco *m* per binari di manovra
—	3796	coaking coal with a high percentage of volatiles	charbon *m* à coke riche en gaz	gasreiche Kokskohle *f*	carbone *m* di coke ricco di gas
—	3797	coaking auger	fleuret *m* hélicoïdal	Spiralbohrer *m*	trivella *f* elicoidale, fioretto *m* elicoidale
—	3798	coaking backer	chargeur *m*	Kohlenlader *m*	caricatore *m* (di carbone)
—	3799	coaking-ball	coal-ball *m*	Kalkknolle *f*	coal-ball *m*
		coal-bearing formation, *s. carboniferous formation*			
—	3800	coal-bed, coal-deposit	gîte *m* houiller	Kohlenlager *n*	giacimento *m* di carbone, giacimento carbonifero

English	French	German	Italian
3801 coal-bin	soute *f*, trémie *f* à charbon	Kohlenbunker *m*	carbonile *m*, silo *m* per carbone
3802 coal-blasting	tir *m* au charbon	Kohlensprengen *n*	abbattimento *m* di carbone con esplosivi
3803 coal brass	inclusion *f* de pyrite dans la houille	Schwefelkies *m* in Kohle	inclusione *f* di pirite nel carbone
coal breaker, *s. coal crusher*			
3804 coal bunker	trémie *f* à charbon	Kohlenbunker *m*	tramoggia *f* a carbone, silo per carbone
3805 coal burning	combustion *f* au charbon	Kohlenverbrennung *f*	combustione *f* a (o del) carbone
3806 coal burning	à charbon	Kohlen-	a carbone
coal carrier, *s. coal heaver*			
3807 coal chute	voie *f* surélevée pour déchargement de charbon	Kohlensturzbahn *f*	binario *m* di rovesciamento del carbone
3808 coal crusher, coal breaker	concasseur *m* à charbon	Kohlenbrecher *m*, Kohlenpochwerk *n*	frantoio *m* (o mulino) per carbone, spaccacarbone
3809 coal crusher and sampler	broyeur *m* de charbon à dispositif d'échantillonnage	Kohlenbrecher *m* zur Entnahme von Mustern	frantoio *m* campionatore per carbone
3810 coal cutter	haveuse *f*	Schrämmaschine *f*	intagliatrice *f* (per carbone)
3811 coal cutter for vertical channeling	rouilleuse *f*	Kerbmaschine *f*	macchina *f* per il taglio verticale del carbone
3812 coal cutting	havage *m*	Schrämen *n*	taglio *m* (orizzontale) del carbone
3813 coal digger	piqueur *m* au charbon	Kohlenhauer *m*	scavatore *m* (o picconatore) di carbone
3814 coal-district	région *f* houillère	Kohlengebiet *n*	regione *f* carbonifera
3815 coal drawing	extraction *f* du charbon	Kohlenförderung *f*	estrazione *f* di carbone
3816 coal dressing	préparation mécanique de charbon	Kohlenaufbereitung *f*	trattamento *m* meccanico del carbone
3817 coal dump	tas *m* de charbon	Kohlenhaufen *m*	mucchio *m* di carbone

		English	French	German	Italian
−	3818	çoal dust, culm powdered coal	poussière *m* de charbon	Kohlenstaub *m*	polvere *f* di carbone, polverino *m* di carbone
°	3819	coal dust furnace	foyer *m* à poussière de charbon	Kohlenstaubfeuerung *f*	focolare *m* a polvere di carbone
−	3820	coal extraction	extraction *f*	Förderung *f*	estrazione *f* di carbone
−	3821	coal field, coal bed	gisement *m* de charbon	Kohlenlager *n*	bacino *m* carbonifero
−	3822	coal-filler	chargeur *m* de charbon	Kohlenlader *m*	caricatore *m* di carbone
°	3823	coal firing	foyer *m* à charbon	Kohlenfeuerung *f*	focolare *m* a carbone
−	3824	coal for gas works	charbon *m* de générateur	Generatorkohle *f*	carbone *m* da gassogeno

coal-formation, *s. carboniferous formation*

°	3825	coal furnace, coal firing	foyer *m* à charbon	Kohlenfeuerung *f*	focolare *m* a carbone
−	3826	coal gangue	gangue *f* de charbon	Kohlenganggestein *n*	ganga *f* del carbone
−	3826a	coal gas	gaz *m* d'éclairage	Leuchtgas *n*	gas *m* illuminante
−	3827	coal getter	piqueur *m* au charbon	Kohlenhauer *m*	picconatore *m* di carbone
−	3828	coal getting	abattage *m* du charbon	Kohlengewinnung *f*	abbattimento *m* di carbone
−	3829	coal grab. bucket grab	pelle *f* automatique, benne *f* de chargement automatique	Greiferkübel *m*, zweiteiliger Kohlenkasten *m*	draga *f* (o scavatore *m* o secchia *f*) a benna, benna *f* automatica
−	3830	coal grinding	broyage du charbon	Kohlenbrechen *n*	polverizzazione *f* del carbone
−	3831	coal-grit	grès houiller	Kohlensandstein *m*	arenaria *f* carbonifera
−	3832	coal handling	amenée *f* du charbon	Kohlenzufuhr *f*	trasporto *m* di carbone
−	3833	coal heaver	élévateur du charbon	Kohlenträger *m*	elevatore *m* di carbone
−	3834	coal-hold	cale *f* à charbon	Kohlenraum *m*	stiva *f* da carbone
−	3835	coal hole, bunker	soute *f* à charbon	Kohlenraum *m*	carbonile *m*, silo *m* per carbone
−	3836	coal hopper	trémie *f* de chargement	Fülltrichter *m*	tramoggia *f* per carbone
−	3837	coal in solid	charbon *m* vierge	anstehende Kohle *f*	carbone *m* vergine

coal levelling bar, *s. rammer*

English	French	German	Italian
3838 **coal measures, carboniferous formation**	formation *f* houillère, terrain houiller	Kohlengebirge *n*	formazione *f* carbonifera, terreno *m* carbonifero
coal mill, *s. coal crusher*			
3839 **coal mine, colliery**	houillère *f*, charbonnage *m*	Steinkohlengrube *f*, Kohlenzeche *f*	miniera *f* di carbone fossile, carboniera *f*
3840 **coal miner**	houilleur *m*	Kohlenbergmann *m*	minatore *m* (di carbone)
3841 **coal of uniform size**	charbon *m* uniforme	gleichmässige Kohle	carbone *m* uniforme
3842 **coal pipe**	veine irrégulière de charbon	ungleichmässige Kohlenflöz *n*	vena *f* irregolare di carbone
3843 **coal producing a light ash**	charbon à cendres légères	leichtaschige Kohle *f*	carbone con ceneri leggere
coal rich in gas, *s. gas-coal*			
3844 **coal seam**	couche *f* de charbon (ou houillère)	kohlenführende Schicht *f*	filone di carbone
3845 **coal shed**	intercalation *f* de charbon, soute *f* à charbon	Kohlenzwischenlage *f*, Kohlenraum *m*	intercalazione *f* di carbone, carbonile *m*, silo *m* per carboni
coal shoot, *s. coal chute*			
3846 **coal shovel**	pelle à charbon	Kohlenschaufel *f*	pala da carbone
coal-slack, *s. small coal*			
coal slimes, *s. coal washings*			
3847 **coal stamping machine**	machine *f* à damer le charbon	Kohlenstampf- maschine *f*	macchina *f* per pigiare il carbone
3848 **coal supplies** *pl* **of recent formation**	charbon de couches de formation récente	jüngeres Kohlenvorkommen *n*	carbone *m* da strati di formazione recente
3849 **coal tar**	goudron *m* de houille	Steinkohlenteer *m*	catrame *m* di carbone
3850 **coal tar oil**	huile *f* de goudron de houille	Steinkohlenteeröl *n*	olio *m* residuo di carbone
3851 **coal-tar pitch**	brai *m*, poix *f* de goudron	Steinkohlenpech *n*	pece *f*, pece minerale, pece *f* di carbon fossile
3852 **coal tub**	berline *f* à charbon	Kohlenhund *m*	vagonetto *m* per carbone

English	French	German	Italian
— 3853 coal wall	front *m* de taille d'une houillère	Kohlenstoss *m*	fonte *m* di taglio di una miniera di carbone
— 3854 coal warrant	argile *f* au mur de la veine de charbon	Ton *m* am Fusse des Kohlenflözes	argilla *f* alla base del filone carbonifero
— 3855 coal washing plant	lavoir *f* à charbon	Kohlenwäsche *f*	reparto per il lavaggio *m* del carbone
— 3856 coal washings or slimes	boue *f* de charbon	Kohlenschlamm *m*	fango *m* di carbone
— 3857 coal wedge	coin *m* à charbon	Kohlenkeil *m*	cuneo *m* da carbone
— 3858 coalmine (colliery, pit)	houillère *f*, mine *f* de houille	Grube *f*, Steinkohlen- zeche *f*, Kohlen- bergwerk *n*	miniera *f* di carbone, pozzo carbonifero
— 3859 coalseam	couche *f* de charbon	Steinkohlenfloez *n*	filone *m* di carbone
— 3860 coalcutter, undercutter	haveuse *f*	Schraemmaschine *f*	tagliatrice *f* di carbo- ne
° 3861 to coalesce	coalescer	zusammenballen	coalescere, appallotto- larsi
° 3862 coalescence	coalescence *f*	Verwachsung *f*	coalescenza *f*
— 3863 coaly facies	faciès *m pl.* charbonneux	kohlehaltige Fazies *f*	«facies» *f* carbonifera
° 3864 coaling door	porte *f* du foyer	Feuertür *f*	porta *f* del focolare
— 3865 coalite	semicoke *m*	Halbkoks *m*	semicoke *m*
— 3866 coaly rashings	schiste *m* tendre carbonifère	weicher Schiefer *m*	scisto *m* carbonifero tenero
° 3867 coaming plates *pl.*	tôles *f pl.* d'hiloire	Süllplatten *f pl.*	lamiere *f pl.* di battente
— 3868 coarse	à gros grain *m*	grobkörnig	grosso
	coarse copper, *s. black copper*		
— 3869 coarse crusher	concasseur *m* de gros	Grobbrecher *m*	frantolo *m* per tritura- zione grossa
— 3870 coarse crushing	broyage *m* grossier	Grobzerkleinerung *f*	triturazione *f* (o frantuma- zione) grossa
— 3871 coarse grain	grain *m* grossier	Grobkorn *n*	grano *m* grosso
— 3872 coarse grained	à gros grain	grobkörnig	a grana grossa

English	French	German	Italian
3873 **coarse grained fracture**	cassure f à gros grain	grosskörniger Bruch m	frattura f a grana grossa
3874 **coarse grained iron, open pig**	fer m à gros grain, fer phosphoreux	Grobkorneisen n, grosskörniges Eisen n	ferro m a grana grossa
3875 **coarse grinding**	broyage m grossier	Grobzerkleinerung f	triturazione f grossa
3875a **coarse metal**	matte f	Stein m, Lech m	metallina f grezza, matta f
3876 **coarse screen**	tamis m à larges mailles	Grobsieb n	vaglio m a maglie larghe
3877 **coarse texture**	texture f à gros grain	grobkörnige Textur f	struttura f a grana grossa
coarse wire, *s. thick wire*			
3878 **coarsely crystalline pig iron**	fonte f miroitante à texture grossière	Grobspiegel m	ghisa f speculare grossolana
3879 **to coat, to paint, to dress**	enduire	schlichten	intonacare, rivestire
to coat with lead, *s. to lead*			
coated electrode, *s. covered electrode*			
coated with lead, *s. lead-cased*			
3880 **coating, blacking, dressing**	enduit m, couche f	Schlichte f	rivestimento m, intonaco m
3881 **coating**	couverture f	Überzug m	copertura f, rivestimento
3882 **coating index**	index m d'enduit	Überzugsindex m	indice m di deposizione
3883 **to cob**	broyer et trier	zerkleinern und scheiden von Erzen	frantumare e grigliare
3884 **cob coal, cobble(s)** *pl.*, **lump coal**	gaillettes f $pl.$, gailletterie f, charbon en grélat	Würfelkohle f	carbone m a dadi (o in cubetti) carbone m in pezzatura f media
3885 **cobalt**	cobalt m	Kobalt m	cobalto m
3885a **cobalt bloom**	fleur f de cobalt	Kobaltblüte f	eritrina f
3886 **cobalt-chromium steel, K.S. magnet steel**	acier m au cobalt-chrome	Kobalt-Chromstahl m	acciaio m al cobalto-cromo
3887 **cobalt-glance, cobaltite**	cobaltine f	Glanzkobalt m, Kobaltin m	cobaltite f

	English	French	German	Italian
°	3888 **cobalt glass**	verre *m* de cobalt	Kobaltglas *n*	vetro *m* al cobalto
°	3889 **cobalt glass bottle**	flacon *m* de cobalt	Kobaltflasche *f*	bòttiglia *f* di cobalto
—	3890 **cobalt oxide**	protoxyde *m* de cobalt	Kobaltoxydul *n*	protossido *m* di cobalto
—	3890a **cobalt pyrite**	linnéite *f*	Kobaltkies *m*	linneite *f*
°	3891 **cobalt steel**	acier *m* au cobalt	Kobaltstahl *m*	acciaio *m* al cobalto
—	3891a **cobaltiferous**	cobaltifère	kobalthaltig	cobaltifero
—	3892 **cobaltite**	cobaltite *f*	Kobaltglanz *m*, Glanzkobalt *m*	cobaltina *f*
—	3893 **cobaltomenite**	cobaltoménite *f*	Kobaltomenit *m*	cobaltomenite *f*
—	3894 **cobbed ore**	mineral *m* scheidé	Scheiderz *n*	minerale *m* in pezzatura media, minerale classifica
—	3895 **cobbles** *pl.*, **lump coal, lumps** *pl.*	gailletin *m*, grélats *m pl.*, grélassons *m pl.*	Würfelkohle *f*	carbone *m* a cubi (o in pezzatura media)
—	3896 **coccolite**	coccolite *f*	Kokkolith *m*	coccolite *f*
°	3897 **cock, tap**	robinet *m*	Hahn *m*	rubinetto *m*
°	3897a **cockle**	ondulation *f*	Wölbung *f*	ondulazione *f*
°	3898 **cocks and valves**	robinetterie *f*	Hahnausruestung *f*	rubinetteria *f*
°	3899 **coefficient of dissociation**	constante *f* de dissociation, constante *f* d'affinité	Dissoziationskonstante *f*	costante *f* di dissociazione o d'affinità

coefficient of draft, *s. coefficient of reduction*

	English	French	German	Italian
°	3900 **coefficient of equivalence**	coefficient *m* d'équivalence	Gleichwertigkeitskoeffizient *m*	coefficiente *m* d'equivalenza
°	3901 **coefficient of reduction**	coefficient *m* de réduction	Abnahmezahl *f*	coefficiente *m* di riduzione
°	3901a **coercive force**	force *f* coercitive	Koerzitivkraft *f*	forza *f* coercitiva
—	3902 **coffer**	coffrage *m*, revêtement d'un puits	Schachtausbau *m*	armamento *m*, armatura *f*, rivestimento d'un pozzo
—	3093 **coffer-dam**	cuvelage *m*	Küvelage *f*	palancolata *f*, argine *m* di contenimento

coffering, *s. coffer*

	English	French	German	Italian
°	3904 **to cog**	ébaucher	vorwalzen	sbozzare
—	3905 **to cog**	remblayer	mit Bergen versetzen	eseguire una ripiena, riempire
—	3906 **cog**	pile *f* de bois	Holzkasten *m*, Holzschrank *m*	pilastro *m* per ripiena

English	French	German	Italian
3907 cog	dyke *m*	Gesteinsgang *m*	dicco *m*
3908 cog **to cog down,** *to roll*	dent *m*	Zahn *m*	dente *m*
3909 cog-wheel, gear	roue *f* à dents, engrenage *m*	Zahnrad *n*, Getriebe *n*	ruota *f* dentata
3910 cogged bloom	lingot *m* dégrossi (ou ébauché)	vorgewalzter Block *m*	lingotto *m* sgrossato
3911 cogger	remblayeur *m*	Versatzarbeiter *m*	addetto *m* alla ripiena
3912 cogging, roughing **cogging,** *s. roughing*	,ébauchage *m*, dégrossissage *m*	Vorstrecken *n*, Vorwalzen *n*	laminazione *f* di sbozza- tura, sbozzatura *f*
3913 cogging mill, blooming mill **cogging pass,** *s. bloom pass*	train *m* ébaucheur ou dégrossisseur	Vorstrecke *f*, Vor- strasse *f*	treno *m* sbozzatore, treno *m* blooming
3914 cogging roll	cylindre *m* de blooming	Blockwalze *f*	cilindro *m* blooming, cilindro sgrossatore
3915 cogman	maçon *m* de puits	Schachtmaurer *m*	muratore *m* di pozzi
3916 cognate xenolith, endogenous enclosure	enclave *f* homéogène (ou endogene)	endogener Einschluss *m*	inclusione *f* endogena
3917 cogs on pinion wheel	anneau *m* denté venu de fonte	angegossener Zahnkranz *m*	ingranaggio *m* (ruota *f* denta- ta) fuso in un sol pezzo
3918 cohenite	cohénite *f*	Cohenit *m*	cohenite *f*
3919 cohesion meter	cohésionmètre *m*	Kohäsionsmessappa- rat *m*	coesimetro *m*
3920 cohesion of sand	cohésion *f* du sable	Bindekraft *f*, Bin- devermögen *n* des Sandes	coesione *f* della terra o della sabbia
3920a coil	rouleau *m*	Rolle *f*	rullo *m*, rotolo *m*
3921 col	bobine *f*	Ring (Draht) *m*	rotolo (vergella)
3922 coled bar	barre *f* en rouleaux	eingerollte Barre *f*	barra *f* in rotoli
3923 coil breaks	coque *f* de bande	Bandknick *m*	piega *f* falsa di ban- da
3924 to coin	estamper, frapper	prägen	coniare
3925 coinage, minting	frappe *f*, brassage *m*	Ausprägen *n*, Ausmünzen *n*	coniatura *f* (di monete)

		English	French	German	Italian
—	3926	**to coke**	cokéfier	verkoken	cokificare
—	3927	**coke**	coke *m*	Koks *m*	coke *m*
—	3928	**coke basket**	corbeille *f* à coke	Kokskorb *m*	paniere *m* da coke
°	3929	**coke bed**	lit *m* de coke	Koksschicht *f*	carica *f* di coke, dote *f*, coke *m* di riscaldo
°	3930	**coke blast furnace**	haut-fourneau *m* au coke	Kokshochofen *m*	alto forno *m* a coke
°	3931	**coke breaker**	concasseur *m* à coke	Koksbrecher *m*	frantoio *m* per coke, trituratore *m* per coke
°	3932	**coke breeze, dust-coke**	poussier *m* de coke	Lösche *f*, Kokslösche *f*	cenerino *m* di carbone
°	3933	**coke cake** **coke coal**, *s. coking coal* **coke charge**, *s. coke split*	saumon *m* de coke	Kokskuchen *m*	pane *m* di coke
°	3934	**coke crushing ring**	anneau *m* de concassage de coke	Koksbrechring *m*	anello *m* cava-coke
°	3935	**coke dross**	coke *m* menu, fraisil *m* de coke	Koksklein *n*	coke *m* minuto
°	3936	**coke dust, powdered coke, small coke**	poussier *m* de charbon	Kohlenpulver *n*, Koksklein *n*	polverino *m* di coke
°	3937	**coke fork**	fourche *f* à coke	Koksgabel *f*	forca *f* per coke
°	3938	**coke furnace, coke oven**	four *m* à coke	Koksofen *m*	forno *m* a coke
°	3938a	**coke guide**	guide-coke *m*	Führungsgitter *n*	guida-coke *m*
°	3939	**coke iron**	fer *m* au coke	Kokseisen *n*	ferro *m* al coke
		coke oven, *s. coke furnace*			
°	3940	**coke oven coke, hard coke**	coke *m* métallurgique	Zechenkoks *m*, Hüttenkoks *m*	coke *m* metallurgico, coke di alto forno
°	3941	**coke oven gas**	gaz *m* de four à coke	Koksofengas *n*	gas *m* dei forni a coke
°	3942	**coke oven with utilization of by--products**	four *m* à coke à récupération	Koksofen *m* für Gewinnung der Nebenerzeugnisse	forno *m* a coke a ricupero
		coke pusher, *s. coke pushing machine*			

English	French	German	Italian
3943 coke pushing machine, coke pusher	défourneuse *f* de coke	Koksausdrück-maschine *f*	macchina *f* per sfornare il coke, estrattrice di carbone
3943a coke quenching tower	chevalet *m* d'extinction	Kokslöschturm *m*	torre *f* di estinzione
3944 coke scrubber	filtre *m* à coke	Koksfilter *n*	depuratore *m* (o filtro) a coke
3945 coke sheet iron	tôle *f* au coke	Koksblech *n*	lamiera *f* al coke
3946 coke split	charge *f* de coke	Satzkoks *m*	coke *m* di fusione
3947 coke storing place	dépôt *m* de coke	Kokslagerplatz *m*	deposito *m* di coke
3948 coke yield	rendement *m* en coke	Koksausbringen *n*	rendimento *m* in coke
3949 cokeite	cokéite *f*	Kokeit *m*	cokeite *f*, coke naturale
3950 coking	cokéfaction *f*	Verkohlung *f*	cokizzazione *f*
3951 coking capacity	pouvoir *m* cokéfiant	Verkokungsfähigkeit *f*	potere *m* cokificante
3952 coking chamber	cellule *f* de cokéfaction	Verkokungskammer *f*	camera *f* di cokefazione
3953 coking-coal, coke coal	charbon *m* à coke	Kokskohle *f*	carbone *m* di coke, coke *m*
3954 coking (-process)	cokéfaction *f*, cokéfication *f*	Verkokung *f*, Koksbildung *f*	cokefazione *f*
coking still, *s. batch still*			
3955 coking stoker	chargeur *m* à gazéification préalable	Verkokungsfeuerung *f*	caricatrice *f* a cokificazione
3955a coking test	essai *m* de coke	Koksprobe *f*	prova *f* di coke
3956 Colby's smelting furnace, Colby furnace	four *m* Colby	Colbyscher Ofen *m*	forno *m* Colby
3957 to cold-draw	étirer à froid	kaltziehen	trafilare a freddo
3958 to cold hammer	écrouir, marteler à froid	kalt hämmern, kalt schmieden	battere (o martellare) a freddo
3959 to cold-roll	laminer à froid, écrouir	kalt walzen	laminare a freddo
3960 to cold-stamp	emboutir (ou étamper ou matricer) à froid	kalt stempeln, kalt kümpeln	imbutire (o stampare) a freddo
3961 cold bending test, cold bend	essai *m* de pliage à froid	Kaltbiegeprobe *f*	prova *f* di piegatura a freddo

		English	French	German	Italian
°	3962	**cold blast**	vent *m* froid	kalter Wind *m*	vento *m* freddo
°	3963	**cold-blast iron**	fonte *f* à air froid	kalt erblasenes Roheisen *n*	ghisa *f* a vento freddo
°	3964	**cold blast slide**	vanne *f* à air froid, régistre à air froid	Kaltwindschieber *m*	registro *f* ad aria fredda
°	3965	**cold brittle**	cassant à froid	kaltbrüchig	fragile a freddo
°	3966	**cold brittleness, cold shortness**	fragilité *f* à froid	Kaltbruch *m*	fragilità *f* a freddo (o a bassa temperatura)
°	3967	**cold chamber machine**	machine à chambre *f* froide	Kaltkammer-Druck-giessmaschine *f*	macchina a camera *f* fredda
°	3968	**cold chamber pressure casting**	fonte *f* en chambre froide	Kaltkammer-Druck-giessen *n*	ghisa *f* a camera fredda per fusioni sotto-pressione
°	3969	**cold charge**	charge *f* froide	kalter Einsatz *m*	carica fredda per il forno, carica solida (del forno)
°	3970	**cold chisel**	ciseau *m* à froid	Kaltmeissel *m*	tagliolo *m* a freddo
°	3970a	**cold compacting**	compression *f* à froid	Kaltpressen *n*	compressione *f* a freddo
°	3971	**cold crack, cold cracking**	tapure *f* à froid	Kaltriss *m*	crepa *f* a freddo, cricca (o incrinatura) a freddo
°	3972	**cold crack**	cassure *f* à froid	Kaltbruch *m*, Kaltriss *m*	rottura *f* a freddo, fessura *f* a freddo
°	3973	**cold-drawing**	écrouissage *m*	Kaltzug, Kaltziehen *n*	trafilatura *f* a freddo, imbutitura *f* a freddo
°	3974	**cold drawing shop**	usine *f* d'étirage à froid	Kaltzieherei *f*	trafileria *f* a freddo
°	3975	**cold drawn steel**	acier *m* écroui. acier étiré à froid	kaltgereckter Stahl *m*, kaltgezogener Stahl *m*	acciaio *m* trafilato a freddo

to cold draw the hammer, *s. to cold hammer*

cold dressed iron, *s. cold strained iron*

°	3976	**cold enamelling**	émaillage *m* à froid	Kaltemaillierung *f*	smaltatura *f* a freddo
°	3977	**cold extrusion**	filer à la presse	Fliesspressen *n*, Kaltpressen *n*, Strangpressen *n*	estrusione *f* a freddo
°	3978	**cold-finished**	fini à froid	kalt ausgearbeitet	finito a freddo
°	3978a	**to cold form**	profiler à froid	kaltformen	formare a freddo

English	French	German	Italian
3979 cold forming	forçage *m* à froid	Kalteinsenken *n*	coniatura *f* a freddo, formatura a freddo
3980 cold forming	façonnage *m* à froid	Kaltbearbeitung*f*	lavorazione a freddo
3981 cold forming tool steel	acier à outils pour le façonnage à froid	Werkzeugstahl *m* für Kaltarbeit	acciaio da utensile per la lavorazione a freddo
3981a cold galvanizing	zincage à froid	Kaltverzinkung*f*	galvanizzazione *f* a freddo
3982 cold impact die	matrice *f* de frappe à froid	Kaltschlagmatrize *f*	matrice *f* per stampare a freddo
3983 cold lahar	torrent *m* boueux	Schlammstrom *m*	torrente *m* fangoso, Lahar *m*
3984 cold lap	reprise *f*	Kaltschweisse *f*	giunto *m* a freddo, ripresa
3984a cold laps	peau *f* de crapaud	Runzeln *f pl*.	pelle *f* di rospo
3985 cold metal	métal *m* froid	kaltes Metall *n*	metallo *m* freddo
3986 cold metal	fonte *f* froide	kaltes Eisen *n*	ghisa *f* fredda
3986a cold piercing	pénétration *f* à froid	Kaltdurchbohrung *f*	penetrazione *f* a freddo
3987 cold pit	puits *m* d'aérage	Wetterschacht *m*	pozzo *m* di ventilazione
3987a cold pressing	étampage *m* à froid	Kaltpressen *n*	stampaggio *m* a freddo
cold pressure welding, *s. cold welding*			
3987b cold quenching	trempe *f* à froid	Kaltabschrecken *n*	tempra *f* a freddo
3988 to cold-roll	écrouir	kaltwalzen	trafilare (o imbutire) a freddo
3989 cold roll	cylindre *m* à froid	Kaltwalze *f*	cilindro *m* per la lavorazione a freddo
3990 cold-rolled	laminé à froid	kaltgewalzt	laminato a freddo
3991 cold rolled magnetic steel	feuillard *m* magnétique	Elektro-Blech *n*	nastro *m* magnetico
3992 cold-rolled plate	tôle *f* laminée à froid	kaltgewalztes Blech *n*	lamiera *f* laminata a freddo
3993 cold-rolled sheet iron	tôle *f* laminée à froid	kaltgewalztes Blech *n*	lamiera *f* passata a freddo
3994 cold-rolled steel	acier *m* laminé à froid, acier écroui	kaltgewalzter Stahl *m*	acciaio *m* laminato a freddo
3995 cold-rolled strip	bandes *f pl.* laminées à froid	kaltgewalztes Band *n*	bande *f pl.* laminate a freddo
3996 cold-rolled strip iron	feuillard *m* laminé à froid	kaltgewalztes Eisen *n*	ferro *m* in nastri laminati a freddo
3997 cold-rolling, cold reduction	laminage *m* à froid	Kaltwalzen *n*	laminazione *f* a freddo

		English	French	German	Italian
o	3998	cold rolling mill for strips	laminoir m à froid pour feuillards	Kaltbandwalzwerk n	laminatoio a freddo per nastri
o	3999	cold saw	scie f à froid	Kaltsägemaschine f	sega f a freddo
o	3999	cold sawing	sciage m à froid	Kaltsägen n	segare a freddo
o	4000	cold short	cassant à froid	kaltbrüchig	fragile a freddo
o	4001	cold-short iron	fer m cassant à froid, fer tendre	kaltbrüchiges Eisen n	ferro m fragile a freddo
o	4002	cold-shortness of iron	aigreur f (ou fragilité f à froid) du fer	Kaltbrüchigkeit f des Eisens	fragilità f a freddo del ferro
o	4003	cold-shut, cold-lap	reprise f	Kaltschweisse f	giunto m a freddo, ripresa
o	4003a	cold sprueing	décapage m à froid	Kaltabbeizen n	decapaggio m a freddo
o	4004	cold straightened iron	fer m dressé à froid	kalt gerichtetes Eisen n	ferro m raddrizzato a freddo
o	4005	cold test	essai m à froid	Kaltprobe f	prova f a freddo
o	4006	cold welding	souder à froid	kaltpressschweissen	saldare a freddo per pressione
o	4007	cold work	travail m à froid	Kaltbearbeitung f	lavorazione f a freddo
o	4008	cold work steel	acier m pour travail à froid	Kaltarbeitsstahl m	acciaio m per lavorazione a freddo
o	4009	cold working	allure f froide	Rohgang m	andamento m o marcia f fredda
o	4010	cold working	écrouissage m	Kaltrecken n, Kaltverformung f	incrudimento m
—	4011	colemanite	colemanite f	Colemanit m	colemanite f
		to collapse, s. to fall in			
—	4012	collapsibility	friabilité f	Zerbrechlichkeit f	friabilità f (delle anime)
—	4013	collapsible bit	trépan m à effacement	ausziehbarer Meissel m	trapano m retrattile
—	4014	collapsible prop	étançon m télescopique	nachgiebiger Stempel m	puntello m (o sostegno) telescopico
o	4015	collar	embase f	Bund m, Flansch m	flangia f (fucinatura)
^	4016	collar	collier m	Kragen m	collare m, manicotto m
—	4017	collar	orifice m (d'un puits)	Schachtmündung f	bocca f (di pozzo)

	English	French	German	Italian
4018	collar buster	brise-manchon *m*	Muffenbrecher *m*	rompiflange *m*
4019	collar finder	localisateur *m* de joint	Muffenseher *m*	localizzatore *m* di giunti
4020	collar of the roll	collet *m* du cylindre	Rand *m* oder Ring *m* der Walze	cordone *m* del cilindro
4021	collared casing	tube *m* manchonné	Muffenrohr *n*	tubo *m* a manicotto
4022	collared pin	goujon *m* à embase	Führungsstift *m* mit Bund	pernio *m* flangiato
	collaring, *s. warping*			
4023	collecting	échantillonner	Probeziehen *n*	campionamento *m*, collezione *f*
4024	collecting flue	carneau *m* collecteur	Sammelfuchs *m*	canale *m* collettore
4025	collecting main	conduite *f* principale	Hauptleitung *f*	condotta *f* collettrice principale
4026	collection of minerals	collection *f* minéralogique	Steinsammlung *f*, Mineraliensammlung *f*	raccolta *f* di minerali
4026a	collector	réactif *m* collecteur	Sammelreagens *n*	reagente *m* collettore
4027	collobrierite	collobriérite *f*	Collobrierit *m*	collobrierite *f*
4028	colloidal clay	argile *f* colloïdale	kolloidaler Ton *m*	argilla *f* colloidale
4029	collyrite	collyrite *f*	Kollyrit *m*	collyrite *f*
4030	colophonite	colophonite *f*	Kolophonit *m*	colofonite *f*
	color temperature, *s apparent temperature with colour pyrometer*			
4031	Coloradian epoch	époque *f* coloradienne	Coloradian *n*	Coloradiano *m*
4032	coloradoite	coloradoïte *f*	Coloradoit *m*	coloradoite *f*
4033	colorados	chapeau *m* de fer	eiserner Hut *m*	cappello *m* di ferro
4034	colorimetry	colorimétrie *f*	Kolorimetrie *f*	colorimetria *f*, analisi *f* colorimetrica
4035	colour comparator pyrometer	pyromètre *m* polychromatique	Farbpyrometer *n*	pirometro *m* policromatico
4036	colouring of flames	coloration *f* de la flamme	Flammenfärbung *f*	colorazione *f* della fiamma
4037	columbite	columbite *f*	Columbit *m*	columbite *f*

	English	French	German	Italian
	columbium, *s. niobium*			
°	**4038 column**	colonne *f*	Säule *f*, Ständer *m*	colonna *f*
°	**4039 column**	pied *m*	Ofenfuss *m*, Ofensäule *f*	piede *m*, colonna *f*
°	**4040 column balance**	balance *f* à colonne	Säulenwaage *f*	bilancia *f* a colonna
—	**4041 column drill, column drilling machine**	perforatrice *f* à colonne	Säulenbohrmaschine *f*	perforatrice *f* a colonna, trapano *m* a colonna
—	**4042 column mounting**	montage *m* sur colonne	Montage *f* auf Säule *f*	montaggio *m* su colonna
^	**4043 column of fluid**	colonne *f* de liquide	Flüssigkeitssäule *f*	colonna *f* di liquido
—	**4044 columnar**	en (forme de) colonnes	säulenförmig	à forma di colonna, colonnare
—	**4045 columnar crystals**	cristaux *m pl.* en colonnes	säulenförmige Kristalle *m pl.*	cristalli *m pl.* colonnari
—	**4046 columnar fracture**	fracture *f* en colonnes ou columnaire	säulenförmiger Bruch *m*	frattura *f* colonnare
	columnar jointing, *s. columnar structure*			
—	**4047 columnar section**	profil *m* stratigraphique	Normalprofil *n*	profilo *m* stratigrafico
—	**4048 columnar structure, prismatic structure, prismatic jointing, columnar jointing**	structure *f* prismatique (ou columnaire)	säulenförmige Absonderung *f*, prismatische Absonderung *f*	struttura *f* prismatica (o colonnare)
—	**4049 comagmatic rock**	roche comagmatique	comagmatisches Gestein *n*	roccia *f* comagmatica
°	**4050 comb-gate casting**	attaque *f* en pluie	fallender Guss *m* mit mehrfachem Metallstrahl	colata *f* a pettine
—	**4051 comb-structure**	structure *f* crêtée	Kammstruktur *f*	struttura *f* a pettine
°	**4052 comb tooth method, peg board method**	procedé «en peigne»	sogenanntes Kammverfahren *n*	procedimento *m* detto a pettine
^	**4053 combination bit**	trépan *m* pour roches à deux taillants à queue de carpe	Doppelfischschwanzmeissel *m*	«rock-bit» con al centro due lame a coda di pesce

	English	French	German	Italian
4054	combination boiler, semitubular boiler	chaudière *f* combinée (ou mixte)	Verbundkessel *m*, kombinierter Kessel	caldaia *f* combinata (o accoppiata o mista)
4055	combination die	moule *m* à éléments différents	kombiniertes Modell *n*	stampo *m* con impronte di particolari diversi
4056	combination dies	jeu *m* de modèles	Modellsatz *m*	serie *f* di stampi per stampaggio e trinciatura
4057	combination of metalloids with iron	combinaison *f* des métalloïdes avec le fer	Verbindung *f* der Metalloide mit dem Eisen	combinazione *f* dei metalloidi col ferro
4058	combination reamer	trépan *m* aléseur avec foret au fond	Räumer *m* mit Bodenmeissel	«reamer» con scalpello al fondo
4059	combination reverse-drawing and cutting tool	outil d'emboutissage par retournement avec découpage	Schnittstülp-ziehwerkzeug *n*	utensile *m* d'imbutitura a capovolgimento con taglio
4060	combination socket	douille *f* combinée	kombinierter Keilfänger *m*	bussola *f* combinata, arpione combinato
4061	combination string	tubage *m* combiné	kombinierte Rohrtour *f*	tubaggio *m* combinato, tubazione combinata
4062	combination turret lathe	tour revolver *m*	Revolverdrehbank *f* mit Leitspindel	tornio *m* meccanico a torretta, tornio a revolver
4063	combined Bessemer and open hearth process	procédés *m pl.* Bessemer et Martin combinés	vereinigtes Bessemer und Martin - Verfahren *n*	processo *m* combinato Bessemer e Martin
4064	combined carbon	carbone *m* combiné	gebundener Kohlenstoff *m*	carbonio *m* combinato
4065	combined silicic acid	silice *f* combinée	gebundene Kieselsäure *f*	silice *f* combinata
4066	combined water tube and fire tube boiler	chaudière *f* à tubes de fumée et à tubes d'eau	kombinierter Wasser Flammrohr-Kessel *m*	caldaia *f* a tubi di fiamma e d'acqua combinati
4067	combining volume	volume *m* de combinaison	Verbindungsvolumen *n*	volume *m* di combinazione
4068	combining weight	poids *m* relatif de combinaison	Verbindungsgewicht *n*	peso *m* di combinazione
4069	combustible	combustible	brennbar, verbrennlich	combustibile

		English	French	German	Italian
°	4070	**combustible constituent**	élément m combustible	brennbarer Bestandteil m	parte f combustibile
°	4071	**combustion**	combustion f	Verbrennung f	combustione, carbonizzazione
°	4072	**combustion at constant pressure**	combustion f à pression constante	Verbrennung f bei gleichbleibendem Druck	combustione f a pressione costante
°	4073	**combustion at constant volume**	combustion f sous volume constant	Verbrennung f bei gleichbleibendem Volumen	combustione f a volume costante
°	4074	**combustion boat**	godet m à fusion	Einsetzer m, Glühschiffchen n	navicella f di fusione
°	4075	**combustion boat**	coupelle f de combustion	Verbrennungsschälchen n	capsula f di combustione
°	4076	**combustion chamber**	chambre f de combustion	Brennkammer f	camera f di combustione
°	4077	**combustion control**	contrôle m de la combustion	Verbrennungskontrolle f	controllo m della combustione
		combustion curve, s. *combustion line*			
°	4078	**combustion furnace**	four m à combustion	Verbrennungsofen m	forno m di combustione
°	4079	**combustion glass**	verre m à fusion	Einschmelzglas n	vetro m fusibile
°	4080	**combustion line**	courbe f de combustion	Verbrennungslinie f	curva f (o linea f) di combustione
°	4081	**combustion residual product**	résidu m de la combustion	Verbrennungsrückstand m	residuo m (o prodotti) della combustione
°	4082	**combustion room**	salle f de combustion	Verbrennungsraum m	reparto m combustione
°	4083	**combustion shaft**	cheminée f de combustion, puits m de combustion	Verbrennungsschacht m	pozzo m di combustione
°	4084	**combustion tube**	tube m à combustion	Verbrennungsröhre f	tubo m di combustione
^	4085	**to come into production**	entrer en production	in Produktion gehen	iniziare la produzione
—	4086	**comendite**	comendite f	Comendit m	comendite f

English	French	German	Italian

commercial iron, *s. universal iron ·*

English	French	German	Italian
4087 commercial quality tube for gas	tube *m* gaz commercial	handelsübliches Gasrohr *n*	tubo *m* gas commerciale
4088 commercial steel, industrial steel	acier commercial, acier du type commercial	Handelsstahl *m*	acciaio *m* commerciale
4089 commercial sulphuric acid	acide *m* sulfurique du commerce	käufliche, rohe Schwefelsäure *f*	acido *m* solforico commerciale
4090 to comminute	broyer finement	fein mahlen	macinare (o frantumare) finemente, polverizzare
4090a comminuted powder	poudre *f* moulue	Mahlpulver *n*	polvere *f* minuta
4091 common balance, druggist's scales	balance *f* de Roberval	Tafelwaage *f*	bilancia *f* da tavolo
4091a common brass	laiton *m* commercial	Handelsmessing *n*	ottone *m* commerciale
4092 common charcoal	charbon de bois noir ou ordinaire	Schwarzkohle *f*	carbone *m* di legna nero o comune
4093 common collecting pipe	tuyau *m* collecteur général	gemeinschaftliches Sammelrohr *n*	tubo *m* collettore generale

common draw size, *s. base size*

English	French	German	Italian
4094 common limb	flanc *m* médian	Mittelschenkel *m*	fianco *m* mediano
4095 common mica	muscovite *f*	Muskovit *m*	muscovite *f*
4096 common opal	opale *f* commune	gemeiner Opal *m*	opale comune
4097 common salt	chlorure de sodium	Natriumchlorid *n*	cloruro *m* di sodio
4098 common water tank	réservoir *m* d'eau (général)	gemeinschaftlicher Wasserbehälter *m*	serbatoio generale dell'acqua
4098a compact	comprimé *m*	Pressling *m*	articolo *m* pressato
4099 compact coke	coke *m* dense	kompakter Koks *m*	coke *m* compatto
4100 compact iron ore	minerai *m* de fer compact	derbes Eisenerz *n*	minerale *m* di ferro compatto

compact slag, *s. dense slag*

English	French	German	Italian
4101 compactibility	aptitude *f* au serrage	Verdichtbarkeit *f*	attitudine *f* alla compressione
	compactibility, *s. flowability*		
4102 compactibility index	indice *m* d'aptitude au serrage	Verdichtbarkeitszahl *f*	indice *m* d'attitudine alla plasticità
4102a compacting crack	crique *f* à la compression	Pressriss *m*	crepa *f* di compressione
4103 compacting pressure	pression *f* de serrage	Pressdruck *m*	pressione *f* di compressione

		English	French	German	Italian

^ 4104 **compaction, gravitational compaction** — tassement *m* — Verdichtung *f* — concentrazione *f*, assestamento *m*

^ 4105 **companion flange** — contrebride *f* — Gegenflansch *m* — controflangia *f*

° 4106 **comparative test** — essai *m* de comparaison — Vergleichsversuch *m* — prova *f* per confronto

° 4107 **comparative value** — valeur *f* comparée — Vergleichswert *m* — valore *m* di confronto

° 4108 **compass spread open** — compas *m* écarté — gespreizter Schenkel *m* — supporto *m* con due gambe, compasso aperto

compass with spread shanks, *s. compass spread open*

° 4109 **compensating hanging** — suspension *f* compensée — Ausgleichaufhängung *f* — sospensione *f* compensata

° 4110 **compensating pipe** — tuyau *m* compensateur — Ausgleichrohr *n* — tubo *m* compensatore

° 4111 **to complete** — achever — fertigmachen — completare, terminare

° 4112 **complete chill** — trempe *f* totale — völlige Weisserstarrung *f* — tempra *f* totale

° 4113 **complete combustion** — combustion *f* complète — vollkommene Verbrennung *f* — combustione *f* completa

° 4114 **complete decarburisation** — décarburation *f* complète — vollständige Entkohlung *f* — decarburazione *f* completa

° 4115 **complete miscibility** — miscibilité *f* totale ou complète — vollständige oder (unbeschränkte) Mischbarkeit *f* — miscibilità *f* completa (o totale)

— 4116 **completion gauge** — résultat quantitatif pour la mise en production d'un puits — Quantumresultat des Produktionsanlaufes — risultato quantitativo della messa in produzione di un pozzo

^ 4117 **completion of well** — ensemble des opérations pour entrer en production — Gesamtarbeiten für den Produktionsanlauf — insieme delle operazioni per mettere in produzione un pozzo

° 4118 **complex-alloy steel** — acier *m* d'alliage complexe — Komplexstahl *m* — acciaio *m* complesso

— 4119 **complex fault** — faille *f* composée — zusammengesetzte Verwerfung *f* — faglia *f* composta

° 4120 **component** — constituant *m*, composante *f* — Komponente *f* — costituente *m*, componente *m*

English	French	German	Italian
4121 composite fold	pli *m* composé	zusammengesetzte Falte *f*	piega *f* composta o composita
4122 composite gneiss	migmatite *f*	Migmatit *m*	migmatite *f*
4123 composite plane	plan *m* de macle	Zwillingsebene *f*	piano *m* di geminazione
4123a composite tube	tube *m* composé	Verbundrohr *n*	tubo *m* composto
4124 composite vein, composite lode	filon *m* composé	zusammengesetzter Gang *m*	filone *m* complesso o composto
4125 composition	constitution *f*, composition *f*	Zusammensetzung *f*	costituzione *f*, composizione *f*
4126 composition of the charge	composition *f* de la charge	Zusammensetzung *f*	composizione *f* della carica
4127 composition of the gas	composition *f* du gaz	Gaszusammensetzung *f*	composizione *f* del gas
compound boiler, *s. combination boiler*			
4128 compound engine	machine *f* compound ou composée	Verbundmaschine *f*	macchina *f* compound o composta
4129 compound fault	faille *f* composée	zusammengesetzte Verwerfung *f*	faglia *f* composta
4130 compound steam pump	pompe *f* à vapeur compound	Verbunddampfpumpe *f*	pompa *f* compound a vapore
4131 compound steel	acier *m* composé	Verbundstahl *m*	acciaio *m* legato
4132 compound vein	filon *m* composé	zusammengesetzter Gang *m*	filone *m* composto
4133 compounded (pump)	compound (pompe)	Vorgelege *n*	pompa *f* «compound»
4134 compressed air	air *m* comprimé	Pressluft *f*	aria *f* compressa
4135 compressed air container	réservoir *m* d'air comprimé	Pressluftbehälter *m*	serbatoio *m* per aria compressa
4136 compressed air hammer	marteau *m* à air comprimé	Luftdruckhammer *m*	maglio *m* ad aria compressa
4137 compressed air sandblaster	sableuse *f* à air comprimé	Druckluftstrahlanlage *f*	sabbiatrice *f* pneumatica (o ad aria compressa)
4138 compressed gas	gaz *m* comprimé	verdichtetes Gas *n*	gas *m* compresso
4139 compressed oxygen	chalumeau *m* à oxygène comprimé	Brenner *m* für Sauerstoff	cannello *m* ad ossigeno compresso

		English	French	German	Italian
°	4150	compressed steel	acier *m* comprimé	Pressstahl *m*	acciaio *m* compresso
°	4151	compressibility	compressibilité *f*	Kompressibilität *f*	compressibilità *f*
°	4152	compressible, telescopic runner pattern	coulée compressible, téléscopique	Teleskop-Trichtermodell *n*	colata *f* compressibile
°	4153	compression condensation	compression *f*, condensation *f*	Kompression *f*, Verdichtung *f*	compressione *f*, condensazione *f*
°	4154	compression cylinder	cylindre *m* de compression	Presszylinder *m*	cilindro *m* a compressione
		compression fault, *s. thrust-fault*			
—	4155	compression joint	piézoclase *f*, fente de compression	Druckspalte *f*, Piäzoklas *n*	piezoclasi *f*
°	4156	compression strain	effort de compression	Druckbeanspruchung *f*	sollecitazione *f* a compressione
°	4157	compression test	essai *m* de compression	Druckversuch *m*	prova *f* alla compressione
°	4158	concave form	forme *f* concave	ausgebauchte Form *f*	forma *f* concava
—	4159	concave roof or crown	voûte *f* surbaissée	abwärts gezogenes Gewölbe *n*	volta *f* ribassata
°	4160	concave shape of hearth	forme *f* concave	Muldenform *f*	forma *f* concava
—	4161	concentration of ore by flotation process	enrichissement *m* des minerais par flottage	Erzaufbereitung *f* durch Sonderung nach Gleichfälligkeit in Stromapparaten	arricchimento *m* dei minerali per flottazione
	4162	concentrated acid	acide *m* concentré	konzentrierte Säure *f*	acido *m* concentrato
—	4163	concentrates, dressed ore	schlich *m*, minerai *m* concentré	Schlich *m*, aufbereitetes Erz *n*	schlich *m*, minerale *m* arricchito (o concentrato)
—	4164	concentrating mill	installation *f* de concentration	Aufbereitungsanlage *f*	impianto *m* di concentrazione
—	4165	concentrating percussion table	table *f* à secousses	Stossherd *m*	tavola *f* a scosse
—	4166	concentration	enrichissement *m*	Anreicherung *f*	concentrazione *f*, arricchimento *m*
		concentration, *s. évaporation*			

English	French	German	Italian
4167 concentration of ions	concentration f des ions	Ionenverdichtung f	concentrazione f degli ioni
4168 concentration ores	enrichissement m des minerais	Anreicherung f der Mineralien	arricchimento m dei minerali
4169 concentration polarisation	polarisation f de concentration	Verdichtungspolarisation f	polarizzazione f di concentrazione
4170 concentration plant	installation f d'enrichissement	Anreicherungsanlage f	impianto m di concentrazione
4171 concession	concession f	Konzession f	concessione f
4172 conchoidal fracture	cassure f conchoïde	muscheliger Bruch m	rottura f concoide
4173 conchoidal structure	structure f conchoïdale	muschelige Struktur f	struttura f concoidale

concordance, s. conformity

4174 concrete base	soubassement m en béton	Betonunterlage f	platea f o basamento in calcestruzzo
4175 concrete die	matrice f en béton	Matrize f aus Beton	matrice in calcestruzzo
4176 concrete iron	fer m pour béton armé	Betoneisen n	ferro m da calcestruzzo
4177 concrete pile	pieu m en béton armé	Stahlbetonpfeiler m	palo m di calcestruzzo armato, palo in cemento armato

concrete steel, s. ferro-concrete

concreted, s. finished

4178 concretion	concrétion f	Erhärtung f, Konkretion f	concrezione f
4179 concretionary	concrétionnaire	konkretionär	concrezionato
4180 concurrent boiler	chaudière f à courant direct	Gleichstromkessel m	caldaia f a corrente diretta
4181 condensation	condensation f	Verdichtung f	condensazione f
4182 condensation tube	tube m de condensation	Kondensationsröhre f	tubo m condensatore
4183 condensate field	gisement m de condensat	Kondensatfeld n	giacimento m di condensato
4184 to condense	condenser	verdichten, kondensieren	condensare

	English	French	German	Italian

condenser discharge spot welding machine, *s. capacitor discharge spot welding machine*

		English	French	German	Italian
○	4185	condensing funnel	entonnoir *m* à trop-plein	Ablauftrichter *m*	imbuto *m* di scolo (o di troppo)
○	4186	condenser coil	serpentin *m* refroidisseur	Kühlschlange *f*	serpentina *f* di raffredda mento o di condensazion
○	4187	condensing tube	tuyau *m* condensateur	Kondensatorrohr *n*	tubo *m* condensatore
○	4188	to condition	conditionner	konditionieren	condizionare
○	4189	condition of core sand	forme *f* des grains de sable	Kernsandbeschaffen- heit *f*	forma *f* o struttura *f* dei grani di sabbia
○	4190	condition of furnace	allure *f* d'un fourneau	Ofengang *m*	marcia *f* d'un forno
—	4191	conditioner	conditionneur *m*	Luftvorbereiter *m*	condizionatore *m*

conditioning, *s. scalping*

		English	French	German	Italian
	4192	conditions *pl.* of supply	conditions *f pl.* de livraison	Lieferungs- bedingungen *f pl.*	condizioni *f pl.* di consegna
○	4192a	conductance	conductance *f*	Wirkleitwert *m*, Konduktanz *f*	conduttanza *f*

conducting air, *s. air conducting*

		English	French	German	Italian
^	4193	conductor	tube *m* conducteur	Standrohr *n*	tubo *m* conduttore
○	4194	conductor	conducteur *m*	Leiter *m*	conduttore *m*
—	4195	conductor	(filon) guide	Leitgang *m*	filone-guida *m*

conductor pipe, *s. conductor string*

		English	French	German	Italian
^	4196	conductor string	tube-guide *m*	Standrohr *n*	tubo-guida *m*

conduit, *s. channel*

cone, *s. funnel or bell*

		English	French	German	Italian
—	4197	cone crusher	concasseur *m* à cônes, broyeur *m* à cônes	Kegelbrecher *m*	frantoio *m* a cono
○	4198	cone head bolt, taper bolt	boulon *m* à tête conique	Bolzen *m* mit konischem Kopf	bullone *m* a testa conica
○	4199	cone (or pan) head rivet	clou *m* à tête à tronc de cône	Niet mit Halbkegelkopf	chiodo *m* a testa tronco conica
—	4199a	cone mixer	mélangeur *m* à double cône	Doppelkonus- mischer *m*	mescolatore *m* a doppio cono
—	4200	cone sheet	filon *m* conique	Kegelschicht *f*	filone *m* conico

English	French	German	Italian
4201 coneshot	sondage *m* en co-lonne de production	Bohren *n* im Produktionsgang	perforazione *f* in colonna di produzione
4202 confetti	confetti *m pl.*	Konfetti *pl.*	coriandoli *m pl.*
4203 conformable fold	pli *m* harmonique	konkordante Falte *f*	piega *f* armonica (o concordante)
4204 conformity, conformability	concordance *f*	Planparallelstruktur *f*, Konkordanz *f*	stratificazione *f* concordante
4205 congealed solution, solidified solution	solution *f* solidifiée	erstarrte Lösung *f*	soluzione *f* solida
to conglomerate, *s. to agglomerate*			
4206 conglomerate	conglomérat *m*	Gemenge *n*, Konglomerat *n*	conglomerato *m*
4207 Congo paper	papier *m* Congo	Kongopapier *n*	carta *f* Congo
4207a congruent melting	fusion *f* congruente	kongruente Schmelzung *f*	fusione *f* congruente
4208 conical	conique	kegelförmig	conico
conical gate, *s. wedge inlet*			
4209 conical hole	trou *m* conique	kegeliges Loch *n*	foro *m* conico
4209a conical reamer	dégorgeoir *m* conique	Raumnadel *f*	alesatore *m* conico
4210 conical roll	cylindre *m* bombé	ballige Walze *f*	cilindro *m* curvato o conico
4211 conical spiral spring	ressort *m* conique	kegelförmige Schraubenfeder *f*, Sprungfeder *f*	molla *f* conica
4212 conical tuyere	tuyère *f* conique	kegelige Düse	tubiera *f* conica, ugello *m* conico
4213 conjugate vein	filon *m* conjugué	durchfallender Gang *m*	filone *m* coniugato
4214 connate water	eau *f* fossile	fossiles Wasser *n*	acqua *f* fossile, acqua interstiziale irriducibile
4215 to connect, to put in gear	embrayer	die Kupplung einrücken	innestare il giunto
4216 to connect	relier, brancher	anschliessen	collegare, giuntare
4217 connecting and branching special	pièce *f* spéciale de raccord et de branchement	Formstück *n*	pezzo *m* speciale di raccordo e derivazione
4218 connecting bridge	pont *m* de communication	Verbindungsbrücke *f*	ponte *m* di comunicazione

		English	French	German	Italian
°	4219	connecting cock	robinet *m* de jonction	Verbindungshahn *m*	rubinetto *m* di congiunzione
		connecting line, *s. junction*			
°	4219a	connecting rod	bielle *f*	Kurbelstange *f*	biella *f*
°	4220	connecting rod	bielle *f*	Kurbelstange *f*	biella *f*
°	4221	connecting screw	boulon *m* d'assemblage	Verbindungsschraube *f*	vite *f* di collegamento, bullone *m* di giunzione
		connecting wire, *s. connector*			
°	4222	connection by welding or by lose flanges	assemblage *m* par soudure ou par brides mobiles	Schweiss-oder Losflansch-Verbindungen *f pl.*	giunzione *f* mediante saldatura o mediante flange mobili
°	4223	connection for exhaust dredge	joint *m* pour drague refouleuse	Saugbaggerverbindung *f*	giunto *m* per draga refluente
°	4224	connector, connecting wire	fil de raccordement, raccordement, liaison	Verbindungsdraht *m*, Schaltdraht *m*	filo di raccordo (o di collegamento)
^	4225	connector	ressort *m* de suspension pour bride	Bügel-Aufhängungsfeder *f*	sospensione *f* a molla per staffoni
—	4226	connellite	connellite *f*	Connellit *m*	connellite *f*
°	4227	Connor runner bar	attaque *f* en bavure	Gratanschnitt *m*	attacco *m* a bava
^	4228	conservation agreement	convention *f* de conservation	Vereinbarung *f* für wirtschaftliche Ausbeutung	accordo *m* di conservazione
°	4229	consisting of several parts	en plusieurs parties	mehrteilig	in più pezzi
°	4230	consisting of two pieces	en deux parties	zweiteilig	in due pezzi
^	4231	consolidation	consolidation *f*	Verfestigung *f*	consolidamento *m*
°	4232	constantan	constantan *m*	Constantan *m*	costantana *f*
°	4233	constituent of a chemical combination	constituant *m* d'une combinaison	Bestandteil *m* einer Verbindung	componente *m* d'una combinazione
°	4234	constituents *pl.* of the gas	constituants *m pl.* du gaz	Gasbestandteile *m pl*	componenti *m pl.* od elementi *m pl.* del gas
°	4235	constructional iron	fer *m* de construction	Baueisen *n*	ferro *m* da costruzione
°	4236	constructional steelwork	acier *m* profilé pour construction	Profilstahl *m*	acciaio *m* profilato per costruzione

	English	French	German	Italian
4237	consumption curve	courbe f de consommation	Verbrauchskurve f	curva f di consumo
4238	consumption of blast	consommation f de vent	Windverbrauch m	consumo m d'aria o di vento
4239	consumption of carbon	consommation f de carbone	Kohlenstoffverbrauch m	consumo m di carbonio
4240	consumption of coal	consommation f de charbon	Kohlenverbrauch m	consumo m di carbone
4241	consumption of current	consommation f de courant	Stromverbrauch m	consumo m di corrente
4242	consumption of electrodes	pertes (ou usure) des électrodes	Abbrand m der Elektroden	calo m od usura f degli elettrodi
4243	consumption of files	consommation f des limes	Feilenverbrauch m	consumo m delle lime
4244	consumption of fuel	consommation f de combustible	Brennstoffaufwand m	consumo m di combustibile (o di carburante)
4245	consumption of water	consommation f d'eau	Wasserverbrauch m	consumo m d'acqua
4246	consumption per ton of steel in kilowatt hours	consommation f par tonne d'acier en kilowatts-heure	Verbrauch m pro Tonne Stahl in Kilowatt-Stunden	consumo m di chilowattora per tonnellata d'acciaio
4246a	contact arc	arc m de contact	Greifbogen m	arco m di contatto
4247	contact deposit	gisement de contact	Kontaktlagerstätte f	giacimento m di contatto
	contact jaw, $s.$ jaw			
4247a	contact lode	filon m de contact	Kontaktgang m	filone m di contatto
4248	contact minerals $pl.$	minéraux m $pl.$ de contact	Kontaktmineralien n $pl.$	minerali m $pl.$ di contatto
4248a	contact plating	dépôt m par contact	Kontaktplattierung f	placcatura f per contatto
	contact tube, $s.$ $wire$-$guide$			
4249	container	conteneur m, réservoir m	Druckbehälter m	serbatoio m, contenitore m, recipiente
4250	containing slag	contenant des scories	schlackenhaltig	contenente scorie
	containing steel, $s.$ $steely$			
4251	content	teneur f	Gehalt m	tenore m, titolo m, contenuto

	English	French	German	Italian
°	4252 **content of fine ore**	teneur f en fines	Feinerzgehalt m	tenore m in minerale minuto
°	4253 **content of gas**	teneur f en gaz	Gasgehalt m	tenore m di gas
°	4254 **content of iron**	teneur f en fer	Eisengehalt m	tenore m in ferro, contenuto m di ferro
—	4255 **content of slate**	teneur f en schiste	Gehalt m an Schiefer, Gehalt m an Bergen	tenore m in schisto
—	4256 **continental facies**	faciès m continental	kontinentale Fazies f	«facies» f continentale
—	4257 **continental segment**	plateau continental, socle continental	Kontinentaltafel f	zoccolo m continentale
—	4258 **continental shelf**	plateforme f continentale	Kontinentalplattform f	piattaforma f continentale
—	4259 **continental slope**	talus continental	Kontinentalböschung	scarpa f continentale
°	4260 **continuous annealing furnace (or line)**	four m continu à recuire	Ofen m für kontinuierliches Glühen, Glühstrasse f	forno m di ricottura continua

continuous blast, s. *uniform blast*

	English	French	German	Italian
°	4261 **continuous blowing**	travail m continu	ununterbrochener Betrieb m	operazione f o marcia f continua
°	4262 **continuous casting**	coulée f continue	Strangguss m	colata f continua

continuous charge furnace, s. *self-feeding furnace*
continuous charging grate, s. *self-feeding grate*

	English	French	German	Italian
°	4262a **continuos cold mill train**	train m continu à froid	kontinuierliche Kaltzwalzstrasse f	treno m continuo a freddo
°	4263 **continuous concrete footing with reinforcements**	semelle f continue en béton avec parties armées	durchgehendes Betonfundament n mit Verstaerkungen	soletta f di fondazione continua in calcestruzzo
°	4264 **continuous conveyor**	carrousel m	Kreisbahn f	giostra f, convogliatore continuo
°	4265 **continuous current plant**	installation f à courant continu	Gleichstromanlage f	impianto m a corrente continua
^	4266 **continous distillation**	distillation f continue	stetige Destillation f	distillazione f continua
°	4267 **continuous furnace, continuous type furnace**	four m continu	Durchlampofen m, Ofen m mit ununterbrochenem Gang	forno m continuo

English	French	German	Italian
4268 continuous gas generation	production *f* de gaz continue	ununterbrochene Gaserzeugung *f*	produzione *f* continua di gas
4269 continuous mill	broyeur-continu	kontinuierlich arbeitender Kollergang *m*	molazza miscelatrice *f* continua, mulino continuo
4270 continuous pickling	décapage *m* continu	Dauerabbeizung *f*, Dauerdekapierung *f*	decapaggio *m* continuo
4270a continuous reheating furnace	four *m* poussant	Stossofen *m*	forno *m* a spingitoio
4271 continuous rod mill	train *m* à fil continu	kontinuierliches Drahtwalzwerk *n*	laminatoio *m* continuo per fili
4272 continuous rolling mill	laminoir *m* à mouvement continu	kontinuierliches Walzwerk *n*	laminatoio *m* continuo
4273 continuous sample	échantillon *m* par prélèvement	ununterbrochene Probeentnahme *f*	campione *m* per prelevamento continuo
4274 continuous sand plant	sablerie *f* continue	kontinuierliche Sandaufbereitung *f*	impianto *m* continuo per sabbie
4275 continuous stove	étuve *f* continue	Durchlauf-Trockenofen *m*	stufa *f* continua
4276 continuous tapping	coulée *f* continue (d'un appareil de fusion)	ununterbrochener Abstich *m*	colata *f* continua, spillatura *f* continua
4277 continuous transition	transition *f* continue	kontinuierlicher Übergang *m*	transizione *f* continua
4278 continuous welding	soudure *f* continue	Nahtschweissung *f*	saldatura *f* continua
4279 continuous working	fonctionnement *m* continu	ununterbrochener Betrieb *m*	funzionemento *m* continuo
4280 contoured chaplet	support *m* de noyau de forme	Profil-Kernstütze *f*	sopporto *m* sagomato (o con piastra curvata)
4281 contour	courbe *f* de niveau	Niveaukurve *f*	curva *f* di livello
4281a contour shaping	formation *f* du modèle	Modellformung *f*	formazione *f* del modello
4282 to contract, to shrink	se contracter	sich zusammenziehen	ritirarsi
4283 contract for the supply of ore	contract *m* de livraison de minerais	Erzlieferungsvertrag *m*	contratto *m* di fornitura di minerali
4284 contraction	retrait *m*	Schwindmass *n*	ritiro *m*, contrazione *f*
4284a contraction allowance	double retrait	doppeltes Schwindmass	doppia contrazione *f* (o ritiro)
4285 contraction distortion	déformation *f* au retrait	Verzug *m* durch Schwindung	deformazione *f* da ritiro (o da contrazione)

contraction pipe, *s. pipe*

	English	French	German	Italian
° 4286	contraction rule	mètre *m* à retrait	Schwindmass - stab *m*	metro *m* per modellisti
° 4287	control	régulation *f*	Regulierung *f*	rasatura *f*, regolazione *f*
° 4288	control bevel gear	couple *m* d'engrenages coniques	Kegelradantrieb *m*	coppia *f* conica di comando
^ 4289	control hook-up	ensemble *m* des «preventers»	Kontrolleinrichtungen *f pl.*	complesso *m* dei preventers
° 4290	controlled atmosphere	atmosphère *f* contrôlée (ou artificielle)	Glühgasatmosphäre *f*, Schutzgasatmosphäre *f*	atmosfera *f* artificiale (o controllata)
° 4291	controlled atmosphere furnace	four *m* à atmosphère contrôlée	Schutzgasatmosphäreofen *m*	forno *m* ad atmosfera controllata (o artificiale)
° 4292	controlling the press	distribution *f* de la presse	Steuern *n* der Presse	distribuzione *f* della pressa
° 4293	convection current	courant *m* de convection	Konventionsstrom *m*	corrente di convezione
° 4294	conventional creep limit	limite *f* conventionnelle de fluage	konventionelle Kriechgrenze *f*	limite *m* convenzionale di scorrimento (viscos<
— 4295	convergence recorder	appareil enregistreur de l'affaissement du toit	Apparat *m* zum Registrieren der Firstensenkung	registratore *m* del cedimento del tetto
° 4296	conversion	conversion *f*	Frischen *n*	conversione *f*

to convert into steel, *s. to steel*

converted bar, *s. blister bar*

| ° 4297 | converted clay | argile *f* métamorphosée | umgewandelter Ton *m* | argilla *f* metamorfosata |

converted loam, *s. converted clay*

converted steel, *s. casehardening steel or blister steel*

° 4298	converter	convertisseur *m*	Konverter *m*, Birne *f*	convertitore *m*
° 4299	converter belly	calotte *f* du convertisseur	Konverterhals *m*	ventre *m* del convertitore
° 4300	converter bottom	moule *m* pour le fond de cornue	Birnenbodenform *f*	forma *f* per il fondo del convertitore
° 4301	converter lining	garnissage *m* de convertisseur	Konverterauskleidung *f*	rivestimento *m* del convertitore

English	French	German	Italian
4302 converter mouth	bec *m* de la cornue	Konverteröffnung *f*	bocca *f* del convertitore
4303 converter nose	bec *m* de cornue	Konverterschnauze *f*	becco *m* del convertitore
4304 converter process	procédé *m* au convertisseur	Birnenverfahren *n*	processo *m* di conversione
4305 converter projections	projections *f pl.* du convertisseur	Birnenauswurf *m*, Konverterauswurf *m*	proiezioni *f pl.* del convertitore
4306 converter shed or shop	halle *f* ou atelier *m* des convertisseurs	Birnenhalle *f*, Konverterhalle *f*	locale *m* dei convertitori
4307 converter stand	support des paliers du convertisseur	Birnenständer *m*	cavalletto *m* di sopporto del convertitore
4308 converter steel	acier *m* au convertisseur	Konverterstahl *m*	acciaio *m* al convertitore
converter support, *s. converter stand*			
4309 converting	affinage *m* au vent	Windfrischen *n*	affinaggio *m* al vento
4310 converting or cementing furnace	fourneau *m* convertisseur	Stahlofen *m*	forno *m* convertitore
4311 converting in large converters	travail *m* en grands convertisseurs	Grossbessemerei *f*	affinaggio *m* in grandi convertitori
4312 converting in small converters	travail *m* en petits convertisseurs	Kleinbessemerei *f*	affinaggio *m* in piccoli convertitori
converting process, *s. cementation process*			
convex crown, *s. convex roof*			
4313 convex roof	voûte *f* convexe	convexes Gewölbe *n*	volta *f* convessa
4313a conveyor furnace	four *m* à tapis	Förderbandofen *m*	forno *m* a nastro trasportatore
conveying, *s. transport*			
4314 conveying belt	bande transporteuse	Förderband *n*	nastro *m* trasportatore
4315 conveying of charge	transport *m* au gueulard	Gichtbeförderung *f*	trasporto *m* alla bocca
4316 conveying trough (shaking)	gouttière *f* transporteuse	Förderrinne *f*	canale *m* di trasporto, scivolo *m*, canalone *m*
4317 conveyor	transporteur *m*, convoyeur *m*	Transportvorrichtung *f*	trasportatore *m*, convogliatore *m*
4318 conveyor bucket	godet de convoyeur	Baggereimer *m*	tazza *f* del trasportatore

	English	French	German	Italian
— 4319	conveyor chain	chaîne f à godets	Förderkette f	catena f a tazze
— 4320	conveyor idlers	rouleaux m pl. de convoyeur	Förderbandrollen f pl.	rulli m pl del trasportatore
— 4321	conveyor jib	bras du convoyeur	Rutschausleger m	braccio m trasportatore
— 4322	conveyor-loader	convoyeur--chargeur m	Selbstlademaschine f	trasportatore-caricatore m
— 4323	conveyor trough	gouttière f à secousses, couloir m oscillant	Förderrinne f	trasportatorè m a scosse
— 4324	conveyorman	ouvrier m de transporteur	Fördererwärter m	addetto m al trasportatore
— 4325	cookeite	cookéite f	Cookeit m	cookeite f
∘ 4326	to cool	refroidir	abkühlen	raffreddare
— 4327	to cool the quartz	étonner le quartz	den Quarz abschrecken	granulare il quarzo
∘ 4328	cooled parts of the blast furnace	parties refroidies du haut-fourneau	gekühlte Teile m pl. des Hochofens	parti raffreddate dell'alto forno
∘ 4329	cooled tuyere	tuyère f refroidie (par circulation d'eau)	wassergekühlte Düse f, Kühldüse f	tubiera f od ugello m raffreddato (a circolazione d'acqua)
	cooled twyer, s. cooled tuyere			
∘ 4330	cooler	sécheur-refroidisseur m	Trockner m mit Kühlstrecke	essicatore m, raffreddatore
∘ 4331	cooling, refrigeration	refroidissement m, réfrigération f	Kühlung f, Abkühlung f	raffreddamento m, refrigerazione f
∘ 4331a	cooling bed	refroidisseur m	Kühlbett n	(letto) reffreddatore m
∘ 4332	cooling box, cooler	bâche f de refroidissement	Kühlkasten m	cassa f di raffreddamento
∘ 4333	cooling chamber	chambre f de refroidissement	Kühlkammer f, Kühler m	camera f refrigerante
∘ 4334	cooling crack	tapure f à froid	Kaltriss m; Spannungskaltriss m	cricca f da raffreddamento
∘ 4335	cooling curve	courbe f de refroidissement	Abkühlungskurve f	curva f di raffreddamento
∘ 4336	cooling device	appareil m réfrigérant	Kühlvorrichtung f	dispositivo m o sistema m di raffreddamento

		English	French	German	Italian
ᵓ	4337	cooling down	refroidissement *m*	Abkühlung *f*, Abkühlen *n*	raffreddamento *m*, refrigerazione
ᵓ	4338	cooling fin	toile *f* de refroidissement	Kühlblech *n*	aletta *f* (o bava *f)* di raffreddamento
ᵓ	4339	cooling method	mode *m* de refroidissement	Abkühlungsart *f*	modo *m* di raffreddamento
ᵓ	4340	cooling of furnace	refroidissement *m* du four	Ofenabkühlung *f*	raffreddamento *m* del forno
ᵓ	4341	cooling pond	bassin *m* de refroidissement	Kühlteich *m*	bacino *m* di refrigerazione
ᵓ	4342	cooling rate	,vitesse *f* de refroidissement	Abkühlungs-geschwindigkeit *f*	velocità *f* di raffreddamento
ᵓ	4343	cooling surface	surface *f* de refroidissement	Abkühlungsfläche *f*	superficie *f* di raffreddamento
ᵓ	4344	cooling tower	tour *f* de réfrigération	Kühlturm *m*	torre *f* di refrigerazione
ᵓ	4345	cooling trough, water tank	bâche *f* à eau, bassin *m* de refroidissement	Wasserkasten *m*, Kühltrog *m*	cassetta *f* d'acqua per raffreddamento
ᵓ	4346	cooling water	eau *m* de refroidissement	Kühlwasser *n*	acqua *f* di refrigerazione o raffreddamento
ᵓ	4347	cooling (with water circulation)	refroidissement (avec circulation d'eau)	Rückkühlung *f*	refrigerazione (a circolazione d'acqua)
		cope, *s. top part*			
ᵓ	4348	cope, lift	chapeau de châssis	Kastendeckel *m*	coperchio *m* (di staffa)
ᵓ	4348a	cope and drag pattern	modèle en deux parties	zweiteiliges Modell *n*	modello *m* in due parti
ᵓ	4349	cope box	châssis *m* de dessus	Oberkasten *m*	coperchio *m* (della staffa), staffa superiore
ᵓ	4350	copper	cuivre *m*	Kupfer *n*	rame *m*
		copper, *s. boiler*			
ᵓ	4351	copper-alloy	alliage *m* de cuivre	Kupferlegierung *f*	lega *f* di rame
		copper-base alloy, *s. copper alloy*			
—	4352	copper-bearing	cuprifère	kupferführend	cuprifero

		English	French	German	Italian
°	4353	copper (-bearing) steel	acier *m* au cuivre	Kupferstahl *m*	acciaio *m* al rame
		copper bit, *s. soldering-iron*			
		copper bolt, *s. soldering iron*			
°	4354	copper boiler	chaudière *f* en cuivre	Kupferkessel *m*	caldaia *f* di rame
°	4354a	copper clad steel	acier *m* cuivré	verkupfter Stahl *m*	acciaio *m* rivestito di rame
°	4355	copper-covered steel wire	fil *m* d'acier cuivré, fil d'acier chemisé	Kupferstahldraht *m*	filo *m* d'acciaio ramato
°	4356	copper-faced stereoplate	cliché-galvano *m*	verkupferte Stereotypplatte *f*	lastra *f* di stereotipia ramata
°	4357	copper-founder	fondeur *m* de cuivre	Rotgiesser *m*	fonditore *m* di ottone
		copper glance, *s. chalcocite*			
°	4357a	copper lead	cupro-plomb *m*	Bleibronze *f*	cupropiombo *m*
°	4358	copper matte	matte *f* de cuivre	Kupferstein *m*	matta *f* di rame, metallina *f* di rame
—	4359	copper nickel	nickéline *f*	Rotnickelkies *m*, Kupfernickel *n*	nichelina *f*
—	4360	copper pitch ore	chrysocolle *f*	Chrysokoll *m*	crisocolla *f*
°	4361	copper-plate	planche *f* (ou plaque) de cuivre	Kupferplatte *f*	lamiera *f* (o piastra o lamina) di rame
°	4362	copper plating	cuivrage *m*	Verkupferung *f*	ramatura *f*
		copper-precipitate, *s. shaped copper*			
°	4363	copper pyrite	chalcopyrite *f*, pyrite *f* cuivreuse	Kupferkies *m*	calcopirite *f*, pirite *f* ramifera
°	4364	copper-shell	coquille *f* galvanoplastique	Kupferniederschlag *m*	deposito *m* di rame
		copper steel, *s. copper-bearing steel*			
°	4365	copper turnings	tournure *f* de cuivre	Kupferdrehspan *m*	trucioli *m pl.* di rame, tornitura *f* di rame
—	4366	copper uranite	chalcocite *f*	Torbernit *m*, Kupferuranglimmer *m*	calcocite *f*, torbernite
°	4367	copper vitriol	chalcanthite *f*	Chalkanthit *n*	cianosio *m*, vetriolo *m* di rame
°	4368	copper wire	fil *m* de cuivre	Kupferdraht *m*	filo *m* di rame

	English	French	German	Italian
4369	copper wire gauze	toile *f* en fil de cuivre	Kupferdrahtnetz *n*	rete *f* in filo di rame
4370	copper's hook	crochet *m* à cercles	vierkantiger Fasshaken *m*	zappetta *f* per botti
	copperas, *s. ferrous sulphate*			
4371	coppered sheet iron	tôle *f* cuivrée	verkupfertes Blech *n*	lamiera *f* ramata
4372	copperplate	plaque *f* de cuivre	Kupferplatte *f*	lastra *f* di rame
	copperplate printing, *s. calcography*			
4373	coppered wire	fil *m* cuivré	Kupferdraht *m*	filo *m* ramato
4374	copperish	cuivré	verkupfert	ramato
4375	copper smith	chaudronnier *m* en cuivre	Kupferschmied *m*	calderaio *m*
4376	coprolith	coprolite *m*	Koprolith *m*	coprolito *m*
4377	copying lathe	tour *m* à copier	Formdrehbank *f*	tornio *m* per copiare
4378	coralline facies	faciès *m* coralligène	koralligene Fazies *f*	«facies» *f* corallina
4379	cordite	cordite *f*	Kordit *n*	cordite *f*
4380	cordierite	cordiérite *f*	Cordierit *m*	cordierite *f*
4381	cordylite	cordylite *f*	Kordylit *m*	cordilite *f*
4382	to core	carotter	kernbohren	carotare
4383	core out a casting	noyauter une pièce	Gussstück mit Kernen konstruieren	preparare le parti di un getto da ottenere con anime
4384	core	noyau *m*	Kern *m*, Formkern *m*	anima *f*
4385	core, dry sand core	noyau *m* en sable étuvé	getrockneter Kern *m*	anima *f* a secco
4386	core	carotte *f*	Bohrkern *m*	carota *f*
4387	core assembly	montage *m* d'assemblage	Kernmontagelehre *f*	ramolaggio *m*
	core bar, *s. core iron*			
4388	core barrel, core iron	lanterne *f* (ou armature *f*) du noyau	Kerneisen *n*, Kernständer, Luftspindel *f*	lanterna *f* (o armatura *f*) per anime

		English	French	German	Italian
—	4389	core barrel	tube *m* carottier	Kernrohr *n*	carotiere *m*, tubo carotiere
○	4390	core barrel	arbre *m* à noyau	Kernspindel *f*	armatura *f* dell'anima
○	4391	core bedding frame	cadre de démoulage, châssis de démoulage	Kernbettrahmen *m*	telaio *m* di sformatura, quadro *m* di sformatura
○	4392	core binder, core binding material	agglomérant *m* (pour noyaux)	Trockensandbinder *m*	agglomerante *m* per anime
—	4393	core bit	couronne de sondage, trépan *m* carottier	Bohrkrone *f*, Kernstossbohrer *m*	corona *f*, punta a corona, trivella a tubo, corona di sondaggio
○	4394	core blower, core blowing machine	machine *f* à souffler les noyaux	Kernblasmaschine *f*	soffiatrice *f* per anime, macchina per soffiare le anime
—	4395	core boring	carottage *m*	Kernbohrung *f*	carotaggio *m*
○	4396	core box	boîte *f* à noyaux	Kernkasten *m*	cassa *f* (o armatura *f*) per anima
○	4397	core box for blowing	boîte *f* à souffler	Kernschiessmaschine *f*	cassa *f* (o armatura) d'anima per anime soffiate
○	4398	core carrier	coquille *f* de séchage	Trockenschale *f*	conchiglia d'essicazione
○	4399	core carrier plate	plaque *f* de séchage	Trockenplatte *f*	piastra *f* d'essicazione
—	4400	core catcher	arrache-carotte *m*	Kernbrecher *m*, Kernfangring *m*	strappa-carote *m*
—	4401	core cutter head	tête *f* de carottier	Kernbohrkopf *m*	scarpa *f* (o scalpello *m*) di un carotiere
○	4402	core diameter	fil *m* pour électrodes	Elektrodendraht *m*	filo *m* per elettrodi
○	4403	core drawback	démouleur de noyau	Kernzug *m*	estrattore d'anima
○	4404	core drier	séchoir de noyaux	Kerntrockner *m*	essicatoio *m* d'anime
—	4405	core drill	couronne *f* de sondage, carotteur *m*	Bohrkrone *f*, Bohrkran *m*, Kernapparat *m*	corona *f* di trivellazione, trivella *f* a tubo, sonda *f* campionatrice
—	4406	core drilling	forage *m* à carottage	Kernbohren *n*	trivellazione *f* (o sondaggio *m*) per carotagg
○	4407	core drying	cuire un noyau	einen Kern trocknen	cuocere un anima
○	4408	core drying oven	four *m* à sécher les noyaux	Kerntrockenofen *m*	forno *m* di essicazione delle anime

	English	French	German	Italian
4409	core drying stove	étuve f à noyaux	Kerntrockenofen m	stufa f per anime
4410	core extractor	presse-carotte m, arrache-carotte m	Kernzieher. m, Kernbohrer m	estrattore m per carote
4411	core fork	pince f à noyau	Kerngabel f	pinzetta f per anima
4412	core frame, core barrel	armature f du noyau	Kerngerippe n	armatura f (o cassa) dell'anima
4413	core grid	armature f du noyau	Armierung f, Kerneisen n	armatura f dell'anima
4414	core hole	trou m pour carottage	Kernbohrung f	foro m per carotaggio
4415	core hole	trou m du noyau	Kerngussloch n	foro m (di getto) formato dall'anima
4416	core interlocking	système m asservi	Folgesteuerung f, Programmsteuerung f	servocomando m, congegno di sicurezza
4417	core iron, core barrel	armature f de fer, tige f de noyau	Kerneisen n, Eiseneinlage f	lanterna f
4418	core jig	montage m de rectification	Kernlehre f	sagoma f di controllo delle anime
4419	core lathe	tour m à noyaux	Kerndrehlade f, Kerndrehbank f	tornio m per anime
	core lifter, s. core extractor			
4420	core line sheave	poulie f sur puits pour câble carottier	auf dem Schachte Kernkabelscheibe f	puleggia f sul pozzo per cavo carotaggio
4421	core maker, pattern maker	ouvrier m noyauteur	Kernarbeiter m, Kernmacher m	animista m, fabbricante d'anime
4422	core making machine, core moulding machine	machine f à noyauter. noyauteuse f	Kernformmaschine f	formatrice f per anime, macchina f per formare le anime
4423	core mark	portée de noyau	Kernmarke f	portata f d'anima
4424	core moulding	moulage des noyaux	Kernformen n	formatura f di anime
4425	core moulding shop	atelier à noyaux	Kernformerei, Kernmacherei f	officina per le anime, reparto m animisti
4426	core of anticline	noyau m anticlinal	Sattelkern m	sella f di anticlinale
4427	core of syncline	noyau m synclinal	Synklinalkern m	sella f di sinclinále

		English	French	German	Italian
o	4428	core of the fracture	noyau *m* de cassure	Kern *m* des Bruch-querschnitts	nocciolo *m* della frattura
o	4429	core oven	étuve *f* à noyaux	Kernofen *m*	forno *m* per anime
o	4430	core plate	porte-noyaux *m*, plaque *f* à noyaux	Kernformwanne *f*, Kernformplatte *f*	piastra-sostegno *f* anime, vassoio *m* per anim
o	4431	core print	portée *f* (de modèle)	Kernmarke *f*	portata d'anima
o	4432	core puller	démouleur *m* de noyau	Kernzug *m*	estrattore *m* d'anima
—	4433	core pusher plunger	bouchon *m* du carottier	Kernbohrerpfropfen *m*	tappo del carotiere
—	4434	core receiving barrel	tube *m* porte-carotte intérieur	Innenkernrohr *n*	tubo *m* porta-carota interno
—	4435	core recovery	récupération *f* de carotte	Kerngewinnung *f*	estrazione *f* (o recupero *m*) di carote
o	4436	core recess or groove	rainure *f* de tuyau	Kerneinschnürung *f*	incavo *m* dell'anima
o	4437	core regeneration	régénération *f* du coeur	Kernregeneration *f*	rigenerazione *f* del nucleo
		core relieving, *s. die coating*			
—	4438	core sample	carotte *f*	Bohrkern *m*	carota *f*
—	4439	core sample	échantillon *m* de carotte	Kernprobe *f*	campione *m* di carota
o	4440	core sand	sable *m* à noyaux	Kernsand *m*	sabbia *f* (o terra *f*) per anime
o	4441	core setting	remmoulage *m*	Kerneinlegen *n*	ramolaggio *m*
o	4442	core setting jig	gabarit *m* de remmoulage	Kerneinlegelehre *f*	sagoma *f* di controllo per anime composte
o	4443	core shift	déplacement des noyaux	Kernverschiebung *f*	spostamento *m* di anime
o	4444	core shooter	machine *f* à tirer les noyaux	Kernschiessmaschine *f*	macchina per tirare le anime
o	4445	core shooting, to shoot a core	tirer un noyau	einem Kern schiessen	tirare un anima
o	4446	core shop	noyautage *m*	Kernmacherei *f*	animisteria *f*
o	4447	core spindle	arbre *m* à noyau	Kernspindel *f*	armatura *f* dell'anima, lanterna *f* per anime

	English	French	German	Italian
4448	core stove	étuve f à noyaux	Kerntrockner m	stufa f per anime
4449	core strenght	résistance f à noyau	Kernwiderstand m	resistenza f a cuore
4450	core strickle, strickle board	trousse f à noyau	Kernschablone f	sagoma f per anima
4451	core structure	structure f à coeur	Kerngefüge n	struttura f nel cuore o nucleo
4452	core templet	trousse f à noyau	Kernschablone f	sagoma f per anima
4453	core tube trimmer shoe	sabot m du tube porte-carotte	Kernrohrschuh m	scarpa f del tubo portacarota
4454	core welding wire	baguette f à noyau	Seelenschweissdraht m	filo m da saldare con anima
	core wire, s. filler wire			
4455	core-drill	forer par outil creux	mit dem Hohlbohrer bohren	forare con utensile cavo
4455a	cored bar	barre f à noyau fusible	Stab m mit Schmelz-kern	barra f ad anima fusibile
4456	cored carbon	charbon m à mèche	Kernkohle f	carbone m a miccia
4457	cored interval	intervalle carotté	Kernstrecke f	intervallo m carotato
4458	cored work	fonte f creuse	Hohlblock m	getto m cavo, getto con cavità inferiore
4459	coreless induction furnace	four m électrique à induction à creuset	Induktions-Tiegelofen m	forno m a induzione a crogiolo (o a sega canale)
4460	coremaker	noyauteur m	Kernmacher m	animista m
4461	coremaking	noyautage m	Kernherstellung f	formatura f d'anime
4462	coreprint	portée f de modèle	Kernmarke f	portata f (del modello), portata d'anima
4463	cores (of one mould)	noyautage m	Kernaufbau m	anime f pl.
	coring, s. core barrel			
4463a	coring	microségrégation f	Mikroseigerung f	microsegregazione f
4464	coring	carottage m	Kerngewinnung f	carotaggio m
4465	coring up, coring	noyautage m	Kernherstellung f	formatura f delle anime
4466	coring vessel	boîte f à carotte	Kernkasten m	scatola f per carote
4467	cork	bouchon m	Kork m	turacciolo m o tappo m (di sughero)
4468	cork borer	drille f à bouchons	Korkbohrer m	foratappi m

	English	French	German	Italian
°	4469 **cork knife**	couteau *m* à liège	Korkmesser *n*	coltello *m* per tappi di sughero
°	4470 **cork pliers**	pince *f* à liège	Korkzange *f*	tenaglia *f* per tappi di sughero
°	4471 **cork plate**	plaque *f* en liège	Korkplatte *f*	lastra *f* di sughero
°	4472 **cork presser**	presse *f* à bouchons	Korkpresse *f*	pressa *f* per tappi di sughero
^	4473 **cork screwed tubing**	tubage *m* déformé en tire-bouchon		«tubing» deformato a cavaturaccioli
°	4474 **cork-sheet**	planche *f* de liège	Korkplatte *f*	lastra *f* di sughero
—	4475 **corkite**	corkite *f*	Corkit *m*	corkite *f*
—	4476 **cornelian**	cornaline *f*	Karneol *m*	cornalina *f*
—	4477 **cornetite**	cornétite *f*	Cornetit *m*	corniola *f*, calcedonio
	4478 **corner**	angle *m*	Ecke *f*	angolo *m*
°	4479 **corner connection**	liaison *f* d'angle	Winkelverbindung *f*	attacco *m* ad angolo
°	4480 **corner pillar**	pilier *m* d'angle	Eckpfeiler *m*	pilastro *m* (d'angolo)
	corner seam, *s. fillet weld in a corner joint*			
°	4481 **corner shaling, corner shelling,**	peau *f*, coquille *f* d'oeuf	Schale *f*, Haut *f*	segregazione *f*, trasudamento *m*
	corner weld, *s. fillet weld in a corner*			
°	4482 **cornflower blue**	bleu-violacé	kornblau	azzurro-scuro
°	4483 **cornice in prefabricated elements**	corniche *f* en éléments préfabriqués	Gesims *n* aus vorgefertigten Teilen	gronda *f* in elementi prefabbricati
°	4484 **Cornish boiler**	chaudière *f* de Cornouailles	Cornwallkessel *m*, Einflammrohrkessel *m*	caldaia *f* di Cornovaglia
—	4485 **cornubianite**	cornubianite *f*	Cornubianit *m*	cornubianite *f*
—	4486 **cornwallite**	cornwallite *f*	Cornwallit *m*	cornwallite *f*
—	4487 **coronadite**	coronadite *f*	Coronadit *m*	coronadite *f*
	to corrode, *s. to etch*			

	English	French	German	Italian
—	4488 corroded crystal, brotocrystal	cristal *m* corrodé	korrodierter Kristall *m*	cristallo *m* corrose
o	4489 corroding brittleness	décapage *m*, fragilité de corrosion	Beizbrüchigkeit *f*	fragilità *f* per corrosione
o	4490 corroding proof	échantillon *m* obtenu par corrosion	Ätzprobe *f*	campione *m* ottenuto con attacco acido
o	4490a corronizing	corronisation *f*	Corronisierung *f*	corronizzazione *f*
o	4491 corrosion	corrosion *f*	Korrosion *f*	corrosione *f*
o	4492 corrosion-resisting steel	acier *m* résistant à la corrosion	nichtrostender Stahl *m*	acciaio *m* resistente alla corrosione
o	4493 corrugated bars for reinforcing concrete	ronds *m pl.* crénelés	geriffeltes Betoneisen *n*	tondi *m pl.* scanalati
o	4494 corrugated flue	foyer *m* ondulé	Wellherd *m*	focolare *m* ondulato

corrugated galvanized sheet iron, *s. galvanized corrugated sheet*

	English	French	German	Italian
o	4495 corrugated friction	tube de repêchage à frottement à corps déformé		pescatore *m* a frizione a corpo deformato
o	4496 corrugated iron	tôle *f* ondulée	Wellblech *n*	lamiera *f* ondulata

corrugated plate, *s. corrugated iron*

	English	French	German	Italian
o	4497 corrugated roll	cylindre *m* cannelé	Riffelwalze *f*	cilindro *m* scanalato
o	4498 corrugated sheet, corrugated (sheet) iron	tôle *f* ondulée (ou ridée)	Wellblech *n*	lamiera *f* ondulata
o	4499 corrugated sheet duraluminum	tôle *f* ondulée de duralumin	Duralwellblech *n*	lamiera *f* ondulata di duralluminio
o	4500 corrugated (sheet) iron for joists	tôle *f* ondulée pour poutres	Trägerwellblech *n*	lamiera *f* ondulata per sostegni
o	4501 corrugated sheet zinc	feuille *f* de zinc ondulée	Zinkwellblech *n*	lamiera *f* di zinco ondulata

corrugated sheets, *s. corrugated sheet iron*

	English	French	German	Italian
o	4502 corrugated shutter iron	tôle *f* ondulée à persiennes	Jalousiewellblech *n*	lamiera *f* ondulata per persiane
o	4503 corrugated surface	surface *f* gondolée (ou ondulée)	wellige Oberfläche *f*	superficie *f* ondulata
—	4504 corsite	corsite *f*	Corsit *m*	corsite *f*
—	4505 corundellite	corundellite *f*	Corundellit *m*	margarite *f*, corundellite *f*

	English	French	German	Italian
− 4506	corundophilite	corundophyllite *f*	Korundophilit *m*	corundofillite *f*
− 4507	corundum	corindon *m*	Korund *m*	corindone *m*
− 4508	corve	chien *m* de mine, berline	Förderwagen *m*	vagoncino *m*
− 4509	corver	réparateur *m* de berlines	Wagenausbesserer *m*	riparatore *m* di vagoncini
− 4510	cosalite	cosalite *f*	Cosalit *m*	cosalite *f*
○ 4511	coslettising	coslettisation *f*	Coslettisierung *f*	coslettizzazione
− 4512	cossyrite	cossyrite *f*	Cossyrit *m*	cossirite *f*
○ 4513	cost of analysis	frais *m pl.* d'analyse	Analysenkosten *pl.*	spese *f pl.* d'analisi
	cost of metal at the spout, *s. molten metal cost*			
○ 4514	cost of power	prix *m* de revient de la force motrice	Kosten *pl.* der Treibkraft	costo della forza motrice
○ 4515	cost of producing, prime cost	prix *m* de revient	Herstellungskosten *pl.*,Gestehungspreis	costo di produzione, prezzo di costo
− 4516	cost of winning	frais *m pl.* d'exploitation	Gewinnungskosten *pl.*	costi *m pl.* d'estrazione
4517	cost price	prix *m* d'achat	Ankaufspreis *m*	prezzo *m* d'acquisto
○ 4518	constancy of temperature	constance *f* de la température de la solution	Temperaturkonstanz *f* der Lösung	costanza *f* di temperatura della soluzione
− 4519	costeaning	prospection *f*	Schürfen *n*	ricerca *f* (mineraria) a mezzo pozzetti
	costs of fettling, *s. costs of relining the furnace (with refractory material)*.			
○ 4520	costs of relining the furnace, costs of repairs or fettling	frais *m pl.* de garnissage	Zustellungskosten *pl.*	spese *f pl.* di rivestimento o di rifacimento (del forno)
○ 4521	cotter	clavette *f*	Keil *m*	chiavetta *f* (trasversale)
○ 4522	cotter bolt, eye bolt and key, joint bolt	boulon *m* à clavette, boulon *m* à goupille	Schliessbolzen *m*, Keilbolzen *m*	bullone *m* a chiavetta
˄ 4523	cottered chain	chaîne *f* à clavette	versplintete Kette *f*	catena *f* a chiavetta
○ 4524	cotton-covered wire	fil *m* sous coton, fil à guipage en coton	Baumwolldraht *m*	filo *m* sotto cotone, filo rivestito di cotone

English	French	German	Italian
4525 **cotunnite**	cotunnite *f*	Cotunnit *m*	cotunnite *f*
couch, *s. rubber cap*			
coulometer, *s. voltameter*			
4526 **counter**	costresse *f*	Teilstrecke *f*	livello *m* intermedio
4527 **counter chute**	cheminée *f* à charbon, cheminée à minerai	Stürzrolle *f*, Förderrolle *f*	scivolo *m* (o piano inclinato) per carbone (o minerali)
4528 **counter-current boiler, down-flue boiler**	chaudière *f* à contre-courant, chaudière *f* à tubes réchauffeurs inférieurs	Gegenstromkessel *m*	caldaia *f* a corrente invertita, caldaia a tubi di riscaldamento inferiori (o a controcorrente)
4529 **counterflush drilling**	forage avec circulation renversée	Bohrung *f* mit Verkehrtspülung	perforazione *f* con circolazione inversa
4530 **counterflush-gangway**	galerie costresse *f*	Teilstrecke *f*	galleria *f* di livello
4531 **counterflush-level**	niveau intermédiaire	Zwischensohle *f*	livello *m* intermedio
4532 **counterflush-lode**	filon croiseur	Quergang *m*	filone *m* trasversale
4533 **counterflow furnace**	four *m* à contre-courant	Gegensaugzugofen *m*	forno *m* a tiraggio rovesciato
4533a **counterlode.**	filon *m* transversal	übersetzender Gang *m*	vena *f* trasversale
4534 **to countermould**	contre-mouler	mehrfachformen	formare a ripetere
4535 **countermoulding**	contre-moulage *m*	Mehrfachformerei *f*	formatura *f* a ripetere
4536 **counterpoise**	contre-poids *m*	Gegengewicht *n*	contrappeso *m*
4537 **countersink bit**	fraise *f* plate	Versenker *m* (flacher spitziger Kopf)	accecatoio *m* piatto, presa *f* per svasatura conica
4538 **countersink bit (flat head and obtuse point)**	fraise *f* plate camuse	Versenker *m* (flacher stumpfer Kopf)	accecatoio *m* piatto camoscio
countersink flat head, *s. countersink bit*			
4539 **counter-sunk bolt**	boulon *m* noyé	versenkter Bolzen *m*	bullone *m* con testa fresata o accecata
4540 **countersunk chequered head nail**	pointe *f* à tête plate fraisée	Nagel *m* mit versenktem kariertem Kopf	punta *f* a testa fresata quadrigliata
4541 **countersunk or flush rivet**	rivet *m* noyé, rivet *m* à tête fraisée	versenkter Niet *m*	chiodo *m* a testa fresata
4542 **counting mechanism, counter**	compteur *m*	Zählwerk *n*	contatore *m*

	English	French	German	Italian
—	4543 **contour map**	carte ƒ d'isobathes	Streichlinienkarte ƒ	carta ƒ delle isobate
—	4544 **country(-rock), adjoining-rock**	roche ƒ encaissante, roche ƒ des parois	Nebengestein n	roccia ƒ delle pareti, roccia ƒ incassante
o	4545 **to couple**	accoupler	kuppeln	accoppiare
^	4546 **to couple**	mettre en batterie	zusammenstellen	avvitare (tubi)
o	4547 **couple (of forces)**	couple ƒ (de forces)	Kräftepaar n	coppia ƒ di forze
o	4548 **coupled tuyeres**	tuyères jumelées	Wechseldüsen ƒ pl.	ugelli accopiati (o doppi)
o	4549 **coupling, coupling box**	manchon m d'ac-couplement	Kupplungsmuffe ƒ	manicotto m (d'accop-piamento)

coupling box, s'. *coupling*

	English	French	German	Italian
o	4550 **coupling spindle**	arbre m d'accouple-ment	Kupplungsspindel ƒ	albero m d'accoppia-mento
o	4551 **couplings**	accouplements m pl.	Kupplungen ƒ pl.	giunti, innesti, giunti m p di accoppiamento
o	4551a **coupon**	lingot-éprouvette m	Probeblock m	provetta ƒ grezza, saggio m
—	4552 **course**	veine ƒ, filon m	Erzgang m, Lage ƒ, Schicht ƒ	vena ƒ, filone m, strato m
o	4553 **course of brickwork**	assise ƒ de briques	Steinschicht ƒ	corso m di mattoni
—	4554 **course of outcrop, line of outcrop**	direction ƒ de l'affleurement	Ausstrich m	direzione ƒ dell'affiora-mento
o	4555 **course of rays** pl.	trajet m des rayons	Strahlengang m	direzione ƒ dei raggi
o	4556 **coursing**	aménagement m du courant d'air	Wetterstromverteilung ƒ mittels Wetterscheider	regolazione ƒ della corrente d'aria
o	4556a **couverture**	scorie ƒ de protection	Schutzschlacke ƒ	scoria ƒ di protezione
—	4557 **covellite**	covelline ƒ	Covellin m	covellite ƒ
o	4558 **to cover, to close**	fermer, couvrir	abdecken	coprire
o	4559 **to cover the fire, to bank the fire**	coucher les feux, couvrir les feux	das Feuer (zu)decken, das Feuer aufdämmen	coprire il fuoco, mette-re il fuoco indietro
o	4560 **to cover with cloth**	recouvrir de drap	mit Tuch überziehen	coprire con tela
o	4561 **to cover with lead**	plomber	verbleien	piombare, impiombare
o	4562 **cover**	couvercle m	Deckel m	coperchio m

English	French	German	Italian

4563 cover (protecting the mould holes) — couvre-jet *m* — Trichterabdeckung *f* — copri-colata *m*

4564 cover dies — étampes *f pl.* de couverts — Besteckstanzen *f pl.* — matrici *f pl.* per posaterie

cover glass, *s. plain glass*

cover strip, *s. top flange plate*

4565 covered and braided wire — fil *m* guipé et tressé — umsponnener und umklöppelter Draht *m* — filo *m* avvolto e intrecciato ·

4566 covered boiler plant — installation *f* de chaudières sous toit — überdachte Kesselanlage *f* — impianto *m* coperto di caldaie

4567 covered finery — foyer *m* comtois couvert — bedecktes Frischfeuer *n* — fuoco *m* d'affinaggio chiuso

4568 covered hearth — creuset *m* couvert — verdeckter Herd *m* — crogiolo *m* chiuso

4569 covered wire — fil *m* couvert, fil guipé — umsponnener Draht *m*, besponnener Draht *m* — filo *m* rivestito, filo *m* ricoperto

4570 covering — couverture *f* — Deckung *f* — copertura *f*

4571 covering — enveloppe *f*, gaine *f* — Umhüllung *f*, Mantel *m* — mantello *m*, camicia *f*, rivestimento *m*

4572 covering flux — couverte *f* — Abdeckmittel *n* — copertura *f*, fondente *m* di copertura

4572a covering power, hiding power — pouvoir *m* couvrant — Streuvermögen *n* — potere *m* coprente, coprenza

4573 covite — covite *f* — Covit *m* — covite *f*

4574 cow hair — poil *m* de vache — Kuhhaar *n* — pelo *m* di vacca

4575 Cowper's stove — appareil *m* à air chaud de Cowper — Winderhitzer *m* nach Cowper — stufa *f* ad aria calda Cowper

4576 coyote hole — fourneau *m* de mine — Sprengkammer *f* — camera *f* (o fornello) di mina

4577 coyoting — gaspillage *m* du gisement — Raubbau *m* — sfruttamento *m* irrazionale del giacimento

C.P. = *cement points*

C.P.JOB = *cementing (through) perforation JOB*

C.P.M. = *cycles per minute*

C.P.S. = *cycles per second*

	English	French	German	Italian
o	4578 crab	chariot *m* de pont-roulant	Laufkatze *f*	carrello-argano *m*, argano *m* a cavalletto
^	4579 to crack	cracker	cracken	ridurre per distillazione, sottoporre a piroscissione
o	4580 crack	tapure *f*	Bruch *m*	crepa *f*, incrinatura *f*
—	4581 crack	crevasse *f*, fissure *f*	Sprung *m*	fessura *f*
o	4582 crack detection	détection *f* de craquelure	Untersuchung *f* auf Anrisse	rilevamento *m* di fessura (o crepa)
	crack impregnation test, *s. paraffine test*			
^	4583 crack per pass	taux *m* de craquage	Koeffizient *m* der Transformation durch Kracken	coefficente *m* di trasformazione cracking
o	4584 cracked	crevassé, fissuré	rissig	screpolato, incrinato
	cracked back, *s: broken back*			
o	4584a cracked edge	fissure *f* d'angle	Querriss *m*	incrinatura *f* ai bordi
^	4585 cracked gasoline	essence de craquage	Krackbenzin *n*	benzina *f* di cracking
—	4586 cracker	cylindre *m* broyeur	Brechwalze *f*	cilindro *m* frantumatore
o	4586a cracker core	crayon *m* de masselotte	Luftkern *m*	animetta *f* di materozza atmosferica
o	4587 cracking	fissuration *f*	Rissebildung *f*	incrinatura *f*, criccatura
^	4588 cracking	craquage *m*	Kracking *n*, Abspaltung *f*	cracking, piroscissione
^	4589 cracking process	procédé *m* de craquage	Krackprozess *m*	processo *m* di cracking
—	4590 cradle	berceau *m*, crible *m* laveur	Wiege *f*	vaglio *m* lavatore
o	4591 cramp	crampon *m*, crampe	Klammer *f*, Klampe *f*	grappa *f*, briglia *f*
—	4592 cramp	massif *m*	Pfeiler *m*	pilastro *m* di minerale
—	4593 cranch	massif *m* de minerai	Erzpfeiler *m*	pilastro *m* di minerale
—	4594 crandallite	crandallite *f*	Crandallit *m*	crandallite *f*
o	4595 crane beam	volée *f*, traverse *f* de grue	Kranbalken *m*	bilanciere *m*
—	4596 crane crab	chariot *m* de pont	Kranlaufkatze *f*	carrello *m* di gru a ponte
o	4597 crane for the reheating furnace, soaking pit crane	grue *f* à lingots pour chaufferie	Tiefofenkran *m*, Blockziehkran *m*	gru *f* scorrevole per forni di riscaldo

		English	French	German	Italian
o	4598	crane hook	crochet m de suspension de la grue	Kranhaken m	gancio m di sospensione della gru
o	4599	crane ladle	poche f de grue	Kranpfanne f	siviera f sospesa a gru
o	4600	crane magnet	aimant m de grue	Kranmagnet m	magnete m da gru
o	4601	crane pneumatic rammer	damoir m à grue à air comprimé	Kranpressluftstampfer m	piletta f pneumatica servita da gru
o	4602	crane with grab gear	grue f dragueuse, grue à mâchoires ou à griffe	Greifkran m	gru f con scavatore automatico
o	4603	crane with special gripping device	grue f avec poinçon et pince d'accrochage	Fingerkran m	gru f con tenaglia da presa
o	4604	craneman	grutier m	Kranmann m	gruista m
o	4605	crank	axe m à manivelle	Triebradachse f	asse m a manovella
o	4606	crank gear	commande f par manivelle	Kurbeltrieb m	manovellismo m
o	4607	crank guard	plaque f de garde, couvre-manivelle, capuchon, gaîne f	Kurbelschutzhaube f	involucro m (o piastra f) di protezione, coperchio m
o	4608	crank pin	bouton m de manivelle, maneton m, tourillon m	Kurbelzapfen m	perno m di biella, bottone m di manovella
o	4609	crankaxle	vilebrequin m	Kurbel f	asse m a manovella
o	4610	crankshaft	vilebrequin m	Kurbelwelle f	albero m a gomiti
--	4611	crater crack	crevasse f du cratère	Kraterriss m	cricca f al cratere
—	4612	crawler mounted	chenillé, sur chenilles	Raupenkettenantrieb	cingolato m

crazing, s. mould crack

cre, s. corrosion resistant

—	4613	crednerite	crednérite f	Crednerit m	crednerite f
—	4614	creedite	créédite f	Creedit m	creedite f
o	4615	creep	fluage m	Kriechen n	deformazione f viscosa, scorrimento m

English	French	German	Italian
° 4616 **creep limit**	limite *f* de fluage	Kriechgrenze **f**	limite *m* di scorrimento viscoso
° 4616a **creep rate (or speed)**	vitesse *f* de fluage	Kriechgeschwindig-keit *f*	velocità *f* di scorrimento
° 4617 **creep resistance**	résistance *f* au fluage	Dauerstandfestigkeit	resistenza *f* allo scorrimento
° 4618 **creep rupture**	résistance au fluage pour une longue durée	Zeitstandfestigkeit	resistenza *f* allo scorrimento a lunga durata
° 4619 **creep strength**	résistance *f* au fluage	Kriechfestigkeit *f*, Dauerstandfestigkeit	resistenza *f* allo scorrimento viscoso
° 4619a **creep stress**	charge *f* de fluage	Kriechlast *f*	carico *m* di scorrimento
— 4620 **creeper**	vis *f* sans fin	Förderschnecke *f*	vite *f* senza fine.
— 4621 **creeper chain**	chaîne *f* sans fin	endlose Kette *f*	catena *f* senza fine
— 4622 **creeping**	boursouflement *m* du sol	Sohlenauftrieb *m*, Absinken *n* der Tagesoberfläche *f*, Rutschung *f*	rigonfiamento *m* del suolo, slittamento *m* del suolo, smottamento *m*, franamento *m* del suolo
° 4623 **creeping limit**	limite d'écoulement, limite *f* de fluage	Dauerstandfestigkeit *f*, Fliessgrenze *f*	limite *m* di scorrimento o di viscosità
° 4624 **creeping test**	essai *m* de fluage	Dauerstandversuch *m*, Kriechfestigkeits-pruefung *f*	prova *f* di scorrimento viscoso
° 4624a **cressing**	réduction *f* de section	Querschnittsabnahme *f*	rastremazione *f* alle e-stremità
— 4625 **crestline**	arête *f* anticlinale	Gewölbelinie *f*, Sattellinie *f*	cerniera *f* della piega an-ticlinale
— 4626 **Cretaceous, Cretaceous period, Cretaceous system**	crétacé *m*, période crétacée, système *m* crétacé	Kreideformation *f*, Quaderformation *f*	cretaceo *m*, sistema *f* cretaceo, periodo *m* cretaceo
° 4627 **crevice corrosion**	corrosion *f* fissu-rante	Risskorrosion *f*	corrosione *f* per fessurazione
— 4628 **crevice-water**	eau *m* de diaclases	Kluftwasser *n*	acqua *f* di diaclasi
— 4629 **crib-bed**	cadre *m* porteur ou de base	Tragkranz *m*	quadro portante (o di base)
— 4630 **crib-ring**	cadre *m* du puits	Schachtgeviert *n*	quadro *m* del pozzo
— 4631 **crib tubing**	cuvelage *m* en bois circulaire	hölzerne Küvelage *f*	armamento (o rivestimento) in legno circolare
— 4632 **cribbed**	boisé par cadres iointifs	schrotgezimmert	rivestito (o armato) in legno
— 4633 **cribbed chute**	cheminée *f* de fagotage	Rolloch *n* mit Schrotzimmerung	scivolo *m* con rivestimento in legno

	English	French	German	Italian
4634	cribbing	montage *m* des piles des bois, boisage *m* du puits en càdres jointifs	Holzschrank- zimmerung *f*, Vollschrotzimmerung *f*	montaggio *m* dei pali di legno, armatura *f* del pozzo
4635	cribwork	cadre *m* du puits, pilier de bois	Schachtgeviert *n*, Geviert *n*, Holzschrank *m*	struttura *f* (o puntelli) in legno, quadro *m* del pozzo
4636	crichtonite	crichtonite *f*	Crichtonit *m*	crichtonite *f*
4637	crinanite	crinanite *f*	Crinanit *m*	crinanite *f*
4638	crinoidal limestone	calcaire *m* à crinoïdes	Crinoidenkalk	calcare *m* a crinoidi
4639	crinoids	crinoïdes *m pl.*	Crinoiden	crinoidi *m pl.*
4640	crippling strain	effort *m* de flambage	Knickbeanspruchung *f*	sollecitazione *f* al carico di punta
4641	crisscross	croisé	gekreutzt	incrociato
4642	cristobalite	cristobalite *f*	Cristobalit *m*	cristobalite *f*
4642a	critical ageing	vieillissement *m* total	vollständige Alterung *f*	invecchiamento *m* completo
4643	critical flow	écoulement *m* critique	kritischer Fluss *m*	scorrimento *m* (o flusso) critico
4644	critical heat	chaleur *f* critique	Umwandlungswärme *f*	calore *m* critico
4645	critical point	point *m* critique	Umwandlungspunkt *m*	punto *m* critico
4646	critical pressure	pression *f* critique	kritischer Druck *m*	pressione *f* critica
4647	critical range	durée *f* critique	Umwandlungsdauer *f*	intervallo *m* critico
4648	critical solidification rate	vitesse *f* critique de solidification	kritische Erstarrungs- geschwindigkeit *f*	velocità *f* critica di solidificazione
4649	critical speed of hardening	vitesse *f* critique de trempe	kritische Härtungs- geschwindigkeit *f*	velocità *f* critica di tempera
4650	critical temperature	température *f* critique	kritische Temperatur *f*	temperatura *f* critica
4651	crocidolite, blue asbestos	crocidolite *f*	blauer Asbest (od. Amiant),Bergflachs	crocidolite *f*
4651a	crocodile press	cingleur *m* à levier	Luppenquetsche *f*	compressore *m* a leva
4652	crocoite	crocoïte *f*	Krokoit *m*	crocoite *f*
4653	cromaltite	cromaltite *f*	Cromaltit *m*	cromaltite *f*

		English	French	German	Italian
—	4654	**Cromerian stage**	Cromérien *m*	Cromerian *n*	Cromeriano *m*
—	4655	**cronstedtite**	cronstedtite *f*	Cronstedtit *m*	cronstendtite *f*
—	4656	**crooked, bent**	tordu	krumm	centinato
—	4657	**crooked hole**	sondage *m* tordu	krummes Bohrloch *n*	foro *m* (o sondaggio) storto
°	4658	**crooked handle**	manivelle *f*	Kurbel *f*	manovella *f*
—	4659	**crookesite**	crookésite *f*	Crookesit *m*	crookesite *f*
°	4660	**crop, cropping, crophead, crop end**	chute *f* de tête de lingot	Abfallende *n*	spuntatura *f* di lingotto
		crop, *s. basset*			
		crop-out, *s. basset*			
—	4660a	**cropping**	coupure *f*, coupe *f*	Zerschneiden *n*	taglio *m*
		cropping, *s. basset*			
°	4660b	**cropping**	éboutage *m*	Schöpfen *n*	spuntatura *f*
^	4661	**cross auger**	tarière *f* en croix	Kreuzmeissel *m*	trivella *f* (o sonda) a croce
—	4662	**cropping-out of the bed**	affleurement *m* de la couche	Ausbeissen *n* der Schicht	affioramento *m* dello strato
°	4663	**cross**	pièce *f* à croix	Kreuzstück *n*	pezzo *m* a croce
°	4664	**cross**	croix *f*	Kreuz *n*	traversa *f*, croce *f*
—	4665	**cross**	travers-bancs *m*	Querschlag *m*	traversobanco *m*
—	4666	**cross-adit**	travers-bancs *m*	Querschlag *m*	imboccatura *f* di galleria, traversobanco *m*
		cross chopping bit, *s. cross bit*			
°	4667	**cross back or baffle**	paroi *f* transversale	querlaufender Rücken *m*	parete *f* trasversale.
—	4668	**cross-bar**	traverse *f*, entretoise	Strebe *f*, Querholz *n*	traversa *f*, briglia *f* di collegamento
—	4669	**cross bar**	tirant *m*	Querstab *m*	tirante *m*, traversa
—	4670	**cross-beam**	poutre *f* transversale	Querbalken *m*	trave *f* trasversale
—	4671	**cross bed**	couche *f* oblique,	schräge Schicht *f*	strato *m* obbliquo (o trasversale)
	4672	**cross-bedding**	stratification *f* croisée	Kreuzschichtung *f*	stratificazione *f* incrociata

	English	French	German	Italian
— 4673	cross bit	taillant *m* en croix	Kreuzschneide *f*	tagliente *m* a croce, scalpello *m* a croce
— 4674	cross board	recoupe de pilier	Pfeilerdurchhieb *m*	incrocio *m* di pilastri
— 4675	cross-course	filon *m* croiseur	Quergang *m*	filone *m* trasversale
⊃ 4676	cross crack, edge crack	crique transversale, fissure *f* d'angle	Querriss *m*, Kanten-riss *m*	fessura *f* o cricca *m* trasversale
— 4677	cross cut, cross heading	coupe *f* transversale	Querschnitt *m*	taglio *m* trasversale
— 4678	cross-cut, cross heading	travers-banc, bowette	Querschlag *m*	galleria *f* in traverso-banco *m*
' 4679	cross-cut chisel	bec *m* d'âne	Kreuzmeissel *m*	unghietta *f*
	cross-cut shears, *s. end shears*			
— 4680	cross-cut stoping	exploitation *f* par recoupes transversales	Querbau *m*, Örterbau *m*	coltivazione *f* di traversobanco
_ 4681	cross cutter	haveuse *f*	Schrämmaschine *f*	intagliatrice *f*
_ 4682	cross drift	recoupe *f*	Querstrecke *f*	galleria *f* in traverso-banco
— 4683	to cross drive	recouper	durchqueren	attraversare, scavare gallerie in traverso-banco
— 4684	cross entry	galerie transversale, recoupe *f*	Querstrecke *f*	galleria *f* in traverso-banco
— 4685	cross fault	faille *f* orthogonale	orthogonale Verwerfung *f*	faglia *f* ortogonale
— 4686	cross faulting	faille *f* transversale	Querverwerfung *f*	faglia *f* incrociata
⊃ 4687	cross flue, transverse flue	carneau *m* transversal	Querzug *m*	canale *m* trasversale
— 4688	cross fold	pliage *m* transversal	Querfalz *m*	piega *f* trasversale
⁰ 4689	cross folding test	essai *m* de pliage	Querfaltversuch *m*	prova *f* di piegatura trasversale
4690	cross-hairs	viseur *m*	Raster *m*	reticolo *m* di mira
— 4691	cross hands	traverse *f*	Querträger *m*	traversa *f*
— 4692	cross head	chapiteau *m* d'entre-toisement supérieur	Kopfplatte *f*, Querhaupt *n*	cappello *m*, traversa *f*, testa *f* a croce
— 4693	cross-heading, cut	traverse *f*, galerie *f* à travers-banc	Querschlag *m*	traversa *f*, galleria *f* in traverso-banco

	English	French	German	Italian
— 4694	cross hole	carnet *m*, recoupe *f* d'aérage	Wetterdurchhieb *m*	galleria *f* in traverso-banco di ventilazione
° 4695	cross iron	fer *m* en croix	Kreuzeisen *n*	ferro *m* a croce
° 4696	cross-joint, shift	déplacement *m* de moule, variation *f*	Gussversatz *m*, Versetzung *f*	spostamento *m* della forma, variazione *f*
— 4697	cross-joint	bathroclase *f*	Bathroklas *n*	batroclasi *f*
— 4698	cross lamination, cross bedding	stratification *f* entrecroisée	Kreuzschichtung *f*	stratificazione incrociata
— 4699	cross lode	filon *m* croiseur	Quergang *m*	filone *m* trasversale
° 4700	cross piece	entretoise *f*	Quersteg *m*	trave *m* di collegamento, tirante *m*, pezzo a croce
° 4700a	cross piling	paquet *m* croisé	Kreuzpaket *n*	pacchetto *m* incrociato
° 4701	to cross roll	laminer par rotation entre cylindres inclinés	friemeln	rullare
^ 4702	cross roller bit	trépan *m* en croix	Rollenmeissel *m*	trapano *m* a croce
° 4703	cross rolling	laminage *m* transversal	Querwalzen *n*, Querauswalzen *n*	laminazione *f* trasversale
° 4704	cross section	section *f*, profil *m*	Querschnitt *m*	sezione *f* trasversale, profilo *m*
° 4705	cross(-section) iron	fer *m* en croix	Kreuzeisen *n*	ferro *m* a croce
	cross-sectional area, *s. interface*			
° 4706	cross sleeper	traverse *f*	Querschwelle *f*	traversa *f*
	cross stone, *s. chiastolite*			
— 4707	cross-stratification, cross-bedding	stratification *f* entrecroisée	Kreuzschichtung *f*	stratificazione *f* incrociata
° 4708	cross wire welding	soudure *f* de fils à croix	Drahtkreuz-schweissung *f*	saldatura *f* di fili (o barrette a croce)
— 4709	cross vein	filon *m* croiseur	Kreuzgang *m*, Quergang *m*	filone *m* trasversale
— 4710	cross work	recoupe *f*	Durchhieb *m*	galleria *f* di collegamento
— 4711	cross working	méthode *f* en travers	Querbau *m*	coltivazione *f* traverso-banco
— 4712	crosscut	travers-bancs *m*, recoupe *f*	Querschlag *m*, Durchhieb *m*	traverso-banco *m*, galleria *f* di collegamento

	English	French	German	Italian
_ 4713	**crosscutting**	avancement *m* de travers-bancs	Durchhiebe *m pl.*	avanzamento di traversobanco
⁰ 4714	**cross-tube boiler**	chaudière *f* à tubes croisés	Quersiederohrkessel *m*, Quersieder *m*	caldaia *f* a tubi incrociati
⁰ 4715	**crossbolt**	verrou transversal	Querriegel *m*	catenaccio *m* transversale
— 4716	**crosscut**	recoupe, travers- -bancs	Querschlag *m*	traversobanco *m*
— 4717	**crosscut stoping**	exploitation *f* par recoupes transversales	Querbau *m*	coltivazione *f* di traversobanco
⁰ 4718	**crossing**	croisement *m*	Kreuzung *f*	incrocio *m*
— 4719	**crossing**	crossing *m*	Wetterkreuz *n*	incrocio *m* di ventila- zione
— 4720	**crossite**	crossite *f*	Crossit *m*	crossite *f*
— 4721	**crow**	pince *f*, levier *m*	Brecheisen *n*	pinza *f*, leva *f*, palanchino
⌃ 4722	**crow's-foot**	caracole, crochet *m* de repêchage, harpon	Fanghaken *m*	pescatore *m*, arpione *m*
— 4723	**crowbar**	levier *m*, pince	Brecheisen *n*	leva *f*, palanchino *m*
⁰ 4723a	**crowfeet** **crowfoot**, *s. crow's-foot*	marques *f pl.* en V	V-formige Ziehspuren	tracce *f pl.* a V
— 4724	**crown**	sommet *m*, crête *f*	Gipfel *m*, Scheitel *m*	cima *f*, vetta *f*, cresta *f*
_ 4725	**crown**	crête *f* anticlinale, front *m*	Sattelkopf *m*, Stirn *f*	cresta *f* anticlinale, fronte *m*, testa *f*
⁰ 4725a	**crown**	voussure *f*	Wölbung *f*	volta *f*, chiave *f*
— 4727	**crown**	chapeau *m*	Kappe *f*	cappello *m*
_ 4728	**crown bit**	fleuret *m* à couronne	Kronenbohrer *m*	fioretto *m* a corona
— 4729	**crown block**	moufle *m* fixe	Turmrollenblock *m*	taglia fissa
⁰ 4730	**crown of fire-box**	dessus (ou ciel) du foyer	Feuerkistendecke *f*, Feuerflur *m*	cielo *m* della cassa focolare
⁰ 4731	**crown plate**	tôle *f* du ciel du foyer	Gewölbeplatte *f*, Feuerbüchsendecke *f*	lamiera *f* del cielo del focolare
⁰ 4732	**crown platform**	plate-forme *f* supérieure	Turmkronenbühne *f*	piattaforma *f* superiore
— 4733	**crown-piece**	chapeau *m*	Kappe *f*	cappello *m*
— 4734	**crown pulley**	poulie *f* de forage	Bohrseilrolle *f*, Bohrrolle *f*	puleggia *f* per trivella- zione

		English	French	German	Italian

—	4735	**crown tree**	chapeau m, rallonge	Kappe f	cappello m, prolunga f
o	4736	**crucible, melting pot**	creuset m de fusion	Schmelztiegel m	crogiuolo m di fusione
o	4737	**crucible belly**	ventre m du creuset	Tiegelbauch m	ventre m del crogiuolo
o	4738	**crucible(cast) steel, pot-steel**	acier m au creuset, acier fondu	Gussstahl m, Tiegel(guss)stahl m	acciaio m al crogiolo
		crucible charge, $s.$ *crucible contents*			
o	4739	**crucible contents, crucible charge**	charge f du creuset	Tiegelinhalt m	contenuto m (o carica) del crogiuolo
o	4740	**crucible furnace crucible melting furnace, pot furnace**	four m à creuset	Tiegelschmelzofen m	forno m a crogiolo
o	4741	**crucible fusion**	fusion f au creuset	Tiegelguss m	fusione f al crogiolo
		crucible material, $s.$ *refractory materials for crucibles*			
o	4742	**crucible of refractory clay**	padelin m, creuset en terre réfractaire	Schmelztiegel m. Glasschmelzpfanne f	padella f o crogiuolo d'argilla refrattaria
		crucible pliers, $s.$ *crucible tongs*			
o	4743	**crucible press**	presse f à creusets	Tiegelpresse f	pressa f per crogiuoli
o	4744	**crucible refining**	affinage m au creuset	Tiegelraffination f	affinazione f al crogiolo
o	4745	**crucible stand**	fromage m, tourte f	Käse m, Untersatz m	formaggio m, graticola f
		crucible steel, $s.$ *crucible cast steel*			
		crucible steel plant, $s.$ *crucible steel works*			
o	4746	**crucible steel process, pot steel process**	fabrication f de l'acier au creuset	Tiegelstahldarstellung f	fabbricazione f d'acciaio al crogiuolo
o	4747	**crucible steel works, crucible steel plant**	aciérie f aux creusets	Tiegelstahlhütte f	acciaieria f con forni a crogiuolo
o	4748	**crucible tongs, pliers**	pince f à creuset	Schmelztiegelzange f	pinza f da crogiuolo
o	4749	**crucible triangle**	anneau m de support pour creusets	Glühring m	triangolo m per crogiuoli
o	4750	**crucible wash**	poteyage m pour creuset	Tiegelschlichte f	vernice f protettiva per il crogiuolo

English	French	German	Italian
4751 crucible works	atelier *m* pour la fabrication des creusets	Tiegelfabrik *f*	impianto *m* per la fabbricazione dei crogiuoli
4752 crude bottom	résidu de distillation du pétrole brut	Rohölrückstand *m*	residuo *m* di distillazione di petrolio grezzo
4753 crude copper	cuivre *m* brut	Rohkupfer *n*	rame *m* grezzo
4754 crude fuel	huile *f* brute, pétrole *m* brut, charbon tout venant	Rohöl *n*, Rohkohle *f*	olio *m* grezzo, petrolio *m* grezzo, carbone *m* grezzo
crude-iron, *s. raw-iron*			
4754a crude steel	acier *m* brut	Rohstahl *m*	acciaio *m* grezzo
4755 crude steel equivalent	équivalent *m* en acier brut	Rohstahlgewicht *n*	equivalente *m* di acciaio grezzo
4756 crumb-structure	structure *f* granuleuse	Krümelstruktur *f*	struttura *f* granulosa
4757 crumbling of the ore	concassage *m* du minerai	Zerfallen *n* des Erzes	frantumazione *f* (o disintegrazione) dei minerali
4758 crumpled	froissé	knitterig	sgualcito
4759 crumpling	froncement *m*	Runzelung *f*	piegamento *m*, pieghettatura *f*, corrugamento *m*
4760 crup	affaissement *m* du toit	Absenkung *f* des Hangenden	cedimento *m* del tetto
4761 to crush ore	bocarder, concasser (ou broyer) le minerai	Erz brechen (od. zerkleinern)	frantumare (o triturare) il minerale
4762 crush	écrasement *m* de joint	Zerdrücken *n* in der Teilung	schiacciamento *m* della forma, cedimento *m* (di terra nella forma)
4763 crush	écrasement *m* de moule	Zerdrücken *n* der Form	sfondamento *m* della forma
4764 crush	écrasement *m* de noyau	Zerdrücken *n* des Kernes	schiacciamento *m* dell'anima
4765 crush	frotte *f*	Reibstelle *f*	sfregamento *m*
4766 crush breccia, fault breccia	brèche de friction	Reibungsbreccie *f*	breccia *f* di frizione o di dislocazione
4767 crush structure	structure *f* cataclastique	kataklastisches Gefüge *n*	struttura *f* cataclastica

English	French	German	Italian
— 4768 crushed coke	coke *m* concassé	Brechkoks *m*, Knabbelkoks *m*	coke *m* spezzato o frantumato
crushed slag aggregate, *s. slag sand*			
— 4769 crushed stone	cailloutis *m*	Steinschlag *m*	pietrisco *m*, ghiaietto *m*
— 4770 crushed zone	zone *f* de broyage	Zertrümmerungszone *f*	zona *f* di frantumazione
— 4771 crusher	concasseur *m*	Brechwerk *n*	frantumatore *m*, frantoio *m*
— 4772 crusher ball	élément broyeur	Mahlkörper *m*	corpo *m* per macinare
— 4773 crusher head	trémie *f* de broyeur	Brechereintrag *m*	tramoggia *f* di frantoio
— 4774 crusher roll	rouleau *m* à broyer	Brechwalze *f*	rullo *m* per frantoio, cilindro *m* frantumatore
— 4775 crushing, disintegration	broyage *m*, concassage *m*	Zerkleinerung *f*	triturazione *f*, macinazione *f*, frantumazione *f*
— 4776 crushing	broyage *m*	Zermahlung *f*, Zerkleinern *n*	macinazione *f*, frantumazione *f*
crushing machine, *s. grinding machine*			
— 4777 crushing mill	concasseur *m* à cylindres	Erzwalzwerk *n*	cilindraia *f* per minerali
— 4778 crushing mill with vertical runners, edge mill	broyeur *m* à meules	Kollergang *m*	molazza *f*
° 4779 crushing of the pigs	cassage des gueuses	Zerkleinerung der Masseln	spezzatura dei masselli
— 4780 crushing plant	installation *f* de broyage	Zerkleinerungsanlage *f*	impianto *m* di frantumazione
— 4781 crushing plate	plaque *f* à triturer	Zerkleinerungsplatte *f*	piastra *f* per triturazione (o di frantumazione)
° 4782 crust	croûte *f*	Kruste *f*	crosta *f*
— 4783 crustificated vein	filon *m* concrétionné	Gang *m* mit Lagen	filone *m* concrezionato
— 4784 cryolite	cryolite *f*	Kryolith *m*	criolite *f*
— 4785 cryolithionite	cryolithionite *f*	Kryolithionit *m*	criolitionite *f*
— 4786 cryptoclastic	cryptoclastique	kryptoklastisch	criptoclastico

English	French	German	Italian
4787 **cryptocrystalline**	cryptocristallin	kryptokristallin	criptocristallino
4788 **cryptogamous**	criptogames *m pl.*	Kryptogamen *f pl.*	criptogami *m pl.*
4789 **cryptolite**	cryptolite *f*	Kryptolith *m*	çriptolito *m*
4790 **cryptoperthite**	cryptoperthite *f*	Kryptoperthit *m*	criptopertite *f*
4791 **crystal**	cristal *m*	Kristall *m*	cristallo *m*
4792 **crystal basement**	soubassement *m* cristallin	kristallines Grundgebirge *n*	basamento *m* cristallino
4793 **crystal boundary**	contour *m* cristallin	Kristallbegrenzung *f*	contorno *m* o forma cristallina
4794 **crystal growth**	croissement *m* de cristal	Kristallwachstum *n*	crescita *f* di cristallo
4795 **crystal habit**	faciès *m* de cristal	Kristallhabitus *m*	facies *f* di cristallo
4796 **crystal lattice**	réseau *m* cristallin	Kristallgitter *n*	reticolo *m* cristallino
4797 **crystal lattice parameters**	paramètres *m pl.* du réseau cristallin	Gitterparameter *m*	parametri *m pl.* del reticolo cristallino
crystal water, *s. water of crystallization*			
4798 **crystalline**	cristallin	kristallinisch	cristallino
4799 **crystalline aggregate**	aggrégat *m* cristallin	kristallinisches Aggregat *n*	aggregato *m* cristallino
4800 **crystalline fracture**	cassure *f* cristalline	kristallinischer Bruch *m*	frattura *f* cristallina
4801 **crystalline gypsum, selenite**	gypse cristallisé (ou spathique) sélénite *f*	Gipsspat *m*, Selenit *m*, Marienglas *n*, Frauenglas *n*	gesso *m* cristallizzato, selenite *f*
4802 **crystalline iron ore**	minerai *m* de fer cristallin	kristallinisches Eisenerz *n*	minerale *m* di ferro cristallino
4803 **crystalline state**	forme *f* cristalline	Kristallform *f*	forma *f* cristallina
4804 **crystalline texture (or structure)**	structure *f* ou texture cristalline	kristallinische Struktur *f*, kristallinisches Gefüge *n*	struttura *f* cristallina
4805 **crystallinity**	cristallinité *f*	Kristallinität *f*	cristallinità *f*
4806 **crystallite**	cristallite *f*	Kristallit *m*	cristallite *f*

		English	French	German	Italian
o	4807	crystallisation vessel	vase *m* à cristallisation	Kristallierungs-gefäss *n*	recipiente *m* di cristallizzazione, cristallizzatore *m*
o	4808	crystallised iron	fer *m* cristallisé	kristallisiertes Eisen, kristallisches Eisen *n*	ferro *m* cristallizzato
—	4809	crystallising basin or pan	coupe *f* de cristallisation	Kristallierschale *f*, Kristallisations-gefäss *n*	bacinella *f* di cristallizzazione
		crystallising pan, *s. crystallising basin*			
—	4810	crystallization	cristallisation *f*	Kristallisierung *f*	cristallizzazione *f*
—	4811	crystallite	cristallite *f*	Kristallit *m*	cristallite *f*
—	4812	to crystallize	cristalliser	kristallisieren	cristallizzare
—	4813	crystalloblastesis	cristalloblastèse *f*	Kristalloblastese *f*	cristalloblastesi *f*
—	4814	crystalloblastic	cristalloblastique	kristalloblastisch	cristalloblastico
—	4815	crystalloblastic texture	texture *f* cristalloblastique	kristalloblastische Struktur *f*	struttura *f* cristalloblastica
—	4816	crystalloluminescence	cristalluminiscence	Kristallumineszenz *f*	cristalloluminescenza *f*

CS = *carbon steel*

C.ST = *centistoke*

CTU = *centigrade thermal unit*

		English	French	German	Italian
—	4817	cubanite	cubane *m*	Cuban *m*	cubano *m*
o	4817a	cube mixer	mélangeur *m* cubique	Würfelmischer *m*	mescolatrice *f* cubica
—	4818	cube ore	pharmacosidérite *f*	Pharmakosiderit *m*	farmacosiderite *f*
—	4819	cube shape	forme *f* cubique	Würfelform *f*	forma *f* di dado (o cubica)
—	4820	cube spar	anhydrite *f*	Anhydrit *m*	anidrite *f*
—	4821	cubic	tessulaire (cubique)	tessularisch	tessulario
		cubic system, *s. isometric system*			
	4822	cubical contents, capacity	capacité *f*, contenance, cube *m*	Rauminhalt *m*	capacità *f*
—	4823	cucalite	cucalite *f*	Cucalit *m*	cucalite *f*
—	4824	cuesta	côte *f*	Abhang *m*	costa *f*, terreno *m* in pendio
—	4825	to cull	cueillir, trier *m*	ausklauben, klauben	cogliere, raccogliere, cernere

	English	French	German	Italian
–	4826 culm, powdered coal	culm *m*	Kulm *m*	culm *m*
–	4827 culm, powdered coal	fraisil *m*, menu *m*, poussière *f* d'anthracite	kleine Anthrazitart *f*,. Kohlenklein *n*, Grus	polvere *f* d'antracite, carbone *m* polveroso
–	4828 culsageeite	culsagééite *f*	Culsageeit *m*	culsageeite *f*
–	4829 cumberlandite	cumberlandite *f*	Cumberlandit *m*	cumberlandite *f*
–	4830 cumbraite	cumbraïte *f*	Cumbrait *m*	cumbraite *f*
–	4831 cumengeite	cumengéite *f*	Cumengeit *m*	cumengeite *f*
–	4832 cummingtonite	cummingtonite *f*	Cummingtonit *m*	cummingtonite *f*
–	4833 cumulophyric texture	texture *f* glommérophyrique	glommerophirische Struktur *f*	struttura *f* cumulorifica
ɔ	4834 cup-and-ball structure	structure *f* en bilboquet	kugelige Absonderung *f*	struttura *f* a coppa
ɔ	4835 cup and cone fracture, cupping	cassure *f* en cône et coupe	Becherriss, Kegel- und Hohlbruch *m*	frattura *f* a cono e coppa
ɔ	4836 cup-headed bolt	boulon *m* à tête bombée	Bolzen *m* mit halbrundem Kopf	bullone *m* a testa bombata
*	4837 cup leather packing	garniture *f* en cuir embouti	Stulpenliderung *f*	guarnizione *f* ad angolo od a manicotto
ɔ	4837a cup test	épreuve *f* de ductilité	Duktilitätsprobe *f*	prova *f* di duttilità
ɔ	4838 cupel	coupelle *f*	Kapelle *f*, Kupelle *f*	coppa*f*, coppella *f*
ɔ	4839 cupellation	coupellation *f*	Kupellieren *n*, Läutern, Abtreiben *n*	coppellazione *f*

cupellation furnace, *s. cupelling furnace*

	English	French	German	Italian
ɔ	4840 cupel(ling-) furnace, cupellation-furnace, assaying furnace	four *m* (ou fourneau) à coupelle(s), four à coupellation	Kapellenofen *m*, Muffelofen *m*, Probierofen *m*	forno *m* a coppella
ɔ	4841 cupola, cupola furnace	cubilot *m*	Giessereischachtofen *m*	forno *m* a cupola, cubilotto *m*
ɔ	4842 cupola body, cupola shaft	corps *m*	Kupolofenschacht *m*	mantello *m* (del cubilotto)
ɔ	4843 cupola charge	charge *f* métallique	Kupolofensatz *m*, Gatticrung *f*	carica *f* di un cubilotto
ɔ	4844 cupola(-furnace)	cubilot, coupelot	Kuppelofen *m*, Kupolofen *m*	cubilotto, forno a cupola

	English	French	German	Italian
o	4845 **cupola iron**	fonte f de cubilot	Kupolofenguss m	ghisa f di cubilotto
o	4846 **cupola keeper**	fondeur m au cubilot	Kupolofenwärter m	fonditore m addetto al cubilotto
	cupola runner trough, s. spout			
	cupola shell, s. cupola body			
o	4847 **cupola stack**	cheminée f	Kupolofenkamin m	camino m del cubilotto
o	4848 **cupola supporting frame**	plaque f de support	Abfangplatte f	anello m di sostegno del refrattario
o	4849 **cupola tender**	cubilotier m	Kupolofen-Schmelzer m	fornaiolo m, operaio m addetto al cubilotto
o	4850 **cupola torch**	allumeur m du cubilot	Anheizbrenner m (des Kupolofens)	accenditore m del cubilotto, bruciatore di cubilotto
o	4851 **cupola with square shaft**	cubilot m avec cuve carrée	Kuppelofen m mit viereckigem Schacht	cubilotto m con tino quadrato
o	4852 **cupping**	cassure f intérieure transversale	Querinnenbruch m	rottura f interna trasversale
—	4853 **cupric chloride**	hypochlorure m de cuivre	Chlorkupfer n, Kupferchlorid n	cloruro m di rame
—	4854 **cupriferous iron ore**	minerai m de fer cuivreux	kupferhaltiges Eisenerz n	minerale m di ferro cuprifero
—	4855 **cupro-lead**	cupro-plomb m	Bleibronze f	cupropiombo m, lega f rame-piombo
—	4856 **cupro-manganese, manganese copper**	cupro-manganèse m	Mangankupfer n	cupromanganese m, lega f rame-manganese
—	4857 **cupro-nickel, nickel-copper**	cupro-nickel m	Kupfer-Nickel n	cupronichelio m, cupro-nickel m
	cupro-silicon, s. silicon-copper			
—	4858 **cuprous chloride**	chlorure m cuivreux ou de cuivre	Kupferchlorid n	cloruro m ramoso
—	4859 **cuprozincite**	cuprozincite f	Cuprozinkit m	cuprozincite f
—	4860 **curb**	rouet m, roulisse, cadre m porteur	Schachtring m, Mauerfuss m	anello m tagliente (per affondare pozzi), cresta f di muro

	English	French	German	Italian
–	4861 curbing	boisage *m* du puits à cadres jointifs	Schachtausbau *m* mit Schrotzimmerung *f*	rivestimento *m* del pozzo a quadri vicini
–	4862 curcuma paper	papier *m* de curcuma	Curcumapapier *n*	carta *f* alla curcuma
–	4863 curite	curite *f*	Curit *m*	curite *f*
°	4864 curium	curium *m*	Curium *n*	curio *m*
–	4865 curling	frisure *f*	Verzierung *f* mit erhobener Arbeit	arricciatura *f*
–	4866 current-bedded	déposé par courant	kreuzgeschichtet	depositato dalla corrente
–	4867 current-bedding	stratification *f* torrentielle ou entrecroisée	Kreuzschichtung *f*, Diagonalschichtung *f*	stratificazione *f* torrenziale
	4868 current meter	ampèremètre *m*	Amperemeter *n*	amperometro *m*
°	4869 current of gas	courant *m* gazeux	Gasstrom *m*	corrente *f* di gas
–	4870 curtain	toile *f* d'aérage	Wettertuch *n*	sbarramento *m* di ventilazione
	curtaining, *s. double skin*			
–	4871 curtaining	ridage *m*	Faltenbildung *f*	velatura *f*
–	4872 curvature	arc *m* de circonférence	Kreisbogen *m*	circonferenza *f*, curvatura *f*
°	4873 to curve	courber, plier	krümmen, biegen	piegare, curvare
°	4874 to curve	entailler	schrämen	intagliare
°	4875 curve	courbe *f*, courbure *f*	Kurve *f*, Krümmung *f*, Bogen *m*	curva, curvatura *f*
	4876 curve of decomposition	courbe *f* de décomposition	Zersetzungskurve *f*	curva *f* di decomposizione
	curve of deflection, *s. bending line*			
°	4877 curve of solubility	courbe *f* de solubilité	Löslichkeitskurve *f*	curva *f* di solublità o di concentrazione
°	4878 curved core	noyau *m* coudé	Krümmerkern *m*	anima *f* curva
°	4879 curved corrugated iron	tôle *f* ondulée cintrée	bogenförmiges Wellblech *n*	lamiera *f* ondulata curvata
°	4880 curved corrugated sheet	tôle ondulée cintrée	bogenfoermiges Wellblech *n*	lamiera *f* ondulata curvata

		English	French	German	Italian
—	4881	**curved fault**	faille f courbée	gebogene Verwerfung f	faglia f curva
o	4882	**curved large radius slecker**	lissoir m cintré à grand congé	Polierknopf m für grosse Verbindungsstücke	lisciatoio m curvo per raccordi m pl. grandi
o	4883	**curved printing plate**	planche f cylindrique	Rundplatte f	lastra f cilindrica
o	4884	**curved surface**	surface f bombée	gekrümmte Fläche f	superficie f curva o bombata
o	4885	**curved tongue or point**	aiguille f courbe	krumme Zunge f	ago m curvo
o	4886	**curvilinear quadrat**	lingot cintré	Bogensteg m, Bogenreglette f	lingotto m curvato
o	4887	**cushion, marquette**	coussinet m de butée (de tôle)	Drucklager n (des Bleches)	cuscinetto m di spinta (lamiera)
—	4888	**cushioned blasting**	tir m avec chambre d'expansion	Hohlraumschiessen n	tiro m con camera d'espansione
—	4889	**cusp**	cap m	Kap n	capo m, apice m
—	4890	**cuspidine**	cuspidine f	Cuspidin m	cuspidina f, custerite f
		custerite, s. cuspidine			
o	4891	**to cut**	tronçonner, couper	trennen, schneiden	tranciare, tagliare
o	4892	**to cut, to chip out**	découper au ciseau	aushauen	tagliar via, asportare
		to cut a thread, s. to screw (-thread)			
o	4893	**to cut off**	détacher, couper	abhauen	tagliare, togliere
o	4894	**to cut outside screw-threads**	fileter (une vis)	Aussengewinde n schneiden	tagliare una filettatura esterna
		to cut screw-threads, s. to screw (-thread)			
		to cut screws on a lathe, s, to turn a thread			
		to cut the jig, s. to cut the pattern			
o	4895	**to cut (or to open) the runner (system)**	trancher la coulée, trancher le jet	den Einguss (od den Lauf) anschneiden	tagliare la colata (o il getto)
o	4896	**to cut to pattern (or jig)**	profiler sur modèle, tailler suivant étalon	nach einer Schablone (od Lehre) ausschneiden	sagomare secondo il campione (o il modello)

	English	French	German	Italian
	cut, *s. cross-heading*			
4897	cut	impureté (en % sur la production)	prozentige Unreinheit *f*	impurità (in % sulla produzione)
4898	cut	fouille, déblai *m*	Abraum *m*, Einbruch *m*, Vertiefung *f*	scavo *m*, sterro *m*
4899	cut	saignée *f*, havée *f*	Schnitt *m*	taglio *m*, intaglio *m*
4900	cut-and-fill method	exploitation *f* par remblayage	Stossbau *m*	coltivazione *f* a ripiena
4901	cut-and-fill stope	taille *f* remblayée par matériel du chantier même	Firstenbau *m* mit Selbstversatz	scavo *m* riempito con materiale del cantiere
4902	cut glass	cristal *m* taillé	geschliffenes Glas *n*	cristallo *m* tagliato
4903	cut glass plate	plaque *f* en verre poli	geschliffene Glasplatte *f*	piastra *f* di vetro arrotato
4904	cut-off tool	outil *m* à tronçonner	Abstecher *m*, Abstechstahl *m*	utensile *m* da taglio
	cut-out, *s. formed*			
	cutt-off wheel, *s. cutting wheel*			
4905	cutter	tronçonneuse *f*	Trennschleifmaschine *f*	troncatrice *f*, tranciatrice *f*, trancia *f*
4906	cutter	haveuse *f*, piqueur *m*	Schrämmaschine *f*, Hauer *m*	intagliatrice *f*, picconatore *m*, tagliatore *m*
4907	cutter	outil *m* de coupe, fraise *f*	Schneideapparat *m*, Fräse *f*	attrezzo *m* per tagliare, fresa *f*
4908	cutter	diaclase transversale	Querspalte *f*	diaclasi *f* travversale
4909	cutter arbor	arbre *m* porte-fraise (à queue)	Fräsdorn *m*	asta *f* porta-fresa
4910	cutter bar	barre *f* de haveuse	Schrämstange *f*	barra *f* d'intagliatrice
4911	cutter head	tête *f* de carottier	Kernbohrkopf *m*	testa *f* di carotiere
4912	cutter-loader	haveuse-chargeuse *f*	Schrämlader *m*,	intagliatrice-caricatrice
4913	cutting	coupe *f*, havage *m*, sous-cavage *m*	Schneiden *n*, Schrämen *n*, Schrämarbeit *f*, Unterhöhlen *n*	intaglio *m*, taglio *m*
4913a	cutting	coupure *f*, coupe *f*	Zerschneiden *n*	taglio *m*
	cutting, *s. sharp*			
4914	cutting action	action *f* (ou effet *m*) de coupe	Schneidewirkung *f*, Schnittwirkung *f*	effetto *m* di taglio

	English	French	German	Italian
°	4915 cutting blowpipe, cutting torch	chalumeau *m* . coupeur	Schneidbrenner *m*	cannello *m* da taglio
°	4916 cutting dies, punching dies	étampes *f pl.*, poinçons *m pl.*	Stanzen *f pl.*	trance *f pl.*, punzoni *m pl.*
—	4917 cutting down	sous-cavage *m*	Unterhöhlen *n*	taglio *m* di sotto
°	4917a cutting down	polissage *m* de la surface	Oberflächen-polierung *f*	lucidatura *f* della superficie
°	4918 cutting edge	burin *m*, lame *f*	Schneide *f*	tagliente *m*, lama *f*
	cutting grooves, *s. grooving*			
°	4919 cutting head	ajutage *m* à découper	Schneidbrenner *m*	testa *f* d'attacco
	cutting-iron, (of a plain), *s. plain iron*			
°	4919a cutting line	ligne *f* de coupe	Schnittlinie *f*	linea *f* di taglio
°	4920 cutting-off lathe	tour à décolleter	Abstechbank *f*	tornio *m* per troncare, tornio *m* troncabarre
—	4921 cutting-out stope	gradin *m* inférieur (dans l'exploitation par gradins renversés)	Feldortstoss *m*	gradino *m* inferiore nella coltivazione a gradini rovesci
°	4922 cutting punch	poinçon *m* à découper	Schnittstempel *m*	punzone *m* da taglio
°	4923 cutting screw-threads	creusement *m* des filets	Gewindeschneiden *n*	(taglio *m* della) filettatura *f*
°	4924 cutting speed	vitesse *f* de coupe	Schnittge-schwindigkeit *f*	velocità *f* di taglio
°	4925 cutting threads on the lathe	filetage *m* sur le tour	Gewindeschneiden *n* auf der Drehbank	filettature *f* al tornio
°	4926 cutting tool	outil *m* à fileter	Schneideisen *n*	utensile *m* per tagliare
°	4927 cutting tool angle	angle *m* de coupe	Schnittwinkel *m*	angolo *m* di taglio
°	4928 cutting wheel, slitting wheel	disque *m* de tronçonnage	Trennscheibe *f*	taglia-colate *m* a disco, disco tranciatore
—	4929 cuttings	débris *m pl.* de forage	Bohrgut *n*, Bohrmehl *n*	detriti di trivellazione
°	4930 cyanide hardening, cyaniding	trempe *f* en bain de cyanure	Zyanbadhärten *n*	cianurazione *f*
°	4931 cyanide of potassium	cyanure *m* de potassium	Cyankalium *n*, Kaliumcyanid *n*	cianuro *m* di potassio
	cyanite, *s. kyanite*			

English	French	German	Italian
4932 cyanite schist	schiste *m* à disthène	Disthenschiefer *m*	scisto *m* a distene
4933 cyanochroite	cyanochroïte *f*	Cyanochroit *m*	cianocroite *f*
4934 cyclone	cyclone *m*, hydro-cyclone	Zyklon *m*	ciclone *m*, idrociclone *m*
4935 cyclopite	cyclopite *f*	Cyclopit *m*	ciclopite *f*, anortite *f*
4936 cylinder	bouteille *f*	Flasche *f*	bombola *f*
4936a cylinder, belly	ventre *m*	Kohlensack *m*	ventre *m*, sacca *f*
cylinder boiler, *s. cylindrical boiler*			
4937 cylinder for compressed gases	bouteille *f* pour gaz comprimés	Stahlflasche *f* für verdichtete Gase	bombola *f* per gas compressi
4938 cylinder for dissolved gases	bouteille *f* pour gaz dissous	Stahlflasche *f* für gelöste Gase	bombola *f* per gas disciolti
4939 cylinder for liquefied gases	bouteille *f* pour gaz liquides	Stahlflasche *f* für flüssige Gase	bombola *f* per gas liquefatti
4940 cylinder furnace	four *m* cylindrique	Zylinderofen *m*	forno *m* cilindrico
4941 cylinder liner	fourrure *f* de cylindre	Zylinderbüchse *f*	camicia *f* di cilindro
4942 cylinder screen	trommel *m*	Siebtrommel *f*	vaglio *m* rotante
4943 cylinder with scale	cylindre *m* avec échelle	Zylinder *m* mit Teilung	cilindro *m* con scala
4944 cylindrical blower	soufflerie *f* à cylindres	Zylindergebläse *n*	soffieria *f* a cilindro
4945 cylindrical boiler, cylinder boiler	chaudière *f* (ou générateur) cylindrique	Walzenkessel *m*, zylindrischer Kessel *m*	generatore *m* cilindrico, caldaia *f* cilindrica
4946 cylindrical boiler with external furnace	chaudière *f* cylindrique à foyer extérieur	Walzenkessel *m* mit Aussenfeuerung	caldaia *f* cilindrica a focolare esterno
4947 cylindrical boiler with internal furnace	chaudière *f* cylindrique à foyer intérieur	Walzenkessel *m* mit Innenfeuerung	caldaia *f* cilindrica a focolare interno
4948 cylindrical pig iron mixer	mélangeur *m* cylindrique de fonte	walzenförmiger Roheisenmischer *m*	mescolatore *m* cilindrico per ghisa
4949 cylindrical shape	forme *f* cylindrique	Walzenform *f*	forma *f* cilindrica
4950 cylindrical shell electrode	électrode *f* cylindrique	zylindrische Mantelelektrode *f*	elettrodo *m* a mantello cilindrico

		English	French	German	Italian
—	4951	**cylindrite**	cylindrite *f*	Zylindrit *m*	cilindrite *f*
—	4952	**cymophane**	cymophane *m*	Cymophan *m*	crisoberillo *m* opalescente
—	4953	**cyprine**	cyprine *f*	Cyprin *m*	cipryna *f*
—	4954	**cyprusite**	cyprusite *f*	Cyprusit *m*	ciprusite *f*

English	French	German	Italian
4955 **dachiardite**	dachiardite *f*	Dachiardite *m*	dachiardite *f*
4956 **dacite**	dacite *f*	Dazit *m*	dacite *f*
4957 **dacitic**	dacitique	dazitisch	dacitico
4958 **dactylite**	dactylite *f*	Daktylit *m*	dactilite *f*
4959 **dactylitic**	digital	daktylitisch	dactilico
4960 **to dad**	ventiler un chantier grisouteux	einen Grubenbau bewettern	ventilare un cantiere contenente grisou
4961 **dahamite**	dahamite *f*	Dahamit *m*	dahamite *f*
4962 **dahllite**	dahllite *f*	Dahllit *m*	dahllite *f*
4963 **daily output**	production *f* journalière	Tagesleistung *f*	produzione *f* giornaliera
4964 **dam, baffle stone**	barrage *m*, dame *f*	Schlackenstein *m*	risalto *m*, pietra *f* di dama, piastra *f* di guardia
4965 **dam (in the sprue basin)**	seuil *m* dans le bassin de coulée	Überlauf *m* (im Giesstümpel), Buckel *m*	risalto *m*, soglia *f* (nel bacino di colata)
4966 **dam**	serrement *m*	Absperrdamm *m*	sbarramento *m* di legno
4967 **dam plate**	plaque *f* de dame	Wallplatte *f*	piastra *f* di guardia
4968 **dam stone**	dame *f*	Dammstein *m*, Wallstein *m*	pietra *f* di dama
4969 **dam type lip ladle**	poche *f* à barrage, poche *f* à dame	Giesspfanne *f* mit Schlackenstein	siviera *f* con ferma-scorie (o con piastra di guardia)
4970 **damage by smoke**	endommagement *m* par la fumée	Rauchbeschädigung *f*	danno *m* causato dal fumo
4971 **damascined**	damassé	damasziert, tauschiert	damaschinato
4972 **damascined steel, damascus steel**	acier *m* damassé, acier *m* damasquiné	damaszener Stahl *m*, Damaskstahl *m*	acciaio *m* damaschinato
4972a **damascening**	damasquinage *m*	Damaszierung *f*	damaschinatura *f*, intarsio *m*
4973 **to damask**	damasquiner	damaszieren	damascare
damask steel, *s. damascined steel*			
4974 **damourite**	damourite *f*	Damourit *m*	damourite *f*
4975 **damouritization**	damourisation *f*	Damouritbildung *f*	damouritizzazione *f*

		English	French	German	Italian
o	4976	to damp, to damp down	suspendre la marche, boucher	dämpfen	spengere temporaneamente il forno
o	4977	to damp down (the furnace)	mettre le four hors feu, refroidir	kalt legen	mettere il forno fuori di marcia, arresto (del forno per chiusura della tubiera
—	4978	damp	grisou m	Schlagwetter n	grisou m
—	4979	damp sheet	toile f d'aérage	Wettertuch n	sbarramento m di ventilazione
o	4980	damper	registre m	Regelschieber m	registro m, paratoia f
o	4981	damping, damping down (of a furnace)	arrêt m momentané, bouchage m	Dämpfen n	arresto f momentaneo (per chiusura della tubiera)
o	4982	damping capacity	capacité f d'amortissement	Dämpfungsvermögen n	capacità f smorzante, potere m antivibratorio
o	4982a	damping down	extinction f temporaire	zeitweilige Löschung f	estinzione f temporanea
o	4983	damping down,	refroidissement m du feu	Kaltlegung f	raffreddamento m del forno
—	4984	damposcope	indicateur de grisou	Schlagwetteranzeiger	indicatore m di grisou
—	4985	dampy	humide, contenant bioxyde de carbone	feucht, kohlensäurehaltig	umido, contenente anidride carbonica
o	4986	damstone, baffle stone	dame f	Wallstein m, Dammstein m	piastra f di dama
—	4987	dan	cuffat m à eau	Wasserkübel m	draga f di caricamento ad acqua
—	4988	danaite	danaïte f	Danait m	danaite f
—	4989	danalite	danalite f	Danalith m	danalite f
—	4990	danburite	danburite f	Danburit m	damburite f
—	4991	dandy	brouette f à deux roues	zweirädrige Karre f	cariola f a due ruote
o	4991a	dandy	four m de premier affinage	Frischereiofen m, Frischofen m	forno m di primo affinaggio
o	4992	dangerous temperature	température f dangereuse	gefährliche Temperatur f	temperatura f pericolosa
o	4993	Daniell's safety cock	robinet m de Daniell	Daniellscher Hahn m	rubinetto m di Daniell
—	4994	danks	schiste m houiller	Kohlenschiefer m	scisto m carbonifero
—	4995	dannemorite	dannemorite f	Dannemorit m	dannemorite f

	English	French	German	Italian
– 4996	dant, slack	charbon *m* menu	Kohlengrus *m*	carbonella *f*
– 4997	dantry	charbon *m* gros	Stückkohle *f*	carbone *m* di grossa pezzatura
⁾ 4998	Darby's gas exit pipe	prise *f* de gaz Darby	Darbys Gasfang *m*	presa *f* di gas Darby
– 4999	darapskite	darapskite *f*	Darapskit *m*	darapskite *f*
	Darby's gas take, *s. Darby's gas exit pipe*			
⁾ 5000	Darby's gas catcher	prise *f* de gaz Darby	Darbys Gasfang *m*	presa *f* di gas Darby
⁾ 5001	dark fumes *pl.*	fumées *f pl.* de couleur foncée	dunkle Dämpfe *m pl.*	vapori *m pl.* scùri
⁾ 5001a	dark glowing	recuit bleu	Blauglühen *n*	ricottura *f* bleu
⁾ 5002	dark gray pig iron	fonte *f* grise foncée	tiefgraues Roheisen *n*	ghisa *f* grigio-nera, ghisa *f* grigio scura
⁾ 5003	(to a) dark red-heat	au rouge sombre	auf dunkle Rotglut	al calor rosso scuro
– 5004	dark red silver	pyrargyrite *f*	Pyrargyrit *m*	pirargirite *f*
– 5005	datolite	datolite *f*	Datolith *m*	datolite *f*
– 5006	datum	repère *m*	Anhaltspunkt *m*	punto *m* di riferimento
– 5007	datum horizon	niveau *m* de repère	Leithorizont *m*	livello *m* di riferimento, orizzonte *m* di riferimento
– 5008	datum level	plan *m* de niveau	Grundebene *f*	piano *m* di livello, piano *m* di riferimento
– 5009	datum line	ligne *f* de référence	Grundlinie *f*	linea *f* di riferimento
	datum plane, *s. datum level*			
⁾ 5009a	daubing	revêtement *m* refractaire	feuerbeständige Beschichtung *f*	rivestimento *m* refrattario
– 5010	daubreeite	daubréeite *f*	Daubreeit *m*	daubreeite *f*
– 5011	daubreelite	draubréélite *f*	Daubreelith *m*	daubreelite *f*
– 5012	dauk	grès *m* argileux	toniger Sandstein *m*	gres *m* argilloso
– 5013	davainite	davainite *f*	Davainit *m*	davainite *f*
– 5014	daviesite	daviésite *f*	Daviesit *m*	daviesite *f*
	davy lamp, *s. safety lamp*			
– 5015	day-drift	fendue *f*, galerie *f*	Stollen *m*	livello *m*, galleria *f*

		English	French	German	Italian
−	5016	**day eye**	puits m incliné	tonlägiger Schacht m	pozzo m inclinato
−	5017	**day fall**	affaissement m du sol au-dessus des travaux miniers	Senkung f der Tagesoberfläche	cedimento m del suolo sopra i lavori di scavo
−	5018	**day-light mine**	mine f à ciel découvert, exploitation au jour	Tagebau m	miniera f a giorno, coltivazione f a giorno
−	5019	**day shift**	poste m de jour	Tagschicht f	turno m giornaliero
−	5020	**day stone**	affleurement m	Ausgehende n	affioramento m
−	5021	**daylight**	lumière f du jour	Tageslicht n	luce f del giorno
−	5022	**daze**	mica f	Glimmer m	mica f
˄	5023	**dea, diethanolamine**	diéthanolamine f	Diäthanolamin n	dietanolammina f
−	5024	**dead**	stérile	taub	sterile
−	5025	**dead area**	zone f morte	totes Gebiet n, druckleeres Gebiet n	zona f sterile (o morta)
−	5026	**to dead-burn**	griller à mort	totbrennen, totrösten	arrostire totalmente
		dead-burning, $s.$ *dead roasting*			
−	5027	**dead end**	cul-de-sac	Blindort m	galleria f cieca, cunicolo m
−	5028	**dead ground**	roche f stérile	taubes Gestein n	roccia f sterile
°	5029	**dead hard steel**	acier m diamant	Diamantstahl m	acciaio m diamante
°	5030	**dead head**	masselotte f	verlorener Kopf m	materozza f
−	5031	**dead hole**	culot m	Pfeife f	fondello m (di cartuccia)
˄	5032	**dead line**	brin m mort	Totseil n	cavo m morto
°	5033	**to dead-melt**	laisser se calmer	abstehen lassen	lasciar calmare
°	5033a	**dead melting**	fusion f surpassée	Überschmelzen n	fusione f sorpassata
°	5034	**dead mild steel**	acier m doux	weicher Stahl m	acciaio m dolce
˄	5035	**dead oil**	huile f de créosote	Kreosotöl n	olio m inerte
		dead-roast, $s.$ *to dead burn*			
−	5036	**dead roasting**	surcuisson f, cuisson f à mort	Totbrennen n	stracottura f, torrefazione f a morte

	English	French	German	Italian
5037	dead soft steel, extra mild steel	acier *m* extra-doux	extraweicher Stahl *m*	acciaio *m* extra dolce
5038	dead soft temper, extra mild temper	trempe *f* extra-douce	extra-weiches Tempern *n*	tempra *f* extradolce
	dead spot, *s. dull spot*			
5039	dead steel	acier *m* calmé	ruhiger Stahl *m*	acciaio *m* calmato
5040	deads	roche *f* stérile, déblais *m pl.*	taubes Gestein *n*	roccia *f* sterile, sterile *m*
5041	deads	perte *f* au feu	Abbrand *m*	perdita *f* al fuoco
5042	dealuminizing	désaluminage *m*	Enteloxieren *n*	eliminazione *f* dell'alluminio, desalluminiatura *f*
5043	dean	chantier *m* en cul-de-sac	Blindort *m*	cantiere *m* a galleria cieca
5044	deaeration	désaréation *f*	Entlüftung *f*	deareazione *f*
5045	deareator	désaréateur *m*	Entgaser *m*	disareatore *m*
5046	deblooming	enlèvement *m* de substances fluorescentes du pétrole	Abscheiden *n* fluoreszenter Stoffe aus dem Erdöl	rimozione *f* di sostanze fluorescenti dal petrolio
	debris, *s. detritus*			
5047	debutanization	débutanisation *f*	Entbutanisierung *f*	debutanizzazione *f*
5048	debutanizer	débutaniseur *m*	Entbutanisierungsapparat *m*	debutanizzatore *m*
5049	decalescence	décalescence *f*	Abschrecken *n*	decalescenza *f*
5050	to decant	décanter	dekantieren, abscheiden	decantare, travasare
5051	decanting	décantage *m*	Schlämmen *n*, Abschlämmen *n*	decantazione *f*
5052	decanting bottle	verre *m* à clarifier	Klärflasche *f*, Abklärflasche *f*	bottiglia *f* di decantazione
5053	decanting vessel	vase *m* à décanter	Abklärgefäss *n*, Dekantiergefäss *n*	recipiente *m* di decantazione
5054	to decarbonize, decarburize	décarburer	entkohlen	decarburare
5055	decarbonized	décarburé	entkohlt	decarburizzato. decarbonizzato

English	French	German	Italian

decarbonization, *s. decarburization*

decarbonizing, *s. decarburization*

to decarburate, *s. to decarbonize*

°	5056 **decarburation**	décarburation *f*	Entkohlung *f*	decarbonizzazione *f*
°	5057 **decarburization, decarburizing**	décarburation *f*	Entkohlung *f*	decarburazione *f*, decarbonizzazione
°	5058 **decarburize**	décarburer	entkohlen	decarburare

decarburizing, *s. decarburization*

°	5059 **decarburizing period**	période *f* de la combustion du carbone	Garfrischentkohlungs-periode *f*	periogo *m* di decarburazione, periodo *m* di combustione del carbonio
—	5059a **decay**	décomposition *f*	Zersetzung *f*	decomposizione *f*,
—	5060 **dechenite**	dechénite *f*	Dechenit *m*	dechenite *f*
°	5061 **decimal balance**	bascule *f* décimale	Dezimalwaage *f*	bilancia *f* decimale
°	5062 **deci-standard electrode**	électrode *f* décinormale	Dezinormalelektrode *f*	elettrodo *m* decinormale
°	5063 **deck support and stanchion**	épontille *f* de cale et d'entrepont	Schiffsraum- und Deckstütze *f*	puntello *m* di stiva e coperta
—	5064 **decking**	encagement *m*, décagement *m*	Einschieben *n*, Ausschieben *n*	ingabbiamento *m*, sgabbiamento *m*

decline, *s. declivity*

—	5065 **decline**	déclin *m*	Abfall, Rückgang	declino *m*
—	5066 **declivity, slope, decline**	déclivité *f*, pente *f*	Abhang *m*, Abfall *m*	declivio *m*
—	5067 **to decompose**	se décomposer	sich zersetzen	decomporsi
—	5068 **to decompose**	se désagréger	Zerfallen *n*	decomporsi

decomposed, *s. rotten*

—	5069 **decomposition of limestone**	décomposition *f* du calcaire	Zersetzung *f* des Kalksteins	decomposizione *f* del calcare
^	5070 **decomposition of the hydrocarbons**	décomposition *f* des hydrocarbures	Zersetzung *f* der Kohlenwasserstoffe	decomposizione *f* degli idrocarburi
—	5071 **decomposition pressure**	tension *f* de décomposition	Zersetzungsspannung *f*	tensione *f* di decomposizione

	English	French	German	Italian
5072	**decomposition value**	valeur f de décomposition	Zersetzungswert m	valore m di decomposizione
	decomposition voltage, *s. decomposition pressure*			
5073	**to decopper, decuper**	décuivrer	entkupfern	deramare
	decoppered lye, *s. decuparated lye*			
5074	**decopperizing**	décuivrage m	Entkupfern n	deramatura f
5075	**decorative iron**	fer m à dessins	Ziereisen n	ferro m decorativo
5076	**decorative sheet iron**	tôle f découpée	Zierblech n	lamierino m perforato da ornamenti
5077	**to decore**	debourrer	entkernen	sterrare (o asportare) le anime
5078	**decoring**	débourrage m	Entkernen n, Entkernung f	sterratura f (o scarico) delle anime
5079	**decolourizing coal**	charbon m décolorant	Entfärbungskohle f	carbone m scolorante
5080	**decrease of solubility**	diminution f de la solubilité	Löslichkeitsverminderung f	diminuzione f (o calo) della solubilità
5081	**decreasing the unctuosity (of clay)**	amaigrir	mager machen	render magro
5082	**decuperated or decoppered lye**	lessive f décuivrée	entkupferte Lauge f	liscivia f deramata
5083	**dedolomitization**	dédolomitisation f	Dedolomitisation f	dedolomitizzazione f
5084	**deduction for excessive percentage of silicic acid**	déduction f pour excès en silice, phosphore et soufre	Abzug m für Mehrgehalt an Kieselsäure	riduzione f per tenore eccessivo in acido silicico, fosforo e zolfo
5085	**deep drawing sheet**	tôle f pour emboutissage profond	Tiefziehblech n	lamiera f per stampaggio profondo
5086	**deep drawing test**	essai m d'emboutissage	Tiefziehprobe f, Tiefungsversuch m	prova f d'imbutitura
5087	**deep drawn**	embouti à la presse	tiefgezogen	imbutito alla pressa f
5088	**deep drawn product**	produit m embouti	Tiefzieherzeugnis n	imbutito m
5089	**deep drawn piece with slight sideheight**	embouti m de faible profondeur	tiefgezogene Teile m *pl.*, geringer Zargerhoehe	imbutito m di piccolo spessore

	English	French	German	Italian
—	5090 **deep-drilling**	forage *m* à grande prodondeur	Tiefbohrung *f*	trivellazione *f* profonda
°	5091 **deep etch test**	épreuve *f* de macro-attaque	Tiefbeizprobe *f*	prova *f* di macroincisione
—	5092 **deep hole**	forage *m* profond	Tiefbohrung *f*	sondaggio (o foro) profondo
—	5093 **deep level**	voie *f* de fond	Grundstrecke *f*	galleria *f* di fondo, livello *m* inferiore
—	5094 **deep level mining**	exploitation des niveaux inférieurs	Tiefgewinnung *f*	coltivazione *f* dei livelli inferiori
—	5095 **deep mine or level**	exploitation *f* en profondeur	Tiefbau *m*	scavo *m* sotterraneo (o in profondità)
—	5095a **deep mining**	exploitation *f* souterraine	Tiefbau *m*	coltivazione *f* sotterranea
—	5096 **deep-sea deposits** *pl.*	dépôts *m pl.* de la mer profonde	Tiefseeablagerungen *f pl.*	depositi *m pl.* di mare profondo
—	5097 **deep-seated rocks** *pl.*	roches *f pl.* de profondeur	Tiefengesteine *n pl.*	rocce *f pl.* plutoniche
°	5098 **deep-webbed U-iron**	fer *m* en U avec âme de grande hauteur	hochstegisches U-Eisen *n*	ferro *m* U ad anima alta
—	5099 **deep well elevator, ejector**	éjecteur *m* placé dans le puits	Tiefbrunnenelevator *m*	elevatore *m* per pozzi profondi
—	5100 **to deepen**	approfondir	vertiefen	approfondire
—	5101 **deepening**	approfondissement *m*	Abteufen *n*	approfondimento *m*
^	5102 **deethanizer**	deséthanisateur *m*	Entethanisierungsapparat *m*	desetanizzatore *m*
°	5103 **defect due to metal-mould, foam**	mousse *f*	Schaum *m*	schiuma *f*
°	5104 **defect in casting**	défaut *m* de fonderie	Gussfehler *m*	difetto *m* di fonderia
°	5105 **defect in the material**	vice *m* (ou défaut) de matière	Materialfehler *m*, Fehler *m* im Material	difetto *m* di materiale
°	5106 **defect in welding**	défaut (ou vice) de soudure	Schweissfehler *m*	vizio *m* di saldatura
°	5107 **defect point**	endroit *m* défectueux	Fehlstelle *f*	punto *m* difettoso
°	5108 **defective**	défectueux	mangelhaft	difettoso

English	French	German	Italian
5109 **defective casting**	défaut *m* de la fonte	Gussschaden *m*	difetto *m* di ghisa

defective condition of the hearth, *s. deterioration of the hearth*

English	French	German	Italian
5110 **defective portion**	endroit *m* défectueux	Fehlerstelle *f*	˙punto *m* difettoso, parte *f* difettosa
5111 **defective roasting**	grillage *m* défectueux	mangelhafte Röstung *f*	torrefazione *f* difetto-sa
5112 **deferment factor**	coefficient *m* différé	Verschiebungsfaktor *m*	coefficente *m* differito
5113 **deferred production**	production *f* différée	verschobene *f* Produktion	produzione *f* differita
5114 **to deflagrate, to squib**	déflagrer	abbrennen, entzünden	deflagrare
5115 **deflagration, squib**	déflagration *f*	Aufbrennen *n*	deflagrazione *f*
5116 **deflagrator**	déflagrateur *m*	Deflagrator *m*, Minenzünder *m*	deflagratore *m*
5117 **deflation**	déflation *f*	Deflation *f*	deflazione *f*, deviazione
5118 **to deflect**	dévier	ablenken	deviare
5119 **deflecting tools**	déviateurs *m pl.*	Ablenkgerät *n*	deviatori *m pl.*
5120 **deflection**	flèche *f*, déflection	Biegepfeil *m*	freccia *f*, deflezione *f*
5121 **deflector brattice**	cloison *f* d'aérage	Wetterscheider *m*	diaframma *f* di ventila-zione
5121a **deflector roll**	rouleau *m* de guide	Leitrolle *f*	rullo *m* di guida
5122 **deflocculation**	défloculation *f*	Ausflockung *f*	defloculazione *f*
5123 **defoamer**	additif *m* anti-mousse	Entschäumer *m*	antischiuma *m*
5124 **deformability**	déformabilité	Verformungs-vermögen *n*	grado *m* di deformazio-ne, deformabilità *f*
5125 **deformation**	déformation *f*	Verformung *f*	deformazione *m*
5126 **to degas**	dégazer	entgasen	degasare
5127 **degassing, degasifying**	dégazage *m*, dégazation	Entgasung *f*, Entgasen *n*	degassificazione *f*, bonifica *f* chimica
5128 **degassing anneal**	recuit *m* de dégazage	Entgasungsglühen *n*	ricottura *f* di degassifi-cazione
5129 **degassing flux**	dégazant *m*	Entgasungsmittel *n*	degasante *m*

	English	French	German	Italian
o	5130 **to degate**	enlever la coulée	Eingüsse *m pl.* beseitigen	togliere il colame
o	5130a **degreasing**	dégraissage *m*	Entfettung *f*	sgrassaggio *m*
o	5131 **degree of carbonisation**	degré *m* de carburation	Kohlungsgrad *m*	grado *m* di carburazione
o	5132 **degree of dissociation**	degré *m* de dissociation	Dissoziationsgrad *m*	grado *m* di dissociazione
o	5133 **degree of dissociation of a solution**	degré *m* de dissociation d'une solution	Zerfallgrad *m* einer Lösung	grado *m* di dissociazione d'una soluzione
—	5134 **degree of hardness**	degré *m* de dureté	Härtegrad *m*	grado *m* di durezza
o	5135 **degree of hardness**	degré *m* de trempe	Härtegrad *m*	grado *m* di tempera
o	5136 **degree of purity**	degré *m* de pureté	Reinheitsgrad *m*	grado *m* di purezza
o	5137 **degree of ramming**	serre *f*, serrage *m*	Verdichtungsgrad *m*	grado *m* di stivaggio
o	5138 **degree of quality**	degré *m* de qualité	Gütestufe *f*	grado *m* di qualità
o	5139 **degree of silication**	teneur *f* en silice, acidité *f*	Silizierungsgrad *m*	grado *m* d'acidità
—	5140 **dehrnite**	dehrnite *f*	Dehrnit *m*	dehrnite *f*
o	5141 **de-ionization rate**	vitesse *f* spécifique de déionisation	Entionisierungsgeschwindigkeit *f*	velocità *f* di deionizzazione
o	5142 **to deionize**	déioniser	entionisieren	deionizzare
o	5143 **deironing**	déferrisation *f*	Eisenabtrennung *f*	separare il ferro
—	5144 **delafossite**	delafossite *f*	Delafossit *m*	delafossite *f*
o	5145 **delay release**	relais *m* à retardement	Zeitschalter *m*	relé *m* a tempo, interruttore *m* a tempo
—	5146 **delessite**	delessite *f*	Delessit *m*	delessite *f*
—	5147 **delf**	filon *m*, couche *f*, chantier	Gang *m*, Schicht *f*, Grubenbau *m*, Grube *f*	filone *m*, strato *m*, giacimento *m*, cantiere *m*, miniera *f*, pozzo *m*
o	5148 **delivery, mouth**	rétrécissement *m* du creuset	Verjüngung *f*	orlo *m* o bocca *f* del crogiuolo
^	5149 **delivery**	refoulement *m*	Druck *f*	erogazione *f*, mandata *f*
o	5150 **delivery air chamber**	réservoir *m* d'air de la conduite de refoulement	Druckwindkessel *m*	camera *f* d'aria premente

	English	French	German	Italian
o	5151 delivery conduit	conduite f de refoulement	Druckleitung f	condotta f premente, tubo m di mandata
—	5152 delivery-end	pied m de taille	Strebausgang m	piede m del taglio
o	5153 delivery of ore	arrivage m des minerais	Anfahren n der Erze	arrivo m dei minerali
o	5154 delivery pipe	tuyau m de refoulement	Druckrohr n, Steigrohr n	tubo m premente, tubo m di mandata
o	5154a delivery ramp	rampe f de sortie	Abfuhrrampe f	rampa f d'uscita
—	5155 dellenite	dellénite f	Dellenit m	dellenite f
—	5156 delorenzite	délorenzite f	Delorenzit m	delorenzite. f
o	5157 delta iron	fer m delta	Delta-Eisen n	ferro-delta m
o	5158 delta metal	métal m delta	Deltametall n	metallo m delta
—	5159 deltaite	deltaïte f	Deltait m	deltaite f
—	5160 delvauxite	delvauxite f	Delvauxit m	delvauxite f
—	5161 to delve	creuser, approfondir	abteufen, graben	approfondire, scavare
o	5161a demagnetization	démagnétisation f	Entmagnetisierung f	demagnetizzazione f
o	5162 demagnetizing apparatus, demagnetizer	démagnétisateur m	Entmagnetisiergerät n	apparecchio m smagnetizzante, smagnetizzatore m
o	5163 demand of fuel	combustible m nécessaire	Brennstoffbedarf m	fabbisogno m di combustibile
—	5164 demantoid	demantoïde f	Demantoid m	demantoide f
—	5165 demethanisation	déméthanisation f	Entmethanisierung f	demetanizzazione f
o	5166 demountable	démontable	zerlegbar	smontabile
^	5167 demulsifier	désémulsionnant m	Demulgator m	demulsificatore m
—	5168 dendrite	dendrite f	Dendrit m	dendrite f
—	5169 dendritic, arborescent	dendritique	dendritisch	dendritico
—	5170 dennisonite	dennisonite f	Dennisonit m	dennisoite f
	dense, s. close-grained			
o	5171 dense charge	chargement m serré	dichte Lagerung f	caricamento m compresso o compatto
o	5172 dense iron ore	minerai m de fer dense	dichtes Eisenerz n	minerale m di ferro a struttura compatta

	English	French	German	Italian
°	5173 dense slag aggregate concrete block	bloc *m* dur en béton de laitier	Hüttenhartstein *m*	agglomerato *m* duro di scorie
°	5174 densener	refroidisseur *m* de forme, coquille *f* extérieure	profilierte Schreckplatte *f*	raffreddatore *m*, refrigerante *m*
—	5175 densifier, thickner	épaississeur *n*	Eindickmaschine *f*, Verdickungsmaschine	addensatore *m*
°	5176 density	densité *f*	Dichte *f*	densità *f*
	density, *s. grain size*			
^	5177 density of a gas	densité *f* d'un gaz	Gasdichte *f*	densità *f* d'un gas
°	5178 dent	bosse *f*	Beule *f*	ammaccatura *f*
°	5178a deoxydant	désoxydant *m*	Reduktionsmittel *n*	deossidante *m*
°	5179 deoxydation	désoxydation *f*	Desoxydation *f*	disossidazione *f*, deossidazione *f*
—	5180 denver mud	bentonite *f*	Bentonit *m*	bentonite *f*
—	5181 denudation-plain	pénéplaine *f*	Rumpffläche *f*	penepiano *m*
°	5182 deoxidizer	désoxydant *m*	Entsäuerungsmittel *n*	disossidante *m*, deossidante
°	5183 deoxidization, deoxidation	désoxydation *f*	Desoxydation *f*	deossidazione *f*
°	5184 deoxidize	désoxyder	desoxydieren	deossidare
°	5185 deoxidizing addition	addition *f* désoxydante	sauerstoffaufnehmender Zuschlag *m*	addizione *f* riduttrice
^	5186 dephlegmator	déflegmateur *m*	Dephlegmator *m*	deflemmatore *m*
°	5187 dephosphorising period	période *f* de déphosphoration	Entphosphorungszeit *f*	periodo *m* di defosforazione
°	5188 dephosphoration or dephosphorization	déphosphoration *f*	Entphosphorung *f*	defosforazione *f*
°	5189 dephosphorize, dephosphorise	déphosphoriser	entphosphoren	defosforare
—	5190 depleted area	surface *f* drainée	entwässerte Oberfläche *f*	superficie *f* drenata
—	5191 depleted sand	sable *m* drainé	entwässerter Sand *m*	sabbia *f* drenata
^	5192 depletion (of gas)	déplétion *f* (de gaz)	Gasentlösungstrieb *m*	esaurimento *m* (di gas)

	English	French	German	Italian
5193	depletion	abbaissement *m* de concentration	Konzentrations- Herabsetzung *f*	abbassamento *m* della concentrazione
5194	depleted reservoir	gisement *m* épuisé	erschöpftes (Erdöl) Vorkommen *n*	giacimento *m* esaurito
5194a	depolarization	dépolarisation *f*	Depolarisation *f*	depolarizzazione *f*
	deposit, *s. body or bed*			
5195	deposit of flue dust	dépôt *m* d'escarbilles	Flugascheablagerung *f*	deposito *m* di cenere volante
5196	deposit of graphit	dépôt *m* de graphite	Graphitablagerung *f*	deposito *m* di grafite
5197	deposit of iron ores	gisement *m* de minerai de fer	Eisenerzlagerstätte *f*	giacimento *m* di minerali di ferro
	deposit weld, *s. building up by weld*			
5198	deposited metal	métal *m* d'apport	aufgeschweisstes Metall *n*	metallo *m* depositato
5199	deposited moraine	moraine *f* déposée	Stapelmoräne *f*	morena *f* depositata
	depositing-out tank, *s. liberator tank*			
5200	deposition	dépôt *m*	Ablagerung *f*	deposito *m*
	deposition efficiency, *s. metal distribution ratio*			
5201	depressant	dépresseur *m*	Inhibitor *m*	inibitore *m*
5202	depropanation	dépropanation *f*	Entpropanisierung *f*	depropanazione *f*
5203	depth	extension *f* en profondeur	Tiefenerstreckung *f*	estensione *f* in profondità
5204	depth gauge	jauge *f* de profondeur, pied *m* de profondeur	Tiefenlehre *f*	calibro *m* di profondità
5205	depth of casting	hauteur *f* de la piece coulée	Abgusstiefe *f*	altezza *f* del pozzo colato
5206	depth of chill	profondeur *f* de trempe	Härtetiefe *f*	profondità *f* di tempra
5207	depth of hardening	pénétration *f* de trempe	Haertungstiefe *f*	penetrazione *f* di tempra
5208	depth of hearth	profondeur *f* de la sole du four	Herdtiefe *f*	altezza *f* del focolare
	depth of indentation, *s. indentation*			
5209	depth of penetration	profondeur *f* de pénétration	Eindringtiefe *f*	profondità *f* di penetrazione
5210	depth of round	avancement *m*	Abschlaglänge *f*, Vortrieb *m*	avanzamento *m*

	English	French	German	Italian
o	5211 **depuration**	dépuration *f*	Rëinigung *f*	depurazione *f*
—	5212 **derbylite**	derbylite *f*	Derbylith *m*	derbylite *f*
—	5213 **dermolith**	dermolithe *f*	Dermolith *m*	dermolite *f*
—	5214 **derrick**	tour *f* de sondage	Bohrturm *m*	torre *f* di perforazione torre *f* di trivellazione
—	5215 **derrick braces**	entretoises *f pl.* de la tour de sondage	Streben *f pl.* des Bohrturmes	diagonali *m pl.* o contro venti *m pl.* della torre di sondaggio
—	5216 **derrick cellar**	avant-puits *m*	Bohrturmkeller *m*, Vorschacht *m*	avanpozzo *m* , cantina *f*
—	5217 **derrick earth anchors**	ancrage *m* à terre pour les entretoises de la tour	Verankerung *f* gegen Turmwind	ancore *f pl.* entroterra per i venti della torre
—	5218 **derrick floor, derrick platform**	plancher *m* de manoeuvre	Arbeitsbühne *f*	piano *m* (di manovra) della torre *f* di trivellazione
—	5219 **derrick grip, type rock anchors**	ancrage *m* en roche pour toises de la tour	Verankerung *f* im Gestein gegen Turmwind	ancora *f* per roccia per i venti della torre
—	5220 **derrick leg**	jambe *f* de la tour	Turmständer *m*	gamba *f* della torre (di perforazione)
—	5221 **derrick man**	gruiste *m*	Turmsteiger *m*	pontista *m*
^	5222 **DERV fuel (Diesel Engine Road Vehicle Fuel)**	combustible DERV	DERV Brennstoff *m*	combustibile DERV
o	5223 **descaled**	écrouté	geschält	scrostato
o	5224 **descaler**	décalamineur *m*	Entzunderungs-apparat *m*	decalaminatore *m*, scrostatore *m*
o	5225 **descaling, pickling, sand-blasting, tumbling**	décalaminage *m*	Entzunderung *f*	scagliatura *f*, decalaminazione, disincrostazione (fucinatura)

descaling blowpipe, *s. flame cleaning blowpipe*

	English	French	German	Italian
—	5226 **to descend, to drop**	descendre	abwärts gleiten	discendere
—	5227 **descending horizontal slicing**	exploitation *f* par tranches horizontales descendantes	Scheibenbau *m* in der Reihenfolge von oben nach unten	coltivazione *f* a trance orizzontali discendenti
—	5228 **descent and ascent**	descente *f* et remontée	Ab-und Aufstieg *m*	discesa *f* e salita

English	French	German	Italian

5229 **descloizite** descloizite *f* Descloizit *m* descloizite *f*
    deseaming, *s. flame scarfing*

5230 **to design the passes** tracer les canne- die Kaliber tracciare i profili (o
    lures entwerfen le scanalature)

5231 **design of rolls, roll** calibrage *m* des Kalibrierung *f* der tracciato *m* dei canali
    drafting cylindres Walzen

5232 **desiccator** dessicateur *m*, Entfeuchter *m* essiccatore. *m*
    séchoir *m*

5233 **desiccator disc** support *m* en porce- Porzellaneinsatz *m* sopporto *m* di porcella-
    laine du dessicateur des Exsiccators na dell'essiccatore

5234 **designation of marks** désignation des Markenbezeichnung denominazione *f* della
    marques *f* qualità

5235 **desilication,** désilicification *f* Entsilizierung *f* desilicificazione *f*
    desiliconization

5236 **desiliconize** désilicifier entsilizieren desilicificare

5237 **to desilt, to deslime** décrotter abschlämmen sfangare

5238 **desilting, desliming** décroûtage *f* Abschlämmung *f* defangatura *f*, sfangatura

5239 **desilver** désargenter entsilbern disargentare

5240 **to deslag** décrasser abschlacken, schiumare, scorificare
    ausschlacken

    to deslime, *s. to desilt*

5241 **deslimer** débourbeur *m* Abschlackmaschine *f* sfangatrice *f*,
    sfangatore *m*

    desliming, *s. desilting*

5242 **desmine** desmine *f* Desmin *m* stilbite *f*

5243 **destinezite** destinézite *f* Destinezit *m* destinezite *f*

5244 **desulphurization** désulfuration *f* Entschwefelung *f* desolforazione *f*

5245 **desulphurize** désulfurer entschwefeln desolforare

5246 **desulphurized pig** fonte *f* désulfurée entschwefeltes ghisa *f* desolforata
    iron Roheisen *n*

5247 **desulphurizer** désulfurant *m* Entschwefeler *m* desolforante *m*

5248 **desulphurizing** briquette *f* entschwefelnder bricchetto *m* desolfo-
    briquette désulfurante Ziegel *m* rante

	English	French	German	Italian
⌃ 5249	desuperheater	désurchauffeur *m*	Entüberhitzer *m*	desurriscaldatore *m*
— 5250	detachable bit, jack-bit	taillant *m* à vis, jack-bit	Einsatzschneide *f*	tagliante *m* a vite, punta di trapano smontabile
° 5251	detachable forged catch	entraîneur *m* forgé amovible	aufsteckbarer, geschmiedeter Mitnehmer *m*	attacco *m* fucinato
° 5252	detachable part	partie *f* rapportée, partie *f* amovible	Formeinsatz *m*	parte *f* riportata, parte smontabile
° 5253	detached arch core	noyau anticlinal étranglé	abgeschnürter Sattelkern *m*	nucleo eroso dell'anticlinale
— 5254	to detar	dégoudronner	entleeren	decatramare
— 5255	detarring	dégoudronnage *m*	Entleerung *f*	decatramatura *f*
° 5255a	detergent	détergent *m*	Reinungsmittel *n*	detergente *m*
° 5256	deterioration of the hearth	détérioration du creuset	Schadhaftwerden *n* des Gestelles	deterioramento *m* del crogiuolo
° 5257	determination of calorific value	détermination *f* de la puissance calorifique *f*	Heizwertbestimmung *f*	determinazione *f* del potere calorico
° 5258	determination of carbon	dosage *m* du carbone	Kohlenstoffbestimmung *f*	dosaggio *m* del carbonio
° 5259	determination of density	détermination *f* de la densité	Dichtebestimmung *f*	determinazione *f* della densità

determination of hardness, *s. measurement of hardness*

	English	French	German	Italian
° 5260	determination of single substances	dosage *m* d'un seul corps	Einzelbestimmung *f*	determinazione *f* di un solo corpo
° 5261	determination of solubility	détermination *f* de la solubilité	Löslichkeitsbestimmung *f*	determinazione *f* della solubilità
° 5262	determination of the conductivity	détermination *f* de la conductance	Leitfähigkeitsbestimmung *f*	determinazione *f* della conduttanza
° 5263	to determine the calorific value	déterminer la puissance calorifique	den Heizwert *m* bestimmen	determinare il potere calorifico
° 5264	to determine the calorific value by the calorimetric method	déterminer la puissance calorifique par voie calorimétrique	den Heizwert durch einen Heizwertmesser ermitteln	determinare il potere calorifico col calorimetro
° 5265	to detin, dezinficate	désétamer	entzinnen	dezincare
° 5265a	detinning	désétamage *m*	Entzinnen *n*	dezincatura *f*

English	French	German	Italian
5266 **detrimental constituent**	substance *f* nuisible	schädlicher Bestandteil *m*	elemento *m* nocivo, sostanza *f* nociva
5267 **detritus**	galets *m pl.*, cailloux roulés	Geschiebe *n*, Geschiebemasse *f*	ciottoli *m pl.*
5268 **deuteric**	deutérique	deuterisch	deuterico
deuterium, *s. heavy hydrogen*			
5269 **deuterogene**	deutérogène	klastisch	clastico. deuterogeno
5270 **deuteromorphic**	deutéromorphique	deuteromorph	deuteromorfico
deuteroprism, *s. prism of the second order*			
5271 **to develop**	préparer	vorrichten	preparare (minerali)
5272 **to develop**	développer	entwickeln	sviluppare, rivelare
5273 **developed ore**	minerai préparé	vorgerichtetes Erz *n*	minerale *m* preparato
5274 **developing**	traçage *m*	Vorrichtung *f*	preparazione *f*, tracciato *m*
5275 **development**	développement *m*	Entwicklung *f*	sviluppo *m*
5276 **development end**	front *m* d'avancement	Arbeitsstoss *m*	avanzamento *m*, fronte *m* d'avanzamento
5277 **development of the texture**	développement *m* de la texture	Entwicklung *f* des Gefüges	sviluppo della tessitura
5278 **development stoping**	abattage *m* en traçage	Förderung *f* aus der Vorrichtung	abbattimento *m* secondo tracciato
5279 **development work**	travail *m* d'accès et de traçage	Ausrichtungs- und Vorrichtungsarbeiten *f pl.*	lavori *m pl.* di accesso e di preparazione
5280 **deviation**	déviation *f*	Abweichung *f*	deviazione *f*
5281 **device for loosening and tightening the nuts**	appareil *m* pour serrer et dégager les boulons	Vorrichtung *f* zum Lockern und Anziehen der Schrauben	tenditore *m*, serraviti *m*
5282 **devil**	chambrière *f*	Remmstange *f*	barra *f* di blocco
5282a **devil**	pot *m* à feu	Feuertopf *m*	caldano *m*
5283 **devil's dice**	limonite *f* en cubes	Limonitwürfel *m*	limonite *f* in cubi
5283a **devitrification**	dévitrification *f*	Entglasung *f*	devetrificazione *f*
5284 **Devonian**	Dévonien *m*	Devon *n*	devoniano *m*
5285 **devonite**	devonite *f*	Devonit *m*	devonite
5286 **dew point**	point *m* de rosée	Taupunkt *m*	punto *m* di rugiada
5287 **dewalquite**	dewalquite *f*	Dewalquit *m*	dewalquite *f*

English	French	German	Italian
— 5288 **to dewater**	déshydrater	entwässern	disidratare
— 5289 **dewaterer**	déshydrateur *m*	Entwässerer *m*, Wasserentzieher *m*	deidratatore *m*
— 5290 **dewaterer**	égoutteur *m*	Entwässerungs- maschine *f*	scolatrice *f*
— 5291 **dewatering**	déshydratation *f*	Wasserentziehung *f*	deidratazione *f*
— 5292 **dewatering**	épuisement *m*, dénoyage *m*	Entwässerung *f*, Sümpfen *n*	prosciugamento *m*, drenaggio *m*
— 5293 **dewatering machine**	décanteur *m*	Sandrückgewinnungs- maschine *f*	decantatrice *f*
— 5294 **dewatering screen**	tamis *m* d'égouttage	Entwässerungssieb *n*	vaglio *m* di drenaggio
— 5295 **dewatering tank**	cuve *f* de décantation	Klärbehälter *m*	bacino *m* (o vasca *f*) di decantazione
^ 5296 **dewaxed (lubricating) oil**	huile *f* déparaffinée	entparaffiniertes Öl *n*	olio *m* deparaffinato
^ 5296a **dewaxing**	déparaffinage *m*	Entparaffinieren *n*	deparaffinazione *f*
— 5297 **deweylite**	deweylite *f*	Deweylith *m*	deweylite *f*
— 5298 **dewindtite**	dewindtite *f*	Dewindtit *m*	dewindtite *f*
° 5299 **dezincification**	dézincage *m*	Entzinkung *f*	dezincatura *f*
— 5300 **diabase**	diabase *f*	Grünsteinschiefer *m*	diabase *f*
° 5301 **diabolo-shaped**	en forme *f* de diabolo	schleuderkreisel- ähnlich	a forma *f* di diabolo
— 5302 **diaboleite**	diaboléite *f*	Diaboleit *m*	diaboleite *f*
— 5303 **diaclase**	diaclase *f*	Diaklase *f*	diaclasi *f*
— 5304 **diadochite**	diadochite *f*	Diadochit *m*	diadochite *f*
— 5305 **diaftoresis**	diaftorèse *f*	Diaphtorese *f*	diaftoresi *f*
— 5306 **diagenesis**	diagenèse *f*	Diagenese *f*	diagenesi *f*
— 5308 **diagonal fault, oblique fault**	faille *f* diagonale, faille *f* oblique	diagonale Verwerfung *f*, schief- streichende Verwerfung *f*	faglia *f* diagonale
— 5309 **diagonal joint**	cassure *f* diagonale	diagonale Spalte *f*	frattura *f* diagonale, giunto *m* diagonale
° 5310 **diagonal rolling**	laminage *m* diagonal	Schrägwalzen *n*	laminazione *f* diagonale

English	French	German	Italian
5311 **diagonal ventilation**	aérage *m* diagonal	diagonale Wetterführung *f*	ventilazione *f* diagonale
5312 **diagram**	diagramme *m*	Schaubild *n*	diagramma *f*
5313 **dial**	boussole *f* de minière	Grubenkompass *m*	bussola *f* da miniera
5314 **diagram of solidification**	diagramme *m* de solidification	Erstarrungsbild *n*, Erstarrungsdiagramm	diagramma *m* delle proporzioni di solidificazione
5315 **dialogite**	dialogite *f*	Dialogit *m*	dialogite *f*, rodocrosite *f*
5316 **diamagnetic**	diamagnétique	quermagnetisch, diamagnetisch	diamagnetico
5317 **diamant mortar**	mortier díamant	Diamantmörser *m*	mortaio *m* d'acciaio diamante
5318 **diameter of furnace**	diamètre *m* du fourneau	Ofendurchmesser *m*	diametro *m* del forno
	diameter of the electrode tip, *s. tip diameter*		
5319 **diameter of wire**	épaisseur *m* du fil	Drahtstärke *f*	grossezza *f* o spessore del filo di ferro
5320 **diamond cleavage**	écailles *f pl.* de diamant	Diamantschlacke *f*	scaglie *f* di diamante
5321 **diamond core drilling, diamond coring**	carottage *m* au diamant	Diamantbohren *n*	carotaggio *m* con corona a diamanti
5322 **diamond crown**	couronne *f* à diamants	Diamantkrone *f*	corona *f* a diamanti
5323 **diamond-drill bit, crown**	outil *m* de forage à couronne de diamant	Kranz der Diamant-Bohrmaschine *f*	scalpello *m* a diamanti
5324 **diamond drill**	foret *m* au diamant	Diamantbohrer *m*	fioretto a punta di diamante, perforatore a punta di diamante
5325 **diamond drilling**	sondage *m* au diamant	Diamantbohren *n*	trivellazione *f* con scalpello a diamanti
5326 **diamond mesh**	tôle *f* étirée avec mailles en forme de losange	Streckmetallblech *n* mit Rhombusmuster	lamiera *f* stirata con maglia a losanga
5327 **diamond pass**	cannelure *f* quadrangulaire	Vierkantkaliber *n*	scanalatura *f* quadrangolare

	English	French	German	Italian
°	5328 diamond plate	plaque *f* en losange	Rautenblech *n*	lastra *f* romboidale
—	5329 diamond point bit	trépan *m* pointu	Spitzmeissel *m*	trapano *m* a punta di diamante
—	5330 diamond rock drill crown	couronne *f* à diamants	Diamantbohrkrone *f*	corona *f* a diamanti
—	5331 diamond rubbish	rebuts *m pl.* de diamants	Diamantabfälle *m pl.*, Bort *m*	detriti *m pl.* e frammenti *m pl.* di diamante
—	5332 diamond spar	corindon *m*	Korund *m*	corindone *m*
°	5333 diamond switch	croisement *m* double	Doppelherzstück *n*	scambio *m*, incrocio doppio
°	5333a diamond wheel	meule *f* diamantée	Diamantschleif-scheibe *f*	mola *f* diamantata
—	5334 diamorphism	diamorphisme *m*	Diamorphismus *m*	diamorfismo *m*
—	5335 diaphorite	diaphorite *f*	Diaphorit *m*	diaforite *f*
°	5336 diaphragm	vase *m* poreux	Tonzelle *f*, Dia-phragma *n*	diaframma *m* di terra-cotta
°	5337 diaphragm	écran *m*	Blende *f*	diaframma *m*
^	5338 diaphragm pump	pompe *f* à membrane	Membranpumpe *f*	pompa *f* a membrana
—	5339 diapir	diapir *m*	Diapyr *m*	diapiro *m*
—	5340 diapir structure	structure *f* diapirique	Diapyrstruktur *f*	struttura *f* diapirica
—	5341 diaschistic	diaschiste	diaschistisch	diascistico
—	5342 diaspore	diaspore *m*	Diaspor *m*	diasporo *m*
°	5343 diastrophism	diastrophisme *m*	Diastrophismus *m*	diastrofismo *m*
—	5344 diatom ooze	boue à diatomées *f*	Diatomeenschlamm *m*	fango *m* a diatomei
—	5345 diatomaceous earth	terre *f* à diatomées	Kieselgur *f*, Diatomeenerde *f*	terra *f* a diatomei, diatomite *f*
°	5346 diatomic molecule	molécule *f* biato-mique	zweiatomiges Molekül *n*	molecola *f* biatomica
—	5347 diatreme	diatrème *f*	Diatreme *f*, Diatrema	diatrema *f*
—	5348 dichroic mineral	minerai *m* dichroïque	dichroisches Mineral	minerale *m* dicroico
—	5349 dichroism	dichroïsme *m*	Dichroismus *m*	dicroismo *m*
—	5350 dichroite	dichroïte *f*	Dichroit *m*	dicroite *f*, cordierite *f*

	English	French	German	Italian
5351	**dickinsonite**	dickinsonite f	Dickinsonit m	dickinsonite f
5352	**dickite**	dickite f	Dickit m	dickite f
5353	**didymium**	didyme m	Didym n	didimio m
5354	**to die cast**	couler en coquille, couler sous pression	spritzen	fondere sotto pressione, fondere in conchiglia
5355	**to die out, to taper out**	finir, terminer	auskeilen, verschwinden	finire, terminare
5356	**die, form**	moule m	Form f	stampo m, matrice f
5357	**die, metallic mold**	filière f	Ziehstein m	filiera f
5358	**die, permanent die**	coquille f, moule m métallique	Kokille f, metallische Form f	conchiglia f, stampo m permanente
5359	**die assembly, die-block**	dispositif m de blocage	Sperrvorrichtung f	dispositivo m di bloccaggio, blocca-stampo m
	die-block, $s.$ *die assembly*			
5359a	**die body**	part f fixe du moule	fester Stempelteil m	parte f fissa dello stampo
5360	**die cast, die casting**	coulée f en coquille	Schalenguss m	colata f in conchiglia, fusione f sotto pressione
5361	**die-cast alloy**	alliage m coulé sous pression	Legierungsguss m unter Druck	lega f colata sotto pressione
5362	**die casting**	moulage mécanique (ou sous pression)	Spritzguss m	pressofusione, fusione f sotto pressione
5363	**die-casting machine**	machine f de moulage par pression	Spritzgussmaschine f	macchina f per fusione sotto pressione
5364	**die coating**	poteyage m pour moule	Formschlichte f	lubrificante m, rivestimento m per stampi
5365	**die collar**	filière f de repêchage	Gewindeschneidmuffe f	campana f filettante di pescaggio
5366	**die counter lock**			tallone m di reazione
5367	**die coupling**	cloche f ou filière de repêchage	Fangglocke f	pescatore m a campana, filiera f per tubi, corona f
5368	**die dressing**	lubrifiant m pour moules	Gesenkschmierstoff m	lubrificante m per stampi
5369	**die mark**	rainure f (ou cannelure f, ou rayure) d'étirage	Ziehriefe f	scanalatura f (provvisoria) della trafilatura, segno m di trafila

		English	French	German	Italian
°	5370	**die matching**	centrage *m* des moules	Gesenkzentrierung *f*	centratura *f* stampi
°	5371	**die mold**	moule *m* pour moulage sous pression	Spritzgussgesenk *f*	stampo *m* per presso-fusione
^	5372	**die nipple**	taraud *m* de repêchage	Fangnippel *m*	maschio *m* di pescatore
°	5373	**die plate**	filière *f*	Ziehdüse *f*	calibro *m* di trafila, trafila *f*, filiera *f*
°	5374	**die punch of the press**	coulisseau *m* (ou coulant) porte-matrice	(Press)Stempel *m*	slitta *f* porta-matrice
°	5375	**die quenching**	refroidissement *m* entre moules	Gesenkabschrek-kung *f*	raffreddamento *m* entro stampi
°	5376	**die radius**	rayon *m* de matrice	Ziehkante *f*	raggio *m* della matrice
°	5377	**die roll**	cylindre *m* à matricer	Matrizenwalze *f*	cilindro *m* a matrice
°	5378	**die rolling**	laminage *m* entre cylindres	Zylinderwalzen *n*	laminatura *f* fra cilindri
		die score, *s. die mark*			
°	5378a	**die set**	monture *f* d'estampe à guidage à colonnes	Säulenführungs-gestell *n*	blocco *m* di stampo a guida colonnare
	5379	**die socket**	cloche *f* à écrou	Schraubentute *f*	pescatore *m* a campana
°	5380	**die spotting**	adaptation *f* de la moule	Formanpassung *f*	adattamento dello stampo
°	5381	**die steel**	acier *m* à matrices	Gesenkstahl *m*, Matrizenstahl *m*	acciaio *m* da matrici
°	5382	**die temper steel**	acier au 0,75% de C	Stahl *m* mit 0,75% C-Gehalt	acciaio *m* al 0,75% di C
°	5383	**dielectric absorption**	absorption *f* diélectrique	dielektrische Absorption *f*	assorbimento *m* dielettrico
°	5384	**di-electric dryer**	séchoir *m* à haute fréquence	Hochfrequenz-trockner *m*	essiccatore *m* ad alta frequenza
°	5385	**dielectric furnace**	four *m* diélectrique	dielektrischer Ofen *m*	forno *m* dielettrico
°	5386	**dielectric heating**	chauffage *m* diélectrique	dielektrische Heizung *f*	riscaldamento *m* dielettrico
—	5387	**dienerite**	diénérite *f*	Dienerit *m*	dienerite *f*

English	French	German	Italian
5388 **Diesel fuel**	carburant *m* Diesel	Dieseltreibstoff *m*	carburante *m* Diesel
5389 **Diesel index**	index *m* Diesel	Dieselindex *m*	indice *m* Diesel
5390 **dietrichite**	dietrichite *f*	Dietrichit *m*	dietrichite *f*
5391 **dietzeite**	dietzéite *f*	Dietzeit *m*	dietzeite *f*
5392 **Differdinger rolled section**	fer *m* à I à larges ailes	Differdinger Eisen *n*, breitflanschiges I-Eisen *n*	ferro *m* a doppio T a larga suola
5393 **difference in analysis**	différence *f* dans les analyses	Analysenunter-schied *m*	differenza *f* d'analisi
5394 **difference in thickness**	différence *f* d'épaisseur	Dickenabweichung *f*	variazione *f* o differenza *f* di spessore
5395 **differential coating**	revêtement *m* différentiel	verschiedenartig aufgebrachter Überzug *m*	rivestimento *m* differenziale
5395a **differential cooling**	refroidissement *m* sélectif	selektive Erhitzung *f*	raffreddamento *m* differenziale
5396 **differential wall sticking**	collage *m* différentiel	Festwerden *n* durch Differenzdruck	incollaggio *m* differenziale
5397 **differentiated dyke**	dyke *m* différencié	differenzierter Gesteinsgang *m*	dicco *m* differenziato
5398 **difficult hardening**	trempe *f* difficile	schwierige Härtung *f*	tempra *f* difficile
5399 **difficult reduction**	réductibilité *f* difficile	schwere Reduzierbarkeit *f*	riducibilità *f* difficile, riduzione *f* difficile
5400 **difficultly reducible ore**	minerai *m* difficile-ment réductible	schwer reduzierbares Erz *n*	minerale *m* difficilmente riducibile
5401 **diffraction mottling**	taches *f pl.* de diffraction	Diffraktionsflecken	macchie *f pl.* di diffrazione
diffraction pattern, *s. normal spectrum*			
5402 **diffuser, diffusor**	diffuseur *m*	Verteilerzapfen *m*	diffusore *m*
5403 **diffusion**	diffusion *f*	Diffusion *f*	diffusione *f*
5403a **diffusion bonding**	corroyage *m* par dif-fusion	Diffusionschweis--sung *f*	saldatura *f* a caldo per diffusione
5404 **to dig up**	creuser	aufgraben	scavare
5405 **digester**	autoclave *m* tubulaire	Autoklaventrommel *f*	autoclave *f*
5406 **digestor**	marmite *f* de Papin	Papinscher Topf *m*	pentola *f* di Papin
5407 **digging**	fouille *f*, prospection	Schürfung *f*, Schurf *m*	scavo *m*, ricerca *f*, esplorazione *f*

	English	French	German	Italian
— 5408	**diggings**	gisements *m pl.*, mines *f pl.*, fouilles *f pl.*, ouvrages *f pl.* souterrains	Lagerstätten *f pl.*, Gruben *f pl.*, Grubenbaue *m pl.*, Schürfungen *f pl.*	giacimenti *m pl.*, miniere *f*, scavi *m pl.*, opere *f pl.* sotterranee
— 5409	**dihydrite**	dihydrite *f*	Dihydrit *m*	dihidrite *f*
— 5410	**dike**	filon *m* rocheux	Gesteinsgang *m*	dicco *m*, filone *m* eruttivo
— 5411	**dike-rocks** *pl.*, **hypabyssal rocks** *pl.*	roches *f pl.* filoniennes	Ganggesteine *n pl.*	roccè *f pl.* filoniane
° 5412	**dilatation**	allongement *m*, dilatation *f*	Dehnung *f*	dilatazione *f*
° 5413	**dilatometer**	dilatomètre *m*	Dilatometer *n*, Dehnungsmesser *m*	dilatometro *m*
° 5414	**dilatometric test**	examen *m* dilatométrique	dilatometrische Prüfung *f*	esame *m* dilatometrico
— 5415	**dillies**	petit plan *m* incliné	kurzer Bremsberg *m*	piccolo piano *m* inclinato
^ 5416	**diluent still**	appareil *m* de distillation du diluant	Verdünnungsmittel-destillierapparat *m*	distillatore *m* del diluente
5417	**diluted acid**	acide *m* dilué	verdünnte Säure *f*	acido *m* diluito
° 5418	**diluting agent**	matière *f* pour retarder la cémentation oxydante	Verdünnungsmittel *n*	sostanza *f* per ritardare la cementazione ossidante
— 5419	**diluvial**	diluvial	diluvial	diluviale
— 5420	**diluvium**	diluvium *m*	Diluvium *n*	diluvio *m*
5421	**dimension**	dimension *f*	Abmessung *f*	dimensione *f*
5422	**dimensional accuracy**	précision *f* dimensionnelle	Massgenauigkeit *f*	esattezza *f* della misura
5423	**dimensional variation**	tolérance *f* dimensionnelle	Massabweichung *f*	tolleranza *f* dimensionale
° 5424	**dimensions of the casting**	dimensions *f pl.* de la pièce de fonte	Abmessung *f* des Gussstückes	dimensioni *f pl.* del pezzo di ghisa
	dimetric system, *s. tetragonal system*			
— 5425	**dimorphism**	dimorphisme *m*	Dimorphie *f*	dimorfismo *m*
— 5426	**dimorphous**	dimorphe	dimorphisch	dimorfico

	English	French	German	Italian
—	5427 **Dinantian stage**	Dinantien *m*	Dinantien *n*	dinantiano *m*
	5428 **Dinas brick**	brique *f* Dinas	Dinasziegel *m*	mattone *m* Dinas
ɔ	5428a **ding**	bosse *f*	Beule *f*	ammaccatura *f*
—	5429 **diopside**	diopside *m*	Diopsid *m*	diopside *f*
—	5430 **dioptase**	dioptase *m*	Dioptas *m*	dioptasio *m*
—	5431 **diorite**	diorite *f*	Diorit *m*	diorite *f*
ɔ	5432 **to dip**	plonger	eintauchen	affondare, immergere
ɔ	5433 **to dip**	plonger	einsenken	immergere
	dip, *s. inclination*			
ɔ	5434 **dip brazing**	brasage *m* à immersion	Tauchhartlöten *n*	brasatura *f* ad immersione
ɔ	5435 **dip coat**	potée *f*	Überzugsmasse *f*	terra *f* di fonderia, staffata *f* verde
—	5436 **dip drift, dip entry**	descenderie *f*	flacher Schacht *m*	galleria *f* di ribasso, discenderia *f*, pozzo *m* inclinato
—	5437 **dip fault, transverse fault**	faille *f* transversale, faille *f* orthogonale	Querverwerfung *f*, orthogonale Verwerfung *f*	faglia *f* trasversale, faglia *f* ortogonale
—	5438 **dip fold**	pli *m* plongeant	Tauchfalte *f*	piega *f* in pendenza
—	5439 **dip heading**	descenderie *f*	einfallender Schacht *m*	discenderia *f*
ɔ	5440 **dip heating**	réchauffement *m* par trempe	Tauchheizung *f*	riscaldamento *m* per immersione
—	5441 **dip joint**	diaclase *f* transversale	Querspalte *f*	diaclasi *f* trasversale
—	5442 **dip meter**	stratimètre *m*	Stratimeter *n*	stratimetro *m*
—	5443 **dip-shift**	rejet *m* en profondeur	Abschiebung *f*	rigetto *m* in profondità
—	5444 **dip (or fall) of the stratum**	inclinaison *f* de la couche	Fallen *n* der Schicht	caduta *f* (o inclinazione) dello strato
—	5445 **dip-slip**	rejet *m* en profondeur	Sprungtiefe *f*	rigetto *m* verticale
—	5446 **dip-slip fault**	faille *f* normale	normale Verwerfung *f*	faglia *f* normale
—	5447 **dip up**	creuser	aufgraben	scavare

	English	French	German	Italian
—	5448 **dip working**	exploitation *f* en aval pendage	Unterwerksbau *m*	coltivazione *f* a valle dell'inclinazione
—	5449 **dipper**	godet *m* de pelle mécanique	Löffel *m*	tazza *f* di escavatrice meccanica
—	5450 **dipper dig**	pelle *f* de profondieur	Tieflöffelbagger *m*	escavatrice *f* di profondità
—	5451 **dipper dredge**	pelle *f* mécanique	Greifbagger *m*	pala *f* meccanica
°	5452 **dipping**	décapage *m*	Abbeizen *n*	decapaggio *m*
°	5453 **dipping in molten metals**	immersion *f* en métaux fondus	Eintauchen *n* in schmelzflüssige Metalle	immersione *f* in metalli fusi

dipping against the bed, *s. fault hading against the dip*

dipping with the beds, *s. fault hading with the dip*

	English	French	German	Italian
—	5454 **dipyre**	dipyre *m*	Dipyr *m*	dipiro *m*
—	5455 **dipyrization**	dipyrisation *f*	Skapolitisation *f*	dipirizzazione *f*
°	5456 **to direct the flames on the hearth**	diriger les flammes vers la sole	die Flammen auf den Herd lenken	dirigere la fiamma sulla suola
°	5456a **direct casting**	coulée *f* directe	direktes Ausgiessen	colata *f* diretta
—	5457 **direct coupled roll**	cylindre *m* commandé	ausgetriebene Walze *f*	cilindro *m* direttamente accoppiato

direct flame boiler, *s. direct-draught boiler*

	English	French	German	Italian
°	5458 **direct-draught boiler, through tube**	chaudière *f* à flamme directe	Kessel *m* mit direkter Flamme	caldaia *f* a fiamma diretta
°	5459 **direct heating**	chauffage *m* direct	unmittelbare Heizung *f*	riscaldamento *m* diretto

direct metal, *s. hot metal*

	English	French	German	Italian
°	5460 **direct pressure closing**	fermeture *f* à pression directe	direkter Kraftschluss *m*	chiusura *f* a pressione diretta
°	5461 **direct pressure hot chamber machine**	machine *f* à chambre chaude à pression directe de l'air sur le métal	Druckluftgiessmaschine *f*	macchina *f* con camera calda a pressione pneumatica diretta sul metallo
°	5461a **direct process**	procédé direct	direktes Verfahren	processo *m* diretto
°	5462 **direct production of wrought iron**	extraction *f* directe du fer de son minerai	Rennen *n*	processo *m* diretto, metodo *m* catalano
°	5463 **direct reduction**	réduction *f* directe	direkte Reduktion *f*	riduzione *f* diretta

English	French	German	Italian
5464 **direct steel from the ore process**	acier *m* fabriqué par le procédé au minerai (ou Siemens)	Erzstahl *m*, Uchatiusstahl *m*	acciaio *m* fabbricato col processo Siemens
5465 **direct transmission of power**	action *f* directe	unmittelbare Kraftübertragung *f*	attacco *m* diretto, trasmissione *f* diretta
direction s. *strike*			
5466 **direction of deviation**	direction *f* de la déviation	Abweichungsrichtung *f*	direzione *f* della deviazione
5467 **direction of movement**	sens *m* du mouvement	Bewegungsrichtung *f*	senso *m* del movimento
5468 **directional drilling**	forage *m* dirigé, sondage *m* dirigé	gerichtetes Bohren *n*, dirigiertes Bohren *n*	perforazione direzionale, perforazione deviata
5469 **directional hole**	forage *m* dirigé	Zielbohrung *f*	pozzo *m* direzionale
5470 **directional solidification**	solidification *f* dirigée	gelenkte Erstarrung *f*, gerichtete Erstarrung *f*	solidificazione *f* direzionale
5471 **directional survey**	mesure *f* de déviation	Abweichmessung *f*	misura *f* di deviazione
5472 **directional well**	puits *m* incliné	schräger Schaft *m*	pozzo *m* inclinato
5473 **directions testing testing conditions**	règlement *m* d'essai	Prüfungsvorschrift *f*	regolamento *m* o prescrizioni *f pl.* di prova
5474 **dirt, broken ore**	minerai *m* broyé (ou de rebut)	zerbrochenes Erz *n*	minerale spezzato (o di scarto)
5475 **dirt band, dirt bed**	intercalation *f* stérile	Bergezwischenlage *f*, Bergemittel *n*	intercalazione *f* sterile
5476 **dirt trap**	nid *m* à crasses, piège *m* à crasses	Schlackenfang *m*	fermascorie *m*, parascorie *m*
5476a **dirt gas**	gaz *m* brut	Rohgas *n*	gas *m* grezzo (non lavato)
5477 **dirtied rock**	roche *f* abattue	Haufwerk *n*	roccia *f* abbattuta
5478 **disappearing filament pyrometer**	pyromètre *m* à disparition de filement	Glühfadenpyrometer *n*	pirometro *m* a filamento evanescente
5479 **disc, guard**	disque *m*	Scheibe *f*	cordone *m*, disco *m*
5480 **disc bit**	trépan *m* à disques	Scheibenmeissel *m*	scalpello *m* a disco
5481 **disc compensator**	compensateur *m* à disque	Scheibenausgleicher *m*	disco *m* compensatore, giunto *m* di dilatazione
5482 **disc bit**	trépan *m* à disques	Scheibenmeissel *m*	trapano *m* a dischi

	English	French	German	Italian
— 5483	disc coal-cutting machine	haveuse f à disque	Radschrämmaschine f	intagliatrice f a disco, tagliatrice di carbone a disco
	disc mill, s. *wheel rolling mill*			
	disc piston, s. *solid piston*			
° 5484	disc plug	diaphragme m de coulée	Tümpelverschlussblech n	diaframma m di colata
° 5484a	disc roller	cylindre m à disque	Scheibenwalze f	cilindro m a dischi
° 5485	disc-spring	ressort m à disque	Scheibenfeder f	molla f a disco
° 5486	disc valve	vanne f à siège horizontal	Tellerventil n	valvola f a sede orizzontale (o piana)
° 5487	discard	chute f	Stumpf m, Abfall m	spuntatura f, intestatura f
° 5488	discard head, lost head	jet m, masselotte f, tête f perdue	verlorener Kopf m	massellotta f, materozza f
° 5489	to discharge	déballer	ausleeren	svuotare
^ 5490	discharge	refoulement m	Druck m	mandata f
	discharge, s. *flume*			
— 5491	discharge air shaft	puits m de ventilation	Wetterschacht m	pozzo m di ventilazione
° 5492	discharge from the converter	déchargement m du convertisseur	Birnenauswurf m	scarico m dal convertitore
^ 5493	discharge head	hauteur f d'élévation	Förderhöhe f	prevalenza f, pressione f di mandata
° 5494	discharge hole, bottom door	porte f de vidange	Bodenklappe f	porta f di scarico, porta f per sfornare
^ 5495	discharge maniflod strainer	filtre m sur le refoulement d'une pompe	Pumpendruckfilter n	filtro m sulla mandata di una pompa
^ 5496	discharge pipe	tube m de décharge	Auspuffrohr n	tubo m di scarico
° 5497	discharge pipe	tuyau m de déchargeur	Schüttrohr n	tubo m di gettata
— 5498	discharge towards both sides of the track	déchargement m des deux côtés de la voie	Entladung f nach beiden Seiten des Gleises	scarico m ai due lati del binario
— 5499	discharging	démoulage m	Ausstoss m	scarico m

English	French	German	Italian
5500 **discharging crane**	grue *f* chevalet de transbordement	Verladebockkran *m*	gru *f* di trasbordo a cavalletto
5501 **discharging end**	bande *f* distributrice	Verteilungstrumm *n*	tratto *m* di nastro distributore
5502 **discharging hole**	ouverture *f* de défournement	Ziehöffnung *f*	foro *m* per lo scarico
5503 **disconformity**	pseudo-concordance *f*	unterbrochene gleichförmige Auflagerung *f*	pseudo-concordanza *f*
5504 **to disconnect, to throw out of gear**	débrayer	die Kupplung ausrücken, entkuppeln	disinnestare (il giunto), disinserire
5505 **discordance**	discordance *f*	Schichtungs-diskordanz *f*	discordanza *f*
5506 **discordant fold**	pli disharmonique	unharmonische Falte *f*	piega *f* discordante
5507 **discordant injection**	intrusion discordante	diskordante Intrusion	intrusione discordante
5508 **disengaging drum**	séparateur *m*	Tropfbecher *m*	separatore *m*
5509 **to dish**	emboutir	tiefziehen	imbutire
5510 **to dish (in a forging)**	bomber, cambrer	ausbauchen, aufwölben	eseguire un'impronta cava
5511 **dish**	cuvette *f*	Schale *f*	bacinella *f*
5512 **dish**	creuset *m*	Tiegel *m*	crogiuolo *m*
5513 **dish**	batée *f*	Waschschüssel *f*	trogolo *m*, batea *f*
5514 **dish for sand bath**	capsule *f* pour bain de sable	Sandbadschale *f*	bacinella *f* per bagno di sabbia
5515 **dish plate**	tôle *f* à emboutir	Kuempelblech *n*	lamiera *f* da imbutire
5516 **dished electrode**	électrode *f* capsulée	Schalenelektrode *f*	elettrodo *m* a capsula
dished form, *s. concave form*			
dished plate, *s. buckle plate*			
5517 **dishing**	cambrure *f*	Wölbung *f*	improntatura *f* cava
5517a **dishing**	emboutissage *m*	Tiefziehen *n*	imbutitura *f*
5518 **to disintegrate, to decompose**	tomber en poussière, s'effriter	zerfallen	polverizzarsi, ridursi in polvere

English	French	German	Italian

to disintegrate, *s. to crush*

° 5518a **disintegrated powder** poudre *f* moulue Mahlpulver *n* polvere *f* minuta

disintegration, *s. breaking or crushing*

° 5519 **disintegrator** diviseur *m*, Schleuder *f* disintegratore *m*
    (of sand) désintégrateur *m*

° 5520 **disintegrator,** broyeur *m* centrifuge, Schleudermühle *f* macina *f* centrifuga,
    centrifugal mill désintégrateur *m* disintegratore *f*

— 5521 **disjunctive rocks** roches *f pl.* lose Trümmersedi- rocce *f pl.* sciolte
     disjonctives mente *n pl.*

^ 5522 **disk and doughnut** tour *f* de distillation Destillationsturm *m* torre *f* di distillazione

— 5523 **disk crusher** broyeur *m* à plateau Tellermühle *f* macina *f* a disco

— 5524 **dislocated deposit** gîte *m* disloqué verworfene giacimento dislocato
     Lagerstätte *f*

— 5525 **dislocation,** dislocation *f* Dislokation *f*, dislocazione *f*
    disturbance Lagerungsstörung *f*

— 5526 **dislocator** filon *m* rejeteur Verwerfer *m* dislocatore *m*, filone
     m dislocatore

to dismantle a joint, *s. to dismantle a mould*

— 5527 **dismantling of a floor** décoffrage *m* d'un Entschalung *f* einer disarmo *m* di un solaio
     plancher Decke

^ 5528 **dispensability** fluidité *f* Flüssigkeit *f* scorrevolezza *f*

° 5529 **dispersed corrosion** corrosion *f* dispersée Fleckenkorrosion *f* corrosione *f* a chiazze

° 5530 **dispersed shrinkage** retassure *f* dispersée Mikroporosität *f* porosità *f* diffusa

dispersion hardening, *s. age hardening*

° 5531 **displacable** mobile verschiebbar spostabile

— 5532 **displaced mass** masse *f* charriée Schubmasse *f* falda *f* di scorrimento

displacement, *s. slip or dislocation*

° 5533 **displacement,** spectres *m pl.* de Dislokations-, spettri *m pl.* di sposta-
    velocity and déplacement, de Geschwindigkeits- mento, di velocità e
    acceleration spectra vitesse et und Beschleunigungs- d'accelerazione
     d'accélération spektren *n pl.*

^ 5534 **displacement meter** compteur *m* de Schiebungsmesser *n* misuratore di spiazza-
     déplacement mento

— 5535 **disrupted bed** couche *f* faillée verworfene Schicht *f* filone *m* spaccato

— 5536 **disrupted fold** pli *m* faillé Bruchfalte *f* piega *f* spaccata

English	French	German	Italian
5537 **disruption**	désintégration f	Zerfall m	disintegrazione f
5537a **disruptive strenght**	résistance f disrupti ve	Zerreissfestigkeit f	rigidità f dielettrica
5538 **dissectible**	démontable	zerlegbar	smontabile
5539 **disseminated**	disséminé	eingesprengt	disseminato
5540 **disseminated ore**	minerai m disséminé	eingesprengtes Erz n	minerale m disseminato
5541 **dissemination**	matières f $pl.$ dissé-minées dans la masse	Einsprengung f	minerali m $pl.$ dissemi-nati in una massa
5542 **to dissociate**	dissocier	zerfallen, dissoziieren	dissociare
5543 **dissociation limit**	limite f de dissociation	Dissoziationsgrenze f	limite m di dissocia-zione
5544 **dissociation temperature**	température f de dissociation	Dissoziationstempe-ratur f	temperatura f di disso-ciazione
5545 **dissociation theory**	théorie f de la dissociation	Dissoziationstheorie f	teoria f della disso-ciazione
5546 **dissolvant**	dissolvant m	Lösungsmittel n	solvente m
5547 **to dissolve**	reprendre avec de l'eau ou de l'acide	aufnehmen (mit Wasser oder Säure)	riprendere (con acqua od acido)
5548 **dissolved gas**	gaz m dissous	gelöstes Gas n	gas m $pl.$ disciolti
5549 **dispersing agents**	produits m $pl.$ dispersants	Dispersionsmittel n	agenti m $pl.$ disperden-ti
5550 **distance between rolls**	écartement m des cylindres	Walzenabstand m	distanza f o scarta-mento m dei cilindri
distance from edges, $s.$ $edge$ $distance$			
disthene, $s.$ $kyanite$			
5551 **to distill**	distiller	destillieren	distillare
5552 **to distill, to dry distill**	distiller à sec	entgasen, trocken verdampfen	distillare (a secco), trasformare in gas
5553 **distillating flask**	ballon m pour la distillation	Destillationskolben m	storta f di distilla-zione
5554 **distillating tube**	tube m de distillation	Destillationsröhre f	tubo m di distillazione
5555 **distillation apparatus**	appareil m de distillation	Destillationsapparat m	apparecchio m per la distillazione

		English	French	German	Italian
°	5556	distillation head	ajoute *f* pour appareil de distillation	Destillations- aufsatz *m*	doppio tubo *m* per apparecchio di distillazione
^	5557	distillation loss	perte *f* de distillation	Destillationsverlust *m*	perdita *f* alla distillazione
^	5558	distillation overlap	chevauchement *m* de distillation	Überlappungs- destillation *f*	sovrapposizione *f* di distillazione
^	5559	distillation pot	vase *m* pour la distillation	Destilliertopf *m*	vaso *m* di distillazione
°	5560	distillation receiver	condenseur *m* d'appareil distillatoire	Destillationsvorlage *f*	condensatore *m*
^	5561	distillation residue	résidu *m* de distillation	Destillationsrest *m*	residuo *m* di distillazione
°	5561a	distillation time	durée *f* de cuisson	Destillationszeit *m*	durata *f* di distillazione
		distillation vessel, *s. distillation pot*			
°	5562	distilled water	eau *f* distillée	destilliertes Wasser *n*	acqua *f* distillata
		distilling flask, *s. distillation flask*			
^	5563	distilling plant	installation *f* de distillation	Destillationsanlage *f*	impianto *m* di distillazione
—	5564	distinct cleavage	clivage *m* distinct	deutliche Spaltbarkeit *f*	sfaldatura *f* distinta, clivaggio *m* distinto
°	5565	distorted pattern	modèle *m* déformé	verzogenes Modell *n*	modello *m* deformato (o distorto)
°	5566	distortion	déformation *f*	Verformung *f*, Verzug *m*	deformazione *f*, distorsione *f*
°	5567	distortion by release of internal stresses	déformation *f* par libération des tensions internes	Verzug *m* durch Auslösung innerer Spannungen	deformazione per liberazione dalle tensioni interne
°	5568	distortion in heat treatment	déformation *f* au traitement thermique	Verzug *m* (oder Verformung *f*) durch Wärmebehandlung	deformazione *f* al trattamento termico
°	5569	distortion of moulding box	déformation *f* de châssis	Verformung *f* des Formkastens	deformazione *f* della staffa
		distortion of phase, *s. phase displacement*			
°	5570	distorsion strength, strain strength	résistance *f* à la déformation	Verformungs- festigkeit *f*	resistenza *f* alla deformazione
°	5571	distributing station	centrale *f* de distribution	Verteilungswerk *n*	stazione *f* di distribuzione

	English	French	German	Italian
o	5572 **distributing tube**	tube *m* de distribution	Verteilungsröhre *f*	tubo *m* di distribuzione
o	5573 **distribution of the pig iron**	distribution *f* de la fonte	Verteilung *f* des Roheisens	distribuzione *f* della ghisa
o	5574 **distribution of the stock**	répartition *f* des matières à fondre	Verteilung *f* der Schmelzstoffe	distribuzione *f* della carica
o	5575 **distribution pipe**	tuyau *m* distributeur	Verteilungsrohr *n*, Windkranz *m*	tubo *m* distributore
o	5576 **distributor**	distributeur *m*	Verteiler *m*	distributore *m*, ripartitore *m*
	disturbance, *s. dislocation*			
—	5577 **ditch cuttings, returns**	déblais *m pl.*, farine de sondage	Bohrgut *n*, Bohrmehl *n*	polvere *f* di perforazione
	ditcher, *s. ditch excavator*			
—	5578 **ditching**	exécution *f* des tranchées	Ziehen *n* von Gräben	lavori *m pl.* di trincee
—	5579 **ditroite**	ditroïte *f*	Ditroit *m*	ditroite *f*
—	5580 **divergent columnar**	columnaire en éventail	radialstengelig	colonnare divergente
—	5581 **divergent structure**	structure *f* divergente	radial-strahlige Struktur *f*	struttura *f* divergente
—	5582 **divergent unconformity**	discordance *f* angulaire	Klinodiskordanz *f*	discordanza *f* angolare
	divide, *s. water-shed*			
	divide-line, *s. water-shed*			
o	5583 **divided rule for the rider**	règle *f* du cavalier	Reiterlineal *n*	regolo *m* del cavaliere
—	5584 **divider**	poussard *m*, cloison *f* du puits	Spreize *f*, Schachtscheider *m*	puntello *m*, paratia *f*, diaframma *f*
o	5585 **dividers** *pl.*	compas *m* diviseur	Zirkel *m*, Spitzzirkel *m*	compasso *m* divisore
	division of the rule for the rider, *s. notches of the rule for the rider*			
—	5586 **division plane**	surface *f* de séparation	Trennungsebene *f*	piano *m* di separazione, superfice di divisione

	English	French	German	Italian
°	5587 **divorced annealing** **divorced cementite**, *s. globular cementite*	sphéroïdisation *f*	Weichglühen *n*	sferoidizzazione *f*, ricottura di coalescenza
—	5588 **dixenite**	dixenite *f*	Dixenit *m*	dixenite *f*
°	5589 **to do over with clay**	glaiser	mit Letten bekleiden	rivestire di creta
—	5590 **docrystalline** **doctor**, *s. sponge electrode*	recristallisé	rekristallisiert	ricristallizzato
^	5591 **Doctor sweetening** **doctoring**, *s. sponge plating*	désulfuration *f* Doctor	Doctor-Süssung *f*	addolcimento *m* Doctor
—	5592 **dog**	cliquet *m*, butée *f*, chambrière *f*	Klinke *f*, Hund *m*, Hemmstange *f*	dente *m* d'arresto, cuscinetto *m*, briglia *f*
—	5593 **dog-and-chain** **dog heated spike**, *s. spike*	arrache-étais *m*	Raubvorrichtung *f*	leva-puntelli *m*
^	5594 **dog-clutch**	accouplement *m* à griffes	Zahnkupplung *f*	innesto *m* a denti
—	5595 **dog hole**	passage *m*, recoupe *f*	Fahrweg *m*, Durchhieb *m*	passaggio *m*, galle- ria *f* di collegamento
—	5596 **dog house**	abri *m* de sondeur	Mannschaftsun- terstand *m*	baracca *f* di sonda
^	5597 **dog leg**	dogleg	Knick *m*	«turn» molto marcato
°	5598 **dog mark**	empreinte *f* de tenailles	Zangeneindruck *m*	impronta *f* di tenaglie
	5599 **dog shift** **dog spike**, *s. spike*	poste *m* de nuit	Nachtschicht *f*	turno *m* di notte
°	5600 **dog spike bar** **dog tooth spar**, *s. derbyshire calcite*	fer *m* à crampons	Nageleisen *n*, Hakeneisen *n*	ferro *m* per arpioni
—	5601 **dolerine**	dolérine *f*	Dolerine *f*	dolerina *f*
—	5602 **dolerite**	dolérite *f*	Dolerit *m*	dolerite *f*
—	5603 **doleritic texture**	texture *f* ophitique	doleritische Struktur *f*	struttura *f* ottica
—	5604 **dolerophanite**	dolérophanite *f*	Dolerophanit *m*	dolerofanite *f*
—	5605 **dolly**	tige *f* de bocard	Pochschlage *f*, Pochstempel *m*	asta *f* del mulino a pestelli
—	5606 **dolly** **dolly**, *s. polishing lap or mop.*	locomotive *f* de manoeuvre	Zubringerlokomotive *f*	carrello *m* di piazzale

English	French	German	Italian
— 5607 **doloma, calcined dolomite**	dolomie *f* cuite, dolomie *f* calcinée	gebrannter Dolomit *m*	dolomite *f* cotta o calcinata
— 5608 **dolomite**	dolomite *f*	Dolomit *m*	dolomite *f*, dolomia *f*
— 5609 **dolomite brick**	brique *f* de dolomie	Dolomitstein *m*	mattone *m* di dolomite
— 5610 **dolomite calcining kiln**	cubilot *m* à dolomie	Dolomitbrennofen *m*	forno *m* per dolomite
— 5611 **dolomite mass**	mélange *m* de dolomie	Dolomitmasse *f*	miscuglio *m* di dolomite
— 5612 **dolomite mixer**	malaxeur *m* à dolomie	Dolomitmischer *m*	mescolatore *m* di dolomite
dolomite plant, s. *dolomite shop*			
— 5613 **dolomite powder**	poudre *f* de dolomie	Dolomitmehl *n*	polvere *f* di dolomite
— 5614 **dolomite sand**	sable dolomitique	Dolomitsand *m*	sabbia *f* dolomitica
— 5615 **dolomite shop**	atelier *m* à dolomie	Dolomithalle *f*	impianto *f* per preparare la dolomite
— 5615 **dolomitic lime**	chaux *f* dolomitique	Dolomitkalk *m*	calce *f* dolomitica
— 5616 **dolomitization**	dolomitisation *f*	Dolomitisation *f*	dolomitizzazione *f*
^ 5617 **dolphin**	pylône *m* d'encrage	Ankermast *m*	pilone *m* d'ancoraggio
— 5618 **domal flank**	flanc *m* du dôme	Kuppelflanke *f*	fianco *m* del duomo
— 5619 **domal structure**	structure *f* en dôme	Domstruktur *f*	struttura *f* a duomo
— 5620 **dome**	dôme *m*, coupole *f*	Dom *m*, Kuppel *f*	duomo *m*, cupola *f*
— 5621 **domestic coke**	charbon *m* domestique	Hausbrandkohle *f*	coke *m* per uso domestico
— 5622 **domeykite**	doméykite *f*	Domeykit *m*	domeykite *f*
— 5623 **dominant fault, main fault**	faille *f* principale	Hauptverwerfung *f*	faglia *f* principale
— 5624 **doming**	formation *f* de dômes	Dombildung *f*	formazione *f* di duomi
— 5625 **domite**	domite *f*	Domit *m*	domite *f*
° 5626 **donkey pump**	chaudière *f* auxiliaire	Hilfskessel *m*	cavallino *m*
— 5627 **dook**	descenderie *f*, plan incliné	einfallender Schacht *m*, Bremsberg *m*	galleria *f* di ribasso, piano *m* inclinato

	English	French	German	Italian
° 5628	**door charging**	charge *f* latérale	Seitenladung *f*, Türladung *f*	caricamento *m* laterale (di un forno)
° 5629	**door counter weight**	contrepoids *m* de la porte	Gegengewicht *n* der Tür	contrappeso *m* della porta
° 5630	**door latch**	fermeture *f* de porte	Türverschluss *m*	lucchetto *m* della porta, fermaporta *m*
° 5631	**door of coke oven**	porte *f* de four à coke	Koksofentür.*f*	porta *f* del forno a coke
° 5632	**door still**	seuil *m* de porte	Türschwelle *f*	soglia *f* della porta
^ 5633	**dope**	pâte *f*, graisse *m*	Fett *n*, Schmiere *f*	grasso *m*, pasta *f*
− 5634	**dope**	matériel absorbant	Absorbtionsmittel *n*	materiale *m* assorbente
^ 5635	**dope**	additif *m*	Zusatzmittel *n*	additivo *m*
− 5636	**dopplerite**	dopplérite *f*	Dopplerit *m*	dopplerite *f*

dormant scrap, *s. home scrap*

	English	French	German	Italian
° 5636a	**dot welding**	soudure *f* d'apport	Aufschweissen *n*	saldatura *f* di apporto
° 5637	**to double**	doubler	verdoppeln	raddoppiare
^ 5638	**double**	jeu *m* de deux	Doppelzug *m*	gioco *m* doppio
° 5639	**double acting**	à double effet	doppelt wirkend	a doppio effetto
° 5640	**double acting elevator**	monte-charges *m* à double effet	doppelt wirkender Aufzug *m*	montacarichi *m* a doppio effetto
° 5641	**double acting pump**	pompe *f* à double effet	doppelt wirkende Pumpe *f*	pompa *f* a doppio effetto
° 5642	**double acting steam hammer**	marteau-pilon *m* à vapeur à double effet	doppelt wirkender Dampfhammer *m*	maglio *m* a vapore a doppio effetto
− 5643	**double arc bit**	taillant *m* double	Zweischneidebohrer *m*	tagliente *m* doppio (di un fioretto)
° 5644	**double base plate**	plaque *f* d'appui double	Doppeltragscheibe *f*	piastrone *m* (fra rotaie)
° 5645	**double boiler**	chaudière *f* double	Doppelkessel *m*	caldaia *f* doppia
° 5646	**double box**	à double femelle	Doppelnut-	a doppia femmina
° 5647	**double branch gate**	jet *m* de coulée en fourche	Gabeleinguss *m*	colata *f* a forcella
° 5648	**double combustion chamber boiler**	chaudière *f* à double boîte à feu	Kessel *m* mit doppeltem Feuerkasten	caldaia *f* a doppia cassa-focolare

	English	French	German	Italian
°	5649 double contraction	double retrait *m*	doppeltes Schwindmass *n*	doppio ritiro *m*, doppia contrazione *f*
−	5650 double core barrel	carottier *m* double	Doppelkernrohr *n*	carotiere *m* doppio
°	5651 double corrugated iron	tôle *f* ondulée double	Doppelwellblech *n*	lamiera *f* ondulata doppia
−	5652 double cutting bit	mèche *f* à deux tranchants	zweischneidiger Bohrer *m*	punta *f* di trapano a due tagli
°	5653 double cylindrical boiler	chaudière *f* cylindrique double	Doppelwalzenkessel, Doppel(zylinder)-kessel *m*	caldaia *f* a due corpi cilindrici sovrapposti
−	5654 double-deck screen	crible *m* à deux plateaux, crible double	Doppelplanrätter *m*	vaglio *m* a due piatti, crivello *m* doppio
°	5654a double-double iron	tôle noire quadruplée	Vielfachschwarzblech *n*	lamiera *f* nera quadrupla
	double dougle iron, *s. Z-bar*			
−	5655 double-drum winch	treuil *m* à deux tambours	Zweitrommelhaspel	argano *m* a due tamburi
°	5656 double-ended boiler	chaudière *f* à double face	zweiseitiger Ofen *m*	caldaia *f* a doppia fronte
°	5657 double ended radius sleeker	gouge *f* creuse	Polier-S *n*	lisciatoio *m* doppio, lisciatoio a S
−	5658 double entry	galeries *f pl.* jumelles	Strecke *f* mit Begleitort	gallerie gemelle
°	5659 double expander	dudgeon *m* double	Doppelrohrwalze *f*	allargatubi *m* doppio
	double fagotted iron, *s. double shear iron*			
^	5660 double flanged	à deux brides	doppelt geflanscht	a doppia flangia
°	5661 double flue boiler	chaudière Lancashire	Lancashirekessel *m*	caldaia *f* Lancashire
°	5662 double hardening	trempe *f* tenace à coeur	Kernzähhärtung *f*	doppia tempra
°	5663 double head rail	rail *m* double tête	Doppelkopfschiene *f*	doppio fungo *f*
°	5664 double headed chaplet	support *m* de noyau à double tôle	Wandstärkenkern-stütze *f*	sopporto *m* con un gambo e due lamiere
	double hemming, *s. seaming*			
°	5665 double J - groove	soudure *f* à double biseau à j	J-Doppelschräg-schweissung *f*	saldatura *f* con doppio bisello a J
°	5666 double muffle furnace	fourneau à moufles doubles	Doppelmuffelofen *m*	forno *m* a muffola doppia

	English	French	German	Italian
	double oblique system, *triclinic system*			
—	5667 **double pick**	pic *m* à deux pointes	Doppelhacke *f*	piccone *m* a due punte
°	5668 **double pin**	à double taraud	Doppelfeder	a doppio maschio
°	5669 **double pipe**	tube *m* double	Doppelrohr *n*	tubo *m* doppio
°	5670 **double pointed nail**	goujon *m* à deux pointes	Verbandstift *m*	punta *m* a due punte
^	5671 **double-platform**	plateforme *f* double	Zwischenbühne für Zweierzug	piattaforma *f* doppia
°	5672 **double producer**	gazogène *m* double	Doppelgenerator *m*	gasogeno *m* doppio
°	5673 **double puddling furnace**	four *m* à puddler double	Doppelpuddelofen *m*	doppio forno *m* per puddellaggio
° °	5674 **double refined steel double shear steel** 5674a **double refining**	acier *m* à double corroyage affinage *m* double	Doppelgärbstahl *m*, doppelraffinierter Stahl *m*	acciaio *m* doppiamente raffinato raffinaggio *m* duplex
°	5675 **double scrubber (steel wire)**	grattoir *m* double en fil d'acier	doppelter Schrubber *m* aus Draht	spazzola *f* doppia in filo d'acciaio
°	5676 **double seat valve**	soupape *f* à double siège	Doppelsitzventil *n*	valvola *f* a doppia sede
	double shear steel, *s. double refined steel*			
° °	5677 **double sided pattern plate** 5677a **double sintering**	plaque-modèle *f* doubleface frittage *m* double	zweiseitige Modell-platte *f* Doppelsintern *n*	placca *f* modello a due facce sinterizzazione *f* doppia
—	5678 **double stope**	front *m* à deux ailes	zweiflügeliger Stoss	fronte *m* a doppia ala
°	5679 **double stopper**	double fermeture *f*	doppelter Gichtver-schluss *m*	chiusura *f* doppia
°	5680 **double studded**	double goujonné	doppelseitiger Stehbolzen *m*	a doppia incavigliatura
°	5681 **double tee-iron with ordinary flanges**	double *m* T à ailes ordinaires	H-Eisen, doppel T-Eisen mit gewöhnlichen Flanschen	ferro *m* a I a suola ordinaria
	double teem, *s. cold shut*			
°	5682 **double (tube) expander**	dudgeon *m* double	Doppelrohrwalze *f*	allargatubi *m* doppio
	double T-iron, *s. ll-iron*			
—	5683 **double tube core barrel**	tube-carottier *m* double	Doppelkernrohr *n*	tubo *m* carotiere doppio

English	French	German	Italian
— 5684 double twisted auger	mèche f torse	Schlangenbohrer m	trivella f a spirale
— 5685 double-unit working	exploitation f par deux tailles jumelles	zweiflügeliger Abbau m	coltivazione f a due tagli gemelli
° 5686 double U leather packing	cuir m embouti double	doppelte Liderung f	guarnizione f a U
^ 5687 double walled	à doubles parois	doppelwandig	a doppia parete
° 5688 double welt	pli m double	Doppelfalz m	doppio avvolgimento
^ 5689 doubles	longueur f de deux tiges	Länge von zwei Böhrstangen	lunghezza f di due aste ciascuna

doubling, s. *stratigraphical overlap*

English	French	German	Italian
° 5690 doubling plate	tôle f de doublure	Verdoppelungsplatte f	lamiera f d'imbottitura
^ 5691 doughnut	tore m, tube m toröidal	Bohrinselschuh m, toroidförmiges Rohr n	tubo m toroidale
— 5692 doughtyite	doughtyite f	Doughtyit m	doughtite f
— 5693 douglasite	douglasite f	Douglasit m	douglasite f
° 5694 dowel pin	faux goujon m	abgesetzter loser Führungsstift m	pernio m a cannone, spina f a cannone
° 5695 Dowlais mill	double-duo m	Doppelzweiwalzwerk Doppelduowalzwerk n	doppio-duo m
— 5696 downcast	courant m d'air descendant, puits m d'entrée d'air	abfallender Wetterstrom m, Einziehschacht m	corrente f d'aria discendente, pozzo d'entrata dell'aria o di ventilazione
— 5696a dowk	baryte f impure	ungereinigter Baryt m	barite f impura
° 5697 down comer	prise f de gaz Faber du Faure	Gasfang m nach Faber du Faure	presa f di gas Faber du Faure
— 5698 down dip	aval-pendage	in der Fallrichtung f	in direzione della pendenza
° 5699 down-draught furnace	foyer à flamme renversée	Feuerung f mit umgekehrter Flamme	focolare a fiamma invertita
— 5700 down fault	faille f normale	normale Verwerfung f	faglia f normale

down-flue boiler, s. *counter-current boiler*
down gate, s. *bottom gate or sprue*

English	French	German	Italian
— 5701 down grade	pente f	Gefälle n	pendenza f

down-hand welding, s. *downward welding in the vertical position*

		English	French	German	Italian

—	5702	down-hill ventilation	aérage *m* descendant, ventilation *f* descendante	abfallende Wetterführung *f*	ventilazione *f* discendente
—	5703	down hole	coup *m* de fond	Unterbohrloch *n*	foro *m* di soglia
—	5704	down hole camera	appareil *m* de prise de vues descendu dans le puits	Bohrlochkamera *f*	macchina *f* fotografica per pozzi
°	5705	down main, service pipe	tuyau *m* descendant	Fallrohr *n*	tubo *m* di scarico
		down runner, *s. down sprue*			
°	5706	down sprue, down runner downgate	canal *m* vertical de coulée	Vertikalfuchs *m*	canale verticale di colata
—	5707	down side	lèvre *f* inférieure	gesenkter Flügel *m*	lembo *m* inferiore
—	5708	down warping	tassement *m* (d'une couche)	Einwölbung *f*	cedimento *m* (d'uno strato)
—	5709	down-cast shaft	puits *m* d'entrée d'air, puits descendant	einziehender Schacht *m*	pozzo *m* di ventilazione discendente
		downcomer, *s. vertical pipe*			
°	5710	downdraft tuyere	tuyère à courant d'air descendant	Düse mit Luftströmung nach unten	ugello *m* con correnti (d'aria) verso il basso
—	5711	downfold	pli synclinal, auge	Synklinale *f*, Synklinalfalte *f*	sinclinale *f*
—	5712	downgate	attaque *f* de front, trou *m* de coulée	Frontanschnitt *m* Trichterzulauf *m*	attacco *m* frontale, foro *m* di colata
—	5713	downslip fault	faille *f* normale	normale Verwerfung *f*	faglia *f* normale, rigetto *m* normale
—	5714	downstream	en aval	abwärts	verso il basso
°	5715	downstroke	coup *m* descendant	Abwärtsgang *m*	colpo *m* discendente
—	5716	downthrow	rejet *m* vers le bas, lèvre *f* affaissée	Abschiebung *f*, gesunkener Flügel *m*	lembo *m* affossato (o affondato)
—	5717	downthrown block	massif *m* affaissé, fossé d'effondrement	Graben *m*	roccia *f* affossata, lembo *m* affondato
—	5718	downward enrichment	enrichissement *m* secondaire	Tiefenanreicherung *f*	arricchimento *m* secondario

	English	French	German	Italian
− 5719	**to doze**	remuer la terre avec un bulldozer	Erdbewegung f mit Bulldozer	smuovere la terra con bulldozer
	dozer, s. bulldozer			
° 5720	**dozzle**	bassin m d'alimentation	Speisebecken n	bacino m di alimentazione
− 5721	**dradge**	minerai m de qualité inférieure	niedrig prozentiges Erz	minerale m di qualità inferiore
° 5721a	**draft**	réduction f	Abnahme f	riduzione f
− 5722	**draft, draught**	tirage m	Zug m	corrente f d'aria,
° 5722a	**draft**	angle m spécifique de réduction	Querschnittsabnahme f	portata f specifica di riduzione
° 5723	**draft**	soupape f de tirage	Zugventil n	valvola f di tiraggio
° 5724	**draft, taper (of a die)**	dépouille f, gale f	Schräge f, Modellschräge f	sformo m, spoglia m (di modello), conicità f
° 5725	**draft**	tirant m (d'eau)	Tiefgang m	pescaggio m
° 5726	**draft angle (of a die)**	angle m de dépouille	Schrägwinkel m	angolo m di spoglia
− 5727	**to drag**	traîner, draguer	baggern, schleppen	tirare, trainare
− 5728	**drag**	retroussement m, incurvation f	Schleppung f, Umbiegung f	stiramento m, incurvatura f
− 5729	**drag**	drague f	Baggerschaufel f, Bagger m	draga f
	drag, s. drag box or bottom part			
− 5730	**drag bit**	trépan m à lames	Spatenmeissel m	trapano m a lame, scalpello m a lame
° 5731	**drag box, drag**	châssis m de dessous, moule m inférieur	Unterkasten m	staffa f inferiore, fondo m
− 5732	**drag classifier**	classificateur m à raclettes	Kratzenklassifikator m	classificatore m a raschiatore
− 5733	**drag fold, minor fold**	pli m d'étirement	Schleppfalte f	piega f di stiramento
° 5733a	**drag-in**	solution f adhérente	Eintrag m	soluzione f aderente
− 5734	**drag-line bucket**	benne f traînante de pelle	Kübel m von Schleppschaufelbagger	benna strisciante (o trainata) di escavatrice
− 5735	**drag-ore**	brèche f minéralisée, minerai m broyé	Erzbreccie f	breccia f mineralizzata, minerale m frantumato
^ 5735a	**drag out**	solution f entraînée	Austrag m	soluzione f estratta

	English	French	German	Italian
°	5735b **drag over mill**	laminoir *m* duo irré-versible	Übergabewalzwerk *n*	laminatoio *m* duo irrevers
—	5736 **drag scraper**	scraper *m*	Schrapper *m*	scraper *m*
—	5737 **drag shoe**	sondeuse *f* à grenaille	Schrotbohrer *m*	trivella *f* a corona di graniglia
—	5738 **drag shovel**	godet *m* rétro	Tieflöffel *m*	cucchiaio *m* rovescio
—	5739 **dragline, dragline--escavator**	pelle *f* à benne trainante, dragline *f*	Löffelbagger *m*	escavatore *m* a benna strisciante o trainata
—	5740 **dragman**	rouleur *m*	Schlepper *m*	addetto *m* ai vagoncini
^	5741 **to drain off**	filtrer par aspiration	absaugen	filtrare per aspirazione
^	5742 **drainable oil**	huile *f* exploitable	gewinnbares Öl *n*	olio *m* estraibile
—	5743 **drainage adit, draining shaft**	galerie *f* d'écoulement	Durchlasskanal *m*, Schluckschacht *m*	galleria *f* di drenaggio, pozzo *m* di drenaggio
—	5744 **drainage area**	surface *f* de drainage	Entölungsgebiet *n* , Entwässerungsgebiet *n*	superfice *f* di drenag-gio
	drainage pit, *s. soakage pit*			
—	5745 **drained**	drainé	ausgeleert	drenato, svuotato
^	5746 **drainer**	tour *f* d'égouttage	Entwässerungsturm *m*	torre *f* di sgocciolamento
^	5747 **draining dish**	passoire *f*, vase *m* à égoutter	Abtropfschale *f*	bacinella *f* di sgoccio-lamento
—	5748 **draining-engine, drainage pump**	machine *f* d'épuise-ment, pompe *f* d'épuisement	Wasserpumpe *f*	pompa *f* per drenaggio
—	5749 **draining screen**	tamis *m* d'égouttage	Entwässerungssieb *n*	vaglio *m* di sgoccio-lamento
—	5750 **drainway**	galerie *f* de draina-ge, albraque	Sumpfstrecke *f*, Entwässerungs-strecke *f*	galleria *f* di drenaggio
°	5751 **draught regulation**	réglage *m* du tirage	Zugregelung *f*	regolazione *m* del tiraggio, registrazione *f* del tiraggio
—	5752 **dravite**	dravite *f*	Dravit *m*	dravite *f*
—	5753 **to draw**	dessiner	zeichnen	disegnare
''	5754 **to draw**	tirer, étirer	ziehen, strecken	tirare, stirare, martellare

	English	French	German	Italian
ˆ	5755 **to draw**	aspirer	saugen	aspirare
—	5756 **to draw**	extraire	fördern, gewinnen	estrarre
○	5757 **to draw**	démouler	ausziehen	sformare, estrarre (le forme)
—	5758 **to draw a drift**	pousser une galerie	eine Strecke *f* auffahren	avanzare (in galleria)
○	5759 **to draw back the nozzles**	reculer les buses	die Düsen zurück-ziehen	levare il portavento
○	5760 **to draw down**	écrouir	recken	battere (a freddo), incrudire
○	5761 **to draw down the iron**	étirer le fer	das Eisen strecken	stirare il ferro
○	5762 **to draw from the furnace**	aspirer du haut-fourneau	aus dem Ofen *m* saugen	aspirare dal forno
○	5763 **to draw into wire**	tréfiler, étirer	drahtziehen	trafilare, tirare in fili
ˆ	5764 **to draw off the mud, to purge**	curer, débourber	abschlacken	scaricare i fanghi
○	5765 **to draw off slag**	décrasser les scories	abschlacken	scorificare, disincrostare
○	5766 **to draw on an apron**	démouler sur cadre	auf Rahmen abheben	sformare sul telaio
○	5767 **to draw on pins**	démouler sur chandelles	auf Stiften abheben	sformare a candele
○	5768 **to draw on roll-over**	démouler par renversement	durch Umrollen ausheben	sformare per ribaltamento
○	5769 **to draw on turn-over**	démouler par retournement	durch Wenden ausheben	sformare per rotazione
○	5770 **to draw out**	éxtraire	fördern	estrarre
○	5771 **to draw out steel**	étirer l'acier en barres	den Stahl schienen, den Stahl strecken	tirare l'acciaio in barre
○	5772 **to draw tubes**	étirer les tubes	Rohre ziehen	trafilare tubi
○	5773 **draw**	retirure *f*	Schwindungshohl-raum *m*	risucchio *m*, fessura *f* in un getto
	draw, *s. lift or stripping*			
○	5774 **draw**	effet *m* Léonard	Blaslunker *m*	effetto *m* Léonard
○	5775 **draw back core**	pièce *f* rapportée	Keilstück *n*	pezzo *m* di anima

	English	French	German	Italian
—	5776 **draw back pillars**	dépilage *m*, dépilement *m*	Rückbau *m* der Pfeiler	demolizione *f* dei pilastri
°	5777 **draw-bar pull**	effort *m* de traction au crochet	Zugkraft *f* am Haken	sforzo *m* di trazione al gancio
°	5778 **draw bead**	bord *m* retourné	Wulst *m*	bordo *m* rivoltato
°	5779 **draw bench**	banc *m* d'étirage, tréfileur *m*	Ziehbank *f*, Drahtziehmaschine *f*	trafila *f*, trafilatrice *f*
—	5780 **draw hole**	cheminée à minerai	Erzrolle *f*, Stürzrolle *f*	scivolo *m* per minerali, trasportatore per minerali
°	5781 **draw hole**	orifice *m* de tréfilage	Ziehloch *n*	apertura *f* di stiratura
°	5782 **draw piece**	poignard *m*	Einziehteil *m*	estrattore *m*
°	5783 **draw plate, die**	filière *f*	Zieheisen *n*	filiera *f*, matrice *f* di trafila
°	5783a **draw rod**	bielle *f* de traction	Zugstange *f*	biella *f* di trazione
—	5784 **draw slate**	faux-toit *m*	Nachfalldach *n*	falso tetto *m*
—	5785 **draw works**	treuil *m* de forage (ou de sondage)	Bohrwinde *f*	argano *m* di perforazione
°	5786 **drawback**	tiroir *m*	Kern- und Formteilzugelement *n*	slitta *f*, parte *f* smontabile
°	5787 **drawability**	capacité *f* d'emboutissage profond, étirabilité *f*	Tiefziehfähigkeit *f*, Ziehbarkeit *f*	imbutibilità *f*, trafilabilità *f*
°	5787a **drawbar**	picot *m*	Aushebeeisen *n*	ferro *m* da scampanare
°	5788 **drawer**	tréfileur *m*, étireur *m*	Zieher *m*	stiratore *m*, trafilatrice *f*
—	5789 **drawer**	rouleur *m*	Schlepper *m*	addetto *m* ai vagoncini
	5790 **drawing, tracing** **drawing**, *s. tube rolling*	tracé *m*	Zeichnung *f*, Aufriss *m*	tracciato *m*, disegno
°	5791 **drawing** **drawing**, *s. tempering*	étirage *m*	Ziehen *m*, Streckung *f*	trafilatura *f*, imbutitura *f*, tiratura *f*
—	5792 **drawing back**	abattage *m*	Hereingewinnung *f*	estrazione *f*, abbattimento *m*
—	5793 **drawing-back the pillars**	dépilage *m*, reprise des piliers	Rückbau *m* der Pfeiler	demolizione *f* dei pilastri
°	5794 **drawing bench**	banc *m* d'étirage	Ziehbank *f*	trafila *f*, banco *m* di trafila

	English	French	German	Italian
5795	drawing cage	cage f d'extraction	Förderkorb m	gabbia f d'estrazione
5796	drawing die	matrice f à étirer, couronne f de forme	Ziehring m	corona f della forma, stampo m per imbutitura, anello m di trafila
5797	drawing down	écrouissage m	Strecken n des Eisens	rincrudimento m del ferro
5798	drawing engine	machine f d'extraction	Fördermaschine f	macchina f da estrazione
	drawing frame, s. drawing cage			
5799	drawing machine with pliers	banc m à étirer à pince	Schleppzangenziehbank f	banco m di stiramento a pinza
5800	drawing machine with spool	banc m de tréfilerie à tambours enrouleurs	Scheibenziehbank f, Leierziehbank f	banco m di stiramento a rulli
5801	drawing mill	tréfilerie f	Drahtzieherei f	trafileria f
5802	drawing of patterns, lifting of patterns, stripping	démoulage m	Herausnehmen n der Modelle	estrazione f dei modelli
5803	drawing of the wire	étirage m du fil	Strecken n des Drahtes	trafilatura f del filo
5804	drawing off the ore	défournement m du minerai	Ziehen n des Erzes	scarico m del forno del minerale
5805	drawing-out	extraction f	Förderung f, Gewinnung f	estrazione f
5806	drawing pass	cylindre m étireur	Streckkaliber n	cilindro m trafilatore
5807	drawing plate, dish plate	plaque f à étirer	Zieheisen n	lamiera f da imbutire
5808	drawing press	presse f à étirer	Ziehpresse f	pressa f per trafilare
5809	drawing punch	poinçon à tirer	Ziehstempel m	punzone m per imbutitura
5810	drawing quality	qualité f pour étirage	Ziehgüte f	qualità f di trafilatura
5811	drawing the temper	revenu m	Nachglühen n, Anlassung f	rinvenimento m
5812	drawing tool	outil m à étirer	Ziehwerkzeug n	utensile m da trafilatura

		English	French	German	Italian
−	5813	**drawn**	puits *m* d'extraction	Förderschacht *m*	pozzo *m* d'estrazione
°	5814	**drawn**	étiré	gezogen	trafilato, stirato
°	5815	**drawn bars**	barres *f pl.* étirées	gezogene Stäbe *m pl.*	barre *f pl.* trafilate
°	5815a	**drawn-in scale**	encroûtement *m*	Eingefressenerzunde *f*	scaglia *f* incrostata
°	5816	**drawn iron**	fer étiré, fer écroui	gestrecktes Eisen *n*	ferro stirato, ferro *m* trafilato
°	5817	**drawn ore**	minerai *m* défourné	gezogenes Erz *n*	minerale *m* sfornato
		drawn out iron, *s. drawn iron*			
−	5818	**drawn out middle limb**	flanc *m* médian étiré	verdünnter Mittelschenkel *m*	fianco *m* mediano stirato
°	5819	**drawn steel**	acier étiré	gezogener Stahl *m*	acciaio *m* stirato, acciaio *m* trafilato
°	5820	**drawn tube**	tube *m* étiré	gezogenes Rohr *n*	tubo *m* trafilato
°	5821	**drawn wire**	fil étiré	Streckdraht *m*	filo *m* trafilato
ˆ	5822	**drawworks**	treuil *m* de manoeuvre	Rotary-Hebewerk *n*	argano *m* di manovra
−	5823	**dredge working, dredging**	dragage *m*	Baggerbetrieb *m*	dragaggio *m*
−	5824	**dredged peat**	tourbe *f* draguée	Baggertorf *m*	torba *f* dragata
−	5825	**dredging**	dragage *m*	Baggerbetrieb *m*	dragaggio *m*
−	5826	**dredging-face**	front *m* de dragage	Front *f* der Baggerung *f*	fronte *m* di dragaggio
−	5827	**dredging scoop**	cuillère *f* de drague	Baggerschaufel *f*	cucchiaia *f* di draga
−	5828	**dredging shovel**	pelle *f* mécanique	Löffelbagger *m*	draga *f* a cucchiaio, escavatrice *f* meccanica
−	5829	**dredgy ore**	roche *f* avec filonnets de minerai	Gestein *n* mit Erzadern	roccia *f* con vene di minerale
−	5830	**dreelite**	dréelite *f*	Schwerspat *m*	dreelite *f*
−	5831	**dreg**	sédiment *m*	Bodensatz *m*	sedimento *m*
−	5832	**dreikanter**	pierre *f* à facettes	Dreikanter *m*	pietra *f* sfaccettata
−	5833	**to dress (ores)**	traiter les minerais	(Erze)aufbereiten	trattare i minerali

English	French	German	Italian
5834 **to dress**	couper à dimension	zurechtschneiden	tagliare a misura
5835 **to dress**	poteyer	schlichten	rivestire
5836 **to dress a grinding wheel**	dresser une meule	eine Schleifscheibe abrichten	ravvivare una mola, equilibrare una mola
5837 **dressed**	préparé, taillé	aufbereitet, behauen	preparato, tagliato
5838 **dressed coal**	charbon *m* préparé	aufbereitete Kohle *f*	carbone *m* preparato
5839 **dressed ore**	minerai *m* préparé	aufbereitetes Erz *n*	minerale *m* preparato o trattato
5840 **dresser**	bocardeur *m*	Pocharbeiter *m*	addetto *m* alla laveria
5840a **dresser**	ébarbeur *m*	Gussputzer *m*	sbavatore *m*
5841 **dresser coupling**		lose Verbindung durch Einstellung der Pumpenansaugung	unione *f* scorrevole per aggiustaggio aspirazione pompe
5842 **dressing, ore dressing**	préparation *f*, triage *m*	Aufbereitung *f*, Scheidung *f*	preparazione *f* (dei minerali), cernita *f*
5843 **dressing-(off), trimming, fettling**	ébarbage *m*	Fertigputzen *n*, Entgraten *n*	finitura *f* (di getto), sbavatura *f*
5844 **dressing plant**	installation *f* de préparation	Aufbereitungsanlage *f*	impianto *m* per il trattamento (del minerale)
dressing shop, *s. fettling room*			
5845 **dressing process**	opérations *f pl.* préparatoires	vorbereitendes Verfahren *n*	processo *m* preparatorio
5846 **dried briquette**	briquette *f* séchée	getrockneter Pressstein *m*	mattonella *f* secca
5847 **dried in the desiccator**	séché dans le séchoir	im Entfeuchter getrocknet	seccato nell'essiccatore
5848 **dried sample**	prise *f* d'essai séchée	getrocknete Probe *f*	campione *m* essiccato
5849 **drift, warp**	alluvion *f*, dépôt *m* alluvien	Verladung *f*, Ablagerung *f*	deposito *m* alluvionale
5850 **drift**	galerie *f* d'avancement	Strecke *f*, Querstollen *m*	galleria *f* di livello
5850a **drift**	perçage *m*	Lochung *f*	punzone *m* caccia-cuneo
drift, *s. creep*			
5851 **drift**	calibre passe-tube	Rohrkaliber *n*	calibro *m* passa tubi

English	French	German	Italian
— 5852 **drift-band**	intercalation *f* stérile	Bergemittel *n*	intercalazione *f* sterile
— 5853 **drift beds**	dépôts *m pl.* glaciaires	glaziale Ablagerungen *f pl.*	depositi *m pl.* glaciali
— 5854 **drift boulder**	bloc *m* erratique	erratischer Block *m*	blocco *m* erratico
— 5855 **drift breccia**	brèche *f* glaciaire	Gletscherbreccie *f*	breccia *f* glaciale
— 5856 **drift cap**	chapeau *m*	Kappe *f*	cappello *m*
— 5857 **drift deposit**	dépôt *m* glaciaire, Diluvium	Gletscherablagerung *f*, Diluvium *n*	deposito *m* glaciale, Diluvium *m*
— 5858 **drift epoch**	époque *f* glaciaire	Eiszeit *f*	epoca *f* glaciale
— 5859 **drift indicator**	indicateur *m* de pendage du puits	Neigungsanzeiger *m*	misuratore *m* d'inclinazione del pozzo
— 5860 **drift mine**	mine *f* à puits	Tiefbau *m*	miniera *f* con accesso a pozzo
— 5861 **drift mining**	exploitation *f* à flanc de coteau	Stollenbetrieb *m*	coltivazione *f* con accesso a pozzo
— 5862 **drift post**	montant *m* de cadre	Türstockbein *n*	montante *m* di quadro
— 5863 **drift-sand, blown sand**	sable flottant. mouvants *m pl.*	Triebsand *m*, Schwimmsand *m*	sabbia *f* mobile o spingente
— 5864 **drift set**	cadre *m*	Türstock *m*	quadro *m*
— 5865 **drift stope**	chantier *m* chassant, galerie d'avancement	Strebe *f*, Richtstrecke *f*	cantiere *m* in direzione, galleria *f* d'avanzamento
— 5866 **drift stoping**	abattage *m* en taille chassante	Abbau *m* durch Richtungsvortrieb	abbattimento *m* con tagli in direzione
— 5867 **drift structure**	stratification *f* entrecroisée	Kreuzschichtung *f*	stratificazione *f* incrociata
— 5868 **drift terrace**	terrasse *f* d'accumulation	Akkumulationsterrasse *f*	terrazza *f* d'accumulo
— 5869 **drift test**	essai *m* de perçage ou de poinçonnage	Lochprobe *f*	prova *f* di foratura o di punzonatura
— 5870 **drift tunnel**	galerie *f* d'exploitation, galerie de direction	Abbaustrecke *f*	galleria *f* di coltivazione, galleria *f* di direzione

English	French	German	Italian
5871 driftage	ouvrage *m* souterrain	Grubenbau *m*	opera *m* sotterranea
5872 driftage drill, drifter	perforatrice *f* d'avancement	Bohrmaschine *f* mit Bohrsäule	trivella *f* d'avanzamento, perforatrice *f* da cantiere
5873 drifting	percement *m* de galeries, extraction	Streckenauffahren *n*, Gewinnung *f*	scavo *m* di galleria, estrazione *f*
5873a drifting	brochage *m*	Dornen *n*	mandrinatura *f*
5874 to drill	forer, percer	bohren	forare, trapanare
5875 to drill from above	percer par-dessus	von oben bohren	trapanare di sopra
5876 to drill from the side	percer sur le côté	von der Seite bohren	trapanare di fianco, trivellare di fianco
5877 to drill lengthways	percer dans le sens de la longueur	in der Längsrichtung bohren	trapanare per lungo
5878 to drill out	reforer	aufbohren	perforare di nuovo
5879 to drill out	percer, débourrer	auskratzen, ausbohren	riperforare (un foro da mina non riuscito), scalzare
5880 to drill through	forer à travers	durchbohren	forare di traverso
5881 drill	fleuret *m* de mine, marteau-perforateur, perforatrice *f*	Bohrer, Bohrstange *f*, Bohrhammer *m*,	fioretto *m* da mina, sonda *f*, trivella *f*, martello perforatore *m*, perforatrice *f*
5882 drill barrel shoe	sabot *m* du carottier	Bohrerhalter *m*	scarpa *f* del carotiere
5883 drill bit, drilling bit	outil *m* de forage, fleuret *m*	Bohrer *m*, Bohrgezähe *n*	trivella *f*, sonda *f*
5884 drill carriage	chariot *m* de perforation	Bohrwagen *m*	carro *m* per sondaggio
5885 drill charger	boutefeu *m*	Sprengmeister *m*	artificiere *m*
5886 drill collar	tige-masse *f*	schwere Stange *f*	asta *f* pesante
5887 drill collar blank	tige-masse à batir sur chantier	schwere Stange am Ort herzustellen	asta *f* pesante da fare in cantiere
5888 drill collar clamp	borne *f* pour tige-masse	Schwerstangenzange *f*	cravatta *f* per aste pesanti
5889 drill column	affût *m* à colonne pour perforatrice	Bohrsäule *f*	affusto *m* a colonna per perforatrice
5890 drill core	carotte *f* de sondage	Bohrkern *m*	carota *f* di sondaggio

English	French	German	Italian
— 5891 **drill-cuttings, drilling muds**	boue *f* de forage, déblais *m* de forage	Bohrschlamm *m*	detriti *m pl*, fanghiglie *f pl*. di perforazione
— 5892 **drill hole**	trou *m* de mine	Bohrloch *n*	foro *m* da mina, foro *m* di trivellazione
— 5893 **drill-hole location**	emplacement *m* de sonde	Bohrungsplatz *m*	postazione *f* di sonda
— 5894 **drill-log**	coupe *f* d'un sondage, rapport *m* de sondage	Bohrprofil *n*, Bohrbericht *m*	sezione *f* d'un sondaggio, rapporto *m* di sondaggi
— 5895 **drill man**	sondeur *m*	Bohrarbeiter *m*	perforatore *m* (operaio), trivellatore, sondatore *m*
— 5896 **drill-off test**	tests sur paramètres de forage	Abbohr-Versuch *m*	prove *f pl*. su parametri di sondaggio
— 5897 **drill pipe**	tige *f* de forage	Gestängerohr *n*, Bohrgestänge *n*	asta *f* di perforazione, asta *f* di sondaggio
— 5898 **drill pipe cutter**	coupe-tube *m*	Gestängeschneider *m*	tagliatubi *m*
— 5899 **drill pipe elevator**	élévateur *m* de tiges	Gestänge-Elevator *m*	elevatore *m* di aste
— 5900 **drill pipe slips**	coins de tige de forage	Bohrrohrfangkeile *m pl*.	cunei *m pl*. dell'asta di perforazione
— 5901 **drill pipe string**	train *m* de sonde	Bohrgestängezug *m*	treno *m* di trivellazione
— 5902 **drill post**	colonne-support *f* de perforatrice	Bohrsäule *f*	colonna-supporto *f* della perforatrice
— 5903 **drill rig**	installation *f* de sondage	Bohranlage *f*	impianto *m* di perforazione
	drill rod, *s. drill pipe*		
— 5904 **drill rod bushing**	raccord *m* pour tiges de sonde	Verbindung *f* für Bohrgestänge	raccordo *m* per aste di perforazione
— 5905 **drill rope**	câble *m* de forage	Bohrseil *n*	fune *f* di perforazione
— 5906 **drill runner**	foreur *m*, sondeur *m*	Bohrhauer *m*, Bohrarbeiter *m*	trivellatore *m* (operaio), addetto *m* ai sondaggi
— 5907 **drill site**	emplacement de sondage	Bohrstelle *f*	postazione *f* di perforazione
° 5908 **drill steel**	acier *m* pour ciseaux	Meisselstahl *m*	acciaio *m* per scalpelli
— 5909 **drill stem**	tige *f* pour sondage à la corde	Stossbohrgestängerohr *n*	asta *f* per perforazione a cavo

English	French	German	Italian
5910 drill stem test	essai *m* aux tiges	Gestängeversuch *m*	prova *f* con aste
drill stoper, *s. stoper*			
5911 drill test	essai *m* de perçage ou de forage	Bohrprobe *f*	prova *f* alla trapanatura, prova di perforazione
5912 drillability	forabilité *f*	Bohrbarkeit *f*	perforabilità *f*
5913 drillable material	matériel *m* de sondage	aufbohrbares Material *n*	materiale *m* di sondaggio
5914 drilled plate	tôle *f* à trous forés	Blech *n* mit gebohrten Löchern	lamiera *f* con fori trapanati
5915 driller	maître sondeur *m*	Bohrmeister *m*	capo-trivellatori *m*
5916 drilling	sondage *m*, perforation *f*	Bohrung *f*	perforazione *f*, trivellazione *f*, sondaggio *m*
drilling bit, *s. drill bit*			
5917 drilling break	augmentation *f* de vitesse d'avancement	plötzliche Zunahme *f* des Bohrfortschrittes	aumento *m* della velocità d'avanzamento
5918 drilling by rotation	forer par rotation	drehbohren	forare per rotazione
5919 drilling clay	argile à boue	Bohrton *m*	argilla *f* per fango
5920 drilling control	contrôle *m* de l'avance	Bohrautomat *m*	controllo *m* dell'avanzamento
5921 drilling crew	équipe *m* de foreurs	Bohrmannschaft *f*	squadra *f* perforatori
5922 drilling drumline	câble *m* de forage	Bohrseil *n*	cavo *m* di manovra
5923 drilling engineer	ingénieur *m* de forage	Bohringenieur *m*	ingegnere *m* addetto alla perforazione
5924 drilling-in unit	appareillage *m* de sondage pour nettoyer le trou de sonde	Vorrichtung *f* zum Reinigen des Bohrloches	apparecchio *m* di sondaggio per pulire il foro di sonda
5925 drilling jar	joint *m* hydraulique	hydraulisches Gelenk *n*	snodo *m* idraulico
5926 drilling machine for iron and steel	perceuse *f* pour fer et acier	Bohrmaschine *f* für Eisen und Stahl	trapano *m* o perforatrice *f* per ferro ed acciaio
5927 drilling machine for opening the tap hole	foret *m* pour trouer le trou de coulée	Bohrmaschine *f* zum Öffnen des Stichloches	macchina *f* per fare il foro di colata

English	French	German	Italian
— 5928 **drilling machine pillar**	chevalet *m* du perforateur	Bohrmaschinengerüst *n*	incastellatura *f* di trapano
— 5929 **drilling machine standard**	chevalet *m* de perforateur	Bohrmaschinengerüst *n*	incastellatura *f* di perforatrice
— 5930 **drilling mast**	mât *m* de forage	Bohrmast *m*	antenna *f*, torre *f* ribaltabile di perforazione
drilling muds, *s. drilling cuttings*			
— 5931 **drilling of a bore-hole (or well)**	ouverture *f* ou forage d'un puits	Brunnenbohren *n*	apertura *f* o trivellazione *f* di un pozzo
— 5932 **drilling parameters**	paramètres *m pl.* de forage	Bohrfaktoren *m pl.*	parametri *m pl.* di trivellazione
— 5933 **drilling pattern**	distribution *f* des puits selon le terrain	Verteilung *f* der Gruben zum Gelände	distribuzione *f* di pozzi rispetto al terreno
^ 5934 **drilling pipe float and well assembly**	clapet *m* de sûreté contre le retour en batterie	Rückschlagventil *n* in der schweren Stange	valvola *f* di sicurezza di non ritorno alla batteria
— 5935 **drilling programme**	programme *m* de forage	Bohrprogramm *n*	programma *f* dei sondaggi
— 5936 **drilling rate**	avancement *m*	Vortrieb *m*	avanzamento *m*
— 5937 **drilling record**	journal *m* de sondage	Bohrtagebuch *n*	giornale *m* dei sondaggi
— 5938 **drilling rig**	installation *f* de forage	Bohranlage *f*	impianto *m* di trivellazione
— 5939 **drilling shot hole**	trou *m* de mine	Bohrloch *n*	pozzetto *m* di scoppio
— 5940 **drilling site**	emplacement *m* du sondage	Bohrstelle *f*	postazione *f* di trivellazione
— 5941 **drilling stem**	train *m* de sondage	Bohrrohrstrang *m*	batteria *f* per sondaggi (o di perforazione) .
— 5942 **drilling string**	train *m* de tiges	Gestängestrang *m*, Bohrgarnitur *f*	batteria *f* di aste
— 5943 **drilling tools**	outils *m pl.* de forage	Bohrwerkzeug *n*	attrezzi *m pl.* di perforazione, fioretti *m pl.* da mina
— 5944 **drilling tender**	barge *f* de ravitaillement	Bohr-Tender *m*	piattaforma *f* di rifornimento
^ 5945 **drilling vessel**	plate-forme *f* de forage flottante	Bohrschiff *n*	piattaforma *f* galleggiante per sondaggi

English	French	German	Italian
5946 **drilling wells**	forage *m* des puits	Brunnenbohren *n*	perforazione *f* di pozzi
5947 **drillings**	copeaux *m pl.* de forage	Bohrspäne *m pl.*	trucioli *m pl.* di trapanatura
5948 **drip**	collecteur *m* de gouttes	Tropfenfänger *m*	estrattore *m* di liquido, tubetto *m* di spurgo
5949 **drip pipe**	collecteur *m* de gouttes	Tropfenfänger *m*	cannula *f* di spurgo

dripping cooling plant, *s. trickling cooling plant*

5950 **dripping pan**	égoutteur *m*, égouttoir *m*	Tropfpfanne *f*	gocciolatoio *m*, scolatoio *m*
5951 **drips**	huile *f* écoulée	Tropföl *n*	olio *m* sgocciolato
5952 **to drive a level**	ouvrir une galerie	einen Stollen bohren	aprire (o perforare) una galleria
5953 **drive**	galerie *f* en direction, chassage *m*	Richtungstunnel *m*	galleria *f* in direzione o lungobanco
5954 **drive clamp**	crampon *m* de fixage	Rammschelle *f*	cravatta *f* di fissaggio
5955 **drive head**	tête *f* de tubage	Rammkopf *m*	testa *f* di tubazione
5956 **drive pipe**	tube *m* de fonçage	Rammrohr *n*	tubo *m* perforatore
5957 **drive shoe**	sabot *m* de fonçage	Rammschuh *m*	scarpa *f* di perforazione

driver, *s. catch*

5958 **driver's lamp**	lampe *f* de mine	Grubenlampe *f*	lampada *f* da minatore
5959 **driving**	avancement *m* traçage *m*	Streckenauffahren *n*	avanzamento *m*, tracciamento *m*
5960 **driving**	transmission *f*	Transmission *f*	trasmissione *f*

driving a well-point, *s. drilling of a bore-hole*

5961 **driving axle**	arbre *m* moteur	Treibachse *f*	asse *m* motore

driving cap, *s. drive head*

5962 **driving engine**	moteur *m*	Antriebsmaschine *f*	motrice *f*, motore di trascinamento
5963 **driving head-ways**	travail *m* préparatoire	Vorrichtungs- arbeiten *f pl.*	lavoro *m* preparatorio
5964 **driving maschine**	machine *f* motrice	Antriebsmaschine *f*	macchina *f* motrice

	English	French	German	Italian
° 5965	driving off carbonic acid	expulsion *f* de l'acide carbonique	Austreiben *n* der Kohlensäure	eliminazione *f* dell'acido carbonico
— 5966	driving pulley	poulie *f* de commande	Antriebsscheibe *f*	puleggia *f* motrice
— 5967	driving pulley	poulie Koepe	Koepe-Treibscheibe *f*	puleggia *f* Koepe
° 5968	driving shaft	arbre *m* d'attaque ou de commande	Antriebswelle *f*	albero *m* motore, albero *m* primario (o di comando)
— 5969	driving trough	couloir *m* d'attaque	Angriffrutsche *f*	scivolo *m* d'attacco
° 5970	driving wheels	roues *f pl.* motrices	Treibräder *n pl.*	ruote *f pl.* motrici
— 5971	to drop out	foncer	herausfallen (des Sandes)	crollare, franare (delle sabbie)
° 5972	to drop forge	estamper, matricer	gesenkschmieden	stampare, forgiare (a caldo)
° 5973	drop (casting defect)	chute *f* de sable	abgefallener Sand *m*	distacco (o caduta) di terra, franatura
— 5974	drop	soulèvement *m* de sable	Hochschwemmen *n* von Sandstücken	sollevamento *m* di terra
° 5975	drop ball, pig breaker	casse-fonte *m*	Fallwerk *n*	berta *f* spezzaghisa
° 5976	drop bottom	fond *m* ouvrant	Bodenklappe *f*	fondo *m* a botola, fondo *m* mobile
— 5977	drop bottom bucket	cuffat *m* à fond mobile	Bodenentleerer *m*, Kübel mit Bodenklappe	draga *f* a fondo mobile
— 5978	drop-bottom skip	skip *m* à fond ouvrant	Fördergefäss *n* mit Bodenklappe	skip *m* a fondo apribile (o a botola)
° 5979	drop casting, top pouring	coulée *f* en chute directe	fallender Guss *m* mit einem Metallstrahl	colata *f* diretta o a caduta
	drop doors, *s. bottom doors*			
— 5980	drop fault	faille *f* normale	normale Verwerfung *f*	faglia *f* normale
° 5981	drop forge	marteau *m* à chute	Gesenkschmiede *f*	maglio *m* a caduta
° 5982	drop-forged	façonné par marteau à chute	mit dem Fallhammer *m* geformt	formato al maglio meccanico

English	French	German	Italian
5983 **drop forging**	estampage m, pièce f étampée	Gesenkschmieden n, Gesenkschmiede- stück n	stampaggio m (a caldo), pezzo m stampato, fuci- natura f a stampo
5984 **drop forging hammer, drop stamping hammer**	mouton m à étampage	Pressrahmen- hammer m, Fall- hammer m	berta f a stampare
5985 **drop gate**	canal m de coulée directe	direkter Gusskanal m	canale m di colata diretta
5986 **drop hammer**	mouton m, marteau m guidé	Gleishammer m, Rahmenhammer m	maglio m a caduta libe- ra, martinetto m libero o parallelo, berta f
5987 **drop hammer die**	matrice pour marteau-pilon	Hammergesenk n	stampo m per maglio
5988 **drop-made column**	colonne f coiffée, demoiselle f	Sandpyramide f	piramide f di sabbia (o di terra)
5989 **drop of the top flame**	extinction f de la flamme du gueulard	Niederschlagen n der Gichtflamme	abbattimento m della fiamma della bocca (d'altoforno)
5990 **drop of pressure**	perte f de pression	Spannungsverlust m	perdita f di pressione
5991 **drop of temperature**	chute f de température	Temperaturabfall m, Sinken n der Tempe- ratur	abbassamento m di temperatura, caduta f di temperatura
5992 **drop-runner**	chenal m de coulée en chute directe	Eingusspfeife f	canale m di colata a caduta diretta
5993 **drop shaft**	cuvelage m descendant	Senkschacht m	tubaggio m discendente
5994 **drop-sheet**	toile f d'aérage	Wettertuch n	sbarramento m di ventila- zione
5995 **drop stamp with Müller drive**	marteau m à planche avec commande Müller	Stangenreibhammer m, mit Müllerschem Antrieb	maglio m con comando sistema Müller
5996 **drop stamping**	estampage m	Gesenkschmieden n	stampaggio m al maglio
5997 **drop-stone**	stalactite f, stalagmite f	Tropfstein m	stalattite f, stalagmite f
5997a **drop test**	essai m au choc	Fallprobe f	prova f dinamica di caduta
5998 **drop through die**	moule f à élément passant (ou à pont)	Stempel m mit durchgehendem Element	stampo m a ponte, stam- po m con impronta passante

English	French	German	Italian
° 5999 **drop weight**	mouton m en forme de boule	Fallkugel f	palla f della berta, martino m
— 6000 **dropped side**	lèvre f affaissée (d'une faille)	gesunkener Flügel m (einer Verwerfung)	lembo m abbassato (di faglia)
— 6001 **dropper**	filon m secondaire	Nebengang m	filone m secondario
— 6002 **dropping**	chute f	Durchgehen n	caduta f
° 6003 **dropping funnel**	entonnoir m compte-gouttes	Tropftrichter m	imbuto m contagoccie
° 6004 **dropping metal**	métal m entré en fusion	abschmelzendes Metall n	metallo m fondente
° 6005 **dropping of the charge**	descente f de la charge	Niedergehen n der Gicht	discesa f della carica
— 6006 **dross**	charbon m menu de rebut	Ausschuss-kohlenklein n	carbone m minuto di scarto
° 6007 **dross**	crasse f, scorie f	Krätze f, Krätz-metall, Aschblei f	scoria f
° 6008 **dross filter**	filtre m à crasses, filtre à scories	Schlackenfang m, Siebplatte f	filtro m fermascorie, filtro m per scorie
° 6008a **dross hole**	trou m à crasse	Schlackenloch n	foro m delle scorie
° 6009 **drossing**	écrémage m	Schmutzentfernung f, Schaumabheben n	rimozione f della feccia, scrematura f
— 6010 **drossy coal**	charbon m pyriteux	schwefelkieshaltige Kohle f	carbone m piritico
— 6011 **drowned valley**	vallée f submergée	ertrunkenes Tal n	valle f sommersa
^ 6012 **drum connection**	tube m de connection	Verbindungsrohr n	tubo m di collegamento
— 6013 **drum-curb**	trousse f	Schachtring m	anello m tagliente, cilindro m cavo
° 6014 **drum ladle**	poche-tonneau f	Giesstrommel f	siviera f di colata a tino, caldata f di colata a botte (o a tino)
— 6015 **drum shaft**	arbre m du tambour	Trommelwelle f	albero m del tamburo
— 6016 **drum washer**	lavoir m rotatif	Trommelwascher m	tamburo m o cilindro m lavatore
— 6017 **drumlin**	colline f arrondie de moraine	Drummel	collina f arrotondata di morena

English	French	German	Italian

drumline, s. drum line

6018 **drumming**	sonder le toit en le frappant	Abklopfen n der Firste	sondare il tetto battendolo
6019 **drummy**	peu sûr	unsicher	malsicuro, poco sicuro
6020 **druse**	druse f	Druse f	drusa f
6021 **druse structure**	structure f drusique	Drusentextur f	struttura f drusica
6022 **drusy**	drusique	drusenförmig	drusico, drusiforme

drusy cavity, s. geodes

6023 **to dry**	sécher	trocknen	essiccare, asciugare
6024 **to dry on the spot**	sécher sur place	am Herstellungsplatz trocknen	asciugare sul posto
6025 **dry back boiler**	chaudière f sans fond mouillé	Kreuztrockenkessel m	caldaia f senza fondo bagnato
6025a **dry bond**	corps m de sable à sec	trockene Sandfestigkeit f	- forza f della terra a secco
6026 **dry-bone**	calamine f	Kalamin m, Smithsonit m	calamina f
6027 **dry boring**	sondage m à sec	Trockenbohren n	trivellazione f a secco

dry burning coal, s. lean coal

dry cleaning, s. dry gas cleaning

6028 **dry coal. lean coal**	charbon m maigre	Trockenkohle f	carbone m magro,
6028a **dry copper**	cuivre m à gros grains	grobkörniges Kupfer	rame m a grano grosso
6029 **dry crushing**	broyage m à sec	Trockenmahlen n, Trockenzerkleinerung	frantumazione f a secco
6030 **dry diggings**	placers m pl. d'alluvion	äolische Seifen f pl.	giacimenti m pl. alluvionali
6031 **dry distillation**	distillation f sèche	Entgasung f, trockene Verdampfung f	distillazione f secca
6031a **dry drawing**	étirage m brillant	Glanzziehen n	trafilatura f brillante
6032 **dry enamelling**	émaillage m au poudré	Puderemaillierung f	smaltatura f a spolvero, smaltatura f a secco
6032a **dry gas cleaning**	épuration f à sec du gaz	trockene Gasreinigung f	epurazione f a secco del gas

dry-gilding, s. hot-golding

dry grinding, s. dry crushing

6033 **dry ore**	minerai m sec	trockenes Erz n	minerale m secco
6034 **dry packing**	remblai m sec	Trockenversatz m	riporto m secco, ripiena con materiale secco
6035 **dry plate**	plaque f sèche	Trockenplatte f	placca f secca

	English	French	German	Italian
˄ 6036	dry point	point *m* de dessication	Trocknungspunkt *m*	punto *m* di essicazione
○ 6037	dry puddling	puddlage *m* à sec	Trockenpuddeln *n*	puddellaggio *m* a secco
˄ 6038	dry purification of the gases	épuration *f* à sec des gaz	Trockenreinigung *f* der Gase	depurazione *f* a secco dei gas
○ 6039	dry sand	sable *m* étuvé	trockener Sand *m*	terra *f* essiccata, sabbia *f* secca
○ 6040	dry sand casting	moulage *m* en terre	Masseguss *m*	pezzo *m* colato a secco
○ 6041	dry-sand molding, dry molding	moulage *m* en sable sec	Masseform *f*, Sandform *f*	formatura *f* a secco
○ 6042	dry sand slab (in foundry)	couche *f* de sable étuvé	trockene Sandschicht *f*	strato *m* di terra a secco
○ 6042a	dry scale	ecaillage *m* sec	trockener Zunder *m*	scagliatura *f* secca
— 6043	dry screening	criblage *m* à sec	Trockensiebung *f*	vagliatura *f* a secco
— 6044	dry separation	triage *m* à sec, triage *m* sec	trockene Scheidung *f*	separazione *f* a secco
— 6045	dry separation of coal	préparation *f* à sec du charbon	trockene Scheidung *f* der Kohle	preparazione *f* a secco del carbone
— 6046	dry sifting	tamisage *m* à sec, criblage *m* à sec	Trockensiebung *f*	vagliatura *f* a secco
— 6047	dry stamping, dry crushing	bocardage *m* à sec, broyage *m* à sec	Trockenpochen *n*, Trockenzerkleinerung *f*	frantumazione *f* a secco
— 6048	dry strength	cohésion *f* à sec	Trockenkohäsion *f*	coesione a secco
— 6049	dry walling	meurtiat *m*	Bergemauer *f*	muratura *f* a secco
— 6050	dry washing	lavage *m* à sec	Trockenwaschen *n*	lavaggio secco (o all'aria)
	dry well, *s. dry hole*			
— 6051	dryer, drier	sécheur *m*	Trockner *m*	essicatore *m*
— 6052	drying	séchage *m*	Trocknung *f*	essiccazione *f*, essiccamento *m*
— 6053	drying and roasting apparatus	étuve *f* à sécher et griller	Trocken- und Röstapparat *m*	apparato *m* d'essiccamento o di calcinazione
˄ 6054	drying apparatus (of gas)	appareil *m* à dessécher (des gaz)	Trockenapparat *m*	essiccatoio *m*, essiccatore *m* (di gas)

English	French	German	Italian
6055 **drying chamber**	étuve *f*, chambre *f* de séchage	Trockenkammer *f*, Darrkammer *f*	stufa *f*, camera *f* di essiccamento
6056 **drying chamber carriage**	chariot *m* d'étuve	Trockenkammer-wagen *m*	carro *m* per essiccatoio
6057 **drying cylinder**	tube *m* de séchage	Trockenzylinder *m*	cilindro *m* essiccatore
6058 **drying cylinder**	tambour *m* sécheur	Trockentrommel *f*	tamburo *m* d'essicca-zione
drying drum, *s. drying cylinder*			
6059 **drying-furnace, drying-kiln**	four *m* de séchage, four *m* sécheur	Trockenofen *m*	forno *m* di essicazione
dry molding, *s. dry-sand molding*			
6060 **drying of the moulds**	séchage *m* des moules	Trocknen *n* der Formen	essiccatura *f* od essic-camento *m* delle forme
6061 **drying oven**	étuve *f* de séchage	Trockenschrank *m*, Trockenkasten *m*	stufa *f* d'essiccazione, essiccatoio *m*
6062 **drying plant**	installation *f* de séchage	Trockenanlage *f*	impianto *m* per l'essic-camento
6063 **drying room**	étuves *f pl.* de séchage	Trockenraum *m*	essiccatoio *m*, essic-catore *m*
6064 **drying stand**	support *m* de séchoir	Trockengestell *n*	supporto *m* o sostegno *m* per essiccatoio
driying stove, *s. drying furnace*			
6065 **drying tube**	tube *m* de séchage	Trockenröhre *f*	tubo *m* d'essiccazione
6066 **drying the blast**	séchage *m* de l'air	Windtrocknung *f*	essiccazione *f* dell'aria
6067 **dual completion well**	puits *m* à double tube	Doppelrohrschacht *m*	pozzo *m* a doppio comple-tamento
6068 **dual producer**	puits *m* à double production	Doppelförderungs-schacht *m*	pozzo *m* a duplice produzione
6069 **dual reservoir**	gisement *m* multiple	Doppelförderungs-vorkommen *n*	giacimento *m* multiplo
6070 **dual system**	sondage *m* double	Doppelbohrung *f*	perforazione *f* doppia
6071 **dual zone well**	puits *m* à double production	Doppelzonenförde-rungsschacht *m*	pozzo *m* producente contemporaneamente da due zone

	English	French	German	Italian
—	6072 **duck-bill**	bec m de canard	Entenschnabel m	pala f caricatrice motorizzata
°	6072a **duct**	conduit m	Rohrleitung f	condotto m
°	6073 **ductile, malleable soft**	ductile, malléable	dehnbar, streckbar, hammerbar	duttile, malleabile
°	6074 **ductile or soft iron**	fer m malléable ou ductile	geschmeidiges Eisen n	ferro m malleabile o duttile
°	6075 **ductility**	ductilité f	Dehnbarkeit f, Streckbarkeit f	duttilità f, fucinabilità f
^	6076 **dud**	puits m stérile	Fehlbohrung f	pozzo m improduttivo
—	6077 **duff**	poussier m, fines f pl. lavées	Nussgruskohle f, gewaschene Feinkohle f	polvere f di carbone, fino m di carbone ottenuto al vaglio
—	6078 **Duff producer**	gazogène m Duff	Duffscher Generator m	gasogeno m Duff
—	6079 **dufrenite**	dufrénite f	Dufrenit m, Kraurit m	dufrenite f
—	6080 **dufrenoysite**	dufrénoysite f	Dufrenoisit m	dufrenoisite f
—	6081 **duftite**	duftite f	Duftit m	duftite f
—	6082 **dug well**	puits m à bras	Handbrunnen m	pozzo m a mano
^	6083 **dull**	cheville f d'ajustage	Einstellstift m	spina f d'aggiustaggio
—	6084 **dull bit**	outil usé	verschlissener Meissel m	scalpello m consumato
—	6085 **dull bit indicator**	indicateur m d'usure d'outil	Verschleissanzeiger m für Meissel	indicatore m d'usura dello scalpello
—	6086 **dull coal**	charbon m mat	Mattkohle f	carbone m amorfo
°	6086a **dull finish**	décapage m au mat	Mattbeizung f	decapaggio m opaco
°	6087 **dull red-hot**	chauffé au rouge sombre	dunkelrotglühend	scaldato al calor rosso scuro
°	6088 **dull or dead spot**	partie f mate	matte Stelle f	superficie f appannata, parte f opaca
—	6088 **dulled**	usé	verschlissen	consumato (di scalpello)
	6090 **dumb**	sans moteur	ohne Motor m	senza motore
—	6091 **dumalite**	dumalite f	Dumalit m	dumalite f

English	French	German	Italian

dumb scab, *s. sand buckle*

6092	**dummy (die forging)**	empreinte *f*	Abdruck *m*	impronta *f*
6093	**dummy riser**	montant *m* aveugle	Blindpfeiler *m*	montante *m* cieco
6094	**dumontite**	dumontite *f*	Dumontit *m*	dumontite *f*
6095	**dumortierite**	dumortiérite *f*	Dumortierit *m*	dumortierite *f*
6096	**dump**	terril *m*, crassier *m*, halde *f*	Schlackenhalde *f*	deposito *m* di loppa, discarica *f*
6097	**dump bailer**	cuiller *f* de cimentation	Zementierbüchse *f*	cucchiaia *f* di cementazione
6098	**dump bucket**	benne *f* basculante	Kippkübel *m*	tramoggia *f* oscillante
6099	**dump car**	wagon *m* basculant	Kippwagen *m*	vagone *m* ribaltabile, vagone a bilico
6100	**dump cradle**	culbuteur *m*	Wipper *m*, Kipper *m*	apparecchio *m* di ribaltamento
6101	**dump pit**	halde *f*, terril *m*	Halde *f*, Schlackenhalde *f*	ammasso *m* di materiale sterile
6101a	**dump test**	essai *m* d'aplatissement	Stauchprobe *f*	prova *f* di ricalcatura

dump truck, *s. dump car*

| 6102 | **dump valve** | vanne *f* à décharger | Ausblaseventil *n* | valvola *f* di scarico |
| 6103 | **dumper** | culbuteur *m* | Kippwagen *m* | ribaltatore *m* |

dumping cart, *s. tipping wagon*

6104	**dumping grate**	grille *f* à scories	Schlackenrost *m*	griglia *f* per scorie
6105	**dumping ground**	dépôt des déblais	Sturzplatz *m*	deposito *m* di rifiuti
6106	**dumping place, dump**	lieu *m* de déversement	Absturzplatz *m*	scarico *m*
6107	**dundasite**	dundasite *f*	Dundasit *m*	dundasite *f*
6108	**dune sand**	sable *m* de dune	Quarzsand *m*	sabbia *f* di duna

dung water, *s. filthy water*

6109	**dungannonite**	dungannonite *f*	Dungannonit *m*	dungannonite *f*
6110	**dunite**	dunite *f*	Dunit *f*	dunite *f*
6111	**dunn bass**	schiste *m* argileux	Tonschiefer *m*	scisto argilloso, argilloscisto *m*

		English	French	German	Italian
		duns, *s. dunn bass*			
°	6112	**duplex process**	procédé duplex	Duplex-Verfahren *n*	procedimento *m* duplex
°	6113	**duplex pump, Worthington pump**	pompe *f* duplex, pompe Worthington	Duplexpumpe *f*, Worthingtonpumpe *f*	pompa *f* duplex, pompa Worthington
°	6114	**duplex steel**	acier duplex	Duplexmetall *n*, Duplexstahl *m*	acciaio *m* duplex
°	6114a	**duplex tube**	tube *m* bimétallique	Bimetallrohr *n*	tubo *m* bimetallico
°	6115	**durain**	durain *m* *	Durit *m*	durite *f*
°	6116	**dural, duralumin**	duralumin *m*	Dural *n*, Duralumin *n*	dural *m*
		duralumin, *s. dural*			
°	6117	**durability**	résistance *f*, dureté	Haltbarkeit *f*	durata *f*, stabilità *f*
°	6118	**duration of heating**	durée *f* de la chauffe	Dauer *f* der Erhitzung	durata *f* del riscaldamen
°	6119	**duration of oscillation**	durée *f* d'oscillation	Schwingungsdauer *f*	durata *f* d'oscillazione
—	6120	**durbachite**	durbachite *f*	Durbachit *m*	durbachite *f*
—	6121	**durdenite**	durdénite *f*	Durdenit *m*	durdenite *f*
—	6122	**durn**	cadre *m* de galerie	Stollenbrett *n*	quadro *m* per armare gallerie
°	6123	**dust**	talquer	mit Talkum einpudern	passare il talco
—	6124	**dust**	poussière	Staub *m*	polvere *f*
—	6125	**dust arrester**	collecteur de poussières	Staubfänger *m*	collettore *m* delle polveri
°	6126	**dust bag**	sac *m* à poudre	Staubsack *m*	sacchetto *m* da spolvero, sacco *m* della polvere
		dust bin, *s. dust pocket*			
		dust bother, *s. dust nuisance*			
		dust box, *s. dust chamber*			
°	6127	**dust catcher**	caisse *f* à poussières	Staubfang *m*, Staubfänger *m*	cassa *f* di raccolta della polvere
°	6128	**dust chamber, dust box**	chambre *f* à poussières	Staubfang *m*, Staubkammer *f*	camera *f* della polvere

English	French	German	Italian
6129 **dust coal**	charbon *m* poussié-reux	Staubkohle *f*	carbone *m* in polvere
dust-coke, *s. coke-breeze*			
dust collector, *s. dust chamber*			
6130 **dust deposits**	dépôts *m pl.* de poussières atmosphériques	Ablagerung *f* von atmosphärischem Stau¹⁾	deposito *m* di pulviscolo atmosferico
6131 **dust exhauster**	aspirateur *m* de poussières	Staubsauger *m*	aspiratore *m* di polveri
6131a **dust exhaustion**	aspiration *f* de poussières	Staubabsaugung *f*	aspirazione *f* di polvere
6132 **dust extractor**	séparateur de poussières, dépoussiéreur *m*	Entstaubungs-vorrichtung *f*	separatore *m* di polvere
6133 **dust from throat of furnace**	poussière *f* du gueulard	Gichtstaub *m*	polvere *f* della gola del forno
6134 **dust laving**	abattage *m* des poussières	Entstauben *n*	abbattimento *m* delle polveri
6135 **dust nuisance**	inconvénient *m* des poussières	Staubbelästigung *f*	inconveniente *m* causato dalle ceneri (o dalle polveri)
6136 **dust pocket**	sac *m* à poussières	Staubsack *m*	sacco *m* da polvere
6137 **dust removal**	dépoussiérage *m*	Entstaubung *f*	rimozione *f* della polvere
6138 **dust removal tool, dust catcher**	dépoussiéreur *m*	Entstaubungs-vorrichtung *f*	depolveratore *m*
6139 **dust trap**	arrêt-barrage *m*	Staubsperre *f*	separatore *m* di polvere
duster, *s. dry hole*			
6140 **duster**	sondage stérile (ou improductif)	Fehlbohrung *f*	sondaggio *m* sterile o improduttivo
6141 **dusting**	talcage *m*	Einpudern *n* mit Talkum	spolverare con talco
6141a **dusting**	poudrage *m* au sulfure	Schwefelbestäubung *f*	impolveramento *m* con zolfo
6142 **dutch gold**	or *m* faux	Rauschgold *n*	oro *m* falso, oro *m* olandese
6143 **duty**	rendement *m*	Nutzleistung *f*	resa *f*, lavoro *m* utile

	English	French	German	Italian
°	6144 **dwarf boiler**	chaudière *f* naine	Zwergkessel *m*	caldaia *f* nana
°	6145 **dwindle away**	épuiser	erschöpfen	esaurire
—	6146 **Dyas**	Dyas, Permien *m*	Dyas *f*, Perm *n*	Dyas *m*, Permiano *m*
°	6147 **dyeing roll**	cylindre *m* applicateur de peinture	Auftragwalze *f*	rullo *m* di applicazione della vernice
—	6148 **dyke**	dyke *m*	Gesteinsgang *m*, Intrusivgang *m*	dicco *m*, filone *m* eruttivo
	dyke rock, *s. dyke*			
^	6149 **dynagraph, dynamometer**	dynagraphe *m*	Dynamometer *n*	dinamometro *m*
^	6150 **dynamic brake**	frein *m* dynamique	Wirbelstrombremse *f*	freno *m* dinamico
—	6151 **dynamic metamorphism**	métamorphisme *m* dynamique	dynamischer Metamorphismus *m*	dinamometamorfismo *m*
°	6151a **dynamic strength**	résistance dynamique	dynamische Festigkeit *f*	resistenza *f* dinamica
°	6152 **dynamic test**	essai *m* dynamique	dynamische Prüfung *f*	prova *f* dinamica
—	6153 **dynamiting**	dynamitage *m*	Dynamitsprengung *f*	esplosione *f* di dinamite
°	6154 **dynamo room**	salle *f* des dynamos	Dynamoraum *m*	sala *f* delle dinamo
°	6155 **dynamo sheet, armature core plate**	tôle *f* pour dynamo	Dynamoblech *n*	lamiera *f* per dinamo
°	6156 **dynamo steel casting**	acier *m* moulé pour dynamo	Dynamostahlguss *m*	acciaio *m* fuso per dinamo
—	6157 **dysanalyte**	dysanalyte *f*	Dysanalyt *m*	disanalite *f*
—	6158 **dyscrasite**	dyscrasite *f*	Dyskrasit *m*	dyscrasite *f*
—	6159 **dyscrystalline**	mal cristallisé	schlecht kristallisiert	mal cristallizzato
—	6160 **dysluite**	dysluite *f*	Dysluit *m*	disluite *f*
—	6161 **dysphotic region**	région *f* dysphotique	dysphotische Region *f*	regione *f* disfotica
—	6162 **dysprosium**	dysprosium *m*	Dysprosium *n*	disprosio *m*
—	6163 **dyssnite**	dyssnite *f*	Dyssnit *m*	dyssnite *f*

	English	French	German	Italian
	eaglestone, s. *aetites*			
6164	**ear (of a ventilator)**	oüïe f d'aspiration (d'un ventilateur)	Ventilatoreinström- öffnung f	bocca f di aspirazione d'un ventilatore
6165	**ear bit**	trépan m à oreilles	Stufenmeissel m	trapano m a alette
6166	**early tertiary**	tertiaire m ancien	Frühneolithikum n	primo terziario m
	earliest section, s. *first section*			
6167	**earth auger**	tarière f à large spire	Tellerbohrer m	trivella f da suolo a larghe spire
	earth borer, s. *earth auger*			
6168	**earth boring machine**	sondeuse f	Bohrkran m	perforatrice f
6169	**earth-creep**	glissement m de terrain	Erdrutsch m	smottamento m di terre- no. frana f
6170	**earth flax**	amiante m, asbeste m	Asbest n	amianto m
6171	**earth ripper**	excavateur m de tranchée	Einschnittbagger m	macchina f scava-trin- cea
6172	**earthy fracture**	cassure f terreuse	erdiger Bruch m	rottura f terrosa
6173	**earthy coal**	charbon m terreux	Erdkohle f	carbone m terroso
6174	**earthy haematite**	ocre f rouge	Blutstein m	ocra f rossa
6175	**earthy iron ore**	minerai m de fer terreux	erdiges Eisenerz n	minerale m di ferro terroso
6176	**earthy oil**	naphte m, pétrole m	Naphtha n, Erdöl n	nafta f, petrolio m
6177	**earthy pillar**	nonne f, pyramide f coiffée, demoiselle f	Erdpyramide f	piramide f di terra, piramide f di sabbia
6178	**earthy wax**	ozokérite f	Ozokerit m	ozocherite f
6179	**easer**	mine f de dégraissa- ge	Hilfsbohrloch n	foro m da mina ausi- liario
6180	**easily fusible iron**	minerai m facilement fusible	leicht schmelzba- res Erz n	minerale m facilmen- te fusibile
6181	**easily reducible ore**	minerai m facilement réductible	leicht reduzierba- res Erz n	minerale m facilmen- te riducibile
	easing, s. *joint breaking or relieving*			
6182	**easy cleavage**	clivage m distinct	deutliche Spaltbar- keit f	sfaldatura f distinta, clivaggio m distinto
6183	**easy reduction**	réductibilité f facile	leichte Reduzierbar- keit f	riducibilità f facile
6184	**ebanite support**	soucoupe f en caout- chouc durci	Untersatz m aus Hartgummi	piattello m di ebanite

		English	French	German	Italian
○	6185	eccentric breaker	presse f à excentrique	Exzenterpresse f	spezzamasselli m ad eccentrico
○	6186	eccentric press	presse f à excentrique	Exzenterpresse f	pressa f ad eccentrico
○	6187	eccentric roll	cylindre m excentrique	exzentrische Walze f	cilindro m eccentrico
—	6188	echinoderm	echinoderme f	Echinoderm	echinoderma f
—	6189	eclogite	éclogite f	Eklogit m	eclogite f
—	6190	economic geology	géologie f économique	angewandte Geologie f	geologia f economica
○	6191	economical grate	grille f économique	Sparrost m	griglia f economica
○	6192	economizer jet	buse f de l'économiseur	Ekonomiseur-Düse. f	ugello m dell'economizzatore
○	6193	economizing tube	tuyau m économiseur	Economizer-Rohr n	tubo m economizzatore
^	6194	eddy	tourbillon m	Wirbel m	turbine m, vortice m mulinello m
^	6194a	eddy current	courant m de Facoult	Wirbelstrom m	corrente f di Facoult
^	6195	eddy flow	écoulement m turbulent	Wirbelströmung f	moto m turbolento
—	6196	edenite	edenite f	Edenit m	edenite f
○	6197	edge	arête f	Kante f	spigolo m, angolo m
○	6198	edge, rim	bord m	Rand m	bordo m orlo m, margine
○	6199	edge angle bar	cornière f d'angle	Eckwinkel m	cantonale m d'angolo
○	6200	edge break	fissure f du bord	Kantenriss m	incrinatura f al bordo
		edge crack, s. cross crack			
○	6201	edge-holding property, cutting hardness	résistance de tranchant, dureté f de tranchant	Schneidhaltigkeit f, Schneidhärte f	durezza f di taglio
—	6202	edge-mill	moulin m chilien	chilenische Mühle f	macinatoio m (o mulino a palmenti
		edge-mill. s. crushing mill with vertical runners			
		edge of a hammer. s. pane			
○	6203	edge of the cylinder	rebord m du cylindre	Rand m des Zylinders	bordo m del cilindro
○	6203a	edge roll	cylindre m de refoulement	Stauchwalze f	cilindro m bordatore

English	French	German	Italian
6204 **edge water**	eau *f* marginale	Randwasser *n*	acqua *f* marginale
6205 **edge water encroachment**	encrochement d'eau de bordure	Vorrücken *n* von Randwasser	avanzamento *m* di acqua marginale
6206 **edge water line**	limite *f* eau-pétrole	Randwasserlinie *f*	limite *m* acqua-petrolio
6207 **edge well**	puits *m* de bordure	Randsonde *f*	limite *m* del bordo
6208 **edged surface**	surface *f* anguleuse	kantige Oberfläche	superficie *f* ad angoli vivi (o ruvida)
6208a **edger**	distributeur *m*	Flachstich *m*	distributore *m*
6209 **edging (rolling mill)**	finissage *m* des bords	Randschlichtdrehen *n*	rifinitura *f* dei bordi
6210 **edging pass**	passe *f* sur les bords	Randfertigpolieren *n*	passata *f* sugli spigoli
6211 **edging stand**	cage *f* finisseuse des bords	Randfertigwalzkorb *m*	gabbia *f* rifinitrice dei bordi, bordatrice *f*
6212 **edging train**	train *m* finisseur des bords, cage *f* de refoulement	Randfertigstrecke *f* Stauchgerüst *n*	treno *m* rifinitore dei bordi
6213 **edingtonite**	edingtonite *f*	Edingtonit *m*	edingtonite *f*
6214 **Edison apparatus**	appareil *m* d'Edison	Scheider *m* von Edison	apparecchio *m* di Edison
6215 **effect of stroke. strenght of blow**	effet *m* du coup force *f* du marteau	Schlagwirkung *f*	portata *f* del martello, effetto *m* del colpo
6216 **to effervesce**	bouillonner	aufbrausen	entrare in effervescenza
effervescing steel, *s. unkilled steel*			
6217 **effuser**	diffuseur *m*	Diffusor *m*	diffusore *m*
6218 **effusive masses**	massifs *m pl.* d'épanchement	Ergussmassen *f. pl.*	ammassi *m pl.* effusivi
6219 **effusive rock, extrusive rock**	roche *f* d'épanchement	Effusivgestein *n* Ergussgestein *n*	roccia *f* effusiva
6220 **egg coal**	boulet *m* d'anthracite	Eierbrikett *n*	ovulo *m* d'antracite
6221 **egg coke cob coal**	coke *m* concassé, gaillettes *f pl,* charbon *m* en grélat	Brechkoks *m*, Eikoks *m*	coke *m* di pezzatura uovo (o a cubetti)
6222 **egg ended boiler**	chaudière *f* cylindrique à fond ovale	Eggsenderkessel *m*	caldaia *f* cilindrica a fondo ovale
6223 **egg shape**	forme *f* ovoïde	Eiform *f*	forma *f* ovoidale

	English	French	German	Italian
− 6224	**egg size**	grosseur f d'œuf	Eigrosse f	grossezza f d'uovo
	egg sleeker. *s. spoon tool*			
− 6225	**egg-stone**	oolithe f	Oolith m,	oolite f, calcare m oolitico
− 6226	**eggette**	briquette f	Brikett n	mattonella f(di carbone)
− 6227	**eglestonite**	eglestonite f	Eglestonit m	eglestonite f
− 6228	**ehlite**	ehlite f	Ehlit m	ehlite f
° 6229	**Ehrhardt's pressing process**	procédé m à la presse Ehrhardt	Pressverfahren n nach Ehrhardt	processo m alla pressa Ehrhardt
° 6230	**Eichorn's hydrometer**	aéro-pycnomètre m d'Eichorn	Senkwaagedichtig-keitsmesser m	-aereo-picnometro m di Eichorn
− 6231	**eichwaldite**	eichwaldite f	Eichwaldit m	eichwaldite f
− 6232	**Eifelian stage**	Eifélien m	Eifel-Stufe f	Eifeliano m
6233	**eight hours shift**	poste m de huit heures	achtstündige Arbeitsschicht f	turno m di otto ore
° 6234	**einsteinium**	einsteinium m	Einsteinium n	einstenio m
° 6235	**to eject**	démouler (en sable)	auswerfen	sformare (in sabbia), estrarre un modello
− 6236	**ejecta**	projections $f. pl.$ volcaniques	Auswürflinge $m pl.$	proiezioni $f pl.$ vulca-niche
° 6236a	**ejection**	éjection f	**Ausstossen** n	eiezione f
° 6237	**ejection heel**	talon m d'éjection	Auswerflappen m	appendice f di estrazion
° 6238	**ejection plate, top ejector plate**	plaque f d'éjection plaque supérieure d'éjection	Ausstosser m	piastra f porta estrattor piastra f superiore d'esp sione
° 6238a	**ejector**	éjecteur m	Ausstosser m	eiettore m
° 6239	**ejector plate stop**	repos m d'éjection	Auswerferanschlag m	spina f guida di estrazi
° 6240	**ejection release**	rappel m d'éjection	Rückdruckstift m	guida m di estrazione
° 6241	**ejector**	éjecteur m	Auswerfer m	espulsore m
− 6242	**ekdemite**	ecdémite f	Ekdemit m	ecdemite f
− 6243	**elæolite**	éléolite f	Eläolith m	eleolite f,nefelina f
° 6244	**elastic buffer**	butoir m élastique	elastischer Puffer m	respingente elastico
° 6245	**elastic limit**	limite f d'élasticité	Elastizitätsgrenze f	limite m di elasticità

	English	French	German	Italian
6246	elastic modulus, Young's modulus	module m d'élasticité, module m Young m	Elastizitätsmodul	modulo m di elasticità modulo m di Young
6246a	elastic strain	déformation f élastique	elastische Formänderung f	deformazione f elastica
6247	elasticity of compression	élasticité f de compression	Druckelastizität f	elasticità f di compressione
6248	elasticity of elongation	élasticité f de traction	Zugelastizität f	elasticità f di trazione
6249	elasticity of flexure	élasticité f de flexion	Biegungselastizität f	elasticità f di flessione
6250	elasticity of materials	élasticité f des matériaux	Elastizität f der Materialie	elasticità f dei materiali
6251	elasticity of torsion	élasticité f de torsion	Torsionselastizität f	elasticità f di torsione
6252	elaterite	élatérite f	Elaterit m	elaterite f
6253	elbow	dressant m	seigeres Flöz n	filone m verticale
6254	elbow, knee	coude m	Krümmer m, Kniestück n	raccordo m a gomito
6255	electric arc	arc m électrique	Lichtbogen m	arco m voltaico, arco m elettrico
6256	electric arc furnace	four m électrique à arc	Lichtbogenofen m	forno m elettrico ad arco
6257	electric arc horizontal furnace	four m électrique à arc horizontal	elektrischer Horizontalofen m	forno m elettrico ad arco orizzontale
6258	electric bench shears	cisaille f d'établi électrique	elektrische Tischschere f	forbici f $pl.$ da banco elettriche, cesoia f da banco elettrica
6259	electric-blasting	tir m électrique, allumage m électrique f	elektrische Zündung	accensione f elettrica
6260	electric-blasting cap	détonateur électrique	elektrischer Zünder	detonatore m elettrico
6261	electric blow pipe electric torch	chalumeau m électrique	elektrisches Lötrohr n	cannello m elettrico
6262	electric boiler	chaudière f électrique	Elektro (dampf) - kessel m	caldaia f elettrica
6263	electric cableduct tube	tube m pour la protection de câbles électriques	Kabelschutzrohr n	tubo m per protezione di cavi elettrici
6264	electric cap-lamp	lampe f électrique de chapeau	elektrische Kopflampe f	lampada f elettrica da elmetto

	English	French	German	Italian
° 6265	electric carbon	charbon *m* électrique	galvanische Kohle *f*	carbone *m* elettrico
° 6266	electrical conductivity	conductivité *f* électrique	elektrische Leitfähigkeit *f*	conduttività *f* elettrica
— 6267	electrical coring	carottage *m* électrique	elektrisches Kernen *n*	carotaggio *m* elettrico
° 6268	electric crucible furnace	four *m* électrique à creuset	Elektrotiegelofen *m*	forno *m* elettrico a crogiuolo
6269	electric current	courant *m* électrique	elektrischer Strom *m*	corrente *f* elettrica
° 6270	electric discharge impuls	pulsation *f* magnétique	elektrischer Entladungsimpuls *m*	impulso *m* magnetico
— 6271	electric driving of the bell winch	commande *f* électrique du treuil de chargement	elektrischer Antrieb *m* der Glockenwinde	comando *m* elettrico dell'argano
° 6272	electric enamelling	émaillage *f* électrique	elektrisches Emaillieren *n*	smaltatura *f* elettrica
6273	electric endosmosis	endosmose *f* électrique	elektrische Endosmose *f*	endosmosi *f* elettrica
° 6274	electric furnace	four *m* électrique	Elektroofen *m*	forno *m* elettrico
° 6275	electric furnace iron, electric furnace pig iron	fonte *f* électrique, fonte *f* au four électrique	Elektroroheisen *n*	ghisa *f* elettrica, ghisa al forno elettrico
° 6276	electric furnace of resistance type with reverberatory arch,	four *m* électrique à résistance à voûte chauffante	elektrischer Ofen *m* für Widerstandsheizung mit strahlendem Deckelgewölbe	forno *m* elettrico a resistenza a riverbero
	electric furnace steel, *s. electric steel*			
6277	electric generator set	groupe *m* électrogène	Generatorsatz *m*	gruppo *m* elettrogeno
° 6278	electric hand drilling machine on stand	foreuse *f* à main électrique d'établi	elektrische Handbohrmaschine auf Ständer	foratrice *f* elettrica a m per banco
— 6279	electric hand-lamp	lampe *f* électrique à main	elektrische Grubenlampe *f*	lampada *f* elettrica a ma
° 6280	electric hearth furnace	four *m* électrique à sole	elektrischer Herdofen *m*	forno *m* elettrico a suol
— 6281	electric hoist	palan *m* électrique	Elektrozug *m*	paranco *m* elettrico
— 6282	electric hoisting	extration *f* électrique puisage *m* électrique	elektrische Förderung *f*	estrazione *f* elettrica

	English	French	German	Italian
6283	electric holding furnace	four m électrique d'attente	elektrischer Warmhalteofen m	forno m elettrico di attesa
6284	electric impact wrench	clef f de serrage électrique	elektrischer Drehmomentschraubenschluessel m	chiave f di serraggio elettrica
6285	electric induction furnace	four m ou fourneau électrique à induction	Induktionsofen m	forno m elettrico a induzione
6286	electric installation	installation f de machines électriques	elektrische Maschinenanlage f	impianto m di macchine elettriche
6287	electric measuring apparatus	appareil m de mesure électrique	elektrischer Messapparat m	apparecchio m di misurazione elettrica
6288	electric melting furnace	four m électrique de fusion	Elektroschmelzofen m	forno m elettrico di fusione
6289	electric muffle furnace	four m à moufle électrique	elektrischer Muffelofen m	forno m elettrico a muffola
6290	electric pig	fonte f crue électrique	Elektroroheisen n	ghisa f grezza elettrica

electric plant, *s. electric installation*

	English	French	German	Italian
6291	electric production of pig iron	production f de fer par le procédé électrique	Elektroroheisenerzeugung f	produzione f di ghisa elettrica od al forno elettrico
6292	electric refining furnace	four m électrique à affiner	elektrischer Frischfeuerofen m	forno m elettrico di affinazione
6293	electric refining of iron	affinage m du fer par le procédé électrothermique	Raffination f des Eisens auf elektrothermischem Wege	affinaggio m del ferro per via elettrotermica
6294	electric resistance	résistance électrique	elektrischer Widerstand m	resistenza f elettrica, reostato m
6295	electric resistance furnace	four m (ou fourneau m) électrique à résistances	elektrischer Widerstandsofen m	forno m elettrico a resistenza
6296	electric resistance furnace	four m électrique à baguettes rayonnantes	Graphitstabofen m	forno m elettrico a resistenza ausiliaria
6297	electric resistance welding	soudure f par résistance électrique	Widerstandsstumpfschweissung f	saldatura f elettrica a resistenza
6298	electric shaft furnace	four m électrique à cuve	Elektroschachtofen m	forno m elettrico a tino

	English	French	German	Italian
° 6299	electric smelting	fonte *f* électrique fusion *f* électrique	Elektroschmelzen *n*	fusione *f* con forno e- lettrico, ghisa *f* elettric
° 6300	electric smelting furnace	four *m* électrique de fusion	Elektroschmelzofen *m*	forno *m* elettrico di fusi ne
° 6301	electric smelting of iron	fusion *f* électrother- mique du fer	Schmelzen *n* des Eisens auf elektro- thermischem Wege	fusione *f* elettrotermica ferro
° 6302	electric soldering- copper (or solde ring iron)	fer *m* à souder élec- trique	elektrischer Lötkol- ben *m*	saldatoio *m* elettrico
	electric soldering-iron, *s. electric soldering-copper*			
° 6303	**electric steam boiler**	chaudière *f* électri- que à vapeur	elektrischer Dampf- kessel *m*	caldaia *f* elettrica a vap
° 6304	**electric steel**	acier *m* électrique	Elektrostahl *m*	acciaio *m* elettrico
° 6305	**electric steel ca- stings**	fontes *f pl.* d'acier électriques	Elektrostahlform- guss *m*	getto *m* d'acciaio elettr
° 6306	**electric steel ma- nufacture, elec- tric steel production**	fabrication *f* (ou pro- duction *f*) d'acier au four électrique	Elektrostahlerzeug- gung *f*	fabbricazione *f* dell'acc al forno elettrico
	electric steel production, *s. electric steel manufacture*			
° 6307	**electric steel strip**	bande *f* d'acier électrique	Elextrostahlband *n*	nastro *m* d'acciaio al fo elettrico
° 6308	**electric steel works**	aciérie *f* électrique	Elektrostahlwerk *n*	acciaieria *f* elettrica
° 6309	**electric tilting appa- ratus**	appareil *m* de renver- sement à commande électrique	elektrische Kippvor- richtung *f*	apparecchio *m* per il rib tamento *m* elettrico
° 6310	**electric tilting fur- nace**	four *m* électrique basculant	elektrischer Kipp- ofen *m*	forno *m* elettrico ribalta le
° 6311	**electric tool steel**	acier *m* à outils au four électrique	Elektro-Werkzeug- stahl *m*	acciaio *m* elettrico per tensili
° 6312	**electric tool tipper, electric tool-tipping machine**	machine *f* électri- que à braser et trai- ter les pointes d'ou- tils	Aufschweissmaschi- ne *f* fuer Schneid- plättchen, elektri- sche Vorrichtung zum Aufschweissen der Schneidplaettchen auf Werkzeuge	macchina *f* elettrica sal punti per utensili
° 6313	**electric tunnel fur- nace**	four *m* à tunnel électrique	elektrischer Röhren- ofen *m*	forno *m* a tunnel elettric
° 6314	**electric weld**	soudure *f* électrique	eleckrische Schweissung *f*	saldatura *f* elettrica

	English	French	German	Italian
6315	electric welded	soudé électrique-ment	elektrisch ge-schweisst	saldato elettricamen-te
6316	electric welder (pe-trol engine driven)	machine f à souder, électrique (à moteur à essence)	elektrische Schweissmaschine f mit Benzinmotor-antrieb	saldatrice f elettrica (con motore a benzina)
6317	electric welding	soudure f électri-que	Elektroschweis-sung f	saldatura f elettrica
6318	electric winder	treuil m électrique	elektrischer Haspel	argano m elettrico
6319	electrical logging	carottage m électri-que	elektrisches Kernen n	carotaggio m elettrico
6320	electrically made pig iron	fonte f électrique	Elektroroheisen n	ghisa f al forno elet-trico
6321	electrical spot-wel-ding	soudure f électrique par pointes	elektrische Punkt-schweissung f	saldatura f elettrica a punti
6322	electro drilling	électroforage m	elektrisches Bohren n	sondaggio m elettrico
	electro steel, s. electric steel			
6322a	electroanalysis	électroanalyse f	Elektroanalyse f	elettroanalisi f
6323	electrochemical la-boratory table	table f pour les es-sais électro-chimi-ques	elektrochemischer Arbeitstisch m	tavolo m per labora-ratorio elettrochimico
6324	electrochemical pickling	décapage m électro-chimique	elektrolytisches Dekapieren n	decapaggio m elettro-chimico
6325	electrochemical process	procédé m électro-chimique	elektrochemisches Verfahren n	processo m elettrochi-mico
6326	electrode-carbon	charbon m à élec-trodes	Elektrodenkohle f	carbone m per elet-trodi
6327	electrode holder	support m d'élec-trodes	Elektrodenhalter m	sostegno m o suppor-to m degli elettrodi
6328	electrode passage	passage f de l'élec-trode	Elektrodendurchfüh-rung f	guida f degli elettro-di
	electrode pick-up, s. pick-up			
	electrode tip, s. working end of an electrode			
6329	electrode wire	fil m pour électro-des	Elektrodendraht m	filo m per elettrodi
6330	electro deposition, electro-plating	galvanoplastie f	Galvanoplastik f	elettrodeposizione f

		English	French	German	Italian
°	6331	electroerosion	électro-érosion *f*	Funkenerosion *f*	elettroerosione *f*
°	6331a	electroforming	électroformage *m*	Galvanoplastik *f*	galvanoplastica *f*
°	6332	electroforging, resistance forging	forgeage *m* par résistance	Elektroschmieden *n*	fucinatura *f* (o forgiatura) per resistenza
°	6333	electro-gilding	dorure *f* galvanique	galvanische Vergoldung *f*	doratura *f* galvanica
°	6333a	electrography	électrographie *f*	Elektrographie *f*	elettrografia *f*
°	6334	to electrolyse	électrolyser	elektrolysieren	elettrolizzare
°	6335	electrolysis	électrolyse *f*	Elektrolyse *f*	elettrolisi *f*
°	6336	electrolyte	électrolyte *m*	Elektrolyt *m*	elettrolito *m*
°	6337	electrolytic analysis	électro-analyse *f*	Elektroanalyse *f*	elettroanalisi *f*
°	6337a	electrolytic cleaning	dégraissage électrolytique	elektrolytische Reinigung *f*	sgrassaggio *m* elettrolitico
°	6338	electrolytic copper	cuivre *m* électrolytique	Elektrolytkupfer *n*, elektrolytisches Kupfer *n*	rame *m* elettrolitico
°	6339	electrolytic copper refining	affinage *m* électrolytique du cuivre	elektrolytische Kupferraffination *f*	affinamento *m* elettrolitico del rame
°	6340	electrolytic deposit	dépôt *m* galvanique	galvanischer Niederschlag *m*	deposito *m* galvanico
°	6341	electrolytic dissociation	dissociation *f* électrolytique	elektrolytische Spaltung *f*	dissociazione *f* elettrolitica
°	6342	electrolytic friction of the ions	frottement *m* électrolytique des ions	elektrolytische Reibung *f* der Ionen	attrito *m* elettrolitico degli ioni
°	6343	electrolytic frictional resistance	résistance *f* de frottement électrolytique	elektrolytischer Reibungswiderstand *m*	resistenza *f* d'attrito elettrolitica
°	6344	electrolytic iron	fer *m* électrolytique	Elektrolyteisen *n*	ferro *m* elettrolitico
°	6345	electrolytic nickel	nickel *m* électrolytique	Elektrolytnickel *n*	nickel elettrolitico
°	6346	electrolytic pickling	décapage *m* électrolytique	Elektrobeizen *n*	pulitura *f* elettrolitica
°	6347	electrolytic refining	affinage *m* électrolytique	elektrolytische Raffination *f*	raffinazione *f* elettrolitica
°	6348	electrolytic separation	séparation *f* électrolytique	elektrolytische Trennung *f*	separazione *f* elettrolitica
°	6349	electrolytic slime	boue *f* électrolytique	Elektrolysenschlamm *m*	fango *m* elettrolitico
°	6350	electrolytic solution pressure	tension *f* électrolytique de la solution	elektrolytischer Lösungsdruck *m*	tensione *f* elettrolitica della soluzione

	English	French	German	Italian
6351	electrolytic tin plate	fer *m* blanc électrolytique	elektrolytisch verzinntes Weissblech	banda *f* stagnata elettrolitica
6352	electrolytic zinc process	électrolyse *f* du zinc	Zinkelektrolyse *f*	elettrolisi *f* dello zinco
6353	to electrolyze	électrolyser	elektrolysieren	elettrolizzare
6354	electrolyzing	électrolyse *f*	Elektrolysierung *f*	elettrolisi *f*
6355	electromagnet	électroaimant *m*	Elektromagnet *m*	elettromagnete *m*
6356	electro magnetic agitation	brassage *m* électromagnétique	induktive Badbewegung *f*,elektromagnetische Badbewegung *f*.	agitazione *f* elettro-magnetica

electro-magnetic circulation, *s. electromagnetic agitation*

6357	electromagnetics	électromagnétisme *m*	Elektromagnetismus *m*	elettromagnetismo *m*
6358	electromagnetism	électromagnétisme *m*	Elektromagnetismus *m*	elettromagnetismo *m*
6359	electromatic control device	appareillage *m* électrique de commande automatique	automatische elektrische Steuerung *f*	apparecchiatura *f* elettrica di comando automatico
6360	electrometallurgy	électrométallurgie *f*	Elektrometallurgie *f*	elettrometallurgia *f*
6361	electrometric measurement	mesure *f* électrométrique	elektrometrische Messung *f*	misurazione *f* elettrometrica
6361a	electropercussion	sondage *m* par percussion	Schlagschweissen *n*	saldatura *f* a percussione
6362	elektron	électron *m*	Elektron *n*	elektron *m*
6363	electro negative	électro-négatif	elektro-negativ	elettro-negativo

electronic heat control, *s. phase shift heat controller*

6364	electronic process	usinage *m* électronique	elektronisches Verfahren *n*	lavorazione *f* elettronica
6365	to electroplate	galvaniser	galvanisieren	trattare con galvanostegia *f*, trattare elettroliticamente

electroplating, *s. electro-deposition*

6366	to electrorefine	affiner par électrolyse	elektrolytisch raffinieren	affinare per elettrolisi

electrorefining, *s. electrolytic refining*

electrorefining copper, *s. electrolytic copper*

6366a	electrostatic bond	liason *f* ionique	Ionenbindung *f*	legame *m* ionico

	English	French	German	Italian
° 6367	electrostatic per-cussion welding	soudure f électro-statique par per-cussion	Entladestossschweis-sung f	saldatura f elettrostatica a percussione
— 6368	electrostatic sepa-ration	séparation électro-statique	elektrostatische Aufbereitung f	separazione f elettrosta-tica
° 6369	electro-stenolysis	électrosténolyse f	Elektrostenolyse f	elettrostenolisi f
° 6369a	electro-striction	électrostriction f	Elektrostriktion f	elettrostrizione f
— 6370	electro teleclinometer	téléclinomètre m é-lectromagnétique	Bohrlochneigungs-messer m	teleclinometro m elet-tromagnetico
° 6371	electrotype-plate electrotyping shell	coquille f galvano-plastique	Galvano n	galvano m, riporto m me-tallico
— 6372	eleolite	éléolite f	Eläolith m	eleolite f
— 6373	eleolite-syenite	syénite f éléolitique	Eläolithsyenit m	sienite f eleolitica

elektron, s. electron

| 6374 | element | élément m | Element n | elemento m |

elephant boiler, s. French boiler

elevated reservoir, s. high level tank

| — 6375 | elevation | élévation f | Aufriss m | sezione f o spaccato verticale, elevazione f |

elevation, s. increase

— 6376	elevation of the well	cote f du sondage	Bohrlochhöhe f	quota f del pozzo
— 6377	elevator	élévateur m	senkrechtes He-bewerk n	montacarichi m
— 6378	elevator, paternoster elevator	noria f élevateur m à godets	Becherwerk n	elevatore m a paternoster

elevator bucket, s. elevator cage

| — 6379 | elevator cage | cage f | Förderschale f | gabbia f del montacari-chi |

elevator frame, s. lift frame

| — 6380 | elevator link | anse f de l'éléva-teur | Elevator-Bügel m | staffa f dell'elevatore |
| — 6381 | eliasite | eliasite f | Eliasit m | eliasite f |

	English	French	German	Italian
6382	elimination of phosphorus	élimination *f* du phosphore	Phosphorabscheidung *f*	eliminazione *f* del fosforo
6383	elimination of sandy ingredients	élimination *f* des matières sableuses	Entfernung *f* sandiger Bestandteile	eliminazione *f* d'elementi sabbiosi
6384	eliquation	liquation *f*	Seigerung *f*	liquazione *f*
	eliquation hearth, *s. liquation furnace*			
6385	ellipsoidal basalt	basalte *m* ellipsoïdal	ellipsoidaler Basalt *m*	basalto *m* ellipsoidale
6386	elliptical wire	fil *m* elliptique	elliptischer Draht *m*	filo *m* ellittico
6387	ellsworthite	ellsworthite *f*	Ellsworthit *m*	ellsworthite *f*
6388	to elongate	étirer, allonger	strecken	stendere, allungare
6389	elongated porosity	porosité *f* à pores allongés	Langporigeporosität *f*	porosità *f* a pori allungati
6389a	elongation	allongement *m*	Dehnung *f*	allungamento *m*
6390	elongation at rupture	allongement *m* à la rupture	Bruchdehnung *f*	allungamento *m* di rottura
6391	elongation proof limit	limite *f* élastique conventionnelle	Prüfdehngrenze *f*	limite *m* di elasticità della prova
6392	elongation strain	limite *f* apparente d'extension	Dehnungsgrenze *f*	limite *m* apparente di allungamento
6393	elpidite	elpidite *f*	Elpidit *m*	elpidite *f*
6394	to elutriate	épurer par lavage et filtrage	entschlämmen	defangare, sfangare
6395	elutriation	élutriation *f*	Aufschlämmung *f*	elutriazione *f*, lavaggio *m* controcorrente
6396	eluvial	éluvial	eluvial	alluvionale
6397	eluvial deposit	éluvion *m*	eluviale Lagerstätte *f*	deposito *m* eluviale
6398	eluvium	éluvion *m*	Eluvium *n*	eluvio *m*
6399	elvan	elvan *m*	Elvan *m*	elvano *m*
6400	to embed	recouvrir, placer dans le ciment	einbetten	rivestire, ricoprire (di cemento)
6401	embedded core	noyau *m* emballé	eingeformter Kern *m*	anima *f* precollocata, anima *f* imprigionata nella sabbia

	English	French	German	Italian
— 6402	embolite	embolite *f*	Embolit *m*	embolite *f*

to emboss the hole, *s. opening out the hole*

embossed floor plate, *s. buckle plate*

	English	French	German	Italian
° 6403	embossed	gaufré	geprägt	goffrato, stampato in rilievo
° 6404	embossing	gaufrage *m*, bosselage *m*	Prägedruck *m*, Reliefarbeit	stampaggio *m* in rilievo, goffratura *f*
° 6405	embossing tool	outil *m* à matricer	Prägewerkzeug *n*	utensile *m* per coniare
° 6406	to embrittle	rendre fragile	spröde machen	infragilire, rendere fragile
° 6406a	embrittlement	accroissement *m* de la fragilité	Versprödung *f*	aumento *m* della fragil
— 6407	emerald	émeraude *f*	Smaragd *m*	smeraldo *m*
— 6408	emerald copper	dioptase *m*	Dioptas *m*	dioptasio *m*
— 6409	emerged bog	tourbe *f* émergée	Überwassermoor *n*	torbiera *f*
° 6410	to emery grind to grind with emery	polir à l'émeri émeriser	(ab)schmirgeln	smerigliare
° 6411	emery	émeri *m*	Schmirgel *m*	smeriglio *m*
° 6412	emery cloth	toile *f* d'émeri	Schmirgelleinen *n*	tela *f* a smeriglio
° 6413	emery disc	meule *f* à émeri	Schmirgelscheibe *f*	mola *f* a smeriglio
° 6414	emery grinding	polissage à l'émeri	Schmirgeln *n*	smerigliatura *f*
° 6415	emery paper	papier *m* à l'émeri	Schmirgelpapier *n*	carta *f* smerigliata
° 6416	emery powder	poudre *f* d'émeri	Schmirgelpulver *n*	polvere *f* di smeriglio

emery wheel, *s. emery disc*

	English	French	German	Italian
— 6417	eminence	hauteur *f*	Höhe *f*	altezza *f*
— 6418	emmonsite	emmonsite *f*	Emmonsit *m*	emmonsite *f*
— 6419	emplectite	emplectite *f*	Emplektit *m*	emplectite *f*
— 6420	empressite	empressite *f*	Empressit *m*	empressite *f*
° 6421	emptying of the oven	défournement *m* du four	Entleerung *f* des Ofens	scarico *m* del forno, sfornamento
° 6422	emptying the furnace	vidange *f* du four	Entleerung *f* des Ofens	vuotatura *f* del forno
— 6423	Emscherian substage	sous-étage emschérien	Emscher *n*	Emscheriano *m*

	English	French	German	Italian
6424	emulsible oil	huile f émulsionable	Emulsionsöl n	olio m emulsionabile
6425	emulsifiability	émulsification f	Emulgierung f	emulsionabilità f
6426	emulsified oil	huile f emulsionnée	emulgiertes Öl n	olio m emulsionato
6427	emulsifier	émulsifiant m	Emulgator m	emulsionatore m
6428	emulsion	émulsion f	Emulsion f	emulsione f
6429	emulsion mud	boue f à l'émulsion	Emulsionsspülung f	fango m emulsionato
6430	to emulsify	émulsifier	emulgieren	emulsionare
6431	enallogene enclave	enclave f énallogène	fremder Einschluss m	inclusione f enallogena
6432	to enamel	émailler	emaillieren	smaltare
6433	enamel	émail m	Glasfluss m	smalto m
6434	enamel insulated wire	fil m sous émail	emaillierter Draht m, Emaildraht m	filo m isolato allo smalto
6435	enamelled iron	fer m émaillé	emailliertes Eisen n	ferro m smaltato
6436	enamelled sheet	tôle f émaillée	Emailblech m	lamiera f smaltata
6437	enamelled wire	fil m émaillé	Lackdraht m	filo m smaltato
6437a	enamelling	émaillage m	Emallieren n	smaltatura f
6438	enamel(ling) furnace	four m à émailler	Emaillierofen m, Emaillierbrennofen m	forno m per smaltare
6438a	enantiotropism	énantiotropie f	Enantiotropie f	enantiotropia f
6439	enargite	énargite f	Enargit m	enargite f
6440	Encke's blower	soufflerie f Encke	Enckesches Gebläse n	soffiante m Encke
6441	enclosed iron grains shot	grains m pl. de fer englobés	eingeschlossene Eisenkörner n pl.	granuli m pl. di ferro incorporati
6442	enclosed slag	scorie f interposée	eingeschlossene Schlacke f	scoria f d'inclusione, scoria interposta
6443	enclosing rock	roche f encaissante	Nebengestein n	roccia f interposta
6444	enclosure	inclusion f	Einschluss m	inclusione f
	enclosing rock, s. country rock			
6445	encrinite,.	calcaire m à crinoïdes	Crinoïdenkalk m	calcare m a crinoidi

		English	French	German	Italian
—	6446	encrinite limestone	calcaire *m* à crinoïdes	Crinoidenkalk *m*	calcare *m* a crinoidi
—	6447	encrochement	envahissement d'eaux latérales	Wassereinbruch *m*	invasione *f*, avanzamento d'acque laterali
°	6448	end	tête *f* du four	Kopfende *n*	testa *f* del forno
	6449	end	bout, extrémité *f*	Ende *n*	fine *f*, estremità *f*
—	6450	end	front de taille	Ort *m*	fronte *m* di taglio
—	6451	to end off	se terminer en coin	auskeilen	finire a cuneo
—	6452	to end on	en direction des limets	in Schlechtenrichtung *f*	in direzione dei filoni
°	6453	end-on welding	soudure *f* en bout	Stossschweissung *f*	saldatura *f* di testa
°	6453a	end quenching	trempe *f* des extrémités	Kopfabschreckung *f*	tempra *f* delle estremità
°	6454	end plate	plaque *f* de fond, plaque *f* tubulaire	Röhrenstützplatte *f*	piastra *f* di fondo, piastra *f* tubolare
^	6455	end point	point *m* final	Endpunkt *m*	punto *m* finale
°	6455a	end shear	cisaille *f* à guillotine	Teilschere *f*	cesoie *f pl.* trasversal
°	6456	end sizing	calibrage *m* de tête de tube	Rohrenendkalibrierung *f*	calibratura *f* della test di tubo

endless band, *s. endless chain*

		English	French	German	Italian
°	6457	endless chain or band	chaîne *f* sans fin	endlose Kette *f*	catena *f* senza fine
°	6458	endless-rope haulage	traction *f* par câble sans fin	Förderung *f* mit endlosem Seil	trazione *f* a fune senza fine
—	6459	endlichite	endlichite *f*	Endlichit *m*	endlichite *f*
—	6460	endogenetic rock	roche *f* endogénétique	endogenes Gestein *n*	roccia *f* endogena

endogenous enclosure, *s. cognate xenolith*

endogenous rocks, *s. igneous rocks*

		English	French	German	Italian
°	6461	endogenous slag inclusion	scorie *f* congénitale	endogene Schlacke *f*	scoria *f* congenita
°	6462	endogenous slag inclusion	inclusion *f* de scorie congénitale ou endogénétique)	Einschluss *m* von endogener Schlakke	inclusione *f* di scoria congenita (o endogena)
—	6463	endomorphism	transormations *f pl.* endomorphes	endomorphe Kontaktwirkungen *f pl.*	azioni *f pl.* di contatto endomorfe

	English	French	German	Italian
6464	endothermic reaction	réaction f endothermique	wärmeverzehrende Reaktion f	reazione f endotermica
	endothermic working, s. working too hot			
6465	endurance	endurance f	Dauerfestigkeit f	resistenza f alla fatica
	endurance limit, s. fatigue strenght			
6466	endurance ratio	rapport m d'endurance	Schwellfestigkeitsverhältnis n	resistenza f alla fatica
6466a	endurance strenght	limite f de fatigue	Dauerschwingfestigkeit f	limite f di fatica
6467	engine casting	moulage m pour pièces de machine	Maschinenguss m	fusione f per pezzo di macchine
6468	engine house	bâtiment m des machines	Maschinenhaus n	edificio m delle macchine
6469	engine lathe	tour m mécanique	Maschinendrehbank f	tornio m a motore
6470	engine pit	puits m d'extraction et d'épuisement	Förder- und Pumpenschacht m	pozzo m d'estrazione e di sfruttamento
6471	engineer	machiniste m	Maschinenwarter m	macchinista m
6472	engineer in charge	ingénieur m de l'exploitation	Betriebsingenieur m	ingegnere m di servizio
6473	engineer in charge	machiniste m du monte-charges	Fördermaschinist m	macchinista m del montacarichi
	engineering alloy, s. structural steel			
6474	engineering cast iron	fonte f mécanique	Guss m für den Maschinenbau, Maschinenguss m	ghisa f per macchine
6475	engineering flow-plan	projet m de procédé	Fliessplan m	progetto m di processo
6476	engineering steel	acier m pour construction	Maschinenbaustahl m	acciaio m da costruzione
6477	englatial melting	ablation f ou englacial interne	inneres Abschmelzen n, inglaziales Abschmelzen n	ablazione f interna
6478	englatial moraine	moraine f interne	Innenmoräne f	morena f interna
6479	English converting furnace	four m anglais à cémentation	englischer Zementierofen m	forno m inglese a cementazione
6480	English method of cutting (tunnel)	méthode f anglaise de percement	englische Tunnelbauweise f	attacco m (di tunnel) col metodo inglese
6481	English pig iron	fonte f anglaise	englisches Roheisen n	ghisa f inglese

	English	French	German	Italian
° 6482	English standard joist	poutrelle *f* anglaise	englischer Träger *m*	trave *f* inglese
° 6483	English system with two convertors	système *m* anglais par deux convertisseurs	paarweise umzechiger Betrieb *m*, englisches System	sistema *m* inglese con due convertitori
° 6484	enlarged coreprint	portée *f* de modèle renforcée	verstärkte Kernmarke *f*	portata *f* di modello rinforzata
− 6485	enlargement	renforcement *m*	Verstärkung *f*	rinforzo *m*
− 6486	enlarger	outil *m* à élargir (pour chambres)	Schachträumer *m*	allargatore *m* (per camere)
− 6487	enlarging	élargissement *m*	Erweiterung *f*	allargamento *m* (per costruzione di camere)
− 6488	enlargment	chambre *f* de cémentation	Zementierkammer *f*	camera *f* di cementazione
6489	enriched gas drive	déplacement *m* de gas enrichi	Verschiebung *f* von angereichertem Gas	spostamento *m* di gas arricchito
6489a	enrichement	enrichissement *m*	Anreicherung *f*	arricchimento *m*
6490	enstatite	enstatite *f*	Enstatit *m*	enstatite *f*
^ 6491	enthalpy	entalpie *f*	Enthalpie *f*	entalpia *f*
− 6492	entombed	enseveli	verschüttet	sepolto *m*, interrotto *m*
^ 6493	entrapped cold shot	goutte *f* froide	Spritzkugel *f*	goccia *f* fredda
^ 6494	entropy	entropie *f*	Entropie *f*	entropia *f*
° 6495	entry side	ouverture *f* d'entrée	Zuführungsöffnung *f*	apertura *f* d'entrata
° 6495a	entry ramp	rampe *f* d'alimentation	Zufuhrrampe *f*	rampa *f* di alimentazione
− 6496	entry stump	pilier *m* de galerie	Streckenpfeiler *m*	pilastro *m* di galleria
− 6497	entry timbering	boisage *m*, soutènement d'une galerie	Streckenzimmerung *f*	sostegno *m* o rinforzo di galleria
− 6498	Eocene	Eocène *m*	Eozän *n*	Eocene *m*
− 6499	eolian	éolien	äolisch	eoliano *m*
− 6500	eosphorite	éosphorite *f*	Eosphorit *m*	eosforite *f*
− 6501	Eozoic era	ère *f* éozoïque	Eozoikum *n*	era *f* eozoica *f*
− 6502	Eozoon structure	structure *f* à éozoon	Eozoon-Struktur *f*	struttura *f* a eozoon

	English	French	German	Italian
6503	**E P lubricant**	lubrifiant *m* pour hautes pressions	Hochdruckschmiere *f*	lubrificante *m* per alte pressioni
6504	**Eparchean series**	Eparchéen *m*	eparchäische Formation *f*	serie *f pl.* eparcheane
6505	**epeirogenesis**	mouvements *m pl.* épirogéniques	Epirogenese *f*	epirogenesi *f*
6506	**epeirogenetic**	mouvement *m* épirogénetique	epirogenetische Bewegung *f*	movimento *m* epirogenetico
6507	**epeirogeny**	épirogénie *f*	Epirogenese *f*	epirogenia *f*
6508	**ephesite**	ephésite *f*	Ephesit *m*	Efesite *f*
6509	**epicentral region**	région *f* épicentrale	Epizentralgebiet *n*	zona *f* epicentrale
6510	**epichlorite**	épichlorite *f*	Epichlorit *m*	epiclorite *f*
6511	**epiclastic**	épiclastique	epiklastich	epiclastico
6512	**epidesmine**	épidesmine *f*	Epidesmin *m*	epidesmina *f*
6513	**epidiabase**	épidiabase *f*	Epidiabas *f*	epidiabase *f*
6514	**epididymite**	épididymite *f*	Epididymit *m*	epididimite *f*
6515	**epidiorite**	épidiorite *f*	Epidiorit *m*	epidiorite *f*
6516	**epidote**	épidote *f*	Epidot *m*	epidoto *m*
6517	**epigene**	épigène	epigenetisch	epigeno
6518	**epigenesis**	épigénèse *f*	Epigenese *f*	epigenesi *f*
6519	**epigenite**	épigénite *f*	Epigenit *m*	epigenite *f*
6520	**epirock**	épi-roche *f*	Epigestein *n*	epiroccia *f*
6521	**epithermal vein**	filon *m* épithermal	epithermaler Gang *m*	filone *m* epitermale
6522	**epizona**	épizone *f*	Epizone *f*	epizona *f*
6523	**equal angle with round edges, angle with equal sides**	cornière *f* à ailes égales et à coins rondis	gleichschenkliges Winkeleisen *n*	cantonale *m* a lati uguali, profilato *m* a lati uguali e spigoli arrotondati
6523a	**equalizing**	égalisation *f*	Ausgleichen *n*	omogenizzazione *f*
6524	**equation of combination**	équation *f* d'une combinaison	Verbindungsgleichung *f*	formula *f* d'una combinazione, equazione *f* chimica
6525	**equation of electrolytic condition**	équation *f* d'état	Zustandsgleichung *f*	equazione *f* di stato

	English	French	German	Italian
	equalization of pressure, s. *balance of pressure*			
^ 6526	**equalizer**	égalisateur m (de pression)	(Druch) Ausgleicher m	eguagliatore m di pres ne
— 6527	**equiaxed crystals**	cristaux m pl. équi- axiques	gleichaxische Kristalle m pl.	cristalli m pl. equiassi
° 6527a	**equicohesive**	equicohésif	gleichkohäsiv	equicoesivo
° 6528	**equilibrium diagram**	diagramme m d'équi- libre	Zustandsschaubild n	diagramma m d'equilibr
° 6529	**equilibrium of dissociation**	équilibre m de dis- sociation	Dissoziationsgleich- gewicht n	equilibrio m di dissocia zione
° 6530	**equi-molecular solution**	solution f équimolé- culaire	äquimolekulare Lö- sung f	soluzione f equimoleco- lare
° 6530a	**equipartition**	équirépartition f	Gleichverteilung f	equiripartizione f
° 6531	**equivalence factor**	facteur m d'équivalence	Äquivalenzfaktor m	fattore m di equivalenz
	equivalence factor, s. *copper equivalent*			
° 6532	**equivalent concen- tration of a solu- tion**	concentration f en grammes équiva- lents d'une solution	Äquivalentkonzen- tration f einer Lö- sung	concentrazione f equiva lente d'una soluzione
— 6533	**equivalent orifice**	orifice m équivalent	äquivalente Gruben- öffnung f	apertura f equivalente
° 6534	**equivalent solution**	solution f équivalen- te	gleichwertige Lö- sung f	soluzione f equivalente
— 6535	**era**	ère f	Epoche n	era f
° 6536	**erbium**	erbium m	Erbium n	erbio m
— 6537	**erect anticline**	anticlinal m droit	aufrechte Antikli- nale f	anticlinale f eretta
— 6538	**erecting prism**	prisme m redresseur	Umkehrprisma n	prisma m d'inversione
— 6539	**Erian division**	division f d'Erié	Erian n	Eriano m
° 6540	**Erichsen cupping test**	essai m d'emboutis- sage	Tiefziehversuch m	prova f d'imbutitura
— 6541	**erikite**	érikite f	Erikit m	erichite f
— 6542	**erinite**	érinite f	Erinit m	erinite f
— 6543	**erionite**	érionite f	Erionit m	erionite f
° 6544	**Erlenmeyer glass flask**	ballon m en verre	Erlenmeyerkolben m	matraccio m conico
— 6545	**erosion**	érosion f	Auswaschung f	erosione f

	English	French	German	Italian
6546	erosion-corrosion	corrosion *f* par érosion	Verreibung *f*	corrosione *f* per erosione
	erosion scab, *s. sand wash*			
6547	erosion thrust	charriage *m* d'érosion	Erosionsüberschiebung *f*	eccedenza *f* d'erosione
6548	erosional gap	lacune *f* d'érosion	Erosionsunterbrechung *f*	lacuna *f* d'erosione
6549	erratic	erratique	erratisch	erratico
6550	erratic block, erratic mass	bloc *m* erratique	erratischer Block *m*	masso *m* erratico
6551	erratic value	valeur *f* de la dispersion	Streuwert *m*	valore *m* di dispersione
6552	errite	errite *f*	Errit *m*	errite *f*
6553	erubescite, bornite	bornite *f*	Bornit *m*	bornite *f*
6554	error in assembly	faute *f* de remmoulage	Fehler *m* beim Zusammenbau der Form	difetto *m* di ramolaggio
6555	error in coring	faute *f* de noyautage	Fehler *m* beim Kernmachen	difetto *m* d'anima
6556	error in fettling	faute *f* d'ébarbage	Fehler *m* beim Putzen	difetto *m* di sbavatura
6557	error in moulding	faute *f* de moulage	Fehler *m* beim Formen	difetto *m* di formatura
6558	eruption	éruption *f*	Ausbruch *m*	eruzione *f*
6559	eruptive vein	veine *f* (éruptive)	Eruptivader *f*	vena *f* eruttiva
6560	erythrite	érythrine *f*	Erythrin *m*	erithrina *f*
6561	erythrosiderite	érythrosidérite *f*	Erythrosiderit *m*	erithrosiderite *f*
6562	escape, leak	fuite *f* de gaz	Gasentweichung *f*	fuga *f* di gas
6563	escape of air	dégagement *m* de l'air	Entweichen *n* der Luft	uscita *f* d'aria, fuga *f* d'aria
6564	escape of heat to upper part	feu *m* au gueulard	Oberfeuer *n*	temperatura *f* alla bocca del forno
6565	escape valve	soupape *f* d'échappement	Auslassventil *n*	valvola *f* di scarico
6566	escaping gas, evolved gas	gaz *m* dégageant	entweichendes Gas *n*	gas *m* sviluppato

		English	French	German	Italian
^	6567	escaping of volatile compounds	dégagement m des produits volatils	Entweichen n flüchtiger Bestandteile	scarico m dei prodotti volatili
—	6568	essential minerals	minéraux m pl. essentiels	wesentliche Mineralien n pl.	minerali m pl. essenziali
	6569	estimate, tender	devis m, offre f	Kostenanschlag m	preventivo m
—	6570	estaurine facies	faciès f lagunaire	lagunäre Fazies f	«facies» f di estuario
o	6571	to etch, to bite, to corrode	attaquer à l'acide	ätzen	attaccare con acido, mordere, corrodere
o	6571a	etchant	corrosif m, caustique	Ätzmittel n	corrosivo, reattivo
o	6572	etching	attaque f à l'acide	Ätzen n	attacco m acido o chimico, mordente m
o	6573	etching figures	figures f pl. de corrosion	Ätzfiguren f pl.	figure f pl. (o disegni) di attacco
o	6574	etching solution for zinc	eau-forte f pour planches de zinc	Zinkätze f	acquaforte f per lastre di zinco
o	6574a	etching pits	pores d'attaque à l'acide	Ätzporen	pori di attacco all'acid
o	6575	etching polishing	polir par attaque à l'acide	Ätzprobe f	prova f dell'attacco aci
^	6576	ether	éther m sulfurique	Schwefeläther m	etere m solforico
—	6577	ettringite	ettringite f	Ettringit m	ettringite f
—	6578	eucairite	eucaïrite f	Eukarit m	eucarite f
—	6579	euchroite	euchroïte f	Euchroit m	eucroite f
—	6580	euclase	euclase f	Euklas m	euclase f
—	6581	eucolite	eucolite f	Eukolit m	eucolite f
—	6582	eucolite-titanite	eucolittitanite f	Eukolit-Titanit m	eucolittitanite f
—	6583	eucrite	eucrite f	Eukrit m	eucrite f
—	6584	eucryptite	eucryptite f	Eukryptit m	eucriptite f
—	6585	eudialyte	eudialyte f	Eudialyt m	eudialite f
—	6586	eudidymite	eudidymite f	Eudidymit m	eudidimite f
—	6587	eudiometer	eudiomètre m	Eudiometer m	eudiometro m
—	6588	eudnophite	eudnophite f	Eudnophit m	eudnofite f
		eugranitic texture, s. granitic texture			
—	6589	euhedral	automorphe, idiomorphe	automorph. idiomorph	amorfo, idiomorfo

	English	French	German	Italian
6590	euphotic region	région f euphotique	euphotische Region f	regione f eufotica
6591	euralite	euralite f	Euralith m	euralite f
6592	eurite	eurite f	Eurit m	eurite f
6593	euritic	euritique	mikrogranitisch	euritico
6594	European process iron	fonte f à coeur blanc	Weisskerneisen n	ghisa f a cuore bianco
6595	europium	europium m	Europium n	europio m
6596	eustatic	eustatique	eustatisch	eustatico
6597	eusynchite	eusynchite f	Eusynchit m	eusinchite f
6598	eutectic	eutectique m	Eutektikum n	eutettico m
6599	eutectic	eutectique	eutektisch	eutettico
6600	eutectic alloy	alliage m eutectique	Eutektikum n	lega f eutettica, eutettico
6601	eutectic cast iron	fonte f eutectique	eutektisches Gusseisen n	ghisa f eutettica
6602	eutectic exudation	ressuage m eutectique	eutektisches Treiben n	bruciatura f di trattamento termico
6603	eutectic mixture	mélange m eutectique	eutektische Mischung f, Eutektikum n	miscela f eutettica

eutectic steel, s. *eutectoid steel*

	English	French	German	Italian
6604	eutectic structure	structure f eutectique	eutektische Textur f	struttura f eutettica
6605	eutectoid	transformation f eutectoïde	eutektoide Unwandlung f	trasformazione f eutettoide
6606	eutectoid	eutectoïde m	Eutektoid n	eutettoide m, perlite f
6607	eutoctoid steel	acier m eutectoïde	eutektoider Stahl m	acciaio m eutectoide
6608	eutomous	à clivage m net	mit deutlicher Spaltbarkeit f	a frattura f netta, a sfaldatura f netta
6609	euxenite	euxénite f	Euxenit m	euxenite f
6610	to evaporate	vaporiser	verdampfen	vaporizzare
6611	to evaporate	évaporer	abdampfen	evaporare

	English	French	German	Italian
— 6612	to evaporate to dryness	évaporer à sic-cité	zum Trocknen ein-dampfen	evaporare a secco
° 6613	evaporating flask	matras *m* à évapo-tion	Abdampfkolben *m*	matraccio *m* d'evapora-zione
° 6614	evaporating basin	capsule *f* à évapo-ration	Abdampfschale *f*	bacinella *f* d'evapora-zione
° 6615	evaporating pan	vase *m* d'évapora-tion	Abdampfkasserolle *f*	caldaia *f* d'evaporazione
° 6616	evaporating pan with revolving helical heating coil, Wetzel type	cuve *f* évaporatrice, système Wetzel, à serpentin réchauffeur tournant	Abdampfpfanne *f* mit rotierender Heiz-spiral *m*	caldaia *f* di evaporazion sistema Wetzel, a serper tino riscaldatore girante
° 6617	evaporating vessel	chaudière *f* d'évapo-ration	Abdampfkessel *m*, Abdampfpfanne *f*	caldaia *f* evaporatrice
6618	evaporation	vaporisation *f*	Verdampfung *f*	vaporizzazione *f*
	evaporation, *s. drying*			
^ 6619	evaporation concen-tration	concentration *f* par évaporation	Eindampfen *n*	condensazione *f* per eva-porazione
^ 6620	evaporation per m2 of heating surface	évaporation *f* par m^2 de la surface de chauffe	Verdampfung *f* per Quadratmeter Heiz-fläche	acqua *f* evaporata al m^2 di superficie riscaldata
— 6621	evaporator	appareil *m* à concen-trer, évaporateur	Eindampfer *m*	evaporatore *m*
^ 6622	evaporator tower	tour *f* d'évaporation	Verdampfturm *m*	torre *f* d'evaporazione
° 6623	even fracture	cassure *f* unie	ebener Bruch *m*	rottura *f* piana
— 6624	even grained	à grain régulier	gleichmässig kör-nig	a grana regolare
— 6625	even with the ground level	au ras du sol, à la surface du sol	mit der Erde gleich, in Erdhöhe	a fior di terra, alla su-perficie del suolo
— 6626	evergreenite	evergreenite *f*	Evergreenit *m*	evergreenite *f*
	evolution, *s. formation*			
° 6627	evolution of heat	dégagement *m* de chaleur	Wärmeausgabe *f*	sviluppo *m* di calore
° 6628	evolution of oxygen	dégagement *m* d'oxy-gène	Sauerstoffabgabe *f*	sviluppo *m* d'ossigeno
— 6629	exact lenght	longueur *f* exacte	genaue Länge *f*	lunghezza *f* esatta

	English	French	German	Italian
6630	exactitude of measurements agreed to	exactitude *f* des dimensions conve-·nues	Genauigkeit *f* der vereinbarten Abmessungen	precisione *f* delle dimensioni convenute
	examination, *s. testing*			
6631	examination according to appearance	appréciation *f* d'après l'aspect éxtèrieur	Beurteilung *f* nach dem Aussehen	·giudizio *m* secondo i dati esterni
6632	examination in dissolved state	analyse *f* par voie humide	Prüfung *f* auf nassem Wege	analisi *f* per via umida
6633	examination in dry state	analyse *f* par ·voie sèche	Prüfung *f* auf trokkenem Wege	analisi *f* per via secca
6634	to examine	essayer, examiner	prüfen, untersuchen	esaminare, provare
6635	excavating bucket	benne *f* piocheuse	Greifer *m*	benna *f* scavatrice
6636	excavator (machine)	excavateur *m*	Bagger *m*	escavatore *m*,
6637	excavateur (worker)	terrassier *m*	Erdarbeiter *m*	terrazziere *m*, scavatore *m* (operaio)
6638	excentric bit, offset bit	trépan *m* excentré	Exzentermeissel *m*	scalpello *m* eccentrico
6639	excess	excès *m*	Überschuss *m*	eccesso *m*
6639a	excess-acetylene flame	flamme *f* réductrice	Reduktionsflamme *f*	fiamma *f* riducente
6640	excess metal	pastille *f*	Tablette *f*	pasticca *f*
6641	excess of oxygen	excès *m* d'oxygène	Sauerstoffüberschuss *m*	eccesso *m* d'ossigeno
6641a	excess-oxygen flame	flamme *f* oxydante	Oxydationsflamme *f*	fiamma *f* ossidante
6642	excess of precipitant	excès *m* de réactif de précipitation	Überschuss *m* des Fällungsmittels	eccesso *m* di precipitante
6643	excess rapping	excès *m* d'ébranlage	zu starkes Losklopfen *n*	scampanatura *f* eccessiva
6644	excess weight	surpoids *m*	Übergewicht *n*	eccesso *m* di peso
6645	exchanging analyses	échange *m* des analyses	Austausch *m* der Analysen	scambio *m* d'analisi
6646	exclusion of air	exclusion *f* d'air	Luftabschluss *m*	esclusione *f* d'aria
6647	excoriation	excoriation *f*	Schürfung *f*	escoriazione *f*
6648	exfoliation, spalling	exfoliation *f*, effeuillage *m*	Exfoliation *f*, Desquamation *f*	desquamazione *f*, sfogliatura *f*, sfaldatura *f*

	English	French	German	Italian
− 6649	exfoliation joint	fissure f d'exfoliation	Exfoliationsspalte f	fessura f di sfaldatura
− 6650	exhaust fan	ventilateur m d'extraction, ventilateur m aspirant	saugender Ventilator m	ventilatore m aspirante
− 6651	exhaust ventilation	aérage m aspirant ventilation f aspirante	saugende Bewetterung f	ventilazione f per aspirazione
− 6652	exhaust pipe	tube m de décharge	Auspuffrohr n	tubo m di scarico
° 6653	exhaust port	ouverture f d'échappement	Ausströmkanal m	apertura f o luce f di scappamento
° 6654	exhaust steam	injecteur m à vapeur d'échappement	Abdampfinjektor m	iniettore m a vapore di scarico (di caldaia)
− 6655	exhauster	ventilateur m aspirant	saugender Ventilator m	ventilatore m aspirante, ventilatore m negativo
° 6655a	exit ramp	rampe f de sortie	Abfuhrrampe f	rampa f di uscita
° 6666	exit side, catcher's side	côté m de la sortie	Austrittseite f	lato m di uscita
− 6657	exogenetic process	phénomène m exogénétique	exogenetischer Prozess m	fenomeno m exogenetico
− 6658	exogenic inclusion	enclave f énallogène, enclave m exogénétique	exogener Einschluss m	inclusione f enallogena
° 6659	exogenous metallic inclusion	inclusion f métallique étrangère	metallischer Einschluss m fremden Ursprungs	inclusione f metallica estranea
° 6660	exogenous non metallic inclusion	inclusion f non métallique étrangère	nichtmetallischer Einschluss m fremden Ursprungs	inclusione f non metallica estranea
− 6661	exomorphism	actions $f.pl.$ de contact exomorphes	exomorphe Kontaktwirkungen $f pl.$	azioni $f pl.$ di contatto esomorfe
° 6662	exothermal reaction	réaction f exothermique	wärmegebende Reaktion f	reazione f esotermica
° 6663	exothermic sleeve	manchon m exothermique	exothermer Trichtereinsatz m	manicotto m esotermico
° 6664	exotic	difficile à usiner	schwer bearbeitbar	di difficile lavorazione

English	French	German	Italian
6665 **expanded metal**	métal *m* déployé	Streckmetall *n*	lamiera *f* stirata
6666 **expander for drill pipe**	appareil *m* pour monter les protecteurs *m* sur les tiges	Bohrrohrausdehner	apparecchio *m* per montare i protettori sulle aste
6667 **expanding anchor**	ancre *f* extensible	Spreizanker *m*	ancora *f* prolungabile
6668 **expanding bar**	épinglette, dégorgeoir	Räumnadel *f*	barra *f* alesatrice
6669 **expanding prop**	étançon extensible	wandernder Stempel *m*	palo *m* di sostegno regolabile
6670 **expanding reamer**	alésoir *m* extensible	elastische Reibahle *f*	alesatore *m* elastico (o a lame registrabili)
6670a **expanding test**	essai *m* de perçage	Lochprobe *f*	prova *f* di punzonatura
6671 **expansion drill**	foret *m* à découper, foret *m* à rallonge	Ausschneidebohrer *m*	trapano *m* ad espansione
6672 **expansion joint**	joint *m* de dilatation	Dilatationsfugenleiste *f*	giunto *m* di dilatazione
6673 **expansion scab**	gale *f* franche	festsitzende Sandschülpe *f*	sfoglia *f* aperta
6674 **expelling of volatile matter**	expulsion *f* des matières volatiles	Austreiben *n* flüchtiger Bestandteile	espulsione *f* di materie volatili
6675 **experiment, test**	analyse *f*, essai *m*	Versuch *m*	analisi *f*, prova *f*, esperimento *m* saggio *m*
6676 **experimental boiler**	chaudière *f* d'essai	Versuchskessel *m*	caldaia *f* di prova
6677 **experimentally**	expérimentalement	versuchsmässig	sperimentalmente
6678 **to explode**	exploser	explodieren	scoppiare
6679 **to exploit**	exploiter	abbauen	sfruttare
6680 **exploration**	exploration *f*	Erforschung *f*	esplorazione *f*
exploring *s. working, or exploration*			
6681 **explosibility**	explosibilité *f*	Explodierbarkeit *f*	esplosibilità *f*
6682 **explosion**	explosion *f*	Sprengung *f*	esplosione *f*
6683 **explosion tuff**	tuf *m* d'explosion	Explosionstuff *m*	tufo *m* d'esplosione
6684 **explosive substance, explosive blasting agent**	matière *f* explosive	Sprengmittel *n*	materia *f* esplosiva
6685 **explosive**	explosif *m*	Explosivstoff *m*	esplosivo *m*

		English	French	German	Italian
−	6686	**explosive D**	explosif *m* D	D-Sprengstoff *m*	esplosivo *m* D
°	6687	**explosive formed boiler front**	fond *m* de chaudière formé par explosion	umgeformte Kesselstirnwand *f*	fronte *f* di caldaia sagomata per esplosione
°	6688	**explosive forming**	formage *m* par explosion	Explosiv-Verfahren *n*	stampaggio *m* ad esplosione
°	6689	**explosive metal cladding**	plaçage *m* à l'explosif	Plattieren *n* mit Schockwellen	placcatura *f* per esplosione
	6690	**to expose (to the light)**	exposer (à la lumière)	belichten	esporre alla luce
	6691	**to expose the structure**	faire apparaître la texture	das Gefüge blosslegen	rivelare la struttura
		exposed base, *s. uncovered base*			
	6692	**exposure**	exposition *f*	Ausbiss *m*	esposizione *f*
−	6693	**exsiccator**	séchoir *m*	Exsikkator *m*	essicatore *m*, stufa di essicamento
		expulsion, *s. splash*			
−	6694	**expulsion of water**	expulsion *f* de l'eau	Austreibung *f* von Wasser	espulsione *f* dell'acqua
°	6695	**extended furnace with horizontal grate**	foyer *m* antérieur à grille horizontale	Planrostvorfeuerung *f*	focolare *m* a graticola orizzontale davanti alla caldaia
°	6696	**extensometer**	extensomètre *m*	Dehnungsmesser *m*	estensimetro *m*, dinamometro
		extent in lateral direction, *s. lenght in lateral direction*			
	6697	**exterior source of light**	source *f* de lumière extérieure	äussere Lichtquelle *f*	sorgente *f* di luce esterna
		external cast, *s. external mould*			
°	6698	**externaly fired boiler**	chaudière *f* à foyer extérieur	Kessel *m* mit Aussenfeuerung	caldaia *f* a focolare esterno
°	6699	**external mo(u)ld, external cast**	moule *m* externe	Abdruck *m*	modello *m* esterno
°	6700	**external screw cutting tool**	outil *m* à fileter extérieurement	Gewindestahl *m*	utensile *m* per filettare
°	6701	**external thread chaser**	peigne *m* à fileter extérieur	Gewindestraehler *m* (Aussengewinde)	pettine *m* da filettare (esteriore)

English	French	German	Italian
6702 **externally fired furnace**	foyer *m* extérieur	Aussenfeuerung *f*	focolare *m* esterno
6703 **extra hard steel, best tool steel**	acier-diamant *m*	Diamantstahl *m*	acciaio *m* diamante
6704 **extra lattens**	tôle *f* extra-fine	Feinstblech *n*	lamiera *f* sottilissima
extra-mild steel, *s. extra-soft steel*			
6705 **extra-soft steel**	acier *m* extra-doux	extraweicher Stahl *m*	acciaio *m* extradolce
6706 **to extract**	extraire	ausziehen, extra-hieren	estrarre
6707 **extracting column**	colonne *f* d'extraction	Extraktionsturm *m*	torre *f* d'estrazione
6707a **extraction**	extraction *f*	Förderung *f*	estrazione *f*
6708 **extraction apparatus**	appareil *m* d'extraction	Auslauger *m*	apparecchio *m* d'estrazione
6709 **extraction drift**	voie *f* de taille, galerie *f* d'extraction	Abbaustrecke *f*	galleria *f* d'estrazione (o di taglio)
6710 **extraction funnel**	entonnoir *m* d'extraction	Auslaugtrichter *m*	imbuto *m* d'estrazione
6711 **extraction shaft**	puits *m* d'extraction	Förderschacht *m*	pozzo *m* d'estrazione
6712 **extraction turbine**	turbine *f* à extraction	Extraktionsturbine *f*	turbina *f* con prese intermedie
6713 **extractive distillation**	distillation *f* extractive	extraktive Destillierung *f*	distillazione *f* per estrazione
6714 **extramagmatic**	extramagmatique	extramagmatisch	extramagmatico
6715 **extreme line casing**	tubage à «extreme line»		rivestimento *m* di pozzi tipo «Extreme line»
6716. **extreme pull**	tir *m* à la limite de portée de l'installation		tiro *m* al limite di portata dell'impianto
6717 **to extrude**	filer à la presse	strangpressen	estrudere
6718 **extruded**	extrudé	stranggepresst	estruso
6719 **extruded forging**	extrudé *m*	Strangpresser-zeugnis *n*	fucinato *m* per estrusione, pezzo *m* estruso
6720 **extruded steel section, stepped hot-extruded steel section**	profil *m* à gradins en acier extrudé à chaud	gestaffeltes warm-stranggepresstes Stahlprofil *n*	profilato *m* a gradini in acciaio estruso a caldo
6721 **extruding press**	presse *f* à filer	Strangpresse *f*	pressa *f* da estrusione

		English	French	German	Italian
°	6722	**extrusion**	extrudage *m*	Strangpressprofil *n*, Strangpressen *n*	estrusione *f*
°	6723	**extrusion billet**	ébauche *m* pour presse à filer	Strangpress_ rohling *m*	blocco *m* da estrudere
°	6724	**extrusion die**	tuyère *f* sous pression	Pressdüse *f*	ugello *m* di pressione
°	6724a	**extrusion pipe**	retassure *f* d'extrusion	Extrusionslunker *m*	risucchio *m* d'estrusion
°	6725	**extrusion press tool**	outil *m* de presse à filer	Strangpresswerkzeug *n*	utensile *m* per l'estrusione
—	6726	**extrusive rock**	roche *f* extrusive	Extrusivgestein *n*	roccia *f* estrusiva
°	6726a	**exudation**	exsudation *f*	Exsudation *f*	essudazione *f*
		exuding of the head,	*s. rising of the head*		
°	6727	**eye, staple**	oreille *f*	Ohr *n*	orecchio *m*
—	6728	**eye agate**	agate *f* œïllée	Augenachat *m*	agata *f* occhiadina
°	6729	**eye bolt, ring bolt, eye screw**	boulon *m* à oeillet	Augenbolzen *m*	bullone *m* con testa ad occhio
—	6730	**eye-gneiss**	gneiss *m* œillé	Augengneiss *m*	gneiss *m* occhiadino
—	6731	**eye piece**	oculaire *m*	Augenlinse *f*	oculare *m*
—	6732	**eye structure or texture**	structure *f* oeillée	Augenstruktur *f*	struttura *f* occhiadina

English	French	German	Italian
-6733 fabric	texture *f*	Textur *f*, Gewebe *n*	struttura *f*
6734 fabricated steel	acier *m* marchand	Handelstahl *m*	acciaio *m* commerciale
-6735 to face	dresser, revêtir	montieren, verkleiden	montare, preparare, rivestire
6736 to face with charcoal powder	saupoudrer de poussier de charbon	mit Kohlenstaub einpudern	ricoprire con polvere di carbone
6737 to face-harden	endurcir superficiellement, cémenter	verhärten, zementieren	indurire superficialmente, cementare
-6738 face	taille *f*, front *m* de taille	Ort *m*, Stoss *m*, Strebfront *f*	taglio *m*, fronte *f* di taglio
-6739 face	face *f*, facette *f*	Kristallfläche *f*	faccia *f*, faccetta *f*
6740 face bend test	essai *m* de flexion de la face de soudure	Oberflächenbiegeprobe der Schweissstelle *f*	prova *f* di flessione della fronte di saldatura
-6741 face conveyor	convoyeur *m* de taille	Strebförderer *m*	convogliatore *m* d'estrazione
face covering, *s. case hardening*			
-6742 face entry	chantier *m* à front normal aux limets	Grubenort mit Stoss·stellung senkrecht zur Schichtenrichtung	cantiere *m* con fronte normale al piano di stratificazione
6743 face guard	masque *m*	Maske *f*, Schutzmaske *f*	maschera *f*
6744 face hardened	cémenté	zementiert	cementato
-6745 face man	abatteur	Häuer *m*	minatore *m*
6746 face milling cutter (inserted teeth)	fraise *f* à lames rapportées	Messerkopf *m*	fresa *f* a lame riportate
-6747 face of a well	fond *m* du sondage	Bohrlochsohle *f*	fondo *m* del sondaggio
-6748 face of coal	stratification *f* de charbon, limet *m*	Kohlenschlechte *f*	stratificazione *f* del carbone
-6749 face of stope	front *m* de taille	Strebfront *f*	fronte *f* di taglio
-6750 face of working	front d'exploitation	Arbeitsstoss *m*	fronte *f* di avanzamento
-6751 face on	front *m* d'attaque parallèle aux limets	Abbaustoss parallel zum Flöz	fronte *f* d'attacco parallelo al piano *m* di stratificazione

	English	French	German	Italian
—	6752 **face prop**	étai *m* posé à front	Firstenstempel *m*, Strebstempel *m*	puntello *m* posato di fronte
°	6753 **face shield**	masque *m* de soudeur	(Schweisser)- -Schutzschild *n*	visiera *f* protettrice
—	6754 **face shovel**	drague *f* à godet poussant	Stosslöffelbagger *m*	escavatore a cucchiaia spingente
—	6754a **facet**	facette *f*	Facette *f*	faccetta *f*
—	6755 **facies**	faciès *m*	Fazies *f*	«facies» *f*
—	6756 **facies fossil**	fossile *m* de faciès	Faziesfossil *n*	fossile *m* di «facies»
°	6757 **facing**	revêtement *m*	Verkleidung *f*	rivestimento *m*
°	6758 **facing, facing sand**	sable *m* de moulage, sable *m* de contact	Formsand *m*, Modellsand *m*	sabbia *f* per modellare, terra *f* da modello, terra *f* fine
	facing, *s. insert*			
°	6759 **facing**	dresser au tour	plandrehen	tornire piano, spianatura
°	6760 **facing sand**	sable *m* de moulage	Formsand *m*	terra *f* (fine) da modello
	factor of safety, *s. safety factor*			
	factor, *s. pile*			
°	6761 **fagotted-iron furnace**	fourneau *m* d'affinage de ferraille	(Paket)-Schweiss-ofen *m*	forno *m* d'affinamento del ferraccio
°	6762 **faggot, fagot**	paquet *m*, fagot *m*	Paket *n*, Faschine *f*	pacchetto *m*, fascina *f*
°	6763 **faggoting**	paquetage *m*	Paketierung *f*	preparazione *f* dei pacchetti di ferro
	fagotting furnace, *s. fagotted-iron furnace*			
—	6764 **fahl-ore, fahlerz, tetrahedrite**	tétraédrite *f*	Tetraedrit *m*	tetraedrite *f*
—	6765 **fahlband**	fahlbande *m*	Fahlband *n*	strato *m* contenente sulfuri metallici
—	6766 **failure**	éboulement *m*	Einsturz *m*	franamento *m*, frana *f*
°	6767 **failure**	panne *f*	Schaden *m*	difetto *m*, avaria *f*
°	6768 **failure crack**	fente *f*	Bruchriss *m*	crepa *f*, fessura *f*
—	6769 **fairfieldite**	fairfieldite *f*	Fairfieldit *m*	fairfieldite *f*
—	6770 **fakes**	grès *m* micacé	Glimmersandstein *m*	gres *m* micaceo

English	French	German	Italian
to fall down, *s. to fall in*			
6771 **to fall (in), to collapse**	s'ébouler, s'écrouler	einfallen, einstürzen	franare, smottarsi
6772 **fall**	pente *f*	Gefälle *n*	caduta *f*, dislivello *m*
fall, *s. lowering or falling in*			
6773 **fall of cage**	chute *f* de la cage	Seilbruch *m*	caduta *f* della gabbia
6774 **fall of ground**	éboulement *m*	Absturz *m*	frana *f*, franamento *m*
6775 **fall of roof**	éboulement *m* du toit	Zubruchgehen *n* der Firste	franamento *m* del tetto
fall of scaffold, *s. slip of scaffold*			
fall of temperature, *s. drop of temperature*			
fall of the stratum, *s. dip of the stratum*			
6776 **fallen-in**	éboulé	zubruchgegangen	franato, smottato
6777 **fallen-in shaft**	puits *m* éboulé	zubruchgegangener Schacht *m*	pozzo *m* franato o crollato
6778 **falling-in, falling down**	écroulement *m*, éboulement *m*	Sturz *m*, Bruch *m*, Einsturz *m*	crollo *m*, franamento *m*
6779 **false bedding**	stratification *f* entrecroisée	Diagonalschichtung *f*	stratificazione *f* incrociata, falsa stratificazione *f*
6780 **false bottom**	faux bedrock *m*	falscher Firstgebirge *n*	falsa roccia *f* di tetto
6781 **false cap**	chapeau *m* provisoire	vorläufige Kappe *f*	cappello *m* provvisorio
6782 **false cleavage**	pseudo-clivage *m*	Ausweichungsclivage *f*	pseudo-stratificazione *f*
6783 **false dam stone**	fausse dame *f*	falscher Dammstein *m*	falsa dama *f*
false galena, *s. sphalerite*			
6784 **false lining**	fausse-chemise *f*	Zwischenschacht *m*	falsa camicia *f*
6784a **false part**	fausse partie *f*	falsche Formhälfte *f*	staffa *f* matta
6785 **false pass**	cannelure *f* à vide	Blindkaliber *n*, blindes Kaliber *n*	falso canale *m*
6786 **false set**	cadre *m* provisoire	Hilfsgeviert *n*	quadro *m* provvisorio

	English	French	German	Italian
—	6787 **false stull**	plateforme *f* mobile	bewegliche Bühne *f*	palchetto *m* volante
—	6788 **false topaz**	citrine *f*	Citrin *m*	citrino *m*
—	6789 **falsework**	échafaudage *m*	Gerüst *n*	gabbia *f*, ponteggio *m*, armatura *f*
—	6790 **famatinite**	famatinite *f*	Famatinit *m*	famatinite *f*
—	6791 **famp**	calcaire *m* décomposé	zersetzter Kalkstein *m*	calcare *m* decomposto
—	6792 **to fan**	ventiler	bewettern	ventilare, aereare
—	6793 **fan**	ventilateur *m*	Ventilator *m*	ventilatore *m*
	fan, *s. low level bog*			
—	6794 **fan blade**	ailette *f* de ventilateur	Schaufelblatt *n* eines Ventilators	lama *f* del ventilatore
—	6795 **fan blower**	ventilateur *m* centrifuge	Schleudergebläse *n*	ventilatore *m* centrifugo
°	6796 **fan cooled**	refroidi par l'air	luftgekühlt	raffreddato ad aria
°	6797 **fan cupola**	cubilot *m* à aspiration	Saugkuppelofen *m*, Saugkupolofen *m*	cubilotto *m* ad aspirazione
—	6798 **fan drift**	galerie *f* de ventilateur	Ventilator-Umlaufstrecke *f*	galleria *f* di ventilatore
—	6799 **fan-fold**	pli en éventail	Fächerfalte *f*	piega *f* a ventaglio
—	6800 **fan glomerate**	conglomérat *m* alluvionnaire	Alluvialkonglomerat *n*	conglomerato *m* alluvionale
—	6801 **fan out screw**	sondage *m* à la corde	Seilbohrung *f*	perforazione a percussione alla fune
—	6802 **fan shaft**	arbre *m* du ventilateur	Flügelwelle *f*	asse *m* del ventilatore
—	6803 **fan-shaped anticline**	anticlinal *m* en évantail	Fächerantiklinale *f*	anticlinale a ventaglio
	fan shaped fold, *s. fan fold*			
°	6804 **fan-shaped ingate**	attaque *f* de coulée en évantail	Fächergussrinne *f*	attacco *m* di colata a ventaglio
—	6805 **fan structure**	structure *f* en éventail	Fächerstruktur *f*	struttura *f* a ventaglio

English	French	German	Italian
6806 fan tailed burner	brûleur *m* circulaire à jet en éventail	Rundstrahlbrenner *m*	becco *m* circolare
6807 fan-talus	cône *m* d'éboulis	Schuttfächer *m*	cono *m* di deiezione
6808 fandrift	galerie *f* de ventilateur	Wetterkanal *m*	cunicolo *m* del ventilatore, galleria *f* di livello a ventilazione forzata
6809 fang	canard *m* d'aérage	Lutte *f*	condotto *m* d'aria
6810 fanglomerate	dépôt *m* clastique grossier	Fanglomerat *n*	deposito *m* clastico grezzo
6811 fanner	ventilateur *m*	Ventilator *m*	ventilatore *m*
6812 fanning	réduction du tirage	Zugverminderung *f*	riduzione *f* del tiraggio
6813 fans	taquets *m pl.*, clichage *m* pour cages	Aufsetzvorrichtung *f*, Keps *m*	sostegni *m pl.*, puntelli *m pl.*, tacchetti *m pl.* per gabbie
6814 farewell rock	témoin *m*	Zeugenberg *m*	testimonio *m*
6815 farmer well	puits *m* peu profond		pozzo *m* poco profondo
6816 faroelite	faröelite *f*	Farölith *m*	faroelite *f*
6817 farrisite	farrisite *f*	Farrisit *m*	farrisite *f*
fash, *s. burr or flash*			
6817a fash	plaque *f* d'écoulement	Auslaufplatte *f*	lamiera *f* da effusione
fashioned iron, *s. section*			
6818 fasibitikite	fasibitikite *f*	Fasibitikit *m*	fasibitichite *f*
6819 fasinite	fasinite *f*	Fasinit *m*	fasinite *f*
6820 fassaite	fassaïte *f*	Fassait *m*	fassaite *f*
6821 fast	fixe, ferme	fest	fisso, fermo
6822 fast-action explosive	explosif *m* brisant	brisanter Sprengstoff *m*	esplosivo *m* dirompente
6823 fast line	câble *m* d'enroulement	Fahrseil *n*	cavo *m* d'avvolgimento
6824 fast to expousure	à l'épreuve des intempéries	wetterfest	a prova d'intemperia
6825 to fasten by pinning	épingler	mit Stiften befestigen	fissare con punte, spillare
fastening by pinning, *s. sprigging*			
fat coal, *s. bituminous coal*			

English	French	German	Italian
^ 6826 fat oil, fatty oil	huile f grasse	fettes Öl n, Fetföl n	olio m grasso
° 6826a fat sand	sable m fort	fetter Sand m	terra f grassa
⌐ 6827 to fathorm	mesurer	messen	misurare
— 6828 fathom	brasse f, toise f	Lachter n	tesa f, braccio m
— 6829 fathom tale	paie f suivant le volume extrait	Bezahlung f mit zu Grunde gelegtem Raummass	paga f a volume di materiale estratto
° 6830 fatigue	fatigue f	Ermüdung f	fatica f
° 6830a fatigue allowance	effort m admissible	Ermüdungszuschlagm	carico m ammissibile
° 6831 fatigue crack	cassure f de fatigue	Dauerschwingbruch m	crinatura f per fatica
° 6832 fatigue fracture	rupture f par fatigue	Ermüdungsbruch m	rottura f per fatica
° 6833 fatigue limit	limite f théorique d'endurance, limite f apparente d'élasticité	konventionelle Dauer-schwingfestigkeit f	limite m convenzionale di resistenza alla fatica
° 6833a fatigue range	zone f de fatigue	Ermüdungszone f	zona f di fatica
° 6834 fatigue strenght	limite f convention-nelle d'endurance	konventionelle Dauerschwingfestig-keit f	limite m convenzionale di resistenza alla fatica
° 6835 fatigue stress	sollicitation f de fatigue	Dauerbeanspruchung f	snervamento m
° 6836 fatigue testing, fatigue test, endurance test	essai m de fatigue, essai m d'endurance	Dauerfestigkeitspro-be f	prova f di fatica
^ 6837 fatty acid	acide m gras	Fettsäure f	acido m grasso
^ 6838 fatty compound	composé m aliphatique	Fettverbindung f	composto m alifatico
— 6839 fault	faille f, dislocation f	Verwerfung f, Verwurf m, Sprung m, Gangspalte f	faglia f, linea f di cedimento
° 6840 fault (in a casting)	défaut m de coulage, grains m pl.	Gussfehler m	difetto m di fusione, paglia f
— 6841 fault bench	gradin m de faille	Verwerfungsstufe f	gradino m di faglia
— 6842 fault block	bloc m, massif faillé	Scholle f	blocco m, blocco m dislocato
— 6843 fault-block walley	vallée f d'effondrement	Grabental n	vallata f di disloca-zione
— 6844 fault-breccia, fault-rock	brèche f de faille, brèche f de friction	Verwerfungsbreccie f, Dislokationsbreccie	breccia f di faglia (o di dislocazione)

English	French	German	Italian
6845 **fault caused by tensional stress**	faille *f* d'extension, faille *f* d'expansion	Dehnungsverwerfung *f*	faglia *f* di estensione, faglia *f* diretta
6846 **fault cliff**	escarpement *m* de faille	Verwerfungswand *f*, Bruchliniestufe *f*	scarpata *f* di faglia
6847 **fault coal**	charbon *m* pauvre	geringwertige Kohle *f*	carbone *m* povero
6848 **fault dip**	inclinaison *f* de faille	Einfallen *n* der Verwerfung	inclinazione *f* di faglia
6849 **fault fissure**	paraclase *f*	Verwerfungsspalte *f*	paraclasi *f*
6850 **fault hading against the dip**	faille *f* contraire	gegenfallende Verwerfung *f*	faglia *f* inversa
6851 **fault hading with the dip**	faille *f* conforme (ou régulière)	rechtfallende Verwerfung *f*	faglia *f* normale
6852 **fault line, fault trace, rift, fault outcrop**	ligne *f* de faille	Verwerfungslinie *f* Abbruchlinie *f*	affioramento della faglia
6853 **fault-line scarp**	escarpement *m* de faille	Bruchwand *f*	scarpa *f* di faglia
6854 **fault outcrop, fault line**	affleurement *m* de faille	Verwerfungslinie *f*	affioramento *m* di faglia
6855 **fault outlier**	lambeau *m* de charriage	Deckscholle *f*	faglia *f* di carriaggio
6856 **fault-pit**	effondrement *m* circulaire	Kesselbruch *m*, Pinge *f*	frana *f* circolare
6857 **fault plane**	plan *m* de la faille	Verwerfungsebene *f*	piano *m* della faglia
6858 **fault-polish**	miroir *m* de glissement	Bleispiegel *m*	specchio *m* di faglia
6859 **fault ridge**	tête *f* de faille	Schollenkante *f*	testa *f* di faglia
fault rock, *s. fault-breccia*			
6860 **fault strike**	direction *f* de faille	Streichen *n* von Verwerfung	direzione *f* di faglia
fault trace, *s. fault line*			
6861 **fault throw**	rejet *m* de la faille	seigere Sprunghöhe *f*	rigetto *m* della faglia
fault zone, *s. shear zone*			

	English	French	German	Italian
—	6862 fault wall	lèvre f de faille	Flügel m (von Verwerfung)	lembo m di faglia
—	6863 faultage	formation f des failles	Sprungbildung f	formazione f di faglie, fagliazione f
—	6864 faulted or dislocated deposit	gîte m disloqué	verworfene oder gestörte Lagerstätte f	giacimento m dislocato
—	6865 faulted structure	terrain faillé	Schollenland n	terreno m dislocato (o fagliato)
	faulting, s. faultage			
°	6866 faultless	sain	fehlerfrei	sano, privo di difetti
—	6867 favourable bed	zone f favorable	günstige Zone f	zona f favorevole
—	6868 fayalite	fayalite f	Fayalit m	fayalite f
—	6869 feather-alum	alun m de plume	Haarsalz n, Halotrichit m	halotrichite f
°	6870 feather edged flat	fers m pl. à arêtes vives	scharfkantiger Stahl m	ferro m a spigoli vivi
°	6871 feather edged halfround	demi-rond m irrégulier	regelloser Halbrundstahl m	mezzo-tondo m irregolare
—	6872 feather-ore	plumosite f	Federerz n	plumosite f
°	6873 feather spline	clavette f	Stift m, Keil m	chiavetta f, linguetta f
°	6874 to feed	nourrir	nachgiessen, speisen	rabboccare, alimentare
°	6875 feed	avance f	Vorschub m	avanzamento m
°	6876 feed boiler	chaudière f alimentaire	Speisekessel m	caldaia f di alimentazione
°	6877 feed box	bassin m de coulée	Eingusskasten m	bacino m di colata
—	6878 feed chute	goulotte f d'alimentation	Abgaberinne f	scivolo m d'alimentazione
	feed head, s. feeder head			
—	6879 feed hopper	trémie f d'alimentation	Aufgabetrichter m, Fülltrichter m	tramoggia f d'alimentazione o di caricamento
—	6880 feed launder for ore	goulotte f alimenteuse pour minerais	Gerinne n Gefluder n	scivolo m alimentatore per minerali

English	French	German	Italian
6881 **feed manifold**	collecteur *m* d'alimentation	Speisefang *m*	collettore *m* di alimentazione
6881a **feed motion**	mouvement *m* d'avancement	Vorschub *m*	movimento *m* d'avanzamento
6882 **feed screw**	vis *f* sans fin d'alimentation	Aufgabeschnecke *f*	vite *f* d'alimentazione
6883 **feed stock**	charge *f*	Charge *f*	carica *f*
6884 **feeder**	conduite *f* d'alimentation	Zufuhrkanal *m*, Speiseleitung *f*	conduttura *f* d'alimentazione, alimentatore *m*
6885 **feeder**	filon *m* nourricier	Nebengang *m*	filone *m* alimentatore
6885a **feeder, riser**	masselotte *f*	Speiser *m*	materozza *f*
feeder, *s. feedhead*			
6886 **feeder head, feader, feed head**	masselotte *f*, jet *m*, nourrice	Speiser *m*, Steiger *m*, Giesskopf *m*, Anguss	materozza *f*
6887 **feeder head (or feed head) with Washburn core**	masselotte *f* à étranglement	Speiser *m* mit Einschnürkern	materozza *f* strozzata
6887a **feeding**	nourrissage *m*	Nachspeisen *n*	rabboccatura *f*
6888 **feeding**	alimentation *f*	Speisung *f*	alimentazione *f*
6889 **feeding**	avancement *m*	Vorschub *m*	avanzamento *m*
6889a **feeding compound**	substance *f* exothermique	exotherme Substanz *f*	sostanza *f* esotermica
6890 **feeding device**	appareil *m* d'alimentation	Speiseapparat *m*	apparecchio *m* d'alimentazione
6891 **feeding gate of a furnace**	gueulard *m* de chargement	Einsatzöffnung *f*, Gicht *f*	bocca *f* (o gola) di caricamento
feeding head, *s. feeder head*			
6892 **feeding hopper**	trémie *f* de chargement, ou d'alimentation	Beschickungstrichter *m*	tramoggia *f* di caricamento
6893 **feeding mouth**	ouverture *f* d'entrée	Maulweite *f*	apertura *f* di bocca
6894 **feeding neck**	col *m* de liaison de la masselotte	Speiserhals *m*, Steigerhals *m*	collarino *m*, collo di raccordo *m* della materozza
6895 **feeding orifice (of injection chamber)**	orifice *m* d'alimentation (de la chambre d'injection)	Mundstück *n*	foro *m* d'alimetazione (della camera d'iniezione)
6896 **to feel, to touch**	tater, tatonner, manipuler, palper	tasten	palpare, tastare,

	English	French	German	Italian
	to feel the ground, s. *to sound the ground*			
o	6897 **feeler**	palpeur *m*	Taster *m*	tasto *m*, chiave *f*, calibro *m*
o	6898 **feeling lever**	levier-palpeur *m*	Tasthebel *m*	leva *m* di tasto
—	6899 **feldspar**	feldspath *m*	Feldspat *m*	feldspato *m*
—	6900 **feldspathic**	feldspathique	feldspathaltig	feldspatico
—	6901 **feldspathization**	feldspathisation *f*	Feldspatisierung *f*	feldspatizzazione *f*
—	6902 **feldspathoid**	feldspathoïde *m*	Feldspatvertreter *m*	feldspatoide *m*
	6903 **fell**	abattre du bois	Holz hauen	abbattere (alberi)
—	6904 **fell**	minerai *m* de plomb	Bleierz *n*	minerale *m* di piombo
—	6905 **fell heap**	tas *m* de minerai	Erzhaufen *n* zur Aufbereitung	mucchio *m* di minerale
—	6906 **felling**	abattage *m*	Hereingewinnung *f*	abbattimento *m*
—	6907 **felsite**	felsite *f*	Felsit *m*	felsite *f*
—	6908 **felsitic**	felsitique *m*	felsitisch	felsitico
—	6909 **felsitic texture or structure**	texture *f* ou structure *f* pétrosiliceuse	felsitische Struktur *f*	struttura *f* petrosiliciosa
—	6910 **felsobanyite**	felsobanyite *f*	Felsöbanyit *m*	felsobanyite *f*
—	6911 **felsophyre**	felsophyre *m*	Felsophyr *n*	felsofiro *m*
	felspar, s. *feldspar*			
	felstone, s. *felsite*			
—	6912 **felt cover**	couverture *f* en feutre	Filzüberzug *m*, Filzstreifen *m*	copertura *f* di feltro
o	6913 **female sub**	réduction *f* à femelle	Nutenverminderung *f*	riduzione *f* a femmina
—	6914 **female tap**	cloche *f* de repêchage	Fangglocke *f*	pescatore *m* a campana
	female thread, s. *internal thread*			
o	6915 **fence bar**	fer *m* à grilles	Gittereisen *n*	ferro *m* da grata
o	6916 **fence diagram**	vue *f* isométrique	Gitterprofil *n*	profilo *m* isometrico (o tridimensionale)

	English	French	German	Italian
6917	fencing wire	fil *m* de fer pour clôture	Draht *m* für Umzäunungen	filo *m* di ferro per recinzioni
6918	fend-off	balancier *m*	Schwengel *m*	bilanciere *m*
6919	ferberite	ferbérite *f*	Ferberit *m*	ferberite *f*
6920	ferghanite	ferghanite *f*	Ferghanit *m*	ferghanite *f*
6921	fergusite	fergusite *f*	Fergusit *m*	fergusite *f*
6922	fergusonite	fergusonite *f*	Fergusonit *m*	fergusonite *f*
6923	fermentation	fermentation *f*	Fermentierung *f*	fermentazione *f*
6924	fermium	fermium *m*	Fermium *n*	fermio *m*
6925	fermorite	fermorite *f*	Fermorit *m*	fermorite *f*
6926	fermorite-leaf crystal	dendrite *f*	Dendrit *m*	dendrite *f*
6927	fernandinite	fernandinite *f*	Fernandinit *m*	fernandinite *f*
6928	ferric oxide	oxyde *m* ferrique	Eisenoxyd *n*	ossido *m* ferrico
6929	ferric sulphate	sulfate *m* ferrique	schwefelsaures Eisenoxyd *n*, Eisenoxydsulfat *n*	solfato *m* ferrico
6930	ferrierite	ferriérite *f*	Ferrierit *m*	ferrierite *f*
6931	ferrinatrite	ferronatrite *f*	Ferrinatrit *m*	ferrinatrite *f*
6932	Ferris wheel feed	alimentation *f* par godets roulants	Ferriskorbspeisung *f*	alimentazione *f* a tazze rotanti
6993	ferrisymplesite	ferrisymplésite *f*	Ferrisymplesit *m*	ferrisymplesite *f*
6934	ferrite	ferrite *f*	Ferrit *m*	ferrite *f*
	ferrite ghost, *s. ghost lines*			
6935	ferritic cast iron	fonte *f* ferritique	ferritisches Gusseisen *n*	ghisa *f* ferritica
6936	ferritic steel	acier *m* ferritique	ferritischer Stahl *m*	acciaio *m* ferritico
6937	ferritization	ferritization *f*	Ferritizierung *f*	ferritizzazione
6938	ferritungstite	ferritungstite *f*	Ferritungstit *m*	ferritungstite *f*
6939	ferro-alloy	ferro-alliage *m*	Ferrolegierung *f*	ferrolega *f*
6940	ferro-aluminium	ferro-aluminium *m*	Aluminium-Eisen *n*	ferro-alluminio

	English	French	German	Italian
° 6941	ferro-boron	ferrobore *m*	Eisenbor *n*	ferroboro *m*
° 6942	ferro-chrome	ferro-chrome *m*	Chrom-Eisen *n*	ferro-cromo *m*
° 6943	ferro concrete, concrete steel	béton *m* armé	Eisenbeton *m*	cemento *m* armato
° 6943a	ferrograph	hystérésigraphie *f*	Hystereseschleifen- schreiber *m*	isteresigrafo *m*
° 6944	ferro-manganese	ferro-manganèse	Manganeisen *n*	ferromanganese *m*
° 6945	ferro-manganese titaniferous	ferromanganèse *m* titanifère	Eisenmangantitan *n*	ferro *m* manganese al titanio
° 6946	ferro-molybdenum	ferro-molybdène *m*	Molybdäneisen *n*	ferro-molibdeno *m*
° 6947	ferro-nickel	ferro-nickel *m*	Nickeleisen *n*, Ferronickel *n*	ferronichelio *m*
° 6948	ferro-phosphorous	fer-phosphore *m*, fer phosphoreux	Eisenphosphor *n*	ferro *m* fosforoso
° 6949	ferro silico- -manganese	ferro-manganèse *m* siliceux	Silikospiegel *m*	ferro *m* al silicio-man- ganese
° 6950	ferro-silicon	ferro-silicium *m*	Ferrosilizium *n*	ferrosilicio *m*
° 6951	ferrous sulphide	sulfure *m* de fer	Schwefelkies *m*	bisolfuro *m* di ferro, pirite *f* di ferro
° 6952	ferro-titanium	ferrotitane *m*	Ferrotitan *n*	ferro-titanio *m*
° 6953	ferro-tungsten	ferro-tungstène *m*	Ferrowolfram *n*	ferro-tungsteno *m*
° 6954	ferro-vanadium	ferro-vanadium *m*	Vanadiumeisen *n*, Ferrovanadium *n*	ferro-vanadio *m*
° 6955	ferrocobalt	ferrocobalt *m*	Ferrokobalt *n*	ferro-cobalto *m*
— 6956	ferrolite	ferrolite *f*	Ferrolit *m*	ferrolite *f*
° 6957	ferromagnetic	ferromagnétique	eisenmagnetisch	ferromagnetico
° 6958	ferrometer	ferromètre *m*	Ferrometer *n*	ferrometro *m*
— 6959	ferropallidite	ferropallidite *f*	Ferropallidit *m*	ferropallidite *f*
° 6960	ferrosilico- -manganese	ferro-manganèse *m* siliceux	Ferro-Siliko- -Mangan *n*	ferro-silico-manganese *m*
° 6961	ferrosilicon	ferrosilicium *m*	Ferrosilizium *n*	ferro-silicio *m*
° 6962	ferrostatical pressure	pression *f* ferro- statique	ferrostatischer Druck *m*	pressione *f* ferrostatica

English	French	German	Italian
6963 ferrous	ferreux, ferro-	ferro-	ferroso
6964 ferrous ammonium sulphate	sulfate *m* de fer ammoniacal	Eisenoxydulammoniumsulfat *n*	solfato *m* ferroso-ammonico, sale *m* di Mohr
6964a ferrous metallurgie	métallurgie *f* du fer	Eisenmetallurgie *f*	metallurgia *f* del ferro
6965 ferrous oxyde	oxyde *m* ferreux	Eisenoxydul *n*	ossido *m* ferroso
6966 ferrons sulphate, green vitriol	sulfate *m* ferreux	Eisenoxydulsulfat *n*	solfato *m* ferroso
6966a ferroxyl	ferroxyle *m*	Ferroxyl	ferrossile *m*
6967 ferrozirconium	ferrozirconium *m*	Ferrozirkon *n*	ferrozirconio *m*
6968 ferruginous sand	sable *m* ferrugineux	Eisensand *m*	sabbia *f* ferruginosa
6969 ferruginous opal, jasper opal	opale *f* ferrugineuse, jaspe-opale	Jàspopal *m*, Eisenopal *m*	opale ferruginoso
6970 to fettle	ébarber	fertigputzen	sbavare
6971 to fettle (the cores)	débourrer	entkernen	svuotare le anime
6972 to fettle	ébavurer	abgraten	sbavare
6973 fettler	ébarbeur *m*	Gussputzer *m*	sbavatore *m* (operaio)
6974 fettling, dressing	ébarbage *m*	Fertigputzen *n*, Entgraten *n*	sbavatura *f* (dei getti)
6975 fettling, trimming	garnissage *m*	Zustellung *f*	rifacimento *m*
6976 fettling-hammer	marteau *m* à ébarber	Abgrathammer *m*	martello *m* sbavatore
6977 fettling-machine	ébarbeuse *f*	Abgratmaschine *f*	sbavatrice *f*
fettling room, *s. fettling shop*			
6978 fettling shop, dressing shop	atelier *m* d'ébarbage	Gussputzerei *f*	reparto *m* sbavatura, sala di ripulitura
6979 fettling the furnace, relining the furnace	garnissage *m* du four	Zustellung *f* des Ofens	rivestimento *m* o rifacimento *m* del forno
6980 fettling tool	outil *m* d'ébarbage	Abgratwerkzeug *n*	sbavatore *m*, sbavatrice *f*
F.H. = *full-hole*			
6981 fibering	stucture *f* fibreuse	Faserstruktur *f*	struttura *f* delle fibre
6982 fibre, fiber	nerf *m*, fibre *f*	Sehne *f*, Faser *f*	fibra *f*, nervatura *f*
6983 fibroblastic texture	texture *f* fibroblastique	fibroblastische Struktur *f*	struttura *f* filamentosa, struttura *f* fibroblastica
6984 fibroferrite	fibroferrite *f*	Fibroferrit *m*	fibroferrite *f*

	English	French	German	Italian
— 6985	**fibrolite**	fibrolite *f*	Fibrolith *m*, Faserkiesel *m*	fibrolite *f*
— 6986	**fibrous**	nerveux, fibreux	sehnig	nervoso, fibroso
° 6987	**fibrous fracture**	cassure *f* fibreuse	faseriger Bruch *m*	frattura *f* fibrosa
° 6988	**fibrous iron**	fer *m* nerveux	sehniges Eisen *n*	ferro *m* fibroso
° 6989	**fibrous iron ore**	minerai *m* de fer fibreux	faseriges Eisenerz *n*	minerale *m* di ferro fibroso
° 6989a	**fibrous fracture**	cassure *f* fibreuse	Faserbruch *m*	frattura *f* fibrosa
— 6990	**fibrous jamesonite**	jamesonite *f* fibreuse	faseriger Jamesonit *m*	jamesonite *f* fibrosa
— 6991	**fibrous lignite**	lignite *m* fibreux	faseriger Lignit *m*	lignite *f* fibrosa
— 6992	**fibrous red iron ore**	fer *m* oligiste concrétionné	roter Glaskopf *m*, Eisenniere *f*	ferro *m* oligisto rosso fibroso
— 6993	**fibrous structure**	structure *f* fibreuse	Faseraufbau *m*	struttura *f* fibrosa
— 6994	**fichtelite**	fichtélite *f*	Fichtelit *m*	fichelite *f*
— 6995	**fiedlerite**	fiedlérite *f*	Fiedlerit *m*	fiedlerite *f*
° 6996	**field energy**	énergie *f* du champ	Feldenergie *f*	energia *f* di campo
° 6997	**field intensity**	intensité *f* de champ	Feldintensität *f*, Feldstärke *f*	intensità *f* di campo
ˆ 6998	**field extension well**	puits *m* de délimitation du gisement	Aufschlussbohrung *f* zur Ermittlung der Grösse des Vorkommens	pozzo *m* di delimitazione del giacimento
° 6999	**field of view**	champ *m* de la lunette	Gesichtsfeld *n*	campo *m* visivo
— 7000	**field test**	essai *m* effectif (sur le terrain)	Feldversuch *m*	prova *f* sul posto
— 7001	**fieldpath**	sentier *m*, chemin	Feldweg *m*	sentiero *m*, viottolo *m*
— 7002	**fiery**	grisouteux	schlagwetterhaltig	contenente grisou
	figure eight wire, *s. shaped wire 8 section* **figure of merit**, *s. quality factor* **figured (bar) iron**, *s. section*			
° 7003	**file**	lime *f*	Feile *f*	lima *f*
° 7004	**file cutter's chisel**	étoile *f* de tailleur de limes	Feilenhauermeissel *m*	tagliatore *m* di lima

		English	French	German	Italian

file dust, *s. filings*

		English	French	German	Italian
°	7005	**file hardening furnace**	four *m* à tremper les limes	Feilenhärteofen *m*	forno *m* per temperare le lime
°	7006	**file steel**	acier *m* à limes	Feilenstahl *m*	acciaio *m* da lime
°	7007	**filings**	limaille *f*	Feilspan *m*, Feilstaub *m*	limatura *f*
°	7008	**to fill and ram the mould**	emballer un noyau	eine Form *f* aufstampfen	riempire e battere la forma
—	7009	**to fill in**	tamponner	hinterfüllen	rincalzare
^	7010	**to fill in**	tamponner	abdichten	sigillare
°	7011	**to fill the mould**	remplir le moule	die Form füllen	riempire la forma
°	7012	**to fill up**	remplir	nachfüllen	riempire
^	7013	**to fill up**	mastiquer	spachteln, verschmieren	mettere del mastice, masticiare
°	7014	**to fill up the casting holes**	boucher les soufflures	die Gusslöcher verstopfen	chiudere o tappare le soffiature
—	7014a	**fill**	poids *m* de remplissage	Füllmenge *f*	volume *m* di riempimento
—	7015	**fill factor**	densité *f* de remplissage	Fülldichte *f*	densità *f* di riempimento
—	7017	**filled flat-back stoping**	exploitation *f* à échelon remblayée	versetzer Firstenabbau mit waagerechter Firste	coltivazione a gradino rovescio con ripiena
—	7018	**filled flat-back stope**	taille *f* en échelon remblayée	versetzter Firstenstoss *m* mit waagerechter Firste	taglio *m* a gradino rovescio con ripiena
—	7019	**filled rill stope**	gradin *m* incliné avec remblayage	versetzter Firstenstoss *m* mit geneigter Firste	gradino *m* inclinato con ripiena
—	7020	**filled stope**	taille *f* remblayée	versetzter Stoss *m*	cantiere *m* riempito
—	7021	**filler material**	colmatant *m*	Füllmaterial *n*	materiale *m* per ripiena
°	7022	**filler metal**	métal *m* d'apport	Zusatzmetall *n*	metallo *m* di apporto
°	7023	**filler plate**	semelle *f* avec le dispositif à tourner en cône	Sattelplatte *f*	suola *f* con congegno da tornire conico

	English	French	German	Italian
⌃ 7024	**filler plug**	bouchon de remplissage	Füllpfropfen *m*	tappo *m* di riempimento
○ 7025	**filler rod, welding rod**	fil *m* à souder	Schweissdraht *m*	filo *m* per saldature, bacchetta *f* d'apporto
○ 7026	**filler sand**	sable *m* de moulage à grain gros, terre *f* de remplissage	grosskörniger Formsand *m*, Füllsand *m*	terra *f* per formatura a grana grossa, terra *f* di riempimento
○ 7027	**fillet**	congé *m*	Hohlkehle *f*	raccordo *m* concavo
○ 7028	**fillet (to be strickled)**	congé *m* à racler	auszuschneidende Kante *f*	raccordo *m* da sagomare
○ 7029	**fillet (in black paint)**	congé *m* au noir	zu brechende Kante *f*	indicazione *f* di raccordo, segno (in nero) di raccordo
	fillet, *s. fillet weld*			
○ 7030	**fillet iron**	fer *m* à congé	Andrückwerkzeug *n* für Lederhohlkehlen	lisciatoio *m* per raccordi
○ 7031	**fillet weld, joint sealing**	cordon *m* d'étanchéité	Dichtungsrand *m*, Randwulst *m*	cordone *m* d'angolo
○ 7032	**fillet welding**	soudure *f* en angle	Raupenschweissung *f*	saldatura *f* a raccordo (o d'angolo o a gola)
— 7033	**filling**	remplissage *m*	Füllen *n*	riempimento *m*
— 7034	**filling frame**	cadre *m* supérieur	Aufsatzrahmen *m*	quadro *m* (o telaio) superiore di riempimento
— 7034a	**filling height**	hauteur *f* de remplissage	Fullhöhe *f*	altezza *f* di riempimento
○ 7035	**filling in**	tamponnage *m*	Verdämmen *n*	tamponatura *f*
○ 7036	**filling (with white metal)**	coulage *m* ou remplissage (en métal blanc)	(mit Weissmetall) Ausgiessen *n*	riempimento *m* (di metallo bianco)
— 7037	**filling material**	matériaux *m pl.* de remblayage	Aufschüttungsmasse *f*	materiali *m pl.* di riempimento o per ripiena
○ 7038	**filling station**	station *f* de service	Tankstation *f*	stazione *f* di servizio
— 7039	**filling system**	système *m* d'exploitation avec remblayage	Abbauverfahren *n* mit Bergeversatz, Versatzverfahren *n*	coltivazione *f* con ripiena
— 7040	**fillowite**	fillowite *f*	Fillowit *m*	fillowite *f*
○ 7040a	**film**	pellicule *f*	Film *m*	pellicola *f*
7041	**to filter**	filtrer	filtern	filtrare
7042	**filter**	filtre *m*	Filter *n*	filtro *m*

English	French	German	Italian
— 7043 **filter bed**	couche _f_ filtrante	Filterschicht _f_	strato _m_ filtrante
○ 7044 **filter cone**	entonnoir _m_ de filtre	Filterkegel _m_	cono _m_ filtrante
○ 7044a **filter core**	noyau-filtre _m_	Siebkern _m_	anima-filtro _m_
○ 7045 **filter disc**	plaque _f_ à filtrer	Filterplatte _f_	piastra _f_ filtrante
— 7046 **filter drum**	tambour _m_ filtrant	Filtertrommel _f_	tamburo _m_ filtrante
○ 7047 **filter funnel**	entonnoir _m_ à filtrer	Filtertrichter _m_	imbuto _m_ filtrante
filter gate, _s. ring (pencil) gate_			
filter glass, _s. welding glass_			
˄ 7048 **filter loss**	perte _f_ en eau libre	Filterverlust _m_	perdita _f_ d'acqua libera
○ 7049 **filter paper**	papier _m_ filtrant	Filterpapier _n_	carta _f_ da filtro
○ 7050 **filter plant**	installation _f_ de filtrage	Filtrationsanlage _f_	impianto _m_ di filtraggio
○ 7051 **filter press**	filtre-presse _m_ ﹨	Filterpresse _f_	filtropressa _m_
○ 7052 **filter pump**	pompe _f_ à filtrer	Filterpumpe _f_	pompa _f_ filtrante
○ 7053 **filter ring**	support _m_ de filtre	Filterhalter _m_	portafiltro _m_
˄ 7054 **filter tank**	réservoir _m_ de filtration	Filtertank _m_	serbatoio _m_ di filtraggio
○ 7055 **filtering-boiler**	chaudière _f_ à filtrer	Filtrierkessel _m_	caldaia _f_ per filtrare
○ 7056 **filtering charcoal**	charbon _m_ à filtrer	Filterkohle _f_	carbone _m_ per filtri
○ 7057 **filtering flask**	flacon _m_ à filtrer dans le vide	Absaugflasche _f_, Nutsche _f_	bottiglia _f_ per filtrazione forzata
○ 7058 **filtering pipette**	pipette _f_ à filtrer	Filterstechheber _m_	pipetta _f_ filtrante
○ 7059 **filtering tube**	tube _m_ à filtrer	Filterröhre _f_	tubo _m_ per filtrare
— 7060 **filthy water**	purin _m_	Jauche _f_	acqua _f_ fetida
— 7061 **filtrate**	produit _m_ filtré	Filtrat _n_	prodotto _m_ filtrato
— 7062 **filtration**	filtration _f_	Filterung _f_	filtrazione, filtraggio
— 7063 **filtration disc**	capsule _f_ à filtrer	Filterschale _f_	disco _m_ filtrante
˄ 7064 **filtration percolation**	filtrage _m_ à percolation	Perkolations-filtration _f_	filtraggio _m_ a percolazione
○ 7064a **fin, flash**	ailette _f_	Rippe _f_	aletta _f_

	English	French	German	Italian
°	7065 **fin**	gerçure f de la lingotière	Kokillenriss m	incrinatura f della lingottiera
°	7065a **fin, overfill**	bavure f de lamination	Walzenbart m	bava f di laminazione
°	7066 **fin crack**	crique f de bavure	Bartriss m	crepa f di bavatura
°	7067 **final hardening**	trempe f finale	Endhärtung f	tempra f finale
°	7068 **final pass**	cylindre m finisseur	Feinwalze f	cilindro m finitore
°	7069 **final section**	section f finale	Endquerschnitt m	sezione f finale
°	7070 **final shape**	forme f finale	Endform f	forma f finale
°	7071 **final test**	essai m final	endgültiger Versuch m	collaudo m finale
°	7072 **to fine, to refine**	affiner, purifier	frischen, raffinieren	affinare, raffinare, purificare
°	7073 **fine bullion**	lingot d'or (ou d'argent pur)	Feinbarrengold (od. Silber)	lingotto m d'oro (o d'argento fino)
—	7074 **fine coal, small coal**	fines f de charbon	Feinkohle f	fini m $pl.$ di carbone, minuto m
—	7075 **fine coal dust**	poudre f de houille	Steinkohlenmehl n	polvere f di carbon fossile
—	7076 **fine coal washer**	laveur m à fines	Feinkohlenwäsche f	lavatrice f per fini
—	7077 **fine crusher**	broyeur m des fines	Feinmühle f	frantoio m (o mulino) per fini
—	7078 **fine crushing**	broyage m fin	Feinzerkleinerung f	macinazione f fina
°	7079 **fine drawing**	tréfilage m fin	Feinzug m	stiramento m fine, trafilatura fine
—	7080 **fine grained**	à grain fin	feinkörnig	a grana fine, finemente granulato
°	7081 **fine grained fracture**	cassure f à grain fin	feinkörniger Bruch m	frattura f a grana fine
°	7082 **fine grained iron**	fer m à grain fin	Feinkorneisen n	ferro m a grana fine
°	7083 **fine grained pig iron**	fonte f grise claire	lichtgraues Roheisen n	ghisa f grigio-chiara, ghisa a grana fine
°	7084 **fine grained steel**	acier m à grain fin	Feinkornstahl m	acciaio m a grana fine

English	French	German	Italian
— 7085 **fine grinding**	broyage *m* fin	Feinzerkleinerung *f*	triturazione *f* fina, macinazione *f* fine
— 7086 **fine iron ore, powdery iron ore**	minerai *m* de fer pulvérulent	pulverförmiges Eisenerz *n*	minerale *m* di ferro polverulento
° 7087 **fine lapping**	fleur *f* (sur les pièces coulée)	Schlierenbildung *f*	fiore *m* (sui pezzi colati)
fine metal, *s. refined metal*			
— 7088 **fine sand**	sable *m* fin	feiner Sand *m*	sabbia *f* minuta
— 7089 **fine sieve**	tamis *m* fin	feines Sieb *n*, Feinsieb *n*	vaglio *m* (o crivello) fine od a maglie fini
fine smelting, *s. fine working*			
° 7090 **fine (or special) steel**	acier *m* de choix, acier *m* fin	Spezialstahl *m*, Sonderstahl *m*	acciaio *m* scelto, acciaio *m* fino
— 7091 **fine texture**	texture *f* fine	Kleingefüge *n*	struttura *f* fine
fine wire, *s. thin (drawn) wire*			
° 7092 **fine working, fine smelting**	travail *m* d'affinage	Feinarbeit *f*	processo *m* d'affinaggio
° 7093 **fined iron, refined iron**	fer *m* affiné	Frischfeuereisen *n*	ferro *m* affinato
fined steel, *s. single-shear steel*			
° 7094 **finely crystalline iron**	fer *m* cristallin fin	feinkristallinisches Eisen *m*	ferro *m* cristallino fino
° 7095 **finely divided**	finement divisé	fein verteilt	finemente diviso
finely divided carbon, *s. powdered coal*			
— 7096 **finely divided concentrates**	concentrés *m pl.* très fins	Schli(e)ch, Schlieg *m*	concentrati *m pl.* sottilissimi
° 7097 **finely machined**	usiné fin	fein bearbeitet	lavorato fine
— 7098 **fineness of grinding**	indice *m* de finesse	Feinheitsgrad *m*	indice *m* di finezza
— 7099 **fineness of grinding**	finesse *f* du broyage	Mahlfeinheit *f*	finezza *f* della macinatura (o della frantumazione)
° 7100 **finer, refiner**	affineur *m*, raffineur *m*	Frischer *m*	operaio *m* addetto all'affinaggio, raffinatore *m*
° 7100a **finery**	four *m* d'affinage	Feinofen *m*	forno *m* d'affinaggio

		English	French	German	Italian
°	7101	finery fire, low hearth	four *m* ou foyer *m* d'affinerie	Frischherd *m*, Frischfeuer *n*	fuoco *m* d'affinaggio
		finery iron, *s. refined iron*			
°	7102	finery process	travail *m* au bas-foyer	Frischfeuerbetrieb *m*	processo *m* d'affinaggio
—	7103	fines, smalls, small coal	fines *f pl.* (de charbon)	Kohlenklein *n*	fino *m* (di carbone)
—	7104	finger board	râtelier *m* à tiges	Gestängerechen *m*	rastrelliera *f* per le aste
—	7105	finger chute	cheminée *f* étroite	enges Rollloch *n*	foro *m* di scarico stretto
°	7106	finger die	étampe *f* à noyau glissant	Stempel *m* mit gleitendem Zapfen	stampo *m* con maschío scorrevole
°	7107	finger slot	fente *f* de levage	Griffschlitz *m*	fenditura *f* di presa
—	7108	finger-type trap ring	arrache-carotte à doigts	Trapring *n* mit Fingern	strappa-carote *m* a stecche
^	7109	fingering	digitation *f*	Fingerbildung *f*	digitazione *f*
°	7110	fining	fabrication *f* de fonte malléable	Tempergusserzeugung *f*	fabbricazione *f* di ghisa malleabile
°	7111	fining process, refining	méthode *f* d'affinage	Frischverfahren *n*, Frischmethode *f*	metodo *m* o processo *m* d'affinaggio
°	7112	to finish	planer, finir	schlichten	rifinire, ripassare
°	7113	to finish	raccorder	ausbessern	riparare
°	7114	to finish bright	polir finement	hochglanzpolieren	lucidare, lavorare a specchio
°	7115	to finish the core	finissage *m* du noyau	Volldrehen *n* des Kernes	rifinitura *f* dell'anima
		finish the molds, *s. to smooth the moulds*			
°	7116	finish grinding, finishing polish	finissage *m* à la meule, finissage de meulage	Fertigschleifen *n*	finitura *f* alla mola
°	7117	finish hardware	quincaillerie *f*	Eisenteile *m pl.*	minuterie metalliche
°	7118	finish machining	finissage *m*	Fertigbearbeitung *f*	finitura *f*, rifinitura *f*
°	7119	finished, completed	achevé, fini	beendigt, fertig	finito, ultimato

English	French	German	Italian
7120 finished dried crucible	creuset *m* cuit	reifer Tiegel *m*	crogiuolo *m* essiccato
finished iron, *s. merchant-iron*			
7120a finished product	produit *m* de laminage	Walzwerkprodukt *n*	prodotto *m* di laminazione
7121 finished sheet	tôle *f* finie, tôle *f* nettoyée	fertiges Blech *n*	lamiera *f* finita
7122 finished sheet iron	tôle *f* nettoyée	geputztes Blech *n*	lamiera *f* finita
7123 finished steel	acier *m* fini	Fertigstahl *m*	acciaio *m* finito
7124 finisher (linisher, belt surfacer,)belt grinder bench type with abrasive disc	ponceuse-surfaceuse *f* d'établi à courroie et à disque abrasif	Tisch-Bandschleifmaschine *f* mit Schmirgelscheibe	affilatrice *f* (lisciatrice), affilatrice *f* a cinghia tipo da banco con disco abrasivo
7125 finishing	raccord *m*	Ausbesserung *f*	raccordo *m*
7126 finishing castings	achèvement *m* (ou finissage) des pièces coulées	Bearbeitung *f* der Gusstücke	rifinitura *f* dei pezzi colati (o fusi)
7127 finishing drum	trommel *m* finisseur	Tratschtrommel *f*	tamburo *m* di lavaggio finitore
7128 finishing groove	finisseur *m*, cannelure *f* finisseuse	Fertigkaliber *n*	canale *m* finitore
7129 finishing impression	empreinte *f* de finissage	Fertigabdruck *m*	impronta *f* di finitura
7130 finishing machine	machine *f* de finissage	Feinbearbeitungsmaschine *f*, Fertigungsmaschine *f*	rifinitrice *f*
7130a finishing mill	laminoir *m* finisseur	Fertigwalzwerk *n*	laminatoio *m* finitore
7131 finishing-mill train	train *m* finisseur	Fertigstrasse *f*	treno *m* finitore
7132 finishing of work(ing) piece	finissage *m* de la pièce	Fertigbearbeitung *f* des Werkstückes	rifinitura *f* del pezzo
7133 finishing pass	cylindre *m* finisseur	Fertigwalze *f*	cilindro *m* finitore
finishing polish, *s. finishing grinding*			
7134 finishing quality	polissabilité *f*	Polierfähigkeit *f*	lucidabilità *f*
7135 finishing roasting	grillage *m* définitif	Garrösten *n*	arrostimento *m* definitivo
7136 finishing roll	cylindre *m* finisseur	Fertigwalze *f*	cilindro *m* finitore

	English	French	German	Italian
° 7137	finishing rolling mill	laminoir *m* finisseur	Fertigwalzwerk *n*	laminatoio *m* finitore
° 7138	finishing rolls	train *m* finisseur	Fertigstrecke *f*, Fertigwalzwerk *n*	treno *m* finitore
° 7138a	finishing shop	atelier *m* de finition	Zurichterei *f*	officina *f* di rifinitura
° 7139	finishing slag	scorie *f* finale	Endschlacke *f*	scoria *f* finale
° 7139a	finishing stand	finisseuse *f*	Fertigwalzgerüst *n*	gabbia *f* finitrice
° 7140	finishing tool	outil *m* de finition	Schlichtstahl *m*	utensile *m* per finitura
° 7141	finishings	corrections *f pl.*	Zusatzberichti-gungen *f pl.*	correzioni *f pl.*
− 7142	finnemanite	finnemanite *f*	Finnemanit *m*	finnemanite *f*
° 7143	finned tube	tubes *m pl.* à ailettes	Rippenröhren *f pl.*	tubi *m pl.* ad alette
° 7144	finned heating tubes	tuyaux *m pl.* à ailettes de chauffage	Rippenrohrheizkoer-per *m*	tubi *m pl.* alettati di riscaldamento
	finning, *s. veining*			
− 7145	fiorite	fiorite *f*	Fiorit *m*	fiorite *f*
	fire-arch, *s. furnace-arch*			
° 7146	to fire	allumer	anfeuern	accendere
° 7146a	fire assaying	coupellation *f*	Kupellation *f*	coppellazione *f*
° 7147	fire bar	barreau *m* de grille	Roststab *m*	sbarra *f* della griglia, barrotto
° 7148	fire-bar bearer	traverse *f* de la grille	Rostträger *m*	traversa *f* della griglia, portabarrotti *m*
° 7149	fire bar iron	fer *m* à barreaux de grilles	Roststabeisen *n*	ferro *m* per sbarre di griglia o per barrotti
	fire barrier, *s. fire wall*			
− 7150	fire blende	pyrostilpnite *f*	Pyrostilpnit *m*	pirostilpnite *f*
− 7151	fire boss	porion *m* d'aérage	Wettersteiger *m*	sorvegliante *m* della ventilazione
° 7152	fire box, stoke hole, chamber	foyer *m*, caisse *f* à feu	Feuerraum *m*	focolare *m*, focolaio *m* cassa *f* a fuoco
° 7153	fire - box boiler	chaudière *f* à caisse feu	Feuerbüchskessel *m*	caldaia *f* a cassa - fo-colare
° 7154	fire-box crown plates	tôles *f* de ciel de boîte à feu	Feuerbüchsdecke *f*	lamiere di cielo della cassa a fuoco

	English	French	German	Italian
7155	fire box plate	tôle f de foyer (de chaudière)	Feuerblech n	lamiera f da focolare
7156	fire-box side plates	parois f pl. latérales de boîte à feu	Feuerbüchsenseiten- wand f	pareti f pl. laterali della cassa focolare
	fire brick, s. chamot			
7157	fire bridge	autel m	Feuerbrücke f	altare m
	fire chamber, s. fire place			
7158	fire clay	argile f réfractaire, terre f à pipe	feuerfester Ton m	argilla f refrattaria
7159	fire clay box	caisse f en matière réfractaire	Tonkiste f	cassa f in terra refrat- taria
7160	fire clay crucible	creuset m en argile	Tontiegel m	crogiuolo m d'argilla
7161	fire clay muffle	moufle m en terre réfractaire	Muffel f aus Schamotte	muffola f in terra refrattaria
7162	fire clay plug	bouchon m ou tampon d'argile réfractaire	Massenpfropfen m	tappo m d'argilla re- frattaria
7163	fire coat	revêtement réfractaire	feuerfeste Verkleidung f	rivestimento m refrat- tario (su metalli)
	fire cracking, s. chill crack			
7164	fire dam	barrage m contre les feux	Branddamm m	sbarramento m antincendio
7165	fire damp	grisou m	Grubengas n	grisou m, miscela f esplosiva
7166	fire dog	chenet m	Feuerbock m	alare m
7167	fire door	porte f contre les feux	Feuertür f	porta f antincendio
7168	fire-engine steam boiler	chaudière f pour pompe à incendie	Feuerspritzenkessel m	caldaia f per pompa antincendio
7169	fire grate	grille f de foyer	Feuerrost m	griglia f del focolare
7169a	fire guilding	dorure f au feu	Feuervergoldung f	doratura f al fuoco
7170	fire hearth-furnace	four m à avant- creuset	Stumpfofen m	forno m con crogiuolo anteriore
7171	fire hydrant with tubular post	bouche f d'incendie à colonne tubulaire	Rohrsäule f für Feuerlösch- hydranten	idrante m per incendio a colonna tubolare
7172	fire kiln	four m de grillage	Röstofen m	forno m d'arrostimento

	English	French	German	Italian
— 7173	fire-opal, flame-opal	opale *f* de feu, opale *f* flamboyante	Feueropal *m*, Sonnenopal *m*	opale di fuoco, girasole
° 7174	fire place, grate	foyer *m*, chauffe *f*	Feuerraum *m*, Heizraum *m*	focolare *m*, focolaio
° 7175	fire plug	poste *m* (ou prise *f*) d'incendie	Hydrant *m*	idrante *m*
° 7176	fire rake	râble *m*	Krücke *f*	gancio *m*
°. 7177	fire-resisting steel	acier réfractaire	feuerbestaendiger Stahl *m*	acciaio *m* refrattario
° 7177a	fire refined	affiné au feu	thermisch vergütet	affinato al fuoco
° 7178	fire sand	sable *m* de moulage	Formsand *m*	sabbia *f* refrattaria, sabbia *f* per forme
° 7178a	fire scale	couche *f* d'oxyde de cuivre	Kupferoxydschicht *f*	strato *m* di ossido di rame
° 7179	fire setting	abattage *m* au feu	Feuersetzen *n*	abbattimento *m* col fuoco
° 7180	fire-tinnel wire	fil étamé au feu	feuerverzinnter Draht *m*	filo stagnato al fuoco
	fire-tools, *s. firing tools*			
° 7180a	fire waste	perte *f* au feu	Materialabbrand *m*	perdita *f* al fuoco
—7181	fire watch	détecteur *m* de feu	Feuermelder *m*	rivelatore *m* d'incendio
	fire welding, *s. forge welding*			
	firebox, *s. furnace with internal horizontal grate*			
— 7182	fireclay, fire-clay	argile *f* réfractaire	feuerfester Ton *m*	argilla *f* refrattaria
— 7183	fireclay, fire-clay	terre *f* réfractaire	feuersester Lehm *m*	terra *f* refrattaria
— 7184	firedamp	grisou *m*	Schlagwetter *n*	aria *f* miscelata con gas
	fireman; *s. stoker*			
° 7184a	firestone	pierre *f* réfractaire	Sandstein *m*	pietra *f* refrattaria
— 7185	fire wall	coupe-feu *m*, rideau *m* de fer	Brandmauer *f*, Brandwand *f*	muro *m* tagliafuoco, parafuoco *m*
— 7186	fireproof	incombustible	fenerbeständig	incombustibile
° 7187	firing	chauffage *m*, chauffe *f*, alimentation *f*	Heizung *f*, Feuern *n*, Speisung *f*	riscaldamento *m*, alimentazione *f*
° 7188	firing	allumage *m*	Anfeuern *n*	accensione *f*
— 7189	firing (of a mine)	tirage *m*	Sprengung *f*	brillamento *m*
° 7190	firing a boiler	allumage du foyer d'une chaudière	Anheizen *n* eines Kessels	accensione *f* di una caldaia

	English	French	German	Italian
— 7191	firing machine	exploseur *m*	Zündmaschine *f*	esploditore *m* elettrico
° 7192	firing of steam boilers	chauffage *m* des chaudières	Befeuerung *f* der Dampfkessel	riscaldamento *m* delle caldaie
° 7193	firing plant	installation *f* de foyers	Feuerungsanlage *f*	impianto *m* di forni
° 7194	firing the enamel	fusion *f* de l'émail au feu	Einbrennen *n* des Emails	fusione *f* dello smalto
° 7195	firing tool(s)	attirail *m* de chauffe	Feuerungsgerät *n*	attrezzi *m* pl. per l'ascensione
— 7196	first class coal	charbon *m* de première qualité	Kohle *f* bester Sorte	carbone *m* di prima qualità
° 7197	first coat	première couche *f*, couche *f* de fond	vorübergehender Anstrich *m*, Grundierung *f*	prima mano *f* di tinta, tintura *f* di base
° 7198	first combustion	combustion *f* primaire	Primärverbrennung *f*	combustione *f* primaria
— 7199	first driving	traçage *m*	Vorrichtung *f*	tracciamento *m*, preparazione *f*
° 7200	first pass	première cannelure *f*	Anfangskaliber *n*	primo canale *m*
° 7201	first section	section *f* initiale	Anfangsquerschnitt *m*	sezione *f* iniziale
° 7202	first shape	dimension *f* primitive	Vorform *f*	dimensione *f* primitiva
— 7203	first working	préparation *f*, travaux de traçage	Vorrichtungsarbeiten *f pl.*	lavori *m* pl. di tracciamento, lavori *m* pl. preparatori (di scavo)
— 7204	firsts	minerai *m* en morceaux	Stückerz *n*	concentrato *m*, minerali *m* in pezzi
— 7205	fischerite	fischérite *f*	Fischerit *m*	fischerite *f*
^ 7206	fish	poisson *m*	Fisch *m*	pesce *m*
^ 7207	to fish	repêcher	fangen	ripescare
^ 7207a	fish eyes	microfissures *f pl.*	Mikrorisse *m* pl.	microfissure *f pl.*
^ 7208	fish grid	écrille *f*, grille *f* à poissons	Fischrechen *m*	griglia *f* per pesci
^ 7209	fish joint	joint *m* à mâchoires	Backenkupplung *f*	giunto *m* a ganasce
° 7210	fish-plate	éclisse *f*	Lasche *f*, Decklatte *f*	stecca *f*, parella *f*, ganascia *f*

English	French	German	Italian
7211 fish plate bolt	boulon *m* d'éclisse, boulon *m* à vis pour fixer les éclisses	Laschenbolzen *m*, Laschenschraube *f*	bullone *m* della stecca (chiavarda)
7212 fish plate pass	cannelures *f pl.* pour éclisses	Laschenkaliber *n*	scanalature *f pl.* per stecche
7213 fish-tail	retassure *f* a V	Lunker *m*	cavità *f* a V
7214 fish-tail bit	trépan *m* en queue de poisson	Fischschwanz- meissel *m*	trapano *m* a coda di carpa (o di pesce)
7215 fish up	retirer une pièce tombée au fond	fangen	pescare un pezzo caduto in fondo
7216 fisherman	expert *m* en repêchage	Fangfachmann *m*	specialista *m* in recuperi
fishhooks, *s. check marks or crowfeet*			
7217 fishing	repêchage *m*	Fangarbeit *f*	ripescaggio *m*, recupero *m*
7218 fishing hook	crochet *m* de repêchage	Fanghaken *m*	gancio *m* pescatore
7219 fishing jars	coulisse *f* de repêchage	Fangrutschschere *f*	snodo *m pl.* di pescaggio
7220 fishing magnet	aimant *m* de repêchage	Fangmagnet *m*	magnete *m* di pescaggio
7221 fishing socket	souricière *f*	Keilfänger *m*	pescatore *m*, ricuperatore *m*
7222 fishing tongs	accrocheur *m* à pinces	Fanggreifer *m*, Fangschere *f*	pescatore *m* a pinze
7223 fishing tap	taraud *m* de repêchage	Spitzfänger *m*	maschio-pescatore *m*
7224 fishing tools	outils *m pl.* de repêchage	Fanggeräte *n pl.*	utensili *m pl.* per recuperi (o per pescaggio)
fishmounting, *s. alligatoring*			
7224a fissure vein	filon *m* de rupture	echter Gang *m*	filone *m* di rottura
7225 fist size	grosseur *f* de poing	Faustgrösse *f*	grossezza *f* di pugno
7226 fitting	raccord *m*	Rohrverbindungs- stück *n*	raccordo *m*
7227 fitting pipe	raccord *m*	Rohrstück *n*	raccordo *m*
7228 five spot	(puits *m*) en quinconce	Schachbrettschacht *m*	(pozzo *m*) a «quinconce»

English	French	German	Italian
fixed boiler, s. stationary boiler			
7229 fixed bottom roll	cylindre m inférieur fixe	festliegende Unterwalze f	cilindro m inferiore fisso
7230 fixed carbon	carbone m combiné	gebundener Kohlenstoff m	carbonio m combinato
7231 fixed die, fixed die-half	bloc m fixe	Formplatte f, Eingussseite f	semistampo m fisso (per pressofusione)
7232 fixed division or partition wall	paroi f de séparation fixe	feste Zwischenwand f	parete f divisoria fissa
7233 fixed furnace	four m fixe	feststehender Ofen m	forno m fisso
fixed grate, s. stationary grate			
fixed jaw, s. current carrying jaw			
7234 fixed ladle	poche f fixe	Standpfanne f	siviera f fissa
7235 fixed measure	mesure f déterminée	festes oder fixes Mass n	misura f fissa
7236 fixed oxygen	oxygène m combiné	gebundener Sauerstoff m	ossigeno m combinato
7237 fixed pan mill	broyeur m à cuve fixe	Kollergang m mit feststehendem Teller	molazza f a vasca fissa
7238 fixed pipe	tubulure f fixe	festliegendes Rohr n	tubo m fisso
7239 fixed plate	plateau m fixe	feste Aufspannplatte	placca f fissa
7240 fixed platform	plate-forme fixe	feststehende Plattform f	piattaforma f fissa
7241 fixed roof (tank)	(réservoir m à) toit fixe	Festdach n (Tank)	serbatoio m (a tetto) fisso
7242 fixed steam crane	grue f fixe à vapeur	feststehender Dampfkran m	gru f fissa a vapore
7243 fixing	fixage m	Fixieren n	fissaggio m
fixing pad, s. padding			
7244 fixture assembly	outillage m de montage	Montagevorrichtung f	attrezzatura f di montaggio
7245 fizelyte	fizélyte f	Fizelyt m	fizelite f

	English	French	German	Italian
	7246 **flag**	plaquette f	Platte f	mattonella f, pietra f da lastrico
—	7247 **flag ore**	hématite f stratifiée	plattiges Erz n	ematite f stratificata
°	7248 **flag pole**	hampe f porte--drapeau	Fahnenstange f	antenna f portabandie-ra
	flagstone, $s.$ $flag$			
	to flake, $s.$ to $scale$			
°	7249 **flake, snow-flake**	lamelle f	Lamelle f, Blättchen n	lamella f, lamina f, fiocco
—	7249a **flake**	flocon m	Flocke f	scaglia f
—	7250 **flake graphite**	graphite m lamellaire ou à lamelles	Lamellengraphit m	grafite f lamellare
°	7250a **flakes**	gerçures f $pl.$	Haarrisse m $pl.$	criccature f $pl.$
	flaky coal, $s.$ $foliated$ $coal$			
—	7251 **flamboyant quartz**	quartz m aventuriné	Aventurin m	aventurina f
°	7252 **flame**	flamme f	Flamme f	fiamma f
—	7253 **flame arrestor**	coupe-feu m	Brandmauer f	tagliafuoco m
°	7254 **flame(-arc) carbon**	charbon m d"arc flambant	Effektkohle f	carbone m per arco elettrico
°	7254a **flame annealing**	recuit au chalumeau	Oberflächen-glühung f	ricottura f alla fiamma
°	7255 **flame baffling**	conduite m des flammes	Flammenführung f	condotto m delle fiamme
	flame carbon, $s.$ $mineralised$ $carbon$			
°	7256 **flame-cleaning, flame-descaling**	décalaminage m à la flamme	Flammenentzunderung f	decalaminazione alla fiamma
	flame coloring, $s.$ $flame$ $proof$			
	flame conditioning torch, $s.$ $flame$ $cleaning$ $blowpipe$			
	flame cutter, $s.$ $cutting$ $blowpipe$			
°	7257 **flame-cutting machine**	machine f à découper au chalumeau	Brennschneidemaschine f	macchina f per taglio alla fiamma
	flame gouging, $s.$ $groove$ $cutting$			
°	7258 **to flame harden, to skin-dry**	flamber	abflammen	indurire alla fiamma, fiammare
°	7259 **flame hardening**	trempe f à la flamme, au chalumeau	Flammenhärtung f	tempera f col cannello, fiammatura, tempra f alla fiamma
°	7260 **flame-hardening machine**	machine f à tremper au chalumeau	Brennhärtemaschine f	macchina f per la tempra alla fiamma

English	French	German	Italian

flame hardening torch, s. *flame hardening blowpipe*

° 7261 **flame hole**   passage *m* de la   Flammenloch *n*   apertura *f* d'entrata
                   flamme   della fiamma

flame-opal, s. *fire-opal*

° 7262 **flame-proof (or test)**   essai *m* à la flamme   Flammenfärbung *f*   prova *f* alla fiamma

° 7263 **flame-proof wire**   fil *m* ignifugé   feuersicherer   filo *m* incombustibile
                                        Draht *m*

° 7263a **flame scaling**   zingage *m* au trempé   Immersionsverzinken   zincatura *f* per immer-
                                        n   sione

° 7264 **flame tube boiler**   chaudière *f* à tubes   Flammrohrkessel *m*   caldaia *f* a tubi di
                         de fumée   fiamma
− 7265 **flaming coal,**   charbon *m* flambant   Flammkohle *f*   carbone *m* a lunga
        bituminous coal   fiamma

flammable, s. *inflammable*

− 7266 **flamper**   minerai *m* de fer   Toneisenstein *m*   minerale *m* di ferro
                         argileux   argilloso

− 7267 **flang**   pic *m* à deux   Doppelkeilhaue *f*   piccone *m* a due
                      pointes   punte

° 7268 **to flange deeply**   emboutir   tiefziehen   imbutire

flange, s. *foot*

flange of fire tube, s. *beaded end of a fire tube*

^ 7269 **flange or flanged**   tuyau *m* à bride   Flanschenrohr *n*   tubo *m* a flangia
        pipe

° 7270 **flange sleeker**   casque *m*   Polierhaken *m*   lisciatoio *m* a S

° 7271 **flange steel**   acier *m* malléable,   Bördelstahlblech *n*   acciaio *m* malleabile
                   acier à refouler   Flussstahl *m*   (per bordature)

° 7272 **flanged plate**   tôle *f* à bord   Kümpelblech *n*,   lamiera *f* ad orlo
                   rabattu   umgebördeltes Blech   rovesciato

° 7273 **flanged profile**   profil *m* biseauté,   Abkantprofil *n*   profilo *m* smussato
                   profil *m* chanfreiné

° 7274 **flanged sections**   profils *m pl.*   Abkantprofile *n pl.*   profilati *m pl.* cian-
                   chanfreinés   frinati

° 7275 **flanging**   pliage *m* de bords,   Randbiegung *f*,   piegatura *f* dei bordi,
                 bordage *m*   Bördeln *n*   bordatura *f*
° 7276 **flanging test**   essai *m* de bordage   Bördelversuch *m*   prova *f* di bordatura

	English	French	German	Italian
^ 7277	**flank well**	puits *m* de flanc	Flankensonde *f*	pozzo *m* laterale
o 7278	**flannel disc**	disque *m* en flanelle	Flanellscheibe *f*	disco *m* di flanella o di panno
— 7279	**flap**	trappe *f*	Klappe *f*	botola *f*
— 7280	**flap**	courroie	Riemen *m*	cinghia *f*
o 7281	**flap valve**	clapet *m*	Klappenventil *n*	valvola *f* a cerniera
o 7282	**flapping**	rupture *f* de la couche de laitiers	Schlacken-schichtaufbrechen *n*	rottura *f* dello strato di scorie
— 7283	**flapping**	battement *m*	Schlagen *n*, Flattern *n*	sbattimento *m*, vibrazione *f*
— 7284	**flapping**	coup *m* de fouet	Schleudern *n* des Förderseils	oscillazione *f* della cinghia, vibrazione *f* della cinghia
— 7285	**to flare**	vaciller	unruhig flackern	vacillare, barcollare
— 7286	**flaser-gneiss**	flasergneiss *m*	Flasergneis *m*	flasergneiss *m*
o 7287	**to flash**	brûler	brennen	bruciare, lampeggiare
— 7288	**to flash**	abattre à l'explosif	niedersprengen	abbattere con esplosivo

to flash off, *s. to melt off*

	English	French	German	Italian
o 7289	**flash**	éclair *m*, feu *m*, éclat *m*	Blitz *m*, Feuer *n*	bagliore *m*, fuoco *m*, lampo *m*
o 7289a	**flash. fash**	plaque *f* d'écoulement	Auslaufplatte *f*	lamiera *f* d'effusione
o 7290	**flash**	bavure *f*	Grat *m*	bavatura *f*, bava *f*,
o 7290a	**flash, fin**	ailette *f* de soudure	Schweissrippe *f*	aletta *f* di saldatura
o 7291	**flash boiler, quick steaming boiler, flasher**	chaudière *f* (à vaporisation) rapide	Blitzkessel *m*, Schnellverdampfungs-kessel *m*	caldaia *f* (a vaporizza-zione) rapida

flash butt welding, *s. flash welding*

	English	French	German	Italian
o 7292	**flash casting**	coulée *f* en châssis	Kastenguss *m*	getto *m* in staffa
^ 7293	**flash drum**	chambre *f* de vaporisation	Verdampfungs-kammer *f*	camera *f* di vaporiz-zazione
o 7294	**flash gutter**	chenal *m* à barbe	Gratrinne *f*	canale *m* di sfogo bava-tura, cavità *f* di sfogo bavatura

English	French	German	Italian
flash hole, s. *flash gutter*			
° 7295 **flash-lift molding machine**	machine *f* à démouler	Abhebeformmaschine *f*	sformatrice *f*
° 7296 **flash mold**	moule *m* en châssis	Kastenform *f*	forma *f* in staffa
° 7297 **flash molding**	moulage *m* en châssis	Kastenformerei *f*	formatura *f* in staffa, staffatura *f*
° 7298 **flash pin**	goujon *m* de châssis	Formkastenstift *m*	pernio *m* per staffa
— 7299 **flash roaster**	four à grillage superficiel	Röstofen *m*	arrostitore *m* istantaneo
— 7300 **flash roasting**	grillage *m* superficiel	Blitzröstung *f*	arrostimento *m* superficiale
^ 7301 **flash tower**	tour *f* de détente	Entspannungsturm *m*	torre *f* d'attesa
° 7302 **flash setting**	prise éclair	abruptes Abbinden *n*	presa *f* rapida
° 7303 **flash welded**	soudé à l'arc	vorgeschweisst	saldato all'arco
° 7304 **flash welder**	soudeuse *f* «flashing»	Stumpfschweiss-maschine *f*	saldatrice *f* per scintillamento
° 7305 **flash welding**	soudure *f* flashing	Funkenschweissung *f*	saldatura *f* per scintillamento
flash welding without preheating, s. *straight flash welding*			
flasher, s. *flash boiler*			
° 7306 **flashing**	plaque *f* de protection	Abweisblech *n*	lastra *f* di protezione
° 7307 **flashing time**	temps d'étincellage	Funkenzeitpunkt *m*	tempo *m* di scintillio
° 7308 **flashless forging**	forgeage *m* sans barbe	Gratlosschmiedung *f*	fucinatura *f* senza bava
° 7309 **flashline**	témoin *m* d'ébarbure, ligne *f* d'ébarbure	Gratlinie *f*	linea *f* di bavatura (traccia di bavatura, testimonio di fucinatura)
° 7310 **flask, box, casting box**	châssis *m* de moulage	Formkasten *m*, Flaschen *m*, Laden *m*	staffa *f* per gettare in forma
° 7311 **flask band**	bande *f* de châssis de moulage	Formkastenband *n*	banda *f* della staffa

	English	French	German	Italian
	flask casting, *s. box casting*			
° 7312	flask for developing gas	flacon *m* à dégagement des gaz	Flasche *f* für Gasentwicklung	fiala *f* per lo sviluppo del gas, bottiglia *f* generatrice di gas
° 7313	flask molding machine	machine *f* à mouler	Formmaschine *f*	formatrice *f* per staffe
° 7314	flask stand	support *m* de ballon	Kolbenträger *m*	supporto *m* per storta
° 7315	flat	plat *m*	Flachstab *m*	piatto *m*
− 7316	flat	plate-forme *f*, basse, estuaire *m*	Plattform *f*, Fläche *f*, Untiefe *f*	piattaforma *f*, pianura *f*, estuario *m*
− 7317	flat back cut and fill method	exploitation *f* par tailles en échelon avec remblayage	Firstenbau *m* mit wagerechter Firste und Versatz	coltivazione *f* a gradino rovescio con ripiena
− 7318	flat-back method	exploitation *f* par tailles en échelon	Firstenbau *m* mit wagerechter Firste	coltivazione *f* a gradino rovescio
− 7319	flat-back overhand stope	taille *f* montante en échelon	Firstenstoss *m* mit wagerechter Firste	cantiere *m* a gradino rovescio in rimonta
− 7320	flat-back square-set stope	taille *f* montante en échelon à boisage parallélépipédique	Firstenstoss *m* mit waagerechter Firste und Rahmenzimmerung	cantiere *m* in rimonta a gradino rovescio con armatura a parallelepipedo
− 7321	flat back stope	taille *f* en échelon	Firstenstoss *m* mit waagerechter Firste	cantiere *m* a gradino rovescio a tagli orizzontali
° 7322	flat bar, flat iron, sheet-billet	larget *m*, brame *f*	Platine *f*	piatto *m*, largo-piatto *m*
° 7323	flat bar steel	acier *m* plat	Flachstahl *m*	acciaio *m* laminato piatto
^ 7324	flat bed			millepiedi *m*
° 7325	flat billet	large-plat *m*	Breiteisen *n*	ferro *m* piatto
	flat bloom, *s. thick slab*			
− 7326	flat bog	tourbière *f* de plaine	Flachlandmoor *n*	torbiera *f* di pianura
° 7327	flat bottom flask	ballon *m* à fond plat	Stehkolben *m*	storta *f* verticale, matraccio *m* a fondo piatto

	English	French	German	Italian
7328	**flat bottom rail, Vignoles rail**	rail *m* Vignole	Vignoleschiene *f*	rotaia *f* vignole
7329	**flat bulb iron**	fer *m* plat à boudin	Flachwulsteisen *n*	ferro *m* piatto a bordino
7330	**flat carved nail**	pointe *f* plate rayée	flacher gestreifter Stift *m*	punta *f* piana rigata
	flat countersunk head rivet, *s. flat top countersunk head rivet*			
7331	**flat curve**	courbe *f* surbaissée	flache Kurve *f*	curva *f* ribassata
7332	**flat drill**	foret *m* à langue d'aspic, mèche *f* plate	Spitzbohrer *m*	punta *f* da trapano
	flat faced fillet weld, *s. mitre filled weld*			
7333	**flat fish plate**	éclisse *f* plate	Flachlasche *f*	stecca *f* piatta, coprigiunto *m* piatto
7334	**flat foundry nail**	pointe *f* à tête plate pour mouleurs	flacher Formstift *m*	punta *f* a testa piana per fonderia
7335	**flat gate, slit gate**	attaque *f* plate	Gussrinne *f*	attacco *m* di colata a piatto, attacco a coltello
7336	**flat half-round, feather edged half-round**	demi-rond *m* plat, demi-rond irrégulier	Flach-Halbrundeisen *n*	barra *f* o ferro *m* mezzo tondo irregolare
7337	**flat head countersunk rivet**	rivet *m* à tête plate noyée	Senkniet *m*	chiodo *m* a testa svasata piana
	flat head machine screw, *s. countersunk head screw*			
7338	**flat head nail**	pointe *f* à tête plate	flacher Stift *m*	punta *f* a testa piana
7339	**flat hole**	trou *m* plat	Flachloch *n*	foro *m* piano
7340	**flat(-iron), flat bar, flats** *pl.*	fer *m* plat, plats *m* *pl.*, bandelette *f*, larget *m*	Flacheisen *n*, Platine *f*	ferro *m* piatto, ferro *m* universale
7341	**flat joint**	diaclase *f* horizontale	schwebende Spalte *f*	diaclasi *f* orizzontale, batroclasi *f*
7341a	**flat lead**	plomb *m* laminé	Walzblei *n*	piombo *m* laminato (o in foglie)
	flat position welding, *s. down-hand welding*			
7342	**flat rammer**	pilette *f*	Plattstampfer *m*	pestello *m*
7343	**flat rope**	cable *m* plat	Flachseil *n*	fune *f* piatta
7344	**flat seam**	couche *f* plate	flachfallendes Flöz *n*	strato *m* piatto

English	French	German	Italian
° 7345 **flat sheet(-metal)**	tôle f (plate)	Blech n	lamiera f, piastra f
— 7346 **flat wall**	mur m	Liegende n	muro m (di miniera)
° 7347 **flat wire**	fil m méplat	Flachdraht m	filo m di ferro piatto
flats, $s.$ *flat-iron*			
— 7348 **to flatten**	élargir	ausbreiten	allargare
° 7349 **flattened round bar**	fer m plat bombé	abgeflachtes Rundeisen n	ferro m tondo appiattito
° 7350 **flattened-strand**	câble m métallique à torons méplats	flachlitziges Drahtseil n	fune f metallica a trefoli piatti
flattener, $s.$ *(roller) leveller*			
— 7351 **flattening**	aplatissement m,	Abflachung f, Abplattung f	appiattimento m, spianatura f
° 7351a **flattening**	brunissage m, lissage m	Glätten n	appiattimento m
° 7352 **flattening machine**	planeuse f	Richtmaschine f	spianatrice f
° 7353 **flatter**	banc m à étirer les bandes	Bandziehmaschine f	trafila f per nastri
— 7354 **flatting**	roulage m de charbon par chevaux	Kohlenförderung f mit Pferden	trasporto m del carbone con cavalli
flatting, $s.$ *kinking*			
° 7355 **flatting mill**	aplatissoire m	Plättmaschine f, Plättwerk n	laminatoio m (per lamiere e nastri), laminatoio per ridurre grani di metallo fragile in polvere
— 7356 **flaxseed coal**	culm m, menu m	kleinstückiger Anthrazit m	minuto m, antracite f
— 7357 **flaxseed ore**	minerai m oolithique	oölithisches Erz n	minerale m oolitico
— 7358 **fleckschiefer**	schiste m tacheté	Fleckschiefer m	scisto m maculato
flaw, $s.$ *fault*			
— 7359 **flaw, crack**	fente f, crevasse f, fissure f	Riss m, Einriss m	fessura f, crepaccio m
° 7360 **flaw**	crique f, soufflure f, défaut m	Kaltschweisse f, Gussblase f, Fehler m	cricca f, fessura f, difetto m, soffiatura f
— 7361 **flaw fault**	faille f à rejet horizontal	Seitenverschiebung f	faglia f a rigetto orizzontale
° 7362 **flaw in the casting**	défaut m de coulée	Gussfehler m	difetto m di fusione (o di colata)

English	French	German	Italian

flaw in the material, s. *defect in the material*

flaw in welding, s. *welding defect*

7363	**flawy iron**	fer *m* paillieux, fer cendreux	unganzes Eisen *n*, abblätterndes Eisen *n*	ferro *m* sfaldato
7364	**fleet angle**	angle *m* de déviation de câble	Seilablenkungs- winkel *m*	angolo *m* di deviazione del cavo
7365	**flexair valve**	vanne à levier	Hebelventil *n*	valvola *f* a leva
7366	**flexible belt drop stamp**	mouton *m* à courroie	Wickelhammer *m*, Riemenfallhammer *m*	maglio *m* a cinghia, berta *f* a cinghia
7367	**flexible metal tube**	tube *m* métallique flexible	Metallschlauch *m*	tubo *m* flessibile metallico
7368	**flexible shaft**	arbre *m* flexible	biegsame Welle *f*	albero *m* flessibile
7369	**flexible tube nozzle**	ajutage *m* pour tuyau flexible	Anschluss *m* fuer flexiblen Schlauch	ugello *m* a tubo flessibile
7370	**flexible wire**	fil *m* souple	flexibler Draht *m*, Leitungsschnur *f*	filo *m* flessibile

flexural center, s. *shear center*

flexural rigidity, s. *bending stress*

flexural test, s. *bend test*

7371	**flexure**	pli *m* de couche, flexure *f*	Schichtfalte *f*, Flexur *f*	piega *f* di strato, flessura *f*
7372	**flexure**	flexion *f*	Durchbiegung *f*	flessione *f*
7373	**flight**	rampe *f*	Treppe *f*	rampa *f*, scalinata *f*
7374	**flight**	raclette *f*, racloir *m*	Kratzblech *n*	raschietto *m*. rastrel- lo *m*, paletta *f*
7375	**flight drag conveyor**	transporteur à raclettes	Kratzbandförderer *m*	trasportatore a rastrelli
7376	**flinkite**	flinkite *f*	Flinkit *m*	flinchite *f*
7377	**flint**	silex *m*, flint *m*, caillou *m*	Flintstein *m*, Kiesel *m*	silice *f*, flint *m*, ciottolo *m*, pietra *f*
7378	**flint clay**	argile *f* à silex. argile *f* flint	Kieselton, Flint-Ton *m*	argilla *f* flint

English	French	German	Italian
— 7379 **flint glass**	flint-glass, cristal d'Angleterre	Flintglas n	flint-glass, vetro m di silice
flint stone, $s.$ $flint$			
— 7380 **flinty**	caillouteux	kieselig, kieselartig	pietroso, vetroso
° 7381 **flinty fracture**	cassure f conchoïdale, fracture conchoïdale	muscheliger Bruch m	frattura f concoidale
— 7382 **flinty ground**	sol m siliceux	Kieselboden m	suolo m silicioso
— 7383 **flinty slate**	schiste m siliceux	Kieselschiefer m	scisto m silicioso
° 7384 **flitch plate**	plaque-éclisse f, plaque de renfort	Verstärkungslasche f. Decklatte f	placca f a stecca, corpigiunto
° 7384a **float**	auge f de sédimentation	Ablagerungsmulde f	trogolo m di sedimentazione
^ 7385 **float collar**	manchon m à soupape	Schwimmuffe f	manicotto m galleggiante
—7386 **float gold**	«couleur», or m flottant	ausgewaschenes Goldteilchen n, Flutgold n	«colore» m, polvere f d'oro finissima
^ 7387 **float indicator**	indicateur de niveau à flotteur	Schwimmerstandanzeiger m	indicatore m di livello a galleggiante
— 7387a **float mineral**	paillettes f $pl.$ flottantes	schwimmendes Erzpulver n	minerale polverizzato galleggiante
—7388 **float shoe**	sabot m à soupape	Schwimmschuh m	scarpa f per tubi con valvola
^ 7389 **float (viscosity) test**	essai m de flottage	Schwimmprobe f	prova f di galleggiamento
^ 7390 **floating head**	tête f flottante	Schwimmkopf m	testa f flottante
^ 7390a **floating plug (or mandrel)**	mandrin m flottant	Pendeldorn m	mandrino m galleggiante
° 7391 **floating reamer**	alésoir m flottant, finisseur m	Pendelreibahle, mit Halter	alesatoio m galleggiante
^ 7392 **floating roof (tank)**	(réservoir à) toit m flottant	Schwimmdach (Tank)	(serbatoio m a) tetto m galleggiante
^ 7393 **flocculation**	floculation f	Flockung f	floculazione f
° 7394 **to flog**	dessabler	entsanden, vorputzen	disterrare, sterrare
— 7395 **floky**	floconneux	flockig	fioccoso
— 7396 **flood-plain terrace**	terrace f fluviale	Inundationsterrasse f	terrazzo m fluviale
^ 7397 **flooded suction**	aspiration f immergée	Flüssigkeitsspiegel-stand über Saugstutzen	aspirazione f immersa

	English	French	German	Italian
— 7398	**flooding**	engouffrement *m*	Überschwemmung *f*	ingolfamento *m*
— 7399	**flooding**	inondation *f*	Überflutung *f*	allagamento *m*
— 7400	**flooding pattern**	patron *m* d'injection	Bohrlochanordnung *f* für Fluten	modello *m* d'iniezione
— 7401	**floor**	plancher *m*, plate-forme *f*	Fussboden *m*	pavimento *m*, piattaforma *f*
— 7402	**floor**	mur *m*	Sohle *f*	suola *f*, muro *m*, piede *m*
— 7403	**floor block**	moufle *m* de plancher	Kabelumlenkrolle *f* auf Arbeitsbühne	paranco *m* da piattaforma
— 7404	**floor level**	plaque intermédiaire d'entretoisement	Zwischenboden *m*	piastra *f* intermedia
— 7405	**floor limb**	flanc *m* inférieur d'un pli couché	liegender Schenkel *m* einer liegenden Falte	fianco *m* (o lembo *m*) inferiore d'una piega adagiata
	floor molding, *s. pit molding*			
ɔ 7406	**floor of foundry**	sol *m* de la fonderie	Flur *m* der Eisengiesserei	piano *m* della fonderia
ɔ 7407	**floor-plate**	tôle *f* pour couvertures de planchers	Fussbodenbelagblech *n*	lamiera *f* per pavimentazione
ɔ 7408	**floor·plates** *pl.*	tôles *f pl.* varangues	Liegerblech *n*	paglinoli *m pl.*
— 7409	**floor of seam**	mur *m* d'une couche	liegende Schicht *f*	muro *m* d'uno strato, suola *f* di un filone
ɔ 7410	**floor work**	moulage *m* à découvert	Formen *n* im Boden	formatura *f* allo scoperto
— 7411	**floored intrusive**	laccolithe *f*	Lakkolith *m*	laccolite *f*
— 7412	**floorman**	aide-sondeur *m*	Hilfsbohrer *m*	aiuto perforatore *m*
— 7413	**florencite**	florencite *f*	Florencit *m*	florencite *f*
ɔ 7414	**floss**	scorie *f* de puddlage	Puddelschlacke *f*	scoria *f* fusa galleggiante, scoria *f* di puddellaggio
ɔ 7415	**floss hole**	trou *m* de laitier	Schlackenauge *n*, Schlackenloch *n*	foro *m* delle scorie, scarico *m* delle scorie
ɔ 7415a	**flotation**	flottation *f*	Flotation *f*	flottazione *f*

	English	French	German	Italian
° 7416	**flotation cell**	cellule *f* de flottaison	Schwimmungszelle *f*	cella *f* di flottazione
— 7417	**flour**	farine *f*	Mehl *n*	farina *f*
— 7418	**flour gold**	or *m* flottant	Flutgold *n*	«colore» *m*
^ 7419	**to flow**	jaillir, érupter	frei fliessen, eruptiv ausfliessen	sgorgare
^ 7420	**to flow by heads. to head**	jaillir par intermittence	stossweise fliessen	sgorgare a intermittenza, fluttuare
	to flow out, *s. to leak*			
^ 7421	**flow bean, flow nipple**	pointeau *m* d'éruption	Ausbruchs- drosselhahn *m*	valvola *f* di regolazio- ne
— 7422	**flow-breccia**	texture *f* bréchoïde	brecciöse Textur *f*	struttura *f* brecciata
7422a	**flow chart**	organigramme *m*	Flussdiagramm *n*	organigramma *m*
— 7423	**flow cleavage**	schistosité *f* de pression	Druckschieferung *f*	scistosità *f* di pres- sione
° 7424	**flow gate**	orifice *m* ou trou de coulée	Einguss *m*	apertura *f* o foro di colata
^ 7425	**flow head**	tête *f* d'éruption	Ausbruchskopf *m*	testa *f* d'eruzione
7426	**flow diagram**	diagramme *m* de procédé	Fliessschema *n*	diagramma *m* (o sche- ma) di processo
° 7427	**flow limit**	limite *f* d'écoulement	Ziehgrenze *f*	limite *m* di stiramento
° 7428	**flow line**	conduite *f* d'écoulement	Abflussleitung *f*	canale *m* (o condotta *f*) di scolo
° 7429	**flow line**	bec *m* de déversement	Ausflussrohr *n*	becco *m* di scarico, li- nea *f* di scorrimento
° 7429a	**flow line**	ligne *f* de fluage	Fliesslinie *f*	linea *f* di flusso
° 7430	**flow lines**	fleurs *f pl.*	Eisblumen *f pl.*	fiori *m pl.*
	flow of fibers, *s. flow line*			
	flow of metal, *s. flow*			
° 7431	**flow of slag**	rigole *f* à laitier	Schlackentrift *f*	scarico *m* della scoria o della loppa
° 7432	**flow-off**	dégorgeoir *m*	Überlauf *m* an einer Form	sfogo *m*, sfioratore *m*, scarico *m*
° 7432a	**flow-off casting**	dégorgement *m* de la coulée	überfliessendes Giessen *n*	trabocco *m* della colata

English	French	German	Italian
° 7433 **flow-off gate**	canal *m* (ou rigole) d'écoulement	Abflussrinne *f*	canale *m* di scarico
° 7434 **flow plate, flow bean. choke**	tuyere	Düse *f*	ugello *m*
^ 7435 **flow spool**	bride *f* d'écoulement	Spülflansch *m*	flangia *f* di scorrimento
° 7435a **flow stress**	effort *m* de fluage	Schubspannung *f*	sforzo *m* di flusso
° 7436 **flow structure, fluxion-structure**	structure *f* fluidale (ou pour déformation plastique)	Fluidaltextur *f* Verschiebungs-struktur *f*	struttura *f* fluidale (o per deformazione plastica
^ 7437 **flow tank**	réservoir d'écoulement	Auffangtank *m*	serbatoio *m* di scolo (o di scorrimento)
^ 7438 **flow wings**	bras *m pl.* de distri-bution de la tête d'éruption		bracci *m pl.* d'eroga-zione «dell'albero di Natale»
° 7439 **flow through**	lavage *m* du moule	Durchgiessen *n* einer Form	lavaggio *m* della forma
° 7439a **flowability**	coulabilité *f*	Viergiessbarkeit *f*	colabilità *f*

flowability, *s. compactability*

flower wire, *s. piano wire*

English	French	German	Italian
— 7440 **flowing bottom hole pressure**	pression *f* de glisse-ment du lit	Fliess-Sohlendruck *m*	pressione *f* di scorri-mento del letto
^ 7441 **flowing by heads**	production *f* intermittente	intermittierende Produktion *f*	produzione *f* intermittente
° 7442 **flowing furnace**	fourneau *m* à fonte	Flossofen *m*, Blauofen *m*	forno *m* a riverbero per minerali di piombo
^ 7443 **flowing life**	durée *f* d'éruption	Dauer *f* des natürlichen Aus-flusses	durata *f* d'eruzione
^ 7444 **flowing well**	puits *m* jaillissant, sonde *f* éruptive	fliessende Sonde *f*, Eruptiersonde *f*	pozzo *m* ad eruzione spontanea
° 7445 **fluctuation of current**	fluctuation *f* de l'intensité du courant	Stromschwankung *f*	variazione *f* nella corrente
° 7446 **fluctuation of voltage**	fluctuation *f* de la tension	Spannungsschwan-kung *f*	variazione *f* nella tensione
^ 7447 **flowing pressure**	pression *f* d'écoulement	Förderdruck *m*	pressione *f* di scorri-mento
^ 7448 **flowing production**	production *f* jaillissante	laufende Produktion *f*	produzione *f* spontanea

	English	French	German	Italian
° 7449	**flue**	carneau *m*	Abzugskanal *m*, Zug *m*	condotto *m*, condotto del forno, canna *f* fumaria
° 7450	**flue boiler**	chaudière *f* à foyer intérieur	Flammrohrkessel *m*	caldaia *f* a focolare interno
° 7451	**flue boiler with cross tubes**	chaudière *f* à tube--foyer avec bouilleurs transversaux	Quersiedekessel *m*	caldaia *f* a focolare interno con bollitori trasversali
° 7452	**flue bridge**	autel *m* du rampant	Fuchsbrücke *f*	ponte *m* del canale
° 7453	**flue damper**	registre *m* ou soupape *f* de tirage	Zugabesperrklappe *f*	valvola *f* di regolazione del fumo
° 7453a	**flue dust**	escarbilles	Gichtstaub *m*	cenere *f* volatile
° 7454	**flue furnace**	foyer intérieur tubulaire	Flammrohr- feuerung *f*	focolare interno
	flue gas, *s. roasting gas*			
° 7455	**flue gas testing apparatus**	appareil *m* d'analyse des gaz brûlés	Rauchgasunter- suchungsapparat *m*	analizzatore *m* del gas bruciato
° 7456	**flue roof**	voûte *f* du rampant	Fuchsdecke *f*	volta *f* del canale
° 7457	**flue tube**	tube-foyer	Feuerrohr *n*, Flammrohr *n*	tubo-focolare
− 7458	**fluellite**	fluellite *f*	Fluellit *m*	fluellite *f*
° 7459	**fluid**	fluide	leichtflüssig	fluido
° 7460	**fluid-bed furnace**	four *m* à lit facilement fusible	Ofen *m* mit leichtflüssigem Bett	forno a letto fluido
° 7461	**fluid-compressed**	comprimé à l'état fluide	flussiggepresst	compresso allo stato fluido
^ 7462	**fluid coupling**	transmission *f* hydraulique	Flüssigkeits- kupplung *f*	trasmissione *f* idraulica
° 7462a	**fluid deformation**	déformation *f* par fluage	fliessende Verzer- rung *f*	deformazione *f* fluida
^ 7463	**fluid level**	niveau *m* de liquide	Flüssigkeitsspiegel *m*	livello *m* del liquido
° 7464	**fluid metal, cast-iron**	fer *m* en lingot, fer fondu	Blockeisen *n*, Flussmetall *n*	ferro *m* in lingotti, metallo *m* omogeneo
^ 7465	**fluid packed pump**	pompe *f* à garniture liquide	Teleskoppumpe *f*	pompa *f* a guarnizione liquida
° 7466	**fluid pressure**	pression *f* du liquide	Flüssigkeitsdruck *m*	compressione *f* del liquido

English	French	German	Italian
7467 **fluid steel, ingot steel**	acier *m* fondu	Flussstahl *m*	acciaio *m* fuso
7468 **fluid structure, flow-structure**	texture *f* fluidale	fluidale Textur *f*, Fluktationsstruktur *f*	struttura *f* fluidale
fluidity, *s. castability*			
7469 **fluidity**	fluidité *f*	Dünnflüssigkeit *f*	fluidità *f*
7470 **fluidity test piece**	éprouvette *f* de coulabilité	Probe *f* für das Fliessvermögen	provetta *f* di colabili- tà
7470a **fluidizer**	fondant *m*	Flussmittel *n*	fondente *m*
7471 **fluke**	curette *f*	Bohrlöffel *m*	raschietto *m*, rastrello *m*
7472 **flume, channel**	rigole *f*	Abflusskanal *m*	canale *m* di scarico
7473 **flumping well**	puits *m* en phase de pompage		pozzo *m* in fase di pompaggio
7474 **fluocerite**	fluocérine *f*	Fluocerit·*m*	fluocerina *f*, fluocerite *f*
fluor, *s. fluorite*			
7475 **fluor-spar, fluor**	fluorine *f*, chaux *f* fluatée	Flussspat *m*, Kalziumfluorid *n*	spatofluoro, fluorina *f*, fluorite *f*
7476 **fluoroscopic examination**	examen *m* fluoroscopique	fluoroskopische Prüfung *f*	esame *m* radioscopico
7477 **fluorine**	fluorine *f*	Flussspat *m*	fluorite *f*
7478 **to flush**	procéder au remplissage hydraulique	mit Spülversatz *m* versetzen	eseguire la ripiena idraulica
7479 **to flush**	débourber	schlämmen	spurgare, lavare (minerali)
7480 **flush**	affleuré	eben, flach	affiorante
7481 **flush**	lavage *m*	Ausspülung *f*	lavaggio
7482 **flush bolt**	verrou d'arête	Kantenriegel *m*	paletto incassato
7483 **flush drilling**	forage *m* avec circulation	Spülbohren *n*	sondaggio *m* a circola- zione
7484 **flush-joint casing**	tube fileté à mi-épaisseur	Rohr mit glatter Verbindung	tubo *m* di rivestimento a «flush-joint»
7485 **flush production**	production *f* éruptive	Ausbruchsproduktion *f*	produzione *f* eruttiva

English	French	German	Italian

flush with the ground, *s. even with the ground*

— 7486 **flushing** — lavage *m* d'or — Goldwaschen *n* — lavaggio *m* dell'oro

— 7487 **flushing** — remblayage *m* hydraulique — Spülversatz *m* — colmata *f* (o ripiena *f*) idraulica

° 7488 **flushing** — décrassage *m* — Entschlackung *f* — rimozione *f* delle scorie di alto forno

flushing and upset travel, *s. preheating*

— 7489 **flushing auger** — tarière à rincer — Spülschappe *f* — trivella *f* aspirante

— 7490 **flushing dredger** — drague *f* aspirante — Saugbagger *m* — draga *f* ad azione aspirante

^ 7491 **flushing oil** — huile *f* de lavage — Ausspülungsöl *n* — olio *m* di lavaggio

— 7492 **flushing shaft** — puits *m* de remblayage — Ausfüllungsschacht *m* — pozzo *m* di colmata

° 7493 **flute** — outil à rainurer — Falzbeitel *m* — scanalatore *m*

° 7493a **flute, fluting** — rupture *f* par flexion — Biegebruch *m* — rottura *f* per flessione

° 7494 **fluted bar** — fer *m* à face concave — Hohlkanteisen *n* — ferro *m* a lati concavi

° 7494a **fluted tube** — tuyau *m* cannelé — kanneliertes Rohr *n* — tubo *m* scanalato

— 7495 **fluviatile facies** — faciès fluviatile — fluviatile Fazies *f* — «facies» fluviale

° 7496 **to flux** — traiter au fondant — bearbeiten mit Flussmitteln — trattare con fondente

° 7497 **flux** — fondant *m* — Flussmittel *n* — fondente *m*

° 7498 **flux-covering** — flux *m* — Flussmittel *n* — fondente *m*

° 7499 **flux (for soldering)** — fondant *m* (pour soudure) — Lotaufbringemittel *n*, Lötflussmittel *n* — fondente *m* (per saldatura)

° 7499a **flux additive bin** — soute *f* pour additions — Zusatzbunker *m* — serbatoio *m* per addizioni

° 7500 **flux medium, fluxing medium** — fondant *m* — Flussmittel *n* — fondente *m*

° 7501 **fluxing, flux-covering** — addition *f* de fondant — Zuschlag *m* — addizione *f* di fondente

° 7502 **fluxing agent** — fondant *m* — Flussmittel *n*, Zuschlag *m* — fondente *m*

° 7503 **fluxing ore** — minerai *m* fondant — Zuschlagerz *n* — minerale *m* fondente

° 7504 **fluxing power** — pouvoir *m* scorifiant — Verschlackungsfähigkeit *f* — potere *m* scorificante

English	French	German	Italian
7505 **fly-ash, brown coal ash binder**	cendre *f* volante	Flugasche *f*	cenere *f* volatile (o impalpabile)
fly ash, *s. ash inclusion*			
7506 **fly cutter arbor**	arbre *m* porte-outil	Stahlhalter-Aufspanndorn *m*	albero *m* porta-utensile
7507 **flying shears**	cisailles *f pl.* à porte-à-faux	Mitlauf-Schopf-schere *f*	apparecchio *m* per tagliare billette e barre in movimento, cesoie volanti
7508 **flynut**	papillon *m*, écrou *m*	Flügelmutter *f*	dado *m* a farfalle (o ad alette), galletto *m*
7509 **flysch**	flysch *m*	Flysch *m*	flysch *m*
7510 **foam condition**	condition *f* de mousse	schaumförmiger Zustand *m*	condizione *f* spumosa
7511 **foamed aluminium**	écume *f* d'aluminium	Aluminiumschaum *m*	alluminio *m* piuma, schiuma *f* di alluminio
7512 **foamed slag**	laitier *m* mousseux	schaumige Schlacke *f*	scoria *f* spumosa
7513 **foaming agent**	produit moussant	Schäumer *m*	prodotto *m* schiumogeno
7514 **focal length**	distance *f* focale	Brennweite *f*	distanza *f* focale
7515 **to focus**	mettre au point	einstellen	mettere a fuoco
7516 **focus**	foyer *m*	Brennpunkt *m*	fuoco *m*, punto *m* focale
7517 **focussing**	mise *f* au point	Einstellung *f*	messa *f* a fuoco
7518 **foids**	feldspathoïdes *m pl.*	Feldspatvertreter *m*	feldspatoidi *m pl.*
7519 **foil, sheet**	feuille *f*, tôle *f*	Blatt *n*, Folie *f*	lamiera *f*, foglio
7520 **fold**	pli *m*	Falte *f*	piega *f*
fold, *s. lap or overlap*			
7521 **fold carpet**	pli-nappe *m*	Deckfalte *f*	piega *f*, falda, falde *f pl.*
7522 **fold-fault**	pli-faille *m*	Bruchfalte *f*	piega-faglia *f*
7523 **folded**	plié	gefalzt, umgebogen	piegato
7524 **folded region**	région *f* plissée	Faltenland *n*	regione *f* ripiegata
folder, *s. folding stick*			
7525 **folding, plication**	plissement *m*	Faltung *f*	piegamento *m*, piega *f*
folding doors, *s. accordion doors*			
7525a **folding test**	essai *m* de pliage	Faltprobe *f*	prova *f* di piegamento

	English	French	German	Italian
° 7526	folia, leaf	feuille *f*, lame *f*	Blatt *n*, Blättchen *n*	foglio *m*, lamina *f*
— 7527	folia	veinule *f*	Äderchen *n*	piccola vena *f*
— 7528	to foliate	se diviser en lamelles *f pl.*	blättern	laminarsi, sfaldarsi
— 7528a	foliated	laminé	lamelliert	laminato
° 7529	foliated, lamellar	feuilleté	blätterig, lamellar	lamellare
— 7530	foliated coal, slaty coal, flaky coal	houille *f* feuilletée	Schieferkohle *f*, Blätterkohle *f*, Schichtenkohle *f*	carbone *m* schistoso, carbone d'ardesia

foliated crystalline rocks, *s. metamorphic rocks*

	English	French	German	Italian
— 7531	foliation	foliation *f*	Schieferung *f*	fogliazione *f*
— 7532	foliation cleavage	schistosité *f*	Schieferung *f*	scistosità *f*
— 7533	foliation structure	structure *f* feuilletée	schieferige Textur *f*	struttura *f* scistosa
— 7534	foliation tellurium	nagyagite *f*	Nagyagit *m*, Blättererz *n*	nagyagite *f*
° 7534a	follow board	plaque *f* porte-modèle	Modellträgerplatte *f*	placca *f* porta-modello
^ 7535	follower, cement retainer	presse-étoupe *m* de cémentation	Zementierkopf *m*	premistoppa *m*
— 7536	following-up system	exploitation *f* en chassant	Vorbau *m*	coltivazione *f* in direzione
—7536a	fool's bold	pyrite *f* de fer	Eisenkies *m*	pirite *f* di ferro
° 7538	foot, base	patin *m*	Fuss *m*, Schienenfuss *m*	base *f*, piede *m*, suola *f* (della rotaia)
° 7539	foot bellows	soufflerie *f* à pédale	Tretgebläse *n*	soffietto *m* a pedale
— 7540	foot block	semelle *f* de boisage	Grundschwelle *f*	cuneo *m* di sostegno
— 7541	foot hole	mine *f* de relevage	Sohlenschussbohrloch *n*	mina *f* di rilevaggio
^ 7542	foot oil, residual oil	pétrole *m* résiduel	Restöl *n*	olio *m* residuo
° 7543	foot-lathe, treadle-lathe	tour *m* à pédale	Fussdrehbank *f*	tornio *m* a pedale
° 7544	foot of rail	patin *m* du rail	Schienenfuss *m*	suola *f* della rotoia

foot-piece, *s. foot-block*

English	French	German	Italian

foot-plate, *s. floor-plate*

7545 **foot product**	résidu *m*	Rückstand *m*	residuo *m* di fondo
7546 **foot roller, guide roller**	galet *m* conducteur	Fussrolle *f*	rotella *f* di base
7547 **foot wall**	mur *m*, sol *m*	Liegende *n*, Sohle *f*	letto *m* (di giacimento), muro *m*, fondo *m*
7548 **foot wall**	lèvre *f* inférieure	tieferer Flügel *m*	bordo *m* inferiore (di una faglia)
7549 **foot wall drift**	galerie *f* au mur	Strecke *f* am Liegenden	galleria *f* sul fondo
7550 **footage**	avancement *m* du forage au mètre	Bohrstrecke *f*	avanzamento *m* della perforazione a metri
7551 **footage per round**	avancement *m* par cycle de travail	Abschlaglänge *f*	avanzamento *m* per ciclo di lavoro
7552 **foraminifera**	foraminifères *m pl*	Foraminifera *m pl.*	foraminiferi *m pl.*
7553 **forbesite**	forbésite *f*	Forbesit *m*	forbesite *f*

force-off time, *s. pressure-off time*

7554 **forced draft, forced draught**	tirage *m* forcé	künstlicher Zug *m*	tiraggio *m* forzato
7555 **forced draught furnace**	foyer *m* à soufflage sous grille	Unterwindfeuerung *f*	focolare *m* a tiraggio forzato
7556 **forced-draught furnace with air injection through hollow grate bars**	foyer *m* à injection d'air à travers les barreaux creux	Unterwindfeuerung *f* mit Luftzuführung durch Hohlroststäbe	focolare *m* con inizione d'aria dall'interno dei barrotti cavi
7557 **forced pump**	pompe *f* foulante	Presspumpe *f*	pompa *f* premente
7558 **forceps**	pincette *f*	Federzange *f*	pinze *f* pl.
7559 **fore hearth**	chaufferie *f*, sole *f* à réchauffer	Vorglühherd *m*	camera *f* di raffreddamento, avancrogiuolo *m*
7560 **fore plate**	plaque *f* d'avant	Vorderplatte *f*	placca *f* o piastra *f* anteriore
7561 **fore plate**	plaque *f* de latéral, paroi *f* de latéral	Arbeitszacken *m*, Brustzacken *m*, Vorderzacken *m*	placca *f* laterale di lavoro

English	French	German	Italian
— 7562 forebreast	front *m* de taille	Arbeitsort *m*	fronte *m* di taglio
° 7563 forehand welding	soudure *f* à gaz à gauche	Linksautogen-schweissung *f*	saldatura *f* a gas in avanti
— 7564 forehead	front *m* d'une galerie	Streckenort *m*	fronte *m* di taglio, fronte *m* di galleria
° 7565 forehearth	avant-creuset *m*	Vorherd *m*	avancrogiolo *m*
° 7566 foreign body	corps *m* étranger	Fremdkörper *m*	corpo *m* estraneo
foreign inclusion, *s. xenolith*			
7567 foreman	surveillant *m*	Aufseher *m*	sorvegliante *m*
— 7568 foreshaft	avant-puits *m*	Vorschacht *m*	avanpozzo *m*
— 7569 forewinning	exploitation *f* des chambres, traçage	Kammerbau *m*, Vorrichtungsarbeiten	coltivazione *f* delle camere
° 7570 to forge	forger	schmieden	fucinare, forgiare
° 7571 to forge, to hammer	étirer (sous le marteau)	ausschmieden	stirare al maglio, fucinare al maglio
° 7572 to forge cold	forger à froid	kaltschmieden	fucinare a freddo
° 7573 to forge hot	forger à chaud	warmschmieden	fucinare (o forgiare) a caldo
° 7574 to forge out	étirer sous le marteau	ausschmieden	stirare al maglio
° 7575 forge, smithy, smithery	forge *f*, atelier *m* de forgeron	Schmiede *f*, Schmiedewerkstatt *f*	fucina *f*
° 7576 forge coal	charbon *m* de forge	Schmiedekohle *f*	crabone *m* da fucina
° 7577 forge coal coke	coke *m* de charbon de forge	Esskohlenkoks *m*	coke *m* di carbone di fucina
° 7578 forge iron	fer *m* forgeable	Schmiedeeisen *n*	ferro *m* fucinabile
° 7578a forge-pig, white cast-iron	fonte *f* d'affinage	Puddelroheisen *n*	ghisa *f* bianca (o d'affinazione)
° 7579 forge pig iron, pig iron for puddling	fonte *f* de puddlage fonte *f* d'affinage	Puddelroheisen *n*	ghisa *f* da pudellaggio, ghisa *f* bianca
° 7579a forge scale	mâchefer *m*	Hammerschlag *m*	scaglia *f* di fucinazione
° 7580 forge steel	acier *m* puddlé	Schmiedestahl *m*	acciaio *m* fucinato
° 7581 forge strain	sollicitation *f* de forgeage	Schmiedenbean-spruchung *f*	sollecitazione *f* di forgiatura

English	French	German	Italian
7582 **forge welding, fire welding**	soudure *f* à chaud suant	Schweissen *n*, Hammerschweissen *n*	saldatura *f* per bolli-tura
7583 **forge work**	forgeage *m*, pièce *f* de forge	Schmieden *n*, Schmiedestück *n*	forgiatura *f*, pezzo *m* fucinato
7584 **forgeability**	forgeabilité *f*	Schmiedbarkeit *f*	fucinabilità *f*
forgeable, *s. ductile*			
7585 **forgeable iron**	fer *m* forgeable	Schmiedeeisen *n*	ferro *m* fucinabile
forged iron, *s. wrought-iron*			
7586 **forged piece**	pièce *f* forgée	Schmiedestück *n*	pezzo *m* fucinato, forgiato *m*, fucinato *m*
7587 **forged steel, wrought steel**	acier *m* forgé	Schmiedestahl *m*	acciaio *m* forgiato, acciaio *m* fucinato
forgeman, *s. forger*			
7588 **forger, forgeman**	forgeur *m*, forgeron *m*	Schmied *m*, Hammerschmied *m*	fucinatore *m*
forger, *s. forging machine*			
7589 **forging**	pièce *f* de forge, pièce *f* forgée	Schmiedestück *n*	pezzo *m* fucinato (o forgiato)
7590 **forging**	forgeage *m*	Schmieden *n*, Schmiedung *f*	fucinatura *f*, forgia-tura *f*
7591 **forging and rolling machine**	machine *f* à forger et laminer	Schmiede-u. Walzemaschine *f*	macchina *f* per la fucinatura e la lami-nazione
7592 **forging billet**	billette *f* pour forge	Schmiedeknüppel *m*	bicchiere *m*, sbozza-to *m* tubolare (o cavo)
7592a **forging brass**	laiton *m* à forger	Schmiedemessing *n*	ottone *m* da fucinare
7593 **forging hammer**	marteau *m* à forger	Schmiedehammer *m*	maglio *m* (da forgia)
forging heat, *s. forging temperature*			
7594 **forging induction heater**	four *m* à induction à forger	Induktionsofen *m*, Induktionsschmiede-ofen *m*	forno *m* o apparecchio a induzione per fuci-natura
7595 **forging machine, forging press**	presse *f* à forger, machine *f* à refouler	Schmiedepresse *f* Stauchmaschine *f*	fucinatrice *f*, pressa per fucinare. pressa *f* per stampaggio a caldo
7595a **forging range**	température *f* idéale de forgeage	ideale Schmiede-temperatur *f*	temperatura *f* ideale per fucinare

English	French	German	Italian
° 7596 **forging rolls, reduce roll**	machine *f* à forger à rouleaux	Walzschmiede-maschine *f*	fucinatrice *f* a rulli, sbozzatrice a rulli
° 7597 **forging scale**	déchets *m pl.* de forge, scorie *f* de forge	Glühspan *m*, Schmiedeabfälle *m pl.*, Hammerschlag *m*	sfridi *m pl.* di fucinatura, scoria *f* di forgia
° 7597a **forging strain**	effort *m* de forgeage	Schmiedespannung *f*	sforzo *m* di fucinatura
° 7598 **forging temperature**	température *f* de forgeage	Schmiedetemperatur *f*	temperatura *f* di forgiatura
° 7599 **forging test**	essai *m* de forgeage, essai *m* au forgeage	Schmiedeprobe *f*	prova *f* di fucinatura
° 7599a **forging tongs**	pince *f* à marteler	Schmiedezange *f*	tenaglie *f pl.* di fucinatura
° 7600 **forgings**	fers *m pl.* forgés	Schmiedeisen *n pl.*	fucinati *m pl.*
° 7601 **fork**	fourche *f* de retenue	Abfanggabel *f*	forcella *f* d'arresto
° 7602 **fork**	fourche *f*	Mitnehmer *m*	forca *f*, forchetta *f*
— 7603 **fork**	bifurcation *f*	Zweigung *f*	biforcazione *f*
— 7604 **fork lift**	élevateur *m* à mâchoires	Gabelheber *m*	elevatore *m* a ganasce
° 7605 **to form, to profile**	façonner, profiler	faconnieren, formen, profilieren	sagomare, profilare

form for block making, *s. mould for block making*

English	French	German	Italian
° 7606 **form oil**	huile *f* à moules	Giessformöl *n*	olio *m* da fonderia
— 7607 **formation**	formation *f*, groupe	Schichtenbildung *f*, Formation *f*	formazione *f*, gruppo
— 7608 **formation factor**	facteur *f* de formation	Formationsfaktor *n*	fattore *m* di formazione
° 7609 **formation of evolution of carbon monoxide**	dégagement *m* de l'oxyde de carbone	Kohlenoxydent-wicklung	formazione *f* dell'ossido di carbonio
° 7610 **formation of cracks**	formation *f* de criques	Rissbildung *f*	formazione *f* di incrinature
° 7611 **formation of heating cracks**	fissuration *f* due au traitement thermique	Warmrissbildung *f*	formazione *f* delle incrinature a caldo
°. 7612 **formation of hydrogen**	dégagement *m* d'hydrogène	Wasserstoffbildung *f*	sviluppo *m* d'idrogeno, formazione *f* d'idrogeno

formation of pipes, *s. funnel formation*

English	French	German	Italian
^ 7613 **formation packer**	packer *m* pour trou découvert	Packer-Formation *f*	packer *m* per foro scoperto

English	French	German	Italian
7614 formation tester	essayeur *m* de formations	Formationsprüfer *m*	apparecchio *m* di prova per formazioni
7614a formation voltage	tension *f* de formation	Formierungsspannung *f*	tensione *f* di formazione
7615 formed, shaped,	façonné, profilé	geformt, profiliert, ausgespart	sagomato, profilato
7616 formed cutter	fraise *f* profilée	Profilfraeser *m*	fresa *f* sagomata
7617 forming, shaping	moulage *m*	Formung *f*	formatura *f*, piegatura
7617a forming die	estampe *f* d'emboutissage	Prägestempel *m*	stampo *m* per imbutitura
forming lathe, *s. copying lathe*			
7618 forming cutter	fraise *f* profilée	Formfräser *m*	fresa *f* a profilo, fresa sagomata
7619 forming power	effort *m* de déformation	Verformungskraft *f*	effetto *m* di deformazione
7620 forming puddle balls, balling	former les loupes	Luppenmachen *n*	formare le palle, formazione di groppi (o masselli)
7621 fornacite	fornacite *f*	Fornacit *m*	fornacite *f*
7622 forsterite	forstérite *f*	Forsterit *m*	forsterite *f*
7623 fortification agate	agate *f* à fortification	Festungsachat *m*	agata *f* perigonica
7624 fortunite	fortunite *f*	Fortunit *m*	fortunite *f*
7625 forward combustion	combustion en avance	mitläufige Teilverbrennung *f*	combustione *f* in avanti
7626 forward welding	soudage *m* en avance	Linksschweissung *f*	saldatura *f* a gas in avanti
7627 to fossick	marauder	die Pfeiler abbauen von einem aufgelassenen Bau	estrarre pilastri di una miniera abbandonata
7628 fossicking	maraudage *m*	Pfeilergewinnung *f* von einem aufgelassenen Bau	ritiro *m* dei pilastri da una miniera abbandonata
7629 fossil, petrification	fossile, pétrification *f*	Fossil *n*, Versteinerung *f*	fossile, petrificazione *f*
7630 fossil charcoal, mineral coal	charbon *m* fossile, charbon *m* minéral	Steinkohle *f*	carbone *m* fossile, carbone *m* minerale
7631 fossil fuel	combustible *m* fossile	fossiler Brennstoff *m*	combustibile *m* fossile

	English	French	German	Italian
— 7632	**fossiliferous**	fossilifère	fossilführend	fossilifero
	fossilism, s. fossilization			
— 7633	**fossilization, petrifaction**	fossilisation f, pétrification f	Fossilisation f, Versteinerung f	fossilizzazione f, pietrificazione f
— 7634	**to fossilize**	fossiliser, pétrifier	fossilisieren, versteinern	fossilizzare, pietrificare, mineralizzare
	fouling, s. scale or incrustation			
° 7635	**to found**	fondre	giessen	fondere
7636	**to found**	fonder	gründen	fondare
— 7637	**foundation**	fondation f	Grundmauer f, Unterbau m	fondazione f, fondamenta f
	foundation plate, s. base-plate			
7638	**founder**	fondateur m	Gründer m	fondatore m
— 7639	**founder**	éboulement m	Einsturz m	franamento, frana f, crollo m
° 7640	**founder**	fondeur m	Giessereibesitzer m, Giessereileiter m, Giesser m	fonditore m
° 7641	**founder's flange**	lissoir m de soudeur	Schweisserspatel m	spatola f da fonditore
° 7642	**founder's sand,**	sable m de fonderie	Formsand m, Modellsand m	sabbia f da formare, terra f da fonderia
° 7643	**founding, casting**	fonte f, moulage m, coulée f, pièce f de fonte	Giessen n, Guss m, Abguss m, Gussstück n	fusione f, fonditura f, colata f, pezzo m colato, pezzo m fuso
° 7644	**founding furnace**	four m de fusion	Giessofen m	forno m di fusione
° 7645	**founding metal**	métal m de coulée	Gussmetall n	metallo m di colata (o di fusione)
° 7646	**founding of rollers**	fonte f de rouleaux	Walzenguss m	fusione f di rulli
° 7647	**foundry**	fonderie f	Giesserei f	fonderia f
° 7648	**foundry air furnace**	four m à réverbère de fonderie	Giessereiflammofen m	forno m a riverbero da fondere

English	French	German	Italian
7649 foundry blacking	noir *m* de fonderie	Kohlenstaub *m*	nero *m* per fonderia
7650 foundry bucket	poche *f* de coulée	Giesspfanne *f*	siviera *f* di colata
7651 foundry car	chariot *m* de pont de coulée	Giesslaufkatze *f*	carro *m* da fonderia o da colata
7652 foundry casting work	coulée *f*, fusion *f*	Guss *m*	colata *f*, fusione *f*
7653 foundry coke	coke *m* de fonderie	Giessereikoks *m*	coke *m* da fonderia
7654 foundry crane	grue *f* de coulée	Giesskran *m*	gru *f* per fonderia o da colata
7655 foundry crane with automatic tipping device	grue *f* de coulée à (dispositif de) bascule ou renversement automatique	Giessereikran *m* mit selbsttätiger Kippvorrichtung	gru *f* da fonderia con dispositivo di scarico automatico
7656 foundry cupola	cubilot *m* de fonderie	Giessereikuppelofen *m*	cubilotto *m* per ghisa
7657 foundry flask	châssis *m* de fonderie (ou de moulage)	Giesskasten *m*, Formkasten *m*	staffa *f*
7658 foundry furnace, melting furnace	four *m* de fonderie	Giessereiofen *m*	forno *m* da fonderia
foundry hand, *s. founder*			
7659 foundry house	halle *f* de fonderie	Giesshalle *f*	reparto *m* fusioni
foundry iron, *s. grey pig*			
7660 foundry ladle, charging ladle	poche *f* (ou creuset) à couler	Gabelpfanne *f*, Wagentiegel *m*	siviera *f* (o caldàia *f* o secchione) di colata
7661 foundry manager	directeur *m* de fonderie	Giessereileiter *m*	direttore *m* di fonderia
7662 foundry molding machine	machine *f* à mouler pour fonderie	Giessereiformmaschine *f*	formatrice *f* per fonderia
7663 foundry of malleable cast-iron	fonderie *f* de fonte malléable	Tempergussgiesserei	fonderia *f* di ghisa malleabile
7664 foundry pattern	modèle *m* de fonderie	Gussmodell *n*	modello *m* di fonderia
7665 foundry-pig (iron)	fonte *f* de moulage	Giessereiroheisen *n*	ghisa *f* per fusioni
foundry pig, *s. foundry iron or grey pig*			

	English	French	German	Italian
° 7666	foundry pig iron for acid proof casting	fonte f de moulage pour pièces résistantes aux acides	Roheisen n für säurebeständigen Guss	ghisa f per fondere pezzi resistenti agli acidi
° 7667	foundry pig iron for fire proof castings	fonte f de moulage pour pièces résistantes au feu	Roheisen n für feuerbeständigen Guss	ghisa f per fondere pezzi resistenti al fuoco
° 7668	foundry pit, casting pit	fosse f de coulée	Dammgrube f	fossa f di colata
° 7669	foundry reverberatory furnace	four m à réverbère de fonderie	Giesserei-flammofen m	forno m a riverbero
° 7670	foundry run	coulée f de fonderie	Abstich m	colata f di fonderia
	foundry sand, $s.moulding\ sand$			
° 7671	foundry sand testing instruments	appareillage m pour l'essai des sables de fonderie	Geräte $f\ pl.$ zur Prüfung von Giessereisand m	apparecchi per prove terre e sabbia di fonderia
° 7672	foundry slewing crane	grue f de fonderie pivotante	Laufkran m	gru f da fonderia girevole
° 7673	foundry tools	outillage m de fondeurs	Geräte $n\ pl.$ für Eisengiesser	utensili $m\ pl.$ per fonderie
° 7674	foundry traveller	pont m roulant de fonderie	Giessportalkran m	gru f a ponte per fonderia
° 7675	foundryology	technique f de fonderie	Giessereiwesen n	tecnica f di fonderia
— 7675a	fountain	chenal m de coulée	Förderrinne f	colatoio m
^ 7676	fountain	puits m tubulaire américain	Rohrbrunnen m	pozzo m tubolare
° 7677	four cycle engine	machine f à quatre temps	Viertaktmaschine f	macchina f a quattro tempi
— 7678	four-cycle stick set	cadre m complet	Viergespann n	quadro completo
° 7679	four-high mill	laminoir m à quatre cylindres verticaux	Walzwerk n mit vier stehenden Walzen	laminatoio m a quattro cilindri verticali
^ 7680	four-part flask	bride f double	Doppelbügel m	staffa f a due staffe
° 7681	four-stand tandem mill	laminoir m continu à quatre cages en tandem	kontinuierliches Walzwerk m mit vier Tandem-Walzgerüsten	laminatoio continuo a quattro gabbie in tandem
— 7682	four-way bit	trépan m à quatre ailettes	Vierflügelbohrer m	trapano m (o scalpello) a quattro taglienti

English	French	German	Italian
7683 four wings bit	burin *m* à quatre ailettes	Vierschneidmeissel *m*	scalpello *m* a quattro lame
7684 fourble	jeu *m* de quatre	Viererzug *m*	serie *f* di quattro aste
7685 foyer	creuset *m* d'attente	Wartetiegel *m*	crogiuolo *m* di attesa
7686 fraction	fraction *f*	Absatz *m*, Unterbrechung *f*	frazione *f*
7687 fractional distillation	distillation *f* fractionnée	fraktionierte Destillation *f*	distillazione *f* frazionata
7688 fractional distillation flask	ballon *m* à fractionner	Fraktionskolben *m*	matraccio *m* per distillazione frazionata
7689 fractional distillation tube	tube *m* à fractionner	Fraktionsröhre *f*	tubo *m* per distillazione frazionata
7690 fractional magma	magma *m* fractionnel	Teilmagma *n*	magma *m* frazionato
7691 fractionating tower	tour *f* de fractionnement	Fraktionierturm *m*	torre *f* di frazionamento, colonna di distillazione
7692 fractionation	fractionnement *m*	Fraktionierung *f*	frazionamento *m*

fractionator, *s. fractionating tower*

English	French	German	Italian
7693 fracture	cassure *f*, fracture *f*	Bruch *m*	frattura *f*, rottura *f*
7694 fracture, fracture grain	grain *m* de cassure	Bruchgefüge *n*	grano *m* di frattura
7695 fracture, surface of fracture	surface *f* de la cassure, section *f* de rupture	Bruchfläche *f*	superficie *f* di rottura
7696 fracture by contre-coup	fracture *f* par contre-coup	Bruch *m* durch Gegenschlag	frattura *f* per contraccolpo
7697 fracture line	ligne *f* de fracture	Bruchlinie *f*	linea *f* di frattura
7698 fracture of chain	rupture *f* de chaîne	Kettenbruch *m*	rottura *f* della catena
7699 fracture on deformation	cassure *f* ductile	Verformungsbruch *m*	rottura *f* per deformazione
7700 fracture of roll	rupture *f* de cylindre	Walzenbruch *m*	rottura *f* del cilindro
7701 fracture plane	plan *m* de rupture	Bruchfläche *f*	piano *m* di frattura
7701a fracture stress	effort *m* de cassure	Bruchspannung *f*	sforzo *m* di frattura
7702 fracture zone	zone *f* de fracture	Bruchzone *f*	zona *f* di frattura

	English	French	German	Italian
°	7703 **fracture structure**	structure f de la cassure	Bruchgefüge n	struttura f di rottura
–	7704 **fractured**	crevassé	klüftig, zerklüfft	lessurato, crepato
–	7705 **fractured zone**	zone fracturée	Bruchzone f	zona f fratturata
–	7706 **fracturing**	formation f des fissures	Zerklüftung f	formazione f di fessure
°	7707 **fragility**	fragilité f	Zerbrechlichkeit f	fragilità f
–	7708 **fragmental texture**	structure f clastique	klastische Struktur f	struttura f clastica
–	7708a **fragmented**	fragmenté	splittrig	frantumato
–	7709 **frame**	cadre m	Rahmen m	inquadratura f
°	7710 **frame**	carcasse f	Formrahmen m	carcassa f
°	7710a **frame**	support m	Gestell n	supporto m
	frame of a mould, *s. box of a mould*			
°	7711 **frame plate**	plaque f à cadre	Rahmenplatte f	piastra f a quadro
°	7712 **framed core box**	boîte-caisson f	Abziehkernkasten m	cassa f d'anima a paniere (o a contenitore)
–	7713 **francium**	francium m	Francium n	francio m
–	7714 **franckeite**	franckéite f	Franckeit m	francheite f
–	7715 **francolite**	francolite f	Frankolith m	francolite f
–	7716 **frangibility**	frangibilité f	Brüchigkeit f	fragilità f
–	7717 **franklinite**	franklinite f	Franklinit m	franklinite f
°	7717a **fraze**	bavure f de découpage	Schnittgrat m	bava f di taglio
–	7718 **to fray out**	se coincer en biseau	auskeilen	terminare
°	7719 **to free**	décramper	die Klammern lösen	togliere i ganci, togliere le graffe
	7720 **free at works**	franco (à l')usine	frei Hütte f	franco stabilimento
–	7721 **free burning coal**	houille f non collante à longue flamme	nicht backende Flammkohle f	carbone m non collante a lunga fiamma
°	7721a **free-cutting brass**	laiton m de décolletage	Automatenmessing n	ottone m facilmente lavorabile
–	7722 **free face**	surface f libre	freie Stossfläche f	superficie f libera
–	7723 **free fall**	chute f libre	Freifall m	caduta f libera
–	7724 **free-fall boring**	forage m à chute libre	Freifallbohren n	perforazione f a caduta libera

English	French	German	Italian
7725 **free-fall jars**	joint *m* à chute libre	Freifallschere *f*	giunto *m* a caduta libera
7725a **free ferrite**	ferrite *f* libre	freier Ferrit *m*	ferrite *f* libera
7726 **free from flaws or cracks**	sans criques *f pl.*	Rissfreiheit *f*	senza fessure *f pl.*, senza crepe *f pl.*
7727 **free from scale**	exempt de pailles	zunderfrei	esente da scaglie
7728 **free from slags**	exempt de scorie	schlackenfrei	esente da scorie
7729 **free from stresses**	sans tension	spannungsfrei	senza tensione
7730 **free gas**	gaz libre	freies Gas *n*	gas *m* libero
7731 **free-machining steel, free-cutting steel**	acier *m* de coupe	Schnellbearbeitungsstahl *m*	acciaio *m* da taglio, acciaio lavorabile ad alta velocità
7732 **free milling ore**	or *m* libre	Freigold *n*	oro *m* libero
7733 **free moulding**	moulage *m* en terre	freie Formerei *f*	formatura *f* senza modello, formatura in terra
7734 **free on trucks, f. o. t.**	franco wagon	frei Waggon	franco vagone
7735 **free point**	point *m* libre	Freiteufe *f*	punto *m* libero
7736 **free shaft**	cuve *f* dégagée	freigelegter Schacht	tino *m* non isolato (o libero)
7737 **free standing bosh**	étalages *m* libres	freistehende Rast *f*	sacca *f* libera
7738 **free standing casing**	tubage *m* libre	nichtzentrierter Futterrohrbereich *m*	tubaggio *m* libero
7739 **free sulphuric acid in purple ore**	acide *m* sulfurique libre dans les résidus	freie Schwefelsäure *f* in Abbränden	acido *m* solforico libero nei residui
7740 **to freeze**	se coincer	verklemmen, festlaufen	incepparsi, bloccarsi
7741 **freeze point**	point *m* neutre d'une colonne en puits	freie Stelle *f* einer Schachtsäule	punto *m* neutro di una colonna in pozzo
7742 **freezing**	solidification *f*, congélation *f*	Erstarrung *f*, Gefrieren *n*	solidificazione *f*, raffreddamento *m*
7743 **freezing**	calage *m*	Klemmung *f*	ingrippamento *m*, bloccaggio *m*
7744 **freezing machine**	machine frigorifique	Kältemaschine *f*	macchina *f* frigorifera

		English	French	German	Italian
°	7745	**freezing of tap hole**	blocage *m* du trou de coulée	Verstopfung *f* des Stichloches	intasamento del foro *m* di colata
—	7746	**freezing out the ore**	préparation *f* des minerais par le froid	Ausfrieren *n* der Erze	metodo *m* di preparazione per congelamento
		freezing point, *s. solidification point*			
—	7747	**freezing process**	procédé *m* de congélation	Gefrierverfahren *n*, Ausfrierungs- verfahren *n*	metodo *m* di congelamento
°	7748	**freezing range**	intervalle *m* de solidification	Erstarrungsintervall *n*	intervallo *m* di solidificazione
°	7749	**freezing shaft**	puits *m* frigorifique	Gefrierschacht *m*	pozzo *m* frigorifero
—	7750	**freibergite**	freibergite *f*	Freibergit *m*	freibergite *f*
—	7751	**freieslebenite**	freislébénite *f*	Freieslebenit *m*	freieslebenite *f*
—	7752	**freirinite**	freirinite *f*	Freirinit *m*	freirinite *f*
—	7753	**fremontite**	frémontite *f*	Fremontit *m*	fremontite *f*
°	7754	**French boiler, elephant boiler**	chaudière à bouilleurs	Siedekessel *m*, französischer Kessel	caldaia *f* francese
		French chalck, *s. talc*			
—	7755	**French method of cutting tunnel**	méthode *f* française de percement (d'un tunnel)	französische Tunnelbauweise *f*	attacco *m* col metodo francese (di tunnel)
°	7755a	**Frenchman**	polissoir *m*	Fugennagel *m*	spatola *f*
		fresh ash coal, *s. lean coal*			
		fresh concrete, *s. green concrete*			
—	7756	**fresh iron ore**	minerai *m* de fer frais	frisches Eisenerz *n*	minerale *m* di ferro scavato di fresco
°	7757	**fresh sand**	sable *m* neuf	Frischsand *m*	sabbia *f* nuova
—	7758	**fresh water limestone**	travertin *m*	Travertin *m*, Kalktuff	travertino *m*
—	7759	**freyalite**	freyalite *f*	Freyalith *m*	freyalite *f*
°	7760	**fret-sawing machine**	scie *f* alternative à découper, sauteuse	Wippsaegemaschine *f*	traforatrice *f*, sega *f* da traforo alternativa
°	7760a	**fretted lead**	ruban *m* en plomb	Bleistreifen *m*	nastro *m* di piombo
°	7761	**fretting corrosion**	corrosion *f* par friction	Reibungskorrosion *f*	corrosione *f* per attrito
°	7762	**fretting fatigue**	fatigue *f* de frottement	Reibungsermüdung *f*	fatica *f* di sfregamento
—	7763	**friable iron ore**	minerai *m* de fer friable	brüchiges Eisenerz *n*	minerale *m* di ferro friabile

English	French	German	Italian
7764 Frick furnace	four *m* Frick	Frickscher Ofen *m*	forno *m* Frick
7765 friction	frottement *m*	Reibung *f*	attrito *m*, frizione *f*
7766 friction breccia, fault-breccia	brèche *f* de friction	Reibungsbreccie *f*	breccia *f* di dislocazione, breccia di frizione
7767 friction coupling	accouplement *m* à friction	Reibungskupplung *f*	giunto *m* a frizione
7768 friction hammer	marteau *m* à friction	Reibungshammer *m*	maglio *m* a frizione
7769 friction roll	rouleau *m* de friction	Reibungsrolle *f*	rullo *m* di frizione
7770 friction roll (top roll)	cylindre *m* libre	Schleppwalze *f*	cilindro *m* libero
7771 friction wire	tire-feu *m*	Kupplungsdraht *f*	filo *m* della frizione
7771a frictional wear	usure *f* par frottement	Reibungsverschleiss *m*	usura *f* per attrito
7772 friedelite	friedélite *f*	Friedelit *m*	friedelite *f*
7773 frieseite	frieséite *f*	Frieseit *m*	frieseite *f*
7774 to frit	fritter ensemble	zusammenbrennen, zusammenfritten	calcinare, agglomerare
7774a frit	fritte *f*	Fritte *f*	matrice *f* vetrosa
fritted sand, *s. fused sand*			
7775 fritting	frittage *m*	Sinterung *f*	sinterizzazione *f*
front, *s. breast or face*			
7776 front end plate	paroi *f* avant	Frontseite *f* eines Kessels	piastra *f* anteriore, testata *f* frontale
front face, *s. front surface*			
7776a front mill table	ligne *f* d'amenée	Zufuhrrollgang *m*	linea *f* di alimentazione
7777 front of a thrust	front *m* de charriage	Faltenstirn *f*	fronte di faglia
7778 front plate	coupe-fonte *m*	Abschlussring *m*	segmentatore *m*
7779 front side	front *m*, face *f*	Stirnseite *f*	parte *f* frontale, fronte *f*, faccia *f*
7780 front surface or face	face *f* de devant	Stirnfläche *f*	lato *m* anteriore, faccia *f* anteriore
7781 front tipper	wagonnet basculant en bout	Vorderkipper *m*	vagonetto *m* a scarico di testa
7781a frosting	matage *m*	Mattierung *f*	smerigliatura *f*
7782 froth flotation	flottation *f* par la mousse	Schaumschwimmaufbereitung *f*	flottazione *f* a spuma
7783 frother	moussant	schaumig	spumeggiante, spumoso
7784 frothing	formation *f* de mousse	Schaumbildung *f*	formazione *f* di schiuma

		English	French	German	Italian
^	7785	frozen pipe	batterie f prise dans le puits		batteria f presa in pozzo
		frying arc, s. hissing arc			
—	7786	fuchsite	fuchsite f	Fuchsit m	fuchsite f
^	7787	fuel	combustible m	Brennstoff m	combustibile m
^	7788	fuel gas	gaz m combustible	Brenngas n	gas m combustibile
—	7789	fuel in dust state, atomised fuel	combustible m (à l'état) pulvérulent	staubförmiger Brennstoff m	combustibile m finemente polverizzato
—	7790	fuel mixed with air	combustible m mélangé d'air	Brennstoff-luftgemisch n	combustibile m misto ad aria
^	7791	fuel-oil	fuel-oil m, mazout m	Heizöl n, Rohöl n	olio m combustibile, nafta f, masut m
^	7792	fuel oil rotameter	fluxmètre m	Kriechgalvanometer n Durchflussmeter n	flussometro m, rotametro m
—	7793	fulgurite	fulgurite f	Fulgurit m	fulgurite f
o	7793a	full ageing	vieillissement m complet	vollständige Alterung f	invecchiamento m totale
o	7794	full anneal	recuire	ausglühen	ricuocere completamente
	7795	full cargo	cargaison f complète	volle Ladung f	carico m completo
—	7796	full circle spear	harpon m de repêchage	vollrunder Speer m, Fanghaken m	pescatore m
—	7797	full dip	ligne f de plus grande pente	stärkstes Einfallen n	linea f di massima pendenza
o	7798	full flame converter blow	allumage m de convertisseur	Zünden n eines Konverters	accensione f di un convertitore
^	7799	full gauge hole	trou m régulier à diamètre constant		foro m regolare e di diametro costante
^	7800	full-hole tool joint	joint m à passage total	Verbinder m mit normalem Durchgang	giunto m a passaggio totale
o	7801	full gauge railway	voie f normale	Vollbahn f, vollspurige Bahn f	binario m a scartamento normale
o	7802	full hard temper	trempe f dure	Harthärtung f	tempra f dura
o	7803	full hardening	trempe f à coeur	Durchhärten n	tempra f completa, tempra f al nucleo
^	7804	full liner	chemise f d'une pièce	Büchse aus einem Stück	camicia f completa (di un pezzo)

	English	French	German	Italian
—	**7805 full mature valley**	vallée f sénile	vollreifes Tal n	vallata f senile
	full pattern, s. block pattern			
—	**7806 full set**	cadre m complet	Viergespann n	quadro m completo
—	**7807 full timbering**	boisage m complet	Vollzimmerung f	armamento m in legno completo
o	**7808 full warming**	réchauffer à coeur	durchwärmen	riscaldare al nucleo
o	**7809 full warming time**	durée f du réchauffement à coeur	Durchwärmzeit f	tempo m di riscaldamento al nucleo
o	**7809a fuller**	dégorgeoir m	Einschnürgerät n	scanalatore m
—	**7810 fuller's earth, smectite**	argile f smectique, terre f à foulon	Walkererde f, Fullererde f	argilla f smectica, argilla f saponaria
o	**7811 fullering**	matage m, dégorgement m	Verstemmen n, Einschnürung f	presellatura f, impronta di rifollatura, scanalatura f
o	**7812 fullering impression**	empreinte f de matage	Verstemmungsdruck m	impronta f per bacchettatura (o per rifollatura)
	fulmicotton, s. gru cotton			
—	**7813 fulminate of mercury**	fulminate m de mercure	Knallquecksilber n	fulminato m di mercurio
—	**7813a fulminating gold**	or m fulminant	Knallgold n	fulminato m d'oro
—	**7814 fuloppite**	fulloppite f	Fuloppit m	fulloppite f
—	**7815 fundamental gneiss**	gneiss m primaire	Primordialgneis m	gneiss m primario
—	**7816 fundamental schist**	schiste m primaire	Primordialschiefer m	scisto m primario
—	**7816a fume**	fumée f	Rauch m	fumo m, esalazione f
o	**7817 fume cupboard**	canal m d'aspiration, hotte f	Abzug m	cappa f d'aspirazione
o	**7818 fuming nitric acid**	acide m nitrique fumant	rauchende Salpetersäure f	acido m nitrico fumante
	7819 fundamental	fondamental	grundsätzlich	fondamentale
o	**7820 funnel, hopper cup**	trémie f, entonnoir m	Trichter m	tramoggia f, imbuto m
	funnel, s. pipe			
	funnel, s. gate (of a mould)			
o	**7821 funnel formation, formation of pipes**	formation f d'entonnoir	Trichterbildung f	formazione f d'imbuto
o	**7822 funnel holder**	support m de filtre	Filtergestell n	sostegno m o supporto m del filtro
o	**7823 funnel with perforated plate**	tamis m à filtrer	Filtersieb n	staccio m o vaglio m filtrante

	English	French	German	Italian
^ 7824	furfural	furfural *m*, furfurol *m*	Furfural, Furfurol *n*	furfurolo *m*
° 7825	furnace, stove	foyer *m*, fourneau *m*, four *m*	Feuerung *f*, Ofen *m*	focolaio *m*, focolare *m*, forno *m*
° 7826	furnace blast	vent *m* de haut fourneau	Hochofenwind *m*	vento *m* di altoforno
	furnace blocking, *s. blocking or pigging up*			
° 7827	furnace bottom	sole *f* de four	Ofensohle *f*	suola *f* del forno
° 7828	furnace brazing	brasage *m* au four	Ofenhartlöten *n*	brasatura *f* al forno
° 7829	furnace bridge	autel *m*, pont *m*	Ofenbrücke *f*, Feuerbrücke *f*	altare *m*, muretto *m* del forno
° 7830	furnace campain	campagne *f* de fourneau	Ofenreise *f*	durata *f* del forno
	furnace charge, *s. charge*			
° 7831	furnace-coal	charbon *m* pour fours métallurgiques	Ofenkohle *f*	carbone *m* per forni metallurgici
	furnace coke, *s. metallurgical coke*			
° 7832	furnace construction	construction du four	Aufbau *m* des Ofens	costruzione del forno
° 7833	furnace crown	ciel *m* du foyer	Feuerbüchsendecke *f*	cielo *m* del focolare
° 7833a	furnace delivery chute	amortisseur *m* de four double	Doppelprellblock *m*	smorzatore *m* di forno doppio
° 7834	furnace delivery table	tablier *m* à rouleaux	Ofenrollgang *m*	tavola *f* a rulli
° 7835	furnace end	extrémité *f* du four	Ofenende *n*	estremità *f* del forno
° 7836	furnace flue	carneau du four	Ofenkanal *m*	condotto *m* del forno
	furnace for coal, *s. coal furnace*			
° 7837	furnace for extraction of by-products	four *m* à extraction de sous-produits	Ofen für Gewinnung von Nebenprodukten	forno *m* per estrazione di sottoprodotti o dei derivati
° 7838	furnace for gaseous fuel	foyer à gaz	Gasfeuerung *f*	focolare a gas
	furnace for hardening, *s. tempering furnace*			
° 7839	furnace for making iron	four *m* de cémentation	Temperofen *m*, Zementierofen *m*	forno *m* di cementazione
° 7840	furnace for oil fuel	foyer à pétrole, foyer à huile lourde	Ölfeuerung *f*	focolare *m* ad olio combustibile

English	French	German	Italian
7841 **furnace for petroleum residue**	foyer *m* pour résidus de la distillation du pétrole	Feuerung *f* mit Petroleumrück- ständen	focolare *m* a residui di petrolio
7842 **furnace for pulverized coal**	foyer *m* à charbon pulvérisé	Kohlenstaubfeuerung *f*	focolare *m* a polvere di carbone
7843 **furnace front**	devanture *f* de foyer	Feuergeschränk *n*	fronte *f* del focolare
furnace grate, *s. fire-grate*			
furnace hand, *s. furnace man*			
7844 **furnace-grate, fire-grate**	grille *f*, grille *f* à foyer	(Feuer) Rost *m*	graticola *f*, griglia *f*
7845 **furnace hoist**	monte-charge *m* de haut fourneau	Gichtaufzug *m*	montacarichi *m* di altoforno
7846 **furnace jacket, furnace lining**	blindage *m* de fourneau, revêtement du four	Ofenmantel *m*	rivestimento *m* del forno
7847 **furnace in front of the boiler, fore hearth**	foyer *m* antérieur	Vorfeuerung *f*	focolare *m* anteriore
7848 **furnace in full heat**	four *m* en pleine température	in voller Hitze befindlicher Ofen *m*	forno *m* a pieno regime
furnace installation, *s. firing plant*			
7849 **furnace lining, furnace jacket**	revêtement *m*, blindage *m*	feuerfeste Ausklei- dung *f*, Ofenmar.tel	rivestimento *m* (di un forno)
7850 **furnace man**	ouvrier *m* de haut-fourneau	Hochofenarbeiter *m*	operaio *m* d'alto forno
furnace of a boiler, *s. boiler furnace*			
7851 **furnace-plate**	tôle *f* de foyer	Feuerblech *n*	lamiera *f* del focolare
7852 **furnace plattform**	plate-forme *f* de haut-fourneau	Ofenbühne *f*	piattaforma *f* d'alto- forno
7853 **furnace scale**	calamine *f* de four	Ofenzunder *m*	scaglia *f* del forno
7854 **furnace shaft**	cuve *f* de four	Ofenschacht *m*	tino *m* del forno
7855 **furnace shaft**	puits *m* pourvu de foyer d'aérage	Wetterschacht *m* mit Feuerung	pozzo *m* con focolare d'aerazione
7856 **furnace shell**	revêtement du four	Ofenmantel *m*	rivestimento *m* del forno

		English	French	German	Italian
°	7857	**furnace slag**	scorie *f* de fourneau	Ofenschlacke *f*	scoria *f* d'altoforno
°	7858	**furnace-top bell**	cloche *f* de haut fourneau	Gichtglocke *f*	campana *f* di altoforno
°	7859	**furnace-top hopper**	trémie *f* de charge- ment de haut fourneau	Gichttrichter *m*	tramoggia *f* di carica- mento per altoforno
		furnace top platform,	*s. charging platform*		
°	7860	**furnace transformer**	transformateur *m* du four	Ofenumformer *m*	trasformatore *m* del forno
°	7861	**furnace unit**	unité *f* de four, charge *f* d'un four	Ofeneinheit *f*	unità *f* di forno, cari- ca *f* di un forno
°	7862	**furnace under the boiler**	foyer *m* inférieur	Unterfeuerung *f*	focolare *m* inferiore
°	7863	**furnace with cooling water circulation through the grate bars**	foyer *m* à circulation d'eau à travers les barreaux de la grille	Feuerung *f* mit Kühlung durch Wasserumlauf in Hohlroststäben	focolaio *m* con circo- lazione d'acqua nei barrotti della griglia
°	7864	**furnace with cylinder grate**	foyer *m* avec grille à rouleau	Walzenrost- feuerung *f*	focolare *m* con griglia a cilindro
°	7865	**furnace with forced draught, forced- -draught furnace**	foyer *m* à soufflage sous grille	Unterwindfeuerung *f*, Feuerung *f* mit Druckluft	focolaio *m* con getto (o ad iniezione) d'aria sotto griglia
°	7866	**furnace with forced draught**	foyer *m* à air comprimé	Pressluftfeuerung *f*	focolare *m* ad aria forzata
°	7867	**furnace with horizontal grate**	foyer *m* à grille horizontale	Planrostfeuerung *f*	focolare *m* a griglia orizzontale
°	7868	**furnace with horizontal grate underneath the boiler**	foyer *m* inférieur à grille horizontale	Planrostunter- feuerung *f*	focolare *m* esterno a griglia orizzontale
°	7869	**furnace with inclined grate, inclined grate furnace**	foyer *m* à grille inclinée	Schrägrostfeuerung *f*	focolare *m* a griglia inclinata
°	7870	**furnace with inclined grate underneath**	foyer *m* inférieur à grille inclinée	Schrägrostinnenfeu- erung *f*	focolare *m* a griglia inclinata sotto alla caldaia
°	7871	**furnace with internal horizontal grate**	foyer *m* intérieur à grille horizontale	Planrostinnenfeu- erung *f*	focolare *m* interno a griglia orizzontale
°	7872	**furnace with movable fire bars**	foyer *m* avec grille à secousses	Schüttelrostfeuerung *f*	focolare *m* con griglia a scosse

English	French	German	Italian
7873 **furnace with movable hearth**	four *m* à sole mobile	Ofen *m* mit fahrbarem Herd	forno *m* a suola mobile
7874 **furnace with multistage grate**	foyer *m* avec grille à étages	Staffelrostfeuerung *f*	focolare *m* con griglia a piani
7875 **furnace with over--grate blower**	foyer *m* à introduction d'air au-dessus de la grille	Feuerung *f* mit Oberluftzuführung	focolare *m* con adduzione d'aria sopra la griglia
7876 **furnace with projecting bridge**	foyer *m* à autel surplombant	Feuerung *f* mit vorstehender Feuerbrücke	focolare *m* con altare sporgente
7877 **furnace with removable bottom**	four *m* à sole amovible	Ofen *m* mit auswechselbarem Boden	forno *m* a suola mobile
7878 **furnace with stepped grate**	foyer *m* avec grille à gradins	Treppenrostfeuerung *f*	focolare *m* con griglia a gradini
7879 **furnaceman**	fondeur *m*	Schmelzer *m*	fonditore *m*
7880 **furniture tube**	tube *m* à meubles	Möbelrohr *n*	tubo *m* per mobili
furrow, *s. fault line*			
7881 **furrowing**	formation *f* des cannelures	Ausfurchung *f*	formazione *f* di scanelature
7882 **furrowing**	corrosion *f* électrolytique	elektrolytische Korrosion *f*	corrosione *f* elettrolitica
7883 **further cleansing**	nettoyage *m* supplémentaire	Nachreinigung *f*	pulitura *f* supplementare
7883a **fusain**	fusain *m*	Fusit *m*	fusite *f*
to fuse, *s. to melt*			
7884 **fuse**	fusée *f*	Zünder *m*	esca *f*
7885 **fuse-wire**	fil *m* fusible	Schmelzdraht *m*	filo *m* fusibile
7886 **fused alumina**	alumine *f* fuse	Flusstonerde *f*	allumina *f* fusa
7887 **fusible alloy**	alliage fusible	Schmelzlegierung *f*	lega *f* fusibile
fusible alloy pattern, *s. wax (or investement) pattern*			
7888 **fusible clay**	terre *f* fusible	schmelzbarer Ton *m*	argilla *f* fusibile
7889 **fusible metal**	métal *m* fusible	Schmelzmetall *n*	metallo *m* fusibile
7889a **fusible plug**	fusible *m*	Schmelzsicherung *f*	tampone *m* fusibile
7890 **fusibility, meltableness**	fusibilité *f*	Schmelzbarkeit *f*	fusibilità *f*
fusing, *s. melting*			

	English	French	German	Italian
° 7891	**fusing agent**	agent de fusion	Schmelzmittel *n*	agente di fusione
° 7892	**fusing burner**	chalumeau *m* coupeur	Schneidbrenner *m*	cannello *m* da taglio
° 7893	**fusion, melting**	fusion *f* liquéfaction	Schmelzen *n*, Schmelzung *f*	fusione *f*, liquefazione *f*
° 7893a	**fusion cutting**	sciage *m* par friction	Reibungssägen *n*	segare per attrito
	fusion steel wire, *s. filler wire*			
° 7893b	**fusion range**	zone *f* de fusion	Schmelzbereich *m*	zona *f* di fusione
° 7894	**fusion welding**	soudure *f* par fusion	Schmelzschweissung	saldatura *f* per fusione
— 7895	**fusulina**	fusulina *f*	Fusulina *f*	fusulina *f*

	English	French	German	Italian
— 7896	**gabarite**	gabarit *m*	Formbrett *n*, Schablone *f*	calibro *m* sagomato
— 7897	**gabbro**	gab(b)ro *m*	Schillerfels *m*, Gabbro *m*	gabbro *m*
— 7898	**gabbroic**	gabbroïque	gabbroïsch	gabbroico
— 7899	**gabbroid**	gabbroïde	gabbroid	gabbroide
— 7900	**gad**	coin *m*, pince *f*, aiguille *f*	Fimmel, Keil *m*, Bergeisen *n*	barra *f* a cuneo, scalpello *m*, pinza *f*
— 7901	**gad picker**	coin *m*, perforatrice *f* à main	Keil, Bergeisen *n*, Handbohrmaschine *f*	cuneo *m*, perforatrice *f* a mano
— 7902	**gadolinite**	gadolinite *f*	Gadolinit *m*	gadolinite *f*
— 7903	**gadolinium**	gadolinium *m*	Gadolinium *n*	gadolinio *m*
— 7904	**gagate**	gagate *m*	Gagat *m*	ambra *f* nera
	gage point, *s. spotting point*			
— 7905	**gageite**	gagéite *f*	Gageit *m*	gageite *f*
○ 7906	**gagger**	crochet *m*	Sandhaken *m*	gancio *m*, «crochet» *m*, armatura. *f*
○ 7906a	**gagger**	tirette *f*	Aushebeband *n*	tirante *m* d'estrazione
○ 7907	**gagging**	(re)dressage *m*	Geraderichtung *f*	raddrizzatura *f*
7908	**gain**	gain *m*	Gewinn *m*	guadagno *m*, profitto *m*
— 7909	**gain**	recoupe *f*, travers-bancs *m*	Durchhieb *m*, Querschlag *m*	galleria *f* di collegamento, traverso-banco
— 7910	**galapectite**	galapectite *f*	Galapektit *m*	galapectite *f*
— 7911	**galaxite**	galaxite *f*	Galaxit *m*	galassite *f*
	galena, *s. lead glance*			
— 7912	**galenite, lead glance**	galène *f*	Bleiglanz *m*	galena *f*, solfuro *m* di piombo
— 7913	**galeno-bismutite**	galénobismuthite *f*	Galenobismutit *m*	galenobismutite *f*
	gallery, *s. mine adit*			
○ 7914	**gallery furnace**	four *m* à tunnel	Tunnelofen *m*	forno *m* a tunnel
— 7915	**gallery framework**	boisage *m* en porte	Türgerüst *n*, Rahmen *m*	armatura *f* della galleria

		English	French	German	Italian
^	7916	**galling**	éraillure *f* écorchure *f*	Korrosion	escoriazione *f*, pregrippag- gio *m*
o	7917	**gallium**	gallium *m*	Gallium *n*	gallio *m*
o	7918	**Galloway boiler**	chaudière *f* (à tubes) Galloway	Gallowaykessel *m*	caldaia *f* (a tubi di) Galloway
—	7919	**gallows**	cadre *m* incomplet	einbeiniger Türstock	quadro *m* incompleto
—	7920	**gallows**	plancher *m*	Bühne *f*	piattaforma *f*
—	7921	**gallows frame,** **head frame**	chevalement *m*	Fördergerüst *n*	castelletto *m* d'estra- zione
—	7922	**galmei**	smithsonite *f*	Galmei, Smithsonit *m*	smithsonite *f*
o	7923	**galvanic**	galvanique	galvanisch	galvanico
o	7924	**galvanic** **metallization**	métallisation *f* galvanique	galvanische Metallisierung *f*	metallizzazione *f* galvanica
o	7925	**galvanic mould,** **galvanic matrix**	moule *m* galvanique	galvanische Matrize *f*	matrice *f* galvanica
o	7926	**galvanisation,** **zincing, zinking**	galvanisation *f*, zincage, zingage *m*	Galvanisation *f*, Galvanisierung *f*, Verzinkung *f*	galvanizzazione *f*, zincatura *f*
o	7927	**galvanism, voltaism**	galvanisme *m*	Galvanismus *m*	galvanismo *m*
o	7928	**to galvanise, to zinc**	galvaniser, zinguer	galvanisieren, verzinken	galvanizzare, zincare
o	7929	**galvanized**	galvanisé	galvanisiert	galvanizzato
o	7930	**galvanized copper** **wire**	fil *m* de cuivre galvanisé (ou zingué)	galvanisierter Kupferdraht *m*	filo *m* di rame galvaniz- zato
o	7931	**galvanized** **corrugated sheet**	tôle *f* ondulée galvanisée	verzinktes Wellblech *n*	lamiera *f* ondulata galvanizzata (o zincata)
o	7932	**galvanized iron**	fer *m* galvanisé, fer *m* zingué	galvanisiertes Eisen, verzinktes Eisen *n*	ferro *m* zincato, ferro *m* galvanizzato
o	7933	**galvanized iron wire**	fil *m* en fer galva- nisé	verzinkter Ei- sendraht *m*	filo *m* di ferro galva- nizzato (o zincato)
o	7934	**galvanized iron** **(sheet)**	tôle *f* galvanisée	verzinktes (Eisen-) Blech *n*	lamiera *f* galvanizzata

galvanized sheet iron, *s. galvanised iron (sheet)*

English	French	German	Italian
° 7935 **galvanized sheet with trapezoidal corrugations**	tôle *f* galvanisée à ondes trapézoïdales	verzinktes Trapezblech *n*	lamiera *f* zincata ad onde trapezoidali
° 7936 **galvanized signal strand**	câble *m* à torons (7 ou 19 fils)	Litzenseil (7 oder 19 Drähte)	fune a trefoli di 7 (o 19) fili
° 7937 **galvanized steel oval wire**	barre *f* à section ovale	Ovalstab· *m*	filo di acciaio ovale zincato, ovaletto *m*
° 7938 **galvanized steel decking**	caillebotis *m pl.* galvanisés	·verzinkte Stabroste *m pl.*	grigliati *m pl.* zincati
° 7939 **galvanized strip**	bande *f* galvanisée	verzinktes Blech *n*	banda zincata
° 7940 **galvanized wire**	fil *m* galvanisé	galvanisierter Draht *m*	filo *m* galvanizzato
° 7941 **galvanized wrought iron**	fer *m* galvanisée	galvanisiertes Eisen	ferro *m* zincato
° 7942 **galvanizing, galvanisation**	galvanisation *f*, zincage *m*	Verzinken *n*, Galvanisierung *f*	zincatura *f*, bagno di zincatura, galvanizzazione
° 7943 **galvanizing by the electrolytic process**	galvanisation *f* électrolytique	kalte (od galvanische) Verzinkung *f*	zincatura *f* elettrolitica
galvanizing of iron, *s. zinking of iron*			
° 7944 **galvanizing process**	procédé *m* de galvanisation	Galvanisierprozess *m*	processo *m* di galvanizzazione (o di zincatura)
gammagraph, *s. gammaradiograph*			
° 7945 **gamma iron**	fer *m* gamma	Gamma-Eisen *n*	ferro *m* gamma
° 7946 **gamma radiography**	gammagraphie *f*	Gammastrahlen-Prüfung *f*	gammagrafia *f*
° 7947 **gamma radiograph**	gammagraphie *f*	Gammastrahlenbild *n*	gammagramma *m*
° 7948 **gamma ray inspection**	contrôle *m* gammagraphique	Gamma-strahlenprüfung *f*	controllo *m* gammagrafico
° 7949 **gamma ray log**	diagraphie *f* de rayons gamma	Gammastrahlenbild *n*	diagrafia *f* dei raggi gamma
° 7950 **gamma rays**	rayons *m pl.* gamma	Gamma-Strahlen *m pl.*	raggi gamma
° 7951 **gang**	équipe *f*	Kolonne *f*, Schicht *f*	**squadra** *f* di operai, turno *m*

		English	French	German	Italian
°	7952	**gang milling**	fraisage *m* multiple	Mehrfachfräsung *f*	fresatura di pezzi in serie (o multipla)
—	7953	**gang rider**	rouleur *m*	Schlepper *m*	addetto *m* ai carrelli
°	7954	**gang slitting machine**	laminoir à bandes d'acier	Bandeisenwalzwerk *n*	laminatoio *m* per bandelle
—	7955	**ganging**	roulage *m*	Förderung *f*	carreggio *m*, trasporto *m*
—	7956	**gangue**	gangue *f*	Ganggestein *n*, Gangart *f*	ganga *f*
—	7957	**gangue deposit**	gisement *m*, filon *m*	gangartige Lager-stätte *f*	giacimento *m* a filone
—	7958	**gangue mineral**	minerai *m* de gangue	Gangmineral *n*	minerale *m* sterile
—	7959	**gangway**	galerie de transport, voie *f* de fond, passage *m*	Förderstrecke *f*, Grundstrecke *f*, Fahrtrumm *m*, Durchgang *m*	galleria *f* di passaggio (o di fondo), passaggio *m*, livello *m* (o galleria *f*) principale
—	7960	**ganister**	ganister *m*	Ganister *m*	ganistro *m*, roccia *f* silicea
—	7961	**ganoid**	ganoïde *m*	Ganoide *n*	ganoide *m*
—	7962	**ganomalite**	ganomalite *f*	Ganomalith *m*	ganomalite *f*
—	7963	**ganophyllite**	ganophyllite *f*	Ganophyllit *m*	ganofillite *f*
°	7964	**gantry (for crane)**	voie *f* de roulement de grue	Kranbahn *f*	cavalletto *m* (di gru)
°	7965	**gantry crane**	pont-roulant *m*	Laufkran *m*	gru *f* a ponte, carro-ponte *m*, gru a caval-letto
		gap, *s. air space*			
	7966	**gap**	gorge *f*, ouverture *f*, fente *f*, trou *m*, brèche *f*	Schlucht *f*, Öffnung *f*, Spalte *f*, Zwischenraum *m*	gola *f*, apertura *f*, vuoto *m*, crepa *f*, fo-ro *m*, breccia *f*
—	7967	**gap**	hiatus *m*	Lücke *f*	lacuna *f*
—	7968	**gap fault**	faille *f* ouverte	klaffende Verwerfung *f*	faglia *f* aperta
		gap in plane of bedding, *s. stratigraphic gap*			
—	7969	**gaping**	bâillement *m*	Spalt *m*	apertura *f*

English	French	German	Italian

gaping fault, open fault, *s. gap fault*

garbage consuming furnace, *s. refuse burning furnace*

° 7970	**garbage incinerator**	four *m* à brûler les ordures	Müllverbrennungs-ofen *m*	inceneratore *m* di rifiuti
− 7971	**garewaite**	garewaïte *f*	Garewait *m*	garewaite *f*
− 7972	**garganite**	garganite *f*	Garganit *m*	garganite *f*
− 7973	**garnet, pyrope**	pyrope *m*, grenat *m* de Bohème	Granat *m*, Pyrop *m*	granato *m*, piropo *m*
− 7974	**garnierite**	garniérite *f*	Garnierit *m*	garnierite *f*

gas absorption, *s. gassing*

^ 7975	**gas absorption plant**	installation *f* d'extraction de gasoline du gaz	Förderanlage *f* für Gasolin	impianto *m* d'estrazione di gasolina da gas
^ 7976	**gas analysis**	analyse *f* du gaz	Gasanalyse *f*	analisi *f* tecnica del gas
^ 7977	**gas analytical apparatus**	appareil *m* pour l'analyse des gaz	gasanalytischer Apparat *m*	apparato *m* per analisi dei gas
^ 7978	**gas anchor**	ancrage *m* de gaz	Gasanker *m*	ancora *f* di gas
° 7979	**gas bag**	sac *m* en caoutchouc pour gaz	Gassack *m*	sacca *f* o polmone *m* di gas
^ 7980	**gas bailer, mammoth pump**	pompe *m* mammouth, pompe *f* pneumatique	Mammutpumpe *f*	pompa *f* pneumatica, pompa *f* mammut
° 7981	**gas balance**	balance *f* à gaz	Gaswaage *f*	bilancia *f* per gas
° 7982	**gas blowing engine**	soufflerie *f* à gaz	Gasgebläse *n*	soffiante *f* o soffieria *f* a gas
^ 7983	**gas blow-out**	dégagement *m* instantané de gaz	Gasausbruch *m*	eruzione *f* di gas

gas brazing, *s. torch brazing*

° 7984	**gas burette**	burette *f* à gaz	Gasmessröhre *f*	buretta *f* a gas
° 7985	**gas-burner**	bec *m* à gaz	Gasbrenner *m*	becco *m* a gas, bruciatore a gas, ugello a gas
^ 7986	**gas cap**	cape de gaz	Gaskappe *f*	cappa *f* di gas

	English	French	German	Italian
˄ 7987	gas cap drive	expansion *f* de gaz, poussée *f* de cape	Gaskappenausdehnung *f*	spinta *f* del gas della cappa
	gas carburation, *s. gas carburising*			
○ 7988	gas carburation, gas carburising	cémentation *f* gazeuse	Gaszementation *f*	carbocementazione a gas, cementazione (carburante) a gas
○ 7989	to gas carburise	cémenter au gaz	gaszementieren	cementare col gas
○ 7990	gas case hardening	cémentation *f* gazeuse	Gaseinsatzhärtung *f*	cementazione *f* gassosa
	gas cavity, *s. blowhole*			
	gas cleaner, *s. gas purifier*			
	gas cleaning, *s. gas purification*			
○ 7991	gas coke	coke *m* de gaz	Gaskoks *m*	coke *m* di gas illuminante, coke *m* di storta
○ 7992	gas collecting tube	tube *m* collecteur de gaz	Gassammelröhre *f*	tubo *m* collettore di gas
○ 7993	gas conservation	conservation *f* de gaz	Gasschonung *f*	conservazione *f* del gas
○ 7994	gas current	courant *m* gazeux	Gasstrom *m*	corrente *f* gassosa
○ 7995	gas current rich in oxygen	courant *m* de gaz riche en oxygène	sauerstoffreicher Gasstrom *m*	corrente *f* di gas ricco d'ossigeno
˄ 7996	gas cut	venue *f* de gaz dans la boue	Gasgehalt *m* im Schlamm	presenza *f* (o ˙venuta) di gas nel fango
	gas cutting, *s. flame cutting*			
— 7997	gas-detector	grisoumètre *m*	Schlagwetteranzeiger *m*	rivelatore *m* di gas
	gas developing bottle, *s. flask for developing gas*			
˄ 7998	gas drive	pompage *m* par injection de gaz	Gaseinpressung *f*	pompaggio *m* ad iniezione di gas
	gas driven generator, *s. gas dynamo*			
○ 7999	gas duct or passage	trajet *m* de gaz	Gasweg *m*	canale *m* del gas
○ 8000	gas dynamo	dynamo *f* à gaz	Gasdynamo *m*	dinamo *f* a gas, generatore *m* a gas

	English	French	German	Italian
°	8001 gas envelope	enveloppe *f* de gaz	Gashülle *f*	inviluppo *m* di gas
^	8002 gas evolution	expansion *f* de gaz	Gasausdehnung *f*	espansione di gas
—	8003 gas explosion	explosion *f* de gaz	Gasexplosion *f*	esplosione *f* di gas
^	8004 gas factor	rapport *m* gaz-pétrole	Gas-Ölverhältnis *n*	rapporto *m* gas-petrolio
^	8005 gas field	champ *m* de gaz	Gasfeld *n*	giacimento *m* di gas
°	8006 gas-fired boiler	chaudière *f* à gaz	Kessel *m* mit Gas-feuerung	caldaia *f* a gas
°	8007 gas fired furnace for hardening	four *m* de trempe au gaz	Gashärteofen *m*	forno *m* a gas per la tempera
°	8008 gas fired muffle furnace	four *m* à moufle au gaz	Gasmuffelofen *m*	forno *m* a muffola a gas
°	8009 gas flue to the hearth	conduite *f* de gaz vers le four	Gasleitung *f* zu dem Herde	arrivo *m* del gas, ca-nale *m* d'arrivo del gas
ᵒ	8010 gas-fuel, gaseous fuel	combustible *m* gazeux	gasförmiger Brennstoff *m*	combustibile *m* gassoso
ᵒ	8011 gas-furnace	four *m* à gaz, four chauffé au gaz	Gasofen *m*	forno *m* à gas
°	8012 gas generating apparatus	gazogène *m*, appa-reil *m* pour la production des gaz	Gasentwicklungs-apparat *m*	apparato *m* generato-re di gas, gasogeno *m*
—	8013 gas generation	gazéification *f*	Gaserzeugung *f*	gassificazione *f*
	gas generator, *s. gas producer*			
°	8013a gas gouging	rainurage *m* à la flamme	autogene Rillung	scanalatura *f* al can-nello
°	8014 gas(-heated) soldering-iron	fer *m* à souder à gaz	Gaslötkolben *m*	saldatoio *m* a gas
°	8015 gas hole	soufflure *f*	Gasblase *f*	soffiatura *f*
—	8016 gas horizon	horizon *m* gazeux	Gashorizont *m*	orizzonte *m* gassoso
—	8017 gas indicator	grisoumètre *m*	Schlagwetter-anzeiger *m*	rivelatore *m* di gas
°	8018 gas inlet	entrée *f* de gaz	Gaszuführung *f*	entrata *f* del gas
°	8019 gas inlet capillary tube	capillaire *m* d'arrivée du gaz	Gaszuführungs-kapillarrohr *n*	tubo *m* capillare d'ammissione del gas
°	8019a gas liberation	dégagement *m* de gaz	Gasausscheidung *f*	liberazione *f* di gas

	English	French	German	Italian
^	8020 gas lift	puisage *m* au gaz	Druckgasförderver- fahren *n*	estrazione *f* con inie- zione di gas
^	8021 gas lift well	puits *m* d'extraction à injection de gaz	Förderschacht *m* zur Einführung von Pressgas	pozzo *m* d'estrazione per immissione di gas
^	8022 gas main	conduite *f* principale de gaz	Hauptgasleitung *f*	condotto principale del gas
^	8023 gas mantle	chemise *f* de gaz	Gasmantelrohr *n*	camicia *f* di gas
o	8024 gas meter	compteur *m* à gaz	Gasuhr *f*	contatore *m* a gas
o	8025 gas mixture	mélange *m* gazeux	Gasgemenge *n*	mescolanza *f* gassosa
—	8026 gas motor coal	charbon pour moteur(s) à gaz	Gasmotorkohle *f*	carbone *m* per motori a gas
^	8027 gas(cut) mud	boue *f* gazéifiée	gashaltige Spülung *f*	fango *m* gassato
—	8028 gas mask	masque *m* antigaz	Gasschutzmaske *f*	maschera *f* antigas
o	8029 gas nitriding	nitrurer au gaz	gasnitrieren	nitrurare col gas
o	8030 gas offtake	prise *f* de gaz (d'un haut fourneau)	Gichtgasabzugsrohr *n*	presa *f* di gas (di un alto forno)
^	8031 gas oil, Diesel oil, solar oil, Diesel fuel	gasoil *m*, huile *f* à gaz	Gasöl *n*, Dieselöl *n*	gasolio *m*, olio *m* Diesel
^	8032 gas-oil interface	surface *f* de contact gas-huile	Gasöl-Kontaktfläche *f*	superficie *f* di contatto gas-olio
o	8033 gas outlet pipe	conduite *f* de départ du gaz	Gasableitungsrohr *n*	condotto *m* d'uscita del gas
o	8034 gas outlet tube	prise *f* de gaz Faber du Faure	Gasfang *m* nach Faber du Faure	presa *f* di gas Faber du Faure
o	8035 gas oxygen lamp	lampe *f* à gaz d'éclairage et à oxygène	Leuchtgassauerstoff- lampe *f*	lampada *f* a gas illu- minante e ad ossige- no
o	8035a gas pickling	décapage *m* au gaz	Gasbeizung *f*	decapaggio *m* al gas
^	8036 gas pipeline	gazoduct *m*	Gasleitung *f*	gasdotto *m*
o	8037 gas piping	tuyauterie *f* de gaz	Gasleitung *f*	tubazione o conduttu- ra del gas

gas pocket, *s. blowhole*

	English	French	German	Italian
^ 8038	gas pocket	poche f de gaz	Gaslager n	cuscinetto di gas
o 8039	gas polarisation	polarisation f d'un gaz	Gaspolarisation f	polarizzazione f d'un gas
o 8040	gas port	parcours m du gaz	Gasweg m	direzione f del gas
o 8041	gas pressure	pression f du gaz	Gasspannung f	pressione f del gas
o 8042	gas producer	gazogène m	Gaserzeuger m	gasogeno m
o 8043	gas-proof	à l'épreuve des gaz, inattaquable par les gaz	gasfest	a prova di gas, inattaccabile dai gas
o 8044	gas-puddling	puddlage m au gaz	Gasfrischen n	puddellatura f a gas
o 8045	gas purification, gas cleaning	épuration des gaz	Gasreinigung f	depurazione del gas
o 8046	gas purifier, gas cleaner	épurateur m (de gaz)	Gasreiniger m	depuratore m (per gas)
o 8047	gas regulator	régulateur m de gaz	Gasregler m	regolatore m di gas
o 8048	gas retort	cornue f à gaz	Gasretorte f	storta f per gas
— 8049	gas rock	roche f gazifère	gasführendes Gestein n	roccia f gassifera
— 8050	gas sand	sable m gazifère	Gassand m	sabbia f gassifera
— 8051	gas schist	schiste m gazifère	gasführender Schiefer m	schisto m gassifero
— 8052	gas scrubber, gas trap	laveur m de gaz	Gaswascher m, Gaswäscher m	separatore m per gas
— 8053	gas scrubbing	épuration f de gaz	Gasreinigung f	depurazione f di gas
— 8054	gas separator	séparateur m de gaz	Gasabscheider m	separatore m di gas
o 8055	gas shell	grenade f à gaz	Gasgranate f	granata f chimica
— 8056	gas showing	traces f pl. de gaz	Gasvorkommen n	tracce f pl. di gas
	gas take, s. *circular gas outlet tube*			
o 8057	gas tee piece	tube m de séparation des gaz	Gasteilungsröhre f	tubo m divisore per gas, separatore m
	gas trap, s. *gas scrubber*			

	English	French	German	Italian
o	8058 gas turbine	turbine *f* à gaz	Gasturbine *f*	turbina *f* a gas
^	8059 gas valve	vanne *f* à gaz	Gasventil *n*	valvola *f* a gas
o	8060 gas vent	évent *m*	Steiger *m*, Steiger-öffnung *f*	respiro *m*
o	8061 gas volumeter	volumètre *m* à gaz	Gasvolumeter *n*	volumetro *m* per gas
o	8062 gas wash bottle	flacon *m* laveur de gaz	Gaswaschflasche *f*	bottiglia *f* di lavaggio per gas
o	8063 gas washer	scrubber *m*, laveur *m* à gaz	Gaswascher *m*, Skrubber *m*	lavatore per gas
o	8063a gas welding	soudure *f* à gaz	Autogenschweissen *n*	saldatura *f* a gas
—	8064 gas well	puits *m* à gaz	Gassonde *f*	pozzo *m* di gas
o	8065 gas well	sondage *m* à gaz	Gasbohrung *f*	sondaggio a gas, trivellazione a gas
o	8066 gas works	usine *f* à gaz	Gaswerk *n*	officina del gas
o	8067 gas (works) coke	coke *m* de gaz	Gaskoks *m*	coke *m* di gas
o	8068 gas yield	rendement *m* en gaz	Gasausbeute *f*	rendimento *m* in gas, resa di gas
o	8069 gaseous atmosphere	atmosphère *f* gazeuse	Gasatmosphäre *f*	atmosfera *f* gassosa
o	8070 gaseous explosive	explosif *m* gazeux	Gassprengstoff *m*	esplosivo *m* gassoso
o	8071 gaseous fuel	combustible *m* gazeux	gasförmiger Brennstoff *m*	combustibile *m* gassoso
—	8072 gaseous mine	mine *f* grisouteuse	Schlagwettergrube *f*	miniera *f* con grisou
	gaseous mixture, *s. fuel mixed with air*			
—	8073 gash vein	filon *m* irrégulier (en chapelet)	«Gash-Gang» *m*	filone *m* irregolare
o	8074 gasification	gazéification *f*	Vergasung *f*	gassificazione *f*
o	8075 gasification of the solid fuel	gazéification *f* du combustible solide	Vergasung *f* des festen Brennstoffes	gassificacazione *f* del combustibile solido
o	8076 to gasify	gazéifier	vergasen	gassificare
o	8077 gasifying action	effet *m* gazéifiant	vergasende Wirkung *f*	effetto *m* gassificante

	English	French	German	Italian
^	8078 **gasket**	garniture f ronde	Runddichtung f	guarnizione f rotonda
^	8078a **gasket cement**	matière f de bourrage	Dichtungsmittel n	cemento m di guarnizione
—	8079 **gasmeter, gasometer**	gazomètre m	Gasometer m	gasometro m
^	8080 **gasoline trap**	appareil m pour l'extraction de la gazoline	Benzin-und Wasserabscheiden m aus Erdgas	apparecchio m per l'estrazione di gasolina
—	8081 **gasproof**	étanche au gaz	gasdicht	stagno ai gas
—	8082 **gasser**	sondage m à gaz	Gasbohrung f	sondaggio a gas, pozzo di gas naturale
o	8082a **gassing**	absorption f de gaz	Gasabsorption f	assorbimento m di gas
o	8083 **gassy**	gazé	vergast	gassato
o	8084 **gassy iron**	fonte f soufflée	Blasenguss m	ghisa soffiata, getto m soffiato
—	8085 **gassy mine**	mine f grisoteuse	Schlagwettergrube f	miniera f con grisou
o	8086 **to gate**	appliquer les attaques de coulée	Anschnitte m $pl.$ einsetzen	mettere le colate
o	8087 **gate or runner (of a mould), geat, git, sprue-hole**	goulot m de coulée. trou de coulée	Einguss(kanal) m, Giessloch n	gola f, foro di colata
o	8088 **gate**	porte f, trappe f	Tür f	portello, porta, botola, foro (di scarico)
o	8089 **gate, gate inlet**	attaque f de coulée	Anschnitt m	attacco m di colata
o	8090 **gate (solidified metal in a gate)**	loupe f (dans l'attaque de coulée)	Bodensatz m im Anschnitt	colame m
	gate, s. *ingate gating*			
o	8091 **gate area**	section f d'attaque	Anschnittquerschnitt m	sezione f d'attacco
o	8092 **gate cutter, gate knife**	outil m à trancher la coulée	Giesskelle f zum Abschneiden des Ablaufes	tagliacolate m, mestolo m per canali di colata
	gate knife, s. *gate cutter*			
o	8093 **gate inlet**	attaque f de coulée	Anschnitt m	attacco m di colata
o	8094 **gate pin, runner pin**	modèle m de jet de coulée	Eingussmodell n	modello m di colata, bastone m verticale di colata

	English	French	German	Italian
— 8095	gate road	voie *f* de roulage, voie *f* de fond	Grundstrecke *f*, Sohlenstrecke *f*,	galleria di carreggio (o di fondo)
° 8096	gate stick	bâton *m* de coulée	Eingussstock *m*	bastone *m* di colata
^ 8097	gate valve	vanne *f* à coin	Schleusenschieber *m*	saracinesca *f* a paratoia, valvola *f* a cassetto
° 8098	gate wash	nettoyage *m* du trou de coulée	Giesslochreinigung *f*	pulitura *f* del canale di colata
° 8099	gated pattern	modèle *m* à entonnoirs	Modell *n* mit Eingusstrichtern	modello *m* con colata attaccata
^ 8100	gathering line	conduite *f* d'amenée	Zuflussleitung *f*	conduttura *f* d'alimentazione, tubazione *f* di captazione
^ 8101	gathering pump	pompe *f* auxiliaire	Hilfspumpe *f*	pompa *f* ausiliaria (o provvisoria)
° 8101a	gathering (surface)	surface *f* irrégulière	unregelmässige Oberfläche *f*	superficie *f* irregolare
° 8102	gathering stock	augmentation *f* de la section transversale	Querschnittsvergrösserung *f*	aumento *m* della sezione trasversale
^ 8103	gathering tank	réservoir *m* collecteur	Sammeltank *m*	serbatoio *m* collettore
° 8104	gating, gate	système *m* d'alimentation	Giesssystem *n*	insieme *m* di canali di colata e montanti
° 8105	gating	attaque *f* de coulée	Anschnitt *m*	applicazione delle colate, attacco di colata
° 8106	gating and risers, runners	jets *m pl.* de coulée	Rücklaufmaterial *n.* Giessabfälle *m pl.*	boccame *m*, colate *f pl.*
	gating with run-off, *s. flow through*			
° 8107	gauge	jauge *f*, calibre *m*	Lehre *f*	calibro *m*
^ 8108	gauge	manomètre *m*	Manometer *n*	manometro *m*
° 8109	gauge	écartement *m* de voie	Spurweite *f*	scartamento *m* dei binari
° 8110	gauge (of thickness)	jauge *f* de remmoulage	Wanddickenlehre *f*	maschera *f* di ramolaggio
° 8111	gauge (template)	calibre *m*	Lehre *f*	calibro *m*
^ 8112	gauge	niveau (productif)	Nutzniveau *n*	livello *m* (produttivo)

	English	French	German	Italian
○ 8113	gauge board	fond *m* de bois gabarié	Lehrboden *m*	tavolozzo *m* portamodello, fondo *m* di legno con modello
_ 8114	gauge door	porte *f* de réglage d'aérage	Wetterklappe *f*	portello *m* per regolare la ventilazione
○ 8115	gauge of wire	numéro *m* du fil, jauge *m* du fil	Drahtnummer *f*	numero *m* del filo, calibro *m* del filo
^ 8116	gauge stick	barre *f* de contrôle	Kontrollstab *m*	asta *f* di controllo
^ 8117	gauging tank	réservoir *m* jaugeur	Messtank *m*	serbatoio *m* graduato
_ 8118	Gault stage	Gault *m*	Gault *n*	Gault *m*
_ 8119	gauteite	gautéïte *f*	Gauteit *m*	gauteite *f*
○ 8120	gauze	toile *f* métallique	Drahtgewebe, Gaze *f*	rete *f* metallica, garza *f*
○ 8121	Gayley's method of blast dry air	procédé *m* Gayley pour le séchage de l'air	Windtrocknungsverfahren *n* nach Gayley	processo *m* d'essiccazione Gayley
_ 8122	gay-lussite	gay-lussite *f*	Gaylussit *m*	gaylussite *f*
_ 8123	geanticline	géoanticlinal .*m*	Geoantiklinale *f*	geoanticlinale *f*
○ 8124	gear, gearing	engrenages *m pl.*	Getriebe *n*	pignoni *m pl.*
○ 8125	gear, drive	engrenage *m*, rouage *m*	Getriebe *n*	ingranaggio *m*
	gear, *s. cast tooth*			
○ 8126	gear casing core (foundry)	noyau *m* de la boîte des engrenages	Räderkastenkern *m*	anima *f* della scatola ingranaggi
○ 8127	gear cutting machine	machine *f* à tailler les engrenages	Zahnradhobelmaschine *f*	macchina *f* dentatrice per ingranaggi
○ 8128	gear grinding machine	machine *f* à rectifier les engrenages	Zahnflankenschleifmaschine *f*	macchina *f* per rettificare gli ingranaggi
○ 8129	gear ring	couronne *f* dentée	Zahnkranz *m*	corona *f* dentata
○ 8130	gear shaft	arbre *m* d'entraînement (ou d'engrenage)	Getriebewelle *f*	albero *m* porta-ingranaggi
○ 8131	gear transmission system	transmission *f* mécanique	mechanische Übertragung *f*	trasmissione *f* meccanica

	English	French	German	Italian
° 8132	gear wheel, cog wheel	roue f dentée	Zahnrad n	ingranaggio m
° 8133	gear wheel moulding machine	machine f à mouler les roues dentées	Zahnräderform-maschine f	macchina f per forma-re ingranaggi
° 8134	gear wheel moulding machine attaching to the wall	machine f à mouler murale	Wandformmaschine f	macchina f da parete o murale per formare
° 8135	gear wheel moulding machine mounted on a column	machine f à mouler les engrenages à colonne	Säulenzahnrad-formmaschine f	macchina f a colonna per formare ingranag-gi
° 8136	gear wheel moulding machine with table	machine f à mouler les engrenages avec table	Tischzahnräderform-maschine f	macchina f a tavola per formare ingranaggi
° 8137	gear wheel moulding machine with two face plates	machine f à mouler les roues dentées avec deux plateaux	Zahnräderform-maschine f mit zwei Planscheiben	macchina f a due piat-taforme per formare ingranaggi
° 8138	geared ladle	poche f à engrenage	Giesspfanne f mit Getriebe-Kippvorrichtung	siviera f a ingranaggi
° 8139	gearing of teeth	engrènement m des dents	Eingriff m der Zähne	ingranaggio m dei denti
° 8140	geat, gate (of a mould), sprue	orifice m (ou jet) de coulée, gueule f du moule	Einguss, Einlauf m	foro m di colata, get-to m (o canale) di colata
— 8141	gedanite	gédanite f	Gedanit m	gedanite f
— 8142	Gedinnian stage	Gédinnien m	Gedinnien n	Gedinniano m
— 8143	gedrite	gédrite f	Gedrit m	gedrite f
— 8144	gehlenite	gehlénite f	Gehlenit m	gehlenite f
— 8145	geikielite	geikielite f	Geikielith m	geichielite f
— 8146	gel cement	gel-ciment m	Gelzement m	gelcemento m
— 8147	gel strenght	effet m tissotropi-que de la boue	Schlammthixotrop-effekt m	effetto m tissotropico del fango
— 8148	gelatinous silicic acid	silice f gélatineuse	gallertartige Kieselsäure f	silice f gelatinosa
— 8149	gelignite	gélignite f	Gelignit m (Spreng-stoff)	gelignite f

English	French	German	Italian
8150 gem	gemme *f*	Edelstein *m*	gemma *f*
8151 geminate crystal	cristal *m* maclé	Zwillingskristall *m*	geminato *m*
gemstone, *s. gem*			
8152 general phenomena in the blast furnace	phénomènes *m pl.* qui se produisent dans le haut-fourneau	allgemeine Vorgänge *m pl.* im Hochofen	andamento *m* generale dell'alto forno
8153 general trend	direction *f* générale	allgemeines Streichen *n*, Hauptstreichen *n*	direzione *f* generale
generator room, *s. dynamo room*			
8154 generator unit	groupe *m* générateur	Generatorsatz *m*	gruppo *m* generatore
8155 genoholotype	géno-holotype *m*	Geno-Holotypus *m*	geno-holotipo *m*
8156 genoparatype	géno-paratype *m*	Geno-Paratypus *m*	genoparatipo *m*
8157 genotype	génotype *m*	Genotypus *m*	genotipo *m*
8158 genthite	genthite *f*	Genthit *m*	genthite *f*
8159 geoanticline	géoanticlinal *m*	Geoantiklinale *f*, Geantiklinale *f*	geoanticlinale *f*
8160 geochemistry	géochimie *f*	Geochemie *f*	geochimica *f*
8161 geochronology	chronologie *f* géologique	Geochronologie *f*	geocronologia *f*
8162 geocratic period	période *m* géocratique	geokratische Zeit *f*	periodo *m* geocratico
8163 geocronite	géocronite *f*	Geokronit *m*	geocronite *f*
8164 geode	géode *m*	Geode *f*	geode *m*
8165 geodesy	géodésie *f*	Geodäsie *f*	geodesia *f*
8166 geodetic	géodésique	geodätisch	geodetico
8167 geodynamics	géodynamique *f*	Geodynamik *f*	geodinamica *f*
8168 geogenesis	géogenèse *f*	Geogenese *f*	geogenesi *f*
8169 geognosy	géologie *f* stratigraphique	Geognosie *f*	geologia *f* regionale, geognosia *f*

	English	French	German	Italian
— 8170	geoide	géoïde *m*	Geoid *n*	geoide *m*
— 8171	geologic(al)	géologique	geologisch	geologico
— 8172	geologic(al) age	âge *f* géologique	geologisches Alter *n*	era *f* geologica
— 8173	geologic(al) clock	tableau *m* chronologique	Zeittafel *f*	tabella *f* cronologica
— 8174	geologic(al) column	profil *m* géologique	geologisches Profil *n*	profilo *m* stratigrafico, profilo *m* geologico
— 8175	geologic(al) record	profil *m* stratigraphique	Normalprofil *n*	profilo *m* stratigrafico
— 8176	geologic(al) section	coupe *f* géologique	geologischer Schnitt *m*	profilo *m* geologico
— 8177	geologic(al) survey	relèvement *m* géologique	geologische Landesaufnahme *f*	rilievo *m* geologico
— 8178	geologic(al) window	fenêtre *f* tectonique	tektonisches Fenster *n*	finestra *f* tectonica
— 8179	geologist	géologue *m*	Geologe *m*	geologo *m*
— 8180	geology	géologie *f*	Geologie *f*	geologia *f*
— 8181	geomorphology	géomorphologie *f*	Geomorphologie *f*	geomorfologia *f*
— 8182	geonomy	géonomie *f*	Geonomie *f*	geonomia *f*
— 8183	geophysical	géophysique	geophysikalisch	geofisico
— 8184	geophysics	géophysique *f*	Geophysik *f*	geofisica *f*
— 8185	geordie	mineur *m* de charbonnage	Bergmann *m*, Knappe *m*	minatore *m* di carbone
— 8186	georgiadesite	georgiadésite *f*	Georgiadesit *m*	giorgiadesite *f*
— 8187	geoscopy	géoscopie *f*	Geoskopie *f*	geoscopia *f*
— 8188	geosyncline	géosynclinal *m*	Geosinklinal *f*	geosinclinale *f*
— 8189	geotechnics	géotechnique *f*	Geotechnik *f*	geotecnica *f*
— 8190	geotectonic geology, structural geology	géologie *f* structurale	strukturelle Geologie *f*	geologia *f* strutturale
— 8191	geothermal	géothermal	geothermisch	geotermico
— 8192	geothermal gradient	gradient *m* géothermique	geothermische Tiefenstufe *f*	gradiente geotermico

English	French	German	Italian
8193 Gerard furnace	four *m* Gérard	Gerardscher Ofen *m*	forno *m* Gérard
8194 gerhardtite	gerhardtite *f*	Gerhardtit *m*	gerhardtite·*f*
8195 German silver, pakfong. Argentan	maillechort *m*, argentan, argent *m* allemand, argental, alfénide	Argentan *n*, Neusilber *n*, Packfong *n*	argentone, argento *m* tedesco, argental *m*, alfenite *f*, pacfong *m*
8196 germanium	germanium *m*	Germanium *n*	germanio *m*
8197 gersdorffite	gersdorffite *f*	Gersdorffit *m*	gersdorffite *f*
8198 to get	abattre	hereingewinnen	abbattere
8199 to get a bone	perforer une roche dure	hartes Gestein *n* bohren	perforare in una roccia dura
8200 to get granite	rencontrer une roche dure	hartes Gestein antreffen	incontrare una roccia dura nello scavo
8201 get	production *f*, rendement *m*	Produktion *f*, Förderung *f*	produzione *f*, rendimento *m*
8202 get down	faire descendre	einfahren	far scendere
8203 get out	monter, remonter, extraire	ausfahren, hinauffahren	montare, rimontare, estrarre
8204 getter	abatteur *m*, piqueur	Abkohler *m*, Hauer *m*	picconatore *m*
8204a getter	dégazeur *m*	Fangstoff *m*	affinatore *m* del vuoto
8205 getting	abattage *m*, exploitation *f*, sous-cavage *m*	Abkohlen *n*, Hereingewinnung *f*, Unterhöhlen *n*	abbattimento *m*, sfruttamento *m*, coltivazione, taglio *m* al di sotto
8206 geyerite	geyérite *f*	Geyerit *m*	geyerite *f*
8207 geyser	geyser *m*	Geyser *n*	geyser *m*
8208 geyserite	geysérite *f*	Geyserit *m*	geyserite *f*
8209 ghizite	ghizite *f*	Ghizit *m*	ghizite *f*
8210 ghost	strie *f* de polissage	Schleifriss *m*, Polierkratzer *m*	stria *f* di lucidatura
8210a ghost (lines)	bande *f* de ferrite libre	freies Ferritband *n*	banda *f* di ferrite libera
8211 giant powder	dynamite *f*	Dynamit *n*	dinamite *f*
8212 gib	cale *f*, clavette *f*	Keil *m*	cuneo *m*, chiavetta *f*
8213 gib	pilot *m*, poussard *m*	Spreize *f*	puntello *m*

		English	French	German	Italian
°	8214	**gib steel**	acier *m* pour clavettes	Keilstahl *m*	acciaio *m* per chiavette
—	8215	**gibbet**	flèche *f* de grue	Kranbalken *m*	braccio *m* di gru
—	8216	**gibbsite**	gibbsite *f*	Gibbsit *m*	gibsite *f*
—	8217	**gibelite**	gibélite *f*	Gibelit *m*	gibelite *f*
—	8218	**gieseckite**	gieseckite *f*	Gieseckit *m*	gieseckite *f*
—	8219	**gig**	machine *f* d'extraction, cage *f* d'extraction à deux étages, benne *f*	Fördermaschine *f*, zweibödiges Fördergestell *n*	macchina *f* d'estrazione, gabbia *f* d'estrazione a due piani, benna *f*
—	8220	**gig house**	bâtiment *m* de machine d'extraction	Fördermaschinengebäude *n*	edificio *m* della macchina d'estrazione
—	8221	**gigantolite**	gigantolite *f*	Gigantolith *m*	gigantolite *f*
—	8222	**gigantostraca**	gigantostraca *f*	Gigantostraken	gigantostraca *f*
—	8223	**gilbertite**	gilbertite *f*	Gilbertit *m*	gilbertite *f*
°	8224	**to gild, to gold-plate**	dorer	vergolden, mit Gold überziehen	dorare, indorare
°	8225	**gilding**	dorure *f*	Vergolden *n*	doratura *f*
°	8226	**gilding by amalgamation**	dorure *f* au mercure	Quecksilbervergoldung *f*	doratura *f* a mercurio
°	8227	**gilding press**	presse *f* à dorer	Vergoldungspresse *f*	pressa *f* da dorare
°	8228	**gilled tube with fins**	tube *m* à ailerons	Rippenrohr *n*	tubo *m* ad alette
°	8229	**gillespite**	gillespite *f*	Gillespit *m*	gillespite *f*
—	8230	**gilsonite**	gilsonite *f*	Gilsonit *m*	gilsonite *f*
—	8231	**gin**	chèvre *f*, treuil *m* d'extraction	Hebezeug *n*, Förderhaspel *m*	capra *f*, argano *m*, paranco *m*
°	8232	**Gin furnace**	four *m* Gin	Ginofen *m*	forno *m* Gin
^	8233	**gin pole**	bigue *f*	Galgen *m*, Montagemast *m*	biga *f*, pontone *m*
—	8234	**giobertite**	giobertite *f*	Magnesit *m*	giobertite *f*
—	8235	**gips**	gypse *m*	Gips *m*	gesso *m*

English	French	German	Italian
8236 girasol	girasol *m*	Feueropal *m*	girasole *m*
8237 giratory crusher	concasseur *m* giratoire	Kreiselbrecher *m*	frantoio *m* giratore
8238 girder, beam	poutrelle *f*, fer *m* plancher	Träger *m*	ferro *m* per travi
8239 girds (derrick)	entretoisage *m*	Verstrebung *f*	controventi *m pl.* della torre
8240 girder for cranes	pont *m* pour grues	Kranbrücke *f*	ponte *m* per gru
8241 girder iron	fer *m* à poutres	Profileisen *n*	ferro *m* per travi (o profilato), profilato *m* di ferro
8242 girder pass	cannelures *f pl.* pour poutrelles	Trägerkaliber *n*	tracciato *m* per travi
8243 girder stores	parc *m* à poutrelles	Trägerlager *n*	deposito *m* di travature metalliche, parco putrelle
8244 Girod furnace	four *m* Girod	Girodofen *m*	forno *m* Girod
8245 girt(h)	entretoise *f*, poussard *m*	Riegel *m*, Spreize *f*	travetto *m* orizzontale di sostegno
8246 girth sheet	tôle *f* latérale	Seitenblech *n*	lamiera *f* laterale d'acciaio (di storta)
8247 gismondite	gismondine *f*	Gismondin *m*	gismondite *f*
git, s. *gate*			
giunk, s. *scrap iron*			
8248 give	affaissement *m* du toit	Senkung *f* der Firste	cedimento *m* del tetto
8249 Givetian stage	givétien *m*	Givetien *n*	givetiano *m*
G.L. *ground level*			
8250 glacial deposits *pl.*	dépôts *m pl.* glaciaires	glaziale Ablagerungen *f pl.*	depositi *m pl.* glaciali
8251 glacial drift	alluvion *m* glaciaire	Glazialgeschiebe *n*	alluvione *m* glaciale
8252 glacial facies	faciès *m* glacial	glaziale Fazies *f*	«facies» *f* glaciale
8253 glacial mud	boue *f* glaciaire	Gletscherschlamm *m*	fango *m* glaciale

	English	French	German	Italian

glacial period, *s. ice age*

— 8254	**glacial ploughing**	labourage *m* glaciaire	Gletscherabtrag *m*	aratura glaciale
— 8255	**glacial poy-hole**	moulin *m* glaciaire	Gletschermühle *f*	mulino *m* glaciale
— 8256	**glacial scour**	strie *f* glaciaire	Gletscherschramm *m*	stria *f* glaciale
— 8257	**glacial sheet**	couverture *f* glaciaire	festländische Eisdecke *f*	copertura *f* glaciale
— 8258	**glacial striae**	stries *f pl.* glaciaires	Gletscherschrammen	strie *f pl.* glaciali
— 8259	**glacial till**	argile *f* à blocaux	Geschiebemergel *m*	argilla *f* a blocchi
— 8260	**glacial trough**	auge *f* glaciaire	Trogtal *n*	truogolo glaciale
— 8261	**glacial valley**	vallée *f* glaciaire	glazial umgeformtes Tal *n*	valle *f* glaciale
— 8262	**glacialism**	théorie *f* de glaciation	Glazialtheorie *f*	glacialismo *m*
— 8263	**glacier**	glacier *m*	Gletscher *m*	ghiacciaio *m*
— 8264	**glacieret**	glacier *m* de second ordre	Hängegletscher *m*	ghiacciaio *m* di secondo ordine
— 8265	**glacis**	glacis *m*	Böschung *f*	scarpata *f*
° 8266	**glade**	couvercle *m* du presse-étoupe	Stopfbüchsendeckel *m*	coperchio *m* del premistoppa
— 8267	**gladkaite**	gladkaïte *f*	Gladkait *m*	gladkaite *f*
— 8268	**glance-coal**	charbon *m* luisant, houille *f* luisante	Glanzkohle *f*, Anthrazit *m*	carbone *m* brillante, antracite *f*
° 8268a	**glancing angle**	angle *m* de Bragg	Glanzwinkel *m*	angolo *m* di Bragg
° 8269	**gland, stuffing box gland**	bride *f*, bride *f* de boîte à presse-étoupe	Brille *f*, Stopfbüchsenbrille *f*	briglia *f*, briglia *f* del premistoppa
° 8270	**glass bead tube**	tube *m* à perles	Perlröhre *f*	tubo *m* con perle
° 8271	**glass bell**	cloche *f* en verre	Glasglocke *f*	campana *f* di vetro
° 8272	**glass box**	boîte *f* en verre	Glaskasten *m*	bacinella *f* di vetro
° 8273	**glass cock**	robinet *m* en verre	Glashahn *m*	rubinetto *m* di vetro

English	French	German	Italian
8274 **glass cover**	couvercle *m* en verre	Deckgläschen *n*	coperchio *m* di vetro
8275 **glass cutter**	coupe-verre *m*	Glasschneidemesser *m*	utensile *m* tagliavetri
8276 **glass-furnace, glass--kiln**	four *m* de verrerie	Glasofen *m*, Glasfabrikofen *m*	forno *m* per vetro, forno *m* per vetreria
8277 **glass hard**	dur comme le verre	glashart	duro come il vetro
8278 **glass hardness**	trempe *f* parfaite	Glashärte *f*	tempera *f* perfetta
glass kiln, *s. glass furnace*			
8279 **glass matrix**	pâte *f* vitreuse	glasige Zwischenmasse *f*	pasta *f* vetrosa
8280 **glass paper**	papier *m* de verre	Glaspapier *n*	carta *f* vetrata
8281 **glass plate**	plaque *f* en verre	Glasplatte *f*	lastra *f* di vetro
8282 **glass powder**	poudre *f* de verre	Glaspulver *n*	polvere *f* di vetro
8283 **glass rod**	baguette *m* en verre	Rührstab *m*, Glasstab *m*	bastoncino *m* o bacchetta *f* di vetro per agitare
8284 **glass-sheet**	plaque *f* de verre	Glastafel *f*, Glasscheibe *f*	lastra *f* di vetro
8285 **glass tube**	tube *m* en verre	Glasröhre *f*	tubo *m* o tubetto *m* di vetro
8286 **glass ware**	appareils *m pl.* en verre	Glasgerät *n*	apparecchi *m pl.* di vetro
glassworks' kiln, *s. glass-furnace*			
8287 **glassy feldspar**	sanidine *f*	Sanidin *m*	sanidina *f*
8288 **Glauber salt**	sel *m* de Glauber	Glaubersalz *n*	sale di Glauber
8289 **glauberite**	glaubérite *f*	Glauberit *m*	glauberite *f*
8290 **glaucochroite**	glaucochroïte *f*	Glaukochroit *m*	glaucocroite *f*
8291 **glaucodot**	glaucodot *m*	Glaukodot *m*	glaucodot *m*
8292 **glaucokerinite**	glaucocérinite *f*	Glaukokerinit *m*	glaucocerinite *f*
8293 **glauconite**	glauconite *f*	Glaukonit *m*	glauconia, glaucо-nite *f*

	English	French	German	Italian
— 8294	glauconitic	glauconieux	glaukonitisch	glauconifero
— 8295	glaucophane	glaucophane *m*	Glaukophan *m*	glaucofane *m*
° 8296	glazed iron, glazy pig	fer *m* à haute teneur en silicium	hochsiliziumhaltiges Eisen *n*	ferro *m* ad alto tenore di silicio
° 8296a	glazing	glaçure *f*	Glasieren *n*	smaltatura *f* a vetro
° 8297	glazing	polissage prélimi-naire	Vorpolieren *n*	lucidatura *f* preliminare
— 8298	glessite	glessite *f*	Glessit *m*	glessite *f*
° 8299	gliding band	ligne *f* de glissement	Gleitband *n*	linea *f* di slittamento
° 8300	glitter	étincellement	Flimmern *n*	scintillamento *m*
— 8301	globe mill	moulin *m* à boulets	Kugelmühle *f*	mulino *m* a palle, macina *f* a palle
^ 8302	globe valve	robinet *m* d'arrêt sphérique	Kugelventil *n*	valvola *f* a sfera
— 8303	globular porosity	porosité *f* globulaire	Kugelporosität *f*	porosità globulare
— 8304	globular structure or structure	structure *f* globu-laire. texture globulaire	kugelige Struktur, sphärolithisches Gefüge *n*	struttura *f* globulare
— 8305	globulite	globulite *f*	Globulit *m*	globulite *f*
— 8306	glomero-blastic structure	structure *f* gloméro--blastique	glomeroblastische Struktur *f*	struttura *f* glomero-blastica
— 8307	glomerophyric	glomérophyrique	glomeroporphyritisch	glomerofirico
° 8308	glory hole, reheating furnace	four *m* à réchauffer, four *m* de réchauffage	Heizofen *m*	forno *m* di riscaldo
° 8309	gloryhole	entonnoir *m* souterrain	Trichterschurre *f*	imbuto *m* sotterraneo
° 8310	gloryhole system	exploitation *f* par entonnoirs souterrains	Trichterbau *m*	coltivazione *f* ad imbuti sotterranei

glossy finish, s. *brillant finish*

gloves of asbestos, s. *welding gloves*

gloves of leather, s. *welding gloves*

glow, s. *red-heat*

English	French	German	Italian
8311 **glow lamp, bulb**	lampe *f* à incandescence	Glühlampe *f*	lampadina *f* ad incandescenza
glowing, *s. weak roasting*			
8312 **glowing cloud**	nuée *f* ardente	Eruptionswolke *f*	nube *f* ardente
8313 **glowing heat, red--heat**	incandescence *f*	Weissglut *f*	incandescenza *f*
glowing iron, *s. red-hot iron*			
8314 **glucinium**	glucinium *m*	Beryllium *n*	glucinio *m*
8315 **to glue**	coller	zusammenleimen	incollare
8316 **glue**	colle *f*	Leim *m*	colla *f*
8316a **glut weld**	soudure en V	V-Schweissung *f*	saldatura *f* a V
8317 **glutenite**	conglomérat *m*	Konglomerat *n*	conglomerato *m*
8318 **gmelinite**	gmélinite *f*	Gmelinit *m*	gmelinite *f*
8319 **gneiss**	gneiss *m*	Gneis *m*	gneiss *m*
8320 **gneissic structure**	structure *f* gneissique	Gneisstruktur *f*	struttura *f* a gneiss
8321 **gneissoid syenite**	syénite *f* gneissique	Gneissyenit *m*	sienite *f* a gneiss
8322 **gneissose granite**	gneiss-granite *m*	Gneisgranit *m*	granito-gneiss *m*
8323 **go devil**	ramoneur *m*	Laufteufel *m*	attrezzo *m* a forma di barra lasciato cadere nel pozzo
8324 **go devil**	installation *f* transportable du plan incliné	tragbare Bremsbergvorrichtung *f*	impianto *m* trasportabile d'un pozzo inclinato
8325 **goaf**	remblai *m*, vieux travaux	Versatz *m*, Berge, Versatzmaterial *n*, alter Mann *m*	ripiena *f*, vecchi lavori *m pl.* di scavo
8326 **goaf stowage**	remblayage *m*	Versatzarbeit *f*, Versetzen *n*	lavori *m pl.* di ripiena, ripiena *f*, colmata *f*
8327 **goaf stower**	machine *f* à remblayer	Versatzmaschine *f*	macchina *f* per ripiena
8328 **to gob**	remblayer	versetzen	eseguire una ripiena, riempire
8329 **gob**	remblai *m*, zone *f* foudroyée	Versatz *m*, Versatzberge, alter Mann *m*	ripiena *f*, zona *f* franata

	English	French	German	Italian
−	8330 **gob fire explosion**	exploision *f* de grisou	Schlagwetterexplosion *f*	esplosione *f* di grisou
−	8331 **gob road**	galerie *f* dans les remblais	Stollen *m* im Bergversatz	galleria *f* nelle ripiene
−	8332 **gob-road system**	exploitation *f* chassante	Vorbau *m*	coltivazione *f* ad avanzamento
−	8333 **gob stower**	remblayeuse *f* mécanique	Versatzmaschine *f*	macchina *f* per ripiena meccanica
−	8334 **gob stowing**	remblayage *m*	Versetzen *n*, Bergversatz *m*	ripiena *f*, colmata *f*, riempimento *m*
−	8335 **gob stuff**	remblai *m*	Versatz *m*	colmata *f*, ripiena *f*
−	8336 **gobbing**	remblayage *m*, remblai *m*	Versatzarbeit *f*, Versatz *m*	colmata *f*, (lavori di) ripiena *f*
−	8337 **gobbing machine**	remblayeuse *f* mécanique	Versatzmaschine *f*	macchina *f* per ripiena
−	8338 **goethite**	goethite *f*	Goethit *m*	goethite *f*
−	8339 **goffering**	froncement *m*, plissotement *m*	Fältelung *f*, Runzelung *f*	pieghettatura *f*, arricciatura *f*
°	8340 **goggles** *pl.*	lunettes *f pl.* protectrices	Schutzbrille *f*	occhiali *m pl.* di protezione
−	8341 **going**	aller *m*	Hingang *m*	andata *f*
−	8342 **goliath crane**	portique *m*	Portalkran *m*	gru *f* a cavalletto
°	8343 **gold**	or *m*	Gold *n*	oro *m*
−	8344 **gold-bearing quartz**	quartz *m* aurifère	Goldquarz *m*	quarzo *m* aurifero
°	8345 **gold blocking**	dorure *f* en feuilles	Blattvergoldung *f*	doratura *f* ad oro battuto
°	8346 **gold blocking press**	presse *f* à dorer et à empreindre	Prägepresse *f* für die Vergoldung	trancia *f* per dorare
°	8346a **gold bullion**	or *m* en lingots	Goldbarren *m*	oro *m* in lingotti
−	8347 **gold digging**	exploitation *f* aurifère	Goldseife *f*	coltivazione *f* di una miniera d'oro
°	8347a **gold foil**	feuille *f* d'or	Blattgold *n*	foglia *f* d'oro
−	8348 **gold pan**	batée *f*	Waschtrog *m*	bacinella *f* per lavare l'oro
°	8349 **gold refining**	affinage de l'or	Goldscheidung *f*	affinamento dell'oro
−	8350 **gold telluride**	tellurure *f* d'or	Goldtellurid *m*	telluride *f* d'oro

English	French	German	Italian
8351 gold vein	veine *f* aurifère	Goldgang *m*	vena *f* aurifera
8352 gold washer	laveur *m* d'or	Goldwäscher *m*	lavatore *m* d'oro
8353 goldfieldite	goldfieldite *f*	Goldfieldit *m*	goldfieldite *f*
8354 goldstone	aventurine *f*	Aventurin *m*	aventurina *f*
gompholite, *s. nagelfluh*			
8355 gonnardite	gonnardite *f*	Gonnardit *m*	gonnardite *f*
8356 Gooch's crucible	creuset *m* de Gooch	Goochscher Tiegel *m*	imbuto *m* di Gooch
8357 good bottom	bon mur *m*	gutes Liegende *n*	fondo *m* buono (di miniera)
8358 good weld	bonne soudure *f*	gute Schweiss-verbindung *f*	saldatura *f* ben fatta
8359 good pack	bon remblai *m*	guter Versatz *m*	ripiena *f* buona
8360 good roof	bon toit *m*	gutes Hangende *n*	tetto *m* buono
8361 goongarrite	goongarrite *f*	Goongarrit *m*	goongarrite *f*
8362 goose neck	col *m* de cygne	Druckbehälter *m*	collo *m* d'oca
8363 goose neck die-casting machine	machine *f* à fondre à air comprimé à chambre mobile	Pressgussmaschine *f* mit beweglicher Kammer	macchina *f* per presso-fusione ad aria compressa a camera mobile
8364 gooseberry stone	grossulaire *f*	Grossular	grossularia *f*
8365 gopher hole	fourneau *m* de mine	Minenkammer *f*	fornello *m* di mina
8366 gopher hole blasting	sautage *m* par chambres	Kammerschiessen *n*	abbattimento *m* con esplosivi a camere
8367 gophering	exploitation *f* irrationnelle	Raubbau *m*	sfruttamento *m* irrazionale
G.O.R. = *gas-oil ratio*			
8368 gordonite	gordonite *f*	Gordonit *m*	gordonite *f*
8369 goslarite	goslarite *f*	Goslarit *m*	goslarite *f*
8370 gossan, iron hat	chapeau *m* de fer	eiserner Hut *m*	cappello *m* di ferro
8371 gothic section	profil méplat	Spitzbogenprofil *n*	profilato *m* semipiatto

English	French	German	Italian
— 8372 **gouge, pug**	argile *f* de frottement	Verwerfungston *m*, Kluftton *m*, Kluftlette, Besteg, Ganglette *f*	argilla *f* d'attrito
— 8373 **gouge bit**	mèche-cuiller *f*	Hohlbohrer *m*	trivella *f* a cucchiaio, trapano *m*
— 8374 **gouging**	attaque *f* par le mur		attacco *m* dal muro (o dal tetto)
° 8374a **gouging, groove cutting**	rainurage *m* à la flamme	autogene Rillung *f*	scanalatura *f* al cannello
° 8375 **governor**	régulateur *m*	Regler *m*	regolatore *m* di pressione
— 8376 **goyazite**	goyazite *f*	Goyazit *m*	goyazite *f*
— 8377 **grab**	benne *f* preneuse pelle *f* automatique	Greiferkübel *m*, Greifer *m*	gru *f* a benna, pala *f* automatica
— 8378 **grab**	accrocheur *m*	Fanggerät *n*	arpione *m* di pescaggio
— 8379 **grab crane**	grue *f* à benne	Greifbagger *m*	gru *f* a benna
— 8380 **grab dredger**	benne *f* preneuse	Greifbagger *m*	gru *f* a benna
— 8381 **grab iron**	accrocheur *m*	Fanggerät *n*	gancio *m* da presa
— 8382 **grab sample**	échantillon *m* pris au grappin	zufälliges Muster *n*	campione *m* prelevato col gancio da presa
8383 **grade**	type *m*, catégorie	Materialgüte *f*	grado *m*, tipo *m* (di materiale)
— 8384 **grading**	classement *m*	Klassifizierung *f*	classificazione *f*
— 8385 **grading**	nivellement *m*	Nivellierung *f*	livellamento *m*
— 8386 **grading**	terrassement *m*	Erdarbeit *f*	terrazzamento *m*
— 8387 **grading, proportion of lump ore**	proportion *f* de gros	Stückgehalt *m*, Geröll *n*	proporzione *f* di minerale in pezzi nel giacimento o deposito
— 8388 **grading**	granulométrie *f*	Korngrössenverteilung *f*	granulometria *f*
— 8389 **grading plant**	installation *f* de triage	Klassieranlage *f*	impianto *m* di cernita
— 8390 **grading screen**	crible *m* classeur	Klassiersieb *n*	vaglio *m* classificatore

English	French	German	Italian
8391 **graduated measuring tube**	tube *m* gradué	graduiertes Messrohr *n*	tubo *m* graduato
8392 **graduated pipette**	pipette *f* graduée	Messheber *m*, Messpipette *f*	pipetta *f* di misurazione o tarata
8393 **graftonite**	graftonite *f*	Graftonit *m*	graftonite *f*
8394 **grahamite**	grahamite	Grahamit *m*	grahamite *f*
8395 **grail**	gravier *m*, sable *m*	Kies, Sand *m*	ciottolo *m*, sabbia *f*
8396 **grain**	grain *m*	Korn *n*	grana *f*, granulo *m*
grain, *s. crystal*			
grain, *s. grist*			
8397 **grain boundary**	limite *f* de grain	Korngrenze *f*	limite *m* del grano
8398 **grain growth**	croissance *f* des grains	Kornwachstum *n*	ingrossamento *m* della grana
grain number, *s. grain size number*			
8399 **grain refinement**	affinage *m* du grain	Kornfeinung *f*	affinazione *f* del grano
8400 **grain refining**	affinement *m* du grain	Kornvergütung *f*	raffinamento *m* del granulo
8400a **grain roll**	rouleau *m* de grenage	Kornwalze *f*	rullo *m* di granitura
8401 **grain size**	grosseur *f* du grain	Korngrösse *f*	grandezza *f* del grano
8402 **grain size number**	indice *m* de grosseur du grain	Korngrössenzahl *f*	numero *m* indice della dimensione del grano
8403 **grain structure, granular structure**	structure *f* granulaire	Kornstruktur *f*,	struttura *f* granulare
8404 **grained iron**	fer *m* à grains	gekörntes (od körniges) Eisen *n*	ferro *m* granulare
8405 **grained rock**	roche *f* grenue, roche *f* plutonienne	körniges Gestein *n*, plutonisches Gestein *n*	roccia *f* granulare, roccia *f* plutonica, roccia *f* di profondità
8405a **graining**	grenage *m*	Kornbildung *f*	granitura *f*
8406 **grains** *pl.*	minerai *m* en grains, grenailles *f pl.* de criblage	Graupe *f*	minerale *m* in pezzi piccoli
8407 **gram molecular volume**	volume *m* d'un gramme-molécule	Gramm-Molekül-volumen *n*	volume *m* d'una grammo-molecola

		English	French	German	Italian
°	8408	gram molecular weight	poids *m* en grammes-molécules	Gramm-Molekül-gewicht *n*	peso *m* in grammo-molecole
—	8409	gramenite	graménite *f*	Gramenit *m*	gramenite *f*
—	8410	grammatite	grammatite *f*	Grammatit *m*	grammatite *f*
°	8411	gramme equivalent	gramme-équivalent *m*	Grammäquivalent *n*	grammo-equivalente *m*
°	8412	gramme ion	gramion *m*, grammeion *m*	Grammion *n*	grammo-ione *m*
°	8413	gramme molecule	grammol *m*, gramme-molécule *m*	Grammol *n*	grammo-molecola *m*
°	8414	grampus	tenaille *f* à billettes	Barrenzange *f*	tenaglie *f pl.* per billette
—	8415	grandidierite	grandidiérite *f*	Grandidierit *m*	grandidierite
—	8416	granite	granit *m*	Granit *m*	granito *m*
—	8417	granite-porphyry	granite-porphyre *m*	Granitporphyr *m*	porfido *m* granitico
—	8418	granite sand	sable *m* granitique	Granitsand *m*	sabbia *f* granitica
—	8419	granitic subsoil	soubassement *m* granitique	granitischer Untergrund *m*	sottosuolo *m* granitico
—	8420	granitic (or eu-granitic) texture	structure *f* granitique	hypidiomorphkörnige Struktur *f*	struttura *f* granitica, struttura granulare
—	8421	granitite	granitite *f*	Granitit *m*	granitite *f*
—	8422	granitization	granitisation *f*	Granitisierung *f*	granitizzazione *f*
—	8423	granitoid, granitic	granitoïde	granitähnlich	granitoide
—	8424	granitoid texture, granitic texture	texture *f* granitoïde	granitische Textur *f*	struttura *f* granitoide o granitica
—	8425	granoblastic texture	texture *f* granoblastique	granoblastische Struktur *f*	struttura *f* granoblastica
—	8426	granodiorite	granodiorite *f*	Granodiorit *m*	granodiorite *f*
—	8427	granolite	roche *f* à structure grenue	Granolit *m*	granolite *f*
—	8428	granopatic texture or granophiric structure	structure *f* granophyrique	granophyrisches Gefüge *n*	struttura *f* granofirica

English	French	German	Italian
8429 granophyre	granophyre *m*	Granophyr *m*	granofiro *m*
8430 granophyric	granophyrique	granophyrisch	granofirico
granophyric texture, *granopatic structure*			
8431 granular crystalline gypsum	albâtre *m*	Alabaster *m*	alabastro *m*
8432 granular fracture	cassure *f* grenue	körniger Bruch *m*	rottura *f* granulare
8433 granular iron, grained iron	fer *m* grenu	körniges Eisen *n*	ferro *m* granulare
8434 granular limestone	calcaire *m* saccharoïde	körniger Kalkstein *m*	calcare *m* granulare, marmo *m*
granular structure, *s. grain structure*			
8435 to granulate	granuler	körnen, granulieren	granulare
8436 granulated carbon	grenaille *f* de charbon	Kohlenkörner *n pl.* Kohlengriess *m*	granuli *m pl.* di carbone, minuto di carbone
8437 granulated cuprous oxide	oxyde *m* de cuivre en grains	körniges Kupferoxyd *n*	ossido *m* di rame granulato
8438 granulated slag	laitier *m* granulé	gekörnte Schlacke *f*	loppa *f* granulata
8439 granulating plant	installation *f* de granulation	Granulationsanlage *f*	impianto *m* di granulazione
8440 granulation	granulation *f*	Körnung *f*, Granulierung *f*	granulazione *f*
8441 granulite	granulite *f*	Granulit *m*	granulite *f*
8442 granulitic structure	structure *f* granulitique	Granulitstruktur *f*	struttura *f* granolitica
8443 granulose	granuleux	körnig	granuloso
8444 granulose texture	texture *f* granoblastique	granoblastische Struktur *f*	struttura *f* granoblastica
8445 grapelike formation	forme *f* de grappe	traubenartige Bildung *f*	formazione *f* a grappoli
8446 graphic texture, eutectic texture	structure *f* (ou texture) pegmatoïde. texture *f* pegmatique, texture *f* graphique	graphische Textur *f*, eutektische Textur *f*	struttura *f* pegmatoide

		English	French	German	Italian
−	8447	graphite, plumbago	graphite *m*, plombagine *f*	Graphit *m*, Plumbago *m*, Reissblei *n*	grafite *f*, piombaggine *f*
o	8448	graphite crucible	creuset *m* en graphite	Graphittiegel *m*	crogiuolo *m* di piombaggine (o di grafite)
o	8449	graphite pyrometer	pyromètre *m* à graphite	Graphithitzemesser *m*, Graphitpyrometer *n*	pirometro *m* a grafite
o	8450	graphite rosette	rosette *f* de graphite	Graphitrosette *f*	rosetta *f* di grafite
o	8451	graphite water	eau *m* de graphite	Graphitwasser *n*	acqua *f* di grafite
−	8452	graphitic	graphitique	graphitisch	grafitico
−	8453	graphitic carbon	carbone *m* graphitique	graphitischer Kohlenstoff *m*	carbonio *m* grafitico, grafite *f*
o	8454	graphitic cast iron	fonte *f* graphiteuse	graphitisches Gusseisen *n*	ghisa *f* grafitosa
^	8455	graphitic oil	huile *f* graphitée	graphitiertes Öl *n*, Graphitöl	olio *m* grafitato
o	8456	graphitic steel	acier *m* graphiteux	graphitischer Stahl *m*	acciaio *m* grafitico
o	8457	graphitisation, graphitization	graphitisation *f*	Graphitisierung *f*	grafitizzazione *f*, ricottura di grafitizzazione
o	8458	to graphitise	graphiter	graphitisieren	grafitizzare
o	8459	graphitiser	graphitisant *m*	Graphitisierungsmittel *n*	grafitizzante *m*

graphitising, *s. graphitisation*

		English	French	German	Italian
^	8460	grapple	harpion (pour câbles)	Fanghaken *m*	arpione *m*
−	8461	grapholith	schiste *m* argileux	Tonschiefer *m*	scisto *m* argilloso
−	8462	graphophyric	granophyrique	granophyrisch	granofirico
−	8463	graptolite	graptolithe *f*	Graptolith *m*	graptolite *f*
−	8464	grass	niveau *m* du sol, surface *f*, carreau *m*	Tagesoberfläche *f*, Rasen *m*	terreno *m* superficiale, livello *m* del suolo
o	8465	grate	grille *f*	Rost *m*	griglia *f*, grata
o	8466	grate area	surface *f* de grille	Rostfläche *f*	superficie *f* della griglia

English	French	German	Italian
8467 grate bar, fire bar	barreau *m* de grille	Roststab *m*	sbarra *f* di griglia
8468 grate bar	grille *f* en rails de fer	Schienenrost *m*	grata *f* a sbarre
8469 grate bars	fer *m* pour barreaux	Roststabeisen *n*	barre *f* per griglie
8470 grate in one section	grille *f* à un seul panneau	Ganzrost *m*	griglia *f* in una sola sbarra
8471 grate cooling	réfrigération *f* du foyer	Rostkühlung *f*	raffreddamento *m* della griglia
8472 grate firing	foyer *m* à grille	Rostfeuerung *f*	focolare *m* a griglia
8473 grate opening, airspace between the grate	vide *m* ou lumière *f* de grille	Rostfuge *f*, Rostspalt *m*	vano *m* tra sbarre
8473a grate platform	palier *m* de grille	Gitterpodest *n*	piattaforma *f* di griglia
8474 grate with external water cooling	grille *f* à ruissellement	Rieselrost *m*	griglia *f* a scorrimento con raffreddamento esterno ad acqua
8475 grate with water circulation	grille *f* à circulation d'eau	Rost *m* mit Wasserzirkulation	grata *f* a circolazione d'acqua
8476 grating structure	structure *f* treillisée	Gitterstruktur *f*	struttura *f* a griglia
8477 gravel	gravier *m*	Kies *m*, Schotter *m*	ghiaia *f*
8478 gravel	sable *m* aurifère	goldführender Sand *m*	sabbia *f* aurifera
8479 gravel mine	carrière *f* de gravier	Kiesgrube *f*	cava *f* di ghiaia
8480 gravel mine	exploitation *f* alluviale	Goldseife *f*	miniera *f* d'oro alluvionale
8481 gravel packing	filtre à gravier	Kiesmantel	filtro *m* a ghiaia
8482 gravimeter	gravimètre *m*	Gravimeter *n*	gravimetro *m*
8483 gravimetric determination	analyse *f* gravimétrique	gravimetrische Bestimmung *f*	analisi *f* gravimetrica
8483a gravity casting	coulée sans pression	Giessen *n* ohne Druck	colata *f* per gravità
8484 gravity concentration	concentration *f* par gravité	Gravitationsaufbereitung *f*	concentrazione *f* per gravità
8485 gravity conveyor	descenseur *m*	Seigerförderer *m*	trasportatore *m* a gravità

		English	French	German	Italian
o	8486	**gravity die-casting, permanent mold gravity casting**	coulée *f* en coquille par gravité	Gravitationsko- killenguss *m*	colata *f* in conchiglia per forza di gravità
—	8487	**gravity drainage**	drainage *m* par gravité	Dränierung *f* durch Schwerkraft	drenaggio *m* per gravità
—	8488	**gravity fault**	faille *f* normale	normale Verwerfung *f*	faglia *f* normale
—	8489	**gravity flow**	écoulement *m* par gravité	Abfliessen *n*	scorrimento *m* per gravità
—	8490	**gravity-hoist**	balance *f* à gravité	Gravitationshebe- zeug *n*	paranco *m* a gravità
—	8491	**gravity incline**	plan *m* incliné	Bremsberg *m*	piano *m* inclinato, scivolo *m*

gravity position welding, *s. down-hand welding*

gravity runway, *s. gravity incline*

—	8492	**gravity separation**	séparation *f* par gravité	Gravitationsaufberei- tung *f*	separazione *f* per gravità
—	8493	**gravity solution**	liqueur *m* dense	schwere Flüssigkeit *f*	soluzione *f* gravitazio- nale
—	8494	**gravity spring**	source *f* de gravitation	Gravitationsquelle *f*	sorgente *f* di gravita- zione
—	8495	**gravity stamp**	bocard *m*	Pochmühle *f*	mulino *m* a pestelli
—	8496	**gravity water**	eau *f* gravitation- nelle	Gravitationswasser *n*	acqua *m* gravitazionale
—	8497	**gray antimony, grey antimony**	stibnite *f*	Antimonit *m*,	antimonite *f*, stibi- na *f*, stibnite *f*

gray cast iron, *s. grey cast iron*

—	8498	**gray clay**	argile *f* grise	grauer Ton *m*	argilla *f* grigia
—	8499	**gray copper**	cuivre *m* gris	Fahlerz *n*	rame *m* grigio

gray iron, *s. gray pig iron*

o	8500	**gray iron fining**	affinage *m* impar- fait, premier affinage	Rohfrischen *n*	affinaggio *m* della ghisa grigia
—	8501	**gray metal**	schiste *m* argileux gris	grauer Tonschiefer *m*	scisto *m* argilloso grigio

English	French	German	Italian
8502 **gray pig iron**	fonte *f* grise ordinaire, fonte *f* grise	gewöhnliches graues Roheisen *n*, graues Roheisen *n*	ghisa *f* grigia, ghisa *f* comune
grease, *s. fat*			
8503 **grease gun**	pistolet-graisseur *m*	Schmierpumpe *f*	ingrassatore *m* a pompetta
8504 **grease hole**	nouveau puits *m*	neuer Schacht *m*	nuovo pozzo *m* petrolifero
8505 **greasy**	graisseux	schmierig	untuoso
8506 **green bond**	corps *m* à vert	Grünstandfestigkeit *f*	forza *f* a verde
8506a **green brick**	brique *f* moulée	ungebrannter Backstein *m*	mattone *m* crudo
8507 **green casting**	moulage *m* à vert	Grüngiessen *n*	fusione *f* in verde, colata in verde
8508 **green clay**	argile *f* maigre	magerer Ton *m*	argilla *f* magra
8509 **green coal**	charbon *m* frais, charbon vierge	frische Kohle *f*	carbone *f* fresco
8509a **green compact**	compact *m* non-fritté	ungesinterter Pressling *m*	compatto *m* non sinterizzato
green concrete, *s. fresh concrete*			
8510 **green copper**	malachite *f*	Malachit *m*	malachite *f*
8511 **green earth**	glauconie *f*	Glaukonit *m*	glauconite *f*
8512 **green lead ore**	pyromorphite *f*	Pyromorphit *m*	piromorfite *f*
8513 **green microline**	amazonite *f*	Amazonenstein *m*	amazonite *f*
green permeabilty, *s. green sand permeability*			
8514 **green sand**	argile *f* verte	grüner Sand *m*, grüner Schlick *m*	argilla *f* verde
8515 **green sand casting**	moulage *m* en sable vert	Grünsandform *f*	getto *m* in forma di terra verde
8516 **green sand core**	noyau *m* en sable vert	grüner Kern *m*	anima *f* a verde
8517 **green sand mould**	moule *m* à vert	Grünsandform *f*	forma *f* a verde
8518 **green sand moulding**	moulage *m* à vert	Grünformen *n*	formatura *f* a verde
8519 **green strength**	cohésion *f* à vert résistance du comprimé	Grünbinderkraft *f* Grünfestigkeit *f*	coesione *f* a verde resistenza *f* del sinterizzato
green vitriol, *s. ferrous sulphate*			
8520 **green wood charcoal**	charbon *m* de bois feuillu	Laubholzkohle *f*	carbone *m* di legna (di ramoscelli)

	English	French	German	Italian
— 8521	**greenalite**	greenalite *f*	Greenalit *m*	greenalite *f*
— 8522	**greenockite**	greenockite *f*	Greenockit *m*	greenockite *f*
— 8523	**greenovite**	greenovite *f*	Greenovit *m*	greenovite *f*
° 8524	**greenstick fracture**	fracture *f* incomplète	Infraktion *f*	frattura *f* incompleta
— 8525	**gregarina** *pl.*	grégarines *f pl.*	Gregarine *f*	gregarine *f. pl.*
— 8526	**greisen**	greisen *m*	Greisen *n*	greisen *m*
— 8526a	**grena**	charbon *m* non-lavé	Rohkohle *f*	carbone *m* non lavato
	grey antimony, *s. antimonite*			
° 8527	**grey cast iron**	fonte *f* grise	Grauguss *m*	ghisa *f* grigia
	grey copper, *s. tetrahedrite*			
° 8528	**Grey-girder, broad flanged rolled girder**	double T à larges ailes	Differdinger Eisen *n.* Greyträger *m*	ferro del profilo Grey, ferro di Differdinger
° 8529	**grey iron, grey pig**	fonte *f* grise	Grauguss *m*	ghisa *f* grigia (o comune)
° 8530	**grey iron foundry**	fonderie *f* à fonte grise	Graugiesserei *f*	fonderia *f* per ghisa grigia
	grey loam, *s. grey clay*			
	grey manganese ore, *s. acerdese*			
° 8531	**grey pig (-iron), foundry-pig, foundry-iron**	fonte *f* grise, fonte *f* tendre, fonte *f* de moulage	Grauguss *m*, graues Roheisen *n*	ghisa *f* grigia
° 8531a	**grey slag**	scorie *f* verte de plomb	grüne Bleischlacke *f*	scoria *f* verde di piombo
— 8532	**greywacke**	grauwacke *f*	Grauwacke *f*	grauwacke *f*
	grid bar iron, *s. fire bar iron*			
° 8533	**grid layout**	quadrillage *m*	Liniennetz *n*	reticolo *m*
° 8534	**grief stem**	tige *f* d'entraînement	Mitnehmerstange *f*	asta *f* motrice
— 8535	**griffy**	sableux	sandig	sabbioso
^ 8536	**grillage**	grille *f*	Gitter *n*	griglia *f*, zatteroni *m pl.* della torre e dei motori
° 8537	**grind**	meuler, polir	schleifen, anschleifen	molare, affilare, levigare

	English	French	German	Italian
8538	grind, mill	broyer	brechen, zerkleinern	molazzare, frantumare
8539	to grind	moudre, pulvériser	mahlen, zerreiben	macinare, polverizza-re
8540	to grind finely	polissage m fin	Feinschleifen n	spianatura f con la lima fine
8541	to grind roughly	polissage m préparatoire	Grobschleifen n	spianatura f con la lima grossa
	to grind with emery	s. to emery grind		
8542	grind	broyage f	Zermahlen n	macinazione f
8543	grinder	meuleur m	Schleifer m	molatore m
8544	grinder	machine f à meuler	Schleifmaschine f, Bockschleifmaschine f	molatrice f, affilatrice f
8545	grinding, sharpening	meulage m affûtage m	Schleifen n	molatura f, smerigliatu-ra f
8546	grinding	broyage m	Zermahlen n	polverizzazione f, macinazione f
8547	grinding	strie f de la plaquette polie	Schleifriss m	striatura f del pezzo levigato
8548	grinding action of glacier ice	action f abrasive de la glace glaciaire	abschleifende Gletschererosion f	azione f (erosiva) del ghiaccio
8549	grinding bench	machine f à meuler	Schleifstuhl m	macchina f da affilare, affilatrice f
8550	grinding board	planchette f à polir	Schleifbrett n	piano m di levigazione
8551	grinding charcoal	charbon m à polir	Schleifkohle f	carbone m di salice per levigare
8552	grinding check	strie f d'usinage	Schleifriss m	incrinatura f di rettifica
8553	grinding emery	émeri m	Schleifschmirgel m	smeriglio m
8554	grinding in	rodage m à l'émeri	Einschleifen n	smerigliatura f
8555	grinding joints	outils-meules m pl.	Schleifscheiben f pl.	utensili m pl. per molare
8556	grinding machine, crusher	concasseur m, broyeur m	Zerkleinerungsma-schine f, Mühle f	macchina f per triturare, polverizzatore m, fran-toio m
8557	grinding machine,	meuleuse f	Schleifmaschine f	macchina f per molare

		English	French	German	Italian
°	8558	**grinding material**	matière *f* à polir	Schleifmittel *n*	materiale *m* per levigare, smeriglio *m*
—	8559	**grinding mill**	moulin *m* chilien	Feinzerkleinerungsmühle *f*	mulino *m* per macinazione fine
°	8560	**grinding pan**	amalgamateur *m*	Amalgamator *m*	amalgamatore *m*
—	8561	**grinding path**	plateau *m* des moules, cuvette *f*	Mahlbahn *f*	piano *m* di macinazione
°	8562	**grinding wheel**	roue *f* à meuler	Schleifscheibe *f*	mola *f* per affilare
—	8563	**grindstone, grinding stone**	pierre *f* meulière	Mühlstein *m*	mola *f*, macina *f* da mulino
°	8564	**to grip or bite the piece**	saisir la barre	das Walzstück *n* erfassen	prendere la barra, afferrare la sbarra
°	8565	**to grip the ingot**	accrocher le lingot	den Block einspannen	attaccare il lingotto, agganciare il lingotto
—	8566	**grip**	parachute *m*, pince *f* d'accrochage	Fangvorrichtung *f*, Mitnéhmer *m*	paracadute *m*, dispositivo *m* d'arresto
°	8567	**grip die**	matrice *f* de machine à forger	Schmiedemaschinengesenke *n*	stampo *m* di fucinatrice
—	8568	**grip gear**	parachute *m*	Fangvorrichtung *f*	paracadute *m*, dispositivo *m* d'arresto
—	8569	**grip shot**	coup *m* de mine incliné	geneigtes Bohrloch *n*	foro *m* di mina inclinato
—	8570	**griphite**	griphite *f*	Griphit *m*	grifite *f*
—	8571	**gripping device**	pince *f* d'accrochage	Mitnehmer *m*	pinza *f* da presa
—	8572	**gripping device**	griffe *f*, mâchoire *f*	Greifer *m*	griffa *f*, ganascia *f*
—	8573	**griquaite**	griquaïte *f*	Griquait *m*	griquaite *f*
—	8574	**grist, grain**	produit *m* broyé	Mahlgut *n*	macinatura *f*, prodotto *m* macinato
—	8575	**grit**	sable *m* gros, grenaille *f*	Grus *m*, Sandstein *m* Schrot *n*	sabbia *f* grossa, graniglia
—	8575a	**grit blasting**	grenaillage *m*	Abstrahlen *n*	granigliatura *f*
—	8576	**gritstone**	grès *m* à gros grains	grobkörniger Sandstein *m*	gres *m* a grana grossa
—	8577	**gritty**	graveleux	kiesig	ghiaioso

English	French	German	Italian
8578 grizzle	charbon *m* pyriteux	pyrithaltige Kohle *f*	carbone *m* piritico
8579 grizzly	grille *f*	Rost *m*, Gittersieb	griglia *f*, vaglio *m*
8580 grizzly elevator	élévateur *m* à grille	Rosthebewerk *n*	elevatore *m* a griglia
8581 grizzly feed	alimentation *f* à grille	Rostspeisung *f*	alimentazione *f* a griglia
8582 grizzly level	niveau *m* de grilles	Rostsohle *f*	livello *m* delle griglie
8582a grog	argile *f* cuite pulvérisée	gebrannter Ton *m*	argilla *f* cotta in polvere
8583 grommet	attache *f* continue du câble sans bout	Ring *m* des Keilriemens	anello *m* continuo di cavo senza estremità
8584 grommet belt	courroie *f* trapézoïdale à deux câbles sans bouts	Keilriemen *m* mit zwei Ringen	cinghia *f* trapezoidale con due «grommets»
8585 to groove	canneler	kehlen, kerben	scanalare
8586 groove	rainure *f*, cannelure *f*, gorge *f*	Rille *f*, Rinne *f*, Kerbe *f*	scanalatura *f*, gola *f*, canale *m*
8587 groove	creux, tranchée *f*	Vertiefung *f*, Schurfgraben *m*	solco *m*, trincea *f*
groove angle, *s. angle of VEE*			
groove brush, *s. brush with side*			
8587a groove cutting	rainurage *m* à la flamme	autogene Rillung *f*	scanalatura *f* al cannello
groove face, *s. fusion face*			
8588 groove sheave	poulie à gorge	Rillenrad *n*	puleggia *f* scanalata
8589 groove weld	cordon *m* frontal	vorderseitlicher Rand *m*	cordone *m* frontale
8590 grooved drum	tambour *m* cannelé	Seiltrommel *f* mit Rillen	tamburo *m* scanalato
8591 grooved part	partie *f* creuse du cylindre	eingeschnittene Stelle *f*	parte *f* intagliata od intaccata
8592 grooved pulley	poulie *f* à gorge	Rillenrad *n*	puleggia *f* scanalata
8593 grooved roll	cylindre *m* à gorge	ausgekehlte Walze *f*	cilindro *m* a gola
8594 grooved roll	cylindre *m* cannelé	Kaliberwalze *f*	cilindro *m* a canali
8595 grooved spring steel	acier *m* cannelé pour ressorts	Rippenfederstahl *m*	acciaio *m* scanalato per molle

		English	French	German	Italian
°	8596	**groover (for anvil)**	outil *m* à canneler (ou rainurer)	Falzbeïtel *m*	scanalatore *m*, attrezzo a scanalare
°	8597	**grooving**	rainurage, rainage	Nuten *n*, Schlitzen *n*	scanalatura *f*
°	8598	**grooving and tonguing**	rainure *f* et languette *f*	Spundung *f*	incastro *m* a maschio e femmína, collegamento *m* a incastro
—	8599	**grorudite**	grorudite *f*	Grorudit *m*	grorudite *f*
°	8600	**gross blowholes**	bouillonnement *m*	Kochen *n*	rifiuto *m* di sbollitura
°	8601	**gross calorific value**	puissance *f* calorifique brute	oberer Heizwert *m*	potere *m* calorifico superiore, potere *m* calorifico massimo
—	8602	**gross measure drift**	galerie *f* transversale	Querschlag *m*	traforo *m* di sonda
	8603	**gross production**	grande production *f*	Massenerzeugung *f*	produzione *f* in massa
	8604	**gross weight**	poids *m* brut	Rohgewicht *n*, Bruttogewicht *n*	peso *m* lordo
—	8605	**grossularite**	grossulaire *f*	Grossular *m*	grossularite *f*
—	8606	**grothite**	grothite *f*	Grothit *m*	grothite *f*
°	8607	**ground, sharpened**	affilé, aiguisé, meulé	scharf, geschliffen	affilato, aguzzato, arrotato
—	8608	**ground auger**	tarière *f*, sonde *f*	Erdbohrer *m*	sonda *f*, trivella *f*
°	8609	**ground bar**	barre *f* rectifiée	geschliffener Stab *m*	barra *f* rettificata
°	8610	**ground clamp**	bride *f* de serrage (pour mise à terre)	Erdschlussklemme *f*	morsetto *m* per terreno
°	8611	**ground coat**	couche *f* de base	Grundiermittel *n*	strato *m* di base
—	8612	**ground coal**	charbon *m* de la partie inférieure de la couche	Grundkohle *f*	carbone *m* del fondo di miniera
—	8613	**ground gypsum**	gypse *m* de qualité supérieure	hochwertiger Gips *m*	gesso *m* di qualità superiore
—	8614	**ground-hog**	contre-poids *m* d'un plan incliné	Gegengewicht *n* im Bremsberg	contrappeso *m* d'un piano inclinato
—	8615	**ground-hog**	terrassier *m*	Erdarbeiter *m*	terrazziere *m*

English	French	German	Italian
8616 ground level	niveau *m* du sol	Grundsohle *f*	livello *m* del suolo, fondo *m*
8617 ground mass	masse *f* microcristalline	Grundmasse *f*	massa *f* microcristallina
8618 ground moraine	moraine *f* de fond	Grundmoräne *f*, Untermoräne *f*	morena *f* profonda
8619 ground products	produits *m pl.* rectifiés	geschliffene Produkte *n pl.*	rettificati *m pl.*
8620 ground sill	semelle *f* de base	Grundschwelle *f*	suola *f* di base, dormiente *m*
8621 ground sluice	canal *m* à sluices	Grundgerinne *n*, Abflussgraben *m*	canale *m* scaricatore
8622 ground water	nappe *f* d'eau souterraine	Grundwasser *n*	acqua *f* sotterranea o freatica
8623 ground-work	sous-oeuvre *f*	Unterbau *m*	lavoro *m* sotterraneo
8624 grounds and lags	modèle *m* en douves	Modellaufbau *m* in Dauben	modello *m* a doghe
8625 group of faults	groupement *m* de failles	Bruchsystem *n*	gruppo *m* di faglie
8626 group of lines	groupe *m* de raies	Liniengruppe *f*	gruppo *m* di linee
8627 group of springs	groupement de sources	Brunnensystem *n*	gruppo di sorgenti
8628 grouting	fonçage *m* des puits par cimentation, cimentation *f* des fissures aquifères	Schachtabteufen *n* nach dem Zementierverfahren, Zementierung *f* wasserführender Klüfte	trivellazione *f* di pozzi per cementazioni, cementazione *f* delle fissure acquifere
8629 grouting machine	machine *f* de cimentation	Zementiermaschine *f*	macchina *f* per cementazione
8630 grouting process	fonçage *m* des puits par la méthode de la cimentation, cimentation *f* des fissures	Schachtabteufen *n* nach dem Zementierverfahren, Versteinungsverfahren *n*	perforazione *f* di pozzi col metodo della cementazione, cementazione *f* delle fissure
8631 grove	travers-bancs *m*, puits *m*, ouvrage *m* souterrain	Schacht *m*, Grubenbau *m*	galleria *f* di traverso-banco, pozzo *m*, opera *f* sotterranea

	English	French	German	Italian
— 8632	**growan**	granite _m_ à tourmaline	Turmalingranit _m_	granito _m_ a tormalína
° 8633	**growth (of cast iron)**	gonflement _m_ (de la fonte)	Wachsen _n_ (des Gusseisens)	rigonfiamento _m_ della ghisa
— 8634	**grunerite**	grunérite _f_	Grünerit _m_	grunerite _f_
— 8635	**grunlingite**	grunlingite _f_	Grünlingit _m_	grunlingite _f_
— 8636	**guadalcazarite**	guadalcazarite _f_	Guadalcazarit _m_	guadalcazarite _f_
— 8637	**guag**	vieux travaux _m pl._	alter Mann _m_	miniera _f_ abbandonata
— 8638	**guanajuatite**	guanajuatite _f_	Guanajuatit _m_	guanajuatite _f_
° 8639	**guaranteed contents**	teneur _f_ garantie	verbürgter Gehalt _m_	tenore _m_ garantito
° 8640	**guaranteed loss**	perte _f_ garantie	garantierter Verlust _m_	perdita _f_ garantita
° 8641	**guard**	carter _m_	Gehäuse _n_	protezione, carter _m_
° 8642	**guard**	garde _f_	Abstreifmeissel _m_	guardia _f_
	guard, _s. disc_			
	guard iron, _s. rail iron_			
	guard plate, _s. screen_			
° 8643	**guard rail, check rail, guide rail**	contre rail _m_	Leitschiene _f_, Radlenker _m_, Zwangsschiene _f_	controrotaia _f_, barriera _f_ di protezione
	guards, _s. roller tables_			
— 8644	**guarinite**	guarinite _f_	Guarinit _m_	guarinite _f_
— 8645	**gubbin**	minerai _m_ de fer argileux	Toneisenerz _n_	minerale _m_ di ferro argilloso
— 8646	**gudmundite**	gudmundite _f_	Gudmundit _m_	gudmundite _f_
— 8647	**guejarite**	guéjarite _f_	Guejarit _m_	guejarite _f_
— 8648	**guest mineral**	métasome _m_	Metasom _n_	metasoma _m_
	guide, _s. stripping plate_			
° 8649	**guide**	guide _m_	Führung _f_	guida _f_, guardia _f_
— 8650	**guide fossil, index-fossil**	fossile _m_ caractéristique	Leitfossil _n_	fossile _m_ caratteristico, fossile-guida

	English	French	German	Italian
8651	**guide mark**	strie f de laminage, marque f de guide	Walzreife f Führungsstangenspur	riga f di laminazione traccia f di guida
8652	**guide pin**	tige f de démouleuse	Abhebestift m	spina f di estrazione
8653	**guide-plate**	plaque f directrice, plan directeur	Gleitplatte f, Leitwand f, Leitblech n	piastra f direttrice, piano m direttore
	guide roller, s. *foot roller*			
	guide scratch, s. *guide mark*			
8654	**guide shoe**	sabot m de guidage	Führungsschuh m	scarpa f di guida
8655	**guide track**	rampe f	Kurvenstück n	ringhiera f, naso m di comando
	guided root bend test, s. *tongue bend test*			
8656	**guiding rolls on both sides of the machine**	serveuses $f\,pl.$ de part et d'autre de la machine	Anlauf- und Ablaufrollgänge $m\,pl.$	coppia f di rulli di rettifica sui due lati della macchina
8657	**guildite**	guildite f	Guildit m	guildite f
8658	**guillotine**	coupe-jet m	Eingussschere f	taglia colate f
8659	**guillotine shear**	cisaille-guillotine f	Tafelschere f	cesoia f a ghigliottina
8660	**gug**	plan m automoteur	selbsttätige Bremsbergvorrichtung f	piano m automatico
8661	**guhr**	terre d'infusoires	Infusorienerde f	terra f d'infusori
8662	**gulch gold**	or m alluvionnaire	Seifengold n	oro m alluvionale
	gullet, s. *gate (of a mould)*			
8663	**gum**	gomme f	Harz n	gomma f
8664	**gum-dynamite**	dynamite-gomme f	Gelatine-Dynamit n	gelatina-dinamite f
8665	**gumbo**	gumbo m	Gumbo m	suolo m argilloso (o molto adesivo)
8666	**gumming of cores**	collage m de noyau	Kernkleben n	incollatura f d'anime
8667	**gummite**	gummite f	Gummit m	gummite f
8668	**gun**	canon m à boucher le trou de coulée	Stopfmaschine f	macchina f per otturare il foro di colata

	English	French	German	Italian
— 8669	gun	canon perforateur	Geschosslocher *m*	fucile *m* perforatore, agitatore del fango
° 8670	gun barrel steel	acier à canons de fusils	Gewehrlaufstahl *m*	acciaio per canne di fucile
— 8671	gun boat	skip *m*	Kippkübel *m*	skip *m*, gabbia *f* da miniera
— 8672	gun cotton, nitrocotton, fulmicotton	coton-poudre *m*	Schiessbaumwolle *f*	cotone *m* fulminante, fulmicotone
° 8673	gun-metal	métal à canons, bronze à canon	Kanonenmetall *n*, Kanonenbronze *f*	metallo *m* per cannoni, bronzo *m* da cannone
— 8674	gun perforator	perforateur *m* à balles, canon *m* perforateur	Geschossrohrlocher *m*, Geschosslocher *m*	perforatore *m* a pallottola, fucile *m* perforatore
° 8675	gun spring steel	acier à ressort(s) pour fusil	Gewehrfederstahl *m*	acciaio *m* per molle di fucili
^ 8676	gush	jaillissement *m*	Ausbruch *m*	eruzione *f*
^ 8677	gusher	puits *m* jaillissant	Springer *m*, Springerquelle *f*, Spritzer *m*	pozzo *m* ad eruzione spontanea
^ 8678	gushing well	puits *m* jaillissant	Spritzer *m*	pozzo *m* ad eruzione spontanea
° 8679	gusset (plate)	gousset *m* (en tôle)	Knotenblech *n*	piastra *f* nodale di testa
° 8680	gusset	gousset *m* d'union	Metallgitter *n*	fazzoletto *m* d'unione
° 8681	guttapercha bottle	bouteille *f* en guttapercha	Guttaperchaflasche *f*	bottiglia *f* di guttaperca
° 8682	guttapercha sheet	carton *m* en guttapercha	Guttaperchapapier *n*	carta *f* di guttaperca
° 8683	guttapercha ware	pièces *f pl.* en guttapercha	Guttaperchagerät *n*	strumenti *m pl.* di guttaperca
° 8684	gutter, trench	rigole *f* de chargement	Einflussrinne *f*	canale *m* di colata
— 8685	gutter	lit *m* de rivière contenant de l'or	Flussbett *n* mit Goldgehalt	letto *m* di fiume contenente oro
— 8686	gutter	gouttière *f*	Wasserrinne *f*, Abflusskanal *m*	canale *m* di scolo acque

English	French	German	Italian
8687 **gutter (for flash)**	canal *m* à ébarbures	Gratrinne *f*	scanalatura *f* per sfogo sbavatura
8688 **to gutter**	rainer, rainurer	schlitzenfräsen	scanalre
8689 **gutter discharge pipes, rainwater down-pipe**	tuyaux *m pl.* de descente pour eaux pluviales	Regenwasser- abflussrohre *n pl.*	tubi *m pl.* per scarichi pluviali
8690 **guy, stay (rope)**	hauban *m*	Ankerdraht *m*	filo *m* d'ancoraggio, tenditore *m*, vento *m*
8691 **guys**	haubans *m pl.* de la tour	Turmankerdrähte *m pl.*	venti *m pl.* della torre
8692 **gwag**	vieux travaux	alter Mann *m*	miniera *f* abbandonata
8693 **gymnite**	gymnite *f*	Gymnit *m*	gymnite *f*
8693a **gypsiferous**	gypsifère	gipsführend	gessifero
8694 **gypsum**	gypse *m*	Gips *m*	gesso *m*, pietra *f* da gesso
8695 **gyratory crusher**	concasseur *m* giratoire	Kreiselbrecher *m*	frantoio *m* giratore
8696 **gyrol**	friction *f* hydraulique	hydraulische Friktion *f*	frizione *f* idraulica
8697 **gyrolite**	gyrolite *f*	Gyrolith *m*	gyrolite *f*

	English	French	German	Italian
—	8967a habit	forme f cristalline	Kristallform f	forma f cristallina
—	8698 habitus	faciès m	Habitus m	facies f
—	8699 hackmanite	hackmanite f	Hackmannit m	hackmannite f
—	8700 hackly fracture	cassure f hachée	zackiger Bruch m	rottura f irregolare (o scagliosa)
—	8701 hade-slip fault	faille f normale	gewöhnlicher Sprung m	faglia f normale
°	8702 Hadfield steel	acier m Hadfield	Hadfieldstahl m	acciaio m Hadfield
—	8703 hading against the dip fault	faille f contraire	gegenfallende Verwerfung f	faglia f contraria
—	8704 hading with the dip fault	faille f conforme	rechtfallende Verwerfung f	faglia f conforme
—	8705 haematite	hématite f	Hämatit. m	ematite f
°	8706 hafnium	hafnium m	Hafnium n	afnio m
—	8707 haidingerite	haidingérite f	Haidingerit m	haidingerite f
—	8707a hair-copper	chalcotrichite f	Chalkotrichit m	calcotrichite f
°	8708 hair crack	fissure capillaire	Haarriss m	incrinatura f (o frattura) capillare
°	8709 hair-cross	réticule m	Fadenkreuz n	reticolo m
—	8709a hair pyrite	millérite f	Millerit m	millerite f
—	8710 hair salt	halotrichite f	Halotrichit m	halotrichite f
°	8710a hair seam	repliure de laminage	Überwalzungsfehler m	difetto m di piegatura
—	8711 hairstone	cheveux m pl. de Vénus	feinadriger Rutil eingewachsen im Bergkristall	capelli m pl. di Venere
	half converting, s. *case-hardening*			
—	8711a half and half solder	soudure f de plombier	Lötmörtel m	stagno m da idraulico
—	8712 half-course	front m d'attaque à 45° avec la direction	Stossstellung f von 45° zum Streichen	fronte m d'attacco a 45° dal piano di stratificazione
—	8713 half-edge seam	couche f inclinée à 45°	Flöz n von 45° Neigung	filone m inclinato
	half-fixed boiler, s. *semiportable boiler*			
	half hard and hard steel, s. *ingot steel*			
°	8714 half-hard steel	acier m mi-dur	Flussstahl m	acciaio m semiduro
	8715 half round	demi-circulaire	halbrund	semicircolare

English	French	German	Italian
8716 **half-round iron** **(or bar), half-rounds**	fer *m* demi-rond, fer *m* mi-rond	Segmenteisen *n*, Halbrundprofil *n*	ferro *m* semitondo, mezzotondo *m*
8717 **half steel**	acier *m* ferreux	Halbstahl *m*	acciaio *m* ferroso
8718 **half-washed semi-** **-bituminous coal**	charbon *m* demi- -gras mi lavé	halbgewaschene Halbpechkohle *f*	carbone *m* semigrasso semilavato
8719 **halide**	halogénure *m*	Halogenid *n*, Haloid *n*	alogenuro *m*
8720 **halite**	halite *f*	Halit *m*, Steinsalz	salgemma *m*
8721 **halleflinta**	hälleflinta *f*	Hälleflinta *m*	hälleflinta *f*
8722 **hallerite**	hallérite *f*	Hallerit *m*	hallerite *f*
8723 **halloysite**	halloysite *f*	Halloysit *m*	
8724 **haloid**	haloide *m*	Haloid *n*	aloide *m*
8725 **halogen**	halogène	halogen	alogeno
8726 **halotrichite**	halotrichite *f*	Halotrichit *m*, Haarsalz *n*	halotrichite *f*
8727 **to hammer**	marteler, forger	hämmern, durch- hämmern, (aus)- schmieden, treiben	martellare, forgiare
to hammer the bloom, *s. to shingle*			
8728 **to hammer the tube** **during the** **hydraulic test**	frapper sur les tu- yaux avec le marteau pendant l'épreuve hydraulique	die Röhre während der Wasserdruckpro- be abhämmern	battere i tubi durante la prova idraulica
8729 **hammer breaker**	broyeur *m* à marteaux	Hammermühle *f*	frantoio *m* a martelli, macina *f* a martelli
8730 **hammer cylinder**	cylindre *m* du mouton	Bärzylinder *m*	cilindro *m* della mazza battente
8731 **hammer drill**	marteau-perforateur	Bohrhammer *m*	martello-perforatore *m*
8732 **hammer drill stoper**	foratrice *f* télescopique	Teleskophammer *m*	perforatrice *f* tele- scopica
8733 **hammer drilling**	forage par battage	stossbohren	sondaggio alla corda (o a percussione)
8734 **hammer face**	panne *f* du marteau	Hammerbahn *f*	penna *f* della mazza battente (o del martello)

	English	French	German	Italian
° 8735	hammer forging	martelage *m*	Hämmern *n*	fucinatura *f* al maglio, martellatura *f*
° 8736	hammer forging	pièce *f* forgée au marteau	Schmiedestück *n*	pezzo *m* fucinato al maglio
	hammer-hardened iron, *s. cold-hammered iron*			
° 8737	hammer head	tête *f* de marteau	Hammerkopf *m*	mazza *f* battente
	hammer mark, *s. dent*			
— 8738	hammer mill, hammer crusher	broyeur *m* à marteaux	Hammermühle *f*	mulino *m* a martelli
° 8739	hammer operated by a crank	marteau *m* à manivelle	Kurbelhammer *m*	maglio *m* a manovella
° 8740	hammer pane	panne *f* de marteau	Hammerfinne *f*	penna *f* del martello
° 8741	hammer piston	piston *m* du marteau	Hammerkolben *m*	stantuffo *m* della mazza
° 8742	hammer scale	battiture *f*, oxydes *m pl.*	Hammerschlag *m*, Zunder *m*	scaglia *f* di martellatura
	hammer shop, *s. forge shop*			
° 8742a	hammer slag	laitier *m* de puddlage	Puddelschlacke *f*	scoria *f* di puddellaggio
° 8743	hammer union	union *f* à marteau	Hammerverbindung *f*	unione *f* a martello
° 8744	hammer valve gear	distribution *f* du marteau	Hammersteuerung *f*	distribuzione *f* (o comando) dell'inversione di marcia della mazza battente
— 8745	hammer weld, hammer welding	soudure *f* par martelage	Hammerschweissung *f*	saldatura *f* mediante martellatura *f* (o per fucinatura)
° 8746	hammered cast steel	acier *m* fondu forgé	gehämmerter Gussstahl *m*	acciaio *m* fuso battuto
	hammered iron, *s. wrought-iron*			
° 8747	hammered sheet iron	tôle *f* martelée	gehämmertes Eisenblech *n*	lamiera *f* martellata
° 8748	hammering	martelage *m*	Hämmern *n*	martellatura *f*
° 8749	hammering test	essai *m* d'élargissement	Ausbreit(e)probe *f*	prova *f* di allargamento

English	French	German	Italian
8750 **hammerman**	forgeron *m*, marteleur *m*	Hammerarbeiter *m*	fabbroferraio *m*, fucinatore *m*, forgiatore *m*
8751 **hancock jig**	tamis *m* hydraulique à étage mobile	Hydraulik-Sieb *n* mit beweglicher Ebene	crivello *m* idraulico a piano mobile
8752 **hancockite**	hancockite *f*	Hancockit *m*	hancockite *f*
8753 **hand-anvil, small anvil**	enclumette *f*, bigorneau *m*	Handamboss *m*, Gegenhalter *m*	incudinuzza *f*, incudine *f* a mano
8754 **hand auger**	tarière *f* à main	Handbohrer *m*	trivella *f* a mano
8755 **hand bellows**	soufflet *m*	Blasebalg *m*	soffietto *m* a mantice
8756 **hand brush**	brosse *f* de nettoyage à main	Handfeger *m*	spazzola *f* a mano
8757 **hand churn drill**	fleuret à main	Handbohrer *m*	fioretto *m* a mano, trivella *f* a mano
8758 **hand dog**	clef *f* à tige	Gestängeschlüssel *m*	chiave *f* ad asta
8759 **hand-drilled well (or hole)**	forage *m* à bras (ou à main)	Handbohrung *f*	perforazione *f* a mano
8760 **hand gilding**	dorure *f* à la main	Handvergoldung *f*	doratura *f* a mano
8761 **hand hole**	regard *m*	Schauklappe *f*	portello *m* d'ispezione
hand iron, *s. electric iron*			
8762 **hand jig**	bac *m* à piston	Handsetzmaschine *f*	vaglio *m* (o crivello *m*) a mano
8763 **hand ladle**	poche *f* à main, cuiller *f* de coulée	Handkelle *f*, Handgiesslöffel *m*	siviera *f* a mano, tazza *f* di colata, tazzina *f*, cassina *f*
8764 **hand-mining**	abattage *m* à la main	Handgewinnung *f*	abbattimento *m* (o estrazione) a mano
8765 **hand-mould**	moule à main	Handgiessinstrument *n*	attrezzo *m* per formatura a mano
8766 **hand moulding**	moulage *m* à main	Handguss *m*	formatura *f* a mano
8767 **hand moulding machine**	machine *f* à mouler à main	Handformmaschine *f*	formatrice *f* a mano
8768 **hand moulding machine for belled articles**	machine *f* pour le moulage à la main de pièces à forme rebondie	Handformmaschine *f* für bauchige Gegenstände	macchina *f* per formare pentole

		English	French	German	Italian
°	8769	hand moulding machine with pin lifting arrangement	machine *f* pour le moulage à la main à tige de soulève- ment	Handformmaschine *f* mit Stiftenab- hebung	macchina *f* da formare a mano con sollevamen- to a spina della staffa
°	8770	hand moulding machine with turnover pattern plate	machine *f* à mouler à la main avec plaque à modèle renversable	Handformmaschine *f* mit Wendeplatte	macchina *f* da formare a mano con piattaforma rovesciabile (attorno a perno orizzontale)
—	8771	hand mucking	roulage *m* à bras	Handförderung *f*	trasporto *m* a mano
—	8772	hand-picked	trié à la main	handgeklaubt	classificatore a mano, vagliato a mano
—	8773	hand picking	triage *m* à la main	Klaubarbeit *f*, Handscheidung *f*	cernita *f* (o vagliatura) a mano
—	8774	hand pneumatic rammer	damoir *m* à main et à air comprimé	Handpressluft- stampfer *m*	martello *m* pneumatico a mano
°	8775	hand puddling	puddlage *m* à la main	Handpuddeln *n*	pudellaggio *m* a mano
	8776	hand pump	pompe *f* à main	Handpumpe *f*	pompa *f* a mano
		hand-rail iron, *s. banister iron*			
°	8777	hand-railing iron	fer *m* main-courante	Handschienen- -Eisen *n*	ferro *m* corrimano
—	8778	hand rammer	pilon *m* à main	Handstampfer *m*	battipalo *m* a mano, piletta *f*, pestello *m*
—	8779	hand ramming	serrage *m* à la main	Handstampfen *n*	stivatura *f* a mano
°	8780	hand-ramming machine	machine *f* à mouler à main	Handformmaschine *f*	formatrice *f* a mano
°	8781	hand regulation	distribution *f* à main	Handsteuerung *f*	distribuzione *f* a mano
	8782	hand scales	balance *f* à main	Handwaage *f*	bilancia *f* a mano
		hand screen, *s. face shield*			
°	8783	hand serial tap	taraud *m*	Satz-Gewindebohrer *m*	masciatore *m*
°	8784	hand shank ladle	poche *f* à main	Handpfanne *f*	siviera *f* a mano, taz- za *f* di colata
		hand shield, *s. face shield*			

English	French	German	Italian
— 8785 **hand shoveling**	pelletage *m* à main	Handschaufelung *f*	scavo *m* a mano
— 8786 **hand-stoping**	abattage *m* à la main	Handgewinnung *f*	abbattimento *m* a mano
⁰ 8787 **hand-tipping ladle**	poche *f* de coulée avec dispositif pour verser à la main	Giesspfanne *f* mit Handkippvorrichtung	siviera *f* di colata con dispositivo di ribaltamento a mano
⁰ 8788 **hand tipping mechanism**	dispositif *m* pour verser à la main	Handkippvorrichtung *f*	apparecchio *m* per versare a mano
hand torch, *s. hand blowpipe*			
— 8789 **hand tramming**	roulage *m* à bras	Handförderung *f*	trasporto *m* a mano
⁰ 8790 **hand-vice, filing--block**	étau à main, mordache *f*	Feilkloben *m*, Handschraube *f*	morsa *f* a mano
⁰ 8791 **hand wheel**	manivelle *f* de serrage	Handrad *n*	manovella *f* di serraggio
⁰ 8792 **hand winch**	treuil *m* à main	Handwinde *f*	argano *m* a mano
⁰ 8793 **handle**	poignée *f*	Kastengriff *m*	manico *m*, impugnatura *f*
⁰ 8794 **handle of peel**	extrémité *f* de levier	Schwengelkopf *m*	estremità *f* della bilancia
⁰ 8795 **handles, pull grips**	mains-courantes	Handgriffe *m pl.*	corrimani *m pl.*
— 8796 **handling**	manutention *f*, transport *m* des matériaux	Handhabung *f*, Material bewegung *f*	manutenzione *f*, movimento *m* dei minerali
⁰ 8797 **handling the converter**	manoeuvre *f* du convertisseur	Betrieb des Konverters	manovra del convertitore
⁰ 8798 **handtight**	serré à la main	von Hand angezogen	stretto (o serrato) a mano
handwelding, *s. manual welding*			
^ 8799 **hang up**	arrêt de la colonne pendant le tubage	Arretierung *f* der Säule	arresto della colonna durante il tubaggio
— 8800 **hangendes**	toit *m* de tunnel	Hängende *n*	cielo *m* (di tunnel)
⁰ 8801 **hanger (foundry)**	chariot *m*, porte-poche	Stütze *f*	portantina *f*
⁰ 8802 **hanger or hanger bracket**	chaise *f* pendante, palier pendant	Hängelager *n*, Transmissionsstütze *f*	sopporto *m* pensile, peduccio *m*
⁰ 8802a **hanger crack**	crique *f* transversale	Querriss *m*	crepa *f* trasversale

	English	French	German	Italian
—	8803 hangfire	long feu *m*	Spätschuss *m*	ritardo di accensione (di mina)
°	8804 hanging	suspension *f*	Aufhängung *f*	sospensione *f*
°	8805 hanging	accrochage *m* des charges	Hängen *n* der Gicht	attacco *m* delle cariche
—	8806 hanging	toit *m*	Hangende *n*	tetto *m* (di un banco), cielo *m* (di tunnel)
—	8807 hanging glacier	glacier suspendu	Gehängegletscher *m*	ghiacciaio *m* sospeso, vedretta *f*
—	8808 hanging layer	toit *m*	Hangende *n*	tetto *m*, cielo *m* (di tunnel)
°	8809 hanging (of the charge)	accrochage *m* des charges	Hängen *n* der Gicht, Feststauen *n*	formazione *f* di volte
—	8810 hanging valley	vallée *f* suspendue	Hängetal *n*	valle *f* sospesa
—	8811 hanging-on	recette *f*	Füllort *m*	stazione *f* di fondo
—	8812 hanging shaker conveyor	couloir *m* oscillant suspendu	Hängerutsche *f*	vaglio *m* oscillante, sospeso
—	8813 hanging wall	toit *m*	Hangende *n*, Firste *f*	tetto *m*, cielo *m* (di galleria)
—	8814 hanging wall	terrains de recouvrement	Deckgebirge *n*	terreno *m* di ricopertura
—	8815 hanging wall	lèvre supérieure	höherer Flügel *m*	lembo *m* superiore
—	8816 hanksite	hanksite *f*	Hanksit *m*	hanksite *f*
—	8817 hannayite	hannayite *f*	Hannayit *m*	hannayite *f*
—	8818 hard-ash coal	charbon *m* maigre	Magerkohle *f*	carbone *m* magro
°	8819 hard cast steel	moulage *m* d'acier dur	harter Stahlguss *m*	acciaio *m* colato duro
°	8820 hard centre	noyau *m* dur	harter Kern *m*	cuore *m* duro
—	8821 hard clay	argile *f* ferme	Hartlehm *m*	argilla *f* soda
—	8822 hard coal, lean coal, anthracite	anthracite *f*	Anthrazit *m*	antracite *f*

hard coke, *s. coke-oven coke*

English	French	German	Italian
8823 **hard copper**	cuivre *m* dur	Hartkupfer *n*	rame *m* duro
8824 **hard-drawn copper wire**	fil *m* de cuivre écroui	Hartkupferdraht *m*	filo *m* di rame crudo stirato
8825 **hard-drawn wire, unannealed wire**	fil *m* écroui à froid	hartgezogener Draht *m*	filo *m* duro a freddo
8826 **hard-facing**	durcissement *m* superficiel	Oberflächenhärtung *f*	indurimento *m* superficiale, riporto duro (per saldatura)
8827 **hard-facing**	garnissage *m* (d'un outil)	Besetzen *n*	
8828 **hard facing metal**	métal *m* dur	Hartmetall *n*	metallo *m* duro
8829 **hard glass**	verre *m* dur	Hartglas *n*	vetro *m* duro
8830 **hard glass beaker**	gobelet *m* en verre dur	Hartglasbecher *m*	bicchiere *m* di vetro infusibile
8831 **hard grain**	grain *m* d'acier dur	Hartkorn *n*	grano *m* d'acciaio duro
8832 **hard head**	concrétion *f* dure dans le grès	harte Konkretion *f* im Sandstein	concrezione *f* dura nel gas
8833 **hard ingot steel**	acier *m* dur en lingots	Masselhartstahl *m*	acciaio *m* duro in masselli (o lingotti)
8834 **hard iron**	fer *m* dur, fer *m* ordinaire	hartes Eisen *n*	ferro *m* duro
8835 **hard iron ore**	minerai *m* de fer dur	hartes Eisenerz *n*	minerale *m* di ferro duro
8836 **hard lead**	plomb *m* antimonié	Bleiantimon *n*	piombo *m* all'antimonio
8837 **hard-metal**	métal dur	Hartmetall *n*	metallo *m* duro
8838 **hard pan**	cuirasse *f* ferrugineuse	Eisenkruste *f*	corrazza *f* ferrugginosa
8839 **hard troostite**	troostite *f*	Troostit *m*	troostite *f*
8840 **hard-solder, brazing (metal)**	brasure *f*, soudure *f* forte	Hartlot *n*, Schlaglot *n*, Messinglot *n*	brasatura *f*, saldatura *f* forte
8841 **hard-solder**	soudure *f* de cuivre	Kupferlot *n*, Hartlot *n*	saldatura *f* di rame (o forte)
8842 **hard spot**	point *m* dur	harte Stelle *f*	punto *m* duro, zona *f* dura

	English	French	German	Italian
°	8843 hard steel	acier m dur	Hartstahl m	acciaio m duro, acciaio m indurito
°	8844 hard white crust with radiated structure	croûte f dure à texture blanche rayonnante	weissstrahlige Hartgusskruste f	crosta f dura a sezione bianca raggiante
°	8845 hard wire	fil m écroui	Hartdraht m	conduttore m crudo
°	8846 to harden, to temper	tremper, durcir	härten	temperare, indurire
°	8847 to harden a metal	tremper un métal	ein Metall härten	temperare un metallo
°	8848 to harden the steel	tremper l'acier	den Stahl härten	temperare l'acciaio
°	8849 hardenable steel	acier m trempable	temperierbarer Stahl m	acciaio m temprabile
°	8850 hardenability	aptitude f à la trempe	Härtungsfähigkeit f	temperabilità f
°	8851 hardened	trempé, durci	gehärtet	temprato
°	8852 hardened and tempered steel	acier m trempé et recuit	vergueteter Stahl m	acciaio m bonificato
°	8853 hardened case	couche f de cémentation	Härteschicht f	strato m cementato, strato m di cementazione
	hardened face, s. steel face			
°	8854 hardened ingot steel plate	plaque f d'acier coulé trempé	gehärtete Fluss·stahlplatte f	piastra f di acciaio omogeneo temperato
°	8855 hardened nickel steel plate	tôle f d'acier au nickel trempé	gehärtete Nickelstahlplatte f	piastra f di acciaio al nichelio temperato
	hardened point, s. steel point			
°	8856 hardened steel	acier m trempé	gehärteter Stahl m	acciaio m temperato
°	8857 hardening	trempe f	Härtung f	tempra f
°	8858 hardening	durcissement m	Verhärtung f	indurimento m
	hardening alloy, s. master alloy			
°	8859 hardening and tempering	trempe f et revenu	Vergütung f	bonifica f
°	8860 hardening bath	bain m de trempe	Härtebad n	bagno m di tempra
°	8861 hardening by nitridation	trempe f par nitruration	Nitrierhärtung f	tempra f per nitrurazione

English	French	German	Italian
8862 hardening compound	composé *m* de cémentation	Härtemittel *n*	composto *m* per cementazione
8863 hardening crack	procédé *m* de trempe	Härtevorgang *m*	processo *m* di tempra
8864 hardening depth	profondeur *f* de trempe	Härtetiefe *f*	profondità *f* di tempra
8865 hardening-furnace, cementing furnace, tempering-furnace	four *m* à tremper	Härteofen *m*	forno *m* di tempera
8866 hardening plant	atelier *m* de trempe	Härteanlage *f*	reparto *m* tempera
8867 hardening process	procédé *m* de trempe	Härteverfahren *n*	processo *m* di tempera
8868 hardening test	essai *m* de trempe	Haertungsprobe *f*	prova *f* di tempra
8869 hardenite	hartite *f*, hardénite *f*	Hartit *m*	hardenite *f*, hartite *f*, martensite *f*
8870 hardfacing alloy	métal *m* d'apport, alliage d'apport	Aufschweisslegierung *f*	lega *f* di saldatura
8870a hardie, hardy	tranchet *m* d'enclume	Setzhammer *m*	tagliolo *m* con codolo
8871 hardness	dureté *f*	Härte *f*	durezza *f*
8872 hardness of steel	degré *m* de trempe de l'acier	Härtegrad *m* des Stahles	durezza *f* dell'acciaio
8873 hardness penetration	profondeur *f* de trempe	Härtetiefe *f*	profondità *f* di penetrazione
8874 hardness testing by indentation	billage *m*	Kugeldruck *m*, Härteprüfung *f*	brinellatura *f*
8875 hardpan	cuirasse *f* ferrugineuse	Eisenkruste *f*	corazza *f* ferrugginosa
8876 hardystonite	hardystonite *f*	Hardystonit *m*	hardystonite *f*
8877 harlequin opal	arlequin *m*	Harlequin *n*	arlecchino *m*
8878 Harmet smelting process	procédé *m* de fusion de Harmet	Harmetschmelzverfahren *n*	processo *m* di fusione Harmet
8879 harmotome	harmotome *m*	Harmotom	harmotome *m*
8880 harrisite	harrisite *f*	Harrisit *m*	harrisite *f*
8881 harstigite	harstigite *f*	Harstigit *m*	harstigite *f*
8882 hartite	hartite *f*	Hartit *m*	hartite *f*

English	French	German	Italian
° 8883 **harveyized plate**	plaque _f_ harveysée	Harveyisierte Platte _f_	piastra _f_ harveyizzata
° 8884 **harvey(iz)ed steel**	acier _m_ harveysé	harveyisierter Stahl _m_	acciaio _m_ harveizzato
— 8885 **harz jig**	crible _m_ hydraulique à étage fixe	Hydraulik-Sieb _n_ mit fester Ebene	crivello _m_ idraulico a piano fisso
— 8886 **hastingsite**	hastingsite _f_	Hastingsit _m_	hastingsite _f_
— 8887 **hatchettolite**	hatchettolite _f_	Hatchettolith _m_	hatchettolite _f_
— 8888 **hatherlite**	hatherlite _f_	Hatherlit _m_	hatherlite _f_
— 8889 **hatter**	chercheur d'or _m_	Goldgräber _m_	cercatore _m_ d'oro
— 8890 **hauchecomite**	hauchecornite _f_	Hauchecornit _m_	hauchecornite _f_
— 8891 **hauerite**	hauérite _f_	Hauerit _m_	hauerite _f_
— 8892 **haul clip**	tenaille _f_ d'attelage	Schlepphaken _m_	pinza _f_ da presa
— 8893 **haul drift**	galerie _f_ de roulage	Förderstrecke _f_	galleria _f_ di carreggio
— 8894 **haul man**	rouleur _m_	Schlepper _m_	addetto _m_ ai carrelli
— 8895 **haul plane**	plan _m_ incliné	Bremsberg _m_	piano _m_ inclinato
haul way, _s. haul drift_			
— 8896 **hauler**	rouleur _m_	Schlepper _m_	trasportatore _m_
— 8897 **hauler**	treuil _m_	Winde _f_	argano _m_
— 8898 **haulway, haulage road**	voie _f_ de roulage	Förderstrecke _f_	galleria _f_ di carreggio
— 8899 **hausmannite**	hausmannite _f_	Hausmannit _m_	hausmannite _f_
— 8900 **hauyne**	haüyne _f_	Hauyn _f_	hauyna _f_
hauynite, _s. hauyne_			
— 8901 **hauynophyre**	haüynophyre _m_	Hauynophyr _m_	hauynofiro _m_
— 8902 **hazle**	grès _m_ schisteux compact	fester schieferiger Sandstein _m_	gres _m_ scistoso compatto
° 8903 **to head, to upset (forging)**	refouler	verformen	ricalcare, rifollare
° 8904 **head**	tête _f_	Kopf _m_	fungo _m_, testa _f_

English	French	German	Italian
8905 **head (of hammer)**	tête *f* de marteau, étampe *f*	Hammerkopf *m*	testa *f* del martello
8906 **head, pressure head**	charge *f* d'eau, hauteur *f* d'élévation	Druckhöhe *f*, Förderhöhe *f*	prevalenza *f* altezza *f* di pressione
8907 **head board**	cale *f*, écoin *m*	Holzkeil *m*	cuneo *m* di legno, puntello *m*
8908 **head cylinder gasket**	joint *m* de culasse	Zylinderkopfpackung *f*	guarnizione *f* per testa del cilindro
8909 **head flow**	refoulement *m* intermittent	intermittierende Versorgung *f*	erogazione *f* intermittente (di petrolio)
8910 **head captain**	porion chef *m*	Obersteiger *m*	capo squadra *m*
8911 **head frame**	chevalement *m*	Fördergerüst *n*, Förderturm *m*	incastellatura *f* d'estrazione, castelletto *m* d'estrazione
8912 **head-frame track limit switch**	évite-molettes *m* de chevalement	Sicherheitsvorrichtung *f* am Förderturm gegen Übertreiben	congegno *m* di sicurezza del castelletto *m* d'estrazione
8913 **head gear**	chevalement *m*	Fördergerüst *n*	castelletto *m* d'estrazione, incastellatura *f* d'estrazione
8914 **head house**	bâtiment *m* d'extraction	Schachtgebäude *n*	edificio *m* d'estrazione
8915 **head melter**	maître-fondeur *m*	Schmelzmeister *m*	capo-forno *m*
8915a **head metal**	métal *m* de masselotte	Steigermetall *n*	metallo *m* di materozza
8916 **head of ingot mould**	tête *f* de la lingotière	Muldenkopf *m*	testa *f* della lingottiera
8917 **head of stamp**	sabot *m* de bocard	Pochschuh *m*	zoccolo *m* del mulino
8918 **head-piece**	chapeau *m*	Kappe *f*	cappello *m* (di armatura in legno)
8919 **head room**	hauteur *f* de voûte	Stosshöhe *f*	altezza *f* della volta (o del soffitto)
	head sheave, *s. head wheel*		
8920 **head slab core**	noyau *m* détachable	loser Kern *m*	anima *f* della lista
8921 **head-stock**	chevalement *m*	Fördergerüst *n*	castelletto *m* (o incastellatura *f*) d'estrazione

	English	French	German	Italian
−	8922 head sword	eau *f* de galerie	Stollenwasser *n*	acqua *f* di galleria
−	8923 head wheel	molette *f*	Seilscheibe *f*	ruota *f* del cavo
−	8924 head work	chevalement *m*	Fördergerüst *n*	castelletto *m* (o incastellatura d'estrazione)
−	8925 header	collecteur *m*	Sammelkammer *f*, Wasserkammer *f*	collettore *m*
−	8926 header, rivet snap	chasse-rivet *m*, bouterolle *f*	Döpper *m*	scalpello *m*
−	8927 header	coup *m* de toit	Kopfschussbohrloch *n*	scoppio di rocce
−	8928 header, manifold	distributeur *m*, claviature *f*	Verteiler *m*, Verteilungssystem *n*	collettore *m*
°	8929 header die	matrice *f* de refoulage	Verformungsform *f*	stampo *m* (o matrice) di ricalcatura
−	8930 headframe	tour *f* d'exploitation	Gewinnungskopfgestell *n*	castelletto *m* o incastellatura *f* di estrazione
−	8931 heading	galerie *f* d'avancement, fendue *f*	Richtstrecke *f*, Stollen *m*	galleria *f* d'avanzamento (o principale)
°	8931a heading	façonnement *m* des têtes	Anköpfen *n*	ricalcatura *f*
^	8932 heading	produit *m* de tête	erstes Destillat *n*	prodotto *m* di testa
−	8933 heading	concentré *m*	Konzentrat *n*	concentrato *m*
−	8934 heading-and-stall method	exploitation *f* par chambres et piliers	Kammerpfeilerbau *m*	coltivazione *f* a camere e pilastri
−	8935 heading face	front *m* d'avancement	Richtstreckenstoss *m*	fronte *m* d'avanzamento
−	8936 heading machine	haveuse *f* de galerie	Streckenschrämmaschine *f*	tagliatrice *f* di galleria, scavatrice *f*
−	8937 heading stope	chantier *m* d'avancement	Richtstrecke *f*	cantiere *m* d'avanzamento
−	8938 headless rivet	rivet *m* à tête perdue	kopfloser Niet *m*	chiodo *m* a testa cieca
°	8939 headplate	plaque *f* frontale, gendarme *m*	Stirnplatte *f*	piastra *f* frontale
−	8940 healing stone	ardoise *f*	Dachschiefer *m*	ardesia *f*

	English	French	German	Italian
—	8941 heap	halde *f*	Halde *f*	terriccio *m* (di mine-rali)
—	8942 heap keeper	terrilleur *m*	Haldenarbeiter *m*	addetto *m* alle scorie (di minerale)
—	8943 heap leaching	lixiviation *f* en tas	Haufenlaugerei *f*	lisciviazione *f* a mucchi
—	8944 heap roasting, roasting in heaps	grillage *m* en meules ou en tas	Haufenröstung *f*	torrefazione *f* in mucchi
	8945 heaped concrete	béton *m* coulé	Schüttbeton *m*	calcestruzzo *m* colato
o	8946 heart, core	noyau *m*	Kern *m*	cuore *m*
o	8947 heart and square trowel	spatule *f*	Lanzette *f*	spatola *f* a piatto e cucchiaio
o	8948 heart cut	fraction *f* de coeur	Herzfraktion *f*	pezzo *m* di anima
o	8949 hearth	laboratoire *m*	Arbeitsherd *m*	aia *f*, focolare *m*, laboratorio *m*
o	8950 hearth	creuset *m*	Herd *m*	crogiuolo *m*
o	8951 hearth	sole *f* de four de fusion	Sohle *f*	suola *f*, letto *m* di fusione del crogiuolo
o	8952 hearth, working hearth	foyer *m* de travail	Arbeitsherd *m*	suola *f* di lavoro
	hearth block, *s. base block*			
o	8953 hearth bottom	fond *m* de creuset	Gestellboden *m*, Herdboden *m*	suola *f* del crogiolo, fondo *m* del crogiolo
o	8954 hearth fining	affinage *m* sur sole	Herdfrischen *n*	affinaggio *m* su suo-la (od in fossa)
o	8955 hearth for heating, fore hearth	foyer *m* à réchauffer, cassin *m*	Vorwärmeherd *m*	forno *m* di riscaldo
o	8956 hearth furnace	four à sole	Herdofen *m*	bassofuoco *m*, forno *m* a suola
o	8957 hearth hole	ouverture *f* de la poitrine	Brustöffnung *f*	apertura *f* del petto
o	8958 hearth jacket	blindage *m* du creuset	Gestellmantel *m*, Herdpanzer *m*	schermatura *f* del crogiuolo
o	8959 hearth level	fond *m* du creuset, sole *f* du creuset	Herdsohle *f*, Ofensohle *f*	suola *f* del crogiuolo

	English	French	German	Italian
°	8960 **hearth lining**	garnissage *m* de la sole	Herdfutter *n*, Ausfütterung *f*, Auskleidung *f*	rivestimento *m* della suola
°	8961 **hearth mould, open sand mould**	moule *m* à découvert	Herdform *f*, offene Form *f*	forma *f* in fossa
°	8962 **hearth moulding**	moulage *m* à découvert	Herdformerei *f*	formatura *f* in fossa
	hearth of a liquation furnace, *s. liquation furnace*			
	hearth opening, *s. hearth hole*			
°	8963 **hearth plate**	plaque *f* du foyer	Herdeisen *n*	placca *f* del focolare
	hearth refining, *s. hearth fining*			
°	8964 **hearth ring machine**	machine *f* à mouler les cercles des fourneaux de cuisine	Herdringmaschine *f*	macchina *f* da formare anelli per cucine o per stufe
°	8965 **hearth steel**	acier *m* Martin	Martinstahl *m*	acciaio *m* Martin
°	8966 **hearth surface**	surface *f* de la sole	Herdfläche *f*	superficie *f* del focolare o della suola
°	8967 **to heat**	s'échauffer	heiss werden	riscaldarsi
°	8968 **to heat the iron**	chauffer la fonte	das Eisen vorwärmen	riscaldare la ghisa
°	8969 **to heat the ladle**	chauffer la poche	die Pfanne anwärmen	asciugare (o scaldare) la siviera
°	8970 **to heat to red heat**	chauffer au rouge	in Rotglut brennen	riscaldare al calor rosso
°	8971 **heat**	chaleur *f*, température *f*	Wärme *f*, Temperatur *f*	calore *m*, temperatura *f*
°	8972 **heat**	bain *m*, coulée *f*, chaude *f*	Bad *n*, Schmelzung *f*	infornata *f*, colata *f*, bagno *m*, calda *f*
°	8972a **heat, melt**	piquée *f*	Abstich *m*	spillata *f*
°	8973 **heat-absorption, thermal absorption**	absorption *f* de chaleur	Wärmeaufnahme *f*, Wärmeabsorption *f*	assorbimento *m* di calore (o termico)
°	8974 **heat accumulator, heat storage**	récupérateur *m* de chaleur	Wärmespeicher *m*	ricuperatore *m* di calore, accumulatore di carbone
°	8975 **heat change due to reaction**	effet *m* calorifique de la réaction	Wärmetönung *f* der Reaktion	effetto *m* calorifico o termico della reazione

		English	French	German	Italian
o	8976	heat color	couleur f de recuit	Glühfarbe f	colore m di ricottura
o	8977	heat conduction, heat conductivity, thermal conduction	conductibilité f calorifique	Wärmeleitung f	conduzione f del calore, conduttività f termica
o	8978	heat consumption	consommation f de chaleur	Wärmeverbrauch m	consumo m di calore
o	8979	heat crack	crique f due à la chaleur	Warmriss m	cricca f (o crepa f) dovuta al calore
o	8980	heat equation, heat balance	bilan m calorifique	Wärmebilanz f	bilancio m calorifico
		heat-fusion, s. igneous fusion			
o	8981	heat in iron and slag	chaleur f de la fonte et du laitier	Eisen- und Schlackenwärme f	calore m della ghisa e della loppa
o	8982	heat insulating sleeve	manchon m isolant	wärmeisolierender Trichtereinsatz m	manicotto m isolante
o	8983	heat insulation	isolation f thermique	Wärmeisolation f	isolamento m termico
o	8984	heat interchange	équilibre m calorifique	Wärmeausgleichung f	equilibrio m termico
o	8985	heat of combination	chaleur f de combinaison	Verbindungswärme f	calore m di combinazione
o	8986	heat of combustion	air m de combustion	Verbrennungsluft f	aria f di combustione
o	8987	heat of dissociation	chaleur f de dissociation	Zerfallwärme f, Dissoziationswärme f	calore m di dissociazione
o	8988	heat of ionisation	chaleur f d'ionisation	Ionisationswärme f	calore m d'ionizzazione
o	8989	heat of reaction	chaleur f de réaction	Reaktionswärme f	calore m di reazione
o	8990	heat passage, heat conduction	conductibilité f thermique	Wärmeleitung f	conduttibilità f termica
o	8991	heat-resistant steel	acier m réfractaire	hitzebeständiger Stahl m	acciaio m refrattario (al calore)
o	8992	heat-resisting	résistant à la chaleur	hitzebeständig	resistente a caldo
o	8993	heat resisting cast iron	fonte f réfractaire, fonte résistante à la chaleur	hitzebeständiges Gusseisen n	ghisa f refrattaria (o resistente al calore)

English	French	German	Italian
° 8994 heat resisting steel	acier *m* résistant à la chaleur	hitzcbeständiger Stahl *m*	acciaio *m* resistente al calore (o refrattario)
heat storage, *s. heat accumulator*			
° 8995 heat storage vessel	chaudière *f* accumulatrice de chaleur	Wärmespeicher *m*, Wärmespeicher-kessel *m*	caldaia *f* accumulatrice di calore
° 8996 heat test, hot test	essai *m* à chaud	Warmprobe *f*	prova *f* a caldo
° 8997 heat treatable	améliorable par trempe et revenu	vergütbar	bonificabile
° 8998 heat treated steel, hardened steel	acier *m* trempé	gehaerteter Stahl *m*	acciaio *m* temprato
° 8999 heat-treating induction heater	appareil *m* pour le traitement thermique	Wärmebehandlungs-apparat *m*	apparecchio *m* a indu-zione per trattamento termico
° 9000 heat-treatment	traitement *m* thermique	Warmbehandlung *f*	trattamento *m* termico
° 9001 heat treatment cycle curve	diagramme *m* de traitement thermique	Glühkurve *f*	diagramma *m* di ricottu-ra
° 9002 heat treatment in a controlled atmosphere	traitement *m* thermique en atmosphère contrôlée	Gästempern *n*	trattamento *m* termico in atmosfera control-lata
° 9003 heat-treatment furnace	four *m* à traitement thermique	Wärmebehandlungs-ofen *m*	forno *m* per il tratta-mento termico
° 9004 heated	chauffé	erwärmt, erhitzt	scaldato
heated soaking pit, *s. soaking pit*			
° 9005 heater and flue tube for smoke-tube boilers	tube bouilleur et réchauffeur pour chaudières à tubes de fumée	Siederohr *n* für Rauchrohrkessel	tubo *m* bollitore e scaldatore per caldaie a tubi di fumo
° 9006 heater tube for fuel-oil	tube *m* pour le réchauffage du mazout	Vorwärmrohr *n* für Heizöl	tubo *m* per riscalda-mento della nafta
° 9007 heating, warming	échauffement *m*, chauffage *m*	Erwärmung *f*, Erwärmen *n*	riscaldamento *m*
heating arc, *s. reverberatory arc*			
° 9008 heating boiler	chaudière *f* à chauffage	Heizungskessel *m*	caldaia *f* per riscalda-mento

English	French	German	Italian
⊙ 9009 **heating chamber**	chambre *f* de chauffe	Heizkammer *f*, Wärmeraum *m*	camera *f* di riscaldamento, camera *f* riscaldante
⊙ 9010 **heating coil**	serpentin *m* de chauffage	Heizschlange *f*	serpentina *f* di riscaldamento
○ 9011 **heating coke**	coke *m* d'allumage	Füllkoks *m*	coke *m* per l'accensione
○ 9012 **heating flue**	carneau *m* de chauff(ag)e	Heizkanal *m*	canale *m* di riscaldamento
○ 9013 **heating furnace, reheating furnace**	four *m* de chauffage	Heizofen *m*	forno *m* di ri scaldamento
○ 9014 **heating grid**	grille *f* de chauffage	Heizgitter *n*	griglia *f* di riscaldamento
heating hearth, *s. smelting hearth*			
○ 9015 **heating jacket**	chemise *f* de réchauffage	Heizhülle *f*	camicia *f* di riscaldo
○ 9016 **heating of the head**	chauffage *m* de la tête du lingot	Heizen *n* des Blockkopfes	riscaldamento *m* del getto
heating ring, *s. annular groove*			
○ 9017 **heating stove**	four *m* à recuire	Glühofen *m*	forno *m* di ricottura
heating torch, *s. heating blowpipe*			
○ 9018 **heating-up time**	temps *m* d'échauffement	Aufheizzeit *f*	tempo *m* di riscaldamento
— 9019 **heave**	gonflement *m* (du mur), boursouflement *m*	Quellen *n*	rigonfiamento *m* del muro
— 9020 **heave**	recouvrement *m* horizontal	horizontale Deckung *f*	ricoprimento *m* orizzontale
— 9021 **heavily pitching seam**	couche *f* en dressant	saigeres Flöz *n*	filone *m* a piombo (o verticale)
○ 9022 **heavily tapered solid core box**	boite *f* à noyaux à pot de fleur	ungeteilter Kernkasten *m*	cassa *f* d'anima troncoconica
— 9023 **heaving bottom**	sol qui gonfle	quellende Sohle *f*	suola *f* che si gonfia
— 9024 **heaving sands**	sable *m* coulant	Schwimmsand *m*	sabbia *f* scorrevole

English	French	German	Italian
– 9025 **heaving shale**	schiste *m* gonflant, argile gonflante	drückender Schiefer *m*	argilla *f* rigonfiante
° 9026 **heavy angle steel, heavy angles**	grosses cornières *f pl.*	schwerer Winkelstahl *m*	angolari *m pl.* pesanti
– 9027 **heavy bedded**	en couches épaisses	dick gebankt	a strati spessi
° 9027a **heavy case**	couche superficielle épaisse	dicke Oberflächenschicht *f*	strato *m* superficiale spesso
° 9028 **heavy duty**	pour services lourds	Strapazier-	sottoposto *m* a forti sollecitazioni
^ 9029 **heavy duty oil**	huile *f* pour service sévère	Strapazieröl *n*	olio *m* per servizi pesanti
^ 9030 **heavy ends**	fractions *f pl.* lourdes	schwere Fraktionen *f pl.*	frazioni *f pl.* pesanti
– 9031 **heavy barytes**	barytine *f*	Schwerspat *m*	baritina *f*
° 9032 **heavy duty tool for rough turning** **heavy earth,** *s. baryte*	outil *m* de coupe (dégrossissage)	Hochleistungs-Laengsdrehstahl *m*, Laengsdrehstahl *m* zum Schruppen	coltello *m* per sgrossare a gran taglio
– 9033 **heavy fluid separation**	séparation *f* par liquides denses	Trennung *f* mittels schwerer Flüssigkeiten	separazione *f* a mezzo liquidi densi
– 9034 **heavy gradient**	pente *f* raide	steiles Gefälle *f*	pendenza *f* erta
° 9035 **heavy metal**	métal *m* lourd	Schwermetall *n*	metallo *m* pesante
– 9036 **heavy minerals**	minéraux *m pl.* lourds	schwere Mineralien *n.pl.*	minerali *m pl.* pesanti
° 9037 **heavy plate, thick sheet**	tôle *f* forte, grosse tôle	Grobblech *n*	lamiera *f* grossa
° 9038 **heavy rapping hammer**	mailloche *f*	Schlegel *m*	mazza *f*
° 9039 **heavy sections** **heavy spar,** *s. barite*	acier *m* profilé fort	schwerer Profilstahl *m*	profilato *m* pesante di acciaio
– 9040 **heavy stratification**	stratification *f* puissante	mächtige Schichtung *f*	stratificazione *f* pesante
° 9041 **heavy structural sections**	profilés *m pl.* lourds, profilés *m pl.* pour la construction	schwere Profile *n pl.*, Bauprofile *n pl.*	profilati *m pl.* pesanti, profilati da costruzione

English	French	German	Italian
9042 heavy wall tube	tube *m* d'épaisseur majorée	dickwandiges Rohr *n*	tubo *m* di grosso spessore
9043 hebronite	hebronite *f*	Hebronit *m*	hebronite *f*
9044 hedenbergite	hédenbergite *f*	Hedenbergit *m*	hedenbergite *f*
9045 hedgehog	drague *f*	Bagger *m*	draga *f*
9046 hedrumite	hedrumite *f*	Hedrumit *m*	hedrumite *f*
9047 hedyphane	hédyphane	Hedyphan *n*	hedyfane
9048 heel	ouverture *f* du trou de mine	Bohrlochkopf *m*	apertura del foro di mina
9049 heel	résidus *m pl.*	Rückstände *m pl.*	fondami *m pl.*
9050 heel (foundry)	réserve liquide de métal	flüssige Metall-reserve *f*	riserva *f* liquida di metallo
9051 heel of coal	pilier *m* de charbon	Kohlenbein *n*	pilastro *m* di carbone
9052 heel of stope	gradin *m* supérieur	oberer Stoss *m*	gradino *m* superiore
9053 heel riser (foundry)	montant latéral	Seitenpfahl *m*	montante *m* laterale
9054 height	hauteur *f*	Höhenlage *f*, Höhe *f*	altezza *f*
9055 height of bosh	hauteur *f* des étalages	Rasthöhe *f*	altezza *f* della sacca
9056 height of hearth	hauteur *f* de l'ouvrage	Gestellhöhe *f*	altezza *f* del crogiuolo
9057 height of stroke	hauteur *f* de chute	Hubhöhe *f*	alzata *f*, altezza *f* di caduta
9058 helical cutter	fraise *f* hélicoïdale	Schneckenfräser *m*	fresa *f* elicoidale, fresa a vite, creatore
9059 helical gear	roue-vis *f* hélicoïdale	Schneckenrad *n*	ruota *f* madre d'una coppia elicoidale
helical gearing, *s. helical tooth*			
9060 helical plain milling	fraise cylindrique rapide à dégrossir	Hochleistungs-Spiralfraeser *m*	coltello *m* elicoidale
9061 helical spring, spiral or coil spring	ressort *m* hélicoïdal	gewundene Feder *f*, Spiralfeder *f*	molla *f* ad elica

	English	French	German	Italian
°	9062 helical tooth	dent *f* à chevron	Winkelzahn *m*	spina *f* di pesce
—	9063 heliodor	héliodor *m*	Heliodor *m*	eliodoro *m*
—	9064 heliophyllite	héliophyllite *f*	Heliophyllit *m*	eliofillite *f*
—	9065 heliotrope	héliotrope *m*	Heliotrop *n*	eliotropio *m*
—	9066 helium	hélium *m*	Helium *n*	elio *m*
°	9067 Hellberger furnace	four *m* Hellberger	Hellbergerscher Ofen *m*	forno *m* Hellberger
—	9068 helmet crew	équipe *f* de sauvetage	Rettungsmannschaft *f*	squadra *f* di salvataggio
°	9069 helmet for sand- -blaster	casque *m* pour sableur	Putzerhelm *m*	casco *m* per sabbiatore

helve, *s. handle*

helve hammer, *s. lift hammer*

helver, *s. lift hammer*

	English	French	German	Italian
—	9070 helvite	helvite *f*	Helvin *m*	helvite *f*
—	9071 helvetian	helvétien *m*	Helvetian *m*	elveziano *m*
—	9072 hemafibrite	hémafibrite *f*	Hämafibrit *m*	hemafibrite *f*
—	9073 hematite	hématite *f*	Hämatit *m*	ematite *f*
°	9074 hematite iron	fonte *f* hématite	Hämatit-Roheisen *n*	ghisa *f* ematite
°	9075 hematite iron ore	fer *m* oligiste concrétionné	roter Glaskopf *m*	ematite *f* a superficie vetrosa
°	9076 hematite pig iron, Bessemer pig iron	fonte *f* Bessemer	Bessemerroheisen *n*	ghisa *f* Bessemer
—	9077 hematolite	hématolite *f*	Hämatolith *m*	ematolite *f*
—	9078 hematostibiite	hématostibiite *f*	Hämatostibiit *m*	ematostibiite *f*
—	9079 hemera	hemera *f*	Hämere *f*	hemera *f*
—	9080 hemicrystalline	hypocristallin	hypokristallin	ipocristallino
—	9081 hemidome	face unique	Pedion	faccia *f* unica
—	9082 hemihedral	hémiédrique	hemiedrisch	emiedrico

	English	French	German	Italian
−	9083 hemimorphism	hémimorphie *f*	Hemimorphie *f*	emimorfismo *m*
−	9084 hemimorphic	hémimorphique	hemimorph	emimorfico
−	9085 hemimorphite	hémimorphite *f*	Hemimorphit *m*	emimorfite *f*
−	9086 hemitropic	hémitrope	hemitrop	emitropico
°	9087 hemp brush	brosse *f* en chanvre	Hanfbürste *f*	spazzola *f* di canapa
°	9088 hemp rope	corde *f* en chanvre	Hanfseil *n*	corda *f* di canapa
°	9089 Hempel furnace	four *m* Hempel	Hempelofen *m*	forno *m* Hempel
°	9090 hemper swab	queue *f* de vache	Quast *m*	coda *f* di canapa
−	9091 henwoodite	henwoodite *f*	Henwoodit *m*	henwoodite *f*
−	9092 hepatic pyrites	marcassite *f*	Leberkies *m*	marcassite *f*
−	9093 heptorite	heptorite *f*	Heptorit *m*	eptorite *f*
−	9094 Hercynian folding	plissement *m* hercynien	hercynische Faltung *f*	piegamento *m* erciniano
−	9095 hercynite	hercynite *f*	Hercynit *m*	ercinite *f*
−	9096 herderite	herdérite *f*	Herderit *m*	herderite *f*
°	9097 heredity	hérédité *f*	Vererblichkeit *f*	eredità *f*
−	9098 heronite	héronite *f*	Heronit *m*	heronite *f*
°	9099 Heroult electric blast furnace	haut-fourneau *m* Héroult	Héroultscher Hochofen *m*	alto forno *m* Héroult
−	9100 herrengrundite	herrengrundite *f*	Herrengrundit *m*	herrengrundite *f*
−	9101 herschelite	herschélite *f*	Herschelit *m*	herschelite *f*
−	9102 hessite	hessite *f*	Hessit *m*	hessite *f*
−	9103 hessonite	hessonite *f*	Hessonit *m*	essonite *f*
−	9104 hetaerolite	hétairite *f*	Hetairit *m*	hetairite *f*
−	9105 heterogenite	hétérogénite *f*	Heterogenit *m*	eterogenite *f*
−	9106 heteromesical deposits *pl.*	dépôts *m pl.* hétéromésiques	heteromesische Ablagerungen *f pl.*	depositi *m pl.* eteromesici
−	9107 heteromorphite	hétéromorphite *f*	Heteromorphit *m*	eteromorfite *f*

		English	French	German	Italian
—	9108	heteromorphic rocks	roches *f pl.* hétéromorphiques	heteromorphe Gesteine *n pl.*	rocce *f pl.* eteromorfe
—	9109	heterotaxial deposit	dépôt *m* hétérotaxique	heterotaxe Ablagerung *f*	deposito *m* eterotassico
—	9110	heterotopical deposit	dépôt *m* hétérotopique	heterotopische Ablagerung *f*	deposito *m* eterotopico
—	9111	Hettangian stage	hettangien *m*	Hettangien *n*	hettangiano *m*
—	9112	heulandite	heulandite *f*	Heulandit *m*	heulandite *f*
—	9113	heumite	heumite *f*	Heumit *m*	heumite *f*
—	9114	hewettite	hewettite *f*	Hewettit *m*	hewettite *f*
—	9115	hewing	havage *m*, sous--cavage *m*	Unterhöhlen *n*, Unterschrämen *n*	taglio *m* orizzontale del carbone, taglio *m* inferiore
—	9116	hewn stone	pierre *f* de taille	Quaderstein *m*	pietra *f* sbozzata
^	9117	hex kelly	tige *f* hexagonale d'entraînement	Sechskantstange *f*	asta *f* motrice esagonale
—	9118	hexad	axe *m* sénaire	sechszählige Achse *f*	asse *m* senario
°	9119	hexagon bar (iron)	fer *m* hexagonal, fer *m* hexagone	Sechskanteisen *n*	ferro *m* esagonale, esagoni *m pl.* di ferro
°	9120	hexagon-headed bolt	boulon *m* à tête hexagonale	Sechskantschraube *f*	bullone *m* a testa esagonale
		hexagon iron, *s. hexagon bar*			
°	9121	hexagonal rod, hexagonal bar iron	fer *m* hexagonal	Sechskanteisen *n*	barra *f* esagonale
—	9122	hexagonal system	système *m* hexagonal	hexagonales System *n*	sistema *m* esagonale
—	9123	hexagonal trapezohedron	trapézoèdre *m* hexagonal	sechsseitiges Trapezoeder *n*	trapezoedro *m* esagonale
°	9124	hexagonal wire	fil *m* hexagonal, fil à six-pans	Sechskantdraht *m*	filo *m* esagonale
°	9125	hexagonal wire netting	treillis *m* à triple torsion	Drahtgeflecht *n* mit dreifacher Verwindung	traliccio *m* a torsione tripla

		English	French	German	Italian
o	9126	**hexagons, hexagon bars**	acier m hexagonal	Sechskantstahl m	esagono m d'acciaio
—	9127	**hexahydrite**	hexahydrite f	Hexahydrit m	esaidrite f
—	9128	**hexakisoctahedron**	hexoctaèdre m	Hexakisoktaeder m	esaottaedro m
—	9129	**hexakistetrahedron**	hexatétraèdre m	Hexakistetraeder m	esatetraedro m
		HF ioniser, $s.$ $high$ $frequency$ $ioniser$			
—	9130	**hiatal texture**	structure f poreuse	poröse Struktur f	struttura f porosa
—	9131	**hiatus**	hiatus m	Hiatus m	hiatus m, lacuna f
—	9132	**hibbenite**	hibbénite f	Hibbenit m	hibbenite f
—	9133	**hibschite**	hibschite f	Hibschit m	hibschite f
—	9134	**hiddenite**	hiddénite f	Hiddenit m	hiddenite f
—	9135	**higginsite**	higginsite f	Higginsit m	higginsite f
o	9136	**high alloy**	alliage m à haute teneur	hochprozentige Legierung f	lega f ad alto tenore
o	9137	**high-alloy steel**	acier m d'alliage riche, acier affiné	hochlegierter Stahl m, Edelstahl m	acciaio m ad alto tenore legante
—	9138	**high angle hole**	puits m à grande déviation	Bohrloch mit starker Neigung	pozzo m (o foro) molto deviato
o	9139	**high-carbon steel**	acier m à haute teneur en carbone	hochgekohlter Stahl m	acciaio m a alto tenore di carbonio
o	9140	**high-carbon structural steel**	acier m fin (de construction) au carbone	unlegierter Baustahl m	acciaio m fino al carbonio da costruzione
o	9141	**high-conductivity copper**	cuivre m à haute conductivité	Kupfer n von hoher Leitfähigkeit	rame m di alta conduttività
o	9142	**high content alloy**	alliage m à haute teneur	hochprozentige Legierung f	lega f a alto tenore
		high-duty boiler, $s.$ $high$-$power$ $boiler$			
o	9142a	**high-duty cast iron**	fonte f résistante	hochfestes Gusseisen n	ghisa f ad alta resistenza
o	9143	**high duty cast iron, high strength cast iron**	fonte f résistante	hochfestes Gusseisen n	ghisa f ad alta resistenza, ghisa f acciarosa (o di alta qualità)
o	9144	**high energy rate forming**	formage m à haute énergie	Hochleistungsumformung f	stampaggio m ad alta energia

	English	French	German	Italian
—	9145 high-explosive, disruptive explosive	explosif brisant	Brisanzsprengstoff *m*	esplosivo *m* dirompente
°	9146 high frequency electric induction welding machine	soudeuse *f* à induction à haute fréquence	Anlage *f* für elektrische Hochfrequenz- -Induktionsschweis- sung *f*	saldatrice *f* ad induzione ad alta frequenza
°	9147 high frequency induction furnace	four *m* à induction à haute fréquence	Hochfrequenz- -Induktionsofen *m*	forno *m* a induzione ad alta frequenza
°	9148 high-frequency furnace	four *m* à haute fréquence	Hochfrequenzofen *m*, Wirbelstromofen *m*	forno *m* ad alta frequenza
°	9149 high furnace	four *m* à cuve, haut fourneau	Schachtofen *m*, Hochofen *m*	forno *m* a tino, alto- forno *m*
°	9150 high-grade cast iron	fonte *f* de première qualité	hochwertiger Guss *m*	ghisa *f* di prima quali- tà
—	9151 high-grade fuel	combustible *m* de très bonne qualité	hochwertiger Brennstoff *m*	combustibile *m* pregia- to, combustibile *m* di ottima qualità
—	9152 high-grade ore	minerai *m* riche	reiches Erz *n*	minerale *m* ricco
°	9153 high-grade steel	acier *m* de qualité supérieure, acier *m* supérieur	hochwertiger Stahl *m*, Qualitätsstahl *m*	acciaio *m* pregiato (o di qualità superiore)
°	9154 high heat	difficilement fusible	schwerflüssig	difficilmente fusibile
°	9155 high-heat salt bath	bain *m* de sel pour températures élevées	hohes Wärme- salzbad *n*	bagno *m* di sale per alte temperature
^	9156 high level tank, elevated reservoir	réservoir *m* suréle- vé ou de distribution	Hochbehälter *m*	serbatoio *m* elevato
°	9157 high light	point *m* brillant	Glanzpunkt *m*	punto *m* brillante
^	9157a high line	câble *m* d'extraction	Förderseil *n*	cavo *m* di manovra al parco tubi
°	9158 high manganese spiegel, specular iron containing a large amount of manganese	fonte *f* spiegel à haute teneur en manganèse	stark manganhaltiges Spiegeleisen *n*	ghisa *f* a tenore composto od a strut- tura compatta
—	9159 high moorland	plateau *m* marécageux	Hochmoor *n*	altopiano *m* paludoso
^	9160 high-octane number fuel	carburant *m* à nom- bre d'octane élevé	Betriebsstoff *m* mit hoher Oktanzahl	carburante *m* ad alto numero di ottano

	English	French	German	Italian
o	9161 high polish	poli fin	hochglanzpoliert	lucidato a specchio
o	9162 high phosphorous iron	fer *m* à haute teneur en phosphore	hochphosphorhaltiges Eisen *n*	ferro *m* con alto tenore in fosforo
o	9163 high-power boiler, high-duty boiler	chaudière *f* à puissance élevée	Hochleistungskessel *m*	caldaia *f* a potenza elevata
o	9164 high pressure	haute pression *f*	Hochdruck *m*, Hauptdruck *m*	alta pressione *f*, pressione *f* finale
o	9165 high-pressure blow-pipe	tubulure *f* à haute pression	Hochdruckrohr *n*	cannello *m* ad alta pressione
o	9166 high-pressure blower	ventilateur *m* à haute pression	Hochdruckgebläse *n*	ventilatore *m* ad alta pressione
o	9167 high-pressure boiler with omega steel tubes	chaudière *f* à tubes d'acier oméga à haute pression	Omega-Stahlrohr-kessel in Hochdruckausführung *f*	caldaia *f* a tubi di acciaio omega ad alta pressione
o	9168 high-pressure pipe	tube *m* pour hautes pressions	Hochdruckrohr *n*	tubo *m* per alte pressioni
o	9169 high-pressure spiral blower	soufflerie *f* hélicoïdale à haute pression	Hochdruckschraubengebläse *n*	ventilatore *m* a spirale ad alta pressione
o	9170 high-pressure steam boiler	chaudière *f* à vapeur à haute pression	Hochdruckdampfkessel *m*	caldaia *f* a vapore ad alta pressione
	high-quality steel, *s. high-grade steel*			
—	9171 high side	lèvre *f* soulevée	gehobener Flügel *m*	lembo *m* sollevato
o	9172 high-silicon (pig) iron, silvery gray	fonte *f* grise riche en silicium, fonte *f* très siliceuse, fonte *f* brillante	siliziumreiches graues Roheisen *n*, Schwarzeisen *n*, Glanzeisen *n*	ghisa *f* grigia siliciosa, ghisa *f* brillante, ghisa *f* nera
^	9173 high-solvency naphta	naphte *m* solvant	Lösungsnaphta *n*	nafta *f* solvente
o	9174 high-speed metal sawing machine	scie *f* à métaux à grande vitesse	schnelle Metallsäge *f*	sega *f* rapida meccanica da metalli
o	9175 high-speed reversing mill	laminoir *m* réversible à haute vitesse	schnellaufendes Reversierwalzwerk *n*	laminatoio *m* reversibile ad alta velocità
o	9176 high speed roll	cylindre *m* à grande vitesse	schnellaufende Walze *f*	cilindro *m* a gran velocità
o	9177 high speed rolling mill	train *m* rapide	Schnellwalzwerk *n*	treno *m* rapido

	English	French	German	Italian
°	9178 high speed steel	acier *m* rapide	Schnellstahl *m*	acciaio *m* rapido
°	9179 high speed tool steel	acier *m* rapide pour outils	Schnellwerkzeug-stahl *m*	acciaio *m* rapido per utensili
°	9180 high-speed turret lathe steel	acier *m* rapide pour tour-révolver	Schnelldreh-Revolverstahl *m*	acciaio *m* rapido per tornio-revolver
—	9181 high stone content asphaltic concrete	béton *m* d'asphalte à gros granulats	Asphaltgrobbeton *m*	calcestruzzo *m* asfaltico grosso
°	9182 high strength	haute résistance *f*	hochwertige Festigkeit *f*	resistenza *f* (alta)

high-strenght brass, *s. manganese bronze*

high-strenght steel, *s. high-tensile*

	English	French	German	Italian
°	9183 high stress grinding abrasion	usure *f* par abrasion sous pression de contact élevée	Verschleiss *m* durch Abrieb unter hohem Kontaktdruck	usura *f* per abrasione ad alta pressione di contatto
°	9184 high stresses obtained by resonance	contraintes *f pl.* élevées dues à la résonnance	durch Resonanz *f* hervorgerufene starke Spannungen	forti sollecitazioni *f pl.* dovute alla risonanza
°	9185 high temperature stability	résistance *f* à chaud	Wärmefestigkeit *f*, Hitzebeständigkeit *f*	resistenza *f* al calore, stabilità *f* al calore
°	9186 high tensile brass, high tension brass	laiton *m* à haute résistance	Sondermessing *n*	ottone *m* ad alta resistenza

high tension steel, *s. high tensile steel*

	English	French	German	Italian
°	9187 high.tensile steel	acier *m* à haute résistance	Festigkeitsstahl *m*	acciaio *m* ad alta resistenza
°	9188 high tensile welding steel	acier *m* soudable à haute résistance	Festigkeitsschweiss-stahl *m*	acciaio *m* saldabile ad alta resistenza
°	9189 high-tension cable	câble *m* d'alimentation à haute tension	Hochspannungs-speisekabel *n*	cavo *m* di alimentazione ad alta tensione
°	9190 high tension plant	installation *f* à haute tension	Hochspannungs-'anlage *f*	impianto *m* ad alta tensione
°	9191 high velocity forming process	formage *m* à très hautes vitesses de déformation	Hochgeschwindig-keitsverformung *f*	processo *m* di formatura rapido
°	9192 high webbed tee-iron	fer *m* à T à âme allongée	hochstegiges T-Eisen *n*	ferro *m* a T ad anima alta
°	9192a highgate resin	copaline *f*	Kopalin *m*	copalite *f*

highest pressure, *s. maximum pressure*

505

	English	French	German	Italian
∘	9193 highest pressure boiler	chaudière f à très haute pression	Höchstdruckkessel m	caldaia f ad altissima pressione
∘	9194 highly radiated pig	fonte f blanche à texture franchement rayonnée	hochstrahliges Roheisen n	ghisa f fortemente raggiata (o radiale)
∘	9195 highly refractory material	pâte f très réfractaire	hochfeuerfeste Masse f	materiale m molto refrattario
−	9196 hillebrandite	hillebrandite f	Hillebrandit m	hillebrandite f
∘	9197 hindered contraction	retrait m contrarié	behinderte Schwindung f	ritiro m contrastato (o ritardato)
−	9198 hinge, bend	charnière f	Umbiegung f, Scharnier n	cerniera f
∘	9199 hinge-block	charnière f	Gelenk n	cerniera f
−	9200 hinge line	ligne f de charnière	Schlossrand m	linea f di cerniera
∘	9201 hinge pin	goujon m	Zapfen m	spinotto m
∘	9202 hinge plate	plaquette f de charnière	Plattengelenk n, Zapfenband n	lamierina f porta-cerniera
∘	9203 hinged	désarticulé, dénoué	gegliedert, gelenkig	snodato
∘	9204 hinged closing trap	trappe f à charnière	Verschlussklappe f	botola f a cerniera
∘	9205 hinged core box	boîte f à noyaux (ou à charnière)	Klappkernkasten m	cassa f d'anima a cerniera
∘	9206 hinged moulding box	châssis m à démotter	Abschlagkasten m, Abschlagrahmen m	staffa f per smottare, staffa f a cerniera
∘	9207 hinged vice, leg-vice	étau ordinaire, étau à pied	Flaschenschraubstock m	morsa f a bottiglia, morsa f con gambo
−	9208 hinsdalite	hinsdalite f	Hinsdalit m	hinsdalite f
−	9209 hintzeite	hintzéite f	Hintzeit m	hintzeite f
∘	9210 Hiorth furnace	four m Hiorth	Hiorthscher Ofen m	forno m Hiorth
−	9211 hippuritic facies	faciès m à hippurites	Hippuriten-Fazies f	facies f ippuritica
−	9212 hirst	banc m de sable	Sandbank f	banco m di sabbia
−	9213 histrixite	histrixite f	Histrixit m	histrixite f

	English	French	German	Italian
°	9214 hitch	attaque *f*, noeud *m*	Haken *m*, Knoten *m*	attacco *m*, nodo *m*
—	9215 hitchcockite	hitchcockite *f*	Hitchcockit *m*	hitchcockite *f*
—	9216 hitcher	encageur *m*	Anschläger *m*	ingabbiatore *m*
°	9217 hob, hub	poinçon *m* d'empreinte	Patrize *f*	punzone *m* d'impronta-tura
°	9217a hob	plateau *m* de four	Ofenplatte *f*	placca *f* di forno
°	9218 hob	vis fraise *f*	Wälzfräser *m*	creatore *m*
°	9219 hobbing	impression *f*	Prägung *f*	improntatura *f*
°	9220 hobbing steel, punch steel	acier *m* à poinçons	Lochstempelstahl *m*, Stempelstahl *m*	acciaio *m* stampigliabi-le, acciaio per punzoni
—	9221 hodgkinsonite	hodgkinsonite *f*	Hodgkinsonit *m*	hodgkinsonite *f*
—	9222 hog back	crête *f* isoclinale	Isoklinalkamm *m*	cresta *f* isoclinale
°	9222a hogging	ébarbage *m* à la flamme	Flammentgratung *f*	sbavatura *f* alla fiamma
—	9223 hogbomite	hogbomite *f*	Hogbomit *m*	hogbomite *f*
—	9224 hoist	monte-charge *m*	Aufzug *m*	montacarichi *m*
—	9225 hoist	palan *m*	Hebezeug *n*, Flaschenzug *m*	paranco *m*, argano *m*
—	9226 hoist drum	tambour *m* de treuil, tambour *m* d'extraction	Fördertrommel *f*	tamburo *m* dell'argano, tamburo *m* d'estrazione
—	9227 hoist frame	charpente *f* du monte-charge	Fördergerüst *n*	armatura *f* del montaca-richi
—	9228 hoist man	machiniste *m* d'extraction	Fördermaschinist *m*	addetto *m* alla macchi-na d'estrazione
	hoist pan, *s. charging pan*			
—	9229 hoisting	extraction *f*, levage	Schachtförderung *f*, Heben *n*	estrazione *f*, solle-vamento *m*
—	9230 hoisting block	moufle *f* mobile	lose Seilscheibe *f*	muffola *f* mobile, puleggia *f* mobile, taglia *f* mobile
—	9231 hoisting cable	câble *m* d'extraction	Förderseil *n*	cavo *m* d'estrazione (o di manovra)
—	9232 hoisting engine	machine *f* d'extrac-tion, machine *f* de levage	Fördermaschine *f*. Aufzugmaschine *f*	macchina *f* d'estra-zione
—	9233 hoisting shaft	puits *m* d'extraction	Förderschacht *m*	pozzo *m* d'estrazione

	English	French	German	Italian
—	9234 hoisting sheave	molette *f*	Seilscheibe *f*	puleggia *f* mobile
—	9235 hoisting string-up	ensemble *m* d'élévation	Hebegruppe *f*	complesso *m* di sollevamento, controtaglia *f*, cavo *m*
—	9236 hoisting winch	treuil *m* d'extraction, treuil *m* de levage	Förderhaspel *f*, Aufzugwinde *f*	argano *m* d'estrazione, argano *m* di sollevamento
—	9237 hokutolite	hokutolite *f*	Hokutolit *m*	hokutolite *f*
—	9238 Holarctic	holarctique *m*	Holoarktik *m*	holoartico *m*
—	9239 hold-back rope	câble *m* de retour du tube	Rohrkabeltragseil *n*	fune *f* di ritorno del tubo
°	9239a hold down	goupille *f* de retenue	Stellspindel *f*	perno *m* di ritenuta
^	9240 hold down bar	barre *f* de fixage	Spannstange *f*	barra *f* di fissaggio
—	9241 holdenite	holdénite *f*	Holdenit *m*	holdenite *f*
°	9242 holding	maintien *m*	Warmhalten *n*	attesa *f*
—	9243 holding apparatus	parachute *m*	Fangvorrichtung *f*	paracadute *m*
°	9244 holding furnace	four *m* de maintien	Warmhalteofen *m*	forno *m* di attesa
^	9245 holding direction	direction *f* de pose (d'un packer)		direzione *f* di posa (di un packer)
°	9246 holding-down plate	plaque *f* d'ancrage, contre-plaque *f*	Spannplatte *f*, Befestigungsplatte *f*	piastra *f* di ritegno, contropiastra *f*
°	9247 holding time	durée *f* d'arrêt	Haltezeit *f*	tempo *m* di permanenza
°	9248 hole	trou *m*, piqûre *f*	Loch *n*	foro *m*
°	9249 hole-bored axle from end to end	arbre *m* percé sur toute sa longueur	Achse *f* mit durchgehender Bohrung	asse *m* perforato per tutta la sua lunghezza
^	9250 hole caliper	diamétreur	Bohrloch-Kaliber *n*	calibro *m* per fori
^	9251 hole gauge	jauge *f* pour trous	Lochlehre *f*	calibro *m* per fori o per diametri
—	9252 hole man	boutefeu *m*	Schiessmeister *m*	artificere *m*
^	9253 hole opener	broche *f* fixe	Festräumer *m*	allargatore *m* fisso
°	9254 holed	havé, entaillé	geschrämt	tagliato, intagliato
°	9255 holed	perforé, percé	perforiert	perforato, forato

	English	French	German	Italian
o	9256 holes punched in the channel back	trous poinçonnés dans le dos du profil	gestanzte Löcher fm Steg des Profils	fori punzonati praticati sul dorso del profilo
^	9257 holiday	partie f de tuyau restée sans vernis	Rohrteil m ohne Anstrich	parte f di un tubo rimasta senza vernice
—	9258 holing-pick	rivelaine f	Schrämeisen n	piccone m per carbone
o	9259 holing-through	percement m	Durchschlag m	perforazione f.
—	9260 hollandite	hollandite f	Hollandit m	hollandite f
o	9261 hollow, groove	creux m	Vertiefung f	cavità f
o	9262 hollow	tube m ébauché	Rohrluppe f	tubo m sbozzato
o	9263 hollow, groove, recess	congé m	Hohlkehle f	raccordo m
o	9264 hollow body	corps m creux	Hohlkörper m	corpo m cavo
o	9265 hollow body for stems and guide tubes of spring buffers	tampon m de choc (tige et enveloppe)	Rohr n für Puffer (Schaft und Hülse)	respingente m (gambo e custodia)
o	9266 hollow cast, hollow casting	fonte f creuse	Hohlguss m	getto m cavo, getto m con cavità inferiore
o	9267 hollow-cast furniture	lingots m pl. en fonte, garniture f creuse	Hohlstege m pl.	lingotti m pl. vuoti
o	9268 hollow casting	coulage m à noyau	Hohlguss m	getto m ad anima, getto m cavo
o	9269 hollow drill steel	acier m pour forets	Hohlbohrstahl m	acciaio m per barramine forate
o	9270 hollow druse	trou m	Druse f	foro m
o	9271 hollow extruded sections	profils m pl. creux extrudés	stranggepresste Hohlprofile n pl.	profilati m pl. cavi estrusi
o	9272 hollow forging	forgeage m creux forgeage à mandrin	Hohlschmieden n Dornschmieden n	fucinatura f cava (o con mandrino)
o	9273 hollow halfround bar steel	fer m demi-rond creux	Hohlhalbrundstahl m	barra f a canalino, cordonata f semplice
o	9274 hollow helical gearing	pignon m creux	hohle Kammerwalze f. Innenverzahnung f	dentatura f interna
o	9275 hollow iron	tube m en fer	Eisenrohr n	tubo m di ferro

English	French	German	Italian
° 9276 **hollow piece**	ébauché *m*	Rohling *m*	sbozzato *m*
° 9277 **hollow pin**	goujon *m* tubulaire	vorstehende Führungsbüchse *f*	boccola *f* per pernio a cannone, colonnetta *f* di guida cava
° 9278 **hollow punch, punch**	pince *f* à emporte—pièce des oeillets	Locheisen *n*, Lochzange *f*	foratoio *m*, tenaglia *f* occhiellatrice *f*
° 9278a **hollow punching**	trépanation *f* par emporte-pièce	Warmbohren mit Locheisen	alesatura *f* a caldo con fustella
^ 9279 **hollow reamer**	tube *m* fissuré à deux pointes	gespaltetes Rohr *n* mit zwei Spitzen	tubo *m* fessurato con due punte per pescare
° 9280 **hollow trunnion**	tourillon *m* creux	hohler Zapfen *m*	perno *m* vuoto, perno *m* del vento
— 9281 **hollow spar**	andalousite *f*	Andalusit *m*	andalusite *f*
— 9282 **hollows**	vieux travaux *m pl.*	alter Mann *m*	scavi *m pl.* abbandonati
° 9283 **holmium**	holmium *m*	Holmium *n*	olmio *m*
— 9284 **holoaxial**	holoaxe	holoachsial	oloassiale
— 9285 **Holocene**	holocène *m*	Holozän *n*	olocene *m*
— 9286 **holocrystalline**	holocristallin	holokristallin	olocristallino
— 9287 **holohedral**	holoédrique	holoedrisch	oloedrico
— 9288 **holohyaline**	holohyalin	holohyalin	oloialino
— 9289 **hololeucocratic**	hololeucocrate	hololeukokrat	ololeucocratico
— 9290 **holomelanocratic**	holomélanocrate	holomelanokrat	olomelanocratico
— 9291 **holomorphic**	holomorphique	holomorphisch	olomorfico
— 9292 **holotype**	holotype *m*	Holotypus *n*	olotipo *m*
holsters, *s. stand*			
—9293 **holyokeite**	holyokéite *f*	Holyokeit *m*	holiokeite *f*
° 9293a **home scrap**	ferrailles de production propre	Hüttenschrott *m*	rottami *m pl.* di produzione propria
^ 9294 **home socket**	tube *m* de repêchage	Fangrohr *n*	asta *f*, tubo *m* di pescaggio
— 9295 **homilite**	homilite *f*	Homilit *m*	omilite *f*
— 9296 **homocline**	homoclinal	homoklinisch	omoclinale
— 9297 **homoeoblastic structure**	structure *f* homoéoblastique	homöoblastische Struktur *f*	struttura *f* omeoblastica

		English	French	German	Italian
—	9298	**homoeomorphous**	homoéomorphe	homoeomorph	omeomorfo
°	9299	**homogenising anneal**	traitement d'homogénéisation	Diffusionsglühen *n*	trattamento *m* di omogeneizzazione
°	9299a	**homopolar bond**	liaison *f* covalente	kovalente Bindung *f*	legante *m* covalente
—	9300	**homotaxial deposit**	dépôt *m* homotaxique	homotaxe Ablagerung *f*	deposito *m* omotassico
—	9301	**honestone, hone**	pierre *f* à aiguiser	Wetzschiefer *m*, Wetzstein *m*	pietra *f* da affilare
—	9302	**honey-stone**	mellite *f*	Mellit *m*	mellite *f*
		honeycomb casting, *s. blown casting*			
°	9303	**honey-combed, blown hollow**	caverneux	löcherig	cavernoso
°	9304	**honey-combed (or porous or spongy or blown) casting**	fonte *f* à soufflures	blasiger Guss *m*	getto *m* soffiato, ghisa *f* soffiata
—	9305	**honeycombed rock**	roche *f* alvéolaire	Felslöcher *n pl.*, Felshöhlen *f pl.*	roccia *f* alveolare
		honey-combed, *s. pumice-stone slag*			
°	9306	**honey combing**	formation *f* de soufflures	Schwalbennestbildung *f*	formazione *f* di soffiatura
°	9306a	**honing**	rectification intérieure	Honen *n*	levigatura *f*
°	9307	**honing machine**	machine *f* à honer	Honmaschine *f*, Läppmaschine *f*	lappatrice *f*
°	9308	**hood**	chapiteau *m* (du cubilot)	Kaminhaube *f*	cappello *m* (del cubilotto)
°	9309	**hood**	hotte *f*	Abzughaube *f*	cappa *f*
°	9310	**hoof or neat's foot meal**	farine *f* de pieds de boeufs	Klauenmehl *n*	farina *f* d'unghia di bue
°	9311	**to hook up**	mettre dans le circuit	einschalten	agganciare, mettere in circuito, innestare
°	9312	**hook, rake**	crochet *m*	Haken *m*, Schaffhaken *m*	rampino *m*
°	9313	**hook block assembly**	moufle à crochet combiné	kombinierter Rollenblock *m* mit Haken	muffola *f* combinata a gancio
°	9314	**hook bolt, hook screw, clip, T-headed bolt**	boulon *m* de fondation	Hammerschraube *f*, Schaufelbolzen *m*	bullone *m* con testa a T, bullone *m* di fondazione
°	9315	**hook foundry nail**	crochet *m* pour mouleurs	Formstift *m*	punta *f* a gancio per fonderia

English	French	German	Italian
o 9316 **hook gagger**	armature f à crochet	Hakengiessform f	armatura f a gancio
o 9317 **hook iron, winder**	fer m à crochet	Hakeneisen n	ferro m da ganci
o 9318 **hook plate**	selle f à crochet	Hakenplatte f	piastrina f a rampone, piastrina f d'attacco
^ 9319 **hook-wall packer**	remblayeuse f pour trou non tubé	Versatzmaschine f für unverrohrtes Bohrloch	packer m per foro scoperto
— 9320 **hooker-on**	accrocheur m	Aufhänger m	ingabbiatore m
o 9321 **hoop**	cercle m (en bois)	Reifen m	cerchio m
o 9322 **hoop**	fer m plat	Bandeisen n	ferro m piatto, nastro m di ferro, reggetta f
o 9323 **hoop, iron belt**	ceinture f en fer plat	umgelegtes Eisenband n, Gürtel m	cerchio m, cintura f
o 9324 **hoop iron, strip iron, band iron**	fer m feuillard, fer m à bandage	Bandeisen n, Eisenreif m	ferro m a nastro, reggetta f di ferro
o 9325 **hoop rolling mill, strip rolling mill**	laminoir m à feuillards	Bandeisenstrecke f	treno m per nastri
o 9326 **hooper**	mélangeur Halliburton	Halliburtonmischer m	mescolatore m ad ugello e tramoggia (Halliburton)
— 9327 **hopeite**	hopéite f	Hopeit m	hopeite f
— 9328 **hopper**	trémie f	Zwischenbehälter m, Speisetrichter m	tramoggia f
— 9329 **hopper brackets**	support m de la trémie	Träger m des Trichters	sostegno m o supporto m della tramoggia
hopper car, s. bottom discharge car			
hopper cup, s. funnel			
— 9330 **horizon**	horizon m, gisement m	Horizont m, Lagerstätte f	orizzonte m mineralizzato, livello m stratigrafico, giacimento m
o 9331 **horizontal air heater**	appareil m à air chaud horizontal	liegender Winderhitzer m	apparecchio m ad aria calda orizzontale
o 9332 **horizontal blower**	machine f soufflante horizontale	liegendes Gebläse n	soffieria f orizzontale
o 9333 **horizontal boiler**	chaudière f horizontale	liegender (Dampf)-Kessel m	caldaia f orizzontale

	English	French	German	Italian
°	9334 horizontal casting	coulée f horizontale	liegender Guss m	colata f orizzontale, getto m coricato
°	9335 horizontal clay mixer	malaxeur m à argile horizontal	waagerechter Tonmischer m	mescolatore m d'argilla orizzontale
—	9336 horizontal cut-and-fill	exploitation f par tailles en échelon avec remblayage	Firstenbau m mit waagrechter Firste und mit Bergeversatz	coltivazione f a tagli a gradino con ripiena
—	9337 horizontal cut-and- -fill stope	taille f en échelon avec remblayage	Firstenstoss m mit waagerechter Firste und mit Bergeversatz	taglio m a gradino con ripiena
—	9338 horizontal displacement	rejet m horizontal	horizontale Schublänge f	rigetto m orizzontale
—	9339 horizontal joint	bathroclase f, diaclase f horizontale	Bathroklas n, schwebende Spalte	batroclasi f, diaclasi f orizzontale
°	9340 horizontal drive	commande f horizontale	liegender Antrieb m	comando m orizzontale
—	9341 horizontal drum	tambour m horizontal	waagrechte Trommel f	tamburo m orizzontale
°	9342 horizontal furnace	four dormant	liegender Ofen m, Horizontalofen m	forno m orizzontale
°	9343 horizontal grate	grille f horizontale	Planrost m	griglia f piana
—	9344 horizontal lining	boisage horizontal	waagrechte Zimmerung f	rivestimento m con tavole orizzontali
—	9345 horizontal overlap	recouvrement m horizontal	horizontale Deckung f	ricoprimento m (tettonico) orizzontale
°	9346 horizontal pipe	tuyau m horizontal	waagrechtes Rohr n	tubo m orizzontale
°	9347 horizontal plane	surface f plane	ebene Fläche f	superficie f piana
°	9348 horizontal plate	plaque f horizontale	waagrechte Platte f	piastra f orizzontale
°	9349 horizontal rotating table	manège m	Drehtisch m	piattaforma f girevole
—	9350 horizontal separation in fault line strike, total heave	rejet horizontal latéral	streichende Sprungweite	rigetto m orizzontale laterale
—	9351 horizontal slicing	exploitation f par tranches horizontales	horizontaler Scheibenbau m	coltivazione f a trance orizzontali

	English	French	German	Italian
°	9352 horizontal steam boiler	chaudière *f* horizontalé	liegender Dampfkessel *m*	caldaia *f* orizzontale
^	9353 horizontal swing	levier de déviation	Umkehrbock *m*	leva *f* di deviazione
—	9354 horizontal throw	rejet *m* horizontal transversal	horizontale Sprungweite *f*	rigetto *m* orizzontale trasversale
—	9355 horizontal thrust fault	faille *f* horizontale	horizontale Verwerfung *f*	faglia *f* orizzontale
°	9356 horizontal-type forging machine, bulldozer	machine *f* à forger horizontale	liegende Schmiedemaschine *f*	fucinatrice *f* orizzontale
—	9357 horn	batée *f*	Sichertrog *m*	batea *f* (per minerali)
°	9358 horn casting	coulée *f* en cornichon	Horngiessen *n*	colata *f* a corno
—	9359 horn charcoal	charbon *m* de corne	Hornkohle *f*	carbone *m* di corno

horn for circumferential seam welding, *s. arm for circumferential seam welding*

horn for longitudinal seam welding, *s. arm for longitudinal seam welding*

	English	French	German	Italian
°	9360 horn-gate	attaque *f* en cornichon	Hornzulauf *m*	attacco a corno
—	9361 horn mercury	calomel *m*	Kalomel *n*	calomelano *m*
°	9362 horn plate	para-essieux	Achsenfutter *n*	parasala *f*
—	9363 horn silver	cérargyrite *f*	Chlorsilber *m*	cerargirite *f*
—	9364 horn socket	tube *m* de repêchage	Hornbüchse *f*	pescatore *m*
^	9365 horn spacing	distance *f* entre les bras		distanza *f* tra i bracci
°	9366 horn welding	soudure *f* par martelage	Hammerschweissung *f*	saldatura *f* a martellatura
—	9367 hornbeam	charme *m*	Weissbuche *f*	carpino *m*
—	9368 hornblei	phosgénite *f*	Phosgenit *m*	fosgenite *f*
—	9369 hornblende	hornblende *f*	Hornblende *f*	orneblenda *f*
—	9370 hornblende schist	schiste *m* à hornblende	Hornblendeschiefer *m*	scisto a orneblenda

	English	French	German	Italian
—	9371 **hornblendite**	hornblendite f	Hornblendefels m	orneblendite f
—	9372 **hornfels**	cornéenne f	Hornfels m	selce f cornea
	hornlead, $s.$ *hornblei*			
—	9373 **horns**	rainures f $pl.$ du tambour d'extraction f $pl.$	Seiltrommelrillen	guide f $pl.$ del tamburo d'estrazione
—	9374 **hornstone**	silice f cornée	Hornstein m	selce f cornea
—	9375 **horse**	inclusion f de stériles dans une veine	eingeklemmte Scholle f	inclusione f di sterile
—	9376 **horse**	chevalet m	Bock, Gerüst n	cavalletto m, capra f
—	9377 **horseback**	intercalation f stérile	eingeklemmte Scholle f	ammasso m sterile
—	9378 **horse-flesh ore**	cuivre m panaché	Buntkupfererz n	bornite f
^	9379 **horse head**	secteur m de suspension	Pferdekopf m	testa f del bilanciere di pompaggio
o	9380 **horse-nail iron**	fer m pour clous à ferrer	Hufeisennagel n	barra f per chiodi da ferro di cavallo
o	9381 **horseshoe**	fer m à cheval	Hufeisen n	ferro m da cavallo
o	9382 **horseshoe bars**	barre f pour fers à cheval	Hufstabeisen n	barra f per ferri da cavallo
o	9383 **horseshoe magnet**	aimant m en fer à cheval	Hufeisenmagnet m	magnete m a ferro di cavallo
—	9384 **horsfordite**	horsfordite f	Horsfordit m	horsfordite f
—	9385 **horst**	horst m	Horst m	horst m
—	9386 **hortonolite**	hortonolite f	Hortonolith m	hortonolite f
^	9387 **hose adapter**	attaque f du tuyau à la tête d'injection m	Schlauchanschluss m	attacco m del tubo alla testa d'iniezione
o	9388 **hose clip**	bande f universelle	Universalschelle f	fascetta f universale
^	9389 **hose union (or coupling)**	goulotte f	Stutzen m	bocchettone m
—	9390 **host mineral**	hôte m	primäres Mineral n	minerale m primario

English	French	German	Italian
9391 **hot air main**	conduite *f* de vent chaud	Heisswindleitung *f*	condotto *m* d'aria calda
9391a **hot bed, cooling bed**	refroidisseur *m*	Kühlbett, Warmlager *n*	raffreddatore *m*
9392 **hot bending test**	essai *m* de pliage à chaud	Warmbiegeprobe *f*	prova *f* di piegatura a caldo
9393 **hot blast**	vent *m* chaud	heisser Wind *m*	vento *m* caldo
9394 **hot blast cupola**	cubilot *m* à vent chaud	Heisswindkupolofen *m*	cubilotto *m* a vento caldo o ad aria calda
9395 **hot-blast furnace**	four *m* à vent chaud	Heisswindofen *m*	forno *m* a vento caldo
9396 **hot-blast iron**	fonte *f* au vent chaud	heissgeblasenes Roheisen *n*	ghisa *f* a vento caldo
9397 **hot-blast main**	conduite *f* de vent chaud	Heisswindleitung *f*	condotta *f* del vento caldo
9398 **hot blast oven**	étuve *f* à air pulsé	Konvektionsofen *m*	forno *m* ad aria pulsata
9399 **hot blast pig iron**	fonte *f* au vent chaud	heiss geblasenes Roheisen *n*, mit heissem windgeblasenem Roheisen *n*	ghisa *f* fabbricata ad alta temperatura
9400 **hot-blast stove**	préchauffeur *m* (d'air)	Luftvorwärmer *m*	preriscaldatore *m* (d'aria)
9401 **hot blast valve**	vanne *f* à air chaud	Heisswindschieber *m*	valvola *f* ad aria calda
9402 **hot brittle iron**	fer *m* cassant à chaud	heissbrüchiges Eisen *n*, rotbrüchiges Eisen *n*	ferro *m* fragile a caldo
9403 **hot brittleness**	fragilité *f* à chaud	Heissbrüchigkeit *f*	fragilità *f* a caldo
9404 **hot chamber machine**	machine à chambre chaude	Warmkammer-Druckgiessmaschine *f*	macchina a camera calda
9405 **hot chamber piston machine**	machine à chambre chaude à piston	Kolbengiessmaschine *f*	macchina a camera calda a pistone
9406 **hot charge, molten charge**	charge *f* chaude, charge *f* liquide	warmer Einsatz *m*	carica *f* calda o liquida per il forno
9407 **hot chisel**	tranche *f* à chaud	Warmschrotmeissel *m*	tagliolo *m* (o scalpello) a caldo
hot compacting, *s. hot pressing*			
9408 **hot crack**	cassure *f* à chaud	Warmbruch *m*	rottura *f* a caldo, cricca di solidificazione

	English	French	German	Italian
o	**9409 hot crack**	tapure *f* à chaud	Warmriss *m*	crepa *f* a caldo, incrinatura *f* a caldo
o	9409a **hot deseamer**	décriqueuse à chaud	Flämmaschine *f*	scriccatore *m* alla fiamma
o	**9411 hot drawing**	étirage à chaud	Warmziehen *n*	trafilatura *f* a caldo
o	**9412 hot drawing and expanding equipment**	installation *f* de tréfilage et d'évasement	Anlage *f* zum Kaltziehen und Warm-Aufweiten	impianto *m* di trafilatura e di allargamento a caldo
o	**9413 hot enamelling**	émaillage *m* à chaud	Puderemaillierung *f*	smaltatura *f* a caldo
o	**9414 hot-extruded special steel sections**	profils *m pl.* d'acier spéciaux extrudés à chaud	warmstranggepresste Sonderprofile *n pl.* aus Stahl	profilati *m pl.* in acciaio ottenuti per estrusione a caldo
o	**9415 hot flat iron**	fer *m* plat à planer à chaud	Polierschaufel *f*	ferro *m* per lisciare a caldo
o	**9416 hot forging**	forgeage *m* à chaud	Warmhämmern *n*	forgiatura *f* a caldo
o	**9417 hot forming**	cintrage *m* à chaud	Warmbiegen *n*	curvatura *f* a caldo
o	**9418 hot galvanizing**	galvanisation *f* à chaud	Feuerverzinkung *f*	zincatura *f* a fuoco (o a caldo)
o	**9419 hot-golding**	dorure *f* au feu	Feuervergoldung *f*	doratura *f* a fuoco
o	**9420 hot iron**	fonte *f* chaude	heisses Gusseisen *n*	ghisa *f* calda
^	**9421 hot laid mixture**	mélange *m* à chaud	Warmgemisch *n*	miscela *f* a caldo
o	**9422 hot metal**	métal *m* chaud	heisses Metall *n*	metallo *m* caldo
o	9422a **hot metal car**	wagon *m* mélangeur	fahrbarer Mischer *m*	carro *m* mescolatore
^	9423 **hot oil, illegal oil**	pétrole *m* illégal	Schwarzöl *n*	petrolio *m* illegale
o	9423a **hot-peening**	trempe *f* chaude	Thermalhärtung *f*	tempra *f* calda
o	**9424 hot quenching**	grenaillage *m* à chaud	Warmkugelstrahlen *n*	pallinatura a caldo
o	**9425 hot plate**	plaque *f* de chauffage	Wärmeplatte *f*	piastra *f* di riscaldamento
o	**9426 to hot-press**	étamper à chaud	Gesenkschmieden *n*	stampare a caldo
o	9426a **hot pressing**	compression *f* à chaud	Warmpressen *n*	compressione *f* a caldo
o	**9427 hot-reducing rolling mill**	laminoir *m* réducteur à chaud	Warmreduzierwalzwerk *n*	laminatoio *m* riduttore a caldo
o	**9428 to hot-roll**	laminer à chaud	warmwalzen	laminare a caldo

	English	French	German	Italian
9429	hot-rolled	laminé à chaud	warmgewalzt	laminato a caldo
9430	hot rolled hoop	feuillard m à chaud	warmgewalztes Bandeisen n	reggetta f da imballo
9431	hot-rolled plate	tôle f laminée à chaud	warmgewalztes Blech n	lamiera f laminata a caldo
9432	hot-rolled steel	acier m laminé à chaud	warmgewalzter Stahl m	acciaio m laminato a caldo
9433	hot rolled steel sections	acier m profilé laminé à chaud	warmgewalzter Formstahl m	profilato m di acciaio laminato a caldo
9434	hot rolled steel strip	feuillard m laminé à chaud	warmgewalztes Bandeisen n	nastro m laminato a caldo
9435	hot-rolled strip iron	fer m feuillard laminé à chaud	heissgewalztes Eisen n	ferro m in nastri laminati a caldo, moietta f
9436	hot-rolling	laminage m à chaud	Warmwalzen n	laminazione f a caldo
9437	hot rolling mill	laminoir m à chaud	Warmwalzwerk n	laminatoio m a caldo
9438	hot saw	scie f à chaud	Warmsäge f	sega f a caldo
9438a	hot scarfing	chalumeautage m	Flämmen	scriccatura f al cannello
9439	hot short	cassant à chaud	warmbrüchig	fragile a caldo
9440	hot-short iron, red-short iron	fer m cassant à chaud	heissbrüchiges Eisen n, warmbrüchiges Eisen n	ferro m fragile a caldo
9441	hot shortness, red shortness	fragilité f à chaud	Warmbrüchigkeit f	fragilità f a caldo
9442	hot smelted iron	fonte f d'allure chaude	heisseingeschmolzenes Eisen n	ghisa f ottenuta con andamento caldo
9443	hot spinning	tournage m en plaques	Plattendrehen n	tornitura f in lastre
9444	hot spot	point m chaud	warme Stelle f	punto m caldo
9445	hot tear	crique f de retrait	Schwindungsriss m	cricca f di ritiro
9446	hot test	essai m à chaud	Warmprobe f	prova f a caldo
9447	hot tin plate	fer-blanc m étamé à chaud	feuerverzinntes Weissblech n	banda f stagnata a caldo
9448	hot tinned wire	fil m étamé au feu	feuerverzinnter Draht m	filo m stagnato al fuoco
9449	hot tinning	étamage m à chaud	Feuerverzinnen n	stagnatura f a caldo
9449a	hot top	masselotte f chaude	Wärmhaube f	coperchio m isolante

		English	French	German	Italian
o	9450	hot water boiler	chaudière f à eau chaude	Heisswasserkessel m	caldaia f ad acqua calda
o	9451	hot water circuit in black plate tubes	circuits m pl. en tube de fer noir	Heisswasserumlauf m in Schwarzblech- rohren	circuiti m pl. in tubo di lamiera nera
o	9452	hot water funnel	entonnoir m à eau chaude	Heisswassertrichter m	imbuto m per acqua calda
o	9453	hot worked	brut m de chaud	warm verformt	lavorato a caldo
o	9454	hot working	façonnage m à chaud	Warmformgebung f	formatura f a caldo
o	9455	hot working	allure f chaude	Gargang m	funzionamento m a caldo (d'un altoforno)
o	9456	hot working tool	outil m pour travail à chaud	Warmarbeits- werkzeug n	utensile m per la la- vorazione a caldo
—	9457	hotching	criblage m par dépôt	Setzarbeit f	stacciatura (o vaglia- tura) per deposito
—	9458	hour-glass structure	structure en sablier	Sanduhrstruktur f	struttura f a clessidra
—	9459	household (or domestic) coal, house-coal	charbon m domesti- que, charbon m de ménage	Hausbrandkohle f	carbone m (per uso) domestico
o	9460	household article	utensile m de ménage	Haushaltgerät n	utensile m domestico
o	9461	housing, stand	montant m de cage	Walzenständer m	sopporto m di laminatoio
o	9462	housing (of a pipe)	tampon m anti-fuite (dans un tuyau)	Dichtungspfropfen m	dispositivo m di tampo- namento di fuga (in un tubo)
o	9463	housing accessories	pièce f de garniture	Einbaustück n	guarnitura f, guarnizio- ni f pl.
o	9464	housing for two rolls	cage f à deux cylindres	Zweiwalzenständer m	gabbia f a due cilindri
o	9465	housing of a rolling mill	cage f du laminoir	Walzenständer m, Gerüstständer m, Walzengestell n	gabbia f (o incastella- tura f) del laminatoio
o	9466	housing	cage f de laminoir	Walzgerüst n	gabbia f del laminatoio
—	9467	hover ground	terre f meuble	loses Gebirge n	terra f mobile

	English	French	German	Italian
– 9468	**howlite**	howlite *f*	Howlith *m*	howlite *f*
▸ 9469	**hub**	moyeu *m*	Nabe *f*	mozzo *m*
– 9470	**hub**	mire *f* de nivellement	Nivellierlatte *f*	biffa *f* di livello
	hubbing, *s. hobbing*			
– 9471	**hubnerite**	hubnérite *f*	Hubnerit *m*	hubnerite *f*
– 9472	**hudge**	benne *f*	Förderkübel *m*	benna *f*
– 9473	**hudge**	traîneau *m*	Schlitten *m*	slitta *f*
– 9474	**hudsonite**	hudsonite *f*	Hudsonit *m*	hudsonite *f*
– 9475	**hugelite**	hugelite *f*	Hugelit *m*	hugelite *f*
– 9476	**Hughes disc bit**	trépan *m* à cônes de Hughes	Hugeskegel- meissel *m*	trapano *m* a coni di Hughes
	hull plate, *s. ship plate*			
– 9477	**hullite**	hullite *f*	Hullit *m*	hullite *f*
– 9478	**hulsite**	hulsite *f*	Hulsit *m*	hulsite *f*
– 9479	**humic**	humique	humin	umico
– 9480	**humidity of air, moisture**	humidité *f* de l'air	Luftfeuchtigkeit *f*	umidità *f* dell'aria
– 9481	**humite**	humite *f*	Humit *m*	umite *f*
– 9482	**hummer-screen**	tamis *m* à vibration magnétique	Hummer-Sieb *n*	vaglio *m* a scosse magnetico
° 9483	**humpy separation**	peau *f* de crapaud	höckerartige Ausscheidung *f*	superficie *f* scabra
– 9484	**hund**	wagonnet *m*, bac *m*	Förderwagen *m*	vagoncino *m*
– 9485	**hung shot**	long feu *m*	Schussverzögerung *f*	ritardo *m* d'accensione
– 9486	**hung up**	coincé	festgeklemmt	inceppato
– 9487	**huntilite**	huntilite *f*	Huntilith *m*	huntilite *f*
	hurley, *s. hund*			
– 9488	**Huronian**	huronien *m*	Huron *n*	huroniano *m*
° 9489	**Hutter's bell**	cloche *f* Hutter	Glocke *f* nach Hutter	campana *f* Hutter
– 9490	**hurrier**	rouleur *m*	Fördermann *m*	spingitore *m*

English	French	German	Italian
— 9491 hussakite	hussakite f	Hussakit m	hussakite f
— 9492 hutch	berline f	Förderwagen m, Grubenwagen m	vagoncino m
— 9493 hutch	concentré m de minerai	Erzkonzentrat n	concentrato m di minerale
— 9494 hyacinth	hyacinthe f	Hyazinth m	giacinto m
— 9495 hyaline	hyalin	hyalin	ialino, vetroso
— 9496 hyaline quartz	quartz m hyalin	Hyalin-Quarz m	quarzo m ialino
— 9497 hyalite	hyalite f	Hyalit m	ialite f
— 9498 hyalocrystalline	hyalocristallin	hyalokristallin	ialocristallino
— 9499 hyalophane	hyalophane m	Hyalophan n	ialofano m
— 9500 hyalopilitic texture	texture f hyalopilitique	hyalopilitische Struktur f	struttura f ialopilitica
— 9501 hyalosiderite	hyalosidérite f	Hyalosiderit m	ialosiderite f
— 9502 hyalotekite	hyalotékite f	Hyalotekit m	ialotekite f
° 9503 hybrid ion	ion m neutre ou hybride	Zwitterion n	ione m neutro
— 9504 hydatogenesis	hydatogenèse f	Hydatogenese f	idatogenesi f
— 9505 hydatogenic	hydatogène	hydatogen	idatogeno
° 9506 hydrant, water post	prise f d'eau	Wasserposten m, Hydrant m	sbocco m d'acqua, idrante m
— 9507 hydrargillite	hydrargillite f	Hydrargillit m	idrargillite f
— 9508 hydrargyrum	mercure m	Quecksilber n	mercurio n
— 9509 hydrate of potash, caustic potash	potasse f caustique	Ätzkali n	potassa f caustica, idrato di potasso
— 9510 hydrated silicate of alumina	silicate m d'alumine hydraté	wasserhaltiges Tonerdesilikat n	silicato m idrato di allumina
° 9511 hydraulic accumulator	accumulateur m hydraulique	Druckwasserspeicher m	accumulatore m idraulico
° 9512 hydraulic accumulator working by compressed air	accumulateur m hydropneumatique	Luftakkumulator m	accumulatore m idraulico a carico d'aria compressa

English	French	German	Italian
9513 hydraulic balancing	équilibrage *m* hydraulique	Gewichtsausgleich- ung *f* durch Wasser- druck	compensazione *f* i- draulica
9514 hydraulic blower	soufflerie *f* hydraulique	Wasserkraftgebläse *n*	soffieria *f* idraulica
9515 hydraulic brake	frein *m* hydraulique	Wasserdruckbremse *f*	freno *m* idraulico
9516 hydraulic brick press	presse *f* à briques hydraulique	Druckwasserstein- presse *f*	pressa *f* idraulica da mattoni
9516a hydraulic bronze	bronze *m* de robinet- terie	Wasserhahnbronze *f*	bronzo *m* per rubi- netteria
9517 hydraulic circulating	forage *m* à injection	Spülbohren *n*	sondaggio *m* a inie- zione
9518 hydraulic classifier	spitz-lutte *m*	Spitzlutte *f*	classificatore *m* idrau- lico
9519 hydraulic coal-burster	coin *m* hydraulique	hydraulische Keilpresse *f*	cuneo *m* idraulico
9520 hydraulic descaler	décalamineur *m* hydraulique	hydraulische Entzunderungs- maschine *f*	decalaminatore *m* i- draulico
9521 hydraulic discharge	débit *m*	Wassermenge *f*	portata *f*
9522 hydraulic feed	avancement *m* hydraulique	hydraulischer Vorschub *m*	alimentazione *f* idraulica
9523 hydraulic forging press	presse *f* à forger hydraulique	Druckwasserschmie- depresse *f*	pressa *f* idraulica per forgiare
9524 hydraulic hammer	marteau *m* hydraulique	Wasserhammer *m*	martello *m* idraulico
9525 hydraulic jack	vérin *m* hydrau- lique	hydraulischer Hebebock *m*	martinetto *m* idrauli- co
9526 hydraulic lift	monte-charges *m* hydraulique	Wasserdruckaufzug *m*	montacarichi *m* idraulico
9527 hydraulic mining	abattage *m* hydrau- lique, exploitation hydraulique	hydraulische Gewinnung *f*	abbattimento *m* idrau- lico, coltivazione *f* idraulica
9528 hydraulic moulding machine	machine *f* à mouler hydraulique	Druckwasserform- maschine *f*	formatrice *f* (o mac- china *f* per formare) idraulica
9529 hydraulic moulding machine with turnover table	machine *f* hydrauli- que à mouler avec plaque renversable à modèle	hydraulische Form- maschine *f* mit Wendeplatte	macchina *f* idraulica per formare a mano con piattaforma rovesciabi- le

	English	French	German	Italian
°	9530 hydraulic moulding press	presse *f* hydraulique à mouler	Druckwasserform-presse *f*	pressa *f* idraulica da formare
°	9530a hydraulic piercing	trépanation *f* hydraulique	hydraulisches Ausbohren *n*	alesatura *f* idraulica
	hydraulic plunger, *s. hydraulic ram*			
°	9532 hydraulic pump	pompe *f* à commande hydraulique	Wasserdruckpumpe *f*	pompa *f* a comando idraulico, pompa *f* idraulica
°	9533 hydraulic pressure	pression *f* hydraulique	Flüssigkeitsdruck *m*	pressione *f* idraulica
°	9534 hydraulic pulling tool	vérin *m* hydraulique	hydraulisches Ziehwerkzeug *n*	martinetto *m* idraulico
°	9535 hydraulic pump	pompe *f* hydraulique	hydraulische Pumpe *f*	pompa *f* idraulica
°	9536 hydraulic ram	piston *m* plongeur	Mönch(s)kolben *m*	stantuffo *m* tuffante
	hydraulic shear (A), *s. hydraulic shearing machine*			
°	9537 hydraulic shearing	cisaille *f* hydraulique pour blooms	hydraulische Blockschere *f*	cesoia *f* idraulica per blumi
—	9538 hydraulic stowage	remblayage *m* hydraulique	Spülversatz *m*	ripiena *f* idraulica
°	9539 hydraulic test	essai *m* hydraulique	Wasserdruckprobe *f*	prova *f* idraulica
°	9540 hydraulic working	commande *f* hydraulique	Druckwasserbetrieb *m*	funzionamento *m* ad acqua compressa
—	9541 hydraulicking	abattage *m* hydraulique	hydraulische Gewinnung *f*	estrazione *f* a getto d'acqua, abbattimento idraulico
—	9542 hydride	hydrure *m*	Hydrid *n*	idruro *m*
—	9543 hydro-separator	hydroséparateur *m*	Hydroabscheider *m*	idroseparatore *m*
—	9544 hydrobios	hydrobios	hydrobios	idrobios
—	9545 hydro-blast	dessablage *m* hydraulique	Nassputzen *n*	idrosterratura *f*
—	9546 hydroboracite	hydroboracite *f*	Hydroboracit *m*	idroboracite *f*
—	9547 hydrocarbons	hydrocarbures *m pl.*	Kohlenwasserstoffe *m pl.*	idrocarburi *m pl.*
—	9548 hydrocerussite	hydrocérussite *f*	Hydrocerussit *m*	idrocerussite *f*

English	French	German	Italian
9549 hydrochloric acid	acide *m* chlorhydrique	Salzsäure *f*	acido *m* cloridrico
9550 hydroclastic rock	roche *f* hydroclastique	hydroklastisches Gestein *n*	roccia *f* idroclastica
9551 hydrocratic movement	mouvement *m* hydrocratique	Senkungsbewegung *f* des Festlandes	movimento *m* idrocratico
9552 hydrocyanite	hydrocyanite *f*	Hydrocyanit *m*	idrocianite *f*
9553 hydrodynamic drawing	emboutissage *m* hydromécanique	hydromechanisches Ziehen *n*	imbutitura *f* idromeccanica
9554 hydrodynamic reverse drawing tool	outil *m* hydromécanique d'emboutissage par retournement	hydromechanisches Ziehen *n* mit begrenztem Stülpzug	utensile *m* idromeccanico per imbutitura a ritroso
9555 hydro-fluoric acid	acide *m* fluorhydrique	Flusssäure *f*	acido *m* fluoridrico
9556 hydroformate	produit *m* d'hydroforming	hydrogeformtes Erzeugnis *n*	idroformato *m*
9557 hydrogen	hydrogène *m*	Wasserstoff *m*	idrogeno *m*
9558 hydrogen embrittlement	fragilité *f* à l'hydrogène	Wasserstoffbrüchigkeit *f*	fragilità *f* da idrogeno
9559 hydrogen embrittlement relief	déhydrogénation *f*	Dehydrierung *f*	deidrogenazione
9560 hydrogen flame	flame *f* d'hydrogène	Wasserstoff-Flamme *f*	fiamma *f* di idrogeno
9561 hydrogen peroxide	eau *f* oxygénée	Wasserstoffsuperoxyd *n*	acqua *f* ossigenata
9562 hydrogenating and synthesis column	batterie *f* pour installations d'hydrogénation et synthèse	Hydrier- und Synthesespeichersäule *f*	colonna *f* di idrogenazione e di sintesi
9562a hydrogenation	hydrogénation *f*	Hydrierung *f*	idrogenazione *f*
9563 hydrohematite	hydrohématite *f*	Hydrohämatit *m*	idroematite *f*
9564 hydrolysis	hydrolyse *f*, électrolyse *f* de l'eau	Hydrolyse *f*	idrolisi *f*
9565 hydromatic brake	frein hydraulique	Wasserbremse *f*	freno *m* idraulico
9565a hydrometallurgy	hydrométallurgie *f*	Hydrometallurgie *f*	idrometallurgia *f*
9566 hydrometamorphism	hydrométamorphisme *m*	Hydrometamorphismus *m*	idrometamorfismo *m*
9567 hydrometer	densimètre *m*, hydromètre	Densimeter *n*	densimetro *m*, idrometro *m*

English	French	German	Italian
− 9568 **hydromuscovite**	hydromuscovite f	Hydromuskovit m	idromuscovite f
− 9569 **hydronephelite**	hydronéphélite f	Hydronephelit m	idronefelite f
− 9570 **hydrophane**	hydrophane m	Hydrophan m	idrofane m
− 9571 **hydrophilite**	hydrophilite f	Hydrophilit m	idrofilite f
° 9572 **Hydrospark-process**	procédé m Hydrospark	Hydrosparkverfahren n	processo m Hydrospark
° 9573 **hydrostatic balance**	balance f hydrostatique	hydrostatische Waage f	bilancia f idrostatica
˄ 9574 **hydrostatic head, head of water**	niveau hydrostatique	hydrostatisches Niveau, Wasserdruck-höhe f	carico m idrostatico
˄ 9575 **hydrostatic pressure**	pression f hydrostatique	hydrostatischer Druck m	pressione f idrostatica
− 9576 **hydrotalcite**	hydrotalcite f	Hydrotalkit m	idrotalcite f
− 9577 **hydroxide of iron**	hydrate m de fer	Eisenhydroxyd n	idrossido m di ferro o ferrico
° 9578 **hydroxyl ion**	ion m hydroxyle	Hydroxylion n	ione m idrossile
− 9579 **hydrozincite**	hydrozincite f	Hydrozinkit m	zinconite f
− 9580 **hygrometer**	hygromètre m	Feuchtigkeitsmesser m, Hygrometer n	igrometro m
− 9581 **hygroscopic water**	eau f hygroscopique	hygroskopisches Wasser n	acqua f igroscopica
− 9582 **hypabyssal**	hypabyssal	hypabyssisch	ipoabissale
− 9583 **hypabyssal rock, dike rock**	roche hypabyssale	hypabyssisches Gestein n	roccia f ipoabissale
− 9584 **hypautomorphic structure**	structure f mi--idiomorphe	hypautomorphe Struktur f	struttura f semi-idio-morfa
° 9585 **hypereutectic**	hypereutectique	übereutektisch	ipereutettico, ipereutettoide
° 9586 **hypereutectic cast iron**	fonte f hypereutectique	übereutektisches Gusseisen n	ghisa f ipereutettica
° 9587 **hypereutectoid cast iron**	fonte f à matrice hypereutectoïde	übereutektoides Gusseisen n	ghisa f a matrice ipereutettoide, ghisa f ipereutettoide

English	French	German	Italian
9588 **hypereutectoid steel, hypereutectic steel**	acier *m* hypereutec-toïde (ou hypereutec-tique)	übereutektoider Stahl *m*	acciaio *m* ipereutettoi-de (o ipereutettico)
9589 **hyperite**	hypérite *f*	Hyperit *m*	hiperite *f*
9590 **hyperquench**	hypertrempe *f*	Abschrecken *n*	ipertempra *f*
9591 **hypersthene**	hypersthène *f*	Hypersthen *m*	iperstene *f*
9592 **hypersthenite**	hypersthénite *f*	Hypersthenit *m*	iperstenite *f*
9593 **hypidiomorphic**	hypidiomorphe	hypidiomorph	ipidiomorfo
9594 **hypochlorite sweeting**	traitement *m* à l'hypochlorite	Hypochlorit-behandlung *f*	trattamento *m* con ipoclorito
9595 **hypocrystalline**	hypocristallin	hypokristallin	ipocristallino
9596 **hypoeutectic, hypoeutectoid**	hypoeutectique	untereutektisch	ipoeutettico, ipoeutet-toide
9597 **hypoeutectoid**	hypoeutectoïde	untereutektoidisch	ipoeutettoide, ipoeutet-tico
9598 **hypoeutectoid steel**	acier *m* hypoeu-tectoïde	untereutektoidischer Stahl *m*	acciaio *m* ipoeutectoi-de
9599 **hypoeutectoid cast iron**	fonte *f* à matrice hypoeutectoïde	untereutektoidisches Gusseisen *n*	ghisa *f* ipoeutettoide (o ipoeutettica)
9600 **hypoeutectoid steel**	acier *m* hypoeutectoïde	untereutektoider Stahl *m*	acciaio *m* ipoeutettoide o ipoeutettico
9601 **hypogene**	hypogène	hypogen	ipogeno
9602 **hyposulphite of sodium**	hyposulfite *m* de soude	Natriumhyposulfit *n*	iposolfito *m* di soda
9603 **hypotaxic deposit**	dépôt *m* superficiel	hypotaxische Lagerstätte *f*	deposito *m* superficia-le
9604 **hypothermal vein**	filon *m* hypothermal	hypothermaler Gang *m*	filone *m* ipotermale
9605 **hypotype**	plesiotype *m*	Plesiotypus *m*	plesiotipo *m*
9606 **hyppuritic facies**	faciès *m* à hippurites	Hippuritenfazies *f*	«facies» *f* ippuritica
9607 **hypsogram**	diagramme *m* de niveau	Niveaudiagramm *n*	diagramma *m* di livello

English	French	German	Italian
— 9608 **hypsometer**	hypsomètre *m*	Hypsometer *n*	ipsometro *m*

English	French	German	Italian

I beam, s. double T beam

I.D. = internal diameter

I.F. = internal flush

	English	French	German	Italian
9609	**I-iron, I-bar**	fer *m* en I, fer à I	I-Eisen *n*	ferro *m* a I
9610	**I-section vertical member**	profil *m* de poteau en I	I-Pfostenprofil *n*	profilato *m* ad I di sostegno
9611	**Ice age, Glacial epoch**	époque *f* glaciaire, période *f* glaciaire	Eiszeit *f*	epoca *f* glaciale, periodo *m* glaciale
9612	**ice-cap**	glacier scandinave, fjell-type	norwegischer Gletscher *m*	ghiacciaio *m* norvegese

ice spar, s. cryolite

	English	French	German	Italian
9613	**Iceland-spar, Iceland crystall**	spath d'Islande	isländischer Doppelspat *m*	spato *m* d'Islanda
9614	**icositetrahedron**	icositétraèdre *m*	Ikositetraeder *n*, Deltoidodekaeder *n*	icositetraedro *m*, trapezoedro *m*
9615	**iddingsite**	iddingsite *f*	Iddingsit *m*	iddingsite *f*
9615a	**ideal gas**	gaz *m* idéal	ideales Gas *n*	gas *m* ideale
9616	**idioblast**	idioblaste *m*	Idioblast *f*	idioblasto *m*
9617	**idiochromatic**	idiochromatique	idiochromatisch	idiocromatico
9618	**idiogenites**	unités *f pl.* idiogènes	idiogene Einheiten *f pl.*	unità *f pl.* idiogene
9619	**idiogenous**	idiogène	idiogen	idiogeno
9620	**idiomorphic**	idiomorphe	idiomorph	idiomorfico
9621	**idle roll, idler**	rouleau *m* tendeur	Blindwalze *f*	rullo *m* tenditore
9622	**idrialite**	idrialite *f*	Idrialin *m*	idrialina *f*
9623	**igneous fusion**	fusion *f* ignée	Zerschmelzen *n* im Feuer	fusione *f* ignea
9624	**igneous metallurgy**	métallurgie *f* par la voie ignée, pyrométallurgie *f*	Pyrometallurgie *f*	pirometallurgia *f*
9625	**igneous rocks** *pl.*, **pyrogenic rocks** *pl.*	roches *f pl.* ignées	Erstarrungsgesteine *n pl.*	rocce *f pl.* eruttive (o endogene)

	English	French	German	Italian
−	9626 **igniter wire**	fil *m* explosif	Zünddraht *m*	filo *m* esplosivo
°	9627 **igniting**	allumage *m*, mise *f* à feu	Anzünden *n*, Anblasen *n*	accensione *f*
°	9627a **ignition alloy**	alliage *m* pyrophore	pyrophore Legierung *f*	lega *f* piroforica
°	9628 **ignition flame**	flamme *f* d'allumage	Zündflamme *f*	fiamma *f* d'accensione
°	9628a **ihrigizing**	imprégnation *f* au silicium	Siliziumimprägnierung *g*	impregnazione *f* al silicio
−	9629 **ijolith**	ijolite *f*	Ijolith *m*	ijoilite *f*
−	9630 **ijussite**	ijussite *f*	Ijussit *m*	iussite *f*
−	9631 **Ilgner system**	groupe *m* Ilgner	Ilgnersystem *n*	gruppo *m* Ilgner
−	9632 **illite**	illite *f*	Illit *m*	illite *f*
	9633 **illuminated object**	objet *m* éclairé	beleuchtetes Objekt *n*	oggetto *m* illuminato
	9634 **illumination**	éclairage *m*	Beleuchtung *f*	illuminazione *f*
	9635 **illumination apparatus**	dispositif *m* d'éclairage	Beleuchtungsvorrichtung *f*	apparecchio *m* d'illuminazione
°	9636 **illuminating gas**	gaz *m* d'éclairage	Leuchtgas *n*	gas *m* illuminante
−	9637 **ilmenite**	ilménite *f*	Ilmenit *m*	ilmenite *f*
−	9638 **ilmenitite**	ilménitite *f*	Ilmenitit *m*	ilmentite *f*
°	9639 **image, virtual image**	image virtuelle	virtuelles Bild *n*	immagine *f* virtuale
°	9640 **image fault**	défaut *m* dans la formation des images	Abbildungsfehler *m*	errore *m* nell'immagine
°	9641 **imbricated plate**	plaque *f* en forme d'écaille	Schuppenblech *n*	lamiera *f* a scaglie
−	9642 **imerged bog**	tourbière *f* immergée	Unterwassermoor *n*	torbiera *f* sommersa
−	9643 **immature crystal**	cristal *m* embryonnaire	Skelettkristall *m*	cristallo *m* immaturo
°	9644 **immersion hardening**	trempe *f* par immersion	Tauchhärten *n*	tempra *f* per immersione
°	9644a **immersion plating** impact, *s. blow*	dépôt au trempé	Eintauchplattierung *f*	deposito *m* per immersione
°	9645 **impact resistance**	résistance *f* au choc, résilience	Schlagfestigkeit *f*	resistenza *f* all'urto
−	9646 **impact screen**	tamis *m* vibreur, tamis *m* à vibrations	Vibrationssieb *n*	vaglio *m* a scosse, crivello *m* a scosse
°	9646a **impact strenght**	résilience *f*	Kerbschlagzähigkeit *f*	resilienza *f* su barrette intagliate

English	French	German	Italian
9647 impact test	essai *m* au choc	Schlagversuch *m*	prova *f* d'urto
9648 impact test (on a notched test bar)	essai *m* de rési-lience	Kerbschlagversuch *m*	prova *f* di resilienza (su provetta intagliata)
9648a impact toughness	résilience *f* au choc	Schlagzähigkeit *f*	resilienza *f* all'urto
9649 impact value measured on notched test bar	résilience *f*	Kerbschagzähigkeit *f*	resilienza *f* su barrette con intaglio, resilienza *f* su provetta intagliata
9650 impacted fracture	fracture *f* pénétrante	durchdringende Fraktur *f*	frattura *f* penetrante
9651 impalpable atomized dust	poudre *f* impalpable atomisée	atomisiertes feines Pulver *n*	polvere *f* impalpabile atomizzata
9652 impeller	roue *f* à aubes	Schaufelrad *n*	ruota *f* a palette
9653 impeller pump	pompe *f* centrifuge	Schleuderpumpe *f*	pompa *f* centrifuga
9654 impeller ramming	serrage *m* par projection	Verdichten *n* durch Schleudern *n*	formatura *f* a proiezione
impermeable barrier, *s. impervious layer*			
9655 impermeable stratum	faille *f* imperméable	wasserdichte Schicht *f*	falda *f* impermeabile
9656 impervious break	intercalation *f* imperméable	undurchlässige Zwischenlage *f*	intercalazione *f* impermeabile
9657 impervious layer	couche *f* imperméable	wasserdichte Schicht *f*	strato *m* impermeabile
9658 impervious rocks *pl.*	roches *f pl.* imperméables	wasserdichte Gesteine *n pl.*	rocce *f pl.* impermeabili
9659 impinging light	lumière *f* incidente	auffallendes Licht *n*	luce *f* incidente
9660 imported coal	charbon *m* d'importa-tion	eingeführte Kohle *f*	carbone *m* d'importazione
9660a impoverishment	appauvrissement *m*	Verarmung *f*	impoverimento *m*
9661 impregnated carbons	charbons *m pl.* imprégnés	imprägnierte Kohlen *f pl.*	carboni *m pl.* imbevuti
impregnated coal, *s. mineralized carbon*			
9662 impregnated deposit	gisement *m* d'imprégnation	Imprägnationsla-gerstätte *f*	giacimento *m* d'impregnazione
9663 impregnated sand	sable *m* imprégné	durchtränkter Sand *m*	sabbia *f* impregnata
9664 impregnation ore	minerai d'imprégnation	imprägniertes Erz *n*	minerale *m* d'impregnazione

	English	French	German	Italian
−	9665 impregnation vein	filon *m* d'impré-gnation	Imprägnationsgang *m*	filone *m* d'impregnazione
°	9666 impression	empreinte *f*	Eindruck *m*	impronta *f*
°	9667 impression block	bloc d'empreinte, couronne de cire	Abdruckstempel *m*, Abdruckbüchse *f*	blocco *m* d'impronta
°	9668 to imprint (the pattern in the sand)	imprimer (le modèle dans le sable)	(das Modell in den Sand) eindrücken	imprimere (il modello nella terra o nella sabbia)
°	9669 improperly set core	noyau *m* mal placé	versetzer Kern *m*	anima *f* mal composta (o mal sistemata)
°	9670 to improve the steel (by heat-treatment)	rectifier l'acier	den Stahl vergüten	bonificare l'acciaio
°	9671 improvable	exploitable	abbauwürdig	sfruttabile
°	9671a improving	affinage *m*	Vergütung *f*	affinazione *f*
°	9672 impurities	impuretés *f pl.*	Unreinheiten *f pl.*	impurità *f pl.*
ˆ	9673 input gas	gaz *m* d'injection	Einpressgas *n*	gas *m* d'iniezione
−	9674 input well, intake well, injection well	puits *m* injecteur	Einlassonde *f*, Einpressonde *f*	pozzo *m* d'immissione (o d'iniezione)
°	9675 in blast	en marche	in Betrieb	in funzione, in servizio
−	9676 in large pieces	en gros morceaux	grossstückig	in pezzi grossi
−	9677 in layers	par couches	schichtweise	a strati
	in open cut, *s. above ground*			
	in operation, *s. in work*			
	in series, *s. by sets*			
ˆ	9678 in situ combustion	combustion in situ	Verbrennung *n* am Ort	combustione *f* sotterranea
°	9679 in the heat treated state	en état de traitement thermique	im vergüteten Zustand	nello stato bonificato
°	9680 in want of repair	nécessitant une réparation	ausbesserungsbedürftig	bisognoso di riparazioni
°	9681 in work, in operation	en service, en marche	in Betrieb	in servizio

English	French	German	Italian
9682 **inbreathing**	inhalation *f*	Einblasen *n*	inalazione *f*
9683 **inby (e)**	vers les chantiers	in Richtung der Grubenbaue	verso il fronte

incandescence, *s. white heat*

incandescent, *s. white hot*

9684 **incandescent gas light**	bec *m* à gaz incandescent	Gasglühlicht *n*	becco *m* a incandescenza

incandescent lamp, *s. glow lamp*

9685 **incandescent layer of coals**	couche *f* de charbon incandescent	glühende Kohlenschicht *f*	strato *m* di carbone incandescente
9686 **incidental constituent**	partie *f* accessoire (de la texture)	Nebengefügebestandteil *m*	costituente *m* secondario
9687 **incinerator**	four *m* à gadoues	Müllfeuerung *f*	inceneratore *m*, forno *m* per distruggere rifiuti

inclinated, *s. inclined*

9688 **inclination, dip**	inclinaison *f*, pendage *m*	Einfallen *n*	inclinazione *f*
9689 **inclination of grate**	inclinaison *f* de la grille	Rostneigung *f*	inclinazione *f* della griglia

inclination of the stratum, *s. dip of the stratum*

9690 **incline**	plan *m* incliné, descenderie *f*, puits *m* incliné	Bremsberg *m* tonnlägiger Schacht	piano *m* inclinato, scivolo *m*, galleria *f* di ribasso
9691 **incline**	pente *f*, inclinaison *f*	Gefälle, Neigung *f*	pendenza *f*, inclinazione *f*, rampa *f*
9692 **incline cut and fill**	exploitation *f* par gradin incliné avec remblayage	Firstenbau *m* mit geneigter Firste und mit Bergeversatz	coltivazione *f* a gradino inclinato con ripiena
9693 **incline engine**	machine *f* pour couloir	Rutschmaschine *f*	macchina per piano inclinato
9694 **incline man**	chargé *m* du couloir	Rutschmann *m*	addetto al piano inclinato
9695 **inclined belt**	bande *f* de transport inclinée	Steigband *n*	nastro *m* inclinato

	English	French	German	Italian
— 9696	**inclined cut-and-fill stope**	gradin *m* incliné avec remblayage	Firstenstoss mit geneigter Firste und mit Bergeversatz	gradino *m* inclinato con ripiena
— 9697	**inclined cut-and fill stoping**	exploitation *f* par gradin incliné avec remblayage	Firstenbau *m* mit geneigter Firste und mit Bergeversatz	coltivazione *f* a gradini inclinati con ripiena
— 9698	**inclined fault**	faille *f* inclinée	geneigte Verwerfung *f*	faglia *f* inclinata
— 9699	**inclined fold**	pli *m* oblique	schiefe Falte *f*	piega *f* obliqua
	inclined fracture, s. *oblique fracture*			
— 9700	**inclined gallery**	descenderie *f*	tonlägiger Schacht *m*	galleria *f* di ribasso
— 9701	**inclined grate**	grille *f* inclinée	Schrägrost *m*	griglia *f* inclinata
	inclined grate furnace, s. *furnace with inclined grate*			
	inclined hoist, s. *inclined lift*			
— 9702	**inclined lift**	monte-charges *m* incliné	Schrägaufzug *m*	montacarichi *m* a piano inclinato
^ 9703	**inclined pipe**	tuyau *m* incliné	geneigtes Rohr *n*	tubo *m* inclinato
— 9704	**inclined pit**	puits *m* incliné	tonnlägiger Schacht *m*	pozzo *m* inclinato
° 9705	**inclined plate**	tôle *f* inclinée	schräg stehendes Blech *n*	lamiera *f* inclinata
° 9706	**inclined rolling mill**	laminoir *m* oblique	Drehherdofen *m*	laminatoio *m* obliquo
— 9707	**inclined top-slicing**	exploitation *f* par tranches inclinées descendantes avec foudroyage	geneigter Scheibenbruchbau *m*	coltivazione *f* a trance inclinate discendenti con franamento
— 9708	**inclined well**	forage *m* oblique	schräge Bohrung *f*	sondaggio *m* obliquo (o inclinato)
^ 9709	**inclinometer**	clinomètre *m*	Neigungsmesser *m*	clinometro *m*
	included slag, s. *enclosed slag*			
— 9710	**included water**	eau *f* d'interposition	Interpositionswasser *n*	acqua *f* di interposizione

English	French	German	Italian

including angle, s. *angle of VEE*

	English	French	German	Italian
9711	inclusion, xenocryst	enclave *f*, inclusion *f*	Einschluss *m*, Fremdling	intrusione *f*, inclusione
9712	inclusion (of sand)	inclusion *f* (de sable)	Einschluss *m* (Sand)	inclusione *f* (di terra)
9713	inclusion, slag, slag trap	inclusion *f* de scorie	Schlackeneinschluss *m*	inclusione di scoria
9713a	inclusion stringer	inclusion *f* allongée	langgereckter Einschluss *m*	inclusione *f* allungata
9714	incompetent	tendre	weich	tenero
9715	incomplete fusion	fusion *f* incomplète	unvolkommene Verschmelzung *f*	fusione *f* incompleta
9716	incomplete set	cadre *m* à un seul montant	halber Türstock *m*	quadro *m* zoppo
9717	incompletely roasted ore	minerai *m* imparfaitement grillé	unvollkommen geröstetes Erz *n*	minerale *m* imperfettamente torrefatto
9718	incorrect pattern	modèle *m* mal concu	schlecht geplantes Modell *n*	modello *m* mal progettato
9719	incorrect pattern	modèle *m* non conforme	nicht passendes Modell *n*	modello *m* non conforme
9720	to incrassate	épaissir, condenser	verdichten	ingrossare, condensare
9721	to increase the output	augmenter la production	die Leistung steigern	aumentare la produzione
9722	to increase the pressure head	rehausser la coulée	aufbauen (den Einguss)	alzare la colata, rialzare la colata
9723	increase in temperature, elevation of temperature	accroissement *m* (ou élévation *f*) de la température	Temperaturzunahme *f*, Temperaturerhöhung *f*	ascesa *f* o aumento *m* della temperatura
9724	increase of heat	augmentation *f* de chaleur	Wärmezunahme *f*	aumento *m* di calore
9724a	increaser	raccord de réduction	Übergangsrohr *n*	manicotto *m* di riduzione
9725	increasing the reductibility	accroissement *m* de la réductibilité	Erhöhung *f* der Reduktionsfähigkeit	aumento *m* della riducibilità
9726	incrustated iron ore	minerai *m* de fer veiné d'autres matières	durchwachsenes Eisenerz *n*	minerale *m* di ferro incrostato
9727	incrustation	incrustation *f*	Verkrustung *f*	incrostazione *f*
9728	incrustation, fouling	formation *f* d'incrustations, entartrage	Krustenbildung *f*	formazione *f* d'incrostazioni

		English	French	German	Italian
°	9729	indentation indentation hardness.	empreinte *f* *s. vickers hardness*	Abdruck *m*	impronta *f*
°	9730	indentation test	essai *m* d'emboutissage	Tiefungsprobe *f*, Tiefzichprobe *f*	prova *f* di imbutitura
°	9731	indipendent «free» blast furnace	haut-fourneau *m* à chemise nue	freistehender Hoch- ofen *m*	alto-forno *m* libero
°	9732	independent crane	grue *f* isolée	freistehender Kran *m*	gru *f* indipendente
°	9733	independent shaft	cuve *f* dégagée	freistehender Schacht *m*	tino *m* libero, tino *m* a camicia libera
—	9734	index fossil	fossile *m* carac- téristique	Leitfossil *n*	fossile *m* caratteristi- co, fossile-guida *m*
—	9735	index of basicity	indice *m* de basicité	Basizitätsgrad *m*	indice *m* (o grado *m*) di basicità
°	9736	Indian steel, Wootz indianite, *s. anorthite*	acier *m* Wootz	Wootzstahl *m*	acciaio *m* Wootz, acciaio *m* indiano
°	9737	indicator on the top of a blast furnace	indicateur des charges	Gichtanzeiger *m*	indicatore *m* delle cariche
—	9738	indicator stand	indicateur *m* d'extraction	Signalständer *m*	indicatore *m* d'estra- zione
—	9739	indigo copper	covelline *f*	Covellin *m*	covellite *f*
°	9740	indigo solution	solution *f* d'indigo	Indigolösung *f*	soluzione *f* d'indaco
—	9741	indigolite	indigolite *f*	Indigolith *m*	indigolite *f*
—	9742	indistinct cleavage	clivage *m* imparfait	undeutliche Spaltbarkeit *f*	clivaggio *m* imperfet- to
°	9743	indirect arc furnace	four *m* à arc indi- rect	indirekter Lichtbogenofen *m*	forno *m* ad arco indiretto
°	9744	indirect heating	chauffage *m* indirect	mittelbare Heizung *f*	riscaldamento *m* indiretto
°	9745	indirect reduction	réduction *f* indirecte	indirekte Reduktion *f*	riduzione *f* indiretta
—	9746	indium	indium *m*	Indium *n*	indio *m*
^	9747	individual pumping unit	unité *f* individuelle	Einzelpumpanlage *f*	unità *f* singola di pompaggio
°	9748	induction forging	forgeage *m* à induction	Induktionsschmieden *n*	fucinatura *f* con ri- scaldamento a induzione

English	French	German	Italian
9749 **induction-furnace**	four *m* à induction	Induktionsofen *m*	forno *m* a induzione
9750 **induction hardening**	trempe *f* par induction	Induktionshärtung *f*	tempra *f* ad induzione
9751 **induction heating**	chauffage *m* par induction	Erhitzung *f* durch Induktion	riscaldamento *m* per induzione
9752 **induction heating equipment**	appareil *m* de chauffage à induction	Induktionsheizapparat *m*	apparecchio *m* per riscaldamento a induzione
9753 **induction log**	carottage *m* électrique	elektrische Kernbohrung *f*	carotaggio *m* elettrico
9754 **induction machine**	machine *f* à induction	Induktionsmaschine *f*	macchina *f* ad induzione
9755 **induction rocking furnace**	four *m* basculant à induction	Induktionskippofen *m*	forno *m* oscillante a induzione
9756 **induction welding**	soudage *m* par induction	induktives Schweissen *n*	saldatura *f* per induzione
9756a **indurated**	durci	gehärtet	indurito
9757 **industrial furnace**	four *m* industriel	Industrieofen *m*	forno *m* industriale
9758 **industrial furnace for gas firing**	four *m* industriel pour le chauffage au gaz	Industrieofen *m* für Gasfeuerung	forno *m* industriale per riscaldamento a gas
industrial steel, *s. commercial steel*			
9759 **inert-base dynamite**	dynamite *f* à base inerte	Inertdynamit *n*	dinamite *f* a base inerte
9760 **inexplosive boiler**	chaudière *f* inexplosible	explosionssicherer Kessel *m*	caldaia *f* inesplodibile
9760a **infection**	progrès de la corrosion	Korrosionsfortschritt *m*	progresso *m* della corrosione
inferior fuel, *s. low grade fuel*			
9761 **infilling**	remplissage *m* (du filon)	Gangausfüllung *f*	riempimento *m* (del filone)
9762 **infilling drilling**	forage *m* intercalaire	Einfüllungsbohrung *f* abteufen	sondaggio *m* intercalare
9763 **infilling well**	puits intermédiaire	Zwischensonde	pozzo *m* intermedio
9764 **infiltrated zone**	zone *f* envahie	infiltrierte Zone *f*	zona *f* infiltrata
9765 **inflammable, flammable**	inflammable	entflammbar, brennbar	infiammabile

		English	French	German	Italian
−	9766	inflow	venue f	Zufluss m	afflusso
^	9767	inflow performance	caractéristiques $fpl.$ de productivité	Förderleistung f	caratteristiche $fpl.$ di produttività
−	9768	influence	influence f	Einfluss m	influenza f
−	9769	influence of the frost	action f de la gelée	Frosteinwirkung f	azione f del gelo
o	9770	influence on solubility	influence f (exercée) sur la solubilité	Löslichkeitsbeeinflussung f	influenza f sulla solubilità
^	9771	influx	afflux m, venue f	Zuströmung, Zulauf	afflusso m, flusso m
o	9772	infra-red dryer	étuve f (ou four) à rayonnement infra--rouge	Infrarot-Trockenofen m	stufa f a raggi infrarossi
o	9773	infusibility	infusibilité f	Unschmelzbarkeit f	infusibilità f
o	9774	infusible, refractory	infusible	unschmelzbar	infusibile, di fusione difficile
−	9775	infusorial earth	terre f d'infusoires	Infusorienerde f	farina f fossile, tripoli m
o	9776	ingate, gate	jet m de moulage	Gusstrichter m	attacco m di colata, canale m di colata
o	9776a	ingate	attaque f dirigée	gerichteter Anschnitt m	attacco m guidato
−	9777	ingate-plot	accrochage m, recette f du fond	Füllort m	stazione f di fondo
o	9778	(in)gate inlet	attaque f de coulée	Anschnitt m	attacco m di colata
o	9779	ingate or runner with side channels	jet m de coulée coudé	angeschnittener Einguss m	colata f di fianco
o	9780	ingoing side of rolling mill	entrée f latérale du laminoir	Walzwerkeingang m	entrata f del laminatoio
o	9781	to ingot	lingoter	blockgiessen	fondere in pani
o	9782	ingot, bar	lingot m, barre, barre, barreau	Block m, Massel f	lingotto m, massello m
o	9783	ingot	saumon m	Barren m	salmone m, pane m
o	9783a	ingot bloom	lingot m prelaminé	Vorblock m	lingotto m preliminare
		ingot buggy; s. *ingot car*			
o	9784	ingot car, ingot buggy	chariot m à lingots	Blockwagen m	carrello m portalingotti

English	French	German	Italian
9785 **ingot charging carriage**	chariot *m* enfourneur des lingots	Blockeinsetzwagen *m*	carro *m* per il caricamento dei lingotti
9786 **ingot charging crane**	enfourneuse *f* de lingots, grue *f* de chargement des lingots	Blockeinsetzkran *m*	gru *f* per caricare i lingotti
9787 **ingot conveyance**	transport *m* des lingots	Blocktransport *m*	trasporto dei lingotti
9788 **ingot copper**	cuivre *m* en lingots	Blockkupfer *n*	rame *m* in lingotti
9789 **ingot crane**	pont *m* roulant pour le transport des lingots	Blockkran *m*, Blockförderkran *m*	gru *f* per il trasporto dei lingotti
9790 **ingot crane**	grue *f* avec pince à lingots	(Block-) Zangenkran *m*	gru *f* a tenaglia per lingotti
9791 **ingot crop end**	tête *f* du lingot	Blockkopf *m*	testa *f* del lingotto
ingot dogs, *s. ingot tongs*			
9792 **ingot gripper, ingot stripper**	tenaille *f* à lingots	Blockgreifer *m*	tenaglie *f pl.* per lingotti, estrattore *m* di lingotti
9793 **ingot holding device**	dispositif *m* pour saisir les lingots	Blockeinspann- vorrichtung *f*	dispositivo *m* da presa per lingotti
9794 **ingot-iron, mild steel, low carbon steel**	fer *m* homogène, fer *m* de fusion, acier extra-doux	Flusseisen *n*, Flussstahl *m*	ferro *m* omogeneo, ferro *m* fuso
ingot metal, *s. ingot iron or soft iron*			
9795 **ingot mould**	lingotière *f*	Stahlwerkskokille *f*	lingottiera *f*
9796 **ingot pit**	four *m* à réchauffer	Vorwärmgrube *f*	forno *m* di riscaldo (o di preriscaldo)
9797 **ingot pusher**	pousseuse *f* des lingots	Blockausdrücker *m*	estrattore *m* di lingotti
9798 **ingot pushing device**	dispositif *m* d'en- fournement des lingots, poussoir *m*	Blockdrücker *m*	dispositivo *m* per introdurre od infornare i lingotti
9799 **ingot slicing machine**	machine *f* à décou- per des lingots	Blockteilmaschine *f*	tagliatrice *f* di lingotti
9800 **ingot-steel, fluid steel, billet**	acier *m* fondu, acier homogène	Flussstahl *m*, Homogenstahl *m*	acciaio *m* fuso, acciaio omogeneo

		English	French	German	Italian
o	9801	ingot stores	parc *m* à lingots	Blocklager *n*	deposito *m* di lingotti, parco *m* lingotti
o	9802	ingot stripper	stripeur *m*, appareil *m* à démouler les lingots	Abstreifer *m*, Stripper *m*	tenaglia *f* da lingotti, slingottatrice *f*
o	9803	ingot stripping crane	pont *m* roulant à démouler	Blockabstreifkran *m*, Stripperkran *m*	gru *f* per estrarre lingotti dalle lingottiere
o	9804	ingot tongs, pincher	tenaille *f* à lingots	Blockzange *f*	tenaglia *f* per lingotti
o	9805	ingotting	lingotage *m*	Blockguss *m*	lingottatura *f*
—	9806	ingression	ingression *f*	Ingression *f*	ingressione *f*
^	9807	inhibitor	inhibiteur *m*	Inhibitor *m*, Hemmstoff *m*	inibitore *m*, catalizzatore *m* negativo
—	9807a	initial creeps	fluage *m* initial	Anfangskriechen *n*	scorrimento *m*
o	9808	injected body	massif *m* d'iniection	Injektionsmasse *f*	massa *f* d'iniezione (o intrusiva)
^	9809	injected fuel	carburant *m* injecté	Injektionsbrennstoff *m*	carburante *m* iniettato
^	9810	injectivity	injectivité *f*	Einpressindex *m*	iniettabilità *f*
^	9811	injectivity profile	courbe d'injectivité	Einpressprofil *n*	curva *f* d'iniettabilità
o	9812	injection	injection *f*	Schussvorgang *m*	iniezione *f*
o	9813	injection chamber	chambre *f* d'injection	Druckkammer *m*	camera *f* d'iniezione
—	9814	injection metamorphism	métamorphisme *m* d'injection	Injektionsmetamorphose *f*	metamorfismo *m* d'iniezione
o	9815	injection moulding	moulage *m* par injection	Spritzguss *m*	formatura *f* per iniezione
—	9816	injection of ribbon	intrusion *f* rubanée	Ribelinjektion *f*	intrusione *f* nastriforme
—	9817	injection well	puits *m* d'injection	Einpressonde *f*	pozzo *m* d'iniezione
o	9818	injector	injecteur *m*	Injektor *m*	iniettore *m*
o	9819	injector channel	buse *f* d'injection	Eingiessbüchse *f*	ugello *m* d'iniezione
o	9820	inlet	entrée *f*, ouverture d'entrée	Eingang *m*, Zuführungsöffnung *f*	entrata *f*, orifizio *m* d'amissione, apertura *f* d'entrata

English	French	German	Italian
9821 **inlet**	orifice *m* de coulée	Gusstrichter *m*	orifizio *m* di colata
9822 **inlet hole**	orifice *m* d'entrée	Eintrittsöffnung *f*	porta *f* d'accesso o di visita, orifizio *m* d'adduzione (o d'ammissione)
9823 **inlier**	fenêtre *f* (géologique)	geologisches Fenster *n*	finestra *f* (geologica)
9824 **inner bar, traverse**	entretoise *f*	Schore *f*, Steg *m*	traversa *f*
9825 **inner core barrel**	tube *m* carottier intérieur	inneres Kernrohr *n*	tubo *m* porta-carote (di un carotiere)
9825a **inner cover**	coiffe *f* de protection	Schutzhaube *f*	cappa *f* interna
9826 **inoculant**	inoculant *m*	Impfstoff *m*	inoculante *m*, correttivo *m*
9827 **inoculation**	inoculation *f*	Impfung *f*	inoculazione *f*, correzione (per ghisa liquida)
9828 **input joint**	pièce *f* d'introduction	Zugangsstück *n*	pezzo *m* d'introduzione
9829 **input well**	sondage *m* d'injection, puits *m* d'alimentation	Einpressonde *f*, Einlassbohrung *f*	sondaggio *m* d'iniezione, pozzo *m* petrolifero sotto pressione
9830 **inrush**	irruption *f*, dégagement *m* instantané	Durchbruch *m*, Ausbruch *m*	irruzione *f*, eruzione *f*
9831 **inrush of water**	coup *m* d'eau	Wasserdurchbruch *m*	irruzione (o colpo) d'acqua
9832 **to insert, carburize**	cémenter, charger, insérer	einsetzen eisatzhärten	cementare, inserire
9833 **insert**	insertion *f*	Eingiessteil *m*	inserto *m*
9833a **insert die**	matrice *f* changeable	Einsatzmatrize *f*	matrice *f* cambiabile
9834 **inserted joint**	joint *m* à emboîtement	Stemmuffenverbindung *f*	giunto *m* a bicchiere
9835 **inserted joint casing**	tube *m* à renflement, tubage *m* à emboîtement	aufgemufftes Rohr *n*, muffenlose Rohrverbindung *f*	tubaggio *m* a incastro
9836 **inserted rib**	nervure *f* rapportée	eingesetzte Rippe *f*	nervatura *f* incassata
9837 **inserting the pig**	mise *f* en place de la gueuse	Einspannen *n* der Massel	collocamento *m* dei masselli, sistemazione *f* dei masselli

		English	French	German	Italian
o	9838	inserting the plug	mise *f* en place du fond	Einsetzen *n* des Bodens	montaggio *m* del fondo
—	9839	inset	recette *f* inférieure	Füllort *m*	stazione *f* di fondo
—	9840	inset, phenocryst	phénocristal *m*	Phenocryst *m*	fenocristallo *m*
o	9841	inset core	pièce *f* battue	loser Ballen *m*, Aussenkern *m*	motta *f*
—	9842	inside calipers *pl.*	(compas *m*) maître *m* de danse	Lochtaster *m*, Innentaster *m*	compasso *m* per fori
^	9843	inside drift	calibre pour manchon	Muffelkaliber *n*	calibro *m* per manicotto
o	9844	insoluble	insoluble	unlöslich	insolubile
o	9845	to inspect the tuyeres	inspecter les tuyères	die Formen nachsehen	controllare le tubiere
	9846	inspection	contrôle *m*	Kontrolle *f*	controllo *m*
o	9847	inspection hole, peep hole	regard *m*	Schauöffnung *f*	spia *f*, foro *m* d'ispezione
	9848	inspector	agent-réceptionnaire	Abnahmebeamter *m*	collaudatore *m*
o	9848a	to inspissate	épaissir	eindicken	ispessire

institute of welding, *s. welding institute*

insulated crane, *s. independent crane*

		English	French	German	Italian
o	9849	insulated wire and cables	câbles *m pl.* et conducteurs isolés	isolierte Kabel und Leiter	cavi *m pl.* e conduttori isolati
o	9850	insulating	isolant	isolierend, Isolier=	isolante
o	9851	insulation joint	joint *m* isolant	Isolierungsstück *n*	giunto *m* isolante
o	9852	insulation to minimize cold bridges	isolation *f* pour éviter la formation de ponts thermiques	Isolation *f* zur Vermeidung von Kaltbruecken	isolamento *m* per evitare la formazione di ponti termici
o	9853	intake	entrée *f*, admission *f*, alimentation *f*	Zutritt, Einnehmen *n*, Speisung *f*	entrata *f*, ammissione *f*, alimetazione *f*, presa *f*
—	9854	intake	chantier *m* d'aérage	Wetterstrecke *f*	galleria *f* di ventilazione
o	9855	intake	orifice *m* de coulée	Gusstrichter *m*	orificio *m* di colata, bocca *f* di colata

English	French	German	Italian
9856 **intake air**	air *m* entrant	einziehendes Wetter *n*, Zuluft *f*	aria *f* d'immissione
9857 **intake pressure**	pression *f* d'introduction	Einlassdruck *m*	pressione *f* d'introduzione
9858 **intake shaft**	puits *m* d'entrée d'air	einziehender Schacht *m*	pozzo *m* d'apirazione dell'aria
9859 **intake well**	sondage *m* d'injection	Einlassbohrung *f*	sondaggio *m* d'iniezione
9859a **intensifier**	renforcateur *m*	Verstärkungsmittel *n*	rinforzatore *m*
9860 **intensity of retention of the ions**	intensité *f* de retenue des ions	Haftstärke *f* der Ionen	intensità *f* di ritenuta degli ioni
9861 **intensity of tensile stress, tension**	tension *f* de traction, traction *f* unitaire	Zugspannung *f*	tensione *f*, coefficiente *m* di trazione
9862 **intensity of torsional stress**	tension *f* de torsion	Drehspannung *f*	tensione *f* di torsione
9863 **intensity value**	grandeur *f* de l'intensité	Spannungsgrösse *f*	grandezza *f* dell'intensità
9864 **interbedded**	interstratifié	zwischenschichtig	interstratificato
9865 **interbedding**	interstratification *f*	Zwischenschichtung *f*	interstratificazione
interblock, *s. block*			
9866 **intercalar texture**	texture *f*, texture *f* intercalaire	Intersertalgefüge *n*	struttura *f* intercalare
9867 **intercalated bed**	intercalation *f*	Einlagerung *f*	interstrato *m*
9868 **intercalation, interstratified bed**	intercalation *f*	Einlagerung *f*, Einschaltung *f*	interstrato *m*, interposizione *f*
9869 **interchangeable**	interchangeable	auswechselbar	intercambiabile
9870 **interchangeable lip**	bec *m* amovible	auswechselbare Schnauze *f*	becco *m* amovibile (o intercambiabile)
9871 **interchangeable mould**	moule *m* élémentaire (ou interchangeable)	auswechselbarer Formeinsatz *m*	stampo *m* semplice, forma *f* intercambiabile
9872 **interchangeable part**	partie *f* interchangeable, partie *f* amovible	auswechselbarer Teil *m*	parte *f* intercambiabile
9873 **intercooler**	réfrigérant *m* intermédiaire	Zwischenkühler *m*	refrigerante *m* intermedio

English	French	German	Italian
— 9874 intercrystalline	intercristalline	interkristallin	intercristallino
— 9875 intercrystalline corrosion	corrosion *f* intergranulaire	interkristalline Korrosion *f*	corrosione *f* intergranulare
— 9876 intercrystalline fracture	fracture *f* intercristalline	interkristalliner Bruch *m*	frattura *f* intercristallina
— 9877 interdendritic	interdentritique	interdendritisch	interndendritico
— 9878 interdendritic graphite	graphite *m* interdentritique	interdendritischer Graphit *m*	grafite *f* interdendritica

interdendritic segregation, *s. microsegregation*

° 9879 interface	surface *f* de séparation	Trennfläche *f*	fascia *f* di separazione
— 9880 interfacial angle	angle *m* des faces	Flächenwinkel *m*	angolo *m* interfacciale
° 9880a interferometer	interféromètre *m*	Interferometer *m*	interferometro *m*
— 9881 interformational sheet	filon-couche *m*	Lagergang *m*	filone *m* parallelo al piano di stratificazione
° 9882 intergranular fracture	cassure *f* intergranulaire	Korngrenzenbruch *m*	frattura *f* intergranulare, crepa *f* intergranulare
— 9883 intergrow	enchevêtrer	verwachsen	concrescere, accavallare
— 9884 intergrown	enchevêtré	verwachsen	concresciuto
— 9885 intergrowth	enchevêtrement *m*	Verwachsung *f*	concrescenza *f*
° 9886 interior of blast furnace	intérieur *m* du haut-fourneau	Hochofeninnere *n*	interno *m* dell'alto-forno
— 9887 interjacent	intercalé, interstratifié	eingebettet	intercalato, interstratificato
— 9888 interlaced scanning	exploration *f* intercalaire	Zwischenzeilenabtastung *f*	esplorazione *f* intercalata
° 9888a intermediate constituent	composé intermétallique	intermetallische Verbindung *f*	composto *m* intermetallico
° 9889 intermediate filleting piece	témoin *m* de congé	Massmarke *f* für eine Hohlkehle	testimonio *m* del raccordo
° 9890 intermediate frequency furnace	four *m* électrique à moyenne fréquence	Mittelfrequenz-Induktionsofen *m*	forno *m* elettrico di frequenza intermedia

intermediate lever, *s. first motion lever*

° 9891 intermediate part	chape *f*	Formmittelteil *n*	fascia *f*, coperchio *m*

	English	French	German	Italian
9892	intermediate rock	roche *f* neutre	intermediäres Eruptivgestein *n*	roccia *f* neutra
9893	intermediate rolls, intermediate train	train *m* préparateur	Zwischenstrecke *f*, Zwischenstrasse *f*	treno *m* preparatore
	intermediate train, *s. intermediate rolls*			
	intermetallic compound, *s. intermediate constituent*			
9894	intermitter	interrupteur *m*	Unterbrecher *m*	interruttore *m*
9895	intermittent gas lift	gaz *m* lift intermittent	periodisches Gas-lift *n*	gas-lift *m* intermittente
9896	intermount basin	bassin *m* structural, cuvette *f*	Faltungsbecken *n*	bacino *m* strutturale
9897	internal chill	réfroidisseur *m* interne	eingegossener Kühlkörper *m*	raffreddatore *m* interno, raffreddatore *m* inglobato
9898	internal combustion engine	moteur *m* à combustion interne	Verbrennungsmotor *m*	motore *m* a combustione interna
9899	internal crack	fissure *f* interne	Innenriss *m*	incrinatura *f* interna
9900	internal flush tool joint	joint lisse interne	Verbinder mit vollem Durchgang	giunto liscio interno
9901	internal friction	frottement *m* interne	innere Reibung *f*	attrito *m* interno, frizione *f* interna
9902	internal mo(u)ld, internal cast	moule *m* interne	Steinkern *m*	modello *m* interno
9903	internal pressure	pression *f* intérieure	Innendruck *m*	pressione *f* interna
9904	internal shrinkage	retassure *f* interne	Innenlunker *m*	risucchio *m* interno
9905	internal stress	tension *f* interne	innere Spannung *f*	tensione *f* interna
9906	internal structure	structure *f* interne	innere Beschaffenheit *f*	struttura *f* interna
9907	internal temperature	température *f* intérieure	Innentemperatur *f*	temperatura *f* interna
9908	internal yield	limite *f* élastique intérieure	innere Streckgrenze *f*	limite *m* elastico interno
9909	internally fired furnace	foyer *m* intérieur	Innenfeuerung *f*	focolare *m* interno

	English	French	German	Italian
°	9910 **inter-pass annealing**	recuits *m pl.* entre passages	Zwischenglühen *n*	ricottura *f* intermedia
—	9911 **interpenetration twins**	macles *f pl.* d'interpénétration	Durchwachsungs-zwillinge *m pl.*	geminazioni *f pl.* d'interpenetrazione
°	9912 **interrupted hardening, interrupted quenching**	trempe *f* interrompue	unterbrochene Härtung *f*	tempera *f* interrotta
°	9913 **interrupted pour**	coulée *f* interrompue	unterbrochener Guss *m*	colata *f* interrotta
—	9914 **intersertal texture**	texture *f* ou structure *f* intersertale	Intersertalstruktur *f*	struttura *f* intersertale
—	9915 **interspersed**	intercalé	eingeschaltet	intercalato
°	9915a **interstitial**	intersti tiel	interstitiell	interstiziale
	interstratified bed, *s. intercalation*			
—	9916 **interstratified tuff**	tuf *m* interstratifié	eingeschaltete Tuffbank *f*	tufo *m* interstratificato
—	9917 **to interstratify**	interstratifier	einlagern	interstratificare
—	9918 **interstream area**	ligne *f* de partage	Wasserscheide *f*	linea *f* di ripartizione, spartiacque *m*
°	9919 **intractable material**	matériau *m* difficilement usinable	schwer zu bearbeitendes Material *n*	materiale *m* difficilmente lavorabile
	intraformational bed, *s. intercalation*			
°	9920 **intragranular fracture**	cassure *f* intragranulaire	intrakristalliner Bruch *m*	frattura *f* infragranulare
°	9921 **intricate**	compliqué	schwicrig	complicato
°	9922 **intricate shape**	forme *f* compliquée	schwierige Form *f*	forma *f* complicata
°	9923 **intrusion**	intrusion *f*	Intrusion *f*	intrusione *f*
—	9924 **intrusive**	intrusif	intrusiv	intrusivo
—	9925 **intrusive bodies**	corps *m pl.* intrusifs	Intrusivkörper *m pl.*	corpi *m pl.* intrusivi
—	9926 **intrusive rocks**	roches *f pl.* intrusives	Intrusivgesteine *n pl,* Gangegestein *n*	rocce *f pl.* intrusive (o plutoniche)
—	9927 **intrusive sheet**	nappe *f* intrusive	Intrusivlager *n*, Lagergang *m*	strato *m* intrusivo
°	9928 **intubation**	tubage *m*	Intubation *f*	canaletti *m pl.*
—	9929 **intumescence**	intumescence *f*	Intumeszenz *f*	intumescenza *f*

English	French	German	Italian
9930 **intumescence of lava**	dôme *m* de lave	Lavadom *m*	duomo *m* di lava
9931 **invar steel**	acier *m* Invar	Invarstahl *m*	acciaio *m* Invar
9931a **inverse annealing**	recuit *m* inverse	inverse Glüh-frischen *n*	ricottura *f* inversa
9932 **inverse chill, inverse chilling**	trempe *f* inverse	umgekehrtes Härten *n*	tempra *f* inversa (o invertita)
9933 **inverted combustion**	combustion *f* renversée	umgekehrte Verbrennung *m*	combustione *f* invertita
9934 **inverted fold**	pli renversé	überliegende Falte *f*	piega *f* inversa
9935 **inverted saddle**	selle *f* inverse	umgekehrter Sattel *m*	sella *f* inversa
inverted trough-iron, *s. zore iron*			
9936 **investigation with the microscope**	examen *m* microscopique	mikroskopische Untersuchung *f*	esame *m* microscopico, esame al microscopio
9937 **investment casting**	microfusion *f*	Genaugiessverfahren *n*	fusione *f* a cera persa industriale, microfusione
investement moulding, *s. lost wax moulding*			
9938 **investement pattern**, *s. wax pattern*			
9939 **iodargyrite**	iodargyrite *f*	Jodsilber, Jodit	iodite *f*, iodargirite *f*
9940 **iodine**	iode *m*	Jod *n*	iodio *m*
9941 **iodine solution**	teinture *f* d'iode	Jodlösung *f*	tintura *f* d'iodio
9942 **iodobromite**	iodobromyrite *f*	Jodobromit *m*	iodobromirite *f*
iodyrite, *s. iodargyrite*			
9943 **iolite, cordierite**	iolite *f*, cordiérite *f*	Jolith, Kordierit *m*	iolite *f*, cordierite *f*
9944 **ion**	ion *m*	Ion *n*	ione *m*
9945 **ionite**	ionite *f*	Jonit *m*	ionite *f*
9946 **ionitriding**	nitrurer par échange d'ions	ionitrieren	ionitrurare
9946a **ionization**	ionisation *f*	Ionisation *f*	ionizzazione *f*
9947 **IPN steel principal rafters**	arbalétriers d'acier	Stahlsparren IPN	puntoni *m pl.* di acciaio IPN
I.P.S. = *Inside Pipe Size*			
9948 **Ireland furnace**	cubilot *m* Ireland	Ireland Ofen *m*	forno *m* Ireland
9949 **irestone**	cornéenne *f*	Hornstein *m*	selce *f* cornea

	English	French	German	Italian
−	9950 **iridium**	iridium *m*	Iridium *n*	iridio *m*
−	9951 **iridosmine**	iridosmine *f*	Iridosmium *n*	iridosmina *f*
°	9952 **iron**	fer *m*	Eisen *n*	ferro *m*
°	9953 **iron air heater**	appareil *m* à air chaud en fonte	eiserner Winderhitzer *m*	apparecchio *m* di ghisa ad aria calda
	iron alum, *s. halotrichite*			
°	9954 **iron and steel products**	produits *m pl.* sidérurgiques	Eisen-und Stahlerzeugnisse *n pl.*	prodotti *m pl.* siderurgici
°	9955 **iron bars**	fers *m pl.* en barres	Stabstahl *m*, Stabeisen *n*	ferro *m* in barre, acciaio *m* in barre, barre *f pl.* di ferro
°	9956 **iron ball**	boule *f* de fer, loupe *f*	Eisenballen *m*	palla *f* di ferro
°	9957 **iron bath**	bain *m* de fer	Eisenbad *n*	bagno *m* di ferro
	iron belt, *s. hoop*			
°	9958 **iron blocks, sow**	loup *m*, bloc *m*	Eisensau *f*, Sau *f*	blocco *m*
	iron bloom, *s. iron loop*			
°	9959 **iron bracket**	console *f* en fonte	eisernes Tragstück *n*	mensola *f* di ferro
°	9960 **iron building**	construction *f* en fer, charpente *f* en fer	Eisenwerk *n*, Eisenverband *m*, Eisenkonstruktion *f*	costruzione *f* in ferro
−	9961 **iron carbide**	carbure *m* de fer	Eisenkarbid *n*	carburo *m* di ferro
°	9962 **iron carbon alloy**	alliage *m* fer-carbone	Eisenkohlenstofflegierung *f*	lega *f* ferro-carbonio
°	9963 **iron-carbon diagram**	diagramme *m* fer-carbone	Eisen-Kohlenstoff-Diagramm *n*	diagramma *f* ferro-carbonio
°	9964 **iron-carbon equilibrium diagram**	diagramme *m* d'équilibre du fer-carbone	Eisenkohlenstoffzustandschaubild *n*	diagramma *f* di stato ferro-carbonio
°	9965 **iron casting**	fusion *f* en fonte	Eisenguss *m*	fusione *f* in ghisa
°	9966 **iron casting**	fonte *f*	Eisenguss *m*	getto *m* in ghisa
°	9967 **iron cement**	mastic *m* de fer	Rostkitt *m*	mastice *m* metallico
°	9968 **iron chill**	lingotière *f*	Kokilleneinlage *f*, Blockgiessform *f*	lingottiera *f*

English	French	German	Italian
9969 **iron containing oxygen, burnt iron**	fer *m* oxydé	sauerstoffhaltiges Eisen *n*	ferro *m* contenente ossigeno, ferro ossidato
iron containing oxygen, *s. rusty iron*			
iron covering, *s. iron shell*			
9970 **iron disulphide**	pyrite *f* (de fer)	Pyrit *m*	pirite *f* (di ferro)
9971 **iron electrode**	électrode *f* en fer	Eisenelektrode *f*	elettrodo *m* di ferro
9972 **iron fittings of the chimney**	armature *f* de la base de la cheminée	Kaminbeschlag *m*	armatura *f* del camino
9973 **iron fittings of the furnace**	armature *f* du four	Ausrüstung *f* des Ofens	armatura *f* del forno
9974 **iron-founder**	fondeur *m* de fer	Eisengiesser *m*	fonditore *m* di ferro
iron for wire, *s. wire iron*			
9975 **iron-foundry**	fonderie *f* de fer	Eisenhütte *f*	fonderia *f* di ferro
9976 **iron framework**	trellis métallique	Metallgitter *n*	traliccio *m* metallico
9977 **iron from washery**	fonte *f* provenant des lavoirs	Wascheisen *n*	ghisa *f* proveniente dai lavatoi
9978 **iron glance, specular iron ore**	oligiste *m*, spécularite *f*	Eisenglanz *m*	oligisto *m*, ematite *f*, speculare
9979 **iron grains**	grains *m pl.* de fer	Eisenkörnchen *n pl.*	granelli *m pl.* o particelle *f pl.* di ferro
iron hat, *s. gossan*			
9980 **iron industry**	industrie *f* sidérurgique	Hüttenindustrie *f*	industria *f* siderurgica
9981 **iron loop**	fer *m* en loupes	Luppeneisen *n*	ferro *m* in blumi
iron loss, *s. iron waste*			
9982 **iron man**	haveuse *f*	Schrämmaschine *f*	tagliatrice *f* orizzontale di carbone
9983 **iron-mine**	mine *f* de fer	Eisengrube *f*	miniera *f* di ferro
9984 **iron-mould**	lingotière *f*	Kokille *f*, Giessform	lingottiera *f*, conchiglia *f*
9985 **iron muffle**	moufle *m* en fer	gusseiserne Muffel *f*	muffola *f* di ferro
iron-nickel, *s. ferro-nickel*			

		English	French	German	Italian
—	9986	iron ochre	minium m' de fer	Eisenmennige f	minio m di ferro
—	9987	iron ore	minerai m de fer	Eisenerz n	minerale m di ferro
—	9988	iron ore containing carbonic acid	minerai m de fer carbonaté	kohlensäurehaltiges Eisenerz n	minerale m di ferro contenente acido carbonico
—	9989	iron ore containing lead	minerai m de fer plombifère	bleihaltiges Eisen- erz n	minerale m di ferro galenico
—	9990	iron ore containing water, water bearing iron ore	minerai m de fer aquifère	wasserhaltiges Eisenerz n	minerale m di ferro con alto tenore di acqua
—	9991	iron ore mine	mine f de fer	Eisenerzgrube f	miniera f di ferro
		iron oxyde, $s.$ iron ore			
—	9991a	iron pan	carapace f de fer	Eisenunterschicht f	giacimento m di ferro
		iron particles, $s.$ iron grains			
°	9992	iron pig	saumon m de fer	Mulde f	massello m, salmo- ne m di ferro
°	9993	iron plate, sole plate	plaque f en fer, sabot m	Eisenplatte f, Fussplatte f	piastra f di fondazio- ne in ferro, piastra f di base
		iron plate, $s.$ iron sheet, sheet iron			
°	9994	iron plated shaft	cuve f avec enveloppe en tôle	Schacht m mit Mantel	tino m blindato
°	9995	iron Portland cement, slag cement	ciment m de laitier Portland	Eisenportlandzement m	cemento m di loppa (o di scorie Portland)
		iron protosulphide, $s.$ iron sulphuret			
°	9996	iron-puddling	puddlage m du fer	Schmiedeisenpuddeln n, Eisenpuddeln n	puddellatura f del ferro
—	9997	iron pyrite	pyrite f de fer	Pyrit m	pirite f di ferro
°	9998	iron rail with steel head	rail m de fer à tête d'acier	Eisenschiene f mit Stahlkopf	rotaia f di ferro con testa d'acciaio
°	9999	iron rake, rabble	crochet m, râble m	Kratze f, Rührhaken	raschiatoio m
°	10000	iron receiver	avant-creuset m	Sammelherd m	crogiuolo m anteriore
°	10001	iron refining	affinage m de la fonte	Eisenfrischerei f	affinaggio m della ghisa

English	French	German	Italian
iron refuse, *s. scrap iron*			
10002 iron reinforcement	boisage *m* en acier (pour mines)	Eisenzimmerung *f*	armatura *f* in ferro
10003 iron rivet, iron nail	rivet *m* en fer	Eisenniet *m*	chiodo *m* in ferro
10004 iron rod, round bar iron	fer *m* rond	Rundeisen *n*, Rundstab *m*	ferro *m* tondo
10005 iron rolling mill	laminoir *m*	Eisenwalzwerk *n*	laminatoio *m*
10006 iron runner	rigole *f* de coulée	Eisenabflussrinne *f*	canale *m* di colata
10007 iron sandstone	grès *m* ferrugineux	eisenhaltiger Sandstein *m*	gres *m* ferruginoso
iron scale, *s. scale*			
10008 iron scrap	débris *m* de fer, ferraille *f*	Schrott *m*	rottame *m* di ferro
10009 iron sections for rolling stock	profilés *m pl.* pour wagons de chemin de fer	Waggonbauprofile *n pl.*	profilati *m pl.* per vagoni
10010 iron separation	ségrégation *f* de fer	Eisenabscheidung *f*	separazione *f* o segregazione *f* di ferro
10011 iron sheet, sheet iron	feuille *f* de fer	Eisenblech *n*	lamiera *f* di ferro, lamina *f* di ferro, foglio *m* di lamiera di ferro
10012 iron shell	manteau *m* en tôle, enveloppe *f* en tôle	Blechmantel *m*	rivestimento *m* di lamiera, mantello *m* in ferro
10013 iron shoe	semelle *f*	Schuh *m*	base *f* del ritto del supporto
10014 iron shot, casting scrap	grenaille *f* de fonte	Gussschrot *m*	graniglia *f* di ghisa
iron sinter, *s. pharmacosiderite*			
10015 iron sleeper, tie	traverse *f* en fer	eiserne Schwelle *f*	traversa *f* di ferro (o metallica)
10016 iron spar, spathic iron	fer *m* oxydé carbonaté	Stahlstein *m*	spato *m* ferroso
10017 iron spark	étincelle *f* de fer	Eisenfunken *m*	scintilla *f* di ferro

	English	French	German	Italian
−	10018 **iron spinel**	pléonaste *m*	Pleonast *m*	pleonasto *m*, ceylanite
−	10019 **iron stageing**	boisage *m* en acier	Eisenzimmerung *f*	armatura *f* in ferro
○	10020 **iron stanchion**	console *f* en fer	Eisenträger *m*	colonna *f* di ferro
○	10021 **iron stores**	magasin *m* à fers	Eisenlager *n*	magazzino *m* o deposito *m* di ferrami
−	10022 **iron sulphuret, iron protosulphide**	fer *m* sulfuré, sulfure *m* de fer	Schwefeleisen *n*, Eisensulfid *n*	solfuro *m* di ferro, solfuro *m* ferroso
−	10023 **iron tourmaline**	tourmaline *f* noire	Schörl *m*	tormalina *f* nera
	iron tube, *s. hollow iron*			
○	10024 **iron ware**	produits *m pl.* de l'industrie du fer	Eisenzeug *n*, Eisenprodukte *n pl.*	prodotti *m pl.* dell'industria metallurgica, articoli di ferro
○	10025 **iron waste**	déchet *m* de fer	Eisenabbrand *m*, Eisenschrott *m*	rottami *m* (o scarti, o ritagli) di ferro
	iron water, *s. chalybeate water*			
○	10026 **iron wire**	fil *m* de fer	Eisendraht *m*	filo *m* di ferro
○	10027 **iron with high contenet of carbon**	fer *m* à haute teneur de carbone	hochkohlenstoffhaltiges Eisen *n*	ferro *m* ad alto tenore di carbonio
○	10028 **iron with small content of sulphur**	fer à faible teneur de soufre	Eisen *n* mit niedrigem Schwefelgehalt	ferro *m* a piccolo tenore di solfo
○	10029 **to ironclad**	cuirasser	panzern	corazzare
○	10030 **ironclad shaft**	four *m* à minerais de mercure	Ofen *m* für Quecksilbererz	tipo di forno per minerale di mercurio
○	10031 **ironing die**	étampe *f* à niveler	Flachstanze *f*	stampo *m* spianatore
○	10032 **ironman**	haveuse *f*	Schrämmaschine *f*	tagliatrice *f* orizzontale di carbone
○	10033 **ironclad shaft**	puits *m* coffré	verkleideter Schacht	pozzo *m* rivestito
○	10034 **ironmaster**	maître *m* des forges	Hüttenmeister *m*	capo-forgia *m*
○	10035 **ironmongery**	ferronnerie *f*	Eisenwaren *f pl.*	ferramenta *f*
−	10035a **ironstone**	minerai *m* de fer argileux	Eisenstein *m*	carbonato *m* di ferro
○	10036 **ironwork**	travail *m* en fer	Eisenwerk *n*	lavoro *m* in ferro
○	10037 **ironworking**	sidérurgie *f*	Eisenmetallurgie *f*	siderurgia *f*

English	French	German	Italian
10038 **irregular bedding**	stratification f discordante ou irrégulière	unregelmässige Schichtung f	stratificazione f irregolare (o discordante)
irregular working, $s.$ *cold working*			
10039 **irregular working of blast furnace**	allure f variable du haut-fourneau	wechselnder Ofengang m	marcia f variabile dell'altoforno
10040 **irregularities of working**	arrêt dans le fonctionnement, perturbation dans le fonctionnement	Betriebsstörungen $f\,pl.$	arresto o perturbazione di funzionamento
10041 **to irrigate**	ruisseler	berieseln	irrigare, innaffiare
10042 **irrigation**	arrosage m	Berieselung f	irrigazione f
10043 **irrigation surface**	nappe f de ruissellement	Rieselfläche f	superficie f d'irrigazione
10044 **irruptive**	intrusif	intrusiv	intrusivo
10045 **irvingite**	irvingite f	Irvingit m	irvingite f
10046 **Ischewsky furnace**	four m Ischewsky	Ischewskyscher Ofen m	forno m Ischewsky
10047 **isenite**	isénite f	Isenit m	Isenite f
10048 **iserine**	isérite f	Iserin m	iserite f
10049 **ishikawaite**	ishikawaite f	Ishikawait m	ishikawaite f
10050 **isinglass stone**	mica f	Glimmer m	mica f
10051 **island drilling**	sondage m de plusiers puits directionnés	Bohren n verschiedener Schachte aus derselben Stellung	perforazione f di diversi pozzi direzionati dalla stessa posizione
10052 **isobutane**	isobutane m	Isobutan n	Isobutano m
10053 **isobutene**	isobutène m	Isobuten n	isobutene m, isobutilene m
10054 **isoclinal anticline**	anticlinal m, isoclinal m	Isoklinalantiklinale f	anticlinale f isoclinale
10055 **isoclinal fold**	pli m isoclinal	Isoklinalfalte f	piega f isoclinale
10056 **isoclasite**	isoclasite f	Isoklas n	isoclasite f

English	French	German	Italian
− 10057 **isocline**	isocline	isokline	isoclino
− 10057a **isodimorphous**	isodimorphe	isodimorph	isodimorfo
^ 10058 **isoformate**	isoformate *m*	Isoformat *n*	isoformato *m*
− 10059 **isogonic line**	ligne *f* isogone	Isogone *f*	linea *f* isogona
− 10060 **isohydric**	isohydrique	isohydrisch	isoidrico
− 10061 **isohydric solutions**	solutions *f pl.* isohydriques	isohydrische Lösungen *f pl.*	soluzioni *f pl.* isoidriche o corrispondenti
− 10062 **isohydry of acid solutions**	isohydrie *f* des solutions acides	Isohydrie *f* der Säurelösungen	isoidria *f* delle soluzioni acide
○ 10063 **isolated chimney**	cheminée *f* indépendante	freistehender Schornstein *m*	camino *m* indipendente
○ 10064 **isolated steam pump**	pompe *f* à vapeur isolée	freistehende Dampfpumpe *f*	pompa *f* a vapore isolata
○ 10065 **isolating casing**	gaine *f* isolante	Isoliermantel *m*	guaina *f* isolante
^ 10066 **isomerate**	isomérate *m*	Isomerat *m*	isomerato *m*
− 10067 **isomesical deposits**	dépôts *m pl.* isomésiques	isomesische Ablagerungen *f pl.*	depositi *m pl.* isomesici
− 10068 **isometric system, monometric system**	système cubique	reguläres Krystallsystem *n*	sistema *f* cubico
− 10069 **isomorph**	isomorphe	isomorph	isomorfo
− 10070 **isomorphism**	isomorphisme *m*	Isomorphismus *m*	isomorfismo *m*
^ 10071 **iso-octane**	iso-octane *m*	Isooktan *n*	isottano *m*
− 10072 **isopach maps**	cartes *f pl.* isopaques	Mächtigkeitskarten *f pl.*	carte *f pl.* isopache
^ 10073 **isoparaffin**	isoparaffine *f*	Isoparaffin *n*	isoparaffina *f*
^ 10074 **isopentane**	isopentane *m*	Isopentan *n*	isopentano *m*
− 10075 **isopical deposits** *pl.*	dépôts *m pl.* isopiques	isopische Ablagerungen *f pl.*	depositi *m pl.* isopici
^ 10076 **isoprene**	isoprène *m*	Isopren *n*	isoprene *m*
− 10077 **isoseismal, isoseismic**	isoséiste	isoseismisch	isosismico

English	French	German	Italian
10078 **isostatic settling**	affaissement *m* isostatique	isostatische Senkung *f*	cedimento *m* isostatico
10079 **isothermal annealing**	recuit *m* isothermique	isotherme Glühung *f*	ricottura *f* isotermica
10080 **isothermic hardening**	trempe *f* isothermique	isothermische Härtung *f*	tempera *f* isotermica
10081 **isothermic transformation**	transformation *f* isotherme	isothermische Umwandlung *f*	trasformazione *f* isoterma
10082 **isotopical deposit**	dépôt *m* isotopique	isotopische Ablagerung *f*	deposito *m* isotopico
10083 **isotropic molecular interaction**	action *f* intermoléculaire isotrope	Isotropen--Molekularwirkung *f*	azione *f* intermolecolare isotropa
10084 **itabirite**	itabirite *f*	Itabirit *m*	itabirite *f*
10085 **italcolumite**	italcolumite *f*	Italcolumit *m*	italcolumite *f*
10085a **Italian asbestos**	amiante trémolitique	Tremolitasbest *m*	amianto *m* tremolitico
10086 **Italian method of cutting tunnel**	méthode *f* italienne de percement d'un tunnel	italienische Tunnelbauweise *f*	atacco *m* col metodo italiano
10087 **ixolite**	ixolite *f*	Ixolith *m*	ixolite *f*
10088 **ixometer**	fluidimètre *m*	Flüssigkeitsmesser *m*	fluidimetro *m*

	English	French	German	Italian
−	10089 **jacinth**	hyacinthe *f*	Hyazinth *m*	giacinto *m*
	jack, black jack, *s. zinc blende*			
−	10090 **jack**	récipient métallique (pour poudres à mines)	Metallbehälter *m* (für Minenpulver)	recipiente *m* metallico (per polvere da mine)
°	10091 **jack**	vérin *m*	Hebebock *m*	martinetto *m*, cricco *m*, binda *f*
−	10092 **jack bit**	taillant *m* amovible	Einsatzschneide *f*	tagliente *m* regolabile
−	10093 **jack hammer**	marteau-perforateur	Bohrhammer *m*	martello *m* perforatore
−	10094 **jack-head pit, jack pit**	puits *m* intérieur	Blindschacht *m*	pozzo *m* interno, pozzo *m* ausiliario
−	10095 **to jack-knife**	se rompre, se gonfler	zusammenbrechen, ausbauchen	rompersi, gonfiarsi
−	10096 **jack-knifing**	écrasement *m* de boisage	Zimmerungsbruch *m*	sfondamento *m* dell'armatura
−	10097 **jack lamp**	lampe *f* Davy	Davysche Sicherheitslampe *f*	lampada *f* Davy
−	10098 **jack pit**	petit puits *m* auxiliaire	kleiner Hilfsschacht *m*	piccolo pozzo *m* ausiliario
°	10099 **jack shaft**	arbre *m* de commande	Antriebswelle *f*	albero *m* motore
−	10099a **jackhammer**	marteau *m* pneumatique	Presslufthammer *m*	martello *m* pneumatico
°	10100 **jacket**	chemise *f*, enveloppe *f*	Mantel *m*, Hülle *f*	camicia *f*, mantello *m*, rivestimento *m*
°	10101 **jacket core**	noyau *m* tubulaire cylindrique	Mantelkern *m*	anima *f* tubolare cilindrica
°	10102 **jacket of the heath**	blindage *m* du creuset	Gestell *n*, Herdmantel *m*	blindaggio *m* del crogiuolo
°	10103 **jacket sheet iron, shell plate**	tôle *f* d'enveloppe	Mantelblech *n*	lamiera *f* da rivestimento
°	10104 **jacketed casting**	jet *m* enveloppé	Mantelguss *m*	getto *m* con intercapedine
°	10105 **jackboard**	planchéiage *m*	Holzgerüst *n*	tavola *f* di sostegno
^	10106 **jacknife rig**	installation *f* à antenne	Antennenanlage *f*	impianto *m* ad antenna
^	10107 **jackrabbit**	calibre *m* «entre»	Gutlehre *f*	calibro-passa *m*

English	French	German	Italian
10108 jackshaft	arbre *m* auxiliaire de poulie	Spillhilfswelle *f*	albero *m* ausiliario dell'argano
10109 jacobsite	jacobsite *f*	Jakobsit *m*	jacobsite *f*
10110 jacupirangite	jacupirangite *f*	Jacupirangit *m*	jacupirangite *f*
10111 to jad	haver, souscaver	unterschrämen, schrämen	tagliare, intagliare
10112 jad	havée *f*	Schram *m*	taglio *m*, intaglio *m*
10113 jadding	havage *m*	Schrämen *n*	taglio *m* orizzontale (del carbone)
10114 jade	jade *m*	Jade *m*	giada *f*
10115 jadeite	jadéite *f*	Jadeit *m*	giadeite *f*
10116 jadeitite	jadéitite *f*	Jadeitit *m*	giadeitite *f*
10117 jag (g)	entaille *f*, encoche *f*	Kerbe *f*, Ausschnitt	intaglio *m*, tacca *f*
10118 to jam	gripper	sich festfressen	grippare
10119 jam nut	contre-écrou *m*	Gegenmutter *f*	controdado *m*
jamb block, *s. rebated walling block*			
10120 jam welding	soudure *f* bout à bout	Stumpfschweissung *f*	saldatura *f* di testa
10120a jammer	support *m* de noyau	Profilkernstütze *f*	supporto *m* sagomato
10121 to japan	vernir au four	japanieren, lackieren	laccare, verniciare al forno
10122 japanned	verni au four, laqué	japaniert, lackiert	laccato, verniciato al forno
10123 japanning	vernissage au four	Lackieren *n*, Japanieren *n*	laccatura *f*, verniciatura *f* al forno
10124 to jar	secouer, vibrer,	schütteln, rütteln stossbohren	scuotere, vibrare, perforare ad urto
10125 jar	coulisse *f*	Rutschschere *f*	snodo *m*
10126 jar crotch sockets	arrache-coulisse *m*	Rutschscherenfänger	pesca-snodi *m*
10127 jar-down spear	arrache-coulisse *m*	Schlagrohrkrebs	pesca-snodi *m*
10128 jar knocker	récupérateur *m*	Regenerator *m*, Fanggerät *n*	recuperatore *m*

		English	French	German	Italian
°	10129	**jar molding machine**	machine *f* de moulage à secousses	Rüttelformmaschine *f*	formatrice *f* a scosse
		jar ramming, *s. jolt ramming*			
˄	10130	**jar safety joint**	outil de repêchage	Fanggerät *n*	attrezzo *m* di pescaggio
˄	10131	**jar socket**	arrache-coulisse *m*	Rutschscherenfänger *m*	pesca-snodi *m*
˄	10132	**jar stem**	corps *m* de la coulisse de forage	Rutschscherenschaft *m*	corpo *m* di uno snodo
		jar tool, *s. jack crotch sockets*			
—	10133	**jargon**	jargon *m*	Jargon *m*	zirconite *f*
—	10134	**jarosite**	jarosite *f*	Jarosit *m*	ocr a *f* di ferro
—	10135	**jarring**	broutage *m* d'un outil,secouage *m*	Rütteln *n*	vibrazione d'un attrezzo, scuotimento
°	10135a	**jarring mark**	marque de vibration	Vibrationsspur	traccia *f* di vibrazione
˄	10136	**jars**	coulisse *f* de forage	Rutschschere *f*	snodo *m* per sondaggi
—	10137	**jasper-agate**	agate *f* jaspée	Jaspisachat *m*	agata-diasporo *f*
		jasper opal, *s. ferruginous opal*			
—	10138	**jasperization**	jaspérisation *f*	Jasperisation *f*	diasperizzazione *f*
—	10139	**jaspilite**	jaspilite *f*	Jaspilit *m*	jaspilite *f*
˄	10140	**jat system**	système *m* de contrôle	Kontrollsystem *n*	sistema *m* di controllo
—	10141	**jaw**	mâchoire *f* (de broyeur)	Brechbacke *f*	mascella *f* (di frantoio)
—	10141a	**jaw breaker (or crusher)**	broyeur *m* à mâchoires	Backenbrecher *m*	mulino *m* a ganasce
°	10142	**jaw chuck**	mandrin *m* à mors	Backenfutter *n*	morsa *f*, mandrino *m* autocentrante, griffa *f*
°	10143	**jaw (of a vice)**	mâchoire *f*	Backe *f*	ganascia *f*
—	10144	**jefferisite**	jefferisite *f*	Jefferisit *m*	jeffersite *f*
—	10145	**jeffersonite**	jeffersonite *f*	Jeffersonit *m*	jeffersonite *f*
°	10146	**Jena glass**	verre *m* de Jena	Jenaer Geräteglas *n*	vetro *m* di Jena per apparati
—	10147	**jenkin**	fausse voie *f*, recoupe de traçage	Blindort, blinde Strecke *f*	galleria *f* cieca
—	10148	**jeremejevite**	jéréméjéwite *f*	Jeremejewit *m*	jeremejevite *f*

English	French	German	Italian
10149 jerk line	câble *m* à secousses	Stosseil *n*	cavo *m* a strappo (o ausiliario)
10150 jeromite	jeromite *f*	Jeromit *m*	jeromite *f*
10150a jerring machine	secoueur *m*	Rüttelmaschine *f*	macchina *f* a scosse
10151 jerry man	boiseur *m*	Zimmerhauer *m*	armatore *m* in vena
10152 jet	jais *m*	Gagat *m*	ambra *f* nera, giavazzo *m*
10153 jet	jet *m*	Einguss *m*	canale *m* di colata
10154 jet, nozzle	gicleur *m*, buse *f*	Düse *f*	spruzzatore *m*, ugello *m*
10155 jet	loupe *f*	Ofenbär, Bodensatz *m*	colame *m*, groppo *m*

jet, *s. suction basket*

jet, *s. air blast or sprue*

English	French	German	Italian
10156 jet charge	charge *f* creuse	Hohlgicht *f*	carica *f* cava
10157 jet-nozzled rock bit	sondage à jet	Düsenbohrung *f*	perforatrice *f* a getto
10158 jet perforator	perforateur *m* à charge creuse	Hohlgichtbohrer *m*	perforatore *m* a carica cava
10159 jet propulsion fuel	combustible *m* pour jets	Brennstoff *m* für Düsenflugzeuge	combustibile *m* per reattori
10160 jet tapping	ouverture *f* explosive du trou de coulée	explosive Abstich-lochöffnung *f*	apertura *f* esplosiva del foro di colata
10161 jet velocity	vitesse *f* du jet	Düsenstrahl-geschwindigkeit *f*	velocità *f* del jet
10162 jetstone	schorl	schwarzer Turmalin *m*	tormalina *f* nera
10163 jetting action	action *f* d'érosion	Spüleffekt *m*	azione *f* d'erosione
10164 jeweller's red	rouge *m* à polir	Polierrot *n*, Juwelierrot *n*	rosso *m* per levigare, rosso *m* inglese
10165 jezekite	jezekite *f*	Jezekit *m*	jezekite *f*
10166 jib	crochet *m*	Haken *m*	gancio *m*
10167 jib crane	grue *f* à flèche	Drehkran *m*	gru *f* a braccio, gru *f* a bandiera
10168 jib cranes on rails	grues à flèche tournante sur rail	Schienendrehkran *m*	gru *f pl.* a braccio girevole su rotaia

English	French	German	Italian
— 10169 **to jig**	laver au crible	setzen	lavare a scosse
— 10170 **jig**	lavoir *m* à secousses	Setzmaschine *f*	crivello *m* (o vaglio *m*) oscillante
jig. *s. core setting jig*			
— 10171 **jig borer**	machine *f* verticale à aléser les gabarits	senkrechte Bohrmaschine für Schablonen	alesatrice *f* verticale per maschere
— 10172 **jig-hitcher**	rouleur *m*	Schlepper *m*	trasportatore *m* (operaio)
— 10173 **jig plane**	plan *m* incliné à voie unique et contrepoids	eintrümmiger Bremsberg *m* mit Gegengewicht	piano *m* inclinato a via unica e a contrappeso
— 10174 **jig tank**	caisse *f* du jig	Siebkasten *m* einer Setzmaschine	cassa *f* del crivello
— 10175 **jigged ore**	minerai *m* lavé	gewaschenes Erz *n*	minerale *m* lavato
— 10176 **jigger (mine worker)**	cribleur *m*	Vorklassierer *m*	crivellatore *m*
— 10177 **jigger**	crible *m*	Setzmaschine *f*	vaglio *m*, crivello *m*
— 10178 **jigger conveyor**	convoyeur *m* à secousses, couloir *m* oscillant	Schüttelrutsche *f*	convogliatore *m* a scosse
— 10179 **jigger work**	criblage *m* par dépôt, lavage *m* par jig	Setzarbeit *f*	vagliatura *f* per deposito, lavaggio *m* al crivello
— 10180 **jigging**	sassage *m*, passage au crible	Durchsieben *n*, Siebsetzarbeit *f*	crivellatura *f*
— 10181 **jigging machine**	lavoir *m* à secousses	Setzmaschine *f*	crivello *m* oscillante o a scosse
— 10182 **jigging of ore**	lavage *m* de minerai	Abläutern der Erze	lavaggio *m* del minerale, crivellatura *f* del minerale
° 10183 **jigging point**	repère de départ d'usinage	Ausgangspunkt *m* für die Bearbeitung	riferimento *m* per la lavorazione meccanica
° 10184 **jigging point**	patte *f* d'usinage	Einspannhilfe *f* für die Bearbeitung	appoggio *m* per la lavorazione
— 10185 **jigging screen**	crible *m* à secousses, crible filtrant	Setzsieb *n*, Schüttelsieb *m*	vaglio *m* (o crivello *m*) a scosse

English	French	German	Italian
10186 **jinny**	treuil *m* de traction	Schlepperhaspel *m*	motore *m* del verricello
10187 **joaquinite**	joaquinite *f*	Joaquinit *m*	joaquinite *f*
job's tears, *s. chrysolite grains*			
10188 **jobbing foundry**	fonderie *f* sur modèles	Kundengiesserei *f*	fonderia *f* per terzi
10188a **jobbing plate**	tôle *f* moyenne	Mittelblech *n*	lamiera *f* media
10189 **jocker chute**	cheminée *f* auxiliaire à minerai	Hilfsrolle *f* für Erze	scivolone *m* ausiliare per minerali
10190 **jockey**	dispositif *m* d'attelage	Kuppelvorrichtung *f*	dispositivo *m* d'attacco, puleggia *f* di tensione
10191 **jockey stick**	barre *f* d'attelage	Kuppelstange *f*	asta *f* d'accoppiamento
10192 **joggle**	mortaise *f*	Zapfenloch *n*	mortisa, gorgia *f*
10193 **johannite**	johannite. *f*	Johannit *m*	johannite *f*
10194 **johnstrupite**	johnstrupite *f*	Johnstrupit *m*	Johnstrupite
10195 **joining balk**	bois *m* de garnissage	Verzug *m*	legno *m* di rivestimento (o per armatura)
10196 **joining by mortise and tenon**	assemblage *m* à tenon et à mortaise	Zapfenverbindung *f*	giunzione *f* a tenone e a mortisa
10197 **joining on butt**	assemblage *m* en bout	Stossverbindung *f*	giunzione *f* ad attestatura
10198 **joint, groove**	joint *m*	Fuge *f*	giunto *m*
10199 **joint**	plaque *f* obturatrice	Verschlusskappe *f*	cappello *m* o cuffia *f* di guardia
10200 **joint**	union *f*, assemblage *m*, articulation *f*	Verbindung *f*	unione *f*, giunzione *f*, connessione *f*, accoppiamento *m*, articolazione *f*
10201 **joint-aid**	support *m* à ressort	Federstütze *f*	sostegno *m* a molla (in fondo al «mouse hole»)
10201a **joint breaking**	dédoublage *m* du moule	Offnung der Form	apertura *f* della forma
10202 **joint face**	plan *m* de joint	Teilungsebene *f*	piano *m* di divisione
10203 **joint line**	ligne *f* de joint	Teilungslinie *f*	linea *f* di divisione, linea *f* di giunzione
10204 **joint of pipe**	élément, tronçon *m* du tuyau	Rohrlänge *f*	sezione *f* (o lunghezza *f*) del tubo

	English	French	German	Italian
—	10205 joint of retreat	joint *m* de retrait	Kontraktionsspalte *f*	giunto *m* di ritiro
—	10206 joint plane	plan *m* de cassure	Kluftfläche *f*	piano *m* di rottura (o frattura)
°	10207 joint sealing	trainée *f* d'étanchéité	Dichtungsrille *f*	sigillatura *f*
°	10208 joint sealing, sealing ring	cordon *m* d'étanchéité	Sandwulst *m*	cordone *m* di sigillatura
^	10209 joint strength	capacité *f* de joint	Abstreiffestigkeit *f* eines Verbinders	capacità *f* di giunto
°	10210 joint with cover plate	joint *m* avec couvre-joint	Laschenverbindung *f*	giunto *m* con copri-giunto
°	10211 jointer	soudeur *m*	Löter *m*	saldatore *m*
	10212 jointer	tronçon *m* court de tubage	Verbohrungsstück *n*	spezzone *m* corto di «casing»
—	10213 jointing	fissuration *f*	Zerklüftung *f*	fissurazione *f*
°	10214 jointing	assemblage *m*	Verbindung *f*	giunzione *f*, connessione *f*
°	10214a jointing nail	polissoir *m*	Fugennagel *m*	spatola *f*
—	10215 joist	entretoise *f*	Querträger *m*, Querbalken *m*	travetto *m*, travicello *m*, tirante *m*
°	10216 ioist, I iron	fers *m pl.* double T	Träger *m*, Doppel T Eisen *n*	profilato *m* a doppio T
°	10217 jolt (foundry)	secousse *f*	Rütteln *n*	scossa *f*
°	10218 jolt molding	moulage *m* par secousses	Rüttelformen *n*	formatura *f* a scossa
°	10219 jolt molding machine	machine *f* à mouler à secousses	Rüttelformmaschine *f*	formatrice *f* a scosse
°	10220 jolt pin-lift moulding machine	machine *f* à mouler à secousses avec démoulage sur chandelles	Rüttelformmaschine *f* mit Stiftabhebung	formatrice *f* a scossa con sformatura a candele
°	10221 jolt ramming	serrage *m* par secousses	Verdichten *n* durch Rütteln	stivatura *f* a scossa
°	10222 jolt rollover draw machine	machine *f* à mouler-en secousses avec démoulage par renversement	Rüttelformmaschine *f* mit Aushebung durch Kippen	formatrice *f* a scosse con sformatura a ribaltamento

English	French	German	Italian
10223 jolt squeeze molding machine	machine *f* de moulage à secousses et pression	Druckrüttelformma-schine *f*	formatrice *f* a scosse e pressione
10224 jolt squeeze pin-lift molding machine	machine *f* à mouler à secousses et pression avec démoulage sur chandelles	Druckrüttelformaschi-ne mit Schiftenabhe-bung	formatrice *f* a scosse e pressione con sformatura a candele
jolter, *s. jolting machine*			
10225 jolting	secousse *f*	Rütteln *n*	scossa *f*
10226 jolting machine	crible *m* laveur à secousses	Setzmaschine *f*	vaglio *m* lavatore a scosse, crivello *m* a scosse
10227 jolting molding machine	machine *f* de moulage à secousses	Rüttelformmaschine *f*	formatrice *f* a scosse
10228 jolting plate	plaque *f* de serrage	Druckplatte *f*	placca *f* di compressione
10229 jordanite	jordanite *f*	Jordanit *m*	jordanite *f*
10230 josefite	josefite *f*	Josefit *m*	josefite *f*
10231 joseite	joséite *f*	Joseit *m*	joseite *f*
10232 josephinite	joséphinite *f*	Josephinit *m*	josefinite *f*
10233 journal friction	frottement *m* du tourillon	Zapfenreibung *f*	sfregamento *m* del collo
10234 journal	châssis *m* du marteau	Büchsensäule *f*	retto *m* del supporto
10235 journal bearing	coussinet *m* de tourillon	Zapfenlager *m*	supporto *m* per perni
10236 journey	train de berlines	Wagenzug *m*	convoglio *m* di vagoncini
10237 jowling	sonder le toit en le frappant	Abklopfen *n* der Firste	sondare il tetto battendolo
10238 jud	charbon *m* coupé d'en bas et de côté, tranche	unterschrämte und gekerbte Kohle *f*, Abschnitt *m*	carbone *m* tagliato dal basso e dal lato, trancia *f*
10239 judd	gros bloc *m* de charbon	grosser Kohlenklumpen *m*	grosso blocco di carbone
10240 juggler	contre-fiche *f*	Strebe *f*	contraffisso *m*, sostegno *m*, puntello *m*

	English	French	German	Italian
—	10241 **julienite**	juliénite *f*	Julienit *m*	julienite *f*
—	10242 **jumbo**	chariot *m* de perforation	Bohrwagen *m*	carrello *m* di perforazione
—	10243 **jumbo rig**	installation *f* de sondage auto-transportée	Mehrfachbohr-maschine *f*,fahrbar	perforatrice *f* multipla su carrello
—	10244 **jumillite**	jumillite *f*	Jumillit *m*	jumillite *f*
°	10244a **jump**	chevauchement	Überlappung *f*	sovrapposizione *f*
—	10245 **jump**	accident, cran	Sprung *m*, Verwerfung *f*	salto *m*, faglia *f*
°	10246 **to jump**	refouler, aplatir, écraser	stauchen, zusammenstauchen	ricalcare, rifollare
—	10247 **jump drilling**	sondage *m* par battage	Stossbohrung *f*	perforazione *f* a percussione
°	10247a **jump joint**	joint *m* refoulé	Stauchverbindung *f*	giunzione *f* ricalcata
ˆ	10248 **jump (of gazoline)**	sensibilité *f* (d'essence)	(Benzin) Empfindlichkeit *f*	sensività *f* (di benzina)

jump test, *s. upbending test*

jump-weld, *s. butt-weld(ing)*

	English	French	German	Italian
—	10249 **jumper**	perforateur *m* à percussion	Stossbohrmaschine *f*	perforatore *m* a percussione
—	10250 **jumper bar**	perçoir, fleuret, refouloir	Bohrer *m*, Stossbohrer *m*, Bohreisen *n*	punta *f* perforatrice a corona, fioretto
°	10251 **jumping**	refoulement *m*, aplatissement *m*, écrasement *m*	Stauchung *f*	schiacciamento *m*, ricalcatura *f*, appiattimento *m*

jumping test, *s. shock crushing test*

	English	French	German	Italian
ˆ	10252 **jumpover**	raccord *m*	Verbindung *f*	raccordo *m*
°	10253 **junction, connecting line**	voie *f* de raccordement	Anschlussgleis *n*	binario *m* di raccordo

juncture, *s. seam*

	English	French	German	Italian
°	10254 **junk**	ferraille *f*, détritus *m*	Abfälle *m pl.*	rifiuto *m* scarto *m*, rottame *m*
ˆ	10255 **junk basket**	panier *m* de sédimentation	Fangkorb *m*	cilindro *m* sullo scalpello per detriti

English	French	German	Italian
^ 10256 **junk casing**	colonne *f* abimée	zerstörte Säule *f*	colonna *f* rovinata
^ 10257 **junk catcher**	collier *m* de repê-chage à lames	Brockenfänger *m*	pescatore *m* a lame
^ 10258 **junk pusher**	outil *m* pour pousser les détritus au fond du puits	Vorrichtung *f* zum Abstossen der Abfälle auf dem Schachtboden	attrezzo *m* per spingere detriti al fondo pozzo
− 10259 **jurupaite**	jurupaïte *f*	Jurupait *m*	giurapaite *f*
− 10260 **jurassic**	jurassique *m*	Jurassisch *m*	giurassico
○ 10261 **to jut**	dépasser, désaffleurer	hervostehen	gettare, sporgere
○ 10262 **jut**	saillie *f*	Erker *m*	getto *m*, sporgenza *f*
− 10263 **juxporite**	juxporite *f*	Juxporit *m*	juxporite *f*
− 10264 **juxtaposition twins**	macles *f pl.* juxtaposées	Juxtapositionszwillinge *m pl.*	geminazioni *f pl.* giustapposte

English	French	German	Italian
— 10265 **kaersutite**	kaersutite *f*	Kaersutit *m*	kaersutite *f*
— 10266 **kainite**	kaïnite *f*	Kainit *m*	cainite *f*, kainite *f*
— 10267 **kainolith**	kaïnolithe *f*	Kainolith *m*	cainolite *f*
— 10268 **kainosite**	kaïnosite *f*	Kainosit *m*	cainosite *f*
— 10269 **kainotype rock**	roche *f* néovolcanique	jungvulkanisches Gestein *n*	roccia *f* neovulcanica
— 10270 **Kainozoic era**	ère *f* cénozoïque	känozoische Formation *f*	era *f* cenozoica
— 10271 **kakoxen**	kakoxen *m*	Kakoxen *m*	kakoxen *m*
— 10272 **kali**	potasse *f*	Potasche *f*	potassa *f*
— 10273 **kaliborite**	kaliborite *f*	Kaliborit *m*	kaliborite *f*
— 10274 **kalinite**	kalinite *f*	Kalinit *m*	kalinite *f*
— 10275 **kaliophilite**	kaliophilite *f*	Kaliophilit *m*	kaliofilite *f*
— 10276 **kalium**	kalium *m*	Kalium *n*	potassio *m*
— 10277 **kalkowskite**	kalkowskite *f*	Kalkowskin *m*	kalkowskite *f*
— 10278 **kallaite**	calaïte *f*	Kallait *f*	calaite *f*, turchese
— 10279 **kamacite**	kamacite *f*	Kamacit *m*	kamacite *f*
— 10280 **kamarezite**	kamarezite *f*	Kamarezit *m*	kamarezite *f*
— 10281 **kammererite**	kammérérite *f*	Kammererit *m*	kammererite *f*
— 10282 **kampylite**	kampylite *f*	Kampylit *m*	kampylite *f*
— 10283 **kaolinite**	kaolinite *f*	Kaolinit *m*	caolinite *f*, caolino *m* puro
— 10283a **kaolinization**	kaolinisation *f*	Kaolinisierung *f*	caolinizzazione *f*
— 10284 **kar**	cirque *m* glaciaire	Kar *m*	circo *m* glaciale
— 10285 **karstenite**	karsténite *f*	Karstenit *m*	karstenite *f*, anidrite *f*
— 10286 **karyinite**	caryinite *f*	Karynit *m*	carynite *f*
— 10287 **kasolite**	casolite *f*	Kasolit *m*	casolite *f*
— 10288 **katagenesis**	katagénèse *f*	Katagenese *f*	catagenesi *f*, sviluppo *m* regressivo

	English	French	German	Italian
10289	katamorphic	katamorphique	katamorph	catamorfico
10290	kataphorite	katophorite *f*	Katophorit *m*	katoforite *f*
10291	katazone	kata-zone *f*	Katazone *f*	catazona *f*
10292	katoptrical	catoptrique	katoptritisch	catoptrico
10293	katoptrite	katoptrite *f*	Katoptrit *m*	catoptrite *f*
10294	kaustobiolite	kaustobiolite *f*	Kaustobiolith *m*	caustobiolite *f*
10295	kawk	fluorine *f*	Fluorit *m*	fluorina *f*
10296	keel block	bloc *m* à quille	Kielprobe *f*	provetta *f* a chiglia
10297	keel plate	tôle *f* de quille	Kielplatte *f*, Kielblech *n*	lamiera *f* di chiglia
10298	keep in stock	stocker	lagern	immagazzinare
10299	keeps	taquets *m pl.*	Aufsetzvorrichtung *f*	sostegni *m pl.* per gabbia, tacche *f pl.*
10300	Keewatin period	période *f* de Keewatin	Keewatin *n*	periodo *m* di Keewatin
10301	kehoeite	kéhoéite *f*	Kehoeit *m*	kehoeite *f*
10302	kelihauite	keilhauite *f*	Keilhauit *m*	keilhauite *f*
10303	kelly, auger stem	tige *f* carrée d'entraînement	Vierkantstange *f*	asta *f* motrice
10304	kelly's rat hole	trou *m* de la tige carrée	Rattenloch *n*	foro *m* dell'asta quadra
10305	kelly bushing	carré *m* d'entraînement	Mitnehmereinsatz *m*	cunei *m pl.* di trascinamento dell'asta motrice
10306	kelly stopcock	robinet *m* de la tige carrée	Absperrhahn *m* für die Spülstange	rubinetto *m* dell'asta motrice
10307	kelper	fondeur *m*	Giesser *m*	fonditore *m*
10308	kelyphite	kélyphite *f*	Kelyphit *m*	kelyfite *f*
10309	kempite	kempite *f*	Kempit *m*	kempite *f*
10310	kentrolite	kentrolite *f*	Kentrolith *m*	kentrolite *f*

keps, *s. catch device*

	English	French	German	Italian
	10311 keramohalite	kéramohalite f	Keramohalit m	keramohalite f
o	10312 kerf	trait de chalumeau	Einschnitt m	taglio m di soffiatore
—	10312a kermesite	kermésite f	Kermesit m	chermesite f, antimonio m rosso
—	10313 kern but	gradin m de faille	Bruchstufe f	gradino m di faglia
	kernel, s. core			
—	10314 kernite	kernite f	Kernit m	kernite f
—	10315 kerogen	kérogène m	Kerogen n	cherogene m
^	10316 kerosene, kerosine	kérosène m	Kerosen n	cherosene m, petrolio raffinato
^	10317 kerosene distillate	kérosène m distillé	distilliertes Kerosen n	petrolio m distillato
	kerosine, s. kerosene			
—	10318 kerrite	kerrite f	Kerrit m	kerrite f
—	10319 kersantite	kersantite f	Kersantit m	kersantite f
—	10320 to kerve	haver, sous-caver	schrämen, schlitzen	scavare, tagliare (al di sotto)
—	10321 kerving	havée f, saignée f	Schram, Schlitz m	taglio m orizzontale, intaglio m, tacca f
—	10322 kettle	bassin m, cirque m glaciaire	Kar n	bacino m, circo m glaciale
—	10323 kettle hole	pli m synclinal	Mulde f, Synklinalfalte f	piega f sinclinale
^	10323a key	coin m de fixation	Verbindungskeil m	cuneo m di fissaggio
o	10324 key bar	acier m pour clavettes	Keilstahl m	acciaio m per chiavette
—	10325 key bed	couche f guide	Leitschicht f	filone-guida m, strato m inferiore
—	10326 key cut holes	coups m pl. de bouchon	Einbruchschüsse m pl.	mine f pl. di rottura
—	10327 key horizon	horizon m repère	Leithorizont m	orizzonte m di riferimento
^	10328 key seat	encoche f de la clavette	Schlüsselloch n, Keilnut m	incastro m della chiavetta

English	French	German	Italian
10329 **key seat wiper**	dispositif *m* pour nettoyer l'encoche de clavette	Keilnutreiniger *m*	dispositivo *m* per prevenire la presa in parete dell'asta pesante
10330 **key well**	puits *m* d'alimentation	Einpress-Sonde *f*	pozzo *m* d'alimentazione
10331 **keyseating**	encoche *f* de clavette	Schlüsselloch *n*, Keilnut *m*	incastro *m* della chiavetta
10332 **keyway**	logement *m* de clavette	Schlüsselgehäuse *n*, Keilgehäuse *f*	alloggio *m* per chiavetta
10333 **khagiarite**	khagiarite *f*	Khagiarit *m*	khagiarite *f*
10334 **kibble**	benne *f*, tonne *f*	Kübel *m*	benna *f*, draga *f*
10335 **kibble filler**	chargeur *m* de bennes	Kübelfüller *m*	draga *f* (o benna *f*) di caricamento
10336 **kibbler**	broyeur *m*	Brecher *m*	frantoio *m*, mulino *m*
10337 **to kick off**	mettre en marche	in Gang setzen	avviare
10338 **kick**	ménisque *m*, forme *f* concave de la surface	Senkung *f* des Metallspiegels, Meniskus *m*	menisco *m* della ghisa
10339 **kick**	vibration *f* du câble de perforation	Schwingung *f* des Bohrseils	vibrazione *f* della corda di perforazione
10340 **kick-back dump**	culbuteur *m* de tête	Kopfwipper *m*	ribaltatore *m* di testa
10341 **kick off**	mise *f* en marche du puits	Inbetriebnahme *f* eines Schachtes	inizio *m* della produzione spontanea d'un pozzo
10342 **kick-off valve, flow valve**	soupape *f* de mise en marche	Startventil *n*	valvola *f* d'avvio
10343 **kick-off point**	point *m* de déviation	Ablenkpunkt *m*	punto *m* di deviazione
10344 **kicker**	éjecteur *m* à déclenchement	Schnappauswerfer *m*	estrattore *m* a scatto
10345 **kicker cylinder**	cylindre *m* éjecteur à déclenchement	Schnappauswerfzylinder *m*	cilindro *m* di estrazione a scatto
10346 **kicking**	puits actif	plötzlicher Zufluss *m* im Bohrloch	pozzo *m* attivo

kidney ore, *s. botryoidal iron ore*

	English	French	German	Italian
−	10347 **kies**	pyrite *f*	Pyrit *m*	pirite *f*
−	10348 **kieselguhr**	kieselguhr *m*	Kieselgur *f*	farina *f* fossile, tripoli *m*
−	10349 **kieserite**	kiésérite *f*	Kieserit *m*	kieserite *f*
^	10350 **to kill a well**	tuer un puits	totpumpen	uccidere un pozzo in eruzione
°	10350a **killed spirits**	eau *f* à souder	Lötwasser *n*	acqua *f* per saldare
°	10351 **killed steel**	acier *m* calmé	beruhigter Stahl *m*	acciaio *m* calmato, acciaio *m* calmo
°	10352 **killing**	calmage *m*, passage à froid	Beruhigung *f*, Kaltbehandlung *f*	calma *f*, lavorazione *f* a freddo finale
°	10353 **killing (of steel)**	désoxydation *f*	Desoxydieren *n*	disossidazione *f*
^	10354 **killing line**	conduit *m* pour tuer le puits	Totpumpleitung *n*	condotta *f* per uccidere il pozzo
°	10354a **killing pickle**	bain *m* épuisé	ausgenutztes Bad *n*	bagno *m* spento
−	10355 **killinite**	Killinite *f*	Killinit *m*	killinite *f*
−	10356 **kiln, roasting furnace**	four *m* (de grillage)	Röstofen *m*	forno *m* d'arrostimento
°	10357 **kiln man**	chef *m* de four	Tiegelbrenner *m*	capo-forno *m*
°	10358 **kiln of Chinaglia's system**	fourneau Chinaglia	Chinaglia-Ofen *m*	fornace *f* (a sistema) Chinaglia
°	10359 **kiln of Hoffmann's system**	fourneau *m* système Hoffmann	Hoffmann-Ofen *m*	fornace *f* Hoffmann
°	10360 **kiln with overlying beds**	four *m* à étages	Etagenofen *m*	forno *m* a ripiani
^	10361 **kilomole**	kilomole *m*	Kilomol *m*	chilomole
−	10362 **kimberlite**	kimberlite *f*	Kimberlit *m*	kimberlite *f*
°	10362a **kindling temperature**	température d'inflammation	Flammpunkt *m*	punto *m* d'infiammazione
−	10363 **kindly ground**	gisement *m* filonien	Ganglagerstätte *f*	giacimento *m* filoniano
−	10364 **kinetigenesis**	kinetogénèse *f*	Kinetogenese *f*	chinetogenesi *f*
−	10365 **king's hook**	barre *f* d'attelage	Königsstange *f*	barra *f* di trazione
−	10366 **king's yellow**	orpiment *m*	Auripigment *n*	orpimento *m*
−	10367 **king post**	pilier *m*	Pfeiler *m*	pilastro *m* montante
°	10367a **kink**	faux pli *m*	Kink *f*, Knick *m*	piega *f* falsa, nodo *m*, groppo *m*
−	10368 **kip**	accrochage *m*	Füllort *m*	stazione *f* di fondo

English	French	German	Italian
10369 Kipp's apparatus	appareil *m* de Kipp	Kippscher Apparat *m*	apparecchio *m* di Kipp
10370 kipushite	kipushite *f*	Kipushit *m*	Kipushite *f*
10371 kir	kir *m*, pétrole *m* solidifié	fossiles Petroleum *n*	kir *m*, petrolio *m* fossile
10372 kirrolite	kirrolite *f*	Kirrolith *m*	Kirrolite *f*
10373 kirve	entaille *f*, havée *f*	Schlitz *m*, Kerbe *f*	intaglio *m*, taglio *m*
10374 to kirve	sous-caver, haver	schrämen, schlitzen	tagliare (al di sotto), intagliare
10375 kirving	havage *m*, sous--cavage	Schrämen *n*, Kerben *n*	taglio *m* (al di sotto), intaglio *m*
10376 kish	écume *f* de graphite	Garschaumgraphit *m*	schiuma *f* di grafite
10377 kish graphite	exsudation *f* de graphite, séparation de graphite	Ausscheidung *f* von Garschaumgraphit	segregazione *f* di grafite
10378 kish graphite inclusions	nids *m pl.* de graphite	Graphitnester *n pl.*	nidi *m pl.* di grafite
10379 kish graphite spots	piqûre *f* de graphite	Graphitporen *f pl.*	vaiolature *f pl.* di grafite
10380 kishy	graphiteux	graphitisch	grafitoso
10381 kisser	mâchefer *m* de contact local	örtlicher Kontakt-zünder *m*	macchia *f* locale per contatto
10382 Kjellin furnace	four *m* Kjellin	Kjellinscher Ofen *m*, Kjellinofen *m*	forno *m* Kjellin
10383 Kjeldahl flask	flacon *m* de Kjeldahl	Kjeldahlkolben *m*	flacone *m* di Kjeldahl
10384 kjerulfine	kjerulfine *f*	Kjerulfin *m*	kjerulfina *f*
10385 klaprothite	klaprothine *f*	Klaprothit *m*	klaprotite *m*
10386 klebelsbergite	klébelsbergite *f*	Klebelsbergit	klebelsbergite *f*
10387 kleinite	kleinite *f*	Kleinit	kleinite *f*
10388 klinoklas	clinoclase *f*	Klinoklas, Strahlerz *n*	clinoclasi *f*
10389 klockmannite	klockmannite *f*	Klockmannit *m*	klockmannite *f*
10390 to knead, to pug	pétrir	kneten	impastare

	English	French	German	Italian
	knife tool, *s. right-hand tool*			
−	10391 **knebelite**	knébélite *f*	Knebelit *m*	knebelite *f*
○	10391a **knitted structure**	structure fréticulée	Netzstruktur *f*	struttura *f* reticolare
	to **knobble**, *s. to shingle*			
	knobbled iron, *s. bloomery iron*			
○	10392 **knobbling, spellerizing**	cinglage *m*	Herdfrischarbeit *f*	fucinatura *f*, forgiatura *f*
○	10393 **to knock**	frapper	klopfen	battere
−	10394 **to knock**	sonder le toit	die Firste abklopfen	sondare il tetto (battendolo)
○	10395 **knock**	coup *m*, choc *m*	Schlag *m*, Stoss *m*	colpo *m*, urto *m*
○	10396 **knock down**	démasselotage *m*	Abschlagen *n* der Steiger	smaterozzatura *f*
	knock-down test, *s. upbending test*			
^	10397 **knock-fuel**	combustible *m* détonant	Klopfbrennstoff *m*	detonante *m*
^	10398 **knock-off, take-off**	décrocher	abschrauben	distaccare, svitare
○	10398a **knock-off feeder head**	masselotte *f* étranglée	eingeschnürter Speiser *m*	materozza *f* strozzata
○	10399 **knock-out, to open the casting**	décocher	ausleeren, abziehen, abtragen	distaffare
○	10400 **knock-out**	décochage *m*	Ausschlagen *n*, Abziehen *n*	distaffatura *f*, distaffaggio *m*
	knock out, *s. shake out*			
○	10401 **knock-out bar**	barre *f* de piquage	Brechstange *f*	barra *f* di sterratura (o per distaffare)
○	10402 **knock-out by jolting**	décochage *m* par secousses	Ausleeren *n* durch Rütteln	distaffatura *f* a scossa
○	10403 **knock out core**	extracteur *m* de carottes	Ausziehvorrichtung *f*	maschio *m* estrattore
−	10404 **knock-out drum**	chambre *f* de séparation	Trennungskammer *f*	camera *f* di separazione
○	10405 **knock-out grid**	grille *f* de décochage	Ausschlagrost *m*	griglia *f* per distaffare
○	10406 **knock-out station**	poste *m* de décochage	Ausschlagstelle *f*	posto *m* per distaffare
	10407 **knock-out time**	temps *m* gâché	verlorene Zeit *f*	tempo *m* perduto

	English	French	German	Italian
o	10408 knocked out (of adjustement)	hors-calibre	unkalibriert	starato
o	10409 knocker	marteau pour signaux	Signalhammer m	martello m segnalatore
o	10410 knocker line	fil m à signaux	Signaldraht m	filo m per segnalazioni
—	10411 knocking	minerai m en morceaux	Stückerz n	minerale m in pezzi
	knocking out, $s.$ knock out			
—	10412 knockings pl., lump ore	minerai m en morceaux, minerai m gros	Stückerz n	minerale m in pezzi
o	10413 knot	noeud m	Knoten m	nodo m
o	10414 knuckle	genouillère f	Kniehebel m	ginocchiera f
o	10415 knuckle joint	fermeture f à genouillère	Kniehebelverschluss m	chiusura f a ginocchiera, giunto m articolato
—	10416 knuckle post	pilier de cabestan	Haspelpfosten m	pilastro m dell'argano
o	10417 knuckle press	presse à matricer	Pressstempel m	pressa f per coniare
o	10417a knurling	moletage m	Kordierung f	zigrinatura f
—	10418 kobellite	kobellite f	Kobellit m	kobellite f
—	10419 kochite	kochite f	Kochit m	kochite f
—	10420 koechlinite	koechlinite f	Koechlinit m	koechlinite f
—	10421 koenenite	koenénite f	Koenenit m	koenenite f
—	10422 kollanite	poudingue m	Puddingstein n	collanite f
—	10423 koneshot	sondage m en colonne	Säulenbohrung f	perforazione f in colonna
—	10424 kongsbergite	kongsbergite f	Kongsbergit m	kongsbergite f
—	10425 koninckite	koninckite f	Koninckit m	koninckite f
—	10426 koppite	koppite f	Koppit m	koppite f
—	10427 kornelite	kornélite f	Kornelit m	cornelite, coquimbite
—	10428 kornerupine	kornerupine f	Kornerupin m	kornerupina f
—	10429 kottigite	kottigite f	Kottigit m	kottingite f

English	French	German	Italian
— 10430 **krablite**	krablite *f*	Krablit *m*	krablite *f*
— 10431 **kramerite**	kramérite *f*	Kramerit *m*	kramerite *f*
— 10432 **krantzite**	krantzite *f*	Krantzit *m*	krantzite *f*
— 10433 **kraurite**	kraurite *f*	Kraurit *m*	kraurite *f*, dufrenite *f*
— 10434 **krausite**	krausite *f*	Krausit *m*	krausite *f*
— 10435 **kremersite**	kremersite *f*	Kremersit *m*	kremersite *f*
— 10436 **krennerite**	krennérite *f*	Krennerit *m*	krennerite *f*
— 10437 **krohnkite**	kroehnkite *f*	Kröhnkit *m*	krohnkite *f*
— 10438 **krypton**	crypton *m*	Krypton *m*	cripto *m*
— 10439 **kukkersite**	kukkersite *f*	Kukkersit *m*	kukkersite *f*
— 10440 **kulaite**	kulaïte *f*	Kulait *m*	kulaite *f*
— 10441 **kullaite**	kullaite *f*	Kullait *m*	kullaite *f*
kulm, *s. culm*			
— 10442 **kunzite**	kunzite *f*	Kunzit *m*	kunzite *f*
— 10443 **kupfferite**	kupfférite *f*	Kupfferit *m*	kupfferrite *f*
— 10444 **kyanite**	cyanite *f*	Cyanit *m*	cianite *f*
— 10445 **kylite**	kylite *f*	Kylit *m*	kylite *f*
— 10446 **kyschtymite**	kyschtymite *f*	Kyschtymit *m*	kyschtymite *f*

	English	French	German	Italian
	L-beams, s. angle steel			
°	10447 **L-iron**	fer m à L	L-Eisen n	ferro m a L
	10448 **label**	étiquette f	Flaschenschild n	etichetta f
°	10449 **laboratory (of a furnace)**	sole f du four	Herd m	suola f
°	10450 **laboratory bench**	table f de laboratoire	Laboratoriumstisch m	tavolo m da laboratorio
°	10451 **laboratory working**	conduite f du laboratoire	Laboratoriumsbetrieb m	esercizio m del laboratorio
−	10452 **labradite**	labradite f	Labradit m	labradite f
	labrador feldspar, s. labradorite			
−	10453 **hornblende**	hypersthène	Hypersthen m, Paulit m	Iperstene m
−	10454 **labradorite, Labrador feldspar**	labradorite f, labrador m	Labrador(it) m, Labradorstein m, Labradorfeldspat m	labradorite f
−	10455 **laccolite**	laccolithe f	Lakkolith m	laccolite f
−	10456 **laccolithic**	laccolithique	lakkolitisch	laccolitico
−	10457 **to lace up**	garnir de planches	verschalen	rivestire (o armare) con tavole di legno
−	10458 **lacing**	chapeau m, bois m de garnissage	Kappe f, Verschalung f	cappello m, rivestimento m in legno, tavole f di rivestimento
°	10459 **lacing flat bar**	plat m de triangulation	Gitterflacheisen n	ferro m piatto di traliccio
°	10460 **to lacquer**	laquer	lackieren	laccare
°	10461 **lacquer**	laque f	Lack m	lacca f, vernice f (a smalto)
°	10462 **lacquer drawn wire, wet drawn wire**	fil m écroui par voie humide	Nassstreckdraht m	filo m trafilato ad umido
−	10463 **lacroixite**	lacroixite f	Lacroixit m	lacroixite f
−	10464 **lad**	galibot m	Knappe m	minatore m
−	10465 **to lade**	charger	laden	caricare

English	French	German	Italian
° 10466 lade	embouchure *f*	Mündung *f*	imboccatura *f*
— 10466a ladder	échelle *f* d'excavateur	Kettentraggerüst *m*	noria *f* di draga
° 10467 ladder sollar	palier *m* de repos	Ruhebühne *f*	piattaforma *f* di riposo
— 10468 laddervein	filon à échelle	Leitergang *m*	filone *m* a gradini
° 10469 ladle (metal container)	poche *f* (de coulée)	Pfanne *f*	siviera *f*, secchia *f* (o secchione *m*) di colata
° 10470 ladle (cup-shaped spoon)	cuiller *f* de coulée	Gusspfanne *f*, Giesskelle *f*	cucchiaione *m*
° 10471 ladle analysis	analyse *f* chimique	chemische Analyse *f*	analisi *f* di colata
° 10472 ladle bail	étrier *m* de la poche de coulée	Giesspfannenbügel *m*, Pfannenbügel *m*	staffa *f* della siviera (o della secchia di colata)
° 10473 ladle bogie, ladle car for casting	chariot *m* porte-poche	Pfannenwagen *m*, fahrbahre Pfanne *f*	carrello *m* caldaia, carrello *m* porta-siviera, carro *m* di colata
° 10473a ladle brick	brique de poche	Pfannenziegel *m*	mattone *m* di caldaia
° 10474 ladle carrier	griffe *f* à poche de coulée	Traggabel *f*	forchetta *f*, portante *m*
° 10475 ladle crane	pont *m* de coulée	Giesspfannenkran *m*	ponte *m* di colata
° 10476 ladle for ring carrier	poche *f* à fourche	Gabelpfanne *f*	siviera *f* a portante
° 10477 ladle guide	guidage *m* de la poche de coulée	Pfannenführung *f*	guida *f* per la secchia (o per la siviera)
° 10478 ladle handle	étrier *m* de la poche de coulée	Giesspfannenbügel *m*, Pfannenbügel *m*	staffa *f* della siviera (o della secchia *f* di colata)
° 10479 ladle lining	revêtement *m* de la poche de coulée	Giesspfannenauskleidung *f*	rivestimento *m* della secchia di colata (o della sivicra)
° 10480 ladle lip	bec *m* de la poche de coulée	Giesspfanneausguss *m*, Giesspfannenschnauze *f*	labbro *m* della secchia di colata (o della siviera)
° 10481 ladle on wheels, ladle car	poche *f* roulante	fahrbare Pfanne *f*	siviera *f* girevole su carrello
° 10482 ladle pouring appliance	orifice *m* de coulée	Auslass *m*	scaricatore *m*
° 10483 ladle sample	prise *f* d'essai de métal liquide	Schöpfprobe *f*	presa *f* di metallo liquido per la prova

English	French	German	Italian
10484 **ladle shank**	étrier *m* de la poche de coulée, brancard	Giesspfannengabel *f* Tragschere *f*	staffa *f* della siviera (o della secchia di colata), portante *m*
10485 **ladle skull**	croûte *f* de poche de coulée	Pfannenkruste *f*	crosta *f* della siviera (o della secchia di colata)
10485a **ladle slag**	laitier *m* de poche	Pfannenschlacke *f*	scoria *f* di siviera
10486 **ladle with rack height adjustment**	poche *f* à crémaillère	Giesspfanne *f* mit Zahnstangengehänge	siviera *f* a cremagliera
10487 **ladler, ladleman**	pocheur *m*	Giesser *m*	fonditore *m*, addetto *m* alle siviere
10488 **to lag**	revêtir	verschalen	rivestire
10489 **lagging**	garnissage *m*, revêtement *m*	Verschalung *f* Schalbretter *n pl.*	guarnissaggio *m*, rivestimento *m*
10490 **lagging board**	palplanche *f*	Verzug *m*	tavola *f* di rivestimento
10491 **lagoon, shallow lake**	lagune *f*	Lagune *f*	laguna *f*
10492 **lakarpite**	lakarpite *f*	Lakarpit *m*	lacarpite *f*
10492a **lake**	colorant *m* à pigment	Pigmentfarbe *f*	colorante *m* al pigmento
10493 **lake deposits** *pl.*	dépôts *m pl.* lacustres	Seeablagerungen *f pl.*	depositi *m pl.* lacustri
10494 **lake sand**	sable *m* de lac	Seesand *m*	sabbia *f* di lago, sabbia lacustre
10494a **lakes**	masse *f* de ségrégation	Seigerungsmasse *f*	massa *f* di segregazione
10495 **lambskin**	anthracite *f* de qualité inférieure	minderwertiger Anthrazit *m*	antracite *f* di qualità inferiore
10496 **lamella, lamina**	lamelle *f*	Lamelle *f*	lamella *f*, lamina *f*
10497 **lamellar**	lamellaire	lamellar	lamellare, laminare
10498 **lamellar serpentine**	antigorite *f*	Antigorit *m*	antigorite *f*
10499 **lamina**	lamelle *f*	Blatt *n*, Schicht *f*	lamina *f*
10500 **laminar**	lamellaire	blätterig, lamellar	laminare
10501 **laminar flow**	écoulement laminaire	laminarer Fluss *m*	scorrimento *m* laminare
10502 **laminar texture**	texture *f* (ou structure) lamelleuse	blättriges Gefüge *n*	struttura *f* lamellare
10503 **to laminate**	laminer	walzen, auswalzen	laminare (in fogli sottili)

	English	French	German	Italian
−	10504 **laminated**	stratifié	geschichtet	stratificato
°	10505 **laminated**	laminé	lamelliert	laminato
	laminated coal, *s. foliated coal*			
−	10506 **laminated fracture**	cassure *f* lamellaire	blättriger Bruch *m*	frattura *f* lamellare
	laminated iron, *s. rolled iron*			
°	10507 **laminating**	calandrage *m*	Kalandrieren *n*	calandratura *f*
°	10508 **laminating machine**	laminoir *m* à tôles	Blechwalzwerk *n*	laminatoio *m* per lamiere (sottili)
−	10509 **lamination**	schistosité *f* de stratification	Absonderung *f* nach den Schichtflächen	scistosità *f* di stratificazione
°	10510 **lamp-carbons** *pl.*	crayons *m pl.*, charbons *m pl.*	Bogenlampenkohlen *f pl.*	carboni *m pl.* per lampada ad arco
−	10511 **lamprophyre**	lamprophyre *f*	Lamprophyr *m*	lamprofiro
−	10512 **lanarkite**	lanarkite *f*	Lanarkit *m*	lanarchite
°	10513 **lamp plate**	assiette *f* de lampe	Lampenteller *m.*	piattello *m* della lampada
	lamp standard, *s. standard*			
−	10514 **lampadite**	lampadite *f*	Kupfermanganerz *n*	lampadite *f*
°	10515 **Lancashire boiler, double flue boiler**	chaudière *f* Lancashire, chaudière *f* à deux tubes-foyers	Lancashirekessel *m*, Doppelflammrohrkessel *m*	caldaia *f* Lancashire, caldaia *f* a due tubi di fiamma
°	10516 **Lancashire boiler with two corrugated flues**	chaudière *f* à deux tubes-foyers ondulés	Zweiwellenrohrkessel *m*	caldaia *f* a due focolari ondulati
	Lancashire hearth, *s. Swedish bloomery fire*			
^	10517 **to land**	placer	absetzen, aufhängen	sistemare, mettere
−	10518 **land**	terrain *m*, terre *f*, continent *m*	Land *n*, Boden *m*, Kontinent *m*	terreno *m*, terra *f*, continente *m*
^	10519 **land**	poser une colonne de tubes	Rohrtour *f* einbauen	discendere una colonna di tubi
−	10520 **land asphalt**	asphalte *m* de qualité inférieure	minderwertiger Asphalt *m*	asfalto *m* di qualità inferiore

English	French	German	Italian
— 10521 **land at bottom**	arriver à la recette inférieure	einfahren zur tiefsten Sohle f	arrivare in fondo, arrivare alla stazione in fondo
° 10522 **land(-type) boiler**	chaudière f terrestre	Landkessel m	caldaia f terrestre
— 10523 **lander**	receveur	Anschläger m	ricevitore m
— 10524 **landfall**	éboulement	Erdrutsch m	frana f, franamento m
— 10525 **landing**	recette f, palier m de repos	Schachthängebank f, Schachtbühne f	fondo pozzo m, stazione f di fondo, piattaforma f di riposo
— 10526 **landing dogs**	taquets, clichage pour cages	Keps m, Aufsetzvorrichtung f	tacche f $pl.$ della gabbia, tacchette f $pl.$
^ 10527 **landing head**	bride f de départ	Abfahrtflansch m	flangia f di partenza
^ 10528 **landing slip**	coin m d'ancrage	Ankerkeil m	cuneo m di ancoraggio
^ 10529 **landing spool**	bobines f $pl.$ d'ancrage de la colonne	Säulenverankerungsrolle f $pl.$	rocchetti m $pl.$ di ancoraggio della colonna
— 10530 **landing stage**	recette du jour, recette f	Hängebank f, Abzugsbühne f	stazione f di fondo, stazione f
— 10531 **landings**	production f	Förderung f	produzione f
landslide, $s.$ $landfall$			
— 10532 **langbanite**	langbanite f	Langbanit m	langbanite f
— 10533 **langbeinite**	langbeinite f	Langbeinit m	langbeinite f
— 10534 **langite**	langite f	Langit m	langite f
— 10535 **lansfordite**	lansfordite f	Lansfordit m	lansfordite f
— 10536 **lanthanite**	lanthanite f	Lanthanit m	lantanite f
— 10537 **lanthanum**	lanthane m	Lanthan n	lantanio m
° 10538 **to lap, to polish**	polir, lisser	polieren, läppen	lappare, smerigliare, levigare
° 10539 **to lap weld**	souder en biseau	überlappt schweissen	saldare a sovrapposizione (o a ricoprimento)
° 10539a **lap**	repliure f de laminage	Überwalzungsfehler m	difetto m di piegatura
° 10540 **lap joint**	joint m à emboîtement	überlappter Stoss m	giunto m a sovrapposizione

English	French	German	Italian
° 10541 lap seam welding	soudure f continue à recouvrement	Überlapptnaht- schweissung f	saldatura f continua a sovrapposizione
° 10542 lap-weld, joint welding	soudure f par (ou à) recouvrement	Überlappungs- schweissung f	saldatura f a ricopri- mento (o a sovrapposi- zione)
° 10543 lap welded tube	tube m soudé par recouvrement	überlappt geschweisstes Rohr n	tubo m saldato ad unghia
lap welding, s. lap weld			
— 10544 lapis-lazuli	lapis-lazuli m	Lapislazuli m, Lasurstein m	lapislazzuli m
° 10544a lapping	rodage m	Läppen n	lappatura f
— 10545 larderellite	lardérellite f	Larderellit m	larderellite f
— 10546 large coal, lump-coal best coal, round coal	charbon m gros, charbon en roche	Stückkohle f, Grobkohle f	carbone m di grossa pezzatura
— 10547 large coke	coke m en morceaux	Grosskoks m	coke m grosso
° 10548 large cylinder for gas transport	réservoir m pour le transport de gaz	Speicherbehälter m zur Gasbeförderung	bombolone m per il trasporto di gas
° 10549 large heart trowel	truelle f à coeur	Herzblatt- polierschaufel f	cazzuola f a cuore
° 10550 large iron bars, blooms	gros fers m pl.	Grobeisen n	ferro m in grossi profili
large pieced coal, s. large coal			
° 10551 large water-capacity- -boiler	chaudière f à grand volume, chaudière f à gros éléments	Grosswasserraum- kessel m	caldaia f a grande corpo
— 10552 larnite	larnite f	Larnit m	larnite f
— 10553 larry	mortier m de ciment	Zementmörtel m	malta f di cemento
— 10554 larry	plate-forme f	Bühne f	piattaforma f
— 10555 larry	berline f	Wagen m	vagoncino m
— 10556 larsenite	larsénite f	Larsenit m	larsenite f
— 10557 lasher	barrage m	Stauung f	sbarramento m, diga f
— 10557a lashing	enlévement m de mi- nerai	Erzabfuhr f	rimozione f di minerale
° 10558 lashing wire	fil m de renforcement	Versteifungsdraht m	filo m di rinforzo
10559 last pass	cannelure f finisseuse	Endkaliber	canale m finitore

English	French	German	Italian
− 10560 **lasurite**	lazurite *f*	Lasurit *m*	lapislazzuli *m*
○ 10561 **latch**	verrou *m*	Klinke *f*	lucchetto *m*, chiavistello *m*
− 10562 **latch**	levé *m* de plan de mine	Markscheiden *n*	confini *m pl.*, linee *f pl.* di demarcazione
^ 10563 **latch jack, boot jack**	fourche *f* à barette (ou cliquet)	Löffelhaken *m*	pescatore *m* a forchetta con chiavistello *m* a molla
^ 10564 **latch-on centralizer**	centralisateur *m* de pression	Druckzentralisator *m*	centralizzatore *m* a cerniera
− 10565 **latching**	levé *m* de plan de mine	Markscheiden *n*, Grubenaufnahme *f*	confini *m pl.*, linee *f pl.* di demarcazione
○ 10566 **latent defect**	vice *m* interne	innerer Verderb *m*	vizio *m* interno
○ 10567 **latent heat**	chaleur *f* latente	gebundene (latente) Wärme *f*	calore *m* latente
^ 10568 **lateral**	dérivation *f* de conduite	Abzweigleitung *f*	derivazione *f* di condotta
− 10569 **lateral crater**	cratère *m* adventif	Adventivkrater *m*	cratere *m* laterale
○ 10570 **lateral flue, side flue**	carneau *m* de dérivation	Umgehungskanal *m*	canale *m* di derivazione
	lateral guide, *s. side guide*		
○ 10571 **lateral pressure**	pression *f* latérale	Seitendruck *m*	pressione *f* laterale
− 10572 **laterite**	latérite *f*	Laterit *m*	laterite *f*
− 10573 **lateritic**	latéritique	lateritisch	lateritico
− 10574 **laterization**	latéritisation *f*	Lateritbildung *f*	lateritizzazione *f*
○ 10575 **lath**	latte, palplanche	Latte *f*, Leiste *f*, Getriebepfahl *m*	listello *m*, stecca *f*, lamella *f*, tavolone *m*
○ 10576 **lathe jaw**	mâchoire *f* de tour	Drehbankbacke *f*	griffa *f* da tornio
○ 10577 **lathe tools**	outils *m pl.* de tour	Drehstähle *m pl.*	utensili *m pl.* da taglio
○ 10578 **lathe with leading screw**	tour *m* à commande par vis-mère	Leitspindeldrehbank *f*	tornio *m* parallelo per filettare
○ 10579 **lathe with variable speed**	tour *m* à vitesse variable	Drehbank *f* mit veränderbarer Drehzahl	tornio *m* a velocità variabile

	English	French	German	Italian
— 10580	latite	latite *f*	Latit *m*	Latite *f*
	latten-brass, *s. plate-brass*			
° 10581	lattice structure	structure *f* fenestrée (ou treillisée)	Gitterstruktur *f*	struttura *f* reticolare
° 10582	lattice unit	corps *m* élémentaire du réseau	Gittereinheit *f*	corpo *m* elementare del reticolo
— 10583	laubanite	laubanite *f*	Laubanit *m*	laubanite *f*
— 10584	laugenite	laugénite *f*	Laugenit *m*	laugenite *f*
— 10585	laumontite	laumonite *f*	Laumontit *m*	laumonite *f*, laumontite *f*
— 10586	launder	batée *f*, rigole *f* lavoir *m*	Waschtrog *m*, Rinne *f*	truogolo *m*, vaschetta *f*, canale *m*, lavatoio *m*
° 10587	launder	rigole de coulée	Giessrinne *f*	canale *m* di colata
— 10588	Laurentian epoch	Laurentien *m*	Laurentium *n*	Laurenziano *m*
— 10589	lava	lave *f*	Lava *f*	lava *f*
— 10590	lavenite	lavénite *f*	Lavenit *m*	Lavenite *f*
— 10591	lawrencite	lawrencite *f*	Lawrencit *m*	lawrencite *f*
— 10592	lawsonite	lawsonite *f*	Lawsonit *m*	lawsonite *f*
^ 10593	to lay down (the drill pipes)	démonter (les tiges)	(Bohrstangen) demontieren	smontare (le aste)
—10594	layer, stratum. bed	couche *f*, strate *f*, lit *m*	Schicht *f*, Lager *f*, Bank *f*	strato *m*, banco *m*, falda *f*
° 10594a	layer lattice	réseau *m* à couches	Schichtgitter *n*	reticolo *m* a strati
° 10595	layer of metal, metal bath	couche *f* de métal, bain *m* de métal	Metallschicht *f*, Metallbad *n*	strato *m* di metallo, bagno *m* di metallo
° 10596	layer of oxide	couche *f* d'oxyde	Oxydschicht *f*	strato *m* d'ossido
° 10597	layer of rust	couche *f* de rouille	Rostschicht *f*	strato *m* di ruggine
° 10598	layer of slag	couche *f* de scorie	Schlackenschicht *f*	strato *m* di scorie
° 10599	laying-in of cores	mise *f* en place des noyaux	Einlegen *n* der Kerne	sistemazione *f* delle anime
° 10600	layout	plan *m* de montage	Montagezeichnung *f*	piano *m* di montaggio,
° 10600a	layout	comparaison *f* des dimensions	Vergleich *m* der Abmessungen	confronto *m* delle dimensioni
—10601	lazulite	lazulite *f*	Lazulit *m*, Blauspat	lazulite *f*

English	French	German	Italian
− 10602 **lazurite**	lazurite *f*	Lasurit *m*	lazurite *f*, lapislazzulite *m*
leaching, *s. lixiviation*			
leaching plant, *s. lixiviation plant*			
leaching vat, *s. lixiviation vat*			
° 10603 **to lead, to coat with lead**	plomber, plaquer de plomb	verbleien, ausbleien	impiombare, placcare con piombo
° 10604 **lead**	plomb *m*	Blei *n*	piombo *m*
° 10605 **lead acetate**	acétate *m* de plomb	Bleiacetat *n*	acetato *m* di piombo
° 10606 **lead alloy**	alliage *m* (à base) de plomb	Bleilegierung *f*	lega *f* (a base) di piombo
° 10607 **lead basin**	capsule *f* en plomb	Bleischale *f*	capsula *f* o bacinella *f* di piombo
° 10608 **lead bath quench**	trempe *f* au plomb	Bleibadhärten *n*	tempra *f* in bagno di piombo, tempera *f* al piombo
° 10609 **lead bottle**	flacon *m* en plomb	Bleiflasche *f*	fiala *f* di piombo
° 10610 **lead bronze, leaded bronze**	bronze *m* au plomb	Bleibronze *f*	bronzo *m* al piombo, metallo *m* rosa
° 10611 **lead-cased, lead-covered**	plombé, plaqué (ou chemisé) de plomb	verbleit	impiombato, placcato (o incamiciato)
lead covered sheet-iron, *s. tern plate*			
lead dish, *s. lead basin*			
° 10612 **lead furniture**	lingots *m pl.* de plomb	Bleistege *m pl.*	lingotti *m pl.* in materiale
^ 10613 **lead(ed) gazoline**	essence *f* éthylée	Bleibenzin *n*	benzina *f* etilata
− 10614 **lead glance, galena, galenit**	galène *f*, mine *f* de vernis	Bleiglanz *m*, Galenit *m*, Bleischuss *m*	galena *f*, piombo *m* solforato
° 10615 **lead harden**	tremper dans un bain de plomb	in Blei *n* anlassen	temprare in un bagno di piombo
lead marcasite, *s. blende*			
− 10616 **lead matte**	matte *f* de plomb, matte plombeuse	Bleistein *m*	matta *f* di piombo

		English	French	German	Italian
o	10617	lead metal	plomb métal *m*	metallisches Blei *n*	piombo *m* metallico
		lead mine, *s. graphite*			
^	10618	lead naphthenate	naphténate *m* de plomb	Bleinaphthenat *n*	naftenato *m* di piombo
—	10619	lead monoxide	litharge *f*	Bleioxyd *n* Bleiglätte *f*	litárgirio *m*
—	10620	lead oleate	oléate *m* de plomb	Bleioleat *n*	oleato *m* di piombo
o	10620a	lead patenting	trempe *f* au plomb	Patentierung *f*	tempra *f* al piombo
o	10621	lead pipe	tuyau *m* en plomb	Bleiröhre *f*	tubo *m* di piombo
o	10622	lead-refining furnace	fourneau *m* d'affinage à plomb	Raffinierofen *m* für Blei	forno *m* d'affinamento per piombo
—	10623	lead spar	anglésite *f*	Anglesit *m*	anglesite *f*
—	10624	lead sulphide	galène *f*	Galenit *m*	galenite *f*
o	10625	lead tempering bath	four *m* à plomb	Bleiofen *m*	bagno *m* di piombo
		lead-vice, *s. hinge vice*			
		lead vitriol, *s. lead spar*			
o	10626	lead wire	fil *m* de plomb	Bleidraht *m*	filo *m* di piombo
—	10627	leader	veinule *f*, veine *f* secondaire	Erzader *f*	vena *f* secondaria
^	10628	leader	conducteur *m*, tube-guide	Leiter *m*, Leitrohr *n*	conduttore *m*, tubo *m*
o	10628a	leader	laminoir *m* polisseur	Polierwalzwerk *n*	laminatoio *m* spianatore
		leaderstone, *s. gauge*			
—	10629	leadhillite	leadhillite *f*	Leadhillit *m*	leadhillite *f*
o	10630	leading	plombage *m*	Verbleiung *f*	piombatura
—	10631	leading	veine *f*, veinule *f*	Ader *f*	vena *f*
o	10632	leading out wire	fil *m* de départ, départ	Ausführungsdraht *m*	filo *m* partente, partenza *f*
		leaf, *s. folia*			
o	10633	leaf of spring, spring leaf or plate	lame *f* de ressort	Federblatt *n*	foglia *f* di molla a balestra
o	10634	leaf spring	ressort-lame *m*	Blattfeder *f*	molla *f* a balestra

English	French	German	Italian
° 10635 to leak, to run out	se vider	auslaufen	vuotarsi
leak, *s. escape*			
° 10636 leaker	caffut *m*	Ausschussstück *n*	fusione scartata alla prova a pressione
° 10637 leaking	non-étanchéité *f*	Undichtheit *f*	permeabilità *f*, fuga *f*
° 10638 leaking of the tuyere	fuite *f* de la tuyère	Lecken *n* der Form	fuga *f* della tubiera
— 10639 lean clay, sandy clay	argile *f* maigre	magerer Ton *m*	argilla *f* magra
— 10640 lean coal, dry coal, blind coal, hard coal	charbon *m* maigre, houille *f* maigre	magere Kohle *f*, Magerkohle *f*, Sandkohle *f*	carbone *m* magro
— 10641 lean coke	coke *m* maigre	Magerkoks *m*	coke *m* magro
^ 10642 lean gas	gaz *m* pauvre	Armgas *n*	gas *m* povero
lean lime, *s. hydraulic lime*			
lean material, *s. lean clay*			
— 10643 lean ore	minerai *m* pauvre	armes Erz *n*	minerale *m* povero
— 10644 lean sand	sable *m* maigre	magerer Sand *m*	terra *f* magra, sabbia *f* magra
— 10645 leap	dislocation *f*	Dislokation *f*	dislocazione *f*
— 10646 leap	filon *m* pauvre	arme Ader *f*	filone *m* di scarso valore
^ 10647 lease tank	réservoirs *m pl.* de production	Feldtanks *m pl.*	serbatoi *m pl.* di produzione
° 10648 leather bellows	soufflet *m* en cuir	lederner Spitzbalg *m*	soffietto *m* di cuoio
° 10649 leather charcoal, leather coal	charbon *m* de cuir	Lederkohle *f*	carbone *m* di cuoio
° 10650 leather cup	cuir *m* embouti	Lederstulp *m*	bordo *m* di cuoio
° 10651 leather fillet	congé *m* de cuir	Lederhohlkehle *f*	raccordo *m* di cuoio
° 10652 leather hollow	congé *m* en cuir	Lederhohlkehle *f*	raccordo *m* in cuoio
° 10653 leather packing	garniture *f* de piston en bagues de cuir	Lederringdichtung *f*	guarnizione *f* di anelli di cuoio

English	French	German	Italian
° 10654 **leather ring**	bague *f* en cuir	Lederring *m*	anello *m* di cuoio
leave, *s. draft or taper*			
— 10655 **lechatelierite**	lechateliérite *f*	Lechatelierit *m*	lechatelierite *f*
— 10656 **lecontite**	lecontite *f*	Lecontit *m*	lecontite *f*
— 10657 **lectotype**	lectotype	Lectotypus *m*	lectotipo *m*
— 10658 **ledeburite**	ledeburite *f*	Ledeburit *m*	ledeburite *f*
— 10659 **ledge**	filon *m* métallifère	Erzgang *m*	filone *m* metallifero
— 10660 **ledmorite**	ledmorite *f*	Ledmorit *n*	ledmorite *f*
— 10661 **leeuwfonteinite**	leeuwfonteinite *f*	Leeuwfonteinit *m*	leeuwfonteinite *f*
° 10662 **left-hand heavy duty turning tool**	outil *m* à gauche pour coupes profondes	schwerer Abdrehstahl *m*	utensile *m* sinistro per tornitura pesante
° 10663 **left-hand light turning and facing tool**	outil *m* à gauche à dresser et à passes droites fines	leichter Abdrehstahl *m*	utensile *m* sinistro leggero per tornitura e piallatura
° 10664 **left-hand (side) tool, knife tool**	couteau coupe--gauche, outil à gauche	linker Messerstahl *m*, Linksmesser *n*	coltello *m* a sinistra, utensile da tagliare a sinistra
° 10665 **leftward welding**	soudure à gaz à gauche	Linksautogen-schweissung *f*	saldatura a gas in avanti
° 10666 **leg**	aile *f* (de cornière)	Schenkel *m* (des Winkeleisens)	lato *m* (di un ferro ad angolo)
° 10667 **leg (of a cupola)**	jambe *f* du cubilot	Kupolofenbein *n*	colonnina *f*
° 10668 **leg piece**	jambe, montant *m*	Stempel, Bein *n*	gamba *f*, montante *m*
leg pipe, *s. pen stock*			
— 10669 **lehiite**	lehiite *f*	Lehiit *m*	lehiite *f*
— 10670 **lehnerite**	lehnerite *f*	Lehnerit *m*	lehnerite *f*
— 10671 **leidleite**	leidléite *f*	Leidleit *m*	leidleite *f*
— 10672 **leifite**	leifite *f*	Leifit *m*	leifite *f*
— 10673 **lenades**	feldspatoides *m pl.*	Feldspatvertreter *m*	feldspatoidi *m pl.*
— 10674 **lengenbachite**	lengenbachite *f*	Lengenbachit *m*	legenbachite *f*
° 10675 **length in lateral direction**	extension *f* horizontale, longueur *f* en direction	streichende Erstreckung *f*	estensione *f* orizzontale

English	French	German	Italian
° 10676 **length of stroke**	hauteur f ou délimitation f de la levée	Hubbegrenzung f	limite m d'alzata
° 10677 **lengthwise rolling**	laminage m dans le sens de la longueur	Längswalzen n	laminazione f nel senso della lunghezza
— 10678 **lennilite**	lennilite f	Lennilith m	lennilite f
— 10679 **lensing**	stratification f lenticulaire	linsenförmige Lagerung f	stratificazione f lenticolare
— 10680 **lenticular vein**	filon lenticulaire	Linsengang m	filone-strato m
— 10681 **leonhardite**	leonhardite f	Leonhardit m	leonardite f, laumontite f
— 10682 **leonite**	léonite f	Leonit m	leonite f
— 10683 **leopardite**	léopardite f	Leopardit m	leopardite f
— 10684 **lepidoblastic texture**	texture f lépidoblastique	lepidoblastische Struktur f	struttura f lepidoblastica
— 10685 **lepidocrocite**	lépidocrocite f	Lepidokrokit m	lepidocrocite f
— 10686 **lepidolite**	lépidolite f	Lepidolith m	lepidolite f
— 10687 **lepidomelane**	lépidomélane m	Lepidomelan m	lepidomelano m
— 10688 **leppey**	travail m facile	leichte Arbeit f	lavoro m facile
— 10689 **leptite**	leptite f	Leptit m	leptite f
— 10690 **leptochlorite**	leptochlorite f	Leptochlorit m	leptoclorite f
— 10691 **leptoclase**	leptoclase f	Leptoklase f	leptoclasi f
— 10692 **leptynite**	leptynite f	Leptynit m	leptynite f
— 10693 **lessingite**	lessingite f	Lessingit m	lessingite f
— 10694 **lestiwarite**	lestiwarite f	Lestiwarit m	lestiwarite f
— 10695 **to let the hammer rebound**	laisser rebondir le mouton	den Hammer m prellen	ammortizzare il colpo della mazza
— 10696 **lettsomite**	lettsomite f	Lettsomit m	lettsomite f
— 10697 **leucaugite**	leucaugite f	Leukaugit m	leucaugite f
— 10698 **leucite**	leucite m	Leucit m	leucite f

	English	French	German	Italian
— 10699	leucitite	leucitite f	Leuzitit m	leucitite f
— 10700	leucitophyre	leucitophyre m	Leuzitporphyr m	leucitofiro m
— 10701	leucochalcite	leucochalcite f	Leukokalzit m	leucocalcite f
— 10702	leucocratic	leucocrate	leukokrat	leucocratico m
— 10703	leucophoenicite	leucophoenicite f	Leukophönicit m	leucofonicite
— 10704	leucopyrite	leucopyrite f	Leukopyrit m	leucopirite
— 10705	leucosphenite	leucosphénite f	Leukosphenit m	leucosfenite
— 10706	leucoxene	leucoxène m	Leukoxen m	leucoxeno m
— 10707	levee	remblai m	Damm m	argine m
	level with the ground, $s.$ *even with the ground*			
— 10708	level course	ouvrage m en direction	streichender Grubenbau m	opera f in direzione
— 10709	level line	ligne horizontale	Horizontallinie f	linea f orizzontale
— 10710	level of ground water	niveau m de la nappe souterraine	Grundwasserspiegel m	livello m idrostatico, livello m della falda sotterranea
— 10711	level of the water-table	niveau hydrostatique	hydrostatischer Spiegel m	livello m idrostatico
— 10712	level pillar	pilier m du puits	Schachtpfeiler m	pilastro m del pozzo
○ 10713	level plate	voûte f plate	scheitrechter Boden	volta f piatta
— 10714	level seam	couche f plate	horizontale Schicht f	filone m (o strato m) orizzontale (o piano)
	level workings, $s.$ *deep mine workings*			
○ 10715	levelling bottle	flacon m de niveau	Niveauflasche f	bottiglia f di livello
10716	livelling rule	règle f à dresser (en métal)	Richtschiene f	regolo m di metallo per livellare
○ 10717	lever	levier m	Hebel m	leva f
	lever gun welding head, $s.$ *lever gun*			
○ 10718	leverage	disposition f des leviers	Hebelwerk n	sistema m di leve

	English	French	German	Italian
−	10719 **leverrierite**	leverri érite *f*	Leverrierit *m*	leverrierite *f*
−	10720 **lewisite**	lewisite *f*	Lewisit *m*	lewisite *f*
−	10721 **lewistonite**	lewistonite *f*	Lewistonit *m*	lewistonite *f*
−	10722 **lherzite**	lherzite *f*	Lherzit *m*	lherzite *f*
−	10723 **lherzolite**	lherzolite *f*	Lherzolith *m*	lherzolite *f*
−	10724 **liassic**	liasique	liasisch	liassico
−	10725 **libethenite**	libeth énite *f*	Libethenit *m*	libethenite *f*
−	10726 **license**	concession *f*	Konzession *f*	concessione *f*
°	10727 **lid**	clapet *m*, couvercle	Deckel *m*, Kappe *f*	cappello *m*, coperchio
−	10728 **lid**	cale *f* de bois	Holzkeil *m*	cuneo *m* di legno, zeppa *f*, puntello *m*
°	10729 **lid of blast box**	plaque *f* de fond de la boîte à vent	Windkastendeckel *m*	placca *f* di fondo della cassa del vento
^	10730 **lie key**	clef *f* de retenue	Abfanggabel *f*	piede *m* di bue, elevatore *m* per aste
−	10731 **liebenerite**	liebenérite *f*	Liebenerit *m*	liebenerite *f*
−	10732 **liebigite**	liebigite *f*	Liebigit *m*	liebigite *f*
−	10733 **lievrite**	liévrite *f*	Lievrit *m*	lievrite *f*, ilvaite *f*
°	10734 **life of furnace**	campagne *f* d'un four	Ofenreise *f*	durata *f* (o campagna) d'un forno
−	10735 **lifeline**	câble *m* de sûreté	Sicherheitskabel *n*	fune *f* di sicurezza
	to lift, *s. to take out*			
°	10736 **to lift off (before casting)**	démotter	den Formrahmen *m* abnehmen	smottare
	to lift the casting, *s. to open the casting*			
−	10737 **to lift the floor**	couper le mur	Sohle *f* nachreissen	tagliare il muro
°	10738 **to lift the piece (to be rolled)**	soulever la barre (à laminer)	das Walzstück *n* anheben	alzare la barra (da laminare)
−	10739 **lift**	monte-charge *m*, ascenseur *m*	Aufzug *m*	montacarichi *m*, ascensore *m*

	English	French	German	Italian
—	10740 lift	hauteur *f* d'éléva-tion, (ou d'extraction)	Förderhöhe *f*	altezza *f* d'elevazione, altezza *f* d'estrazione
—	10741 lift	hauteur de l'étage	Bauhöhe *f*	altezza *f* del livello (d'estrazione)
—	10742 lift	jeu des pompes étagées	Pumpensatz *m*	serie *f* di pompe
—	10743 lift	cordée	Treiben *n*	avanzamento *m*
°	10744 lift, draw	démoulage *m*	Herausnehmen *n* des Modells	sformatura *f*
°	10745 lift, cope	partie *f* de dessus	Formoberteil *n*	mezzaforma *f* superiore
°	10746 lift	formation *f* de dôme	Bogenbildung *f*	incupolamento *m*
°	10747 lift frame, elevator frame	charpente *f* du monte-charge	Fördergerüst *n*	armatura *f* del monta-carichi
°	10748 lift hammer, helver, helve hammer	marteau *m* à soulè-vement	Aufwerfhammer *m*	martello *m* frontale
°	10749 lift-out furnace	four *m* à creuser extractible	Auszugtiegelofen *m*	forno *m* a crogiolo estraibile
°	10750 lift shafts	cage *f* d'ascenseur	Aufzugschacht *m*	gabbia *f* di ascensore
°	10751 lift truck	chariot *m* élévateur	Hubkarren *m*	carrello *m* elevatore
°	10752 lift with rope drive	monte-charge *m* à câble	Seilaufzug *m*	montacarichi *m* a cavo
—	10753 lifted side	lèvre *f* soulevée	gehobener Flügel *m*	lembo *m* sollevato (di una faglia)
°	10754 lifter	dispositif *m* de levage	Aufzugvorrichtung *f*	dispositivo *m* di sollevamento
—	10755 lifter	mine *f* de relevage	Sohlen-schussbohrloch *n*	mina *f* di rilevaggio
—	10756 lifter	bocard *m* pilon *m*	Pochstempel *m*, Stempel *m*	mulino *m*, pestello *m*
°	10756a lifter, gagger	crochet *m*	Sandhaken *m*	gancio *m*
°	10757 lifter	happe *f*	Tiegelzange *f*	tenaglione *m*
—	10758 lifter	tirant *m* d'extraction	Aushebeband *n*	tirante *m* d'estrazione
—	10759 lifting	élévation *f*, remonte *f*	Ausfahrt *f*	sollevamento *m*, ri-monta *f*

English	French	German	Italian
10760 **lifting**	soulèvement *m* de moule	Heben *n* der Form	sollevamento del coperchio
10761 **lifting apparatus for the cover**	dispositif *m* pour enlever le couvercle	Deckelabhebevor- richtung *f*	macchina *f* per alzare il coperchio
10762 **lifting ball**	étrier *m* d'élévation	Stangenbügel *m*	staffa *f* di sollevamento
10763 **lifting beam**	palonnier *m*	nicht verstellbares Tragbalken *m*	bilancino *m*, traversa *f* (non regolabile)
10764 **lifting beam, adjusting lifting beam**	balancier *m*	Tragbalken *m* Schwengel *m*	bilancino *m*, traversa *f* regolabile
10765 **lifting blocks**	installation *f* de crochetage	Überhebvorrichtung *f*, Überhebevorricht- ung *f*	supporto *m* del rampino
10766 **lifting device**	démouleuse *f*	Abhebevorrichtung *f*	dispositivo *m* per estrarre la mezza staffa
10767 **lifting device**	appareil *m* d'élévation	Hebevorrichtung *f*	apparecchio (o dispo- sitivo) di sollevamento
10768 **lifting handle**	poignée *f* pour enlever le modèle	Modellheber *m*	maniglia *f* a vite per estrarre il modello
10769 **lifting iron (for patterns)**	petite tige *f* à enlever les modèles	Modellhebestift *m*	asticella *f* di estra- zione
10770 **lifting jack**	vérin *m*, cric *m*	Winde *f*	martinetto *m*
10771 **lifting of ingots**	démoulage *m*, enlè- vement *m* des lingots	Heben *n* der Blöcke	sollevamento *m* dei lingotti
lifting of patterns, s. *drawing of patterns*			
10772 **lifting pin**	chandelle *f* à enlever les modèles	Abhebestift *m*	candela *f* (di sforma- tura) dei modelli
10773 **lifting plate**	plaque *f* de levage, plaque à enlever les modèles	Aushebeplatte *f*	piastra *f* di estrazione, tappo *m* d'estrazione
10774 **lifting plung**	bouchon *m* de levage	Hebestück *m*	tappo *m* d'estrazione
10774a **lifting rod**	noyau *m* mobile	Vorheber *m*	costa *f* mobile
10775 **lifting table**	tablier *m* à rouleaux	Hebetisch *m*	tavola *f* a rulli
10776 **lifting type machine for flat castings**	machine *f* à démou- ler pour pièces plates	Abhebemaschine *f* für flache Gegen- stände	sformatrice *f* per pez- zi piatti

	English	French	German	Italian
° 10777	to light the fire	allumer le feu	das Feuer anzünden, anfeuern	accendere il fuoco
° 10778	light alloy	alliage *m* léger	Aluminiumlegierung *f*, Leichtlegierung *f*	lega *f* leggera, lega *f* d'alluminio
10779	light bundle	faisceau *m* lumineux	Lichtbündel *n*	fascio *m* luminoso
° 10780	light duty	pour service leger	Leichtdienst- *m*	sottoposto a solle-citazioni non eccessi-ve
ˆ 10781	light ends	fractions *f pl.* légères	leichte Fraktionen *f pl.*	frazioni *f pl.* finali leggere
° 10782	light filter	filtre *m* à lumière	Lichtfilter *m*	filtro *m* luminoso
° 10783	light grey pig iron	fonte *f* grise claire	hellgraues Gusseisen *n*	ghisa *f* grigio-chiara
° 10784	light metal	métal *m* léger	Leichtmetall *n*	metallo *m* leggero
° 10784a	light plate	tôle *f* moyenne	Mittelblech *n*	lamiera *f* media
° 10785	light sections	profils *m pl.* légers	Leichtprofile *n pl.*	profilati *m pl.* leggeri
— 10786	light shaft	puits *m* au jour, prise *f* de lumière	Lichtschacht *m*	pozzo *m*, cavedio *m* di luce
° 10787	light standard rail	petit rail *m*	kleine Schiene *f*	rotaietta *f*
ˆ 10788	light-string	équipement *m* électrique dans la tour	elektrische Anlage *f* (im Turm)	impianto *m* elettrico in torre
ˆ 10789	light thermal by-pass naphta	naphte *m* léger	Leichtnaphtha *n*	nafta *f* leggera
° 10790	light tubular torch	torche *f* tubulaire légère	leichte Rohrfackel *f*	torcia *f* tubolare leggera
° 10791	light turning and facing tool	outil *m* à dresser et à passes droites fines	leichter Abdreh- und Anflachstahl *m*	utensile leggero per tornitura e spiana-tura

light well, *s. light shaft*

— 10792	lighter	allège *f*	Leichter *m*	alleggio *m*, barcone *m*, piatta *f*
10793	lighting and power station	installation *f* d'éclairage et de distribution d'éner-gie	Beleuchtungs- und Kraftübertragungs-werk *n*	stazione *f* per l'ero-gazione e la distri-buzione dell'energia

	English	French	German	Italian
− 10794	lighting carbon	charbon *m* à lumière	Beleuchtungskohle *f*	carbone *m* per illuminazione
° 10795	lighting hole	porte *f* (ou orifice *m*) d'allumage	Anzündöffnung *f*	porta *f* d'ascensione, portello *m* d'ascensione
10796	lighting installation	installation *f* d'éclairage	Beleuchtungsanlage *f*	impianto *m* d'illuminazione
° 10797	lightning rods in step tapered sections	tiges *f pl.* à paratonnerre à troncs rétrécis	abgesetzte Blitzableiterstangen *f pl.*	aste *f pl.* per parafulmini a tronchi rastremati
10798	lighting station	centrale *f* d'éclairage	Beleuchtungswerk *n*, Beleuchtungszentrale *f*	centrale *f* per illuminazione elettrica
° 10799	lighting up	allumage *m*	Anzünden *n*	accensione *f*, messa *f* in marcia, avviare (un forno)
° 10800	lightly mottled pig iron	fonte *f* demi-truitée	schwach halbiertes Roheisen *n*	ghisa *f* semitrotata
° 10801	lightweight section	profilé *m* leger	Formstahl *m*, Feinstahl *m*	profilato *m* leggero, sagomato *m* leggero
− 10802	lignite	lignite *m*	Lignit *m*	lignite *f*
° 10803	lignite fired furnace	foyer *m* à lignite	Braunkohlenfeuerung *f*	focolare a lignite
− 10804	lignitiferous	lignitifère	lignitisch	lignitifero
− 10805	ligroin	ligroïne *f*	Ligroin *n*	ligroina *f*
− 10806	lillianite	lillianite *f*	Lillianit *m*	lillianite *f*
− 10807	limb	lèvre *f* (d'une faille), flanc *m* (d'un anticlinal)	Verwerfungsflügel *m*, Antiklinalschenkel *m*	lembo *m*, fianco *m*, ala *f*, gamba *f* (di faglia)
− 10808	limber assembly	ensemble souple	flexibler Bohrstrang *m*	serie di funi flessibili per perforazione
− 10809	limburgite	limburgite *f*	Limburgit *m*	limburgite *f*
− 10810	lime, oxide of calcium	chaux *f*, oxyde *m* de calcium	Kalk *m*, Kalziumoxyd *m*	calce *f*, ossido *m* di calcio
° 10811	lime bin	rigole *f* à chaux	Lutte *f*	canale *f* per calce

lime brick, *s. clay brick*

	English	French	German	Italian
— 10813	lime feldspar	feldspath *m* calcaire	Kalkfeldspat *m*	feldspato *m* calcare, anortite *f*
	lime ferritic electrode, *s. basic electrode*			
— 10814	lime flux	castine *f*	Kalkzuschlag *m*	castina *f*
° 10815	lime light	lumière *f* de Drummond	Kalklicht *n*	luce *f* di Drummond
° 10816	lime kiln, lime-pit	four *m* à chaux	Kalkofen *m*	forno *m* per calce
— 10817	lime uranite	autunite *f*	Kalkuranglimmer,	autunite *f*
° 10817a	lime washing	bain *m* au lait de chaux	Weisseln *n*	imbiancatura *f*
— 10818	lime water	lait *m* de chaux	Kalkmilch *f*, Kalkwasser *n*	latte *m* di calce, acqua *f* di calce
	limesoda feldspar, *s. gabbro*			
° 10819	limestone flux	castine *f*, calcaire *m*, fondant *m*	Kalkstein *m*	calcare *m*, fondente *m*, castina *f*
— 10820	limestone-rock	roche *f* calcaire	Kalkstein *m*, Kalkfelsen *m*	roccia *f* calcarea
° 10821	limit of elasticity	limite *f* élastique vraie, limite *f* d'élasticité	Elastizitätsgrenze *f*	limite d'elasticità
° 10822	limit of error of analysis	limite *f* d'erreurs d'analyse	Analysen--Fehlergrenze *f*	limite *m* d'errore dell'analisi
° 10823	limit of proportionality	limite *f* de proportionnalité	Proportionalitätsgrenze *f*	limite *m* di proporzionalità
° 10824	limit value	valeur *f* limite	Grenzwert *m*	valore *m* limite
° 10825	limited solubility	solubilité *f* limitée	beschränkte Löslichkeit *f*	solubilità *f* limitata
° 10826	limiting conductivity of the electrolyte	conductance *f* limite de l'électrolyte	Endleitfähigkeit *f* des Elektrolyten	conduttanza-limite *f* d'elettrolito
— 10827	limnic	limnique	limnisch	limnico
— 10828	limonite, brown iron ore	oxyde *m* de fer hydraté, limonite *f*	Brauneisenstein *m*, Limonit *m*	sesquiossido *m* di ferro idrato, limonite *f*
	lindblad, *s. electric hearth furnace Groenwall*			
— 10829	lindoite	lindöite *f*	Lindöit *m*	lindoite *f*

English	French	German	Italian
− 10830 **lindstromite**	lindströmite *f*	Lindströmit *m*	lindstromite *f*
° 10831 **to line the furnace with fire bricks**	revêtir la boîte à feu de briques réfractaires	den Feuerraum mit feuerfesten Steinen auskleiden	rivestire il focolare con mattoni refrattari
− 10832 **line bumper**	amortisseur *m* du câble	Kabeldämpfer *m*	ammortizzatore *m* (o paracolpi *m*) del cavo
− 10833 **line of dip**	ligne *f* de plongement	Einfallslinie *f*	linea *f* d'inclinazione
° 10834 **line of force**	ligne *f* de force	Kraftlinie *f*	linea *f* di forza
− 10835 **line of fracture**	ligne *f* de fracture	Bruchlinie *f*	linea *f* di frattura
line of fusion, *s. melt run*			
− 10836 **line of lode**	direction *f* du filon	Gangrichtung *f*	direzione *f* del filone
− 10837 **line of outcrop course of outcrop**	ligne *f* d'affleurement	Ausgehende *n*, Ausstrich *m*,	linea *f* d'affioramento
° 10837a **line of segregation**	limite *f* de ségrégation	Seigerungsgrenze *f*	limite *m* di segregazione
− 10838 **line of strike**	direction *f* de stratification	Streichlinie *f*	direzione *f* (o linea *f*) di stratificazione
° 10839 **line pipe**	tuyau *m* pour conduite	Leitungsrohr *n*	tubo *m* per condotte
° 10840 **line shaft**	arbre *m* de renvoi	Vorgelegewelle *f*	albero *m* di rinvio
line welding, *s. seam welding*			
− 10841 **linear foliation, fibrous structure**	texture *f* fibreuse	gestreckte Struktur *f*, faseriges Gefüge *n*	struttura *f* a fibre
° 10841a **liner**	bande *f* de garnissage	Einlegestreifen *m*	striscia *f* di riempimento
^ 10842 **liner**	tubage *m* perdu, tube *m* perdu	verlorene Verrohrung *f*	colonna *f* perduta, colonna *f* fenestrata
° 10843 **liner, shim**	séparateur *m*, chemise *f*	Blecheinlage *f*	spessore *m*
^ 10844 **liner cleaner**	laveur *m* du tube perdu	Filterrohrwascher *m*	lavatore *m* della colonna perduta
^ 10845 **liner hanger**	support *m* du tube perdu	Filterrohrhänger *m*	supporto *m* della colonna perduta
^ 10846 **liner hanger packer and setting tool**	packer *m* du support de la colonne perdue avec dispositif de fixage	Filterrohrhänger-packer mit Spanneinrichtung *f*	packer *m* per colonna perduta con dispositivo di fissaggio

English	French	German	Italian
^ 10847 **liner hanger packer with setting and resetting tool**	packer *m* du support de la colonne perdue avec dispositif d'extraction	Filterrohrgreifer mit Fass–und Nachfassvorrichtung	packer *m* con relativo dispositivo di manovra
^ 10848 **liner setter**	joint *m* du packer	Filterrohrabsetzverbindung *f*	giunto *m* del packer
° 10849 **lining**	garnissage *m*	feuerfeste Auskleidung *f*, Futter *n*	rivestimento *m* refrattario, guarnizione *f*
° 10850 **lining**	brasque *f*	Tiegelglasur *f*	materiale *m* di rivestimento (per crogiuoli)
— 10851 **lining**	damage *m*	Ausstampfen *n*	pigiatura *f*, costipamento *m*
° 10852 **lining a bearing**	régulage *m*	Lagerausguss *m*	rivestimento *m* con metallo antifrizione
° 10853 **lining for bearings**	fourrure *f* d'un palier, revêtement d'antifriction	Lagerfutter *n*. Lagerschalenausguss *m*	rivestimento *m* del cuscinetto, guarnizione *f* del cuscinetto
° 10854 **lining material for repairs**	masse *f* servant à réparer le garnissage	Ausbesserungsmasse *f*	materiale *m* per arricchire il rivestimento
° 10855 **lining of shaft**	chemise *f* réfractaire	Kernschacht *m*	camicia *f* refrattaria, rivestimento *m* refrattario
lining plate, *s. stiffener*			
° 10856 **lining the converter**	garnissage *m* en briques du convertisseur	Ausmauern *n* der Birne	rivestimento *m* di mattoni del convertore
linisher *s. finisher*			
° 10857 **linkage**	tringlerie *f*	Gelenkverbindung *f*	biellismo *m*
^ 10858 **links**	coulisses *f pl.*	Gelenke *n pl.*	articolazioni *m pl.*
° 10859 **linseed oil varnish**	vernis *m* à l'huile de lin	Leinölfirnis *m*	vernice *f* all'olio di lino
° 10859a **lintel girder**	marâtre *m*	Tragkranz *m*	anello *m* dell'involucro
° 10860 **lip**	bec *m*, évasement *m*	Schnauze *f*, Auskragung *f*	becco *m*, dilatamento *m*
° 10861 **lip-pour ladle**	poche *f* de coulée à bec	Giesspfanne *f* mit Ausgussschnauze	siviera *f* (o canale) di colata a becco

	English	French	German	Italian
10862	lip of drill	taillant *m* de fleuret	Bohrschneide *f*	tagliante *m* di fioretto
10863	lip ring	garniture *f* à bec	Lippenpackung *f*	guarnizione *f* a labbro (o a becco)
10864	liparite	liparite	Liparit *m*	liparite *f*
10865	lipopalingenesis	lipopalingénèse *f*	Lipopalingenese *f*	lipopalingenesi *f*
	liquated portion, *s. segregated portion*			
10866	liquation	liquation *f*, ressuage *m*	Seigerung *f*	liquazione *f*
10867	liquation-furnace, sweating-furnace, (e)liquation-hearth	four *m* de liquation, four *m* à ressuage	Seigerherd *m*, Treibofen *m*	forno *m* separatore
10868	liquation lead	plomb *m* de ressuage	Seigerblei *n*	piombo *m* di liquazione
10869	liquation pan	chaudière *f* de liquation	Seigerpfanne *f*	caldaia *f* di liquazione
10870	liquation slag	scorie *f* de ressuage	Seigerschlacke *f*	scoria *f* di segregazione (o di liquazione)
10871	liquid ammonia	eau *f* ammoniacale	Ammoniakwasser *n*	acqua *f* ammoniacale
10872	liquid cooled	refroidi par liquide	flüssig abgekühlt	raffreddato a liquido
10873	liquid end	devant d'une pompe	Pumpenvorderteil *n*	parte *f* anteriore di una pompa
10874	liquid explosive	explosif *m* liquide	flüssiger Sprengstoff *m*	esplosivo *m* liquido
10875	liquid fuel	combustible *m* liquide	flüssiger Brennstoff *m*	combustibile *m* liquido
10876	liquid fuel furnace	four *m* à combustible liquide	flüssiger Brennstoffofen *m*	focolare *m* a combustibile liquido
	liquid honing, *s. vapour blasting*			
10877	liquid iron	fer *m* liquide	flüssiges Eisen *n*	ferro *m* liquido
10878	liquid oxygen explosive	explosif *m* à l'oxygène liquide	Sauerstoffsprengmittel *n*	esplosivo *m* all'ossigeno liquido
10879	liquid petroleum gas, L.P.G.	gaz *m* liquide de pétrole	Flüssigpetroleumgas *n*	gas *m* liquefatto di petrolio, G.P.L.
10880	liquidus	liquidus *m*	Liquiduslinie *f*	liquido *m*

Emglish	French	German	Italian
— 10881 liroconite	liroconite *f*	Lirokonit *m*	liroconite *f*
— 10882 liskeardite	liskeardite *f*	Liskeardit *m*	liskeardite *f*
— 10883 litchfieldite	litchfieldite *f*	Litchfieldit *m*	litchfieldite *f*
— 10883a lithia mica	lépidolite *f*	Lepidolith *m*	lepidolite *f*
— 10884 lithification	pétrification *f*	Versteinerung *f*	pietrificazione *f*
— 10885 lithium	lithium *m*	Lithium *n*	litio *m*
— 10886 lithoclase	lithoclase *f*	Lithoklase *f*	litoclasi *f*
— 10887 lithogeneous	lithogène	lithogen	litogeno
— 10888 lithographic stone	pierre *f* lithographique	lithographischer Stein *m*	pietra *f* litografica
— 10889 lithology	lithologie *f*	Lithologie *f*	litologia *f*
— 10890 lithophysa	lithophyse *f*	Lithophysa *f*	litofisa *f*
— 10891 lithosphere	lithosphère *f*, croûte *f* terrestre	Lithosphäre *f*, Zone *f* des Katamorphismus	litosfera *f*
° 10892 litmus paper	papier *m* de tournesol	Lackmuspapier *n*	carta *f* di tornasole
° 10893 litmus solution	teinture *f* de tournesol	Lackmustinktur *f*	tintura *f* di tornasole

littoral area, *s. littoral zone*

— 10894 littoral deposits *pl.*	dépôts *m pl.* littoraux	Strandablagerungen *f pl.*	depositi *m pl.* litoranei
— 10895 littoral facies	faciès *m* littoral, faciès *m* de rivage	litorale Fazies *f*	facies *f* litorale
— 10896 littoral winds	puits *m* intérieur, bure *f*	Blindschacht *m*	pozzo *m* interno, pozzo *m* ausiliare
—10897 littoral zone, littoral area	région *f* littorale	Küstengebiet *n*	zona *f* litoranea
^ 10898 live oil	huile *f* riche	gasreiches Öl *n*	olio *m* ricco di gas
° 10898a live roller	rouleau *m* auto moteur	Elektrorolle *f*	rullo *m* automotore
° 10899 live rolling mill	plan *m* à rouleaux commandé	angetriebener Rollgang *m*	piano *m* a rulli comandato
—10900 livingstonite	livingstonite *f*	Livingstonit *m*	livingstonite *f*
—10901 lixiviation plant	installation *f* de lessivage	Laugeanlage *f*	impianto *m* di lisciviazione

	English	French	German	Italian
−	10902 lixiviation residue	résidu *m* de lessiva-ge	Laugerückstand *m*	residui *m pl.* di lavaggio
−	10903 lixiviation vat	cuve *f* à lessiver	Laugebottich *m*	tino *m* di lisciviazione
−	10904 lizard-stone	marbre *m* serpentin	Serpentinmarmor *m*	marmo *m* serpentino
^	10905 LNG	gaz naturel liquéfié	LNG (verflüssigte Erdgase)	gas *m* naturale liquido
o	10906 to load or to charge (a furnace)	charger, enfourner (les matériaux)	beschicken	caricare, infornare
	load, *s. seam*			
	load, *s. carriage capacity*			
o	10907 load at the 0,2% proof stress	charge *f* à la limite conventionnelle d'élasticité à 0,2%	Belastung *f* an der 0,2%-Grenze	carico *m* al limite convenzionale di elasticità 0,2%
o	10908 load at proportional limit	charge *f* à la limite des allongements proportionnels	Belastung *f* an der Proportionalitäts-grenze	carico *m* al limite di proporzionalità
−	10909 load binder	tendeur *m* à chaîne	Kette *f* mit Spannschloss	tenditore *m* a catena
o	10910 load capacity	capcité *f* de charge	Belastungsfähigkeit	capacità *f* di carico
−	10911 load-conveyor	chargeuse-convoyeur *f*	Selbstladetransport-band *n*	caricatrice *f* trasportatrice
−	10912 load metamorphism	métamorphisme *m* par pression	Belastungs-metamorphose *f*	metamorfismo *m* per pressione
^	10913 load oil	huile *f* d'amorçage	Anlassöl *n*	petrolio *m* d'adescamento
^	10914 load water	eau *f* d'amorçage	Anlasswasser *n*	acqua *f* di adescamento
−	10915 loader	drague *f* chargeuse	Kübelfüller *m*	draga *f* di caricamento
−	10916 loading, charging loading factor, *s. fill factor*	chargement *m*	Verladung *f*	caricamento *m*
o	10917 loading gauge	gabarit *m* de chargement	Ladeschablone *f*, Ladeprofil *n*	sagoma *f* di carico
−	10918 loading hopper	trémic *f* de chargement	Füllrumpf *m*, Schüttrumpf *m*	tramoggia *f* di caricamento

	English	French	German	Italian
°	10919 loading plant with rotary crane above	installation f de chargement à grue pivotante et roulante supérieure	Verladeanlage f mit obenlaufendem Drehkran	impianto m per trasbordo a gru girevole mobile
°	10920 loading plant and trasporting installations	installation f de chargement et de transport	Verlade- und Beförderungsvorrichtung	impianto m di caricamento e di trasporto
—	10921 loading ramp or wharf	rampe f de chargement	Verladerampe f	rampa f di caricamento
°	10921a loading range	limites f $pl.$ de charge	Belastungsgrenzen f $pl.$	limiti m $pl.$ di carico
	loading staiths, $s.$ *loading wharf*			
—	10922 loading wharf or staiths	quai m de chargement	Verladekai m	banchina f di caricamento
—	10923 loadstone	aimant m naturel	Magneteisenstein m	magnetite f
—	10924 loam	terre f glaise	Lehm m	terra f argillosa
—	10925 loam brick	brique f de terre glaise	Lehmstein m	mattone m crudo
°	10926 loam casting	moulage m en argile	Lehmguss m	getto m in forma di argilla
°	10927 loam core	noyau m en terre glaise	Lehmkern m	anima f di terra
°	10928 loam mould	moule m en terre glaise	Lehmform f	forma f in terra grassa
°	10929 loam moulding	moulage m en terre glaise	Lettenformen n	formatura f in terra grassa
—	10930 loam rock	marne f	Mergel m	marna f
°	10931 loamy addition	addition f de matière argileuse	lehmige Beimengung f	aggiunta f argillosa
°	10932 loamy paste	pâte f grasse collante	klebriger Brei m	pasta f grassa
—	10933 loamy sand	sable gras	fetter Formsand m, Masse f	sabbia f (o terra f) grassa
—	10934 lob	scheider, trier	scheiden	vagliare, crivellare
—	10935 lob	filon m à échelle	Leitergang m	filone m a gradini
—	10936 lobe	lobe m	Lobus m	lobo m
°	10936a local annealing	recuit m sélectif	selektives Frischglühen n	ricottura f selettiva
°	10937 local stress relieving	stabilisation f locale	Spannungsfreiglühen n	distensione f locale

English	French	German	Italian
° 10938 **local weldability**	soudabilité f locale	Lokalschweissbar-keit f	saldabilità f locale
° 10939 **localized oxidized pinholes**	piqûres f pl. hétérogènes oxydées	ungleichmässig verteilte oxydierte Poren f pl.	camolatura f eterogenea ossidata
° 10940 **localized reaction pinholes**	piqûres f pl. hétérogènes bleuâtres	ungleichmässig verteilte blau gefärbte Poren f pl.	camolatura f eterogenea azzurrognola
° 10941 **localized unoxidized pinholes**	piqûres f pl. hétérogènes brillantes (ou non oxydées)	ungleichmässig verteilte glänzenden Poren f pl.	camolatura f eterogenea lucida (o non ossidata)
° 10942 **locating cones** pl. **for mould assembly**	bicône m, repère m de remmoulage	Führungskegel m	riferimento m a doppio cono, (o di ramolaggio)
^ 10943 **location**	emplacement m	Ansatzpunkt m, Lokation f	postazione f
lock, s. *anti-chamber*			
° 10943a **lock**	irrégularité f	Unebenheit f	irregolarità f
° 10944 **lock die**	moule f avec talon de réaction	Unebenheit f	stampo m con tallone di reazione
° 10945 **lock plate**	(corps de) platine f	Schlossblech n	(corpo della) piastrina f
° 10946 **locking**	verrouillage m	Verriegelung f	bloccaggio m
° 10947 **locking plate**	clapet m de fermeture	Verschlussklappe f	piastra f di chiusura
° 10948 **locomotive boiler**	chaudière f de locomotive	Lokomotivkessel m	caldaia f di locomotiva
° 10949 **locomotive flue tube**	tube m à fumée pour locomotives	Lokomotivrauchrohr n	tubo m da fumo per locomotive
locomotive furnace, s. *furnace with internal horizontal grate*			
° 10950 **locomotive steam crane**	grue f roulante à vapeur	fahrbarer Dampfkran m	gru f mobile a vapore
° 10951 **locomotive steam crane for unloading ships**	grue f roulante à vapeur pour le déchargement des bateaux	(fahrbarer) Dampfkran m zum Löschen der Schiffsladung	gru f mobile a vapore per lo scarico di navi
° 10952 **locomotive steel**	acier m à locomotives	Lokomotivstahl m	acciaio m per locomotive

English	French	German	Italian
° 10953 **locomotive wheel set**	train *m* pour locomotives	Lokomotivradsatz *m*	asse *m* montato per locomotive
— 10954 **lode, seam**	filon *m*, veine *f*	Gang *m*, Erzgang *m*	filone *m*, vena *f*
— 10955 **lode-gold**	or *m* filonien	Ganggold *n*	oro *m* filoniano
— 10956 **lode-mining**	exploitation *f* filonienne, exploitation *f* des filons	Gangbergbau *m*	coltivazione *f* dei filoni
— 10957 **lode plot**	filon horizontal	flacher Gang *m*	filone *m* orizzontale
— 10958 **lode rock**	gangue *f*	Ganggestein *n*	ganga *f*
— 10959 **lodestone**	magnétite *f*	Magnetit *m*	magnetite *f*
— 10960 **lodestone**	minerai *m* de filon	Gangerz *n*	minerale *m* filoniano
— 10961 **lodgement**	albraque	Sumpfstrecke *f*	galleria *f* di scolo
— 10962 **loess-soil**	sol *m* loessien	Loessboden *m*	terreno *m* loessiano
— 10963 **lofting**	boisage *m* du toit	Zimmerung *f* der Firste	armamento *m* del tetto
— 10964 **log**	enregistrement *m*, diagramme *m*	Indikatordiagramm *n*	registrazione *f*, diagramma *m*
— 10965 **logging line**	câble *m* de carottage électrique	Elektrokernbohrungsseil *n*	cavo *m* per carotaggio elettrico
— 10966 **lollingite**	lollingite *f*	Löllingit *m*	lollingite *f*
— 10967 **Londinian stage**	étage *m* londinien	Londinian *n*	londiniano *m*
^ 10968 **long armed**	à fléau long	langarmig	a bracci lunghi
— 10969 **long borer**	barre *f* double	Abbohrer *m*	barra *f* doppia
° 10970 **long boss tool with interchangeable heads**	colonne *f*	Polierknopf *m*	lisciatoio *m* a tampone
— 10971 **long horn**	front *m* d'attaque à 30° avec les limets	Stossstellung *f* von 30° zur Schichtenrichtung	fronte *m* d'attacco a 30° rispetto al piano di stratificazione
— 10972 **long pillar work**	exploitation *f* par panneaux	Pfeilerbau *m* mit langen Pfeilern	coltivazione *f* a lunghi pilastri

		English	French	German	Italian
°	10973	long shaft pendulum tool	fouloir m de grand modèle	langer Spitzstampfer m	pestello m, pilletta f
°	10974	long slot burner	brûleur m à embouchure oblongue	Langlochbrenner m	becco m ad imboccatura oblunga
^	10975	long string	colonne f de production	Produktionssäule f	colonna f di produzione
^	10976	long stroke pump	pompe f à longs coups	Langhubpumpe f	pompa f a lunga corsa
^	10977	long threads	filetage m type long	Langgewinde n	filettatura f lunga
—	10978	long-wall working	exploitation f par tailles chassantes à front continu	Langfrontbau m	coltivazione f a lunghi fronti in direzione
°	10979	longitudinal crack	crique f longitudinale	Längsriss m	fessura f o cricca f longitudinale
°	10979a	longitudinal curl	cambrure f longitudinale	Längswölbung f	volta f longitudinale
—	10980	longitudinal fold	pliage m en long	Längsfalz m	piega f longitudinale
°	10981	longitudinal groove	rainure f longitudinale	Längsfurche f	scanalatura f longitudinale
°	10982	longitudinal reinforcing iron bar, supporting reinforcement	armature f longitudinale	Längsbewehrung f	armatura f longitudinale (o portante)
°	10983	longitudinal rib	côte f longitudinale	Längsrippe f	costa f (o costola) longitudinale
—	10984	longitudinal sampling	échantillonnage m en long	Längsprobenabnahme f	campionatura f longitudinale
°	10985	longitudinal sleeper	longrine f	Längsschwelle f	longherina f, longarina f
—	10986	longitudinal valley	vallée f longitudinale	Längstal n	valle f longitudinale
—	10987	longulite	longulite f	Longulit m	longulite f
—	10988	longwall	grand front m aligné	Langfront f	grande fronte m in direzione
—	10989	longwall advancing	méthode m de grandes tailles chassantes	Strebbau m mit breitem Blick nach der Baugrenze fortschreitend	coltivazione f a grande fronte in direzione

English	French	German	Italian
— 10990 **longwall coal cutter**	haveuse f pour grands fronts	Longwall--Schrämmaschine f	tagliatrice f per grandi fronti
— 10991 **longwall face**	grand front m aligné	Abbaustoss m bei Strebbau mit breitem Blick	grande fronte m in direzione
— 10992 **longwall mining**	exploitation f par longwall	Strebbau m mit breitem Blick	coltivazione f per grandi fronti in direzione
— 10993 **longwall retreating**	exploitation f par longwall en rabattant	Strebbau m mit breitem Blick von der Baugrenze rückschreitend	coltivazione f a lunghi tagli in ritirata
— 10994 **longwall stoping**	exploitation f par longwall	Langfrontbau m	coltivazione f a lunghi tagli in direzione
	looking-glass ore, s. *specular iron ore*		
° 10995 **loop**	boucle f	Schleife f	nodo m, anello m, occhiello m
° 10996 **loop**	loupe f	Luppe f	lingotto m incandescente
° 10997 **loop expansion**	courbe f de dilatation	Ausdehnungskurve f	curva f di dilatazione
° 10998 **loop iron**	fer m en loupe	Luppeneisen n	ferro m in lingotti
^ 10999 **loop line**	canalisation f parallèle	Nebenleitung f	canalizzazione f parallela
° 10999a **looping pit**	fosse f à boucles	Schlingengrube f	fossa f a cappi
	looping mill, s. *wire mill*		
— 11000 **looping pit**	emmagasineur m	Schlingengrube f	accatastatore m
— 11001 **loose, (argillaceous) iron ore**	minerai m de fer argileux non compact	lockeres, toniges Eisenerz n	minerale m di ferro cavernoso (od argilloso)
° 11002 **loose bottom**	fond m amovible	Losboden m	fondo m mobile, falsa f staffa
^ 11003 **loose flange**	bride f mobile	loser Flansch m	flangia f mobile
— 11004 **loose kibble**	benne f flottante	Förderkübel m ohne Führungsschlitten	benna f oscillante
° 11005 **loose pattern**	modèle m démontable	Korbmodell n	modello m scomponibile, modello sciolto

English	French	German	Italian
o 11006 **loose piece**	partie *f* démontable, bossage *m* volant	Losteil *n*, lose Nabe *f*	parte *f* amovible, tassello *m*, parte sciolta
o 11007 **loose piece, loose part**	partie *f* séparée	Losteil *n*	parte *f* sciolta
o 11008 **loose pin**	broche *f* de remmoulage	loser Führungsstift *m*	pirone *m* mobile
— 11009 **loose pulley**	poulie *f* folle	Losscheibe *f*	puleggia *f* folle
o 11010 **loose tool**	outil *m* à main (pour forger)	Herdgerät *n*	attrezzo *m* a mano (per fucinatura)
o 11011 **to loosen the pattern, to rap**	dégager le modèle	das Modell lockern	scampanare il modello
o 11012 **loosening of the brickwork**	désagrégation *f* de la maçonnerie	Lockerung *f* des Steinverbandes	disgregazione *f* della muratura, crepatura della muratura
— 11013 **loosing**	descente *f* de la cage d'extraction	Senken *n* des Förderkorbes	discesa *f* della gabbia
o 11014 **lost-wax casting**	coulée *f* en cire perdue	Modellausschmelze *f*	fusione *f* a cera persa, fusione *f* di precisione, microfusione *f*
— 11015 **loparite**	loparite *f*	Loparit *m*	loparite *f*
— 11016 **lorandite**	lorandite *f*	Lorandit *m*	lorandite *f*
— 11017 **loranskite**	loranskite *f*	Loranskit *m*	loranskite *f*
— 11018 **lorenzenite**	lorenzénite *f*	Lorenzenit *m*	lorenzenite *f*
— 11019 **lorettoite**	lorettoïte *f*	Lorettoit *m*	lorettoite *f*
— 11020 **lorry**	berline *f*, camion *m*	Förderwagen *m*, Kraftwagen *m*	vagoncino *m*, autocarro *m*
— 11021 **loseyite**	loséyite *f*	Loseyit *m*	loseyite *f*
o 11022 **loss by friction**	perte *f* par frottement	Reibungsverlust *m*	perdita *f* per attrito
o 11023 **loss by spring back**	perte *f* par repliage	Rückbiegungsverlust *m*	perdita *f* per ripiegatura
— 11024 **loss due to dressing**	perte *f* au triage	Aufbereitungsverlust *m*	perdita *f* per trattamento
— 11025 **loss due to roasting**	perte *f* au grillage	Röstverlust *m*	perdita *f* per torrefazione

	English	French	German	Italian
–	11026 **loss due to screening**	perte *f* au triage	Aufbereitungs-verlust *m*	perdita *f* per tratta-mento termico
°	11027 **loss in melting**	perte *f* de fusion	Schmelzverlust *m*	perdita *f* di fusione
°	11028 **loss of a property**	évanouissement *m* d'une propriété	Abklingen *n* einer Eigenschaft	scomparsa *f* d'una proprietà
°	11029 **loss of gas**	perte *f* de gaz, fuite *f* de gaz	Gasverlust *m*	perdita *f* di gas
°	11030 **loss of heat**	perte *f* de chaleur	Wärmeverlust *m*	perdita *f* di calore
°	11031 **loss of metal**	perte *f* en métal	Metallverlust *m*	perdita *f* di metallo
°	11032 **loss of pressure**	perte *f* de pression	Druckverlust *m*	perdita *f* di pressione
°	11033 **loss of weight**	perte *f* de poids	Gewichtsverlust *m*	perdita *f* di peso
–	11034 **losses**	résidus *m pl.*, déchets *m pl.*	Abfälle *m pl.*, Abräume *m pl.*	detriti *m pl*, residui *m pl.*
°	11035 **lost head**	masselotte *f*	verlorener Kopf *m*	materozza *f*
˄	11036 **lost circulation**	perte *f* de circulation	Spülungsverlust *m*	perdita *f* di circola-zione
°	11037 **lost head nail for shoes**	pointe *f* à tête--homme pour chaus-sures	Schuhnagel *m* mit gestauchtem Kopf	punta *f* a testa a grappino
–	11038 **lost record**	lacune *f* stratigraphique	stratigraphische Lücke *f*	lacuna *f* stratigrafica
°	11039 **lost sand core**	noyau *m* perdu	verlorener Sandkern *m*	anima *f* perduta
°	11040 **lost wax moulding**	coulée *f* en cire perdue	Genaugiessverfahren *n*	fusione *f* a cera persa
–	11041 **lotrite**	lotrite *f*	Lotrit *m*	lotrite *f*
–	11042 **louderbackite**	louderbackite *f*	Louderbackit *m*	louderbackite *f*
°	11043 **loupe**	loupe *f*	Luppe *f*	massello *m*, palla *f* di ferro
–	11043a **love arrows**	quartz *m* rutilé	Rutilnadeln *f pl.*	quarzo *m* rutilato
°	11044 **low-alloy steel**	acier *m* d'alliage pauvre, acier *m* à faible alliage	armlegierter Stahl *m*	acciaio *m* di lega povera
–	11045 **low-bed**	mille-pieds *m pl.*		millepiedi *m*
°	11046 **low-carbon steel, ingot steel**	acier *m* à faible te-neur en carbone	Stahl *m* mit niedri-gem Kohlenstoff-gehalt	acciaio *m* con basso tenore di carbonio

English	French	German	Italian
11047 low frequency electric induction furnace	four *m* électrique à induction à basse fréquence	Netzfrequenz- Induktionsofen *m*	forno *m* elettrico a induzione a bassa frequenza
11048 low-frequency induction furnace	four *m* à induction à basse fréquence	Niederfrequenz- Induktionsofen *m*	forno *m* a induzione a bassa frequenza
11049 low hearth	four *m* d'affinerie	Frischherd *n*	fuoco *m* d'affinaggio
low hydrogen electrode, *s. basic electrode*			
11050 low-grade anthracite	houille *f*	Steinkohle *f*	litantrace *m*
11051 low grade or inferior fuel	mauvais combustible *m*	minderwertiger Brennstoff *m*	cattivo combustibile *m*, combustibile *m* scadente
11052 low-grade ore	minerai *m* pauvre, minerai *m* de basse teneur	armes Erz *n*	minerale *m* povero, minerale *m* a basso tenore
11053 low level bog, black bog	tourbière *f* basse	Grünlandmoor *n*, Wiesemoor, Moss *n*	torbiera *f* bassa
11054 low lighting power	pouvoir *m* éclairant faible	geringe Leuchtkraft *f*	potere *m* illuminante debole
11055 low-melting-point alloy	alliage *m* à bas point de fusion	niedrigschmelzende Legierung *f*	lega *f* di basso punto di fusione
11056 low-phosphorous steel	acier *m* à faible teneur en phosphore	Stahl *m* mit niedrigem Phosphorgehalt	acciaio *m* con basso tenore di fosforo
11057 low pressure, preliminary pressure	basse pression *f*, pression *f* préliminaire	Niederdruck *m*, Vordruck *m*	pressione *f* iniziale
11058 low pressure steam boiler	chaudière *f* à vapeur à basse pression	Niederdruckdampf- kessel *m*	caldaia *f* a vapore a bassa pressione
11058a low shaft	cuve *f* basse	Niederschacht *m*	tino *m* basso
11059 low side	lèvre *f* affaissée, lèvre abaissée (d'une faille)	gesunkener Flügel, (einer Verwerfung)	ala *f* (o gamba *f*) abbassata, lembo *m* abbassato (di faglia)
11060 low silicon pig	fonte *f* rapide (pauvre en silicium et manganèse)	garschmelziges Roheisen *n*	ghisa *f* povera di silicio e manganese
11061 low solids mud	boue *f* à faible teneur en solides	Spülung *f* mit niedrigem Feststoffanteil	fango *m* a basso tenore di solidi
11062 low steel, mild steel	acier *m* à faible teneur en carbone	niedriggekohlter Stahl *m*	acciaio *m* con basso tenore di carbone

	English	French	German	Italian
° 11063	low tension plant	installation f à basse tension	Niederspannungs-anlage f	impianto m a bassa tensione
— 11064	lower bend	charnière f inférieure	Muldenscharnier n	cerniera f inferiore
° 11065	lower box, bottom box	châssis m inférieur	Unterkasten m	fondo m
° 11066	lower cylinder, lower drum	chaudière f inférieure	Unterkessel m	caldaia f inferiore
	lower drum, s. lower cylinder			
° 11067	lower electrode, bottom electrode	électrode f de la sole	Bodenelektrode f	elettrodo m del fondo
— 11068	lower limb	flanc m inférieur	liegender Schenkel m	fianco m inferiore
° 11069	lower part	partie f inférieure	unterer Teil m	parte f inferiore
° 11069a	lower punch	estampe f inférieure	Unterstempel m	stampo m inferiore
— 11070	lower wall	mur m, sol m	Liegende n	muro m, suolo m
— 11071	lower wall	lèvre affaissée (d'une faille)	gesunkener Flügel m, gesenkter Flügel m (einer Verwerfung)	ala f (o gamba f) abbassata
— 11072	lowered side	lèvre inférieure (d'une faille)	gesunkener Flügel m (einer Verwerfung)	ala f (o gamba f) inferiore abbassata (di una faglia)
	lowering, s. screwing up			
	lowering of bell, s. lowering of cone			
° 11073	lowering of cone	descente f du cône	Senkung f des Kegels	abbassamento m od apertura f del cono
° 11074	lowering of temperature	abaissement m de la température	Temperatursenkung f	abbassamento m di temperatura
° 11075	lowering stage	chargeur m descendant	Senkbühne f	piattaforma m mobile
11076	lowering the casing	descente f de tubage	Einbau m der Verrohrung	discesa f del tubaggio
	lowland moor, s. low level bog			
— 11077	loxoclase	loxoclase f	Loxoklas n	loxoclasi f
^ 11078	LPG	gaz de pétrole liquéfié	LPG (verflüssigte Erdölgase)	gas m di petrolio liquefatto

	English	French	German	Italian
´	11079 **lube. lubrificant**	lubrifiant _m_	Schmiere _f_	lubrificante _f_
^	11080 **lubricator**	chambre-écluse	Rohrschleuse _f_	lubrificatore _m_
—	11081 **lugs**	molettes _f pl_, taquets _m pl._	Klinken _f pl._	arresti _m pl_, tacche _f pl._, risalti _m pl._
—	11082 **ludlamite**	ludlamite _f_	Ludlamit _m_	ludlamite _f_
—	11083 **ludwigite**	ludwigite _f_	Ludwigit _m_	ludwigite _f_
°	11084 **lug**	oreille _f_	Führungslappen _m_	orecchio _m_, orecchione _m_, orecchia _f_
—	11085 **lugarite**	lugarite _f_	Lugarit _m_	lugarite _f_
—	11086 **lujaurite**	lujaurite _f_	Lujaurit _m_	lujaurite _f_
—	11087 **lumachelle**	lumachelle _f_	Lumachell _m_	lumachella _f_
°	11088 **luminous flame**	flamme _f_ éclairante	selbstleuchtende Flamme _f_	fiamma _f_ illuminante

lump, s. _bloom_

lump coal, s. _cobbles_

	English	French	German	Italian
°	11089 **lump breaker**	casse-gueuse _m_	Masselbrecher _m_	frangigrumi _m_
—	11090 **lump-fuel**	combustible _m_ en morceaux	stückiger Brennstoff _m_	combustibile _m_ a pezzi

lump of puddled steel, s. _ball of puddled steel_

	English	French	German	Italian
—	11091 **lump ore**	minerai _m_ gros, minerai _m_ en morceaux	Stückerz _n_	minerale _m_ grosso (o a pezzi)
—	11092 **luneburgite**	luneburgite _f_	Lüneburgit _m_	luneburgite _f_
—	11093 **lunnite**	lunnite	Lunnit _m_	lunnite _f_
°	11094 **Lürmann slag tuyere**	tuyère _f_ à laitier Lürmann	Lürmannsche Schlackenform _f_	tubiera _f_ per la scoria o loppa Lürmann
°	11095 **Lürman's stuffing box**	joint _m_ de dilatation de Lürmann, presse-étoupes de Lürmann	Lürmannsche Stopfbüchse _f_	giunto _m_ di dilatazione Lürmann
—	11096 **luscladite**	luscladite _f_	Luscladit _m_	luscladite _f_
—	11097 **lusitanite**	lusitanite _f_	Lusitanit _m_	lusitanite _f_
—	11098 **lussatite**	lussatite _f_	Lussatit _m_	lussatite _f_

	English	French	German	Italian

lustrous coal, s. *glance-coal*

		English	French	German	Italian
o	11099	**lute a mould**	luter un moule	einen Formkasten abdichten	lutare una forma, sigillare una forma
—	11100	**lutecite**	lutécite *f*	Lutecin *m*	lutecite *f*
—	11101	**lutecium, lutetium**	lutécium *m*	Lutetium *n*	lutezio *m*
—	11102	**Lutetian stage**	Lutétien *m*	Lutetian *n*	luteziano *m*
—	11103	**lutite**	lutite *f*	Lutit *m*	lutite *f*
o	11104	**Luxemburg pig iron**	fonte *f* de Luxembourg	Luxemburger Roheisen *n*	ghisa *f* del Lussemburgo
—	11105	**luxullianite**	luxullianite *f*	Luxullianit *m*	luxullianite *f*
—	11106	**luzonite**	luzonite *f*	Luzonit *m*	luzonite *f*
—	11107	**lycopodium**	poudre *f* de lycopode	Lykopodium *n*	polvere *f* di licopodio
o	11108	**lye containing zinc**	lessive *f* zincifère	zinkhaltige Lauge *f*	lisciva *f* di zinco
o	11109	**lye boiler**	chaudière *f* à lessive	Laugekessel *m*	caldaia *f* per lisciva
—	11110	**lying side**	mur *m*, sol *m*	Liegende *n*	muro *m*, suola *f*
—	11111	**lytomorphic**	lythomorphique	lytomorphisch	litomorfico

English	French	German	Italian
11112 macaroni pipe	macaroni tube	Makkaronirohr *n*	tubo *m* sottile
11113 macaroni string	batterie *f* de macaroni	Makkaronirohr-batterie *f*	batteria *f* di piccolo diametro per lavori entro le aste
11114 macedonite	macédonite *f*	Macedonit *m*	macedonite *f*
11115 macgovernite	macgovernite *f*	Macgovernit *m*	macgovernite *f*
11116 machinability	usinabilité *f*	Bearbeitbarkeit *f*	lavorabilità *f*
11117 machinability of a material	usinabilité *f* d'un matériau	Bearbeitbarkeit *f* eines Materials	lavorabilità *f* di un materiale
11118 machinable cast iron	fonte *f* douce	weiches Gusseisen *n*	ghisa *f* dolce

to machine, *s. to finish*

11119 machine cast	coulé à la machine	Maschinen-gegossen	colato alla macchina
11120 machine casting	moulage *m* pour pièces de machine	Maschinenguss *m*	ghisa *f* per pezzi di macchine
11121 machine drill	marteau *m* perforateur	Bohrhammer *m*	martello *m* perforatore
11122 machine driller	ouvrier *m* sondeur	Bohrhauer *m*	trivellatore *m* (operaio)
11123 machine finishing	finissage à la machine	maschinelle Fertigbearbeitung *f*	finitura *f* a macchina
11124 machine for testing tensile strength	appareil *m* pour l'essai de traction	Zerreissmaschine *f*	macchina *f* per la prova di trazione
11125 machine for moulding gear wheels by means of a tooth block	machine *f* à mouler les engrenages au moyen d'un fouloir porte-segment	Zahnräderschabloniermaschine *f*	macchina *f* a sagoma od a sciablona per formare ingranaggi
11126 machine for moulding large pulleys	machine *f* à mouler les poulies de grand diamètre	Riemenscheiben-formmaschine *f*	macchina *f* per formare puleggie di grande diametro
11127 machine for tensile strength testing	appareil *m* pour l'essai de traction	Zerreissmaschine *f*	macchina *f* per la prova di trazione
11128 machine grinding	moulage *m* à la machine	Maschinenschliff *m*	molatura *f* meccanica
11129 to machine mould	mouler à la machine	auf der Maschine formen	formare a macchina, formare meccanicamente

	English	French	German	Italian
— 11130	machine holing	perforation f mécanique	maschinelles Bohren n	perforazione f meccanica
° 11131	machine man	machiniste m	Maschinist m	macchinista f
— 11132	machine mining	abattage m mécanique	maschinelle Gewinnung f	estrazione f meccanica
° 11133	machine moulding	moulage m à la machine	Maschinenformerei f	formatura f meccanica (o a macchina)
° 11134	machine puddling	puddlage m mécanique	Maschinenpuddeln n	pudellaggio m meccanico
° 11135	machine reamer with Morse taper shank	alésoir m de machine à fût conique Morse	Maschinenreibahle f mit Morsekonus	alesatore m meccanico con cono Morse
° 11135a	machine steel	acier m à outils	Werkzeugstahl m	acciaio m da utensili
° 11136	machine tool	machine-outil f	Werkzeugmaschine f	macchina f utensile
° 11137	machine work	travail m à la machine	Maschinenarbeit f	lavoro m a macchina
	machine welding, s. automatic welding			
° 11138	machinery castings	fonte f mécanique	Maschinenguss m	ghisa f per macchine
— 11139	machinery stoping	abattage m mécanique	maschinelle Gewinnung f	abbattimento m meccanico
° 11139a	machining	façonnage m	maschinelle Bearbeitung f	-lavorazione f a macchina
° 11140	machining allowance	surépaisseur f d'usinage	Bearbeitungszugabe f	soprametallo m (di lavorazione), sovrametallo m
— 11141	mackensite	mackensite f	Mackensit m	mackensite f
— 11142	macle	chiastolite f	Chiastolith m, Andalusit m	chiastolite f, andalusite f
— 11143	macled	maclé	verzwillingt	geminato
— 11144	maconite	maconite f	Maconit m	maconite f
— 11145	macro etch test	attaque f macrographique	makrographische Ätzung f	attacco m acido macrografico
— 11146	macroclastic	macroclastique	makroklastisch	macroclastico
— 11147	macrocrystalline	macrocristallin	makrokristallin	macrocristallino
— 11148	macrodome	macrodôme m	Makrodom m	macrodomo m
— 11149	macrography	macrographie f	Makrobild n	macrografia f

English	French	German	Italian
- 11150 **macrographic test**	examen *m* macrographique	makrographische Untersuchung *f*	esame *m* macrografico
- 11151 **macrography**	macrographie *f*	Makrographie *f*	macrografia *f*
- 11152 **macromeritic structure**	structure *f* macroméritique	makromeritische Struktur *f*	struttura *f* macromeritica
- 11153 **macropinacoid**	macropinacoïde *m*	Makropinakoid *m*	macropinacoide *m*
- 11154 **macroprism**	macroprisme *m*	Makroprisma *n*	macroprisma *m*
- 11155 **macroscopic examination**	observation *f* macroscopique	makroskopische Beobachtung *f*	osservazione *f* macroscopica
⊃ 11156 **macro-segregation**	ségrégation *f* majeure, macro- -ségrégation *f*	Makroseigerung *f*	macrosegregazione *f*
⊃ 11157 **macrostructure**	macrostructure *f*	Makrogefüge *n*, Makrostruktur *f*	macrostruttura *f*
- 11158 **maculose structure**	structure *f* tachetée	Flecktextur *f*	struttura *f* maculata
- 11159 **madeirite**	madéirite *f*	Madeirit *m*	madeirite *f*
- 11160 **madupite**	madupite *f*	Madupit *m*	madupite *f*
- 11161 **maenaite**	maenaite *f*	Maenait *m*	maenaite *f*
- 11162 **mafic mineral**	minerai *m* ferromagnésien	mafisches Mineral *n*	minerale *m* ferromagnesico
- 11163 **mafite**	mafite *f*	Mafit *m*	mafite *f*
- 11164 **mafraite**	mafraite *f*	Mafrait *m*	mafraite *m*
○ 11165 **magamp regulation**	réglage *m* par amplificateurs magnétiques	Regulierung *f* mit Magnetverstärkern	regolazione con amplificatori magnetici
- 11166 **magazine mining**	exploitation *f* par chambres–magasins	Magazinbau *m*	coltivazione *f* a camere-magazzino
magistral, *s. roasted copper pyrite*			
- 11167 **magma**	magma *m*	Magma *n*	magma *m*
- 11168 **magmatic digestion**	assimilation *f* magmatique	magmatische Assimilation *f*	assimilazione *f* magnetica
- 11169 **magmatic ore deposits**	gîtes *m pl.* magmatiques	magmatische Erzlagerstätten *f pl.*	giacimenti *m pl.* magmatici

English	French	German	Italian
— 11170 **magmatic stoping**	effondrement *m* magmatique du toit	Aufstemmung *f*	abbattimento *m* magmatico, cedimento *m* magmatico del tetto
— 11170a **magnesia**	magnésie *f*	Magnesia *f*	magnesia *f*
— 11171 **magnesiochromite**	magnésiochromite *f*	Magnesiumchromit *m*	magnesiocromite *f*
— 11172 **magnesioferrite**	magnésioferrite *f*	Magnesiumferrit *m*	magnesioferrite *f*
— 11173 **magnesioludwigite**	magnésioludwigite *f*	Magnesiumludwigit *m*	magnesioludwigite *f*
— 11174 **magnesite**	magnésite *f*	Magnesit *m*	magnesite *f*
— 11175 **magnesite brick**	brique *f* de magnésite	Magnesitziegel *m*	mattone *m* di magnesite
— 11176 **magnesite lining**	revêtement *m* de magnésite	Magnesitauskleidung *f*	rivestimento *m* di magnesite
— 11177 **magnesite mass**	masse *f* de magnésite	Magnesitmasse *f*	massa *f* di magnesite
— 11178 **magnesium**	magnésium *m*	Magnesium *n*	magnesio *m*
— 11179 **magnesium aluminium garnet**	grenat alumino--magnésien	Magnesiatongranat *m*	granato *m* allumino-magnesico
— 11180 **magnesium lamp**	lampe *f* au magnésium	Magnesiumlampe *f*	lampada *f* al magnesio
magnesium mica, *s. phlogopite*			
— 11181 **magnesium oxide**	magnésie *f*	Magnesia *f*	magnesia *f*
— 11182 **magnesium ribbon**	bande *f* de magnésium	Magnesiumband *n*	nastro *m* di magnesio
magnesium shock cooling, *s. shock cooling*			
° 11183 **magnet**	aimant *m*	Magnet *m*	magnete *m*
° 11184 **magnet steel**	acier *m* magnétique, acier *m* à aimants	Magnetstahl *m*	acciaio *m* magnetico, acciaio *m* per magneti
° 11185 **magnetic**	magnétique	magnetisch	magnetico
° 11186 **magnetic attractive**	pouvoir *m* d'attraction magnétique	magnetische Anziehungskraft *f*	potere *m* d'attrazione magnetica
— 11187 **magnetic bearing**	direction *f* magnétique	magnetisches Streichen *n*	direzione *f* magnetica
— 11188 **magnetic chuck**	plateau *m* magnétique	magnetisches Futter *n*	piano *m* magnetico
— 11189 **magnetic concentration of ores**	traitement *m* magnétique des minerais	magnetische Aufbereitung von Erzen	trattamento *m* magnetico dei minerali

English	French	German	Italian
11190 **magnetic dressing**	préparation *f* magnétique	magnetische Aufbereitung *f*	trattamento *m* magnetico
11191 **magnetic drum**	tambour *m* magnétique	Magnettrommel *f*	tamburo *m* magnetico
11192 **magnetic field**	champ *m* magnétique	magnetisches Feld *n*	campo *m* magnetico
11193 **magnetic iron (ore), magnetite**	fer *m* magnétique, magnétite *f*, fer *m* oxydulé	Magneteisenstein *m*, Magnetit *m*	ferro *m* magnetico, magnetite *f*
11194 **magnetic iron pyrites**	pyrrhotine *f*	Magnetopyrit *m*	pirite *f* magnetica
11195 **magnetic loss**	perte *f* magnétique	magnetischer Verlust *m*	peruita *f* magnetica
11196 **magnetic needle**	aiguille *f* aimantée	Magnetnadel *f*	ago *m* magnetico
magnetic oxide of iron, *s. magnetic iron*			
11197 **magnetic particle inspection**	examen *m* magnétoscopique	Magnetpulver- untersuchung *f*	esame *m* magneto- scopico
11198 **magnetic permeability**	perméabilité *f* magnétique	magnetische Durchlässigkeit *f*	permeabilità *f* magnetica
11199 **magnetic pulley**	poulie *f* magnétique	Magnetscheibe *f*	puleggia *f* magnetica
11200 **magnetic pyrites**	pyrite *f* magnétique	Magnetkies *m*	pirite *f* magnetica
11201 **magnetic resistance**	résistance *f* magnétique	magnetischer Widerstand *m*	resistenza *f* magnetica
11202 **magnetic sand**	sable *m* magnétique	Magneteisensand *m*	sabbia *f* di magnetite
magnetic sensibility, *s. magnetic attractive capacity*			
11203 **magnetic separator**	séparateur *m* magnétique	Magnetscheider *m*	separatore *m* magnetico
magnetic sheet iron, *s. lamination*			
magnetic stone, *s. magnetic iron*			
11204 **magnetic survey**	prospection *f* magnétique	magnetisches Schürfen *n*	prospezione *f* magnetica
11205 **magnetisation**	aimantation *f*	Magnetisierung *f*	magnetizzazione *f*

	English	French	German	Italian
—	11206 **magnetism**	magnétisme *m*	Magnetismus *m*	magnetismo *m*
—	11207 **magnetite**	magnétite *f*	Magnetit *m*	magnetite *f*
°	11208 **magnetizable**	magnétisable	magnetisierbar	magnetizzabile
°	11209 **magnetizing roasting**	grillage *m* magnétisant	magnetisierende Röstung *f*	arrostimento *m* magnetizzante
°	11209a **magnetography**	magnétographie *f*	Magnetographie *f*	magnetografia *f*

magnetomotive potential, *s. magnetomotive tension*

	English	French	German	Italian
°	11210 **magnetomotive tension**	tension *f* magnétomotrice	magnetische Kraftspannung *f*	tensione *f* magnetomotrice
—	11211 **magnetoplumbite**	magnétoplumbite *f*	Magnetoplumbit *m*	magnetoplumbite *f*
°	11212 **magnification**	grossissement *m*	Vergrösserung *f*	ingrandimento *m*
	11213 **magnifier**	loupe *f*	Lupe *f*	lente *f*
—	11214 **magnoferrite**	magnoferrite *f*	Magnoferrit *m*	magnetoferrite *f*
—	11215 **magnophyric**	à gros phénocristaux	grobporphyrisch	a grandi fenocristalli
—	11216 **maiden field**	gisement *m* vierge	jungfräuliches Gebiet *n*	giacimento *m* vergine
—	11217 **maidenhair**	rutile *m* aciculaire	langstrahliges Rutil, nadeliges Rutil *n*	rutilo *m* acicolare

maillechort, *s. German silver*

	English	French	German	Italian
°	11217a **main bell**	grande cloche *f*	grosse Glocke *f*	gran cono (o campana)
°	11218 **main blast entry**	embouchure *f* principale du carneau	Eintritt *m* für die Hauptgebläseleitung	imboccatura *f* del condotto principale del vento (di alto forno)
—	11219 **main bottom**	roche de fond	festes Gebirge *n*	roccia *f* di fondo, roccia *f* di letto
—	11220 **main drive**	galerie *f* principale	Hauptstrecke *f*	galleria *f* principale

main fault, *s. dominant fault*

	English	French	German	Italian
°	11221 **main flue**	carneau *m* de la cheminée	Abzugkanal *m*	canale *m* del camino
°	11222 **main gate**	chenal *m* (ou canal) de coulée	Gussrinne *f*	canale *m* di colata
°	11223 **main jet**	coulée *f* principale	Hauptguss *m*	getto *m* principale
—	11224 **main level**	voie *f* de niveau	Grundstrecke *f*	galleria *f* di fondo, galleria *f* principale

English	French	German	Italian
11225 main rope	câble-tête *m*	Vorderseil *n*	cavo *m* principale, cavo *m* di testa
11226 main runner	fossé *m*, chenal *m*	Gosse *f*, Graben *m*	canale *m*, solco *m* principale di colata
11227 main track	voie *f* principale	Hauptgleis *n*	binario *m* principale
11228 major fold	pli *m* principal	Hauptfalte *f*	piega *f* principale
11229 major joint	diaclase *f* principale	Hauptspalte *f*	diaclasi *f* principale
11230 to make footage	avancer, chasser	vortreiben	perforare, avanzare perforando
11231 to make the joint	visser (les tiges ou le tuyaux)	(Rohr) anschrauben	avvitare (le aste o i tubi)
11232 to make the mixture	préparation *f* du lit de fusion	Möllerung *f*	preparazione *f* (del letto di fusione)
11233 to make up	visser les tiges de sonde	Rohre zusammen- schrauben	avvitare le aste di perforazione
to make visible, *s. to develop*			
11234 make of casing	descente de tubage	Einbau *m* der Verrohrung	discesa *f* del tubag- gio
11235 make-up torque	couple *f* de blocage	Verschraub- drehmoment *n*	coppia *f* di bloccaggio
11236 making hole	profondeur *f* du sondage	Bohrlochtiefe *f*	profondità *f* del sondaggio
malacca tin, *s. straits tin*			
11237 malachite	malachite *f*	Malachit *m*	malachite *f*
11238 malacolite	malacolite *f*	Malakolith *m*	malacoite *f*
11239 malacon	malacon *m*	Malakon *m*	malacon *m*
11240 malchite	malchite *f*	Malchit *m*	malchite *f*
11241 maldonite	maldonite *f*	Maldonit *m*	maldonite *f*
11242 male fishing tap	taraud *m* mâle de repêchage	Fangzapfen *m*, Spitzfänger *m*	pescatore *m* a maschio
11243 male sub	réduction *f* à mâle		riduzione *f* a maschio

English	French	German	Italian
^ 11244 **male thread**	filetage mâle	Zapfengewinde *n*	filettatura *f* a maschio (o esterna)
— 11245 **malignite**	malignite *f*	Malignit *m*	malignite *f*
— 11246 **malladrite**	malladrite *f*	Malladrit *m*	malladrite *f*
— 11247 **mallardite**	mallardite *f*	Mallardit *m*	mallardite *f*
o 11248 **malleability, ductility**	malléabilité *f,* ductilité *f*	Schmiedbarkeit *f*	malleabilità *f,* duttilità *f*
malleable, *s. ductile*			
o 11249 **malleable cast-iron, malleable casting(s)**	fonte *f* malléable, fonte *f* douce de moulage	Temperguss *m,* Temperstahlguss *m*	ghisa *f* malleabile, ghisa *f* bianca (o dolce da fonderia)
malleable iron, *s. malleable pig iron*			
o 11250 **malleable iron casting, mitis casting**	coulée *f* de fonte	Temperguss *m,* Weichguss *m*	getto *m* di ghisa malleabile
o 11251 **malleable iron wire**	fil *m* de fer malléable	weicher Draht *m*	filo *m* di ferro ricotto
o 11252 **malleable steel**	acier *m* malléable, acier *m* doux	Schweissstahl *m*	acciaio *m* malleabile, acciaio *m* dolce
o 11253 **malleablizing**	malléabilisation *f*	Tempern *n*	malleabilizzazione *f*
o 11254 **malleablizing anneal**	recuit *m* de malléabilisation	Tempern *n*	ricottura *f* di malleabilizzazione
o 11255 **malleablizing by decarburisation**	malléabilisation *f* par décarburation	Glühfrischen *n*	malleabilizzazione *f* per decarburazione
o 11256 **malleablizing by graphitisation**	malléabilisation *f* par graphitisation	Tempern *n* durch Graphitisieren	malleabilizzazione *f* per grafitizzazione
o 11257 **to malleate**	marteler, forger	hämmern	martellare, forgiare
malmstone, *s. firestone*			
o 11258 **man hole**	trou *m* d'homme, regard de visite	Einsteigöffnung *f,* Mannloch *n*	passaggio *m* d'ispezione, foro *m* d'uomo
o 11259 **man in charge of throat**	ouvrier *m* au gueulard	Gichtarbeiter *m*	operaio *m,* addetto *m* alle cariche (dell'altoforno)
— 11260 **manandonite**	manandonite *f*	Manandonit *m*	manandonite *f*
— 11261 **mandelstone**	roche *f* amygdaloïde	Mandelstein *m*	roccia *f* amigdaloide

English	French	German	Italian
11262 mandrel	pic *m* à deux pointes	Doppelkeilhaue *f*	piccone *m* a due punte
11263 mandrel	olive *f*	Profilkörper *m*	oliva *f*, corpo *m* sagomato
11264 mandrel (of drawbench)	mandrin *m* d'étirage	Ziehdorn *m*	mandrino *m* di trafila
11265 mandrel roll for welded tubes	cylindre *m* à mandrin pour tubes soudés	Dornwalze *f* für geschweisste Rohre	cilindro *m* a mandrino per tubi saldati
11266 manganese	manganèse *m*	Mangan *n*	manganese *m*
11267 manganese-aluminium garnet	spessartine *f*	Spessartin *m*	spessartite *f*
manganese blende, *s. alabandite*			
11268 manganese bronze	bronze au manganèse, bronze manganeux	Manganbronze *f*	bronzo *m* al manganese
11269 manganese cast iron	fonte *f* manganésée	manganhaltiges Gusseisen *n*	ghisa *f* al manganese
11270 manganese-copper, cupro-manganese	cuivre *m* au manganèse, cuivre *m* manganèse	Mangankupfer *n*	rame *m* manganesifero
11271 manganese dioxide	peroxyde *m* de manganèse	Mangansuperoxyd *n*	perossido *m* di manganese, biossido *m* di manganese
11272 manganese pig	fonte *f* manganésée	Mangangusseisen *n*	ghisa *f* al manganese
11273 manganese-silicon steel, silico(n)-manganese steel	acier *m* mangano-siliceux	Silizium-Manganstahl *m*	acciaio *m* mangano-silicioso, acciaio *m* mangano-silicico
11274 manganese spar, carbonate of manganese, rhodonite	carbonate *m* de manganèse. dialogite *f*	Manganspat *m*, Dialogit *m*	spato *m* manganico, carbonato *m* di manganese
11275 manganese spectrum	raie *f* du manganèse	Manganspektrum *n*	linea *f* del manganese
11276 manganese spiegel	fonte *f* spéculaire au manganèse	Manganspiegel *m*	ghisa *f* speculare al manganese
11277 manganese steel, Hadfield steel	acier *m* Hadfield, acier *m* au manganèse	Manganhartstahl *m*, Manganstahl *m*	acciaio *m* Hadfield, acciaio *m* al manganese
11278 manganese steel frog	coeur *m* en acier au manganèse	Manganstahl-herzstück *n*	cuore *m* in acciaio al manganese

English	French	German	Italian
— 11279 manganesian iron	ferromanganèse *m*	Manganeisen *n*	ferromanganese *m*
— 11280 manganesiferous	manganésifère	manganführend	manganifero
— 11281 manganic oxide	sesquioxyde *m* de manganèse	Manganoxyd *n*	ossido *m* manganico
— 11282 manganiferous	manganésé	manganhaltig	manganico
— 11283 manganiferous iron ore	minerai *m* de fer manganésé	manganhaltiges Eisenerz *n*	minerale *m* di ferro manganesifero
— 11284 manganiferous zinc ore	minerai *m* de zinc manganésé	manganhaltiges Zinkerz *n*	minerale *m* di zinco manganesifero
° 11285 manganin wire	fil de manganine	Manganindraht *m*	filo *m* di manganina
· — 11286 manganite	manganite *f*,	Manganit *m*	manganite *f*
— 11287 manganocalcite	manganocalcite *f*	Manganokalzit *m*	manganocalcite *f*
— 11288 manganophyllite	manganophyllite *f*	Manganphyllit *m*	manganofillite *f*
— 11289 manganosite	manganosite *f*	Manganosit *m*	manganosite *f*
— 11290 manganous	manganeux	manganhaltig	manganoso
— 11291 manganous oxide, manganese oxide	oxyde *m* manganeux	Manganoxydul *n*	ossido *m* di manganese
— 11292 mangerite	mangérite *f*	Mangerit *m*	mangerite *f*
° 11292a mangling	redressage *m*	Geraderichten *n*	raddrizzatura *f*
manhole, *s.* man hole			
^ 11293 manifold, header	claviature *f*	Rohrverteiler *m*	collettore *m*, condotta *f*
° 11294 Manilla rope	corde *f* (Manilla)	Hanftau *n*	corda *f* di Manilla
manipulator, *s. tilter*			
° 11295 Mannesman process	procédé *m* Mannesmann	Schrägwalzverfahren *n* nach Mannesmann	processo *m* Mannesmann
— 11296 mannitol, mannite	mannite *f*	Mannit *m*	mannite *f*
^ 11297 manometer, pressure gauge	manomètre *m*	Druckmesser *m*	manometro *m*
° 11298 manometric efficiency	rendement *m* manométrique	manometrischer Wirkungsgrad *m*	rendimento *m* manometrico
— 11299 to mantle	couvrir, revêtir	bedecken	coprire, rivestire
° 11299a mantle	enveloppe *f*	Mantel *m*	mantello *m*, involucro *m*

	English	French	German	Italian
°	11300 mantle	couronne *f*, marâtre *f* d'un haut fourneau	Tragkranz *m* (eines Hochofens)	corona *f* (d'altoforno)
°	11301 mantle	surmoule *m*	Formmantel *m*	sovrastampo *m*
°	11302 mantle bracket	support *m* du massif, couronne *f* de la marâtre, couronne *f* de support	Mantelplatte *f*, Eisenkranz *m*. Tragkranz *m*, Tragring *m*	corona *f* di supporto (d'altoforno)
°	11303 mantle ring	marâtre *f*	Tragkranz *m*	anello *m* dell'involucro
°	11304 mantle sheet iron	tôle *f* d'enveloppe	Manteleisen *n*	lamiera *f* di rivestimento
	manual blowpipe, *s. hand blowpipe*			
	11305 manual labour	travail *m* à la main	Handarbeit *f*	lavoro *m* a mano, lavoro *m* manuale
	manual torch, *s. hand blowpipe*			
	manufacture of blister steel, *s. cementation process*			
	manufacture of cement steel, *s. cementation process*			
°	11306 manufacture of crucibles	fabrication *f* des creusets	Tiegelherstellung *f*	fabbricazione *f* dei crogiuoli
°	11307 manufacture of ingot metal in the reverberatory furnace	fabrication *f* de l'acier sur sole	Frischen *n* auf Flusseisen im Flammofen	fabbricazione *f* dell'acciaio su suola
	manufacture of steel in the electric furnace, *s. electric steel*			
°	11308 manufacturer (steam) boiler	chaudière *f* (à vapeur) industrielle ou manufacturière	Gewerbekessel *m* Industriekessel *m*	caldaia *f* (a vapore) industriale
—	11309 manway raise	montage *m* de circulation	Fahrüberhauen *n*	montaggio *m* di circolazione
^	11310 manway-up	montage *m* de circulation	Fahrüberhauen *n*	montaggio *m* di circolazione
^	11311 map of distributing system	plan *m* du réseau	Leitungsplan *m*	piano *m* delle condutture
°	11311a maraging	vieillissement *m* martensitique	Martensitalterung *f*	invecchiamento *m* martensitico
—	11312 marble plate	plaque *f* de marbre	Marmorplatte *f*	lastra *f* di marmo
—	11313 marcasite	marcasite *f*	Markasit *m*	marcassite *f*, pirite *f* bianca

	English	French	German	Italian
−	11314 **margarite**	margarite *f*	Margarit *m*	margarite *f*
−	11315 **margarosanite**	margarosanite *f*	Margarosanit *m*	margarosanite *f*
−	11316 **marginal facies**	faciès *m* marginal	Randfazies *f*	facies *f* marginale
−	11317 **marginal fold**	pli *m* marginal	Randfalte *f*	piega *f* marginale
−	11318 **marialite**	marialite *f*	Marialith *m*	marialite *f*
−	11319 **marignacite**	marignacite *f*	Marignacit *m*	marignacite *f*
−	11320 **marine clay**	argile *f* (des polders)	Marschenton *m*	argilla *f* dei «polders»
−	11321 **marine deposits** *pl.*	dépôts *m pl.* marins	Meeressedimente *n pl.*	sedimenti *m pl.* marini
^	11322 **marine drilling**	forage *m* en mer	Bohren in der See	sondaggio *m* in mare
−	11323 **marine facies**	faciès *m* marin	marine Fazies *f*	«facies» *f* marina
°	11324 **marine(type)boiler**	chaudière *f* de marine	Schiffskessel *m*,	caldaia *f* marina
°	11325 **marine water-tube boiler**	chaudière *f* aquatubulaire marine	Schiffssiederohr-kessel *m*	caldaia *f* marina a tubi d'acqua
−	11326 **mariposite**	mariposite *f*	Mariposit *m*	mariposite *f*
−	11327 **mariupolite**	mariupolite *f*	Mariupolit *m*	mariupolite *f*
	to mark, *s. to stamp*			
°	11328 **mark out**	tracer	anreissen	tracciare
°	11329 **mark, sign**	marque *f*	Kennzeichen *n*	marca *f*
°	11330 **marker**	repère *m*	Markierung *f*	contrassegno *m*, riferimento *m*
−	11331 **marker horizon**	horizon *m* repère	Leithorizont *m*	orizzonte *m* guida
−	11332 **markfieldite**	markfieldite *f*	Markfieldit *m*	markfieldite *f*
°	11333 **marking gauge, carpenter's gauge**	trusquin *m*	Streichmass *n*	tracciatore *m* a mano
°	11334 **marking off**	traçage *m*	Anreissen *n*	tracciatura *f*
−	11335 **marl**	marne *f*	Mergel *m*	marna *f*
−	11336 **marloesite**	marloésite *f*	Marloesit *m*	marloesite *f*

	English	French	German	Italian
— 11337	marly clay	argile *f* marneuse	Mergelton *m*	argilla *f* marnosa
— 11338	marly soil	sol *m* marneux	Mergelboden *m*	suolo *m* marnoso
— 11339	marmatite	marmatite *f*	Marmatit *m*	marmatite *f*
— 11340	marmolite	marmolite *f*	Marmolith *m*	marmolite *f*
o 11341	marquenching	refroidissement *m* rapide martensitique	Abschreckung *f*	tempera *f* in due tempi
— 11342	marscoite	marscoïte *f*	Marscoit *m*	marscoite *f*
	marsh damp, *s. firedamp*			
— 11343	marshite	marshite *f*	Marshit *m*	marscite *f*
— 11344	marshy soil	sol *m* marécageux	sumpfiger Boden *m*	terreno *m* palustre (o paludoso)
	martempering, *s. step quenching*			
o 11345	Martens microscope stand	support *m* de microscope d'après Martens	Mikroskopgestell *n* nach Martens	sostegno *m* Martens da microscopio
— 11346	martensite	martensite *f*	Martensit *m*	martensite *f*
o 11347	martensite quench	trempe *f* martensitique	Martensithärtung *f*	tempra *f* martensitica
o 11348	martensitic cast iron	fonte *f* martensitique	martensitisches Gusseisen *n*	ghisa *f* martensitica
o 11349	Martin blower	soufflerie *f* Martin	Kapselhochdruckgebläse *n*	soffiante *m* Martin
	Martin-Siemens process, *s. acid open-hearth process*			
	Martin steel, *s. open hearth steel*			
— 11350	martinite	martinite *f*	Martinit *m*	martinite *f*
— 11351	martite	martite *f*	Martit *m*	martite *f*
— 11352	masanite	masanite *f*	Masanit *m*	masanite *f*
— 11353	mascagnite	mascagnite *f*	Mascagnin *m*	mascagnite *f*
o 11354	mash seam welding	soudure *f* plastique continue	plastische Nahtschweissung *f*	saldatura *f* plastica continua
o 11355	masonry	muraillement *m*	Ausmauerung *f*	muratura *f*
o 11356	masonry shaft	puits *m* maçonné	Schacht *m* mit Ziegelmauerung	pozzo *m* in muratura
o 11357	mass effect	effet *m* de masse	Masseneffekt *m*	effetto *m* di massa
o 11358	massicot	massicot *m*	Massicot *n*	massicot *m*

	English	French	German	Italian
−	11359 massive structure	structure *f* massive	Massivstruktur *f*	struttura *f* massiccia
°	11359a master	modèle *f* à étalon	Mustermodell *n*	modello *m* campione
°	11360 master alloy	alliage-mère *m*	Vorlegierung *f*	lega-madre *f*
°	11360a master block	porte-poinçon *m*	Stempelhalter *m*	portastampo *m*
−	11361 master borer	chef foreur *m*	Bohrmeister *m*	capo *m* trivellatore
^	11362 master bushing	boisseau *m* principal	Haupteinsatz *m*	cunei *m* pl. della tavola rotary
^	11363 master gate	vanne *f* de sûreté	Hauptschieber *m*	«preventer» *m* a saracinesca
°	11363a master form	forme *f* maîtresse	Urform *f*	forma *f* madre
^	11364 master gauge	rapporteur *m*	Urkaliber *n*	manometro *m* campione
−	11365 master lode	filon *m* principal	Hauptgang *m*	filone *m* principale
°	11366 master pattern	pré-modèle *m*	Muttermodell *n*	premodello *m*, modello *m* madre
°	11366a mat etching	décapage *m* au mat	Mattbeizung *f*	decapaggio *m* matto
°	11367 mat sheet	tôle *f* mate	Mattblech *n*	latta *f* matta
°	11368 match plate job	travail *m* par plaque-modèle	Modellplattenarbeit *f*	lavoro *m* mediante placca modello
°	11369 match plate molding	moulage *m* par plaque-modèle	Modellplattenformen *n*	formatura *f* con piastra modello
°	11370 matched	centré	zentriert	centrato (di stampo)
°	11371 matching	centrage *m*	Zentrieren *n*	centratura *f* degli stampi
°	11372 material containing ferric oxide	substance *f* riche en oxyde de fer	eisenoxydhaltiges Gut *n*	sostanza *f* ferrosa
°	11373 material for plug	masse *f* ou matière *f* pour boucher	Gestübbe *n*	terra *f* per tappare
−	11374 material handling	manipulation *f* de matériel	Materialbehandlung *f*	trattamento *m* del materiale
−	11375 matildite	mathildite *f*	Matildit *m*	matildite *f*
−	11376 matlockite	matlockite *f*	Matlockit *m*	matlockite *f*
°	11377 matrix, bottom die	étampe *f* de dessous	Untermodell *n*	stampo *m* inferiore, matrice *f*
°	11378 matrix	matrice *f*, forme *f*	Matrize *f*, Form *f*	matrice *f*, forma *f*, stampo *m*
°	11379 matrix	matrice *f*	Grundmasse *f*	matrice *f*

	English	French	German	Italian
- 11380	matrix	matrice *f*, magma *m* de second temps	Gangstein *m*	matrice *f*
ᵒ 11381	matte	matte *f* de cuivre	Lech *m*, Stein *m*	metallina *f* grezza
- 11382	matting	platelage *m*	Matten *n*	piano *m* di tavole per fondazione
- 11383	mattock	pioche *f*, pic *m*	Breithacke *f*	piccone *m*
- 11384	maucherite	mauchérite	Maucherit	maucherite *f*
- 11385	mauzeliite	mauzeliite *f*	Mauzeliit *m*	mauzeliite *f*
ᵒ 11386	maximum load	charge *f* maximale	Höchstlast *f*	carico *m* massimo
ᵒ 11387	maximum pressure	pression *f* maxima	Höchstpressung *f*	pressione *f* massima
	meadow ore, *s. limonite*			
	meager coal, *s. lean coal*			
ᵒ 11387a	mean free path	libre parcours *m* moyen	mittlere freie Weglänge *f*	cammino *m* medio libero
— 11388	meander belt	zone *f* des méandres	Mäanderstreifen *m*	zona *f* dei meandri
ᵒ 11389	to measure	mesurer	messen	misurare
ᵒ 11390	to measure the temperature of a body by means of its radiation	mesurer la température d'un corps par son rayonnement	die Temperatur *f* eines Körpers aus seiner Strahlung messen	misurare la temperatura d'un corpo per mezzo della sua radiazione
ᵒ 11391	to measure the test piece	mesurer les dimensions de l'éprouvette	die Probe *f* ausmessen	misurare le dimensioni della provetta
11392	measure	mesure *f*	Mass *n*	misura *f*
— 11393	measure	couche *f*, lit *m*	Flöz *n*, Schicht *f*	strato *m*, filone *m*, vena *f*, letto *m*
11394	measurement measure	mesurage *m*, prise *f* de mesures, mesure *f*	Messung *f*, Mass	misura *f*, misurazione *f*
ᵒ 11395	measurement or determination of hardness	mesure *m* ou détermination *f* de la dureté	Härtemessung *f*	misura *f* della durezza
— 11396	measuring chain	chaîne *f* d'arpenteur	Messkette *f*	catena *f* di misurazione
ᵒ 11397	measuring error	erreur *f* de mesure	Messfehler *m*	errore *m* di misurazione

	English	French	German	Italian
° 11398	measuring flask	ballon m jaugé	Messkolben m	pallone m di misura, matraccio m tarato
° 11399	measuring glass	vase m gradué	Messkelch m	provetta f
° 11400	measuring instrument	instrument m de mesure	Messwerkzeug n	strumento m di misura
° 11401	measuring point	point m de repère	Messpunkt m	punto m di riferimento
° 11402	measuring wire	fil m de mesure	Gefälldraht m	filo m di misura
− 11403	M.C.F.	mille pieds cubes	Tausende f an Kubikfuss	migliaia f di piedi cubi

mechanical charging, s. mechanical stoking

− 11404	mechanical coal pick	marteau piqueur m	Abbauhammer m	martello m perforatore
− 11405	mechanical dressing	préparation f mécanique	maschinelle Aufbereitung f	preparazione f meccanica
° 11406	mechanical gas fired furnace for hardening	four m de trempe mécanique au gaz	mechanischer Gashärteofen m	forno m meccanico a gas per la tempera
° 11407	mechanical jack	vérin m mécanique	mechanischer Schneckenbohrer m	martinetto m meccanico
° 11408	mechanical knock--out by vibration	décochage m par vibrations	Ausleeren n durch Vibration	distaffatura f mediante vibrazioni
° 11409	mechanical properties	caractéristiques f pl. mécaniques	mechanische Eigenschaften f pl.	caratteristiche f pl. meccaniche

mechanical pudding, s. machine pudding

° 11410	mechanical puddler	puddleur m mécanique	mechanischer Puddler m	pudellatore m meccanico
° 11411	mechanical reaction on the material	action f mécanique sur le matériau	mechanische Wirkung f auf den Werkstoff	azione f meccanica sul materiale
− 11412	mechanical shovel	choleur m, pelle mécanique	Schaufellader m	pala f meccanica
♂ 11413	mechanical stoker, automatic stoker	foyer m mécanique	mechanische Feuerung f	focolare m meccanico, alimentatore m meccanico
° 11414	mechanical stoking	chauffage m mécanique	selbsttätige Rostbeschickung f	alimentazione f automatica della griglia

English	French	German	Italian
11415 mechanical strainer	appareil *m* de tamisage mécanique	mechanische Siebvorrichtung *f*	crivello *m* (o vaglio *m*) meccanico
11416 mechanical test	essai *m* mécanique	mechanische Prüfung *f*	prova *f* meccanica
mechanical torch, *s. mechanical blowpipe*			
11416a mechanical twins	macle *f* de déformation	Verzerrungszwillings-kristall *m*	cristalli *m pl.* geminati da deformazione
11417 mechanical undercutter	haveuse *f*	Schrämmaschine *f*	intagliatrice *f* per carbone
11418 mechanical workshop	atelier *m* de construction mécanique	mechanische Werkstätte *f*	officina *f* meccanica
11419 mechanically driven ore grinder	triturateur *m* de minerai commandé mécaniquement	mechanisch betriebener Erzzerreiber *m*	trituratore *m* di minerali a comando meccanico
11420 mechanized winning	abattage *m* mécanique	maschinelle Gewinnung *f*	abbattimento *m* meccanico
11421 Meco-Moore cutter loader	haveuse-chargeuse *f* Meco-Moore	Meco-Moore Schraemlademaschine *f*	scavatrice *f* e caricatrice Meco-Moore
11422 mediophyric	à grain moyen	mittelporphyrisch	medioporfirico
11423 mediosilicic	neutre	neutral	neutro
medium and high carbon steel, *s. ingot steel*			
11423a medium carbon steel	acier *m* demi-doux	halbharter Stahl *m*	acciaio *m* semi-dolce
11424 medium drawing	tréfilage *m* moyen	Mittelzug *m*	stiramento *m* medio, trafilatura *f* media
11425 medium grained	à grain moyen	mittelkörnig	a grano medio
11426 medium hard foundry pig iron	fonte *f* de moulage moyennement dure	mittelhartes Giessereieisen *n*	ghisa *f* da fonderia semidura
11427 medium-hard steel	acier *m* (de)mi-dur	mittelharter Stahl *m*	acciaio *m* semiduro
11428 medium iron train	laminoir *m* à fers moyens	Mittelstrecke *f*	laminatoio *m* medio
11429 medium phosphorus iron	fonte *f* semi-phosphoreuse	halbphosphorisches Gusseisen *n*	ghisa *f* semifosforosa
11430 medium plate	tôle *f* moyenne	Mittelblech *n*	lamiera *f* media
11431 medium-pressure boiler	chaudière *f* à moyenne pression	Mitteldruckkessel *m*	caldaia *f* a media pressione

	English	French	German	Italian
° 11432	medium pressure steam boiler	chaudière *f* à vapeur à pression moyenne	Mitteldruckdampf- kessel *m*	caldaia *f* a vapore a media pressione
— 11433	medium sand	sable *m* à grain moyen	mittelkörniger Sand *m*	sabbia *f* a grana media
° 11434	medium section	profil *m* moyen	mittelschweres Profil *n*	profilato *m* medio
° 11435	medium shape, medium section	profil *m* moyen	mittelschweres Profil *n*	profilato *m* medio
° 11436	medium soft-steel	acier *m* (de)mi-doux	halbweicher Stahl *m*	acciaio *m* semidolce
° 11437	medium steel	acier mi-dur	mittelharter Stahl *m*	acciaio *m* semiduro
° 11438	medium water- -capacity boiler	chaudière *f* à volume moyen	Mittelwasser- raumkessel *m*	caldaia *f* a medio corpo
— 11439	meerschaum	sépiolite *f*	Sepiolith *m*	schiuma *f* di mare, sepiolite *f*
— 11440	meeting the demand for iron ore	approvisionnement *m* en minerai	Deckung *f* des Erzbedarfes	coprire le richieste dei minerali

M.H. = *medium hardness*

	English	French	German	Italian
— 11441	meionite	méionite *f*	Mejonit *m*	meconite *f*
— 11442	melaconite	mélanconite *f*	Melaconit *m*	melaconite *f*
— 11443	melanite	mélanite *f*	Melanit *m*	melanite *f*
— 11444	melanocerite	mélanocérite *f*	Melanocerit *m*	melanocerite *f*
— 11445	melanocratic	mélanocrate	melanokrat	melanocratico
— 11446	melanophlogite	mélanophlogite *f*	Melanophlogit *m*	melanoflogite *f*
— 11447	melanotekite	mélanotékite *f*	Melanotekit *m*	melanotechite *f*
— 11448	melanovanadite	mélanovanadinite *f*	Melanovanadinit *m*	melanovanadinite *f*
— 11449	melanterite	mélantérite *f*	Melanterit *m*	melanterite *f*
— 11450	melaphyr(e)	mélaphyre *m*	Melaphyr *m*	melafiro *m*
— 11451	melilite	mélilite *f*	Melilith *m*	melilite *f*
— 11452	melinite	mélinite *f*	Melinit *m*	melinite *f*
— 11453	melinophane	mélinophane *m*	Melinophan	melinofano *m*

	English	French	German	Italian
— 11454	mellite	mellite *f*	Mellit *m*	mellite *f*
— 11455	melonite	melonite *f*	Melonit, Tellurnickel *m*	melonite *f*
° 11456	to melt	fondre	schmelzen	fondere
	to melt down, *s. to smelt*			
° 11457	to melt off, to melt out	séparer par fusion	abscheiden durch Schmelzen	separare mediante fusione
° 11458	melt	piquée *f*	Abstich *m*	colata *f*, spillata *f*
° 11459	meltable	fusible	schmelzbar	fusibile
° 11460	melted	fondu	geschmolzen	fuso
	melted iron, *s. liquid iron*			
° 11461	melter	creuset *m*, bassin *m* de coulée	Schmelztiegel *m*, Schmelzkessel *m*	bacino *m* di fusione
° 11462	melter, smelter, founder, ladler	fondeur *m*	Giesser *m*	fonditore *m*
° 11463	melting, fusing, fusion	fusion *f*	Schmelzen *n*	fusione *f*
° 11464	melting down	fusion *f*	Einschmelzen *n*	fusione *f*
° 11465	melting down process (pig iron and scrap)	procédé *m* par fusion de fonte et riblons	Zusammen-schmelzverfahren *n*	sistema *m* di fabbricazione dell'acciaio con ghisa e rottami
° 11466	melting-furnace, smelter	four *m* de fusion, fourneau *m* de fonderie	Schmelzofen *m*, Giessofen *m*	forno *m* di fusione, forno *m* fusorio, stufa *f* per fondere
° 11467	melting furnace for bronze	four *m* à bronze	Brennschmelzofen *m*	forno *m* fusorio per il bronzo
° 11468	melting-furnace for white metal	four à métal blanc	Weissmetallschmelz-ofen *m*	forno *m* fusorio per metallo bianco
° 11469	melting in a cupola furnace	fusion *f* au cubilot	Kuppelofenschmel-zen *n*	fusione *f* al cubilotto
° 11470	melting iron	gouttelettes *f pl.* de fonte	heruntersickerndes Eisen *n*	sgocciolamento *m* della ghisa
° 11471	melting kettle	creuset *m* de fonderie	Schmelztiegel *m*	crogiuolo *m* di fonderia

English	French	French	Italian
° 11472 **melting ladle**	poche f de coulée	Schmelzlöffel m, Giesspfanne f	siviera f di colata
° 11472a **melting loss**	pertes f pl. de fusion	Schmelzverluste m pl.	perdite f pl. di fusione
° 11473 **melting of slags**	fusion f du laitier	Schlackenver-schmelzen n	fusione f della loppa o della scoria
° 11474 **melting of the alloy**	fusion de l'alliage	Verschmelzung f der Legierung	fusione f della lega, liquazione f
° 11475 **melting point**	point m de fusion	Schmelzpunkt m	punto m di fusione
° 11476 **melting pot, crucible**	creuset, bassin de coulée	Tiegel m, Schmelzkessel m	crogiuolo m, bacino m di colata
° 11477 **melting range**	intervalle m de fusion	Schmelzintervall n	intervallo m di fusio-ne
° 11477a **melting rate**	vitesse f de fusion	Schmelzge-schwindigkeit m	velocità f di fusione
° 11478 **melting stock**	charge f	Beschickung f, Einsatz m	carica f
° 11479 **melting table**	table f de coulée	Giesstisch m	tavola f di colata
° 11480 **melting temperature**	chaleur f de fusion	Schmelzhitze f	temperatura f di fusione
° 11481 **melting tube**	petit tube m à fusion	Schmelzröhrchen n	tubetto m di fusione
° 11482 **melting under controlled at-mosphere**	fusion f en atmosphère contrô-lée	Schmelzen n unter Schutzgas	fusione f in atmosfe-ra controllata
° 11483 **melting unit**	four m de fusion	Schmelzofen m	forno m fusorio
° 11484 **melting zone**	zone f de fusion	Schmelzzone f	zona f di fusione
— 11485 **menaccanite**	ilménite f	Menaccanit m	menaccanite f
° 11486 **to mend**	surcharger	überlasten	sovraccaricare
11487 **to mend**	réparer	ausbessern	riparare
° 11488 **to mend cast iron**	souder la fonte	Gusseisen m schweissen	saldare la ghisa
— 11489 **mendelyeevite**	mendelyeevite f	Mendelejewit m	mendeleyevite f
— 11490 **mendipite**	mendipite f	Mendipit m	mendipite f
— 11491 **mendozite**	mendozite f	Mendozit m	mendozite f
— 11492 **meneghinite**	meneghinite f	Meneghinit m	meneghinite f
— 11493 **menhir**	menhir m	Menhir m	menhir m

English	French	German	Italian
— 11494 menilite	ménilite *f*	Menilit *m*	menilite *f*
⊃ 11495 Menne method	procédé *m* Menne	Menneverfahren *n*	processo *m* Menne
mercantile iron, *s. merchant-iron*			
merchant bar, *s. merchant iron*			
⊃ 11496 merchant-iron, commercial iron, mercantile iron, bar iron, finished iron	fer marchand, profilés *m pl.* (ou profils *m pl.)* du commerce	Handel(s)eisen *n*, Merkantileisen *n*	ferro *m* commerciale, ferro *m* mercantile, profilati *m pl.* commerciali
⊃ 11497 merchant-mill	laminoir *m* à fers marchands	Handelseisen-walzwerk *n*	laminatoio *n* per profilati commerciali
⊃ 11498 merchant steel	acier marchand	Handelsstahl *m*	acciaio *m* commerciale (o industriale)
— 11499 mercuric chloride	chlorure *m* de mercure	Quecksilberchlorid *n*	cloruro *m* di mercurio, sublimato *m* corrosivo
— 11500 mercuric oxide	oxyde *m* de mercure	Quecksilberoxyd *n*	ossido *m* di mercurio
— 11501 mercuric sulphide	sulfure *m* de mercure	Quecksilbersulfid *n*	sulfuro *m* di mercurio, cinabro *m*
— 11502 mercurous chloride	bichlorure *m* de mercure	Quecksilberchlorür *n*	cloruro *m* mercuroso, calomelano *m*
— 11503 mercury, quick silver	mercure *m*, vif-argent *m*	Quecksilber *n*	mercurio *m*
○ 11504 mercury boiler	chaudière *f* à mercure	Quecksilberkessel *f*	caldaia *f* a mercurio
○ 11505 mercury box	réservoir *m* à mercure	Quecksilberbüchse *f*	serbatoio *m* per mercurio
○ 11506 mercury lamp	lampe *f* à mercure	Quecksilberlampe *f*	lampada *f* a mercurio
○ 11507 mercury pressure gauge	manomètre *m* à mercure	Quecksilbermano-meter *n*	manometro *m* a mercurio
○ 11508 mercury steel bottle	récipient *m* à mercure	Quecksilberbehälter *m*	recipiente *m* per mercurio
○ 11509 mercury tongs	pince *f* à mercure	Quecksilberzange *f*	pinzetta *f* per mercurio
○ 11510 mercury trough	cuve *f* à mercure	Quecksilberwanne *f*	vasca *f* di mercurio
○ 11511 mercury vessel	récipient *m* à mercure	Quecksilbergefäss *n*	vaso *m* per mercurio

	English	French	German	Italian
−	11512 merocrystalline	hypocristallin	hypokristallin	ipocristallino
−	11513 meroxene	méroxène *m*	Meroxen *n*	meroxene *m*
−	11514 merrillite	merrillite *f*	Merrillit *m*	merrillite *f*
−	11515 merwinite	merwinite *f*	Merwinit *m*	merwinite *f*
o	11516 mesh	maille *f*	Masche *f*	maglia *f* (metallica)
o	11517 mesh iron sheet	tôle *f* striée	geriffeltes Blech *n*	lamiera *f* di ferro striata
−	11518 mesh sieve	tamis *m* à mailles	Maschensieb *n*	staccio *m* a maglie
−	11519 mesh structure	structure *f* maillée	Maschenstruktur *f*	struttura *f* a maglie (o reticolare)
−	11520 meshed	maillé, réticulé	gemascht	a maglie, reticolare
−	11521 mesocratic	mésocrate	mesocrat	mesocrato
−	11522 mesolite	mésolite *f*	Mesolith *m*	mesolito *m*
−	11523 mesosilicic rock	roche *f* neutre	mesosilizisches Gestein *n*	roccia *f* neutra
−	11524 mesostasis	mésostasis *f*	Mesostasis *f*	mesostasi *f*
−	11525 mesothermal vein	filon *m* mésothermal	mesothermaler Gang *m*	filone *m* mesotermale
−	11526 mesothorium	mésothorium *m*	Mesothorium *n*	mesotorio *m*
−	11527 mesotype	mesotype *m*	Mesotyp *m*	mesotipo *m*
−	11528 Mesozoic era	groupe *m* mésozoïque	Mesozoikum *n*	mesozoico *m*
−	11529 mesozone	mésozone *f*	Mesozone *f*	mesozona *f*
−	11530 messelite	messélite *f*	Messelit *m*	messelite *f*
−	11531 metabrushite	métabrushite *f*	Metabrushit *m*	metabruscite *f*
−	11532 metacinnabarite	métacinabre *m*	Metacinnabarit *m*	metacinabro *m*
−	11533 metacryst(al)	porphyroblaste *m*	Porphiroblast *m*	porfiroblasto *m*
−	11534 metaheulandite	métaheulandite *f*	Metaheulandit *m*	metaheulandite *f*
−	11535 metahewettite	métahewettite *f*	Metahewettit *m*	metahewettite

English	French	German	Italian
11536 to metal	réguler	Lager mit Weissmetall ausgiessen	rivestire con metallo bianco
11537 metal	métal *m*, mincrai *m*, fonte *f*	Metall *n*, Erz *n*, Gusseisen *n*	metallo *m*, minerale *m*, ghisa *f*
11538 metal alloy	alliage *m* métallique	Metallegierung *f*	lega *f* metallica
metal bath, *s. layer of metal*			
11539 metal cutting	façonnage *m* par enlèvement de copeaux	spanabhebende Verformung *f*	lavorazione *f* con asportazione di truccioli
11540 metal cutting tools	outils *m pl.* pour l'usinage des métaux	Werkzeuge *n pl.* für Metallbearbeitung	utensili *m pl.* per tagliare metallo
11541 metal degreasing	dégraissage *m*	Entfettung *f*	sgrassatura *f*
11542 metal drift	galerie *f* au stérile	Gesteinsstrecke *f*	galleria *f* in roccia
11542a metal fog	brouillard *m* métallique	Metallnebel *m*	nebbia *f* metallica
11543 metal for medals, medal bronze	bronze *m* à monnais	Münz(en)bronze *f*, Medaillenbronze *f*	bronzo *m* da monete
11544 metal framework	structure *f* métallique	Stahlgerüst *n*	struttura *f* metallica
11545 metal gauze	toile métallique	Metallgewebe *n*	rete *f* metallica
11546 metal goods	articles *m pl.* en métal	Metallwaren *f pl.*	oggetti *m pl.* metallici
11547 metal high-level opening lights	chassis-impostes *m* ouvrants en acier	Kippflügelober-lichter aus Stahl	serramenti *m pl.* in acciaio apribili
11548 metal insert	pièce *f* d'usure de boîte	Verschleisseinlage *f* des Kernkastens	inserto *m* metallico
11549 metal-man	mineur *m* à la roche	Felshauer *m*	minatore *m* alla roccia
11550 metal mixer	mélangeur *m* de fonte	Roheisenmischer *m*	mescolatore *m* di ghisa
11551 metal mould	coquille *f*	Kokille *f*	conchiglia *f*
11552 metal moulds for reinforced concrete castings	caissons *m pl.* métalliques pour bétonnages	Metallschalen *f pl.* für Betonguss	casserature *f pl.* metalliche per getti in cemento armato
11553 metal notch	trou *m* de coulée	Abstichöffnung *f*	foro *m* di colata

	English	French	German	Italian
°	11554 **metal packing**	garniture *f* métallique	Metalldichtung *f*	guarnizione *f* metallica
—	11555 **metal penetration**	abreuvage *m*	Einbrennen *n* des Eisens	infiltrazione *f* (metallica)
°	11556 **metal penetration**	défoncement *m*	abgerissene Form *f*	sfondamento *m*, penetrazione *f* di metallo (nella forma)
°	11557 **metal penetration**	coquille *f* d'oeuf abreuvante	Schalenbildung *f*	segregazione *f* infiltrata
°	11557a **metal polish**	moyen *m* de polissage	Putzmittel *n*	pasta *f* per lucidare
—	11558 **metal prop**	étançon *m* métallique	Metallpyrometer *n*	pirometro *m* metallico
°	11559 **metal pyrometer**	pyromètre *m* métallique	Metallpyrometer *n*	pirometro *m* metallico

metal rolled bar, *s. flat*

metal shaving, *s. chips of metal*

	English	French	German	Italian
°	11560 **metal sheetings with continuous support**	feuilles *f pl.* de métal sur appui continu	Metalldachplatten *f pl.* auf Schalung	lamiere *f pl.* metalliche su appoggio continuo
—	11561 **metal sieve**	tamis *m* à mailles	Maschensieb *n*	setaccio *m* (o vaglio) a maglia
°	11562 **metal spraying**	metallisation *f* au pistolet	Metallspritzen *n*	metallizzazione *f* a spruzzo
°	11563 **metal sprazing gun**	pistolet *m* pour métallisation	Metallspritzpistole *f*	pistola *f* spruzzatrice per metalli
°	11564 **metal-turning lathe**	tour *m* à métaux	Metalldrehbank *f*	tornio *m* per metalli
°	11565 **metal working**	travail *m* des métaux	Metallbearbeitung *f*	lavorazione *m* dei metalli
°	11566 **metallic**	métallique	metallisch	metallico
—	11567 **metallic arsenic**	arsenic *m* natif	Scherbenkobalt *n*, metallisches Arsen *n*	arsenico *m* nativo
°	11567a **metallic coating**	revêtement *m* métallique	Metallüberzug *m*	rivestimento *m* metallico
°	11568 **metallic iron**	fer *m* métallique	metallisches Eisen *n*	ferro *m* metallico
°	11569 **metallic mercury**	mercure *m* métallique	metallisches Quecksilber *n*	mercurio *m* metallico
°	11570 **metallic raw**	matières premières métalliques	metallische Rohstoffe *m pl.*	materie *f pl.* prime metalliche

	English	French	German	Italian
11571	metallic salt	sel *m* métallique	Metallsalz *n*	sale *m* metallico
11572	metallic silver	argent *m* métallique	metallisches Silber *n*	argento *m* metallico
11573	metallic sounding	rendant un son métallique	metallisch klingend	di suono metallico
	metallic vein, *s. mineral vein*			
	metalliferous, *s. ore bearing*			
11574	metallization	métallisation *f*	Metallisierung *f*	metallizzazione *f*
11575	to metallize	métalliser	metallisieren	metallizzare
11576	metallized carbons	charbons *m pl.* métallisés	metallisierte Kohlen *f pl.*	carboni *m pl.* metallizzati
11577	metallizing	métallisation *f*	Metallisierung *f*	metallizzazione *f*
11578	metallogenetic	métallogénétique	metallogenetisch	metallogenetico
11579	metallogenic	métallogénique	metallogenisch	metallogenico
11580	metallographic equipment	installation *f* métallographique	metallographische Einrichtung *f*	impianto *m* metallografico
11581	metallographic examination	recherche *f* métallographique	Metalluntersuchung *f*	ricerca *f* metallografica
11582	metallographic test	examen *m* métallographique	metallographische Untersuchung *f*	esame *m* metallografico
11583	metallography	métallographie *f*	Metallographie *f*	metallografia *f*
11584	metalloid	métalloïde *m*	Metalloid *n*	metalloide
11585	metallurgical coke	coke *m* métallurgique	Hüttenkoks *m*	coke *m* metallurgico
11586	metallurgical furnace	four *m* métallurgique	metallurgischer Ofen *m*	forno *m* metallurgico
11587	metallurgical industry	industrie *f* métallurgique	Hüttenindustrie *f*	industria *f* metallurgica
11588	metallurgical process	procédé métallurgique	hüttenmännischer Vorgang *m*	processo *m* metallurgico
11589	metallurgical treatment	traitement *m* métallurgique	hüttenmännische Behandlung *f*	trattamento *m* metallurgico

	English	French	German	Italian
o	11590 metallurgy of ferrous metals	métallurgie f des métaux ferreux	Eisenmetallurgie f	metallurgia f dei metalli ferrosi
o	11591 metallurgy of non- -ferrous metals	métallurgie des métaux autres que le fer	Nichteisenmetal- lurgie f	metallurgia f dei metalli non férrosi
—	11592 metamorphic	métamorphique	metamorphisch	metamorfico
—	11593 metamorphic rocks, phyllocrystalline rocks	roches f pl. cristal- lophylliennes, ro- ches f pl. métamor- phiques	metamorphe Gesteine n pl.	rocce f pl. metamorfi- che
—	11593a metamorphism	métamorphisme m	Metamorphie f	metamorfismo m
—	11594 metamorphosed rock	roche f métamor- phisée	metamorphes Gestein n	roccia f metamorfiz- zata
—	11595 metapepsis	métamorphisme m régional	Regionalmetamor- phose f	metamorfismo m regio- nale
—	11596 metarossite	métarossite f	Metarossit m	metarossite f
—	11597 metasilicate	métasilicate m	Metasilikat n	metasilicato m
—	11598 metasomatic deposit	gisement m métasomatique	metasomatische Lagerstätte f	giacimento m metaso- matico
—	11599 metasomatic vein	filon métasomatique	metasomatischer Gang m	filone m metasomatico
—	11600 metasomatism	métasomatose f, substitution f	Metasomatose f, Verdrängung f	metasomatosi f, sostituzione f
—	11601 metasome	métasome m	Metasome m	metasome m
—	11602 metastibnite	métastibnite f	Metastibnit m	metastibnite f
—	11603 metathenardite	métathénardite f	Metathenardit m	metatenardite f
—	11604 metatype	métatype m	Metatypus m	metatipo m
—	11605 metavariscite	métavariscite f	Metavariszit m	metavariscite f
—	11606 metavoltine	métavoltite f	Metavoltin m	metavoltite f
—	11607 meteoric iron	fer m météorique	Meteoreisen n	ferro m meteorico
o	11608 meter scale	mètre m pliant	Metermassstab m	scala f metrica
o	11609 metering distributor	distributeur-doseur m	Zuteiler m, Dosiereinrichtung f	distributore-dosatore m
o	11610 metering separator	séparateur calibré	Mess-Separator m	separatore m calibrato

	English	French	German	Italian
^ 11611	methane pipeline	conduite *f* de méthane	Methanfernleitung *f*	metanodotto *m*
	method, *s. system*			
11612	method of analysis	méthode *f* d'analyse	Analysenmethode *f*	metodo *m* d'analisi
	method of calcination, *s. method of roasting*			
− 11613	method of mining	méthode *f* d'exploitation	Abbauverfahren *n*	metodo *m* di coltivazione
− 11614	method of roasting	procédé *m* de grillage	Röstverfahren *n*	procedimento *m* di torrefazione
− 11615	method of treatment	mode *m* de traitement	Behandlungsweise *f*	modo *m* di trattamento
− 11616	meymacite	meymacite *f*	Meymacit *m*	meymacite *f*
− 11617	miargyrite	miargyrite *f*	Miargyrit *m*	miargirite *f*
− 11618	miarolitic cavity	cavité *f* miarolitique	miarolitischer Hohlraum *m*	cavità *f* miarolita
− 11619	miarolitic texture	texture *f* miarolitique	miarolithische Textur *f*	struttura *f* miarolitica
− 11620	miascite, miaskite	miaskite	Miaskit *m*	miaschite *f*
− 11621	mica	mica *f*	Glimmer *m*	mica *f*
− 11622	mica flakes	paillettes *f pl.* de mica	Glimmerschuppen *f pl.*	lamelle *f pl.* di mica
− 11623	mica schist, mica slate	micaschiste *m*	Glimmerschiefer *m*	micascisto *m*
	mica-slate, *s. mica-schist*			
− 11624	mica plate	plaque *f* en mica	Glimmerplatte *f*	lastrina *f* di mica
° 11625	mica spectacles	lunettes *f pl.* en mica	Glimmerbrille *f*	occhiali *m pl.* di mica
− 11626	micaceous iron-ore	fer *m* micacé, fer oligiste	Eisenglimmer *m*	(ferro) *m* oligisto micaceo
− 11627	micaceous structure	structure *f* feuilletée	blätterige Struktur *f*	struttura *f* lanellare
− 11628	micanite	micanite *f*	Mikanit *n*	micanite *f*

English	French	German	Italian
— 11629 microaphanitic texture	structure f pétrosiliceuse	mikrofelsitische Struktur f	struttura f petrosiliciosa
— 11630 microchemical analysis	analyse f microchimique	mikrochemische Analyse f	analisi f microchimica
— 11631 microclastic	microclastique	mikroklastisch	microclastico
— 11632 microcline	microcline f	Mikroklin m	microcline f
— 11633 microcline-perthite	microcline-perthite	Mikroklinperthit m	microclinpertite f
— 11634 microcrypto--crystalline	microcrypto-cristallin	mikrokryptokristallin	microcriptocristallino
— 11635 microfelsitic texture	structure f pétrosiliceuse	mikrofelsitische Struktur f	struttura f petrosilicea, struttura f felsofirica
— 11636 microgranitic texture	structure f microgranitique	mikrogranitische Struktur f	struttura f microgranitica
° 11637 micrograph	micrographie f	Mikrobild n	micrografia f
° 11638 micrographic	micrographique	mikrographisch	micrografico
— 11639 micrographic intergrowth	structure f micrographique	mikropegmatitische Struktur f	struttura f micrografica
micrographic texture, $s.$ micrographic intergrowt			
° 11639a microhardness	microdureté f	Mikrohärte f	microdurezza f
— 11640 microlite	microlite f	Mikrolith m	microlite f
— 11641 microlitic	microlitique	mikrolitisch	microlitico
° 11642 micrometer calipers $pl.$	compas m d'épaisseur micrométrique	Feinschraubzirkel m, Mikrometerzirkel m	compasso m micrometrico
° 11643 micrometer screw gauge	palmer m, jauge f micrométrique	Feinstellschraube f, Mikrometerschraube f	micrometro m
— 11644 micromeritic	microméritique	mikromeritisch	micromeritico
— 11645 micropaleontology	micropaléontologie f	Mikropaleontologie f	micropaleontologia
— 11646 micropegmatite	micropegmatite f	Mikropegmatit m	micropegmatite
— 11647 microperthite	microperthite f	Mikroperthit m	micropertite
— 11648 microphyric	microphyrique	mikrophyrisch	microfirico
— 11649 micropoikilitic texture	structure f micropoecilitique	mikropoikilitische Struktur f	struttura f micropoecilitica

English	French	German	Italian
11650 microscope lamp	lampe f pour microscope	Mikroskoplampe f	lampada f da micro-scopio
° 11651 microscopy	examen m microscopique	mikroskopische Untersuchung f	microscopia f
° 11652 micro-section, micro-slice	plaquette f polie micrographique	Mikroschliff m	pezzo m levigato
° 11653 micro-segregation	ségrégation f mineure	Mikroseigerung f, Kornseigerung f	microsegregazione f
° 11654 micro-shrinkage	microretassure f	Mikrolunker m	microrisucchio m, microritiro m
microasphanitic texture, s. microfelsitic texture			
° 11655 microstructure	microstructure f	Mikrogefüge n, Feingefüge n	microstruttura f
— 11656 microtinite	microtinite f	Mikrotinit m	microtinite f
° 11657 microwelding phenomena	phénomènes m $pl.$ de microsoudure	Mikroschweissphä-nomene n $pl.$	fenomeni m $pl.$ di microsaldatura
˄ 11658 mid-continent petroleum	pétrole avec paraf-fine et asphalte	Erdöl mit Paraffin u. Asphalt	petrolio m con paraf-tina e asfalto
° 11658a mid-part	chape f	Formmittelteil m	fascia f
° 11659 middle	goulot m	Einschnüren n	strozzatura f
° 11660 middle box	châssis m intermédiaire	Mittelkasten m	fascia f
— 11661 middle limb	flanc m médian	Mittelschenkel m	fianco m mediano
— 11662 middle man	intercalation f stérile (entre deux couches)	Zwischenmittel n	intercalazione f sterile (fra due strati)
° 11663 middle pass	cannelure f intermédiaire	Entwicklungskaliber n	calibro m interme-diario
° 11664 middle ring	ceinture f intermédiaire	Zwischenring m	anello m intermedio
° 11665 middle roll	cylindre m médian	Mittelwalze f	cilindro m di mezzo
° 11666 middling	forgeage du goulot	Einschnüren-schmieden n	fucinatura f della strozzatura
— 11667 middling	mixte m	Mittelgut n	granaglia f
— 11667a middling	coupe f intermé-diaire	Zwischenschnitt m	taglio m intermedio

	English	French	German	Italian
^ 11668	midget ratchet wrench	manche *m* à cric pour clefs à douille	Handgriff *m* für Kompassschlüssel	impugnatura *f* a cricco per chiavi a bussola
— 11669	miersite	miersite *f*	Miersit *m*	miersite *f*
— 11670	miesite	miésite *f*	Miesit *m*	miesite *f*
— 11671	migmatite	migmatite *f*	Migmatit *m*	migmatite *f*
— 11672	miharaite	miharaïte *f*	Miharait *m*	miharaite *f*
— 11673	mijakite	mijakite *f*	Mijakit *m*	mijakite *f*
— 11674	milarite	milarite *f*	Milarit *m*	milarite *f*
° 11675	mild iron	fer *m* doux	Weicheisen *n*	ferro *m* dolce
	mild carbon steel, *s. soft steel*			
° 11676	mild cast steel	acier *m* fondu soudable	schweissbarer Gussstahl *m*	acciaio *m* fuso saldabile
° 11677	mild cauliflowering	rochage *m*	Blumenkohlbildung *f*	ribollimento *m*, formazione *f* di cricche sulla crosta superficiale
° 11678	mild steel, low (carbon) steel, ingot iron	acier *m* doux, fer homogène	Weichstahl *m*, Schiffbaustahl *m*	acciaio *m* dolce, ferro *m* omogeneo
° 11679	mild steel for automatic lathes	acier *m* doux de décolletage	Automatenweichstahl *m*	acciaio *m* dolce per torni automatici
° 11680	mild steel plate	tôle *f* en acier doux	Flusseisenblech *n*	lamiera *f* di ferro omogeneo
	milk white opal, *s. white opal*			
— 11681	milky quartz	quartz *m* laiteux	Milchquarz *m*	quarzo *m* lattiginoso
° 11682	to mill	moudre, laminer, fräsen	mahlen, walzen, fräsen	macinare, laminare, fresare
^ 11683	to mill away	détruire une section de casing	eine Casingstrecke *f* abhauen	distruggere un tratto di casing
° 11684	to mill off	réduire à la fraise	auf der Fräsbank *f* reduzieren	ridurre alla fresa
— 11685	mill	moulin *m*, broyeur *m*	Mühle *f*	mulino *m*, frantoio *m*
11686	mill	usine *f*	Fabrik *f*	fabbrica *f*
— 11687	mill	installation *m* de préparation mécanique	Aufbereitungsanlage *f*	impianto *m* di laveria meccanica

	English	French	German	Italian
°	11688 **mill**	laminoir *m*	Walzwerk *n*	laminatoio *m*, treno *m* di laminazione
°	11689 **mill**	fraise *f*	Fräse *f*	fresa *f*
–	11690 **mill**	cheminée *f* à minerai	Stürzrolle *f*	scivolo *m*, piano *m* inclinato
	mill approach table, *s. run-up table*			
°	11691 **mill bar**	fer *m* ébauché	Rohschiene *f*	ferro *m* sbozzato
°	11692 **mill cinder, mill scale**	battitures *f pl.* des laminoirs	Walzensinter *m*	scaglie *f pl.* di laminatoio, scoria *f* di puddellaggio
°	11693 **mill defects**	défauts *m pl.* de laminage	Walzfehler *m pl.*	difetti *m pl.* di laminatura
°	11693a **mill finish**	finissage *m* au laminoir	Walzfertigung *f*	finitura *f* al laminatoio
–	11694 **mill hole**	cheminée *f* à minerai, trémie *f* dans la roche	Stürzrolle *f*, Trichterschurre *f*	piano *m* inclinato (o scivolo *m*) per minerali, tramoggia *f* nella roccia
	mill housing, *s. mill stand*			
°	11695 **mill limit**	tolérance de laminage	Walzentoleranz *f*	tolleranza *f* di laminazione
°	11696 **mill man**	lamineur *m*	Walzer *m*	laminatore *m*
°	11697 **mill pack**	paquet *m* de tôles	Plattenpaket *n*	pacco *m* di lamiere
	mill process, *s. direct process*			
–	11698 **mill run**	campagne *f* du bocard	Pochwerk-Laufzeit *f*	campagna *f* del frantoio
°	11699 **to mill sand**	frotter un sable	einen Sand mischkollern	molazzare una sabbia
°	11700 **mill scale**	calamine *f* de recuit	Glühzunder *m*	scaglia *f* di ricottura
°	11701 **mill steel wire**	fil *m* d'acier fondu	Flussstahldraht *m*	filo *m* d'acciaio fuso
°	11701a **mill table**	ligne *f* des rouleaux	Rollgang *m*	linea *f* dei rulli
°	11702 **mill train, train of rolls**	train *m* de laminoir	Walzstrecke *f*, Walzstrasse *f*	treno *m* del laminatoio
°	11703 **milled**	laminé	gewalzt	laminato
°	11704 **milled nail for fruit packing**	pointe *f* fraisée pour caisses à fruits	gefräster Stift *m* für Obstkisten	punta *f* fresata per casse da frutta
–	11705 **millerite**	millérite *f*	Millerit *m*	millerite *f*
–	11706 **milling**	broyage *m*	Brechen *n*	macinazione *f*, frantumazione
°	11706a **milling**	fraisage *m*	Fräsen *n*	fresatura *f*

	English	French	German	Italian
°	11707 milling	frottage *m*	Kollern *n*	molazzatura *f*
°	11707a milling	moletage *m*	Rändeln *n*	granitura *f*
°	11708 milling cutter	fraise *f*	Fräser *m*	fresa *f*
°	11709 milling guide	cloche *f* à fraise	Fräserglocke *f*	campana *f* di guida a fresa
−	11710 milling ore	minerai de broyage	aufbereitetes Erz *n*, Pocherz *n*	minerale *m* da macinare
−	11711 milling pit	cheminée *m* à minerai	Trichterschurre *f*	piano *m* inclinato (o scivolo) per minerali
−	11712 milling shoe	sabot *m* de fraisage	Frässchuh *m*	scarpa *f* per «overshot»
−	11713 milling system	exploitation *f* par entonnoirs souterrains	Gewinnung *f* mit Trichterschurren	coltivazione *f* ad imbuti sotterranei
^	11714 milling tools	outils *m pl.* de fraisage	Fräswerkzeuge *n pl.*	attrezzi *m pl.* per uscire da un casing (o per ricostituire una filettatura a maschio)
−	11715 millisite	millisite *f*	Millisit *m*	millisite *f*
°	11716 millstone	meule *f*	Mühlstein *m*	mola *f*
−	11717 millstone grit	grès *m* houiller	Kohlensandstein *m*	arenaria *f* carbonifera, gres *m* carbonifero
−	11718 miloschite	miloschine *f*	Miloschin *m*	miloschine *f*
−	11719 mimesite	mimésite *f*	Mimesit *m*	mimesite *f*, mimosite *f*
−	11720 mimetesite	mimétésite *f*	Mimetesit *m*	mimetesite *f*
−	11721 minable	exploitable	abbauwürdig	coltivabile
−	11722 minder	encageur	Anschläger *m*, Füllortarbeiter *m*	ingabbiatore *m*
−	11723 to mine	miner, creuser, creuser, exploiter	minieren, abbauen	minare, scavare, coltivare, sfruttare (una miniera)
−	11724 mine	mine *f*	Grube *f*, Bergwerk *n*	miniera *f*
−	11725 mine adits, galleries	galeries *f pl.*	Stollen *m pl.*	gallerie *f pl.*

English	French	German	Italian

mine air, s. air in a mine

mine car, s. trolley

— 11726 mine dam	serrement *m*	Grubendamm *m*	sbarramento *m*
— 11727 mine dial	boussole *f* de mineur	Grubenkompass *m*	bussola *f* per miniere
— 11728 mine drainway	albraque	Sumpfstrecke *f*	galleria *f* di drenaggio
— 11729 mine earth	gîte *m* de minerai de fer	Eisenerzlager *n*	giacimento *m* di minerale di ferro
— 11730 mine face	front *m* de taille	Grubenort *m*	fronte *m* d'avanzamento (o di taglio)
— 11731 mine foreman	porion *m*, maître-mineur	Obersteiger *m*	capo-squadra *m*
— 11732 mine gallery	galerie *f* au jour	Stollen *m*	galleria *f* a giorno
— 11733 mine head frame	chevalement *m*	Fördergerüst *n*	castelletto *m*, incastellatura
— 11734 mine igniter	boutefeu *m*	Schiessmeister *m*	artificiere *m*
— 11735 mine level	galerie *f* de niveau	Niveaustrecke *f*	galleria *f* di livello
— 11736 mine openings	travaux *m pl.* préparatoires	Vorrichtungsbaue *m pl.*	lavori *m pl.* preparatori
— 11737 mine out	exploiter	gewinnen	coltivare, sfruttare
— 11738 mine prop	étançon *m* de mines	Grubenstempel *m*	puntello *m* di miniera
— 11739 mine run	tout-venant *m*	Fördererz *n*	minerale *m* di prima estrazione
— 11740 mine-shaft	puits (d'une mine)	Schacht *m*	pozzo *m* (di miniera)
— 11741 mine slack	menus non classés	Fördergrus *m*	minerale *m* non cernito
— 11742 mine station	gare *f* d'usine	Hüttenbahnhof *m*	stazione *f* metallurgica
— 11743 mine tin	étain *m* de roche	Bergzinn *n*	stagno *m* di roccia
— 11744 mine transit	tachéomètre *m* pour mines	Tachometer *m* für Gruben	tacheometro *m* per miniera
— 11745 mine ventilation	aération *f* (ou aérage) des mines	Grubenlüftung *f*	aerazione *f* (o ventilazione) delle miniere

English	French	German	Italian
— 11746 **miner**	mineur *m*	Bergmann *m*, Bergknappe *m*	minatore *m*
— 11747 **miner's lamp**	lampe de mineur	Grubenlampe *f*	lampada *f* da miniera
— 11748 **miner's rammer**	refouloir *m*	Schlägel *m*, Stampfer *m*	calcatoio *m*
— 11749 **mineral** **mineral caoutchouc**, *s. elastic bitumen* **mineral charcoal**, *s. fossil charcoal*	minerai *m*	Mineral *n*	minerale *m*
— 11750 **mineral colour**	couleur *f* minérale	Mineralfarbe *f*	colore *m* minerale
— 11751 **mineral deposit**	gisement *m* minéral, gîte minier	Lagerstätte *f* eines Minerals	giacimento *m* minerario
— 11752 **mineral extracted**	charbon *m* extrait, houille *f* extraite	gewonnene Kohle *f*	carbone *m* estratto
^ 11753 **mineral oil, crude oil, crude**	huile (minérale), pétrole *m*	(Erd)öl, Petroleum *n*	olio *m* minerale, petrolio *m*, olio *m* grezzo
— 11754 **mineral spot**	inclusion *f* minérale	Mineraleinschluss *m*	inclusione *f* minerale
^ 11755 **mineral spirits**	ligroïne *f*	Lackbenzin *n*, Testbenzin *n*	distillati *m pl.* leggeri
— 11756 **mineral vein**	filon (métallifère)	Gang *m*, Erzgang *m*	filone *m* (metallifero)
— 11757 **mineralizable**	minéralisable	vererzbar	mineralizzabile
— 11758 **mineralization**	minéralisation *f*	Vererzung *f*	mineralizzazione *f*
— 11759 **to mineralize**	minéraliser	mineralisieren	mineralizzare
— 11760 **mineralized carbon, impregnated coal**	charbon minéralisé	Flammkohle *f*	carbone *m* a fiamma (o mineralizzato)
— 11761 **mineralized product**	produit *m* riche en métal	haltiges Gut *n*	prodotto *m* utile
— 11762 **miineralizing agents**	agents *m pl.* minéralisateurs	Mineralbildner *m pl.*	agenti *m pl.* mineralizzanti
— 11763 **mineralizing fault**	faille *f* nourricière	mineralisierende Verwerfung *f*	faglia *f* mineralizzata
— 11763a **mineralogy**	minéralogie *f*	Mineralogie *f*	mineralogia *f*
— 11764 **minery**	district *m* minier	Grubenbezirk *m*	distretto *m* minerario
— 11765 **minette**	minette *f*	Minette *f*	minetta *f*

	English	French	German	Italian
− 11766	minguetite	minguétite *f*	Minguetit *m*	minguetite *f*
11767	minimum demand	demande *f* minimum (d'énergie)	geringster Bedarf *m*	consumo *m* minimo
○ 11768	minimum hot yield point	limite *f* inférieure d'étirage à chaud	Mindest-Warmstreckgrenze *f*	limite *m* minimo di snervamento a caldo
− 11769	mining	exploitation *f* minière, industrie *f* minière	Bergbau *m*	coltivazione *f* di miniere, industria *f* mineraria, lavoro *m* di scavo
− 11770	mining by blasting	abattage *m* par explosifs	Sprengarbeit *f*	abbattimento *m* con esplosivi
− 11771	mining cable	câble *m* de mine	Grubenkabel *n*	cavo *m* per miniere
− 11772	mining car, miner's waggon, miner's truck	wagonnet *m*, chien *m*	Grubenwagen *m*, Hund *m*, Förderhund *m*	vagonetto *m* per miniera
− 11773	mining drill steel	acier *m* pour perforation de roches	Gesteinsbohrstahl *m*	acciaio *m* per barramine
− 11774	mining floor	niveau *m* d'abattage	Abbausohle *f*	livello *m* d'abbattimento
− 11775	mining geology	géologie *f* minière	Montangeologie *f*	geologia *f* mineraria
− 11776	mining industry	industrie *f* minière	Bergbau *m*	industria *f* mineraria
− 11777	mining machine	haveuse *f*, machine de mine	Schrämmaschine *f*, Bergwerksmaschine *f*	intagliatrice *f* per carbone, machina *f* per miniera
− 11778	mining method	méthode *m* d'exploitation	Abbauverfahren *n*	metodo *m* d'estrazione (o di coltivazione)
− 11779	mining retreating	exploitation *f* en rabattant	Rückbau *m*	coltivazione *f* in ritirata
	mining supplies, *s. mining tools*			
− 11780	mining tools *pl.*	outillage *m* de mines	Werkzeuge für Bergwerke	utensili *m pl.* per mine
− 11781	miniphyric structure	texture *f* microporphyrique	mikroporphyrische Struktur *f*	struttura *f* microporfirica
− 11782	minor arch	anticlinal *m* secondaire	Nebensattel *m*	anticlinale *f* secondaria

English	French	German	Italian
− 11783 **minor fold, secundary fold**	pli secondaire, ondulation *f* secondaire	Spezialfalte *f*	piega *f* secondaria
− 11784 **minor intrusion**	petite *f* intrusion	Kleinintrusion *f*	piccola intrusione *f*, intrusione *f* minore
− 11785 **minor mineral**	minéral *m* accessoire	zusätzliches Erz *n*	minerale *m* accessorio
to mint, *s. to coin*			
minting, *s. coinage*			
− 11786 **minus -minerals**	minéraux *m pl.* formés avec réduction de volume	Minusmineralien *n pl.*	minerali *m pl.* formati con riduzione di volume
− 11787 **minute folding**	plissement *m*	Fältelung *f*	pieghettatura *f*
− 11788 **minverite**	minvérite *f*	Minverit *m*	minverite *f*
− 11789 **Miocene epoch**	miocène *m*	Miozän *n*	miocene *m*
− 11790 **mirabilite**	mirabilite *f*	Mirabilit *m*	mirabilite *f*
− 11791 **mire**	terrain boueux	Schlammgrund *m*	terreno *m* impantanato di fango
mirror bronze, *s. speculum metal*			
− 11792 **mirror - stone**	muscovite *f*	Muskovit *m*	muscovite *f*
^ 11793 **misaligned**	non centré	unzentriert	non centrato, non allineato
∘ 11794 **miscibility**	miscibilité *f*	Mischbarkeit *f*	miscibilità *f*
∘ 11795 **miscibility gap**	intervalle *m* de miscibilité	Mischungslücke *f*	intervallo *m* di miscibilità
∘ 11796 **miscible**	miscible	mischbar	miscibile
− 11797 **misenite**	misénite *f*	Misenit *m*	misenite *f*
− 11798 **misfire, failure**	allumage *m* défectueux	Fehlzündung *f*	accensione *f* difettosa
∘ 11799 **mismatch**	variation *f*	Gussversatz *m*	variazione *f*, spostamento *m* sul giunto
∘ 11799a **mismatch**	déplacement *m*	Veschiebung *f*	spostamento *m*
∘ 11800 **mismatch in core**	variation *f* de noyau	versetzter Kern *m*, Kernversatz *m*	anima *f* variata (o spostata), variazione *f* dell'anima

English	French	German	Italian
o 11801 **mismatch in metal mould**	variation *f* de coquille	versetzte Kokille *f*, Kokillenversatz *m*	conchiglia *f* variata (o spostata), variazione *f* della conchiglia
o 11802 **mismatch in mould**	variation *f* de moule	Formversatz *m*	forma *f* variata (o spostata), variazione *f* della forma
o 11803 **mismatch in pattern**	variation *f* de modèle	versetztes Modell *n*, Modellversatz *m*	variazione *f* del modello
o 11804 **mismatch in pattern-plate**	variation *f* de plaque modèle	versetzte Modellplatte *f*	placca *f* variata, variazione *f* della placca
mispickel, *s. arsenical pyrites*			
o 11805 **misplaced core**	noyau *m* déplacé	verlorener Kern *m*	anima *f* perduta
o 11806 **misrun**	mal venu	schlecht ausgelaufen	difettoso
o 11807 **misrun casting**	fusion *f* mal venue	schlecht ausgelaufener Guss *m*	fusione *f* difettosa
missing fire, *s. failure*			
— 11808 **missourite**	missourite *f*	Missourit *m*	missourite *f*
^ 11809 **mist condition**	condition de brume	nebelförmiger Zustand *m*	condizione *f* di nebbia
^ 11810 **mist drilling**	forage à l'air humide	Feuchtluftbohrung *f*	perforazione *f* pneumatica con iniezione di acqua
— 11811 **mist projector**	pulvérisateur *f* d'eau	Brause *f*	polverizzatore *m* d'acqua
— 11812 **misy**	copiapite *f*	Copiapit *m*	copiapite *f*
— 11813 **mitis casting**	jet *m* de fer malléable, fonte *f* malléable	Temperguss *m*	getto *f* di ferro malleabile, ghisa *f* malleabile
— 11814 **mitis metal**	fonte *f* malléable	Temperguss *m*	ghisa *f* malleabile
— 11815 **mitred angle bars** *pl.*	fer *m* travaillé en onglet	auf Gehrung *f* gearbeitetes Eisen *n*	ferro *m* tagliato ad ugnatura
— 11816 **to mix**	malaxer	kneten	impastare
— 11817 **to mix**	mélanger	mischen	miscelare, mescolare, mischiare

	English	French	German	Italian
°	11818 **to mix together**	mélanger	(durcheinander-) mischen	mescolare insieme
^	11819 **mixed aniline point**	point *m* d'aniline	Anilinpunkt *m*	punto *m* di anilina
^	11820 **mixed-base oil**	pétrole *m* de base mixte	Mischöl *n*	petrolio *m* a base mista
−	11821 **mixed coke**	coke tout venant	unsortierter Koks *m* aller Korngrössen	coke *m* come viene (o non cernito)
−	11822 **mixed crystals** *pl.*	cristaux *m pl.* mixtes	Mischkristalle *m pl.*	cristalli *m pl.* misti
°	11823 **mixed iron**	fer *m* pour le mélange	Mischeisen *n*	ferro *m* da mescolare
°	11824 **mixed scrap**	ferraille *f*	Schrott *m*	rottame *m* ferroso
−	11825 **mixer**	malaxeur *m*	Kneter *m*	impastatrice *f*, macchina *f* per impastare
°	11826 **mixer**	mélangeur *m*	Mischer *m*	mescolatore *m*
°	11826a **mixer metal**	fonte *f* brute de mélangeur	Mischerroheisen *n*	ferro *m* crudo di mescolatore
°	11827 **mixer platform**	plate-forme *f* des mélangeurs	Mischerbühne *f*	piano *m* dei mescolatori
°	11828 **mixing**	malaxage *m*	Kneten *n*	impastatura *f*, impasto
°	11829 **mixing apparatus**	mélangeur *m*	Mischapparat *m*	mescolatore *m*
°	11830 **mixing cone**	trémie *f* de mélange	Mischtrichter *m*	tramoggia *f* mescolatrice
°	11831 **mixing furnace**	(four) mélangeur *m*	Roheisenmischer *m*	forno *m* mescolatore
°	11832 **mixing ladle**	poche *f* mélangeuse, poche à mélanger	Mischerpfanne *f*	mescolatore *m*, siviera *f* mescolatrice
°	11833 **mixing machine**	malaxeur *m*, mélangeur *m*	Mischmaschine *f*	mescolatrice *f*
°	11834 **mixing shed**	halle *f* des mélangeurs	Mischerhaus *n*, Mischergebäude *n*	locale *m* dei mescolatori
°	11835 **mixing shed**	halle *f* de mélange	Möllerhaus *n*	locale *m* per mescolare o dosare
−	11836 **mixite**	mixite *f*	Mixit *m*	mixite *f*
°	11837 **mixture**	mélange *m*	Mischung *f*	miscela *f*, miscuglio *m*

English	French	German	Italian
– 11838 mixture of ores	mélange *m* de minerais	Erzgemenge *n*	miscuglio *f* di mine-rali
° 11839 mixture of ores and fluxes	lit *m* de fusion	Möller *m*	letto *m* di fusione
– 11840 mizpah	trachyte *f*	Trachyt *m*	trachite *f*
– 11841 mizzonite	mizzonite *f*	Mizzonit *m*	mizzonite *f*, dipiro *m*
– 11842 MMCF	millions de pieds cubes	Millionen *f pl.* an Kubikfuss	milioni di piedi cubi
– 11843 moat	tranchée noyée	Wassergraben *m*	trincea *f* allagata, fossato *m* allagato
– 11844 mobile belt elevator	sauterelle *f*	fahrbares Transportband *n*	trasportatore *m* a nastro mobile
– 11845 mobile crane	grue *f* mobile	fahrbarer Kran *m*	gru *f* mobile, gru *f* trasportabile
– 11846 mobile platform	plate-forme mobile	bewegliche Bohrplattform *f*	piattaforma *f* mobile
– 11847 mobile rig	jig *m* (ou tarière) mobile	beweglicher Bohrer *m*	trivella *f* mobile
^ 11848 mobility ratio	coéfficient *f* de mobilité	Mobilitätsverhältnis *n*	coeffcente *m* di mobilità
– 11849 mocha stone	agate *f* moka	Mokkastein *m*	agata *f* muscosa
– 11850 mock lead, blende	blende *f*	Zinkblende *f*	blenda *f*
mock ore, *s. mock lead*			
– 11851 modderite	modderite *f*	Modderit *m*	modderite *f*
– 11852 mode	pourcentage en poids (d'une roche)	prozentuale Gewichtszusammen-setzung *f* (eines Felsens)	composizione *m* percentuale in peso
° 11852a model	platine *f*	Platine *f*	platina *f*
modern bloomery fire, *s. Lancashire hearth*			
° 11853 modification of the method	variantes *f pl.* du procédé	Abarten *f pl.* des Verfahrens	varianti *f pl.* di fab-bricazione
° 11854 modifier	modificateur *m*	Modifizierungs-mittel *n*	agente *m* modificante
° 11855 modulus of elasticity, Young's modulus	module *m* d'élasti-cité	Elastizitätsmodul *m*	modulo *m* d'elastici-tà

English	French	German	Italian
— 11856 mofette	mofette *f*	Mofette *f*	mofetta *f*
mohr's clip, *s. clip*			
— 11857 moil	coin *m*, pic *m*	Spitzeisen *n*, Keil *m*	piccone *m*, cuneo *m*
— 11858 moiling	travail *m* à la massette	Hereintreibearbeit *f*	lavoro *m* alla mazzetta
— 11859 moissanite	moissanite *f*	Moissanit *m*	moissanite *f*
— 11860 to moisten	mouiller	anfeuchten	inumidire
— 11861 moistened cinders	fraisil *m* humide	angefeuchtete Kohlenlösche *f*	cenere *f* umida
— 11862 moistmeter, moisture teller (or tester)	mesureur *m* d'humidité	Feuchtigkeitsmesser *m*	misuratore *m* di umidità
— 11863 moisture	humidité *f*	Feuchtigkeit *f*	umidità *f*
— 11864 moja	lave *f* boueuse	Schlammlava *f*	lava *f* fangosa
— 11865 mol	molécule-gramme *f*	Grammolekül *n*	molecola-grammo *m*
— 11866 molasse	molasse *f*	Molasse *f*	molassa *f*
to mold, *s. to mould*			
mold, *s. mould*			
— 11867 moldavite	moldavite *f*	Moldavit *m*	moldavite *f*
molded brick, *s. green brick*			
° 11868 molder	mouliste *m*	Former *m*	formatore *m*
molder, *s. moulder*			
° 11869 molding	moulage *m*	Formen *n*	formatura *f*
molding, *s. moulding*			
^ 11870 mole per cent	teneur *m* molaire	Molargehalt *m*	percentuale *f* molare
° 11871 molecular volume	volume *m* moléculaire	Molekularvolumen *n*	volume *m* molecolare
° 11872 molecular weight	poids *m* moléculaire	Molekulargewicht *n*	peso *m* molecolare
° 11873 moleculary composition	structure *f* moléculaire	molekulare Zusammensetzung *f*	struttura *f* o composizione *f* molecolare
° 11874 molecule, group of atoms	molécule *f*, groupe *m* d'atomes	Molekül *n*, Atomgruppe *f*	molecola *f*, gruppo *m* di atomi
—11875 molengraaffite	molengraaffite *f*	Molengraaffit *m*	molengraaffite *f*

	English	French	German	Italian
— 11876	molera	terre f à diatomées, diatomite	Diatomeenerde f, Infusorienerde f, Kieselerde f	diatomite f, farina f fossile
∘ 11877	molten, melted	fondu	geschmolzen	fuso
∘ 11878	molten, cast	coulé, moulé	schmelzflüssig, flüssig	gettato
∘ 11879	molten metal cost, cost at the spout	fonte f liquide (au prix de revient)	flüssiges Gusseisen n (als Kostenträger)	ghisa f liquida (prezzo di costo)
∘ 11880	molten test sample	éprouvette f de métal liquide prélevée	flüssig entnommenes Eisen n	provetta f liquida, presa per la prova
— 11881	molybdenite	molybdénite f	Molybdänit m	molibdenite f
— 11882	molybdenum	molybdène m	Molybdän n	molibdeno m
∘ 11883	molybdenum steel	acier m au molybdène	Molybdänstahl m	acciaio m al molibdeno
∘ 11884	molybdic acid	acide m molybdique	Molybdänsäureanhydrid n	acido m molibdico
— 11885	molybdite	molybdite f	Molybdit m	molibdite f
— 11886	molybdomenite	molybdoménite f	Molybdomenit m	molibdomenite f
— 11887	molybdophyllite	molybdophyllite f	Molybdophyllit m	molibdofillite f
— 11888	molysite	molysite f	Molysit m	molisite f
	moment of flexion, $s.$ bending moment			
∘ 11889	moment of inertia	moment m d'inertie	Trägheitsmoment n	momento m d'inerzia
∘ 11890	monatomic molecule	molécule f mono-atomique	einatomiges Molekül n	molecola f monoatomica
— 11891	monazite	monazite f	Monazit m	monazite f
— 11892	monchiquite	monchiquite f	Monchiquit m	monchiquite f
— 11893	mondhaldeite	mondhaldéite f	Mondhaldeit m	mondaeldeite f
∘ 11894	Monel metal	métal m Monel	Monel-Metall n	metallo m Monel
— 11895	monetite	monétite f	Monetit m	monetite f
— 11896	monheimite	monheimite f	Monheimit m	monheimite f

	English	French	German	Italian
— 11897	monimolite	monimolite *f*	Monimolit *m*	monimolite *f*
— 11898	monite	monite *f*	Monit *m*	monite *f*
— 11899	monitor	monitor *m*	Monitor *m*	monitor
	monitor lathe, *s. turret lathe.*			
— 11900	monkey	mouton *m*	Rammbär *m*	battipalo *m*, berta *f*
— 11901	monkey	recoupe de ventilation	Wetterdurchhieb *m*	galleria *f* (o cunicolo *m*) di ventilazione
° 11901a	monkey cooler	refroidisseur *m* du trou de laitier	Schlackenformküh-ler *m*	raffreddatore *m* del foro delle scorie
— 11902	monkey drift	galerie *f* d'exploration	Aufschlussstrecke *f*	galleria *f* d'esplorazione
— 11903	monkey gangway	recoupe *f* de ventilation, passage	Wetterdurchhieb *m*	galleria *f* (o cunicolo *m*) di ventilazione
° 11904	monkey wrench	clef *f* universelle	Universalschlüssel *m*	chiave *f* universale (o inglese)
— 11905	monmouthite	monmouthite *f*	Monmouthit *m*	monmouthite *f*
° 11906	monochromatic optical pyrometer	pyromètre *m* optique monochromatique	Teilstrahlungs-pyrometer *n*	pirometro *m* ottico monocromatico
— 11907	monoclinal valley	vallée *f* monoclinale, combe *f*	Isoklinaltal *n*	valle *f* monoclinale
— 11908	monoclinic system, monosymmetric system, oblique system	système *m* binaire (ou monoclinique)	monoklines System *n*	sistema *f* monoclino
° 11909	mono-cylindrical	monocylindrique	einzylindrig	monocilindrico
— 11910	monogene rock	roche monogénique	monogenes Gestein *n*	roccia *f* monogenica
— 11911	monogenetic	monogénique	monomineralisch	monogenico
° 11912	monolithic lining	garnissage monolithe	Stampffutter *n*	rivestimento *m* monolitico
° 11913	monolithic lining material	pisé *m*	Stampfmasse *f*	pigiata *f*
	monometric system, *s. isometric system*			
— 11914	monomineral rock	roche *f* monominérale	monomineralisches Gestein *n*	roccia *f* monominerale
° 11915	monorail type jib crane	grue-vélocipède *f*	Velozipedkran *m*	gru *f* a bicicletta, gru a monorotaia

English	French	German	Italian

monozite, *s. monazite*

— 11916 monrepite	monrepite *f*	Monrepit *m*	monrepite *f*
— 11917 Monroean subdivision	formation *f* de Monroean	Monroe Vorkommen *n*	formazione *f* di Monroe
— 11918 montanite	montanite *f*	Montanit *m*	montanite *f*
— 11919 Montian stage	montien *m*	Montian *n*	montiano *m*
— 11920 monticellite	monticellite *f*	Monticellit *m*	monticellite *f*
— 11921 montmorillonite	montmorillonite *f*	Montmorillonit *m*	montmorillonite *f*
— 11922 montrealite	montréalite *f*	Montrealit *m*	montrealite *f*
— 11923 montroydite	montroydite *f*	Montroydit *m*	montroidite *f*
— 11924 monzonite	monzonite *f*	Monzonit *m*	monzonite *f*
— 11925 monzonitic texture	texture *f* monzonitique	monzonitische Textur *f*	struttura *f* monzonitica
— 11926 moonstone	oeil-de-poisson	Mondstein *m*	pietra *f* della luna
— 11927 moor rock	grès *m* à gros grain	Grobsandstein *m*, Sandstein *m*	gres *m* a grana grossa
mop, s. polishing lap			
— 11928 moraine	moraine *f*	Moräne *f*	morena *f*
— 11929 moraine belt	ceinture *f* morainique	Moränengürtel *m*	cintura *f* morenica
— 11930 moraine lodge	loge *f* de moraine	Moränenamphytheater *n*	anfiteatro *m* morenico
— 11931 morenosite	morénosite *f*	Morenosit *m*	moresonite *f*
∘ 11932 Morgan producer	gazogène *m* Morgan	Morganscher Generator *m*	gasogeno *m* Morgan
— 11933 morganite	morganite *f*	Morganit *m*	morganite *f*
— 11934 morion	quartz *m* enfumé	Morion *m*	quarzo *m* affumicato
— 11935 moroxite	moroxite *f*	Moroxit *m*	moroxite *f*
— 11936 mortar	mortier *m*	Mörtel *m*	malta *f*
— 11937 mortar	mortier *m*, cuvette *f* à broyer	Reibschale *f*	mortaio *m* da miscela

English	French	German	Italian
° 11938 **mortise**	mortaise *f.*	Zapfenloch *n*	incastro *m* per il dente di una mortisa
° 11939 **to mortise, to punch**	poinçonner	auslochen	punzonare
− 11940 **mosaic texture, cellular texture**	structure en mosaïque (ou alvéolée)	Pflasterstruktur *f,* Hornfelsstruktur *f*	struttura *f* alveolare
− 11941 **mosandrite**	mosandrite *f*	Mosandrit *m*	mosandrite *f*
− 11942 **mosesite**	mosesite *f*	Mosesit *m*	mosesite *f*
− 11943 **moss**	mousse *f*	Moos *n*	muschio *m*
− 11944 **moss** **moss agate,** *s. mocha stone*	tourbière *f*	Moor *n*	torbiera *f*
− 11945 **moss-box**	boîte *f* à mousse	Moosbüchse *f*	scatola *f* per muschio
− 11946 **mossite**	mossite *f*	Mossit *m*	mossite *f*
− 11946a **mossy zinc**	grenaille *f* de zinc	Zinkgries *m*	granuli *m pl.* di zinco
− 11947 **mother gate**	galerie *f* principale	Hauptstrecke *f*	galleria *f* principale
^ 11948 **mother hubbard**	trépan type normal	Backenmeissel *m*	trapano *m* normale
− 11949 **mother lode**	filon *m* principal	Hauptgang *m*	filone *m* principale
mother lye, *s. mother liquor*			
^ 11950 **mother oil**	pétrole *m* brut	Rohöl *n*	petrolio *m* grezzo
− 11951 **motive column**	dépression *f* de la mine	Widerstandsdruckhöhe *f*	depressione *f* della miniera
° 11952 **motor-generator body**	carter *m* de moteur-générateur	Motor-Generator-Gehäuse *n.* Umformer-gehäuse *n*	cassa *f* del motore generatore
° 11953 **motor for polishing**	moteur *m* à polir	Poliermaschine *f*	motore *m* per levigare
° 11954 **motorised crane**	grue *f* automotrice	selbstfahrender Kran *m*	gru *f* automotrice, gru *f* meccanica
° 11955 **mottle zone**	trempe *f* primaire partielle à transition truitée	weisserstarrte Zone *f* mit meliertem Übergang	tempra *f* primaria parziale a transizione trotata
mottled cast iron, *s. mottled pig iron*			
° 11956 **mottled (pig-)iron, mottled cast iron**	fonte *f* truitée	halbiertes (od. meliertes) Roheisen	ghisa *f* trotata (o marezzata)
° 11957 **mottled structure**	structure *f* mouchetée (minerais)	gepunkte Struktur *f* (Erze)	struttura *f* marezzata

English	French	German	Italian
o 11958 **mottled white pig iron**	fonte *f* truîtée blanche	halbiertes Roheisen *n*, Forelleneisen *n*	ghisa *f* trotata bianca
o 11958a **mottling**	tiqueture *f*	Tüpfelung *f*	screziatura *f*
o 11960 **to mould**	mouler	formen, einformen	formare, costruire la forma
o 11961 **to mould from a casting**	surmouler	nach dem Gussstück formen	formare dal pezzo
o 11962 **to mould in a pit**	mouler en fosse	in der Grube formen	formare in fossa
o 11963 **to mould in a snap flask**	mouler en motte	kastenlos formen	formare a motta
o 11964 **to mould on an oddside**	mouler sur couche	mit Sparhälfte *f* formen	formare su falsa placca
o 11965 **to mould on end**	mouler debout	stehend formen	formare verticalmente
o 11966 **to mould on the flat**	mouler à plat	liegend formen	formare orizzontalmente
o 11967 **to mould the crucibles**	mouler les creusets	Tiegel formen	impastare i crogiuoli
o 11968 **mould**	moule *m*	Form *f*, Giessform *f*, Gussform *f*	forma *f*
— 11969 **mould**	terre végétale, humus	Humus, fetter Ton *m*	terra *f* vegetale, humus
— 11970 **mould**	empreinte *f*	Abdruck *m*	impronta *f* (di un fossile)
o 11971 **mould assembly**	remmoulage *m*	Giessfertigmachen *n* der Form	ramolaggio *m*
	mould carriage, *s. mould trolley*		
o 11972 **mould casting**	moulage *m* en châssis	Formguss *m*	pezzo *m* formato in staffa
o 11973 **mould cavity**	empreinte *f*	Formhohlraum *m*	forma *f*, impronta *f*
o 11974 **mould closing mechanism**	dispositif de fermeture *f* du moule	Formschliessmechanismus *m*	dispositivo di chiusura *f* dello stampo
o 11975 **mould closing piston**	piston *m* de fermeture (du moule)	Schliesskolben *m*	pistone *m* di chiusura
o 11976 **mould crack**	craquelure *f* du moule	Haarriss *m* der Form	criccatura *f* dello stampo

	English	French	German	Italian
°	11977 **mould-dryer**	four *m* de séchage des moules	Gussformtrockenofen *m*	forno *m* di essicazione delle forme
°	11978 **mould drying area**	séchoir *m* à moules	Formtrockenplatz *m*	essiccatoio *m* per forme
	mould-drying oven, *s. mould-drier*			
°	11979 **mould for bakeries**	moule *m* pour pâtisserie	Rohr *n* für Backofen.	stampo *m* per pasticcerie
°	11980 **mould frame**	moule *m*	Formrahmen *m*	cassetta *f* per la forma
°	11981 **mould hardness**	degré *m* de serrage	Verdichtungsgrad *m*	grado *m* di compressione
°	11981a **mould jacket**	jaquette *f*	Giessrahmen *m*	giacchetta *f*
°	11982 **mould joint**	joint *m* de moulage	Formteilung *f*	ritrovatura *f*
°	11983 **mould joint, joint surface**	joint *m* de moule	Teilungsfläche *f*, Formteifläche *f*	piano *m* di divisione di una forma
—	11984 **mould peat**	tourbe *f* moulée	Streichtorf *m*	torba *f*
°	11985 **mould ready for casting**	moule *m* prêt pour la coulée	giessfertige Form *f*	forma *f* pronta per colare
°	11986 **mould release trigger**	doigt *m* de démoulage	Schrägstift *m*	perno *m* inclinato di comando dei maschi
	mould shift, *s. mismatch in mould*			
°	11987 **mould trolley**	chariot *m* de machine à mouler	Formwagen *m*	carrello *m* portastaffa
°	11988 **mould with interchangeable parts**	moule *m* à éléments interchangeables	Form *f* mit auswechselbaren Einsätzen	forma *f* a elementi intercambiabili
°	11989 **mouldable, moldable**	moulable, formable	formbar	formabile
°	11990 **moulded in place,**	noyé	eingegossen	incorporato nella fusione, preso in fonderia
°	11990a **moulder**	dimension *f* primitive	Vorform *f*	forma *f* primitiva
°	11991 **moulder**	mouliste *m*, mouleur *m*	Formenbauer *m*, Former *m*	formatore *m*
°	11992 **moulder bench**	banc *m* de mouleur	Formerbank *f*	banco *m* da formatore
°	11993 **moulder's hammer**	marteau *m* de mouleur	Modellhammer *m*	mazzuolo *m* da formatore
°	11994 **moulder's peel**	pelle *f* de mouleur	Formerschaufel *f*	pala *f* da formatore

	English	French	German	Italian
	moulder scoop, *s. casting laddle*			
○ 11995	**mouldering**	cassant	spröde	fragile
○ 11996	**moulders adjustable depth gauge**	sonde *f* de mouleur	Tiefenmass *n*	calibro *m* a sonda, sonda *f* da formatore
○ 11997	**mo(u)lding**	moulage *m*	Formen *n*	formatura *f*
○ 11998	**moulding allowance**	garantie *f*, surépaisseur *m* prevu sur le modèle	garantierte Werkstoffzugabe *f* am Modell	sovraspessore *f* di sicurezza
○ 11999	**moulding bay, moulding floor**	atelier *m* de moulage, chantier *m* de moulage	Formerei *f*, Formhalle *f*, Formplatz *m*	reparto *m* di formatura
○ 12000	**moulding bench**	banc *m* de moulage	Formbank *f*	banco *m* di formatura (o di formazione)
○ 12001	**moulding board, bar plate**	planche *f* à imprimer	Profilklotz *m*, Pressplatte *f*	piano *m* per formare
○ 12002	**moulding box**	châssis *m*	Formkasten *m*	staffa *f*, cassa *f* di formatura
○ 12003	**moulding box for pulley moulding machine**	châssis *m* de la machine à mouler les poulies	Formkasten *m* der Riemenscheibenformmaschine	staffa *f* speciale per puleggie
○ 12004	**moulding clay, casting loam**	argile *f* à mouler	Formlehm *m*	argilla *f* da modellare
	moulding flask, *s. moulding box*			
	moulding floor, *s. moulding bay*			
○ 12005	**moulding from a casting**	surmoulage *m*	Formen *n* (oder Formerei) nach dem Gussstück *n*	formatura *f* dal pezzo
○ 12006	**moulding hall**	halle *f* de moulage	Formhalle *f*, Formerei *f*	tettoia *f* per formatura, reparto *m* formatura
	moulding-hole, *s. casting-pit*			
	moulding in boxes, *s. moulding in flasks*			
○ 12007	**moulding in dry sand**	moulage à sec	Trockensandformen *n*	formatura *f* a secco
○ 12008	**moulding in flask, closed moulding**	moulage *m* en châssis	Kastenformerei *f*	formatura *f* in staffa

		English	French	German	Italian
o	12009	moulding in green sand	moulage m en sable vert	Nassgussformen n	formatura f a verde
o	12010	moulding in place	moulage m noyé, noyé	Eingiessen n, eingegossen	incorporamento nella fusione, preso in fondita
o	12011	moulding knife grinder	machine f à affûter les fers profilés	Vielfachschleifmaschine f für Formeisen	affilatrice f multipla per ferri da profilare (o da sagomare)
o	12012	moulding loam	terre à mouler	Formsand m	terra f per formature
o	12013	moulding loop, moulding reel	carrousel m	Karussel n	giostra f forme
o	12014	moulding machine	machine f à façonner les moules, machine f à mouler	Formmaschine f	macchina f per formare, formatrice f
o	12015	moulding machine for ribbed pipes	machine f à mouler les tuyaux à ailettes	Rippenrohrformmaschine f	macchina f per formare tubi alettati
o	12016	moulding machine with double ramming action	presse f à mouler à double effet	Doppelpresse f, doppelte Formpresse f	formatrice f a due facce
o	12017	moulding machine with lifting carriage	machine f à démouler à chariot élévateur	Abhebe(form)maschine f mit Hebekarren	formatrice f con estrazione della forma a carrello elevatore
o	12018	moulding machine with rotary table	machine f à mouler avec plateau tournant	Drehtischformmaschine f	formatrice f con piattaforma girevole
o	12019	moulding machine with two travelling pattern tables	machine f à mouler à double effet	Doppelformmaschine f	formatrice f doppia
o	12020	moulding materials	matériaux m $pl.$ de moulage	Formstoffe m $pl.$, Formmaterialien n $pl.$	materiali m $pl.$ per la formatura
		moulding nails, $s.$ $sand$ $piece$			
o	12021	moulding of gear wheels	moulage m de roues dentées	Formen n von Zahnrädern	formatura f d'ingranaggi
		moulding piece, $s.$ $sand$ $piece$			
o	12022	moulding press	machine f à mouler par pression, presse f à mouler	Formpresse f, Pressformmaschine f	pressa f da formare

	English	French	German	Italian
○	12023 **moulding of gear wheels with stripping plates**	moulage *m* des engrenages avec modèle à segments traversant la table	Formen *n* der Zahnräder mit Durchzugringen	formatura *f* a pettine (od a settore) degli ingranaggi
○	12024 **moulding pit**	fosse *f* de moulage	Formgrube *f*	fossa *f* per formatura
○	12025 **moulding plate**	plaque-support *f* de moule	Unterlegbrett *n*	vassoio *m*, tavoletta *f*, piano *m* per formare
	moulding press, *s. moulding machine*			
○	12026 **moulding press with rotatable turnover plate**	presse *f* à mouler avec plaque renversable	Formpresse *f* mit drehbarer Wendeplatte	pressa *f* da formare con piattaforma spostabile
	moulding reel, *s. moulding loop*			
○	12027 **moulding-sand, moulder's sand**	sable *m* de moulage	Formsand *m*, Modellsand *m*	sabbia *f* da formare, sabbia da fonderia
○	12028 **moulding shop**	atelier *m* de moulage	Formerei *f*	reparto *m* formatura
	moulding stakes, *s. sand piece*			
○	12029 **moulding technique**	procédé *m* de moulage	Formverfahren *n*	procedimento *m* di formatura
—	12030 **mound**	monticule, butte	Hügelchen *n*, Erdwall *m*, Wall *m*	montagnola *f*, puntello *m*
○	12030a **mountain cork**	liège *f* fossile	Bergkork *m*	sughero *m* di montagna
—	12031 **mountain glacier**	glacier *m* alpin	alpiner Vergletscherungstypus *m*	ghiacciaio *m* alpino
○	12032 **mountain green**	vert *m* de montagne	Berggrün *n*	verde *m* minerale, verde *m* ungherese
—	12033 **mountain intrusive**	batholite *f*	Batholith *m*	batholite *f*
—	12034 **mountain leather**	amiante *m* flexible	Bergleder *n*	amianto *m* in lamine flessibili
	mountain soap, *s. rock soap*			
	12035 **mounted on wheels**	monté sur chariot *m*	fahrbar	montato su carro
○	12036 **mounting core**	noyau-galette *m*	Kernlagerverstärkung *f*	galletta *f*
—	12037 **mounting gallery**	montage *m*	Schwebende *n*	rimonta *f*
^	12038 **mouse hole**	trou de souris, avant-trou *m*	Loch zum Abstellen eines Bohrgestänges	pozzetto *m* d'alloggio dell'asta di manovra

English	French	German	Italian
12039 mouse trap	souricière f à clapet	Fangklappe f	pescatore m svincola-bile
12040 mouth (of a mine shaft)	embouchure f	Mündung f	imboccatura f (di pozzo)
12041 mouth	mâchoire f	Backe f	mascella f
12042 mouth (of a furnace)	bure f	Gichtöffnung f	bocca f di carica-mento
mouth, s. delivery			
12043 mouth-blow pipe	chalumeau à bouche	Blaslötrohr n, Löt-rohr n mit Mundstück	cannello m ferrumina-torio
12044 mouth of a blast furnace, feeding gate of a blast furnace	bure d'un haut fourneau	Gichtöffnung f eines Hochofens	bocca f di un alto-forno
12045 mouth of a pit	tête f du puits	Schachtöffnung f	bocca f del pozzo
12046 movable boiler	chaudière f mobile	beweglicher Kessel	caldaia f mobile
12047 movable die	bloc m mobile	Auswerfformhälfte f	semistampo m mobile
12048 movable magnet	aimant m mobile	beweglicher Magnet	magnete m mobile
12049 movable pin	broche f de remmou-lage	loser Führungs-stift m	pirone m mobile
12050 movable plate	plateau m mobile	bewegliche Aufspannplatte f	placca f mobile
12051 movable steel road section (temporary)	route f en acier amovible (provisoi-re)	umsetzbare Stahlstrasse f (provisorische)	strada f in acciaio amovibile (provvi-soria)
12052 movement of the lever	course f du levier	Bewegung f des Hebels	movimento m della leva
12053 movement of the rider	déplacement m du cavalier	Reiterverschiebung f	spostamento m del cavaliere
12054 moving iron	fer m mobile	Dreheisen n	ferro m mobile
12055 moyle	pointeau m, coin m	Spitzeisen n, Keil m	punteruolo m, cuneo
M.S. = mild steel			
12056 mucilaginous	mucilagineux, visqueux	schleimig	mucillagginoso
12057 to muck	charger une berline	einen Wagen beladen	caricare un vagonetto

English	French	German	Italian
– 12058 **muck**	déblai *m*, tas *m* à charger	Haufwerk *n*	sterro *m*, scavo *m*, copertura *f*
° 12059 **muck bar**	fer *m* brut, fer *m* ébauché (de puddlage)	Rohbarren *m pl*, Rohschiene *f*	ferro *m* grezzo, ferro *m* sbozzato (di puddellaggio), barra *f* greggia, barra *f* da rilaminare
·° 12059a **muck iron**	fer *m* brut	Roheisen *n*	ferro *m* grezzo
° 12060 **muck mill**	train *m* préparatoire	Vorwalzwerk *n*	treno *m* preparatorio
– 12061 **muck pile**	tas *m* à charger	Haufwerk *n*	mucchio *m* da caricare
° 12062 **muck rolls**	cylindres *m* ébaucheurs	Vorwalzen *f pl.*	cilindri *m pl.* sbozzatori, cilindri *m pl.* sgrossatori
– 12063 **muck soil**	terre *f* noire	Schwarzerde *f*	terra *f* nera
– 12064 **mucker**	pelleteur *m*	Schaufler *m*, Wagenlader *m*	scavatore *m*
– 12065 **mucking**	chargement *m*	Abfüllarbeit *f*, Wegschaufeln *n*	rimozione *f* (caricamento di minerali ecc.)
– 12066 **mucking machine**	chargeuse *f* mécanique	Lademaschine *f*	caricatrice *f* meccanica
˄ 12067 **to mud**	embourber, embouer	verschlämmen	otturare con fango
˄ 12068 **to mud-off, to seal-off**	colmater, enduire	abdichten, verkleistern	tamponare, otturare, interrare
to mud up, *s. to mud*			
˄ 12069 **mud**	boue, vase, limon	Schlamm *m*, Lehm *m*	fango *m*, mota *f*
˄ 12070 **mud acid**	·boue *f* acide	saurer Schlamm *m*	fango *m* acido
˄ 12071 **mud additive**	produit *m* de traitement des boues	Spülungszusatz *m*	prodotto *m* di trattamento dei fanghi
˄ 12072 **mud analysis logging**	contrôle *m* des boues	Schlammkontrolle *f*	˙controllo *m* del fango
– 12073 **mud auger**	tarière *f* à boues	Schlammbohrer *m*	·trivella *f* (o cucchiaia *f*) di pulizia
– 12074 **mud box**	puisard *m*	Spülgrube *f*	pozzetto *m* (o bacino *m*) dei fanghi

	English	French	German	Italian
ˆ 12075	mud cake, mud lining	pâte f de boue	Spülungskuchen m, Wandbelag m	panello m di fango
— 12076	mud ditch	rigole f à boue	Spülrinne f	canale m (di raccolta) dei fanghi
— 12077	mud drum	collecteur à boues	Schlammfang m, Schlammtrommel f	collettore m del fango
— 12078	mud flow	coulée f de boue	Schlammlava f	lava f di fango
— 12079	mud fluid	fluide m boueux	Spülung f	fluido m fangoso, fango m d'iniezione
— 12080	mud gun	bocheuse f	Stichlochstopfmaschine f	macchina f per tamponatura
ˆ 12081	mud line	conduite à boues	Schlammleitung f	condotta f del fango
ˆ 12082	mud logging	diagraphies f pl. de boues	Messen n von Spülungs- eigenschaften	diagrafie f pl. dei fanghi
ˆ 12083	mud loss	perte f de circulation	Zirkulationsverlust m	perdita f di circolazione
ˆ 12084	mud mixing plant	centrale f de malaxage de boue	Schlammischanlage f	centrale f di preparazione dei fanghi
— 12085	mud pit	bassin m de décantation	Schlammgrube f	bacino m di decantazione, vasca f del fango
— 12086	mud pitting	piquage m par la boue	Korrosion durch Spülung	corrosione f da fanghi
ˆ 12087	mud pressure	pression f de la boue	Schlammpressung f	pressione f del fango

mud pocket, s. mud drum

	English	French	German	Italian
ˆ 12088	mud pump	pompe f à boue	Schlammpumpe f	pompa f per fango
ˆ 12089	mud sheat, cake	pâte de boue	Schlammbeschlag m	pannello m di fango
— 12090	mud socket	cuiller f à clapet	Schlammbüchse f, Schlammlöffel m	cucchiaia f di pulizia
ˆ 12091	mud tank	bac m à boue	Spülungstank m	serbatoio m dei fanghi
— 12092	mud thickener	épaississeur m des boues	Schlammverdichter m	addensatore m di fanghi

English	French	German	Italian
^ 12093 mud thinner, thinning agents	fluidifiant *m*	Verflüssiger *m*	fluidificante *m*
^ 12094 mudding	envasement *m*	Verschlammung *f*	interramento *m*, otturazione con fango
— 12095 mudstone	schiste *m* argileux	Schieferton *m*	schisto *m* argilloso
∘ 12096 muffle	moufle *m*	Muffel *f*	muffola *f*
∘ 12097 muffle-furnace, chamber-furnace, blind roaster	four *m* à moufle, moufle *m*	Muffelofen *m*	forno *m* a muffola, muffola *f*
∘ 12098 muffle-furnace for coal	moufle au charbon	Muffelofen *m* für Kohlenheizung	muffola *f* a carbone
∘ 12099 muffle-furnace for gas	four *m* à moufle au gaz	Muffelofen *m* für Gasheizung	muffola *f* a gas

muffle-oven, *s. muffle-furnace*

^ 12100 mule head	tête *f* du balancier	Schwingbalkenkopf*m*	testa *f* del bilanciere
— 12100a muller	frotteur *m*	Mischkollergang *m*	molazza *f* mescolatrice
— 12101 mulling	broyage *m* par moulins chiliens	Feinzerkleinerung *f* auf Kollergänge	macinazione *f*, molazzatura *f*, polverizzazione *f*

mulling, *s. milling*

— 12102 mullite	mullite *f*	Mullit *m*	mullite *f*
— 12103 mullock	stérile	Berge *pl.*	detriti *m pl.*, sterile *m*
— 12104 mullocking	travail *m* au rocher	Gesteinsarbeit *f*	lavoro *m* alla roccia
— 12105 mullochy	stérile	taub	sterile
^ 12106 multiflex scratchers	gratteur *m* de tubage horizontal	waagerechter Kratzer *m*	baffi *m pl.* di gatto orizzontali

multiflue boiler, *s. tubular boiler*

∘ 12107 multigrip floor	tôle bossée	Bossenblech *n*	lamiera *f* bugnata
∘ 12108 multi-handled heavy-hammer	casse-gueuse *m*	Masselhammer *m*	mazza *m* rompighisa, macchina *f* rompighisa

multiple boiler, *s. multitubular boiler*

∘ 12109 multiple core box	boîte *f* à noyaux multiples	Mehrfachkernkasten *m*	cassa *f* d'anima multipla, cassa *f* ad anime multiple

	English	French	German	Italian
°	12110 **multiple coreprint**	portée f commune	gemeinsame Kernmarke f, merfache Kernmarke f	portata f multipla, portata f comune
°	12111 **multiple crucible furnace**	four m à plusieurs creusets	mehrtiegliger Ofen m	forno m per più crogiuoli
°	12112 **multiple cylindrical boiler**	chaudière f à plusieurs corps cylindriques superposés	mehrfacher Walzenkessel m	caldaia f a più corpi cilindrici
—	12113 **multiple fault**	faille f multiple	Verwerfung f	faglia f multipla

multiple impulse welding, s. *pulsation welding*

	English	French	German	Italian
°	12114 **multiple mould cavity**	moule m à empreintes multiples	Mehrfachform f	stampo m multiplo, forma f multipla
°	12115 **multiple pass weld**	soudure f à passes multiples	Vielfachgangschweissung f	saldatura f a passate multiple
°	12116 **multiple projection welding**	soudure f multiple en relief	Vielfach-Relief-schweissung f	saldatura f multipla a rilievo
^	12117 **multiple pumping**	pompage m accouplé	mit Kehrradantrieb pumpen f pl.	pompaggio m multiplo (o accoppiato)
^	12118 **multiple sand exploitation**	exploitation f de faisceaux de sables	Gewinnung f von Horizontkomplexen m pl.	coltivazione f delle fasce di sabbia

multiple screw thread, s. *multiple thread*

	English	French	German	Italian
°	12119 **multiple spot welding**	soudure f continue par points	Punktnahtschweissung f	saldatura f continua a punti
°	12120 **multiple stage boiler**	chaudière f à étages	Etagenkessel m	caldaia f a bollitori sovrapposti, caldaia a piani
—	12121 **multiple stage cementing**	cimentation f étagée	stufenweise Zementierung f	cementazione f a stadi (o graduale)

multiple storied boiler, s. *multiple stage boiler*

	English	French	German	Italian
—	12122 **multiple twinning**	macles f pl. polysynthétiques	Wiederholungszwillinge m pl.	geminazioni f pl. polisintetiche
°	12122a **multiple tool**	outillage m multiple	Mehrfachwerkzeug n	utensile m multiplo
^	12123 **multiple well derrick**	derrick m pour forage multiple	Bohrturm m zum Mehrfachbohren	torre f per perforazioni multiple
°	12124 **multiple wire system**	système m à plusieurs conducteurs	Mehrleitersystem n	sistema m a più conduttori

	English	French	German	Italian
^ 12125	multiplex cementing collar	manchon *m* de cimentation étagée	Etagenzementierungsmuffe *f*	manicotto *m* per cementazione a più stadi
o 12126	multiplier	multiplicateur *m*	Hubvergrösserer *m*	moltiplicatore *m*
— 12127	multistage grate	grille *f* à étages	Staffelrost *m*	griglia *f* a piani
o 12128	multitubular boiler	chaudière *f* multitubulaire	Vielröhrenkessel *m*	caldaia *f* pluritubolare
o 12129	multivalent ion	ion *m* multivalent	mehrwertiges Ion *n*	ione *m* polivalente
— 12130	mundic, iron pyrite	pyrite *f*	Pyrit, Schwefelkies	pirite *f*
— 12131	muniongite	muniongite *f*	Muniongit *m*	muniongite *f*
o 12132	Muntz metal, yellow metal	métal *m* Muntz	Muntzmetall *n*	metallo *m* Muntz
— 12133	mur	mur *m*	Lagerung *f*, Lager *n*	piano *m* di scavo, fondo *m*, letto *m*
— 12134	murbruck structure	structure *f* en mortier	Mörtelstruktur *f*	struttura *f* a malta
— 12135	murchisonite	murchisonite *f*	Murchisonit *m*	murchisonite *f*
— 12136	murmanite	mourmanite *f*	Murmanit *m*	murmanite *f*
— 12137	Muschelkalk subdivision	Trias *m* moyen	Muschelkalk *n*	Trias *m* medio
— 12138	muscovadite	muscovadite *f* ·	Muscovadit *m*	muscovadite *f*
— 12139	Muscovite	mica *m* commun, muscovite *f*	Muskovit *m*	mica *f* potassica, mica *f* bianca
o 12140	mushroom core print	portée *f* débordante	über die Modellaussenfläche vergrösserte Kernmarke *f*	portata *f* maggiorata (o debordante)
— 12141	mushroom fold	pli *m* en champignon	Pilzfalte *f*	piega *f* a fungo
o 12142	mushroom-head rivet	rivet *m* à tête demi-ronde aplatie	Rundniet *m* mit grossem Kopf	chiodo *m* a testa semitonda larga
— 12143	mushroom rock	rocher *m* en forme de champignon	Pilzfelsen *m*	fungo *m*
^ 12144	mushroom valve	tiroir *m* à coquille	Muschelschieber *m*	valvola *f* a conchiglia (o a cono, o a fungo)

	English	French	German	Italian
^	12145 **mushroom vent**	soupirail *m* à vent	Lüftungsgerät *n*	aereatore *m* a vento
—	12146 **mushy**	poreux	porig	poroso
°	12146a **mushy stage**	état *m* pâteux	Teigelzustand *m*	stato *m* pastoso
	music wire, *s. piano wire*			
—	12147 **muthmannite**	muthmannite *f*	Muthmannit *m*	muthmannite *f*
—	12148 **mylonite**	mylonite *f*	Mylonit *m*	milonite *f*
—	12149 **mylonitic texture**	texture *f* mylonitique	mylonitische Struktur *f*	struttura *f* milonitica (o frantumata)
—	12150 **mylonitization**	mylonitisation *f*	Mylonitisierung *f*	milonitizzazione *f*
—	12151 **myrmekits**	myrmékite *f*	Myrmekit *m*	myrmechite *f*

English	French	German	Italian
– 12152 **nablock**	concrétion *f* arrondie	gerundete Konkretion *f*	concrezione *f* rotonda
– 12153 **nacreous-lustre, pearly lustre**	éclat *m* nacré (ou perlé)	Perlmutterglanz *m*	splendore *m* perlaceo
– 12154 **nacrite**	nacrite *f*	Nakrit *m*	nacrite *f*
– 12155 **nadorite**	nadorite *f*	Nadorit *m*	nadorite *f*
– 12156 **maëgite**	naégite *f*	Naegit *m*	naegite *f*
– 12157 **nagatelite**	nagatelite *f*	Nagatelit *m*	nagatelite *f*
– 12158 **nagelfluh**	poudingue *m*	Nagelfluh *f*	puddinga *f* (calcarea)
– 12159 **nagyagite**	nagyagite *f*	Nagyagit *m*	nagyagite *f*
– 12160 **nahcolite**	nahcolite *f*	Nahcolit *m*	nahcolite *f*
° 12161 **nail iron for horse-shoes**	fer *m* pour clous à ferrer	Hufnageleisen *n*	barra *f* per chiodi del ferro da cavallo
° 12162 **nail pass**	cannelures *f pl.* pour clous	Nagelkaliber *n*	tracciato *m* per chiodi
° 12163 **nail rod, nail-iron, nail rod iron**	fer *m* à clous, fer en barres pour clous	Nageleisen *n*	ferro *m* per chiodi
° 12164 **nail without head**	pointe *f* sans tête	kopfloser Stift *m*	punta *f* senza testa
° 12165 **nailed and welded pole**	pal *m* riveté et soudé	genieteter und geschweisster Pfahl	palo *m* chiodato e saldato
° 12166 **nailing**	chauffage *m* progressif de creusets vers le rouge	schrittweise Heizung von Tiegeln bis Rotglut	riscaldamento *m* progressivo al rosso dei crogiuoli
– 12167 **nantokite**	nantokite *f*	Nantokit *m*	nantochite *f*
^ 12168 **naphthalene**	naphtalène *m*	Naphthalin *n*	naftalina *f*, naftalene
^ 12169 **naphthenate**	naphtenate *m*	Naphthenat *n*	naftenato *m*
^ 12170 **naphthene index**	indice *m* naphténique	Naphthenzahl *f*	indice *m* naftenico
^ 12171 **naphthene**	naphtène *m*	Naphthen *n*	nafteno *m*
^ 12172 **naphthenic**	naphténique	naphtenisch	naftenico
Naples yellow, *s. lead antimonate*			
– 12173 **napoleonite**	napoléonite *f*	Napoleonit *m*	napoleonite *f*

	English	French	German	Italian
−	12174 **nappe inlier**	fenêtre *f*	geologisches Fenster *n*	finestra *f* geologica
−	12175 **nappe outlier**	témoin *m* de chevauchement, lambeau de charriage	Deckscholle *f*, Überschiebungs- rest *m*	testimonio *m* di carreggiamento
°	12176 **narrow flame**	flamme *f* pointante	Stichflamme *f*	fiamma *f* concentrata
−	12177 **narrow gauge railway**	voie *f* étroite	Schmalspurbahn *f*	binario *m* a scarta- mento ridotto
	narrow strap, *s. top flange plate*			
−	12178 **narrowing**	rétrécissement *m*	Verengung *f*	restringimento *m*
°	12179 **Nathusius furnace**	four *m* Nathusius	Nathusiusscher Ofen *m*	forno *m* Nathusius
−	12180 **native arsenic**	arsenic *m* natif	metallisches Arsen *n*	arsenico *m* metal- lico
−	12181 **native asphalt**	asphalte *m* naturel	Naturalasphalt *m*	asfalto *m* naturale
−	12182 **native rock**	roche *f* mère	Muttergestein *n*	roccia *f* madre
−	12183 **natroalunite**	natroalunite *f*	Natroalunit *m*	natroalunite *f*
−	12184 **natroborocalcite**	boronatrocalcite *f*	Boronatrokalzit *m*	boronatrocalcite *f*
−	12185 **natrochalcite**	natrochalcite *f*	Natrochalcit *m*	natrocalcite *f*
−	12186 **natrojarosite**	natrojarosite *f*	Natrojarosit *m*	natrojarosite *f*
−	12187 **natrolite**	natrolite *f*	Natrolith *m*	natrolite *f*
−	12188 **natrophilite**	natrophylite *f*	Natrophilit *m*	natrofilite *f*
−	12189 **natural ageing**	vieillissement *m* naturel	Kaltauslagern *n*	invecchiamento *m* spontaneo
−	12190 **natural draught**	tirage *m* naturel	natürlicher Zug *m*	tiraggio *m* naturale
−	12191 **natural fuel**	combustible *m* naturel	natürlicher Brennstoff *m*	combustibile *m* natu- rale
^	12192 **natural flow**	courant *m*	Fluss *m*	corrente *f*, flusso *m*
^	12193 **natural gas**	gaz naturel	Naturgas *n*	gas *m* naturale
^	12194 **natural gasoline, casinghead gasoline**	essence de gaz naturel, gazoline *f* naturelle	Naturgasolin *n*	gasolina *f* naturale
°	12195 **natural hardness**	trempe *f* naturelle	Naturhärte *f*	tempera *f* naturale
	natural iron, *s. native iron*			

	English	French	German	Italian
–	12196 **natural sand**	sable *m* naturel	Natursand *m*	terra *f* naturale (o sabbia *f*)
–	12197 **natural slope**	talus *m* naturel	natürliche Böschung *f*	scarpata *f* naturale
–	12198 **natural water**	eau *f* brute, eau *f* naturelle	Rohwasser *n*, Naturwasser *n*	acqua *f* impura, acqua *f* naturale
–	12199 **naujaite**	naujaïte *f*	Naujait *m*	naujaite *f*
–	12200 **naumannite**	naumannite *f*	Naumannit *m*	naumannite *f*
–	12201 **nauruite**	nauruite *f*	Nauruit *m*	nauruite *f*
–	12202 **navite**	navite *f*	Navit *m*	navite *f*
–	12203 **navvy**	drague, excavateur *m*	Bagger *m*	draga *f*, scavatrice *f*

n.butane, *s. normal butane*

	English	French	German	Italian
o	12204 **neck**	col *m*, collet *m*, tourillon *m*, bec *m* d'un convertisseur	Hals *m*, Hals *m* einer Bessemerbirne	collo *m*, colletto *m*, becco *m* d'un convertitore
^	12204a **necking, necking down**	réduction *f* de section	Querzusammenziehung *f*	contrazione *f* diametrale
o	12205 **needle**	épinglette *f*	Schiessnadel *f*	punta *f*, ago *m* d'espulsione
o	12206 **needle bearing**	roulement *m* à aiguilles	Nadellager *n*	cuscinetto *m* ad aghi

needle bottom, *s. perforated bottom*

	English	French	German	Italian
–	12207 **needle ironstone**	goethite *f*	Goethit *m*	goethite *f*
o	12208 **needle jet**	jet *m* reglé à aiguille conique	Nadelguss *m*	getto *m* regolato ad ago conico
–	12209 **needle ore**	aikinite *f*	Nadelerz *n*, Aikinit *m*	aikinite *f*
–	12210 **needle shaped, acicular**	aciculaire, aiguillé	nadelförmig	a forma d'aghi, aghiforme. aciculare
–	12211 **needle zeolite**	zéolite *f* aciculaire	Faserzeolith *m*	zeolite *f* aciculare
o	12211a **needled bottom**	fond *m* en baguettes	Nadelboden *m*	fondo *m* perforato
o	12212 **negative**	négatif *m*, épreuve *f* négative	Negativ *n*, Patrize *f*	negativa *f*, matrice *f* negativa
–	12213 **negative carbon**	charbon *m* négatif	negative Kohle *f*	carbone *m* negativo
o	12214 **negative hardening**	trempe *f* négative	negative Härtung *f*	tempera *f* negativa o non riuscita

	English	French	German	Italian
− 12215	nelsonite	nelsonite *f*	Nelsonit *m*	nelsonite *f*
− 12216	nemaphyllite	némaphyllite *f*	Nemaphyllit *m*	nemafillite *f*
− 12217	nematoblastic texture	texture *f* nématoblastique	nematoblastische Struktur *f*	struttura *f* nematobla-stica
− 12218	Neocomian stage	néocomien *m*	Neokom *n*	neocomiano *m*
− 12219	Neodevonic period	dévonien *m* supérieur	Neodevon *n*	devoniano *m* superio-re
− 12220	neodymium	néodyme *m*	Neodym *n*	neodimio *m*
− 12221	neogenic	néogène	neogen	neogeno
− 12222	Neolithic stage	néolithique *m*	Neolithikum *n*	neolitico *m*
° 12223	neon	néon *m*	Neon *n*	neon *m*
° 12224	neoprene gaskets	joints *m pl.* obturés au neoprène	Fugenverschluss *m* aus Neopren	guarnizioni *m pl.* di neoprene
− 12225	neotantalite	néotantalite *f*	Neotantalit *m*	neotantalite *f*
^ 12226	neohexane	neohexane *m*	Neohexan *n*	neoesano *m*
− 12227	Neozoic group	groupe *m* néozoïque	neozoische Gruppe *f*	gruppo *m* neozoico
− 12228	nepheline	néphéline *f*	Nephelin *m*	nefelina *f*
− 12229	nepheline basalt	basalte *m* à néphéline	Nephelinbasalt *m*	basalto *m* alla nefe-lina
− 12230	nephelinite	néphélinite *f*	Nephelinit *m*	nefelinite *f*
	nephelite, *s. nepheline*			
− 12231	nephelite syenite	syénite *f* à néphéline	Nephelinsyenit *m*	sienite *f* nefelinica
− 12232	nephrite	néphrite, jade *m*	Nephrit *m*, Jade *f*	nefrite *f*, giada *f*
− 12233	nepouite	népouite *f*	Nepouit *m*	nepouite *f*
− 12234	neptunic rocks	neptunites *f pl.*	neptunische Gesteine *n pl.*	rocce *f pl.* nettuni-che
− 12235	neptunite	neptunite *f*	Neptunit *m*	nettunite *f*
−12236	neptunium	neptunium *m*	Neptunium *n*	nettunio *m*
− 12237	neritic	néritique	neritisch	neritico

	English	French	German	Italian
—	12238 **neritic facies**	faciès *m* néritique	neritische Fazies *f*	facies *f* neritica
—	12239 **nesquehonite**	nesquehonite	Nesquehonit *m*	nesquehonite *f*
—	12240 **nest of ore**	poche de minerai	Erznest *n*	sacca *f* di minerali
⁰	12241 **net calorific value**	puissance *f* calorifique nette	unterer Heizwert *m*	potere *m* calorifico minimo
^	12242 **net pay**	zone *f* productive effective	Nettomächtigkeit *f*	zona *f* effettivamente produttiva
^	12243 **net sand**	sable *m* net	Nettomächtigkeit *f* eines Sandsteins	sabbia *f* effettivamente produttiva
⁰	12244 **net shaped, reti-culated**	réticulaire	netzförmig	reticolare, a forma di rete
⁰	12245 **net shaped electrode**	électrode *f* réticulaire	Netzelektrode *f*	elettrodo *m* reticolato
—	12246 **net slip**	rejet *m* net	wahre Schublänge *f*	rigetto *m* netto
	net structure, *s. cellular structure*			
	12247 **net weight**	poids *m* net	Reingewicht *n*	peso *m* netto
—	12248 **netted structure**	structure *f* maillée	Maschenstruktur *f*	struttura *f* a maglie, struttura *f* reticolare
—	12249 **network of faults**	réseau *m* de failles	Sprungnetz *n*	rete *f* di faglie
—	12250 **network of veins**	réseau *m* de veines	Gängenetz *n*	rete *f* di filoni
⁰	12251 **Neumann bands**	lignes *f pl.* de Neumann	Neumannlinien *f pl.*	linee *f pl.* di Neumann
	neutral, *s. neutral wire*			
⁰	12251a **neutral point**	zone *f* neutre	Fliessscheide *f*	zona *f* neutra
—	12252 **neutral rock**	roche *f* neutre	neutrales Gestein *n*	roccia *f* neutra, roccia *f* intermedia
—	12253 **neutral substance**	substance *f* neutre	neutrale Substanz *f*	sostanza *f* neutra
⁰	12254 **neutral wire, third wire**	conducteur *m* neutre troisième conducteur *m* ou fil	Mittelleiter *m*, Nullleiter *m*	filo *m* neutro o di compensazione
⁰	12255 **to neutralise**	neutraliser	neutralisieren, abstumpfen	neutralizzare
—	12256 **neve-glacier**	glacier de névé	Firngletscher *m*	nevaio, nevato
—	12257 **nevyanskite**	newjanskite *f*	Newjanskit *m*	newjanskite *f*
	new-billet steel, *s. billet*			

English	French	German	Italian
− 12258 new sand	sable *m* neuf	Neusand *m*	sabbia *f* nuova
− 12259 new soil	sol *m* vierge	Neuland *n*	suolo *m* vergine
− 12260 newberyite	newberyite *f*	Newberyit *m*	newberite *f*
to newcast, *s. to remelt*			
− 12261 newlandite	newlandite *f*	Newlandit *m*	newlandite *f*
° 1226 la nib	compact *m* terminé	fertiger Pressling *m*	compatto *m* terminato
° 1226 lb nibbling	grignotage *m*	Knabbern *n*	spinatura *f*
° 12262 nibbling machine	poinçonneuse *f*	Lochpresse *f*, Stanzmaschine *f*	macchina *f* punzonatrice
− 12263 niccolite	niccolite *f*	Nickelin *m*	niccolite *f*, nichelina *f*
° 12264 nick	encoche *f*, entaille *f*	Kerbe *f*	intaglio *m*, tacca *f*
° 12265 nicked fracture test	essai *m* de fracture par choc sur barreaux entaillés	Einkerbbruchprobe *f*	frattura *f* su barretta intagliata
− 12266 nickel ores	minerais *m.pl.* de nickel	Nickelvorkommen *n pl.*	minerali *m pl.* di nichel
° 12267 to nickel	nickeler	vernickeln	nichelare
° 12268 nickel	nickel *m*	Nickel *n*	nichel *m*
12269 nickel-alloy	alliage *m* à base de nickel	Nickellegierung *f*	lega *f* di nichelio
° 12270 nickel-aluminium steel	acier *m* au nickel--aluminium	Nickelaluminiumstahl *m*	acciaio *m* al nichel--alluminio
nickel bloom, *s. annabergite*			
° 12271 nickel-bronze	bronze *m* au nickel	Nickelbronze *f*	bronzo *m* al nichelio
° 12272 nickel-copper alloy	bronze *m* blanc	Nickelkupfer *n*	bronzo *m* bianco
° 12273 nickel-chrome steel	acier *m* au nickel--chrome	Nickelchromstahl *m*	acciaio *m* al nichel--cromo
° 12274 nickel hardening method	procédé *m* de trempe au nickel	Nickelhärtungsverfahren *n*	processo *m* di tempera al nickel
− 12275 nickel matte	matte *f* de nickel	Nickelstein *m*	matta *f* di nichel
° 12276 nickel-molybdenum	alliage *m* de molybdène et nickel	Molybdännickel *n*	lega *f* di molibdeno e nickel
− 12277 nickel-ore	minerai *m* de nickel	Nickelerz *n*	minerale *m* di nichel
− 12278 nickel oxide	oxyde *m* de nickel	Nickeloxydul *n*	ossido *m* di nickel
° 12279 nickel-plated sheet iron	tôle *f* nickelée	vernickeltes Blech *n*	lamiera *f* nichelata

	English	French	German	Italian
° 12280	nickel silver	maillechort *m*	Neusilber *n*	alpacca *f*
° 12281	nickel steel	acier *m* au nickel	Nickelstahl *m*	acciaio *m* al nichel(io)
° 12282	nickel steel plate	plaque *f* d'acier au nickel	Nickelstahlplatte *f*	piastra *f* di acciaio al nichelio
° 12283	nickel-vanadium steel	acier *m* au nickel--vanadium	Nickelvanadiumstahl *m*	acciaio *m* al nichel--vanadio
° 12284	nickelage,	nickelage *m*	Vernickelung *f*	nichelatura *f*
° 12285	nickeliferous iron ore	minerai *m* de fer nickelifère	nickelhaltiges Eisenerz *n*	minerale *m* di ferro nickelifero
° 12286	to nickelplate	nickeler	vernickeln	nickelare
− 12287	nicking	rouillure *f*, entaillage	Kerbe *f*, Kerben *n*	intaccatura *f*, tacca *f*
− 12288	nickings	charbon *m* menu	Kohlenklein *n*	carbone *m* minuto
° 12289	nidging	taille *f* de la pierre	Steinebehauen *n*	taglio *m* della pietra
− 12290	nife-zone	nife	Nife-Zone *f*	nife
^ 12291	nigger boy	soupape *f* de sûreté	Sicherheitsventil *n*	valvola *f* di sicurezza
− 12292	nigger head	tambour *m* à l'extré-mité de l'axe d'un treuil	Spill *n*, Spill-Kopf *m*, Spill-Trommel *f*	tamburo *m* (o campana) dell'argano
° 12293	night latch	verrou de sûreté	Nachtriegel *m*	stanghetta *f* di sicurezza
12294	night shift	poste *m* de nuit	Nachtschicht *f*	turno *m* di notte
− 12295	nigrine, nigrite	nigrine *f*, nigrite *f*	Nigrin *m*	nigrina *f*, nigrite *f*
− 12296	niobate	niobate *m*	Niobat *m*	niobate *m*
° 12297	niobium	niobium *m*	Niobium *n*	niobio *m*
− 12298	nip	amincissement *m*, étreinte *f*	Auskeilen *n*, Verdrückung *f*	restringimento *m* a cuneo, contrazione *f*
− 12299	nip	éboulement *m*	Bruch *m*, Zerdrücken *n*	franamento *m*, frana *f*
− 12300	nip out	amincissement *m*, étreinte *f*	Auskeilen *n*, Verdrückung *f*	restringimento *m*, contrazione *f*
° 12301	nipper	tenailles *f pl.*, pinces *f pl.*	Zange *f*	tenaglie *f pl.*, pinze *f pl.*

English	French	German	Italian
12302 **nipper**	aide-ouvrier *m*	Hilfsarbeiter *m*	manovale *m*
12303 **nippers** *pl.*, **tongs** *pl.*	tenaille *f* à déclic	Auslösevorrichtung *f*, Teufelsklaue *f*	tenaglia *f* con dispositivo di scatto
12304 **nipping fork**	clef *f* de retenue	Abfanggabel *f*	chiave *f* di ritenuta
12305 **nipple**	raccord *m* fileté	Nippel *m*	raccordo *m* a vite, raccordo *m* filettato
12306 **nitrate of cobalt**	nitrate *m* de cobalt	Kobaltnitrat *n*	nitrato *m* di cobalto
12307 **nitrate of palladium**	nitrate *m* de palladium	Palladiumnitrat *n*	nitrato *m* di palladio
nitrated steel, *s. nitrited steel*			
12308 **nitratite**	nitratine *f*	Nitratin *m*, Natronsalpeter *m*	nitratina *f*, sodanitro
12309 **nitric acid**	acide *m* nitrique	Salpetersäure *f*	acido *m* nitrico
12309a **nitride**	nitrure *m*	Nitrid *n*	nitruro *m*
12310 **nitrided alloy steel**	alliage *m* d'acier nitruré	Nitrierstahllegierung *f*	lega *f* di acciaio nitrurato
12311 **nitrided layer**	couche *f* nitrurée	nitrierte Schicht *f*	strato *m* nitrurato
nitrited steel, *s. nitriding steel*			
12312 **nitriding**	nitruration *f*	Nitrieren *n*	nitrurazione *f*
12313 **nitriding process**	procédé *m* de nitruration	Nitrierverfahren *n*	processo *m* di nitrurazione
12314 **nitriding steel, nitrogenhardened steel**	acier *m* nitruré, acier *m* de nitruration	Nitrierstahl *m*, Nitrogenstahl *m*	acciaio *m* nitrurato
12315 **nitrification**	nitrification *f*	Salpeterbildung *f*	nitrificazione *f*
12316 **nitrobarite**	nitrobaryte *f*	Nitrobarit *m*	nitrobarite *f*
12317 **nitrocalcite**	nitrocalcite *f*	Nitrokalzit *?*	nitrocalcite *f*
nitrocotton, *s. gun cotton*			
12318 **nitrogelatine**	nitro-gélatine *f*	Nitrogelatine *f*	nitrogelatina *f*
12319 **nitrogen**	azote *m*	Stickstoff *m*	azoto *m*, nitrogeno *m*
12320 **to nip, to nip out**	se terminer en coin	sich auskeilen	restringersi a cuneo
12321 **nitrogen hardening**	nitruration *f*	Nitrieren *n*, Nitrierhärtung *f*	nitrurazione *f*
nitrogen hardened steel, *s. nitrided steel*			

English	French	German	Italian
12322 **nitroglauberite**	nitroglaubérite *f*	Nitroglauberit *f*	nitroglauberite *f*
12323 **nitroglycerine explosive**	explosif *m* à base de nitroglycérine	Nitroglyzerinspreng- stoff *m*	esplosivo *m* alla nitroglicerina
12324 **nitrometer** **nitrostarch,** *s. xyloidin*	nitromètre *m*	Nitrometer *n*	nitrometro *m*
12325 **nitro, nitrous**	nitreux	nitrös	nitroso
12326 **nivenite** **nobbing, nobbling,** *s. nobling*	nivénite *f*	Nivenit *m*	nivenite *f*
12327 **nobelium**	nobélium *m*	Nobelium *n*	nobelio *m*
12328 **noble metal**	métal *m* précieux	Edelmetall *n*, edles Metall *n*	metallo *m* nobile
12329 **noble opal, precious opal**	opale *f* noble	edler Opal *m*, Edelopal *m*	opale *m* nobile
12329a **nobling**	cinglage *m*	Zängen *n*	eliminazione *f* di scorie
12330 **nocerite**	nocérite *f*	Nocerin *m*	nocerite *f*
12331 **nodular**	nodulaire	knötchenförmig	nodulare, a noduli
12332 **node of the fault**	pont *m* de faille	Brücke *f* einer Verwerfung	ponte *m* di faglia
nodular cast iron, nodular iron, *s. spheroidal graphite cast iron*			
12333 **nodular graphite**	graphite *m* nodulaire	Knötchengraphit *m*, Knotengraphit *m*	grafite *f* nodulare
12334 **nodular graphite cast iron, nodular iron**	fonte *f* à graphite nodulaire	Gusseisen *n* mit Knotengraphit	ghisa *f* nodulare
12335 **nodular ore, kidney ore**	minerai *m* en rognons, roussier *m*	Nierenerz *n*	minerale *m* reniforme (o nodulare)
12336 **nodule**	nodule *m*	Knötchen *n*	nodulo *m*
12337 **nominal size**	cote *f* nominale	Nennmass *n*	misura *f* nominale
12338 **non-aging steel**	acier *m* non vieillissant	alterungsfreier Stahl *m*, alterungs- beständiger Stahl *m*	acciaio *m* antinvec- chiante
12339 **non alloy steel, carbon steel**	acier *m* non allié	unlegierter Stahl *m*	acciaio *m* non legato (o al carbonio)
12340 **non-baking**	non collant	nichtbackend	magro, non bitumi- noso

English	French	German	Italian
— 12341 **non-baking coal**	houille f maigre, charbon m non collant	Magerkohle f	carbone m magro (o non bituminoso)
— 12342 **non-bituminous or non-baking coal**	houille f maigre	Magerkohle f	carbone m magro
° 12343 **non-burning steel**	acier m résistant à haute température	hitzebeständiger Stahl m	acciaio m resistente alle alte temperature
— 12344 **non-caking coal, non-clinkering coal**	houille f non-collante (ou à flamme vive)	Sinterkohle f	carbone m non fondente (o a fiamma viva)
— 12345 **non clinkering coal**	charbon m non scorifère	schlackenreine Kohle f	carbone m senza scorie
non-cocking coal, s. *non-caking coal*			
— 12346 **non-conformable**	discordant	diskordant	discordante
non-corroding steel, s. *stainless steel*			
°· 12347 **non-destructive measurement**	mesure f non destructive	zerstörungsfreie Messung f	misura f non distruttiva
non-corroding steel, s. *stainless steel*			
° 12348 **non-destructive testing**	contrôle m non destructif	zerstörungsfreie Prüfung f	controllo m non distruttivo
° 12349 **non-ferrous metal**	métal m non ferreux, petit métal	Nichteisenmetall n	metallo m non ferroso
— 12350 **non-gassing coal**	charbon m pauvre en gaz	gasarme Kohle f	carbone m povero di gas
— 12351 **non-graphitic**	non graphitique	nichtgraphitisch	non grafitico
— 12352 **non homogeneous**	non homogène	durchwachsen	non omogeneo
— 12353 **non-inflammable, flameproof**	résistant au feu, ignifuge	feuersicher, feuerfest	non infiammabile, ignifugo
— 12354 **non-magnetic**	non-magnétique	nicht magnetisch	non magnetico
° 12355 **non-magnetic cast iron**	fonte f amagnétique	unmagnetisches Gusseisen n	ghisa f amagnetica
^ 12356 **non-magnetic drill collar**	masse-tige m Schwerstange f	nichtmagnetische Schwerstange f	asta f pesante non magnetica
° 12357 **non-magnetic steel**	acier m anti-magnétique (ou amagnétique)	unmagnetisierbarer Stahl m, Antimagnetstahl m	acciaio m non magnetico (o amagnetico)
° 12358 **non-metallic inclusion**	inclusion f non métallique	nichtmetallischer Einschluss m	inclusione f non metallica

English	French	German	Italian
– 12359 non-mineralised product, tailings	produit *m* stérile, stérile *m*	steriles Gut *n*	prodotto *m* sterile
ᵓ 12360 non-phosphorized steel	acier *m* non phosphoré	Nichtphosphorstahl *m*	acciaio *m* non fosfora-to
ᵓ 12361 non polarized machine	machine *f* non polarisée	unpolarisierte Maschine *f*	macchina *f* non polarizzata
ᵓ 12362 non-reversing mill	laminoir *m* irréversible	kontinuierliche Stabeisenstrasse *f*	laminatoio *m* non reversibile
ᵓ 12363 non-scaling	inoxydable	zunderbeständig	inossidabile
12364 non self-propelled	non automoteur	nicht selbstfahrend	non automotore
ᵒ 12365 non-slip tread	plaque *f* striée	Gleitschutzbelag *m*	lastra *f* ferma-piede (o rigata)
non-splintering, *s. splinter-proof*			
ᴬ 12366 non upset	sans refoulement	nicht verdickt	non pressato, non compresso
non-stationary boiler, *s. portable (local type)*			
ᵒ 12367 non-warping steel	acier *m* indéformable	verzugfreier Stahl *m*	acciaio *m* inderforma-bile
– 12368 nonesite	nonésite *f*	Nonesit *m*	nonesite *f*
nonsizing, *s. running out*			
– 12369 nontronite	nontronite *f*	Nontronit *m*	nontronite *f*
– 12370 nonwetted	non mouillable	unbenetzbar	non bagnabile
– 12371 norbergite	norbergite *f*	Norbergit *m*	norbergite *f*
– 12372 nordenskioldine	nordenskiöldite *f*	Nordenskiöldin *m*	nordenskioldite *f*
– 12373 noria excavator	excavateur *m* à noria	Schöpfradbagger *m*	scavatore *m* a noria
– 12374 norite	norite *f*	Norit *m*	norite *f*
ᵒ 12375 normal bending quality sheet U-beams	solives-hourdis *f pl.* en tôle pliées en U	U-Traeger aus Falzblech	nervature-riempimen-to *f pl.* di lamiera piegata ad U
– 12376 normal displacement	déplacement *m* normal (d'une faille)	saigere Sprunghöhe *f*	dislocazione *f* norma-le
– 12377 normal fault, down--throw fault, drop fault, gravity fault	faille *f* normale	normale Verwerfung *f*, echte Verwerfung *f*, Abgleitung *f*, Verwerfung *f*	faglia *f* normale
normal fold, *s. upright fold*			

	English	French	German	Italian
−	12378 **normal granite**	granit m à biotite	Biotitgranit m	granito m a biotite
−	12379 **normal habitus**	faciès m normal	isometrischer Habitus m	facies f normale
−	12380 **normal horizontal separation**	distance f horizontale des affleurements	laterale horizontale Trennung f	distanza f orizzontale dell'affioramento
°	12381 **normal nitrided steel**	acier m normal de nitruration	normaler Nitrierstahl m	acciaio m normale da nitrurazione
	normal spectrum, *s. diffraction spectrum*			
−	12382 **normal superposition**	superposition f normale	normale Lagerung f	sovrapposizione f normale
−	12383 **normal throw**	rejet m	Sprunghöhe f	rigetto m
°	12384 **normal working**	allure f normale	Gargang m	andamento m o marcia f normale
°	12385 **normalise**	normaliser	normalglühen	normalizzare
°	12386 **normalised steel**	acier m normalisé	normalisierter Stahl m	acciaio m normalizzato
°	12387 **normalising (grain refining)**	recuit m d'affinage structural, recuit m de régénération	Normalglühen n	ricottura f di affinazione strutturale, ricottura f di rigenerazione
°	12388 **normalising**	trempe f à l'air, normalisation f	Lufthärtung f, Normalisierglühung f	normalizzazione f, tempra f all'aria
°	12389 **northupite**	northupite f	Northupit m	northupite f
°	12390 **nose of a Bessemer converter**	bec m d'un convertisseur Bessemer	Hals m einer Bessemerbirne	becco m di un convertitore Bessemer
°	12391 **nose (of a lathe)**	pointe de tour	Drehbankspitze f	punta f da tornio
−	12392 **nosean**	noséane m	Nosean n	noseano m
−	12393 **noseanite**	noséanite f	Noseanit m	noseanite f
°	12394 **notch**	entaille f, encoche f	Einschnitt m, Kerbe f	intaglio m, incavatura f, tacca f
−	12395 **notch**	tranchée f	Schürfgraben m	trincea f
°	12396 **notch brittleness**	fragilité f à l'entaille	Kerbsprödigkeit f	fragilità f all'intaglio
°	12397 **notch bar test**	essai m de choc sur éprouvette entaillée	Kerbschlagprobe f	prova f d'urto con provetta intagliata

	English	French	German	Italian
○	12398 **notch effect**	effet d'entaille	Kerbwirkung f	effetto m d'intaglio
○	12399 **notch gun**	canon m à boucher le trou de coulée	Stopfmaschine f	macchina f per tappare fori di colata
○	12400 **notch sensitivity**	sensibilité f à l'entaille	Kerbempfindlichkeit f	sensibilità f all'intaglio
○	12400a **notch toughness**	résilience f d'entaille	Kerbzähigkeit f	resilienza f d'intaglio
○	12401 **notched, toothed** **notched,** s. serrated	dentelé	kleinzackig	dentellato
○	12401a **notched ingot**	lingot m entaillé	vorgekerbter Block m	lingotto m intagliato
○	12402 **notches of the rule** **for the rider**	cran m de la règle du cavalier	Teilung f des Reiterlineals	suddivisione f del regolo del cavaliere
○	12403 **notching**	entaillage m, entaille f	Schlitz m, Einschnitt m	intagliatura f
—	12404 **noumeite**	nouméite f	Numeait m	numeaite f
○	12405 **nowel, core**	noyau m	Kern m	anima f
○	12406 **noxious**	nocif	schädlich	nocivo, dannoso
○	12407 **nozzle**	busette f de coulée	Lochstein m	sede f di colata
○	12408 **nozzle**	brûleur m	Brenndüse f	becco m di combustione
○	12409 **nozzle**	busette f (de soufflet)	Blasdüse f	ugello m
○	12410 **nozzle**	lance f à jet de sable	Strahlrohr n	tubo m a getto
○	12411 **nozzle, teeming** **nozzle**	orifice m ou siège m de coulée	Ausflussöffnung f	foro m di colata
○	12412 **nozzle box**	tubulure f de coulée	Auslassstutzen m	tubo m di colata
○	12413 **nozzle brick sleeve**	tube m réfractaire	gebrannte Hülse f	involucro m o tubo m refrattario
○	12414 **nozzle (of bellows)**	buse f (de soufflet)	Düse f, Blasebalgrohr n	canna f (di mantice)
○	12415 **nozzle plate**	plaque f de tuyère	Düsenplatte f	piastra f di ugelli
○	12416 **nozzle section**	section f de la buse	Düsenquerschnitt m	sezione f dell'ugello
○	12416a **nozzling**	frettage m	Aufschrumpfen n	calettamento m
^	12417 **nuclear log**	diagraphie f nucléaire	Radioaktivitätslog n	diagrafia f nucleare

English	French	German	Italian
° 12418 **nuclear magnetism log**	diagraphie f de magnétisme nucléaire	Kernmagnetismuslog n	diagrafia f di magnetismo nucleare
nucleous number, $s.$ *mass number*			
° 12419 **nucleus**	germe m, noyau m	Keim m, Kern m	germe m, nucleo m
– 12420 **nugget**	pépite f	Goldklumpen m, Klumpen m	pepita f
– 12421 **nuggeting**	recherches d'or	Prospektieren n nach gediegenem Gold, Goldsuche f	ricerche d'oro
12422 **number of kind**	numéro m de la série	Gattungsnummer f	numero m d'ordine
– 12423 **number of year**	indication f de l'année	Jahreszahl f	annata f
number one bar, $s.$ *best or muck bar*			
– 12424 **nummulite**	nummulite f	Nummulit m	nummulite f
– 12425 **nummulitic facies**	faciès m nummulitifère	Nummulitenfazies f	facies f nummulifera
– 12426 **nummulitic limestone**	calcaire nummulitique	Nummulitenkalk m	calcare m nummulitico
° 12427 **nut**	écrou m	Schraubenmutter f	dado m
– 12428 **nut coal, nuts** $pl.$	gailletteries f $pl.$, noisettes f $pl.$	Nusskohle f	carbone m in pezzatura noce
– 12429 **nut coke**	noix de charbon, coke concassé	Nusskoks m, Knabbelkoks m	koke m in pezzatura noce
nutz, $s.$ *nut coal*			

	English	French	German	Italian
12430	O.B. alloy	bronze *m* au plomb (8%)	Bleibronze *f* (8%)	bronzo *m* al piombo (all'8%)
12431	object of separation	but *m* du triage	Scheidezweck *m*	scopo *m* della separazione
12432	objective	objectif *m*	Objektiv *n*	obbiettivo *m*
12433	oblique bedding	stratification *f* oblique	Diagonalschichtung *f*	stratificazione *f* obliqua
12434	oblique fracture	cassure *f* en sifflet	schiefer Bruch *m*	frattura *f* o rottura *f* obliqua
12435	oblique prism	prisme *m* oblique	schiefes Prisma *n*	prisma *m* obliquo
	oblong iron, *s. square bar*			
12436	observation	observation *f*	Beobachtung *f*	osservazione *f*
12437	obsidian	obsidienne *f*	Obsidian *m*	ossidiana *f*
12438	obsidianite	obsidianite *f*	Obsidianit *m*	ossidianite *f*
12439	obtuse	émoussé	stumpf	ottuso
12440	obtuse angle iron	cornière *f* biaise	schiefes Winkeleisen *n*	cantonale sghembo
12441	obtuse angle Z (or zed iron)	fer *m* à Z à aile inclinée	schiefwinkliges Z-Eisen *n*	ferro *m* a Z sghembo
12442	occluded	inclus, enfermé, emprisonné	eingeschlossen	occluso
12443	occluded gas	gaz *m* inclus (ou enfermé ou emprisonné)	eingeschlossenes Gas *n*	gas *m* occluso
12444	occlusion	partie *f* peu dense	lockere Stelle *f*	parte *f* spugnosa
12445	occlusion	occlusion *f*	Einschluss *m*	occlusione *f*
12446	occurance of gas	venue *f* de gaz	Gasvorkommen *n*	manifestazione di gas
12447	ocellar structure	structure *f* kélyphitique	Ocellartextur *f*	struttura *f* ocellare
12448	ochre, ocher	ocre *f*, sanguine *f*, craie *f* rouge	Ocker *m*	ocra *f*, creta *f* rossa
	ochry-brown, *s. brown iron-ore*			
12449	ochrolite	ochrolite *f*	Ochrolith *m*	ocrolite *f*
12450	oct kelly, octagonal kelly	tige *f* octagonale	achteckige Mitnehmerstange *f*	asta *f* ottagonale

English	French	German	Italian
° 12451 octagonal bar	fer *m* octogonal	Achtkantstahl *m*	ottagono *m*, ferro *m* ottagono
° 12452 octagonal block	bloc *m* octogonal	achtkantiger Block *m*	massello *m* ottagonale
^ 12453 octane	octane *m*	Oktan *n*, Octan	ottano *m*
^ 12454 octane rating	indice *m* d'octane	Oktanwert *m* Oktanzahl *f*	gradazione *f* ottanica, livello *m* ottanico
° 12454a octet structure	octet *m* électronique	Elektronenoktett *m*	ottetto *m* elettronico
O.D. — *outside diameter*			
° 12455 oddside	fausse couche *f*, plaque-modèle *f*	Sparhälfte *f*, Modellplatte *f*	letto *f* falso, falso piano *m*, falsa placca *f*, placca *f* modello
— 12456 odinite	odinite *f*	Odinit *m*	odinite *f*
— 12457 odontolite	odontolite *f*	Odontolith *m*	odontolite *f*
^ 12458 odorizer	substance *f* odorante	Aromastoff *m*	odorizzante *m*
12459 of equal weight	de poids égal	gleichschwer	di eguale peso
° 12460 off gauge	écart *m* effectif	Massabweichung *f*	fuori dimensioni
° 12460a off-heat	piquée *f* défecteuse	Ausfallabstich *m*	spillata *f* difettosa
— 12461 offretite	offrétite *f*	Offretit *m*	offretite *f*
12462 to offset	balancer, compenser	balancieren, ausgleichen	bilanciare, compensare
— 12463 offset	distance *f* horizontale des affleurements	laterale horizontale Trennung *f*	spostamento *m* orizzontale degli affioramenti
— 12464 offset	recoupe *f*	kurzer Einbruch *m*	breve galleria *f* di derivazione
— 12465 offset	forage *m* de limite	Schutzbohrung *f*	sondaggio *m* anticlinale
^ 12466 offset agreement	accord *m* limite	Schutzabkommen *n*	accordo *m* limite
— 12467 offset area	zone *f* limite	Schutzgebiet *n*	area *f* limite
— 12468 offset of the bed	ramification *f* d'une couche	Ausläufer *m*	ramificazione *f* di uno strato, apofisi *f*

English	French	German	Italian
12469 offset production	production f limite	Schutzproduktion f	produzione f limite
12470 offset well	puits m de limite, forage m de limite	Grenzbohrung f	sondaggio m di delimitazione
12471 offshore drilling	sondage submarin	Unterwasserbohrung f	trivellazione f in mare aperto
12472 offshore rig	sonde f submarine	Unterwasserbohrer m	impianto m di perforazione marina
offshoot, *s. apophyse*			
12473 offstream	hors de service	ausser Betrieb m	fuori servizio
12474 offtake, air vent	traînée f d'air	Entlüftungsnut f	canale m d'aria,(di sfogo d'aria da una forma)
12475 offtake	débit m	Förderung f	produzione f, flusso m
12476 O.H,(oil hardening)	trempe f à l'huile	Olhärtung f	tempera f in olio
12476a O.H. & T.	trempé à l'huile et revenu	in Öl gehärtet und nachgeglüht	temprato in olio e rinvenuto
12477 to oil, to rub over with oil	huiler, graisser	einölen	oliare , ingrassare
12478 oil	huile f	Öl n	olio m
12479 oil bank	front m d'huile	Ölbank f	banco m di petrolio
12480 oil bath	bain m d'huile	Ölbad n	bagno m d'olio
12481 oil bloom	fluorescence f de pétrole	Ölfluoreszenz f	fluorescenza f di petrolio
oil bonded sand, *s. oil sand*			
12482 oil bunker	réservoir à pétrole	Ölbehälter m	serbatoio m per petrolio
oil-burning boiler, *s. oil-fired boiler*			
12483 oil can	burette f à huile	Öler m	oleatore m
oil-chalk test, *s. paraffine test*			
12484 oil concession	concession f pétrolifère	Erdölkonzession f	concessione f petrolifera
12485 oil dehydrating plant	installation f de déshydratation d'huile	Dehydrierungsanlage f	impianto m di disidratazione del petrolio
12486 oil deposit	gisement m de pétrole	Ölvorkommen n	giacimento m di petrolio
12487 oil derrick	tour f de sondage à pétrole	Erdölbohrturm m, Ölförderturm m	torre f di perforazione petrolifera

	English	French	German	Italian
^	12488 **oil drain**	boue f à l'huile	Ölschlamm m	fango m all'olio
^	12489 **oil field**	champ m de pétrole	Ölfeld n	cantiere m (o campo m) petrolifero
o	12490 **oil-fired boiler**	chaudière f ànaphte	Dieselkessel m	caldaia f a nafta
o	12491 **oil-furnace**	four à pétrole, four chauffé au pétrole	Petroleumofen m	forno m a petrolio
o	12492 **oil gas burner**	brûleur m à huile lourde	Ölgasbrenner m	bruciatore m a gas a olio pesante
o	12493 **oil-hardened steel**	acier trempant à l'huile	Ölhärtungsstahl m	acciaio m temprante in olio
o	12494 **oil-hardening**	trempe f à l'huile	Ölhärtung f	tempera f in olio

oil hardening steel, s. *oil hardened steel*

	English	French	German	Italian
^	12495 **oil in place**	huile f en place	Öl n am Ort	olio m sul posto
^	12496 **oil in water emulsion**	émulsion f d'huile dans l'eau	Öl-Emulsion in Wasser	emulsione f d'olio nell'acqua
^	12497 **oil industry**	industrie f pétroli-fère	Erdölindustrie f	industria f petrolife-ra
^	12498 **oil layer**	nappe f pétrolifère	Ölschicht f	strato m petrolifero
^	12499 **oil lens**	lentille f de sable pétrolifère	Öllinse f	lente f di sabbia petrolifera
^	12500 **oil mine**	mine f de pétrole	Erdölbergwerk n	miniera f petrolifera
^	12501 **oil mining**	exploitation f de mines pétrolifères	Erdölbergbau m	coltivazione f di giacimenti petroliferi
^	12502 **oil pit**	fosse f à huile	Ölloch n	fossa f per olio
^	12503 **oil plant**	installation f pétrolifère	Erdölanlage f	impianto m petro-lifero
^	12504 **oil pool**	accumulation f de pétrole	Ölanreicherung f,	accumulo m di petrolio
^	12505 **oil rights**	droits d'exploita-tion du pétrole	Erdölförderungs-rechte f pl.	diritti di estrazione del petrolio
^	12506 **oil sand**	sable m à huile	Ölsand m	sabbia f petrolifera, gres m petrolifero

	English	French	German	Italian
^	12507 oil saver	racleur *m* d'huile	Ölabstreifer *m*	raschia-olio *m*
^	12508 oil seepage	infiltration *f* pétrolifère	Ölinfiltration *f*	infiltrazione *f* petrolifera
^	12509 oil shale	schiste bitumineux	Ölschiefer *m*	scisto bituminoso
^	12510 oil show, oil indication	indication *f* de pétrole	Ölanzeichen *n*	manifestazione *f* di petrolio
^	12511 oil strike	découverte *f* du pétrole	Erdölentdeckung *f*	ritrovamento *m* del petrolio
^	12512 oil string, production string	colonne *f* d'exploitation (ou de production)	Förderkolonne *f*	colonna *f* tubante (o di produzione)
^	12513 oil thief	jauge *f* d'échantillonnage	Ölprobenehmer *m*	pescatore *m* di campioni di petrolio (nel serbatoio)
^	12514 oil trap	siphon *m* de pétrole, deshuileur *m*	Ölabscheider *m*	zona *f* d'arresto del petrolio
^	12515 oil well	puits *m* à pétrole	Ölsonde *f*, Ölquelle *f*	pozzo *m* petrolifero, sonda *f* petrolifera
^	12516 oil well plunger pump	pompe *f* de fond pour puits de pétroie	Untergrundpumpe *f* für Erdölgruben	pompa *f* di fondo per pozzi di petrolio
^	12517 oil withdrawal	enlèvement *m* de pétrole	Ölentnahme *f*	prelevamento *m* di petrolio
^	12518 oil yard	chantier *m* pétrolifère	Ölfeld *n*	cantiere *m* petrolifero
°	12518a oiling	protection *f* à l'huile	Ölschutz *m*	protezione *f* con olio
—	12519 oisanite	oisanite *f*	Oisanit *m*	oisanite *f*
—	12520 okenite	okénite *f*	Okenit *m*	okenite *f*
°	12521 old crucible material	débris *m pl.* de creusets	Tiegelscherben *f pl.*	rifiuti *m pl.* o detriti *m pl.* dei crogiuoli
	old iron, s. scrap iron			
—	12522 old man	vieux travaux *m pl.*	alter Mann *m*	miniera *f* abbandonata
°	12523 old sand	sable vieux	Altsand *m*	sabbia *f* vecchia
—	12524 olefin	oléfine *f*	Olefin *n*	olefina *f*
—	12525 oleaginous	oléagineux	ölhaltig	oleoso, untuoso
—	12526 oleic acid	acide *m* oléique	Ölsäure *f*	acido *m* oleico

	English	French	German	Italian
^	12527 olein	oléine *f*	Olein *n*	oleina *f*
^	12528 oleum liver	film *m* d'oléum	Oleumfilm *m*	pellicola *f* oleosa
^	12529 oleum spirit	esprit *m* d'huile	Ölspiritus *m*	spirito *m* di petrolio
o	12530 oligist iron	fer *m* oligiste	Eisenglanz *m*	ferro *m* oligisto, specularite *f*
—	12531 Oligocene	oligocène, système oligocène	Oligozän *n*	oligocene *m*
—	12532 oligoclase	oligoclase *m*	Oligoklas *m*	oligoclasio *m*
—	12533 oligoclasite	oligoclasite *f*	Oligoklasit *m*	oligoclasite *f*
—	12534 oligonite	oligonite *f*	Mesitinspat *m*	oligonite *f*
—	12535 olivenite	olivénite *f*	Olivenit *m*	olivenite *f*
o	12535a oliver	marteau *m* à pédale	Tritthammer *m*	martello *m* a pedale
o	12536 olivine	olivine *f*	Olivin *m*	olivina *f*
o	12537 omitted core	noyau *m* oublié	verlorener Kern *m*	anima *f* dimenticata
—	12538 omphacite	omphazite *f*	Omphacit *m*	onfacite *f*
^	12539 on-and off	monté et fini	an und aus	intrapreso e finito, montato e levato
^	12540 on-and-off attachment	attaque *f* à accrochage et décrochage	an und aus Verbindung	attacco *m* ad aggancio e sgancio
o	12540a on end	debout	stehend	dritto
^	12541 on position	en position de travail	in Arbeitsstellung *f*	in posizione di lavoro
^	12542 on stream	en marche productive	in Produktionsgang *m*	in marcia produttiva
^	12543 on structure	placé sur anticlinal productif	auf der Struktur *f* gelagert	sistemato su anticlinale produttivo
^	12544 on the pump	en phase *f* de pompage	beim Pumpen	in fase *f* di pompaggio
	on the surface, *s. above ground*			
^	12545 on trip barrel	fût *m* productif	produktives Ölfass *n*	fusto *m* produttivo
^	12546 once run, once through	à procédé direct	ohne Rücklauf *m*	a processo diretto
—	12547 onegite	onégite *f*	Onegit *m*	onegite *f*
—	12548 onkilonite	onkilonite *f*	Onkilonit *m*	onkilonite *f*

	English	French	German	Italian
– 12549	onofrite	onofrite *f*	Onofrit *m*	onofrite *f*
– 12550	onsetter	accrocheur *m*	Anschläger *m*	addetto *m* alle gabbie
– 12551	oolitic iron ore, minette	fer *m* oolithique, minette *f*	Rogenstein *m*, Minette *f*	f rro *m* oolitico
– 12552	oolitic texture, pisolitic texture	structure *f* oolithique (ou pisolithique)	oolithische Struktur *f*, pisolithische Struktur *f*	struttura *f* oolitica (o pisolitica)
– 12553	onsetting	encagement *m*	Einschieben *n* der Förderwagen	ingabbiamento *m*
^ 12554	onstream	en service	in Betrieb	in esercizio
	onyx, *s. banded agate*			
– 12555	opal	opale *f*	Opal *m*	opale *m*
	opal jasper, *s. ferruginous opal*			
– 12556	opdalite	opdalite *f*	Opdalit *m*	opdalite *f*
° 12557	open a large mould	dédoubler un moule	eine grosse Form *f* öffnen	aprire una forma (grande)
– 12558	open a stope	ouvrir une taille	eine Abbaustrecke *f* aufhauen	aprire *f* una galleria
12559	to open automatically	s'ouvrir automatiquement	sich selbsttätig öffnen	aprirsi automaticamente
° 12560	to open the casting, to lift the casting	décocher, démouler la fonte	(den Formkasten) ausleeren, entformen	sformare o sterrare
	to open the mold, *s. to open the casting*			
° 12561	to open the tap hole by electric arc	dégager le trou de coulée à l'arc électrique	das Stichloch mittelst elektrischem Lichtbogens öffnen	aprire il foro di colata con l'arco elettrico
° 12562	open annealed	recuit *m* à l'air	unter Luftzutritt ausgehärtet	ricotto all'aria
12563	open annealing, black annealing	recuit à l'air, recuit en noir	Luftaushärtung *f*, Schwarzglühen *n*	ricottura *f* all'aria (o in nero)
– 12564	open-burning coal	charbon *m* flambant	Gasflammkohle *f*	carbone *m* a fiamma lunga
° 12564a	open cast	coulée *f* à découvert	offener Herdguss *m*	colata *f* allo scoperto
– 12565	open cast	mine *f* à ciel ouvert, travail à ciel ouvert	Tagebau *m*	miniera *f* a cielo aperto, lavoro *m* a cielo aperto
– 12566	open cast mining	exploitation *f* à ciel ouvert	Tagebau *m*	coltivazione *f* a cielo aperto
° 12567	open coil	bobine *f* ouverte	offene Rolle *f*	bobina *f* aperta

	English	French	German	Italian
o	12568 open cycle output	production f à cycle ouvert	Leistung f in offenem Zyklus	produzione f in ciclo aperto
o	12568a open die	estampe f ouverte	offener Stempel m	stampo m aperto
o	12569 open-die forging	forgeage m libre	Herdformschmieden n	fucinatura f libera
—	12570 open fault	faille f ouverte, faille f disjonctive	klaffende Verwerfung f	faglia f aperta
^	12571 open flow test	essai m à plein	offener Fliess-versuch m	prova f a pieno flusso
—	12572 open fold	pli m ouvert	flache Falte f	piega f aperta
o	12573 open hearth	foyer m découvert	offener Herd m	focolare m (o crogiuo-lo) aperto, suola f aperta
o	12574 open-hearth furnace	four Martin, four à sole	Siemens-Martin--Ofen m, Herdofen m	forno Martin (Siemens)
o	12575 open-hearth furnace plant	aciérie f Martin	Martinwerk n	acciaieria Martin--Siemens
o	12576 open hearth pig iron	fonte f Martin ou pour acier	Martinroheisen n, Stahlroheisen n	ferro m Martin o per acciaio
o	12577 open-hearth plant, open hearth furnace plant	aciérie f Martin	Martinwerk n	acciaieria f Martin Siemens
o	12578 open-hearth process	procédé m Siemens-Martin	Siemens-Martin-verfahren n	processo m con forno a riverbero
o	12579 open-hearth refining	affinage m par four Siemens-Martin	im Siemens-Martin-ofen raffinieren	affinazione f su suo-la
o	12580 open hearth steel	acier m Martin	Martinstahl m	acciaio m Martin
o	12581 open hearth steel works	aciérie f Siemens--Martin	Martinstahlhütte f	acciaieria f Martin
—	12582 open hole	sondage m (ou trou) non tubé	unverrohrtes Loch n	foro m scoperto (o aperto)
o	12582a open joint	joint m ouvert	offene Formteilung f	ritrovatura f aperta
—	12583 open mill	mélangeur m ouvert	offener Mischer m	mescolatore m aperto
	open mine, s. open cast			
—	12584 open mining	exploitation f à ciel ouvert	Tagebau m	coltivazione f a cie-lo aperto
o	12585 open mould	moule m à découvert	offene Form f	forma f allo scoperto

	English	French	German	Italian
— 12586	open overhand stope	gradin *m* renversé sans remblayage	Firstenstoss *m* ohne Bergeversatz	gradino *m* rovescio senza ripiena
	open pig (iron), *s. coarse-grained iron*			
○ 12587	open pass	cannelure *f* ouverte	offenes Kaliber *n*	canale *m* aperto
	open pig (iron), *s.coarse-grained iron*			
— 12588	open pit	exploitation *f* à ciel ouvert	Tagebau *m*	coltivazione *f* a cielo aperto, trincea *f* a cielo aperto
	open pit mining, *s, open pit*			
— 12589	open quarry	carrière *f* à ciel ouvert	Steinbruch *m*	cava *f* a cielo aperto
○ 12590	open range boiler plant	installation *f* de chaudières découvertes	freistehende Kesselanlage *f*	impianto *m* scoperto di caldaie
— 12591	open sand	sable *m* poreux	poriger Sand *m*	sabbia *f* porosa
○ 12592	open sand casting	coulée *f* à découvert	offener Herdguss *m*	colata *f* allo scoperto, formatura *f* allo scoperto
	open sand mold, *s. hearth mold*			
○ 12593	open sand molding	moulage *m* à découvert	Herdguss *m*	colata *f* allo scoperto
	open steel, *s. rimming steel*			
— 12594	open stope	chantier *m* à ciel ouvert	Tagebau *m*	cantiere *m* a giorno, cantiere *m* aperto
— 12595	open stopes	exploitation *f* par piliers abandonnés	Festenbau *m*, Stützbau *m*	coltivazione *f* a pilastri abbandonati
— 12596	open stulled stope	taille *f* boisée non remblayée	unversetzter Stoss *m* mit Stempelzimmerung	taglio *m* rinforzato senza ripiena
○ 12597	open tool	outil *m* ouvert	offenes Gerät *n*	utensile *m* aperto
○ 12598	open top feeder	masselotte *f* ouverte, masselotte *f* directe	offener Speiser *m*, verlorener Kopf *m*	materozza *f* (superiore) aperta
○ 12599	open top side feeder	masselotte *f* ouverte à talon	seitlich offener Speiser *m*	materozza *f* aperta a tallone (o lateralmente)
○ 12600	open topped housing	cage *f* à chapeau rapporté	Kappenständer *m*	gabbia *f* aperta o con cappello
—12601	open underhand stope	gradin *m* droit non remblayé	Strossenstoss *m* ohne Bergeversatz	gradino *m* dritto senza ripiena

	English	French	German	Italian
	12602 **open up**	ouvrir	aufschliessen	aprire
—	12603 **open wagon**	wagon *m* ouvert	offener Wagen *m*	carro *m* aperto
	open water drilling, *s. offshore drilling*			
	open working, *s. open mining*			
°	12604 **open white pig**	fonte *f* blanche	garschmelziges Eisen *n*	ghisa *f* bianca porosa
—	12605 **opencast**	à ciel ouvert, au jour	im Tagebau *m*	allo scoperto *m*, a cielo *m* aperto, a giorno
	12606 **openwork**	exploitation *f* à ciel ouvert	Tagebaugewinnung *f*	coltivazione *f* a cielo aperto
—	12607 **open working**	travaux *m pl.* à ciel ouvert, abattage au jour	Tagebau *m*, Tagebruch *m*	lavori *m pl.* a cielo aperto
°	12608 **opened top or throat**	gueulard *m* ouvert	geöffneter Gichtverschluss *m*	bocca *f* di caricamento aperta, cono *m* aperto
	opened throat, *s. opened top*			
°	12609 **opening a large mould**	dédoublage *m*	Auseinandernehmen *n*	apertura di una formatura
°	12610 **opening of the tuyere**	oeil *m* de la tuyère	Auge *n* der Form	apertura *f* dell'ugello
—	12611 **opening out**	préparation *f*	Vorrichtung *f*	preparazione *f*
°	12612 **opening out the hole, to emboss the hole**	agrandir le trou	das Loch auftreiben	allargare il foro
—	12613 **operated**	exploité	benutzt	sfruttato
	12614 **operating cycle**	cycle *m* d'exploitation	Betriebskreisprozess	ciclo *m* di lavorazione
°	12614a **operating platform**	banc *m* de manoeuvre	Kanzel *f*	piattaforma *f* di servizio
	operating time, *s. weld cycle time for repetitive welding*			
°	12615 **operating valve, regulating slide valve**	valve *f* d'admission	Steuerschieber *m*	cassetto *m* di distribuzione, valvola *f* d'ammissione
	operator, *s. gas welder*			
—	12616 **ophite**	ophite *f*	Ophit *m*	ofite *f*

	English	French	German	Italian
—	12617 **ophitic texture**	texture f ophitique	ophitische Struktur f, Gabbrostruktur f	struttura f ofitica
—	12618 **opposed**	opposé	gegenwärtig , entgegengesetzt	opposto, contrapposto
	O.Q., *s. oil quenched*			
—	12618a**orange lead**	rouge m au plomb	Orangemennige f	tetrossido m di piombo
—	12619 **orangite**	orangite f	Orangit m	orangite f
—	12620 **orbicular structure**	structure f orbiculaire	sphäroidische Textur f	struttura f sferoidale
—	12621 **orbite**	orbite f	Orbit m	orbite f
—	12622 **ordanchite**	ordanchite f	Ordanchit m	ordanchite f
o	12623 **order of abundance**	ordre m de fréquence		ordine m di frequenza
	ordinary flattened drill, *s. arrow headed drill*			
o	12624 **ordinary or simple housing**	cage f fermée ordinaire	Walzenständer m für stetige Lagerung	gabbia f chiusa ordinaria
o	12625 **ordinary quality soft steel**	acier doux de qualité courante	gewöhnlicher Fluss. stahl	acciaio dolce ordinario
—	12626 **ordinary shaft-sinking**	fonçage m à niveau vide	gewöhnliches Abteufverfahren n	approfondimento m a livello aperto
	ordinary steel, *s. carbon steel*			
—	12627 **ore assay**	analyse f quantitative des minerais	quantitative Erzanalyse f	analisi f quantitativa del minerale
—	12628 **ore assaying**	essai m des minerais	Erzprobenehmen n	prova f dei minerali
—	12629 **ore bearing**	métallifère	metallhaltig, erzführend	metallifero
—	12630 **ore benefication**	enrichissement des minerais	Erzaufbereitung f	arricchimento m dei minerali
—	12631 **ore bin**	soute à minerai	Erzbunker m	tramoggia f per minerali
	ore body, *s. solid ore deposit*			
—	12632 **ore breaking**	abattage m de minerai	Erzabbau m	abbattimento m di minerali
—	12633 **ore breaking**	concassage m de minerai	Erzzerkleinerung f	frantumazione f di minerale
—	12634 **ore-briquette**	briquette f de minerai	Erzbrikett n, Erzziegel m	mattonella f di minerale

English	French	German	Italian
— 12635 ore briquetting	agglomération f de minerais	Erzbrikettierung f, Mineralagglomeration f	agglomerazione f di minerali
— 12636 ore burner	grilleur de minerai	Erzröster m	arrostitore m di minerale
° 12637 ore charge, charge of ore	charge f de minerai	Erzgicht f	carica f di minerale
— 12638 ore chute	cheminée à minerai	Erzrolle f	scivolo m per minerali
— 12639 ore column	colonne f de minerai	Erzsäule f	colonna f di minerale
ore concentration, s. ore dressing			
— 12640 ore deposit	gîte f métallifère	Erzlagerstätte f	giacimento m metallifero
— 12641 ore distributer	distributeur m de minerai	Erzverteiler m	distributore m del minerale
— 12642 ore-dressing	traitement m mécanique	Aufbereitung f, Zubereitung f	trattamento m meccanico dei minerali
— 12643 ore dust, fines	poussière f de minerai	Erzstaub m	polvere f di minerale
ore enrichment, s. enrichment			
— 12644 ore-leaching plant	installation f de lixiviation des minerais	Erzlaugerei f	impianto m per lisciviazione dei minerali
— 12645 ore level	galerie f d'exploitation	Förderstollen m	galleria f d'estrazione
— 12646 ore loading device	appareil m de chargement des minerais	Erzladevorrichtung f	caricatore m per minerali
— 12647 ore-mass	amas m de minerai	Erzkörper n	massa f (o ammasso m) di minerali
— 12647a ore pocket	nid m, poche f	Erznest n	nido m di minerale
ore process, s. direct process			
— 12648 ore puddling	puddlage m de minerai	Erzpuddeln n	puddellaggio m di minerale
— 12649 ore pulp, ore mud	fines m pl. de minerai	Erztrübe f pl., Erzschlemme f	minerale m macinato con acqua, torbida f
— 12650 ore raising	extraction f des minerais	Erzförderung f	estrazione f dei minerali
— 12651 ore shoot	cheminée f de minerais	Erzschlauch m,	scivolo m (o piano inclinato) di minerali

English	French	German	Italian
— 12652 ore sintering	agglomération f des minerais	Erzsinterung f	agglomerazione f dei minerali
— 12652a ore sizing	triage m des minerais	Erzklassierung f	classificazione f dei minerali
— 12653 ore-sorting	triage m de minerai	Erzscheiden n	cernita f del minerale
— 12654 ore stamp	bocard m	Pochwerk n	mulino m a pestelli
— 12655 ore stock	réserve f de minerai	Erzvorrat m	riserva f di minerale

stock work, s. *solid ore deposit*

— 12656 ore storing place	dépôt m de minerais	Erzlagerplatz m	deposito m di minerali
— 12657 ore to be roasted	matière f à griller	Röstgut n	materiale m da torrefare
— 12658 ore wagon	wagonnet m à minerais	Erzwagen m, Erzförderwagen m	vagone m (o carrello) per minerale
— 12659 ore washery	lavoir m à minerais, laverie f	Wäsche f, Erzwäsche f	lavatoio m per minerali
— 12660 ore winning	extraction f de minerai	Erzförderung f	estrazione f di minerale
— 12661 ore working	traitement m du minerai	Erzverarbeitung f	trattamento m del minerale
— 12662 orendite	orendite f	Orendit m	orendite f
— 12663 organic material	matière f organique	organischer Stoff m	sostanza f organica

organic substance, s. *organic material*

— 12664 oriental ruby	rubis oriental	orientalischer Rubin	rubino m orientale
— 12665 oriental topaz	corindon m jaune	orientalischer Topas m	corindone m giallo

oriental turquoise, s. *agaphite*

— 12666 orientite	orientite f	Orientit m	orientite f
— 12666a original mineral	minerai primaire	primäres Mineral n	minerale m primario
— 12667 original stratification	stratification f primaire	primäre horizontale Schichtung f	stratificazione f primaria
^ 12668 orifice	orifice	Stauscheibe f	orifizio m
^ 12669 orifice flange	bride f d'orifice	Düsenflansch m	flangia f dell'orifizio
^ 12670 orifice meter	indicateur m à orifice	Staurandmesser m	venturimetro m
^ 12671 orifice plate	plaque f perforée	Lochplatte f	piastra f perforata

	English	French	German	Italian
—	12672 oriented core	carotte *f* orientée	orientierter Kern *m*	carota *f* orientata
°	12673 ornamental moulding	profilé *m* d'enjolivage	Zierleiste *f*	profilato *m* ornamentale
°	12674 ornamentation of the surface	embellissement *m* de la surface	Oberflächenver-schönerung *f*	abbellimento *m* della superficie
—	12675 ornoite	ornoïte *f*	Ornoit *m*	ornoite *f*
—	12676 orogenesis	orogénèse *f*	Orogenese *f*	orogenesi *f*
—	12677 orographic fault	faille *f* orographique	orographische Verwerfung *f*	faglia *f* orografica
—	12678 orpiment	orpiment *m*	Auripigment *n*	orpimento *m*
°	12679 Orsat apparatus orthite, *s. allanite*	analyseur *m* d'Orsat	Orsatscher Apparat *m*	apparecchio *m* di Orsat, apparecchio *m* per analisi dei gas
—	12680 orthoclase	orthoclase *m*	Orthoklas *m*	ortoclasio *m*
—	12681 orthophyric texture	texture ortho-phyrique	orthophyrische Struktur *f*	struttura *f* ortofirica
—	12682 orthorhombic	orthorhombique	orthorhombisch	ortorombico
—	12683 orthorhombic prism	prisme *m* orthorhombique	orthorhombisches Prisma *n*	prisma *m* rombico
—	12684 (ortho)rhombic system, prismatic system	système *m* tertiaire	rhombisches System *n*	sistema *m* (trimetrico) rombico
	orthosymmetric system, *s. orthorhombic system*			
—	12685 orthosilicate	orthosilicate *m*	Orthosilikat *n*	ortosilicato *m*
—	12686 oscillating sieve	tamis *m* oscillant	Schwingsieb *n*	setaccio *m* oscillante, crivello *m* a scosse
	oscillating crystal, *s. rotating crystal*			
	oscillating trough, *s. rocking trough*			
°	12687 osmium	osmium *m*	Osmium *n*	osmio *m*
—	12688 osmondite	osmondite *f*	Osmondit *m*	osmondite *f*
—	12689 osmotic pressure	pression *f* osmotique	osmotischer Druck *m*	pressione *f* osmotica
	outburst, *s. basset*			
°	12690 out of repair	en mauvais état	baufällig	in cattico stato
°	12691 out of work, shut down, out of operation	hors service	ausser Betrieb *m*	fuori servizio

	English	French	German	Italian
˄ 12692	**out-step well, out-step**	puits *m* d'extension	Erweiterungssonde *f*	pozzo *m* d'allargamento
— 12693	**to outcrop**	affleurer (d'un gisement)	ausgehen (einer Lagerstätte)	affiorare (di un giacimento)
— 12694	**outcrop**	affleurement *m*, sopement *m*	Ausgehen *n*, Ausbeissen *n*	affioramento *m* superficiale, cappello
— 12695	**outcrop of a lode**	affleurement d'un filon	Gangausbiss *m*, Ausgehen *n*	affioramento *m* di un filone
— 12696	**outer barrel**	tube *m* carottier extérieur	äusseres Kernrohr *n*	corpo *m* di carotiere
° 12697	**outer brickwork of shaft**	enveloppe *f* extérieure de la cuve, gaine *f*	Hintermauerung *f* des Kernschachtes	muratura *f* esterna della camicia
	outer core barrel, *s. outer barrel*			
° 12697a	**outer cover**	cloche *f* chauffante	Heizhaube *f*	cappa *f* di riscaldamento
° 12698	**outer mains**	conducteur *m* extérieur	Aussenleiter *m*	conduttore *m* esterno
12699	**outfit**	outillage *m*	Ausrüstung *f*	attrezzatura *f*, dotazione *f*
˄ 12700	**outflowing**	écoulement *m*, décharge *f*	Abfluss *m*	effluente *m*
	outgate, *s. riser*			
° 12701	**outgoing side of rolling mill**	sortie *f* du laminoir	Walzwerkausgang *m*	uscita del laminatoio
° 12702	**outlet**	orifice *m* de départ	Entziehungsöffnung *f*	apertura *f* (o foro) d'uscita, bocca *f* di scarico
° 12703	**outlet of liquid ballast**	évacuation *f* du ballast liquide	Ablassen *n* des flüssigen Ballastes	evacuazione *f* della zavorra liquida
˄ 12704	**outlet plug**	bouchon *m* de vidange	Ablassschraube *f*	tappo *m* di scarico
° 12705	**outlet tube**	tuyau *m* de prise de gaz	Entziehungsrohr *n*, Ablassrohr *n*	tubo *m* di presa del gas
— 12706	**outlier**	témoin *m*	Zeugenberg *m*, Zeuge *m*	testimonio *m*

	English	French	German	Italian
°	12707 **outline of pattern**	contour *m* du modèle	Modellumriss *m*	contorno *m* del modello
^	12708 **outpost**	emplacement *m* d'exploitation	Förderungsstelle *f*	postazione *f* di coltivazione
^	12709 **outpost well**	puits hors du gisement	Schacht *m* ausserhalb des Lagers	pozzo *m* fuori del giacimento
	output, *s. yield*			
^	12710 **output meter**	compteur *m* de débit	Leistungsmesser *m*	contatore *m* di uscita
°	12711 **output of water supply per hour**	quantité *f* d'eau par heure de la distribution d'eau	stündliche Leistung *f* mit Wasserversorgung	portata *f* oraria dell'impianto d'acqua
°	12712 **output per hour**	productibilité *f* par heure	stündliche Leistung *f*	producibilità *f* oraria
—	12713 **outset**	recette *f* du jour	Hängebank *f*	stazione *f* di fondo
°	12714 **outside calipers**	compas *m* d'épaisseur	Aussentaster *m*	compasso *m* di spessore
	outside-fired boiler, *s. external furnace boiler*			
—	12715 **outstope**	taille *f* chassante	Strebe *f*	taglio *m* in direzione
—	12716 **outstope process**	exploitation *f* par tailles chassantes	Vorbau *m*	coltivazione *f* a tagli in direzione
—	12717 **outtake**	voie *f* de sortie d'air	ausziehende Wetterstrecke *f*	galleria *f* per l'uscita dell'aria
^	12718 **outrigger**	hauban *m*	Ausleger *m*	controvento *m*
—	12719 **outwash plain**	plaine *f* de levage	Schuttfeld *n*	piana *f* di lavaggio
—	12720 **ouvarovite**	ouvarovite *f*	Uwarowit *m*	uvarovite *f*
°	12721 **oval bar, ovals**	fer *m* olive	Ovaleisen *n*	ferro *m* ad oliva
°	12722 **oval boiler**	chaudière *f* à section ovale	Ovalkessel *m*	caldaia *f* a sezione ovale
°	12723 **oval bush**	bague *f* ovale	Ovalbüchse *f*	boccola *f* oblunga
°	12724 **oval iron**	fer *m* ovale	Ovalstahl *m*	ferro *m* ovale
°	12725 **oval pass**	cannelure *f* ovale	Ovalkaliber *n*	canale *m* ovale
	oval wire, *s. elliptical wire*			
	oven, *s. kiln*			
°	12726 **oven battery**	batterie *f* de fours	Ofenbatterie *f*	batteria *f* di forni

English	French	German	Italian
— 12727 oven for carbonizing	four *m* de carbonisation	Verkohlungsofen *m*	forno *m* di carbonizzazione
— 12728 over ground	moulu trop fin	totgemahlen	macinato troppo fino
— 12729 over pitched	à faille *f* très inclinée	sehr geneigte Verwerfung *f*	falda *f* molto inclinata
^ 12730 over point, dew point	point *m* de condensation	Taupunkt *m*	inizio *m* di condensazione
° 12731 overageing, overaging	vieillissement *m* poussé	getriebene Aushärtung *f*	invecchiamento *m* spinto
° 12732 overall dimensions	encombrement *m*	Ausmasse *f*	(dimensioni di) ingombro *m*
° 12733 overannealing overbending, *s. springback allowance*	recuit *m* excessif	zu weit getriebener Glühprozess *m*	ricottura *f* eccessiva
° 12734 overblowing	sursoufflage *m*	Überblasen *n*	sovraossidazione *f*
— 12735 overburden	couverture *f*	Gebirgsdruck *m*	copertura *f*, terreno *m* di copertura
— 12736 overburden pressure	pression *m* de surcharge	Überlastungsdruck *m*	pressione *f* di sovraccarico
— 12737 overcast	crossing d'aérage	Wetterbrücke *f*	incrocio *m* di ventilazione
— 12738 overdeeping	surcreusement *m*	Übertiefung *f*	scavo *m* eccessivo
° 12738a overdraft	recourbure *f*	Kräuseln *n*	arricciatura *f*
— 12739 overfall	digue *f* à déversoir	Überlaufdeich *m*	stramazzo *m*
— 12740 overfault overfill, *s. fin*	faille *f* inverse	inverse Verwerfung *f*, Aufschiebung *f*	faglia *f* inversa (o anormale)
— 12741 over-feed stoker	chargeur *m* à alimentation par en--dessus	Feuerung *f* mit Beschickung von oben	caricatrice *f* ad alimentazione superiore
— 12742 overflow level	trop-plein *m*	Überlauf *m*, Niveau *n*	canale *m* di sfioro, pozzetto *m* di sfioro
— 12743 overflow pipe	tube *m* de trop-plein	Überlaufrohr *n*	tubo *m* dello sfioratore o di troppo pieno
° 12744 overflow well	talon *m* de lavage	Entlüftungssack *m*	pozzetto *m* di lavaggio
— 12745 overfolding	recouvrement *m*	Überfaltung *f*	sovrapposizione *f*

English	French	German	Italian
— 12746 **overhang stope**	gradin *m* renversé	Firstenstoss *m*	cantiere *m* a gradini rovesci
— 12747 **overhang stoping**	abattage *m* en gradins	Firstenbau *m*	abbattimento *m* (o coltivazione *f)* a gradini
^ 12748 **overgauge hole**	trou *m* hors calibre	Bohrloch *n* mit grösserem Durch-messer als Meisseldurchmesser	foro *m* fuori calibro
° 12748a **overgrowt**	surcroissance *f*	Verwachsung *f*	aggregamento *m*
12749 **to overhaul**	reviser	revisionieren, überholen	revisionare
^ 12750 **overhead**	flux *m* de tête	Kopffluss *m*	flusso *m* di testa
— 12751 **overhead**	en gradins renversés	firstenbauartig	a gradini a rovescio
— 12752 **overhead-cavity**	cloche *f* du toit	Glocke *f*	campana *f* (del tetto)
— 12753 **overhead crane**	grue *f* cantilever, grue-tour *f*	Auslegerkran *m*	gru *f* sopraelevata
^ 12754 **overhead drum**	accumulateur *m*	Akkumulator *m*	accumulatore *m*, condensatore *m*
— 12755 **overhead endless-rope**	câble *m* flottant	schwebendes Seil *n* ohne Ende	cavo *m* aereo senza fine
— 12756 **overhead grinding machine**	machine *f* à meuler suspendue	hängende Schleif-maschine *f*	macchina *f* da spiana-re sospesa

overhead line, *s. aerial line*

English	French	German	Italian
— 12757 **overhead rope railway**	transporteur *m* aérien à câble	Seilbahn *f*	trasportatore *m* aereo
— 12758 **overhead traveller**	pont-roulant *m*	Laufkran *m*	gru *f* a ponte

overhead welding, *s. overhead position welding*
overheated iron, *s. burnt iron*

English	French	German	Italian
° 12759 **overheated steel**	acier *m* surchauffé	überhitzter Stahl *m*	acciaio *m* surriscaldato
° 12760 **overheating of the iron**	surchauffe *f* de la fonte	Überhitzung *f* des Eisens	surriscaldamento *m* della ghisa
° 12761 **overheating**	sensibilité *f* à la surchauffe	Überhitzungs-empfindlichkeit *f*	sensibilità *f* al surriscaldamento
— 12762 **overhoisting**	mise *f* aux molettes	Übertreiben *n* der Förderkörbe	messa *f* della gab-bia alle molette

	English	French	German	Italian
— 12763	**overland transport**	transport *m* par terre	Landfracht *f*	trasporto *m* per terra
° 12764	**to overlap**	recouvrir	überlappen	sovrapporre
	overlap, *s. stratigraphical overlap*			
— 12765	**overlap fault**	faille *f* inverse	abnormale Verwerfung *f*, Aufschiebung *f*	faglia *f* inversa
	overlap in plane of bedding, *s. stratigraphical overlap*			
° 12766	**overlap welding**	soudure *f* par recouvrement	Überlapt-schweissung *f*	saldatura *f* per sovrapposizione
° 12767	**overlapping**	recouvrement *m*	Überlappung *f*	sovrapposizione *f*
— 12768	**overlying beds**	toit *m*	Hängende *n*	tetto *m*
— 12769	**overlying strata**	couche de couverture	Deckschicht *f*	strato *m* di copertura
— 12770	**overman**	porion *m*	Steiger *m*	capo-squadra *m*
^ 12771	**to overoil**	graisser en excèss	überschmieren	lubrificare eccessivamente
° 12771a	**overpickling**	surdécapage *m*	Überbeizung *f*	sovradecapaggio *m*
° 12772	**overpole**	surperchage *m*	Überpolung *f*	supertrattamento *m* al legno fresco
° 12773	**overpoled**	surperché	überpolt	supertrattato al legno fresco
° 12774	**overpressure**	surpression	Überdruck *m*	sovrapressione *f*, iperpressione *f*
^ 12775	**overriding royalty**	redevance *f* supplémentaire	Zusatzabgabe *f*	diritti *m pl.* supplementari
^ 12776	**overrunning clutch**	embrayage *m* à roue libre	Überhol-Kupplung *f*	innesto *m* a ruota libera
— 12777	**overshot**	souricière *f* à tiges	Klappenfänger *m*	pescatore *m* svincolabile per aste
— 12778	**oversize**	refus *m*	Rückstand *m*	rifiuto *m*, scarto *m*
° 12778a	**oversize grain**	gros grain *m*	Überkorn *n*	grano *m* sovradimensionato
	overthrust, *s. thrust fault*			
— 12779	**overthrust fold**	pli *m* déversé	Überschiebungs-falte *f*	piega *f* di carreggiamento
— 12780	**overthrust mass**	masse *f* charriée	überschobene Masse *f*	massa *f* di carreggiamento
— 12781	**overthrust plane**	surface *f* de carriage	Überschiebungs-fläche *f*	superfice *f* di carreggiamento o di scorrimento

English	French	German	Italian
— 12782 **overturned anticline**	anticlinal *m* renversé	überkippte Antiklinale *f*	anticlinale *f* rovescia-ta
— 12783 **overturned fold**	pli *m* renversé	überkippte Falte *f*	piega *f* rovesciata
— 12784 **overturning skip**	skip *m* basculant	Kippkübel *m*	skip *m* ribaltabile
— 12784a **overvoltage**	surtension *f*	Überspannung *f*	sovratensione *f*
— 12785 **overwind**	aller aux molettes	Übertreiben *n* der Förderkörbe	arrivare a fine corsa
— 12786 **overwind preventer**	évite-molettes *m*	Vorrichtung *f* gegen das Uebertreiben	evita-mollette *f*, freno di sicurezza per fine corsa
overwinding, *s. overwind*			
— 12787 **oxalic acid**	acide *m* oxalique	Oxalsäure *f*	acido *m* ossalico
— 12788 **oxammite**	oxammite *f*	Oxammit *m*	oxammite *f*
— 12789 **oxidation**	oxydation *f*	Oxydation *f*	ossidazione *f*
— 12790 **oxidation inhibitor**	antioxydant *m*	Antioxydationsmittel	antiossidante *m*
— 12791 **oxidation process**	procédé *m* d'oxydation	Inoxydationsver-fahren	processo *m* d'ossida-zione
— 12792 **oxidation zone**	zone *f* d'oxydation	Oxydationszone *f*	zona *f* di ossidazione
— 12793 **oxidationite**	produit *m* d'oxydation	Oxydationsprodukt *n*	prodotto *m* d'ossida-zione
— 12793a **oxide**	oxyde *m*	Oxyd *n*	ossido *m*
— 12794 **oxide of barium**	protoxyde *m* de baryum	Baryt *m*	ossido *m* di bario
— 12795 **oxide layer**	couche *f* de calamine	Zunderschicht *f*	strato *m* di scaglia
— 12796 **trimanganic tetroxide**	oxyde *m* manganeux ou manganique, oxy-de *m* salin	Manganoxyduloxyd *n*	ossido *m* manganoso o manganico
oxide of calcium, *s. lime*			
— 12797 **oxide of copper**	oxyde *m* cuivrique	Kupferoxyd *n*	ossido *m* di rame
— 12798 **oxide of iron from the coal tar industry**	oxyde *m* de fer pro-venant de la fabri-cation des couleurs tirées du goudron	Eisenoxyd *n* von der Teerfarbenerzeugung	ossido *m* di ferro dalla fabbricazione dei colori di catrame
— 12799 **oxide of lead**	oxyde *m* plombique	Bleioxyd *n*	ossido *m* di piombo

English	French	German	Italian
— 12800 oxide of magnesium	oxyde *m* de magnésium	Magnesia *f*	ossido *m* di magnesio
— 12801 oxide of zinc	oxyde *m* de zinc	Zinkoxyd *n*	ossido *m* di zinco
— 12802 oxide scale	croûte *f* d'oxyde de fer	Glühspanschicht *f*	strato *m* d'ossido di ferro
— 12803 oxide-scaling	calamination *f*	Verzunderung *f*	ossidazione *f*
° 12804 oxiding-fusion	fusion *f* oxydante	oxydierendes Schmelzen *n*	fusione *f* ossidante
— 12805 to oxidise	oxyder	oxydieren	ossidare
oxidised, *s. blued*			
° 12806 oxidised blowholes	effet *m* Custer	oxydierte Blase *f*	soffiature *f pl.* ossidate
— 12807 oxidised cap	chapeau *m* de fer	eiserner Hut *m*	cappello *m* ossidato
— 12808 oxidising	oxydant	oxydierend	ossidante
— 12808a oxidising	oxydation *f*	Oxydieren *n*	ossidazione *f*
oxidising action, *s. oxidising effect*			
° 12809 oxidising addition	addition *f* oxydante	oxydierender Zusatz *m*	aggiunta *f* ossidante
— 12810 oxidising effect of the air on coal	action *f* oxydante de l'air sur le charbon	oxydierende Wirkung *f* der Luft über Kohle	azione *f* ossidante dell'aria sopra il carbone
° 12810a oxidising flame	flamme *f* oxydante	Oxydationsflamme *f*	fiamma *f* ossidante
— 12811 oxidising roasting	grillage *m* oxydant	oxydierende Röstung *f*	torrefazione *f* ossidante
° 12812 oxidising smelting	fusion *f* oxydante	oxydierendes Schmelzen *n*	fusione *f* per ossidazione
oxidizing smelting, *s. oxiding-fusion* **oxyacetylene cutting**, *s. flame cutting* **oxyacetylene welding**, *s. acetylene welding*			
° 12813 oxyacetylene welding	soudure *f* oxy- -acétylénique	Sauerstoff-Azetylen- schweissung *f*	saldatura *f* ossiaceti- lenica
° 12814 oxyhydrogen blow pipe	chalumeau *m* oxhydrique	Knallgasgebläse *n*	fiamma *f* ossidrica di gas tonante
— 12815 oxyhydrogen gas	gaz *m* détonant	Knallgas *n*	gas *m* fulminante od ossidrico
° 12816 oxyhydrogen welding	soudure *f* oxydrique	Sauerstoff- -Wasserstoffschweis- sung *f*	saldatura *f* ossidrica

	English	French	German	Italian
—	12817 **oxygen**	oxygène *m*	Sauerstoff *m*	ossigeno *m*
—	12818 **oxygen compound**	composé *m* oxygéné	Sauerstoffverbindung *f*	composto *m* ossigenato
o	12819 **oxygen cutting tube**	chalumeau *m* pour découpage à l'oxygène	Sauerstoffbrenner-rohr *n*	cannello *m* per ossitaglio
o	12819a **oxygen lance**	lance *f* d'oxygène	Sauerstofflanze *f*	lancia *f* di ossigeno
o	12820 **oxygen nipple**	embout *m* à oxygène	Sauerstoffnippel *m*	raccordo *m* ad ossigeno
o	12820a **oxygenation**	oxygénation *f*	Anreicherung *f* mit Sauerstoff	ossigenazione *f*
—	12821 **ozocerite**	ozocérite *f*	Ozokerit *m*, Bergwachs *n*	ozocerite *f*
—	12822 **ozone paper**	papier *m* à ozone	Ozonpapier *n*	carta *f* ozonoscopica

	English	French	German	Italian
— 12823	**pachnolite**	pachnolite	Pachnolith *m*	pachnolite *f*
° 12824	**to pack**	emballer	einpacken	stivare, incassare
— 12825	**to pack**	remblayer	versetzen	riempire
— 12826	**to pack, tighten**	étancher, rendre étanche	abdichten	calafatare, guarnire, rendere stagno
° 12827	**pack**	paquet *m*	Paket *n*	pacchetto *m*
— 12828	**pack (packing)**	remblai *m*, remblayage *m*	Bergversatz *m*	muratura *f* di sostegno
° 12829	**pack annealing**	recuit *m* en paquet	Paketglühen *n*	ricottura *f* in pacchetto
° 12830	**pack carburising**	cémentation *f* en caisse	Kastenzementierung *f*	cementazione *f* in cassetta
° 12831	**pack hardening**	cémentation (par refroidissement dans l'huile)	Zementierung (durch Abkühlung in Öl)	cementazione *f* (con raffreddamento in olio)
^ 12832	**pack-off**	porte-garnitures *m* complet	kompletter Dichtungsträger *m*	porta-guarnizioni *m* completo
^ 12833	**pack-off assembly**	dispositif *m* de contrôle du débit d'un puits	Kontrollgerät *n* für die Schachtströmung	dispositivo *m* di controllo del flusso di un pozzo
^ 12834	**pack-out unit**	partie en caoutchouc du «bag preventer»	Gummiteil *m* des «bag preventer»	parte *f* in gomma del «bag preventer»
— 12835	**pack-prop**	étai *m* métallique extensible	ausdehnbare Metallstrebe *f*	puntello *m* metallico allungabile
° 12836	**pack-rolling**	laminage *m* multiple, laminage *m* en paquet	Mehrfachwalzen *n* Paketwalzen *n*	laminazione *f* a pacco (o multipla)
— 12837	**pack wall**	mur *m* de remblai	Bergemauer *f*	muro *m* per ripiena
— 12838	**package**	compact *m*	Aggregat *n*	aggregato *m*
^ 12839	**packed column**	colonne *f* garnie	Füllkörpersäule *f*	colonna *f* a riempimento
^ 12840	**packed tower**	tour *f* de percolation	Füllkörpersäule *f*	torre *f* a riempimento
° 12841	**packer**	emballeur *m*	Einpacker *m*	imballatore *m*, svitatore *m*, caricatore *m*
— 12842	**packer**	remblayeur *m*	Versatzarbeiter *m*	addetto *m* alla ripiena

	English	French	German	Italian
°	12843 packing	emballage *m*	Einpacken *n*	stivatura *f*, caricamento *m*
°	12843a packing	encastrement *m*	Einbettung *f*	incastratura *f*
—	12844 packing	remblai, remblayage	Versatz *n*, Versetzen *n*	. ripiena *f*, muratura *f* di sostegno
^	12845 packing, stuffing	bourrage *m*, garniture *f*	Packung *f*, Abdichtung *f*	guarnizione *f*
—	12846 packing case	dame *f* de remblai, mur *m* de remblais	Bergemauer *f*	argine *m* (o muro *m*) di sostegno
°	12847 packing drum	cylindre *m* étanche	Dichtungswalze *f*	cilindro *m* (o tamburo *m*) di guarnizione
	packing effect, *s. mass effect*			
^	12848 packing gland	presse-étoupe *m*	Stopfbüchse *f*	premistoppa *m*
^	12849 packing gland crossover	allonge *f* du presse--étoupe	Verlängerung *f* der oberen Stopfbüchse	prolungamento dell'anello superiore di tenuta sopra i cunei d'inflangiatura
°	12850 packing joint	joint *m*	Dichtungsfuge *f*	giunto *m* a guarnizione
—	12851 packing material	matières *f pl.* de remplissage	Ausfüllstoff *m*	materiale *m* di riempimento
^	12852 packing off attachment	attaque *f* pour faire circuler le tube de repêchage à travers le poisson	Umlaufvorrichtung *f* für «releasing spear»	congegno *m* per far circolare il «releasing spear» attraverso il pesce
°	12853 packing surface	surface *f* de contact étanche	Dichtungsfläche *f*	superficie *f* di contatto
—	12854 packs	remblai *m*	Versatz *m*	ripiena *f*
—	12855 packsand	grès *m* à grain fin	feinkörniger Sandstein *m*	gres *m* a grana fine
°	12856 pad	nodule *m* de soudure	Schweissknoten *m*	ringrosso *m* di saldatura
^	12857 pad, rubber pad	tampon *m*	Pfropfen *m*	tampone *m* con gli ettrodi nel microlog
°	12857a pad	saillie *f*	Ansatz *m*	pezzo *m* di giunzione
°	12858 padding, fixing pad	surépaisseur *f* d'alimentation	giesstechnische Verstärkung *f*	sovraspessore *m* di alimentazione
—	12859 paddle mixer	mélangeur *m* à ailettes	Paddelmischer *m*	mescolatrice *f* ad alette
—	12860 paddock	dépôt provisoire	vorläufiger Lagerplatz *m*	spiazzo *m* di deposito temporaneo

	English	French	German	Italian
− 12861	paigeite	paigéite *f*	Paigeit *m*	paigeite *f*
	to paint, *s. to coat*			
° 12862	to paint black, to blacken	peindre en noir	schwarz streichen	tingere in nero
^ 12863	paint pot	source *f* de boue bouillonnante	heisser Schlammsprudel *m*	sorgente *f* di fango in ebollizione
− 12864	paint rock	ocre *f* de fer, argile *f* schisteuse et ferrugineuse	Eisenocker *m*, eisenhaltiger, schieferiger Ton *m*	ocra *f* di ferro, argilla *f* scistosa e ferruginosa
− 12865	paisanite	paisanite *f*	Paisanit *m*	paisanite *f*
	pakfong, *s. German silver*			
− 12866	palaeobotany	paléobotanique *f*	Paläobotanik *f*	paleobotanica *f*
− 12867	Palaeocene period	paléocène *m*	Paläozän *n*	paleocene *m*
− 12868	palaeoclimatology	paléoclimatologie *f*	Palaeoklimatologie *f*	paleoclimatologia *f*
− 12869	Palaeodevonic period	dévonien ancien *m*	Unterdevon *n*	paleodevoniano *m*
− 12870	palaeolithic	paléolithique	paläolithisch	paleolitico
− 12871	palaeotypal	paléotypique	paläotyp, altvulkanisch	paleotipico
− 12872	Palaeozoic era	paléozoïque *m*	Paläozoikum *n*	paleozoico *m*
− 12873	palagonite	palagonite *f*	Palagonit *m*	palagonite *f*
− 12874	palaite	palaïte *f*	Palait *m*	palaite *f*
− 12875	palatinite	palatinite *f*	Palatinit *m*	palatinite *f*
− 12876	paleontological facies	faciès *m* paléontologique	paläontologische Fazies *f*	«facies» *f* paleontologica
− 12877	paleontologic geology	géologie *f* paléontologique	paleontologische Geologie *f*	geologia *f* paleontologica
− 12878	palladium	palladium *m*	Palladium *n*	palladio *m*
− 12879	palladium asbestos	asbeste *m* en palladium	Palladiumasbest *m*	asbesto *m* od amianto *m* al palladio
° 12879a	palladium plating	placage *m* au palladium	Palladium-plattierung *f*	placcatura *f* al palladio
° 12880	pallet, slide	glissière *f*	Gleitfläche *f*	superfice *f* di scorrimento

	English	French	German	Italian
°	12881 **pallet**	palette *f*	Flachpalette *f*	piattaforma *f*, tavolazzo *m*
−	12882 **palm oil, palmitin**	huile *f* de palme	Palmfett *n*	palmitina *f*
−	12883 **palmerite**	palmérite *f*	Palmerit *m*	palmerite *f*
−	12884 **palmierite**	palmiérite *f*	Palmierit *m*	palmierite *f*
−	12885 **pan**	batée *f*, cuve *f*, auge *f*	Waschtrog *m*, Kessel *m*, Pfanne *f*	batea *f*, vaschetta *f*, truogolo *m*
−	12886 **pan amalgamator**	amalgamateur *m* à cuve	Pfannenamalgamator *m*	amalgamatore *m* a bacinella (o a vaschetta)
−	12887 **pan-allotriomorphic texture**	texture *f* aplitique	panallotriomorphe Struktur *f*	struttura *f* aplitica
°	12888 **pan head with tapered neck**	rivet à tête cône tronque avec collet	halbversenkter Niet *m*	chiodo *m* a testa conica troncata con colletto
−	12889 **pan-idiomorphic texture**	texture *f* panidiomorphe	panidiomorphe Struktur *f*	struttura *f* panidiomorfa
°	12890 **pan of the mill**	sole *f* de frotteur	Teller *m* des Kollergangs	vasca *f* (o disco) della molazza
°	12891 **pan of the sand mill**	cuve *f* de frotteur	Schüssel *f* des Kollergangs	vasca *f* della molazza (per sabbia)
−	12892 **panabase**	panabase *f*	Tetraedrit *m*	tetraedrite *f*
−	12893 **pandermite**	pandermite *f*	Pandermit *m*	pandermite *f*
°	12894 **pane**	panne *f* du marteau	Finne *f*	penna *f* del martello
−	12895 **panel**	panneau *m*	Abbaufeld *n*	pannello *m*
°	12896 **panel fin**	pointe *f* à tête très large	Breitkopfstift *m*	punta *f* a testa piana larga
−	12897 **panel entry**	galerie *f* d'exploitation	Abbaustrecke *f*	sezione *f* di scavo, camera *f*
−	12898 **panel system**	système *m* d'exploitation par panneaux	Pfeilerbau *m*	sistema *m* di coltivazione a sezioni (o a camere)
−	12899 **panel work**	exploitation *f* par panneaux	Pfeilerbau *m*	coltivazione *f* a sezioni (o a camere)

English	French	German	Italian
— 12900 **panning**	lavage *m* de l'or à la batée	Goldwaschen *n* im Waschtrog	lavaggio *m* dell'oro alla batea
— 12901 **pantellerite**	pantellérite *f*	Pantellerit *m*	pantellerite *f*
_ 12902 **pantograph seal**	garniture *f* de toit	Dachabdichtung *f*	guarnizione *f* per tetto
○ 12902a **pap**	pièce *f* de raccord	Anschlussglied *n*	pezzo *m* di connessione
— 12903 **paper schist**	schiste-carton *m*	Papierschiefer *m*	scisto-cartone *m*
○ 12904 **paper covered wire**	fil *m* sous papier	papierisolierter Draht *m*	filo *m* isolato in carta
○ 12905 **paper-insulated enamelled wire**	fil *m* émaillé sous papier	Lackpapierdraht *m*	filo *m* smaltato isolato in carta
○ 12905a **paper mould**	moule *m* en papier	Pappform *f*	forma *f* di carta
^ 12906 **paraffin**	paraffine *f*	Paraffin *n*	paraffina *f*
^ 12907 **paraffin-base oil**	pétrole *m* paraffinique	paraffinöses Öl *n*	petrolio *m* paraffinico
^ 12908 **paraffin go-devil**	passediable *m* à paraffine	Paraffinschabekolben *m*	raschiatore *m* per paraffina
^ 12909 **paraffin scraper**	racleur *m* à paraffine	Paraffinkratzer *m*	raschiatore *m* per paraffina
paraffin test, *s. crack impregnation test*			
^ 12910 **paraffin trouble**	embarras *m* de paraffine	Paraffinstörung *f*	ostruzione *f* di paraffina
^ 12911 **paraffin (slack) wax**	cire *f* de paraffine	Paraffinwachs *n*	pasta *f* (o cera) di paraffina
— 12912 **paragenesis**	paragénèse *f*	Paragenese *f*	paragenesi *f*
_ 12913 **paragneiss**	paragneiss *m*	Paragneis *m*	paragneiss *m*
— 12914 **paragonite**	paragonite *f*	Paragonit *m*	paragonite *f*
— 12915 **parahopeite**	parahopéite *f*	Parahopeit *m*	parahopeite *f*
— 12916 **paralaurionite**	paralaurionite *f*	Paralaurionit *m*	paralaurionite *f*
— 12917 **paralic**	paralique	paralisch	paralico
— 12918 **parallel extinction**	extinction *f* droite	gerade Auslöschung *f*	estinzione *f* parallela
parallel throw, *s. stratigrafic gap*			
— 12919 **parallel transgression**	transgression *f* concordante	Parallel-transgression *f*	discordanza *f* concordante (o parallela)
— 12920 **parallel unconformity**	transgressivité *f* parallèle	Paralleldiskordanz *f*	discordanza *f* parallela

		English	French	German	Italian
°	12921	**parallel row**	rangée *f* parallèle	Parallelreihe *f*	disposizione *f* parallela
°	12922	**parallel seam welding**	soudure *f* continue parallèle	Parallelnaht-schweissung *f*	saldatura *f* continua parallela
°	12923	**parallel spot welding**	soudure *f* parallèle à points	Parallelpunkt-schweissung *f*	saldatura *f* parallela a punti
—	12924	**paraluminite**	paraluminite *f*	Paraluminit *m*	paralluminite *f*
°	12925	**paramagnetic**	paramagnétique	paramagnetisch	paramagnetico
—	12926	**paramorphic**	paramorphique	paramorph	paramorfo
—	12927	**paramorphism**	paramorphose *f*	Paramorphose *f*	paramorfismo *m*
—	12928	**paraurichalcite**	parauricalcite *f*	Paraurikalzit *m*	parauricalcite *f*
—	12929	**paravauxite**	paravauxite *f*	Paravauxit *m*	paravauxite *f*
°	12930	**parcel**	rouleau *m* de fil	Drahtbündel *n*	rotoli di filo, matasse di filo
°	12930a	**parcel plating**	dêpot *m* limité	Teilgalvanisierung *f*	deposito *m* limitato
°	12931	**parchment-insulated wire**	fil *m* isolé au parchemin	Pergamentdraht *m*	filo *m* isolato con pergamena
°	12932	**parchment pipe**	tuyau *m* en parchemin	Pergamentschlauch *m*	tubo *m* di pergamena
—	12933	**parent (al) magma**	magma *m* primaire	Muttermagma *n*	magma *m* primario
°	12933a	**parent metal**	métal *m* base	Basismetall *m*	metallo *m* base
		parian cement, *s. Keene's cement*			
—	12935	**parianite**	parianite *f*	Parianit *m*	parianite *f*
—	12936	**parisite**	parisite *f*	Parisit *m*	parisite *f*
°	12937	**parkerization**	parkérisation *f*	Parkerisieren *n*	parkerizzazione *f*
°	12938	**parrot coal,** *s. candle coal or cannel coal* **Parry gas exit pipe**	prise *f* de gaz Parry	Parryscher Gasfang *m*	presa *f* di gas Parry
—	12939	**parsettensite**	parsettensite *f*	Parsettensit *m*	parsettensite *f*
—	12940	**parsonsite**	parsonsite *f*	Parsonsit *m*	parsonsite *f*
°	12941	**partial fusing in annealing**	fusion *f* partielle au recuit	teilweises Schmelzen *n* beim Glühen	rifusione *f* parziale di ricottura

	English	French	German	Italian
o	12942 **partial miscibility**	miscibilité f partielle	beschränkte Mischbarkeit f	miscibilità f parziale (o limitata)
	partial vacuum, s. rarefaction			
	particle, s. powder particle			
o	12943 **parting (parting sand)**	sable m de séparation	Streusand m	sabbia f isolante (o di separazione)
o	12944 **parting (between two sections of a mould)**	joint de séparation	Gesenkoberfläche f	giunto m (o superfice) di separazione
—	12945 **parting**	intercalation f stérile, nerf	Bergemittel n, taubes Gestein n	intercalazione f sterile
—	12946 **parting**	division f, limet m	Absonderung f, Lage f	divisione f, linea f di divisione
o	12947 **parting**	séparation f	Trennung f	separazione f, divisione f
o	12947a **parting compound**	isolant m	Formpuder m	isolante m, spolvero m
o	12948 **parting furnace**	four m de départ	Scheideofen m	forno m di separazione
	parting line, s. joint face			
—	12949 **parting plane**	plan m de stratification	Schichtfläche f	piano m di stratificazione
o	12950 **parting powder**	poncif m, isolant m	Trennpuder m, Modellpuder m	spolvero m, isolante m
o	12951 **parting silver**	argent m de départ	Scheidesilber n	argento m raffinato
o	12952 **parting tool**	outil m à détalonner	Einstechstahl m, Abstechstahl m	utensile m da taglio
—	12953 **partition**	cloison f	Zwischenwand f, Scheidewand f	parete f di separazione, tramezzo m, divisorio m
—	12954 **partition rock**	roche f encaissante	Nebengestein n	roccia f adiacente
	partition wall, s. fixed division			
—	12955 **parts per thousand**	mise f au mille	pro Tausend n	resa f per mille
o	12956 **pass, groove**	rainure f de cylindre	Kalibervertiefung f der Walze	canale m di cilindro
	pass, s. welding seam			
o	12957 **pass in welding**	passe f	(Schweiss)gang m	passata f
o	12958 **pass**	passage m, passe f	Durchgang m, Stich m	passaggio m
o	12958a **pass schedule**	programme m de laminage	Stichtabelle f	tavola f delle passate
o	12959 **passage opening**	passage m	Durchgangsöffnung f	passaggio m
o	12960 **passivation**	passivation f	Passivierung f	passivazione f

	English	French	German	Italian
° 12961	passive hardness, wear hardness	trempe f passive	passive Härte f, Abnutzungshärte f	resistenza f allo sfregamento
° 12961a	paste solder	pâte à souder	Lötpaste f	pasta f per saldare
° 12962	pasty	pâteaux	teigig	pastoso
° 12963	pasty iron	fer m à l'état pâteux	teigig gewordenes Eisen n	ferro m pastoso

to patch, *s. to finish*

° 12964	patch	retorcher	flicken	ripristinare, riparare (un rivestimento), rappezzare
− 12965	patch-like	à morceaux	stückweise	a pezzi
− 12966	patch of ore	poche de minerai	Erznest n	ammasso m (o sacca) di minerale
° 12967	patching	retorchage m	Ausbesserung f	riparazione f (d'un rivestimento), rappezzatura f
° 12968	patent core nail	pointe f à noyau brevetée	Patentkernnagel m	supporto m per anime brevettato

patent-fuel, *s. briquett(e)*

12969	patenting	patentement m	Patentierung f	patentamento m
− 12970	paternoite	paternoïte f	Paternoit m	paternoite f
° 12970a	patina finish	patine f artificielle	künstliche Patina f	patina f artificiale
− 12971	patronite	patronite f	Patronit n	patronite f
° 12972	pattern	modèle m	Gussmodell n	modello m
° 12973	pattern	calibre m	Schablone f	calibro m, sagoma f
− 12974	pattern	structure f	Struktur f	struttura f

pattern, *s. template*
pattern blacking, *s. pattern varnish*
pattern board, *s. pattern plate*

° 12975	pattern deformed during ramming	modèle m déformé au serrage	beim Stampfen verformtes Modell n	modello m deformato nella stivatura

pattern draft, *s. pattern draw*

° 12976	pattern draw	démoulage m des modèles	Modellabhebung f	sformatura f dei modelli
° 12977	pattern-draw molding machine	démouleur m par extraction du modèle	Abhebeformmaschine f	formatrice f ad estrazione modello

	English	French	German	Italian
12978	pattern half	moitié f de modèle	Modellhälfte f	metà f di modello
12979	pattern heating	réchauffage m du modèle	Modellheizung f	riscaldamento m del modello
12980	pattern holder with horizontal and vertical movement	fouloir m porte-segment mobile horizontalement et verticalement	allseitig beweglicher Schablonenhalter m	portasagoma m (bandiera) mobile universale
12981	pattern incorporating the runner system	modèle m comportant le système d'alimentation	Modell n mit Eingüssen und Steigern	modello m con incorporato il sistema di alimentazione
12982	pattern maker	modeleur m	Modellbauer m	modellista m
12983	pattern maker	plaquiste m	Modellplattenformer	platorista m
12984	pattern making	modelage m	Modellherstellung f	modellatura f
12984a	pattern metal	alliage m de modèle	Modellegierung f	lega f di modello
12985	pattern miller (foundry)	fraiseuse à modèles	Modellfräsmaschine	fresatrice f per modelli
12986	pattern mouldery	moulage m avec modèles	Modellformerei f	formatura f con modelli
12987	pattern plate	plaque-modèle f	Modellplatte f	placca f (o piastra f) modello
12988	pattern plate molding, match plate molding	moulage m au gabarit	Modellplattenformen n	formatura f a placca modello
12989	pattern plate raising and lowering gear	guide m du porte-segment	Formstösselführung f	guida f del portasagoma
12990	pattern screw	tire-fond m à modèle	Aushebeschraube f	estrattore m a vite per modelli
12991	pattern setter	ajusteur m de modèles	Modell-Adjustierer m	aggiustatore m di modelli
12992	pattern shop	modelage m, atelier de modelage	Modellwerkstatt f	modelleria f
12993	pattern shrinkage allowance	majoration f du modèle pour (compenser) la contraction	Modellübermetall n zum Ausgleichen der Schrumpfung	maggiorazione f del modello per (compensare) il ritiro
12994	pattern store, storage	magasin m de modèles	Modellager n	magazzino m dei modelli
12995	pattern tie bar	barre f à reboucher	Dämmleiste f	traversa f di rinforzo da chiudere

	English	French	German	Italian
—	12996 pawl	harpon *m*, cliquet *m* d'arrêt	Haspe *f*, Sperrklinke *f*	arpione *m*, nottolino *m* d'arresto
—	12997 pay bed	couche *f* minéralisée	Erzflöz *n*	strato *m* mineralizzato
—	12998 pay ore	minerai *m* payant	abbauwürdiges Erz *n*	minerale *m* produttivo
—	12999 pay ore-body	gîte *m* justifiant l'exploitation	abbauwürdige Lagerstätte *f*	giacimento *m* produttivo
—	13000 pay rock	formation *f* géologique payante	abbauwürdiges Vorkommen *n*	formazione *f* geologica produttiva
^	13001 pay sand, pay	sable *m* payant	wirtschaftlich lohnender Sand *m*	sabbia *f* petrolifera produttiva
^	13002 pay streak	couche *f* de sable payante	abbauwürdige Sandschicht *f*	strato di sabbia *f* produttivo
^	13003 pay zone	zone *f* productive	produktive Zone *f*	zona *f* produttiva
—	13004 pea	grain *m*	Korn *n*	grano *m* (di pirite di ferro)
—	13004a pea iron ore	minerai *m* pisiforme	Linsenerz *n*	minerale *m* pisiforme
—	13005 peach	chlorite *f*	Chlorit *n*	clorite *f*
—	13006 peach coke	grésillon *m*	Perlkoks *m*	coke minuto
—	13007 peach stone	chloritoschiste *m*	Chloritschiefer *m*	cloritoscisto *m*
—	13008 peacock coal	charbon *m* luisant	Glanzkohle *f*	antracite *f*
—	13009 peacock copper ore	bornite *f*	Bornit *m*	bornite *f*
^	13010 peak torque	couple *f* maximum	max. Drehmoment *n*	coppia *f* motrice massima
°	13011 pear shaped mandrel	mandrin *m* piriforme	birn(en)förmiger Dorn *m*	mandrino *m* piriforme
—	13012 pear spar	fluorine *f*	Fluorit *m*	fluorina *f*, fluorite *f*
—	13013 pearceite	pearcéite *f*	Pearceit *m*	pearceite *f*
°	13014 pearl ash solutions	eau *f* potassique	Holzaschenwasser *n*	acqua *f* con ceneri di legno
—	13015 pearl sinter pearl spar, *s. dolomite*	opale *f* perlière	Perlspat *m*	spato *m* perlaceo
·—	13016 pearlite	perlite *f*	Perlit *m*	perlite *f*
—	13017 pearlitic	perlitique	perlitisch	perlitico

	English	French	German	Italian
°	13018 **pearlitic cast iron**	fonte *f* perlitique	perlitisches Gusseisen *n*	ghisa *f* perlitica
°	13019 **pearlitic steel**	acier *m* perlitique	perlitischer Stahl *m*	acciaio *m* perlitico
°	13020 **pearly**	grenu	gekörnt	granulato
—	13021 **pearly**	nacré	perlartig	perlaceo
—	13022 **pearly lustre**	éclat *m* nacré	Perlmutterglanz *m*	bagliore *m* perlaceo
	peas, *s. pea coal*			
—	13023 **peat, turf**	tourbe *f*	Torf *m*	torba *f*
—	13024 **(peat-) bog, peat-bed**	tourbière *f*	Moor *n*	torbiera *f*
—	13025 **peat briquette**	aggloméré *m* de tourbe	Torfbrikett *n*	agglomerato *m* di torba
—	13026 **peat coal**	charbon *m* de tourbe	Torfkohle *f*	carbone *m* di torba
—	13027 **peat cutter**	trieur *m* de tourbe	Torfstecher *m*	separatore *m* di torba
—	13028 **peat mould**	tourbe *f* terreuse	Torferde *f*	torba *f* terrosa
—	13029 **peat moor, peatery**	tourbière *f*	Torfmoor *n*	torbiera *f*
—	13030 **pebble bed**	couche *f* de galets	Schotterbett *n*	strato *m* ghiaioso
—	13031 **pebble jack**	blende *f*	Zinkblende *f*	blenda *f*
—	13032 **pebble filter**	filtre *m* à gravier	Kiesfilter *n*	filtro *m* di ghiaia
—	13033 **pebble mill**	broyeur *m* à galets	Kugelmühle *f*	mulino *m* a palle
—	13034 **pebble stone**	galet *m*	Gerölle, Geschiebe *n*	ciottolo *m*
	pebbles, *s. alligator skin*			
—	13035 **peckhamite**	peckhamite *f*	Peckhamit *m*	peckhamite *f*
—	13036 **pectolite**	pectolite *f*	Pektolith *m*	pectolite *f*
—	13037 **pedocal**	sol *m* calcaire	Kalkboden *m*	suolo *m* calcareo
°	13038 **pee-pee**	chenal *m* de laitier	Schlackenloch *n*	canale *m* di colata delle scorie
°	13039 **peel, charge shovel**	pelle *f* de chargement	Einsatzschaufel *f*	pala *f* per caricare, pala *f* caricatrice

	English	French	German	Italian

peel test, *s. slug test*

°	13040 **peeled-calibrated bar**	barre *f* dégrossie-calibrée	geschälter gedrehter Stahl *m*	barra *f* pelata calibrata
–	13041 **peeling**	desquamation *f*	Desquamation *f*	desquamazione *f*
°	13042 **peeling off**	délaminage *m*	Abschälen *n*	spellatura *f*
°	13043 **peening**	écrouissage *m*, matage *m*	Kalthämmern *n*, Verstemmung *f*	trafilatura *f* a freddo, ribaditura *f*
°	13044 **peep hole**	regard *m*	Schauöffnung *f*	foro *m* di spia
°	13045 **peg (block for forging tools)**	pièce *f* d'écartement	Distanzstück *n*, Abstandsblock *m*	spessore *m*, pezzo *m* distanziatore

peg rammer, *s. flat rammer*

–	13046 **pegmatite**	pegmatite *f*	Pegmatit *m*	pegmatite *f*
–	13047 **pegmatization**	pegmatisation *f*	Pegmatisierung *f*	pegmatizzazione *f*
–	13048 **pegmatoid**	pegmatoïde	pegmatitähnlich	pegmatoide
–	13049 **pegging rammer**	damoir *m* en pointe	Spitzstampfer *m*	piletta *f* a punta
–	13050 **pelagic deposits** *pl.*	dépôts *m pl.* pélagiques	pelagische Ablagerungen *f pl.*	depositi *m pl.* pelagici
–	13051 **pelagic facies**	faciès pélagique	(eu)pelagische Fazies *f*	«facies» *f* pelagica
–	13052 **pelicanite**	pélicanite *f*	Pelikanit *m*	pelicanite *f*
–	13053 **pelitic texture, argillaceous texture**	structure *f* pélithique (ou argileuse)	pelitische Struktur *f*	struttura *f* pelitica
–	13054 **pellicle of oxide**	pellicule *f* d'oxyde	Häutchen *n*, Oxydhäutchen *n*	pellicola *f* d'ossido
°	13054a **pen stock**	coude *m* de porte--vent	Anschlussstutzen *m*	gomito *m* del porta-vento
°	13055 **pencil core, cracker core**	crayon *m* de masselotte	Luftkern *m*, Luftstift *m*	animetta *f* di materozza
°	13056 **pencil gate, pop-gate**	attaque *f* en pluie	Siebeingussrinne *f*	attacco *m* di colata a pioggia
°	13057 **pencil ring gate**	attaque *f* par collier-douche	Ringsiebeinguss *m*	attacco *m* a pioggia anulare
–	13058 **pencil-stone**	pyrophyllite *f*	Pyrophyllit *m*	pirofillite *f*

English	French	German	Italian
^ 13059 **pendulum**	poteau oscillant	Pendelstützbock *m*	palo *m* oscillante
o 13060 **pendulum conveyor**	balancelle *f*	Gehänge *n*	bilancella *f*, convogliatore a pendolo
— 13061 **peneplain, plain of erosion**	pénépiaine	Rumpffläche *f*, Fastebene *f*	penepiano, rasopiano *m*
penetrameter, *s. image quality indicator*			
o 13062 **penetrant testing**	examen *m* pénétrant	Eindringversuch *m*	saggio *m* di penetrazione
— 13063 **penetration rate**	vitesse *f* d'avancement	Bohrfortschritt *m*	velocità d'avanzamento
— 13064 **penetration-twins**	macle *f* de pénétration	Durchwachsungszwillinge *m pl.*	geminazione *f* di penetrazione
— 13065 **penetrative rock**	roche *f* intrusive	Intrusivgestein *n*	roccia *f* intrusiva
— 13066 **penfieldite**	penfieldite *f*	Penfieldit *m*	penfieldite *f*
— 13067 **pentagonal prism**	prisme *m* pentagonal	fünfseitiges Prisma *n*	prisma *m* pentagonale
— 13068 **pennine**	pennine	Pennin *m*	pennino *m*
— 13069 **pennystone**	sphérosidérite *f*	Sphärosiderit *m*	sferosiderite *f*
— 13070 **penroseite**	penroséite *f*	Penroseit *m*	penroseite *f*
— 13071 **penthouse**	plancher *m* de sûreté	Sicherheitsbühne *f*	impalcatura *f* di sicurezza
o 13072 **penthouse**	hangar *m*	Schutzdach *n*	tettoia *f* ad un solo sporgente
— 13073 **pentlandite**	pentlandite *f*	Pentlandit *m*	pentlandite *f*
o 13073a **pepper blister**	piqûres de surface	Oberflächenporen *f pl.*	camolatura *f* superficiale
o 13074 **percent elongation**	allongement *m* pour cent après rupture	Bruchdehnung *f*	allungamento *m* percentuale dopo rottura
o 13075 **percentage of ashes**	teneur *f* en cendres	Aschgehalt *m*	tenore *m* in cenere, contenuto di cenere
13076 **to percolate**	filtrer	filtrieren	filtrare
o 13076a **percussion welding**	sondage *m* par percussion	Schlagschweissen *n*	saldatura *f* a percussione
— 13077 **percylite**	percylite *f*	Percylith *m*	percilite *f*
o 13078 **perfect combustion**	combustion *f* complète	vollkommene Verbrennung *f*	combustione *f* completa

	English	French	German	Italian
° 13079	perfect solubility	solubilité *f* complète	vollkommene Löslichkeit *f*	solublità *f* completa
° 13080	perforated bottom, needle bottom	fond *m* en terre réfractaire perforé avec des baguettes	Nadelboden *m*	fondo *m* forato
° 13081	perforated pipe	tube perforé	durchlöchertes Rohr *n*	tubo *m* perforato
° 13082	perforated sheet iron	tôle *f* perforée	gelochtes Blech *n*	lamiera *f* perforata
° 13083	perforated tube	tube *m* percé	gelochtes Rohr *n*	tubo *m* perforato
− 13084	perforating job	forage *m* à canon perforateur	Geschosslochbohrung *f*	perforazione *f* con fucile
° 13085	perforation	poinçonnage *m*	Lochung *f*	foratura *f*, perforazione *f*
− 13086	perhyaline	structure *f* perhyaline, structure ultravitreuse	perhyalinische Struktur *f*	struttura *f* perialina
− 13087	periclase	périclase *m*	Periklas *n*	periclasio *m*
− 13088	periclinal structure	structure *f* périclinale	periklinale Struktur *f*	struttura *f* periclinale
− 13089	pericline	péricline *m*	Periklin *n*	periclino *m*
− 13090	peridot	péridot *m*	Peridot *m*	peridot *m*, olivina *f*
− 13091	perimagmatic	périmagmatique	perimagmatisch	perimagmatico
− 13092	perimorph	périmorphose *f*	Perimorphose *f*	perimorfosi *f*
° 13093	peripheric blisters	soufflures *f pl.* périphériques	Randblasen *f pl.*	soffiature *f pl.* periferiche
	period of roasting, *s. burning period*			
13094	period of unloading	délai *m* de déchargement	Löschfrist *f*	termine *m* di scaricamento
° 13095	period of working charge	durée *f* de passage de la charge	Durchsetzzeit *f*	durata *f* del passaggio della carica
° 13096	periodical pass	cannelures *f pl.* à bossages	periodisches Kaliber *n*	profilo *m* con intacchi ad intagli

English	French	German	Italian
13097 **perknite**	perknite *f*	Perknit *m*	perknite *f*
13098 **perlite**	perlite *f*	Perlit *m*	perlite *f*
13099 **perovskite**	pérovskite, pérowskite	Perovskit *m*	perovskite *f*
13100 **peroxide of lead**	peroxyde *m* de plomb	Bleisuperoxyd *n*	perossido *m* di piombo, biossido *m* di piombo
13101 **peroxide of sodium**	bioxyde *m* de sodium	Natriumsuperoxyd *n*	perossido *m* di sodio, biossido *m* di sodio
13102 **perished steel**	acier *m* dénaturé	abgestandener Stahl *m*	acciaio *m* denaturato
13103 **peritectic transformation**	transformation *f* péritectique	peritektische Umwandlung *f*	trasformazione *f* peritettica
13104 **permanent coat**	peinture *f* définitive	bleibender Anstrich *m*	tintura *f* stabile (o definitiva)
13105 **permanent coil**	bobine *f* magnétique durable	Magnetspule *f* für den Dauergebrauch	bobina *f* permanente
13106 **permanent magnet**	aimant *m* permanent	Dauermagnet *m*	magnete *m* permanente
13107 **permanent magnet steel**	acier *m* à aimants permanents	Dauermagnetstahl *m*	acciaio *m* per calamite permanenti
13108 **permanent mould**	forme *f* fixe	starre Form *f*, beständige Form *f*	forma *f* fissa

permanent mould casting, *s. die-casting*

permanent mold gravity casting, *s. gravity die-casting*

English	French	German	Italian
13109 **permeability**	perméabilité *f*	Durchlässigkeit *f*	permeabilità *f*
13110 **permeability curve**	courbe *f* de perméabilité	Durchlässigkeitskurve *f*	curva *f* di permeabilità
13111 **permeability to gases**	perméabilité *f* aux gaz	Durchlässigkeit *f* für Gase	permeabilità *f* ai gas
13112 **permeable rock**	roche *f* perméable	durchlässiges Gestein *n*	roccia *f* permeabile
13113 **permissible aberration**	écart *m* toléré	zulässige Abweichung *f*	differenza *f* ammessa

English	French	German	Italian
° 13114 **permissible stresses**	contraintes *f pl.* admissibles	zulässige Spannungen	sollecitazioni ammissibili
permitted explosive, *s. safety explosive*			
— 13115 **persilicic**	acide	sauer	acido
— 13116 **persistent fossil**	fossile *m* persistant	Dauerfossil *n*	fossile longevo
— 13117 **perthite**	perthite *f*	Perthit *m*	pertite *f*
— 13118 **pestle**	pilon *m* de mortier	Stösser *m*, Reiber *m*	pestello *m*
— 13119 **petalite**	pétalite *f*	Petalit *m*	petalite *f*
ˆ 13120 **petals**	segments *f pl.*	Segmente *pl.*	segmenti *m pl.* di un ombrello di cementazione
° 13121 **petcok**	robinet *m*	Hahn *m*	rubinetto *m*
petrification, *s. fossilization*			
— 13122 **petrogenesis**	pétrogenèse *f*	Petrogenese *f*	petrogenesi *f*
to petrify, *s. fossilize*			
— 13123 **petrographic**	pétrographique *m*	petrographisch	petrografico
— 13124 **petrographical facies**	faciès pétrographique	petrographische Fazies *f*	«facies» *f* petrografica
— 13125 **petrography**	pétrographie *f*	Petrographie *f*	petrografia *f*
ˆ 13126 **petrolatum**	pétrolatum. *m*	Petrolatum *n*	petrolato *m*
ˆ 13127 **petrolatum wax**	cire *f* de paraffine	Petrolatumwachs *n*	paraffina *f* amorfa
ˆ 13128 **petrolene**		Petrolen *n*	petrolene *m*
ˆ 13129 **petroleum**	pétrole *m*	Petroleum *n*	petrolio *m*
petroleum butter, *s. petrolatum*			
ˆ 13130 **petroleum coke**	coke *m* de pétrole	Petrolkoks *m*	coke *m* di petrolio
petroleum-furnace, *s. oil-fuel furnace*			
ˆ 13131 **petroleum injector**	injecteur *m* à pétrole	Petroleumeinspritzer *m*	iniettore *m* di petrolio
ˆ 13132 **petroleum jelly**	vaseline *f*	Vaselin *n*	vasellina *f*
ˆ 13133 **petroleum spirit**	éther *m* de pétrole	Petroläther *m*	ragia *f* di petrolio
13134 **petroleum stove**	fourneau *m* à pétrole, réchaud *m* à pétrole	Petroleumkocher *m*	fornello *m* a petrolio

English	French	German	Italian
13135 petroleum tailings	résidus *m pl.* de pétrole	Petroleum-rückstände *m pl.*	fondami *m pl.* petroliferi
13136 petroleum tester	appareil *m* pour l'essai du pétrole	Petroleumprüfer *m*	verificatore *m* di petrolio
13136a petrology	pétrologie *f*	Petrologie *f*	petrologia *f*
13137 petzite	petzite *f*	Petzit *m*	petzite *f*
13138 pewter	peltre *m*, alliage *m* d'étain et de plomb	Zinn *n*, Hartzinn *m*	peltro *m*, lega *f* di stagno e di piombo
13139 pewtery	stannifère	Zinn-, zinnhaltig	stannifero
13140 phacelite	phacélite *f*	Phakelit *m*	facelite *f*
13141 phacoidal structure	structure *f* filamenteuse	Flasertextur *f*	struttura *f* filamentosa
13142 phacolite	phacolite *f*	Phakolith *m*	facolite *f*, oolite *f* ferruginosa
13143 phaneric	phanérogène	phanerokristallin	fanerogeno
13144 pharmacolite	pharmacolite *f*	Pharmakolith *m*	farmacolite *f*
13145 pharmacosiderite	pharmacosidérite *f*	Pharmakosiderit *m*	farmacosiderite *f*
13146 phase	phase *f*	Phase *f*	fase *f*
13146a phase diagram	diagramme des phases	Zustandsdiagramm *n*	diagramma *m* delle fasi
13147 phenacite	phénacite *f*	Phenakit *m*	fenacite *f*
13148 phengite	phengite *f*	Phengit *m*	fengite *f*
13149 phenocryst(al), inset	cristal du premier stade, phénocristal	Erstling *m*, Einsprengling *m*	cristallo *m* di prima generazione
13150 phenole	phénol *m*	Phenol *m*	fenolo *m*
13151 phenolic resin	résine *f* phénolique	Phenolharz *n*	resina *f* fenolica
13152 phenolphtalein paper	papier *m* à la phénolphtaléine	Phenolphtaleinpapier *n*	carta *f* alla fenolftaleina
13153 philadelphite	philadelphite *f*	Philadelphit *m*	filadelfite *f*
13154 phillipsite	phillipsite *f*	Phillipsit *m*	fillipsite *f*
13155 phlogopite	phlogopite *m*	Phlogopit *m*	flogopite *m*
13156 phoenicochroite	phoenicochroïte *f*	Phönicochroit *m*	fenicocroite *f*
phoenix column section, *s. quadrant iron*			
13157 pholerite	pholérite *f*	Pholerit *m*	folerite *f*

		English	French	German	Italian
−	13158	pholidolite	pholidolite *f*	Pholidolith *m*	folidolite *f*
−	13159	phonolite	phonolite *f*	Phonolith *m*, Klingstein *m*	fonolite *f*
−	13160	phosgenite	phosgénite *f*	Phosgenit *m*	fosgenite *f*
−	13161	phosphate chalk	craie *f* phosphatée	Phosphatkreide *f*	creta *f* fosforosa
−	13162	phosphate coating	phosphater	phosphatieren	fosfatare
−	13163	phosphate of calcium	phosphate *m* de chaux	Calciumphosphat *n*	fosfato *m* calcico
−	13164	phosphate of iron	phosphate *m* de fer	Eisenphosphat *n*	fosfato *m* di ferro
−	13165	phosphate of sodium	phosphate *m* de soude	phosphorsaueres Natron *n*, Natriumphosphat *n*	fosfato *m* sodico
−	13166	phosphatic iron ore	minerai *m* de fer phosphoreux	phosphorhaltiges Eisenerz *n*	minerale *m* di ferro fosforoso
°	13167	phosphatic slag	scorie *f* de déphosphoration	basische Schlacke *f*	scoria *f* basica
°	13168	phosphating	phosphatation *f*	Phosphatierung *f*	fosfatazione *f*
°	13168a	phosphide banding	bande *f* de phosphure	Phosphidband *n*	banda *f* di fosfuro
°	13169	phosphide sweat	diamant *m*	Phosphidperle *f*	goccia *f* fosforosa
−	13170	phosphoferrite	phosphoferrite *f*	Phosphoferrit *m*	fosfoferrite *f*
−	13171	phosphophyllite	phosphophyllite *f*	Phosphophyllit *m*	fosfofillite *f*
°	13172	phosphor bronze	bronze *m* phosphoreux	Phosphorbronze *f*	bronzo *m* fosforoso
°	13173	phosphor-bronze wire	fil *m* de bronze phosphoreux	Phosphorbronzedraht *m*	filo *m* di bronzo fosforoso
°	13174	phosphor compound	composé *m* phosphorique	Phosphorverbindung *f*	composto *m* fosforico
°	13175	phosphor copper	cupro-phosphore *m*	Phosphorkupfer *n*	rame *m* fosforoso
°	13176	phosphor-manganese	mangano-phosphore *m*	Phosphormangan *n*	manganese *m* fosforoso
°	13177	phosphor steel	acier *m* phosphoreux	Phosphorstahl *m*	acciaio *m* fosforoso
°	13178	phosphor tin	étain *m* phosphoreux	Phosphorzinn *n*	stagno *m* fosforoso
−	13179	phosphoric anhydride	anhydride *m* phosphorique	Phosphorsäureanhydrid *n*	anidride *f* fosforica

English	French	German	Italian
13180 **phosphoric iron**	fonte *f* Cleveland	phosphorhaltiges Roheisen *n*	ghisa *f* Cleveland
13181 **phosphoric pig iron**	fonte *f* phosphoreuse	phosphorhaltiges Roheisen *n*, Phosphorroheisen *n*	ghisa *f* fosforosa
13182 **phosphorite**	phosphorite *f*	Phosphorit *m*	fosforite *f*
13183 **phosphorus**	phosphore *m*	Phosphor *m*	fosforo *m*
phosphorous steel, *s. phosphor steel*			
13184 **phosphosiderite**	phosphosidérite *f*	Phosphorsiderit *m*	fosfosiderite *f*
13185 **phosphuranylite**	phosphuranylite *f*	Phosphoranylit *m*	fosfuranilite *f*
13185a **photochemical**	photochimique	photochemisch	fotochimico
13186 **photographic apparatus**	appareil *m* photographique	Photo - Apparat *m*	apparecchio *m* fotografico
13187 **photographic plate**	plaque *f* photographique	photographische Platte *f*	lastra *f* fotografica
13188 **phreatic eruption**	explosion *f* phréatique	phreatische Explosion *f*	esplosione *f* freatica
13189 **phthanite**	phtanite *f*	Phthanit *m*	ftanite *f*
13190 **phyllite**	phyllite *f*	Phyllit *m*	fillite *f*
phyllocrystalline rocks, *s. metamorphic rocks*			
13191 **physical and chemical preparation**	préparation *f* physique et chimique	physikalische und chemische Vorbereitung *f*	preparazione *f* meccanica e chimica
13191a **physical metallurgy**	métallurgie physique	physikalische Metallurgie *f*	metallurgia *f* fisica
13192 **physical mixture**	mélange *m* physique	physikalisches Gemisch *n*	miscela *f* fisica
13193 **physical properties**	caractéristiques *f* *pl.* physiques	physikalische Eigenschaften *f pl.*	caratteristiche *f pl.* fisiche
13194 **physical test**	essai *m* physique	physikalische Prüfung *f*	prova *f* fisica
13195 **physico-chemical apparatus**	appareils physico-chimiques	physikalisch-chemische Geräte *n pl.*	apparecchi *m pl.* fisico-chimici
13196 **piano wire, flower wire**	fil *m* pour cordes de piano	Klavierdraht *m*, Klaviersaite *f*	filo *m* armonico
13197 **Piat furnace**	four *m* Piat, four à creuset-transportable	Piatofen *m*	forno *m* Piat
13198 **to pick**	trier au marteau ou à la main	ausklauben	spaccare il minerale in pezzi
13199 **to pick**	localiser (une couche)	lokalisieren (eine Schicht)	localizzare (un contatto di strato)

	English	French	German	Italian
—	13200 to pick off	trier	ausklauben	cernere, scegliere, classificare, separare
—	13201 to pick up	hisser	aufheben	'sollevare in torre
—	13202 pick	pioche *f*	Keilhaue *f*	piccone *m*
—	13203 pick-and-shovel work	travail *m* au pic et à la pelle	Keilhauen- und Wegfüllarbeit *f*	lavoro *m* al piccone e alla pala
	pick hammer, *s. chipping hammer*			
—	13204 pick machine, coal--cutting machine	haveuse *f* à pic	stossend wirkende Schrämmaschine *f*	intagliatrice *f* a piccone
^	13205 pick-up and slack-off		Zug *m* und Rückzug *m* der Schachtsäule	tiro *m* e ritiro *m* della colonna in pozzo
—	13206 pick-up grab	pince *f* de repêchage	Fangzange *f*	pescatore *m*
—	13207 pick-up truck	autogrue *f*	Kranwagen *m*	autocarro-gru *m*
—	13208 picked ore	concentré *m* de triage	Scheideerz *n*	concentrato *m* di minerale scelto
—	13209 picked sample	échantillon *m* choisi	ausgesuchtes Muster *n*	campione *m* scelto
—	13210 picker	trieur *m*, marteau *m* de triage	Klauber *m*, Klaubhammer *m*	addetto *m* alla cernita, martello *m* per la cernita
—	13211 picker	pic *m*, fleuret *m* d'amorçage	Keilhaue *f*	piccone *m*, fioretto *m* d'innescamento
°	13211a picker	picot *m*	Aushebeeisen *n*	ferro *m* da scampanare
—	13212 pickeringite	pickeringite *f*	Pickeringit *m*	pickeringite *f*
—	13213 picking	triage *m* à main	Klaubarbeit *f*	cernita *f* a mano, picconatura *f*
—	13214 picking belt	bande *f* de triage	Klaubeband *n*	cinghia *f* di cernita
—	13215 picking ore	minerai *m* trié au marteau ou à la main	Klauberz *n*	minerale *m* spaccato a mano (o col martel-lo)
°	13216 to pickle	décaper à l'acide	mit Säure beizen	pulire con acido
°	13216a pickle	décapant *m*	Beize *f*	liquido *m* di decapag-gio
°	13217 pickle, pickling bath	bain *m* de dérochage ou de décapage	Säurebad *n*, Dekapierflüssigkeit *f*	bagno *m* di decapag-gio
°	13218 pickle test	essai *m* de décapage	Säureprobe *f*	prova *f* in acido

	English	French	German	Italian
○	13219 **pickled**	décapé	gebeizt	decapato
○	13220 **pickled plate,** **pickling sheet**	tôle *f* décapée	gebeiztes Blech *n*	lamiera *f* decapata
○	13221 **pickled sheet**	tôle *f* mate	Mattblech *n*	latta *f* matta
○	13222 **pickling bat**	cuve *f* de décapage	Beiztrog *m*	vasca *f* di decapaggio
○	13223 **pickled wire**	fil de fer *m* décapé	gebeizter Draht *m*	filo *m* di ferro decapato
○	13224 **pickler**	décapeur	Abbeizungsarbeiter *m*	addetto *m* al decapaggio
○	13225 **pickling**	décapage *m*	Beizung *f*	decapaggio *m*
	pickling bath, *s. pickle*			
○	13226 **pickling conveyor** **for castings**	transporteur *m* pour jets de fonderie	Gussförderer *m*	trasportatore *m* per getti di fonderia
○	13227 **pickling crack**	crique *f* de décapagc	Abbeizungsriss *m*	cricca *f* di decapaggio
○	13228 **pickling line**	installation *f* de décapage continu	Beizanlage *f*	impianto *m* di decapaggio continuo
○	13229 **pickling the wire**	décapage *m* du fil	Beizen *n* des Drahtes	pulitura *f* del filo
○	13230 **pickling tube or bath**	bac *m* de décapage	Beiz-Bottich *m*	vasca *f* di decapaggio
○	13230a **pickup**	métal *m* adhérent	Ansatz *m*	metallo *m* aderente
○	13231 **picnometer**	pycnomètre *m*	Dichtigkeitsmesser *m*	picnometro *m*
—	13232 **picotite**	picotite *f*	Pikotit *m*	picotite *f*
—	13233 **picrite**	picrite *f*	Pikrit *m*	picrite *f*
—	13234 **picrolite**	picrolite *f*	Pikrolith *m*	picrolite *f*
—	13235 **picromerite**	picromérite *f*	Pikromerit *m*	picromerite *f*
○	13236 **piece for use**	pièce *f* à employer	Gebrauchsstück *n*	pezzo *m* pronto all'uso
○	13237 **piece to be cleaned**	pièce *f* à ébarber	Putzstück *n*	pezzo *m* da sbavare
○	13238 **piece to be rolled**	pièce *f* à laminer, barre *f*	Walzstück *n*	pezzo *m* da laminare, barra *f*
—	13239 **pienaarite**	pienaarite *f*	Pienaarit *m*	pienaarite *f*
○	13240 **to pierce**	forer	bohren	perforare

		English	French	German	Italian
°	13241	**to pierce, to bore**	percer	bohren	forare
°	13242	**to pierce the tap-hole**	déboucher le trou de coulée	Aufstechen *n* des Abstichloches	sturare il foro di colata
		pierced hole, *s. drilled hole*			
°	13243	**piercer, punch**	chasse-pointes *m*, poinçon *m*	Durchschlag *m*, Lochdorn *m*	punzone *m*
°	13244	**piercing**	poinçonnage *m*	Stanzen *n*, Lochen *n*	punzonatura *f*
—	13245	**pierite**	dolomie *f*	Dolomit *m*	dolomite *f*
°	13246	**to pig**	couler la fonte en gueuses	die Luppen *f pl.* giessen	colare la ghisa in pani
°	13247	**to pig-back**	ajouter de la fonte brute	Roheisen *n* zusetzen	aggiungere ghisa grezza
°	13248	**pig**	fosse *f* de coulée pour gueuses	Barrenschmelzgrube *f*	fossa *f* di colata per lingotti
°	13249	**pig, sow**	gueuse *f*, saumon *m*, gueuset *m*	Massel *f*, Luppe *f*, Roheisenmassel *f*	massello *m* (o pane *m*) di ghisa
		pig, *s. pig casting machine*			
°	13250	**pig and ore process**	procédé *m* à la fonte et au minerai	Siemens-Prozess *m*	processo *m* Siemens
°	13251	**pig bed, casting bed**	couche *f* de coulée, lit *m* de coulée	Giessbett *n*, Sandbett *n*	letto *m* per la colata
°	13252	**pig boilling**	puddlage *m* gras ou bouillant	Schlackenfrischen *n* Kochpuddeln *n*	puddellaggio *m* bollente (o grasso)
°	13253	**pig breaker**	casse-gueuse *m* ·	Masselbrecher *m*	rompighisa *m*
°	13254	**pig breaker**	casse-fonte *m*	Fallwerk *n*	berta *f* spezza-rottami
°	13255	**pig casting machine**	machine *f* à couler les gueuses	Masselgiess-maschine *f*	fonditrice *f* per masselli
°	13256	**pig casting yard**	lit *m* de coulée	Giessbett *n*, Masselbett *n*	letto *m* (o fossa *f*) di colata
°	13257	**pig copper**	cuivre *m* en saumons	Luppenkupfer *n*	rame *m* in salmoni
°	13258	**pig for remelting**	gueuse *f* de refonte	Rohmasseln *f pl.*	focaccia *f* da rifondere
°	13259	**pig iron, pig**	fonte *f* brute	Roheisen *n*	ghisa *f* grezza (o nuova)

	English	French	German	Italian
13260	**pig iron bath**	bain *m* de fonte	Roheisenbad *n*	bagno *m* di ghisa
13261	**pig iron bed**	lit *m* de coulée pour gueuses	Giessbett *n*	letto *m* di colata per lingotti
	pig iron casting, *s. cast iron castings*			
13262	**pig iron containing nickel**	fonte *f* au nickel ou contenant du nickel	nickelhaltiges Roheisen *n*	ghisa *f* al nickel
13263	**pig iron charge**	charge *f* de fonte	Roheisengichtsatz *m*	carica *f* di ghisa
	pig iron for castings, *s. cast iron*			
	pig iron for malleable castings, *s. malleable iron*			
	pig iron for refining, *s. charcoal hearth cast iron*			
13264	**pig iron mixer**	mélangeur *m* de fonte	Roheisenmischer *m*	mescolatore *m*
13265	**pig iron wagon**	wagon *m* pour la fonte	Roheisenwagen *m*	vagone *m* per trasportare la ghisa
13266	**pig-lead**	saumon (ou pain) de plomb	Ofenblei *n*, Bleiklumpen *m*	pane *m* (o salmone *m)* di piombo
13267	**pig-machine**	machine *f* à couler les gueuses	Masselgiessmaschine *f*	macchina *f* per fondere masselli (o i salmoni)
13268	**pig mold**	moule *m* de gueuses	Masselform *f*	forma *f* di massello (o di salmone)
13269	**pig sow**	chenal *m* de coulée à lingots	Barrengussrinne *f*	canale *m* di colata per lingotti
13270	**pig tin**	étain *m* en saumon	Blockzinn *n*	stagno *m* in pani (o salmoni)
13270a	**pig washing**	affinage *m* de fonte brute	Frischen *n* von Roheisen	affinazione *f* di ghisa grezza
	pigging, *s. ingotting*			
	pigging back, *s. carburization material*			
13271	**piglet (foundry)**	petite gueuse *f*	kleine Luppe *f*	panotto *m*, piccolo *m* pane
13272	**pigment-gilding**	dorure *f* à mordant	Beizvergoldung *f*	doratura *f* a mordente
13273	**pigsty**	anneau *m* de cuvelage, pile *f* de bois	Stützring *m* Holzpfeiler *m*	anello *m* di rinforzo, pilastro *m*, catasta *f*

	English	French	German	Italian
—	13274 **pigsty timbering**	soutènement *m* par piles de bois	Holzpfeilerzimmerung *f*	armatura *f* a pilastri di legno
—	13275 **pilandite**	pilandite *f*	Pilandit *m*	pilandite *f*
o	13276 **to pile**	paqueter	paketieren	formare un pacchetto
o	13277 **to pile up, to ball**	tasser, agglomérer	in Haufen setzen, austapeln	dividere in piccole palle
o	13278 **pile**	pile *f*, tas *m*, amas *m*	Haufen *m*, Stapel *m*	mucchio *m*, ammasso *m*
o	13279 **pile, fagot**	paquet *m* de fer à souder	Schweisspaket *n*	pacchetto *m* di ferro da puddellare
—	13280 **pile foundation**	fondation *f* sur pilotis	Fundament *n* auf Pfahlrost	fondazione *f* su platea di palafitte
o	13281 **pilger mill**	laminoir *m* à pas de pélerin	Pilgerwalzwerk *n*	laminatoio *m* a passo di pellegrino
o	13282 **pilger roll**	cylindre *m* de laminoir à pas de pélerin	Pilgerwalze *f*	cilindro *m* a passo di pellegrino
o	13283 **piling, fagoting**	préparation *f* des paquets, paquetage *m*	Paketieren *n*	fabbricazione *f* o preparazione *f* dei pacchetti
o	13284 **piling**	empilage *m*, empilement *m*	Aufstapelung *f*	ammucchiare, accatastare
—	13285 **piling**	battage *m* de pieux	Pfahlrammen *n*	battitura *f* dei pali
—	13286 **piling**	poussage *m* par palplanches	Getriebezimmerung *f*	armatura *f* a tavoloni
o	13287 **piling and welding of steel**	corroyer, corroyer l'acier	gärben, Stahl *m* schmieden	fucinare, fucinare l'acciaio
o	13287a **pill press**	presse *f* à briquettes	Pastillenpresse *f*	pressa *f* per compatti
o	13288 **pillar**	colonne *f*	Säule *f*	colonna *f*, pilastro *m* (di macchina)
—	13289 **pillar**	pilier *m*	Pfeiler *m*	pilastro *m*

pillar and breast stoping, s. *pillar and room*

—	13290 **pillar-and-room**	exploitation *f* par chambres et piliers	Kammerpfeilerbau *m*	coltivazione *f* a camere e pilastri

pillar and stall, s. *pillar-and-room*
pillar bolt, s. *stay bolt*

English	French	German	Italian
13291 pillar coal	charbon *m* en piliers	Pfeilerkohle *f*	carbone *m* in pilastri
13292 pillar crane	grue *f* à potence	Säulendrehkran *m*	gru *f* a bracci
pillar die set, *s. die set*			
13293 pillar drawing	dépilage *m*	Verhieb *m*, Abbau *m* der Pfeiler	demolizione *f* (o ritiro) dei pilastri
pillar-iron, *s. quadrant iron*			
13294 pillar mining	exploitation *f* par piliers abandonnés	Kammerbau *m*	coltivazione *f* a pilastri abbandonati
13295 pillaring	exploitation *f* par piliers, dépilage *m*	Pfeilerbau *m*, Pfeilerabbau *m*	coltivazione *f* a pilastri, demolizione *f* dei pilastri
13295a pillaring	colonne *f* froide	kalte Säule *f*	colonna *f* fredda
13296 pillow	coussinet *m*	Lager *n*	cuscinetto*m*
13297 pillow structure	division *f* en oreillers empilés	wollsackförmige Absonderung *f*	divisione *f* in cuscinetti
13298 pilot bit	trépan-pilote *m*	Führungsmeissel *m*	trapano *m* pilota
13299 pilot hole	trou *m* pilote	vorgebohrtes Loch *n*	foro *m* pilota
13300 pilot raise	montage *m* auxiliaire	kurzer Aufbruch *m*	montaggio *m* ausiliare
13301 pilotaxitic texture	texture *f* pilotaxitique	pilotaxitische Struktur *f*	struttura *f* pilotaxitica
13302 pimple	matte *f* de cuivre	Metallin *n*	metallina *f*, matta *f* di rame
13302a pimpling	granulation *f* superficielle	Pickelbildung *f*	granulazione *f* superficiale
13303 pimpling	soufflures *f pl.*	Blasen *f pl.*	bollicine *f pl.* (in un getto)
13304 to pin	goujonner	Führungsstifte *m pl.* anbringen	fissare con perni
13305 pin	broche *f*, goujon *m*	Stift *m*	perno *m*
13306 pin	boulon *m* de guidage	Führungsstift *m*	perno *m* di guida
13307 pin	tenon *m*, cheville *f*	Dübel *m*, Stift *m*	spina *f*, caviglia *f*
13308 pin closure	engoujonnage *m*	Zusammenpassen *n* mit Führungsstiften	riferimento *m*, accoppiamento *m* con perni
13309 pin joint	assemblage par goupille	Bolzengelenk *n*	articolazione *f* a perni
13309a pin lift	démoulage *m* sur chandelles	Abheben auf Stiften	sformatura *f* a candele
pincers, *s. wire pliers*			
13310 to pinch	se contracter	schrumpfen	contrarsi
13311 pinch	pli *m* longitudinal	Längsfalte *f*	piega *f* longitudinale
13311a pinch	onde *f*, repliure *f*	Welle *f*	onda *f* (di laminazione)

English	French	German	Italian
^ 13312 **to pinch (in), to choke**	étrangler	drosseln	ridurre volontariamente il flusso del pozzo
° 13312a **pinch pass**	dressage *m*	Dressierwalzung *f*	laminazione *f* raddrizzatrice
° 13313 **pinch roll**	rouleau *m* entraîneur	Greifwalze *f*, Treibrolle *f*	cilindro *m* di presa, rullo *m* di azionamento
pincher, *s. ingot tongs*			
— 13314 **pine charcoal**	charbon *m* de bois de conifères	Nadelholzkohle *f*	carbone *m* di legna (di conifere)
— 13315 **pinguite**	pinguite *f*	Pinguit *m*	pinguite *f*
pinhead blisters, *s. pepper blisters*			
° 13316 **pinholes**	piqûres *f pl.*	Nadelstichporen *f pl.*	camolatura *f*, porosità *f* puntiforme
° 13317 **pinholes**	piqûres *f pl.* panachées	verschiedenfarbige Poren *f pl.*	camolatura *f* mista
° 13318 **pinholes**	piqûres *f pl.* de scorie	Schlackenporen *f pl.*	camolatura *f* da scoria
° 13319 **pinion**	pignon *m* à chevrons	Kammwalze *f*	pignone *m* a spina di pesce
° 13320 **pinion shaft**	arbre *m* du pignon	Antriebswelle *f*	albero *m* del pignone
° 13320a **pinion stand**	cage *f* à pignons	Kammwalzgerüst *n*	gabbia *f* a pignoni
° 13321 **pinion steel**	acier *m* à pignons	Triebstahl *m*	acciaio *m* da rocchetti od ingranaggi
° 13322 **pinion trunnion**	tourillon *m* à pignon	Wanderzapfen *m*	perno *m* con ingranaggio
— 13323 **pinnoite**	pinnoïte *f*	Pinnoit *m*	pinnoite *f*
— 13324 **pintadoïte**	pintadoïte *f*	Pintadoit *m*	pintadoite *f*
— 13325 **piotine**	saponite *f*	Saponit *m*	saponite *f*
^ 13326 **to pipe**	refouler	liefern	erogare
° 13327 **to pipe**	formation *f* de retassements	Lunkerbildung *f*	formarsi di cavità di ritiro (risucchiare)
° 13328 **pipe (foundry)**	cuiller (de coulée)	Giesskelle *f*, Giesslöffel *m*	cucchiarozzo, cucchiaio *m*
° 13329 **pipe, funnel**	retassement *m*, retassure *f*, cavité *f*	Lunker *m*	risucchio *m*, soffiatura, cavità di ritiro, cono di risucchio
° 13329a **pipe chaplet**	support *m* de noyau	Kernstütze *f*	supporto *m* per anima
^ 13330 **pipe chocking**	encrassement *m* d'un tuyau	Rohrverstopfung *f*	ostruzione di un tubo

	English	French	German	Italian
13331	pipe-clay	terre *f* de pipe	Pfeifenton *m*	terra *f* da pipa
13332	pipe coupling	manchon *m*	Rohrnippel *m*	manicotto *m*
13333	pipe crossing joint	croix *f*	Kreuz-Stück *n*	pezzo a croce (per tubi)
13334	pipe-cutter	coupe-tubes *m*	Rohrschneider *m*	tagliatubi *m*
13335	pipe dog	clef *m* à tubes	Rohrschlüssel *m*	chiave *f* per tubi
13336	pipe fitting	tubulure *f*	Rohrverbindungen *f pl.*	raccorderia *f*
13337	pipe for chemical plants	tube *m* pour les industries chimiques	Rohr *n* für chemische Anlagen	tubo *m* per impianti chimici
13338	pipe for conveying industrial water	tube *m* pour canalisations d'eau industrielle	Rohr *n* für Industrie--Wasserversorgung	tubo *m* per condotte di acqua industriale
13339	pipe for gas lines	tube *m* pour canalisations de gaz naturel	Erdgasrohr *n*	tubo *m* per gasdotti
13340	pipe for heat exchangers	tube *m* pour échangeurs de chaleur	Rohr *n* für Wärmeaustauscher	tubo *m* per scambiatori di calore
13341	pipe for hydroelectric penstocks	tube *m* pour conduites forcées	Rohr *n* für Druckwasserleitungen	tubo *m* per condotte forzate
13342	pipe for natural gas	tube *m* pour gaz, canalisations de méthane	Leitungsrohr *n* für Erdgas	tubo *m* per metanodotti
13343	pipe for refinery	tube *m* pour raffinerie	Rohr *n* für Raffinerieanlagen	tubo *m* per raffineria
13344	pipe for thermic plants	tube *m* pour installations thermiques	Rohr *n* für thermische Anlagen	tubo *m* per installazioni termiche
13345	pipe for town gas	tube *m* pour canalisations de gaz de ville	Leitungsrohr *n* für Stadtgas	tubo *m* per gas di città
13346	pipe for waters main	tube *m* pour aqueducs	Rohr *n* für Wasserleitungen	tubo *m* per acquedotti
13347	pipe grab	accroche-tube	Rohrfänger *m*	pescatore *m* per tubi
13348	pipe grip, pipe wrench	pince *f* à griffe	Rohrzange *f*	stringitubi *m*

	English	French	German	Italian
^ 13349	**pipe hanger**	support *m* pour tuyaux	Rohrschelle *f*	supporto *m* (o collare) per tubi, raccordo *m* a sospensioni per tubi
o 13350	**pipe hole**	retassement *m*	Lunkerung *f*, Lunker *m*	soffiatura *f*, cavità *f*
o 13351	**pipe junction**	raccord *m* de tuyau	Rohransatz *m*	raccordo *m* per tubi
^ 13352	**pipe lagging**	enveloppe *f* de tuyaux	Rohrmantel *m*	rivestimento *m* (o copertura) di tubi
^ 13353	**pipe layer**	machine *f* pose--tuyaux	Leitungslege-vorrichtung *f*	macchina *f* posa-condotte
^ 13354	**pipe laying**	pose *f* de tuyaux	Rohrlegen *n*	messa *f* in opera (o montaggio *m*) di tubi
^ 13355	**pipe line**	pipe line *m*, conduite *f*, canalisation *f* à pétrole	Rohrleitung *f*, Ölleitung *f*	condotta *f*, conduttura *f*, tubatura *f*, oleodotto *m*
^ 13356	**pipe line oil**	brut *m* de pétrole commercial	Pipe-Line Öl *n*	olio *m* purissimo, grezzo *m* commerciale
^ 13357	**pipe lining**	enveloppe *f* de tuyaux	Rohrmantel *m*	rivestimento *m* di tubi
^ 13358	**pipe man**	tuyauteur *m*	Rohrleger *m*	posatore *m* di tubi
^ 13359	**pipe nipple**	manchon *m*	Rohrnippel *m*	manicotto *m* (per tubi)
— 13360	**pipe of ore**	colonne *f* de minerai	Erzfall *m*	colonna *f* di minerale
^ 13361	**pipe opener**	machine *f* à élargir les tubes	Rohrreibahle *f*	allargatubi *m*
^ 13362	**pipe rack**	parc à tiges et tuyaux	Gestänge-u. Röhrlager *n*	parco *m* per aste e tubi
^ 13363	**pipe ramp**	couloir *m* de la tour	Turmrutscher *m*	piano *m* di scivolo della torre
o 13364	**pipe rolling mill**	laminoir *m* à tubes	Rohrwalzwerk *n*, Röhrenwalzwerk *n*	laminatoio *m* per tubi
^ 13365	**pipe set back**	gerbage *m*	Gestänge-Abstellfläche *f*	deposito *m* dei tubi
o 13366	**pipe sleeker**	lissoir *m* à tuyaux	Polierknopf *m*	lisciatoio *m* a squadra
o 13367	**pipe sleeve**	tuyau *m* à manchon	Muffenrohr *n*	tubo *m* a manicotto

	English	French	German	Italian
	pipe stand, s. *pipe hanger*			
	pipe stove, s. *radiant tube furnace*			
13368	pipe union	raccord-union *m*, raccord à trois pièces	Rohrverschraubung *f*	raccordo *m* a tre vie, giunzione *f* a vite di tubi
13369	pipe vice	étau à tubes	Rohrklemme *f*	morsa da tubi
13370	pipe with bevelled ends	tube *m* avec extrémités chanfreinées	Rohr *n* mit abgeschrägten Enden	tubo *m* con estremità smussate
13371	pipe with loose flanges	tube *m* avec assemblages par brides mobiles	Leitungsrohr *n* mit Losflanschverbindungen	tubo *m* con giunti a flange mobili
13372	pipe yard	parc *m* à tuyaux	Rohrlager *n*	parco *m* tubi
13373	piped billet	ébauche tubulaire	Rundrohling *m*	bicchiere *m*, sbozzato *m* tubolare
	pipeline, s. *pipe line*			
	pipeline network, s. *piping network*			
13374	pipeline run	débit de pipe-line	Ölleitungszufluss *m*	portata *f* dell'oleodotto
13375	piper	soufflard *m*	Bläser *m*	fessura *f* di scarico
13376	piperno	piperno *m*	Piperno *m*	piperno *m*
13377	pipette	pipette *f*	Pipette *f*, Stechheber *m*	pipetta *f*
13378	pipette bottle	flacon *m* à pipette	Pipettenflasche *f*	bottiglia *f* a pipetta
	pipette holder, s. *pipette stand*			
13379	pipette stand	étagère *f* à pipettes	Pipettenständer *m*	porta-pipette *m*
13380	piping	conduite *f*, tuyauterie *f*	Rohrleitung *f*	condotto *m* conduttura *f*, tubazione *f*
13381	piping	retassure *f*	Lunkerung *f*	cavità *f* di ritiro
13382	piping	abattage *m* à l'eau	hydraulische Gewinnung *f*	estrazione *f* idraulica
13383	piping	retassement *m*, formation *f* de retassures	Lunkern *n*, Saugen *n* Lunkerblockbildung *f*	ritiro *m*, formazione *f* di risucchi

	English	French	German	Italian
^	13384 **piping for reprocessing plants**	tuyauterie *f* pour installations de retraitement	Rohrleitung *f* für Wiedergewinnungs- anlagen	tubazione *f* per impianti di rigenerazione
^	13385 **piping system**	réseau *m* de canalisation	Rohrleitungsnetz *n*, Leitungsnetz *n*	rete *f* di tubazioni
—	13386 **pisolite**	pisolite *f*	Pisolit *m*, Pisolith *m*	pisolite *f*
—	13387 **pisolitic iron, bean ore**	minerai *m* de fer en grains	Bohnerz *n*	limonite *f* pisolitica o in grani
	pisolitic texture, *s. oolitic texture*			
°	13388 **pistol pipe**	tuyau *m* à pistolet	Hauptwindrohr *n*, Kranzrohr *n*	canna *f* di pistola
°	13389 **piston**	piston *m*	Kolben *m*	stantuffo *m*, pistone *m*
	piston blade, *s. piston vane*			
—	13390 **piston drill**	marteau perforateur	Bohrhammer *m*	martello *m* perforatore
°	13391 **piston pin**	tourillon *m* de piston	Kolbenbolzen *m*	perno *m* (o spinotto) di pistone
°	13392 **piston ring**	segment du piston	Kolbenring *m*	anello *m* dello stantuffo
°	13393 **piston rod**	tige *f* de pompe	Pumpenstock *m*	stelo *m* di pompa
°	13394 **piston valve gear**	distribution *f* par piston	Kolbensteuerung *f*	distribuzione *f* a mezzo stantuffo
°	13395 **piston vane**	ailette *f* formant piston	Kolbenflügel *m*	aletta *f* di stantuffo
°	13396 **pit, casting pit**	fosse *f* de coulée, coulée *f* en fosse	Giessgrube *f*, Grubenguss *m*	fossa *f* di colata, colata *f* in fossa
—	13397 **pit**	puits *m*, mine *f*, carrière	Schacht *m*, Grube *f*, Bergwerk *n*, Steinbruch *m*	pozzo *m*, cava *f*, miniera *f* (di carbone)
	pit, *s. soaking furnace (or pit)*			
—	13398 **pit barring**	soutènement *m* du puits	Schachtausbau *m*	armatura *f* di pozzo
—	13399 **pit bottom**	accrochage *m*	Füllort *m*	stazione *f* di fondo
—	13400 **pit cage**	cage *f* de mine	Fördergestell *n*	gabbia *f* di miniera
°	13401 **pit cast**	coulée *f* dans la fosse de coulée	in Giessgrube *f* gegossen	colata *f* in fossa

English	French	German	Italian
13402 **pit casting**	jet *m* coulé en fosse	Grubenguss *m*	getto (eseguito) in fossa
13403 **pit coal**	houille *f*	Steinkohle *f*	carbone *m* fossile
13404 **pit eye**	fond *m* du puits	Sohle *f*	fondo *m* di pozzo
13405 **pit frame**	chevalement *m*	Fördergerüst *n*	castelletto *m* d'estrazione
13406 **pit furnace**	four *m* potager	Tiegelkammerofen *m*	forno *m* a pozzo
13407 **pit gas**	grisou *m*	Grubengas *n*	grisou *m*
13408 **pit-gear**	appareillage *m* de puits	Grubenanlagen *f pl.*, Bergwerksanlagen *f pl*	attrezzatura *f* di miniera
13409 **pit head, pit top**	entrée *f* de mine	Grubeneingang *m*	entrata *f* del pozzo
13410 **pit molding**	moulage *m* en fosse	Grubenformen *n*	formatura *f* in fossa
13410a **pit sample**	prise *f* d'essai de fonte	Gussprobeentnahme *f*	prelievo *m* di ghisa
13411 **pitch**	brai *m*, poix *f*	Pech *n*	pece *f*
13411a **pitch**	cannelure *f*	Walzenkaliber *n*	calibro *m* di cilindri
13412 **pitch**	degré, pente *f*	Gefälle *n*, Neigung *f*	grado *m*, pendenza *f*
13413 **pitch blende**	pechblende *f*, uraninite *f*	Pechblende *f*, Uraninit *m*	pechblenda *f*, uranite *f*
13414 **pitch diameter**	diamètre *m* moyen de filetage	mittlerer Gewindedurchmesser *m*	diametro *m* medio di filettatura
13415 **pitch glance**	éclat *m* résineux	Pechglanz *m*	bagliore *m* resinoso
13416 **pitch kettle**	chaudière *f* à poix	Pechkessel *m*	caldaia *f* per pece
13417 **pitch-stone**	rétinite *f*	Pechstein *m*	retinite *f*
13418 **pitchy coal**	houille *f* poisseuse	Pechkohle *f*	carbone *m* di pece
13419 **pitchy lignite**	houille *f* poisseuse	Pechkohle *f*	lignite *f* picea
13420 **pitching**	incliné	geneigt	inclinato
13421 **pitching seam**	couche *f* inclinée	geneigtes Flöz *n*	strato *m* (o filone *m*) inclinato
13422 **pitman**	mineur *m*, puisatier *m*	Bergmann *m*, Häuer *m*	minatore *m*, picconiere *m*
13423 **pitman**	bielle *f*	Pleuelstange *f*	biella *f*
13424 **pitman stirrup**	étrier *m* (de suspension)	Zugstangenbügel *m*	staffa *f* (di sospensione)

		English	French	German	Italian
°	13425	**Pitot tube**	tube *m* de Pitot	Pitot-Rohr *n*	tubo *m* di Pitot
°	13426	**pitted surface**	surface *f* grippée	angefressene Oberfläche *f*	superficie *f* a vaiolatura
—	13427	**pitting**	exécution *f* des fouilles de recherche	Schürfen *n*, Schürfung *f*	prospezione *f*, ricerca *f* (di giacimenti)
°	13428	**pitting**	formation *f* de piqûres, corrosion	Lochfrass *m*	butteratura, formazione *f* dì cavità, vaiolatura *f*
°	13429	**pitting corrosion**	corrosion *f* par piqûre	Lochfrass *m*	corrosione *f* a fossette
—	13430	**pittinite**	pittinite *f*	Pittinit *m*	pittinite *f*
°	13431	**pivot**	pivot *m*, tenon *m*	Drehzapfen *m*	perno *m* (di testa), tenon
°	13432	**pivoted**	pivoté	verbolzt	imperniato
°	13433	**to place edgeways, to up-edge**	placer de champ	hochkantig stellen	piazzare in piano
	13434	**place of loading**	lieu *m* de chargement	Ladestelle *f*	luogo *m* di carico
—	13435	**placer**	placer *m*	Seife *f*	giacimento *m* alluvionale
—	13436	**placer gold**	or *m* alluvionnaire	Seifengold *n*, Alluvialgold *n*	oro *m* alluvionale
—	13437	**placer workings**	exploitation *f* de placers	Seifenwerk *n*	coltivazione *f* di giacimento alluvionale
		placing the crucible, *s. setting-in the crucible*			
—	13438	**plagioclase**	plagioclase	Plagioklas *m*	plagioclasio
—	13439	**plagionite**	plagionite *f*	Plagionit *m*	plagionite *f*
—	13440	**plagiophyre**	plagiophyre *m*	Plagiophyr *m*	plagiofiro *m*
		plain back iron, *s. back iron*			
°	13441	**plain bearing**	palier *m* lisse	Gleitlager *n*	supporto a scorrimento
		plain-bit, *s. plain-iron*			
°	13442	**plain end cylindrical tube**	tube *m* à bouts lisses de section cylindrique	Glattrohr *n* mit rundem Querschnitt	tubo *m* liscio cilindrico
°	13443	**plain ends merchant quality tube (boiler tube)**	tube *m* lisse (bouilleur) de qualité commerciale	handelsübliches Glattrohr *n*	tubo *m* liscio commerciale
		plain-knife, *s. plain-iron*			

English	French	German	Italian
13444 plain pipette	pipette *f* jaugée	Vollstechheber *m*	pipetta *f* tarata
13445 plain plate, smooth plate	tôle *f* lisse	glattes Blech *n*	lamiera *f* liscia
13446 plain superrefined steel	acier *m* spécial sans alliage	unlegierter Edelstahl *m*	acciaio *m* speciale senza lega
13447 plain-parallel structure	concordance *f* des couches	Planparallelstruktur *f*	concordanza *f* degli strati
13448 plain plate	tôle *f* lisse	glattes Blech *n*	lamiera *f* liscia
13448a plain thermit	thermite *f* normale	normaler Thermit *m*	termite *f* normale
13449 plain tubing	tube *m* de pompage normal	Pumprohr ohne Endverstärkung	tubo *m* di pompaggio normale
13450 to plane by filing	polir à la lime	mit der Feile ebnen	spianare con la lima
13451 to plane	dresser, raboter	aushobeln, hobeln	piallare
13452 plane	plan *m* d'appui, entaille *f* du couteau	Pfanne *f*	piano *m* d'acciaio (d'appoggio)
13453 plane	plan *m*	Fläche *f*, Ebene *f*	piano *m*, pianura *f*
13454 plane	plan incliné	Bremsberg *m*	piano *m* inclinato
13455 plane-iron, cutting-iron, cutter	fer (de rabot), crochet, fer à raboter	Hobeleisen *n*, Hobelstahl *m*	ferro *m* o lama *f* (di pialla), coltello *m*
13456 plane of cleavage	plan *m* de clivage	Spaltfläche *f*	piano *m* di scorrimento
13457 plane of throat	niveau *m* du gueulard	Gichtebene *f*	piano *m* della bocca
13458 plane schistosity	schistosité *f* plan-parallèle	ebene Schieferung *f*	scistosità *f* piano--parallela
	plain sheet iron, *s. smooth plate*		
13459 plane-table survey	levé *m* à la planchette	Messtischaufnahme *f*	rilevamento *m* alla tavoletta *f* (pretoriana)
13460 planed fault	faille *f* nivelée	geebnete Verwerfung *f*	faglia *f* rasata. faglia *f* piatta
13461 planerite	planérite *f*	Planerit *m*	planerite *f*
13462 planished plate, burnished plate	tôle *f* lustrée (ou polie ou brunie)	(Hoch)Glanzblech *n*, glattes (Eisen)Blech	lamiera *f* lisciata (o brunita)
	planished steel, *s. polished steel*		
13463 plank dam	cloison *f* en planches	Holzwasserscheider *m*	tramezzo *m* di tavole

	English	French	German	Italian
—	13464 **planking**	planchéiage *m*	Bretterschalung *f*	assito *m*
—	13465 **planoferrite**	planoferrite *f*	Planoferrit *m*	planoferrite *f*
	planparallel structure, *s. conformity*			
°	13466 **plant boiler**	chaudière *f* de service	Betriebskessel *m*	caldaia *f* di servizio
°	13467 **plaster casting**	coulée *f* en plâtre	Gipsguss *m*	colata *f* in gesso
°	13468 **plaster mould**	moule en plâtre	Gipsmatrize *f*	forma *f* di gesso
°	13469 **plaster moulding, gypsum moulding**	moulage *m* en plâtre	Gipsformverfahren *n*	formatura *f* in gesso
—	13470 **plastic clay, potter's clay**	argile plastique, terre *f* à potier, terre *f* glaise	plastischer Ton *m*, Töpferton *m*	argilla *f* plastica, argilla *f* da modellare
°	13471 **plastic coating**	enduit *m* plastique	Plastik-Überzug *m*	rivestimento *m* plastico
°	13472 **plastic material**	matière *f* plastique	plastisches Material *n*	materia *f* plastica
°	13472a **plastic metall**	métal de coussinet	Lagermetall *n*	metallo *m* plastico
°	13473 **plasticiser**	plastifiant *m*	Plastifiziermittel *n*	plastificante *m*
°	13474 **plasticity**	plasticité *f*	Plastizität *f*	plasticità *f*
—	13475 **plastotype**	plastotype *m*	Plastotypus *m*	plastotipo *m*
°	13476 **plat-band**	moulure *f* de la face	Bandgesims *n*	(cornice *f* di) fascia *f*
°	13477 **to plate**	plaquer	plattieren	placcare
°	13478 **to plate with copper**	cuivrer	verkupfern	ramare
	to plate with gold, *s. to gold-plate*			
°	13479 **plate**	plaque *f*, lame *f*	Platte *f*, Tafel *f*	placca *f*, piastra *f*
°	13480 **plate**	bloom *m*	Barren *m*	blumo *m*
°	13481 **plate, plating**	placage *m*	Plattierung *f*	placcatura *f*
°	13482 **plate (mill)**	cylindre *m* à tôles	Blechwalze *f*	cilindro *m* per lamiere
—	13483 **plate, scale (casting defect)**	écaillage *f*, buse *f*	Blätterung *f*	sfogliatura *f*
°	13483a **plate**	plaque-filière *f*	Zieheisen *n*	filiera *f*, trafila *f*
°	13484 **plate**	plaque *f*, feuille *f*	Platte *f*, Täfelchen *n*	piastra *f*, lastra *f*
°	13485 **plate (flanging quality), soft sheets**	tôle *f* pour emboutissage	Bördelblech *n*	lamiera *f* flangiata
°	13486 **plate amalgamation**	amalgamation *f* sur plaques	Plattenamalgamation *f*	amalgamazione *f* su piastre

English	French	German	Italian
13487 **plate bending machine**	machine *f* à cintrer les tôles	Blechbiege-maschine *f*	piegatrice *f* per lamiere
13488 **plate brass, sheet--brass**	laiton en planches	Messingblech *n*	ottone *m* in lastroni
13489 **plate conveyor**	transporteur *m* à palettes	Plattenförderband *n*, Standbahn *f*	trasportatore *m* a placche (o a piastre)
13490 **plate glass base**	glace *f* du fond de la balance	Grundplatte *f* aus Spiegelglas	specchio *m* di base della bilancia
13491 **plate-heating--furnace**	four *m* dormant à tôle	Blechglühofen *m*	forno *m* per ricuocere piastre
13492 **plate in contact with the flame**	planche *f* léchée par les flammes	Heizfläche *f*	piastra *f* lambita dalle fiamme
plate iron, *s. sheet iron*			
13493 **plate lapped by the water**	tôle *f* léchée par l'eau	von Wasser über-spülte Platte *f*	piastra *f* lambita dall'acqua
plate mill, *s. sheet rolling mill*			
13494 **plate-mill roll**	cylindre *m* à tôles	Blechwalze *f*	cilindro *m* per lamiere
13495 **plate mould**	mouler sur plaque	mit der Modellplatte formen	formare con placca
13496 **plate of porous porcelain**	assiette *f* en porcelaine poreuse	Teller *m* aus porigem Porzellan	piatto *m* di porcellana porosa
plate roll, *s. plate mill roll*			
plate rolling, *s. sheet rolling*			
13497 **plate rolling mill**	laminoir *m* à tôles	Blechwalzwerk *n*	laminatoio *m* per lamiere
13498 **plate spring**	ressort *m* à disques	Tellerfeder *f*	molla *f* a disco
13499 **plate steel**	acier *m* à plaques	Plattenstahl *m*	acciaio *m* per piastre
13500 **plate thickness**	épaisseur *m* de tôle	Blechstärke *f*	spessore *m* della lamiera
plate with patterns, *s. moulding board*			
plateau, *s. table-land*			
13501 **platen spacing, horn spacing**	distance entre les bras	Armabstand *m*	distanza tra i bracci
13502 **plates**	plateaux *m pl.*	Aufspannplatten *f pl.*	piani *m pl.*
13502a **plates**	lamelles *f pl.* de poudre	Pulverplättchen *n*	lamelle *f pl.* di polvere

	English	French	German	Italian
° 13503	plates in contact with water	tôles *f pl.* léchées par l'eau	mit dem Wasser in Berührung stehende Platten *f pl.*	piastre *f pl.* lambite dall'acqua
° 13504	plating with brass	laitonnage *m*	Vermessingung *f*	ottonatura *f*
° 13505	platform	plate-forme *f*	Palette *f* auf Füssen	piattaforma *f*, vassoio
— 13506	platform	plate-forme *f*	Zwischenbühne *f*	piattaforma *f*
— 13507	platform brackets	support *m* de la plateforme du gueulard	Träger *m* des Gichtbelages	supporto *m* della piattaforma di caricamento
— 13508	platform of weigh- - bridge	pont *m* (de la bascule)	Brücke *f*	ponte *m* della basculla
— 13509	platform scale	pont *m* à bascule	Wiege *f*, Kippbrücke *f*	ponte *m* a bilico
— 13510	platiniridium	platiniridium *m*	Iridiumplatin *n*	platino *m* iridiato
° 13511	platinization	platinage *m*	Platinierung *f*	platinatura *f*
° 13512	plating	placage, revêtement *m*	Verkleidung *f* Plattieren *n*	placcatura *f*, rivestimento *m*
— 13513	platinic chloride	chlorure *m* de platine	Platinchlorid *n*	cloruro *m* di platino
° 13514	platinum	platine *m*	Platin *n*	platino *m*
° 13515	platinum basin	capsule *f* en platine	Platinschale *f*	capsula *f* di platino
° 13516	platinum bearing	platinifère	platinhaltig	platinifero
° 13517	platinum boat	nacelle *f* en platine	Platinschiffchen *n*	navicella *f* di platino
° 13518	platinum cone	entonnoir *m* en platine	Platinkegel *m*, Platinkonus *m*	cono *m* di platino
° 13519	platinum crucible	creuset *m* en platine	Platintiegel *m*	crogiuolo *m* in platino
° 13520	platinum incineration dish	capsule *f* en platine pour incinérations	Platinveraschungsschale *f*	capsula *f* di platino per incenerazione
° 13521	platinum knife	couteau *m* en platine	Platinmesser *n*	coltello *m* di platino
° 13522	platinum metal	métal *m* de platine	Platinmetall *n*	metallo *m* di platino
° 13523	platinum muffle	moufle *m* en platine	Platinmuffel *f*	muffola *f* di platino
° 13524	platinum plating	platinage *m*	Platinierung *f*	platinatura *f*

English	French	German	Italian
13525 platinum pin	aiguille *f* de platine	Platinnadel *f*	ago *m* di platino
13526 platinum sheet	feuille *f* de platine	Platinblech *n*	lamiera *f* di platino
13527 platinum spatula	spatule *f* en platine	Platinspatel *m*	spatola *f* di platino
13258 platinum spoon	cuillère *f* en platine	Platinlöffel *m*	cucchiaio *m* di platino
13258a platinum sponge	éponge *f* de platine	Platinschwamm *m*	platino *m* spugnoso
13529 platinum ware	utensiles en platine	Platingerät *n*	utensili di platino
13530 platinum wire	fil *m* de platine	Platindraht *m*	filo *m* di platino
13531 platman	accrocheur *m*	Anschläger *m*	ingabbiatore *m*
13532 platt	recette *f*	Füllort *m*	stazione *f* di fondo
13532a platter	masse *f* totale de fer à forger	Gesamtmasse *f* des Schmiedemetalls	massa *f* totale di ferro di fucinatura
13533 plattnerite	plattnérite *f*	Plattnerit *m*	plattnerite *f*
13534 platy	en plaquettes	plattenförmig	in tavole

platy pig iron, s. *white crystalline iron*

English	French	German	Italian
13535 to play out	s'épuiser	erschöpfen	esaurirsi
13536 play	jeu *m*, tolérance *f*	Spielraum *m*	giuoco *m*, tolleranza *f*
13537 play of the weighing machine	jeu *m* de la bascule	Spiel *n* der Waage	oscillazione *f* della basculla o bilancia
13538 plazolite	plazolite *f*	Plazolith *m*	plazolite *f*
13539 Pleiocene	pliocène *m*	Pliozän *n*	pliocene *m*
13540 Pleistocene	pléistocène *m*	Pleistozän *n*	pleistocene *m*
13541 plenum	soufflant	blasend	soffiante
13542 plenum system of ventilation	ventilation *f* soufflante	blasende Bewetterung *f*	ventilazione *f* soffiante
13543 pleochroism	pléochroïsme *m*	Pleochroismus *m*	pleocroismo *m*
13544 pleonaste	pléonaste *m*	Pleonast *m*	pleonasto *m*
13545 plesiosaurus	plésiosaure *m*	Plesiosaurus *n*	plesiosauro *m*
13546 plesiotype	plesiotype *m*	Plesiotypus *m*	plesiotipo *m*
13547 plessite	plessite *f*	Plessit *m*	plessite *f*
13548 pliable, pliant	flexible, pliable	biegbar, biegsam	flessibile, pieghevole

	English	French	German	Italian
−	13549 **plication**	plissotement *m*	Runzel *f*	corrugamento *m*
o	13550 **pliers**	pinces *f pl.*	Zange *f*	pinze *f pl.*
−	13551 **Pliocene epoch**	pliocène *m*	Pliozän *n*	pliocene *m*
−	13552 **plot**	plan *m*, tracé *m*, parcelle *f*, faire le plan	Plan *m*, Riss *m*, Parzelle *f*	piano *m*, tracciato *m*, appezzamento *m* (di terreno)
o	13553 **plough steel**	acier de charrues	Pflugstahl *m*	acciaio *m* da aratri
−	13554 **plucking**	érosion *f* par éclatement	splitternde Gletschererosion *f*	erosione *f* per esplosione
o	13555 **plug (in foundry)**	carotte *f*	Stichlochpfropfen *m*	carota *f*, chiodo *m*
o	13556 **plug**	bouchon *m*	Schlusspfropfen *m*	coperchio *m*, tappo *m*
^	13557 **to plug**	boucher	verdämmen	cementare un pozzo
o	13558 **to plug the tap hole**	boucher le trou de coulée	das Stichloch *n* verschliessen	tappare il foro di colata
o	13559 **plug (of a cock)**	taraud *m*	Schneidbohrer *m*	maschio *m*
o	13560 **plug and feather(s)**	aiguille *f* infernale	Treibkeil *m*	ago *m* infernale
−	13561 **plug bit**	trépan *m* à carottier continu	Plug Bit	scalpello *m* per carotieri continui
−	13562 **plug container**	tête *f* de cimentation avec bouchons	Zementierkopf *m* mit Pfropfen	testa *f* di cementazione contenente tappi
o	13562a **plug line, plug scratch**	traces de mandrin	Dornspuren	tracce di mandrino
−	13563 **plug ramming machine**	machine *f* à damer les fonds	Bodenstampfmaschine *f*	·macchina *f* per costipare il fondo
^	13564 **plug valve**	robinet *m* à boisseau	Kegelventil *n*	valvola *f* a maschio
o	13565 **plugged pouring basin**	bassin *m* de coulée à flotteur	Giesstümpel *m* mit Schwimmer	bacino *m* a tampone galleggiante
	plugger, *s. jackhammer*			
	plugging, *s. botting*			
−	13566 **plugging**	colmatage *m*, bouchage *m*	Verstopfung *f* Schliessen des Stichlochs	riempimento *m*, tamponatura *f*
−	13567 **plugging agent**	colmatant *m*	verstopfende Zusätze *m pl.*	agente *m* per tamponare

English	French	German	Italian
– 13568 plumb bob	fil *m* à plomb	Senklot *n*, Senkblei *n*	piombino *m*, filo *m* a piombo
– 13569 plumb line, plumb rule	niveau *m* de maçon	Setzwaage *f*	archipenzolo *m*, livella *f*
– 13570 plumbago	graphite *m*	Graphit *m*	grafite *f*
– 13571 plumbago, clay-graphite mixture	plombage *m*	Graphitschwärze *f*	piombaggine *f*, nero *m* di grafite
° 13571a plumber's solder	soudure *f* de plombier	Lötmörtel *n*	stagno *m* da idraulico
– 13572 plumbocuprite	plombocuprite *f*	Plumbokuprit *m*	piombocuprite *f*
plum padding-stone, *s. padding-stone*			
° 13573 to plunge in water	saisissement *m* dans l'eau	Abschrecken *n*	immersione *f* rapida nell'acqua
– 13574 plunge of axis	inclinaison *f* axiale	Achsneigung *f*	inclinazione assiale
° 13575 plunger, piston	piston *m*	Förderkolben *m*	pistone *m*
^ 13575a plunger	quenouille *f*	Stopfenstange *f*	asta *f* del tampone
° 13576 plunger displacement	course *f* du piston	Kolbenverdrängung *f*	corsa *f* del pistone
° 13577 plunger lift	levée *f* du piston	Kolbenhub *m*	levata *f* del pistone
^ 13578 plunger pump	pompe *f* à piston plongeur	Tauchkolbenpumpe *f*	pompa *f* a stantuffo tuffante
° 13579 plunger rod	tige *f* de piston	Kolbenstange *f*	asta *f* di pistone
° 13580 plunger-type die-casting machine	machine *f* à fondre à piston	Kolbenspritzguss-maschine *f*	macchina *f* per pressofusione a stantuffo
plutonic rocks, *s. deep-seated rocks*			
° 13581 plutonium	plutonium *m*	Plutonium *n*	plutonio *m*
plymetal, *s. clad metal*			
– 13582 pneumatic chisel	burin *m* à air comprimé	Luftdruckmeissel *m*	scalpello *m* ad aria compressa
– 13583 pneumatic-feed column	colonne *f* à avancement pneumatique	Bohrsäule *f* mit Pressluftvorschub	affusto *m* a colonna pneumatica, trivella *f* pneumatica a colonna
– 13584 pneumatic hammer	marteau *m* pneumatique	Presslufthammer *m*	martello *m* pneumatico
– 13585 pneumatic hoist	palan *m* pneumatique (ou à air comprimé)	Pressluft-flaschenzug *m*	paranco *m* pneumatico

		English	French	German	Italian
—	13586	pneumatic jack	vérin *m* pneumatique (ou à air comprimé)	pneumatischer Hebebock *m*	martinetto *m* pneumatico
—	13587	pneumatic knock-out	décochage *m* pneumatique (ou à air comprimé)	pneumatisches Ausleeren *n*	distaffatura *f* pneumatica
—	13588	pneumatic lift	monte-charge *m* pneumatique	Luftdruckaufzug *m*	montacarichi *m* pneumatico
—	13589	pneumatic packing	remblayage *m* pneumatique (ou à air comprimé)	Blasversatz *m*	ripiena *f* pneumatica
—	13590	pneumatic power drill	perceuse *f* pneumatique	Pressluftbohrmaschine *f*	trapano *m* ad aria compressa
—	13591	pneumatic power hammer	marteau *m* pneumatique	Lufthammer *m*	martello *m* pneumatico
—	13592	pneumatic process	fonçage *m* avec sas à air	Schachtabteufen *n* unter Anwendung von Pressluft	approfondimento *m* del pozzo ad aria compressa
—	13593	pneumatic rammer	damoir *m* à air comprimé	Pressluftstampf-maschine *f*	costipatrice *f* (o piletta) pneumatica
°	13594	pneumatic ramming	serrage *m* pneumatique (ou à air comprimé)	Verdichten *n* mit Druckluft	formatura *f* a proiezione pneumatica (o ad aria compressa)
—	13595	pneumatic rock-drill	machine *f* à forer (foreuse) pneumatique	Druckluftgesteins-bohrmaschine *f*	scalpello *m* pneumatico
—	13596	pneumatic separation	préparation *f* à air comprimé (ou pneumatique)	Windaufbereitung *f*	preparazione *f* pneumatica
—	13597	pneumatic separator	séparateur *m* pneumatique	Pressluft-Abscheider *m*	separatore *m* pneumatico
—	13598	pneumatic stowage	remblayage *m* pneumatique	Blasversatz *m*	ripiena *f* pneumatica
—	13599	pneumatic table	table *f* d'épuration pneumatique	Luftherd *m*	tavola *f* per la separazione pneumatica
—	13600	pneumatic test	essai *m* pneumatique	pneumatische Kontrolle *f*	prova *f* pneumatica
—	13601	pneumatic trough	cuve *f* pneumatique	pneumatische Wanne	vasca *f* pneumatica

		English	French	German	Italian
−	13602	pneumatic tube conveyor	transporteur *m* pneumatique	pneumatische Transportvorrichtung *f*	trasportatore *m* pneumatico
−	13603	pneumatolysis	pneumatolyse *f*	Pneumatolyse *f*	pneumatolisi *f*
−	13604	pocket	poche *f*	Tasche *f*	tasca *f*, sacca *f*
°	13605	pocket (in a casting)	cavité *f*	Lunker *m*	cavità *f*
		pocket print, *s. tail print*			
−	13606	pod	lentille allongée de minerai	Erzlineal *n*	lente *f* allungata di minerale
−	13607	podolite	podolite *f*	Podolit *m*	podolite *f*
−	13608	poikilitic texture	texture *f* poecilitique	poikilitische Struktur *f*	struttura *f* poecilitica
		to point, *s. to sharpen*			
°	13609	point locking	blocage *m* des aiguilles	Weichensicherung *f*	blocco *m* degli scambi
		point man, *s. pipeliner*			
°	13610	point of a crossing, tongue of crossing	pointe *f* du coeur	Herzstückspitze *f*	punta *f* del cuore
−	13611	point of decomposition	point *m* de décomposition	Zersetzungspunkt *m*	punto *m* di decomposizione
−	13612	point of the horse	point *m* de ramification d'un filon	Abzweigungspunkt *m* eines Ganges	punto *m* di ramificazione di un filone
°	13613	point of tongue	pointe *f* d'aiguille	Zungenspitze *f*	punta *f* dell'ago
		pointed, *s. sharp*			
		pointed rabble, *s. puddling bar*			
°	13614	pointed soldering-iron	fer à souder droit	Spitzlötkolben *m*	saldatoio *m* a punta
°	13614a	pointing	taillage *m*	Ausspitzung *f*	smussatura *f*
		pointing, *s. tagging*			
		poke welding, *s. push welding*			
°	13615	poker, rabble	ringard *m*	Schürfstange *f*	attizzatoio *m*, agitatore *m*
°	13616	polarisation capacity	capacité *f* de polarisation	Polarisationskapazität *f*	capacità *f* di polarizzazione
		polarisation filter, *s. quarter wave plate*			
°	13617	polarity reversing	inverseur *m* de polarité	Polumschalter *m*	commutatore *m* della polarità
	13618	polarography	polarographie *f*	Polarographie *f*	polarografia *f*, analisi *f* polarografica

English	French	German	Italian
— 13619 **pole jack**	vérin arrache- étai	Stempelrauberwinde *f*	binda strappapuntelli
— 13620 **polianite**	polianite *f*	Polianit *m*	polianite *f*
— 13621 **policeman**	chapeau *m* en caoutchouc	Gummikappe *f*	cappuccio *m* di gomma
— 13622 **poling**	perchage *m*	Polen *n*	trattamento *m* al legno verde, riduzione *f* con pali di legno verde
° 13623 **to polish**	polir	polieren	levigare, lustrare
° 13624 **to polish, to scour**	blanchir, polir	blank reiben	pulire
— 13625 **polish, slickensides**	miroir de faille	Spiegel, Harnisch *m*	specchio *m* della faglia
° 13626 **polish**	poli *m*, lustre *m*	Politur, Glätte *f*,	lucentezza *f*, brunitura *f*
° 13626a **polish etch**	attaque *m* chimique polisseuse	polierende Ätzung *f*	attacco *m* da pulitura
° 13627 **polishable**	polissable	polierbar	lucidabile
	polished plate, *s. planished plate*		
˄ 13628 **polished rod**	tige *f* étanche	Polierstange *f*	asta *f* liscia (di torre)
° 13629 **polished steel, bright steel**	acier *m* bruni, acier *m* lissé	polierter Stahl *m*, geglätteter Stahl	acciaio *m* brunito
° 13630 **polished surface**	surface *f* polie	polierte Oberfläche *f*	superficie *f* lucidata
° 13630a **polishing**	brunissage *m*	Polieren *n*	brunitura *f*, lucidatura
° 13631 **polishing bob**	touffe *f* polisseuse	Schwabbel *f*	brunitoio *m*
° 13631a **polishing scrachtes**	stries *f pl.* de polissage	Polierkratzer *m*	striature *f pl.* di lucidatura
	polishing slicker, *s. square corner smoother*		
— 13632 **poll pick**	pic *m* ordinaire	einfache Keilhaue *f*	piccone *m* comune
— 13633 **pollenite**	pollénite *f*	Pollenit *m*	pollenite *f*
— 13634 **pollucite**	pollucite *f*	Pollux *m*	pollucite *f*
— 13635 **polonium**	polonium *m*	Polonium *n*	polonio *m*
— 13636 **polyadelphite**	polyadelphite *f*	Polyadelphit *m*	poliadelfite
— 13637 **polyargite**	polyargite *f*	Polyargit *m*	poliargite *f*
— 13638 **polyargyrite**	polyargyrite *f*	Polyargyrit *m*	poliargirite *f*
— 13639 **polyarsenite**	polyarsénite *f*	Polyarsenit *m*	poliarsenite
— 13640 **polybasite**	polybasite *f*	Polybasit *m*	polibasite

English	French	German	Italian
— 13641 **polychroilite**	polychroïlite f	Polychroilith m	policroilite f
— 13642 **polycrase**	polycrase m	Polykras m	policraso m
— 13643 **poly-cylindrical**	à plusieurs cylindres	mehrzylindrig	a più cilindri
— 13644 **polymorphous**	polymorphe ,	polymorph	polimorfo
^ 13645 **polystyrene**	polystyrène m	Polystyrol m	polistirene m
^ 13646 **polystyrene twinning**	macles f pl. polysynthétiques	Wiederholungs- zwillinge m pl.	geminazioni polisinte- tiche
^ 13647 **polyethylene**	polyéthylène m	Polyäthylen n	polietilene m, politene m
^ 13648 **polyvinyl resin**	résine f polyvinylique	Polyvinylharz n	resina f polivinilica
° 13648a **pony rougher**	cage f dégrossisseu- se	Vorsteckgerüst n	gabbia f sgrossatrice
— 13649 **pool**	travail m au coin	Hereintreibearbeit f	lavoro m al cuneo
— 13650 **pool**	gisement m d'hydrocarbures	Hydrokarburvor- kommen n	giacimento m d'idro- carburi
— 13651 **pool opener**	sondage m positif	Nutzbohrung f	sondaggio m positivo
— 13652 **poor boy**	remède, expédient	Arrangement n	ripiego m, arrangia- mento m
— 13653 **poor coal**	charbon m pauvre	minderwertige Kohle f	carbone m povero
— 13654 **poor in graphite**	pauvre en graphite	graphitarm	povero di grafite
— 13655 **poor pack**	mauvais remblai m	schlechter Versatz m	ripiena f cattiva
— 13656 **poor rock**	minerai m pauvre	armes Erz n	minerale m povero
— 13657 **pop**	petit coup m de mine	kleines Schussloch n	piccolo foro di mina
pop gate,s. pencil gate			
^ 13658 **pop joint, jointer**	bout m de tuyau	Rohrsplitter m	spezzone m di tubo
° 13658a **pop-up, vent**	trou m d'air	Entlüftung f	tirata f d'aria
— 13659 **poppet**	chevalement m	Fördergerüst n	castelletto m d'estra- zione
° 13660 **porcelain beaker**	gobelet m en porcelaine	Porzellanbecher m	bicchiere m di porcellana
° 13661 **porcelain calcining furnace**	four m à cuire la porcelaine	Porzellanbrennofen m	forno m per cuocere la porcellana
° 13662 **porcelain-crucible**	creuset m en porcelaine	Porzellantiegel m	crogiuolo m di porcel- lana

	English	French	German	Italian
o	13663 porcelain eva- porating basin	vase *m* d'évapora- tion en porcelaine	Porzellanabdampf- schale *f*	bacinella *f* d'evapora- zione in porcellana
o	13664 porcelain funnel	entonnoir *m* en porcelaine	Porzellantrichter *m*	imbuto *m* di porcella- na
o	13665 porcelain measuring vessel	mesure *f* de porce- laine	Porzellanmass *n*	misuratore *m* di porcellana
o	13666 porcelain ring	anneau *m* de porcelaine	Porzellanring *m*	anello *m* di porcella- na
o	13667 porcelain trough	cuve *f* en porcelaine	Porzellanwanne *f*	vasca *f* di porcellana
o	13668 porcelain tube	tube *m* en porcelaine	Porzellanröhre *f*	tubo *m* di porcellana
o	13669 porcelain ware	appareils *m pl.* en porcelaine	Porzellangeräte *n pl.*	apparecchi *m pl.* di porcellana
o	13670 pore space	volume *m* des pores	Porenraum *m*	spazio *m* dei pori
o	13671 porosity, porous texture	porosité *f*	Porosität *f*, poröse Struktur *f*	porosità *f*, struttura *f* porosa
o	13672 porous	spongieux	schaumig	schiumoso
o	13673 porous casting	jet *m* caverneux	luckiger Guss *m*	getto *m* poroso
o	13673a porous chrome	chromage dur poreux	poröse Hartver- chromung *f*	cromatura *f* dura po- rosa
o	13674 porous iron	fer *m* poreux, fer *m* caverneux	luckiges Eisen *n*	ferro *m* poroso
—	13675 porous iron ore	minerai *m* de fer poreux	poriges Eisenerz *n*	minerale *m* di ferro poroso
o	13676 porous piece	morceau *m* poreux	Schaumstück *n*	pezzo *m* poroso
o	13677 porous pig iron, open grain pig	fonte *f* caverneuse	luckiges Floss *n*	ghisa *f* cavernosa
	porous slag, *s. pomicestone like slag*			
o	13678 porous texture	structure *f* poreuse	poröse Struktur *f*	struttura *f* porosa
—	13679 porpezite	porpézite *f*	Porpezit *m*	porpezite *f*
—	13680 porphyrite	porphyrite *f*	Porphyrit *m*	porfirite *f*
—	13681 porphyritic	porphyrique	porphyrartig	porfirico
—	13682 porphyroblastic texture	texture *f* porphyro- blastique	porphyroblastische Struktur *f*	struttura *f* porfiro- blastica
—	13683 porphyroid	porphyroïde *m*	Porphyroid *m*	porfiroide *m*

	English	French	German	Italian
o	13684 **port**	carneau *m*	Gasabzugsöffnung *f*	condotto *m*
o	13685 **port**	orifice *m*, ouverture *f*	Öffnung *f*	luce *f* d'entrata e d'uscita, apertura
	portable, *s. dissectable*			
o	13686 **portable air-furnace**	fourneau *m* portatif	tragbarer Ofen *m*	fornace *f* portatile
—	13687 **portable cleansing mill**	moulin *m* de nettoy-age transportable	tragbare Putzmühle *f*	mola *f* trasportabile
o	13688 **portable crucible, on wheels**	creuset *m* sur roues	Wagentiegel *m*	crogiuolo *m* trasporta-bile
o	13689 **portable electric grinder**	affûteuse *f* portative électrique	elektrische Handschleifmaschine *f*	affilatrice *f* portabile elettrica
—	13690 **portable grinder**	meuleuse *f* portative	Handschleifmaschine *f*	molatrice *f* portabile
o	13691 **portable (loco type) boiler**	chaudière *f* locomobile	beweglicher Kessel, Lokomobilkessel *m*	caldaia *f* locomobile
—	13692 **portable drilling rig**	installation *f* portative de forage	fahrbarer Bohrkran *m*	impianto *m* di perfora-zione mobile
o	13693 **portable mould dryer**	four sécheur *m* transportable	fahrbarer Trocken-ofen *m*	stufa *f* portatile
o	13694 **portable muller (foundry)**	broyeur *m* à moules tranportable	fahrbahre Mühle *f*	molazza *f* portatile
o	13695 **portable pig breaker**	casse-gueuses *m* sur roues	fahrbarer Masselbrecher *m*	spezzamasselli *m* portatile
—	13696 **portable railway**	voie *f* portative	Feldbahn *f*, Waldbahn *f*	binarietto *m* portatile
	portable welding gun, *s. portable spot welding head*			
—	13697 **portal crane**	grue *f* à portique	Torkran *m*, (Portalkran *m*)	gru *f* a portico
o	13698 **porter**	barre *f* avec bout à forger	Stab *m* mit zu schmiedendem Ende	barra *f* con estremo da forgiare
o	13699 **porter (forging tool)**	cingleresse *f*	Schmiedezange *f*	tenaglie *f pl.* per fucinare
o	13699a **porter bar**	porte-lingot *m*	Blockhalter *m*	portalingotto *m*
—	13700 **portion of the texture**	constituant *m* de la texture	Gefügebestandteil *m*	costituente *m* della struttura
—	13701 **positioning dowel**	piquet-repère *m*	Führungspfahl *m*	picchetto *m* (di riferi-mento)

English	French	German	Italian
– 13702 **positive**	positif _m_, épreuve _f_ positive	Positiv _n_	positiva _f_
'– 13703 **positive blower**	ventilateur _m_ soufflant	blasender Ventilator _m_	ventilatore _m_ soffiante
– 13704 **positive carbon**	charbon _m_ positif	positive Kohle _f_	carbone _m_ positivo
° 13705 **post**	arbre _m_ de trousseau (ou de troussage)	Spindel _f_	albero _m_ per sagomare, albero _m_ per sagomatura
° 13706 **post (charge of mineral)**	charge _f_	Charge _f_	carica _f_
– 13707 **post**	montant _m_, poteau _m_, pieu _m_	Posten _m_, Stempel _m_, Pfahl _m_	montante _m_, palo _m_, pilastro _m_, puntello _m_
– 13708 **post-and-bar**	cadre _m_ à un seul montant	halber Türstock _m_	quadro _m_ ad un sol montante

post-and-cap, _s. post-and-bar_

English	French	German	Italian
– 13709 **post-and-stall**	exploitation _f_ par traçage et dépilage	Pfeilerbau _m_	estrazione _f_ a colonne e a gallerie
– 13710 **post drill**	perforatrice _f_ à colonne	Säulenbohrmaschine _f_	perforatrice _f_ a colonna
° 13710a **post-heating**	réchauffage _m_ de la soudure	Nachwärmung der Schweissstelle	post-riscaldamento _m_ dell zona saldata
– 13711 **post puller**	arrache-étais _m_	Raubvorrichtung _f_	estrattore _m_ di puntelli
– 13712 **post puncher**	haveuse _f_ percutante à colonne	stossend wirkende Säulenschrämmaschine _f_	intagliatrice _f_ a percussione a colonna
– 13713 **post stone**	grès _m_ à grain fin	feinkörniger Sandstein _m_	gres _m_ a grana fine
° 13714 **post-tensioning**	post-tension _f_	nachträglicher Verbund _m_	post-tensione _f_
° 13715 **pot, metal crucible**	creuset _m_ métallique	Metallschmelztiegel _m_	crogiuolo _m_ metallico
° 13716 **pot annealed**	recuit en boîtes (ou en caisse)	kastengeglüht	ricotto in cassetta (o cassa)
° 13717 **pot annealing**	recuit _m_ en boîtes	Kastenglühung _f_	ricottura _f_ in cassetta (o cassa)
° 13718 **pot annealing furnace**	four _m_ à pots pour recuire	Kastenglühofen _m_	forno _m_ di ricottura a cassette

	English	French	German	Italian
○	13719 **pot furnace**	four *m* à creuset	Metalltiegelschmelz-ofen *m*	forno *m* a crogiuolo metallico
○	13720 **pot hole**	marmite *f*	Riesenkessel *m*	marmitta *f*
	pot-steel, *s. crucible cast steel*			
○	13721 **potash bulb**	appareil *m* à potasse	Kaliapparat *m*	apparecchio *m* per potassa
○	13722 **potash hardening**	cémentation *f* au prussiate de potasse	Einbrennhärtung *f*	cementazione *f* al cianuro
—	13723 **potassium chlorate**	chlorate *m* de potasse	Kaliumchlorat *n*	clorato *m* di potassa
—	13724 **potassium cyanide**	cyanure *m* de potassium	Cyankalium *n*	cianuro *m* di potassio
—	13725 **potassium ferrocyanide**	ferrocyanure *m* de potassium	gelbes Blutlaugensalz *n*	ferrocianuro *m* di potassa
—	13726 **potassium ferricyanide**	ferrocyanide *m* de potasse	rotes Blutlaugensalz *n*	ferricianuro *m* potassico
—	13727 **potassium iodide and starch paper**	papier *m* d'amidon à iodure de potassium	Jodkali umstärke-papier *n*	carta *f* all'amido e allo ioduro di potassio
—	13728 **potassium iodide paper**	papier *m* à l'iodure de potassium	Jodkaliumpapier *n*	carta *f* all'ioduro di potassio
—	13729 **potassium iodide**	iodure *m* de potassium	Jodkalium *n*	ioduro *m* di potassio
—	13730 **potassium nitrate**	nitre *m*, salpêtre *m*	Kalisalpeter *m*	salnitro *m*, nitrato *m* di potassa
—	13731 **potelot**	molybdénite *f*	Molybdänglanz *m*	molibdenite *f*
—	13732 **potential of decomposition**	potentiel *m* de décomposition	Zersetzungs-potential *n*	potenziale *m* di decomposizione
—	13733 **potential production**	production *f* potentielle	Förderpotential *n*	produzione *f* potenziale
	potter's clay, *s. ball clay*			
○	13734 **potter's lathe**	tour *m* ou roue *f* à potier	Töpferscheibe *f*	ruota *f* del pentolaio
—	13735 **pounding machine**	bocard *m*	Pochhammer *m*	mulino *m* a pestelli
—	13736 **pounding trough**	caisse du bocard	Pochtrog *m*	cassa *f* del mulino a pestelli
○	13737 **pour**	couler	giessen	colare

		English	French	German	Italian
°	13738	**to pour (out)**	déverser	ausgiessen	versare
°	13739	**to pour from below**	couler en source	von unten her giessen	colare in sorgente
°	13740	**to pour on end**	couler debout	stehend giessen	colare in piedi
°	13741	**to pour white metal in bearings**	couler du métal blanc dans les coussinets	Lager mit Weissmetall ausgiessen	colare metallo bianco nei cuscinetti
°	13742	**pour, sprue**	descente *f* de coulée	Eingusskanal *m*, Einlauf *m*	imboccatura (o foro) di colata
°	13743	**pour point**	température *f* de coulée	Fliesspunkt *m*	punto *m* di scorrimento
^	13744	**pour point depressant**	inhibiteur *m* de coagulation	Antigerinnsel *m*, Stockpunkterniédriger *m*	inibitore *m* di coagulazione
°	13745	**pour reversion, pour instability**	instabilité *f* à l'écoulement	Flussinstabilität *f*	instabilità *f* allo scorrimento
°	13746	**poured, cast**	coulé	gegossen	colato
		pouring, *s. casting*			
°	13747	**pouring basin, casting basin**	bassin *m* de coulée	Giesstümpel *m*, Gusstümpel *m*	bacinella *f* di colata
°	13748	**pouring basin, casting basin**	entonnoir *m* de coulée	Eingusstrichter *m*	imbuto *m* di colata
°	13749	**pouring basin**	cône *m* de coulée	Trichterkopf *m*	cono *m* di colata
°	13750	**pouring basin with baffles**	bassin *m* de coulée à chicanes	Giesstümpel *m* (od. Gusstümpel) mit Umlenkungen	bacino *m* di colata a trappole fermascorie
°	13751	**pouring bed**	lit *m* de coulée	Giessbett *n*	letto *m* di colata
°	13752	**pouring bush**	godet *m* de coulée	aufgebauter Eingusstrichter *m*	rialzo *m* di colata
°	13753	**pouring channel**	chenal de coulée	Gussrinne *f*	canale di colata
°	13754	**pouring crane**	grue *f* de coulée	Giesskran *m*, Gusskran *m*	gru *f* di colata
°	13755	**pouring cup**	poche *f* de coulée	Giesslöffel *m*	siviera *f* di colata
°	13756	**pouring gate**	trou *m* de coulée, entonnoir de coulée, jet de coulée	Eingusstrichter *m*, Giesstrichter *m*	foro di colata, getto di colata, imbuto di colata

	English	French	German	Italian
° 13757	**pouring hall**	halle de coulée	Giesshalle f, Giesshaus n	campo m di colata
° 13758	**pouring head, git channel, inlet sprue**	jet m, gueule f du moule	Eingusskanal m	colata f, canale m di colata
° 13759	**pouring ladle**	poche f de coulée	Giesspfanne f	siviera f di colata, secchione m
° 13760	**pouring level**	niveau m de coulée	Abstichsohle f	piano m di colata
° 13761	**pouring lip**	bec m de coulée	Giessschnauze f	becco m di colata
	pouring nozzle, s. *teeming nozzle*			
° 13762	**pouring outfit**	accessoires m pl. d'une fonderie	Giesseinrichtung f	accessori m pl. di fonderia
° 13762a	**pouring pit**	fosse f de coulée	Giessgrube f	fossa f di colata
° 13763	**pouring platform**	plate-forme f de coulée	Giessbühne f	piattaforma f di colata
	pouring side, s. *tapping side*			
	pouring spout, s. *runner*			
° 13764	**pouring through pencil gate**	attaque f en pluie	fallender Guss mit mehrfachem Metallstrahl	**attacco** m **a pioggia, attacco** m **di colata a pioggia**
° 13765	**pouring truck**	chariot m de coulée	Giesspfannenwagen	carro m di colata
	pouring vessel, s. *pouring ladle*			
	powder burning, s. *cutting by powder*			
° 13766	**powder carburizing**	cémenter à poudre	pulveraufkohlen	cementare in polvere
— 13766a	**powder compacting**	moulage m par pression	Pulverpressen n	compressione f della polvere
— 13767	**powder dry**	sec comme la poudre	pulvertrocken	secco come la polvere
— 13768	**powder ore**	minerai m disséminé	eingesprengtes Erz n	minerale m disseminato
— 13769	**powdered birch charcoal**	charbon m de bouleau pulvérisé	pulverisierte Birkenkohle f	carbone m di betulla in polvere
— 13770	**powdered coal, dust coal, culm**	charbon m en poudre (ou pulvérisé)	Staubkohle f, Kohlenpulver m, Kohlenstaub m	polvere f di carbone
	powdered coke, s. *coke dust*			
	powdered flux, s. *welding powder*			
	powdered fuel, s. *pulverised fuel*			
— 13771	**powdered graphite**	poussier m de graphite	Graphitstaub m	polvere f di grafite

	English	French	German	Italian
— 13772	powdered peat	poudre f de tourbe	Torfmehl n	polvere f di torba
	powdery iron ore, s. *fine iron ore*			
— 13773	powellite	powellite f	Powellit m	powellite f
— 13774	power consumption	consommation f de force	Kraftverbrauch m	consumo m di forza o d'energia
— 13775	power crane	grue f automotrice	selbstfahrender Kran m	gru f automotrice
— 13776	power distribution	distribution f de force	Kraftverteilung f	distribuzione f di forza
— 13777	power drill	perforateur m mécanique	mechanische Bohrmaschine f	perforatore m meccanico
— 13778	power driven hand tools	outillage m électrique et pneumatique	Handwerkzeuge n $pl.$ mit Kraftantrieb	utensili m $pl.$ portatili elettrici e pneumatici
— 13779	power efficiency	rendement m	Wirkungsgrad m	resa f, rendimento m
— 13780	power electric drill	perceuse f électrique	elektrische Handbohrmaschine f	trapanatrice f portatile elettrica
— 13781	power feed	alimentateur m mécanique	mechanische Vorschubvorrichtung f	alimentatore m meccanico
° 13782	power forging	fer m forgé mécaniquement	mechanisches Schmiedestück n	fucinato m ottenuto meccanicamente
^ 13783	power gauge	manomètre m de pression	Druckmanometer n	manometro m per pressione
^ 13784	power end	arrière m d'une pompe à boue	Schlammpumpenrückseite f	parte f posteriore di una pompa
^ 13785	power kerosene	huile f combustible	Heizöl n	petrolio m carburante
^ 13786	power loader (12 BU Joy)	chargeuse f mécanique	Raupenkettenlader m	caricatore meccanico cingolato
^ 13787	power loader (Goodman Duckbill)	chargeuse f mécanique	mechanischer Lader m	caricatore m meccanico
° 13788	powder metallurgy	métallurgie f des poudres	Pulvermetallurgie f	metallurgia f delle polveri
	power of the light, s. *candle power*			
° 13789	power press (inclinable-), punch press	presse mécanique, inclinable	neigbare Stanzpresse f	pressa f meccanica, inclinabile, pressa a punzone

English	French	German	Italian
^ 13790 power pump	motopompe f à combustion interne	Brennkraftmotor-pumpe f	pompa f con motore a combustione interna
— 13791 power rig	installation f de forage actionnée par moteurs à combustion interne	Anlage f mit Explosionsmotoren-antrieb	impianto m azionato da motori a combustione interna
— 13792 power shovel	pelle f mécanique	Löffelbagger m	escavatore m meccanico
— 13793 power shoveling	pelletage m mécanique	mechanische Schaufelung f	scavo m meccanico
— 13794 power slip	coin m actionné directement à pression	mit Druck direkt betätigter Keil m	cuneo m azionato direttamente a pressione
— 13795 power station	centrale f de force motrice	Kraftwerk n, Kraftstation f	centrale f per forza motrice, centrale f elettrica
^ 13796 power stroke	course f d'expansion	Ausdehnungshub m	corsa f d'espansione
^ 13797 power tong	clef f suspendue entrainée mécanique-ment	mechanisch betätig-ter loser Schlüssel m	chiave sospesa azio-nata meccanicamente
13798 power transmission	transport m d'énergie	Kraftübertragung f	trasmissione f di forza
13799 power unit	groupe moteur m	Motorgruppe f	gruppo m motori
13800 powered directly (by motor)	entraînée directe-ment (par moteur)	direkt(von einem Motor) betätigt	azionata direttamente (da motore)
— 13801 praseodimium	praséodyme m	Praseodym n	praseodimio m
— 13802 praseolite	praséolite f	Praseolith m	praseolite f
— 13803 prasinite	prasinite f	Prasinit m	prasinite f
— 13804 Precambrian system precious metal, s. nobel metal	précambrien m	Präkambrium n	precambriano m
— 13805 precipitant	précipitant m	Fällmittel n	reagente m precipi-tante
— 13806 to precipitate	précipiter	fällen, ausfällen	precipitare
— 13807 to precipitate by sulphuretted hydrogen	précipiter par l'hydrogène sulfuré	mit Schwefelwasser-stoff fällen	precipitare coll'idro-geno solforato

	English	French	German	Italian
° 13808	to precipitate in boiling heat	précipiter en ébullition	in der Siedehitze ausfällen	precipitare all'ebolli- zione
° 13809	precipitate, deposit	précipité m, dépôt m	Niederschlag m	precipitato m, deposito
⌃ 13810	precipitated copper	cuivre m de précipitation	Niederschlagkupfer n	rame m di concentra- zione
— 13811	precipitating column	tour f de précipitation	Niederschlagturm m	torre f di precipita- zione
— 13812	precipitation, structural sepa- ration	précipitation f structurale, sépara- tion structurale	Gefügeausscheidung f	precipitazione f strutturale
° 13813	precipitation anneal	recuit m de précipitation	Aushärten n	ricottura f di precipitazione
° 13814	precipitation electrode	électrode f de précipitation	Niederschlag- elektrode f	elettrodo m di preci- pitazione
° 13815	precipitation hardening	durcissement m structural, trempe f par précipitation	Aushärtung f	indurimento m strut- turale, tempera f per precipitazione
⌃ 13816	precipitation naphta	naphte m de précipitation	Niederschlag- naphtha n	nafta f di precipita- zione
° 13817	precipitation of impurites	précipitation f des impuretés	Ausfällung f der Verunreinigung	precipitazione f del- le impurità
⊖ 13817a	precipitation value	produit m de solubi- lité	Löslichkeits- produkt n	prodotto m di solubi- lità
° 13818	precision balance	balance f de précision	Feinwaage f, Präzisionswaage f	bilancia f di precisio- ne
° 13819	precision blower	soufflerie f de précision	Präzisionsgebläse n	ventilatore m di precisione
° 13820	precision casting	fusion f de précision	Feinschmelzen n	fusione f di preci- sione
° 13821	precision fitting	précision f de l'ajustage	Passgenauigkeit f	precisione f nell'ag- giustaggio
° 13822	precision forging	forgeage m de précision	Feinschmiedung f, Feinschmieden n	fucinatura f di precisione
⌃ 13823	precision ground	finement rectifié	feingeschliffen	rettificato di preci- sione
° 13824	precision moulding, lost wax moulding	moulage m à la cire perdue	Modellausschmelzver- fahren n	formatura f a cera persa, formatura di precisione

	English	French	German	Italian
°	13825 **precision tube**	tube *m* de précision	Präzisionsrohr *n*	tubo *m* di precisione
^	13826 **precoat**	adjuvant *m* pour filtre	Filterzusatz *m*	coadiuvante *m* per filtro
°	13827 **pre-coating of strip**	prérevêtement *m* du feuillard	Vorummantelung *f* des Bandes	prerivestimento *m* del nastro
—	13828 **pre-crusher**	broyeur *m* primaire	Vorbrecher *m*	mulino *m* a pestelli primario, frantoio *m* primario
—	13829 **pre-crushing**	broyage *m* primaire	Vorbrechen *n*	macinazione *f* preliminare
—	13830 **predazzite**	prédazzite *f*	Predazzit *m*	predazzite *f*
°	13831 **pre-drawing**	préétirage *m*	Vorzug *m*	prestampaggio *m*
°	13832 **prefabricated welded steel sections with riveted connections in the field**	profils *m pl.* soudés préfabriqués assemblés sur place par rivetage	vorgeferitigte geschweisste Stahlprofile *n pl.* mit an der Baustelle genieteten Verbindungen	profilati *m pl.* saldati, prefabbricati montati sul posto mediante ribaditura
—	13833 **preferred orientation**	orientation *f* préférentielle	Hauptorientierung *f*	orientamento *m* privilegiato
°	13834 **pre-formed part**	ébauche *f*	Rohling *m*	sbozzo *m*, sbozzato
^	13835 **preformed wire rope**	câble *m* préformé	vorgeformtes Drahtseil *n*	cavo *m* preformato
°	13835a **preforming**	préformage *m*	Vorformung *f*	preformazione *f*
^	13836 **prefractionnator**	préfractionneur *m*	Vorfraktionator *m*	prefrazionatore *m*
°	13837 **preheat**	préchauffer	vorwärmen	preriscaldare
°	13838 **preheated**	pré-chauffé	vorgewärmt	preriscaldato
°	13839 **preheated chill, warmed chill**	coquille *f* chauffée	angewärmte Schale *f*	conchiglia *f* riscaldata
°	13840 **preheater**	rehausse *f* (de creuset)	Tiegelaufsatz *m*	rialzo *m* (del crogiuolo)
°	13841 **preheating**	préchauffage *m*	Vorwärmung *f*	preriscaldamento *m*
°	13842 **prehnite**	prehnite *f*	Prehnit *m*	prehnite *f*
—	13843 **preliminary breaking**	avant-broyage *m*	Vorzerkleinerung *f*	frantumazione *f* (o macinazione) preliminare

	English	French	German	Italian
o 13844	preliminary drawing	tréfilage *m* grossier ou initial	Grobzug *m*	stiramento *m* iniziale o preliminare
o 13845	preliminary experiment	essai *m* préliminaire	Vorversuch *m*	prova *f* od analisi *f* preliminare
o 13846	preliminary heating	chauffage *m* préalable	Vorwärmung *f*	riscaldamento *m* preliminare
o 13847	preliminary heating zone	zone *f* de chauffage préalable	Vorwärmezone *f*	zona *f* di riscaldamento, zona *f* di preparazione

preliminary melting of scrap, *s. smelting of scrap iron*

preliminary pressure, *s. low pressure*

	English	French	German	Italian
— 13848	preliminary survey	levé *m* préliminaire	Vorvermessung *f*	rilevamento *m* preliminare
o 13849	preliminary test	essai *m* préliminaire	Vorprobe *f*	prova *f* preliminare
— 13850	preliminary washing drum	trommel *m* de préparation	Rauhwaschtrommel *f*	tamburo *m* per primo lavaggio
— 13851	premature setting	prise *f* prématurée	vorzeitiges Abbinden *n*	presa *f* prematura
^ 13852	premium gasoline	supercarburant *m*	Superbrennstoff *m*	supercarburante *m*
o 13852a	premodelling	prémodellage *m*	Vormodellierung *f*	premodellatura *f*
o 13853	preparation of test piece	préparation *f* des éprouvettes	Herrichten *n* der Probe	preparazione *f* della provetta
o 13854	preparation of the mixture	préparation *f* de la pâte	Herstellung *f* des Teiges	confezione *f* dell'impasto
o 13855	preparation of the stones	confection *f* des briques	Herstellung *f* der Steine	fabbricazione *f* dei mattoni
o 13856	preparation room	salle *f* de préparation des échantillons	Vorbereitungsraum *m*	sala *f* per la preparazione dei campioni
— 13857	to prepare the loam cake	ébaucher la galette d'argile	Lehmkuchen *m* herrichten	sbozzare la torta di argilla
o 13858	prepared lughole	oreille *f* régulée	Führungslappen *m* mit ausgegossenem Loch	orecchio *m* imboccolato, orecchio *m* regolato
o 13858a	prepared scrap	bonne mitraille *f*	Kernschrott *m*	rottami *m* pl. assortiti
o 13859	preparing the slides	préparation *f* des surfaces polies	Herstellung *f* der Schliffe	preparazione *f* delle superfici levigate
— 13860	preroast	grillage *m* préliminaire	Vorröstung *f*	arrostimento *m* preliminare

	English	French	German	Italian
o	13861 **prescribed length**	longueur f prescrite	vorgeschriebene Länge f	lunghezza f prescritta
o	13862 **preservative compound**	vernis m antirouille	Rostschutzfarbe f	vernice f antiruggine
o	13863 **preservatives**	produits m $pl.$ protecteurs	schützende Zusätze n $pl.$	sostanze f $pl.$ protettive
o	13863a **presintering**	préfrittage m	Vorsintern n	presinterizzazione f
o	13864 **pre-smelting unit**	installation f de préfusion	Vorgiessanlage f	impianto m di prefusione
o	13865 **to press**	comprimer, presser	pressen	pressare
o	13866 **to press the pattern home**	asseoir le modèle	einklopfen	imprimere il modello
o	13867 **press**	presse f	Presse f	pressa f
o	13868 **press-cross beam**	sommier m de presse	Pressholm m	sommità f del compressore
^	13869 **press(ed) drip**	huile f de presse	Pressöl n	olio m di pressatura
o	13870 **press-forge**	forger à la presse	presschmieden	fucinare alla pressa
o	13871 **press gilding**	dorage m à la presse, dorure f à la presse	Pressvergoldung f	doratura f alla trancia
o	13872 **press molding machine**	machine à mouler à compression	Pressformmaschine f	formatrice f a pressione
o	13873 **press of a joiner's bench**	étau m d'établi de menuisier	Schraubstock m	morsa f da banco di falegname
o	13874 **press plate**	plateau m de compresseur, plateau m tournant	Pressplatte f	placca f girevole
o	13875 **press plunger**	piston m de compression	Presskolben m	stantuffo m premente o di compressione
—	13876 **pressed coal**	charbon m comprimé	gepresste Kohle f	carbone m compresso, carbone m in mattonelle
—	13877 **pressed cork**	aggloméré de liège	Presskork m	agglomerato m di sughero
o	13878 **pressed metal assembly**	travail m d'emboutissage	Zieharbeit f	lavorazione f d'imbutitura

	English	French	German	Italian
–	13879 **pressed mica**	mica pressé	Pressglimmer *m*	mica *f* pressata
–	13880 **pressed peat**	tourbe *f* comprimée	Presstorf *m*	torba *f* compressa
°	13881 **pressed sleeper**	traverse *f* emboutie	gepresste Schwelle *f*	traversa *f* pressata
°	13882 **pressed steel**	acier *m* estampé	Gesenkstahl *m*	acciaio *m* stampato
°	13883 **pressed steel building component**	élément *m* de construction en acier estampé	Gesenkstahlbauteil *m*	elemento *m* di costruzione in acciaio stampato
°	13884 **pressed steel plate**	tôle *f* en acier embouti	aus Stahlblech gepresste Platte *f*	lamiera *f* imbutita
°	13885 **pressed steel sheet**	tôle *f* en acier embouti	gepresstes Stahlblech *n*	lamiera *f* in acciaio imbutita
°	13886 **pressed to shape**	façonné à la presse	durch Pressen *n* hergestellt	sagomato alla pressa
°	13887 **presser plate with throw over motion**	plaque *f* de pression à bascule	ausschwenkbare Gegendruckplatte *f*	traversa *f* superiore ribaltabile
^	13888 **pressing cut**	distillat *m* avec paraffine séparée en cristaux	destilliert mit Paraffin in Kristallform	distillato *m* con paraffina separata in cristalli
°	13889 **pressing die**	matrice *f* pour presses	Pressmatrize *f*	matrice *f* per presse
°	13890 **pressing of the bricks**	compression *f* des briques	Pressen *n* der Ziegel	compressione *f* dei mattoni
	pressing slag, *s. slip crack*			
°	13891 **pressing skin**	peau *m* du comprimé	Presshaut *f*	pelle *f* del prodotto sinterizzato
°	13891a **pressings**	pièces *f pl.* embouties	Presserzeugnis *n*	pezzi *m pl.* prodotti con imbutitura
	13892 **pressure**	pression *f*	Pressen *n*	pressione *f*
–	13893 **pressure above the atmospheric**	pression *f* effective	Überdruck *m*	pressione *f* effettiva
	pressure blasting, *s. air blasting*			
–	13894 **pressure blower**	ventilateur *m* soufflant	blasender Ventilator *m*	ventilatore *m* soffiante
°	13895 **pressure boiler**	chaudière *f* à pression	Druckkessel *m*	caldaia *f* a pressione
–	13896 **pressure bomb**	mesureur *m* et enregistreur *m* de la pression d'une couche	Mess-und Schreibgerät *n* für den Schichtdruck	misuratore *m* e registratore della pressione di strato

		English	French	German	Italian
o	13897	**pressure build up**	remontée *f* de pression	Druckaufbau *m*	aumento *m* di pressione
o	13898	**pressure casting, pressure die casting**	coulée *f* sous pression	Druckguss *m*	colata *f* sotto pressione, pressofusione *f*
o	13899	**pressure casting mold**	moule *m* de moulage sous pression	Pressgussform *f*	forma *f* di pressofusione
o	13900	**pressure decline**	déclin de pression	Druckabfall *m*	caduta *f* di pressione
o	13901	**pressure die casting**	moulage *m* (ou pièce *f* moulée) sous pression	Spritzgiessen *n*, Spritzguss *m*	pressofusione *f*, pressofuso *m*
^	13902	**pressure distillate**	distillat *m* sous pression	Druckdestillat *n*	distillato *m* di Cracking
—	13903	**pressure drilling**	forage *m* sous pression	Druckbohren *n*	trivellazione *f* sotto pressione
—	13904	**pressure fan, pressure blower**	ventilateur *m* soufflant	blasender Ventilator *m*	ventilatore *m* soffiante
o	13905	**pressure feeder**	masselotte *f* à pression de gaz	Gasdruckspeiser *m*	materozza *f* a pressione di gas
o	13905a	**pressure filter**	filtre *m* à pression	Druckfilter *m*	filtro *m* a pressione
o	13906	**pressure fluid**	liquide *m* sous pression	Druckflüssigkeit *f*	liquido *m* premente
—	13907	**pressure flexion**	structure *f* fluidale	Flussgefüge *n*	struttura *f* fluidale

pressure gauge, *s* *manometer*

		English	French	German	Italian
^	13908	**pressure head**	hauteur *f* de refoulement	Druckhöhe *f*	altezza *f* della pressione, colonna premente
o	13909	**pressure loss**	perte *f* de pression	Druckverlust *m*, Lagerungsdruck *m*	perdita *f* di pressione
o	13910	**pressure of the rolls**	pression *f* de laminage	Walzendruck *m*	pressione *f* di laminazione
o	13911	**pressure of top roll**	étirage *m* dû au cylindre supérieur	Oberdruck *m* der oberen Walze	pressione *f* verticale del cilindro
o	13912	**pressure on the bosh**	pression *f* des étalages	Rastdruck *m*	pressione *f* sulla ´ sacca
o	13913	**pressure pipe**	conduite *f* forcée	Presswasserleitung *f*	condotta *f* forzata

	English	French	German	Italian
^	13914 **pressure pump**	pompe f à compression	Presspumpe f	pompa f a compressione
^	13915 **pressure pump**	pompe f de compression	Druckpumpe f	pompa f premente
o	13916 **pressure port or passage**	conduit m d'admission de l'air comprimé	Druckkanal m	canale m di compressione
^	13917 **pressure reservoir**	pression f du gisement	Lagerdruck m	pressione f del giacimento
^	13918 **pressure side**	côté m du refoulement	Druckseite f	lato m premente
^	13919 **pressure spring adjusting screw**	vis m de réglage de la pression	Druckeinstellschraube f	vite f di regolazione della pressione
^	13920 **pressure still installation**	installation f de distillation sous pression	Druckdestillationsanlage f	impianto m di distillazione a pressione
	pressure test, s. hydraulic test			
—	13921 **pressure texture**	structure f cataclastique	Kataklasgefüge n	struttura f cataclastica
^	13922 **pressure transmittor**	multiplicateur m de pression	Druckübersetzer m	moltiplicatore m di pressione
ˇ	13923 **pressure valve**	soupape f de refoulement	Druckventil n	valvola f premente
o	13924 **pressure sequence welding**	soudure f progressive par compression	progressive Druckschweissung f	saldatura f progressiva a pressione
o	13924a **pressure tight**	non-poreux	nicht porös	non poroso
o	13925 **pressure vacuum**	épreuve f de pression à vide	Vakuumdruckprobe f	prova f di pressione a vuoto
—	13926 **pressure well**	puits m d'injection	Einpressonde f	pozzo m d'iniezione
o	13927 **pre-tensioning**	pré-tension f	sofortiger Verbund m	precaricamento m
—	13928 **prian**	argile f blanche tendre	weicher weisser Ton m	argilla f primaria bianca
o	13929 **price of the unit of iron and manganese**	prix m unitaire du fer et du manganese	Einheitspreis für Eisen und Mangan	prezzo m unitario del ferro e del manganese
—	13930 **priceite**	pricéite f	Priceit m	priceite f
	to prick the molten metal, s. to stir vertically			

English	French	German	Italian
° 13931 **pricker**	poinçon *m* pour trous d'air	Luftspiess *m*	spillo *m* (o ago *m)* per l'aria
^ 13932 **pricker, stirring rod**	baguette *f* de pompage	Pumpenstock *m*	barra *f* per pompare
— 13933 **prill**	pépite *f*	Erzklumpen *m*	pepita *f*
^ 13934 **primage**	eau *f* d'amorçage	Anlasserwasser *n*	acqua *f* di adescamento
° 13935 **primary air**	air *m* primaire	Unterwind *m*	aria *f* primaria
— 13936 **primary air**	air *m* primaire	Zerstäuberluft *f*	aria *f* primaria (per la polverizzazione)
^ 13937 **primary cementation**	cimentation *f* primaire	Primärzementation *f*	cementazione *f* primaria
° 13938 **primary constituent**	métal *m* de base	Grundmetall *n*	metallo *m* base, costituente *m* primario
° 13938a **primary creep**	fluage *m* primaire	primäres Kriechen *n*	scorrimento *m* primario
—13939 **primary dip**	inclinaison *f* primaire	primäre Schichtenneigung *f*	inclinazione *f* primaria
—13940 **primary exploitation**	exploitation *f* primaire	Erstgewinnung *f*	sfruttamento *m* primario
—13941 **primary graphite**	graphite *m* primaire	Primärgraphit *m*	grafite *f* primaria
—13942 **primary jaw crusher**	concasseur *m* primaire	Primärbackenbrecher *m*	frantoio *m* a mascelle primario
° 13942a **primary pipe**	retassure *f* ouverte	offener Lunker *m*	risucchio *m* aperto
—13943 **primary recovery**	récupération *f* primaire	primäre Förderung *f*	recupero *m* primario
—13944 **primary station**	station *f* primaire	Hauptwerk *n*	stazione *f* primaria
—13945 **to prime a mine**	étoupiller une mine	eine Mine loslassen	innescare una mina
^13946 **to prime a pump**	amorcer une pompe	eine Pumpe *f* anlassen	adescare una pompa
^13947 **prime cut naphta**	naphte *m* primaire	Primärnaphtha *n*	nafta *f* primaria
prime mover, *s. driving engine*			
^13948 **prime white oil**	pétrole *m* primaire	Primärpetroleum *n*	petrolio *m* primario
—13949 **primer, percussion cap, cap**	cartouche-amorce *f*	Schlagpatrone *f*	fulminante *m*, innesco
°13950 **primes, first quality sheets**	tôle de première qualité	erstklassiges Blech *n*	lamiera *f* di prima qualità

	English	French	German	Italian
^ 13951	priming	injection f	Kraftstoffzufuhr f	«cicchetto» (per facilitare l'avviamento)
— 13952	priming	préparation f de la cartouche-amorce	Fertigmachen n der Schlagpatrone	preparazione dell'innesco
^ 13953	priming	amorçage m	Anlassen n	adescamento m (della pompa)
o 13954	priming coat with pigment	primer m pigmenté	Haftgrundmittel n mit Pigmentierung	fondo m pigmentato
— 13955	priming wire	fil m d'amorce	Zünddraht m	innesco m
	principal spectrum, $s.$ zero line			
13956	to print	tirer une épreuve	kopieren	copiare, stampare, tirare una copia
♂ 13957	prints	portées f $pl.$	Kernmarken f $pl.$	portate f $pl.$
— 13958	priorite	priorite f	Priorit m	priorite f
— 13959	prism of the second order	prisme m de seconde espèce, deutéro-prisme	Prisma n zweiter Ordnung	prisma f di secondo ordine
— 13960	prism of the third order, tritoprism	prisme m de troisième espèce	Tritoprisma n	prisma f di terzo ordine
— 13961	prism with oblique cross section	prisme m à section oblique	schief abgeschnittenes Prisma n	prisma m a sezione obliqua
— 13962	prismatic	prismatique	prismatisch	prismatico
— 13963	prismatic cleavage	clivage m prismatique	prismatische Spaltbarkeit f	sfaldatura f prismatica
— 13964	prismatic jointing	séparation f prismatique	säulenförmige Absonderung f	separazione f prismatica
	prismatic structure, $s.$ columnal structure			
— 13965	prismatic system	système m orthorhombique	rhombisches System n	sistema ortorombico
— 13966	prismatine	prismatine f	Prismatin m	prismatina f
— 13967	prismoid	prismatoïde m	Prismatoid n	prismoide m
— 13968	to probe	explorer, sonder	prüfen, sondieren	esplorare, sondare
— 13969	probe	sonde f, tarière f	Erdbohrer m	sonda f, trivella f
— 13970	probertite	probertite f	Probertit m	probertite f
— 13971	probing	prise f d'échantillons du sol	Entnahme f von Bodenproben	prelevamento m di campione del suolo

English	French	German	Italian
— 13972 **procedure of analysis**	procédé d'analyse	Gang der Analyse	processo f d'analisi
° 13972a **process alloy**	addition f	Zusatz m	aggiunta f
° 13973 **process annealing**	recuit m intermédiaire	Zwischenglühung f	ricottura f intermedia
° 13974 **process lag**	retard m du procédé	Verzögerung f	ritardo m operativo
° 13974a **process metallurgy**	métallurgie f des minerais	Erzmetallurgie f	metallurgia f dei minenerali
° 13975 **process of coking**	marche f de la carbonisation	Vorgang m beim Verkoken	processo m di formazione del coke
° 13976 **process of combustion**	processus m de (la) combustion	Verbrennungsvorgang m	processo m di combustione
° 13977 **process of hardening**	marche f de la trempe	Härtevorgang m	andamento della tempera
° 13978 **process of refining**	procédé m d'affinage	Veredelungsverfahren n	processo m d'affinaggio
— 13979 **process of separation**	marche f des opérations de séparation	Trennungsvorgang m	processo m di separazione
° 13980 **process of smelting**	allure f de la fusion	Schmelzverlauf m	andamento m della fusione
° 13981 **process stock**	charge f	Charge f	carica f
° 13982 **processed steel**	acier m fabriqué	bearbeiteter Stahl m	acciaio m lavorato
° 13983 **processing**	traitement m	Verarbeitung f	lavorazione f
— 13984 **processing**	recette f au niveau du sol	Rasenhängebank f	stazione f di fondo
— 13985 **prochlorite**	prochlorite f	Prochlorit m	proclorite f
° 13986 **procuring of water**	captage de l'eau	Wassergewinnung f	presa d'acqua
— 13987 **procuring water from a subterranean source**	captage m d'eau souterraine	Grundwassergewinnung f	presa f d'acqua sotterranea
° 13987a **producer gas**	gaz m pauvre	armes Gas n	gas m povero
° 13988 **producers**	générateurs m $pl.$, gazogènes m $pl.$	Generatoren m $pl.$	gasogeni m $pl.$
° 13989 **product of combustion**	produit m de la combustion	Verbrennungsprodukt n	prodotto della combustione
— 13990 **product of decomposition**	produit m de la décomposition	Zersetzungsprodukt n	prodotto m della decomposizione

	English	French	German	Italian
^ 13991	product of distillation	produit *m* de distillation	Entgasungs-erzeugnis *n*, Destillat *n*	prodotto *m* della distillazione
− 13992	product of dressing	produit *m* du triage	Aufbereitungsgut *n*	prodotto *m* della cernita
− 13993	product of roasting	produit *m* du grillage	Rösterzeugnis *n*	prodotto *m* di torre-fazione
° 13994	product ready for smelting	produit *m* utilisable pour la fusion	verhüttbares Gut *n*	prodotto *m* pronto per altoforno
− 13995	production derrick	chevalement *m* de production	Förderturm *m*	castelletto *m* d'estra-zione
13996	production line	chaîne *f* de production	Fertigungslinie *f*	catena *f* di produzio-ne
° 13997	production of coke	fabrication *f* du coke	Kokserzeugung *f*	produzione *m* di coke
^ 13998	production string	colonne *f* d'exploitation	Förderkolonne *f*	colonna *f* d'estrazio-ne
13999	productiveness	capacité *f* de production	Leistungsfähigkeit *f*	produttività *f*
14000	productivity index	indice *f* de productivité	Produktivitätsindex *m*	indice *m* di produtti-vità
° 14000a	profile, section	profil *m*, section *f*	Profil *n*	profilo *m*
° 14001	profile album	album *m* des profils	Profilalbum *n*	album *m* dei profili
° 14002	profile cutter	fraise *f* à profil	Profilfräser *m*	fresa *f* a profilo
	profiled copper, *s. shaped copper*			
° 14003	profiled sheet iron	tôle *f* profilée	Formblech *n*	lamiera *f* profilata
14004	profitability	rentabilité *f*	Wirtschaftlichkeit *f*	rendimento *m*
° 14005	progress of melting	marche *f* de fusion	Schmelzgang *m*	andamento *m* della fusione
° 14005a	progressive ageing	vieillissemnt *m* pro-gressif	progressive Alterung *f*	invecchiamento *m* pro-gressivo
− 14006	prometheum	prométhéum *m*	Promethium *n*	promezio *m*
° 14006a	proof bar	barre *f* de comparai-son	Vergleichsstab *m*	barra *f* comparatrice
° 14007	proof stress	limite *f* convention-nelle d'élasticité	Elastizitätsgrenze *f*	limite *f* di elasticità convenzionale
° 14008	prop	béquille *f* (du cubilot)	Stütze *f* (der Bo-denklappe)	puntello *m* (del cu-bilotto)
− 14009	prop and sill	montant *m* et semelle	Stempel *m* und Grundschwelle	montante *m* e suola

English	French	German	Italian
— 14010 **prop drawer**	déboiseur *m*, arrache-étais *m*	Stempelrauber *m*	estrattore *m* di puntelli
— 14011 **prop drawing**	déboisage *m*	Holzrauben *n*	disarmo *m* (di miniera)
— 14012 **prop puller**	arrache-étais *m*	Raubvorrichtung *f*	estrattore *m* dei puntelli
— 14013 **prop slicing**	exploitation *f* par tranches avec foudroyage	Scheibenbruchbau *m*	estrattore *f* a trance con franamento
— 14014 **prop stay**	étai *m*, butte *f*	Stempel *m*	puntello *m*
^ 14015 **propane, propylene**	propane *m*, propylène *m*	Propan *n*, Propylen *n*	propano *m*, propilene
— 14016 **to propel**	refouler	treiben	spingere
— 14017 **propellent explosive, propellant**	explosif *m* de lance-ment, propulsif *m*	Treibmittel *n*	esplosivo *m* di lancio , propellente
— 14018 **propelling charge**	charge *f* de lance-ment	Treibladung *f*	lancio, carica di lancio
— 14019 **proper manganese ore**	minerai *m* de manganèse pro-prement dit	eigentliches Manganerz *n*	minerale *m* di manga-nese propriamente detto
— 14020 **proper roasting**	grillage *m* bien réussi	gut gelungene Röstung *f*	torrefazione *f* ben riuscita
— 14021 **proportion by weight**	proportion *f* en poids	Gewichtsverhältnis *n*	proporzione *f* in peso
proportion of lump ore, s. *grading*			
° 14022 **proportional basicity**	rapport *m* de basicité, basicité proportionnelle	Basizitätsgrad *m*	rapporto *m* di basici-tà
° 14023 **proportional part**	partie *f* aliquote	einfacher Bruchteil *m*	parte *f* proporzionale, aliquota *f*
° 14024 **proportionality limit**	limite *f* de proportionnalité	Proportionalitäts-grenze *f*	limite *m* di proporzio-nalità
— 14025 **propping**	étaiement *m*	Stempelzimmerung *f*	armatura *f*, puntella-mento *m*
— 14026 **propping agent**	agent *m* de soutènement	Stützvorrichtung *f*	agente *m* di sostegno
— 14027 **props**	bois *m* de mine	Grubenholz *n*	legname *m* per miniere

	English	French	German	Italian
— 14028	**propylite**	propylite *f*	Propylit *m*	propilite *f*
— 14029	**propylitization**	propylitisation *f*	Propylitisation *f*	propilizzazione *f*
^ 14030	**proration agreement**	convention *f* de rationnement	Einschränkungs-vereinbarung *f*	convenzione *f* di razionamento
^ 14031	**prosopite**	prosopite *m*	Prosopit *m*	prosopito *m*
— 14032	**to prospect**	prospecter, explorer	schürfen	prospettare, esplorare, sondare
— 14033	**prospect**	prospection *f*	Aufsuchen *n*	prospezione *f*, ricerca
— 14034	**prospect hole**	trou *m* de recherche	Aufschlussbohrung *f*	foro *m* di sondaggio (o di ricerca)
— 14035	**prospect pit**	puits *m* de recherche	Schürfschacht *m*	pozzo *m* di ricerca (o di sondaggio)
— 14036	**prospecting**	prospection *f*	Schürfen *n*	prospezione *f*, ricerca *f*
— 14037	**prospecting hammer**	marteau *m* de prospecteur	Prospektierhammer *m*	martello *m* del prospettore
— 14038	**prospecting licence**	permis *m* de recherches	Schürfschein *m*	permesso *m* per le ricerche
— 14039	**prospector**	prospecteur *m*	Prospektor *m*	prospettore *m*
° 14040	**protecting cap**	enveloppe *f* de protection	Schutzhaube *f*	copertura *f*, guardia *f*
	protecting plate, *s. baffle plate*			
— 14041	**protecting roofs**	appentis	Pultdaecher *n pl.*	tettoie *f pl.*
° 14042	**protecting shield, baffle-plate**	contre-porte *f*	Schutzwand *f*, Schutzplatte *f*	contro-porta *f*
° 14043	**protection against corrosion**	protection *f* contre la corrosion	Korrosionsschutz *m*	protezione *f* contro la corrosione
— 14044	**protection hole**	sondage *m* à l'avancement	Vorbohrloch *n*	foro *m* di protezione, sondaggio d'avanzamento
° 14045	**protective atmosphere**	gaz *m* protecteur	Schutzatmosphäre *f*	atmosfera *f* protettiva
° 14046	**protective funnel**	entonnoir *m* de sûreté	Schutztrichter *m*	imbuto *m* di sicurezza

	English	French	German	Italian
°	14047 protective gas furnace	four *m* à atmosphère gazeuse protectrice	Schutzgasofen *m*	forno *m* con atmosfera protetta
—	14048 protoactinium	protactinium	Protactinium *n*	protoattinio *m*
—	14049 protobastite	protobastite *f*	Protobastit *m*	protobastite *f*
—	14050 protoclastic structure	texture *f* protoclastique	protoklastische Struktur *f*	struttura *f* protoclastica
—	14051 protogine	protogine *m*	Protogin *m*	protogino *m*
—	14052 protomylonite	protomylonite *f*	Protomylonit *m*	protomilonite *f*
—	14053 protoparaffin	protoparaffine *f*	Protoparaffin *n*	protoparaffina *f*
—	14054 protusion	protrusion *f*	Protrusion *f*	protrusione *f*
—	14055 proustite	proustite *f*	Proustit *m*	proustite *f*
—	14056 proved reserve	réserve *f* sûre	sichere Reserve *f*	riserva *f* sicura
—	14057 prover (metering)	appareil *m* de contrôle	Eichgerät *n*	apparecchio *m* di controllo
—	14058 proving hole	sondage *m* de recherche	Aufschlussbohrung *f*, Schürfschacht *m*	sondaggio *m* di ricerca, pozzo *m* di prova
—	14059 proving method	méthode *f* de contrôle	Eichmethode *f*	sistema *m* di controllo
—	14060 proxy-mineral	minerai *m* de remplacement	Stellvertreter *m*	minerale *m* di sostituzione
—	14061 to pry out	enlever par action de levier	mit Hebelwirkung ausheben	togliere facendo leva
—	14062 pryan	minerai *m* en menus galets mélangé avec de l'argile	kleine abgerollte Erzstücke *n pl.* in Ton eingebettet	minerale *m* in piccoli ovuli mescolato con argilla
	prybar gun, *s. lever gun*			
—	14063 psammite	psammite *f*	Psammit *m*	psammite *f*
—	14064 psammitic texture	texture *f* psammitique	psammitische Textur *f*	struttura *f* psammitica
—	14065 psephicity	structure *f* pséphitique	psephitische Struktur *f*	struttura *f* psefitica
—	14066 psephite	pséphite *f*	Psephit *m*	psefite *f*

English	French	German	Italian
— 14067 **psephitic texture**	texture *f* pséphitique	psephitische Struktur *f*	struttura *f* psefitica
— 14068 **psephyte**	pséphite *f*	Psephit *m*	psefite *f*
— 14069 **pseudo-anticlinale**	faux anticlinal *m*	falscher Sattel *m*	pseudo anticlinale *f*
— 14070 **pseudoboleite**	pseudoboléite *f*	Pseudoboleit *m*	pseudoboleite *f*
— 14071 **pseudobrookite**	pseudobrookite *f*	Pseudobrookit *m*	pseudobrookite *f*
° 14071a **pseudocarburizing**	pseudocémentation *f*	Pseudozementieren *n*	pseudocementazione *f*
— 14072 **pseudocrystalline**	pseudocristallin	pseudokristallin	pseudocristallino
pseudo-galena, *s. blende*			
— 14073 **pseudoglaucophane**	pseudoglaucophane	Pseudoglaukophan *n*	pseudoglaucofano *m*
— 14074 **pseudolamination**	pseudoschistosité *f*	falsche Schieferung *f*	pseudoscistosità *f*
— 14075 **pseudoleucite**	pseudoleucite *f*	Pseudoleucit *m*	pseudoleucite *f*
— 14076 **pseudomalachite**	pseudomalachite *f*	Pseudomalachit *m*	pseudomalachite *f*
— 14077 **pseudomorph**	pseudomorphe	pseudomorph	pseudomorfo
— 14078 **pseudomorphism**	pseudomorphisme *m*	Pseudomorphose *f*	pseudomorfismo *m*, pseudomorfosi *f*
° 14078a **pseudonitriding**	pseudonitruration *f*	Pseudonitrierung *f*	pseudonitrurazione *f*
— 14079 **·pseudophenocryst**	porphyroblaste *m*	Porphyroblast *m*	porfiroblasto *m*
— 14080 **pseudophite**	pseudophite *f*	Pseudophit *m*	pseudofite *f*
— 14081 **pseudoschistosity**	pseudoschistosité *f*	falsche Schieferung *f*	pseudoscistosità *f*
— 14082 **pseudotachylyte**	pseudotachylyte *f*	Pseudotachylyt *m*	pseudotachilite *f*
pseudo-volcanic eruption, *s. phreatic eruption*			
— 14083 **pseudowavellite**	pseudowavéllite *f*	Pseudowavellit *m*	pseudowavellite *f*
— 14084 **P.S.I.**	livres pour pouce carré	Pfunde *f pl.* für Quadratfusse	libbre *f pl.* per pollice quadrato
— 14085 **psilomelane, black iron ore**	braunite *f*, oxyde *m* manganique	Psilomelan *m*	psilomelano *m*, ossido *m* manganico
— 14086 **psittacinite**	psittacinite *f*	Psittacinit *m*	psittacinite *f*
— 14087 **Psychozoic era**	ère *f* psychozoïque	Psychozoische Ära *f*	era *f* psicozoica
— 14088 **ptilolite**	ptilolite *f*	Ptilolit *m*	ptilolite *f*
— 14089 **ptygmatic structure**	structure *f* ptygmatique	ptygmatische Textur *f*	struttura *f* ptigmatica
— 14090 **pucherite**	puchérite *f*	Pucherit *m*	pucherite *f*
— 14090a **pucker**	pli *m*	Falte *f*	piega *f*
— 14091 **puckering**	froncement *m*, plissotement	Fältelung *f*, Runzelung *f*	corrugamento *m*, pieghettatura *f*

English	French	German	Italian
— 14092 **pudding stone**	poudingue *m*	Puddingstein *m*	conglomerato *m*, puddinga *f*
° 14093 **to puddle**	puddler	puddeln	puddellare
° 14094 **to puddle, to rabble**	puddler, brasser	rühren, durchrühren	mescolare
° 14094a **puddle**	bain *m* de fusion	Schmelzbad *n*	bagno *m* di fusione
° 14095 **puddle ball**	loupe *m* de puddlage	Puddelluppe *f*	palla *f* di puddellaggio
puddle slag, *s. puddled cinder*			
° 14096 **puddled bar**	fer *m* ébauché	Rohbarren *m*	ferro *m* sbozzato, ferro *m* puddellato
° 14097 **puddled cinder**	scorie *f* de puddlage	Puddelschlacke *f*	scoria *f* di puddellaggio
— 14098 **puddled clay**	pisè *m*	Tonschlag *m*	fanghiglia *f*
° 14099 **puddled iron**	fer *m* puddlé	Puddeleisen *n*, Massel *f*	ferro *m* puddellato
° 14100 **puddled iron bars**	fer *m* ébauché	Rohschienen *f pl.*	ferro *m* grezzo
° 14101 **puddled mill**	train *m* de puddlage	Puddeleisenwalzwerk *n*	laminatoio *m* per puddellaggio
° 14102 **puddled roll**	cylindre *m* ébaucheur,	Puddelwalze *f*	cilindro *m* sbozzatore, cilindro *m* sgrossatore
° 14103 **puddled steel**	acier *m* puddlé	Puddelstahl *m*	acciaio *m* puddellato
° 14104 **puddle(d) steel**	acier puddlé	Puddelstahl *m*, Herdfrischstahl *m*	acciaio *m* puddellato
° 14105 **puddler'**	puddleur *m*	Puddler *m*	operaio *m* puddellatore
° 14105a **puddler's candles**	flamme *f* de puddlage	Puddelflamme *f*	fiamma *f* di puddellaggio
° 14106 **puddling**	puddlage *m*	Puddeln *n*, Puddelprozess *m*	puddellaggio *m*
° 14107 **puddling bar, pointed rabble**	ringard *m* pointu, poinçon *m*	Spitz *m*, Brechstange *f*	stanga *f* a punta
° 14108 **puddling for crystalline iron**	puddlage *m* en fer à grains	Kornpuddeln *n*, Puddeln *n* auf Korn	puddellaggio *m* a grana
° 14109 **puddling-furnace**	four *m* à puddler	Puddelofen *m*	forno *m* di puddellaggio
° 14110 **puddling furnace with revolving hearth**	four *m* à sole tournante	Tellerofen *m*	forno *m* di fusione a piatto girevole
° 14111 **puddling machine**	puddleur *m* mécanique	Puddelmaschine *f*	puddellatrice

	English	French	German	Italian
° 14112	puddling of fibrous iron	puddlage m de fer nerveux	Sehnepuddeln n	puddellaggio m di ferro fibroso
° 14113	puddling of steel	puddlage m de l'acier	Stahlpuddeln n	puddellaggio m del-l'acciaio
° 14114	puddling process	procédé m de puddlage	Puddelverfahren n	puddellaggio m
	puddling steel, s. puddled steel			
° 14115	puddling works	usine f de puddlage	Puddelhütte f, Puddelwerk n	stabilimento m di forni per puddellaggio
° 14115a	puffed bar	barre f creuse gonflée	geschwellter Hohlstab m	barra f cava gonfiata
	to pug, s. to knead			
— 14116	to pug	pétrir	kneten	impastare
— 14117	pug	salbande f argileuse	Verwerfungston m, Lettenbesteg m	salbanda f argillosa
— 14118	pug hole	cheminée f	Stürzrolle f	scivolo m piano m inclinato
	pug mill, s. crushing mill with vertical runners			
— 14119	puglianite	puglianite f	Puglianit m	puglianite f
— 14120	pulaskite	pulaskite f	Pulaskit m	pulaskite f
^ 14121	pulking	entraînement m de liquide dans la va-peur de distillation		trascinamento m di liquido nel vapore di distillazione
— 14122	to pull (a pillar)	dépiler	abpfeilern	demolire (i pilastri)
^ 14123	to pull	détuber, extraire	entrohren, ziehen	togliere i tubi, tirare
— 14124	to pull out	relever, sortir	aufholen, ausbauen	tirar via, far uscire
° 14125	pull, tension	traction f	Zug m	trazione f
° 14126	pull	effort de traction	Zugkraft f	sforzo m di trazione
° 14127	pull	crique f transversale	Querriss m	cricca f trasversale (di lingotto)
° 14128	pull grips	mains courantes f pl.	Hangriffe m pl.	corrimani m pl.
° 14128a	pull-over mill	laminoir m duo irré-versibile	Übergabwalzwerk n	laminatoio m duo irre-versibile
° 14129	pull rod, shackle	tige f d'entraînement	Zugstange f	asta f di trasmissione
° 14130	pull rod line, shackle line, jerk line	tringles de transmission	Feldgestänge n pl.	aste f pl. pesanti di trasmissione

English	French	German	Italian
○ 14131 **pull through of pattern**	moulage *m* par introduction et enlèvement du modèle ou par modèle rentrant	Durchziehen *n* (von Modellteilen)	estrazione *f* del modello su macchina a pettine
— 14132 **pulley, driving pulley**	poulie *f* de commande ou motrice	Triebscheibe *f*	puleggia *f* di comando
— 14133 **pulley block hoist**	palan *m* à moufle	Flaschenzug *m*	paranco *m* a taglia
— 14134 **pulley shaft**	puits *m* d'extraction	Förderschacht *m*	pozzo *m* d'estrazione
— 14135 **pulleying**	mise *f* aux molettes	Übertreiben *n*	messa *f* della gabbia alle molette
○ 14136 **pulling**	traction *f*	Traktion *f*	trazione *f*
— 14137 **pulling**	extraction *f*	Ziehen *n*, Ausholen *n*	estrazione *f*
— 14138 **pulling back**	dépilage *m*	Rückbau *m* der Pfeiler, Abpfeilern *n*	demolizione *f* dei pilastri
— 14139 **pulling machine**	treuil *m* auxiliaire	Ziehkran *m*	argano *m* ausiliare
— 14140 **pulling pillars**	dépilage *m*	Abpfeilern *n*, Abbau *m* der Pfeiler *m*	demolizione *f* dei pilastri
— 14141 **pull-shovel**	godet *m* rétro	Tieflöffel *m*	cucchiaio *m* rovescio
^ 14142 **pulp, slime**	eau boueuse *f* des bocards	Pochtrübe *f*	fango *m* del palmento
○ 14143 **pulp boiler**	chaudière *f* lessiveuse à pâte	Zellstoffkocher *m*	caldaia *f* lisciviatrice da polpa
^ 14144 **pulp thickener**	épaississeur *m* des boues	Trübeverdicker *m*	addensatore *m* di fanghi
○ 14145 **pulsation dampener**	amortisseur de pulsation	Pulsationsdämpfer *m*	ammortizzatore *m* di pulsazioni
— 14145a **pulsator jig**	crible *m* à grille mobile	Schüttelmaschine *f*	vaglio *m* a griglia mobile
— 14146 **pulsometer**	pulsomètre *m*	Pulsometer *n*	pulsometro *m*
— 14147 **pulverised coal**	charbon *m* pulvérisé	Kohlenstaub *m*	carbone *m* polverizzato, carbone in polvere
— 14148 **pulverised fuel**	combustible *m* pulvérisé	Pulverbrennstoff *m*	combustibile *m* polverizzato
— 14149 **pulverised quartz**	quartz *m* finement broyé	fein gemahlener Quarz *m*	quarzo *m* finemente macinato
— 14150 **pulveriser**	pulvérisateur *m*	Zerstäuber *m*	polverizzatore *m*

English	French	German	Italian
o 14151 pulverizer for washed argilla-ceous earth	pulvérisateur *m* d'argile finement lavée	Zerstäuber *m* für geschlämmte Tonerde	polverizzatore *m* per argilla lavata
pumcret, *s. pumped concrete*			
— 14152 pumice concrete block	parpaing de pierre ponce	Bimsstein *m*	agglomerato *m* di po-mice, cemento *m* di pomice
o 14153 pumice sand	sable *m* de (pierre) ponce	Bimssand *m*	sabbia *f* di pietra pomice
o 14154 pumicestone like, honeycombed	boursouflé, poreux	bimssteinartig	spugnoso
^ 14155 to pump off	vider par une pompe	leerpumpen	vuotare con una pompa
^ 14156 pump back	reflux *m*	Rückfluss *m*	riflusso *m*
— 14157 pump compartment	compartiment *m* de l'exhaure	Pumpentrumm *m*	reparto *m* pompe (di prosciugamento)
pump plonger, *s. pump piston*			
o 14158 pump piston	piston *m* de pompe	Pumpenkolben *m*	stantuffo *m* della pompa
pump-water, *s. well water*			
^ 14159 pumped off	épuisé	erschöpft	esaurito
^ 14160 pumping plant	installation *f* de pompes	Pumpanlage *f*	stazione *f* di pompaggio
^ 14161 pump power-end	corps *m* hydraulique de pompe	hydraulischer Pumpenkasten *m*	corpo *m* idraulico di pompa
— 14162 pump shaft	puits *m* d'exhaure	Wasserschacht *m*	pozzo *m* di prosciu-gamento
^ 14163 pumper	pompiste *m*	Pumpwärter *m*	addetto *m* alle pompe
^ 14164 pumping beam, beam	balancier *m* de pompage	Schwengel *m*	bilanciere *m* di pompa
^ 14165 pumping jack	chevalement *m* de pompage	Winkelhebel *m*	congegno *m* di pompag-gio idraulico
^ 14166 pumping jack with underhand pull	chevalet *m* avec renvoi inférieur	Winkelhebel *m* mit Unterzug	bilanciere *m* di pompa con rinvio inferiore
pumping station, *s. pumping plant*			

	English	French	German	Italian
^ 14167	**pumping power**	centrale de pompage	Zentralgetriebe *n*	centrale *f* di pompaggio
^ 14168	**pumping string**	colonne *f* de tubes de pompage	Pumprohr *n*	colonna *f* di pompaggio
^ 14169	**pumping rate**	taux *m* de pompage	Pumpgeschwindigkeit *f*	velocità *f* di pompaggio
^ 14170	**pumping unit**	unité *f* de pompage	Pumpanlage *f*	impianto *m* di pompaggio
^ 14171	**pumping well, pumper**	puits *m* en pompage	Pumpensonde *f*	pozzo *m* in fase di pompaggio
	to punch, s. *to mortise*			
° 14172	**to punch**	percer, poinçonner	durchlochen	forare, punzonare
° 14173	**to punch (holes)**	poinçonner	ausstanzen, lochen	punzonare
° 14174	**to punch holes**	poinçonner les trous (de rivets)	Löcher *n pl.* stanzen	punzonare i fori
—14175	**punch**	butte *f*	Stempel *m*	puntello *m*
° 14176	**punch, stamp**	poinçon *m*, étampe *f*	Lochstempel *m*, Stanze *f*	punzone *m*
	punch, s. *die*			
	punch, s. *conical reamer*			
	punch, s. *piercer*			
	punch mark, s. *measuring point*			
	punch press, s. *inclinable power press*			
—14177	**punch prop**	étai *m*, pilot *m*	Stempel *m*, Bolzen *m*	puntello *m*, palo *m*
° 14178	**punch steel**	acier *m* à poinçons	Lochstempelstahl *m*	acciaio *m* per punzoni
°14178a	**punched cavity**	découpage *m* à l'emporte-pièce	Locheisenhohlraum *m*	cavità *f* punzonata
	punched hole, s. *drilled hole*			
° 14179	**punched plate**	tôle *f* perforée	gelochtes Blech *n*	lamiera *f* forata
—14180	**puncher**	haveuse *f* à pic	stossend wirkende Schrämmaschine *f*	intagliatrice *f* a piccone, perforatore *m*, perforatrice *f*
° 14181	**puncher**	poinçon *m*, poinçonneur *m*	Stanze *f*, Stanzer *m*	punzone *m*
° 14182	**punching, stamping**	découpage *m*	Stanzen *n*, Schneiden *n*	tranciatura *f*

	English	French	German	Italian
° 14183	punching die	calibre *m* de perçage	Stanzmatrize *f*, Lochkaliber *n*	stampo *m* (della pressa)
— 14184	punching machine	haveuse *f* à pic	stossend wirkende Schrämmaschine *f*	tagliatrice *f* a piccone
^ 14185	pup joint	joint *m* de tube court	Gestängewechsel *m* (kurze Stange)	riduzione *f* con due diversi diametri per aste
— 14186	puppet	chevalement *m*	Fördergerüst *n*	incastellatura *f* d'estrazione, castelletto *m* d'estrazione
° 14187	pure iron	fer *m* pur	reines Eisen *n*	ferro *m* puro
° 14188	pure oxygen blown steel	acier *m* à l'oxygène pur	reiner O2-Stahl *m*	acciaio *m* all'ossigeno puro
	pure slag, *s. raw slag*			
° 14189	pure tin	étain *m* pur	reines Zinn *n*	stagno *m* puro
	to purge, *s. to draw off the mud*			
— 14190	purging	lavage *m*	Abwaschung *f*, Waschen *n*	bonifica *f*, lavaggio *m*
° 14190a	purified gas	gaz *m* purifié	gereinigtes Gas *n*	gas *m* purificato
— 14191	purified water	eau *f* épurée	gereinigtes Wasser *n*	acqua *f* depurata
° 14192	to purify	épurer	reinigen	depurare
° 14193	purple	pourpre	purpurn	porporino
— 14194	purple copper ore	bornite *f*	Bornit *m*	bornite *f*
	purple ore, *s. calcined pyrites*			
— 14195	purpurite	purpurite *f*	Purpurit *m*	purpurite *f*
° 14196	push bench	banc *m* d'étirage	Ziehbank *f*	banco *m* per trafilatura
— 14197	push conveyor	transporteur *m* à racloirs ou raclettes	Kratzerförderer *m*	trasportatore *m* a raschiatoio
— 14198	push-down machine	exploseur *m* à poignée	elektrische Zündmaschine *f*	esploditore *m* elettrico
	push gun, *s. poke gun*			
— 14199	push moraine	moraine *f* de poussée	Staumoräne *f*	morena *f* viaggiante

English	French	German	Italian
ᴾ 14200 **pusher**	défourneuse de coke	Ausdrücker *m*, Koksausdrück- maschine *f*	estrattrice *f*, estratto- re *m* di coke
° 14201 **pusher furnace**	four *m* poussant	Stossofen *m*	forno *m* a spinta
−14202 **pushing trough**	gouttière *f* mobile ou conduit *m* mobi- le à racloirs	Schubrinne *f*, Schub- förderrinne *f*	canale *m* trasportato- re a spinta
push-up, s. *allowance*			
° 14203 **push-up**	affaissement *m* du moule	Formsenkung *f*	cedimento *m* della forma
° 14204 **push welding**	soudure *f* à poussée	Stossschweissung *f*	saldatura *f* a spinta
to put in gear, s. *to connect*			
° 14205 **to put-on the upper box**	placer le châssis supérieur	den Oberkasten aufsetzen	piazzare il coperchio
−14206 **putter**	chargeur *m*, traîneur *m*	Lader *m*, Wagenlader *m*	caricatore *m*
putting in blast, s. *starting*			
putting in blast again, s. *restarting*			
−14207 **pycnometer**	pycnomètre *m*	Pyknometer *n*	picnometro *m*
° 14208 **pyramid shaped plate**	plaque *f* en tronc de pyramide	pyramidenförmige Platte *f*	piastra *f* piramidale
−14209 **pyramid stoping**	exploitation *f* à mi-pente	Schrägbau *m*	coltivazione *f* a piramide
pyramidal system, s. *tetragonal system*			
−14210 **pyrargillite**	pyrargillite *f*	Pyrargillit *m*	pirargillite *f*
−14211 **pyrargyrite**	pyrargyrite *f*	Pyrargyrit *m*	pirargirite *f*
−14212 **pyrgom**	pyrgome *m*	Pyrgom *m*	pirgome *m*
−14213 **pyribole**	roche composée de pyroxène et d'amphi- bole	Pyribol *m*	piribolo *m*
−14214 **pyrite**	pyrite *f*	(Kupfer)kies *m*, Pyrit *m*	pirite *f*
−14215 **pyritized ammonite**	ammonite *f* pyritisée	pyritisierter Ammonit	ammonite *f* piritica
−14216 **pyritohedron**	pyritoèdre *m*	Pyritoeder *m*	piritoedro *m*

English	French	German	Italian
− 14217 **pyroaurite**	pyroaurite *f*	Pyroaurit *m*	piroaurite *f*
− 14218 **pyrobelonite**	pyrobelonite *f*	Pyrobelonit *m*	pirobelonite *f*
− 14219 **pyrobitumen**	pyrobitume *m*	Pyrobitumen *n*	pirobitume *m*
− 14220 **pyrochlore**	pyrochlore *m*	Pyrochlor *n*	pirocloro *m*
− 14221 **pyrochroite**	pyrochroïte *f*	Pyrochroit *m*	pirocroite *f*
− 14222 **pyroclastic**	pyroclastique	pyroklastisch	piroclastico
− 14223 **pyrocrystalline**	pyrocristallin	pyrokristallin	pirocristallino
− 14224 **pyroelectricity**	pyroélectricité *f*	Pyroelektrizität *f*	piroelettricità *f*
− 14225 **pyrogenic decomposition**	pyrogénation *f*	Crackverfahren *n*	piroscissione *f*
− 14226 **pyrogenetic rock**	roche *f* pyrogène	pyrogenes Gestein *n*	roccia *f* pirogena
− 14227 **pyrolusite**	pyrolusite *f*	Pyrolusit *m*	pirolusite *f*
− 14228 **pyrolysis**	pyrolyse *f*, thermolyse *f*	Pyrolyse *f*, thermische Zersetzung *f*	pirolisi *f*
° 14228a **pyrometallurgy**	pyrométallurgie *f*	Pyrometallurgie *f*	pirometallurgia *f*
− 14229 **pyrometamorphism**	pyrométamorphisme *m*	Pyrometamorphose *f*	pirometamorfosi *f*
° 14230 **pyrometer**	pyromètre *m*	Pyrometer *n*	pirometro *m*
° 14231 **pyrometric measurement of temperature**	mesure *f* des températures, pyrométrie *f*	Temperaturmessung *f*	pirometria *f*
−14232 **pyromorphite**	pyromorphite *f*	Pyromorphit *m*	piromorfite *f*
˄ 14233 **pyronaphtha**	huiles lourdes dérivées du pétrole	Schweröle *n pl.*	pironafta *f*
−14234 **pyrope**	pyrope *m*	Pyrop *m*	piropo *m*
−14235 **pyrophanite**	pyrophanite *f*	Pyrophanit *m*	pirofanite *f*
−14236 **pyrophyllite**	pyrophyllite *f*	Pyrophyllit *m*	pirofillite *f*
−14237 **pyrophysalite**	pyrophysalite *f*	Pyrophysalit *m*	pirofisalite *f*
−14238 **pyroshale**	pyroschiste *f*	Brandschiefer *m*	piroscisto *m*
−14239 **pyrosmalite**	pyrosmalite *f*	Pyrosmalith *m*	pirosmalite *f*
° 14240 **pyrostat**	thermostate *m*	Thermostat *m*	termostato *m*

English	French	German	Italian
—14241 **pyrostilpnite**	pyrostilpnite *f*	Pyrostilpnit *m*	pirostilpnite *f*
—14242 **pyroxene**	pyroxène *m*	Pyroxen *m*	pirossene *m*
—14242a **pyrrhosiderite**	goethite *f*	Goethit *m*	goethite *f*
—14242b **pyrrhotite**	pyrrhotite *f*	Magnetkies *m*	pirrotite *f*

English	French	German	Italian
− 14243 **quadrangular prism**	prisme *m* quadrangulaire	vierseitiges Prisma *n*	prisma *f* quadrangolare
° 14244 **quadrant iron**	fer *m* en quart de rond (ou à colonnes)	Quadranteisen *n* Säuleneisen *n*	ferro *m* quadrante, ferro *m* a colonne
° 14244a **quadrant plate**	cavalier *m*	Kulisse *f*	testa *f* di cavallo
− 14245 **qualitative examination**	analyse *f* qualitative	qualitative Untersuchung *f*	analisi *f* qualitativa
° 14246 **qualities of iron, grades of iron**	sorte *f* de fer	Eisensorte *f*	qualità *f* di ferro
° 14247 **quality**	qualité *f*, nature *f*	Beschaffenheit *f*	qualità *f*, natura *f*
14248 **quality control**	contrôle *m* de qualité	Qualitätsprüfung *f*	controllo *m* di qualità
° 14249 **quality of wire**	qualité *f* de fil de fer	Drahtsorte *f*	qualità *f* del filo di ferro
° 14250 **quantitative examination**	analyse *f* quantitative	Mengenuntersuchung *f*	analisi *f* quantitativa
° 14251 **quantity of light**	quantité *f* de lumière	Lichtmenge *f*	quantità *f* di luce
° 14252 **quantity of water**	quantité *f* d'eau	Wassermenge *f*	quantità *f* d'acqua
° 14253 **quantity weighed for analysis**	pesée *f*	Wiegen *n*	pesata *f*
° 14253a **quantum**	quant *m*	Quant *n*	quanto *m*
− 14254 **quaquaversal dip**	pendage *m* rayonnant	umlaufendes Einfallen *n*	inclinazione *f* divergente
− 14255 **quaquaversal structure**	structure *f* périclinale	periklinale Faltenstruktur *f*	struttura *f* periclinale, duomo *m*
− 14256 **quarfeloid**	agrégat *m* quartz-feldspath	Quarz-Feldspat Aggregat *n*	aggregato *m* di quarzo-feldspato
− 14257 **to quarry**	extraire ou tirer (d'une cave)	(Steine) hauen	estrarre da una cava
− 14258 **quarry, pit**	carrière *f*	Bruch *m*, Grube *f*	cava *f*
− 14259 **quarry sand**	sable *m* de carrière	Grubensand *m*	sabbia *f* di cava
− 14260 **quarry spall**	résidu *m* de carrière	Steinbruchabfälle *n pl*	residui *m pl*. di cava
− 14260a **quarry waste**	menus de carrière	Grubenklein *n*	rifiuti *m pl*. di cava
− 14261 **quarry-water**	eau *f* de carrière	Steinbruchwasser *n*	acqua *f* di cava
− 14261a **quartation**	inquartation *f*	Quartscheidung *f*	quartazione *f*
° 14262 **quarter bend**	coude *m* rond au ¼	Normalkrümmer *m*	curva *f* a 90°

	English	French	German	Italian
° 14263	quarter-wawe plate	lamelle *f* quart d'onde	Filterpolarisator *m*	lamina *f* quarto d'onda
° 14264	quartering the sample	réduction *f* de la prise d'essai	Quartieren *n* des Probegutes	riduzione *f* del campione
° 14264a	quartering way	plan *m* de cassure	Bruchfläche *f*	piano *m* della frattura
— 14265	quartz	quartz *m*	Quarz *m*	quarzo *m*
— 14266	quartz-crystal	cristal *m* (de quartz)	(Quarz) Kristall *m*	cristallo *m* (di quarzo)
— 14267	quartz-diorite	diorite *f* quartzifère	Quarzdiorit *m*	diorite *f* quarzifera
— 14268	quartz in lumps	quartz *m* en morceaux	Stückquarz *m*	quarzo *m* in pezzi
— 14269	quartz-porphyry	porphyre *m* quartzifère	Quarzporphyr *m*	porfido *m* quarzifero
— 14270	quartz reef	filon *m* de quartz	Quarzgang *m*	filone *m* di quarzo
— 14271	quartz rock	quartzite *f*	Quarzit *m*	quarzite *f*
	quartz-sinter, *s. siliceous sinter*			
— 14272	quartz ware	utensiles *m pl.* en quartz	Quarzgerät *n*	utensili *m* di quarzo
— 14273	quartzite	quartzite *f*	Quarzit *m*	quarzite *f*
— 14274	quartzose sand	sable *m* quartzeux	Quarzsand *m*	sabbia *f* quarzosa
— 14275	quartzy	quartzeux	quarzig	quarzifero
— 14276	quartzy grains *pl.*	grains *m pl.* quartzeux	quarzige Körner *n pl.*	grani *m pl.* di quarzo
— 14277	quartzy sandstone	grès *m* quatzeux	Quarzsandstein *m*	gres *m* quarzifero
—14278	quartzy period	quaternaire *m*	Quartär *m*	quaternario *m*
	quaternary system, *s. tetragonal system*			
° 14279	to quench	tremper	abschrecken	spegnere, temprare
° 14280	to quench hot	tremper très chaud dans l'eau	heiss ablöschen	temperare al calor rosso nell'acqua
° 14281	to quench in water	tremper dans l'eau	ablöschen	temperare nell'acqua
° 14282	to quench the steel in water	tremper l'acier dans l'eau	Stahl in Wasser abschrecken	temperare l'acciaio in acqua
° 14283	quench	trempe *f*	Abschrecken *n*, Härten *n*	tempra *f*, raffreddamento rapido
° 14284	quench ageing	vieillissement *m* dû à refroidissement soudain	Abschreckalterung *f*	invecchiamento *m* dovuto a rapido raffreddamento

English	French	German	Italian
° 14285 quench crack	tapure f de trempe	Härteriss m	crepa f o incrinatura di tempra
° 14285a quench hardening	durcissement m par refroidissement rapide	re-Abschreckhärtung f	indurimento m per raffreddamento rapido
° 14286 quenched in oil	refroidi à l'huile	in Öl abgekühlt	raffreddato nell'olio
° 14287 quenched in water	refroidi à l'eau	in Wasser abgekühlt	raffreddato in acqua
° 14288 quenched steel	acier m trempé à l'eau	abgeschreckter Stahl m	acciaio m temprato in acqua
° 14289 quenching	trempe f	Abschreckung f	tempra f
° 14290 quenching	refroidissement m	Abschreckung f	raffreddamento m rapido (di tempera)
° 14291 quenching bath	bain m de trempe	Kühlbad n	bagno m di tempera
° 14291a quenching charge	charge f refroidie	abgeschreckte Charge f	carica f raffreddata
° 14292 quenching hardening	trempe f à l'eau	Abschreckhärtung f	tempra f all'acqua
° 14292a quenching media	bain m de trempe	Härtemittel n	bagno m di tempera

quenching of the coke, *s. damping down of the coke*

English	French	German	Italian
° 14293 quenching temperature	température f de trempe	Abschreckungstemperatur f	temperatura f di spegnimento
° 14294 quenching time	durée f de trempe	Abschreckdauer f	durata f di spegnimento
− 14295 quenching tower	tour f d'extinction	Löschturm m	torre f d'estrazione

quevenne's iron, *s. reduced iron*

English	French	German	Italian
^ 14296 quick-action joint	joint m rapide	Schnellkupplung f	giunto m rapido
° 14297 quick-aging	vieillissement m soudain	Abschreckalterung f	invecchiamento m rapido
14298 quick balance	balance f rapide	Schnellwaage f	bilancia f rapida
° 14299 quick blow	battage m rapide	Schnellschlag m	battitura f rapida
° 14300 quick-detachable connector	connecteur m rapide	schnellauslösbare Kabelkupplung f	tipo m di connessore a stacco immediato
− 14301 quick lime	chaux f vive	gebrannter Kalk m	calce f viva
− 14302 quick match	mèche f rapide	Schnellzündschnur f	miccia f a rapida combustione

quick raising steam boiler, *s. flash boiler*

quick silver, *s. mercury*

English	French	German	Italian
° 14303 quick wear of the furnace	usure f rapide du four	rasche Abnützung f des Ofens	consumo m rapido del forno
° 14304 to quicken the draught	activer le tirage	den Zug beschleunigen	attivare il tiraggio

	English	French	German	Italian
° 14305	**quickening, quicksilver water**	eau *f* mercurielle	Quickwasser *n*	acqua *f* mercuriale
° 14306	**quiescent pouring**	coulée *f* tranquille	wirbelfreies Giessen *n*	colata *f* tranquilla
° 14307	**to quiet**	laisser se calmer	abstehen lassen	lasciar riposare
— 14308	**quisqueite**	quisquéite *f*	Quisqueit *m*	quisqueite *f*

	English	French	German	Italian
−	14309 rabban	chapeau *m* de fer	eiserner Hut *m*	cappello *m* di ferro
^	14310 rabbit	jauge *f* pour tuyaux	Rohrkaliber *n*	calibro *m* per tubi
o	14311 rabbit stand	poupée *f* de rabat, ordon *m*	Reitelsäule *f*	cavalletto *m* per la trave elastica
o	14312 to rabble to rabble, *s. to stir* to rabble, *s. to puddle* rabble, *s. iron rake*	ringarder	schüren	bucare un forno, spillare
o	14313 rabble	agitateur *m*	Rührwerk *n*	agitatore *m*
o	14314 rabble, rake	ringard *m*	Feuerhaken *m*	barra *f*, sbarra *f*, palo *m*, mandriale, gancio *m* da fuoco
o	14315 rabbling	brassage *m* d'un bain	Umrühren *n* eines Bades	rimescolatura *f* di un bagno
o	14316 rabbling	puddlage *m*	Puddeln *n*	puddellaggio *m*
o	14317 rabbling mechanism	mécanisme *m* à brasser	Rühreinrichtung *f*	meccanismo *m* per rimescolare
−	14318 racewinite	racewinite *f*	Racewinit *m*	racewinite *f*
^	14319 raceway	canalisation *f*	Kanalisation *f*	canalizzazione *f*
o	14320 rack	crémaillère *f*	Zahnstange *f*	cremagliera *f*
^	14321 rack-and-pinion jack rack drawn, *s. bench drawn*	cric *m* à crémaillère	Zahnstangenwinde *f*	martinetto *m* a crema-gliera
o	14321a rack feed	engranage *m* à cré-maillère	Zahnstangenantrieb *m*	avanzamento *m* a cre-magliera
o	14322 rack for moulds	étagere *f* à moules	Ablage *f* für Formen	scaffale *m* per forme
o	14323 rack railway, cog--wheeled railway	chemin de fer *m* à crémaillère	Zahnradbahn *f*, Zahnstangenbahn *f*	cremagliera *f*
o	14324 rack with pinion	crémaillère *f* avec pignon moteur	Zahnstange *f* mit Getriebe	cremagliera *f* a pignone
^	14325 racking capacity	capacité de stockage du derrick	Gestänge-Ablegekapazität *f*	lunghezza totale de-gli stands o di tubing contenuta in una torre

English	French	German	Italian
○ 14326 **radial drilling machine**	perceuse *f* radiale	Radialbohrmaschine *f*, Auslegerbohr-maschine *f*	trapanatrice *f* radiale
— 14327 **radial fault**	faille' *f* radiale	Radialsprung *f*	faglia *f* radiale
— 14328 **radial pressure**	pression *f* radiale	radialer Druck *m*	pressione *f* radiale
radial stone, *s. chimney engineering brick*			
— 14329 **radial test**	épreuve *f* radiale	Radialprobe *f*	prova *f* radiale
○ 14330 **radiant tube furnace**	four *m* à tubes radiants	Strahlrohrofen *m*	forno *m* a tubi radianti
○ 14331 **radiated, radiolated**	rayonnant	strahlig	irradiato, raggiante
○ 14332 **radiation of heat**	rayonnement *m* de la chaleur	Wärmestrahlung *f*	irradiazione *f* del calore
○ 14332a **radiation hardening**	durcissement *m* par rayonnement	Strahlungshärtung *f*	indurimento *m* per radiazione
radiation pyrometer, *s. optical pyrometer*			
— 14333 **radiolarian rock**	roche *f* à radiolaires	Radiolariengestein *n*	roccia *f* a radiolari
— 14334 **radiolite**	radiolite *f*	Radiolith *m*	radiolite *f*
○ 14335 **radioactive isotope**	isotope *m* radioactif	radioaktives Isotop *n*	isotopo *m* radioattivo
○ 14336 **radio mast**	antenne *f* pour radio	Rundfunkmast *m*	antenna *f* per radio
14337 **radiograph**	radiographie *f*	Röntgenbild *n*, Radiographie *f*	radiofotografia *f*
radiolated, *s. radiated*			
— 14338 **radiolith structure**	structure *f* radiée	radialstrahlige Struktur *f*	struttura *f* radiale
○ 14338a **radiometallurgy**	radiométallurgie *f*	Röntgenmetallurgie *f*	radiometallurgia *f*
— 14339 **radiophyllite**	radiophyllite *f*	Radiophyllit *m*	radiofillite *f*
14340 **radioscopy**	radioscopie *f*	Röntgen--Durchleuchtung *f*	radioscopia *f*
○ 14341 **radium**	radium *m*	Radium *n*	radio *m*
○ 14342 **radiussed curved top edge sleeker**	lissoir *m* d'équerre cintré à congé	Polierknopf *m*	lisciatoio *m* a squadra
○ 14343 **radiussed straight top edge sleeker**	lissoir *m* d'équerre droit à congé	Stumpfkantpolier-knopf *m*	lisciatoio *m* a squadra per spigoli smussati

English	French	German	Italian
− 14344 **radon**	radon *m*	Radon *n*	rado *m*, radon *m*
− 14345 **rafter**	chevron *m*, poutre *f*	Dachsparren *m*, Balken *m*	falso-puntone *m*, travetto *m* inclinato
− 14346 **rafter set**	cadre *m* complexe	Polygonzimmerung *f*	quadro *m* complesso
− 14347 **to rag**	vorscheider	vorklauben	preparare (minerali)
° 14348 **rag**	pierre *f* à aiguiser, roche dure pour construction	Schleifstein *m*, harter Baustein *m*	mola *f* per affilare, roccia *f* dura per costruzioni
° 14348a **rag, scale pit**	impureté *f*	Fremdkörper *m*	impurità *f*
° 14349 **rag**	bavure *f*, barbe *f*	Schlacke *f*	bava *f*, bavatura *f*
° 14350 **rag bolt**	boulon *m* de scellement	Steinschraube *f*	bullone *m* d'ancoraggio
− 14351 **rag stone**	moellon *m* schisteux	Pläner *m*	ciottolo *m* scistoso
° 14351a **ragged**	rugeux	aufgerauht	rugoso
° 14352 **ragging**	lit de grenailles	Setzbett *n*	letto *m* di graniglie
° 14353 **ragging (on roughing rolls)**	sillons *m pl.* antidérapants	rutschsichere Mulden *f pl.*	solchi *m pl.* antislittamento
− 14354 **raglanite**	raglanite *f*	Raglanit *m*	raglanite *f*
− 14355 **rail for mines**	rail *m* pour mines	Grubenschiene *f*	rotaia *f* per miniera
° 14356 **rail for trunk lines, heavy rail**	rail *m* de grande voie ou de voie normale	Vollbahnschiene *f*	rotaia *f* per ferrovia normale
° 14357 **rail for light railway**	rail *m* pour voie étroite	Kleinbahnschiene *f*	rotaia *f* per ferrovia a scartamento ridotto
° 14358 **rail head**	champignon *m*, tête *f* de rail	Schienenkopf *m*	fungo *m* della rotaia
° 14359 **rail iron**	lisse, ferrure *f*	Geländereisen *n*, Holm *m*	corrente *f* del parapetto, ferro *m* del parapetto
° 14360 **rail joint**	raccord *m* de rails, embranchement	Passschiene *f*, Schienenanschlussstück *n*	raccordo *m* di binario
° 14360a **rail-joint bar**	éclisse *f*	Lasche *f*	brida *f*
° 14361 **rail pass**	cannelures *f pl.* à rails	Schienenkaliber *n*	tracciato *m* per rotaie
° 14362 **rail rolling mill**	laminoir *m* à rails	Schienenwalzwerk *n*	laminatoio *m* per rotaie

	English	French	German	Italian
° 14363	rail spike, dog headed spike	crampon *m*	Krampe *f*, Haken *m*	arpione *m*, morsetto *m*
° 14364	rail-steel	acier *m* à rails	Schienenstahl *m*	acciaio *m* da rotaie
° 14365	railing	guide-mains *m*	Geländer *n*	corrimano *m*
14366	railway freight	transport *m* par chemin de fer	Eisenbahnfracht *f*	nolo *m* ferroviario
° 14367	railway materials	produits *m pl.* pour chemins de fer	Eisenbahnmaterial *n*	materiale *m* ferroviario
− 14368	raimondite	raimondite *f*	Raimondit *m*	raimondite *f*
− 14369	rain pillar	pyramide *f* coiffée	Erdpyramide *f*	piramide di terra
− 14370	to raise	monter, remonter, élever	aufziehen, erheben	montare, elevare, rimontare
14371	to raise	construire	errichten	costruire
− 14372	raise	montage *m*, remonta- ge	Aufhauen *n*, Aufbruch *m*	salita *f*, rimonta *f*, fornello *m*
− 14373	raise-stope	taille *f* montante	Schwebe *f*	taglio *m* in rimonta
− 14374	raise stoping	abattage *m* en remontage	Schwebebau *m*	abbattimento *m* in rimonta
− 14375	raise work	remontage *m*	Auffahren *n* eines Aufhauens	lavoro *m* in rimonta
− 14376	raised beach	terrasse *f* littorale	Strandterrasse *f*	terrazza *f* littorale
° 14377	raised top boiler	chaudière *f* à boîte à feu surhaussée	Kessel *m* mit überhöhtem Feurbüchsmantel	caldaia *f* con cassa-fo- colare rialzata
− 14378	raising	extraction, montage	Förderung *f*, Aufheben *n*	estrazione *f*, solle- vamento *m*
− 14379	raising of water	élévation de l'eau	Wasserförderung *f*	elevazione d'acqua
° 14380	to rake out slag	décrasser	abschlacken	scorificare
° 14381	rake	râteau *m*, croc à feu, crochet *m*	Rechen *m* Rührstange *f*	rastrello *m*, gancio *m* per rimescolare
− 14382	rake	inclinaison *f*, pendage *m*	Einfallen *n*	inclinazione *f*, pendenza *f*
− 14383	rake vein	filon *m* vertical, filon croiseur	steiler Gang *m*, Quergang *m*	filone *m* verticale

English	French	German	Italian
— 14384 raker	curette *f* de mineur	Krätzer *m*, Löffelräumer *m*	raschietto *m* da minatore
○ 14385 raking out the slag	décrassage *m*	Entschlackung *f*, Ausschlacken *n*	scorificazione *f*
— 14386 ralstonite	ralstonite *f*	Ralstonit *m*	ralstonite *f*
— 14387 ram a lining, to reline	damer	stampfen, rammen	pigiare, stivare
— 14388 to ram	fouler	stampfen	costipare
— 14389 to ram	bourrer	besetzen	rincalzare
○ 14390 to ram down the mould	enterrer le moule	den Formsand einstampfen, den Formsand in die Form drücken	sotterrare la forma
○ 14391 ram	mâchoire *f*	Backe *f*	mascella *f*
○ 14392 ram	défourneuse *f* de coke	Koksausdrück-maschine *f*	estrattrice *f* di coke
— 14393 ram	cric *m*	Winde *f*, Hebebock *m*	binda *f*, cricco *m'*
— 14394 ram-off	fausse variation *f*	scheinbare Versetzung *f*	pseudo variazione *f*
— 14395 ramble	faux toit *m*	Dachberge *m pl.*	falso tetto *m*
— 14396 ramdohrite	ramdohrite *f*	Ramdohrit *m*	ramdohrite *f*
○ 14397 ramie covered wire	fil sous ramie	Ramiedraht *m*	filo *m* isolato in ramié
— 14398 ramirite	ramirite *f*	Ramirit *m*	ramirite *f*
— 14399 rammelsbergite	rammelsbergite *f*	Rammelsbergit *m*	rammelsbergite *f*
— 14400 rammer	pilon *m*, mouton *m*, demoiselle *f*	Stampfer *m*, Rammbär *m*	piletta, pestello *m*, ariete *m*
— 14401 rammer	bourroir *m*	Ladestock *m*	mazza *f* a rincalzare
— 14402 rammer, tamper	damoir *m*, fouloir	Stampfe *f*	piletta *f*, battola *f*
— 14403 ramming	serrage *m* (du pisè)	Verdichtung *f* (der Stampfmasse)	battuta *f* (della pigiata)
— 14404 ramming a lining	damage *m*	Ausstampfen *n*	pigiatura *f*, pestatura *f*, costipamento *m*
○ 14404a ramming board	plaque *f* à fouler	Stampfplatte *f*	piastra *f* a costipare

	English	French	German	Italian
° 14405	**ramming piston**	piston *m* plongeur	Mönch *m*	stantuffo *m*
° 14406	**ramming plate**	plaque *f* de serrage	Zwischenplatte *f*	piastra *f* di serraggio
	ramming scab, *s. sand scab*			
° 14407	**ramming the mould**	serrage *m* du moule	Verdichten *n* der Form	stivaggio *m* (o stivatura *f)* di una forma
	ramp, *s. reverse fault*			
− 14408	**ramsayite**	ramsayite *f*	Ramsayit *m*	ramsayite *f*
− 14409	**rance**	marbre *m* belge	belgischer Marmor *m*	marmo *m* belga
− 14410	**randanite**	diatomite *f*	Infusorienerde *f*	diatomite *f*
− 14411	**randing**	recherche *f* par fouilles	Schürfen *n*	prospezione *f*, ricerca *f* (di giacimento)
− 14412	**range, extent**	rangée *f*, étendue *f*	Umfang *m*	perimetro *m*, contorno *m*
° 14412a	**range of stress**	gamme *f* des efforts	Spannungsbereich *m*	gamma *f* degli sforzi
○ 14413	**range of temperature**	étendue *f* de la température	Temperaturspanne *f*	intervallo *m* di temperatura
^ 14414	**rank wildcat**	puits *m* de recherche en zone imconnue	Aufschlussschacht *m* in unbekanntem Gebiet	pozzo *m* esplorativo in zona sconosciuta
− 14415	**ransomite**	ransomite *f*	Ransomit *m*	ransomite *f*
− 14416	**to rap**	sonder le toit	Firste *f* abklopfen	sondare il tetto
	to rap the pattern, *s. to loosen the pattern*			
° 14417	**rapid cupola, rapid**	cubilot *m* à rigole	Spurofen *m*	cubilotto *m* con avancrogiuolo
° 14418	**rapid series of sparks**	étincelles *f pl.* produites à une fréquence élevée	rasche aufeinanderfolgende Funken *m pl*	scintille *f pl.* prodotte ad una frequenza elevata
° 14418a	**rapid steel**	acier *m* rapide	Schnellstahl *m*	acciaio *m* rapido
° 14419	**rapper**	ébranloir *m*	Losklopfer *m*	ferro *m* per scampanare, barra *f* per scampanare
° 14420	**rapping**	ébranlage *m*	Losklopfen *n*	scampanatura *f*, branatura *f*
° 14421	**rapping bar, knock out bar**	barre *f* à ébranler, barre d'ébranlage	Losschlageisen *n*	ferro *m* per scampanare
○ 14422	**rapping device**	dispositif *m* d'ébranlage	Abklopfvorrichtung *f*	dispositivo *m* per scampanare

		English	French	German	Italian
°	14423	**rapping hammer**	maillet *m* conique	Spitzhammer *m*	mazzuolo conico *m*
°	14424	**rapping hammer (with one head)**	maillet *m* à une bobine	Flachspitz-hammer *m*	mazzuolo *m* conico con testa, mazzuolo *m* semplice
°	14425	**rapping hammer (with two heads)**	maillet *m* à deux bobines	Doppelkopfhammer *m*	mazzuolo *m* doppio, mazzuolo *m* conico a doppia testa
°	14425a	**rapping hole**	trou *m* d'ébranlage	Losklopfloch *n*	foro *m* di scampanatura
°	14426	**rapping pin**	picot *m* démouleur	Aushebeeisen *n*	ferro *m* da scampanare o per branatura
°	14427	**rapping plate**	plaque *f* d'ébranlage	Losschlagplatte *f*	piastra *f* per scampanare o per branatura
°	14428	**rapping spike**	pointe *f* à boucle	Aushebeeisen *n*	punta *f* a squadra (per modelli)
°	14429	**rarefaction, partial vacuum**	raréfaction *f* de l'air	Luftverdünnung *f*	rarefazione *f* d'aria
—	14430	**rash**	charbon *m* terreux	erdige Kohle *f*	carbone *m* terroso
°	14431	**rasp**	râpe *f*	Raspel *f*	raspa *f*
—	14432	**raspite**	raspite *f*	Raspit *m*	raspite *f*
		rat, *s. sticker*			
—	14433	**rat hole**	trou *m* de la tige	Rattenloch *n*, Spülstangenloch *n*	foro *m* dell'asta motrice, foro *m* ridotto, pozzetto *m* deviato
°	14434	**rat tail**	ver *m*	Rattenschwanz *m*	coda *f* di topo
—	14435	**ratchet drill**	cliquet *m*	(Bohr) Knarre *f*	trapano *m* a cricchetto
°	14435a	**rate of feed**	vitesse *f* d'avance	Vorschubgeschwindig-keit *f*	velocità *f* d'avanzamento
°	14436	**rate weight (of wind)**	débit *m* d'air	Windmenge *f*	portata *f* del vento
—	14437	**ratebane**	orpiment *m*	Auripigment *n*	orpimento *m*
—	14438	**rathite**	rathite *f*	Rathit *m*	rathite *f*
—	14439	**to rathole**	sonder au préalable	vorbohren	perforare un foro ridotto
°	14440	**rating plate**	plaque *f* signalétique	Leistungsschild *n*	targa *f* indicatrice
°	14441	**ratio rolling**	réduction *f* de laminage	Walz-Verhältnis *n*, Querschnittabnahme	rapporto *m* di laminazione

	English	French	German	Italian
° 14442	ratio of forging reduction	réduction *f* de forgeage	Schmiede--Verhältnis *n*	rapporto *m* di fucina-tura
° 14443	rattail scab	ver *m*	Rattenschwanz *m*	coda *f* di topo, tacco-ne a coda di topo
— 14444	rattle jack	schiste *m* houiller	Kohlenschiefer *m*	scisto *m* carbonifero
— 14445	rattler	cannel-coal *m*	Kannelkohle *f*	carbone *m* a lunga fiamma
° 14446	rattler	tambour *m* dessableur	Putztrommel *f*	tamburo *m* pulitore (di sabbia)
° 14447	rattling	dessablage *m* au tonneau	Gussputzerei *f* in Putztrommeln	pulitura *f* dalla sabbia
— 14448	rauchwacke	grauwacke *f*	Grauwacke *f*	grauwacke *f*
— 14449	raumite	raumite *f*	Raumit *m*	raumite *f*
— 14450	rauvite	rauvite *f*	Rauvit *m*	rauvite *f*
° 14451	raw block	lingot de départ	Abfahrtsmassel *f*	lingotto *m* di partenza
— 14452	raw coal	charbon *m* brut	Rohkohle *f*	carbone *m* grezzo
— 14453	raw dolomite	dolomie *f* crue	Rohdolomit *m*	dolomite *f* cruda
° 14454	raw-iron, crude-iron	fer *m* cru	Roheisen *n*	ferro *m* crudo (o grezzo)
— 14455	raw iron ore	minerai *m* de fer brut ou rugueux	rauhes Eisenerz *n*	minerale *m* di ferro crudo
° 14456	raw material	matière *f* première	Rohstoff *m*	materia *f* prima
— 14457	raw matte	matte *f* brute de cuivre	Kupferrohstein *m*	matta *f* grezza di rame
— 14457a	raw mine	minerai *m* de fer	Eisenerz *n*	minerale *m* di ferro
— 14458	raw ore	minerai *m* brut ou cru	Roherz *n*	minerale *m* grezzo
— 14459	raw shale	schiste *m* dur	fester Schiefer *m*	scisto *m* duro
° 14460	raw sheet iron	tôle *f* brute	Rohblech *n*	lamiera *f* grezza
° 14461	raw or poor slag	laitier *m* froid	Rohschlacke *f*	loppa *f* fredda
^ 14462	raw-water-white	distillat *m* léger	Leichtdestillat *n*	distillato *m* leggero
° 14463	raw zink	zinc *m* d'oeuvre	Werkzink *n*	zinco *m* grezzo
° 14464	razor blade	lame *f* de rasoir	Rasierklinge *f*	lama *f* per rasoio

English	French	German	Italian
− 14465 reacher	tenard *m*	Spreize *f*	puntello *m*
° 14466 to react	réagir	reagieren	reagire
° 14467 reaction	réaction *f*	Reaktion *f*	reazione *f*
° 14468 reaction blowholes	soufflures *f pl.* bleutées	blaugefärbte Blasen *f pl.*	soffiature *f pl.* azzurrognole
° 14469 reaction pinholes	piqûres *f pl.* homo-gènes bleutées	gleichmässig verteilte blau gefärbte Poren *f pl.*	camolatura *f* omoge-nea azzurrognola
ready, *s. finished*			
° 14470 ready for analysis	prêt pour l'analyse	analysenfertig	pronto per l'analisi
° 14471 reagent	réactif *m*	Reagens *n*	reattivo *m*, reagente *m*
° 14472 reagent bottle	flacon *m* à réactifs	Reagentienflasche *f*	bottiglia *f* per reagenti
° 14473 reagents	réactifs *m pl.*	Reagentien *n pl.*, Chemikalien *n pl.*	reattivi *m pl.*, reagenti *m pl.*
° 14474 real magnification	grossissement *m* réel	Eigenvergrösserung *f*	ingradimento *m* reale
° 14474a real strenght	charge *f* maximale	Höchstlast *f*	carico *m* massimo
− 14475 realgar	réalgar *m*	Realgar *m*	realgar *m*
− 14476 realigning	réparation *f* du boisage	Zimmerungs-ausbesserung *f*	riparazione *f* dell'arma-tura
− 14477 to ream	aléser	erweitern	alesare, allargare
− 14478 reamer	trépan aléseur	Räumer *m*, Nachnahmebohrer *m*	trapano *m* alesatore
− 14479 reaming	alésage *m*	•Aufbohrung *f*	alesaggio *m*, alesatura *f*
− 14480 reaming bit	trépan *m* aléseur	Nachnahmebohrer *m*	trapano *m* alesatore
− 14481 rear stand	colonne *f* d'arrière	Hintersäule *f*	cavalletto *m* poste-riore
° 14482 reboiler	rebouilleur *m*	Wiederaufkocher *m*	ribollitore *m*
° 14483 reboiler coil	serpentin *m* réfrigérant	Kühlschlange *f*, Kühlspirale *f*	serpentino *m* refrige-rante
° 14484 rebound	retour *m* élastique	Zurückfederung *f*	resa *f* elastica
° 14485 recarburisation	recarburation *f*	Rückkohlung *f*	ricarburazione *f*
° 14486 recarburize	recarburer	wiederaufkohlen	ricarburare

English	French	German	Italian
14487 to recase	recuveler	Küvelage *f* überholen	rivestire
14488 receiver	récipient *m*	Sammelgefäss *n*	serbatoio *m*
14489 receiver	avant-creuset *m*	Eisensammelraum *m*	crogiuolo *m* anteriore, avancrogiuolo *m*
14489a recess	gorge *f*	Hinterschneidung *f*	scanalatura *f* incanalata
14490 recess	refuge *m*	Schiessort m	rifugio *m* antimine
14491 recessing tool	outil *m* à chambrer	Bohrstahl *m*	utensile *m* da alesare interni
14492 to reciprocate	soulever et baisser alternativement	wechselweise heben und senken	alzare e abbassare alternativamente (il casing)
14493 reciprocating hearth	sole *f* oscillante	Schwingherd *m*	suola *f* oscillante
14494 reciprocating (pump)	(pompe) *f* alternative	Kolben(pumpe)	pompa *f* alternativa
14495 reciprocating mill	laminoir *m* à mouvement alternatif, train *m* réversible	Reversierwalzwerk *n*, Kehrwalzwerk *n*	laminatoio *m* a movimento alternato
14496 reciprocating scratchers	gratteurs *m pl.* de tubage horizontales	waagerechte Kratzer *m pl.*	baffi *m pl.* di gatto orizzontali
14497 reclaimed oil	huile *f* régénérée	Regeneratöl *n*	olio *m* rigenerato
14498 reclaiming and conveying screw	vis *f* sans fin d'extraction et transport	Extraktionförderschnecke *f*	coclea *f* estrattrice e trasportatrice
14499 reclaiming timber	déboisage *m*	Holzrauben *f*	disarmo *m*
14500 recleaner	finisseuse *f*	Nachreiniger *m*	fucinatrice *f*
14501 recoil, spring beam	billot *m*, rabat *m*	Prellung *f*, Prellklotz *m*	trave *f* elastica
14502 recoil spindle	tige *f* de butée	Prellbolzen *m*	stelo *m* ammortizzatore
14503 recoil spring	ressort *m* de rappel	Rückschnellfeder *f*	mollone *m* di recupero
14503a recompacting	recompression *f*	Nachpressen *n*	ricompressione *f*
14504 recondition	effectuer une révision	revisionieren	revisionare
14505 reconditioned sand	sable *m* régénéré	aufbereiteter Sand *m*	sabbia *f* rigenerata
14506 reconstructed glacier	glacier *m* régénéré	regenerierter Gletscher *m*	ghiacciaio *m* rigenerato

	English	French	German	Italian
^ 14507	recording truck	camion *m* enregistreur	Registrier-Lastwagen *m*	autocarro *m* registrátore
^ 14508	recovered acid	acide *m* de récupération	Rückgewinnungssäure *f*	acido *m* di recupero
^ 14509	recovery plant	installation *f* de récupération	Rekuperativanlage *f*	impianto *m* di recupero
^ 14510	recovery	récupération *f*	Wiedergewinnung *f*	recupero *m*, rigenerazione *f*
14511	recovery	rendement *m*	Ausbringen *n*	resa *f*
° 14512	recovery oven	four *m* à coke avec récupération des sous-produits	Nebenprodukt-koksofen *m*	forno *m* a coke con recupero dei sotto prodotti
− 14513	recrusher	broyeur *m* secondaire	Zwischenbrecher *m*	frantoio *m* secondario
− 14514	recrushing	broyage *m* secondaire	Zwischenzerkleinern *n*	frantumazione *f* secondaria
− 14515	recrystallisation	recristallisation *f*	Rekristallisation *f*	ricristallizzazione *f*
	recrystallising, *s. normalising*			
° 14516	rectangular billet	billette *f* méplate ou rectangulaire	Flach-Knüppel *m*	biletta *f* rettangolare
− 14517	rectangular funnel-shaped truck	wagon *m* trémie rectangulaire	vierseitiger, trichter-förmiger Wagen *m*	vagone - tramoggia *m* rettangolare
° 14518	rectangular ingot, slab ingot	lingot *m* rectangulaire	rechteckiger Block *m*	lingotto *m* a sezione rettangolare
° 14519	rectangular tube	tube *m* de section rectangulaire	rechteckiges Rohr *n*	tubo *m* rettangolare
^ 14520	rectification	rectification *f*	Rektifikation *f*	rettificazione *f*
^ 14521	rectifier	rectificateur *m*	Rektifikator *m*	rettificatore *m*
− 14522	recumbent anticline	anticlinal *m* incliné	anliegende Antiklinale *f*	anticlinale *f* coricata (o rovesciata)
− 14523	recumbent fold	pli couché	liegende Falte *f*	piega *f* coricata (o inclinata)
° 14524	recuperative furnace	four *m* à récupération de chaleur	Rekuperativofen *m*	forno *m* a ricuperatore di calore
° 14525	recuperator	récupérateur *m*	Rekuperator *m*	ricuperatore *m* (di calore)

	English	French	German	Italian
^ 14526	to recycle	recirculer	rezyklieren	ritornare in ciclo
^ 14527	recycle gas	gaz de circuit	Kreislaufgas n	gas m di riciclo
^ 14528	recycle ration	rapport m de récirculation	Zirkulations- verhältniss n	rapporto m di riciclo
^ 14529	recycling	récyclage m, récirculation f	Rezyklus m	riciclo m, ritorno m in ciclo
o 14530	red border	bord m rouge	rote Umränderung f	contorno m rosso
o 14531	red brass	laiton m rouge, bronze m	Rotguss m, rotes Messing n	bronzo m rosso
	red-caster, s. copper-founder			
−14532	red clay	argile f rouge	roter Tiefseeton m	argilla f rossa
−14533	red copper ore	cuprite f	Cuprit m	cuprite f
o 14534	red gas stream	jet m de gaz rouge, flamme f rouge	rot erleuchteter Gasstrom m	fiamma f rossa
o 14535	red hard	cassant à chaud	rotbrüchig	fragile a caldo
o 14536	red-hard steel	acier m rapide	Schnellstahl m	acciaio m rapido
o 14537	red hardness	dureté f au rouge	Rotglühhärte f	durezza f al rosso
o 14538	to a red-heat	au rouge	zum Glühen	al rosso
o 14539	red heat	rouge (au feu), au rouge	rotwarm, (rot) glühend	arroventato, riscalda- to al rosso, al colore rosso
o 14540	red-heat, glow	chaude f rouge, rouge chaude f, chaleur f d'incan- descence	Rotglut f, (Rot)Glühhitze f	calore rosso, caldo rosso, calore rovente
−14541	red hematite	oxyde m de fer anhydre, hématite f rouge	Roteisenstein m	sesquiossido m di ferro, ematite f rossa
o 14542	red-hot iron	fer m rouge	Glüheisen n	ferro m arroventato
−14543	read lead ore	crocoïte	Krokoit m	crocoite f
	red ooze, s. red clay			
−14544	red oxide	oxide m mercureux	Quecksilberoxyd n	ossido m di mercurio
o 14545	red rust	rouille f	Rost m	ruggine f
_14546	red sandstone	grès m rouge	roter Sandstein m	arenaria f rossa

	English	French	German	Italian
○ 14547	**red-short, hot-short**	cassant à chaud	rotbrüchig, heissbrüchig	fragile a caldo
○ 14548	**red-short iron**	fer *m* cassant à chaud	rotbrüchiges Eisen *n*	ferro fragile a caldo
○ 14549	**red-shortness, hot-shortness**	fragilité *f* à chaud	Heissbrüchigkeit *f*	fragilità *f* al caldo, o al rosso
− 14550	**red silver ore**	proustite *f*, pyrargyrite *f*	lichtes Rotgültig *m*, Proustit *m*	proustite *f*, pirargirite *f*
− 14551	**red tourmaline**	tourmaline *f* rouge	roter Turmalin *m*	turmalina *f* rossa
○ 14551a	**red stain**	tache *f* rougeâtre	rötlicher Flecken *m*	macchia *f* rossastra
− 14552	**red zinc ore**	zincite *f*	Zinkit *m*	zincite *f*
− 14553	**reddish clay**	argile *f* rosée	rötlicher Ton *m*	argilla *f* rosa
− 14554	**reddle**	ocre *f* rouge	Blutstein *m*	ocra *f* rossa
^ 14555	**redistillation**	redistillation *f*	Redestillation *f*	ridistillazione *f*
○ 14556	**redrawing**	emboutissage *m* de reprise	Ziehen *n* im Weiterschlag	imbutitura *f* di ripresa
○ 14557	**to redrill**	reforer	neubohren	riforare
○ 14558	**redruthite**	chalcosine *f*	Redruthit *m*	redruite *f*
○ 14559	**to reduce**	réduire	reduzieren	ridurre
○ 14560	**to reduce the output**	diminuer la production	die Leistung vermindern	diminuire la produzione
	reduce-roll, *s. forging roll*			
^ 14561	**reduced crude**	huile *f* réduite	Reduktionserdöl *n*	crudo *m* ridotto
○ 14562	**reduced iron**	fer *m* réduit	reduziertes Eisen *n*	ferro *m* ridotto
^ 14563	**reducer**	manchon *m* de réduction	Reduzierstück *n*	manicotto *m* riduttore
○ 14564	**reducing**	réduisant, désoxydant	reduzierend	riducente
○ 14564a	**reducing**	réduction *f* d'épaisseur	Abnahme *f* beim Walzen	riduzione *f* di spessore
○ 14565	**reducing agent**	réducteur *m*	Reduktionsmittel *n*	riducente *m*
○ 14566	**reducing and sizing mill**	laminoir *m* réducteur et calibreur	Kaltreduzier- und Kalibrierwalzwerk *n*	laminatoio *m* riduttore e calibratore
○ 14567	**reducing die**	matrice *f* à réduire	Reduziergesenk *n*	**stampo** *m* di riduzione
○ 14567a	**reducing flame**	flamme *f* réductrice	Reduktionsflamme *f*	fiamma *f* riducente

English	French	German	Italian
° 14568 **reducing furnace**	four *m* de réduction	Reduktionsofen *m*	forno *m* di riduzione
reducing-fusion, *s. reducing-smelting*			
° 14569 **reducing mill**	laminoir *m* réducteur	Kalibrierwalzwerk *n*	laminatoio *m* riduttore
° 14570 **reducing-smelting**	fusion *f* réductrice, fondage de réduction	reduzierendes Schmelzen *n*	fusione *f* riduttiva
° 14571 **reduction**	désoxydation *f*, réduction *f*	Desoxydation *f*, Reduzieren *n*	disossidazione *f*, riduzione *f*
° 14572 **reduction furnace**	four *m* de réduction	Reduktionsofen *m*	forno *m* di riduzione
° 14573 **reduction in area**	coefficient *m* de striction	Einschnürung *f*	coefficiente *m* di strizione, coefficiente *m* di riduzione
° 14574 **reduction of cross section, drawing down**	réduction *f* de section	Querschnittsverminderung *f*	diminuzione *f* della sezione
° 14575 **reduction of furnace dust**	réduction *f* de la poussière au fourneau	Gichtstaubverminderung *f*	diminuzione *f* di polvere (alla bocca) del forno
° 14576 **reduction or draft of passes**	réduction *f* de section des cannelures	Abnahme *f* des Kalibers	riduzione *f* di sezione dei canali
° 14576a **reduction ratio**	degrée *f* de réduction	Reduktionsgrad *m*	grado *m* di riduzione
° 14577 **reduction slag**	scorie *f* réductrice	Reduktionsschlacke *f*	scoria *f* riduttrice
° 14578 **reduction temperature**	température *f* de réduction	Reduktionstemperatur *f*	temperatura *f* di riduzione
° 14579 **reduction zone**	zone *f* de réduction	Reduktionszone *f*	zona *f* di riduzione
reduplication, *s. stratigraphical overlap*			
° 14580 **reed, non metallic inclusion**	inclusion *f* non métallique	nichtmetallischer Einschluss *m*	inclusione non metallica (difetto di laminazione)
° 14580a **reed, shrinkhole**	cavité *f*	Lunkerstelle *f*	risucchio *m*
— 14581 **reed**	mèche *f*	Zündschnur *f*	miccia *f*
— 14582 **Reed roller bit**	trépan *m* à molettes de Reed	Reed-Rollenmeissel *m*	trapano *m* di Reed
— 14583 **reef**	récif *m*	Riff *n*	scogliera *f*
— 14584 **reef**	filon *m* aurifère	Goldgang *m*	filone *m* aurifero (o tabulare)
— 14585 **reef band**	filon *m* tabulaire	Tafelflöz *n*	filone *m* tabulare
— 14586 **reef drive**	gallerie *f* de chassage	Richtungstunnel *m*	galleria *f* in direzione entrobanco

English	French	German	Italian
— 14587 **reef facies**	faciès *m* récifal	Rifffazies *f*	facies *f* di scogliera
° 14587a **reeler, reeling mill**	laminoir lisseur pour tubes	Friemelwalzwerk *n*	laminatoio *m* lisciatore di tubi
—— 14588 **to reeve**	passer le câble dans le moufle	Einführen des Drahtseils in den Flaschenzug	passare (il cavo) nella taglia
— 14589 **reeved up**	monté, fixé	montiert	montato, fissato
14590 **reference book**	répertoire *m*	Nachschlagewerk *n*	manuale *m* di consultazione
° 14591 **reference gauge**	calibre *m* de référence	Messkaliber *n*	calibro *m* di riferimento
14592 **reference N. of basic material**	numéro de matière	Werkstoff-Nummer *f*	numero *m* unificato di materiale
° 14593 **to refine**	affiner, raffiner, épurer	feinen, reinigen, raffinieren, frischen	affinare, raffinare
° 14594 **to refine steel**	(r)affiner l'acier	den Stahl gärben	affinare l'acciaio
° 14595 **to refine (the cast) iron**	affiner (ou mazer) la fonte	das Roheisen frischen	affinare la ghisa
° 14596 **to refine the tin**	affiner l'étain	das Zinn verfeinern	affinare lo stagno
° 14597 **refined and hardened, R & H**	affiné et trempé	verfeinert und gehärtet	affinato e temprato
refined copper, *s. tough pitch-copper*			
° 14598 **refined graphite, washed graphite**	graphite *m* lavé	gereinigter Graphit *m*	grafite *m* lavata o purificata
° 14599 **refined iron, refined pig iron**	fonte *f* affinée, fonte *f* mazée	verfeinertes Gusseisen *n*	ghisa *f* affinata (o raffinata)
° 14600 **refined iron**	fer *m* affiné	Frischfeuereisen *n*	ferro *m* affinato
° 14601 **refined iron, special iron**	fer *m* spécial, fer *m* de qualité	Qualitätseisen *n*	ferro *m* di qualità
refined pig iron, *s. refined iron*			
° 14602 **refined steel**	acier *m* fin	Edelstahl *m*	acciaio *m* raffinato
refined zone, *s. weld junction* **refinement,** *s. refining* **refiner,** *s. finer*			
° 14603 **refinery**	affinerie *f*	Umschmelzwerk *n*	affineria *f*, raffineria *f*
° 14604 **refinery slag**	scorie *f* d'affinage	Raffinierschlacke *f*, Garschlacke *f*	scoria *f* d'affinazione

English	French	German	Italian
14605 **refining**	raffinage *m*, affinage	Affinieren *n*	affinaggio *m*, raffinazione
14606 **refining, fining process**	méthode *f* d'affinage	Frischenmethode *f*, Vergütung *f*	affinazione *f*, affinamento *m*, processo *m* d'affinamento
14607 **refining**	épuration *f*	Reinigung *f*	depurazione *f*
14608 **refining boiler**	chaudière *f* de raffinage	Läuterungskessel *m*	caldaia *f* di raffinazione
14609 **refining (cast iron) in the reverberatory furnace**	affinage (de la fonte) au four à réverbère	Flammofenfrischen *n*	affinamento (della ghisa) al forno a riverbero
14610 **refining flux**	épurant *m*	Reinigungsmittel *n*	depurante *m*
14611 **refining foam**	bourre *f*, limaille *f*	Garschaum *m*	lustrino *m*
14612 **refining forge slag**	scorie *f* de feu d'affinerie	Frischfeuerschlacke *f*	scoria *f* di forno d'affinazione
14613 **refining furnace**	four *m* d'affinage	Frischofen *m*, Raffinierofen *m*	forno *m* d'affinazione, raffinatoio per metalli
14613a **refining heat**	température *f* d'affinage	Feinungstemperatur *f*	temperatura *f* d'affinazione
14614 **refining in open hearth**	affinage au bas-foyer	Herdfrischen *n*	affinaggio al basso fuoco
14615 **refining of metals**	affinage des métaux	Läutern *n* (Raffinieren *n*) der Metalle	affinamento dei metalli
14616 **refining process**	procédé *m* de raffinage	Raffinierprozess *m*, Frischverfahren *n*	processo *m* di raffinazione
14617 **refining puddling**	affinage *m*	Feinpuddeln *n*	affinaggio *m* affinatura *f*, raffinazione *f*
14618 **refining (of) steel**	affinage (ou corroyage) de l'acier	Raffinieren *n* des Stahls	affinaggio (o affinamento) dell'acciaio
14619 **refining with iron ore**	affinage *m* avec du minerai de fer	Erzglühfrischen *n*	affinaggio *m* col minerale di ferro
— 14620 **reflection shooting**	sismique *f* à réflexion	Reflexsismik *f*	sismica *f* a riflessione
^ 14621 **reflux tower**	colonne *f* de distillation à reflux	Flussdestillationssäule *f*	colonna *f* di distillazione a riflusso
to refond, *s. to remelt*			
^ 14622 **reformed gasoline**	essence *f* réformée	Reformbenzin *n*	benzina *f* riformata

	English	French	German	Italian
− 14623	refraction shooting	sismique à réfraction	Refraktionssismik *f*	sismica *f* a rifrazione
° 14624	refractoriness	réfractaireté *f*, résistance au feu	Feuerfestigkeit *f*	refrattarietà *f*, resistenza *f* al fuoco
° 14625	refractory	réfractaire *m*	feuerfester Stoff *m*	refrattario *m*, materiale *m* refrattario
° 14626	refractory	réfractaire	feuerfest	refrattario
° 14627	refractory brick	brique *f* réfractaire	feuerfester Stein *m*	mattone *m* refrattario
° 14628	refractory cement	ciment *m* réfractaire	feuerfester Zement *m*	cemento *m* refrattario
	refractory clay, *s. fire clay*			
° 14629	refractory dressing	poteyage *m*, garnissage réfractaire	Schlichten *n*, feuerfeste Auskleidung *f*	rivestimento *m* refrattario
° 14630	refractory furnace lining	garnissage *m* réfractaire du four	feuerfeste Auskleidung *f* des Ofens	rivestimento *m* refrattario del forno
° 14631	refractory iron ore	minerai *m* difficilement fusible	schwer schmelzbares Erz *n*	minerale *m* difficilmente fusibile
° 14632	refractory lining	garnissage *m* réfractaire	feuerfestes Futter *n*	rivestimento *m* refrattario
° 14633	refractory materials for crucibles	matière *f* pour creusets	Tiegelmasse *f*	materiale *m* refrattario per crogiuoli
° 14634	refractory mortar	mortier *m* réfractaire, coulis réfractaire	feuerfester Mörtel *m*	malta *f* refrattaria
	refractory wash, *s. refractory mortar*			
° 14635	refractory wash, refractory dressing	poteyage *m*	Schlichte *f*	rivestimento *m* isolante
	refrigeration, *s. cooling*			
° 14636	refuge chamber	refuge *m*	Schiessort *m*	rifugio *m* antimine
14637	refusal of acception	refus *m* de réception	Annahmeverweigerung *f*	rifiuto *m* d'accettazione
− 14638	refuse	déblai *m*	Berge *f*	sterile *m*, rifiuti *m pl.*
° 14639	refuse burning furnace, garbage-consuming furnace, garbage incinerator	four à brûler les ordures, foyer pour incineration des ordures	Müllverbrennungsofen *m*	inceneratore di rifiuti
° 14640	refuse coke	rebut *m* de coke	Koksabfall *m*	scarti *m pl.* di coke

English	French	German	Italian
14641 **refuse destructor furnace**	foyer *m* à gadoues, foyer *m* à ordures ménagères	Müllfeuerung *f*	focolare *m* da spazzatura
14642 **refuse dump**	terril *m*, crassier *m*	Berghalde *f*	deposito *m* dei rifiuti
14643 **refusion**	fusion *f*, anatexis *f*	Anatexis *f*	anatessi *f*, fusione *f*
14644 **regenerated gas**	gaz *m* réchauffé	vorgewärmtes Heizgas *n*	gas *m* rigenerato
14645 **regenerative coke oven**	four *m* régénérateur à coke	Regenerativkoksofen *m*	forno *m* rigeneratore a coke
14646 **regenerative furnace**	foyer *m* à récupération intermittente	Regenerativfeuerung *f*	focolare *m* a rigenerazione
14647 **regenerative velocity of the ions**	vitesse *f* de régénération des ions	Neubildungsgeschwindigkeit *f* der Ionen	velocità *f* di rigenerazione degli ioni

regenerative chamber, *s. regenerator*

14648 **regenerator, regenerative chamber**	régénérateur *m*, récupérateur *m*	Wärmespeicher *m* Regenerator *m*	rigeneratore *m*, ricuperatore *m*, camera *f* di rigenerazione
14649 **to register**	engoujonner	verdübeln	accoppiare

register pin, *s. safety stake*

14650 **region of melting**	région *f* d'ablation	Zehrgebiet *n*	regione *f* d'ablazione
14651 **regrinding**	rectifier	nachschleifen	rettificare ulteriormente
14652 **regular lay wire-rope**	câble métallique tordu spiroïdal	Spiralseil *n*	fune *f* metallica ritorta a spirale
14653 **regular tool joint**	joint *m* normal	Verbinder *m* mit verengtem Durchgang	giunto *m* normale
14654 **regular working of the furnace**	marche *f* régulière du four	gleichmässiger Ofengang *m*	andamento *m* regolare del forno
14655 **regulating agent**	stabilisant *m*	Stabilisator *m*	stabilizzante *m*
14656 **regulating cock**	robinet *m* de réglage	Regulierhahn *m*	rubinetto *m* regolatore

regulating slide valve, *s. operating valve*

14657 **regulation, adjustment**	réglage *m*	Einstellung *f*	registrazione *f*

English	French	German	Italian
° 14658 **regulation box**	boîte *f* de distribution	Schaltgehäuse *n*	cassa *f* di distribuzione
^ 14659 **regulation by stop cock**	distribution *f* par robinet	Hahnsteuerung *f*	distribuzione *f* a rubinetto
° 14660 **regulation of the air current**	réglage *m* de l'air	Regelung *f* des Luftstromes	regolazione *f* dell'aria
° 14661 **regulation of water pressure**	réglage *m* de la pression d'eau	Wasserdruck-regelung *f*	regolazione *f* della pressione dell'acqua
° 14662 **regulation door**	porte *f* à guichet	Stromverteilungstür *f*	porta *f* per regolare l'aria
— 14662a **reguline deposit**	dépôt *m* regulin	regulinischer Niederschlag *m*	deposito *m* compatto
° 14663 **regulus**	régule *m*, culot *m*	Regulus *m*, Speise *f*	metallo *m* antifrizione
° 14664 **regulus furnace**	four *m* à régule	Regulusofen *m*	forno *m* di metallo antifrizione
° 14665 **to reheat**	réchauffer	wiedererwärmen	riscaldare
° 14666 **to reheat**	recuire	anlassen	ricuocere
to reheat, *s. to temper*			
reheat treating, *s. retreating*			
° 14667 **reheating**	chauffage *m*	Erhitzen *n*	riscaldamento
° 14668 **reheating chamber**	chambre *f* de recombustion	Wiederverbrennungs-kammer *f*	camera *f* di ricombustione
° 14669 **reheating-furnace**	four *m* à réchauffer	Tiefofen *m* Wiederhitzungsofen *m*	forno *m* di riscaldamento
° 14670 **reheating furnace slag, tap cinder**	scorie *f* de réchauffage	Schweissofen-schlacke *f*	scoria *f* di ricottura
° 14671 **reheating furnace with movable hearth**	four *m* à réchauffer à sole mobile	Wärmofen *m* mit beweglichem Herd	forno *m* di riscaldo a suola mobile
— 14672 **reheating oven**	calorifère *m*	Heizofen *m*	forno *m* di riscaldamento
° 14673 **reheating timbering**	boisage *m* armé	verstärkte Zimmerung *f*	armatura *f* rinforzata, rivestimento *m* armato
— 14674 **reichardite**	reichardtite *f*	Reichardtit *m*	reichardite *f*
— 14675 **reinforced concrete**	beton *m* armé	Eisenbeton *n*	cemento *m* armato
reinforced seam, *s. resistance-butt weld*			

English	French	German	Italian
14676 reinforcing pad	plaque f de renfort	Verstärkungsplatte f	piastra f di rinforzo
14677 reinforcing rod	fer m bétonné	Betoneisen n	ferro m di armatura
14678 reinite	reinite f	Reinit m	reinite f
14679 reissite	reissite f	Reissit m	reissite f
14680 to reject the test	refuser l'échantillon	die Probe verwerfen	rifiutare la prova
14681 to rejuvenate	rajeunir	verjüngen, wiederauffrischen	ringiovanire
1468la relative density	densité f relative	relative Dichte f	densità f relativa
14682 release	déclenchement m	Auslösung f	liberazione f
14683 releasing spear	taraud m rattrappe--tube intérieur à coin dégagéable	Innenrohrfänger m mit trennbarem Keil	pescatore m interno a cuneo svincolabile
14684 reliction	régression f	Regression f	regressione
14685 relief edged squeeze board	plateau m à bordure	Pressplatte f mit Randwulst	placca f bordata, piastra f bordata
14686 relief hole	forage m de secours	Entlastungsbohrung f	sondaggio m d'inter- vento
relief plate, s. balance plate			
14687 relief polishing	polissage m en relief	Reliefpolieren n	lucidatura f in rilievo
14688 relief valve	ventouse f à air	Entlüftungsventil n	valvola f per l'aria
14689 relief well	puits m auxiliaire	Hilfsbohrloch n	pozzo m di sfogo, pozzo m d'intervento
14690 reliever	trou m auxiliaire m	Hilfsbohrloch n	foro m ausiliare
relieving lathe, s. backing-off lathe			
14691 relieving temperature	température f de distension	Dehnungs- temperatur f	temperatura f di distensione
relieving, s. easing or joint breaking			
14692 relieving timbers	reboisage m	Auswechseln n der Zimmerung	sostituzione f del- l'armatura
14693 reline	brasquage m	Glasurbrand m	rivestimento m
relining, s. ramming a lining			
relining the furnace, s. fettling the furnace			
14694 reloading die	matrice f à recalibrer	Kalibriermatritze f	matrice f per ricali- brare
14695 to remelt, to recast	refondre	einschmelzen, umgiessen	rifondere

	English	French	German	Italian
° 14696	to remain red hot	rester rouge	glühend bleiben	restare rosso
° 14697	remelted iron	fonte *f* refondue	umgeschmolzenes Eisen *n*	ghisa *f* rifusa
° 14698	remelted steel	acier *m* refondu	umgeschmolzener Stahl *m*	acciaio *m* rifuso
° 14699	remelting	refusion *f*, refonte *f*	Umschmelzen *n*	rifusione *f*
° 14700	remelting furnace	four *m* à refondre	Umschmelzofen *m*	forno *m* di rifusione
° 14701	remelting process	procédé *m* de refonte	Umschmelzverfahren	processo *m* di rifusione
° 14702	remote control switch	interrupteur *m* commandé à distance	Fernschalter *m*	interruttore *m* tele-comandato
	removable cap, *s. screwed-on cover*			
° 14703	removable (conical) plug	fond *m* amovible (conique)	Losboden *m*	fondo *m* ricambiabile (conico)
° 14704	removable core	noyau *m* détachable	Losteil *n*	anima-tassello *f*
° 14705	removable cover	couvercle *m* mobile	abnehmbarer Deckel *m*	coperchio *m* mobile
° 14706	removable cylindrical plug	fond *m* cylindrique perforé	Durchziehboden *m*	fondo *m* ricambiabile cilindrico
	removable hood, *s. removable top*			
° 14707	removable hood	chapeau *m*	Kappe *f*	cappello *m*
° 14708	removable inner boiler	chaudière *f* intérieure mobile	herausnehmbarer Einsatzkessel *m*	caldaia *f* interiore asportabile
° 14709	removable top	chapeau *m*	Kappe *f*	cappello *m*
° 14710	removal of ashes	enlèvement *m* des cendres	Aschenabfuhr *f*	trasporto *m* della cenere
° 14711	removal of clinker	nettoyage *m* des grilles	Rostschlagen *n*	pulizia *f* delle griglie
° 14712	removal of the plug	enlèvement *m* du fond	Ausstossen *n* des Bodens	estrazione *f* del fondo
° 14713	removable parts *pl.*	parties *f pl.* amovibles	trennbare Teile *m pl.*	pezzi *m pl.* o parti *f pl.* di ricambio
° 14714	removable tubular boiler	chaudière *f* à foyer amovible	Kessel *m* mit ausziehbarer Feuerung	caldaia *f* a focolare asportabile

English	French	German	Italian
— 14715 to remove pillars	dépiler	Pfeiler abbauen, abpfeilern	disarmare (un pozzo)
o 14716 to remove the dust	dépoussiérer	entstauben	depolverare, spolverare
o 14717 to remove the heads	démasselotter	die Speiser abschlagen, die Steiger entfernen	smaterozzare
o 14718 to remove the seam	enlever les bavures de joint	die Gussnaht entfernen	togliere la sbavatura, sbavare
o 14719 to remove the strain	détendre	entspannen	distendere
o 14720 removing the dust	séparation f des poussières	Entstaubung f	separazione f delle polveri
o, 14721 removing heads	démasselottage m	Abschlagen n der Speiser	smaterozzatura f
o 14722 removing of the scale	enlèvement m des battitures	Beseitigung f des Glühspans	rimozione delle battiture
o 14723 removing the pickling acid	battage m du fil	Poltern n	battitura del filo
— 14724 renardite	renardite f	Renardit m	renardite f
rending explosive, s. high-explosive			
— 14725 renewed fault	faille f réouverte	wiedereröffneter Sprung m	faglia f riaperta
o 14725a reniform	réniforme	nierenförmig	reniforme
— 14726 rensselaerite	rensselaerite f	Rensselaerit m	rensselaerite f
— 14727 rent	fissure f, fracture f, fente f	Spalte f, Kluft f, Bruch m	fessura f, crepa f, frattura f, cricca f
— 14728 reopened vein	filon m de rem-plissage secondaire	wiedereröffneter Gang m	filone m di riempi-mento secondario
— 14729 to reoxidize	réoxyder	reoxydieren	riossidare
o 14730 to repair the mould	réparer le moule	die Form f nacharbeiten	riparare la forma
o 14731 repair shop	atelier m de répa-ration	Ausbesserungs-werkstatt f	officina f delle ripa-razioni
repairing the lining, s. fettling the furnace			
o 14732 repeated impact test, repeated blow test	essai m de fatigue par choc	Dauerschlagversuch m	prova f di fatica a urti ripetuti
o 14733 repeated shocks, repeated impact	chocs m pl. répétés	wiederholte Schläge m pl.	urti m pl. ripetuti

	English	French	German	Italian
°	14734 repeated transverse impact test	essai *m* de flexion au choc(s) répété	wiederholter Schlagbiegeversuch *m*	prova *f* di flessione agli urti ripetuti
°	14735 repeated use	réemploi *m*	Wiederverwendung *f*	secondo impiego *m*
°	14736 repeated use of water	emploi *m* répété des eaux	wiederholte Benutzung *f* des Wassers	uso *m* ripetuto dell'acqua
°	14737 replace pattern in mould	rappuyer	Modell nochmals eindrücken	ribattere, ripiazzare
	replacement, *s. metasomatism*			
°	14738 replacing pattern in the mould	rappuyage *m*	Prüfen *n* der Form durch nochmaliges Einlegen des Modells	ripiazzatura *f*
°	14738a repouse	repoussé *m*	getriebene Arbeit *f*	cesellatura *f*
—	14739 repressuring	remise *f* en pression	Gaseinpressen *n*	rimessa *f* in pressione, ricostituzione *f* della pressione negli strati
—	14740 to rerun	redescendre dans le puits	wiedereinfahren	ridiscendere in pozzo
^	14741 rerun oil	huile *f* redistillée	wiederdestilliertes Öl *n*	olio *m* ridistillato
^	14742 rerunning	redistillation *f*	wiederholte Destillierung *f*	ridistillazione *f*, rettifica *f*
^	14743 reserve estimate	estimation *f* des réserves	Reserveschätzung *f*	stima *f* delle riserve
^	14744 reserve of fuel	carburant *m* de réserve	Brennstoffreserve *f*	riserva *f* di carburante
	reserve piece, *s. spare piece*			
^	14745 reservoir, tank	réservoir d'eau	Wasserbehälter *m*	serbatoio *m* d'acqua, serbatoio *m*
	reservoir, *s. air chamber*			
—	14746 reservoir energy	pression *f* souterraine	unterirdischer Druck *m*	pressione *f* sotterranea
—	14747 reservoir engineering	technique *f* d'exploitation des gisements	Lagerförderungstechnik *f*	tecnica *f* di coltivazione dei giacimenti
^	14748 reservoir gas-oil ratio	rapport *m* gaz-huile dans le gisement	Gas-Öl Verhältnis *n* im Lager	rapporto *m* gas-olio nel giacimento

English	French	German	Italian
^ 14749 reservoir pressure	pression _f_ de gisement	Schichtendruck _m_	pressione _f_ di giacimento
^ 14750 reservoir rock	roche-magasin _f_	Speichergestein _n_	roccia-magazzino _m_
^ 14751 reservoir sample	échantillon _f_ de gisement	Sohlenprobe _f_	campione _m_ di giacimento
^ 14752 reset control	contrôle _m_ de déviation	Verschiebungs-kontrolle _f_	controllo _m_ di deviazione
^ 14753 residual, residuum	résidu _m_	Rückstand _m_	residuo _m_
o 14753a residual elements	éléments associés	Begleitelemente _n pl._	elementi associati
— 14754 residual liquor	magma _m_ résiduel	Restmagma _n_	magma _m_ residuo
^ 14755 residual oil	pétrole _m_ restant	Restöl _n_	petrolio _m_ residuo
o 14756 residual scale	calamine _f_ résiduelle	Zunderreste _m pl._	strato _m_ residuo di ossido
— 14757 residual soil	résidu _m_ de la décomposition	Verwitterungs-rückstand _m_	residuo _m_ di decompressione
^ 14758 residual stocks	fractions _f pl._ résiduelles	Restfraktionen _f pl._	frazioni _f pl._ residue
o 14758a residual stress	effort _m_ résiduel	Eigenspannung _f_	sforzo _m_ residuo
residual welding stress, _s. welding stress_			
residue, _s. waste_			
^ 14759 residue unsoluble in acid	résidu _m_ insoluble dans l'acide	in Säure unlöslicher Rückstand _m_	residuo _m_ insolubile nell'acido
o 14760 resilience	résilience _f_	Federung _f_, Federsteife _f_	resilienza _f_
o 14761 resin, rosin	résine _f_	Harz _n_	resina _f_
o 14762 resin	colophane _f_	Kolophonium _n_	colofonia _f_, pece _f_ greca
o 14763 resin-cored solder	soudure _f_ en tube avec décapant intérieur	Rozhrlötzinn _n_	saldatura _f_ in filo preparata
o 14763a resintering	refrittage _m_	Nachsintern _n_	risinterizzazione _f_
o 14764 resistance against fire	résistance _f_ à l'action du feu	Feuerbeständigkeit _f_	resistenza _f_ al fuoco
o 14765 resistance alloy	alliage _m_ pour résistances électriques	Widerstandslegie-rung _f_	lega _f_ di resistenza
resistance butt welding, _s. butt welding_			
o 14766 resistance capacity of the vessel	capacité _f_ de résis-tance de la cuve	Widerstandsfähigkeit _f_ des Behälters	capacità _f_ di resisten-za del recipiente

English	French	German	Italian

resistance forging, *s. electroforging*

° 14767 **resistance-furnace** — four *m* à résistance — Widerstandsofen *m* — forno *m* à resistenza

° 14768 **resistance heating** — chauffage *m* par résistance — Widerstandserhitzung *f* — riscaldamento *m* a resistenza

° 14769 **resistance pyrometer** — pyromètre *m* à résistance — Widerstandsthermo-meter *n* — pirometro *m* a resistenza

° 14770 **resistance to alternation of stresses** — résistance *f* aux efforts alternés — Wechselfestigkeit *f* — resistenza *f* a esigenze alternate

° 14771 **resistance to corrosion** — résistance *f* à la corrosion — Korrosionsbestän-digkeit *f* — resistenza *f* alla corrosione

° 14772 **resistance to heat** — résistance *f* à la chaleur — Hitzebeständigkeit *f* — resistenza *f* al calore

° 14773 **resistance to pressure** — résistance *f* à la pression — Druckfestigkeit *f* — resistenza *f* alla pressione

° 14774 **resistance to pressure and friction** — résistance *f* à l'écrasement et au frottement — Widerstandsfähigkeit *f* gegen Druck und Zerreibung — resistenza *f* alla pressione e alla frantumazione

° 14775 **resistance to shock** — résistance *f* au choc — Schlagfestigkeit *f* — resistenza *f* all'urto

° 14776 **resistance to tensile stress** — résistance *f* à la traction — Zugfestigkeit *f* — resistenza *f* alla trazione

° 14777 **resistance to wear** — résistance *f* à l'usure — Verschleisshärte *f* — resistenza *f* allo sfregamento (o all'usura)

° 14778 **resistance welding** — soudure *f* par résistance — Widerstandsschweis-sung *f* — saldatura *f* per resistenza

° 14779 **resistance wire** — fil *m* pour résistances électriques — Widerstandsdraht *m* — filo *m* di resistenza

° 14780 **resistant** — résistant — widerstandsfähig — resistente

° 14780a **resistivity** — résistivité *f* — spezifischer Widerstand — resistività *f*

° 14781 **resistor alloy** — alliage *m* par rhéostat — Widerstandslegie-rung *f* — lega *f* per reostati

° 14781a **resolution** — rédissolution *f* — Wiederauflösung *f* — ridissoluzione *f*

° 14782 **response of the environmental forces** — réaction *f* des facteurs de milieu — Auswirkung *f* der naturgegebenen Kräfte — reazione *f* delle forze ambientali sismiche

° 14782a **rest period** — temps de repos — Ruhezeit *f* — tempo *m* di riposo

restandardize, *s. back titration*

	English	French	German	Italian
° 14783	**restarting**	resoufflage *m*	Wiederanblasen *n*	rimessa in marcia
° 14784	**restoration of spoilt steel**	régénération *f* de l'acier altéré	Auffrischen *n* von verdorbenem Stahl	rigenerazione *f* dell'acciaio alterato
° 14785	**restored acid**	acide *m* régénéré	regenerierte Säure *f*	acido *m* rigenerato
° 14786	**restriction crack**	crique *f* de retrait	Schrumpfriss *m*	cricca *f* di ritiro, incrinatura di calettamento
° 14786a	**restrained contraction**	retrait *m* contrarié	behinderte Schwindung *f*	ritiro *m* contrastato
^ 14787	**restriction of license**	restriction *f* de concession	Konzessionsbeschränkung *f*	restrizione *f* di concessione
° 14787a	**restriking**	frappe *f* de finition	Nachschlagen *n*	colpo *m* di rifinitura
14788	**result of analysis**	certificat *m* d'analyse	Analysenbefund *m*	certificato *m* d'analisi
14789	**result of test**	résultat *m* de l'essai	Versuchsergebnis *n*	risultato *m* della prova
° 14790	**retarder**	retardateur *m* de prise	Verzögerer *m*	agente *m* ritardante
14791	**retest**	contre-essai *m*	Wiederholungsversuch *m*	ripetizione *f* della prova
	reticulated, *s. net shaped*			
−14792	**to retimber**	reboiser	Zimmerung *f* auswechseln	riarmare, sostituire l'armatura
−14793	**retimbering**	reboisage *m*	Auswechseln *n* der Zimmerung	sostituzione *f* dell'armatura, riarmamento
−14794	**retinite**	rétinite *f*	Retinit *m*	retinite *f*
° 14795	**retort, still**	cornue *f*	Glühkolben *m*	storta *f*
	retort of laboratory, *s. plain retort*			
° 14796	**retort carbon**	charbon *m* de cornue	Retortenkohle *f*	carbone *m* di storta
° 14797	**retort furnace**	four *m* à cornues	Retortenofen *m*	forno *m* a storte
° 14798	**retort gasification**	gazéification *f* à la cornue	Retortenvergasung *f*	gassificazione *f* alla storta
° 14799	**retort graphite**	graphite *m* de cornue	Vergasergraphit *m*	carbone *m* di storta
₀ 14800	**retort stand**	support *m* de cornue	Retortenhalter *m*	sostegno *m* per la storta

English	French	German	Italian
14801 **retorting**	distillation f à la cornue	Retortendestillation f	distillazione f alla storta
° 14801a **retreating**	traitement thermique répété	wiederholte Wärmebehandlung	trattamento m termico ripetuto
° 14802 **retreating system**	exploitation f en rabattant, exploitation f en retraite	Rückbau m	coltivazione f in ritirata
— 14803 **retrograde metamorphism**	métamorphisme m régressif	rückschreitende Metamorphose f	metamorfosi f regressiva
° 14804 **retrogression of dissociation**	rétrogradation f de la dissociation	Dissoziationsrückgang m	retrogradazione f della dissociazione
— 14805 **retrogressive erosion**	érosion f remontante	rückschreitende Erosion f	erosione f regressiva
^ 14806 **retubing**	retubage m	Verrohrung f	ritubaggio m
^ 14807 **to retube**	retuber	verrohren	ritubare
° 14808 **to return**	repasser	zurückgehen, nacharbeiten	ripassare
—.14809 **return-airway**	galerie f de retour d'air	ausziehende Wetterstrecke f	galleria f di ritorno dell'aria
° 14810 **return bend**	courbe f à 180°	180° Kurve f	curva f a 180°
o 14811 **return flame boiler**	chaudière f à retour de flamme	Kessel m mit wiederkehrender Flamme	caldaia f a ritorno di fiamma
° 14812 **return flue**	carneau m de retour	zurückkehrender Feuerzug m	condotto m di ritorno

return force, s. *backward force*

return pressure, s. *backward pressure*

° 14813 **return scrap**	retours m $pl.$ de fabrication	Kreislaufstoffe m $pl.$	ricuperi m $pl.$ di produzione
— 14814 **return shaft**	puits m de sortie d'air	Ausziehschacht m	pozzo m d'uscita dell'aria

return-tube boiler, s. *return flame boiler*

° 14815 **returns**	déchets m $pl.$	Abfälle m $pl.$	sfridi m $pl.$
° 14816 **returning**	retour m	Rückgang m	ritorno m

to reveal the structure, s. *to expose the structure*

° 14817 **reverberatory furnace**	four m de fusion à réverbère	Schmelzflammofen m	forno m a riverbero

	English	French	German	Italian
o	14818 reverberatory furnace with long hearth	four *m* à réverbère à longue sole	Flammofen *m* mit gestrecktem Herd	forno *m* a riverbero a suola lunga
o	14819 reversal	renversement *m*	Umkehr *f*	inversione *f*
o	14819a reverse bend test	essai *m* de flexion alternée	Hin-und Herbiege- probe *f*	prova *f* di tensione alternata
o	14820 reverse combustion	combustion *f* inverse	gegenläufige Teilverbrennung *f*	combustione *f* inversa
—	14821 reverse of dip	changement *m* de pendage	Wechsel *m* des Gefälles	modifica *f* della pendenza
—	14822 reverse of mine ventilation	renversement *m* d'aérage	Umkehr *f* der Stromrichtung des Wetterzuges	inversione *f* della ventilazione
—	14823 reverse fault, thrust, overfault	faille *f* anormale, faille *f* inverse	abnorme Verwerfung *f*, Aufschiebung *f*	faglia *f* inversa, faglia *f* di contrazione
o	14824 reverse reduction gear	réducteur *m*	Verminderer *m*	riduttore *m*
o	14825 reverse rotation	rotation *f* en sens inverse	entgegengesetzte Drehung *f*	cambiamento *m* di marcia
	reversed brass, *s. fontainemoreau alloy*			
o	14826 reversed combustion	combustion *f* renversée	inverse Verbrennung *f*	combustione *f* rovesciata
	reversed fault, *s. reverse fault*			
o	14827 reversible machine	machine *f* réversible	umkehrbare Maschine *f*	macchina *f* reversibile
o	14828 reversible pattern plate	plaque-modèle *f* réversible	Umschlagplatte *f*	placca *f* modello reversibile
	reversing, *s. switching*			
o	14829 reversing cogging mill	laminoir *m* réversible à lingots	Umkehrblock- walzwerk *n*	laminatoio *m* reversibile per lingotti
o	14830 reversing cold rolling mill	laminoir *m* réversible pour laminage à froid	Reversierwalzwerk *n* für Kaltwalzen	laminatoio *m* reversibile per la laminazione a freddo
o	14831 reversing hot finishing mill	laminoir *m* réversible pour le finissage à chaud	Reversierwalzwerk *n* für Warmfertigwalzen	laminatoio *m* reversibile per la finitura a caldo
o	14831a reversing mill	laminoir réversible	Umkehrwalzwerk *n*	laminatoio *m* reversibile
o	14832 reversing plate mill	laminoir *m* réversible à tôles	Reversierblechwalz- werk *n*	laminatoio *m* reversibile per lamiere
o	14833 reversing rolling	laminoir *m* réversible	Reversier- walzwerk *n*	laminatoio *m* o treno *m* reversibile

	English	French	German	Italian
°	14834 reversing the rolls	renversement du laminage	abwechselnde Bewegungsrichtung f	cambiamento m del senso di laminazione
	14835 to revive	faire revivre	wiederbeleben	far rivivere
°	14836 to revolve	tourner	drehen	tornire
—	14836a revolving distributor	trémie tournante	Drehtrichter m	tramoggia f rotante
°	14837 revolving furnace	four m rotatif	rotierender Ofen m	forno m rotativo
°	14838 revolving grate revolving kiln, s. rotary kiln	grille f rotative	Drehrost m	griglia f mobile
—	14839 revolving picking table	table f de triage tournante	Drehherd m	tavola f di cernita girevole
°	14840 revolving puddling	puddlage m rotatif	Drehpuddeln n	puddellaggio m rotativo
°	14841 revolving puddling furnace	four m à puddler rotatif	Drehpuddelofen m	forno m a puddellaggio rotativo
—	14842 revolving screen	crible m rotatif	Trommelsieb n	crivello m (o vaglio) rotativo
—	14843 revolving tippler	culbuteur m rotatif	Kreiselwipper m	scaricatore m meccanico rotativo
°	14844 revolving tubular kiln	four tubulaire tournant	Drehrohrofen m	forno m tubolare rotativo
—	14845 revolving washing drum	tambour m laveur rotatif	sich drehende Waschtrommel f	tamburo m per lavaggio rotativo
^	14846 to rework a well	reprendre un puits		riprendere un pozzo
—	14847 rezbanyite	rezbanyite f	Rézbanyit m	rezbanite f
—	14848 rhabdophanite	rhabdophane m	Rhabdophan m	rabdofanite f
—	14849 Rhaetian stage	rhétien m	Rhätische Stufe f	retiano m
—	14850 rhaetizite	rhaetizite f	Rhätizit m	ratcizite f
—	14851 rhagite	rhagite f	Rhagit m	ragite f
—	14852 rheolaveur coal--washing plant	lavoir à rhéolaveurs	Rheowäsche f	lavatoio m a reolavatori
	14852a rhodazing	placage m au rhodium	Rhodonisieren n	rodanizzazione f
—	14853 rhodizite	rhodizite f	Rhodizit m	rodizite f
—	14854 rhodochrosite	rhodochrosite f	Rhodochrosit m	rodocrosite f
—	14855 rhodonite	rhodonite f	Rhodonit m	rodonite f
—	14856 rhodotilite	rhodotilite f	Rhodotilith m	rodotilite f

	English	French	German	Italian
—	14857 rhodusite	rhodusite *f*	Rhodusit *m*	rhodusite *f*
—	14858 rhomb spar	dolomie *f*	Dolomit *m*	dolomite *f*
—	14859 rhomb porphyry	rhomben-porphyre *m*	Rhombenporphyr *m*	romben-porfido *m*
—	14860 rhombic mica	phlogopite *m*	Phlogopit *m*	flogopite *m*
	rhombic system, *s. orthorhombic sistem*			
—	14861 rhonite	rhonite *f*	Rhŏnit *m*	rhonite *f*
—	14862 rhums	schiste *m* bitumineux	Brandschiefer *m*	scisto *m* bituminoso
—	14863 rhyacolite	rhyacolite *f*	Rhyakolith *m*	rhyacolite *f*
—	14863a rhymer	alésoir *m*	Reibahle *f*	alesatore *m*
°	14864 rib	nervure *f*	Rippe *f*	nervatura *f*
°	14865 ribbed bar	fer *m* à nervures centrales	Rippeneisen *n*	ferro *m* piatto con nervatura centrale
°	14866 ribbed casting	jet *m* nervuré	Rippenguss *m*	getto *m* con nervatura
°	14867 ribbed flat bar	barre *f* plate nervurée	Rippenschiene *f*	barra *f* piatta con nervatura
°	14868 ribbed galvanized sheet-steel	tôle *f* d'acier nervurée galvanisée	geripptes verzinktes Stahlblech *n*	lamiera *f* d'acciaio nervata zincata
	ribbon agate, *s. banded agate*			
—	14869 ribbon structure	structure rubanée	Lagentextur *f*	struttura *f* nastriforme
°	14869a ribbon saw	scie *f* à lame	Blattsäge *f*	sega *f* alternativa
°	14870 rich finery cinder, slag	scorie *f*	Schwal *m*, Schlacke *f*	scoria *f*
°	14871 rich fining slag	scorie *f* douce, scorie *f* riche	Feinschlacke *f*	scoria *f* ricca di ossidi
^	14872 rich gas	gaz *m* riche	Reichgas *n*, Nassgas *n*	gas *m* ricco (o umido)
°	14873 rich in clay	alumineux	tonerdereich	alluminoso
°·	14874 rich in ferric oxide	riche en oxyde de fer	eisenoxydreich	ricco d'ossido di ferro
°	14875 rich in graphite	riche en graphite	graphitreich	ricco di grafite
°	14876 rich in lime	calcareux	kalkreich	calcareo
°	14877 rich in silicic acid	riche en silice	kieselsäurereich	ricco in silice
°	14877a rich low brass	laiton *m* rouge	rotes Messing *n*	ottone *m* rosso
°	14878 rich slag	laitier *m* chaud	Garschlacke *f*	loppa *f* calda
—	14879 richterite	richtérite *f*	Richterit *m*	richterite *f*

	English	French	German	Italian
— 14880	**rickardite**	rickardite *f*	Rickardit *m*	rickardite *f*
— 14881	**ricket**	cloison *f* d'aérage	Wetterscheider *m*	diaframma *m* di ventilazione
— 14882	**to riddle**	cribler	sieben, sichten	cernere, setacciare
— 14883	**riddle**	crible *m* laveur	Sieb *n*	crivello *m*, vaglio *m*
— 14884	**rider**	nerf *m*, inclusion *f* de stérile dans une veine	Schichtenpacket *n*, Flemmstück *n*	nervo *m*, inclusione *f* di sterile in una vena
— 14885	**rider** **rider strip**, *s, cover strip*	crible *m*	Sieb *n*	vaglio *m*, crivello *m*
— 14886	**ridge**	crête *f*	Kamm *m*	cresta *f*, linea *f* spartiacque
— 14887	**riding**	rupture *f* de boisage	Bruch *m* der Verzimmerung	rottura *f* dell'armatura
— 14888	**riebeckite**	riebeckite *f*	Riebeckit *m*	riebeckite *f*
° 14889	**rifle bar**	barre *f* de rotation	Drehbohrstange *f*	barra *f* di rotazione
— 14890	**rifle drill**	foret *m* à canon	Kanonenbohrer *m*	punta *f* a cannone
° 14891	**rifled plate**	tôle *f* rainurée, tôle *f* striée	Riffelblech *n*	lamiera *f* striata
° 14892	**riffler**	lime *f* d'entrée, rifloir *m*	Lochfeile *f*	lima *f* da fori
— 14893	**rift** **rift**, *s. quartering way*	joint *m*, fil *m*, crevasse *f*	versteckte Spalte *f*, Riss *m*, Spaltbarkeit	giunto *m*, filo *m*, fessura *f*
— 14894	**to rig**	appareiller	grubenrichten	attrezzare
— 14895	**to rig, down**	démonter	demontieren	smontare
— 14896	**to rig up**	installer, monter	einrichten, montieren	installare, montare
— 14897	**rig**	installation *f* de forage	Bohranlage *f*	impianto *m* di perforazione
— 14898	**rig floor**	plan *m* de la tour de sondage	Bohrturmplattform *f*	piano *m* della torre di sondaggio
— 14899	**rig hoists**	élévateur pour sondes	Bohrerhebezeug *n*	elevatore *m* per trivelle
— 14900	**rig shift**	déplacement de la tour	Bohrturmverlegung *f*	spostamento *m* dell'impianto di trivellazione

	English	French	German	Italian
−	14901 **rigging**	mécanisme *m* de sondage	Bohrvorrichtung *f*	meccanismo *m* di trivellazione
−	14902 **rigging time**	temps de sondage	Bohrzeit *f*	tempo *m* di perforazione
°	14903 **right and left hand turn off**	aiguillage *m* double	Doppelweiche *f*, Folgeweiche *f*	scambio *m* doppio
°	14904 **right angle rapping spike**	pointe *f* en équerre à boucle	winkliges Aushebeeisen *n*	punta *f* a occhiello per l'estrazione dei metalli
°	14905 **right-hand (side) tool**	couteau *m* coup-à--droite	rechter Messerstahl *m*	(ferro *m* a) coltello *m* a destra
	14906 **right prism**	prisme *m* droit	gerades Prisma *n*, normales Prisma *n*	prisma *m* retto
°	14907 **rightward welding**	soudure *f* à gaz à droite	Rückgasschweissung *f*	saldatura *f* a gas all'indietro
°	14908 **rigid frame construction**	construction *f* à ossature rigide	steifer Skelettbau *m*	costruzione *f* ad ossatura rigida
−	14909 **rill**	trace *f*, sillon *m*	Rillë *f*, Furche *f*	traccia *f*, solco *m*
−	14910 **rill (cut)**	taille *f* à mi-pente	Schrägstreb *n*	taglio *m* inclinato
−	14911 **rill slice**	taille *f* à mi-pente	Schrägstreb *n*	trancia inclinata
−	14912 **rill stope**	gradin *m* incliné	Firstenstoss *m* mit geneigter Firste	gradino *m* inclinato
−	14913 **rill stoping**	méthode *m* de l'avancement par rabattage	Firstenbau *m* mit geneigter Firste	metodo *m* d'avanzamento a gradini inclinati
−	14914 **rim**	rim *m*	Kraterrand *m*	bordo *m* del cratere
°	14915 **rim of furnace**	rebord *m* du four	Ofenrand *m*	bordo *m* del forno
°	14916 **rim of ladle**	bord *m* de la poche	Pfannenrand *m*	bordo *m* della siviera
°	14917 **rim pattern**	modèle *m* à couronne	Kranzmodell *n*	modello *m* di una corona
°	14917a **rimer**	alésoir *m*	Reibahle *f*	alesatore *m*
	rimmed steel, *s. unkilled steel*			
°	14918 **rimming steel**	acier *m* non calmé (ou effervescent)	unruhiger Stahl *m*	acciaio *m* effervescente
^	14919 **rims (pulleys)**	jantes *f pl.* (poulies)	Kranz *m*	cerchione *m* (di puleggia)

	English	French	German	Italian
°	14920 ring	anneau *m*, couronne *f*	Ring *m*	anello *m*, corona *f*
°	14921 ring	anneau *m* de soutènement	Schachtring *m*	anello *m* di sostegno
°	14921a ring core	noyau *m* annulaire	Ringkern *m*	anima *f* anulare
—	14922 ring dike	filon *m* éruptif annulaire	Ringader *f*	filone *m* eruttivo anulare
^	14923 ring gasket	garniture *f* annulaire	Dichtungsring *m*	guarnizione *f* ad anello
°	14924 ring gate	attaque *f* annulaire	Ringeinguss *m*, Ringanschnitt *m*	attacco *f* anulare
°	14925 ring gear	couronne *f* dentée	Zahnkranz *m*	corona *f* dentata
°	14926 ring heart	chenal *m* annulaire	Rundkanal *m*	canale *m* circolare
^	14927 ring joint flange	bride *f* à joint circulaire	Flansch *m* mit Dichtungsring	flangia *f* con guarnizione ad anello
—	14928 ring ore	minerai *m* en cocarde	Kokardenerz *n*	minerale *m* a coccarda
	ring-oven, *s. circular kiln*			
—	14929 ring roll mill	moulin *m* à cylindres annulaires	Ringwalzenmühle *f*	frantoio *m* a cilindri anulari
	ring runner, *s. ring gate*			
°	14930 ring shaped pattern	modèle *m* annulaire	ringförmiges Modell *n*	modello *m* anulare
°	14931 ring weight, weight ring	anneau *m* de charge	Belastungsring *m*	anello *m* di contrappeso
—	14932 ringer	massette *f*, pince *f* de mineur	Handfäustel *m*, Treibfäustel *m*, Brechzange *f*	mazzetta *f* (o pinza *f*) da minatore
—	14933 rinkite	rinkite *f*	Rinkit *m*	rinchite *f*
—	14934 rinkolite	rinkolite *f*	Rinkolit *m*	rincolite *f*
—	14935 rinneite	rinnéite *f*	Rinneit *m*	rinneite *f*
—	14936 rinsing vat	tambour *m* laveur	Waschtrommel *f*	tamburo *m* per lavaggio minerali
—	14937 to rip the roof	recouper le toit	Firste *f* nachreissen	ritagliare il tetto
—	14938 ripidolite	ripidolite *f*	Rhipidolith *m*	ripidolite *f*
°	14939 ripple weld	soudure *f* ondulée	wellige Schweissstelle *f*	saldatura *f* ondulata

	English	French	German	Italian
°	14940 rippled surface	surface *f* ondulée	Welloberfläche *f*	superficie *f* con linee di ripresa
−	14941 to rise	percer en montánt	aufhauen	forare in rimonta
−	14942 rise	cheminée *f*, remontage, remontée	Aufhauen *n*, Überhauen *n*	fornello *m*, rimonta *f*, salita *f*
−	14943 rise	montée, élévation *f*	Anstieg *m*, Steigung *f*	salita *f*, elevazione *f*
−	14944 rise heading	plan *m* incliné	Bremsberg *m*	piano *m* inclinato
	rise of temperature, *s. temperature increase*			
−	14945 rise working	remontage *m*	Aufbrechen *n*	scavo *m* in rimonta
−	14946 riser	montage, remontage	Aufhauen *n*	rimonta *f*, salita *f*, fornello *m*
°	14947 riser	évent *m*, lingotière mère	Haupteinguss *m*, Steiger *m*,	respiro *m*, materozza *f*, montante *m*
−	14948 riser	faille inverse	Aufschiebung *f*	faglia *f* inversa
^	14949 riser (pipe)	tuyau *m* de refoulement	Druckleitung *f*	colonna *f* montante
°	14950 riser bush, pouring bush	rehausse *f* de coulée	Trichterverlängerung *f*, Aufbautrichter *m*	sopralzo *m* di colata
°	14951 riser head	main-courante *f*	Führungschuh *m*	guida *f*
°	14952 riser head	évent *m*	Steigetrichter *m*	tirata *f* d'aria, respiro
^	14953 riser main	tuyau *m* de refoulement	Druckleitung *f*	tubo *m* premente, colonna *f* montante
°	14954 riser pin	cône *m* des évents	Steigetrichterkopf *m*	cono, modello per montanti
°	14955 risering	appliquer les évents	Anbringung *f* der Steigetrichter	applicazione *f* dei montanti
−	14956 rising	remontage *m*	Aufbrechen *n*	fornello *m*
−	14957 rising	montée *f*, ascension	Steigung *f*, Anhöhe *f*	salita *f*, ascensione
°	14958 rising air current	courant *m* d'air montant	aufsteigender Luftstrom *m*	corrente *f* d'aria ascendente
°	14959 rising of the head	boursouflement *m* de la masselotte	Aufblähung *f* des Speisers	rigonfiamento *m* della materozza

English	French	German	Italian
° 14960 **rising of the iron in the mould**	remontée f de la fonte	Treiben n des Eisens	trasudamento m della ghisa
^ 14961 **rising pipe**	tuyau m de refoulement	Druckrohr n, Steigrohr n	colonna f montante, tubo m premente
14962 **rising pouring**	coulée f en source	steigender Guss m	colata f in sorgente
° 14692a**rising steel**	acier m imparfaitement désoxydé	unvollständig desoxydierter Stahl m	acciaio m imperfettamente deossidato
– 14693 **rising top**	champignon m	aufgeblähter Speiser m	fungo m
° 14964 **risque of cracking on hardening**	risque m de formation des fissures par la trempe	Härterissgefahr f	rischio m d'incrinatura di tempra
–14965 **rittingerite**	rittingérite f	Rittingerit m	rittingerite f
14966 **river boat, barge**	chaland m	Flussschiff n	pontone m
–14967 **river sand**	sable m de rivière	Flussand m	sabbia f di fiume
–14968 **river terrace**	terrasse f fluviale	Inundationsterrasse f	terrazzo m fluviale
–14969 **river transport**	transport m fluvial	Flussfracht f	trasporto m fluviale
14970 **river-water**	eau f de rivière	Flusswasser n	acqua f di fiume
–14971 **riversideite**	riversidéite f	Riversideit m	riversideite f
° 14972 **rivet head, nail head**	tête f de rivet	Nietkopf m	testa f di chiodo
° 14973 **rivet iron**	fer m à rivets	Nieteisen n	ferro m per ribattini
° 14974 **rivet-steel**	acier m à rivets	Nietstahl m	acciaio m per chiodi, ferro m per chiodi
14974a**rivet test**	essai m des rivets	Nietenprüfung f	prova f di chiodi
° 14975 **rivet wire, nail wire**	fil m pour rivets, fil m pour clous	Draht m für Nieten, Nageldraht m	filo m per chiodi
° 14976 **riveted angle iron rim**	couronne f rivetée en fers cornières	aufgenieteter Kranz m aus Winkeleisen	corona f formata da ferri d'angolo inchiodati
° 14977 **riveted handle**	manche m riveté	angenieteter Stiel m	manico m ribadito
° 14978 **riveted steel plate catch**	entraîneur m en tôle d'acier rivetée	angenieteter Mitnehmer m aus Stahlblech	attacco m chiodato in lamiera d'acciaio
° 14979 **rivetless head**	casque m de soudeur en une pièce	nietloser Kopfschutz (fuer Schweisser), nietlose Schutzmaske	elmo m protettore senza chiodi

815   RIZZONITE

	English	French	German	Italian
— 14980	**rizzonite**	rizzonite *f*	Rizzonit *m*	rizzonite *f*
— 14981	**road material, ballast**	matériaux *m pl.* pour la construction des routes	Wegebaustoff *m*	materiali *m pl.* per la costruzione delle strade
14982	**road pack**	mur *m* de pierres	Bergemauer *f*	muro *m* di pietre
— 14982a	**roak, roke**	soufflure *f* éclatée	geplatzte Blase *f*	soffiatura *f* spaccata
— 14983	**to roast (ores)**	griller (les minerais)	(Erze) rösten	arrostire (i minerali)
— 14984	**roast heap**	tas *m* de minerai à griller	Rösthaufen *m*	ammasso *m* di minerali da arrostire
— 14985	**roasted ore**	minerai *m* grillé	**geröstetes** Erz *n*	minerale *m* torrefatto
— 14986	**roaster**	four *m* de grillage	Röster *m*	arrostitore *m*
— 14987	**roasting**	grillage *m*	Rösten *n*	arrostimento *m*
— 14988	**roasting bed**	lit *m* de grillage	Röstbett *n*	letto *m* di torrefazione
— 14989	**roasting core**	noyau *m* de grillage	Röstkern *m*	nucleo *m* di torrefazione
— 14990	**roasting-furnace**	four de grillage	Röstofen *m*, Röster *m*	forno *m* di arrostimento
— 14991	**roasting gas, flue gas**	gaz *m* de grillage, gaz *m* brulé	Röstgas *n*	gas *m* di torrefazione o d'arrostimento
	roasting in heaps, *s. heap roasting* **roasting kiln,** *s. roasting-furnace*			
— 14992	**roasting (ores)**	grillage *m* (des minerais)	Rösten *n* (von Erzen)	arrostimento *m* (dei minerali)
— 14993	**roasting or calcining plant**	installation *f* de grillage	Röstanlage *f*	impianto *m* d'arrostimento
— 14994	**roasting temperature**	température *f* de grillage	Rösttemperatur *f*	temperatura *f* di torrefazione
— 14995	**to rob**	dépiler, déboiser	abpfeilern, rauben	disarmare, demolire i pilastri
— 14996	**robbing**	dépilage *m*	Abpfeilern *n*	demolizione *f* dei pilastri, disarmo *m*
— 14997	**robbing pillars**	dépilage *m*	Abpfeilern *n*, Depilage	demolizione *f* dei pilastri
— 14998	**robble**	faille *f*	Verwerfung *f*	faglia *f*

English	French	German	Italian
° 14999 **roche alum**	alun *m* de roche	Steinalaun *m*	allume *m* di rocca
14999a **rochelle salt**	sel *m* de seignette	Natronweinstein *m*	roccella *f*
15000 **Roechling-Roden-** **hauser furnace**	four *m* Röchling- Rodenhauser	Röchling-Roden- hauserscher Ofen *m*	forno *m* Röchling- Rodenhauser
° 15001 **Roechling-Roden-** **hauser three-phase** **furnace**	four *m* à courant triphasé de Röchling- -Rodenhauser	Röchling-rodenhau- serscher Dreiphasen- ofen *m*	forno *m* Röchling- -Rodenhauser a cor- rente trifase
15002 **to rock**	osciller	schwingen	oscillare
^ 15002 **rod pump, insert** **pump**	pompe auxiliaire	Einsatzpumpe	pompa *f* ausiliare
^ 15003 **to rock**	inverser les circuits	schaukeln	invertire i circuiti
— 15004 **rock, stone**	rocher *m*	Fels *m*, Felsen *m*	roccia *f*
15005 **rock bar**	verrou *m*	Riegel *m*	chiavistello *m*
— 15006 **rock basin**	bassin *m* de surcreusement	Felsbecken *m*	bacino *m* di roccia
— 15007 **rock bench**	plateforme *f* d'abrasion	Brandungsplatte *f*	terrazzo *m* roccioso
— 15008 **rock bend**	pli *m*	Falte *f*	piega *f*
— 15009 **rock bit, cone bit**	trépan *m* pour roches	Steinmeissel *m*	trivella *f* per rocce
— 15010 **rock blanket**	couche *f* horizontale	flache Schicht *f*	strato *m* orizzontale
rock boring bar, *s. jumper bar*			
— 15011 **rock burst**	coup *m* de toit	Felssturz *m*	cedimento *m* di roc- cia
— 15012 **rock chute**	cheminée *f* à remblai	Bergerolle *f*	scivolo *m* per·ripiena
— 15013 **rock clay**	argillite *f*	Argillit *m*	argillite *f*
— 15014 **rock crystal**	cristal *m* de roche	Bergkristall *m*	cristallo *m* di roccia
— 15015 **rock-drift**	galerie *f* au rocher	Gesteinsstrecke *f*	galleria *f* in roccia
— 15016 **rock drill**	trépan *m* pour roches	Steinmeissel *m*	perforatrice *f* da roc- cia
— 15017 **rock drill hose**	tube *m* flexible pour sondages	Bohrschlauch *m*	manichetta *f* per trivellazioni
— 15018 **rock drill steel**	acier *m* à fleurets	Bohrstahl *m*	acciaio *m* per fioretti
— 15019 **rock-dust barrier**	arrêt-barrage *m*	Staubsperre *f*	barriera *f* antipolvere

English	French	German	Italian
— 15020 **rock dusting**	schistification *f*	Gesteinsstäubung *f*	scistificazione *f*
— 15021 **rock exposure**	affleurement *m*	Ausbiss *m*	affioramento *m*
— 15022 **rock fill**	remblayage *m*	Versetzen *n*	ripiena *f*
— 15023 **rock foot wall drift**	galerie *f* en roche au mur	Strecke *f* im Liegenden	galleria *f* in roccia sul fondo
— 15023a **rock flour**	cilice *f*	Steinmehl *n*	farina *f* di roccia
— 15024 **rock gangway**	galerie *f* au rocher	Gesteinsstrecke *f*	galleria *f* in roccia
15024a **rock pressure**	pression *f* de la terre	Erddruck *m*	spinta *f* della terra
— 15025 **rock rubble**	brèche *f* de dislocation	Verwerfungsbreccie	breccia *f* di dislocazione
— 15026 **rock salt**	sel gemme *m*	Steinsalz *n*	salgemma *m*
— 15027 **rock shaft**	cheminée à remblais, puits à remblais	Versatzschacht *m*	pozzo *m* a ripiena
— 15028 **rock shelter**	roche *f* surplombante	überhängendes Gebirge *n*	roccia *f* a piombo
— 15029 **rock slope**	puits *m* incliné au rocher	geneigter Gesteinsschacht *m*	pozzo *m* inclinato in roccia
15029a **rock soap**	savon *m* de montagne	Bergseife *f*	sapone *m* di montagna
— 15030 **rock step**	seuil de cirque	Karschwelle *f*	soglia *f* di circo
— 15031 **rock tar**	pétrole *m*, naphte *f*	Petroleum *n*, Erdöl *n*, Naphta *n*	petrolio *m*, nafta *f*, olio *m* minerale
— 15032 **rock terrace**	terrasse *f* rocheuse	Felsterrasse *f*	terrazzo *m* roccioso
15032a **rock wool**	laine minéral	Steinwolle *f*	lana *f* minerale
— 15034 **rocker**	balancier *m*	Schwengel *m*	bilanciere *m*
— 15035 **rocker shovel**	chargeuse *f* mécanique	Lademaschine *f*	caricatrice *f* meccanica
^ 15036 **rocking**	oscillation *f* avec fluide dans le puits	Schwingung *f* mit dem Fluss im Schacht	altalena *f* col fluido in pozzo
— 15037 **rocking**	lavage *m* sur tables oscillantes	Herdarbeit *f* auf bewegtem Herde	lavaggio *m* su tavole oscillanti
— 15038 **rocking feeder**	alimentateur *m* oscillant	bewegliche Aufgabevorrichtung *f*	alimentatore *m* oscillante
° 15039 **rocking furnace**	four *m* oscillant	Schaukelofen *m*	forno *m* oscillante
— 15040 **rocking-grate**	grille *f* à secousse(s)	Schüttelrost *m*	griglia *f* a scosse

English	French	German	Italian
⊃ 15041 **rocking lever**	levier *m* basculant	Kipphebel *m*	bilanciere *m*
15041a **rocking mill**	bocard *m* à pilons	Pochmühle *f*	mulino *m* a piloni
° 15042 **rocking stone**	pierre *f* branlante	Wackelstein *m*	roccia *f* traballante
° 15043 **rocking trough**	conduit *m* oscillant	Schwingrinne *f*	canale *m* trasportatore oscillante
° 15044 **Rockwell hardness**	essai *m* de dureté Rockwell	Rockwellhärteprobe *f*	prova *f* di durezza Rockwell
— 15045 **rocky soil**	sol *m* rocheux	felsiger Boden *m*	terreno *m* roccioso
° 15046 **rod, round iron**	fer *m* rond	Rundeisen *n*	ferro *m* tondo, tondino *m* (di ferro)
— 15047 **rod**	1/160 d'acre	1/160 Acre	1/160 di acro
ˆ 15048 **rod**	tige *f* de sonde	Gestänge *n*	asta *f* di sonda
° 15049 **rod**	barre *f*, bielle *f*	Stab *m*, Leiste *f*	barra *f*, biella *f*
15049a **rod crack**	crique *f* longitudinale	Längeriss *m*	incrinatura *f* longitudinale
ˆ 15050 **rod elevator**	élévateur *m* de tige	Gestängeaufzug *m*	elevatore *m* d'aste
15051 **rod feed**	pomper	pumpen	pompare
15052 **rod feeding**	pompage *m*	Pumpen *n*	pompaggio *m*
° 15053 **rod guide**	lanterne *f* de guidage	Gestängeführung *f*	lanterna *f* di guida
° 15054 **rod iron, iron rods** *pl.*	fer *m* en baguettes	Eisenstäbe *m pl.*, Eisenstangen *f pl.*	ferro *m* in verghette
° 15055 **rod mill**	broyeur *m* à barreaux	Stab-Rohrmühle *f*	mulino *m* a barre
° 15055a **rod mill**	laminoir *m* à barres	Stabwalzwerk *n*	laminatoio *m* a barre
° 15056 **rod milling**	laminage *m* d'un fil	Drahtwalzung *f*	laminazione *f* d'un filo
° 15057 **rod milling plant**	atelier *m* des laminoirs à fils	Drahtwalzwerkstatt *m*	laminatoio *m* per fili
° 15057a **rod pump**	pompe *f* auxiliaire	Einsatzpumpe *f*	pompa *f* ausiliare
° 15058 **rod pass**	cylindre *m* de laminoir à fils	Rundeisenkaliber *n*	cilindro *m* di laminatoio per fili
° 15059 **rod rolling**	laminage *m* d'un fil	Rundeisenwalzung *f*	laminazione *f* d'un filo
° 15059a **rod wire**	fil *m* laminé	Walzdraht *m*	filo *m* laminato (o di ferro)
° 15060 **rodding**	transmission *f* rigide	starre Gestängeverbindung *f*	trasmissione *f* rigida
— 15061 **rodding**	réparation *f* d'un guidage	Reparatur *f* der Schachtführungen	riparazione *f* della guida del pozzo

English	French	German	Italian
— 15062 **rodingite**	rodingite *f*	Rodingit *m*	rodingite *f*
rods, *s, bar-iron*			
— 15063 **roeblingite**	roeblingite *f*	Röblingit *m*	roeblingite *f*
— 15064 **roepperite**	roeppérite *f*	Roepperit *m*	roepperite *f*
° 15065 **Roessler's furnace**	four *m* de Roessler	Rösslerscher Ofen *m*	forno *m* di Roessler
^ 15066 **roily oil**	huile *f* trouble	trübes Öl *h*	olio *m* torbido
° 15067 **to roll down, to cog down**	laminer	abwalzen, auswalzen	laminare
° 15068 **to roll for finishing**	finir de laminer	fertig walzen	finire di laminare
° 15069 **to roll in**	cylindrer	einwalzen	cilindrare
° 15070 **to roll on**	enrouler	zusammenrollen	avvolgere
° 15071 **to roll on return pass**	laminer en arrière	zurückwalzen	laminare all'indietro
° 15072 **to roll together**	laminer ensemble	gemeinsam walzen	laminare insieme
° 15073 **roll**	cylindre *m*	Walze *f*	cilindro *m* (di laminatoio)
° 15074 **roll caliber**	calibre *m* de cylindre de laminoir	Walzenkaliber *n*	calibro *m* del cilindro di laminatoio
° 15074a **roll camber**	bombage *m* du cylindre	Walzenbombierung *f*	bombatura *f* del cilindro
° 15075 **roll casting machine**	machine pour la production des cylindres par centrifugation	Maschine *f* zur Rollenherstellung durch Zentrifugierung	macchina *f* per produzione rulli mediante centrifugazione
° 15075a **roll compacting**	laminage *m* de poudre	Pulvernwalzen *n*	laminazione *f* di polvere
15076 **roll crusher, roll breaker**	broyeur *m* à cylindres	Walzenbrecher *m*	frantoio *m* a cilindri
roll drafting, *s. design of rolls*			
roll electrode, *s. electrode wheel*			
° 15077 **roll face width**	longueur *f* du laminoir	Walzenlänge *f*	lunghezza *f* del cilindro (laminatoio)
15077a **roll forging**	forgeage *m* par laminage	Walzenschmieden *n*	fucinatura *f* per laminazione
15078 **roll forming machine**	machine à former à cylindres	Walzenprofilformmaschine *f*	profilatrice *f* a rulli
° 15079 **roll grinding machine**	rectifieuse *f* à cylindres de laminoir	Aussenrundschleifmaschine *f*	rettificatrice *f* per rulli
° 15080 **roll lathe**	tour *m* à cylindres de laminoir	Walzendrehbank *f*	tornio *m* per cilindri di laminatoio

	English	French	German	Italian
° 15081	roll mandrel	mandrin *m*	Walzdorn *m*	mandrino *m*
1508 1a	roll marks	traces du cylindre·	Walzspuren *f pl.*	traccie *f pl.* di cilindro
15082	roll of copper wire	toile *f* en fil de cuivre enroulée	Kupferdrahtnetzrolle *f*	rotolo *m* di rete in filo di rame
	roll opening, *s. groove*			
° 15083	roll-over machine	retourneur *m* de moule	Umrollvorrichtung *f*	ribaltatrice *f*
° 15084	roll pass	calibre *m* de laminoir	Walzkaliber *n*, Walzenkaliber *n*	calibro *m* de lamina-toio
° 15084a	roll pass	passe *f*	Stich *m*, Durchgang *m*	passata *f*
° 15085	roll-pick-up	piqûre *f* due au laminage	Walznarbe *f*	difetto *m* di laminazio-ne
° 15086	roll pot or vat	bac *m* à cylindres	Walzkessel *m*	caldaia *f* a cilindri
° 15087	roll scale	écaille *f* de laminage	Walzenschlacke *f*	scaglia *f* di laminazio-ne
15088	roll size effect	effet *m* du diamètre des cylindres	Wirkung *f* des Walzendurchmessers	effetto *m* del diametro dei cilindri
15088a	roll spindle	allonge *m* du cylindre	Walzenspindel *f*	asse *m* del cilindro
	roll spot welding, *s. roller spot welding*			
° 15089	roll stand	cage *f* de laminoir	Walzgerüst *n*	gabbia *f* del laminatoio
° 15090	roll turning	tournage *m* des cylindres	Eindrehen *n* der Kaliber	tornitura *f* dei cilindri
	roll vat, *s. roll pot*			
° 15091	roll welding	soudage à cylindres	Walzenschweissung *f*	saldatura *f* (per bolli-tura) a rulli
° 15092	rollable	laminable	walzbar	laminabile
° 15093	roll neck	tourillon *m* de cylindre	Walzenzapfen *m*	collo *m* d'un cilindro
° 15094	rolled	laminé, cylindré	gewalzt, ausgewalzt	laminato
	rolled bars, *s. rolled iron*			
° 15095	rolled edge	bord *m* de laminage	Walzkante *f*	bordo *m* di laminazione
° 15096	rolled mild steel disk wheel	roue *f* à disque laminée en acier doux·	gewalztes flusseisernes Scheibenrad *n*	ruota *f* a disco lami-nata in acciaio dolce
° 15097	rolled-iron, rolled steel	fer *m* laminé (ou cylindré)	Walzeisen *n*, Stabeisen *n*	ferro *m* laminato
	rolled plate, *s. rolled sheet (iron)*			
° 15098	rolled section	fer *m* laminé profilé	Walzprofil *n*	profilo *m* di laminazione

	English	French	German	Italian
○ 15099	rolled sheet (iron)	tôle f laminée	Walzblech n	lamiera f laminata
	rolled sheet metal, *s. rolled sheet (iron)*			
○ 15100	rolled steel	acier m laminé	Walzstahl m	acciaio m laminato
○ 15101	rolled steel section	acier m profilé ou façonné	Profilstahl m, Profileisen n	laminato m di acciaio
○ 15102	rolled structural steel sections	profilés m $pl.$ de construction laminés en acier	gewalzte Baustahlprofile n $pl.$	profilati m $pl.$ per costruzioni laminati in acciaio
○ 15103	rolled wire	fil m laminé	Walzdraht m	filo m laminato
○ 15104	roller	rouleau m, cylindre m, galet m	Rolle f, Walze f, Laufrolle f	rullo m, cilindro m, cuscinetto m
○ 15105	roller	lamineur m	Walzer m	cilindratore m, laminatore m
○ 15106	roller bearing	palier m à rouleaux	Rollenlager n	sopporto m a rulli
— 15107	roller bit	trépan m à molettes	Rollenmeissel m	trapano m ad archetto
○ 15108	roller conveyor	transporteur m à rouleaux (ou à galets)	Rollenbahn f	trasportatore m a rulli
— 15109	roller crusher	concasseur à cylindres	Walzenquetsche f	frantoio m a cilindri
15110	roller feed (for logs)	amenage m par rouleaux	Walzenrolenvorschub m	alimentazione f a rulli
	roller for electric welding, *s. electrode wheel*			
15111	roller hot-press	calandre f à cylindres rechauffés	Kalander m mit geheizten Walzen	calandra a cilindri riscaldati
○ 15112	roller leveling	cylindrage m	Zylindrieren n, Mangeln n	calandratura f
15112a	roller leveller	dresseuse f à galets	Rollenrichtmaschine f	raddrizzatrice f a rulli
— 15113	roller mill	moulin m à cylindres	Walzenmühle f	macina f a cilindri
○ 15114	roller-mould	moule à fondre des rouleaux	Walzengiessform	forma f per la fusione dei rulli
15114a	roller scale	croûte f de laminage	Walzzunder m	scaglia f di laminazione
○ 15115	roller tables, guards	tables de laminoir	Walztische m $pl.$	placche f $pl.$
— 15116	roller screen	crible-classeur m à rouleaux	Rollenklassiersieb n	vaglio m classificatore a rulli
— 15117	roller shaker	couloir m oscillant à galets	Rollenrutsche f	scivolo m oscillante a rulli

English	French	German	Italian
−15118 rolley	berline *f*	Förderwagen *m*	vagoncino *m*
−15119 rolley way	voie *f* de roulage	Förderstrecke *f*	galleria *f* di carreggio
° 15120 rolling	laminage *m*	Walzen *n*, Auswalzen *n*, Strecken *n*	laminazione *f*
−15121 rolling	roulement *m*	Rollen *n*	rotolamento *m*
−15122 rolling crusher, rolling breaker	broyeur *m* à cylindres	Walzenbrecher *m*, Walzwerk *n*	mulino *m* a cilindri
° 15123 rolling defect	défaut *m* de laminage	Walzfehler *m*	difetto *m* di laminazione
° 15124 rolling direction	sens *m* du laminage	Walzrichtung *f*	direzione *f* di laminazione
° 15125 rolling machine	laminoir *m*	Walzmaschine *f*	laminatoio *m*
° 15126 rolling method	méthode *f* de laminage	Walzverfahren *n*	procedimento *m* di laminazione
° 15127 rolling-mill	laminoir *m*	Walzwerk *n*	laminatoio *m*
rolling mill, *s. plate mill*			
rolling mill process, *s. rolling*			
rolling mill scale, *s. scale*			
° 15128 rolling mill train	train *m* de laminoir	Walzstrecke *f*	treno *m* di laminatoio
15128a rolling pressure	pression *f* de laminage	Walzendruck *m*	pressione *f* di laminazione
° 15129 rolling scale	écaille *f* de laminage	Walzensinter *m*	scaglia *f* di laminazione
15129a rolling schedule	séquence *f* de laminage	Stichfolge *f*	tavola *f* delle passate
−15130 rolling stock	parc *m* à wagons	Wagenpark *m*	parco *m* dei vagoni
° 15131 rolling train	train *m* de laminoir	Walzenstrasse *f*	treno *m* di laminatoio
15131a rollover board	plaque *f* à fouler	Stampfplatte *f*	piastra *f* a pilettare
° 15132 rollover pattern-draw molding machine	démouleur *m* basculant à extraction machine *f* agglomératrice	kippbare Abhebeformmaschine *f* Pulverpressmaschine *f*	formatrice *f* e sformatriçe ribaltabile
15132a rolls			macchina *f* agglomerante
ˆ 15133 rolly oil	émulsion *f* naturelle d'huile et eau	natürliche Erdöl- -und Wasseremulsion	emulsione *f* naturale di petrolio e acqua
−15134 romeite	roméite *f*	Romeit *m*	romeite *f*
−15135 romerite	roemérite *f*	Roemerit *m*	roemerite *f*
−15136 to roof (in)	couvrir d'une toiture	überdachen	coprire con tetto
−15137 roof	ciel, toit *m*	Firste, Dach *n*	cielo *m*, tetto *m*

English	French	German	Italian
o 15138 roof	voûte *f*	Herdgewölbe *n*	volta *f* del crogiuolo
— 15139 roof	roche *f* du toit	Hangende *n*	roccia *f* del tetto, cielo *m*
— 15140 roof and pillar system	exploitation *f* par grands massifs	massiver Abbau *m*	coltivazione *f* a grandi massicci
— 15141 roof fall	éboulement du toit	Firstenbruch *m*	franamento *m* del tetto
— 15142 roof hole	coup de couronne	Firstenschuss *m*, Kopfschuss *m*	colpo *m* di corona
— 15143 roof limb	flanc *m* supérieur	hangender Schenkel *m*	fianco *m* superiore
— 15144 roof (of a gallery)	toit *m*	(Strecken) Firste *f*	tetto *m* (di galleria)
o 15145 roof of furnace	voûte *f* du four	Ofenabdeckung *f*	volta *f* del forno
— 15146 roof subsidence	affaissement du toit	Absenkung des Hangenden	cedimento *m* del tetto
— 15147 roof-tilelike structure	structure *f* en tuile	Dachschieferstruktur *f*	struttura *f* a tegole
— 15148 room and pillar stoping	exploitation *f* par chambres et piliers	Kammerpfeilerbau *m*	coltivazione a camere e pilastri
— 15149 room entry	voie *f* d'exploitation	Abbaustrecke *f*	galleria *f* d'estrazione
o 15150 room for metallographical researches	salle *f* des recherches métallo-graphiques	Raum *m* für metallo-graphische Unter-suchungen	sala *f* per le analisi metallografiche
— 15151 room for sampling	salle *f* des prises d'échantillon	Raum *m* für die Probenahme	sala *f* dei saggi o dei campioni
o 15152 root form	forme *f* du fond de filet	Gewinde-Endform *f*	forma *f* del fondo filetto
— 15153 root groove	affaissement *m*	Senkung *f*	insellatura (difetto saldatura)
— 15154 root of a fold	racine *f* de charriage	Uberschiebungs-wurzel *f*	radice *f* di una piega
	root opening, *s. root gap*		
o 15155 Root's blower	soufflerie *f* Root, ventilateur *m* de Root	Rootgebläse *n*, Kapselgebläse *n*	ventilatore *m* Root
o 15156 Root's boiler	chaudière *f* Root	Rootkessel *m*	caldaia *f* Root

English	French	German	Italian
−15157 **rope choker**	sondeur m à câble	Seilbohrer m (Arbeiter)	operatore m a corda
^ 15158 **rope clamp**	mâchoire f de serrage	Seilklemme f	ganascia f di serraggio
−15159 **rope drilling**	sondage m à la corde	Seilbohren n	sondaggio m alla fune (o a percussione)
−15160 **rope drive**	transmission f par câbles	Seilübertragung f	trasmissione a funi
−15161 **rope driven machine**	machine f à commande par câbles	Maschine f für Seilbetrieb	macchina f con trasmissione a fune
−15162 **rope drum**	tambour m d'enroulement	Seiltrommel f	tamburo m d'avvolgimento
−15163 **rope duct**	tuyau m pour câbles	Seilrohr n	tubo m per cavi
−15164 **rope grab**	grappin m à câble	Sailfänger m	pescatore m per funi
−15165 **rope knife**	coupe-corde m	Seilmesser n	tagliacavi m
−15166 **rope lubricator**	appareil m de graissage du câble	Seilschmierer m	ingrassatore m per funi
−15167 **rope railway**	transporteur m funiculaire	Drahtseilbahn f	ferrovia f funicolare aerea
−15168 **rope roll**	tambour m d'extraction	Fördertrommel f	tamburo m d'estrazione
−15169 **rope socket**	cosse f de câble	Seilhülse f	occhio m di cavo, capocorda m
−15170 **rope spear**	harpon m à câble	Seilspeer m	arpione m per corde
−15171 **rope speed**	vitesse f d'extraction	Fördergeschwindigkeit f	velocità f d'estrazione
−15172 **ropy lava**	lave f cordée	Sticklava f	lava f cordata
−15173 **ropy structure**	structure f ondulée	Flussgefüge n	struttura f ondulata
−15174 **rosasite**	rosasite f	Rosasit m	rosasite f
−15175 **roscherite**	roschérite f	Roscherit m	roscherite f
−15176 **roscoelite**	roscoélite f	Roscoelit m	roscoelite f
° 15177 **rose bit**	taillant m en croix	Kreuzschneide f	accecatoio m

English	French	German	Italian
° 15178 **rose countersink bit**	fraise *f* champignon	Versenkbohrer *m*	accecatoio *m* rigato
° 15179 **rose-engine**	tour *m* à guillocher, machine à guillocher	Guillochiemaschine *f*	tornio *m* a rabescare
° 15180 **rose steel**	acier *m* à la rose	Rosenstahl *m*	acciaio *m* con frattura rosa
— 15181 **roselite**	rosélite *f*	Roselith *m*	roselite *f*
— 15182 **rosenbuschite**	rosenbuschite *f*	Rosenbuschit *m*	rosenbuschite *f*
° 15183 **rosette copper**	cuivre *m* rosette	Rosettenkupfer *n*	rame *m* puro
— 15184 **rosette graphite**	graphite *m* en rosettes	Rosettengraphit *m*	grafite *f* a rosette
— 15185 **rosette structure**	structure *f* en cocarde	Kokardenstruktur *f*	struttura *f* a coccarda
— 15186 **rosickyite**	rosickyite *f*	Rosickyit *m*	rosickyite *f*
— 15187 **rosieresite**	rosiérésite *f*	Rosieresit *m*	rosieresite *f*
^ 15188 **rosin**	colophane *f*	Kolophonium *n*	colofonia *f*
— 15189 **rosin jack**	blende *f*	Honigblende *f*	blenda *f*
— 15190 **rosite**	rosite *f*	Rosit *m*	rosite *f*
— 15191 **rossite**	rossite *f*	Rossit *m*	rossite *f*
^ 15192 **rotameter**	débitmètre *m*	Durchflussmeter *m*	rotametro *m*, flussometro *m*
° 15192a **rotary axis**	axe *m* rotatif	Drehachse *f*	asse *m* rotativo
° 15193 **rotary blower**	soufflerie *f* rotative	Drehkolbenpumpe *f*	ventilatore *m* rotativo
° 15194 **rotary body**	surface *f* de révolution	Rundkörper *m*	corpo *m* di rotazione, superfice *f* di rivoluzione
— 15195 **rotary boring**	sondage *m* rotary	Drehbohren *n*	sondaggio *m* a rotazione
— 15196 **rotary core bit**	trépan *m* rotary	Rotary-Meissel, Rotationsmeissel *m*	scalpello *m* a centro rotante
— 15197 **rotary dividing table**	diviseur *m* rotatif	drehbarer Teiltisch *m*	piattaforma *f* girevole graduata
— 15198 **rotary drawwork**	treuil *m* rotary	Rotary-Hebewerk *n*	argano *m* a rotazione
° 15198a **rotary drier**	sécheur *m* rotatif	rotierender Trockner *m*	essiccatoio *m* rotativo

English	French	German	Italian
— 15199 **rotary drill**	perforatrice *f* rotative	Drehbohrmaschine *f*	sonda *f* a rotazione
⌃ 15200 **rotary drilling**	forer à système rotary	rotarybohren	**sondagg**io *m* a rota-zione
⌃ 15201 **rotary drilling rig**	installation *f* de sondage rotary	Rotary-Bohranlage *f*, Rotary-Bohrkran *m*	impianto *m* di trivella-zione a rotazione
° 15202 **rotary feeding plate**	sole *f* doseuse	Zuteilteller *m*	disco *m* dosatore
° 15203 **rotary file, spherical centre**	mèche de centrage sphérique	Kugelbohrer *m* mit zylindrischem Schaft	trapano *m* sferico a gambo diritto
° 15204 **rotary files**	outils-fraises *m pl.*	Fräser(und) Feilen *f pl.*, Rotationsfeilen *f pl.*	lime *f pl.* rotanti
° 15205 **rotary filing machine with flexible shaft**	limeuse *f* rotative avec arbre souple	Drehfeilmaschine *f* mit biegsamer Welle	limatrice *f* rotativa con albero flessibile
⌃ 15206 **rotary fishing jar**	coulisse *f* rotary	Rotary-Schlagschere *f*	pescatore *m* Rotary
° 15207 **rotary furnace**	four *m* rotatif	Trommelofen *m*	forno *m* rotativo o rotatorio
° 15208 **rotary gas furnace**	four *m* rotatif chauffé au gaz	rotierender Ofen *m* mit Gasheizung	focolaio *m* rotatorio scaldato a gas
° 15209 **rotary grate shaft kiln**	four *m* vertical à grille tournante	vertikaler Ofen *m* mit Drehrost	forno *m* verticale a griglia rotatorio
° 15210 **rotary hearth furnace**	four *m* rotatif (ou tournant)	Drehofen *m*, Rotierofen *m*	forno *m* rotativo (a suola girevole)
— 15211 **rotary hose**	manche de rotary	Rotary-Spülschlauch *m*	tubo *m* di gomma al-la testa
— 15212 **rotary hose adapter**	attaque *f* du manche à la tête	Gummischlauch-Anschluss *m*	attacco *m* del tubo di gomma alla testa
° 15213 **rotary kiln**	four *m* rotatif	Drehofen *m*	forno *m* rotatorio
° 15214 **rotary puddling furnace**	four *m* à puddler tournant	Wendeofen *m*, wend-barer Puddelofen *m*	forno *m* da puddellag-gio girevole
° 15214a **rotary piercing mill**	laminoir *m* à cylin-dres obliques	Schrägwalzwerk *n*	laminatoio *m* a cilin-dri obliqui
— 15215 **rotary pump**	pompe *f* rotative	Drehkolbenpumpe *f*, Rotationspumpe *f*	pompa *f* rotativa
— 15216 **rotary screen**	trommel *m*, tamis *m* rotatif	Trommelsieb *n*	vaglio *m* a tamburo ruotante
— 15217 **rotary squeezer**	cingleur *m* rotatif	Luppenmühle *f*	compressore *m* rotativo

English	French	German	Italian
^ 15218 rotary shoe	sabot *m* denté de rotary	gezahnter Rohrschuh *m*	scarpa *f* dentata per sonda a rotazione
− 15219 rotary swivel	tête *f* d'injection de rotary	Rotary-Spülkopf *m*	testa *f* d'iniezione della sonda a rotazione
− 15220 rotary system	système *m* rotary	Rotary-Bohr-verfahren *n*	sistema *f* di sondaggio a rotazione
− 15221 rotary table	table *f* de rotary	Drehtisch *m*	tavola *f* della sonda a rotazione
− 15222 rotary tipper	culbuteur *m* basculant	Kreiselwipper *m*	ribaltatore *m* girevole
^ 15223 rotary tong	clef *f* de serrage	Gestängezange *f*	chiave *f* di serraggio
^ 15224 rotary tower crane	grue *f* pivotante géante	Turmdrehkran *m*	gru *f* a torre girevole
^ 15225 rotary type side	carottier de parois «rotary»	Rotary-Stoss-kernbohrer *m*	carotiere di parete «rotary»
^ 15226 rotary wash overshoe	sabot *m* pour tube de lavage	Rotary-Wascher *m*	scarpa *f* per tuta di lavaggio
− 15227 rotating apparatus	appareil *m* de renversement	Wendevorrichtung *f*	apparecchio *m* per l'inversione o ribaltamento
− 15228 rotating crystal	cristal *m* tournant	Drehkristall *m*	cristallo *m* rotante
° 15229 rotating cylinder	cylindre *m* hydraulique pour le renversement	Wendezylinder *m*	cilindro *m* idraulico ruotante
− 15230 rotating pan mill	broyeur *m* à cuve tournante	Kollergang *m* mit umlaufendem Teller	molazza *f* a vasca girevole
^ 15231 rotating scratchers	gratteurs *m pl.* de tubage avec de pointes à brosse	Wendekratzer *m pl.*	baffi *m pl.* di gatto verticale con punte a spazzola
° 15231a rotating top	tremie *f* tournante	Drehtrichter *m*	tramoggia *f* ruotante
° 15232 rotation in the same direction	rotation *f* dans le même sens	gleichbleibende Richtung *f*	rotazione *f* nello stesso senso
° 15232a rotation lag	retard *m* de rotation	Rotationsverzögerung *f*	ritardo *m* di rotazione
° 15233 rotation of rolls	rotation *f* des cylindres	Walzenbewegung *f*	rotazione *f* dei cilindri
°'15233a rotational slip	glissement *m* rotatif	Drehungsgleiten *n*	sfaldamento *m* rotativo
° 15234 rotator	four *m* à puddler tournant	Puddeldrehofen *m*	forno *m* rotativo per puddellaggio
− 15235 rotatory fault	faille *f* rotatoire	Drehverwerfung *f*	faglia *f* rotativa

		English	French	German	Italian
o	15236	**Rothe's ether apparatus**	appareil *m* à éther d'après Rothe	Äther-Extraktions-apparat *m* nach Rothe	apparecchio *m* per etere secondo Rothe
^	15237	**roto-wall cleaners**	gratteurs *m pl.* de tubage verticaux	Vertikalkratzer *m pl.* mit der Spitze auf einem einigen Draht	baffi di gatto verticali con la punta su un unico filo
		rottenstone, *s. tripoli*			
—	15238	**rotten lode**	filon *m* pourri	zersetzter Gang *m*	filone *m* putrefatto
—	15239	**rotting**	putréfaction *f*	Verwesung *f*	putrefazione *f*
—	15240	**rotting**	érosion *f*	Verwitterung *f*	erosione *f*
o	15240a	**rouge**	rouge *m* à polir	Polierrot *n*	rosso *m* inglese
—	15241	**rougemontite**	rougemontite *f*	Rougemontit *m*	rougemontite *f*
o	15242	**to rough down blooms**	ébaucher, laminer	vorwalzen	sbozzare al laminatoio
o	15243	**to rough-forge**	forger grossièrement	vorschmieden	prefucinare
o	15244	**rough**	balafré	narbig	intagliato, fregiato
o	15245	**rough blanking**	cisaillage *m* grossier	Rohauschneiden *n*	prima tranciatura *f*
o	15246	**rough-cast**	brut de coulée	roh gegossen	fuso grezzo
o	15247	**rough casting**	pièce *f* brute de fonderie	Rohguss *m*	getto *m* grezzo
—	15248	**rough coal**	tout-venant *m*, charbon *m* brut	Förderkohle *f*, Rohkohle *f*	carbone *m* grezzo di fonderia
o	15249	**rough-forged**	forgé brut	roh geschmiedet	fucinato grezzo
o	15249a	**rough grinding**	dégrossissage *m* à la meule	Zuschleifen *n*	sgrossatura *f* alla mola
o	15250	**rough-machined**	ébauché, préparé	vorbearbeitet	sgrossato
o	15251	**rough masonry**	massif *m* en maçonnerie	Rauhgemäuer *n*	camicia *f* esterna in muratura
o	15252	**rough rolled**	brut de laminage	rohgewalzt	grezzo di laminazione
o	15253	**rough-rolled ingot**	bloom *m*	vorgewalzter Block *m*	lingotto *m* pre-laminato
o	15254	**rough sheets**	couches *f pl.* dures	feste Schichten *f pl.*	strati *m pl.* duri
o	15255	**rough-worked iron**	fer dégrossi	grob bearbeitetes Eisen *n*	ferro *m* sgrossato
o	15256	**roughened**	ébauché	vorgewalzt	sbozzato
		roughener, *s. roughing mill*			

	English	French	German	Italian
°	15257 **rougher**	dégrossisseuse *f*	Vorreiniger *m*	laminatoio *m* sgrossatore
°	15257a **roughing, cogging**	laminage *m* des lingots	Blockwalzen *n*	laminazione *f* di lingotti
°	15258 **roughing**	dégrossissage *m*	Vorwalzen *n*	sgrossatura *f*
°	15259 **roughing lathe**	tour *m* à dégrossir	Schruppdrehbank *f*	tornio *m* per sgrossatura
°	15260 **roughing mill**	train *m* ébaucheur	Vorblockwalze *f*	treno *m* sbozzatore
°	15261 **roughing rolls, roughing train**	train *m* ébaucheur	Luppenwalzwerk *n*	treno *m* sbozzatore o cilindri *m pl.* sgrossatori
°	15262 **roughing stand**	cage *f* de laminoir dégrossisseur	Blockgerüst *n*	gabbia *f* del laminatoio
	roughing train, *s. roughing rolls*			
°	15263 **roughing tool**	outil *m* à dégrossir	Schruppstahl *m*	utensile *m* per sbozzare
—	15264 **roughneck**	aide-mineur *m*	Hilfsarbeiter *m*	manovale *m*
°	15266 **roughness**	rugosité *f*	Rauheit *f*	rugosità *f*
	to round off, *s. to splay*			
	15267 **round**	rond	rund, runden	rotondo
—	15268 **round**	série de trous de mine	Bohrlochreihe *f*	serie *f* di fori da mina, volata *f*
°	15269 **round bar**	barre *f* ronde	Rundstab *m*	tondo *m*
°	15270 **round-(bar-)iron, iron rod**	fer *m* rond, ronds *m pl.*	Rundeisen *n*, Rundstab *m*	ferro *m* tondo, tondino *m*
°	15271 **round bar steel**	rond (en acier)	Rundstahl *m*	tondo *m*
°	15272 **round bars for reinforcing concrete**	ronds *m pl.* à béton	Armierungseisen *n*, Moniereisen *n*, Betonstahl *m*	tondi *m pl.* per cemento armato
°	15273 **round bottom flask**	ballon *m* rond	Rundkolben *m*	matraccio *m* a fondo rotondo
—	15274 **round buddle**	table *f* ronde	Rundherd *m*	tavola *f* tonda
°	15275 **round bush**	bague *f* ronde	Führungsbüchse *f* mit Rundloch	boccola *f* cilindrica, boccola *f* tonda
—	15276 **round coal**	gros (charbon)	Stückkohle *f*	carbone *m* in pezzi

	English	French	German	Italian
°	15277 round die	filière f ronde, peigne m à fileter	Gewindeschneideisen n	filiera f rotonda
°	15278 round-edged flat	plat à arêtes arrondies	rundkantiger Flachstahl m	piatto m a costa arrotondata
°	15279 round-edged section iron	fer m profilé à arêtes arrondies	rundkantiges Formeisen n	ferro m profilato arrotondato
°	15280 round ground surface	surface f arrondie par frottement	rundgeriebene Oberfläche f	superficie f arrotondata
°	15281 round head contersunk rivet	rivet m à tête ronde noyée	Linsensenkniet m	chiodo m a testa svasata con calotta
°	15282 round head nail	pointe f à tête bombée	Rundkopfstift m	punta f a testa bombata
°	15283 round-headed bolt, head button bolt	boulon m à tête ronde	Bolzen m mit rundem Kopf	bullone m a testa tonda
°	15284 round ingot	lingot m rond	Rundbarre f	lingotto m tondo
°	15285 round iron	fer m rond	Rundeisen n	ferro m tondo
°	15286 round iron anchorage	ancrage m en fers ronds	Rundanker m	ancoraggio m in ferri tondi
°	15287 round nosed trowel	truelle f à bout arrondi	Polierschaufel f mit rundem Blatt	cazzuola f a punta arrotondata
°	15288 round pass	calibre m rond	Rundkaliber n	calibro m rotondo
°	15289 round porosity	porosité f à pores ronds	Rundporenporosität f	porosità f a pori sferici
°	15290 round (or snap or button) rivet	rivet m à tête demi-ronde	Rundniet m, Halbrundniet m	chiodo m a testa semitonda
°	15291 round sleeker	pièce f à lisser ronde	Rundknopf m	lisciatore m rotondo
°	15292 round steel	acier m rond	Rundstahl m	acciaio m tondo
°	15293 round-strand rope	câble m à torons ronds	Rundlitzenseil n	cavo m a trefoli rotondi
	round top head rivet,	s. knobbled countersunk head rivet		
—	15294 round trip	opération f de remontée et de descente des tiges de forage	Aus- und Einbau m des Bohrgestänges	operazione f di salita e di discesa delle aste di sondaggio

	English	French	German	Italian
	rounds, *s. bar iron*			
°	15295 **rounds in coils**	fer *m* rond en couronne	Rundstahl *m* in Ringen	tondi *m pl.* in rotoli
°	15296 **routing**	mortaisage *f*	Stanzen *n*	contornitura *f*
°	15297 **routing machine**	mortaiseuse *f*	Nutenreisser *m*	contornitrice *f*
—	15298 **routivarite**	routivarite *f*	Routivarit *m*	routivarite *f*
—	15299 **rouvillite**	rouvillite *f*	Rouvillit *m*	rouvillite *f*
^	15300 **royalty**	redevance *f*	Lizenzgebühren *f pl.*	diritti *m pl.* di licenza
^	15301 **royalty oil**	droits *m pl.* de concession pétrolifère	Erdölkonzessionsrechte *n pl.*	diritti *m pl.* di concessione petrolifera
°	15302 **row of tuyeres**	rangée *f* de tuyères	Düsenreihe *f*	ordine *m* d'ugelli
	R.P.M. = *rounds per minute* **to rub with emery**, *s. to emery grind*			
	15303 **to rub with spirits**	frotter à l'esprit de vin	mit Spiritus einreiben	stropicciare con spirito di vino
	15304 **rubber**	caoutchouc *m*	Gummi *m*	gomma *f*
^	15305 **rubber**	protecteur *m* des tiges	Stangenschutz *m*	protettore *m* delle aste
°	15306 **rubber ball**	poire *f* en caoutchouc	Gummiball *m*	pera *f* di gomma
°	15307 **rubber cap**	chapeau *m* en caoutchouc	Gummikappe *f*	cappuccio *m* di gomma
°	15308 **rubber cap, policeman**	plaquette *f* en caoutchouc	Gummifahne *f*	foglio *m* di gomma
	rubber coupling, *s. rubber union*			
°	15309 **rubber finger stall**	doigt *m* en caoutchouc	Gummifinger *m*	dito *m* o ditale *m* di gomma
°	15310 **rubber glove**	gant *m* en caoutchouc	Gummihandschuh *m*	guanto *m* di gomma
°	15310a **rubber mould**	moule *m* en caoutchouc	Gummiform *f*	forma *f* di gomma
^	15311 **rubber pad**	tampon *m* avec les électrodes dans le microlog	Pfropfen *m* mit Elektroden im Mikrolog	tampone *m* con gli elettrodi nel microlog

	English	French	German	Italian
°	15312 rubber plate	plaque *f* en caout-chouc	Gummiplatte *f*	lastra *f* o foglio *m* di gomma
˄	15313 rubber sleeve core barrel	carottier *m* à chemise	Kernrohr *n* mit Gummischlauch	carotiere *m* con involucro di gomma
°	15314 rubber stopper	bouchon *m* en caoutchouc	Gummistopfen *m*, Gummistöpsel *m*	tappo *m* di gomma
°	15315 rubber strip	fil *m* en caoutchouc	Gummifaden *m*	filo *m* di gomma
°	15316 rubber-taped wire	fil *m* sous ruban en caoutchouc	mit Gummiband umwickelter Draht *m*	filo *m* rivestito di nastro di gomma
°	15317 rubber tubing	tuyau *m* en caout-chouc	Gummischlauch *m*	tubo *m* di gomma
°	15318 rubber union	raccord *m* de tuyau	Schlauchkupplung *f*	giunto *m* per tubo flessibile
°	15319 rubbing	frottement *m*	Friktion *f*, Reibung *f*	sfregamento *m*, frizione *f*
°	15320 rubbing	polissage *m*	Schleifen *n*	levigatura *f*
—	15321 rubbing	broyage *m* de minerai	Erzzerkleinerung *f*	frantumazione *f* fine
—	15321a rubbing board	batte *f*	Schlagholz *n*	pestello *m*, battola *f*
˄	15322 rubbing oil	huile *f* de polissage	Polieröl *n*	olio *m* per lucidare
—	15322a rubbing stone	pierre *f* à broyer	Reibstein *m*	pietra *f* per macinare
—	15323 rubble filling	remblayage de galets	Kiesversatz *m*	gettata *f* di ciottoli
—	15324 rubble stone, rubble	caillou *m* roulé, galet *m*	Geröll *n*, Füllstein *m*	ciottolo *m*, selce *f*, breccia *f*
—	15325 rubellite	rubellite *f*	Rubellit *m*	rubellite *f*
—	15326 rubicelle	rubicelle *f*	Rubicell *m*	rubicella *f*
—	15327 rubidium	rubidium *m*	Rubidium *n*	rubidio *m*
—	15328 rubric	hématite *f* rouge	Roteisenerz *n*	ematite *f* rossa
—	15329 ruby	rubis *m*	Rubin *m*	rubino *m*
—	15330 ruby silver	pyrargyrite *f*	Pyrargyrit *m*	pirargirite *f*
—	15331 ruby spinel	rubis *m* balais	Balasrubin *m*	spinello *m* rosso
	ruby suphur, *s. realgar*			
—	15332 rudaceous texture, psephitic texture	structure saccaroïde	psephitische Struktur *f*	struttura *f* psefitica
—	15333 ruddle	ocre *f* rouge	roter Ocker *m*	ocra *f* rossa

	English	French	German	Italian
— 15334	rudite, rudyte	roche *f* sédimentaire à gros grain	Rudit *m*	roccia *f* sedimentaria a grana grossa
	rules for testing, *s. directions for testing*			
	rumbler, *s. tumbling barrel or rattler*			
° 15335	rumpf (welding)	passe *f*	(Schweiss)Gang *m*	passata *f*
— 15336	rumpfite	rumpfite *f*	Rumpfit *n*	rumpfite *f*
° 15337	to run	alimenter	speisen	alimentare
— 15338	to run	ébouler	zu Bruch gehen	franare
— 15339	to run an adit	pousser une galerie	einen Stollen *m* absenken	approfondire una galleria
^ 15340	to run a swab	descendre un piston dans le puits	Pumpenstempel *m* niederbringen	abbassare un pistone nel pozzo
° 15341	to run a metal	couler un métal	(Metall)giessen	colare un metallo
^ 15342	to run a tank	pomper un réservoir pour le vider	Tankauspumpen	pompare un serbatoio per svuotarlo
^ 15343	to run casing, to set casing	entuber, tuber	verrohren, auskleiden	tubare, applicare il tubaggio
° 15344	to run gates	appliquer les attaques de coulée	Ausgussanschlüsse *f pl.* anbringen	applicare gli attacchi di colata
° 15345	to run hot, to heat	s'échauffer	heiss werden, heiss laufen	riscaldarsi
^ 15346	to run in	insérer, introduire	niederbringen	inserire, introdurre, far scendere
° 15347	to run idle	marcher à vide	leergehen	girare a vuoto
	to run light, *s. to run idle*			
° 15348	to run off	dégorger	durchgiessen	sgorgare, colare
	to run out, *s. to leak*			
	run (welding), *s. pass*			
° 15349	run	marche *f*, fonctionnement *m*	Gang *m*, Lauf *m*	marcia *f*, funzionamento *m*, tragitto *m*
—15350	run	éboulis	Schutt *m*	ammasso *m* di detriti
—15351	run	chute *f* de la cage	Seilbruch *m*	caduta *f* della gabbia

English	French	German	Italian
— 15352 run	plan *m* incliné	Bremsberg *m*	piano *m* inclinato
— 15353 run	longueur *f* du trou de mine	Bohrlänge *f*	lunghezza *f* del foro
^ 15354 run-back	tubes *m pl.* de retour	rückkehrende Rohre *n pl.*	tubi *m pl.* di ritorno
^ 15355 run-down lines	tubes *m pl.* d'adduction	Zuleitungsrohre *n pl.*	tubi *m pl.* di convogliamento
^ 15356 run-down tank	réservoir *m* intermédiaire	Zwischentank *m*	serbatoio *m* intermedio (o di lavorazione)
^ 15357 run of casing	opération *f* de tubage	Verrohren *n*	operazione *f* di tubaggio
run of mine, *s. rough coal*			
run-off, *s. overflow channel or flow-off*			
° 15358 run-off	dégorgement *m*	Überfliessen *n*	traboccamento *m*
° 15358a run-off casting	dégorgement *m* de la coulée	uberfliessendes Giessen *n*	trabocco *m* della colata
° 15359 run-off riser	jet *m* de remonte	verlängerter Steigkanal *m*	montante *m*
° 15360 run out	moule *m* vidé	durchgegangene Form *f*	forma *f* svuotata, getto *m* incompleto
° 15361 run out table	table *f* à rouleau de sortie	Abfuhrrollgang *m*	piano *m* di uscita, tavola con rulli d'uscita
run steel, *s. cast steel*			
° 15361a run up table	table *f* à rouleaux d'arrivage	Zufuhrrollgang *m*	tavola *f* con rulli d'entrata
^ 15362 run way	couloir *m* du portail de la tour	Rutsche *f* des Turmportales	scivolo *m* del portale di torre
° 15363 runner	canal *m* d'alimentation	Lauf *m*	alimentatore *m*
° 15364 runner	jet *m* de coulée	Einguss *m*	getto *m* di colata
° 15365 runner	barre *f* d'alimentation	Lauf *m*	canale *m* distributore
° 15366 runner, running channel	rigole *f* de coulée, canal *m* de coulée	Querlauf *m*, Giessrinne *f*	canale *m* distributore, collegamento di colata
° 15367 runner	curseur *m*	Läufer *m*	cursore *m*
^ 15368 runner	roue *f* de pompe	Pumpenlaufrad *n*	ruota *f* di pompa
—15369 runner	rouleur *m*	Schlepper *m*	trasportatore *m* (operaio)

English	French	German	Italian
15370 **runner** **runner (box)**, s. diffuser	guidage m	Führung f, Spurlatte f	guida f, slittoni m pL.
15371 **runner**	meule f supérieure d'un moulin	oberer Mühlstein m	mola f superiore d'un mulino
15371a**runner bush**	godet de coulée	aufgebauter Einguss- trichter m	rialzo m di colata
15372 **runner gate**	chenal m de coulée	Gussrinne f	canale m di colata
15373 **runner-on** **runner pin**, s. gate pin	encageur m, rouleur m	Anschläger m, Schlepper m	ingabbiatore m, tra- sportatore m
15374 **runner pipe**	chenal m de coulée	Giessrinne f	canale m di colata
15375 **runner scrap**	galette f	Angussrest m	materozza f
15376 **runner stick**, **gate pin**	modèle pour coulée	Gussmodelltrichter m	cono-modello m per colate
15376a**runner through**	canal de coulée	Förderinne f	colatoio m
15377 **runners** pl.	jets m pl. de coulée	Rücklaufmaterial n, Giessabfälle m pl.	boccame m
15378 **running**	alimentation f	Speisen n	alimentazione f
15379 **running and** **feeding layout**	dispositif m d'ali- mentation des pièces	Giesssystem n	dispositivo m di ali- mentazione dei pezzi
15380 **running and** **feeding system** **running casing**, s. run casing	masselottage m, système m d'alimen- tation	Speisersystem n, Giesssystem n	materozzatura f, sistema m di alimen- tazione
15381 **running gate**	jet m de coulée, trou de coulée	Einguss m, Eingusskanal m	foro m di colata, get- to di colata
15381a**running-out fire**	four m de premier affinage	Frischereiofen m	forno m di primo affi- naggio
15382 **running in** **running time**, s. burning time	descente f	Einlassen n	discesa f
15383 **runout, run-out**	jet m non venu, moule m vide	durchgegangene Form f	getto m incompleto (o svuotato)
15384 **runs**	teneur f du minerai	Metallgehalt n von Erz	contenuto m di mine- rale
15385 **rupture ductility**	allongement m de rupture par fluage	Zeitdehnbruch m	rottura f di scorri- mento viscoso
15386 **rupture strength**	résistance f à la traction	Zerreissfestigkeit f	resistenza f alla rottura

		English	French	German	Italian
−	15387	**ruptured zone**	zone f de rupture	Bruchzone f	zona f di rottura
^	15388	**rush**	affluence f	Zulauf m	afflusso m, flusso m
o	15389	**rush gold**	or m rouillé	rostiges Gold n	oro m arrugginito
o	15390	**to rust**	rouiller	rosten	arrugginire
o	15391	**rust**	rouille f	Rost m	ruggine f
−	15392	**rust about**	aide-ouvrier m	Hilfsarbeiter m	manovale m
o	15393	**rustproof**	inoxydable	nicht rostend	inossidabile
o	15394	**rustproof steel**	acier m inoxydable	nichtrostender Stahl m	acciaio m inossidabile
o	15395	**rust protection agent**	enduit m contre la rouille	Rostschutzmittel n	agente m antiruggine
o	15396	**rust resisting**	résistant à la rouille	rostfrei, rostbeständig	resistente alla ruggine
o	15396a	**rust remover**	dissolvant m de rouille	Rostlösungsmittel n	dissolvente m della ruggine
o	15397	**rustless iron**	fer m inoxydable	nichtrostendes Eisen n	ferro m inossidabile
		rustless steel, $s.$ $stainless$ $steel$			
o	15398	**rusty iron, burnt iron**	fer m oxydé, fer m contenant de l'oxygène	sauerstoffhaltiges Eisen n	ferro m contenente ossigeno
o	15399	**ruthenium**	ruthénium m	Ruthenium n	rutenio m
−	15400	**rutherfordine**	rutherfordine f	Rutherfordin m	rutherfordite f
−	15401	**rutile**	rutile m	Rutil m	rutilo m
−	15402	**ruttles**	brèche f de friction	Reibungsbreccie f	breccia f di frizione

	English	French	German	Italian
15403	S. hook	crochet _m_ en S	S- Haken _m_	gancio _m_ ad esse
15404	sack borer	tarière à sac	Sackbohrer _m_	trivella _f_ a sacco
15405	sack conveyor	transporteur _m_ pour sacs	Sackförderer _m_	trasportatore _m_ di sacchi a nastro
15406	saddening	forgeage _m_ de prépa- ration	Vorschmiedung _f_	fucinatura _f_ di preparazio- ne
15407	saddle	gâche _f_ pour tubes	Schelle _f_	sella _f_ cavalletto _m_
15408	saddle	anticlinal _m_ en for- me de selle	Sattel _f_	anticlinale _m_ a forma di sella
15408a	saddle	support _m_ de dégor- geoir	Räumnadel _f_, Stütze _f_	supporto _m_ di alesatrice
15409	saddle axis	axe _m_ anticlinal	Sattelachse _f_	asse _m_ anticlinale
15410	saddle plate	selle _f_ avant de boî- te à feu	Stiefelknechtplat- te _f_ , Kropfwand _f_	lamiera _f_ a sella della cas- sa focolare
15411	saddle reef	couche _f_ ondulée	wellenförmiges Flöz _n_	strato _m_ ondulato, filone _m_ tabulare inclinato
15412	saddleback stool	fromage _m_ à V	V - Bühne _f_	palchetto _m_ a V
15413	safety belt	ceinture· _f_ de sûreté	Rettungsgürtel _m_	cintura _f_ di sicurezza
15414	safety clamp	bride _f_ de sûreté	Sicherheitsglieder- klemme _f_	flangia _f_ di sicurezza
15415	safety device, safety valve	dispositif _m_ de sû- reté	Sicherheitsvorrich- tung _f_	dispositivo _m_ di sicu- rezza, valvola _f_ di sicurez- za
15416	safety funnel	tube _m_ de sûreté	Sicherheitsröhre _f_	tubo _m_ di sicurezza
15417	safety explosive	explosif _m_ de sûre- té	Sicherheitssprerg- stoff _m_	esplosivo _m_ di sicurezza
15418	safety joint	joint de sûreté	Sicherheitsmuffe	giunto _m_ di sicurezza
15419	safety lamp. Davy lamp	lampe _f_ de sûreté	Sicherheitslampe _f_	lampada _f_ di sicurezza
15420	safety layout, safety device	dispositif _m_ de sé- curité	Schutzvorrichtung _f_ Sicherheitsvorrich- tung	dispositivo _m_ di sicurezza, congegno _m_ di sicurezza
15421	safety net	filet _m_ protecteur	Schutznetz _n_	rete _f_ di protezione
15422	safety oil-lamp	lampe _f_ à pétrole à flamme de sûreté	Sicherheitsöl- lampe _f_	lampada _f_ di sicurezza ad olio
15423	safety plattform and finger	pont _m_ d'attelage	Gestängebühne _f_	piattaforma _f_ d'attacco

		English	French	German	Italian
o	15424	**safety stake**	pieu *m* de guidage	Führungspfahl *m*	picchetto *m* di guida
^	15425	**safety valve**	soupape *f* de sûreté	Sicherheitsventil *n*	valvola *f* di sicurezza
o	15426	**safety wedge**	cale *f* de sécurité	Verriegelungskeil *m*	cuneo *m* di sicurezza, cuneo *m* di bloccaggio
—	15427	**sagenite**	sagénite *f*	Sagenit *m*	sagenite *f*
o	15427a	**sagger**	boîte *f* réfractaire	Brennkaspel *f*	cassetta *f* refrattaria
—	15428	**sagging of beds on hill sides**	glissement *m* de couches superficielles	Oberflächenschicht- enrustsche *f*	slittamento *m* di strati superficiali
^	15429	**sagging production**	production *f* devenant pire en qualité	Schlimmherstellung *f*	produzione *f* declinante in qualità
—	15430	**sagvandite**	sagvandite *f*	Sagvandit *m*	sagvandite *f*
—	15431	**Sahelian stage**	Sahélien *m*	Sahelian *n*	Saheliano *m*
—	15432	**sahlite**	salite *f*	Salit *m*	salite *f*
—	15433	**sal ammoniac, ammonium chloride**	chlorure *m* d'ammoniaque	Salmiak *m* Chlorammonium *n*	cloruro *m* ammonico o ammoniaco
o	15434	**salamander**	loup *m*	Ofenwolf *m*	materiale *m* residuo non fuso, loppa *f*
—	15435	**salband**	salbande *f*	Salband *n*	salbanda *f*
	15436	**sale**	vente *f*	Verkauf *m*	vendita *f*
—	15437	**salfemic**	salfemique	salfemisch	salfemico
—	15438	**salite**	salite *f*	Salit *m*	salite *f*
—	15439	**salmiac**	salmiac *m*	Salmiak *m*	salmiak *m*
—	15440	**salmonsite**	salmonsite *f*	Salmonsit *m*	salmonsite *f*
—	15441	**Salopian stage**	Salopien *m*	Salopian *n*	salopiano *m*
ọ	15442	**salt bath furnace**	four *m* à bain de sel	Salzbadofen *m*	forno *m* a bagno di sale
◡	15443	**salt bath quench, salt bath hardening**	trempe *f* en bain de sel	Salzbadhärten *n* , Salzbadhärtung *f*	tempra *f* in bagno di sale
—	15444	**salt dome, salt plug**	dôme *m* de sel	Salzdom *m*, Salzstock *m*	duomo *m* salino
		salt plug, *s. salt dome*			
o	15445	**salt spray testing**	test *m* au brouillard salin	Salzsprühversuch *m*	prova *f* in nebbia salina
—	15446	**salt water disposal**	élimination *f* de l'eau saline	Salzwasserentfernung *f*	eliminazione *f* dell'acqua salina

	English	French	German	Italian
15447	salpetre, salpeter	salpêtre m	Salpeter m	salnitrò m, nitrato di potassio
15448	to salvage	recouvrer	wiedergewinnen	recuperare
15449	samarium	samarium m	Samarium m	samario m
15450	samarskite	samarskite f	Samarskit m	samarskite f
15451	samiresite	samirésite f	Samiresit m	samiresite f
15452	sammelkristalli-sation	cristallisation f collective	Sammelkristallisa-tion f	cristallizazione f collettiva
15453	sample	échantillon m	Muster n	campione m
15454	sample	prise f d'essai	Probemenge f, Probe f	prelievo m, saggio m
15455	sample bag	boîte f à carottes	Kernkasten m	cassetta f per carote
15456	sample bottle	flacon m à échantillons	Probeglas n	flacone m per campioni
15457	sample box	boîte f à échantillons	Probeschachtel f	scatola f per campioni
	sample quartering, s.	quartering the sample		
15458	sample-taking	canon m carottier	Geschosskerner m	cannone m carottiere
15459	sampler	sonde f de prise d'échantillon	Probesonde f	sonda f campionatrice
15460	sampling	prélèvement m de échantillon, prise f d'essai	Probenahme f	campionatura f
15461	sampling material	prise f d'essai	Probegut n	campionatura f
15462	sampling (side wall)	carottage m du mur	Schachtstoss-Kern-bohrung f	carotaggio m di parete
15463	sampling spoon	louche f	Probelöffel m	cucchiaia f di colata
15464	samson post	support m de levier de battage	Schwengelbock m	cavalletto m di sostegno del bilancere
15465	samsonite	samsonite f	Samsonit m	samsonite f
15466	to sand blast	sabler	strahlen, absanden	sabbiare
15467	to sand up	ensabler	versanden	insabbiare
15468	to sand-cast	mouler en sable	sandformen	gettare (a colare) in terra, gettare in forma di terra
15469	sand	sable m	Sand m	sabbia f

		English	French	German	Italian
		sand additive, *s. foundry blacking*			
o	15470	sand bath	bain *m* de sable	Sandbad *n*	bagno *m* di sabbia
o	15471	sand bed	couche *f* de coulée	Giessbett *n*	piano *m* (o letto) di colata
o	15472	sand blast	jet *m* de sable	Sandstrahl *m*	getto *m* di sabbia
o	15473	sand blast apparatus	machine *f* à jet de sable	Sandstrahlgebläse *n*	macchina *f* a getto di sabbia
o	15474	sand-blast nozzle, sand blowing nozzle	busette *f* de sablage, buse *f* à jet de sable	Strahldüse *f* für Putzvorrichtung	ugello *m* del getto di sabbia
o	15475	sand-blast nozzle	lance *f* de sablage	Strahlmittellanze *f*	lancia *f* da sabbiare
o	15476	sand-blaster	dessableur *m*	Gussputzer *m*	sabbiatore *m*, macchina per sabbiatura
o	15477	sand-blasting	sablage *m*	Strahlen *n*, Absanden, Strahlputzen *n*	sabbiatura *f*
o	15478	sand-blasting apparatus	dessableuse *f*	Putzmaschine *f*	sabbiatrice *f*, macchina *f* a getto di sabbia
o	15479	sand-blasting barrel	tambour *m* de sablage	Strahlputztrommel *f*	sabbiatrice *f* a tamburo
o	15480	sand-blasting cabinet	cabine *f* à manches	Putzkammer *f* mit Aussenbedienung	cabina *f* a maniche
o	15481	sand-blasting chamber, sand blasting room	cabine *f* de sablage, chambre *f* de dessablage	Strahlkammer *f*, Putzhaus *n*	camera *f* di sabbiatura
o	15482	sand-blasting gun	pistolet *m* de sablage	Strahlmittelpistole *f*	pistola *f* per sabbiare
o	15483	sand-blowing nozzle	brise *f* à jet de sable	Strahldüse *f* für Putzvorrichtung	ugello *m* del getto di sabbia
o	15484	sand bond, cohesion	corps *m* du sable	Standfestigkeit *f* des Sandes	forza *f* della terra, coesione *f* della sabbia
o	15484a	sand bottom	sole *f* en sable	Sandboden *m*	suola *f* in terra
o	15485	sand buckle	échilles *f pl.*	Hammerschlag *m*	taccone *m* falso, falsa sfoglia *f*
		sand burning, *s. metal penetration*			
o	15486	sand cast	coulé en sable	in Sand *m* gegossen	fuso in terra
o	15487	sand cast iron, sand cast pig	fonte *f* coulée en sable	in Sandformen gegossenes Roheisen *n*	ghisa *f* colata in sabbia

	English	French	German	Italian
	sand cast pig, *s. sand cast iron*			
15488	sand cast tube	tuyau *m* coulé en sable	Sandgussrohr *n*	tubo *m* colato in sabbia
15489	sand casting	moulage *m* en sable	Sandguss *m*	colata *f* in sabbia
15490	sand casting	jet *m* coulé en sable	Sandguss *m*	getto *m* in forma di terra
15490a	sand cutter	diviseur *m* du sable	Sandschleuder *m*	disintegratore *m* della sabbia
15491	sand cutting	division *f* de sable	Sandschleudern *n*	divisione *f* della terra
15492	sand drying stove	four *m* à sécher le sable	Sandtrockenofen *m*	forno *m* di essicazione della sabbia
15493	sand edge	languette *f* à sable	Sandleiste *f*	sporto *m* della staffa
15494	sand exclusion	élimination *f* du sable	Verhütung *f* von Sandzufluss	eliminazione *f* della sabbia
15495	sand filling	saupoudrer avec du sable	Aufstreuen *n* von Sand	copertura *f* con sabbia
15496	sand flag	grès *m* se débitant en dalles	plattiger Sandstein *m*	gres *m* in lastre
15497	sand for dry moulds	sable *m* d'étuve	Trockengusssand *m*	terra *f* a secco
15498	sand frame	rehausse *f* de châssis	Füllrahmen *m*	rialzo *m* della staffa
15498a	sand fritting	frittage *m* du sable	Sandzusammenbacken *n*	sinterizzazione *f* della terra
15499	sand hole (casting defect)	trou *m* de sable	Sandloch *n*	cavità *f* con terra
15500	sand inclusion	inclusion *f* de sable	Sandeinschluss *m*	inclusione *f* di terra
15501	sand line	câble *m* de curage	Schlammseil *n*	cavo *m* del tornello veloce
15502	sandline spool	treuil *m* de curage	Schlämmhaspel *f*	argano *m* di spurgo della sabbia
15503	sand mill	frotteur *m*, mélangeur *m* de sable	Kollergang *m*	molazza-mescolatrice *f* (di sabbia)
15504	sand mixer, mixing machine	malaxeur de sable	Sandmischer *m*	mescolatrice *f* per sabbia molazza *f* per terra da fonderia
15505	sand mould	moule *m* en sable	Sandform *f*	forma *f* in sabbia
15506	sand moulding	moulage *m* en sable	Sandformerei *f*	formatura *f* in sabbia o in terra

		English	French	German	Italian
°	15507	sand moulding and foundry work machines	machines *f pl.* à mouler (pour fonderies)	Form- und Giesserei-maschinen *f pl.*	macchine *f pl.* per formare e per fonderia
°	15508	sand packing	obturation *f* au sable	Sandverdichtung *f*	otturazione *f* con sabbia
°	15509	sand paper	papier *m* à sable	Sandpapier *n*	carta *f* smeriglio
°	15510	sand pattern	faux-modèle *m*	Sandmodell *n*, Sparhälfte *f*	falso modello *m*, modello di sabbia
°	15511	sand pins, moulding pins	épingles *f pl.* des pointes *f pl.*	Hakenstifte *m pl.*, Formerstifte *m pl.*	spilli *m pl.* da fonderia
°	15512	sand pipe	tuyau *m* de sablage	Sandrohr *n.*	tubo *m* sabbiatore
°	15513	sand plant	sablerie *f*	Sandaufbereitungs-anlage *f*	impianto *m* per preparare le sabbie, reparto lavorazione terre
—	15514	sand pump	pompe *f* à sable	Sandpumpe *f*	pompa *f* per sabbia
^	15515	sand reel, sand-line reel	treuil *m* de curage	Schlammhaspel *f*	tornello *m* veloce
°	15516	sand reconditioning, sand reclamation	régénération *f* du sable	Altsandaufberei-tung *f*	recupero *m* della terra
^	15517	sand sheave	poulie *f* de curage	Schlammrolle *f*	puleggia *f* del tornello veloce
°	15517a	sand sieve grading	granulomètrie *f*	Korngrössenverteil-ung *f*	granulometria *f*
°	15518	sand skin	croûte *f* de sable	Sandkruste *f*	crosta *f* di sabbia
°	15518a	sand slinger	projecteur *m* de sable	Wanfschleuder *m*	lanciaterra *m*
°	15519	sand sticking to	collage *m* de sable	Kleben *n* des Sandes	asportazione *f* di terra
^	15520	sand thickness	épaisseur *m* de sable	Sanddicke *f*	spessore *m* dello strato poroso
		sand wash, *s. erosion scab*			
°	15521	sandblast barrel	tambour *m* à jet de sable	Trommelgebläse *n*	tamburo *m* a getto di sabbia
°	15522	sandblast machine	sableuse *f*	Sandstrahlmaschine *f*	sabbiatrice *f*
°	15523	sandblast room	chambre *f* de dessablage (au jet de sable)	Sandblastraum *m*, Sandstrahlputzhaus	camera *f* per sabbiatura (a getto di sabbia)
°	15524	sandblast sand	sable *m* de nettoyage	Putzsand *m*	sabbia *f* di pulitura
—	15525	sandblasted pebble	pierre *f* à facettes	Windkanter *m*, Dreikanter *m*	pietra *f* sfaccettata
°	15525a	sandblasting	sablage *m*	Strahlputzen *n*	sabbiatura *f*

English	French	German	Italian
15526 **sanded, polished with sand**	grésillé, poli au sable	mit Sand poliert	levigato con sabbia
15526a **sandhole**	nid *m* de sable	Sandnest *n*	nido *m* di terra
15527 **sandless pig iron**	fonte *f* sans sable	sandfreier Guss *m*	ghisa *f* priva di sabbia
15527a **sandling**	polissage *m* mécanique	Feinschleifen *n*	pulitura *f* meccanica
15528 **sandslinger**	projecteur *m* de terre	Wurfschleuder *m*	proiettore *m* di terra
15529 **sandstone**	grès *m*, grès *m* rouge	Sandstein *m*	arenaria *f*, gres *m*
15530 **sandstone**	pierre *f* de taille	Quadersandstein *m*	pietra *f* da taglio, concio *m*
15531 **sandstone in blocks**	bloc *m* de grès	Quadersandstein *m*	pietra *f* arenaria in blocchi
15531a **sandwich die**	matrice *f* à éléments empilés	Stapelmatrize *f*	matrice *f* a elementi sovrapposti
15532 **sandwich rolling**	laminage *m* à sandwich	Sandwichwalzen *n*	laminazione *f* a sandwich
15533 **sandy facies**	faciès *m* sableux	sondige Fazies *f*	«facies» *f* sabbioso-arenaria
15534 **sandy iron ore**	minerai *m* de fer sablonneux	sandiger Eisenstein *m*	minerale *m* di ferro sabbioso
15535 **sanidine**	sanidine *m*	Sanidin *m*	sanidino *m*
15536 **sanidinite**	sanidinite *f*	Sanidinit *m*	sanidinite *f*
15537 **Sonnoisian stage**	Sannoisien *m*	Sannoisian *n*	Sannoisiano *m*
15538 **santorinite**	santorinite *f*	Santorinit *m*	santorinite *f*
15539 **sanukite**	sanukite *f*	Sanukit *m*	sanukite *f*
15539a **sap**	noyau *m* non cémenté	nichtzementierter Kern *m*	nucleo *m* non cementato
15540 **saponite**	saponite *f*	Saponit *f*	saponite *f*
15541 **sapphire**	saphir *m*	Saphir *m*	zaffiro *m*
15542 **sapropelite**	sapropélite *f*	Sapropelit *m*	sapropelite
15543 **sarcolite**	sarcolite *f*	Sarkolith *m*	sarcolite *f*
15544 **sarcopside**	sarcopside *m*	Sarkopsid *m*	sarcopside *f*
15545 **sard**	sardoine *f*	Sarder *m*	sarda *f*, corniola *f*
15546 **sardonyx**	sardoine *f*	Sardonyx	sardonio *m*
15547 **sarkinite**	sarkinite *f*	Sarkinit *m*	sarkinite *f*
15548 **sarnaite**	sarnaite *f*	Sarnait *m*	sarnaite *f*
15549 **sartorite**	sartorite *f*	Sartorit *m*	sartorite *f*

		English	French	German	Italian
o	15550	sash-bar, sash-iron	fer *m* à vitrage	Sprosseneisen *n*	ferro *m* per spranghe
—	15551	sassolite	sassolite *f*	Sassolin *m*	sassolite *f*
—	15552	saussurite	saussurite *f*	Saussurit *m*	saussurite *f*
—	15553	saussuritization	saussuritisation *f*	Saussuritisation *f*	saussuritizzazione *f*
o	15554	satellitic injection	foyer périphérique	peripherischer Herd *m*	focolare *m* periferico
o	15554a	satin finish	finissage *m* à brosse	Feinen mit Metall- bürste	finitura *f* a spazzola
—	15555	satin spar	sélénite *f* fibreuse	faseriger Gips *m*	selenite *f* fibrosa
^	15556	saturation pressure	pression *f* de satu- ration	Sättigungsdruck *m*	pressione *f* di satu- razione
o	15557	saw blade	lame *f* de scie	Sägeblatt *n*	lama *f* di sega
		saw bow, *s. saw frame*			
o	15558	saw clamp	étau d'affûtage pour scies	Sägefeilkluppe *f*	morsa *f* per affilare le seghe
o	15559	saw frame	cadre *m* de scie	Sägebogen *m*	telaio *m* della sega
o	15560	saw steel	acier *m* à scies	Sägestahl *m*	acciaio *m* da seghe
o	15561	saw tooth bit	couronne *f* dentée	Sägezahnkrone *f*	corona *f* dentata
o	15562	saw tooth dirt trap	piège *m* à crasses en dents de scie	Sägezahnlauf *m*	fermascoria *m* a den- ti di sega
o	15563	saw-toothed crown	couronne *f* à dents de scie	Sägezahnkrone *f*	corona *f* dentata
		saw web, *s. saw blade*			
o	15563a	sawing	sciage *m*	Sägen *n*	segare
—	15564	Saxonian stage	Saxonien *m*	Saxonian *n*	sassoniano *m*
o	15565	say ladle (foundry)	cuiller *f* à éprou- vettes	Giesslöffel *m*	cucchiaino *m* piccolo per saggi di metallo fuso
o	15566	scab, sand inclusion	inclusion *f* de sable	Sandeinschluss *m*	inclusione *f* di terra
o	15567	scab	gale *f* volante	abgespülte Sand- schülpe *f*	spoglia f. rappezzo *m*, sfoglia *f* libera
o	15568	scab	écaille *f*, battiture *f* de fer, tartre *m*	Hammerschlag *m*	scaglia *f*, incrostazio- ne *f*, inclusione *f* di ferro
o	15568a	scab	éclat *m*	Splitter *m*	scheggia *f*
—	15569	scab	renard *m*	Streikbrecher *m*	crumiro *m*

	English	French	German	Italian
– 15570	**to scab**	tailler la pierre	einen Stein *m* behauen	tagliare la pietra
15571	**scabbard**	enveloppe *f* de la tige carrée d'entraî-nement	Vierkantstangen-futter *n*	fodero *m* dell'asta qua-dra
– 15572	**to scabble**	tailler la pierre	einen Stein *m* behauen	tagliare la pietra
– 15573	**scad**	pépite *f*	Naturgold *n*	pepita *f*
° 15574	**scaffold**	accrochage *m*	Versetzung *f*	arresto *m*, ostruzione *f*
° 15575	**scaffold**	couronne *f*	Gewölbe *n*	ponte *m*, volta *f*
– 15576	**scaffold**	échafaud *m*, échafaudage *m*	Baugerüst *n*, Schachtbühne *f*	impalcatura *f*, incastel-latura *f*, armatura *f*

scaffolding, *s. scaffold*

scaffolding (of the roasting furnace), *s. clogging up of the roasting furnace*

	English	French	German	Italian
–15577	**scaffolding**	échafaudage *m*	Schachtbühne *f*	impalcatura *f*
–15578	**to scale, to flake**	s'effeuiller	abblättern	sfaldarsi, disfarsi in scaglie
° 15579	**to scale, to descale**	décalaminer	entzundern	togliere le scaglie
° 15580	**to scale, to scrape off the scale**	désincruster	entkrusten, den Kesselstein *m* entfernen	disincrostare, to-gliere le incrostazioni
° 15581	**scale, fouling (of a boiler)**	croûte *f* (de chau-dière)	Kesselstein *m*	incrostazione *f* (di cal-daie)
° 15582	**scale, scaling**	écaillage *m*	Zunderschicht *f*	scagliatura *f*
° 15583	**scale (met), iron scale, mill scale**	pailles *f pl.* d'oxy-de de fer, calamine *f*	Glühspan *m*, Ham-merschlag *m*, Walz-sinter *m*	scaglie *f pl.* (d'ossido di ferro), calamina *f*
15584	**scale**	bascule *f*	Gattierungswaage *f*	pesa *f*, bilico *m*
15585	**scale**	paraffine brute en écailles	Schuppenparaffin *m*	paraffina *f* grezza in scaglie
15586	**scale**	échelle *f*	Skala *f*	scala *f*
° 15587	**scale, measuring rule**	règle *f* divisée	Massstab *m*	regolo *m* (con divi-sioni)
° 15587a	**scale breaker**	laminoir casse-oxyde	Zunderbrechwalze *f*	laminatoio *m* per ri-muovere le scaglie
15588	**scale deposit**	calcination *f*	Versinterung *f*	calcinazione *f*

		English	French	German	Italian
—	15589	scale door	porte f d'aérage à guichet	undichte Wettertür f	porta f di ventilazione non ermetica
o	15590	scale of hardness	échelle f de dureté	Härtenskala f	scala f delle durezze
o	15590a	scale pit	impureté f	Fremdkörper m	impurità f
o	15591	scale resisting steel	acier m inoxydable	zunderbeständiger Stahl m	acciaio m resistente allo scagliamento
—	15592	scale stone	wollastonite f	Wollastonit m	wollastonite f
^	15593	scale wax	paraffine f en écailles	Schuppenparaffin n	scaglie f $pl.$ di paraffin
—	15594	scalenohedron	scalénoèdre m	Skalenoeder m	scalenoedro m
—	15595	scaling	écaillage, écaillement	Abblätterung f, Abschuppen n	scagliatura f, formazione di scaglie, sfaldatura f
o	15596	scaling	incrustation f, formation f d'écaillage	Schlackenbildung f, Zunderbildung f	formazione f di scoria (su acciaio)
o	15597	scaling, descaling	désincrustation f	Kesselsteinentfernung f	disincrostazione f
—	15598	scaling	purger le toit	Bereissen n der Firste	disgaggio m
o	15599	scaling furnace	fourneau m à décaper	Glühofen m	forno m d'arroventamento (o di ricottura)
o	15600	scaling hammer	marteau m à ébarber	Entgratungshammer m, Abschlackungshammer n	martellina, f per sbavare
o	15600a	scalping	enlèvement m de la couche superficielle écailleux, conchoidale	Beseitigung f der Oberfläche schuppig	rimozione, f dello strato superficiale squamoso, concoidale
o	15601	scaly, laminated			
o	15602	scandium	scandium m	Scandium n	scandio m
—	15603	scapolite	scapolite f	Skapolith m	scapolite f
		to scarf, $s.$ to $chamfer$			
o	15604	scarf, scarfing	assemblage m à mi-bois	Verblattung f	fare un giunto ad ammorsatura f
o	15605	scarf-weld	soudage f en biseau	Zusammenschweissen n	bollitura f a quartabuono
		scarfing (in welding), $s.$ $chafering$			
		scarfing torch, $s.$ $deseaming$ $blowpipe$			

	English	French	German	Italian
– 15606	scarn	skarn *m*	Skarn *m*	scarn *m*
	scarfed, *s. rough*			
– 15607	scarp wall	épaulement *m*	Böschungsmauer *f*	muro *m* di scarpa
15608	scavenge oil	huile *f* récupérée	Tropföl *n*	olio *m* di recupero
	scavanger, *s. scavenging agent*			
15609	scavenging agent,	épurateur *m*	Reinigungsmittel *n*	depuratore *m,* agente *m* antipiombo
15610	scavenging the hole	récurage *m* du trou	Bohrloch klarpsü-len	pulizia *f* del foro
– 15611	scawtite	scawtite *f*	Scawtit *m*	scawtite *f*
– 15612	schafarzikité	schafarzikite *f*	Skafarzikit *m*	schafarzikite *f*
– 15613	schairerite	schairerite *f*	Schairerit *m*	schairerite *f*
– 15614	schalenblende	schalenblende *f*	Schalenblende *f*	schalenblenda *f*
– 15615	schallerite	schallérite *f*	Schallerit *m*	schallerite *f*
– 15616	schalstein	schalstein *m*	Schalstein *m*	schalstein *m*
– 15617	schapbachite	schapbachite *f*	Schapbachit *m*	schapbachite *f*
– 15618	scheelite	scheelite *f*	Scheelit *m*	scheelite *f*
– 15619	scheererite	schéerérite *f*	Scheererit *m*	scheererite *f*
– 15620	schefferite	schefférite *f*	Schefferit *m*	schefferite *f*
– 15621	schertelite	schertelite *f*	Schertélit *m*	schertelite *f*
– 15622	schiller	éclat *m* schilléri-sant	Schiller *m*	schiller *m*
– 15623	schiller spar	schillerspath *m*	Schillerspat *m*	schillerspato *m*, ba-stite
– 15624	schillerization	schillérisation *f*	Schillern *n*	schillerizzazione *f*
– 15625	schirmerite	schirmérite *f*	Schirmerit *m*	scirmerite *f*
– 15625a	schist	schiste *m*	Schiefer *m*	scisto *m*
– 15626	schizolite	schisolite *f*	Schizolith *m*	schisolite *f*
– 15627	schneebergite	schneebergite *f*	Schneebergit *m*	schneebergite *f*
– 15628	schoepite	schoepite *f*	Schoepit *m*	schoepite *f*
– 15629	schorlomite	schorlomite *f*	Schorlomit *m*	schorlomite *f*

	English	French	German	Italian
° 15630	schreibersite	schreibersite *f*	Schreibersit *m*	schreibersite *f*
— 15631	schultenite	schultenite *f*	Schultenit *m*	schultenite *f*
° 15632	Schultz boiler	chaudière *f* Schultz	Schultzkessel *m*	caldaia *f* Schultz
— 15633	schuppen structure	structure *f* écailleuse	Schuppenstruktur *f*	struttura *f* scagliosa
— 15634	schwartzembergite	schwartzembergite *f*	Schwartzembergit *m*	schwartzembergite *f*
— 15635	schwazite	schwatzite *f*	Schwazit *m*	schwazite *f*
° 15636	sclerometer	scléromètre *m*	Ritzhärteprüfer *m*	sclerometro *m*
° 15636a	scleroscope	scléroscope *m*	Härtemesser *m*	scleroscopio *m*
— 15637	scolecite	scolécite *f*	Skolezit *m*	skolecite *f*
— 15638	to scoop	enlever à la pelle, puiser, épuiser	ausschaufeln ausschöpfen	scavare, vuotare, prosciugare
— 15639	scoop	pelle *f,* godet *m*	Spaten *m*, Schaufel *f*, Baggereimer *m*	pala *f*, paletta *f*, tazza *f*
— 15640	scoop chain	chaîne *f* à godets	Eimerkette *f*	catena *f* a tazze
— 15641	scoop dredger	drague *f* à godets	Eimerkettenbagger *m*	draga *f* a tazze, draga *f* a noria
° 15642	to score, to scratch	strier	streifen, kratzen	rigare
° 15643	to score	endenter	einkerben	dentellare
— 15644	to score	corroder	korrodieren	erodere, corrodere
— 15644a	scoria	scorie *f* volcanique	Gesteinsschlacke *f*	scoria *f* vulcanica
— 15645	scoring	abrasions *f pl.*	Abrasionen *f pl.*	abrasioni *f pl.*
° 15646	scoring	formation *f* de rainures, rayage *m*	Riefenbildung *f*, Ritzbildung *f*	formazione *f* di scanalature, rigatura *f*
— 15647	scorodite	scorodite *f*	Skorodit *m*	scorodite *f*
° 15648	scotch blast furnace	haut-fourneau *m* écossais	schottischer Hochofen *m*	alto forno *m* scozzese
— 15649	Scotch Boghead coal	(charbon *m)* boghead écossais	schottische Bogheadkohle *f*	carbone *m* scozzese
° 15650	scotch cleaner	crochet *m* de mouleur	Putzhäkchen *n*	uncinetto *m* da formatore
— 15651	scotch hearth	four *m* à minerai de plomb	Bleierzofen *m*	forno *m* per minerale di piombo
° 15652	scotch pig iron	fonte *f* écossaise	schottisches Roheisen *n*	ghisa *f* scozzese

	English	French	German	Italian
15653	scotch trowel	truelle *f* à lisser	Polierschaufel *f*	cazzuola *f* per fonderia
15654	to scour	curer, débourber, décaper	putzen, spülen, schlämmen	pulire, defangare, decapare
15654a	scouring	dérochage *m*	Scheuern *n*	strofinio *m*
15655	scrap	bocage *m*	Gussbruch *m*	boccame *m*
15655a	scrap	ferraille *f*	Schrott *m*	rottami *m pl.*
15656	scrap bailing	paquetage de chutes	Schrottpaketierung *f*	impacchettatura *f* dei rottami
15657	scrap chute	couloir *m* à chutes	Schrottrinne *f*	scivolo *m* per sfridi
15658	scrap cutter	cisaille *f* à scraps	Schrottschere *f*	cesoia *f* per rifiuti o per sfridi
15659	scrap flattening roll	laminoir *m* à scraps	Schrottwalzwerk *n*	laminatoio *m* per sfrido lamiere
15660	scrap(-iron), junk(-iron)	ferraille *f*, vieux-fer *m*	Schrott *m*	rottame *m* di ferro, ferraccio *m*
15661	scrap iron box	cuiller *f* à mitraille	Schrottmulde *f*	cassetta *f* per rottami piccoli
	scrap metal, *s. scrap iron*			
15662	scrap value	valeur *f* des chutes	Abfallwert *m*	valore *m* degli scarti
15663	scrap process	système *m* à chutes	Schrottverfahren *n*	metodo *m* al rottame
15664	to scrape	racler, gratter	schaben	raschiare
	to scrape off the scale, *s. to scale*			
15665	scraper	raclette *f*	Abstreicheisen *n*	rasatore *m*, sbavatore *m*
15666	scraper	racloir *m*	Schrapper *m*	raschietto *m*, rastrello *m*
15667	scraper	curette *f*	Krätzer *m*, Räumlöffel *m*	allargatore *m* per pozzi, raschietto *m* a cucchiaio
15668	scraper chain	chaîne *f* à raclettes	Förderkette *f*	catena *f* a rastrelli
15669	scraper chain conveyor	convoyeur *m* à raclettes	Kratzbandförderer *m* Kratzband *n*	trasportatore *m* a catena dei detriti
15670	scraper conveyor	transporteur *m* à raclettes, convoyeur *m* à raclettes	Schubleistenförderer *m*, Kratzerkettenförderer *m*	trasportatore *m* a rastrelli
15671	scraper disc	racloir *m*	Kratzerscheibe *f*	raschiatore *m*, raschietto *m*
15672	scraper knife	lame *f*, grattoir *m*	Schab(e)messer *n*	raschiatoio *m*, lama *f* per raschiare
	scraper plate, *s. scraper disc*			

		English	French	German	Italian
°	15673	**scraping**	grattage *m*	Schaben *n*	raschiatura *f*
—	15674	**scraping**	raclage *m*	Schrapperförde-rung *f*	raschiatura *f*, raschiett. tura *f*
°	15675	**scraping belt**	ruban *m* à racloirs	Kratzband *n*	nastro *m* a raschietti (a rastrelli)
°	15676	**scraping device, scraper**	ramasseur *m*	Schab(e)vorrich-tung *f*	apparecchio *m* per ra-schiettare
°	15677	**scraping of the slag on the converter nose**	enlèvement *m* du loup	Losdrücken *n* der Mündungsbären	rimozione *f* della scoria (o del groppo)
°	15678	**scrapman**	ouvrier aux chutes	Schrottmann *m*	addetto al rottame
°	15679	**scrapper, waster**	caffut *m*	Ausschuss *n*	scarto *m*, pezzo *m* da scartare, rifiuto *m*
°	15679a	**scratch**	rayure *f*	Ritz *m*, Kratzer *m*	graffio *m*, graffiatura *f*
°	15680	**scratch brush**	gratte-boësse (pour joints de soudure)	Putzbürste *f* (für Schweissnaht)	spazzola *f* raschiatrice
		scratch brush finish, *s. satin finish*			
°	15681	**scratch hardness**	résistance *f* au striage	Ritzhärte *f*	durezza *f* sclerometrica
°	15682	**scratch test**	essai *m* scléromé-trique	Ritzversuch *m*	prova *f* sclerometrica o di penetrazione per striatura
—	15683	**scratched boulder**	galet *m* strié	geritztes Ge-schiebe *n*	detrito *m* striato
^	15684	**scratcher**	gratteur de tubage	Kratzer *m*	baffi di gatto
—	15685	**scratching**	striage *m*	Ritzung *f*	scalfittura *f*, striatura *f*
		to screen, *s. to cob*			
°	15686	**screen, guard plate**	tôle *f* protectrice	Schutzblech *n*	lamiera *f* protettrice
°	15687	**screen analysis**	analyse *f* granulo-métrique	Korngrössenanalyse *f*	analisi *f* granulometrica
—	15688	**screen pipe**	tube *m* filtre	Filterrohr *n*	tubo-filtro *m*
°	15689	**screen vent**	filtre *m* de souf-flage	Abblasefilter *m*, Siebdüse *f*	filtro *m* sfiatatoio
—	15690	**screened (or sifted) coal**	charbon *m* criblé, charbon *m* trié	gesiebte Kohle *f*	carbone *m* crivellato, carbone *m* classifica-to
^	15691	**screened liner**	tube *m* perdu filtrant	Filterrohrhanger *m*	colonna *f* perduta fil-trante

	English	French	German	Italian
– 15692	**screened ore**	minerai *m* 'trié, minerai *m* riche	Scheiderz *n*	minerale *m* scelto
– 15693	**screening**	criblage *m*, tamisage *m*	Siebung *f*, Sieben *n*	vagliatura *f*, crivellatura *f*
– 15694	**screening device**	installation *f* de triage	Scheidevorrichtung *f*	impianto *m* di vagliatura
– 15695	**screening drum**	tambour *m* de tamisage	Siebtrommel *f*	tamburo *m* di vagliatura
– 15696	**screening plant**	installation *f* de criblage	Siebanlage *f*	impianto *m* di vagliatura
– 15697	**screenings**	déchets *m pl.* de criblage	Siebrückstand *m*	rifiuti *m pl.* di vagliatura
	screeve, *s. joint sealing*			
° 15698	**to screw(-thread)**	tailler un filet, fileter	Gewinde schneiden gewindeschneiden	tagliare una filettatura, filettare
° 15699	**to screw together**	assembler par vis	zusammenschrauben	chiudere la staffa con bulloni
° 15700	**screw, eye bolt, ring bolt**	boulon *m* à oeillet	Augenbolzen *m*	bullone *m* con testa ad occhio
° 15701	**screw auger**	mèche *f* styrienne *m*	Schneckenbohrer *m*	succhiello *m* ad elica
– 15702	**screw bell**	cloche *f* de repêchage	Fangglocke *f*	pescatore *m* (a campana)
° 15703	**screw bolt, threaded bolt**	boulon *m* fileté	Schraubenbolzen *m*	bullone *m* filettato
	screw caliper, *s. screw gauge*			
– 15704	**screw conveyor**	transporteur *m* à vis	Schnecken-Transportrinne *f*	trasportatore *m* a vite, alimentatore *m* a coclea
° 15705	**screw-cutting on**	filetage *m* sur le tour	Gewindeschneiden *n* auf der Drehbank	filettatura *f* al tornio
° 15705a	**screw down**	vis *f* de réglage	Stellschraube *f*	vite *f* di regolazione
° 15706	**screw elevator**	élévateur *m* à vis	Schnecken-Hubförderer *m*	elevatore *m* a vite
° 15707	**screw gauge,**	jauge *f* à vis	Schraublehre *f*	calibro *m* a vite
° 15708	**screw head nail, dummy screws**	fausse vis *f pl.*	scheinbares Gewinde *n*	(punte) false viti *f pl*
° 15709	**screw jack**	vérin *m* mécanique	Schraubenwinde *f*	martinetto *m* meccanico

		English	French	German	Italian
°	15710	screw-plate, side-plate	porte-vis, contre-platine f	Schraubenblech n	porta-vite m, contro-piastrina f
°	15711	screw steel	acier m à boulonne-rie	Schraubeneisen n	acciaio m per bulloni
°	15712	screw tap	taraud m	Gewindebohrer m	maschio m
°	15713	screw-thread screw threading, s. screwing	filet m	Gewinde n	filettatura f
^	15714	screw type anchor	ancrage m à boulon	Schraubenanker m	ancoraggio m a bullone
—	15715	screw washer	lavoir m à vis	Schneckenerzwa-scher m	lavatrice f a coclea o a spirale
°	15716	screwed-on cover, bolted cover	chapeau m boulon-né	aufgeschraubter Deckel m	cappello m avvitato od inchiavardato
°	15717	screwed pipe of the gas type	tube m taraudé «gaz»	Rohr n mit Gas-gewinde	tubo m filettato del tipo «gas»
°	15718	screwing, bolting together	boulonnage m	Verschraubung f	avvitatura f
°	15719	screwing, screw-cutting	creusage f des fi-lets	Gewindeschneiden n	taglio m della filettatu-ra
		screwing down, s. screwing up			
°	15720	screwing up raising	changement m de profil	Verstellung f, Profilwechsel m	cambio m del profilo
^	15721	scrubber	épurateur m à gaz	Gaswascher m	torre f di lavaggio
^	15722	scrubber	fermeture f étanche	Abdichtung f	chiusura f a tenuta
^	15723	scrubber	trou f de décharge	Ablassloch n	foro m di scarico
^	15724	scrubbing	lavage m (de gaz)	(Gas) Gewäsche f	lavaggio m (di gas)
°	15725	scrubbing pot	cuve f de barbotage	Scrubber m	vasca f di gorgoglia-mento
°	15726	scruff (of a tinning bath	scorie f de bain d'é-tamage	Zinnbadschlacke f	scoria f di bagno di stagnatura
°	15727	scull, skull	fond m de poche	Pfannenrest m, Pfannenbär m	crosta f, fondo di cal-daia. culaccio m, rag-grumazione f
—	15727 a	scum	filonnet m	kleines Flöz n	vena f, piccolo filone m
°	15728	scum	écume f	Schlacke f	scoria f, schiuma
°	15729	scumming hole	trou m à crasse	Schlackenloch n	foro m delle scorie

		English	French	German	Italian
°	15730	scythe	faux *f*	Sense *f*	falce *f*
	15731	sea green	vert mer	meergrün	verde-mare
		sea coal, *s. pit coal*			
—	15732	sea sand	sable *m* de mer	Quartzsand *m* aus dem Meer	sabbia *f* di mare
°	15733	to seal	cacheter	versiegeln	sigillare
°	15734	seal	scellement *m*	Verschliessung *f*	sigillo *m*, otturazione *f*
—	15735	seal	barrage *m*	Branddamm *m*	diaframma *f* (antincendi)
°	15735a	seal, sealing	joint étanche	Dichtung *f*	sigillatura *f*
^	15736	seal pot	réservoir *m* du fluide d'étanchéité	Flüssigkeitsbehälter *m*	serbatoio *m* del fluido di tenuta
°	15737	sealed	étanche	luftdicht	stagno *m*, a tenuta
—	15738	sealed working	chantier *m* barré	abgesperrter Bau *m*	cantiere *m* sbarrato
°	15739	sealing liquid	liquide *m* d'arrêt	Sperrflüssigkeit *f*	liquido *m* di chiusura
°	15740	sealing wedge	quille *f* de scellement	Zapfen *m* für Kernverbindungskanal	perno *m* di giunzione
°	15741	sealing wire	fil *m* pour soudure dans le verre	Glaseinschmelzdraht *m*	filo *m* per incrostare il vetro
^	15742	sealoading line	conduite sous-marine	Unterwasserleitung *f*	condotta *f* sottomarina
°	15742a	seam, hair seam	repliure *f* de laminage	Überwalzungsfehler *m*	difetto *m* di piegatura
—	15743	seam, bed, vein	couche *f*, lit *m*, filon *m*	Flöz *n*	banco *m*, vena *f*, filone *m*, strato *m*
°	15744	seam, weld	couture *f*	Fuge *f*	linea *f* di giunzione
°	15745	seam, burr	ébarbure *f*	Grat *m*	bava *f*, riccio *m*
	15746	seam (surface defect)	paille *f*	Grat *m*	paglia *f*
—	15747	seam of coal	couche *f* de houille	Kohlenschicht *f*	giacimento *m*, (filone o banco) di carbone
°	15748	seam welder	machine *f* a souder	Nahtschweissmaschine *f*	saldatrice *f* per giunti
°	15749	seam welding	soudure *f* continue, soudage *m* au galet	Nahtschweissung *f*	saldatura *f* continua (o a rulli)
°	15750	seaming, double hemming, clamping	crampage *m*, agrafage *m*	Verklammern *n* Falzrandverbindung *f*	aggraffatura *f* (lavorazione lamiere)

	English	French	German	Italian
°	15750a **seaming die**	moule *m* pour coutures	Verklammerngesenke *f*	stampo *m* per aggraffature
°	15751 **seamless**	sans soudure	nahtlos	senza giunzioni
°	15752 **seamless casing**	tube *m* sans soudure	nahtloses Rohr *n*	tubo *m* senza saldature
°	15753 **seamless tube**	tube *m* sans soudure	nahtloses Rohr *n*	tubo *m* senza saldature
—	15754 **searchlight carbon**	charbon *m* pour projecteurs	Scheinwerferkohle *f*	carbone *m* per proiettori
—	15755 **searing**	lissage *m*	Polieren *n*	lisciatura *f*
—	15756 **searlesite**	searlésite *f*	Searlesit *m*	searlesite *f*
—	15757 **season cracking**	corrosion *f* intergranulaire spontanée	spontane Korngrenzkorrosion *f*	corrosione *f* intercristallina spontanea
—	15758 **sebastianite**	sebastianite *f*	Sebastianit *m*	sebastianite *f*
—	15759 **second mining**	abattage, dépilage	Hereingewinnung *f*	abbattimento *m*, demolizione *f*
—	15760 **second outlet**	deuxième sortie *f*	zweiter Ausgang *m*	seconda uscita *f*
°	15761 **second tinning pot**	bac *m* de lavage	Durchführkessel *m*	caldaia *f* di passaggio per la seconda stagnatura
—	15762 **second working**	abattage *m*	Hereingewinnung *f*	abbattimento *m* (del carbone)
°	15763 **secondary air**	air *m* secondaire	Sekundärluft *f*	aria *f* secondaria
°	15764 **secondary alloy**	alliage *m* de deuxième fusion	Umschmelzlegierung	lega *f* di seconda fusione
	secondary cell, *s. accumulator or storage cell*			
°	15765 **secondary constituent**	substance *f* ou métal *m* secondaire	Nebenbestandteil *m*, Beimetall *n*	elemento *m* ausiliare, metallo *m* secondario
—	15766 **secondary era**	Secondaire *m*	Mesozoikum *n*	Secondario *m*
˄	15767 **secondary exploitation**	exploitation *f* secondaire	Zweitgewinnung *f*	sfruttamento *m* secondario
	secondary fold, *s. minor fold*			
°	15768 **secondary hardening**	durcissement *m* secondaire	Sekundärhärte *f*	indurimento *m* secondario
°	15769 **secondary ingot**	lingot *m* de deuxième fusion	Schmelzmassel *f*	lingotto *m* di seconda fusione
°	15769a **secondary pipe**	retassure *f* intérieure	Innenlunker *m*	risucchio *m* inferiore
˄	15770 **secondary recovery**	récupération *f* secondaire	sekundäre Forderung	recupero *m* secondario
—	15771 **secondary ventilation**	ventilation *f* auxiliaire	Nebenbelüftung *f*	ventilazione *f* ausiliare

	English	French	German	Italian
15772	section profil iron, fashioned iron	(fer *m*) profilé, fer *m* façonné	Formeisen *n*, Fassoneisen *n*, Profileisen *n*	(ferro *m)* profilato, ferro *m* sagomato, sagomati *m pl.*
15773	section bar	bar *f* de fer profilé	Profileisenschiene *f*	barra *f* di profilato, profilato
15774	section gauge	diamétreur *m*	Kaliberlog *n*	calibro *m* per diametri
15775	section iron	(fer *m*) profilé *m*	Formeisen *n*	ferro *m* profilato
15776	section iron with sharp corner	fer *m* profilé à arêtes vives	scharfkantiges Formeisen *n*	ferro *m* profilato a spigolo vivo
15777	section iron with round corners	fer *m* profilé à arêtes arrondies	rundkantiges Formeisen *n*	profilato *m* di ferro a spigoli arrotondati
15778	section mill	laminoir *m* à profilés	Profilwalzwerk *n*	laminatoio *m* per profilati
15778a	section modulus	couple *m* résistant	Widerstandsmoment	modulo *m* di resistenza
15779	section of pass	profil *m* de laminage	Walzform *f*, Profil *m*	profilo *n* (di laminazione)
	section rolling mill, *s. section mill*			
15780	section sensitivity	sensibilité *f* à l'épaisseur	Wanddickenempfindlichkeit *f*	sensibilità *f* allo spessore
15780a	section tube	tube *m* profilé	Profilrohr *n*	tubo *m* profilato
	section steel, *s. shaped steel*			
15781	sectional boiler	chaudière *f* sectionnelle	Gliederkessel *m*	caldaia *f* a sezioni
	sectional chamber water tube boiler, *s. semitubular boiler*			
15782	sectional grate	grille *f* à plusieurs panneaux	geteilter Rost *m*	griglia *f* di più sbarre
15783	sectional iron	fer *m* profilé	Profileisen *n*	ferro *m* profilato
15784	sectional pattern	modèle *m* en deux parties	geteiltes Modell *n*	modello *m* in due pezzi
15785	sectional steel	acier *m* profilé	Profilstahl *m*	acciaio *m* profilato
15786	sectional type cast iron boiler	chaudière *f* sectionnelle à tubes d'eau	Sektionskessel *m*	caldaia *f* divisa ad elementi smontabili
15787	sectional water tube boiler	chaudière *f* sectionnelle à tubes d'eau	Sektionswasserrohrkessel *m*	caldaia *f* a tubi d'acqua in sezioni
15788	sections for truck building	profils *m pl.* pour construction de wagons	Wagenbauprofile *n pl.*	profilati *m pl.* per costruzione vagoni
15789	sections of boshes	profils *m pl.* des étalages	Rastformen *f pl.*	sezioni *f pl.* della sacca
15790	sections with sharp edges	profils *m pl.* à angles vifs	scharfkantige Profile *n pl.*	profilati *m pl.* a spigoli vivi

		English	French	German	Italian
		sediment, *s. mud*			
−	15791	sedimentary clay	argile *f* sédimentaire	sedimentärer Ton *m*	argilla *f* sedimentaria
−	15792	sedimentary deposits	dépôts *m pl.* sédimentaires	Ablagerungen *f pl.*	depositi *m pl.* sedimentàri
−	15793	sedimentary overlap	stratification *f* concordante	konkordante Lagerung *f*	stratificazione *f* concordante
−	15794	sedimentary rocks	roches *f pl.* sédimentaires	Absatzgesteine *n pl.*	rocce *f pl.* sedimentarie
−	15794a	sedimentation	sédimentation *f*	Ablagerung *f*	sedimentazione *f*
−	15795	seebachite	seebachite *f*	Seebachit. *m*	seebachite *f*
°	15796	seemless steel pipe	tube *m* en acier sans soudure	nahtloses Stahlrohr *n*	tubo *m* d'acciaio senza saldatura
^	15797	seep (gas), escape	dégagement *m* de gaz	Schwaden *m*	emanazione, esalazione *f* di gas
−	15798	segger clay	terre *f* à cassettes, chamotte	Schamotte *f*	terra *f* refrattaria
°	15799	segment core	noyau *m* à segments	Segmentkern *m*	anima *f* a sezioni
°	15799a	segment die	estampe *f* démontable	zerlegbarer Stempel *m*	stampo *m* smontabile
°	15800	segmental arched footbridge	passerelle *f* en arc de cercle	kreisrunder Laufsteg *m*	passerella *f* ad arco di cerchio
°	15801	segment	cerce *f*	Segment *n*	centina *f*
°	15802	segregated portion	gouttelette *f* séparée par liquation	ausgeseigerter Tropfen *m*	goccia *f* segregata
°	15803	segregation, liquation	phénomène *m* de liquation	Seigerungserscheinung *f*, Saigerungserscheinung *f*	fenomeno *m* di separazione
°	15803a	to seize	écorcher	fressen	scorticare
°	15804	to seize with tongs	saisir avec la tenaille	mit der Zange erfassen	afferrare con la tenaglia
°	15804a	seizing	conglomération *f*	Zusammenbacken *n*	conglomerazione *f*
°	15805	selected scrap	riblons *m pl.*	Schrott *m*	rottami scelti *m pl.*
°	15806	selection of motive power	choix *m* de la force motrice	Wahl *f* der Betriebskraft	scelta *f* della forza motrice
°	15807	selection of test pieces	choix *m* des échantillons	Probeauswahl *f*	scelta *f* dei campioni
°	15807a	selective annealing	recuit *m* sélectif	selektives Frischglühen *n*	ricottura *f* selettiva
°	15808	selective quenching	trempe *f* partielle	Teilabschreckung *f*	tempra *f* parziale
−	15809	selenite	sélénite *f*	Selenit *m*	gesso *m* cristallizzato, selenite *f*

	English	French	German	Italian
⊃ 15810	selenium	sélénium *m*	Selen *n*	selenio *m*
⊃ 15811	self-acting clutch	préhension *f* automatique	selbsttätiges Greifen *n*	presa *f* automatica
− 15812	self-acting incline	plan *m* incliné automoteur	sebsttätiger Bremsberg *m*	piano *m* inclinato automotore
⌃ 15813	self-aligning	auto-centrant	selbstzentrierend	autocentrante
○ 15814	self-annealing	auto-recuit *m*	Selbstglühen *n*	autoricottura *f*
⌃ 15815	self contained platform	plate-forme *f* autonome	selbsttragende Plattform *f*	piattaforma *f* autonoma
○ 15816	self-cooling	refroidissement *m* automatique	Selbstkühlung *f*	raffreddamento *m* automatico
○ 15816a	self corrosion	action *f* locale	örtliche Einwirkung *f*	azione *f* locale
○ 15817	self-discharger	cuiller à déchargement automatique	Selbstentlader *m*	scaricatore *m* automatico
○ 15818	self-discharging wagon	wagon *m* à déchargement automatique	Selbstentlader *m*	vagone *m* a scarico automatico
− 15819	self-dumping cage	cage *f* à déchargement automatique	Selbstentladekorb *m*	gabbia *f* a scarico automatico
− 15820	self-dumping skip	skip *m* à déversement automatique	Kippkübel *n*	skip *m* a scarico automatico
⌃ 15821	self emptying tool	tarière *f* à soupape	Ventilbohrer *m*	trivella *f* a valvola
○ 15822	self-feeding furnace	foyer *m* à alimentation automatique, foyer *m* à alimentation continue	Schüttrostfeuerung *f*, Füllschachtfeuerung *f*	focolare *m* a caricamento automatico, focolare *m* a pozzo di riempimento
	self flussing ore, *s. self-fusible ore*			
○ 15822a	self fluxing	autofondant	selbstgehend	autofondente
− 15823	self-fusible ore	minerai *m* de fer fusible par lui-même	selbstschmelzbares Erz *n*	minerale *m* autofusibile
○ 15823a	self hardening	trempe *f* à l'air	Lufthärtung *f*	tempra *f* all'aria
○ 15824	self-hardening	auto-trempant	selbsthärtend	autotemprante
○ 15825	self-hardening steel	acier *m* auto-trempant	naturharter Stahl *m*, Lufthärtungsstahl *m*	acciaio *m* autotemprante
○ 15826	self-heating soldering iron	fer *m* à souder à chauffage automatique	selbstwärmender Lötkolben *m*	saldatoio *m* ad autoriscaldamento
○ 15827	self lighting flame	flamme *f* auto-lumineuse	selbstleuchtende Flamme *f*	fiamma *f* autoluminosa
⌃ 15828	self potential	polarisation *f* spontanée	Eigenpotential *n*	potenziale *m* spontaneo

		English	French	German	Italian
°	15829	self-skimming	autodécrassant	selbstentschlackend	auto-scorificante
↗	15830	self-sealing coupling	joint *m* étanche	abdichte Verbindung *f*	giunto *m* stagno
°	15831	self-slagging tuyere	tuyère *f* auto-décrassante	selbstentschlackende Düse *f*	ugello *m* autoscorificante
°	15832	supporting pantiles in galvanized steel sheet	bacs *m pl.* autoportants en tôle d'acier galvanisée	selbsttragende Pfannen *f pl.* aus verzinktem Stahlblech	elementi *m pl.* autoportanti in lamiera di acciaio zincata
—	15833	seligmannite	séligmannite *f*	Seligmannit *m*	seligmannite *f*
—	15834	sellaite	śellaite *f*	Sellait *m*	sellaite *f*
—	15835	selvage	salbande *f*	Salband *n*	parete *f* laterale, salbanda *f*
—	15836	semianthracite	houille *f* anthraciteuse	anthrazitische Kohle *f*	carbone *m* antracitico
—	15837	semi-bituminous coal	houille *f* demi-grasse	halbfette Kohle *f*	carbone *m* semigrasso

semi-center spinning, *s. semi-centrifugal casting*

°	15838	semi-centrifugal casting	semi-centrifugation *f*	Schleuderguss *m* mit Kernen, Halbschleuderguss *m*	semicentrifugazione *f*
°	15838a	semi-chilled cast iron	fonte *f* semi-dure	Halbhartguss *m*	ghisa *f* semidura
°	15839	semi circular	fosse *f* de coulée demicirculaire	halbkreisförmige Giessgrube *f*	fossa *f* di colata semicircolare
°	15840	semi-continous mill	train *m* semi-continu	halbkontinuierliche Strasse *f*	treno *m* semicontinuo
°	15840a	semi-finished flat	platine *f*	Platine *f*	piatto *m*
°	15841	semi-finished product	demi-produit *m*	halbfertiges Erzeugnis *n*, Halbfabrikat *n*	semiprodotto *m*
°	15842	semifinished steel	acier *m* semifini	halbfertiger Stahl *m*, Stahlrohling *m*	acciaio *m* sbozzato al laminatoio, acciaio *m* in barre
°	15843	semi-fluid hardening medium	matière *f* à tremper épaisse	dickflüssiges Härtemittel *n*	sostanza *f* densa per tempera
°	15844	semi-Goliath crane	semi-portique *m*	Halbportalkran *m*, Halbbockkran *m*	gru *f* a cavalletto zoppo
°	15845	semi-killed steel	acier *m* semi-calmé, acier *m* semi-effervescent	halbberuhigter Stahl *m*	acciaio *m* semi-calmato (o semieffervescente)

semi-longitudinal fault, *s. diagonal fault*
semimild steel, *s. mild carbon steel*

°	15846	semi-permanent mold	moule *m* semi-permanent	halbständige Form *f*	forma *f* semipermanente

		English	French	German	Italian
ɔ	15847	**semiportable boiler**	chaudière *f* semi fixe	halbfeststehender Dampfkessel *m*	caldaia *f* (a vapore) semifissa
ɔ	15848	**semi-steel**	fonte *f* aciérée	Halbstahl *m*	ghisa *f* acciaiosa
–	15849	**semi trailer**	semi-remorque *f*	einachsiger Anhänger *m*	rimorchio *m* a un assale
		semi-transverse fault, *s. diagonal fault*			
ɔ	15850	**semi-tubular boiler**	chaudière *f* semi-tubulaire	Halbröhrenkessel *m*	caldaia *f* semi-tubolare
`	15851	**semi-water gas**	gaz *m* mixte	Mischgas *n*	gas *m* misto
–	15852	**semseyite**	semséyte *f*	Semseyit *m*	semseite *f*
–	15853	**senaite**	sénaite *f*	Senait *f*	senaite *f*
–	15854	**senarmontite**	sénarmontite *f*	Senarmontit *m*	senarmontite *f*
–	15855	**Senoman stage**	étage *m* cénomanien	Senoman *n*	stadio *m* Cenomaniano
	15856	**sensitive**	sensible	empfindlich	sensibile
–	15857	**sensitive drill**	mèche *f* sensitive	empfindlicher Bohrer *m*	trapano *m* sensitivo
	15858	**sensitiveness**	sensibilité *f*	Empfindlichkeit *f*	sensibilità *f*
°	15859	**sensitivty to temperature**	sensibilité *f* à la température	Temperaturempfindlichkeit *f*	sensibilità *f* alla temperatura
–	15860	**to separate, to screen**	trier	abscheiden	separare, cernere
		separated blast furnace, *s. independent blast furnace*			
°	15861	**separately cast test bar**	barreau *m* coulé à part	getrennt gegossener Probebarren *m*	saggio *m* colato a parte
°	15862	**separately cast test bar**	éprouvette *f* coulée à part	getrennt gegossener Probestab *m*	provetta *f* colata a parte
°	15863	**separating and shaking apparatus**	séparateur *m* avec agitateur	Abscheide-und Schüttelvorrichtung *f*	apparecchio *m* separatore ed agitatore
°	15864	**separating funnel**	entonnoir *m* séparateur	Scheidetrichter *m*	tramoggia *f* separatrice
°	15865	**separating plant**	installation *f* de triage	Abscheideanlage *f*	impianto *m* di separazione
°	15866	**separating shears**	cisaille *f* à tronçonner	Trennschere *f*	troncatrice *f*

		English	French	German	Italian
—	15867	separating wall	cloison f	Scheidewand f	tramezzo m, paratia f
—	15868	separation	séparation f	Ausscheidung f	separazione f, disgregazione f
—	15869	separation by hand	triage m à la main scheidage m	Abscheidung f von Hand	separazione f a mano
—	15870	separation door	porte f de ventilation	Wettertür f	porta f di ventilazione
—	15871	separation of carbon	séparation f de carbone	Kohlenstoffausscheidung f	separazione f di carbonio
—	15872	separation of graphite	dépôt m de graphite	Graphitausscheidung f	deposito m di grafite
○	15873	separation of iron	triage m du fer	Eisenausscheidung f	separazione m del ferro
○	15874	separation of phosphorus	déphosphoration f	Phosphorabscheidung f	defosforazione f
○	15875	separation of slag	séparation f du laitier	Abscheiden n der Schlacke	decantazione (o separazione) f delle scorie
○	15876	separation of the constituents of the charge	séparation f des éléments de la charge	Abscheidung der Bestandteile der Mischung	separazione f degli elementi della carica
○	15877	separation of the ore dust	séparation f des poussières	Abscheidung f des Erzstaubes	separazione f delle polveri
^	15878	separator	séparateur m	Abscheider m	separatore m
^	15879	separator box	bassin m à décantation	Scheidebecken n	vasca f di separazione
^	15880	separatory funnel	ampoule f à décantation	Abscheidetrichter m	imbuto m separatore
○	15881	separator with permanent magnet	séparateur m à aimant permanent	Abscheidevorrichtung f mit Dauermagnet	separatore m con magnete permanente
—	15882	sepiolite	sépiolite f	Sepiolith m	sepiolite f
—	15883	septarian nodules, septaria	septaria f	Septarie f	septaria f
—	15884	septum	septum m	Septum n	setto m
—	15885	septum	flanc m médian	Mittelschenkel m	fianco m mediano
—	15886	Sequanian stage	Séquanien m	Sequan m	Sequaniano m

		English	French	German	Italian
○	15887	sequence timer	syncroniseur *m* de séquences		temporizzatore *m* di sequenza
–	15888	serandite	sérandite *f*	Sérandit *m*	serandite *f*
–	15889	serendibite	serendibite *f*	Serendibit *m*	serendibite *f*
–	15890	seriate fabric	structure *f* à grain hétérogène	irregulär körniges Gefüge *n*	struttura *f* a grano e-terogeneo
–	15891	sericite	séricite *f*	Serizit *m*	sericite *f*
–	15892	sericitic	séricitique	serizitisch	sericitico
–	15893	sericitization	séricitisation *f*	Serizitisierung *f*	sericitizzazione *f*
○	15894	series seam welding	soudure *f* continue en série	Reihennaht-schweissung *f*	saldatura *f* continua in serie
–	15895	serpentine	serpentine *f*, ophite *f*	Serpentin(fels) *m*	serpentino *m*
○	15896	serpiginous hollow	moulage *m* creux compliqué	verzettelter Hohl-raum *m*	vuoto *m* sagomato
○	15897	serrated, notched	dentelé, hérissé	zackig	dentato
^	15898	serrated drive shoe	sabot de fonçage avec denture en saillie	gezahnter Ramm-schuh *m*	scarpa *f* di perforatio-ne dentata
^	15899	service pressure rating	pression *f* d'utili-sation	Betriebsdruckstufe *f*	pressione *f* di utilizza-zione
–	15900	service raise	montage *m* de cir-culation	Fahraufhauen *n*	montaggio *m* di circola-zione
–	15901	service shaft	puits auxiliaire	Hilfsschacht *m*	pozzo *m* ausiliario
○	15901a	service stress	effort *m* de travail	Betriebsspannung *f*	tensione *f* di servizio
	15902	to set	poser, monter, placer	montieren, setzen, legen, stellen	mettere, posare, mon-tare, sistemare
	15903	set	série *f*, jeu *m*, grou-pe *m*	Serie *f*, Satz *m*,	serie *f*, gruppo *m*
–	15904	set	cadre *m*	Türstock *m*	quadro *m*
–	15905	set	siège *f* d'extraction	Schachtanlage *f*	zona *f* (o sede) d'estra-zione
○	15905a	set, pitch	plan *m* de solidifica-tion	Erstarrungsebene *f*	piano *m* di solidificazio-ne
○	15906	set	orifice de coulée	Giessloch *n*	foro *m* (o orificio) di colata
○	15907	set of castings	série *f* de pièces de fonte	Gussatz *m*	serie *f* di getti

	English	French	German	Italian
° 15908	set of driving wheels	train *m* de roues motrices	Treibradsatz *m*	treno *m* di ruote motrici
° 15909	set of machines	groupe *m* de machines	Maschinensatz *m*	gruppo *m* di macchine
° 15910	set of pulley patterns	jeu *m* de modèles pour machines à mouler les poulies	Riemenscheiben-modellsatz *m*	serie *f* di modelli per formare una puleggia
— 15911	set of sieves	série *f* de tamis	Siebsatz *m*	serie *f* di stacci (o crivelli)
— 15912	set of timber	cadre *m*	Türstock *m*	quadro *m*
15913	setting	installation *f*, montage *m*	Zusammenstellen *n*	impianto *m*, montaggio *m*
15914	setting	prise *f* (de béton)	Abbindung *f* (von Beton)	presa *f* (di calcestruzzo)
° 15915	set of two single sided pattern-plates	plaque-modèle *f* double	doppelte Modellplatte *f*	placca *f* modello doppio
^ 15916	set screw	vis *f* de blocage	Klemmschraube *f*	vite *f* d'arresto o di pressione
° 15917	set steel	acier *m* au 0,875 de C.	Stahl mit 0,875 C-Gehalt	acciaio *m* al 0,875 di C
	setter, *s. binder*			
	setting, *s. solidification*			
^ 15918	setting depht	profondeur *f* de pose en puits	Setztiefe *f*	profondità *f* di posa in pozzo
° 15919	setting in the crucible	enfournement *m* du creuset	Einsetzen *n* des Tiegels	collocamento *m* o posa *f* del crogiuolo
° 15920	setting point	point *m* de congélation	Stockpunkt *m*	punto *m* di fusione
^ 15921	to settle	décanter	absetzen, klären	depositare, decantare
^ 15922	settled production	production *f* stabilisée	stabilisierte Produktion *f*	produzione *f* stabilizzata
^ 15923	settler	appareil *m* de décantation	Absetzapparat *m*, Klärgefäss *n*	decantatore *m*
° 15923à	settling	sédiment, dépôt *m*	Sediment *n*, Absetzung *f*	sedimento *m*, deposito *m*
^ 15924	settling ditch	rigole *f* de décantation	Absetzgrube *f*, Klärgrube *f*	canale *m* di decantazione
^ 15925	settling tank	bassin *m* décantateur	Klärteich *m*, Klärbecken *n*	bacino *m* di decantazione

	English	French	German	Italian
15926	setting tank	bac *m* décanteur	Klärbehälter *m*	decantatore *m*, serbatoio *m* di decantazione
15927	severity factor	facteur *m* de sévérité	Mussfaktor *m*	fattore *m* di severità
15928	sextant iron	(fer *m*) sextain	Sextanteisen *n*	(ferro *m*) sestante
15929	seybertite	seybertite *f*	Seybertit *m*	seybertite *f*
15930	shackle		Stiel *m*	gambetto *m*
15930a	shadow lines	structure *f* zonale	Zeilenstruktur *f*	struttura *f* zonale
15931	shadowing	effet *m* d'écran	Blenden *n*	effetto *m* di schermo
15932	shaft, pit	puits *m*	Schacht *m*	pozzo *m*
15933	shaft (of a blast furnace)	cuve *f*, ventre *m*	Schacht *m*	sacca *f*, ventre *m*, tino *m*
15933a	shaft	axe *m*, arbre *m*	Welle *f*, Achse *f*	asse *m*, albero *m*
15934	shaftbottom, pitbottom	accrochage *m*	Füllort *m*	stazione *f* di fondo
15935	shaft brick	brique *f* de cuve	Schachtstein *m*	mattone *m* del tino
15936	shaft collar	orifice *m* du puits	Schachtöffnung *f*	bocca *f* del pozzo
15937	shaft crucible furnace	four *m* à cuve pour creusets	Tiegelschachtofen *m*	forno *m* a manica od a vento per crogiuoli
15938	shaft frame	cadre *m* du puits	Schachtgeviert *n*	quadro *m* del pozzo
15939	shaft-furnace, shaft-kiln	four *m* à cuve, four *m* à manche	Schachtofen *m*	forno *m* a pozzo, forno *m* a manica
15940	shaft furnace for hardening	four *m* de trempe à cuve	Schachthärteofen *m*	forno *m* a cilindro per la tempera
15941	shaft furnace for reheating	four *m* à cuve à recuire	Schachtglühofen *m*	forno *m* a ricottura
15942	shaft gate	barrière *f* de puits	Schachtgitter *n*	barriera *f* del pozzo
15943	shaft hammer	marteau *m* à levier	Stielhammer *m*	martello *m* a leva
15944	shaft hauling	exploitation *f* à puits	Schachtgewinnung *f*	estrazione *f* a mezzo di pozzo
15945	shaft-head frame	charpente *f* du chevalement	Fördergerüst *n*	incastellatura *f* d'estrazione
15946	shaft hoist	treuil *m* d'extraction	Schachtfördermaschine *f*	argano *m* d'estrazione
15947	shaft installation	installation *f* d'un puits	Schachtanlage *f*	impianto *m* di pozzo

		English	French	German	Italian
o	15948	shaft kiln	four m vertical à cuve	Schachtofen m	forno m verticale a tino
—	15949	shaft-landing	accrochage m	Füllort m	stazione f di fondo
o	15950	shaft lining	maçonnerie f de la cuve	Schachtausmaue-rung f	muratura f del tino
o	15951	shaft of a blast-furnace	cuve f d'un haut fourneau	Schacht m eines Hochofens	tino m (o ventre) di un alto forno
—	15952	shaft pillar	massif m de pro-tection	Schachtpfeiler m	massiccio m di pro-tezione (di un pozzo)
o	15953	shaft of rivet, rivet shank, shaft of nail	tige f de rivet, corps de rivet	Nietschaft m	asta f del chiodo

shaft plant, s. *shaft installation*

		English	French	German	Italian
^	15954	shaft pump	pompe f de puits	Schachtpumpe f	pompa f per pozzi
—	15955	shaft siding	recette f inférieure	Füllort m	stazione f di fondo
—	15956	shaft sinking cementation process	fonçage m de puits par cimentation	Schachtabteufen n nach dem Zemen-tierverfahren	approfondimento m del pozzo con ce-mentazione
—	15957	shaft sinking freezing process	procédé m de fonça-ge par congélation	Gefrierverfahren n beim Schachtabteu-fen	metodo m di approfon-dimento per congela-mento
—	15958	shaft timbering	boisage m du puits	Schachtausbau m	armamento m del pozzo
o	15959	shaft top	gueulard m	Gicht f	bocca f di alto forno

shaft top, s. *pit top*

		English	French	German	Italian
—	15960	shaft tower	chevalement m	Schachtgerüst n	castelletto m, inca-stellatura f
o	15961	shaft wall	chemise f de la cuve	Schachtwandung f	camicia f del tino
—	15962	shaft working	fonçage m	Schachtabteufen n	scavo m, trivellazio-ne f
—	15963	shaftman	avaleur m	Schachthäuer m	picconiere m
—	15964	shaft-top, pit top	recette f, clichage m	Schachtoeffnung f	entrata f del pozzo
o	15965	shaft wall	chemise f de la cuve	Schachtwandung f	camicia o parete f del tino (d'altoforno)
o	15965a	shake	gerçure	Spalt m, Riss m	fenditura f, crepa f
	15966	shake out, knocking out, stripping	décochage m	Ausleeren n, Ausschlagen n	distaffaggio m, sfor-matura

		English	French	German	Italian
		shake-out grate, *shaking grate*			
o	15967	shake-out machine	décocheuse *f*	Ausleerrüttler *m*	distaffatrice *f* a scosse
–	15968	shaker	crible *m* à secousse	Schüttelsieb *n*	vaglio *m* (o crivello *m*) a scosse
–	15969	shaker conveyor	convoyeur *m* à secousses	Schüttelrutsche *f*	convogliatore *m* a scosse
o	15970	shaker hearth furnace	four *m* à sole à secousses	Ausschlagofen *m*	forno *m* con suola a scosse
		shanker screen, *s. shaker* shaking down, *s. stirring up*			
–	15971	shaking grate	grille *f* mobile	beweglicher Rost *m*	griglia *f* mobile
–	15972	shaking sieve	tamis *m* à secousse	Schüttelsieb *n*	vaglio *m* a scosse
–	15973	shaking trough	conduit *m* de transporteur	Rinnentrog *m*	corpo *m* dello scivolone
–	15974	shaking table	table *f* à secousses	Schütteltisch *m*	tavola *f* a scosse
–	15975	shaking trough	gouttière *f* à secousse	Schüttelrinne *f*	piano *m* inclinato a scosse
–	15976	shale, argillite	schiste *m* argileux	Tonschiefer *m*	scisto *m* argilloso
^	15977	shale break	passée *f* d'argile	Toneinlagerung *f*	passata *f* d'argilla
–	15978	shale coal, slaty coal, foliated coal, bass	houille *f* feuilletée ou schisteuse	blätterige Kohle *f*, Buschelkohle *f*	carbone *m* schistoso
–	15979	shale dusting	schistification *f*	Streuung *f*	scistificazione *f*, stratificazione *f*
–	15980	shale out	devenir argileux	Vertonung, tonig werden	divenire argilloso
–	15981	shale separator	déschisteur *m*	Entschieferer *m*, Schieferabscheider *m*	separatore *m* d'argilla
		shale shaker, *s. shaking sieve*			
o	15981a	shank, bewel	brancard *m*	Tragschere *f*	portante *m*
–	15982	shank	puits *m* intérieur	Blindschacht *m*	pozzo *m* interno (o ausiliare)
–	15983	shank	flanc *m* d'un pli	Schenkel *m*	fianco *m* d'una piega
–	15984	shank	jambe *f*, tige *f*	Schenkel *m*, Schaft *m*	gamba *f*, perno *m* di scalpello, asta *f*
o	15985	shank ladle, handle ladle	poche *f* à fourche	Gabelpfanne *f*	siviera *f* a forcella

		English	French	German	Italian
		shank of the blowpipe, s. *handle of the blowpipe*			
o	15985a	**shape cutting**	formation *f* par enlè-vement des coupeaux	Spanung *f*	conformazione *f* per tagli
o	15986	**shape of brick**	forme *f* de brique	Steinform *f*	forma *f* del mattone
o	15987	**shape of passe**	contour *m* du profil	Profilbegrenzung *f*	contorno *m* del pro-filo
o	15988	**shape roll**	cylindre *m* profilé	Profilwalze *f*	cilindro *m* sagomato
o	15989	**shape rolling mill**	laminoir *m* à profi-lés	Profilwalzwerk *n*	laminatoio *m* per profi-lati
o	15990	**shaped copper, pre-cipitated copper**	cuivre *m* cémentoi-re, cuivre *m* régéné-ré	Zementkupfer *n*	rame *m* cementato, ra-me *m* rigenerato
—	15991	**shaped charge**	charge *f* creuse	Hohlcharge *f*	carica *f* cava
o	15992	**shaped core spindle**	arbre *m* à noyau pro-filé	unrunde (profilierte) Kernspindel *f*	lanterna *f* scannellata per anima
o	15993	**shaped iron**	fer *m* profilé	Profileisen *n*	ferro *m* profilato
o	15994	**shaped steel, rolled steel sections**	acier *m* profilé, profilés *m pl.*	Formstahl *m*, Pro-filstahl *m*, Profil-eisen *n*	acciaio *m* (o ferro *m*) profilato, profilati *m pl.*
o	15995	**shaped tube**	tube *m* profilé	profiliertes Rohr *n*	tubo *m* profilato
o	15996	**shaped wire**	fil *m* profilé	Profildraht *m*	filo *m* profilato (o sago-mato)
o	15997	**shaped wire, figure 8 section**	fil *m* en 8	achtlitziger Draht *m*	filo *m* a (sezione di) 8
o	15998	**shaping, forming**	façonnage *m*, pro-filage *m*	Fassonieren *n*, Formen *n*	formatura *f*, sagomatu-ra *f*
o	15999	**shaping groove**	ébaucheur *m*	Vorkaliber *n*	canale *m* sbozzatore
o	16000	**shaping pass**	cannelures *f pl.* profilées	Formkaliber *n*	canale *m* profilato
o	16001	**sharp, cutting**	affilé, tranchant	scharf, spitz(ig)	affilato, aguzzo. ta-gliente
o	16002	**sharp angle curved top edge sleeker**	lissoir *m* d'équerre cintré	Polierknopf *m*	lisciatoio *m* a squadra
o	16003	**sharp angle straight top edge sleeker**	lissoir *m* d'équerre droit vif	Scharfkantenpolier-knopf *m*	lisciatoio *m* a squadra per spigoli vivi
o	16004	**sharp-edged**	à arête vive	scharfkantig	a bordo vivo
—	16005	**sharp sand**	sable *m* à arêtes vives. sable *m* cru	scharfer Sand *m*	sabbia *f* o terra *f* a spi-goli vivi, sabbia *f* gros-sa

		English	French	German	Italian
o	16006	**to sharpen**	affiler, aiguiser	schärfen, spitzen	affilare, appuntire
—	16007	**to sharpen the bit** sharpened, *s. ground*	affiler le foret	den Meissel schärfen	rinfrescare lo scalpel-lo
o	16008	**sharpening**	affûtage, meulage	Schleifen *n*, Schär-fen *n*, Scharfschlei-fen *n*	affilatura *f*, arrotatura *f*
—	16009	**shastaite**	shastaite *f*	Shastait *m*	shastaite *f*
—	16010	**shastalite**	shastalite *f*	Shastalith *m*	shastalite *f*
—	16011	**shatter**	briser en pièces, fragment *m*	sich zersplittern, zerbrechen, Bruch-stück *n*	andare (o mandare) in pezzi, frammento *m*
—	16012	**shatter breccia**	brèche *f* de friction	Reibungsbreccie *f*	breccia *f* di frizione
o	16012a	**shatter crack**	gerçure *f*	Haarriss *m*	criccatura *f*
		shatter value, *s. sand bond*			
—	16013	**shattered rock**	roche *f* broyée	zertrümmertes Ge-stein *n*	roccia *f* frantumata
—	16014	**shattered zone**	zone *f* de broya-ge	Zertrümmerungszone *f*	zona *f* di frantumazio-ne
—	16015	**shattering**	broyage *m*	Erschütterung *f*, Zerkleinerung *f*	frantumazione *f*
—	16016	**shattuckite**	shattuckite *f*	Shattuckit *m*	shattuckite *f*
—	16017	**sheaf-like structure**	structure *f* en gerbes	Garbenstruktur *f*	struttura *f* a covoni
o	16018	**to shear, to cut out**	couper, cisailler	scheren, abscheren	tagliare, tranciare
o	16019	**shear to length**	couper à longueur	ablängen auf Mass schneiden	tagliare a misura
o	16020	**shear**	cisaillement *m*	Scherung *f*	taglio *m*
—	16021	**shear**	rouillure *f*	Kerbe *f*	tacca *f*
		shear, *s. shearing*			
o	16022	**shear, shears, shearing machine**	cisaille *f*	Schere *f*	cesoia *f*
o	16022a	**shear crack**	crique *f* par cisaille-ment	Schubriss *m*	cricca *f* da taglio
o	16023	**shear pin**	tourillon *m* tranchable	schneidbarer Stift *m*	perno *m* tranciabile
o	16023a	**shear rigidity**	rigidité *f* de glissement	Schubsteife *f*	rigidità *f* di scorrimento
o	16024	**shear steel**	acier *m* de cémenta-tion corroyé	Zementgärbstahl *m*	acciaio *m* di cementazio-ne affinato
o	16025	**shear test**	essai *m* de cisail-lement	Scherversuch *m*	prova *f* al taglio

English	French	German	Italian
— 16026 **shear thrust**	charriage *m* de ci-saillement	Abscherungsüber-schiebung *f*	smottamento *m* degli strati
— 16027 **shear zone**	zone *f* de faille	Zertrümmerungszo-ne *f*	zona *f* della faglia
° 16027a **shered edge**	bord *m* rogné	beschnittene Kante *f*	bordo *m* tagliato
° 16028 **shearing defect**	défaut *m* de cisaille-ment	Scherenfehler *m*	difetto *m* di taglio
° 16028a **shear(ing) lag**	retard *m* de glissement	Schubverzögerung *f*	ritardo *m* di scorrimento
° 16029 **shearing line, shear line**	ligne *f* de cisaille-ment	Scherenschnitt *m*, Scherenstrasse *f*	sezione *f* di taglio, li-nea *f* di taglio
° 16030 **shearing machine**	machine *f* à cisail-ler, cisaille *f*	Maschinenschere *f*	cesoia *f*, tranciatrice *f*, trancia *f*
° 16031 **shearing machine**	rouilleuse *f*	Kerbmaschine *f*	trancia *f*
— 16032 **shearing of core**	coupe *f* de la ca-rotte	Kernschnitt *m*	taglio *m* della carota
° 16033 **shearing resistance**	résistance *f* du tran-chant	Schneidhaltigkeit *f*	resistenza *f* al taglio
° 16034 **shearing strain**	effort *m* tranchant	Scherspannung *f*	deformazione *f* al ta-glio
° 16035 **shearing strenght**	résistance *f* au ci-saillement	Scherfestigkeit *f*	resistenza *f* al taglio
° 16036 **shearing stress**	sollicitation *f* de ci-saillement	Scherbeanspruchung *f*	sollicitazione *f* di ta-glio
° 16037 **shearing test**	essai *m* de cisaill-lement	Scherversuch *m*	prova *f* al taglio
° 16038 **shears**	cisaille *f*	Schere *f*	forbici *f pl.*, cesoie *f pl.*
° 16039 **shears knife**	lame *f* de cisaille	Scherenmesser *m*	coltello *m*, cesoia *f*
— 16040 **sheating (of a well) shaft-timbering**	boisage *m* du puits	Futter *n* eines Brunnens	armatura *f* del pozzo
— 16041 **shed coal**	intercalation *f* de charbon	Kohlenzwischenlage *f*	intercalazione *f* di carbone
^ 16042 **shed section**	section *f* de base	Basisschnitt *m*	sezione *f* di base
— 16043 **scheelite**	scheelite *f*	Scheelit *m*	scheelite *f*
° 16044 **sheet**	tôle *f*, plaque *f*	Blech *n*, Blatt *n*	foglio *m* di lamiera, lamiera *f*, latta *f*
— 16045 **sheet**	intercalation *f*, banc *m*	Zwischenlage *f*, Decke *f*	intercalazione *f*, ban-co *m*, stratificazione *f*

		English	French	German	Italian
°	16046	sheet aluminium	tôle f d'aluminium	Aluminiumblech n	lamiera f d'alluminio
°	16047	sheet bar	larget m	Platine f	bidone m, piatto m
°	16048	sheet billet mill, sheet bar mill	laminoir m à largets	Platinenwalzwerk n	laminatoio m per bidoni
°	16049	sheet billet.	larget m	Platine f	piatto m
°	16050	sheet-brass	tôle f de laiton	Messingsblech n	lamiera f o lamierino m di ottone
°	16051	sheet-copper	tôle f de cuivre	Kupferblech n	lamiera f di rame
°	16052	sheet cutting machine	machine f à découper les tôles	Blechschneidemaschine f	cesoia f a rulli per tagli circolari di lamiere
°	16053	sheet dural(uminium)	tôle f de duralumin	Duralblech n	lamiera f di duralluminio
o	16054	sheet electron	tôle f électron	Elektronblech n	lamiera f di electron
°	16055	sheet gauge	jauge f pour les tôles	Blechlehre f	calibro m per lamiere
°	16056	sheet glass	verre m étiré	ausgezogenes Glas n	vetro m tirato
°	16057	sheet iron	tôles $f\,pl.$	Bleche $n\,pl.$	lamiere $f\,pl.$
°	16058	sheet iron, iron plate	fer m en lame(s), tôle f en fer	Blechplatte f, Eisenblech n	lamiera f di ferro
°	16059	sheet iron ring	anneau m en tôle de fer	Eisenblechring m	anello m in lamiera di ferro
°	16060	sheet iron scraps	tôle f de rebut	Ausschussblech n	lamiera f di scarto
°	16061	sheet iron shell	enveloppe f en tôle de fer	Eisenblechmantel m	blindaggio m
°	16062	sheet iron tube	tuyau m en tôle	Blechrohr n	tubo m in lamiera
o	16063	sheet iron with projections	tôle f gauffrée	Warzenblech n	lamiera f a prominenze
°	16064	sheet jointing	séparation f en feuilles	bankige Absonderung f	separazione f in lamine
—	16065	sheet joints	diaclases horizontales	schwebende Spalte f	diaclasi $f\,pl.$ orizzontali
°	16066	sheet-lead	tôle f de plomb, plomb m laminé	Bleiblech n, Rollenblei n, Bleiplatte f	lamina f di piombo, piombo m laminato
°	16067	sheet magnesium	tôle f de magnésium	Magnesiumblech n	lamiera f di magnesio

		English	French	German	Italian
o	16068	**sheet-metal**	tôle *f*, feuille *f*	Blech *n*	lamiera *f*, piastra *f*
o	16069	**sheet metal free from oxides**	tôle *f* décapée	oxydfreies Blech *n*	lamiera *f* deossidata
o	16070	**sheet metal gauge**	jauge *f* d'épaisseur	Blechlehre *f*	calibro *m* per lamiere
o	16071	**sheet metal roller strain relieving machine**	machine *f* à étirer à cylindres pour tôles	Blechwalzenstreck-maschine *f*	snervatrice *f* a rulli per lamiera
o	16072	**sheet metal work**	tôlerie *f*	Blecharbeit *f*	lavori *m pl.* in lamiera
o	16073	**sheet mill**	laminoir *m* à tôles	Blechwalzwerk *n*	laminatoio *m* per lamiere
o	16074	**sheet mill train**	train *m* à tôles	Blechstrecke *f*	treno *m* per lamiere
o	16074a	**sheet pack**	tôle *f* en forme de paquet	Blech *n* in Paket-form	lamiera *f* a forma di pacchetti
—	16075	**sheet piling, sheet pile**	palplanche *f*	Spundpfahl *m*	palancola *f*, tavolone *m*
o	16076	**sheet roll**	cylindre *m* à toles	Blechwalze *f*	cilindro *m* per lamiere
o	16077	**sheet rolling**	laminer les tôles	blechwalzen	laminare le lamiere
o	16078	**sheet rolling mill**	laminoir *m* à tôles	Blechstrecke *f*	treno *m* per lamiere
o	16079	**sheet scraps**	tôle *f* de rebut	Ausschussblech *n*	lamiera *f* di scarto
o	16080	**sheet shearing**	cisaille *f* à tôles	Blechschere *f*	cesoia *f* da lamiere
o	16081	**sheet-steel**	tôle *f* d'acier	Stahlblech *n*	lamiera *f* d'acciaio
—	16082	**sheet structure**	division *f* en plaques	bankige Absonde-rung *f*	divisione *f* lamellare
o	16083	**sheet tin**	feuilles *f pl.* d'étain	Zinnblech *n*	stagno *m* laminato
—	16084	**sheet vein**	filon *m*, couche *f*	Lagergang *m*	filone *m*, strato *m*
o	16085	**sheet zinc**	tôle *f* de zinc	Zinkblech *n*	lastra *f* (o lamiera) di zinco
—	16086	**sheeted**	stratifié	geschichtet	stratificato
o	16087	**sheeting**	blindage *m*	Verkleidung *f*	armatura *f*
—	16088	**sheeting**	stratification *f*	Schichtung *f*	stratificazione *f*
^	16089	**sheeting**	tubage *m*	Verrohrung *f*	tubaggio *m*
—	16090	**sheeting plane**	plan *m* de stratifi-cation	Schichtfläche *f*	piano *m* di stratifica-zione
—	16091	**sheets**	tôle *f* d'aérage	Wettertuch *n*	paratia *f* di ventila-zione

		English	French	German	Italian
−	16092	shelf	plateforme f continentale	Schelf, Untiefe f Sandbank f	piattaforma f continentale
°	16092a	shell, electrotyping shell	coquille f	Galvano m	riporto m metallico
−	16093	shell	coquille f	Muschel f, Schale f	conchiglia f, guscio m
°	16093a	shell, splash	peau f	Haut f, Schale f	trasudamento m
°	16094	shell	croûte f	Abraumdecke f	crosta f
		shell, s..fused electrolyte container			
°	16095	shell und tube unit	échangeur m à faisceaux	geschlossener Wärmeaustauscher m	scambiatore m a tubi e mantello
−	16096	shell auger	tarière f à cuiller	Löffelbohrer m	trivella f cava
°	16097	shell boiler, cylindrical boiler	chaudière f cylindrique	Zylinderkessel m	caldaia f cilindrica
°	16098	shell cast	moulé en coquille f	in Schalen f pl. gegossen	fuso (o colato) in guscio m
°	16099	shell casting	moulage m en coquille	Schalenguss m	fusione f a guscio, colata f in guscio
°	16100	shell core	noyau-carapace m	Maskenkern m	anima f a guscio
^	16101	shell innage	hauteur f du liquide (dans le réservoir)	Flüssigkeitshöhe f (im Behälter)	altezza f del liquido in serbatoio
°	16101a	shell mould	moule-carapace m	Maskenform f	forma f a guscio
		shell moulding, s. shell casting			
°	16102	shell moulding machine	machine f à mouler en coquille	Schalenguss- maschine f	macchina f per formatura a guscio
°	16103	shell of bosh	enveloppe f des étalages	Rastmantel m	mantello m della sacca
°	16104	shell of tension	enveloppe f de tension	Tensionsschale f	rivestimento m di tensione
−	16105	shell rock	lumachelle f	Muschelkalk m	lumachella f
°	16106	shell of blast furnace	enveloppe f d'un haut fourneau	Hochofenbekleidung f, Ofenmantel m	camicia f (o rivestimento) d'altoforno
−	16107	shell of well	cadre m de puits	Schachtkranz m	anello m (o corona f) d'un pozzo
^	16108	shell outage	hauteur f du vide (dans le réservoir)	Vakuumhöhe f (im Behälter)	altezza f del vuoto (in serbatoio)
°	16109	shell pattern	modèle m au naturel	Naturmodell n	modello m al naturale
°	16110	shell plate (of a boiler)	tôle f de coque (de chaudière)	Kesselwand(ung) f	lamiera f di corpo (della caldaia)

		English	French	German	Italian
°	16111	shell reamer (carbide tipped)	alésoir m ébaucheur, manchon m	Aufsteckreibahle (mit Hartmetallschneidplättchen)	alesatoio m interno (con estremità di carburo)
°	16112	shell steel	acier m pour obus	Granatenstahl m	acciaio m per granate
˄	16113	shell still	distillateur m à chaudière	Kesseldestillierapparat m	distillatore m a caldaia
−	16114	shelley	coquilleux	kokillenförmig	a forma di conchiglia
−	16115	shelley	charbon m trituré	zerkleinerte Kohle f	carbone f triturato
−	16116	shelved waggon	wagonnet m étagé	Etagenwagen m	vagoncino m a più piani
°	16117	sherardising	shérardisation f	Sherardisieren n	sherardizzazione f,
−	16118	shet	toit m éboulé	zubruchgegangenes Hangende n	tetto m franato
°	16118a	shielded arc-welding	soudage m à arc protégé	Lichtbogenschweissen n	saldatura f ad arco schermato
°	16119	shielded electrode	électrode f enrobée	umhüllte Elektrode f	elettrodo m rivestito
		shielded inert gas metal arc-welding, s. inert gas arc welding			
°	16120	shielding	projection f, abri m	Schutz m	protezione f, riparo m
°	16120a	shielding	effect m d'écran	Abschirmung f	effetto m di schermo
−	16121	shift	rejet m horizontal	Seitenverschiebung f	rigetto m orizzontale
	16122	shift	poste m	Schicht f	turno m
	16123	shift boss	chef m de poste	Schichtsteiger m	capo-turno m
−	16124	shift fault	faille f de rejet horizontale	Seitenverschiebung f, Horizontalverschiebung f	faglia f di rigetto orizzontale
°	16125	shifted casting	variation f de moule	versetzte Form f	getto m spostato, forma f variata, getto sdetto
°	16126	shifted core, mismatch in core	variation f du noyau	versetzter Kern m	anima f spostata, anima f variata
−	16127	shifter	encageur m	Anschläger m	ingabbiatore m
°	16128	shifting	déplacement m	Verschiebung f	spostamento m, variazione f
−	16129	shifting	migration f des vallées, déplacement m de côtes	Talverlegung f Küstenversetzung f	migrazione f delle valli, spostamento m delle coste
°	16129a	shim	chemise f	Blecheinlage f	spessore m, camicia f

	English	French	German	Italian
° 16130	to shingle, to hammer the bloom shingle, *s. detritus*	cingler, expulser la scorie	zängen	eliminazione *f* delle scorie al maglio, puddellare al maglio
° 16131	shingle	caillou *m*	Geröll *n*	ciottolo *m*
° 16132	shingled ball	lopin cinglé	gezängte Luppe *f*	palla *f* pudellata al maglio
° 16133	shingler	cingleur *m*	Luppenschmied *m*	fucinatrice *f*
° 16134	shingling (of iron)	cinglage *m*,	Zängen *n*	disincrostazione *f*, scavezzamento *m*
° 16135	shingling rolls	cylindres *m pl.* à cingler	Zängewalzen *f pl.*	cilindri *m pl.* fucinatori (o sgrossatori)
° 16136	shingling squeezer	moulin *m* à cingler	Luppenmühle *f*	fucinatore *m* rotante
° 16137	ship plate	tôle *f* de navire	Schiffsblech *n*	lamiera *f* per navi
° 16138	shipping port	port *m* d'embarquement	·Verschiffungshafen *m*	porto *m* d'imbarco
° 16139	shirt	enveloppe *f*, chemise *f*	Hochofenmantel *m*	camicia *f*, rivestimento (di altoforno)
— 16140	schistosity, foliation	foliation *f*, shistosité *f*	Schieferung *f*	struttura *f* fogliacea
— 16141	shoad	fragment *m* de minéral	Erzfragment *n*	frammento *m* di minerale
— 16142	shoading	prospection *f* d'après les fragments trouvés	Aufsuchen *n* der Lagerstätte auf Grund von Bruchstücken derselben	prospezione *f* secondo i frammenti trovati
16143	shock bending test	essai *m* de flexion au choc	Schlagbiegeprobe *f*	prova *f* di flessione all'urto
° 16143a	shock cooling	réfroidissement *m* par choc thermique	schroffe Abkühlung *f*	raffreddamento *m* per sbalzo termico
° 16144	shock crushing test	essai *m* d'écrasement au choc	Stauchprobe *f*	prova *f* di appiattimento o di schiacciamento
° 16145	shock damp	gaz *m* d'explosion	Schussschwaden *m*	gas *m* d'esplosione
° 16146	shock-forming	moulage *m* par choc	Schlagformerei *f*	formatura *f* ad urto
° 16147	shock stress	contrainte *f* au choc	Schlagbeanspruchung *f*	sollecitazione *f* di un corpo all'urto
° 16148	shock test	essai *m* au choc	Schlagversuch *m*	prova *f* d'urto

		English	French	German	Italian
°	16149	**shock test on notched bar**	essai *m* au choc sur éprouvette en-taillée	Kerbbiegeprobe *f*	prova *f* di flessione su campione intaccato
—	16150	**shoe**	sabot *m*	Senkschuh *m*	scarpa *f*, anello del palo
—	16151	**shoe**	main courante *m* de cage	Gleitschuh *m*, Führungschuh *m*	ringhiera *f* della gabbia
°	16152	**shoe**	sabot *m*	Bremsschuh *m*	ganascia *f* del freno
°	16153	**shoe brake**	frein *m* à sabot	Backenbremse *f*	freno *m* a ganasce
^	16154	**shoe guide**	tampon-guide *m* du sabot	Schuhführung *f*	tampone-guida *m* della scarpa
°	16155	**shoe nails**	clous *m pl.* pour chaussures	Schuhnägel *m pl.*	broccame *m*
°	16156	**shoe tingles**	semences *f pl.*	Zwickstifte *m pl.*	sellerine *f pl.*
^	16157	**shoes string sand**	couche *f* filiforme	fadenförmige Schicht *f*	strato *m* filiforme
—	16158	**shonkinite**	shonkinite *f*	Shonkinit *m*	shonkinite *f*
—	16159	**shoofly**	recoupe *f*	Querstrecke *f*	galleria *f* di collegamento
—	16160	**to shoot**	tirer, abbatre à l'explosif	sprengen, schiessen	esplodere, far saltare, abbattere con esplosivo
—	16161	**shoot**	colonne *f* de minerai riche	Erzstock *m*, Erzfall *m*	colonna *f* di minerale (ricco)
—	16162	**shoot**	couloir *m*	Rutsche *f*, Schütt-rinne *f*, Gleitbahn *f*	scivolo *m*, piano *m* inclinato (per carbone)
		shoot, *s. chute*			
—	16163	**shooter**	boute-feu *m*	Sprengmeister *m*	artificiere *m*
—	16164	**shooting**	tir *m* des mines, torpillage *m*	Sprengarbeit *f*, Bohrlochsprengen *n*	esplosione *f* di mine, torpedinamento *m*
—	16165	**shooting off the solid**	abattage *m* par explosif sans havage préalable	Kohlensprengen *n* ohne Unterschrämen	abbattimento *m* con esplosivo senza taglio preventivo
—	16166	**shooting off water**	fermeture *f* des eaux	Wasserabsperrung *f*	sbarramento *m* delle acque
—	16167	**to shore**	étrésillonner, boiser	unterstützen	puntellare

		English	French	German	Italian
−	16168	**shore**	plage *f*, côte *f*, rivage *f*, bord *m*, terre *f*	Ufer *n*, Strand *m*, Küste *f*, Land *n*	spiaggia *f*, costa *f*, riva *f*, bordo *m*, terra *f*
−	16169	**shore**	contrefiche *f*, entretoise *f*	Strebe *f*, Stütze *f*	puntello *m*, contrafisso *m*, saettone *m*
−	16170	**shore deposit**	accumulation *f* littorale	Anschwemmung *f*	accumulazione *f* litorale
°	16171	**Shore hardness**	dureté *f* Shore	Shorehärte *f*	durezza *f* Shore
−	16172	**shore processes**	actions *f pl.* littorales	litorale Tätigkeit *f*	azioni *f pl.* litorali
−	16173	**shoring**	étaiement *m*	Stempelzimmerung *f*	puntellamento *m*
		shorl, s. *schorl*			
−	16174	**short borer**	fleuret *m* d'amorçage	kurzer Bohrer *m*	fioretto *m* corto, trivella corta
°	16175	**short brittle**	rouverain, cassant à chaud	rotbrüchig	fragile a caldo
°	16176	**short cast**	fonte *f* cassante	sprödes Roheisen *n*	ghisa *f* fragile a caldo
−	16177	**short columnar mineral**	minérai *m* en prismes raccourcis *m*	kurzsäuliges Mineral *n*	minerale *m* in prismi corti
−	16178	**short cut**	recoupement *m* du méandre	Mäanderverkürzung *f*	ritaglio *m* del meandro
°	16179	**short (of strip)**	chutes *f pl.*	Abfallende *n*	estremità *f* dello scarto, sfrido *m*
		short flaming coal, s. *steam coal*			
−	16180	**short horn**	front *m* d'attaque à 60° avec les limets	Stossstellung *f* von 60° zur Schlechtenrichtung *f*	fronte *f* d'attacco a 60° col piano di stratificazione
°	16181	**short-iron, brittler**	fer *m* cassant, fer aigre	sprödes Eisen *n*, faulbrüchiges Eisen *n*	ferro *m* fragile (o vetrino o friabile)
°	16182	**short radius bends**	coude *m* de petit rayon	Rohrbogen *m* mit engem Radius	curva *f* a raggio stretto
°	16183	**short run**	coulé court	mit zu wenig Metall gegossen	mancanza *f* di metallo, colato con poco metallo
°	16184	**short run**	manque *m* (de métal)	unvollständiger Guss *m*	scarso (di metallo)

		English	French	German	Italian
°	16185	short run	non venu	nicht ausgelaufen	incompleto
°	16186	short shaft pendulum tool	fouloir *m* d'établi	Bankstampfer *m*	pestello *m* da banco
°	16187	shortness	fragilité *f*	Sprödigkeit *f*	fragilità *f*
°	16188	shortening of the melting period	réduction *f* de la durée de la fusion	Verkürzung *f* der Schmelzzeit	riduzione *f* del tempo di fusione
		shorterizing, *s. torch (or flame) hardening*			
—	16189	shortwall	petite taille *f*	kurzer Abbaustoss	piccolo taglio *m*
°	16189a	shortness	fragilité *f*	Brüchigkeit *f*	fragilità *f*
—	16190	shoshonite	shoshonite *f*	Shoshonit *m*	shoshonite *f*
°	16191	shot	explosion *f*, coup *m*	Explosion *f*, Schuss *m*	esplosione *f*, colpo *m*
	16192	shot	balle *f*	Kugel *f*	palla *f*
°	16193	shot, grit	grenaille *f*	Schrot *m*, Gries *m*	graniglia *f*
—	16194	shot-bit	couronne *f* à grenailles	Schrotbohrkrone *f*	corona *f* a graniglia
°	16195	to shot blast	grenailler	strahlen, abstrahlen	granigliare, pallinare
°	16196	shot-blasted	décalaminé par grenaillage *m*	durch Strahlen *n* entzundert	trattato a granigliatura *f*
°	16197	shot-blasting chamber	cabine *f* de grenaillage	Putzhaus *n* mit Schleuderrad	camera *f* o cabina di granigliatura
°	16197a	shot-blasting, shot peening	grenaillage *m*	Abstrahlen *n*	granigliatura *f*
	16198	shot blasting unit	unité *f* de grenaillage	Schleuderstrahlenmaschine *f*	pulitrice *f* con graniglia meccanica
°	16199	shot-blasting	dessablage *m* par jet de grenaille	Putzen *n*, Schleuderstrahlen *n*, Strahlputzen *n*	sterratura *f* a getto di graniglia
—	16200	shot boring	sondage *m* à la grenaille	Schrotbohren *n*,	perforazione *f* con corona a graniglia
—	16201	shot core drilling	carottage *m* à la grenaille	Schrotkernbohren *n*	carotaggio *m* con corona a graniglia
°	16201a	shot defect	ressuage *m*	Schwitzkugel *f*	trasudamento *m*
—	16202	shot firer	boute-feu *m*	Sprengmeister *m*	artificiere *m*
—	16203	shot firing	allumage *m* des coups	Bohrlochsprengung *f*	accensione *f* del colpo, tiro *m*
—	16204	shot hole	trou *m* de mine	Bohrloch *n*, Sprengloch *n*	foro *m* da mina, pozzetto *m* di scoppio
°	16205	shot peening	grenaillage *m* d'écrouissage	Strahlverfestigung *f*	pallinatura *f*
°	16205a	shotted metal	métal *m* en grenailles	Schrottmetall *n*	metallo *m* in graniglie

		English	French	German	Italian
o	16206	shotting	formation f de métal granulaire	Körnermetallbildung f	formazione f di metallo granulare (o in pallini)
o	16207	shotty gold	or m granulaire	körniges Gold n	oro m granulare
o	16208	shotweld	soudure f par points	Punktschweissung f	saldatura f a punti
		shoulder, s. underside			
⌃	16209	shoulder	repos m	Absatz m	sede f della tubazione
o	16209a	shoulder (ed)core	noyau m à épaulement	Schulterkern m	anima f a colletto liscio
—	16210	shoulder of the bit	épaule du trépan	Meisselschulter f	spalla f del trapano
—	16211	shove	rejet m horizontal	horizontale Schublänge f	rigetto m orizzontale
—	16212	shovel, peel	pelle f	Schippe f	pala f
—	16213	shovel dredger	drague f à pelle	Löffelbagger m	draga f a cucchiaia, escavatore m a cucchiaio
o	16214	shovel steel	acier m à pales	Schaufelstahl m	acciaio m per pale
—	16215	shovelling	pelletage m	Schaufelung f	spalatura f, scavo m
—	16216	shovelling stoker	chargeur m à pelletage automatique	Schaufelfeuerung f	caricatrice f ad avanzamento continuo
⌃	16217	show of oil	manifestation f d'huile	Ölvorkommen n	manifestazione f di olio
o	16218	shower bath	douche f	Brausebad n	doccia f
⌃	16219	shows	manifestation f de gaz	Gasvorkommen n	manifestazione f di gas
o	16220	to shrink	retasser	lunkern	risucchiare
—	16221	to shrink	se contracter, rétrecir	schwinden, schrumpfen	ritirarsi, contrarre, restringere
o	16222	shrink	retrait m	Schwund m	ritiro m
—	16223	shrink	chambre-magasin m	Magazinbau m	camera-magazzino f
o	16224	to shrink on	emmancher par frettage	aufschrumpfen	calettare
o	16224a	shrink-away	retassement m	Lunkern m	formazione f di risucchi
o	16225	shrink grip	prise f par retrait	Schrumpfverbindung f	presa f per ritiro
o	16226	shrinkage, shrinking	retrait m, contraction	Schwinden n, Schwund m	ritiro m, contrazione f

		English	French	German	Italian
°	16227	shrinkage cavity, shrinkage hole	cavité f de retrait, retassure f	Lunker m	cavità f di ritiro, risucchio m
°	16228	shrinkage crack	crique f de retassure	Schrumpfriss m	crepa f di risucchio, cricca f (incrinatura) di ritiro
		shrinkage hole s. *shrinkage cavity*			
—	16229	shrinkage of backfilling	tassement m du remblai	Senken n des Versatzes	assestamento m della ripiena
°	16230	shrinkage of the steel	gauchissement m de l'acier	Verziehen n des Stahls	contrazione f dell'acciaio
°	16231	shrinkage porosity	porosité f de retassure	Schrumpfporosität f	porosità f di ritiro
—	16232	shrinkage stope	chambre-magasin f	Magazinabbau m	camera-magazzino f
—	16233	shrinkage stoping	exploitation f par chambres-magasins	Magazinbau m,	coltivazione f a camere-magazzino
°	16234	shrinking box	boîte f de retrait	Schrumpfbüchse f	bussola f montata a caldo
—	16234a	shrink(ing)-on	emmanchement m à chaud	Aufziehen n	calettatura f a caldo
°	16235	shrunk	joint	verkeill	calettato
—	16236	shungite	schungite f	Schungit m	schungite f
—	16237	shunting cable railway	voie f funiculaire de manœuvre	Verschiebeseilbahn f	ferrovia f funicolare di manovra
—	16238	shunting drum	cabestan m de manœuvre	Verschiebewinde f	argano m di manovra
—	16239	shunting station	gare f de manœuvre ou de triage	Verschiebebahnhof m	stazione f di manovra o di smistamento
—	16240	shunting track	voie f auxiliaire	Nebengleis n	binario m secondario
°	16241	to shut	serrer, fermer	schliessen, verschliessen	serrare, chiudere
—	16242	shut	taquet m de cage	Aufsetzvorrichtung f	dispositivo m d'arresto
		shut down, s. *out of work*			
		shut down, s. *stopping down*			
°	16243	shut (in welding)	cordon m de soudure	Schweissnaht f	cordolo m della saldatura

		English	French	German	Italian
−	16244	shut, lap	chevauchement m	Überlappung f	sovrapposizione f, piega f
−	16245	shut-in well	puits m fermé	geschlossene Sonde f	pozzo m chiuso
°	16246	shutting off the blast	arrêt m du soufflage	Abstellen n des Gebläses n	arresto m del forno
−	16247	sial	sial m	Sial n	sial m
−	16248	sialma	sialma f	Sialma f	sialma f
−	16249	siberite	sibérite f	Siberit m	siberite f
−	16250	sicklerite	sicklérite f	Sicklerit m	sicklerite f
−	16251	siddle	pendage m du charbon	Kohleneinfallen n	inclinazione f del carbone
−	16252	side	côté, paroi f	Wand f, Seite f	lato m, parete f
−	16253	side	pente f, versant m	Abhang m	inclinazione f, pendenza f, versante m
−	16254	side	lèvre f (d'une faille), flanc m (d'un pli)	Verwerfungsflügel m, Flanke f (einer Falte)	labbro m (o bordo m) d'una faglia, fianco m (d'una piega)
−	16255	side	paroi f latérale	Stoss m	parete f laterale
−	16256	side benching	exploitation f par recoupes transversales	Querbau m	coltivazione f per trance trasversali
°	16256a	side blown converter	convertisseur m Tropenas	Birne f mit Seitenwind	convertitore m a soffiaggio laterale
−	16257	side chamber	chambre f latérale	Seitenkammer f	camera f laterale
		side cramp, s. side thrust			
−	16258	side drag	tir m latéral	Seitenzug m	tiro m laterale
−−	16259	side drift	galerie f horizontale d'accès	Tagesstollen m	galleria f orizzontale d'accesso
−	16260	side dump car	wagon m basculant de côté	Seitenkipper m	vagone m ribaltabile di lato
	16261	side elevation	profil m, vue f latérale	Seitenansicht f	profilo m, visto di lato
−	16262	side entry	accès m latéral	Seitenöffnung f	entrata f laterale
°	16263	side flue	carneau m latéral	Seitenzug m	condotto m laterale
°	16264	side gate	attaque f dirigée directe	gerichteter Aufprallanschnitt m	attacco m guidato diretto
°	16264a	side guide	guidage m latéral	Seitenführung f	guida f laterale

	English	French	German	Italian
− 16265	**side hole**	mine *f* de maizières	Seitenschussbohr-loch *n*	foro *m* da mina laterale
− 16266	**side lacing**	coffrage *m* latéral	Seitenverschalung *f*	rivestimento *m* laterale
° 16267	**side leg, branch**	branche *f*	Schenkel *m*	braccio *m*
16268	**side milling**	fraise *f* plate (ou latérale)	Scheibenfräser *m*	fresa *f* a disco
− 16269	**side of work**	panneau *m* d'exploitation	Abbaufeld *n*	pilastro *m* da coltivare
° 16270	**side-plate**	tôle *f* latérale, flasque *f*	Seitenblech *n*	piastra *f* laterale

side penetration, s. *depth of the side fusion zone*

	English	French	German	Italian
° 16271	**side runner**	attaque *f* à talon	Guss *m* mit seitlichem Anschnitt	colata *f* in sorgente a tallone
° 16271a	**side shearing**	taillage *m*	Zuschneiden *n*	taglio *m* dei bordi
° 16272	**side step gating**	coulée *f* en échelons, coulée *f* étagée, coulée échelonnée	steigender Guss *m* mit Stufenanschnitten	colata *f* a piani
° 16273	**side stick**	blanc *m* de marge	Seitensteg *m*	lingotto *m* di fianco
° 16274	**side stone**	costière *f*	Seitenstein *m*	costiera *f*
− 16275	**side stoping**	abattage *m* latéral	Hereingewinnung *f* von der Seite aus	abbattimento *m* laterale
− 16276	**side test**	essai *m* latéral	Seitenprobe *f*	prova *f* laterale
^ 16277	**side stream**	fraction *f* latérale	Seitenfraktion *f*	frazione *f* laterale
− 16278	**side tester**	carottier *m* latéral	Gebirgsprobenentnehmer *m*	carotiere *m* laterale
− 16279	**side tracking**	forage *m* dévié	Weiterbohren *n* neben einem im Bohrloch steckengebliebenem Werkzeuge	trivellazione *f* deviata
° 16279a	**side thrust**	pression *f* latérale	seitlicher Druck *m*	pressione *f* laterale
− 16280	**side-wall**	paroi *f* latérale	Herdwand *f*	parete *f* laterale, cordone *m*
− 16281	**side-wall core, side-wall sample**	carotte *f* latérale	seitlicher Kern *m*	carota *f* di parete
− 16282	**side-wall coring side step gate casting**	carottage *m* latéral	seitlich Kerne *m pl.* entnehmen	carotaggio *m* di parete
−16283	**siderite**	fer *m* spathique	Spateisenstein *m*	ferro *m* spatico, siderite *f*

		English	French	German	Italian
−	16284	**siderolite**	sidérolite *f*	Siderolith *m*	siderolite *f*
−	16285	**sideronatrite**	sidéronatrite *f*	Sideronatrit *m*	sideronatrite *f*
−	16286	**siderophylite**	sidérophyllite *f*	Siderophyllit *m*	siderofillite *f*
°	16287	**siderurgy**	sidérurgie *f*	Eisenmetallurgie *f*	siderurgia *f*
°	16288	**Siegerland pig iron**	fonte *f* de Siegen	Siegerländer Roheisen *n*	ghisa *f* di Siegen
°	16289	**Siegerland shaft furnace**	four *m* à cuve du Siegerland	Siegerländer *m*	forno *m* a tino di Siegerland
°	16290	**Siemens' butterfly valve**	valve *f* à papillon de Siemens	Siemenssche Wechselklappe *f*	valvola *f* a farfalla di Siemens
°	16291	**Siemens' electromagnetic apparatus**	appareil *m* électromagnétique de Siemens	elektromagnetischer Apparat *m* von Siemens	apparecchio *m* elettromagnetico di Siemens
°	16292	**Siemens-kiln**	four *m* Siemens	Siemens-Ofen *m*	fornace *f* Siemens
°	16293	**Siemens Martin open hearth furnace**	four *m* Martin	Siemens-Martin Ofen *m*	forno *m* Martin Siemens
°	16294	**Siemens process**	procédé *m* Siemens	Siemens-Prozess *m*	processo *m* Siemens
°	16295	**Siemens producer**	gazogène *m* Siemens	Siemens-Generator *m*	gasogeno *m* Siemens
−	16296	**to sieve, to sift**	tamiser	sieben	vagliare, stacciare
−	16297	**sieve**	claie *f*, crible *m*	Wurfsieb *n*	crivello *m*, vaglio *m*
−	16298	**sieve, strainer**	tamis *m*	Sieb *n*	staccio *m*, crivello *m*
°	16298a	**sieve fraction**	fraction *f* granulométrique	Siebfraktion *f*	frazione *f* granulometrica
−	16299	**sieve grate**	grille-tamis *f*	Siebrost *m*	griglia *f* a crivello
−	16300	**sieve mesh**	maille *f* de tamis	Siebmaschine *f*	maglia *f* del setaccio
−	16301	**sieve texture**	structure *f* en tamis	Siebstruktur *f*	struttura *f* a setaccio
−	16302	**sieving**	blutage *m*	Beutelung *f*	stacciatura *f,* vagliatura *f*
		to sift: *s. to sieve*			
−	16303	**siftage**	matières *f pl.* tamisées	Unterkorn *n*	materiale *m* vagliato
−	16304	**sifted coke**	coke *m* criblé	Siebkoks *m*	coke *m* vagliato
−	16305	**sifting**	tamisage *m*, triage *m*	Siebung *f*	vagliatura *f*, cernita *f*

		English	French	German	Italian
—	16306	**sifting device**	dispositif *m* de tamisage	Siebvorrichtung *f*	dispositivo *m* per vagliare
°	16307	**sighting mark**	repère *m* à vue	Kennzeichen *n*	segno *m* di riferimento
—	16308	**sigma phase**	phase *f* sigma	Sigmastadium *n*	fase *f* sigma
—	16309	**sil-o-cel**	diatomite *f*	Diatomeenerde *f*	diatomite *f*
—	16310	**silex**	silex *m*	Kiesel *m*	silicio *m*
—	16311	**silica**	silice *f*	Kieselerde *f*, Kiesel *m*	silice *f*
—	16312	**silica**	anydride *m* siliceux	Kieselsäure *f*, Siliziumdioxyd *n*	anidride *f* silicea
—	16313	**silica brick** **silica sand,** *s. sharp sand*	brique *f* acide	saurer Stein *m*	mattone *m* acido o siliceo
—	16314	**silicarenite**	grès *m* quartzeux	Quarzsandstein *m*	gres *m* quarzifero
—	16315	**silicate of aluminium**	silicate *m* d'alumine	Tonerdesilikat *m*	silicato *m* d'alluminio
—	16316	**siliceous**	siliceux	kieselig	siliceo
—	16317	**siliceous calamine**	hydrosilicate *m* de zinc	Kieselzinkerz *n*	silicato di zinco idrossido
—	16318	**siliceous earth**	diatomite *f*	Diatomeenerde *f*	diatomite *f*
°	16319	**seliceous flux**	fondant *m* siliceux	Kieselzuschlag *m*	fondente *m* siliceo
—	16320	**siliceous sinter**	opale *f* incrustante	Kieselsinter *m*	opale incrostante
°	16321	**siliceous stamping mass**	pisé *m* siliceux	kieselige Stampfmasse *f*	impasto *m* o malta *f* silicea
°	16322	**to silicify**	silicifier	verkieseln	silicare
—	16323	**silicium**	silicium *m*	Silizium *n*	silicio *m*
°	16324	**silico-spiegel**	fer *m* manganèse siliceux	Silikospiegel *m*	ferro *m* silicomanganese
—	16325	**silicon**	silicium *m*	Silizium *n*	silicio *m*
°	16326	**silicon bronze**	bronze *m* siliceux	Siliziumbronze *f*	bronzo *m* al silicio
°	16327	**silicon-bronze wire**	fil *m* de bronze siliceux	Siliziumbronzedraht *m*	filo *m* di bronzo al silicio
—	16328	**silicon carbide**	carborundum *m* carbure de silicium	Siliziumkarbid *n*, Karborundum *n*	carburo *m* di silicio, carborundum *m*

	English	French	German	Italian
°	16329 **silicon copper**	cuivre m au sili-cium	Siliziumkupfer n, Kuprosilizium n	rame m al silicio
°	16330 **silicon-steel**	acier m au silicium	Siliziumstahl m	acciaio m al silicio
—	16331 **silicosis**	silicose f	Silikose f	silicosi f
—	16332 **silicotel**	silicotel m	Silikotel m	silicotel m
°	16333 **silk-covered wire**	fil m sous soie	Seidendraht m	filo m rivestito di seta
°	16334 **silky fracture**	fracture f soyeuse	seidiger Bruch m	frattura f a grano fino
°	16335 **sill**	semelle f, solive f	Sohlenholz n, Grund-schwelle f	soglia f, soletta f, tra-ve f
°	16336 **sill**	base f, fondation f	Basis f	base f, fondazione f
—	16337 **sill**	sill m, nappe f d'in-trusion	Sill n, Lagergang m Intrusivlager n	letto m, filone-strato m, strato m intrusivo
—	16338 **sill (of a mine)**	mur m	Liegende n	muro m
—	16339 **sill floor**	niveau m de fond	Grundsohle f	livello m di fondo
—	16340 **sill floor stope**	chantier m du ni-veau de fond	Ort m auf der Grund-sohle	cantiere m a livello di fondo
—	16341 **sill-floor timbering**	boisage m du niveau de fond	Verzimmerung f der Grundsohle	armatura f d'un livel-lo di fondo
—	16342 **sille**	filon-couche m	Lagergang m	filone-strato m
—	16343 **sillimanite**	sillimanite f	Sillimanit m	sillimanite f
—	16344 **silling**	préparation f du ni-veau de base	Vortrieb n der Gerundsohle	preparazione f della soletta di base
°	16345 **sills**	pièces f $pl.$ d'appui	untere Rahmenhöl-zer n $pl.$	soglie f $pl.$
—	16346 **silt**	limon m	Silt m	limo m
°	16347 **silt, scum**	scorie f	Schlacke f	scoria f
—	16348 **Silurian period**	Silurien m	Silur n	siluriano m
°	16349 **to silver**	argenter	versilbern	(in)argentare
°	16350 **silver**	argent m	Silber n	argento m
°	16351 **silver alloy**	alliage m d'argent	Silberlegierung f	lega f d'argento
°	16351a **silver brazing**	brasage m àl'argent	Silberhartlötung f	brasatura f all'argento
°	16352 **to silver-coat**	argenter	versilbern	argentare

	English	French	German	Italian
— 16353	silver glance	argentite f	Argentit m	argentite f
— 16354	silver nitrate	nitrate m d'argent, pierre f infernale	Höllenstein m, Silbernitrat n	nitrato m d'argento pietra f infernale
° 16355	to silver plate	argenter	versilbern	argentare
° 16356	silver plated	argénté	versilbert	argentato
° 16357	silver-plating, silvering	argenture f	Versilberung f	argentatura f
° 16358	silver refining	affinage m de l'argent	Silberscheidung f	affinamento m dell'argento
— 16359	silver ruby	pyrargyrite f	Pyrargyrit m	piragirite f
— 16359a	silver sand	sable m siliceux	Silbersand m	sabbia f silicea
° 16360	silver-solder	soudure f à l'argent, paillon d'argent	Silberlot n	saldatura f all'argento
° 16361	silver-steel	acier m argenté	Silberstahl m	acciaio m argentato

silvering, s. *silver plating*

	English	French	German	Italian
° 16362	silvery, silver	argenté	silbern	argenteo, di argento
° 16363	silvery iron	fonte f grise riche en silicium	siliziumreiches graues Roheisen n	ghisa f grigia siliciosa
— 16364	simetite	simétite f	Simetit m	simetite f
° 16365	similor	similor m	Prinzmetall n	similoro m
° 16366	simple alloy steel	acier m ternaire	Ternärstahl m	acciaio m ternario
° 16367	simple blow	essai m d'endurance à la rupture au choc	Bruchstosswiderstandsprobe f	prova f di resistenza alla rottura all'urto
° 16368	simple fracture	fracture f simple	einfacher Bruch m	frattura f semplice
° 16369	simple gate	jet m de coulée rond	runder Einguss m	colata f rotonda
° 16370	simple grate firing	foyer m simple à grille	einfache Rostfeuerung f	focolare m semplice a griglia
° 16371	simple hardening	trempe f simple	einfache Härtung f	tempera f semplice
° 16372	simple points	changement m simple	einfache Weiche f	scambio m semplice
° 16373	simple span roofs with trussed rafters	combles m $pl.$ à deux versants simples sur fermes	einfache Sparrendächer n $pl.$	tetti m $pl.$ a due falde su capriate

		English	French	German	Italian
^	16374	simplex cementing collar	manchon *m* pour cimentation «Simplex»	Muffe *f* für mehrstufige Zementierung	manicotto *m* per cementazione
−	16375	simultaneous drilling	forage *m* simultané	gleichzeitiges Bohren	trivellazione *f* simultanea
	16376	simultaneous maximum demand	demande *f* maximum et simultanée d'énergie	gleichzeitiger Höchstbedarf *m*	consumo *m* massimo simultaneo
−	16377	sinclinal fold	pli *m* sinclinal	Sinklinalfalte *f*	piega *f* sinclinale
^	16378	single	rallonge *f*	Einzelzug *m*	asta *f* singola
°	16379	single acting	à simple effet	einfach wirkend	a semplice effetto
°	16380	single-acting cylinder	cylindre *m* à simple effet	einfachwirkende Walze *f*	cilindro *m* a semplice effetto
−	16381	single acting lift	monte-charges *m* à simple effet	einfach wirkender Aufzug *m*	montacarichi *m* a semplice effetto
^	16382	single acting pump	pompe *f* à simple effet	einfach wirkende Pumpe *f*	pompa *f* a semplice effetto
°	16383	single acting steam hammer	marteau-pilon *m* à simple effet	einfach wirkender Dampfhammer *m*	maglio *m* a vapore a semplice effetto
−	16384	single-bench quarrying	exploitation *f* à ciel ouvert à gradin unique	einstufiger Tagebau *m*	coltivazione *f* a cielo aperto a gradino unico
−	16385	single boiler	chaudière *f* formée d'un simple corps cylindrique	Einfachkessel *m*	caldaia *f* semplice
−	16386	single conductor cable	câble *m* à conducteur unique	einadriges Kabel *n*	cavo *m* a conduttore unipolare
°	16387	single crucible furnace	four *m* à un seul creuset	eintiegliger Ofen *m*	forno *m* per un sol crogiuolo
°	16388	single (cylindrical) boiler	chaudière *f* (cylindrique) simple	Einfach(walzen)- kessel *m*	caldaia *f* (cilindrica) semplice
°	16389	single-ended boiler	chaudière *f* à foyers d'un seul côté	Einderkessel *m*	caldaia *f* con focolari ad una estremità
−	16390	single entry	galerie *f* unique	einfache Strecke *f*	galleria *f* unica
−	16391	single fault	faille *f* simple	einfache Verwerfung *f*	faglia *f* semplice
°	16392	single-fire fixed forge	forge *f* fixe à un feu	Einfeuerstand- schmiede *f*	fucina *f* fissa ad un fuoco

		English	French	German	Italian
o	16393	**single lifting table**	table f tournante à levée	Aushubtisch m	piattaforma f spostabile
o	16394	**single-line roll train**	laminoir m simple	einachsige Strasse f	laminatoio m semplice
o	16394a	**single particle**	grain élémentaire	Primärteilchen n	grano m elementare
o	16395	**single phase current plant**	installation f monophasée	Einphasenstromanlage f	impianto m a corrente monofasica
o	16396	**single-phase furnace**	four m à courant monophasé	Einphasenofen m	forno m a corrente monofase
o	16397	**single-pitched latticed trusses built up of light**	fermettes f $pl.$ en treillis composées de cornières légè-	Fachwerkbinder m aus leichten Winkelprofilen n $pl.$	capriatelle f $pl.$ a traliccio formate con angolari leggeri
o	16397a	**single potential**	potentiel m d'électrode	Elektrodenpotential n	potenziale m di elettrodo
o	16398	**single refining slag bottom process**	affinage m au bain de scorie	Einmalschmelzerei f, Schwalarbeit f	affinaggio m al bagno di scorie
—	16399	**single-rope haulage**	plan m incliné de voie unique	eintrümmiger Bremsberg m	piano m inclinato a via unica
o	16400	**(single-) shear steel, refined steel**	acier m affiné, acier m raffiné	Gärbstahl m, Raffinierstahl m	acciaio m affinato, acciaio m raffinato
ˆ	16401	**single-shot**	opération f unique		operazione f unica
o	16402	**single sided pattern plate**	plaque- modèle f simple face	einseitige Modellplatte f	placca f modello semplice (od a una faccia)
ˆ	16403	**single-stage pumping**	épuisement m en un seul jet m	Wasserhebung f, ohne Unterbrechung bis zu Tage	pompaggio m in un sol stadio
—	16404	**single-stamp mill**	bocard m à pilon simple	Einstempel-Pochwerk n	mulino m ad un pestello
—	16405	**single stope**	taille f unique	einflügeliger Abbaustoss m	taglio m unico
o	16406	**single test**	essai m isolé	Einzelversuch m	prova f singola
—	16407	**single tube core barrel**	tube m carottier simple	einfaches Kernrohr n	tubo m carotiere
—	16408	**single vein**	filon m simple	einfacher Gang m	filone m semplice
—	16409	**to sink a hole**	faire un sondage	eine Bohrung f niederbringen	perforare, approfondire un pozzo
—	16410	**to sink the floor**	rebancher le mur	Sohle f nachreissen	trivellare il muro

		English	French	German	Italian
°	16411	sink	poquette *f*	Einfallstelle *f*	avvallamento *m*
—	16412	sink	évier *m*	Ausguss *m*	acquaio *m*
—	16413	sink-and-float method, heavy media separation	méthode de séparation à liquide dense	Schwimm- und Sinkverfahren *n*	metodo *m* di separazione con liquidi densi
°	16413a	sink-head	masselotte *f* chaude	Wärmhaube *f*	coperchio *m* isolante
—	16414	sink-hole	effondrement *m*	Versenkung *f*	cedimento *m*, sprofondamento *m*
—	16415	sink bar, sinker bar	maîtresse-tige *f*	Schwerstange *f*	asta *f* pesante, barra *f* appesantatrice
°	16415a	sinker	larget *m*	Platine *f*	piatto *m*, platina *f*
—	16416	sinking	fonçage *m*	Abteufung *f*, Abteufen *n*	perforazione *f*, trivellazione *f*, scavo *m*
—	16417	sinking	affaissement *m*, tassement *m*	Absenkung *f*	sprofondamento *m*, cedimento *m*
°	16418	sinking, impression	empreinte *f*	Abdruck *m*	impronta *f*, incisione *f*
—	16419	sinking beneath pentice	fonçage *m* sous stot	Unterfahrung *f* eines Schachtes	approfondimento *m* del pozzo
—	16420	sinking bucket	benne *f* de creusement	Abteufkübel *m*	benna *f* di scavo
—	16421	sinking by piling	fonçage *m* au poussage	Abtreiben *n* des Schachtes	approfondimento *m* del pozzo
—	16422	sinking drum	trousse *f* coupante	Senkschuh *m*	tamburo *m*
—	16423	sinking frame	cadre *m* de boisage	Traggeviert *n*	quadro *m* di sostegno
—	16424	sinking hammer	marteau *m* à puits	Abteufhammer *m*	martello *m* per pozzi
°	16424a	sinking mill	laminoir *m* réducteur	Reduzierwalzwerk *n*	laminatoio *m* di riduzione
—	16425	sinking pump	pompe *f* de fonçage	Abteufpumpe *f*	pompa *f* abbassabile nel pozzo
—	16426	sinking tipple	chevalement *m* de fonçage	Abteufgerüst *n*	armatura *f* da pozzo
—	16427	sinopite	sinopite *f*	Sinopit *m*	sinopite *f*
^	16428	sinous flow	mouvement *m* turbulent	Wirbelbewegung *f*	moto *m* turbolento
—	16429	to sinter	agglomérer par frittage, s'agglutiner	sintern	agglomerarsi per compressione a caldo
—	16430	sinter	sinter *m*	Sinter *m*	tufo *m*
°	16431	sinter, dross of iron	scorie *f*	Schlacke *f*	scoria *f*

		English	French	German	Italian
○	16432	**sintered briquette**	briquette f frittée	gesinterter Press-stein m	mattonella f sinterizza-ta
○	16432a	**sintered iron**	fer m fritté	Sintereisen n	ferro m sinterizzato
○	16433	**sintering**	agglutination f, frittage m	Sinterung f	agglutinamento m, sinterizzazione f
○	16434	**sintering**	grésage m, frittage m	Sintern n	greificazione f, sinterizzazione f
—	16435	**sintering coal**	houille f grasse à longue flamme	Sinterkohle f	carbone m grasso a fiamma lunga
○	16435a	**sintering furnace**	four m à fritter	Sinterofen m	forno m di sinterizzazion
○	16436	**sintering point**	point m de grésage	Sinterprunkt m	punto m di sinterizzazion
—	16437	**sintering sand coal**	houille f maigre sableuse	sinternde Sandkohle f	carbone m magro a fiamma lunga
—	16438	**sinterite**	dépôt m des sources	Sinterablagerung f	deposito m delle sorgenti
○	16438a	**sinter skin**	peau f de frittage	Sinterhaut f	pelle f di sinterizzazione
—	16439	**sipylite**	sipylite f	Sipylit m	sipilyte f
—	16440	**sit**	écrasement m des piliers, affaissement m du toit	Pfeilerzerdrückung f, Absenkung f der Firste	cedimento m dei pilastri, cedimento m del tettò
—	16441	**sitaparite**	sitaparite f	Sitaparit m	sitaparite f
—	16442	**six-point bit**	taillant m en couronne	Kronenschneide f	tagliente m a corona
—	16443	**size, size of coal**	grosseur f du grain, grosseur f du charbon	Kohlengrösse f, Korngrösse f	pezzatura f del grano
○	16443a	**size fraction**	fraction f granulométrique	Kornfraktion f	frazione f granulometrica
—	16444	**size of well**	capacité f de production par jour	Tagesproduktion f	capacità f produttiva giornaliera
—	16445	**sized coal**	charbon m calibré	gesiebte Kohle f	carbone m vagliato (o classificato)
○	16445a	**sizing**	calibrage m	Kalibrieren n	calibratura f, taratura f
○	16446	**sizing or grading (by sifting)** sizing, s. coining sizing, s. metal tube sizing	détermination f de la grosseur par criblage	Bestimmung f der Stückgrösse durch Absieben	classificazione f granulometrica
○	16447	**sizing mill**	laminoir m calibreur	Reduzierwalzwerk n	laminatoio m calibratore
○	16448	**skeleton pattern**	squelette m	Skelettmodell n	scheletro m
○	16448a	**skelp**	bande f à tube	Rohrstreifen m	banda f di tubo
	16449	**skew**	oblique	schief, schräg	obliquo
—	16450	**skew**	apophyse f d'un filon	Gangapophyse f	apofisi f d'un filone

		English	French	German	Italian
−	16451	skewer	épinglette *f*	Schiessnadel *f*	punta *f*, ago *m* d'espulsione
^	16452	to skid the derrick	riper une tour de sondage	Bohrturm *m* walzen	raschiare la torre di perforazione
^	16453	skid	patte *f*	Schuh *m*	pattino *m*, zeppa *f*
^	16454	skid mounted	monté sur patte		montato su zatteroni
o	16455	skillet	creuset *m*	Tiegel *m*	crogiuolo *m*
o	16456	skillet cast-steel	acier *m* fondu au creuset	Tiegelgussstahl *m*	acciaio *m* fuso al crogiuolo
^	16457	to skim	éliminer la fraction de kéroséne du pétrole brut	Kerosenabsonderung *f* von -Erdöl	togliere dal petrolio la frazione di cherosene
o	16458	to skim	écrémer	abschlacken	scremare, schiumare
o	16459	to skim	écumer	abschäumen	scorificare, scrostare
o	16460	skim gate, slag trap	canal *m* de détente	Stufeneinlauf *m*, Treppenlauf *m*	attacco *m* di colata
−	16460a	skim gate. skimmer core	crible *m* de laitier	Schlackensieb *n*	vaglio per scorie
o	16461	skimmer	écrémoir *m*, pelle *f* de retenue	Schlackenlöffel *m*,	scrematore *m*, schiumatore *m*, filtro *m*
o	16461a	skimmer	dame *f* de laitier	Schlackendamm *m*	dama *f* di scorie
−	16462	skimmer skimmer, *s. skimming tool*	pelle *f* niveleuse	Abstreicher *m*	escavatore *m* a cucchiaia livellatrice, pala *f* per livellare
o	16463	skimmer brick	brique-barrage *f*	Dammstein *m*	mattone *m* parascorie
^	16464	skimming	élimination *f* d'une fraction gazeuse	Toppen *n*	riduzione *f*, cimatura *f*
o	16465	skimming	écrémage *m*	Abkrammen *n*	schiumatura *f*
^	16466	skimming plant	installation *f* de distillation non poussée	primäre Destillationsanlage *f*	impianto *m* di distillazione primaria
o	16467	skimming tool	écumoire *f*	Schaumlöffel *m* Schlackenlöffel *m*, Krammstock *m*	schiumatore *m*
−	16468	skimping	criblage *m* par dépôt	Setzarbeit *f*	vagliatura *f* per deposito
o	16469	to skin	écrémer	abschlacken	scorificare, scremare

		English	French	German	Italian
o	16470	**to skin dry a mould**	flamber un moule	eine Form abflammen	fiammare una forma
o	16471	**skin**	croûte *f* de la fonte	Gusshaut *f*, Haut *f*	crosta *f* della ghisa
		skin bob, *s. slag pocket*			
o	16471a	**skin dried mould**	moule *m* flambé	abgeflammte Form *f*	forma *f* fiammata
o	16472	**skin dried molding**	formage *m* à sec	Masseform *f*, Sandform	formatura *f* a secco
o	16473	**skin drying**	flambage *m*	Abflammen *n*	fiammatura *f*
o	16474	**skin due to rolling**	couche *f* d'oxyde du laminage	Walzhaut *f*	crosta *f* o strato *m* d'ossido sul pezzo laminato
o	16475	**skin hardening**	trempe *f* superficielle	Oberflächenhärtung *f*	tempra *f* superficiale
o	16476	**skin hardness**	dureté *f* superficielle	Oberflächenhärte *f*	durezza *f* di superficie
o	16477	**skin hole (on an ingot)**	trou *m* superficiel	Oberflächenloch *n*	foro *m* sulla pelle
o	16478	**skin layer**	couche *f* marginale	Randschicht *f*	strato *m* marginale
o	16479	**skin of casting**	croûte *f* de la fonte	Gussrinde *f*, Gusshaut *f*	crosta *f* della ghisa
o	16479a	**skin pass**	finissage *m*	Polierstich *m*	finitura *f*
o	16480	**skip**	skip *m*, benne *f* du chargement	Aufzugkübel *m*	elevatore *m* a benna, benna *f* di caricamento
—	16481	**skip, wheel barrow**	brouette *f* de chargement	Erzkarren *m*	vagoncino *m* per minerale
—	16481a	**skip**	godet *m*	Korb *m*, Kübel	tazza *f*, secchio *m*
—	16482	**skip hoist**	monte-charge *m* incliné	Schrägaufzug *m*	montacarichi inclinato
—	16483	**skip pocket**	trémie *f* de chargement de skips	Bunker *m* fur Förderkübelbeschickung	tramoggia *f* di caricamento degli skips
—	16484	**skip road**	compartiment *m* des skips	Förderkübelabteilung *f*	reparto *m* degli skips
o	16484a	**skip welding**	soudage *m* à pas de pélerin	Pilgerschrittschweissen *n*	saldatura *f* a passo di pellegrino
^	16485	**skirt sheet**	cuvelage *m*	Verkleidung *f*, Mantel *m*	incamiciatura *f*
—	16486	**sklodowskite**	sklodowskite *f*	Sklodowskit *m*	sklodowskite *f*
—	16487	**skogbolite**	skogbolite *f*	Skogbolit *m*	skogbolite *f*
o	16488	**skull**	fond *m* de poche	Pfannenrest *m*	fondo *m* di caldaia, fondo *m* di colata

		English	French	German	Italian
°	16489	**skum, kish**	écume *f*	Schaum *m*	schiuma *f*, scoria *f*
—	16490	**skutterudite**	skutterudite *f*	Skutterudit *m*, Tesseralkies *m*	skutterudite *f*
—	16491	**Skytic stage**	epoque *f* scythienne	scytische Stufe *f*	piano *m* scitiano
—	16492	**slab**	dosse, écoin *m*	Verzugsbrett*n*	tavola *f* per la soletta, rivestimento *m*
—	16493	**slab**	dalle *f*, plaque *f*	Schwartenbrett *n*	lastra *f*, piastra *f*, soletta *f*
—	16494	**slab**	brame *f*	Schirbel , Bramme	bramma *f*, slebo *m*
°	16495	**slab bloom**	brame *f*	Bramme *f*	blumo *m*, bramma *f*
—	16496	**slab down**	abatage *m* du stérile décollé	loses Gebirge *n* abräumen	abbattimento *m* dello sterile
°	16496a	**slab edging**	presse *f* à rogner les rives de la brame	Kantenbeschneider *m*	pressa *f* per bordare le piastre
°	16497	**slab-heating furnace**	four *m* de réchauffage pour brames	Brammentiefofen *m*	forno *m* di riscaldamento per slebi
—	16498	**slab hole**	trou *m* de mine auxiliaire	Hilfsbohrloch *n*	foro *m* da mina ausiliario
°	16499	**slab ingot**	brame *f* brute	Rohbramme *f*	bramma *f* grezza
°	16500	**slab iron**	fer *m* en brames	Brammeneisen *n*	ferro *m* per slebi
°	16501	**slab mill**	laminoir *m* à brames	Brammenwalzwerk *n*	laminatoio *m* per slebi
°	16502	**slab shears**	cisailles *f pl.* à brames	Brammenschere *f*	cesoie *f pl.* per slebi
—	16503	**slab structure**	division *f* en plaques	Absonderung *f*	divisione *f* in lastre
°	16503a	**slab yard**	parc *m* à lingots	Blocklager *m*	parco lingotti
—	16504	**slabbing**	décollement *m* de la roche	Ablösung *f* des Gebirges	distacco *m* della roccia
°	16505	**slabbing** **slabbing mill**, *s. slab mill*	laminage des brames	Brammen *n*	laminazione *f* degli slebi
—	16506	**to slack off**	tirer	abschiessen	mollare un tiro
—	16507	**slack, slack coal**	charbon *m* fin, fines *f pl.*	Gruskohle *f*, Kohlengrus *m*	carbone *m* fino, minuto
°	16508	**slack**	déchet *m* (de tôle)	Abfall *m*	sfrido *m* (di lamiere)
^	16509	**slack barrel**	fût *m* léger	Kanister *m*	fusto *m* leggéro

		English	French	German	Italian
—	16510	**slack hopper**	trémie *f* pour charbon menu	Gruskohlenbunker *m*	tramoggia *f* per carbone minuto
^	16511	**slack off**	dégager la colonne dans le puits		rilascio *m* della colonna in pozzo
o	16511a	**slack quenching**	réfroidissement *m* rapide différé		raffreddamento *m* rapido differito
^	16512	**slack wax**	paraffine *f* brune	Paraffingatsch *m*, Gatsch *m*	pasta *f* di paraffina
o	16513	**to slacken the combustion**	ralentir la combustión	die Verbrennung *f* verlangsamen	rallentare la combustione
o	16514	**slacken**	scorie *f* ajoutée au métal avant la fusion	Schlackenzugabe *f* vor dem Schmelzen des Metalles	scoria (aggiunta al metallo prima della fusione)
		slackening, *s. joint breaking*			
—	16515	**slacking**	décollement *m*	Ablösung *f*	allentamento *m*, scollamento *m*
o	16516	**slacking**	réfroidissement *m*	(Hochofen) Kühlung *f*	raffreddamento *m*, (d'alto forno)
		slacking down. *s. damping down*			
o	16517	**to slag**	scorifier	verschlacken	scorificare
o	16518	**to slag-off, to tap off the slag**	décrasser	abschlacken	scorificare, schiumare
o	16519	**slag**	crasse *f*, laitier *m*	Schlacke *f*, Krätze *f*	scoria *f*, loppa *f*
o	16520	**slag addition**	addition *f* de scories	Schlackenzuschlag *m*	aggiunta *f* di scorie
o	16521	**slag adhering to the converter nose**	loup *m* de bec de cornue	Mündungsbär *m*	deposito *m* di scoria sul becco del convertitore
o	16522	**slag ball**	balle *f* de scorie	Schlackenkugel *f*	palla *f* di scoria
o	16523	**slag bath**	bain *m* de scories	Schlackenbad *n*	bagno *m* di scorie
o	16524	**slag bed, slag bottom**	fond *m* en scorie	Garschlackenboden *m*	suola *f* di scorie
o	16525	**slag block**	bloc *m* de laitier	Schlackenblock *m*	blocco *m* di loppa
o	16526	**slag blowholes**	soufflures *f pl.* de scorie	Schlackenblasen *f pl.*	soffiatura *f* da scoria
		slag bottom process, *s. single refining*			
		slag bottom, *s. slag bed*			
o	16527	**slag breaker**	moulin *m* à scories	Schlackenmühle *f*	mulino *m* per scorie (o per loppa)
o	16528	**slag brick**	brique *f* de laitier	Schlackenstein *m*	mattone *m* di loppa

		English	French	German	Italian
		slag buggy, s. *slag wagon*			
		slag car. s. *slag wagon*			
°	16529	slag cake	gâteau *m* de laitier	Schlackenkuchen *m*	blocco *m* di loppa
°	16530	slag cement	ciment *m* de laitier	Zement *m* mit Schlackenzusatz	cemento *m* di scorie·
		slag chamber, s. *slag pocket*			
°	16531	slag cover	couverture *f* de laitier	Schlackendecke *f*	copertura *f* della loppa
°	16532	slag crust	croûte *f* de scorie	Schlackenkruste *f*	crosta *f* di scorie
°	16533	slag discharge, slag hole	rigoles *f pl.* à laitier	Schlackenabfluss *m*	canale *m* delle scorie
°	16534	slag dump	crassier *m*	Schlackenhalde *f*	deposito *m* di scorie
°	16535	slag forming	scorifiant, formant du laitier	schlackenbildend	· scorificante
°	16536	slag forming period	période *f* de formation des scories	Schlackenbildungsperiode *f*	periodo *m* di formazione delle scorie
°	16537	slag free iron	fer *m* exempt de scorie	schlackenreines Eisen *n*	ferro *m* privo di scorie
°	16538	slag hearth	sole *f* en scories	Schlackenherd *m*	focolare *m* a rivestimento di scorie
°	16539	slag hole, slag notch	trou *m* à laitier	Schlackenloch *n*	foro *m* per la scoria o per loppa. canale per le scorie
°	16540	slag inclusions	inclusions *f pl.* de laitier	Schlackeneinschlüsse *m pl.*	inclusioni *f pl.* di scoria
	16541	slag ladle	poche *f* à crasse	Schlackenpfanne *f*	secchia *f* (o sacca *f*) per le scorie
°	16542	slag notch, scum hole	trou *m* à crasse. chenal *m* de laitier	Schlackenloch *n*	foro *m* (o canale *m)* delle scorie
°	16543	slag-off, slag tap	décrassage *m*	Abschlacken *n*	scorificazione *f* (del bagno)
°	16544	slag out	déloupage *m*	Beseitigen *n* von Ofenbären	scorificazione *f*, eliminazione *f* delle scorie
ʼ°	16545	slag plate	tôle *f* d'écoulement de la scorie	Schlackenblech *n*	lamiera *f* di sbarramento delle scorie

	English	French	German	Italian
° 16546	**slag pocket**	cul d'œuf *m*	Schlackenfangmulde *f*	pozzetto *m* per le scorie
° 16547	**slag poor in iron**	scorie *f* pauvre en fer	eisenarme Schlacke *f*	scoria *f* povera di ferro
° 16548	**slag poor in phosphorous**	scorie *f* pauvre en phosphore	phosphorarme Schlacke *f*	scoria *f* povera di fosforo
	slag Portland cement, *s. iron Portland cement*			
° 16549	**slag press**	presse *f* à laitier	Schlackenpresse *f*	pressa *f* da loppa (o per scorie)
° 16550	**slag pudding**	puddlage *m* gras	Schlackenpuddeln *n*	pudellaggio *m* grasso
° 16551	**slag rich in iron**	scorie *f* riche en fer	eisenreiche Schlacke *f*	scoria *f* ricca di ferro
° 16552	**slag rich in phosphorous**	scorie *f* riche en phosphore	phosphorreiche Schlacke *f*	scoria *f* ricca di fosforo
° 16552a	**slag runner**	rigole *f* de laitier	Schlackenrinne *f*	canale *m* della scoria
° 16553	**slag sand**	sable *m* de laitier	Schlackensand *m*	sabbia *f* di loppa
° 16554	**slag spout**	chenal *m* de laitier	Schlackenloch *n*	canale *m* delle scorie
° 16555	**slag taken away**	scorie *f* entrainée	mitgerissene Schlacke	scoria *f* trascinata dalla colata
° 16556	**slag tap**	décrassage *m*	Abschlackung *f*	scorificazione *f*
° 16557	**slag tapper**	trou *m* à laitier	Schlackenloch *n*	foro *m* delle scorie
° 16558	**slag-tapping, slagging**	coulée *f* de laitier	Schlackenabstich *m*	colata *f* di scorie
	slag tapping hole, *s. slag tapper*			
° 16559	**slag thread**	fil *m* de laitier	Schlackenfaden *m*	filo *m* di loppa
° 16560	**slag tip**	crassier *m*	Schlackenhalde *f*	scarico *m* (o deposito) delle scorie
° 16561	**slag trap**	canal *m* de détente	Schlackenkanal *m*	canale *m* fermascorie
° 16562	**slag tuyere**	tuyère *f* à laitier	Schlackenform *f*	tubierina *f* per la scoria
° 16563	**slag wagon, slag buggy, slag car**	chariot *m* à laitier	Schlackenwagen *m*	vagone *m* per loppa, carro per rimozione scorie
° 16564	**slag washing process**	affinage *m* au bain de scories	Schwalarbeit *f*	affinaggio *m* al bagno di scorie

		English	French	German	Italian
o	16565	**slag wool**	laine *f* de laitier	Schlackenwolle *f*	lana *f* di loppa (o di scorie), lana *f* minerale
o	16566	**slagging**	coulée *f* du laitier	Schlackenabstich *m*	colata *f* di scorie
o	16567	**slagging**	scorification *f*	Schlacken *n*	scorificazione *f*
o	16568	**slagging of coating**	scorification *f* d'enduit	Verschlackung *f* von Schlichte	scorificazione *f* di tinta
o	16569	**slagging of sand**	scorification *f* de sable	Verschlackung *f* von Sand	scorificazione *f* di terra
o	16570	**slagging of the phosphorus**	scorification *f* du phosphore	Verschlackung *f* des Phosphors	scorificazione *f* del fosforo
—	16571	**slaked lime**	chaux *f* éteinte	gelöschter Kalk *m*	calce *f* spenta
—	16572	**sland**	galerie *f* en pente	abfallender Stollen *m*	galleria *f* in pendenza
—	16573	**slat conveyor**	transporteur *m* à écailles	Gliederbandförderer *m*	trasportatore *m* a piastre. convogliatore *m* a piastre
—	16574	**slate** **slate clay**, *s. argillite* **slate coal**, *s. shale coal*	ardoise *f*	Schiefer *m*	ardesia *f*
o	16575	**slate peg, slater's nail (or tack)**	pointe *f* à ardoise	Schiefernagel *m*	punta *f* per ardesie
o	16576	**slatted box**	boîte *f* à noyaux en douelles	Kernkasten *m* mit Dauben	cassa *f* d'anima a doghe
—	16577	**slaty clay**	argile *f* schisteuse	schieferiger Ton *m*	argilla *f* scistosa
		slaty coal, *s. shale coal*			
—	16578	**slaty structure or texture**	structure *f* schisteuse	schiefrige Struktur *f*	struttura *f* scistosa
—	16579	**slavikite**	slavikite *f*	Slavikit *m*	slavikite *f*
o	16580	**sled**	traîneau *m*	Schlitten *m*	slitta *f*
—	16581	**sledge**	masse *f*	Zuschlaghammer *m*	mazza *f*
—	16582	**sledging**	triage *m*	Scheiden *n*	crivellatura *f*, cernita *f*
o	16583	**to sleek**	lisser	polieren	lisciare
o	16584	**sleeker**	lissoir *m*	Polierknopf *m*, Polierschaufel *f*	lisciatoio *m*, spatola *f* per lisciare
o	16585	**sleeking**	lissage *m*	Polieren *n*	lisciatura *f*

	English	French	German	Italian
° 16586	**sleeper**	traverse f, semelle f	Schwelle f, Grundschwelle f	traversa f, trave m, travetto m
° 16587	**sleeper pass**	cannelures $f pl.$ à traverses	Schwellenkaliber n	tracciato m per traverse
° 16588	**sleeper screw, screw spike**	tirefond m	Schienenschraube f	caviglia f, gancio m
— 16589	**sleeping-table**	table f dormante	Grundschwelle f	dormiente m
° 16590	**sleeve**	tube m réfractaire	feuerfeste Hülse f	tubo m refrattario
^ 16591	**sleeve**	manchon m pour tuyaux	Rohrmuffe f	manica f, pezzo m tubolare
° 16592	**sleeve**	cuve f pour moulage sous pression	Spritzgussbehälter m	contenitore m (nella presso-fusione)
	sleeve joint, $s.$ $muff$ $joint$			
° 16593	**sleeve rod**	quenouille f	Ventilstange f	colonnetta f del tappo
— 16594	**sleeve splice**	épissure f à manchon d'un câble	Verbleiung f eines Kabels	impiombatura f a manicotto di un cavo
° 16595	**sleeve valve**	soupape f à manchon	Muffenventil n	valvola f a fodero
° 16596	**slice**	tranche f, enlevure f	Scheibe f, Einbruch m	trancia f
° 16597	**slice**	écaille f	Schuppe f, Lamelle f	scaglia f, lamina f
— 16598	**sliced structure**	structure f finement lamellaire	feinlamellare Struktur f	struttura f lamellare
— 16599	**slicing**	exploitation f par tranches	Scheibenbau m	coltivazione f a trance
— 16600	**slicing and caving**	exploitation f avec foudroyage en tranches horizontales	Scheibenbruchbau m	coltivazione f per franamento in trance orizzontali
16601	**slick**	lisse	glatt	liscio
— 16602	**slick**	sable m noir	Schlamm m	sabbia f nera
— 16603	**slickensides**	surface f de glissement	Rutschfläche f	superficie f di slittamento
° 16604	**slicker**	lissoir m	Spatel m	spatola f
^ 16605	**slidable basket**			ombrello m scorrevole per cementazione

		English	French	German	Italian
—	16606	to slide	glisser	gleiten	scorrere, scivolare
—	16607	slide	éboulement *m*	Bergrutsch *m*	crollo *m*, frana *f*
—	16608	slide	glissement *m* dans le plan *m* des couches, surface *f* de charriage	schichtenparallele Verwerfung *f*, Schichtensprung *m*	superficie *f* di slittamento, slittamento *m* sul piano di stratificazione
o	16609	slide	plaque *f* mince	Dünnschliff *m*	piastrina *f*, lastrina *f*
o	16610	slide	glissière *f*	Führung *f*	guida *f* di scoriamento
o	16611	slide	chariot *m*	Schlitten *m*	slitta *f*, carrello *m*
o	16612	slide (rest-) lathe, sliding	tour *m* à charioter	Supportdrehbank *f*	tornio *m* a carrello
o	16612a	slide preparation	préparation *f* de meulage	Schiffanfertigung *f*	preparazione *f* dei pezzi levigati
—	16613	slide rock	cône *m* de déjection	Gehängeschutt *m*	cono *m* di deiezione
o	16614	slide valve	régistre *m*, vanne *f*	Schieberventil *n*	valvola *f* a cassetto
o	16615	slide valve gear	distribution *f* par tiroir	Schiebersteuerung *f*	distribuzione *f* a cassetto
o	16616	sliding and folding doors	portes *f pl.* glissantes et pliantes	Schiebe-Falttüren *f pl.*	porte *f pl.* scorrevoli e pieghevoli
o	16617	sliding bottom	fond *m* à coulisse	Schieberboden *m*	fondo *m* scorrevole
o	16618	sliding box	châssis *m*	Schiebekassette *f*	cassetta *f*
o	16619	sliding clutch	embrayage *m* mobi-	ausrückbare Kupplung *f*	manicotto *m* mobile
o	16619a	sliding die upset	refoulage *m* à estampe glissante	Stauchen *n* mit Schwebestempel	ricalcatura *f* a stampo scorrevole
o	16620	sliding door	porte-glissière *f*, porte *f* à coulisses	Schiebetür *f*	porta *f* a corsoio
o	16621	sliding falsework	coffrages *m pl.* glissants	Gleitschalungen *f pl.*	armature *f pl.* scorrevoli
o	16622	sliding gate	barrière *f* roulante	Gleitverschluss *m*	saracinesca *f*
o	16623	sliding grate	grille *f* coulissante	Schieberost *m*	griglia *f* oscillante
		sliding-lathe, *s. slide (rest-) lathe*			
—	16624	sliding peat	marais *m*	Morast *m.*	palude *f*
o	16625	sliding pulley	rouleau *m* glisseur	Gleitrolle *f*	rullo *m* di scorrimento
—	16626	slim hole	forage *m* à faible diamètre	Bohrloch *n* mit kleinem Durchmesser	foro *m* a piccolo diametro
—	16627	slime, slim	boue *f*	Lehm *m*, Schlamm *m*	limo *m*, fango *m*, spurgo *m*

English	French	German	Italiano
− 16628 **slime pit**	bassin *m* à schlamms	Schlammsumpf *m*	bacino *m* dei fanghi
− 16629 **slime pulp**	boue *f* schlammeuse	Schlammtrübe *f*	poltiglia *f*
− 16630 **slime pump**	pompe *f* à schlamms	Schlammpumpe *f*	pompa *f* per fanghi
− 16631 **slime separator**	séparateur *m* de boues	Schlammscheidemaschine *f*	separatore *m* di fango
− 16632 **slime table**	caisson *m* allemand	Schlammherd *m*	cassone *m* per fanghi
− 16633 **slime washer**	lavoir *m* à schlamms	Schlammwäsche *f*	lavatoio *m* per fanghi
− 16634 **slime water**	eau *f* schlammeuse	Schlammwasser *n*	acqua *f* fangosa
slimer, *s. slime table*			
− 16635 **slimes-box**	boite *f* à slimes	Schlammkasten *m*	cassa *f* per fanghi
− 16636 **slimes-concentrator**	concentrateur *m* à boues	Schlammkonzentrator *m*	concentratore *m* per fanghi
− 16637 **sliming**	slimage *m*, broyage *m* fin	Feinmahlung *f*	sfangatura *f*, frantumazione *f* fine
− 16638 **slimy**	limoneux	schlammig	fangoso, limaccioso
− 16639 **slimy sapropel**	saprocolle *m*	Saprokoll *m*	saprocollo *m*
° 16640 **to sling**	élinguer	schleudern	imbragare
° 16641 **sling**	élingue *f*	Schlinge *f*	imbragatura *f*, cappio *m*
° 16642 **sling hook**	crochet *m* de levage	Hebehaken *m*	gancio *m* di sollevamento
° 16643 **slinger**	projeteur *m*	Wurfschleuder *f*	lanciateria *m*, lanciasabbia *m*
− 16644 **to slip**	glisser	gleiten, rutschen	scivolare, slittare, franare
− 16645 **slip**	grain *m*, fil *m*, crin *m*, limet *m*	Korn *m*, Fader *m*, Erzäder *f*	grano *m*, filo *m*, vena *f*
− 16646 **slip**	rejet *m*	Ausmass, Mass	rigetto *m*, slittamento *m*
− 16647 **slip and seal assembly**	garniture *f* d'étanchéité à coins	Abhänge-und Adichtungselemente *n pl.*	guarnizione *f* stagna a cunei
− 16648 **slip cleavage**	faux clivage *m*	falsche Spaltbarkeit *f*	falsa sfaldatura *f*

		English	French	German	Italian
°	16649	slip crack	crique f de glissement	Rutschriss m	cricca f di scorrimento
—	16650	slip fault	faille f normale	normale Verwerfung f	faglia f normale
°	16651	slip flask	moule m coulissant	gleitende Gussform f	staffa f scorrevole e ripiegabile
°	16652	slip form machines	machines f $pl.$ dite à coffrages glissants	Strassenbau- maschinen f $pl.$ mit Gleitschalungen	macchine f $pl.$ dette slip form machines
—	16653	slip handle	manche m du coin	Keilgriff m	manico m del cuneo
°	16654	slip line (on drawn parts)	ligne f de mouvement	Gleitlinie f	linea f di movimento
°	16655	slip of scaffold	chute f des charges	Stürzen n der Gicht	caduta f delle cariche
—	16656	slip plane	plan m de faille	Schubfläche f	piano m delle faglie
—	16657	slip scraper	racloir m	Schrapper m	raschietto m, rastrello m
^	16658	slip socket	souricière f	Keilfänger m	pescatore m a corona a cunei
—	16659	slip vein	filon m de faille	Verwerfungsgang m	filone m di faglia
°	16660	slipper	main-courante m	Führungsschlitten m	ringhiera f della gabbia
°	16661	slipping surface	surface m de glissement	Verwerfungsfläche f	superficie f di scorrimento
^	16662	slips	coins m $pl.$ grippeurs	Rohrklemmkeile m $pl.$	cunei m $pl.$ per aste e tubi
—	16663	slips	surface f de glissement, miroir m de glissement	Gleitfläche f, Rutschfläche f	superficie f di scorrimento
^	16664	slip-type core catcher	arrache-carottes m à coins	Keilkernzieher m	strappa-carote m a cunei
—	16665	slippage	glissement m	Rutschen n	slittamento m
^	16666	slipping practice	ripage m et coupe du câble de forage	das Fahrseil nachnehmen	raschiatura f e taglio della fune di perforazione
°	16667	to slit	fendre	spalten	intagliare, fendere
°	16668	slit	entaille f, fente f	Spalt m, Schlitz m	intaglio m, incisione f
—	16669	slit	recoupe m	Querstrecke f	galleria f trasversale di collegamento

		English	French	German	Italian
°	16670	slit gate	attaque _f_ à fente	Schlitzanschnitt _m_	attacco _m_ a bava
°	16671	slit gate	attaque _f_ dirigée latèrale	gerichteter seitlicher Anschnitt _m_	attacco _m_ guidato laterale
—	16672	slitter	pic _m_	Keilhaue _f_	piccone _m_
°	16673	slitting gang cutters	cisailles _f pl._ circulaires multiples	Rollenschere _f_	cesoie _f pl._ circolari multiple
°	16674	slitting mill	machine _f_ à refendre	Schneider _m_	taglierina _f_
—	16675	sloam	couche _f_ d'argile	Tonlage _f_	strato _m_ d'argilla
^	16676	slop oil	résidu _m_ huileux	Ölrückstand _m_	residuo _m_ oleoso
—	16677	slope	inclinaison _f_, plongée _f_, pente _f_, talus _m_	Neigung _f_, Einfallen _n_, Rampe _f_	inclinazione _f_, pendio _m_, pendenza _f_, scarpa _f_, scarpata _f_
—	16678	slope	versant _m_	Abhang _m_	versante _m_
—	16679	slope	puits _m_ plat, descenderie _f_	flacher Schacht _m_, Bremsberg _m_	pozzo _m_ piatto, discendenza inclinata, galleria _f_ inclinata
—	16680	slope-carriage	chariot-porteur _m_	Bremsgestell	carrello _m_ di coda
—	16681	slope linie	ligne _f_ de pente	Neigungslinie _f_	linea _f_ di pendenza
°	16682	sloping roofs with steel truss	toitures _f pl._ inclinées avec fermes en acier	geneigte Dächer mit Stahlsparren	tetti _m pl._ inclinati con capriate in acciaio
—	16683	to slot	sous-caver, haver	unterschrämen	scavare al di sotto
°	16684	slot	fente _f_, mortaise _f_	Spalt _m_, Nut _f_, Schlitz _m_	fessura _f_, fenditura _f_, tacca _f_, incastro _m_
°	16685	slot	rigole _f_ de coulée	Spur _f_, Schlitz _m_	canale _m_ di colata
°	16686	to slot a bar	encocher une barre	eine Stange schlitzen	scanalare una sbarra

slot atomiser, _s. slot sprayer_

slot fumace, _s. channel type furnace_

| — | 16687 | slot sprayer | pulvérisateur _m_ à fente | Schlitzzerstäuber _m_ | polverizzatore _m_ a fessura |

slot weld. _s. plug weld_

| ° | 16688 | slotted pipe | crépine _f_ à stries | Schlitzrohr _n_ | tubo _m_ a fenditura |

		English	French	German	Italian
°	16689	**slotted tube**	tube *m* fissuré	geschlitztes Rohr *n*	tubo *m* fessurato
°	16690	**slotting cutter**	fraise *f* d'entrée	Lochfräser *m*	fresa *f* da fori
°	16691	**to slough**	décroûter	abkratzen	staccarsi , distaccarsi (di croste)
°	16692	**to slow down**	ralentir	verlangsamen	rallentare
		slow cooling, *s. tempering*			
°	16693	**slow dipping**	plonger lentement	langsames Eintauchen *n*	immersione *f* lenta
—	16694	**sludge**	boue *f*, limon *m*	Schlamm *m*	fango *m*, limo *m*
—	16695	**sludge**	débris *m*, farine de sondage	Bohrmehl *n*	rifiuti *m pl.*, polveri *f pl.* di perforazione
°	16696	**sludge hole**	orifice *m* de nettoyage	Schlammloch *n*	foro *m* di pulizia
˄	16697	**sludge pump, sludger**	cloche *f* à boulet	Schlammpumpe *f*	pompa *f* per fango
		sludger, *s. sludge pump*			
—	16698	**sludgy**	boueux	schlammig	fangoso, limaccioso
—	16699	**sluffing**	décollement *m* de la roche	Ablösung *f* des Gebirges an der Firste	scollamento *m* della roccia
—	16700	**slug**	morceau *m*	Klumpen *m*	zolla *f*
—	16701	**slug**	trommel *m*	Trommelsieb *n*	vaglio *m* rotante
°	16702	**slug**	masselotte *f*	Steiger *m*	materozza *f*
°	16703	**slug, burr**	barbe *f*, ébarbure *f*	Grat *m*	sbavatura *f*, bava *f*
		slug (in welding), *s. nugget*			
		slug test, *s. upending test*			
—	16704	**slugger**	bandage *m* de cylindre broyeur	Walzenring *m*	anello *m* del cilindro frantumatore
°	16705	**slugging**	poinçonnage sans détachement de la pièce	Stanzen *n* onhe Stückauslösung	punzonatura *f* senza distacco del pezzo
°	16706	**sluggish**	réfractaire, difficilement fusible	strengflüssig	refrattario, difficilmente fusibile

	English	French	German	Italian
°	16707 **sluggish**	lent	langsam	lento, lungo a trattare
—	16708 **sluice**	écluse f, sluice f, canal m	Schleuse f, Rinne f, Waschrinne f	chiusa f, canale di chiusa
—	16709 **sluice box**	sluice f	Waschrinne f	chiusa f
—	16710 **sluicing**	lavage m aux sluices	Waschrinnenarbeit f	lavaggio m
—	16711 **to slump**	glisser	stürzen	scivolare, slittare, franare
—	16712 **slump**	glissement m, éboulement m	Einsturz m	scivolamento m, slittamento m, frana f
^	16713 **slunk oil**	huile f odoriférante	riechendes Öl n, Riechöl n	olio m odorizzante
—	16714 **slurry**	barbotine f	Tonschlämme f	malta f liquida
—	16715 **to slush**	procéder au remblayage hydraulique	mit Spulversatz versetzen	procedere alla ripiena idraulica
—	16716 **slush**	boue f	Schlamm m	fango m, mota f
°	16717 **slush casting**	moulage m au renversé	Sturzguss m	colata f (o fusione f in conchiglia) a rigetto
—	16718 **slush pit**	bassin m à boue	Schlammkuhle f	vasca f del fango
—	16719 **slush pump**	pompe f à boue	Spülpumpe f	pompa f del fango
°	16720 **slusher**	râcloir m	Schrapper m	raschietto m, raschino m
—	16721 **slushing**	transport m par scrapper	Schrapperarbeit f, Schrapperförderung f	trasporto m con ruspa
—	16722 **slushing**	méthode f de remblayage hydraulique	Spülversatz m	colmata f idraulica
^	16723 **slushing oil**	huile f liquide	Flüssigöl n	olio m liquido
—	16724 **slyne**	chantier m suivant clivage	auf Schlechten zugstellter Stoss	cantiere m secondo il piano di sfaldatura
°	16725 **small arm steel**	acier m pour armes	Waffenstahl m	acciaio m da armi
°	16726 **small Bessemer convertor**	petit convertisseur m	Kleinbessemerbirne f	piccolo m convertitore
—	16727 **small coal, fine**	charbon m menu, houille f menue	Kohlenklein n, Feinkohle f	carbone m minuto,

English	French	German	Italian
— 16728 small coke	coke *m* menu, braise *f*	Koksklein *n*, Koksgries *m*	coke *m* minuto
° 16729 small cupola	petit cubilot *m*	Kleinkuppelofen *m*	piccolo cubilotto *m*
° 16730 small gear wheel moulding machine	machine *f* à mouler les petites roues dentées	Formmaschine *f* für kleine Zahnräder	macchina *f* per formare piccoli ingranaggi
° 16731 small iron bars, billets	petits fers *m pl.*	Feineisen *n*	ferro *m* in piccoli profili
° 16732 small iron fittings for the permanent way	petites pièces *f pl.* en fer de la voie	Kleineisenzeug *n*	piccolo materiale d'armamento
small iron ore, *s. fine iron ore*			
° 16733 small-iron ware	accessoires *m pl.* en fer, petites pièces *f pl.* en fer	Kleineisen *n*	piccolo materiale *m* metallico
° 16734 small metal products	menuiserie *f* metallique	Metalltischlerei *f*	minuterie *f pl.* metalliche
° 16735 small mill	petit train *m*	Feinstrecke *f*	piccolo treno *m*
° 16736 small post for street signs	support *m* pour panneaux indicateurs	Ständer *m* für Wegweiserschilder	paletti *m* per cartelli indicatori
° 16737 small scrap	poussière *f* de coke	Kokspulver *n*	polverino *m* di coke
small section rolling mill, *s. small mill*			
° 16738 small section wire	fil *m* profilé	Formdraht *m*	filo *m* profilato
small-sized coal, *s. small coal*			
° 16739 small steel bottle for respirators	petite bouteille *f* pour appareils de respiration	Sauerstofflasche *f*	bomboletta *f* per respiratori
— 16740 smalls, fines	fines *f pl.*, menu *m* de la mine	Grubenklein *n*	minerale *m* in pezzatura minuta
— 16741 smaltite	smaltine *f*	Smaltin *m*	smaltina *f*
— 16742 smaragd	émeraude *f*	Smaragd *m*	smeraldo *m*
— 16743 smaragdite	smaragdite *f*	Smaragdit *m*	smaragdite *f*
— 16744 smectite	smectite *f*	Smektit *m*, Walkerde *f*	paletta *f*
— 16745 to smelt from the ore	traiter les minerais	verhütten	trattare i minerali

	English	French	German	Italian
	to smelt, *s. to melt*			
	smelter, *s. melter*			
° 16746	smelter coke	coke *m* de fonderie	Schmelzkoks *m*	coke *m* di fonderia
— 16747	smelting	traitement *m* des minerais	Verhüttung *f*	trattamento *m* dei minerali
	smelting, *s. founding*			
° 16748	smelting furnace	four *m* de fusion	Schmelzofen *m*	forno *m* di fusione o fusorio
° 16749	smelting hearth, heating hearth	foyer *m* de chauffage, creuset *m*	Schmelzherd *m*	crogiuolo *m*, suola *f* di fusione
° 16750	smelting house	fonderie *f*	Schmelzerei *f*	fonderia *f*
	smelting of iron by electrothermal methods, *s. electric smelting*			
° 16751	smelting of scrap iron	fusion *f* des riblons	Einschmelzen *n* von Eisenschrot	fusione *f* dei rottami
° 16752	smelting works. smelting house	usine *f* sidérurgique	Schmelzhütte *f*	fonderia *f*, stabilimento *m* siderurgico
	Smith's coal, *gas coal*			
° 16753	smithing	forgeage *m*	Schmieden *n*	forgiatura *f*
° 16754	smithing coal	charbon *m* de forge	Schmiedekohle *f*	carbone *m* di forgia
— 16755	smithite	smithite *f*	Smithit *m*	smithite *f*
— 16756	smithsonite	smithsonite *f*	Smithsonit *m*	smithsonite
° 16757	smithy, forge	forge *f*	Schmiede *f*	forgia *f*, fucina *f*
° 16758	to smoke	enfumer	räuchern	sottoporre all'azione del fumo, affumicare
° 16759	smoke black	noir *m* de fumée	Schwärze *f*	nerofumo *m*
° 16760	smoke-box	boîte *f* à fumée	Rauchkammer·*f*	camera *f* a fumo, cassa *f* a fumo
° 16761	smoke-consuming grate	grille *f* fumivore	Rauchverzehrungsrost *m*	graticola *f* fumivora
° 16762	smoke flue	carneau *m* à fumées	Rauchkanal *m*	condotto *m* del fumo
° 16763	smoke point	point *m* de fumée	Rauchpunkt *m*	punto *m* di fumo

English	French	German	Italian
° 16764 **smoke-preventing furnace**	foyer *m* fumifuge	rauchverhütende Feuerung *f*	focolare *m* fumifugo
° 16765 **smoke tube, stove tube**	tuyau *m* de fumée	Rauchrohr *n*	tubo *m* da fumo
° 16766 **smoke-tube boiler,**	chaudière *f* tubulaire	Heizröhrenkessel *m*	caldaia *f* a tubi di fumo
— 16767 **smoke wacke**	dolomite *f* vacuolaire	Rauhwacke *f*	dolomite *f* vercicolare
— 16768 **smokeless coal**	charbon *m* sans fumée	rauchlose Kohle *f*	carbone *m* senza fumo
— 16769 **smoky quartz**	quartz *m* enfumé	Rauchquarz *m*	quarzo *m* affumicato
— 16770 **to smooth to grind**	meuler	schleifen	arruotare, affilare
° 16771 **to smooth the moulds**	polir les moules	die Gussformen glätten	pulire o lisciare o riparare le forme
° 16772 **smooth fracture**	cassure *f* nette	glatter Bruch *m*	rottura *f* netta
° 16773 **smooth plate**	tôle *f* unie	glattes Blech *n*	lamiera *f* liscia
° 16774 **smoother**	planchette *f* à lisser	Dämmbrett *n*	paletta *f* per lisciare
— 16775 **smudge**	schlamme *f* de houille	Kohlenschlamm *m*	fanghiglia *f* di carbone, morchia
^ 16776 **smudge oil**	huile *f* fumigène	Rauchöl *n*	olio *m* fumogeno
— 16777 **smut**	charbon *m* terreux, charbon *m* tendre de mauvaise qualité	erdige Kohle *f*, weiche schlechte Kohle *f*	carbone *m* ferroso, carbone *m* tenero di cattiva qualità
° 16778 **snagging belt**	transporteur *m* à ébarber	Putzförderer *m*	convogliatore *m* di sbarbatura
° 16779 **snap flask**	châssis *f* à charnière	Abschlagformkasten *n*	staffa *f* da aprirsi lateralmente o a cerniera
° 16780 **snap flask mould**	motte *f*	kastenloser Formblock *m*	motta *f*, staffa *f* apribile per forme
° 16781 **snap flask moulding machine**	assembleuse-démotteuse	kastenlose Formmaschine *f*	accoppiatrice-smottatrice
° 16782 **snap gauge**	calibre *m* à mâchoires	Rachenlehre *f*	calibro *m* a forcella

	English	French	German	Italian
°	16783 **snap head die**	bouterolle *f*	Nietstempel *m*	batti-chiodi *m*
^	16784 **snap-on tong**	clé *f* à tubes mania-ble avec une seule main	mit einer Hand hantierbarer Rohr-schlüssel *m*	chiave *f* per tubing manovrabile con una sola mano
^	16785 **snap-on tools**	outils *m pl.* faci-lement maniables	leicht hantierbare Werkzeuge *n pl.*	utensili *m pl.* mano-vrabili facilmente a mano
—	16786 **snatch block**	poulie *f* à crochet	Hakenrolle *f*	carrucola *f* ad unci-no
—	16787 **snarling**	enchevêtrement *m* du câble de la poulie	Seilverschlingung *f* im der Seilrolle	ingarbuglarsi del ca-vo nella puleggia
—	16788 **snore piece**	crépine *f*	Saugkorb *m*	succhierola *f*
°	16789 **snort valve (blast fumace)**	soupape *f* de réduc-tion de la pression	Druckreduzier-ventil *n*	valvola *f* di riduzio-ne della pressione
	snow-flake, *s. flake*			
—	16790 **to snub**	sous-caver	unterschrämen	scavare al di sotto, allungare uno scavo
—	16791 **snub-line**	câble *m* porteur	Tragseil *n*	fune *f* di sostegno (o portante)
—	16792 **snubber**	coup *m* de bou-chon	Einbruchschuss *m*	tiro *m* di sfondamento
^	16793 **snubbing unit**	équipement *m* de forage sous pres-sion	Vorrichtung *f* für den Krafteinbau des Gestänges in ein unter Druck stehendes Bohrloch	attrezzatura *f* per la perforazione a pres-sione
°	16794 **snug bolt**	boulon *m* à ergot	Hakenschraube *f*, Nasenschraube *f*	bullone *m* a nasello
—	16795 **soakage pit**	puits *m* perdu	Sickerloch *n*	pozzo *m* perdente
°	16795a **soaking**	égalisation *f*	Vorwärmen *n*	termodiffusione *f*
—	16796 **soaking pit**	puits *m* ordinaire	Ausgleichgrube *f*, Wärmegrube *f*	pozzo *m* ordinario
°	16796a **soaking pit**	four *m* d'égalisation	Ausgleichofen *n*	forno *m* a pozzo

soaking pit crane, *s. crane for rehating furnace*

English	French	German	Italian
○ 16797 **soaking pot**	pot *m* de trempage	Tränkgefäss *n*	vasca *f* d'immersio-ne
○ 16797a **soaking zone**	zone *f* d'égalisation	Ausgleichzone *f*	zona *f* di termodiffu-sione
○ 16798 **soap**	savon *m*	Seife *f*	sapone *m*
○ 16799 **soap drawing**	tréfilage *m* à sec	Trockenwalzen *n*	trafilatura *f* a secco
○ 16800 **soap drawn wire**	fil *m* étiré à sec	trockengewalzter Draht *m*	filo *m* trafilato a sec-co
	soap earth, *s. soapstone*		
○ 16801 **soap solution**	solution *f* de savon	Seifenlösung *f*	soluzione *f* di sapone
− 16802 **soapstone**	stéatite *f*	Steatit *m*	steatite *f*
− 16803 **soapy clay**	argile *f* grasse	fetter Ton *m*	argilla *f* grassa
− 16804 **soapy lustre**	éclat *m* gras	Fettglanz *m*	bagliore *m* grasso
○ 16805 **socket**	pied *m* de l'arbre à calibre	Spindelfuss *m*	piede *m*, base *f* (del-l'albero da sagomare)
− 16806 **socket**	attaque *f*	Verbindung *f*	attacco *m* (di fune)
˄ 16807 **socket horn**	tige *f* de repêcha-ge	Fanghaken *m*	asta *f* di pescaggio
○ 16808 **socket pipe joint**	tuyau *m* à emboî-tement	Muffenrohr *n*	tubo *m* a raccordo, tubo *m* a bicchiere
	socket wrench, *s. screw key* **soda feldspar,** *s. albite*		
− 16809 **soda lime**	chaux *f* sodée	Natronkalk *m*	calce *f* sodata
− 16810 **soda-lime feldspar**	feldspath *m* sodico-calcique	Kalknatronfeldspat *m*	feldspato *m* sodico-calcico
− 16811 **soda lye**	lessive *f* de soude	Sodalauge *f*, Natron-lauge *f*	liscivia *f* di soda, i-drossido di sodio
− 16812 **soda niter**	nitratine *f*	Natronsalpeter *m*, Natronit, Chillsal-peter *m*	nitratina *f*, natronite
− 16813 **soda-orthoclase**	anorthose *f*	Anorthoklas *m*	anortosi *f*
− 16814 **sodalite**	sodalite *f*	Sodalith *m*	sodalite *f*
− 16815 **soddyite**	soddyite *f*	Soddyit *m*	soddite *f*
○ 16816 **Soderberg electrode paste**	pâte *f* électrolytique Söderberg	Paste *f* für Söder-berg-Elektroden	pasta *f* elettrodica Söderberg

	English	French	German	Italian
— 16817	sodium	sodium *m*	Natrium *n*	sodio *m*
— 16818	sodium ammonium phosphate	phosphate *m* de sou- de et d'ammoniaque hydraté	Phosphorsalz *n*	fosfato *m* sodico ammo- nico
— 16819	sodium arsenite	arsénite *f* de soude	Natriumarsenit *n*	arsenito *m* sodico
— 16820	sodium bicarbonate	bicarbonate *m* de soude	Natron *n*, Natrium- bikarbonat *n*	bicarbonato *m* sodico o di soda
	sodium borate, *s. borax*			
— 16821	sodium flame	flamme *f* de sodium	Natriumflamme *f*	fiamma *f* del sodio
— 16822	sodium line	raie *f* de sodium	Natriumlinie *f*	linea *f* del sodio
— 16823	sodium pliers	pince *f* à sodium	Natriumzange *f*	pinzetta *f* per sodio
— 16824	sodium press	presse *f* à sodium	Natriumpresse *f*	torchio *m* per sodio
— 16825	sodium sulphite	sulfite *m* de sodium	Natriumsulfit *n*	solfito *m* di sodio
	soft, *s. ductile*			
° 16826	soft and brittle iron	fer *m* mou et tenace	weiches und sprö- des Eisen *n*	ferro *m* molle e tenace
° 16827	soft annealed	recuit complètement fonte *f* douce	weichglüht	ricotto completamente
° 16827a	soft cast iron		weiches Gusseisen *m*	ghisa *f* dolce
° 16828	soft cast steel	moulage *m* en acier doux	weicher Stahlguss *m*	acciaio *m* colato dolce
° 16829	soft charcoal iron	fer *m* doux au bois	weiches Holzkoh- leneisen *n*	ferro *m* molle a carbo- ne di legna
— 16830	soft clay	argile *f* plastique	plastischer Ton *m*	argilla *f* plastica
— 16831	soft coal	houille *f* grasse, houille *f* bitumineuse	bituminöse Kohle *f*, Weichkohle *f*	carbone *m* bituminoso
° 16832	soft copper	cuivre *m* doux	Weichkupfer *n*	rame *m* dolce
° 16833	soft copper wire	fil *m* de cuivre doux	Weichkupferdraht *m*	filo *m* di rame dolce
° 16833a	soft facing	rechargement *m* doux	Weichmetallauftrag- schweissen *n*	rivestimento *m* dolce
° 16834	soft foundry pig iron	fonte *f* douce de mou- lage	weiches Giesserei- eisen *n*	ghisa *f* dolce per fon- dere pezzi di macchine
° 16835	soft iron	fer *m* doux, fer *m* mou	Weicheisen *n*, schmiedbares Ei- sen *n*	ferro *m* dolce, ferro *m* malleabile
° 16836	soft iron ore	minerai *m* de fer tendre	weiches Eisenerz *n*	minerale *m* di ferro tenero
° 16837	soft metal	métal *m* mou (ou tendre)	Weichmetall *n*	metallo *m* tenero, me- tallo *m* dolce

	English	French	German	Italian
^ 16838	soft paraffin	paraffine *f* tendre	weiches Paraffin *n*	paraffina *f* molle
° 16839	to soft solder	souder à l'étain	weich löten	saldare a stagno
° 16840	soft solder	soudure *f* tendre, soudure *f* à l'étain	Weichlot *n*, Weisslot *n*, Schnellot *n*	saldatura *f* dolce, saldatura *f* a stagno
° 16841	soft solder	étain *m* à souder	Weichlot *n*, Lötzinn *n*	lega *f* per saldatura dolce
° 16842	soft-soldered	soudé tendre	weichgelötet	saldato a dolce
° 16843	soft soldering	soudure *f* à l'étain	Weichlöten *n*	saldatura *f* a stagno
° 16844	soft steel, semi-mild steel	acier *m* demi-doux, acier *m* non trempé	halbweicher Stahl *m*, ungehärteter Stahl *m*	acciaio *m* semidolce, acciaio *m* non temperato
° 16845	soft tempering	trempe *f* douce	Weichhärtung *f*	tempera *f* dolce
° 16846	soft wire copper	fil *m* de cuivre cuit	Weichkupferdraht *m*	filo *m* di rame ricotto (o dolce)
° 16847	to soften the steel	adoucïr l'acier	den Stahl enthärten	addolcire l'acciaio
° 16847a	softening	ramollissement *m*	Erweichung *f*	rammollimento *m*
° 16848	softening	adoucissement *m*	Enthärtung *f*	addolcimento *m*
° 16849	(softening) anneal, annealing	recuit *m* d'adoucissement	Weichglühen *n*	ricottura *f* di addolcimento
° 16849a	softening point	point *m* d'émollition	Erweichungspunkt *m*	temperatura *f* di rammollimento
— 16850	softness	mollesse *f*	Weichheit *f*	mollezza *f*, plasticità *f*, sofficità *f*
° 16851	softness	ductilité *f*	Ziehbarkeit *f*	duttilità *f*
— 16852	soggendalite	soggendalite *f*	Soggendalit *m*	soggendalite *f*
16853	soggy	humide, mouillé	feucht, durchnässt	umido, bagnato
— 16854	soil, natural soil	sol *m* naturel	gewachsener Boden *m*	terreno *m* naturale
— 16855	soil flow	solifluction *f*	Bodenfluss *m*	solifluzione *f*
— 16856	soil sampler	sonde *f* de prise d'échantillon	Probesonde *f*	sonda *f* campionatrice
— 16856a	sol	sol *m*	Sol *m*	sole *m*
	solar oil, *s. gas oil*			
° 16857	to solder	souder	löten	saldare
° 16858	solder	produit *m* à souder	Lötmittel *n*	lega *f* per saldatura
° 16858a	solder	soudure *f*	Lot *n*	saldatura *f*
° 16859	solderer	soudeur *m*	Löter *m*	saldatore *m*

		English	French	German	Italian
°	16860	**soldering** **soldering bit,** s. *soldering-iron*	soudage *m*	Löten *n*	saldatura *f*
°	16861	**soldering carbon**	charbon *m* à souder	Lötkohle *f*	carbone *m* per saldare
°	16862	**soldering-iron**	fer *m* à souder	Lötkolben *m*	ferro *m* per saldare
°	16863	**soldering flux**	fondant *m* à souder	Lötrohrfluss *m*.	fondente *m* per saldatura
°	16864	**soldering pewter**	étain *m* à souder	Lötzinn *n*	stagno *m* per saldatura
°	16865	**soldering seam**	cordon *m* de soudure	Lötstelle *f*	cordolo *m* della saldatura a stagno
°	16866	**soldering with** **the blow pipe**	soudure *f* au chalumeau	Flammenlötung *f*	saldatura *f* alla fiamma
°	16867	**soldering with** **the soldering bit**	soudure *f* au fer à souder	Kolbenlötung *f*	saldatura *f* al saldatoio
–	16868	**sole**	socle *m*, substratum *m*	Sohle *f*, Unterlage *f*	zoccolo *m*, substrato *m* suola *f*, base *f*
°	16869	**sole**	sole *f*	Herd *m*	suola *f* (di forno)
°	16870	**sole and dam plates**	sole *f*	Bodenstein *m*	suola *f*, soglia *f*, platea *f*
–	16871	**sole pieces** **sole plate,** s. *iron plate*	semelle *f*	Grundschwelle *f*	suola *f*, dormiente *m*
°	16872	**sole plate of furnace**	sole *f* de foyer	Herd *m*	suola *f* (del forno)
°	16873	**sole weight**	poids *m* mort	Eigengewicht *n*	peso *m* morto
	16874	**solid, durable**	durable	haltbar	durevole
–	16875	**solid back**	toit *m* solide non boisé	feste unverzimmerte Firste *f*	tetto *m* solido non armato
°	16876	**solid car wheel**	roue *f* monobloc	Rad *n* aus einem Stück	ruota *f* monoblocco
–	16877	**solid carbon**	charbon *m* homogène	Homogenkohle *f*	carbone *m* omogeneo
°	16877a	**solid carburizing**	cémentation *f* par solides	Zementieren mit Feststoffen	cementazione *f* per solidi
°	16878	**solid casting**	pièce *f* de fonte pleine	Vollguss, volles Gussstück *n*	pezzo *m* massiccio
°	16879	**solid die**	filière *f* fermée	geschlossene Ziehbank *f*	filiera *f* chiusa
°	16880	**solid-drawn**	étiré de la loupe	aus der Massel gezogen	trafilato *m* da massello

		English	French	German	Italian
–	16881	**solid explosive**	explosif *m* solide	festes Sprengmittel *n*	esplosivo *m* solido
o	16882	**solid fuel**	combustible *m* solide	fester Brennstoff *m*	combustibile *m* solido
o	16883	**solid half-round iron**	fer *m* demi-rond	Halbrundeisen *n*	ferro *m* semitondo pieno
–	16884	**solid ore deposit**	gisement *m* en amas	Erzstock *m*	giacimento *m* massiccio
o	16885	**solid piston, disc piston**	piston *m* à plaque ou à disque	Scheibenkolben *m*	stantuffo *m* a piatto (od a disco)
o	16886	**solid solution**	solution *f* solide, solution *f* cristallisée	feste Lösung *f*, Mischkristall *m*	soluzione *f* solida, soluzione *f* cristallizzata
o	16886a	**solid steel**	acier *m* calmé	beruhigter Stahl *m*	acciaio *m* calmo
o	16887	**solid web truss**	ferme *f* à âme pleine	Vollandbinder *m*	capriata *f* ad anima piena
o	16888	**soldering furnace**	four *m* à souder	Schweissofen *m*	fornello *m* per saldare
o	16889	**soldering liquid**	eau *f* à souder	Lötwasser *n*	liquido *m* per saldare
o	16890	**solid wire**	fil *m* plein	Volldraht *m*	filo *m* pieno
o	16891	**solidification, setting**	solidification *f*	Erstarren *n*	solidificazione *f*
o	16892	**solidification range, freezing range**	intervalle *m* de solidification	Erstarrungsbereich *m*	intervallo *m* di solidificazione
o	16893	**solidified sample**	éprouvette *f* de métal solidifié	erstarrte Metallprobe *f*	provetta *f* solidificata
		solidified solution, *s. congealed solution*			
o	16894	**solidus, solidus curve**	solidus *m*	Soliduslinie *f*	diagramma *m* della soluzione solida
–	16895	**solifluction**	solifluction *f*	Bodenfluss *m*	solifluzione *f*
	16896	**soluble**	soluble	löslich	solubile
^	16897	**soluble cutting oil**	huile *f* de coupe soluble	lösliches Schneidöl *n*	olio *m* da taglio solubile
o	16898	**soluble phosphoric acid**	acide *m* phosphorique	lösliche Phosphorsäure *f*	acido *m* fosforico solubile
	16899	**solubility**	solubilité *f*	Löslichkeit *f*	solubilità *f*

		English	French	German	Italian
°	16900	**solution**	dissolution *f*	Auflösung *f*	soluzione *f*
−	16901	**solution cavity**	cavité *f* de dissolution	Lösungshohlraum *m*	cavità *f* di dissoluzione
^	16902	**solution gas drive**	production *f* par expansion de gaz dissous	Gasentlösungstrieb *m*	produzione *f* per espansione di gas in soluzione
^	16903	**solution mixer**	mélangeur *m* pour solution	Lösungsmischer *m*	miscelatore *m* per soluzione
°	16904	**solution of chloride of calcium**	solution *f* de chlorure de calcium	Chlorcalciumlösung *f*	soluzione *f* di cloruro di calcio
^	16905	**solution of resins in turpentine**	solution *f* de résine dans la térébenthine	Lösung *f* von Harz in Terpentin	soluzione *f* di resina in trementina
°	16906	**solution of sulphate of copper**	solution *f* de vitriol	Vitriollösung *f*	soluzione *f* di vetriolo
°	16906a	**solution stripping**	dépouillage *m* chimique	chemische Entplattierung *f*	degalvanizzazione *f* chimica
^	16907	**solvatation**	solvatation *f*	Solvatation *f*	solvatazione *f*
^	16908	**solvency**	pouvoir *m* dissolvant	Lösungsfähigkeit *f*	capacità *f* di solvente
^	16909	**solvent decarbonizing**	décarbonisation *f* au solvant	Entkohlung *f* mit Lösungsmittel	decarbonizzazione *f* con solvente
^	16910	**solvent dewaxing**	déparaffinage *m* par solvant	Solvent-Entparaffinierungsverfahren *n*	deparaffinazione *f* con solventi
^	16911	**solvent refined oil**	huile *f* raffinée par solvant	mit Lösungsmittel raffiniertes Öl	olio *m* raffinato con solventi
^	16912	**solvent refinery**	raffinage *f* par dissolvant	Solvent-Raffination *f*	raffinazione *f* con solvente
−	16913	**solvsbergite**	solvsbergite *f*	Sölvsbergit *m*	solvsbergite *f*
−	16914	**sommaite**	sommaite *f*	Sommait *m*	sommaite *f*
^	16915	**sonic log**	log *m* sonique	akustisches Log *n*	log *m* acustico
°	16915a	**sonic testing**	essai *m* acoustique	akustische Prüfung	prova *f* acustica
°	16916	**sonium**	inclusion *f* (non métallique)	nichtmetallscher Einschluss *m*	inclusione *f* (non metallica)
°	16917	**soot**	calamine *f*, suie *f*	Russ *m*, Kalamin *m*	calamina *f*
°	16918	**sooty**	fuligineux	russig	fuligginoso

	English	French	German	Italian
− 16919	sooty coal	houille f fuligineuse, charbon m fumant	Russkohle f	carbone m fuligginoso
− 16920	sorbite	sorbite f	Sorbit m	sorbite f
° 16921	sorbitic cast iron	fonte f sorbitique	sorbitisches Gusseisen n	ghisa f sorbitica
− 16922	sordawalite	sordawalite f	Sordawalit m	sordawalite f
° 16922a	sorption	sorption f	sorption f	assorbimento m
− 16923	to sort	trier, séparer, cribler	sichten, sortieren	cernere, crivellare, classificare
16924	sort	sorte f	Marke f	tipo m, specie f
− 16925	sorter	classeur m	Sortierer m	classificatore m, vaglio m
− 16926	sorting	triage m, classification f	Scheidung f, Sortierung f	cernita f, vagliatura f
− 16927	sorting belt	bande f de triage	Leseband n	banda f di selezione
− 16928	sorting plant	installation f de classification	Klassieranlage f	impianto m di classificazione
− 16929	souesite	souesite f	Souesit m	souesite f
− 16930	sough	galerie d'écoulement de l'eau, rigole f d'écoulement	Wasserstollen m, Wasserrösche f, Wassergraben m	galleria f di scolo dell'acqua, canale m di scolo
− 16931	soumansite	soumansite f	Soumansit m	soumansite f
− 16932	to sound	sonder	loten	sondare, scandagliare
− 16933	sound	détroit	Meerenge f	stretto m
16934	sound	solide, en bon état	stark, kräftig	sano, solido, in buon stato
− 16935	to sound the ground	sonder le terrain	untersuchen	scandagliare il terreno
− 16936	to sound the soil	sonder le terrain	den Boden aufbohren ·	sondare il terreno
° 16937	sound casting	jet m sain	Heilguss m	getto m sano
° 16938	sound part	partie f saine	gesunde Stelle f	parte f sana
− 16939	sound-stone	phonolite f	Phonolit m	fonolite f
− 16940	sound wood	bois m sain	gesundes Holz n	legno m sano

	English	French	German	Italian
° 16941	soundness	santé f d'une pièce	Fehlerfreiheit f	integrità f di un pezzo
— 16942	soundproof drilling	sondage m silencieux	geräuschlose Bohrung	perforazione f silenziosa
— 16943	soup wagon	camion m à explosifs	Sprengstoffwagen m	autocarro m con esplosiv
˄ 16944	sour gas	gaz m naturel acide	saures Gas n	gas m acido
˄ 16945	sour well	puits m de gaz corrosif	saure Bohrung f	pozzo m di gas corrosivo
16946	source of electricity	source f d'électricité	Elektrizitätsquelle f	sorgente f d'elettricità
— 16947	source rock	roche-mère f	Muttergestein n	roccia-madre f
o 16948	sow, feeder	gueuse f intermédiaire, gueuse-mère	Nebenkanäle m pl., Muttermassel f	canale m secondario, madre f di colata
° 16948a	sow, bear	bloc m	Eisensau f, Sau f	blocco m
° 16949	sow block	enclume f porte-matrice	Gesenkhalteramboss m	incudine f portastampi
° 16949a	sow block	lit m de l'estampe	Stempelbett n	letto m dello stampo
° 16950	sow channel	rigole f de coulée	Masselgraben m	canale m di colata per lingotti
o 16951	sow iron, salamander	loup m, loupe f	Sau f, Bodensatz m, Ofenbär m	metallo m solidificato nel canale di colata, materiale m non fuso
° 16952	space cavity	cavité f	Hohlraum m	cavità f
° 16952a	space group	groupe m spatial	Raumgruppe f	gruppo m spaziale
° 16953	space lattice	reseau m cristallin	Raumgitter n	reticolo m spaziale
— 16954	spacer	entretoise f	Strebe f	briglia f di collegamento, traversa f
— 16955	spacer	fil m métallique séparant les cartouches d'un trou de mine chambré	Drahtbügel m zum Hohlraumschiessen	filo m metallico per separare le cariche in un foro da mina
— 16956	spacer ring	bague f entretoise	Abstandsring m	anello m distanziatore
° 16957	spacing	espacement m, écartement m, intervalle m	Klaffen n, Weite f, Intervall n	spaziatura f, scartamento m, intervallo m, distanza f
— 16958	spacing of the levels	distance f entre les étages	Sohlenabstand m	distanza f fra i piani di scavo
— 16959	spadaite	spadaite f	Spadait m	spadaite f

	English	French	German	Italian
16960	spaddle	mastic *m*	Spachtelfarbe *f*	mastice *f*
16961	to spade	bêcher	graben	scavare, vangare
16962	spade	bêche *f*, grattoir *m*	Spaten *m*, Kratzer *m*	vanga *f*, raschiatore *m*
16963	spall	éclat *m* de pierre	Steinsplitter *m*	scheggia *f* di pietra
16964	to spall	tailler la pierre, broyer à la main	einen Stein *m* behauen, zerklei- nern von Hand	tagliare una pietra, ma- cinare a mano
16965	spall-off	fonçage *m*, débal- lage *m*	Herausfallen *n* (des Sandes)	crollo *m* (delle sabbie)
16966	spalling	scheidage *m*	Scheidung *f*	cernita *f* a mano
16967	spalling	chute des roches de la paroi	Nachfall *m*, Stein- splittern *n*	caduta *f* di rocce dalla parete, scheggiatura *f*
	spalling, *s. exfoliation*			
16968	spalling resistance	résistance *f* aux variations de tempé- rature	Temperaturwechsel- beständigkeit *f*	resistenza *f* a tempera- ture alternate
16968a	spalling test	essai *m* d'effrittement	Zerbröcklung *f*	prova *f* di sgretolamento
16969	span	portée *f*	Stützweite *f*, Spann *m*	portata *f*
16970	span of 78' 9''	24 m de portée	Stuetzweite von 24 m	24 m di luce
16971	span wire	fil *m* redresseur, hauban *m* tendeur	(Ab)spanndraht *m*	filo *m* tenditore
16972	spangle gold	or *m* en feuilles	Goldfolie *f*	oro *m* in foglie
16973	spangles	fleurs *f pl.* de zinc	Zinkblumen *f pl.*	fiori *m pl.* di zinco
16974	spanner	clé *f* à écrous	Gabelschlüssel *m*	chiave *f* per dadi
16975	spar	spath *m*	Spat *m*	spato *m*
16976	spare boiler	chaudière *f* de ré- serve	Reservekessel *m*	caldaia *f* di riserva
16977	spare piece	pièce *f* de réserve, éprouvette *f* de ré- serve	Ersatzstück *n*	pezzo *m* di riserva
16978	sparger, sparger pipe	arroseur *m* rotatif, tube *m* disperseur	Zerstäuber *m*	tubo *m* di dispersione
16979	spark arrester, spark catcher	pare-étincelles *m*	Funkenfänger *m*	parascintille *m*

		English	French	German	Italian
o	16980	spark cap	éclateur m	Funkenstrecke f	tratto m a scintilla
o	16981	spark chamber	chambre f à étin-celles	Funkenkammer f	camera f parascintille
—	16982	spark fuse	amorce f à étin-celle	Spaltzünder m	esca f a scintilla
o	16983	spark quenching apparatus	appareil m pour éteindre les étin-celles	Funkenlöschvorrich-tung f	apparecchio m per spe-gnere le scintille
o	16984	spark screen, spark arrester	pare-étincelles m	Funkenfänger m	parascintille m
o	16985	spark test	essai m à l'étin-celle	Funkenprobe f	prova f delle scintille alla mola
—	16986	sparker box	tableau m de mise	Schiess.Schalter m	tabella f di messa a fuo-co
o	16987	sparking	projection f d'étin-celles	Funkensprühen n	proiezione f di scin-tille
o	16987a	sparking alloy	alliage m pyrophore	pyrophore Legie-rung f	lega f piroforica
o	16988	sparking time	durée f d'usinage (électro-érosion)	Ausfunkzeit f	durata f di lavorazio-ne (elettroerosione)
		sparly iron, s. spathic iron			
—	16989	Sparnacian stage	étage m sparnacien	Sparnacian n	Sparnaciano m
—	16990	sparry iron ore	minerai m carbonaté grillé	Rostspat m	minerale m carbonato torrefatto, siderite f calcinata
—	16991	sparry limestone	marbre m à gros grain	grobkörniger Marmor m	marmo m a grana gros-sa
^	16992	spars, scaffold	tiges f pl. de pompe	Pumpengestänge n	aste f pl. della pompa
—	16993	spathic, spathose	lamellaire	blätterig, tafelig	lamellare
—	16994	spathic iron, siderite	fer m spathique, si-dérite f	Spateisenstein m, Eisenspat m	ferro m spatico, side-rite f
o	16995	spatter	éclaboussure f	Verspritzen n	gocce f pl. sparse
—	16996	spatter pipe	tube m pour exploi-tation hydraulique des sables	Wasserzuleitung f für die hydraulische Sandgewinnung	tubo m per lo scavo idraulico della sab-bia
—	16997	spatter work	abattage m à l'eau	hydraulische Gewin-nung f	abbattimento m idrau-lico
o	16998	spatula	spatule f	Spatel m	spatola f

	English	French	German	Italian
— 16999	spear	taraud _m_ rattrape- -tube	Rohrfänger _m_	pescatore _m_ di tubi, arpione _m_ a cavo per recupero
17000	spear spear-pointed drill, _s._	tige _f_ de pompe _arrow headed drill_	Pumpenstange _f_	asta _f_ della pompa
— 17001	spear pyrite	pyrite _f_ crêtée	Speerkies _m_	pirite _f_ lanceolata
17002	(special) aeroplane -steel	acier _m_ (spécial) pour aéroplanes	Flugzeugstahl _m_	acciaio _m_ (speciale) per aeroplani
° 17003	special automotive steel	acier _m_ spécial pour automobiles	Spezialstahl _m_ für Kraftwagen	acciaio _m_ speciale per automobili
° 17004	special bar	profil _m_ spécial	Sonderprofilei- sen _n_	verga _f_ profilata in acciaio
^ 17005	special boiling point spirit	distillat _m_ spé- cial	Sonderdestillat _n_	distillato _m_ speciale
° 17006	special bronze	bronze _m_ spécial	Sonderbronze _f_	bronzo _m_ speciale
° 17007	special box	châssis _m_ de for- me, châssis _m_ coupé	Konturformkasten _m_	staffa _f_ sagomata
° 17008	special cast iron	fonte _f_ fine, fonte _f_ spéciale	hochwertiges Guss- eisen _n_	ghisa _f_ speciale
° 17009	special charge	charge _f_ spéciale	Sondersatz _m_	carica _f_ speciale
° 17010	special elements shop	fabrication _f_ d'élé- ments spéciaux	Erzeugung _f_ von Spezialteilen	fabbricazione _f_ di elementi speciali
° 17011	special faceworks for ceilings	matériaux _m pl._ d'é- tayage pour l'étaie- ment	spezielle provi- sorische Decken- stuetzen _f pl._	materiali _m pl._ di pun- tellamento e di arma- mento provvisorio dei solai
° 17012	special fittings	pièces _f pl._ spécia- les	Form- und Verbin- dungsstücke _n pl._	pezzi _m pl._ speciali
° 17013	special foundry, specialty foundry	fonderie _f_ sur album	Giesserei _f_ für Handels-und Bauguss	fonderia _f_ specializ- zata, fonderia _f_ su catalogo
° 17014	special hardening special iron, _s. special profile iron_	trempe _f_ spéciale	Sonderhärtung _f_	tempera _f_ speciale
° 17015	special metallogra- phy	métallographie _f_ spéciale du fer	spezielle Metallo- graphie _f_ des Ei- sens	metallografia _f_ spe- ciale del ferro
° 17016	special hardening method	méthode _f_ de trem- pe spéciale	besonderes Här- tungsverfahren _n_	metodo _m_ speciale di tempera

		English	French	German	Italian
°	17017	special plate	tôle *f* façonnée	Formblech *n*	lamiera *f* profilata
°	17018	special (profile) iron	profilé *m* spécial	Spezialprofileisen *n*	ferro *m* profilato speciale
°	17019	special purpose mill	laminoir *m* pour travaux spéciaux	Sonderwalzwerk *n*	laminatoio *m* per lavori speciali
°	17020	special sections	profils *m pl.* spéciaux	Sonderprofile *n pl.*	profilati *m pl.* speciali
°	17021	special steel	acier *m* spécial	Sonderstahl *m*	acciaio *m* speciale
	17022	special tariff	tarif *m* spécial	Ausnahmesatz *m*	tariffa *f* speciale
^	17023	specific density	densité *f*	Dichte *f*	densità *f*
^	17024	specific gravity	poids *m* spécifique	Dichte *f*	gravità *f* specifica
^	17025	specific gravity flask	picnomètre *m*	Pyknometer *m*	picnometro *m*
°	17026	specific heat	chaleur *f* spécifique	spezifische Wärme *f*	calore *m* specifico
°	17027	specification	prescription *f*	Vorschrift *f*	prescrizione *f*
°	17028	specification of quality	prescriptions *f pl.* de qualité	Gütevorschrift *f*	prescrizioni *f pl.* per la qualità
°	17029	specified width	épaisseur *f* prescrite	vorgeschriebene Stärke *f*	spessore *m* prescritto
°	17030	specimen	éprouvette *f*	Probe *f*	provetta *f*
_	17031	speckled	marbré, tacheté	gefleckt	picchiettato *m*
		speckled metal, *s. pinholed surface*			
_	17032	spectral polarization	extinction *f* ondulée	undulöse Auslöschung *f*	polarizzazione *f* spaziale
°	17033	spectrography	spectrographie *f*	Spektralanalyse *f*	spettrografia *f*
°	17034	spectroscope	spectroscope *m*	Spektroskop *n*	spettroscopio *m*
°	17035	spectroscopical analysis	analyse *f* spectrale	Spektralanalyse *f*	analisi *f* spettrale
°	17036	spectroscopical test	recherches *f pl.* au spectroscope	spektralanalytische Untersuchung *f*	analisi *f* allo spettroscopio
°	17037	specular	spéculaire	spiegelnd	specolare

		English	French	German	Italian
	17038	specular cast-iron	fonte *f* spéculaire	Spiegeleisen *n*	ghisa *f* specolare
	17039	specular forge pig iron	fonte *f* spiegel pour puddlage	Puddelspiegel *m*	ghisa *f* specolare per puddellaggio
	17040	specular iron (-ore)	fer *m* spéculaire	Eisenglanz *m*	ferro *m* specolare
-	17041	specular schist	itabirite *f*	Itabirit *m*	itabirite *f*
-	17042	specular stone	mica *f*	Glimmer *m*	mica *f*
		specularite, *s. specular iron*			
*	17043	speculum metal	bronze *m* pour miroirs	Spiegelmetall *n*	bronzo *m* per specchi
		speed of travel, *s. rate of travel*			
-	17044	speiss	speiss *m*	Speiss *m*	speiss *m*
*	17045	spellerizing	laminage *m* d'acier avec affinage	Stahlwalzen *n* mit Glühen	laminazione *f* d'acciaio con affinaggio
'	17046	spelter	zinc *m*	Zink *n*	zinco *m*
'	17047	spelter solder	soudure *f* de laiton	Messinglot *n*	saldatura *f* all'ottone
'	17048	spelter works	fonderie *f* de zinc	Zinkhütte *f*	fonderia *f* di zinco
-	17049	spencerite	spencérite *f*	Spencerit *m*	spencerite *f*
-	17050	sperrylite	sperrylite *f*	Sperrylit *m*	sperrylite *f*
-	17051	spessartite	spessartine *f*	Spessartin *m*	spessartite *f*
-	17052	sphærocobaltite	sphérocobaltite *f*	Sphärokobaltit *m*	sferocobaltite *f*
-	17053	sphaelerite	sphalérite *f*, blende *f*	Sphalerit *m*, Zinkblende *f*	sfalerite *f*, blenda *f*
-	17054	sphene	titanite *f*	Titanit *m*	titanite *f*
-	17055	sphenoid	sphénoèdre *m*	Sphenoid *m*	sfenoide *m*
-	17056	sphenolith	massif *m* intrusif ayant la forme d'un coin	Sphenolith	sfenolite *f*
	17057	sphere	sphère *m*	Sphäre *f*	sfera *f*
-	17058	sphere ore	minerai *m* sphérique	Kokardenerz *n*	minerale *m* sferico

		English	French	German	Italian
	17059	**spheric**	sphérique	sphärisch	sferico
○	17060	**spherical pot**	chaudière f ronde	Rundkessel m	caldaia f rotonda
—	17061	**spherical shell**	couche f concentrique	Kugelschale f	strato m concentrico
^	17062	**sphericone**	réservoir m à forme de goutte	Sphäroid n	sferoide m, serbatoio m a forma di goccia
^	17063	**sperm oil**	huile f de spermacéti	Walratöl n, Spermazetöl n	olio m di spermaceti
○	17064	**spheroid**	sphérule f	Kügelchen n	sferula f
	17065	**spheroidal**	sphéroïdal	kugelförmig	sferoidale
—	17066	**spheroidal graphite**	graphite m sphéroïdal	Kugelgraphit m	grafite f sferoidale
○	17067	**spheroidal graphite cast iron**	fonte f à graphite sphéroïdal	Gusseisen n mit Kugelgraphit	ghisa f sferoidale
○	17068	**spheroidal graphite casting**	jet m en fonte sphéroïdal	Sphäroguss m	getto m in ghisa sferoidale
—	17069	**spheroidal jointing**	séparation f sphéroïdale	sphäroidische Absonderung f	separazione f sferoidale
○	17070	**spherodisation**	sphéroïdisation f	Kugelbildung f	sferoidizzazione f, ricottura f di coalescenza
—	17071	**spherodised cementite**	cémentite f sphéroïdale	Sphärozementit n	cementite f sferoidale
—	17072	**spheroidised pearlite, spheroidite**	perlite f globulaire, sphérolite f	körniger Perlit m, Sphärolith m	perlite f globulare, sferodite f
—	17073	**spherolitic**	sphérolitique	sphärolitisch	sferolitico
—	17074	**spherosiderite**	sphérosidérite f	Sphärosiderit m	sferosiderite f
—	17075	**spherule texture. spherulitic structure**	texture sphérolitique	sphärolitische Textur f	struttura f sferolitica

spherulitic iron, *s. spheroidal graphite cast iron*

^	17076	**spider**	collier m à coins	Rohrkeilklemme f,	arpione m a cuneo (per tubi)
○	17077	**spider**	lanterne f	Kernspindel f, Kernrohr n	armatura f, lanterna f

	English	French	German	Italian
17078	spiegel, spiegel iron	fonte f spiegel, fonte f spéculaire	Spiegeleisen n	ghisa f speculare
	spigot and sucket joint, s. spigot joint			
17079	spike, dog, rail spike	crampon m, krampe f	Schienennagel m, Krampe f	arpione m, morsetto m, briglia f
17080	spike bar	tige f à harpon		barra f per arpioni
17081	spike disintegrator	diviseur m à broches	Stiftenkorbschleuder m	disintegratore m a perni
17082	spiky	à tiges	stengelig	gambuto
17083	spile	palplanche f	Getrieblpfahl m	palafitta f, tavolone m
17084	spiling	poussage m	Getriebezimmerung f	metodo m del marcia-avanti, armatura f a tavolone
17085	spilite	spilite f	Spilit m	spilite f
17086	spilitic	spilitique	spilitisch	spilitico
17086a	spill, scab	éclat m	Splitter m	scheggia f
	spilling, s. spiling			
17086b	spills	défauts internes	Innengussfehler m	incrinature f pl. interne
17087	spill pipe	tube m de retour	barometrisches Rohr n	tubo m di ritorno (o barometrico)
	spin gate, s. tangential runner			
17088	spindle	broche f, lanterne f	Kernspindel f, Kernrohr n	lanterna f (o armatura f.) per anime
17089	spindle	porte-calibre m	Spindelstock m	albero m
17090	spindle and socket	arbre m à calibre	Spindel f, Schablonenspindel f	asse m della sagoma
17091	spindle box	cage f à pignons	Kammwalzenständer m	gabbia f a pignoni
17092	spindle core	broche f	Stiftkern m	spillo-mandrino m
	spindle housing, s. spindle box			
17093	spindle temper steel	acier m à 1,125 de C.	Stahl m mit 1,125 C-Gehalt	acciaio m all'1,125 di C.
17093a	spin hardening	indurcissement m par rotation	Drehungshärtung f	tempera f per rotazione
17094	spinel	spinelle m	Spinell m	spinello m

		English	French	German	Italian
°	17095	**spinning chain**	chaîne *f* de vissage	Spillkette *f*	catena *f* d'avvolgimento
°	17096	**spinner survey**	contrôle *m* d'essuage	Treibenkontrolle *f*	controllo *m* di trasudamento
^	17097	**spiral auger**	tarière *f* à vis cylindrique	zylindrischer *m* Schneckenbohrer *m*	trivella *f* (o fioretto) elicoidale
		spiral drill, *s. twist drill*			
°	17098	**spiral end mill (cylindrical shank)**	fraise *f* à queue à cannelures hélicoïdales	Spiral-Fingerfräser *m* mit zylindrischem Schaft, Hochleistungs-Schaftfräser *m*	fresa *f* con coda a scanalatura elicoidale
°	17099	**spiral end mill (two lipped) for milling**	fraise *f* à rainures (ou à gorges)	Nutenfräser *m*, Langlochfräser *m* (mit zwei Schneiden)	fresa *f* a scanalatura
°	17100	**spiral gears**	engrenage *m* en spirale	Schraubenräder *n pl.*	ingranaggio *m* a spirale
°	17101	**spiral spring**	ressort *m* à spiral	Spiralfeder *f*	molla *f* a spirale
^	17102	**spiral welded tube**	tube *m* soudé en spirale	spiralgeschweisstes Rohr *n*	tubo *m* saldato a spirale
	17103	**spirit lamp**	lampe *f* à esprit de vin	Spirituslampe *f*	lampada *f* a spirito
		spirit level, *s. water level*			
—	17104	**to spit**	tirer, mettre à feu les coups de mine	abschiessen,	tirare, mettere a fuoco i colpi da mina
—	17105	**spit**	bêche *f*	Spaten *m*	vanga *f*
—	17106	**spitting**	tir *m*, volée *f*	Zündung *f*	tiro *m*, volata *f*
—	17107	**spitzkasten**	caisse *f* pointue	Spitzkasten *m*	cassa *f* appuntita
—	17108	**spitzlutte**	spitzlutte *f*	Spitzlutte *f*	classificatore *m* idrauli-
°	17108a	**splash, shell**	peau *f*	Schale *f*	trasudamento *m*
°	17109	**splash**	bavure *f*	Spritzer *m*	gocce *f pl.*
°	17110	**splash core**	plaque *f* anti-érosion	Prallplatte *f*	mattonella *f* antierosione
^	17111	**splash lubrication**	graissage *m* par barbotage	Ölnebelschmierung *f*	lubrificazione *f* a sbattimento
^	17112	**splash zone**	zone *f* d'éclaboussement	Benetzungszone *f*	zona *f* d'irrigazione
°	17113	**splashing**	projection *f*	Spratzen *n*	proiezione *f*

		English	French	German	Italian
⊃	17114	**to splay,** **to round off**	s'ovaliser	unrundwerden	ovalizzarsi, farsi o- vale
⊃	17115	**splayed circular** **· pass**	cannelure f ogive	Spitzbogenkaliber n	canale m ogivale
⊃	17115a	**splice bar**	éclisse f	Lasche f	stecca f, ganascia f
—	17116	**splint**	houille f matte, du- rain m	Durit m	durite f
—	17117	**splint**	morceau m, écaille f	Splitter m	scheggia f, scaglia f
—	17118	**splint coal**	charbon m bitumineux dur	Splitterkohle f	carbone m bitumino- so duro
⌃	17119	**splint pipe**	tube m fissuré	geschlitztes Rohr n	tubo m fenestrato
⊙	17120	**splinter, chip**	paille f de laminage	Walzsplitter m	scaglia f di lamina- zione
⋄	17121	**splinter-proof**	à l'épreuve des éclats	splitterfest	a prova di scheggia- tura
⊙	17122	**splintery fracture**	cassure f écailleu- se	splittriger Bruch m	rottura f scheggiata, frattura f scagliosa
⊙	17123	**split**	crique f longitudina- le	Längsriss m	incrinatura f longitu- dinale
⊙	17124	**to split**	fendre, faire éclater	spalten, zerspal- ten	fendere, separare, spaccare
⊙	17125	**split**	fente f, crevasse f	Spalt m, Riss m, Bruch m, Härteriss m	fessura f, fenditura f crepaccio m
—	17126	**split**	dérivation f (d'air), courant m partiel	Teilstrom m	derivazione f (d'aria), corrente f parziale
⊙	17127	**split centre**	crevasse f dans le coeur	Kernriss m	fenditura f centrale
⊙	17127a	**split core box**	boîte f à noyaux en deux parties	zweiteiliger Kern- kasten m	cassa f per anime in due parti
⊙	17128	**split chuck**	manchon m de serrage	Spannpatrone f	bussola f di chiusura
⊙	17128a	**split die**	matrice f assemblée	geteilte Matrize f	matrice f sezionata
⊙	17129	**split gate**	attaque f de coulée sur le plan de jonction	Gratanschnitt m	attacco m di colata sul piano di giunzio- ne, attacco m a bava
⊙	17130	**split open ended** **core box**	boîte à noyaux- cadre f	offener Kern- kasten m mit losen Teilen	cassa f d'anima a telaio
⊙	17131	**split pattern**	modèle m en deux parties	zweiteiliges Mo- dell n	modello m in due par- ti (o diviso o scom- ponibile)

		English	French	German	Italian
°	17132	**split shank**	compas *m* à ressort	federnder Schenkel *m*	gambo *m* del supporto per anima
—	17133	**splitter**	riffleur *m*	Riffelprobenteiler *m*	divisore *m*
^	17134	**splitter**	tour *f* de fractionnement à deux sorties	Fraktionierturm mit zwei Ausgängen	torre *f* di frazionamento a due uscite
—	17135	**splitting**	fendage *m*	Aufspaltung *f*	separazione *f*, divisione *f*
—	17136	**splitting**	dédoublement *m* (de couche)	Verdopplung *f*	sdoppiamento *m* (di strato)
°	17137	**splitting up of ions**	dédoublement *m* des ions	Ionenpaltung *f*	sdoppiamento *m* degli ioni
°	17138	**spluttering**	soufflure *f*	Blasenbildung *f*	soffiatura *f*
—	17139	**spodiophyllite**	spodiophyllite *f*	Spodiophyllith *m*	spodiofillite *f*
—	17140	**spodumene**	spodumène *m*	Spodumen *m*	spodumene *m*
—	17141	**spoil**	matériel *m* dragué, stérile *m*	Baggergut *n*, taubes Gestein *n*	materiale *m* dragato, sterile *m*
°	17142	**spoiled casting**	pièce *f* manquée, moulage *m* froid	Fehlguss *m*, Wrackguss *m*	pezzo *m* di scarto, getto *m* mal riuscito
°	17143	**spoiled steel sponge plating**, *s. doctoring*	acier *m* altéré	verdorbener Stahl *m*	acciaio *m* alterato
°	17144	**spongy iron, porous iron**	fer *m* spongieux, fer *m* poreux	schwammiges Eisen *n*, Eisenschwamm *m*	ferro *m* spugnoso, ferro *m* poroso
°	17145	**spongy structure**	texture *f* spongieuse	schwammige Textur *f*	struttura *f* spugnosa
°	17145a	**spongy top**	champignon *m*	aufgeblähter Speiser	fungo *m*, rigonfiamento *m*
	17146	**spontaneous generation**	génération *f* spontanée	Urzeugung *f*	generazione *f* spontanea
°	17147	**spontaneous heating**	échauffement *m* spontané	Selbsterhitzung *f*	riscaldamento *m* spontaneo
°	17148	**spool**	enrouleur *m*, bobine *f*	drehbare Haspel *f*	rullo *m*, bobina *f*
°	17149	**spool, bobbin, coil**	dévidoir *m*, bobine *f* enrouleuse *f*	Spule *f*	spola *f*, bobina *f*
^	17150	**spool flange**	bride *f* d'ancrage	Spülflansch *m*	flangia *f* d'ancoraggio

		English	French	German	Italian
o	17151	**spoon**	cuiller *f*, cuillère *f*	Löffel *m*	cucchiaio *m*, cucchiaia *f*
o	17152	**spoon for sampling, sampling spool**	cuiller *f*	Probenlöffel *m*	cucchiaio *m*
o	17152a	**spoon sample**	échantillon *m* du four	Ofenmuster *n*	campione *m* di forno
o	17153	**spoon tool**	lissoir *m* à cuiller	Polierlöffel *m*	cucchiarozzo *m*
−	17154	**sporogelite**	sporogélite *f*	Sporogelith *m*	sporogelite *f*
−	17155	**spot**	rainure *f*	Einschnitt *m*	intaccatura *f*
−	17156	**spot coring**	carottage *m* à la demande	Informationskernen *n*	carotaggio *m* a piccoli intervalli
o	17157	**spot facing tool, spot facing cutter**	fraise *f* à dégrossir	Stirnsenker *m*	alesatoio *m* per sgrossare
o	17158	**spot test**	essai *m* à la goutte	Tropfprobe *f*	prova *f* alla goccia
o	17159	**spot test**	essai *m* à la touche	Tüpfelanalyse *f*	prova *f* alla tocca
o	17160	**to spot weld**	souder par points	punktschweissen	saldare a punti
o	17161	**spot weld, spot welding**	soudure *f* par points	Punktschweissung *f*	saldatura *f* a punti
o	17162	**spot welded**	soudé par points	punktgeschweisst	saldato a punti
o	17163	**spot welder**	soudeuse *f* par points	Punktschweissmaschine *f*	saldatrice *f* elettrica a punti
o	17164	**spot-weld(ing)**	soudure *f* par points	Punktschweissung *f*	saldatura *f* a punti
o	17165	**spot welding machine**	machine *f* à souder par points	Punktschweissmaschine *f*	saldatrice *f* a punti
−	17166	**spotted**	tacheté, moucheté	fleckig, gefleckt	picchiettato, macchiato
−	17167	**spotted schist**	schiste *m* tacheté	Fleckschiefer *m*	schisto *m* picchiettato
o	17167a	**spotting**	apparition *f* de taches	Fleckigwerden *n*	comparsa *f* di macchie
o	17168	**spotting drill**	foret à centrer	Zentrierbohrer *m*	punta *f* per centrare
o	17168a	**spotting dut**	souillures *f pl.*	Ausblühungen *f pl.*	macchie *f pl.* di essudazione
o	17169	**spotting point**	départ *m* d'usinage	Bezugsebene *f*	piano *m* di riferimento
o	17170	**spout discharging lip**	bec *m* de coulée	Giessschnauze *f*	becco *m* di colata
o	17171	**spout, launder**	chenal *m* de coulée	Abstichrinne *f*, Rinne *f*	canale *m* di colata
	17172	**spout feed**	alimentation *f* à chenal de coulée libre	Freirinnespeisung *f*	alimentazione *f* a bocca libera

		English	French	German	Italian
°	17173	spout slag	scorie f de canal	Rinnenschlacke f	scoria f di canale
^	17174	spouter	puits jallissant	Eruptivsonde f, Springer m	pozzo m petrolifero
–	17175	spouting horn	caverne f karstique	Karsthöhle f	caverna f carsica
°	17176	to sprag	pointer	Formerstifte stecken	mettere le punte
–	17177	spragger	freineur m	Bremser m	frenatore m
–	17178	spragging	freinage m	Bremsen n	frenatura f
–	17179	to spray	arroser	bespritzen, zerstäuben	spruzzare, irrorare, polverizzare
–	17180	spray	vaporisateur m	Zerstäuber m, Spritze f	vaporizzatore m, polverizzatore m
–	17181	spray	apophyse f d'un filon	Gangapophyse f	apofisi f d'un filone

spray (foundry), *s. auxiliary gate*

°	17182	spray	grappe f	Giesstraube f, Stapelguss m	grappolo m di pezzi fusi
°	17183	spray casting	coulée f en grappe	Stapelguss m	colata f a pioggia (o a grappolo)
°	17184	spray nozzle	tuyère f de pulvérisation	Streudüse f	spruzzatore m, polverizzatore m
°	17184a	spray quenching	refroidissement m rapide par eau atomisée	Abschiecken durch Spritzen	raffreddamento m rapido a spruzzi
°	17185	sprayer nozzle	pulvérisateur m à tuyère	Streudüsenzerstäuber m	polverizzatore m ad ugello
°	17186	spraying	pulvérisation f	Zerstäubung f	polverizzazione f
°	17187	spraying and fusing	projection f et fusion	Ausspritzen n und Einbrand m	proiezione f e fusione
°	17188	spraying furnace	foyer m à brûleur	Brennerherd m	focolare m a bruciatore
°	17188a	spread	marge f	Marge f	margine m
^	17189	spreader	solutionneur m	Lösungsmittel n	soluzionatore f
°	17190	spreader	plaque f de jonction	Verbindungsplatte f	piastra f di unione
°	17191	sprig, gagger	épingle f	Winkelstift m	punta f a gancio, chiodo m di rinforzo, punta f per fonderia
°	17191a	sprigging	épinglage m	Stiftbefestigung f	fissaggio m con punte

spring beam, *s recoil*

°	17191b	spring brass	laiton m de ressort	Federmessing n	ottone m per molle

English	French	German	Italian
17192 spring buffer	tampon *m* élastique	Federpuffer *m*	respingente *m* elastico
17192a spring chaplet	support *m* de noyau	Fassonkernstütze *f*	supporto *m* sagomato
17193 spring collet	manchon-pince *m*	Spannhülse *f*	mandrino *m*
spring compass, *s. split shank*			
17194 spring cushioning	amortissement *m* par ressort	Federprellung *f*	ammortizzazione *f* a molla
17195 spring leaf	lame *f* de ressort	Federblatt *n*	balestra *f*
17196 spring pressure gauge	manomètre *m* métallique	Federmanometer *n*	manometro *m* metallico, manometro *m* a tubo elastico
17197 spring release	sommier *m*	Auswurfkasten *m*	scatola *f* porta espulsori
17198 spring retaining ring bar	fer *m* pour cercles de fixation du bandage	Sprengring-Stahl *m*	barra *f* per cerchielli di fissaggio della ruota al cerchione
17199 spring screw thread die	filière *f* réglable, cage *f* de filetage	Gewindeschneidbacken *f pl.* für Bolzen (einstellbar)	filiera *f* aggiustabile
17200 spring-steel	acier *m* à ressort	Federstahl *m*	acciaio *m* per molle
17201 spring steel wire	fil *m* d'acier à ressort	Federstahldraht *m*	vergella*f* d'acciaio per molle
17202 spring washer, spring lock washer	rondelle *f* élastique	Federring *m*	rondella *f* elastica
17203 spring wire	fil *m* pour ressort	Federdraht *m*, Federring *n*	filo *m* per molle
17203a springback	gonflement *m*	Atmen *n*	rigonfiamento *m*
17204 Springer's puddling furnace	four *m* à puddler système Springer	Springerscher Puddelofen *m*	forno *m* da puddellaggio sistema Springer
17205 springing	agrandissement *m* par explosion du fond d'un trou de mine	Auskesseln *n* der Bohrlöcher	allargamento *m* con esplosivo di un foro da mina
17205a springing	répartition *f* des efforts résiduels	Verteilung *f* der Restspannungen	ripartizione *f* degli sforzi residui
to sprinkle, *s. to wet*			
17206 sprinkler	pulvérisateur *m*, crépine *f*	Regner *m*, Wasserbrause *f*	polverizzatore *m*, spruzzatore *m*, succhierola *f*
17207 sprinkling	arrosage *m*	Berieselung *f*	irrigazione *f*

	English	French	German	Italian
— 17208	**sprinkling**	inclusion f de minerai dans la roche en faible quantité	eingesprengtes Erz n	inclusione f di minerale nella roccia in piccola quantità
° 17209	**sprinkling apparatus**	appareil m à arroser	Benetzvorrichtung f	apparecchio m per irrigare
° 17210	**sprocket chain**	chaîne f d'entraînement	Antriebskette f	catena f di trasmissione
° 17211	**sprue, gate, geat**	jet m (de coulée), descente f de coulée	Anguss m, Gusszapfen m, Eingusskanal m, Einlauf m	materozza f, colatoio m
	sprue bottom, *s. locating cone or assembly mark*			
° 17212	**sprue cutter**	ébarbeuse f	Abgratmaschine f	sbavatrice f di colata
° 17213	**sprue hole**	goulot m de coulée, trou m de coulée	Eingusskanal m, Giessloch n, Einlaufrinne f	bocca f di colata
° 17214	**sprue pin**	diffuseur m	Verteilerzapfen m	spargicolata f, diffusore m
° 17215	**sprueing, spruing**	coupage m des coulées, enlèvement m des entonnoirs de coulée	Abstichunterbrechung f	troncatura f delle colate, rimozione f degli imbuti di colata
— 17216	**to spud**	travailler en spudding, forer par battage, forer	schlagbohren, bohren	perforare a percussione, trivellare
^ 17217	**to spud in**	débuter	ansetzen	imprimere un violento moto alternativo lungo la verticale
— 17218	**spud**	pilotis	Stutzen m	palafitta f
— 17219	**spud**	gouge f à repêchage, spatule f de dégagement	Spatenspeer m, Zungenbohrer m	punta f a spatola per pescatore
— 17220	**spudder**	treuil m léger au câble	leichtes Kabelbohrgerät n	argano m leggero a cavo
— 17221	**spudding**	perforation f à câble des sondages peu profonds	Schlagbohren n für geringe Tiefe	perforazione f iniziale alla corda di giacimenti poco profondi
— 17222	**spudding pulley**	poulie f de forage au câble	Rolle f zum Seïlbohren	puleggia f di perforazione al cavo
— 17223	**spudding shoe**	sabot m de spudding, sabot m de battage	Bohrschaufelschuh m	zoccolo m di «spudding»

	English	French	German	Italian
— 17224	**spur**	éperon *m*	Bergsporn *m*	sperone *m*
— 17225	**spur**	contrefort *m*, contrefiche *f*	Strebe *f*, Spreize *f*	contrafforte *m*, saetta *f*, saettone *m*
° 17226	**spur gear**	engrenage *m* cylindrique	Stirnrad *n*	ingranaggio *m* cilindrico
° 17227	**spur gear bob**	fraise *f* à tailler les engrenages droits	Abwälzfräser *m*, für Stirnräder	fresa *f* per tagliar pignoni
— 17228	**spurn**	jambe *f*	Kohlenbein *n*	gamba *f* (di carbone)
— 17229	**spurrite**	spurrite *f*	Spurrit *m*	spurrite *f*
° 17230	**to spurt, to spit**	cracher	spratzen	scintillare, spruzzare
^ 17231	**spurting**	jaillissement *m*	Spratzen *n*	eruzione *f*
° 17231a	**sputtering**	pulvérisation *f* cathodique	Katodenzerstäubung *f*	polverizzazione *f* catodica
° 17232	**square bar(-iron), square-iron**	fer *m* carré, fer *m* rectangulaire	Quadrateisen *n*, Vierkanteisen *n*	ferro *m* quadro, quadretto *m*
° 17233	**square billet**	billette *f* carrée	Vierkant-Knüppel *m*	billetta *f* quadrata
— 17234	**square buddle**	caisse *f* allemande	Schlämmgraben *m*	cassa *f*

square groove, *s. square pass*

	English	French	German	Italian
° 17235	**square corner smoother**	équerre *f* à lisser	Polierknopf *m*	squadra *f* per lisciare
° 17236	**square-headed bolt**	boulon *m* à tête carrée	Bolzen *m* mit Vierkantkopf	bullone *m* a testa quadrata
° 17237	**square ingot**	lingot *m* carré	Vierkantblock *m*	lingotto *m* quadrato

square iron, *s. square bar*

	English	French	German	Italian
° 17238	**square oblong iron**	fer *m* plat rectangulaire	Vierkanteisen *n*	ferro *m* piatto rettangolare
° 17239	**square nosed trowel, square pointed trowel**	truelle *f* à bout carré	Polierschaufel *f* mit geradem Blatt	cazzuola *f* rettangolare
° 17240	**square pass**	cannelure *f* carrée	Quadratkaliber *n*	scanalatura *f* quadrata
° 17241	**square plate**	plaque *f* carrée	quadratische Platte *f*	piastra *f* quadrata
° 17242	**square section**	section *f* carrée	quadratischer Querschnitt *m*	sezione *f* quadrata
— 17243	**square set, set timbering**	boisage *m* parallélépipédique	Fachwerkausbau *m*	armatura *f* a parallelepipedo

		English	French	German	Italian
−	17244	square-set-and-fill	explotation *f* avec boisage parallélépipédique et remblayage	Abbau *m* mit Rahmenzimmerung und mit Bergeversatz	coltivazione *f* con armatura
−	17245	square-set stope, set stoping	chantier *m* avec boisage parallélépipédique	Abbaustoss *m* mit Rahmenzimmerung	cantiere *m* con armatura a parallelepipedo
−	17246	square-set stoping	exploitation *f* avec boisage parallélépipédique	Abbau *m* mit Rahmenzimmerung	coltivazione *f* con armatura a parallelepipedo
−	17247	square setting	boisage *m* (du toit)	(Dach)Verkleidung *f*	armamento *m*
°	17248	square steel	acier *m* carré	Vierkantstahl *m*, Vierkanteisen *n*	acciaio *m* in barre quadrate
°	17249	square tube	tube *m* de section carrée	viereckiges Rohr *n*	tubo *m* quadro
−	17250	square up	tir *m* auxiliaire	Abschiessen *n* der Hilfssprengschüsse	tiro *m* ausiliare
°	17251	square wire	fil *m* carré	Vierkantdraht *m*	filo *m* quadrato
°	17252	square wire netting	treillis *m* à simple torsion	Drahtgeflecht *n* mit einfacher Verwindung	traliccio *m* a torsione semplice
−	17253	square work	exploitation *f* par piliers	Pfeilerbau *m*	coltivazione *f* a pilastri
°	17254	squares, square bars	fers *m pl.* carrés	Vierkanteisen *n*	barre *f pl.* quadre
°	17254a	squaring shear	cisailles à ébouter	Kopfschere	cesoie *f pl.* da squadrare
−	17255	squeeze	affaissement *m* du toit	Absenkung *f* des Hangenden, Zerdrückung *f*	cedimento *m* (o sprofondamento) del tetto
°	17256	to squeeze	presser	drücken	pressare, comprimere
−	17257	to squeeze	bocarder	pochen, stampfen	spremere, macinare
°	17258	squeeze board	plateau *m* à bordure	Pressplatte *f* mit Randwulst	placca *f* bordata
^	17259	squeeze cementation	cémentation *f* par pression	Druckzementierung *f*	cementazione *f* per pressione
°	17260	squeeze head	plateau *m* de serrage	Pressplatte *f*	placca *f* di compressione
^	17261	squeeze job	pompage *m* par pression	Auspumpen *n* unter Druck	pompaggio *m* sotto pressione

		English	French	German	Italian
o	17262	squeeze moulding	serrage *m* par pression	Verdichten *n* durch Pressen	formatura *f* a pressione
o	17263	squeezer, alligator	presse *f* à cingler, cingleur *m* à levier	Luppenquetsche *f*	fucinatrice *f*, formatrice *f* a compressione
		squeezing, *s. bloom pressing*			
o	17264	squeezing molding machine	machine *f* à compression	Pressformmaschine *f*	formatrice *f* a compressione
o	17264a	squeezing the ball	cinglage *m*	Zängen *n*	eliminazione *f* delle scorie
—	17265	to squib	déflagrer	abbrennen	deflagrare
—	17266	squib	mèche *f*, raquette *f*	Zündschnur *f*	miccia *f*, petardo *m*
—	17267	squibbing	agrandissement *f* par explosion du fond d'un trou de mine	Auskesseln *n* der Bohrlöcher	allargamento *m* del fondo di un foro da mina con esplosioni
∧	17268	to stab	guider (une tige dans le raccord)	Einführen des Zapfens in ein Muffengewinde	guidare un asta nel raccordo
∧	17269	stabbing board	plate-forme *f* d'accrochage	Verrohrungsbühne *f*	passerella *f* di manovra per tubaggi
o	17270	stabilised dolomite	dolomie *f* stabilisée	stabilisierter Dolomit *m*	dolomite *f* stabilizzata
o	17271	stabilising	stabilisation *f*	Spannungsfreiglühen *n*	stabilizzazione *f*
∧	17272	stable emulsion	émulsion stable	hartnäckige Emulsion *f*	emulsione *f* stabile
o	17273	stable pig breaker	casseur *m* de gueuses fixe	standfester Masselbrecher *m*	spezzamasselli *m* fisso
—	17274	staccato injection	injection *f* multiple	wiederholte Injektion *f*	iniezione *f* multipla
o	17275	to stack boxes	gerber les châssis	die Formkästen stapeln	accatastare le staffe
o	17275a	stack	cuve *f*	Schacht *m*	tino *m*, bacino *m*
o	17275b	stack cutting	coupage *m* des tôles en paquets	Schneiden von Blechpaketen	taglio *m* delle lamiere in pacchetti
o	17276	stack moulding	coulée *f* en grappe	Stapelguss *m*	colata *f* a grappolo
o	17277	stack mould	grappe *f*	Giessbaum *m*, Stapelabguss *m*	grappolo *m*
o	17278	stacked mould	moule *m* à éléments superposés	Form *f* mit überlagerten Teilen	forma *f* ad elementi sovrapposti
—	17279	stacker	élévateur *m* d'empilage	Stapler *m*, Stapelkran *m*	accatastatore *m*, carrello a piattaforma sollevabile

		English	French	German	Italian
^	17280	**stacking a rig**	démonter une sonde	einen Bohrer demontieren	disarmare una sonda
°	17281	**staff (forging tool)**	porte-lingot *m*	Blockalter. *m*	portalingotto *m*
—	17282	**staffelite**	staffélite *f*	Staffelit *m*	staffelite *f*
	17283	**stage**	étage *m*	Stufe *f*	stadio *m* , piano *m*
—	17284	**stage**	plate-forme *f*	Gerüst *n*	piattaforma *f*
	17285	**stage**	degré *m*, phase *f*	Stadium *n*, Phase *f*	stadio *m*, grado *m*, fase *f*
—	17286	**stage crushing**	broyage *m* étagé	stufenweise Zerkleinerung *f*	frantumazione *f* graduale
—	17287	**stage flotation**	flottation *f* étagée	stufenweise Flotation *f*	flottazione *f* graduale (o progressiva)
°	17288	**stage for the slide**	porte-objet *m*	Objekttisch *m*	portaoggetti *m*
°	17289	**stage-hardening**	trempe *f* à gradins	Stufenhärtung *f*	tempera *f* differenziale
^	17290	**stage pumping**	épuisement *m* en répétitions	satzweises Pumpen *n*	pompaggio *m* a ripetizione
—	17291	**stage working**	exploitation *f* à ciel ouvert	Tagebau *m*	coltivazione *f* a cielo aperto
^	17292	**staggered well**	puits disposé en quinconce	zickzackförmig angeordnete Sonde	pozzo *m* disposto a quinconce
—	17293	**stage staging, scaffolding**	échafaudage *m*	Bühne *f*	impalcatura *f*, ponteggio *m*
°	17294	**stagings round furnace**	plate-forme *f* de visite	Laufbühne *f*	terrazza *f*, piattaforma *f*
—	17295	**stainierite**	stainiérite *f*	Stainierit *m*	stainierite *f*
—	17296	**stainless**	inoxydable	korrosionsbeständig	inossidabile
—	17297	**stainless steel**	acier *m* inoxydable, acier *m* inattaquable	unoxydierbarer Stahl *m*, rostfreier Stahl *m*	acciaio *m* inossidabile
°	17297a	**stake**	piquet-repère *m*	Führungspfahl *m*	picchetto *m*
—	17298	**stalagmite**	stalagmite *f*	Stalagmit *m*	stalagmite *f*
		stalhane, *s. electric hearth furnace Groenwall*			
°	17299	**stalk of a core**	boîte *f* à noyau	Kernformkasten *m*	armatura *f* d'anima

	English	French	German	Italian
— 17300	stall-and-breast	exploitation *f* par chambres et foudroyage des piliers	Kammerpfeilbruchbau *m*	coltivazione *f* a camere con franamento dei pilastri
— 17301	stall-and-room work	exploitation *f* par chambres et piliers	Kammerpfeilerbau *m*	coltivazione *f* a camere e pilastri
˄ 17302	stall collar	manchòn *m* d'arrêt du deuxième bouchon	Befestigungsmuffe *f* für den zweiten Pfropfen	manicotto *m* d'arresto per il secondo tappo
° 17303	stall roasting	grillage *m* en stalles	Stadelröstung *f*	torrefazione *f* all'aria
— 17304	to stamp	damer	einstampfen	battere, costipare
° 17305	to stamp, to mark to stamp out	poinçonner, estampiller	stempeln	punzonare, marcare
— 17306	to stamp	bocarder	stampfen, pochen	frantumare
— 17307	stamp stamp, *s. piercer or punch*	pilon *m* de bocard	Pochstempel *m*	martello *m*, mazzabattente *m*
° 17308	stamp	poinçon *m* de réception	Abnahmestempel *m*	punzone *m* di collaudo
— 17309	stamp battery	batterie *f* de bocard	Pochwerk *n*	macchina *f* per sgretolare il materiale aurifero
— 17310	stamp box	caisse *f* de bocard	Pochtrog *m*	cassa *f* di frantoio
° 17311	stamp die	dé *m* de bocard	Pochsohle *f*	stampo *m* del frantoio
— 17312	stamp mill	bocard *m*	Pochwerk *n*	mulino *m* a pestelli
— 17313	stamp milling	bocardage *m*	Pochen *n*	frantumazione *f*
— 17314	stamp rock	minerai *m* à bocarder	Pocherz *n*	minerale *m* da frantumare
— 17315	stamped concrete	béton *m* damé	Stampfbeton *m*	calcestruzzo *m* battuto
° 17316	stamped iron ladle	poche *f* en tôle emboutie	gestanzte Giesspfanne *f*	caldaia *f* di ferro stampato
° 17317	stamped metal	métal estampé	Stanzmetall *n*	metallo *m* stampato
— 17318	stamped ore	minerai *m* bocardé	Pochmehl *n*	minerale *m* frantumato
° 17319	stamped plate	tôle *f* emboutie	(gepresstes) Formblech *n*	lamiera *f* stampata o imbutita

	English	French	German	Italian
	stamper, *s. rammer*			
− 17320	Stampian stage	étage *m* stampien	Stampien *n*	Stampiano *m*
° 17321	stamping. marking, punching	poinçonnage *m*, estampillage *m*	Stempeln *n*	punzonatura *f*
° 17321a	stamping	découpage *m*	(Aus)Stanzen *n*	stampaggio *m*
− 17322	stamping	tassage *m*, damage *m*	Einstampfen *n*	costipamento *m*
° 17322a	stamping	pièce *f* estampée	Pressling *m*	(pezzo) stampato *m*
° 17323	stamping board	planche *f* de damage	Aufstampfboden *m*	tavolozzo *m*, tavola *f*, per modelli
° 17324	stamping die	matrice *f* à estamper	Stanzmatrize *f*	matrice *f* per stampi
° 17325	stamping form	moule *m* de pilonnage	Stampfform *f*	forma *f*, stampo *m*
° 17326	stamping machine driven by electric motor	pilonneuse *f* électrique	Stampfmaschine *f* mit elektrischem Antrieb	costipatrice *f* elettrica
− 17327	stamping mill	bocard *m*	Pochwerk *n*	mulino *m*, frantoio *m*
° 17328	stamping press	presse *f* à matricer	Prägwerk *n*	pressa *f* per coniare o per stampare
° 17329	stamping tool	matrice *f*, étampe *m*	Prägestempel *m*	punzone *m* da coniare
− 17330	stand, crucible stand	fromage *m*, tourte *f*	Käse *m*, Untersatz *m*	formaggio *m*, graticola *f*, piastra *f*
° 17331	stand, holsters	cage *f* à cylindres	Walzkorb *m*	gabbia *f*, incastellatura *f* per i cilindri
° 17332	stand	support *m*	Gestell *n*, Ständer *m*	treppiede *m*, supporto *m*
^ 17333	stand	trait *m*	Zug *m*	lunghezza *f* (3/4 aste)
° 17333a	stand	cage *f*	Gerüst *n*	gabbia *f*
17334	stand by	auxiliaire	Hilfs−	ausiliario, di riserva
	stand-by boiler, *s. spare boiler*			
° 17335	stand of rolls	cage *f* de laminoir	Walzgerüst *n*	gabbia *f* del laminatoio
^ 17336	stand off	distance *f* entre l'épaulement du joint et le calibre	Schulterabstand *m*	distanza *f* fra la scarpa del giunto e il calibro

		English	French	German	Italian
^	17337	**stand oil**	huile f épaissie	Dicköl n, Standöl	olio m di lino cotto
—	17338	**stand pipe**	colonne f montante	Druckrohr n	colonna f montante
—	17339	**stand up formation**	roche f ferme	festes Gebirge n	roccia f ferma
o	17340	**standard, lamp standard**	mât m de lanterne	Beleuchtungsmast m	palo m per illuminazione
o	17341	**standard. frame**	chevalet m	Bock m, Gerüst n	cavalletto m, incastellatura f a cavalletto
o	17342	**standard analysis**	analyse f de comparaison	Vergleichsanalyse f	analisi f di confronto (o di riferimento)
o	17343	**standard channel**	fers m $pl.$ à U normaux	normales U-Eisen n	ferro m ad U normale
—	17344	**standard coal**	charbon m normal	Normalkohle f	carbone m normale
o	17345	**standard electrode**	électrode f normale	Normalelektrode f	elettrodo m normale
—	17346	**standard mineral**	minerai m normatif	Standardmineral n	minerale m normale
o	17347	**standard points or switch**	changement m normal	Normalweiche f, Regelweiche f	scambio m normale
—	17348	**standard sand**	sable m normal	Normalsand m	sabbia f normale
o	17349	**standard scale**	table f normale	Normaltabelle f	tabella f normale
o	17350	**standard sections with round edges**	profils m $pl.$ à coins arrondis	rundkantige Profile n $pl.$	profilati m $pl.$ a spigoli arrotondati
o	17351	**standard solution**	solution f normale	Normallösung f	soluzione f normale
o	17352	**standard specification**	spécification f normale, normes f $pl.$	Normalangabe f	specificazione f normale
o	17353	**standard steelworks mold**	moule m normal pour aciérie	Stahlwerknormalform f	forma f normale per acciaieria
o	17354	**standard strength of a solution**	titre m d'un liquide	Gehalt m einer Flüsssigkeit	titolo m o composizione f d'un liquido
o	17354a	**standard test piece**	éprouvette étalon	Normalprobestab m	provetta f campione
o	17355	**standard tube**	tuyau m normal	Normalrohr n	tubo m normale
o	17356	**standard weight**	poids m normal	Sollgewicht n	peso m normale
o	17357	**standard wheel set**	train m normal	Radsatz m normaler Bauart	asse m montato normale
o	17358	**standard wire**	fil m normal	Normaldraht m	filo m normale

	English	French	German	Italian
17359	standardized	normalisé	genormt	unificato
— 17360	stander	pilier m de charbon	Kohlenpfeiler m	pilastro m di carbone
^ 17361	standing valve	clapet m de pied	Fussventil n	valvola f d'aspirazione
° 17362	standoff	serrage m de couplage à vis	Verschraubung f	serraggio m di un accoppiamento a vite
— 17363	stank	serrement m	Wasserscheider m	sbarramento m
— 17364	stannary	mine f d'étain	Zinngrube f	miniera f di stagno
— 17365	stannate	stannate m	zinnsaures Salz n	stannato
— 17366	stannic	stannique	Zinn~	stannico
— 17367	stannic chloride	hypochlorure m d'étain ou stannique	Zinnchlorid n	cloruro m stannico
— 17368	stanniferous	stannifère	zinnhaltig	stannifero
— 17369	stannite	stannite f	Stannin m, Zinnkies m	stannite f
— 17370	stannous chloride	chlorure m stanneux	Zinnchlorür n	cloruro m stannoso
— 17371	staple	puits m intérieur, bure f, cheminée f	Gesenk n, Blindschacht m Stürzrolle f	pozzo m ausiliare, scivolo m, piano m inclinato
° 17372	staple	crampon m	Krampe f	punta f cambretta, grappa f
— 17373	staple	entrepôt m	Ladeplatz m	deposito m
— 17374	staple pit (winze)	bure f	Blindschacht m	pozzo m interno (o ausiliare)
° 17375	staples for staves	crampon m pour douves	Schlaufe f für Fassdauben	punta f cambretta p. doghe
— 17375a	star antimony	antimoine m pur	reines Antimon n	antimonio m puro
— 17376	star bit	trépan m en couronne	Sternmeissel m	trapano m a croce
° 17377	star like sparks	étincelles f $pl.$ étoilées	sternbildende Funken m $pl.$	faville f $pl.$ (o scintille) a stella
17378	starch	amidon m	Stärke f	amido m

		English	French	German	Italian
°	17379	starch paper	papier *m* à amidon	Stärkepapier *n*	carta *f* all'amido
−	17380	starter	fleuret *m* d'amorça-ge	Anfänger *m*	trivella *f* d'avviamen-to
	17381	starter button	bouton *m* de mise en route, bouton-démar-reur *m*	Schaltknopf *m*	bottone *m* d'avviamen-to
°	17382	starting, blo-wing in	mise *f* en feu	Anblasen *n*	messa *f* in marcia, ac-censione *f*
°	17383	starting effort	effort *m* de traction, au démarrage	Anfahr(dreh)mo-ment *n*	sforzo *m* di trazione all'avviamento
°	17384	starting impulse	pulsation *f* d'anima-ge	aufgeschalteter Zündimpuls *m*	impulso *m* di accensio-ne
°	17385	starting machine	machine *f* de démar-rage	Anlassmaschine *f*	macchina *f* d'avviamen-to
^	17386	starting pressure	pression *f* de démar-rage	Anfahrdruck *m*	pressione *f* d'avviamen-to
°	17386a	starting sheet starting sheet blank,	feuille *f* de départ *s. mother blank*	Mutterblech *n*	lamierino *m* catodico
°	17387	Stassano furnace	four *m* Stassano	Stassanoscher O-fen *m*, Stassano-Ofen *m*	forno *m* Stassano
°	17388	Stassano's electric blast furnace	haut-fourneau *m* Stassano	Stassanoscher Hochofen *m*	alto forno *m* Stassano
°	17389	starved portion of cast with insuf-ficient metal	partie *f* peu den-se	lockere Stelle *f*	parte *f* spugnosa
−	17390	stassfurtite	stassfurthite *f*	Stassfurtit *m*	stassfurtite *f*
°	17391	state of equilibrium	état *m* d'équilibre	Gleichgewichts-zustand *m*	stato *m* d'equilibrio
°	17392	static bell-tipe furnace	four *m* statique sous cloche	arbeitender Glochenofen *n*	forno *m* statico del tipo a campana
^	17393	static bottom hole pressure	pression *f* statique de fond	Bodenschliess-druck *m*	pressione *f* statica del fondo
^	17394	static gravimeter	gravimètre *m* stati-que	statisches Gravi-meter *n*	gravimetro *m* statico
°	17395	static test	essai *m* statique	statische Prü-fung *f*	prova *f* statica
^	17396	stationary barrel	cylindre *m* fixe de pompe	stehender Zylinder *m*	cilindro *m* fisso di pompa

		English	French	German	Italian
o	17397	**stationary boiler**	chaudière f fixe	feststehender (Dampf)Kessel m	caldaia f fissa
o	17398	**stationary converter**	convertisseur m stationnaire	festehendes Konverter m	convertitore m fisso (o stazionario)
o	17399	**stationary grate**	grille f fixe	fester Rost m	griglia f fissa
o	17400	**stationary magnet**	aimant m fixe	feststehender Magnet m	magnete f fisso
o	17401	**statuary bronze**	bronze m statuaire	Kunstbronze f	bronzo m d'arte
–	17402	**staurolite**	staurolite f	Staurolith m	staurolite f
o	17403	**staves**	bande f d'acier des centralisateurs à éléments longitudinau	Stahlbänder n pl. der Zentriervorrichtungen mit longitudinalen Elementen li	nastri m pl. d'acciaio dei centralizzatori a elementi longitudinali
o	17403a	**staving**	épaississement de l'extrémité	Rohrendverstärkung f	ispessimmento m dell'estremità d'un tubo
o	17404	**stay bolt, pillar bolt**	boulon m d'entretoisement	Stehbolzen m, Zugbolzen m	bullone m tirante
o	17405	**stay plate**	plaque f d'appui	Unterlagplatte f	piastrina f d'appoggio
o	17406	**stay tube**	tube m tirant	Ankerrohr n	tubo m tirante
–	17407	**staying**	étayage m étayement m	Stempelsetzen n	puntellamento m
–	17408	**staying of the crown**	armature f du ciel	Deckenverankerung f	puntellatura f
o	17409	**stays**	support m du cadre	Stütze f des Rahmens	sopporto m (o puntello) del quadro
o	17410	**Stead's brittleness**	fragilité f pour groississement du grain	Brückigkeit f durch Kornvergrösserung	fragilità f per ingrossamento del grano
–	17411	**steadite**	steadite f	Steadit m	steadite f
o	17412	**steady pin (foundry)**	portée f	Kernmarke f	portata f d'anima
		steady stress component, s. principal (or mean) stress			
	17413	**steam**	vapeur f d'eau	Wasserdampf m	vapore m d'acqua
o	17414	**steam admitted above the piston**	vapeur f admise au dessus du piston m	Oberdampf m	vapore m immesso sopra al pistone
o	17415	**steam admitted below the piston**	vapeur f admise au-dessus du piston	Unterdampf m	vapore m immesso inferiormente (sotto al pistone)

		English	French	German	Italian
°	17416	steam bath	bain *m* de vapeur	Dampfbad *n*	bagno *m* di vapore
°	17417	(steam-)boiler	chaudière *f* (à vapeur)	(Dampf)Kessel *m*	caldaia *f* (a vapore)
°	17418	(steam) boiler with mechanical stokers	chaudière *f* (à vapeur) avec grilles mécaniques	Dampfkessel *m* mit mechanischer Feuerung	caldaia *f* (a vapore) con griglie meccaniche
°	17419	steam blower	soufflerie *f* à vapeur	Dampfgebläse *n*	soffieria *f* a vapore
°	17420	steam chest	boîte *f* de distribution	Steuerkasten *m*	camera *f* di distribuzione, duomo *m* (di vapore)
—	17421	steam coal. short flaming coal	charbon *m* à courte flamme	kurzflammige Kohle *f*	carbone *m* a corta fiamma
—	17422	(steam) collier	charbonnier *m* (à vapeur)	(Dampf)Kohlenschiff *n*	(piroscafo) carboniero *m*, nave *f* carboniera
°	17423	steam-cooled	refroidi par vapeur d'eau	dampfgekühlt	raffreddato a vapore d'acqua
°	17424	steam crane	grue *f* à vapeur	Dampfkran *m*	gru *f* a vapore
°	17425	steam cylinder	cylindre *m* à vapeur	Dampfstiefel *m*	cilindro *m* a vapore
°	17426	steam developer	générateur *m* à vapeur	Dampfentwickler *m*	generatore *m* di vapore
°	17427	steam distillation	distillation *f* à la vapeur d'eau	Vergasung *f* mit Wasserdampf	distillazione *f* con vapore acqueo
°	17428	steam dynamo	dynamo *f* à vapeur	Dampfdynamo *f*	dinamo *f* a vapore
°	17429	steam exhaustor	exhausteur *m* à vapeur	Dampfsauger *m*	aspiratore *m* a vapore
°	17430	steam funnel	entonnoir *m* à tuyau de vapeur	Dampftrichter *m*	imbuto *m* a tubo per vapore
°	17431	steam generating downcomer and screen tube	tube *m* vaporisateur, tube *m* de circulation et tube *m* écran	Siede, Fall-und Strahlungsrohr *n*	tubo *m* vaporizzatore, di circolazione e di schermo
°	17432	steam generator	générateur *m* de vapeur	Dampferzeuger *m*	generatore *m* di vapore
°	17433	steam hammer	marteau-pilon *m* à vapeur	Dampfhammer *m*	maglio *m* a vapore

		English	French	German	Italian
°	17434	**steam hammer admitting steam above the piston**	marteau-pilon *m* à vapeur avec admission sur le piston	Dampfhammer *m* mit Oberdampf	maglio *m* a vapore con immissione superiore del vapore
°	17435	**steam hammer with fixed cylinder**	marteau-pilon *m* avec cylindre fixe	Dampfhammer *m* mit feststehendem Zylinder	maglio *m* a vapore a cilindro fisso
°	17436	**steam hammer with single standard**	marteau-pilon *m* avec montant en col de cygne	Dampfhammer *m* mit einseitigem oder C-förmigem Gestell	maglio *m* a vapore ad un sol montante
°	17437	**steam-jacked boiler**	chaudière *f* chemisée de vapeur	Kessel *m* mit Dampfmantel	caldaìa *f* con camicia di vapore
°	17438	**steam jet blower**	souffleur *m* à vapeur	Dampfstrahlgebläse *n*	ventilatore *m* a getto di vapore
°	17439	**steam jet sprayer**	pulvérisateur *m* à jet de vapeur	Dampfstrahlzerstäuber *m*	polverizzatore *m* a getto di vapore
°	17440	**steam locomotive**	locomotive *f* à vapeur	Dampflokomotive *f*	locomotiva *f* a vapore
°	17441	**steam pot**	autoclave *m*	Dampftopf *m*	autoclave *f*
°	17442	**steam power forging press**	presse *f* à forger à vapeur	Dampfdruck-schmiedepresse *f*	pressa *f* a vapore per forgiare
°	17443	**steam pump**	pompe *f* à vapeur	Dampfpumpe *f*	pompa *f* a vapore
^	17444	**steam ratio**	rapport *m* d'humidité	Feuchtigkeitsverhältnis *n*	titolo *m* d'umidità
—	17445	**steam shovel**	pelle *f* à vapeur	Dampfschaufel *f*	escavatore *m* a vapore
—	17446	**steam shovel excavation**	dragage *m* à la pelle à vapeur	Dampfschaufel-betrieb *m*	escavazione *f* o scavo *m.* a vapore
^	17447	**steam soak**	imprégnation *f* de vapeur	Dampfeinsaugen *n*	impregnazione *f* di vapore
^	17448	**steam still**	distillateur *m* à vapeur	Dampfdestillierapparat *m*	distillatore *m* a vapore
°	17449	**steam superheater**	surchauffeur *m* à vapeur	Dampfüberhitzer *m*	surriscaldatore *m* di vapore
°	17450	**steam trap**	séparateur *m* d'eau	Dampfentwässerer *m*	essiccatore *m* di vapore
°	17451	**steam winch**	treuil *m* à vapeur	Dampfwinde *f*	argano *m* a vapore

		English	French	German	Italian
—	17452	steatite	stéatite *f*	Speckstein *m*, Steatit *m*	steatite *f*
°	17453	**to steel, to acierate**	acérer. aciérer	stählen, ansthäh- len, verstählen	acciaiare, converti- re in acciaio
°	17454	**steel**	acier *m*	Stahl *m*	acciaio *m*
°	17455	**steel alloy**	alliage *f* d'acier	Stahllegierung *f*	lega *f* d'acciaio
°	17456	**steel arch**	cintre *m* d'acier	Streckengestell *n*	centinatura *f* d'accia- io
		steel ball, *s. steel lump* **steel ball peening,** *s. cloud bursting* **steel beam,** *s. steel bearer*			
°	17457	**steel bearer, steel beam**	poutre *f* en acier	Stáhlträger *m*	trave *f* d'acciaio
°	17458	**steel bloom**	loupe *f* d'acier	Stahlluppe *f*	massello *m* d'acciaio
°	17459	**steel boiler**	chaudière *f* d'acier	Stahlkessel *m*	caldaia *f* d'acciaio
°	17460	**steel bridge construction**	pont *m* en fer	Eisenbrücke *f*	ponte *m* metallico
°	17461	**steel cast**	coulé en acier	aus Stahl ge- gossen	colato in acciaio
°	17462	**steel-bronze**	bronze-acier *m*	Stahlbronze *f*	bronzo *m* acciaio
°	17463	**steel casting(s), cast steel**	acier *m* moulé, acier *m* de moulage	Stahl(form)guss *m*, Gussstahl *m*	acciaio *m* colato, ac- ciaio in getti
°	17464	**steel cellar frame**	châssis *m* de cave en acier	Kellerrahmen *m pl.* aus Stahl	telai *m pl.* di canti- na in acciaio
°	17465	**steel cementing furnace**	four *m* à acier cé- menté	Zementstahlofen *m*	forno *m* di cementa- zione
°	17466	**steel door**	porte *f* métallique	Eisentür *f*	porta *f* metallica
°	17467	**steel face of ar- mour plate**	face *f* aciérée de la plaque de blin- dage	Stahlseite *f* der Panzerplatte	rivestimento *m* o fiancata *f* d'acciaio della piastra da co- razza
°	17468	**steel-faced**	aciéré	stählern	acciaiato, d'acciaio
°	17469	**steel for case- hardening, blister steel**	acier *m* de cémenta- tion	Einsatzstahl *m*	acciaio *m* da cemen- tazione
°	17470	**steel for corset springs**	acier *m* pour balei- nes de corsage	Korsettfederstahl *m*	acciaio *m* per balene di corsetti

		English	French	German	Italian
o	17471	steel for dies and stamps	acier *m* pour bouterolles et étampes	Döpperstahl *m*	acciaio *m* per stampi
o	17472	steel for punches	acier *m* pour poinçons	Lochstempelstahl *m*	acciaio *m* per punzoni
o	17473	steel for safes	acier *m* à coffres-forts	Geldschrankstahl *m*	acciaio *m* per casse-forti
o	17474	steel for screw taps	acier *m* pour tarauds	Gewindebohrstahl *m*	acciaio *m* per madre viti.
o	17475	steel-foundry	fonderie *f* d'acier	Stahlgiesserei *f*	fonderia *f* d'acciaio
o	17476	steel framework for curtain walls	structure *f* de support en acier pour murs-rideaux	Tragwerk *n* aus Stahl für Mantelwände (Vorhangwände)	struttura *f* di sostegno in acciaio per pareti-cortina
o	17477	steel gray	gris *m* acier	stahlgrau	grigio acciaio
o	17477a	steel grit	grenaille *f* d'acier	Stahlschrot *m*	graniglia *f* d'acciaio
o	17478	steel hammer	marteau *m* d'acier	Stahlhammer *m*	martello *m* d'acciaio
o	17479	steel hardening	cémentation *f* de l'acier	Stahlhärtung *f*	cementazione *f* dell'acciaio
o	17480	steel hoop	bande *f* d'acier	Stahlbandeisen *n*	bandella *f* di acciaio
o	17481	steel ingot	lingot *m* d'acier	Stahlblock *m*	lingotto *m* d'acciaio
o	17482	steel ladle	poche *f* à acier	Stahlpfanne *f*	siviera *f* per acciaio
o	17483	steel magnet	aimant *m* d'acier	Stahlmagnet *m*	magnete *m* d'acciaio
		steel mantle, *s. sheet iron shell*			
		steel mill, *s. steel plant*			
o	17484	steel mix cast iron	fonte *f* aciérée	Gusseisen *n* mit Stahlzusatz	ghisa *f* acciaiosa
o	17485	steel mortar	mortier *m* en acier	Stahlmörser *m*	mortaio *m* d'acciaio
o	17486	steel nose of breaker	pilon *m* en acier	Stahlstössel *m*	mazza *f* d'acciaio
o	17487	steel of a reverberatory furnace	acier *m* au four à réverbère	Flammofenstahl *m*	acciaio *m* di forno a riverbero
o	17488	steel panels for central heating	éléments *m pl.* chauffants en plaques d'acier	Stahlplattenheizkörper *m*	elementi *m pl.* scaldanti a piastre d'acciaio
o	17489	steel pig	lingot *m* d'acier	Stahlblock *m*	massello *m* d'acciaio

		English	French	German	Italian
°	17490	**steel piling, sheet piling, sheet pile**	palplanches *f pl.*	Spundpfahl *m*, Spundwand *f*	palancola *f*
°	17491	**steel plant**	aciérie *f*	Stahlwerk *n*	acciaieria *f*
°	17492	**steel plate**	tôle *f* d'acier	Stahlblech *n*	lamiera *f* d'acciaio
°	17493	**steel-plate road sign**	panneau *m* de signalisation routière en acier	Wegweiser *m* aus Stahlblech	indicatore *m* stradale in lamiera
°	17494	**steel platforms on columns anchored in the rock**	plates-formes *f pl.* métalliques sur poteaux ancrés dans la roche	Stahlplattformen *f pl.* auf im Felsen verankerten Stützen	piattaforme *f pl.* metalliche su colonne ancorate alla roccia
°	17495	**steel plating**	aciérage *m*	Verstählung *f*	acciaiatura *f*
°	17496	**steel plug pin**	baguette *f* en acier	Stahlnadel *f*	ago *m* d'acciaio
°	17497	**steel point**	pointe *f* aciérée	verstahlte Spitze *f*	punta *f* d'acciaio
°	17498	**steel poor in carbon**	acier *m* doux	kohlenstoffarmer	acciaio *m* povero di carbonio, acciaio *m* dolce
°	17498a	**steel powder**	poudre *f* d'acier	Stahlpulver *n*	polvere *f* d'acciaio
'°	17499	**steel prop**	étançon *m* d'acier	Stahlstempel *m*	puntello *m* d'acciaio
°	17500	**steel-puddling**	puddlage *m* du fer	Stahlpuddeln *n*	puddellatura *f* dell'acciaio
°	17501	**steel roll**	rouleau *m* en acier	Stahlwalze *f*	cilindro *m* d'acciaio
°	17502	**steel rolling mill**	laminoir *m* d'acier	Stahlwalzwerk *n*	laminatoio *m* d'acciaio
°	17503	**steel roof support**	étançon *m* métallique	Stahlstempel *m*	puntello *m* metallico
°	17504	**steel roof truss**	charpente *f* métallique de toiture	Metalldachgerüst *n*	carpenteria *f* metallica del tetto
°	17505	**steel rope (or cable)**	câble *m* métallique	Drahtkabel *n*	fune *f* metallica
°	17506	**steel rotary hose**	tube *m* flexible pour tête d'injection	biegsames Rohr *n* für Einspritzkopf *m*	tubo *m* snodato per testa d'iniezione
		steel scrap, *s. iron scrap*			
⌐	17507	**steel set**	cadre *m* d'acier	Stahltürstock *m*	quadro *m* d'acciaio
°	17508	**steel sharpening**	affûtage *m* des fleurets	Bohrernachschärfung *f*	affilatura *f* dei fioretti
°	17508a	**steel sheet**	tôle *f* d'acier	Stahlblech *n*	lamiera *f* d'acciaio

		English	French	German	Italian
°	17509	steel shell	enveloppe *f* en tôle	Blechgefäss *n*	rivestimento *m* di lamiera
—	17510	steel shuttering steel softening, *s. softening* steel stanchion, *s. iron stanchion*	boisage *m* en acier	Stahlgerüst *n*	armatura *f* di ferro
°	17511	steel string piece, steel stringer	limon *m* d'acier	Stahltreppen-baum *m*	trave *f* di rampa di acciaio
°	17512	steel strip	bande *f* d'acier	Stahlbandeisen *n*	nastro *m* d'acciaio
°	17513	steel support	étançon *m* d'acier	Stahlstempel *m*	sostegno *m* d'acciaio
—	17514	steel timbered shaft	puits *m* de mine à revêtement d'acier	Schacht *m* mit Stahlausbau	pozzo *m* di miniera con armatura in acciaio
—	17515	steel timbering	soutènement *m* en acier	Stahlausbau *m*	rivestimento *m* d'acciaio
—	17516	steel tub	berline *f* en acier	Förderwagen *m* aus Stahlblech	vagonetto *m* in acciaio
°	17517	steel window	fenêtre *f* métallique	Stahl-Fenster *n*	finestra *m* metallica
°	17518	steel wire	fil *m* d'acier	Stahldraht *m*	filo *m* d'acciaio
°	17519	steel wool	paille *f* de fer	Stahlwolle *f*	lana *f* d'acciaio
°	17520	steel work	structure *f* en acier	Stahlstruktur *f*	struttura *f* in acciaio
°	17521	steel worker	ouvrier *m* d'aciérie	Stahlwerkarbeiter *m*	lavoratore *f* d'acciaieria
°	17522	steel-works	aciérie *f*	Stahlhütte *f*, Stahlwerk *n*	acciaieria *f*
°	17523	steeling	aciérage *m*	Stählung *f*, Verstählen *n*	acciaiatura *f*
°	17524	steely	aciéreux	stahlartig	acciaioso
°	17525	steely iron, semisteel	fer *m* aciéreux	Feinkorneisen *n*	ferro *m* acciaioso, acciaio *m* extradolce
°	17526	steely pig-iron	fonte *f* aciéreuse	Feinkorn(guss)-eisen *n*	ghisa *f* acciaiosa
°	17527	steep curve	courbe *f* en ogive	steile Kurve *f*	curva *f* ad ogiva (o stretta)
—	17528	steep seam	couche *f* en dressant	steil gelagerte Schicht *f*	filone *m* in pendenza

	English	French	German	Italian
— 17529	steep vein	filon m de fort pendage	steiler Gang m	filone m in forte pendenza
— 17530	steep working	exploitation f en dressant	Abbau m im steilen Flöz n	coltivazione f di filoni in pendenza
— 17531	stellated structure	structure f radiée	radiale Struktur f	struttura f radiale
— 17532	to stem	bourrer	besetzen	rincalzare
° 17533	stem	tige f, tronc m	Stange f, Stamm m	asta f, stelo m, gambo m
— 17534	stem	sabot m de bocard	Pochschuh m	zoccolo m del mulino
— 17535	to stem a hole	bourrer un coup de mine	Bohrloch n besetzen	costipare un foro da mina
° 17536	stem chaplet	support m de noyau à tige	Stammkernstütze f	chiodo m a gambo
— 17537	stemmer	bourroir m	Ladestock m	costipatore m
— 17538	stemming	bourrage m	Besatzeinbringen n	rincalzamento m
— 17539	stemming cartridge	cartouche f de bourrage	Besatzpatrone f	cartuccia f di costipamento
— 17540	stemple, stempel	étai m, butte f	Stempel m	puntello m
— 17541	stence	bois m de mine	Grubenholz n	legname m per mine
— 17542	stenton	recoupe f	Durchhieb m	galleria f di collegamento
	step-back welding, $s.$ *back step welding*			
° 17543	step-bar	éprouvette f en gradins	Stufenprobe f	provetta f a gradini
— 17544	step bit	trépan m à redans	Stufenmeissel m	trapano m a stadi
° 17545	step-down test	essai m de tournage en gradins	Stufendrehprobe f	prova f di tornitura a scala
— 17546	step-fault	faille f en gradins	Staffelbruch m	gradinata f di faglie
— 17547	step fold	pli m monoclinal	Monoklinalfalte f	piega f monoclinale
— 17548	step freezing	congélation f étagée	gradweises Gefrieren n	congelazione f graduale
	step gate casting, $s.$ *side step gating*			
° 17548a	step gating	attaque f de réchauffage	oberer Etagenanschnitt m	attacco m di riscaldamento
° 17549	step-grate	grille f à gradins	Treppenrost m	griglia f a gradini

		English	French	German	Italian
°	17550	**step-hardening**	trempe *f* étagée	Stufenhärtung *f*	tempra *f* per gradi
°	17551	**step melting**	fusion *f* à gradins	Treppenschmelzen *n*	fusione *f* per gradi
°	17552	**step quenching**	trempe *f* interrompue ou étagée	gebrochenes Härten *n*, gestaffelte Martensit Härtung	tempra *f* interrotta o isotermica
—	17553	**step shaped**	à gradins	treppenartig	a gradini
—	17554	**Stephanian stage**	étage *m* stéphanien	Stephanien *n*	stefaniano *m*
—	17555	**stephanite**	stéphanite *f*	Stephanit *m*	stefanite *f*
°	17555a	**stepped anneal**	recuit *m* échelonné	Stufenglühung *f*	ricottura *f* a gradini
°	17556	**stepped grate**	grille *f* à gradins	Treppenrost *m*	griglia *f* a gradini
°	17557	**stepped grate producer**	gazogène *m* avec grille à gradins	Treppenrost-generator *m*	gasogeno *m* con griglia a gradini
°	17558	**stepped hot--extruded steel section**	profil *m* à gradins en acier extrudé à chaud	gestaffeltes, warmstranggepresstes Stahlprofil *n*	profilato *m* a gradini in acciaio estruso a caldo
°	17559	**stepped joint**	joint *m* gauche	profilierte Teilung *f*	falso piano *m* di divisione, piano *m* di divisione irregolare
°	17560	**stepped joint**	joint *m* décroché	abgesetzte Teilfläche *f*	ritrovatura *f*
°	17561	**stepped roll**	cylindre *m* à gradins	Stufenwalze *f*	cilindro *m* a gradini
°	17561a	**stepped runner**	canal *m* d'alimentation en cascade	Stufeneingusskanal *m*	canale *m* d'alimentazione a cascata
°	17562	**stepped side gate**	attaque *f* de réchauffage	oberer Etagenanschnitt *m*	attacco *m* di riscaldamento
°	17563	**stepped sprue**	descente *f* braisée de coulée, descente *f* à talons multiples	Stufeneingusskanal *m*	colata *f* a gradini
		stepped test bar, *s. step bar*			
—	17564	**stepping**	exploitation *f* en gradins renversés	Firstenbau *m*	coltivazione *f* a gradini rovesci
—	17565	**stercorite**	stercorite *f*	Sterkorit *m*	stercorite *f*
°	17566	**stern frame plates**	tôles *f pl.* de l'arcasse	Heckplatten *f pl.*	lamiere *f pl.* dell'arcaccia
—	17567	**sternbergite**	sternbergite *f*	Stenbergit *m*	sternbergite *f*
—	17568	**sterny**	à gros grain	grobkörnig	a grana grossa

	English	French	German	Italian
− 17569	stewartite	stewartite *f*	Stewartit *m*	stewartite *f*
− 17570	stewing	mijotage *m*	Abstehen *n*	rimescolamento *m*
− 17571	stibial	antimonieux	Antimon–	antimonioso
− 17572	stibiconite	stibiconite *f*	Stibiconit *m*	stibiconite *f*
− 17573	stibiopalladinite	stibiopalladinite *f*	Stibiopalladinit *m*	stibiopalladinite *f*
·− 17574	stibiotantalite	stibiotantalite *f*	Stibiotantalit *m*	stibiotantalite *f*
− 17575	stibium	antimoine *m*	Antimon *n*	antimonio *m*
− 17576	stiblite	stiblite *f*	Stibiconit *m*	stiblite *f*
− 17577	stibnite	stibine *f*	Antimonglanz *m*	stibina *f*
− 17578	stichtite	stichtite *f*	Stichtit *m*	stichite *f*
− 17579	stick caustic potash	potasse *f* caustique en bâtonnets	Ätzkali *n* in Staugen	potassa *f* caustica in bacchette o cannelli
	stick gun, *s. poke gun*			
° 17580	sticker, rat, scab	adhérence *f*	Adhärenz *f*	aderenza *f*
° 17581	stickiness	collage *m*, viscosité *f*	Kleben *n*	appiccicosità *f*
− 17582	sticking	coincement *m*	Festwerden *n*	inceppamento *m* (d'aste)
° 17583	sticking of the casting to the die	collage *m* de la pièce sur le moule	Kleben *n* des Gussstücks in der Form	incollamento *m* (o aderenza) del getto alla forma
− 17584	sticky coal	faux-toit *m*	Nachfalldach *n*	falso tetto *m*
° 17585	stiff slag	scorie *f* pâteuse	steife Schlacke *f*	scoria *f* secca o pastosa
° 17586	stiffener	raidisseur *m*	Versteifungselement *n*	tenditore *m*
° 17587	stiffener	(tôle *f* de) fourrure *f*	Futterblech *n*	(lamiera *f* di) imbottitura
° 17587a	stiffening	renforcement *m*	Verstärkung *f*	rinforzo *m*
° 17588	stiffening girder	poutre *f* de rigidité	Versteifungsträger *m*	trave *f* di rinforzo
° 17589	stiffening of the tube walls	renforcement *m* des parois du tube	Versteifung *f* der Rohrwände	rinforzo *m* dei tramezzi

	English	French	German	Italian
17590	**stiffening-plate**	tôle f de renfort	Verstärkungsplatte f	lamiera f di rinforzo
	stiffness, *s. torsional strenght*			
17591	**stilbite**	stilbite f	Stilbit m	stilbite f
17592	**still**	alambic m distillatoire	Destillierblase f	storta f di distillazione, alambicco m
17593	**still coke**	coke m d'alambic	Destillierapparate-koks m	coke m di storta
17594	**still gas**	gaz m de raffinerie	Raffiniergas n	gas m di raffineria
17595	**still grease**	graisse f distillée	destillierte Schmiere f	grasso m distillato
17596	**still wax**	paraffine f de distillation	destilliertes Paraffin n	cera f di distillazione
17597	**stilling well**	puits m de repos	Ruhegrube f	pozzo m di riposo
17598	**stillman**	ouvrier m spécialisé de raffinerie	Raffinerie-Arbeiter m	operaio m qualificato di raffineria
17599	**stilpnochloran**	stilpnochloran m	Stilpnochloran m	stilpnoclorano m
17600	**stilpnomelane**	stilpnomélane m	Stilpnomelan m	stilpnomelano m
17601	**stimulation**	stimulation f	Stimulation f	stimulazione f
17602	**stinger**	combinaison f de trépan pour roches et alésoir	Kombination f von Steinmeissel u. Räumer	combinazione f di trapano per roccie e di alesatore
17603	**stink-damp**	gaz m d'explosion de grisou	Explosionsschwaden m	idrogeno m solforato
17604	**stinkstone**	calcaire m fétide	Stinkkalk m	antraconite f
17605	**to stir a bath**	brasser un bain	eine Schmelze umrühren	agitare un bagno
17606	**to stir in the water**	agiter dans l'eau	im Wasser schwenken	agitare nell'acqua
	to stir up, *s. to puddle*			
17607	**to stir vertically**	pomper	pumpen	pompare
	stirrer, *s. stirring device*			
17608	**stirring**	mise f en suspension par agitation	Umrühren n	agitazione f, rimescolamento m
17609	**stirring device**	agitateur m, mélangeur-agitateur	Rührvorrichtung f	agitatore m, miscelatore-agitatore m

		English	French	German	Italian
°	17610	**stirrup**	étrier *m*	Bügel *m*	staffa *f*, redancia *f*
		stirrup; *s*: *strap*			
°	17610a	**stich welding**	soudure *f* à points continue	Steppnahtschweissen *n*	saldatura *f* continua a punti
°	17611	**stock**	amas *m*, stock *m*	Stock *m*, Vorrat *m*	ammasso *m*, scorta *f*, giacenza *f*
°	17612	**stock**	surépaisseur *f* d'usinage	Bearbeitungszugabe *f*	sovrametallo *m* di lavorazione
—	17613	**stock**	production *f* journalière	Tagesförderung *f*	produzione *f* giornaliera
	17614	**stock**	tronc *m*	Klotz *m*, Stamm *m*	tronco *m*, fusto *m*, ceppo *m*
°	17615	**stock**	charge *f*	Gicht *f*	carica *f*
°	17616	**stock, forging stock**	bout *m* à forger	schmiedbares Stück *n*	spezzone *m*, pezzo *m* da forgiare
°	17617	**stock , wrench (for dies)**	tourne à gauche *m*, filière *f* à coussinet	Schneidkluppe *f*	filiera *f*, giramaschi *m*, trafila *f* a cuscinetti
°	17618	**stock column**	colonne *f* des charges	Beschickungssäule *f*	colonna *f* delle cariche
°	17619	**stock crane**	grue *f* de magasin ou de dépôt	Lagerkran *m*	gru *f* da deposito
°	17620	**stock ground**	parc *m*	Lagerplatz *m*	piazzale *m*, deposito *m*
°	17621	**stock indicator (of a blast furnace)**	indicateur *m* de charge	Gichtanzeiger *m*	indicatore *m* di carica (di altoforno)
°	17622	**stock line**	surface *f* de la charge	Beschickungsoberfläche *f*	superficie *f* della carica
°	17623	**stock line gauge**	indicateur *m* de la descente des charges	Gichtanzeiger *m*	indicatore *m* della discesa delle cariche
—	17624	**stock-piling**	entassement *m*	Häufeln *m*	ammucchiamento *m*
°	17625	**stock-rail**	rail *m* d'applique	Backenschiene *f*	contro-ago *m*
^	17626	**stocktank oil**	huile *f* de stockage	Tanköl *n*	olio *m* di stoccaggio
		stock-yard, *s. stock ground*			
		stocker, *s. stoker*			
—	17627	**stockwork**	stockwerk *m*	Stockwerk *n*	fascio *m* di vene mineralizzate
°	17628	**stoichiometric(al) equivalent**	équivalent *m* stœchiométrique	stöchiometrisches Äquivalent *n*	equivalente *m* stechiometrico

		English	French	German	Italian
°	17629	stoichiometric(al) method of Mrazek	méthode f stœchio-métrique de Mrazek	Mrazeks stöchio-metrisches Verfah-ren n	metodo m stechiome-trico Mrazek
°	17630	to stoke	charger (ou alimen-ter) les chaudières	Feuerung f beschik-ken	governare (o caricare) le caldaie, alimenta-re le caldaie
°	17631	to stoke by hand	charger à la main	mit der Hand be-schicken	caricare a mano
°	17632	to stoke mechani-cally	charger automati-quement	den Rost mecha-nisch beschicken	caricare il focolare meccanicamente
°	17633	stoke-hole, stoke room	chambre f de chauffe	Heizraum m, Feuer-raum m	locale m caldaie, ca-mera f dei forni
°	17634	stoker, fireman	chauffeur m	Heizer m	fuochista m
°	17635	stoker	foyer m automatique, chargeur m automati-que	selbständige Rost-beschickungsvor-richtung f	griglia f meccanica
°	17636	stoker	ringard m	Ofenkrücke f	alimentatore m di com-bustibile, agitatore m
°	17637	stoking	chauffage m, char-gement m	Beschickung f, Heizen n	alimentazione f, ri-scaldamento
—	17638	stolpenite	stolpénite f	Stolpenit m	stolpenite f
—	17639	stolzite	stolzite f	Stolzit m	stolzite f
—	17640	stone bind	grès m	Sandstein m	gres m
—	17641	stone breaker	concasseur m à calcaire ou à mi-nerais	Steinbrecher m, Erzquetsche f	mulino m a mascelle, frantoio m per pietre
		stone coal, s. anthracite stone crusher, s. stone breaker			
—	17642	stone drift	galerie f en rocher, bacnure f	Gesteinsstrecke f	galleria f in roccia
—	17643	stone drill	mèche f à pierre	Gesteinsbohrer m	trivella f per pietre
—	17644	stone-dust stopping	arrêt-barrage m de poussière	Gesteinsstaub-schrank m	diaframma f antipolve-re
—	17645	stone lattice	réseau m d'érosion	Steingitter n	reticolo m d'erosione
^	17646	stone oil	pétrole m	Steinöl n, Erdöl n	petrolio m
—	17647	stone-pick	pic m au rocher	Gesteinshacke f	piccone m per rocce

	English	French	German	Italian
— 17648	stone pillar	pilier m en pierres	Steinpfeiler m	pilastro m di pietra
° 17649	stone ring	anneau m en briques	Steinring m	anello m di mattoni
— 17650	stone shaft	puits m à remblai	Versatzschacht m	pozzo m a ripiena
° 17651	stony slag	laitier m pierreux	steinige Schlacke f	loppa f pietrosa
— 17652	stone tubing	cuvelage m en maçonnerie	wasserdichte Schachtmauerung f	tubaggio m in muratura
— 17653	stone wedge	coin m à pierre	Steinkeil m	cuneo m da pietra
° 17654	stone work	appareillage m des briques	Steinzustellung f	lavoro m in pietra
— 17655	stook	pilier m de charbon, jambe f	Kohlenpfeiler m, Kohlenbein n	pilastro m di carbone, gamba f
° 17656	stool	fromage m	Bodenstein m	formaggella f
— 17657	stoop	pilier m de protection	Sicherheitspfeiler m	pilastro m di protezione
— 17658	stoop	butte f	Stempel m	puntello m
— 17659	stoop system	exploitation f par piliers	Pfeilerbau m	coltivazione f a pilastri
— 17660	stooper	dépileur m	Schrämhauer m	tagliatore m di carbone
— 17661	stooping	dépilage m, dépilement m	Pfeilerabbau m	coltivazione f dei pilastri
° 17662	stop	point m d'accrochage	Anschlagpunkt m	punto m d'agganciamento
^ 17663	stop cock	robinet m d'arrêt	Abschlusshahn m	rubinetto m di regolazione o d'arresto
^ 17664	stop collar	manchon m (de cimentation)	Befestigungsring m	manicotto m di cementazione
— 17665	to stope	abattre le minerai	Erz abbauen	coltivare (a gradini), abbattere (estrarre) il minerale
— 17666	stope	chantier m en gradins, chantier m d'abattage	Abbauort m, Abbaustoss m	cantiere m a gradini, cantiere m (o scavo) d'abbattimento
	stope drill, s. stoper			
—17667	stope face	taille f d'abattage	Abbauort m	fronte f di coltivazione

	English	French	German	Italian
− 17668	stope hole	trou m en semelle	Sohlenloch n	foro m in soletta
− 17669	to stope in	s'ébouler	zubruchgehen	franare
− 17670	stope ore pass	cheminée f à mine-rai	Erzrolle f	scivolo m per minera-li
− 17671	stope rejection	roche f stérile	taubes Gestein n	roccia f sterile
− 17672	stoped out	exploité	abgebaut	sfruttato, esaurito
− 17673	stoped up	foudroyé	eingestürzt, abgerutscht	franato, smottato
− 17674	stoper	perforatrice f (pour creusement en mon-tant)	Teleskop-Hammer m	fucile m perforatore
− 17675	stoper	forage m en faîte	Firstenbohrloch n	perforazione f del tetto
− 17676	stoping	abattage m	Abbau m	coltivazione f, scavo m
− 17677	stoping face. stope face	taille f d'abattage	Abbauort m	fronte f di coltivazione
− 17678	stoping ground	zone f d'exploita-tion	Abbauzone f	zona f di coltivazione
° 17679	stoppage of the blast furnace	arrêt m de la marche du fourneau	Stillstand m des Hochofenbetriebes	arresto m nel funziona-mento del forno
° 17679a	stopper, plunger	quenouille f	Stopfenstange f	asta f del tampone
° 17680	stopper end	tampon m de que-nouille	Stopfen m	tampone m, tappo m
	stopper, s. peg stopper bell, s. small bell stopper head, s. stopper plug			
° 17681	stopper ladle	poche f de coulée à busette	Pfanne f mit Stopfen-ausguss	siviera f di colata ad ugello
° 17682	stopper lifting device	mécanisme m de commande de la quenouille	Stopfenhebevorrich-tung f	apparecchio m di ma-novra del tappo
° 17683	stopper of throat	fermeture f du gueulard	Abschluss m des Schachtes	chiusura f della boc-ca del forno
° 17684	stopper plug, stopper head	tampon m	Stopfen m	tappo m
° 17685	stopper rod	quenouille f	Stopfenstange f	asta f del tampone (o del tappo)
° 17686	stoppered pour-ing basin	bassin m de coulée à quenouille	Birneneinguss m	bacino m di colata a tappo

	English	French	German	Italian
17687	**stopping**	cloison *f* d'aérage	Wetterdamm *m*, Wetterscheider *m*	diaframma *f* di ventilazione
	stopping, *s. shutting off*			
17688	**stopping down, shut down of the furnace**	arrêt *m* du haut-fourneau	Ausserbetriebsetzung *f*	spengimento *m* del forno
17688a	**stopping off**	isolation *f*	Abdeckung *f*	isolante *m*
	stopping up, *s. botting*			
17689	**storage**	stockage *m*	Lagern *n*	immagazzinaggio *m*, deposito *m*
	storage battery. *s. accumulator*			
17690	**storage tank**	réservoir *m* de stockage	Vorratstank *m*	serbatoio *m* di stoccaggio
	to store, *s. to accumulate*			
17691	**store, stock room**	magasin *m*	Vorratsraum *m*	magazzino *m*
17692	**store tank, bin**	réservoir *m*	Vorratsbehälter *m*	serbatoio *m*
	stored heat, *s. accumulated heat*			
17693	**storing reservoir for ore**	réservoir *m* à minerais	Vorratsbehälter *m* für Erz	serbatoio *m* (o deposito) per minerali
17694	**to stove**	étuver	trocknen	essiccare
17695	**stove, oven**	étuve *f*	Trockenofen *m*	stufa *f*
17696	**stove blacking**	noir *m* d'étuve	Schwärze *f*	nero *m* da stufa
17697	**stove coal**	anthracite *m*	Anthrazit *m*	antracite *f*
17698	**stove pipe**	tuyau *m* de poêle	Ofenrohr *n*	tubo *m* da stufa
17699	**stove with air recirculation**	étuve *f* à recirculation d'air	Trockenofen *m* mit Luftumwälzung	stufa *f* con ricircolazione d'aria
17700	**stoving**	étuvage *m*	Trockenvorgang *m*	essiccazione *f* in stufa
17701	**stoving type acrylic resin paint**	peinture *f* à base de résine acrylique thermodurcissable	auf hitzehärtbarem Akrylharz basierender Anstrich *m*	vernice *f* a base di resina acrilica termoindurente
17702	**to stow**	remblayer	versetzen	riempire, eseguire una ripiena

	English	French	German	Italian
− 17703	stowage	remblayage *m*	Versetzen *n*	ripiena *f*
− 17704	stowage machine	remblayeuse *f* mécanique	Versatzmaschine *f*	macchina *f* per ripiena meccanica
⌃ 17705	straddle packer	packer *m* composé de deux éléments	Straddle-Packer	packer *m* a due elementi
⌃ 17706	straight bow centralizer	centralisateur *m* à éléments longitudinaux	Zentriervorrichtung *f* mit Längsteilen	centralizzatore *m* a elementi longitudinali
° 17707	straight carbon steel	acier *m* au seul carbone	Kohlenstoffstahl *m*	acciaio *m* al solo carbonio
− 17708	straight-flute drill	foret *m* à canon	kanonenartiger Bohrer *m*	punta *f* a cannone
⌃ 17709	straight-fraction- ation	fractionnement *m* primaire	Primärfraktionie- rung *f*	frazionamento *m* primario
° 17710	straight grained	à fibres droites	geradefaserig	a fibra dritta
° 17711	straight large radius sleeker	lissoir *m* droit à grand congé	Polierknopf *m*	lisciatoio *m* per raccordi
° 17712	straight pass	cannelure *f* d'étirage	Streckkaliber *n*	scanalatura *f* di trafilatura
⌃ 17713	straight piping	tubage *m* à diamètre constant	Rohrleitung *f* mit konstantem Durchmesser	tubazione *f* a diametro costante
⌃ 17714	straight-run	distillé directement	direkt destilliert	distillato direttamente
⌃ 17715	straight-run gasoline	essence *f* de distillation	Destillationsbenzin *n*	benzina *f* di distillazione
⌃ 17716	straight-run pitch	résidu *m* primaire	Primärrückstände *m pl.*	residuo *m* primario
⌃ 17717	straight run stock	huiles *f pl.* primaires	Primäröle *n pl.*	oli *m pl.* primari
− 17718	straight shank three-flutes reamer	mèche *f* de centrage flûtée	Grundbohrer *m* mit zylindrischem Schaft	trapano *m* scanalato a gambo diritto
− 17719	straight shank, twist drill	mèche *f* spirale à fût droit	Spiralbohrer *m* mit zylindrischem Schaft	trapano *m* elicoidale a gambo dritto
⁹ 17720	straight tongue	aiguille *f* droite	gerade Zunge *f*	ago *m* diritto

		English	French	German	Italian
°	17721	**to straighten**	dresser	gerade richten	raddrizzare
°	17722	**to straighten the sheets**	planer les tôles	die Blechtafeln ausrichten	raddrizzare o spianare le lamiere
°	17723	**strainghtened**	tôle *f* dressée	ausgerichtete Platte *f*	lamiera *f* raddrizzata
°	17723a	**strainghtening**	redressage *m*	Geraderichten *n*	raddrizzatura *f*
°	17724	**straightening hammer**	marteau *m* à dresser	Schlagwerkzeug *n*	maglio *m* per raddrizzare, maglio *m* spianatore
°	17725	**straightening machine**	machine *f* à dresser	Richtmaschine *f*	raddrizzatrice *f*, spianatrice *f*
°	17726	**straightening plate**	taque *f* à dresser en fonte	eiserne Richtplatte *f*	placca *f* in ghisa per raddrizzare
°	17727	**straightening press**	presse *f* à dresser	Richtpresse *f*	pressa *f* raddrizzatrice
°	17728	**straightening roll**	cylindre *m* de dressage	Richtwalze *f*	rullo *m* spianatore
°	17729	**straightening shop**	atelier *m* de cisaillage	Zurichtungshalle *f*	locale *m* per l'aggiustaggio
°	17730	**strain. straining**	effort *m*, travail *m*	Beanspruchung *f*,	sforzo *m*, sollecitazione *f*
°	17731	**strain aging**	vieillissement *m* par déformation plastique	Stauchalterung *f*	invecchiamento *m* dovuto all'incrudimento
°	17732	**strain figures**	figure *f* d'écoulement ou d'étirage	Fliessfigur *f*	aspetto *m* di frattura stirata
°	17732a	**strain gauge**	extensomètre *m*	Dehnungsmessstreifen *m*	estensimetro *m*
°	17733	**strain-hardening**	durcissement *m* par écrouissage	Verhärtung *f*	indurimento *m* dovuto all'incrudimento
°	17734	**strain portal of electric railways**	portique *m* pour lignes ferroviaires électriques	portalartiger Fahrleitungsmast *m* für elektrische Bahnen	portale *m* di ammaraggio di ferrovie elettriche
−	17735	**strain-slip cleavage**	pseudo-clivage *m*	Ausweichungsspalten *n*	pseudo-sfaldatura *f*
°	17735a	**strained casting**	dégorgement *m* de la coulée	überliessendes Giessen *n*	trabocco *m* della colata
°	17736	**strainer**	crépine *f* (de pompe), filtre *m*, tamis *m*	Saugkorb *m*, Filter *m*, Sieb *n*	succhiarola *f* (di pompa), filtro *m*, crivello *m*
°	17737	**strainer core**	noyau-filtre *m*	Siebkern *m*	anima-filtro *f*, anima *f* portafiltro

		English	French	German	Italian
°	17738	**straining chamber**	chambre f de filtration	Siebkammer f	camera f di decantazione
°	17739	**straining dish, strainer**	cuvette f du tamis	Siebschale f	bacino m dello staccio
°	17740	**straits tin**	étain m de Malacca	Malakkazinn n	stagno m di Malacca
—	17741	**strake**	trait m, bande f	Strich m, Band n	striscia f, linea f, nastro m, truogolo m

stranded welding wire, s. *stranded electrode*
stranded wire, s. *steel rope*

		English	French	German	Italian
—	17742	**strange**	allochtone	allochton	alloctono
°	17743	**strap, stirrup**	étrier m, bride f	Bügel m	briglia f, cinghia f
°	17744	**strap iron, strap, hoop-iron**	feuillard m de fer	Flacheisen n, Bandeisen n	bandella f, sbarra f, nastro m di ferro

strapped joint, s. *joint with butt strap*

		English	French	German	Italian
^	17745	**strapping a tank**	mesurage m du réservoir	Tankmessung f	misurazione f del serbatoio
—	17746	**strata**	couches f $pl.$, strates f $pl.$	Schichten f $pl.$, Lage f	falde f $pl.$
—	17747	**stratifield ore deposit**	gisement m stratifié	geschichtete Lagerstätte f	giacimento m stratificato
—	17748	**stratigrapher**	stratigraphe m	Stratigraph m	stratigrafo m

stratigraphic (al) break, s. *stratigraphic gap*

		English	French	German	Italian
—	17749	**stratigraphic gap, parallel throw**	hiatus m stratigraphique	stratigraphische Sprungbreite f in der Schichtebene	lacuna f stratigrafica
—	17750	**stratigraphic separation**	rejet m stratigraphique	stratigraphische Sprunghöhe	rigetto m perpendicolare (o stratigrafico)
—	17751	**stratigraphical overlap, doubling reduplication**	recouvrement m stratigraphique	stratigraphische Wechselbreite f	ricoprimento m stratigrafico

stratigraphical throw, s. *stratigraphic separation*

		English	French	German	Italian
—	17752	**stratigraphy**	stratigraphie f, géologie f historique	Stratigraphie f, historische Geologie f	stratigrafia f, geologia f storica
—	17753	**stratum**	couche f, lit m	Schicht f, Lage f	falda f, strato m, letto m

	English	French	German	Italian
	17754 **straw**	paille *f*	Stroh *n*	paglia *f*
^	17755 **straw oil**	huile *f* de paille	Strohöl *n*	olio *m* paglierino
o	17756 **straw ring**	couronne *f* de paille	Strohkranz *m*	poggiastorte *m*, anello *m* di paglia
o	17757 **straw rope spinning machine**	machine *f* à faire des tresses de paille	Strohseilspinn- maschine *f*	macchina *f* per intrecciare la paglia
o	17758 **straw yellow**	jaune-paille	hellstrohgelb	giallo-paglia
—	17759 **stray**	formation *f* géologique imprévue	unvorhergesehene geologische Formation *f*	formazione *f* geologica imprevista
—	17760 **streak**	trait *m*	Strich *m*	striscia *f*, banda *f*
—	17761 **streak**	filet *m* de minerai	Erzschnur *f*, Erzader *f*	piccola vena *f* di minerale
—	17762 **streaked**	interstratifié	eingebettet, eingeschaltet	interstratificato, intercalato
o	17763 **streaked**	strieux	gestreift	rigato, a righe
o	17764 **streaked casting**	fusion *f* striée	gestreiftes Schmelzen *n*	fusione *f* rigata
—	17765 **streaked texture**	structure *f* des roches écrasées.	Gesteinsstruktur *f*, Flasertextur *f*	roccie *f pl.* a strati sottili
—	17766 **streaks**	schlieren	Schlieren *f*	filoni *m pl.*, vene *f pl.*
—	17767 **streaky**	strieux	gestreift	striato, a righe
—	17768 **streaky structure**	structure *f* strieuse	schlierige Textur *f*	struttura *f* marezzata
o	17769 **stream**	jet *m* de métal, coulée *f*	Giessstrahl *m*, Guss *m*	getto *m* di metalli, colata *f*
—	17770 **stream gold**	or *m* alluvionaire, or *m* alluvien	Seifengold *n*	oro *m* alluvionale
o	17771 **stream hardening**	trempe *m* par jet d'eau	Strahlhärtung *f*	tempera *f* al getto di acqua
o	17772 **stream tin**	étain *m* d'alluvion	Stromzinn *n*, Seifenzinn *n*	stagno *m* alluvionale
—	17773 **stream works**	alluvion *m* stannifère	Zinnseife *f*	alluvione *m* stannifero
—	17774 **strengite**	strengite *f*	Strengit *m*	strengite *f*

		English	French	German	Italian
o	17775	**strength**	résistance f	Festigkeit f	resistenza f, forza f
o	17776	**strength of blow**	force f du damage	Schlagstärke f	forza f della battuta
o	17777	**strength of pole**	intensité f polaire	Polstärke f	intensità f polare

strength under shock, *s. resistance to shock*

strength weld, *s. weld capable of taking stresses*

		English	French	German	Italian
o	17778	**strenght yield**	résistance f à l'étirage	Streckfestigkeit f	resistenza f a snervamento
o	17779	**strength tensile**	résistance f à la traction	Zugfestigkeit f	resistenza f a trazione
o	17780	**to strengthen the sand**	renforcer le sable	den Sand standfester machen	rinforzare la terra (o la sabbia)

strengthened coreprint, *s. enlarged coreprint*

		English	French	German	Italian
o	17781	**strengthening band**	ceinture f	Bandage f	cintura f, banda f di rinforzo
o	17782	**stress**	sollicitation f, effort m	Beanspruchung f	sollecitazione f, sforzo m
o	17783	**stress**	tension f	Spannung f	tensione f
o	17783a	**stress concentration**	concentration f d'efforts	Spannungskonzentration f	concentrazione f degli sforzi
o	17784	**stress crack**	crique f de tension	Spannungsriss m	cricca f di tensione
o	17784a	**stress cycle**	alternance f des efforts	Spannungswechsel	alternanza f delle tensioni
o	17785	**stress-free annealing**	recuit m de détente	Spannungsfreiglühen n	ricottura f di distensione
o	17786	**stress corrosion**	corrosion m sous tension	Spannungskorrosion f	corrosione f sotto tensione
o	17787	**stress relief anneal**	recuit m de détente	spannungsfreies Glühen n	ricottura f di distensione
o	17788	**stress relief contour**	rainure f pour la détente de tension	Entlastungsrille f	scanalatura f per eliminare la tensione
o	17789	**stress relieving**	recuit m pour l'élimination des tensions, stabilisation	Spannungsfreiglühen n	ricottura f di eliminazione delle tensioni, stabilizzazione f
o	17790	**stress relieving grooving**	décriquage m	Rissbeseitigung f	scriccatura f, rimozione delle cricche
o	17791	**stretched beam or girder**	poutrelle f étirée	gestreckter Balken m	trave f stirata

		English	French	German	Italian
—	17792	stretched out middle limb	flanc *m* médian étiré	ausgezogener Mittelschenkel *m*	fianco *m* mediano stirato
°	17793	stretched pole	pal *m* étiré	gestreckter Pfahl *m*	palo *m* stirato
—	17794	stretcher	tirant *m*	Zugbalken *m*	tirante *m*
—	17795	stretcher	tenseur *m*	Spannvorrichtung *f*	tenditore *m*
—	17796	stretcher-bar	affût *m* à colonne	Spannsäule *f*, Bohrsäule *f*	affusto *m* a colonna, trapano *m* a colonna
°	17796a	stretcher leveller	planeuse *f*	Richtmaschine *f*	raddrizzatrice *f* a stiramento
°	17797	stretching	étirage *m*	Ziehen *n*	stiratura *f*
°	17798	stretching force	effort *m* de tension	Spannkraft *f*	sforzo *m* di tensione
—	17799	stria	strie *f*	Rutschstreifen *m pl.*	stria *f*
—	17800	striated	strié	gestreift	striato
—	17801	striated boulder	gravier strié	gekritzeltes Geschiebe *n*	ghiaia *f* striata

striated pebble, *s. striated boulder*

		English	French	German	Italian
—	17802	striation	stries *f pl.*	Rutschrillen,*f pl.* Rutschstreifen *m pl.*	strie *f pl.*
°	17802a	striking	amorçage *m*	Vorgalvaniseren *n*	attivazione *f*
°	17803	to strickle (moulds)	calibrer, trousser	abstreichen	sagomare la forma
°	17804	strickle	trousseau *m*	Schabloniereinrichtung *f*	apparecchio *m* per sagomare
°	17805	strickle	racloir *m*	Abstreichwerkzeug *n*	raschiatoio *m*, raschietto *m*
°	17806	strickle	trousse *f*	Schablone *f*	sagoma *f*
°	17807	strickle bench board	plaque *f* de calibre	Ziehplatte *f*	placca *f* per sagomare
°	17808	strickle board	planche *f* principale	Hauptschablone *f*	sagoma *f* principale
°	17809	strickle board	planche *f* à trousser	Schablonierbrett *n*	sagoma *f*
°	17810	strickle board	drapeau *m*	Schablonenarm *m*	bandiera *f*
°	17811	strickling	troussage *m*	Schablonieren *n*	sagomatura *f*
°	17812	strickling board	trousse *f* ou calibre *m* amovible	Ziehschablone *f*	sagoma *f*
—	17813	to strike	frapper, percer	anbohren, klopfen	battere, perforare

		English	French	German	Italian
°	17814	**to strike money, to strike coins**	battre monnaie, monnayer	prägen, Gëld prägen	battere moneta
°	17815	**to strike off**	araser	abstreichen	rasare
		to strike the core, *s. to finish the core*			
—	17816	**strike, run**	direction *f*, allongement *m*	Streichen *n*	direzione *f*
^	17817	**strike**	découverte *f* de pétrole	Ölentdeckung *f*	scoperta *f* di petrolio
—	17818	**strike-fault**	faille *f* longitudinale	streichende Verwerfung *f*	faglia *f* longitudinale
°	17819	**strike**	racloir *m*, trousse *f*	Abstreicher *m*	raschietto *m*
—	17820	**strike break-through**	recoupe *f*	Durchhieb *m*	galleria *f* di collegamento
—	17821	**strike fault**	faille *f* longitudinale	Längsverwerfung *f*	faglia *f* longitudinale
—	17822	**strike joint**	diaclase *f* longitudinale	Längsspalte *f*	diaclasi *f* longitudinale
—	17823	**strike shift**	déplacement *m* suivant la direction	Verschiebung *f* im Streichen	spostamento *m* secondo la direzione
—	17824	**strike slip**	rejet *m* horizontal	horizontale Schublänge *f*	rigetto *m* orizzontale
—	17825	**strike-slip fault**	faille *f* à rejet horizontal	Seitenverschiebung *f*	faglia *f* a rigetto orizzontale
—	17826	**striker**	receveur, accrocheur, moulineur	Abzieher *m*, Anschläger *m*	ingabbiatore *m*
°	17827	**striking bar, post**	arbre *m* de trousseau	Spindel *f*	palo *m* di sagoma. albero *m* per sagomare
°	17828	**striking off (or up) sand**	réglage *m* du sable	Abstreichen *n* des Sandes	lisciatura *f* della superficie di una forma stivata d'argilla
°	17829	**striking plate**	gáche *f*	Schliessblech *n*	bocchetta *f*
°	17830	**to string**	lier	binden	legare
—	17831	**string**	petit filon *m*, veinule *f*	Ader *f*	filone *m*
	17832	**string**	fil *m*, ficelle *f*	Bindfaden *m*	filo *m*

		English	French	German	Italian
o	17833	string bead	cordon *m* à passe étroite	gerade Naht *f*	cordone *m* a passata stretta, cordone *m* rettilineo
^	17834	string of casing	colonne *f* de tubage	Rohrtour *f*, Rohrfahrt *f*	colonna *f* di tubaggio
—	17835	string water	colonne *f* de fermeture des eaux	Wasserschluss-kolonne *f*	colonna *f* di chiusura delle acque
		stringer, *s. line inclusion*			
—	17836	stringer	veinule *f*, filet *m*	Ader *f*, Erzschnur *f*	vena *f*, cordone *m*
o	17837	stringer plate	tôle *f* gouttière	Stringerplatte *f*	lamiera *f*, trincarino *m*
—	17838	stringing-piece	chapeau *m*	Kopfstück *n*	cappello *m* (d'armatura)
o	17839	to strip	dégalvaniser	entgalvanisieren	degalvanizzare
—	17840	to strip	rectifier	rektifizieren	rettificare
o	17841	to strip	démouler	Modell ausheben	sformare
—	17842	to strip	dépiler, enlever, découvrir, exploiter	abräumen, abdekken, gewinnen, abbauen	demolire (i pilastri), togliere, scoprire, estrarre, coltivare
		to strip the casting, *s. to open the casting*			
o	17843	to strip the ingots	démouler le lingot hors des lingotières	abstreifen strippen den Block aus der Kokille drücken	slingottare, strippare
o	17844	strip	bande *f*, feuillard *m*	Streifen *m*, Bandeisen *n*	nastro *m*, reggetta *f*
o	17845	strip chart	abaque *m* pour enregistrement de variables	Samplerlog	registro *m* delle variabili
		strip iron, *s. band iron or hoop iron*			
o	17846	strip mill, tire mill	train *m* à bandages	Bandstreifenwalzwerk *n*	laminatoio *m* per piattine
o	17847	strip mill train	train *m* à feuillards	Bandstrasse *f*	treno *m* di laminatoio per nastri
—	17848	strip mine	mine *f* à ciel ouvert	Tagebau *m*	miniera *f* a cielo aperto
—	17849	strip mining	exploitation *f* par excavateurs	Gewinnung *f* mittels Bagger	coltivazione *f* con scavatrici
o	17850	strip of material	bande *f* de matériel	Materialstreifen *m*	nastro *m* o striscia *f* di materiale

	English	French	German	Italian
— 17851	strip packing	remblayage *m* partiel (par arêtes de remblai)	Teilversatz *m*	ripiena *f* parziale
— 17852	strip pit	carrière *f*, exploitation a ciel ouvert	Steinbruch *m*, Tagebau *m*	cava *f*, coltivazione *f* a cielo aperto
° 17853	strip plate	large plat *m*	Platine *f*	largo piatto *m*
° 17854	strip rolling mill	laminoir *m* à feuillards	Bandwalzwerk *n*	laminatoio *m* per nastri
° 17855	strip steel	acier *m* feuillard	Bandstahl *m*	acciaio *m* in moietta
° 17856	strip thickness	épaisseur *m* du feuillard	Bandstärke *f*	spessore *m* del nastro
° 17857	stripped	démoulé *m*	abgezogen	strippato
^ 17858	stripped gas	gaz *m* dégazoliné	entbenziniertes Gas *n*	gas *m* degasolinato
° 17858a	stripper punch	poinçon *m* éjecteur	Ausstossstempel *m*	punzone *m* con espulsore
^ 17858b	stripper tank	cuve *f* de dépouillage	Mutterblechbad *n*	cella *f* di strappamento
^ 17859	stripper well	puits *m* presque épuisé	Melksonde *f*	pozzo *m* pompato con scarsa produzione
— 17860	stripped peneplain	pénéplaine fossile	Rumpffläche *f*	penepiano *m* fossile
^ 17861	stripper	tour *f* de rectification	Rektifizierungsturm *m*	torre *f* di rettifica
° 17862	stripper	grue-démouleuse *f*	Stripperkran *m*, Abstreifer *m*	slingottatore *m*
— 17863	stripper	déboiseur *m*	Holzrauber *m*	disarmatore *m*
— 17864	stripper	excavateur *m*	Bagger *m*	escavatore *m*
° 17865	stripping	démoulage *m*	Herausnehmen *n* des Modells aus der Form	sformatura *f*, disfattaggio *m*
° 17865a	stripping	écartement *m* du mandrin	Dornentfernung *f*	rimozione *f* del mandrino
° 17866	stripping	dégalvanisation *f*	Entgalvanisierung *f*	degalvanizzazione *f*
— 17867	stripping	découverture *f*, dépilage *m*	Freilegen *n*, Pfeilergewinnung *f*	rimozione *f* della copertura, disarmo *m* dei pilastri
^ 17868	stripping	distillation *f* primaire du pétrole	erste Destillation *f* des Erdöls	distillazione *f* primaria del petrolio
— 17869	stripping	exploitation *f* par excavateurs	Gewinnung *f* mittels Bagger	estrazione *f* con escavatori

		English	French	German	Italian
o	17870	**stripping crane, stripper**	grue-démouleuse f	Stripperkran m	gru f di sformatura
o	17870a	**stripping force**	force f de retrait	Abziehkraft f	forza f di ritiro
o	17871	**stripping machine**	démotteuse f	Aushebevorrich- tung f	smottatrice f, sfor- matrice f
o	17872	**stripping plate (foundry)**	peigne m	Abstreifkamm m, Abstreifplatte f	pettine m, piastra f di sformatura (o d'e- spulsione)
o	17873	**stripping plate gear wheel moulding machine**	machine f à mouler les engre- nages avec pla- teau-peigne	Zahnräderdurch- zugformmaschine f	formatrice f per in- granaggi a pettine
ˆ	17874	**stripping tower**	tour f de rectifi- cation	Rektifizierungsturm m	torre f di rettifica- zione
ˆ	17875	**stroke counter**	compte-coups m	Hubzähler m	conta-colpi m
–	17876	**stromeyerite**	stromeyérite f	Stromeyerit m	stromeyerite f
o	17877	**strong boiling**	bouillonnement m violent	heftiges Kochen n	ebollizione f violen- ta
o	17878	**strong sand**	sable m fort, sable m gras	fetter Sand m	terra f grassa
		strong welding, s. *strength welding*			
o	17879	**strongly mottled , pig iron**	fonte f truitée	stark halbiertes Roheisen n	ghisa f trotata
–	17880	**strontian**	strontiane f	Strontian m	stronziana f
–	17881	**strontianite**	strontianite f	Strontianit m	stronzianite f
–	17882	**strontium**	strontium m	Strontium n	stronzio m
o	17883	**structural alloy steel**	acier m de construc- tion allié	legierter Baustahl m	acciaio m legato da costruzioni
o	17884	**structural casting**	moulage m de cons- truction	Bauguss m	ghisa f da costruzio- ni
–	17885	**structural discor- dance**	discordance f méca- nique	tektonische Dis- kordanz f	discordanza f tettoni- ca
o	17886	**structural iron**	fer m profilé	Profileisen n	ferro m profilato
o	17887	**structural iron work**	fer m pour construc- tions, profils de fer	Formeisen n, Pro- fileisen n, Profile n pl.	profilati m pl. di fer- ro, sagomati m pl. (di ferro)
		structural mill, s. *shape rolling mill*			

		English	French	German	Italian
o	17888	structural part	pièce f de construc-tion	Konstruktionsteil m	pezzo m di costruzio-ne
o	17889	structural shape	profil m, profilé m	Profileisen n, Formeisen n	profilato m
o	17890	structural sheet iron	tôle f pour la cons-truction	Konstruktionsblech n	lamiera f da costru-zione
o	17891	(structural) ship steel	acier m pour cons-truction navale	Schiffbaustahl m	acciaio m per costru-zione navale
o	17892	structural steel	acier m (de) cons-truction	Baustahl m, Kon-struktionsstahl m	acciaio m da costru-zione
o	17893	structural steel for bridges	acier m pour la cons-truction des ponts	Brückenbaustahl m	acciaio m per costru-zione di ponti
o	17894	structural steel plate	tôle f de construction	Baublech n	lamiera f da costru-zione
o	17895	structure of iron ore	structure f des minerais de fer	Gefüge n des Ei-senerzes	struttura f del mine-rale di ferro
—	17896	structure test-hole	sondage m d'explo-ration	Schürfbohrung f	sondaggio m esplora-tivo
o	17897	struddle	pilot m, montant m	Schachtbolzen m	palo m, montante m, bullone m
—	17898	strutting	entretoisement m	Verstrebung f	puntellamento m
—	17899	strutting board	bois m de garnis-sage	Schalholz n	legno m di rivesti-mento
—	17900	strüverite	strüvérite f	Struverit m	struverite f
—	17901	struvite	struvite f	Struvit m	struvite f
—	17902	stub	pilier m de galerie	Streckenpfeiler m	pilastro m di galleria
—	17903	stud	tige f	Stift m	asta f
o	17903a	stud	support m d'âme	Kernstütze f	supporto m per anima
o	17904	stud bolt, set pin, stud	prisonnier m	Stiftschraube f, Passtift m	bullone m senza te-sta (prigioniero)
o	17904a	studding	soudure f à prisonniers	Schweissen mit Stiftbolzenverstär-kung f	saldatura f con perni prigionieri
—	17905	stuff	gangue f	Gangmineral n	ganga f

stuffed seam, s. resistance butt weld

stuffing box gland, s. gland

| — | 17906 | stull | butte f. étançon m | Stempel m, Strebe f | ponte m di lavoro, palchetto m, puntel-lo m |

		English	French	German	Italian
−	17907	stull timbering	boisage *m* étayé	Stempelschlag *m*	armatura *f* rinforzata, palchetto *m* rinforzato
−	17908	stulled stope	taille *f* étayée	verzimmerter Stoss *m*	taglio *m* rinforzato
−	17909	stull heading	cale *f* de bois	Stützhholz *n*	puntello *m* di sostegno, zeppa *f*
−	17910	stulm	fendue *f*, galerie *f* au jour	Stollen *m*	cunicolo *m* (laterale), galleria *f* a giorno
−	17911	stump	pilier *m*, stot *m*	Bein *n*, Pfeiler *m*	pilastro *m*, ceppo *m*
−	17912	stump pillar	pilier *m* de galerie	Streckenpfeiler *m*	pilastro *m* di galleria
−	17913	stutzite	stutzite *f*	Stützit *m*	stutzite *f*
−	17914	stylolite	stylolithe *f*	Stylolith *m*	stilolite *f*
−	17915	stylolitic structure	structure *f* styloliti-que	stylolithische Textur *f*	struttura *f* colonnare
°	17916	Styrian pig iron	fonte *f* de Styrie	steierisches Roheisen *n*	ghisa *f* di Stiria
°	17917	Styrian roasting furnace	four *m* de grillage styrien	steirischer Röst-ofen *m*	forno *m* di torrefazione stiriano
°	17918	sub blank	réduction *f* sans filetage	Reduktion *f* ohne Gewinde	riduzione *f* senza filet-tatura
		sub-boundary structure, *s. veining*			
−	17919	subdrift	voie *f* intermédiaire	Teilstrecke *f*	galleria *f* intermedia
−	17920	subdrift caving	exploitation *f* en sous-étages avec foudroyage	Zwischensohlen-bruchbau *m*	coltivazione *f* a strati intermedi con franamento
^	17921	sub-drill pipe nipples	joint *m* de tube court	Gestängewechsel *m* für kurzen Stangen	riduzione *f* con due dia-metri diversi per aste
°	17922	to subject	recuire intermé-diairement	zwischenglühen	ricuocere ad intermitten-za
		sublevel caving, *s. subdrift caving*			
°	17923	to sublimate	sublimer	sublimieren	sublimare
°	17924	sublimation	sublimation *f*	Sublimation *f*	sublimazione *f*
°	17925	sublimation apparatus	appareil *m* de su-blimation	Sublimationsappa-rat *m*	apparecchio *m* di subli-mazione
−	17926	submagma	magma *m* secondaire	sekundäres Magma *n*	magma *m* secondario

		English	French	German	Italian
−	17927	submarine valley	vallée f sous-marine	Unterseetal n	valle f sottomarina
^	17928	submersible barge	ponton m de forage submersible	versenkbare Bohrplattform	piattaforma f sommergibile
°	17929	sub-press die	moule m demi-libre	halbfreier Stempel m	stampo m semilibero
°	17930	subsequent treatment	traitement m postérieur	Nachlehandlung f	trattamento m posteriore
−	17931	subsidiary anticline	anticlinal m secondaire	sekundäre Antiklinale f	anticlinale f secondaria
		subsidiary-fault, s. branching fault			
−	17932	sub-soil	sol m inerte	Mineralboden m	suolo m inerte
°	17932a	sub-sow block	plaque f d'assise du moule	Stempelunterplatte f	pezzo m di riempimento dello stampo
°	17933	substitute steel	acier m de remplacement	Austauschstahl m	acciaio m di sostituzione
°	17934	substructure	soubassement m	Unterbau m	sottostruttura f, basamento m
		subtuberant mountain, s. batholith.			
°	17935	sub-zero treatment	traitement m par le froid	Tieftemperaturbehandlung f	trattamento m sotto zero
°	17936	sub-zero treatment	réfrigération f	Tiefkühlung f	sub-raffreddamento m
−	17937	succinite	succinite f	Succinit m	succinite f, ambra f
−	17938	sucker rod	tige f de pompage	Pumpengestänge n	asta f di pompaggio
−	17939	sucker-rod line	câble m pour les tiges de pompage	Seil für Pumpengestänge n	cavo m per le aste di pompaggio
−	17940	sucker-rod spear	taraud m pour tiges de pompage	Fangdorn m für Pumpengestänge n	maschio m per le aste di pompaggio
−	17941	to suck-in the air	aspirer l'air	die Luft ansaugen	aspirare l'aria
−	17942	to suck	filtrer par aspiration	abnutschen, absaugen	filtrare per aspirazione
^	17943	sucker, suction hose	tuyau m d'aspiration	Saugschlauch m	tubo m di aspirazione
−	17944	sucker rod	barre f de pompage	Pumpenständer m	asta f di pompaggio
^	17945	sucker elevator	élévateur m de tige	Gestängeelevator m	elevatore m di aste
^	17946	sucker rod guide	lanterne f de guidage	Gestängeführung f	guida f dell'asta di pompaggio
^	17947	sucker rod hanger	râtelier m des tiges de pompage	Rechen m für Pumpengestänge	rastrelliera f delle aste di pompaggio

	English	French	German	Italian
^ 17948	**sucker rod pumping**	pompage *m* par barre de pompage	Auspumpen *n* durch Pumpenständer	pompaggio *m* con albero di aspirazione
^ 17949	**sucker sand**	sable *m* absorbant	einsaugender Sand *m*	sabbia *f* assorbente
o 17949a	**sucking**	réduction *f* locale du diamètre	örtliche Querschnittsabnahme *f*	riduzione *f* locale del diametro
o 17950	**suction air**	air *m* aspiré	Saugluft *f*	aria *f* aspirata
o 17951	**suction air chamber**	chambre *f* à air de la conduite d'aspiration	Saugwindkessel *m*	camera *f* d'aria aspirante
— 17952	**suction bailer**	drague *f* à succion	Vakuumbüchse *f*	draga *f* aspirante
o 17953	**suction basket, jet**	crépine *f* d'aspiration	Saugkorb *m*	succhierola *f*
o 17953a	**suction casting**	coulée *f* sous vide	Vakuumguss *m*	colata *f* sotto vuoto
o 17954	**suction conduit**	conduite *f* d'aspiration	Saugleitung *f*	condotto *m* aspirante
o 17955	**suction conveyor**	suceuse *f*	Saugvorrichtung *f*	impianto *m* aspirante
	suction cupola, *s. fan cupola*			
o 17955a	**suction gas**	gaz *m* pauvre d'aspiration	Sauggas *n*	gas *m* scarso d'aspirazione
^ 17956	**suction hose**	tube *m* flexible d'aspiration	Saugschlauch *m*	tubo *m* flessibile di aspirazione
	suction passage, *s. suction port*			
o 17957	**suction pipe**	tuyau *m* d'aspiration	Absaugerohr *n*	tubo *m* d'aspirazione
o 17958	**suction port or passage**	conduit *m* d'aspiration	Saugkanal *m*	canale *m* d'aspirazione
— 17959	**suction pump**	pompe *f* aspirante	Saugpumpe *f*	pompa *f* aspirante
o 17960	**suction side**	côte *f* de l'aspiration	Saugseite *f*	lato *m* aspirante
^ 17961	**suction valve**	soupape *f* d'aspiration	Saugventil *n*	valvola *f* aspirante
— 17962	**suction ventilator**	aérateur *m* aspirateur	Luftabsauger *m*	areatore *m* aspiratore
o 17963	**sudden change of temperature**	variation *f* brusque de température	plötzlicher Temperaturwechsel *m*	cambiamento *m* improvviso di temperatura
	sulfide, *s. sulphide*			
^ 17964	**sulfonate**	sulfonate *m*	Sulfonat *n*	solfonato *m*
^ 17965	**sulfonic acid**	acide *m* sulfonique	Sulfonsäure *f*	acido *m* sulfonico

	English	French	German	Italian
17966	sulforization	sulfuration *f.* sulfitage *m*	Schwefelung *f*	solforazione *f*
^ 17967	sulfurized oil	huile *f* sulfurée	Schwefelöl *n*	olio *m* solforato
° 17968	sull	couche *f* d'oxyde	Eisenoxydschicht	strato *m* d'ossido di ferro
° 17968a	sulling	oxydation *f* après décapage	Oxydation nach Beizung *f*	ossidazione *f* post-de-capaggio
° 17969	sulphate of calcium, gypsum	sulfate *m* de chaux, plâtre *m*	schwefelsaurer Kalk *m*, Gips *m*	solfato *m* di calcio, gesso *m*
° 17970	sulphate of copper, blue vitriol	sulfate *m* de cuivre, vitriol *m*	Kupfervitriol *m*, Kupfersulfat *n*	solfato *m* di rame
° 17971	sulphate of magnesium	sulfate *m*	schwefelsaures Magnesium *n*	solfato *m* di magnesio
° 17972	sulphate of potassium	sulfate *m* de potasse	schwefelsaures Kali *n*, Kaliumsulfat *n*	solfato *m* potassico o di potassa
° 17973	sulphate of sodium	sulfate *m* de soude	schwefelsaures Natron *n*	solfato *m* sodico o di soda
° 17974	sulphate of zinc, white vitriol	sulfate *m* de zinc	Zinkvitriol *n*, Zinksulfat *n*	solfato *m* di zinco
° 17975	sulphatising roasting	grillage *m* de sulfatation	sulfatisierende Röstung *f*	torrefazione *f* per eliminazione dello zolfo
° 17976	sulphide of antimony	sulfure *m* d'antimoine	Schwefelantimon *n*	solfuro *m* d'antimonio
° 17977	sulphide roast	grillage *m* sulfatant (ou de sulfatation)	sulfatisierende Röstung *f*	torrefazione *f* per eliminazione dello zolfo
— 17978	sulphoborite	sulfoborite *f*	Sulfoborit *m*	sulfoborite *f*
° 17979	sulphocyanide of ammonium	sulfocyanure *m* d'ammonium	Rhodanammonium *n*	solfocianuro *m* ammonico
— 17980	sulphohalite	sulfohalite *f*	Sulfohalit *m*	sulfohalite *f*
— 17981	sulphur	soufre *m*	Schwefel *m*	zolfo *m*
° 17982	sulphur compound	composé *m* sulfuré	Schwefelverbindung *f*	composto *m* solforato
° 17983	sulphur-furnace	four *m* à soufre	Schwefelofen *m*	forno *m* di zolfo
° 17984	sulphur print	essai *m* Baumann	Baumannabdruck *m*	prova *f* Baumann

		English	French	German	Italian
°	17985	sulphuretted hydrogen	hydrogène *m* sulfuré	Schwefelwasserstoff *m*	idrogeno *m* solforato, acido *m* solfidrico
°	17986	sulphuretted hydrogen chamber	chambre *f* d'hydrogène sulfuré	Schwefelwasserstoffraum *m*	camera *f* per l'idrogeno solforato
°	17987	sulphurous acid	acide *m* sulfureux	schweflige Säure *f*	acido *m* solforoso
—	17988	sulphurous iron ore	minerai *m* de fer sulfureux	schwefelhaltiges Eisenerz *n*	minerale *m* di ferro solforoso
°	17989	sulphuric anhydride	anhydride *m* sulfurique	Schwefelsäureanhydrid *n*	anidride *f* solforica
—	17990	sulvanite	sulvanite *f*	Sulvanit *m*	sulvanite *f*
—	17991	sump	puisard *m*	Schachtsumpf *m*	foro *m* di scarico per le acque
—	17992	sump	bassin *m* à boue	Schlammgrube *f*	pozzo *m* (pozzetto) di scolo
^	17993	sump hole	puisard *m*	Schlammbehälter *m*	bacino *m* di raccolta dei fanghi
—	17994	sump pump	pompe *f* de mines	Grubenpumpe *f*	pompa *f* da miniera
—	17995	sump shot	coup *m* de bouchon	Einbruchschuss *m*	colpo *m* di rottura
^	17996	sump tank	réservoir *m* de dépôt	Absatzbehälter *m*	serbatoio *m* di riserva
—	17997	sumping cut	havée *f* initiale	Einbruchschnitt *m*	taglio *m* iniziale
—	17998	sun crack	fissure *f* de dessiccation	Trockenriss *m*, Trocknungsriss *m*	fessura *f* per disseccazione
—	17999	sunk well	fonçage *m* tubulaire, puits *m* à enfocement sous charge	Senkbrunnen *m*	pozzo *m* tubolare, perforazione *f* tubolare
—	18000	sunstone	pierre *f* de soleil	Sonnenstein *m*	pietra *f* del sole
°	18001	supercooling	surfusion *f*	Unterkühlung *f*	soprafusione *f*
°	18002	super cutting steel	acier *m* à coupe rapide	Schnellstahl *m*	acciaio *m* ad altissima velocità
°	18003	superficial stress	tension *f* superficielle	Oberflächenbeanspruchung *f*	tensione *f* superficiale
°	18004	superficial treatment	traitement *m* superficiel	Oberflächenbehandlung *f*	trattamento *m* superficiale
^	18004a	superfines	fraction *f* fine	Feinstanteil *m*	frazione *f* fine

		English	French	German	Italian
o	18005	superheat	surchauffe f	Überhitzung f	surriscaldamento m, calore m di surriscaldamento
o	18006	superheated iron	fonte f surchauffée	überhitztes Eisen n	ghisa f eccessivamente riscaldata
o	18007	superheater	surchauffeur m	Überhitzer m	surriscaldatore m
o	18008	super-heater collector	collecteur m surchauffeur	Überhitzer-Sammelkammer f	collettore m del surriscaldatore
o	18009	superheater boiler	chaudière f à réchauffeur	Kessel f mit Überhitzer	caldaia f con riscaldatore
o	18010	superheater and coil	tube m et serpentin surchauffeurs	Ueberhitzer m und Rohrschlange	tubo m e serpentino surriscaldatori
o	18011	superheating, superheat	surchauffe f, surchauffage m	Überhitzen n, Überhitzung f	calore m di surriscaldamento
o	18012	superheating coil	serpentin m surchauffeur	Heizrohrschlange f	serpentino m surriscaldatore
o	18013	superheating tube	tuyau m surchauffeur	Ueberhitzerrohr n	tubo m surriscaldatore
^	18014	super heavy oil	huile f extra-dense	überdichtes Öl n	olio m superdenso
o	18015	superhigh speed steel, S.H.S.S.	acier m extra-rapide, acier m extra-dur	Extraschnellstahl m	acciaio m extrarapido
—	18016	superincumbent	superposé	überliegend	sovrapposto
—	18017	superincumbent bed	couche f du toit	Hangendflöz n	strato m del tetto
o	18018	to supersaturate	sursaturer	übersättigen	sovrasaturare
o	18019	supersaturated	sursaturé	übersättigt	soprasaturo
o	18020	supersaturated iron	fer m sursaturé	übersättigtes Eisen n	ferro m soprasaturato
o	18021	super saturation	sursaturation f	Übersättigung f	sovrasaturazione f
o	18022	supersonic, magnaflux, magnetic powder apparatus	appareil m à ultrasons métalloscopique à poudres magnétiques	Ultraschallgerät n mit Magnetpulver	apparecchiatura f ad ultrasuoni metalloscopica a polveri magnetiche

		English	French	German	Italian
o	18023	super-sulphated cement	ciment *m* sursul- faté	Sulfat-Hütten- zement *m*	cemento *m* metallurgi- co sursolfatato
	18024	supervision	surveillance *f*	Aufsicht *f*	sorveglianza *f*
	18025	supplementary cargo	cargaison *f* sup- plémentaire	Beiladung *f*	carico *m* supplementa- re
o	18026	supply of coal by means of a screw conveyor	amenée *f* du charbon par vis sans fin	Kohlenzufuhr *f* durch Förder- schnecke	trasporto *m* di carbo- ne a coclea
o	18027	supply oh heat	adduction *f* de chaleur	Wärmezufuhr *f*	adduzione *f* di calore
o	18028	supplying the coal	amenée *f* du charbon	Anfahren *n* der Kohlen	trasporto *m* del carbo- ne
o	18029	support for water supply pipe	étrier *m* de sus- pension du tuyau d'arrivée	Hängeeisen *n* des Zuflussrohres	tirante *m* sospeso del tubo d'entrata
o	18030	support of the funnel	support *m* de la trémie	Unterstützung *f* des Trichters	sostegno *m* della tra- moggia
—	18031	supported stope	taille *f* boisée	gezimmerter Stoss *m*	taglio *m* rinforzato
—	18032	supported stopes	exploitation *f* avec soutènement du toit	Abbau *m* mit Un- terstützung des Hangenden	coltivazione *f* con pun- tellamento del tetto
—	18033	supporting	soutènement *m*	Unterstützung *f*	puntellamento *m*, soste- gno *m*
o	18034	supporting brackets	support *m*	Tragpratzen *f pl.*, Tragpratze *f*	supporto *m*, mensola *f* di sostegno
o	18035	supporting column	colonne *f* de sou- tènement	Stützrohrsäule *f*	colonna *f* di sostegno
—	18036	supporting curb	cadre *m* porteur	Tragkorb *m*, Traggeviert *n*	quadro *m* portante
o	18037	supporting girders	treillis *m* de pou- tre	Trägerüst *n*	traliccio *m* di travi
—	18038	supporting pack	arête *f* de rem- blai	Bergerippe *f*	spigolo *m* della ripiena

supporting reinforcement, *s. longitudinal reinforcing iron bar*

o	18039	supporting ring	rondelle *f* de sup- port de ballon	Unterlagring *m*	anello *m* portastorte

	English	French	German	Italian
18040	surface	surface f, aire f	Oberfläche f	superficie f
— 18041	surface	jour m	Tagesoberfläche f	cielo aperto
^ 18042	surface-active agent	agent m tensio-actif	oberflächenaktives Mittel n	agente m tensio-attivo
— 18043	surface casing	tube-guide m	Standrohr n	tubo-guida m
° 18043a	surface checking	fissuration f superficielle	geritzte Oberfläche f	incrinatura f superficiale
° 18044	surface chill	refroidisseur m de surface	Aussenkokille f	raffreddatore m superficiale
° 18045	surface condition	état m de surface	Oberflächenbeschaffenheit f	natura f della superficie
	surface converting, s. case hardening			
° 18046	surface crack	crique f à la surface	Oberflächenriss m	fessura f (o cricca f) superficiale
° 18047	surface crust	croûte f superficielle	Oberflächenkruste f	crosta f superficiale
° 18048	surface defect	défaut m de surface	Oberflächenfehler m	difetto m superficiale
° 18049	surface development	développement m de la surface	Oberflächenentwicklung f	sviluppo m della superficie
° 18050	surface folding	rides $f pl.$	Runzeln $f pl.$	rughe $f pl.$
° 18051	surface folding	peau f de crapaud, friasses $f pl.$	Schlieren $f pl.$	rugosità f, pelle f di rospo
° 18052	surface gauge	trusquin m	Parallelreisser m	tracciatore m, traccia-parallele m
° 18053	to surface harden	tremper superficiellement	oberflächenhärten	temprare alla superficie
° 18054	surface hardening	trempe f superficielle	Oberflächenhärtung f	tempra f superficiale
^ 18055	surface hole	trou m pour colonne de tubage	Oberflächenrohrtourloch n	foro m per la «surface string»
° 18056	surface in contact with the steam	plaques $f pl.$ baignées par la vapeur	vom Dampf berührte Fläche	piastre $f pl.$ a contatto col vapore
—18057	surface mining	exploitation f à ciel ouvert	Tagebau m	coltivazione f a cielo aperto
	surface converting, s. case hardening			
°18058	surface of solubilty	surface f de solubilité	Löslichkeitsfläche f	superficie f di solubilità

		English	French	German	Italian
—	18059	**surface out-croppings**	affleurements *m pl.*	Ausgehende *n*	affioramenti *m pl.*
—	18060	**surface plant**	carreau *m*	Tagesanlage *f*	piazzale *m* (di minie-ra)
°	18061	**surface pinholes**	piqûres *f pl.* de sur-face	Oberflächenpo-ren *f pl.*	camolatura *f* superfi-ciale, butteratùre *f pl.* superficiali
—	18062	**surface pit**	carrière *f* à ciel ouvert	Tagegrube *f*	cava *f* a cielo aperto
°	18063	**surface play of iron**	miroitement *m* de la fonte	Spiel *n* des Eisens	giuoco *m* della ghisa
°	18064	**surface protection**	protection *f* superfi-cielle	Oberflächenschutz *m*	protezione *f* superficia-le
°	18065	**surface roughness**	rudesse *f* de la sur-face	Oberflächenrauheit *f*	scabrosita *f* della su-perficie
°	18066	**surface shrinkage**	retassure *f* ouverte	offener Lunker *m*, Aussenlunker *m*	risucchio *m* aperto
—	18067	**surface shooting**	tir *m* des mines à partir de la surface	Abschiessen *n* von der Oberfläche aus	esplosione *f* di mine partendo dalla super-ficie
°	18068	**surface tempera-ture**	température *f* exté-rieure	Aussentemperatur *f*	temperatura *f* esterna
—	18069	**surface termina-tion**	affleurement *m*	Ausgehende *n*	affioramento *m*
°	18070	**surface treatment**	traitement *m* su-perficiel	Oberflächenbehand-lung *f*	trattamento *m* super-ficiale
		surface vitrification, *s. sintering*			
—	18071	**surface winning**	exploitation *f* à ciel ouvert	Tagebaubetrieb *m*	coltivazione *f* a cie-lo aperto
ˆ	18072	**surfactant muds**	boues *f pl.* tensio-actives	Spülungen *f pl.* mit oberflächenentspan-nenden Zusätzen	fanghi *m pl.* tensio-attivi
ˆ	18073	**surge chamber**	chambre *f* d'une pompe	Pumpenkammer *f*	bottiglia *f* di una pom-pa
ˆ	18074	**surge drum**	accumulateur *m* de compensation	Kompensations-sammler *m*	accumulatore *m* di compensazione
ˆ	18075	**surge tank**	réservoir *m* de com-pensation	Kompensations-behälter *m*	serbatoio *m* di com-pensazione

English	French	German	Italian

surplus, *s. overmeasure*

18076	**suroxide**	péroxyde *m*	Superoxyd *n*	perossido *m*
18077	**suspended ring**	anneau *m* suspendu	niederhängender Ring *m*	anello *m* sospeso
18078	**suspended solids**	particules *f pl.* en suspension	suspendierte Teilchen *n pl.*	particelle *f pl.* in sospensione
18079	**suspended tube**	tuyau *m* suspendu	hängendes Rohr *m*	tubo *m* sospeso

suspension, *s. hanging*

18080	**suspension hook**	étrier *m* de suspension	Aufhängebügel *m*	gancio *m* di sospensione
18081	**suspension iron**	fer *m* de suspension	Hängeeisen *n*	ferro *m* di sospensione
18082	**suspension wire**	fil *m* de suspension	Aufhängungsdraht *m*	filo *m* di sospensione
18083	**sutural joint**	stylolithe *f*	Stylolith *m*	stilolite *f*
18084	**svabite**	svabite *f*	Svabit *m*	svabite *f*
18085	**svanbergite**	svanbergite *f*	Svanbergit *m*	svanbergite *f*
18086	**to swab**	pistonner	pistonieren	pistonare
18087	**to swab in**	mettre en production par pistonnage	ankolben	avviare la produzione con pistonaggio

swab, *s. dusting brush*

18088	**swab**	piston *m*	Kolben *m*	pistone *m* (valvolato)
18089	**swabbing**	pistonnage *m*	Pistonieren *n*	pistonaggio *m*
18089a	**swabbing**	enduit *m*	Schlechtung *f*	rivestimento *m*
18090	**swabbing cup**	cuvette *f* du piston pour pistonnage	Pistonierkolbengehäuse *n*	coppetta *f* del pistone per pistonare il pozzo
18091	**swabbing effect**	effet *m* de pistonnement	Kolbenwirkung *f*	effetto *m* del pistonaggio
18092	**swabbing line**	câble *m* de piston	Pistonierseil *n*	cavo *m* di pistone
18093	**swabbing production**	production *f* par pistonnage	Kolbenproduktion *f*	produzione *f* per pistonaggio
18094	**swabbing test**	essai *m* par pistonnage	Kolbenversuch *m*	prova *f* per pistonaggio

		English	French	German	Italian
^	18095	**swabbing well**	puits *m* en piston-nage	gekolbte Sonde *f*	pozzo *m* in pistonaggio
—	18096	**swag**	affaissement *m* du toit	Absenkung *f* der Firste	cedimento *m* del tetto
°	18097	**to swage**	estamper, matricer	gesenkschmieden	forgiare su stampo, stampare
^	18098	**swage**	effilement *m*	Verjüngung *f*	oliva *f*, rastremazione *f*
°	18099	**swage**	moulure *f*	Gesimskranz *m*	modanatura *f* (d'irriga-mento)
°	18100	**swaging**	effilement *m*	Verjüngung *f*	rastremazione *f* alle estremità
°	18100a	**swaging**	réduction *f* de section	Querschnittsab-nahme *f*	riduzione *f* di sezione
°	18101	**sweat**	peau *f*	Schale *f*, Haut *f*	segregazione *f*
°	18102	**sweater**	chaudière *f* de res-suage	Schwitzkessel *m*	caldaia *f* di essuda-zione
^	18103	**sweating, sweat out**	ressuage *m*	Schwitzen *n*, Ausschwitzen *n*	essudazione *f*
^	18104	**sweating oven**	four *m* de ressuage	Schwitzofen *m*	forno *m* per la rimozio-ne della paraffina in cristalli
°	18104a	**sweating out**	apparition *f* de glo-bules	Kügelchenbildung *f*	apparizione *f* di globuli
^	18105	**swedge**	dégorgeoir *m*. à olive	Reduktionsbohrer *m*	allargatore *m* ad oliva
^	18106	**swedge nipple**	robinet *m* de réduction	Reduktionshahn *m*	rubinetto *m* di riduzione
°	18107	**Swedish bloomery fire, Lancashire hearth**	bas-foyer *m*, feu d'affinerie sué-dois	Lancashire-Frisch-herd *m*	fuoco *m* d'affinaggio Lancashire
°	18108	**Swedish charcoal iron**	fer *m* au bois dit de Suède	schwedisches Holzkohleneisen *n*	ferro *m* Svezia a car-bone di legna
°	18109	**Swedish iron**	fer *m* de Suède	schwedisches Eisen *n*	ferro *m* di Svezia
°	18110	**Swedish modern bloomery fire**	bas-foyer *m*, feu *m* d'affinerie suédois	Lancashire-Frisch-herd *m*	fuoco *m* d'affinaggio Lancashire
°	18111	**Swedish pig iron**	fonte *f* de Suède	schwedisches Roheisen *n*	ghisa *f* di Svezia
°	18112	**to sweep the mould, to strickle**	trousser le moule	die Form abdrehen	sagomare la forma
°	18112a	**sweep**	planche *f* à trousser	Schablonierbrett *n*	sagoma *f*, randa *f*

		English	French	German	Italian
°	18113	sweep moulding	moulage *m* au ga-barit	Schablonenformerei *f*	formatura *f* a sagoma
°	18114	sweep templer, strickle board	planche *f* à trousser	Armschablone *f*	sagoma *f* principale -
°	18115	sweeping	troussage *m*	Schablonenforme-rei *f*	formatura *f* a sagoma, (o a bandiera)
°	18116	sweeping out, sweeping	balayage *m*	Spülen *n*, Spülgas-behandlung *f*	lavaggio *m* gassoso
^	18117	sweet crude	brut *m* adouci	entschwefeltes Rohöl *n*	greggio *m* non solforo-so
^	18118	sweeting, sweetening	adoucissement *m*	Entschwefelung *f*	addolcimento *m*
	18119	to swell	forcer	treiben	forzare
	18120	to swell	gonfler, bomber	aufquellen	gonfiare, bombare, di-latare
	18121	swell	bombement *m*, renflement *m*	Ausbauchung *f*	rigonfiamento *m*, bom-batura *f*
	18122	swell	remous *m*	Wellenschlag *m*	vortice *m*, onda *f* lun-ga
°	18123	swell	forçage *m*	Treibstelle *f*	forzatura *f*, rigonfia-mento *m*, prominenza *f*
_	18124	swelling shale	argile *f* gonflante	aufquellender Ton *m*	argilla *f* rigonfiante
°	18125	swept core	noyau *m* troussé	schablonierter Kern *m*	anima *f* sagomata
^	18126	swilling tank	cuve *f* de lavage	Waschtrog *m*	vasca *f* di lavaggio
—	18127	swine-stone	anthraconite *f*, calcaire *m*	Anthrakonit *m*	antraconite *f*
°	18128	swing crane	grue *f* pivotante	Drehkran *m*	gru *f* girevole
^	18129	swing pipe	tube *m* à genouil-lère	Schwenkrohr *m*	tubo *m* a ginocchiera
^	18130	swinging point	attaque *f* pivotante	Drehverbindung *f*	attacco *m* girevole
°	18131	swinging spray	pistolet *m* oscillant	Schwingspritz-pistole *f*	pistola *f* oscillante

swinging sieve, *s. shaking sieve*

	English	French	German	Italian
° 18132	switch tongue	aiguille *f* de changement de voie	Weichenzunge *f*	ago *m* da scambio
18133	switchboard	tableau *m* de distribution	Schaltbrett *n*	quadro *m* di distribuzione
— 18134	switchboy, switchman	aiguilleur *m*	Weichensteller *m*	guardascambio *m*
° 18135	switching, reversing	renversement *m*	Umkehrung *f*, Umschaltung *f*	inversione *f*
° 18136	switching arrangement, reversing arrangement	appareil *m* de renversement	Umsteuervorrichtung *f*	apparecchio *m* d'inversione
— 18137	swivel	émerillon *m*	Spülkopf *m*	perno *m* (girevole)
— 18138	swivel, swivel rod	tête *f* d'injection	Spülkopf *m*	testa *f* di sonda
^ 18139	swivel bail adapter	manche *m* de prise placé sur la tête d'injection	Adapter *m* am Einspritzkopf angeordnet	manico *m* di presa per elevatori posto sulla testa di iniezione
° 18140	swivel damper	registre *m* tournant	Drehschieber *m*	registro *m* girevole
— 18141	swivel book	croc *m* à tourniquet	Wirbelhaken *m*	gancio *m* a molinello
— 18142	swivel joint	attaque *f* à joints en acier	bewegliche Stahlzapfenlagerung *f*	attacco *m* snodato in acciaio
18143	sworn chemist	chimiste *m* assermenté	vereidigter Chemiker *m*	chimico *m* giurato
— 18144	syenitic porphyry	porphyre *m* syénitique	Syenitporphyr *m*	porfido *m* sienitico
— 18145	syenoid	syénite *f* à feldspathoïde	Syenoid *m*	sienite *f* a feldspatoidi
— 18146	sylvanite	silvanyte *f*	Sylvanit, Schrifterz *n*	silvanite *f*
— 18147	sylvester	arrache-étais *m*	Raubvorrichtung *f*	strappa-puntelli *m*
— 18148	sylvite, sylvin	sylvine *f*	Sylvin *m*	silvite *f*
— 18149	symmetric anticline	anticlinal *m* symétrique	symmetrische Antiklinale *f*	anticlinale *f* simmetrica
— 18150	symmetrical fold	pli *m* symétrique	symmetrische Falte *f*	piega *f* simmetrica

		English	French	German	Italian
—	18151	symplektic intergrowth	association *f* symplectique	symplektische Durchwachsung *f*	associazione *f* simplettica
—	18152	symplektic texture	texture *f* symplectique	symplektische Struktur *f*	struttura *f* simplettica
—	18153	symplektite	symplectite *f*	Simplektit *m*	simplectite *f*
—	18154	symplesite	symplésite *f*	Symplesit *m*	simplesite *f*
—	18155	synadelphite	synadelphite *f*	Synadelphit *m*	sinadelfite *f*
—	18156	synchronous deposits	dépôts *m pl.* synchroniques	synchrone Ablagerungen *f pl.*	depositi *m pl.* sincroni
—	18157	synclinal fault	faille *f* synclinale	synclinale Verwerfung *f*	faglia *f* sinclinale
—	18158	synclinal limb	flanc *m* synclinal	Muldenflügel *m*	fianco *m* sinclinale
—	18159	synclinal turn	charnière *f* synclinale	Muldenbiegung *f*, Muldenscharnier *n*	cresta *f* sinclinale
—	18160	synclinal valley	vallée *f* synclinale	Muldental *n*, Synklinaltal *n*	valle *f* di sinclinale
—	18161	syncline	pli *m* synclinal	Synkline, Synklinale *f*	sinclinale *f*, piega *f* sinclinale
—	18162	synclinorium	synclinorium *m*	Synklinorium *n*	sinclinorio *m*
^	18163	syneresis	synérèse *f*	Sinerese *f*	sineresi *f*
—	18164	syngenesis	syngénèse *f*	Syngenese *f*	singenesi *f*
—	18165	syngenite	syngénite *f*	Syngenit *m*	singenite *f*
—	18166	syngony	syngonie *f*	Symmetrie *f*	simmetria *f*
—	18167	syntexis	syntexis *f*, assimilation *f* magmatique	Syntexis *f*, magmatische Assimilation *f*	sintesi *f*, assimilazione *f* magmatica
^	18168	synthesis pipe	tube *m* pour installations de synthèse	Rohr *n* für Syntheseanlagen	tubo *m* per sintesi
^	18169	synthetic fuel	carburant *m* de synthèse	synthetischer Brennstoff *m*	carburante *m* sintetico
°	18170	synthetic iron	fonte *f* synthétique (ou de synthèse)	synthetisches Roheisen *n*	ghisa *f* sintetica
°	18171	synthetic sand	sable *m* synthétique	synthetischer Sand *m*	terra *f* (o sabbia *f*) sintetica

		English	French	German	Italian
°	18172	**syphon**	siphon *m*	Heber *m*, Siphon *n*	sifone *m*
°	18173	**syphon-boiler**	chaudière *f* à siphon	Siphon-Kessel *m*	caldaia *f* a sifone
°	18174	**syphon brick**	brique-siphon *f*	Siphonstein *m*	mattone *m* a sifone per separare le scorie
°	18175	**syphon pipe, U-pipe**	tube *m* en trompette	Hosenrohr *n*, Siphonrohr *n*	tubo *m* a due braccia, tubo *m* ad U
°	18176	**syphon runner**	coulée *f* en siphon	Siphoneinguss *m*	colata *f* a sifone, getto *m* a sifone
°	18177	**syrup consistence**	consistance *f* sirupeuse	Sirupdichte *f*	consistenza *f* sciropposa
—	18178	**system of conjugated fractures**	système *m* conjugué de cassures	Bruchsystem *n*	sistema *m* di fratture
—	18179	**system of crystallization**	système *m* cristallin	Kristallsystem *n*	sistema *m* cristallino
		system of joints, *s. system of conjugated fractures*			
—	18180	**system of lenses**	système *m* de lentilles	Linsensystem *n*	sistema *m* di lenti, (o lenticolare)
—	18181	**system or method of working (mining)**	méthode *f* d'extraction	Gewinnungsart *f*	metodo *m* d'estrazione
—	18182	**szaibelyite**	szaibélyite *f*	Szaibelyit *m*	szaibelite *f*
—	18183	**szmikite**	szmikite *f*	Szmikit *m*	szmikite *f*
—	18184	**szomolnokite**	szomolnokite *f*	Szomolnokit *m*	szmolnokite *f*

		English	French	German	Italian
o	18185	**T-head bolt**	crampon *m* à vis	Hakenschraube *f*	chiavarda *f* a becco
o	18186	**T-iron, T-bar**	fer *m* à T	T-Eisen *n*, T-Träger *m*	ferro *m* a T, profilati *m pl.* a T
		T-joint, *s. Tee-joint*			
−	18187	**table**	table *f*	Tisch *m*	piano *m*, tavola *f*, tavolo *m*
−	18188	**table clamp**	étau *m* de la table	Tischgreifhaken *m*	clampa *f* della tavola
−	18189	**table clamping (for drilling)**	blocage *m* de la table	Tischsperrung *f*	bloccaggio *m* della tavola
−	18190	**table of atomic weights**	tableau *m* des poids atomiques	Tabelle *f* der Atomgewichte	tabella *f* dei pesi atomici
o	18191	**table-land**	plateau *m*	Hochebene *f*	altipiano *m*
^	18192	**table thrust bearing**	coussinet *m* portant de la table rotary	Rotarytischlagerung *f*	cuscinetto *m* portante della tavola Rotary
−	18193	**tabling**	triage *m* du minerai par tables inclinées	Erzabscheidung *f* mit schiefen Ebenen	separazione *f* dei minerali con tavole inclinate
−	18194	**tabular**	tabulaire	tafelig, tafelförmig	tabulare
		tabular spar, *s. wollastonit*			
o	18195	**tack welding**	soudure *f* par points	Punktschweissung *f*	saldatura *f* a punti, puntatura *f*
−	18196	**tackle**	moufle *f*, palan *m*	Flaschenzug *n*, Tauwerk *n*	paranco *m*, taglia *f*
o	18197	**tacky**	gluant	klebrig	appiccicoso
−	18198	**tachylyte**	tachylyte *f*	Tachylyt *m*	tachilite *f*
o	18199	**taffrail round platform**	garde-corps *m* du gueulard	Geländer *n* der Gichtbühne	ringhiera *f* della piattaforma
o	18200	**tag**	fragment *m* métallique	Metallsplitter *m*	frammento *m* metallico
o	18201	**tagger**	tôle *f* très mince	Bekleidungsblech *n*	lamierino *m* sottilissimo
ɔ	18202	**tagging**	effilement *m*, pointage *m*	Verjüngung *f*, Zugspitzen *n*	rastrematura *f* d'estremità
o	18203	**tail**	queue *f*	Schwanz *m*	coda *f*

	English	French	German	Italian
18204	tail (front and tails)	produits *m pl.* légers	Leichtprodukte *n pl.*	prodotti *m pl.* leggeri
18205	tail (heavy and tails)	produits *m pl.* lourds	Schwerprodukte *n pl.*	prodotti *m pl.* pesanti
18206	tail hammer	martinet *m* ou marteau *m* à queue	Schwanzhammer *m*	martello *m* ad altalena
18207	tail pipe	tube *m* de queue	Verlängerungs-rohr *n*	tubo *m* di coda
18207a	tail print	portée *f* montante	Kernmarke *f*	portata *f* alla francese
18208	tail product	produit *m* de queue	Endprodukt *n*	prodotto *m* di coda
18209	tail production	production *f* de queue	Endproduktion *f*	produzione *f* di coda
18210	tail pump	pompe *f* actionnée par le groupe moteur	Pumpe *f* vom Motoraggregat angetrieben	pompa *f* comandata dal gruppo motore
18211	tail pulley	poulie *f* de queue	Umkehrscheibe *f*	puleggia *f* di ritorno
18212	tail rope	câble *m* de renvoi	Unterseil *n*	fune *f* di rinvio
18213	tail rope haulage	traction *f* par câble tête et câble queue	Förderung *f* mit Vorder- und Hinterseil *n*	trazione *f* per cavo di testa e cavo di rinvio
18213a	tail scale	battitures infiltrées	eingesickerter Hammerschlag *m*	battiture *f pl.* infiltrate
18214	tailing out	amincissement *m* en coin	Auskeilen *n*	restringimento *m* a cuneo
18215	taillings, tails	résidus *m pl.*	Rückstände *m pl.*	residui *m pl.*
18216	taimyrite	taimyrite *f*	Taimyrit *m*	taimyrite *f*
18217	to take a sample of gas, to sample the gas	prendre un échantillon de gaz	eine Gasprobe *f* nehmen	prendere un campione di gas
18218	to take out or lift the crucibles	enlever ou retirer les creusets	die Tiegel *m pl.* herausnehmen	levare i crogiuoli
18219	to take the thickness	moucheter	zur Wanddickenkontrolle *f* Lehmpfropfen *m* einlegen	applicare le mosche(o le spie)
18220	taking from the stores	reprise *f* du magasin	Aufnehmen *n* vom Lager	prelevare dal deposito, togliere dal magazzino
18221	taking out the pillars	dépilage *m* (des piliers)	Rückbau *m* der Pfeiler	abbattimento *m* (dei pilastri)

		English	French	German	Italian
—	18222	talc-schist	talcschiste *m*	Talkschiefer *m*	scisto *m* talcoso
—	18223	tallingite	tallingite *f*	Tallingit *m*	tallingite *f*
°	18224	tallow	suif *m*	Rindstalg *m*, Rindertalg *m*	sego *m*
°	18225	tallow pot	chaudière *f* à graisse	Fettkessel *m*	caldaia *f* per il grasso
—	18226	tamanite	tamanite *f*	Tamanit *m*	tamanite *f*
—	18227	tamaraite	tamaraïte *f*	Tamarait *m*	tamaraite *f*
—	18228	to tamp	bourrer	verdämmen	intasare
—	18229	to tamp	damer	stampfen	costipare
—	18230	to tamp	bourrer	besetzen	eseguire una ripiena
°	18231	tamped or pud-dled clay	construction *f* en pisé réfractaire damé	Bau *m* aus Stampf-masse	costruzione *f* al pesto-ne
—	18232	tamper	bourroir *m*	Ladestock *m*	mazza *f* a rincalzare
—	18233	tamper	dame *f*	Stampfer *m*	mazzaranga *f*
—	18234	tamping	bourrage *m*, ma-tière *f* à bourrer	Besetzen *n*, Be-satz *m*	costipamento *m*, mate-riale *m* per ripiena
—	18235	tamping bar	bourroir *m*	Ladestock *m*	mazzaranga *f*
		tamping stick, *s. tamping bar*			
	18236	tan, tan bark	tan *m*	Gerberlohe *f*	polvere *f* di concia
—	18237	tangeite	tangéite *f*	Tangeit *m*	tangeite *f*
°	18238	tandem engine	machine *f* tandem	Tandemmaschine *f*	mazzaranga *f*
°	18239	tandem pistons	pistons *m pl.* en tandem, pistons *m pl.* concentriques	hintereinanderlie-gende Kolben *m pl.*	stantuffi *m pl.* sovrappo-sti a tandem
°	18239a	tandem mill	laminoir *m* tandem	Tandemwalzwerk *n*	laminatoio *m* tandem
°	18240	tandem stand high	finisseur *m* à chaud à cages en tandem	Tandemgerüst-Warm-walzwerk *n*	laminatoio *m* a caldo con gabbie in tandem per la finitura
°	18241	tangential casting	coulée *f* tangentiel-le	Tangentialguss *m*	colata *f* tangenziale
°	18242	tangential straining	contrainte *f* tangen-tielle	Tangentialkraft *f*	tensione *f* tangenziale

		English	French	German	Italian
o	18243	**tangential test**	essai *m* tangentiel	Tangentialprobe *f*	prova *f* tangenziale
–	18244	**tangential thrust**	charriage *m* tangentiel	tangentialer Schub *m*	spinta *f* tangenziale
^	18245	**tank**	citerne *f*	Tanker *m*	cisterna *f*
^	18246	**tank battery**	groupe *m* de réservoirs	Tanklager *n*	gruppo *m* di serbatoi
^	18247	**tank bottoms**	résidus *m pl.* de réservoir	Tankrückstände *m pl.*	sedimenti *m* di serbatoio
^	18248	**tank breather tube**	tube *m* d'aérage du réservoir	Tankbelüftung *f*	tubo *m* di respirazione (o d'aerazione) del serbatoio
^	18249	**tank dome**	regard *m* de réservoirs	Tankschauloch *n*	portello *m* d'ispezione per serbatoi
^	18250	**tank farm**	parc *m* de réservoirs	Tankpark *m*	parco *m* di stoccaggio
^	18251	**tank outage**	perte *f* de pétrole du réservoir	Tankölverlust *m*	perdita *f* di petrolio del serbatoio
o	18252	**tank sheet iron**	tôle *f* à réservoirs	Behälterblech *n*	lamiera *f* per serbatoi
^	18253	**tank strapper**	mesureur *m* de réservoirs	Tankmesser *m*	misuratore *m* di serbatoi
^	18254	**tank thief**	sonde *f* de prise d'échantillons	Probeentnahmebohrer *m*	sonda *f* per campionatura
^	18255	**tank vent pipe**	tube *m* d'égout	Ölbehälterentlüftungsrohr *n*	tubo *m* di sfiato
o	18255a	**tank voltage**	tension *f* de cuve	Badspannung *f*	tensione *f* della vasca
^	18256	**tank wagon**	wagon *m* citerne	Tankwagen *m*	carro *m* cisterna, autobotte *m*
^	18257	**tankage**	stockage *m* du pétrole	Erdöleinlagern *n*	stoccaggio *m* del petrolio
^	18258	**tankage**	contenu *m* d'un réservoir	Tank-Fassungsvermögen *n*	contenuto *m* d'un serbatoio
–	18259	**tantalite**	tantalite *f*	Tantalit *m*	tantalite *f*
–	18260	**tantalum**	tantale *m*	Tantal *n*	tantalio *m*
o	18261	**to tap**	piquer	abstechen	spillare
o	18262	**to tap the hearth**	vider le creuset	den Herd entleeren	vuotare il crogiuolo

to tap off the slag, *s. to slag out*

	English	French	German	Italian
° 18263	**tap**	taraud *m* aléseur	Gewindebohrer *m*	maschio filettante
° 18264	**tap**	piquée *f*	Abstich *m*	colata *f*, spillata *f*
° 18265	**tap and reamer wrench**	tourne-à-gauche *m* pour tarauds et a-lésoirs	Windeisen *n* für Reibahlen und Gewindebohrer	volta maschi per ale-satori
° 18265a	**tap bar**	barre *f* de contrôle de cémentation	Zementierungs-kontrollstab *m*	barra *f* di controllo della cementazione
	tap cinder, *s. reheating furnace slag*			
° 18266	**tap cinder**,	scorie *f* de puddlage	Puddelschlacke *f*	scoria *f* di puddellaggio
° 18266a	**tap density**	densité *f* de la poudre (après secouage)	Rütteldichte *f*	densità *f* della polvere (dopo scuotimento)
° 18267	**tap hole, tapping hole**	trou *m* de coulée	Stichloch *n*	foro *m* di colata, foro *m* di spillatura
° 18268	**tap hole gun**	machine *f* à obtu-rer le trou de cou-lée	Stichlochstopf-maschine *f*	macchina *f* per ottura-re il foro di colata
° 18269	**tap hole stopping machine, mud gun, clay gun**	machine *f* à bou-cher le trou de coulée	Stichlochstopf-maschine *f*	macchina *f* per fare la bocchetta
	tap-out bar, *s. tapping bar*			
° 18270	**to tap slag**	décrasser les scories	abschlacken	scorificare
— 18271	**tapalpite**	tapalpite *f*	Tapalpit *m*	tapalpite *f*
18272	**tape measure**	mètre *m* à ruban	Bandmass *n*, Messband *n*	metro *m* a nastro
° 18273	**taped wire**	fil *m* sous ruban isolant	mit Band isolierter Draht	filo *m* sotto nastro i-solante
— 18274	**taper**	pic *m*, pointerolle	Spitzeisen *n*, Spitzmeissel *m*	piccone *m*, punteruolo *m*
— 18275	**to taper**	rétrécir, se termi-ner en pointe	sich verjüngen, auskeilen	terminare a punta
— 18276	**to taper**	effiler	schärfen	affilare
— 18277	**to taper**	se terminer en coin	auskeilen	rastremare, terminare a punta
— 18277a	**taper**	cône *m* d'entrée	Eingangskonus *m*	cono *m* d'entrata
° 18278	**taper**	renflement *m*	Exzentrizität *f*, Verjüngung *f*	eccentricità *f*, coni-cità *f*
° 18278a	**taper, draft**	dépouille *f*	Schräge *f*	sformo *m*, spoglia *f*
^ 18279	**taper**	raccord *m* conique	Kegelverbindung *f*	raccordo *m* conico
° 18279a	**taper**	angle *m* de retrait	Ausziehwinkel *m*	angolo *m* d'invito o di sforno
° 18280	**taper attachment**	tirette *f*	Ansatzschablone *f* für Unterschneidun-gen	spoglia *f* di un model-lo
° 18281	**taper bit**	aléseur *m* conique	Kegelbohrer *m*	alesatore *m* conico

		English	French	German	Italian
°	18282	taper of a cone	conicité f	Konizität f	conicità f
°	18282a	taper rimer	dégorgeoir m conique	Kegelreibahle f	alesatore m conico
−	18283	taper rope	câble m à section décroissante	verjüngtes Seil n	cavo m a sezione decrescente
−	18284	taper shank straight drill	mèche f droite à fût conique	Bohrer m mit gerader Ausfraesung und konischem Schaft	trapano m diritto a gambo rastremato
−	18285	tapered	conique	verjüngt	rastremato
°	18286	tapered flask	châssis m à démoulage intérieur	Formkasten m mit Innenherausnehmen	staffa f con sformatura interna
		tapered roller, s. conical roller			
°	18287	tapered slip flask	châssis m amovible à démoulage intérieur	ausziehbahrer Formkasten m mit Innenherausnehmen	staffa f estraibile con sformatura interna
^	18288	tapered string	train m de tiges	kombiniertes Gestange n	batteria f di aste
^	18289	tapered tap	taraud aléseur de repêchage	Fanggewindebohrer m	maschio m filettante di pescaggio
°	18290	tapering	effillement m progressif	Verjüngung f	rastremazione f
°	18291	tapering pass	cannelure f interrompue	unterbrochenes Kaliber n	canale m interrotto
−	18292	tapering pod auger, pointed funnel auger	tarière f en entonnoir	Trichterbohrer m	trivella f a imbuto
^	18293	tapped gas pipes	tubes m pl. taraudés type gaz	Gasgewinderohre n pl.	tubi m pl. filettati del tipo gas
°	18294	tappet, cam	came f	Daumen m, Hebekopf m	palmola f, camma f
°	18295	tappet cam drum	bague f à cames	Daumentrommel f, Nockenwelle f	albero m a camme
°	18296	tappet slab core, removable core	noyau m détachable	Losteil n, loser Kern n	anima f del tassello punteria
°	18297	tapping	coulée f du métal en fusion	Abstich m	colata f di metallo in fusione
°	18298	tapping	piquée f	Abstich m	spillatura f, cavata f
°	18299	tapping cutting threads in holes	taraudage m	Gewindebohren n	maschiatura f
°	18300	tapping attachment	machine f à tarauder	Rohrgewindeschneidmaschine f	apparecchio m per filettare con maschi

		English	French	German	Italian
°	18301	tapping bar	barre *f* à piquer	Stichlochspiess *m*	barra *f* per spillare
°	18302	tapping floor	plateforme *f* de coulée	Giessbühne *f*	piattaforma *f* di colata
		tapping hole, *s. tap hole*			
°	18303	tapping interval	intervalle *m* entre les coulées	Abstichpause *f*	intervallo *m* fra le colate
°	18304	tapping in the lathe	filetage *m* sur le tour	Drehbankgewinde *n*	filettatura *f* sul torno
°	18305	tapping iron	ringard *m*	Stichlochspiess *m*	agitatore *m*
°	18306	tapping iron or bar	ringard *m* en fer	eiserner Spiess *m*	stanga *f* di ferro
°	18307	tapping of blast furnace	coulée *f*	Abstich *m*	colata *f*
°	18308	tapping of the slag	lâchage *m* de la scorie	Ablassen *n* der Schlacke	colata *f* della scoria
°	18309	tapping sample	prise *f* d'essai à la coulée	Abstichprobe *f*	prendere il campione di colata
°	18310	tapping shovel	pelle *f* de barrage	Abstichschaufel *f*, Schütze *f*	pala *f* d'arresto o di chiusura
°	18311	tapping side, pouring side	face *f* arrière	Rückseite *f*	lato *m* del foro di colata
°	18312	tapping slag	scorie *f* de coulée	Abstichschlacke *f*	scoria *f* di spillatura
°	18313	tapping spout	rigole *f* de coulée	Abstichrinne *f*	canale *m* di colata
—	18314	tar	goudron *m*	Teer *m*	catrame *m*
—	18315	tar boiling	chauffage *m* du goudron	Teerkocherei *f*	riscaldamento *m* del catrame
—	18316	tar distillate	distillat *m* de goudron	Teerdestillat *n*	distillato *m* di residuo
—	18317	tar distillation plant	installations *f pl.* pour la distillation du goudron	Teerdestillationsanlage *f*	impianto *m* per la distillazione del catrame
—	18318	tar furnace	foyer *m* à goudron	Teerfeuerung *f*	focolare *m* a catrame
—	18319	tar plug	vanne *f* pour résidus	Rückstandventil *n*	valvola *f* per residui

		English	French	German	Italian
—	18320	tar-pot, tar boiler	chaudière f à goudron	Teerkessel m	caldaia f per catrame
❋	18321	tar still	distillateur m de goudron	Teerdestillations-apparat m	distillatore m per residui
	18322	to tare	tarer	ausgleichen	tarare
	18323	tare	tare f, poids mort	Leergewicht n	tara f
	18324	tare or bird shot	plomb m à tarer	Ausgleichschrot m	pallini m pl. di piombo per tarare
—	18325	tarapacaite	tarapacaite f	Tarapacait m	tarapacaite f
_	18326	tarbuttite	tarbuttite f	Tarbuttit m	tarbuttite f
∘	18327	tared pipe	tuyau m goudronné	geteertes Rohr n	tubo m catramato
—	18328	tarn	lac m de cirque	Karsee m	lago m di circo
❋	18328a	tarnish	ternissure f	trüber Belag m	appannatura f
—	18329	tarnowitzite	tarnowitzite f	Tarnowitzit m	tarnowitzite f
—	18330	tar(r)y gas	gaz m riche en goudron	teerhaltiges Gas n	gas m ricco di catrame
∘	18331	tartaric acid	acide m tartrique	Weinsäure f	acido m tartarico
	18332	task wage	salaire m au rendement	Akkordlohn m	salario m a cottimo
—	18333	tasmanite	tasmanite f	Tasmanit m	tasmanite f
—	18334	taurite	taurite f	Taurit m	taurite f
	18335	taut	bien serré	fest angezogen	ben stretto
—	18336	tavistockite	tavistockite f	Tavistockit m	tavistockite f
—	18337	tavolatite	tavolatite f	Tavolatit m	tavolatite f
—	18338	tawite	tawite f	Tawit m	tawite f
—	18339	taxite	taxite f	Taxit m	taxite f
—	18340	taxitic structure	structure f taxitique	taxitische Struktur f	struttura f taxitica
—	18341	taylorite	taylorite f	Taylorit m	taylorite f
∘	18341a	tea lead	calin m	Teeblei n	piombo m in lamine
∘	18342	tea-pot spout laddle	poche-théière f, poche-siphon f	Siphonpfanne f	siviera f (o caldaia f) di colata a sifone
—	18343	teallite	teallite f	Teallit m	teallite f

		English	French	German	Italian
°	18344	tear	inclusion *f*	Einschluss *m*	inclusione *f*
°	18345	to tear, to break	se rompre par traction	zerreissen	rompersi per trazione
	18346	to tear	déchirer, rompre	zerreissen	strappare, rompere
—	18347	to tear out	démonter	abbauen	smontare
—	18348	tear and wear	détérioration *f*	Verfall *n*, Verderben *n*	deperimento *m*
—	18349	technecium	technétium *m*	Technetium *n*	tecnezio *m*
°	18350	Teclu burner	brûleur *m* de Teclu	Teclubrenner *m*	becco *m* di Teclu
—	18351	tectomorphic	tectomorphique	tektomorphisch	tectomorfico
—	18352	tectonic	tectonique	tektonisch	tettonico
°	18352a	tedge	entonnoir *m* d'augmentation	Speisertrichter *m*	imbuto *m* d'alimentazione
°	18353	tee welding	soudure *f* en T	T-Schweissung *f*	saldatura *f* a T
°	18354	to teem	verser, couler	giessen, ausgiessen	versare, colare
°	18355	teemer	fondeur *m*	Giesser *m*	fonditore *m*
°	18356	teeming	coulée *f*	Guss *m*, Giessen *n*	colata *f*
°	18357	teeming lap	pli *m* de coulée	Gussfalte *f*	piega *f* di colata
°	18358	teeming nozzle	orifice *m* de coulée	Ausflussöffnung *f*	foro *m* di colata
°	18359	teeming platform	plate-forme *f* de coulée	Giessbühne *f*	piattaforma *f* di colata

teeming temperature, *s. casting temperature*
telescope carriage, *s. truck*

		English	French	German	Italian
°	18360	telescopic moulding machine for pulleys	machine *f* télescopique à mouler les poulies	Teleskopriemenscheibenformmaschine *f*	macchina *f* a telescopio per formare puleggie
°	18361	telescopic raising	surélévation *f* télescopique	teleskopartige Verlängerung *f*	sopralzo *m* telescopico
°	18362	telescopic roof supporting joint	étançon *m* tubulaire à télescope pour ossature de plancher	teleskopartiger Stahlrohrstempel *m* als Dachgeschossstütze	puntello *m* tubolare a canocchiale per armatura di solaio
^	18363	tell-tale	regard *m*	Messloch *n*	misuratore *m*, spia *f*
^	18364	tell-tale hole	regard *m*	Schauloch *n*	foro *m* di spia
—	18365	tellurine	diatomite *f*	Diatomeenerde *f*	diatomite *f*

		English	French	German	Italian

		English	**French**	**German**	**Italian**
—	18366	**tellurite**	tellurite *f*	Tellurit *m*	tellurite *f*
—	18367	**tellurium**	tellure *m*	Tellur *n*	tellurio *m*
—	18368	**tellurium-bearing**	tellurifère	tellurführend	tellurifero
—	18369	**temiskamite**	temiskamite *f*	Temiskamit *m*	temiskamite *f*
○	18370	**to temper, to reheat**	adoucir. recuire	anlassen, nach-lassen	ricuocere
○	18370a	**temper**	revenu *m*	Anlassen *n*	rinvenimento *m*
○	18371	**to temper**	faire revenir	anlassen	rinvenire
○	18372	**to temper the steel**	faire revenir l'acier	den Stahl *m* anlassen	far rinvenire l'acciaio
○	18372a	**temper**	trempe *f*	Härtegrad *n*	tempera *f*
○	18373	**temper brittleness**	fragilité *f* de revenu	Anlasssproedig-keit *f*	fragilità *f* di rinveni-mento
○	18373a	**temper carbon**	carbone *m* de revenu	Anlasskohlenstoff *m*	carbonio *m* di rinvenimen-to
○	18374	**temper colour**	couleur *f* de recuit	Anlassfarbe *f*	colore *m* di ricottura
○	18375	**temper hardening**	durcissement *m* par revenu	Anlasshärtung *f*	invecchiamento *m* arti-ficiale
○	18375a	**temper pass mill**	laminoir *m* à dresser	Nachwalzwerk *n*	laminatoio *m* per induri-mento superficiale
○	18376	**temper screw**	vis *f* de rallonge	Nachlass. spindel *m*	vite *f* di prolungamento
○	18377	**temper steel**	acier *m* trempé à l'1,0% de C.	gehärteter Stahl *m* mit 1,0% C.	acciaio *m* all' 1,0% di C.
—	18378	**temperament**	tempérament *m*	Temperament *n*	temperamento *m*
○	18379	**temperature**	température *f*	Temperatur *f*	temperatura *f*
○	18380	**temperature cycle stressing**	sollicitation *f* aux chocs thermiques	Temperaturwechsel-beanspruchung *f*	sollecitazione *f* a tem-perature alternate
○	18381	**temperature error**	erreur *f* de tempé-rature	Temperaturfehler *m*	errore *m* di temperatura
○	18382	**temperature gra-dient**	gradient *m* de tem-pérature	Wärmegradient *m*	gradiente *m* di tempera-tura
○	18383	**temperature in the blast furnace**	température *f* dans le haut-fourneau	Temperatur *f* im Hochofen	temperatura *f* nell'alto-forno
○	18384	**temperature increase**	accroissement *m* de température	Wärmezunahme *f*	aumento *m* di tempera-tura
○	18385	**temperature log**	thermométrie *f*	Thermometrie *f*	termometria *f*
○	18386	**temperature of coking**	température *f* de carbonisation	Verkokungstempe-ratur *f*	temperatura *f* di riduzio-ne in coke

		English	French	German	Italian
o	18387	temperature of incandescence	chaleur *f* d'incandescence	Glühhitze *f*	calore *m* d'incandescenza
o	18388	temperature of reaction	température *f* de la réaction	Reaktionstemperatur *f*	temperatura *f* della reazione
o	18389	tempered steel	acier *m* revenu	angelassener Stahl *m*	acciaio *m* rinvenuto
o	18390	tempering bath	bain *m* de revenu	Anlassbad *n*	bagno *m* di rinvenimento
o	18391	tempering, slow cooling	refroidissement *m* lent	Tempern *n*, langsames Abkühlen *n*	raffreddamento *m* lento
o	18392	tempering brittleness	fragilité *f* de revenu	Anlasssprödigkeit *f*	fragilità *f* di rinvenimento
o	18393	tempering flame furnace	four *m* à réverbère à tremper	Härteflammofen *m*	forno *m* a riverbero per la tempera
o	18394	tempering forge	feu *m* de trempe	Härteschmiedefeuer *n*	fucina *f* per la tempera, focolare *m* di fucina
o	18395	tempering furnaces	fours *m pl.* à tremper	Härteöfen *m pl.*	forni *m pl.* di rinvenimento
o	18396	tempering hardness	trempe *f* de recuit	Anlasshärte *f*	tempera *f* di ricottura
o	18397	tempering oil	huile *f* de revenu	Anlassöl *n*	olio *m* per rinvenimento (o per tempera)
		tempering-stove, *s. hardening-furnace*			
o	18398	tempering temperature	température *f* du recuit	Anlauftemperatur *f*	temperatura *f* di ricottura
o	18399	tempering time	durée *f* de revenu	Anlassdauer *f*	durata *f* di rinvenimento
o	18400	template, templet	calibre *m*, gabarit *m*	Lehre *f*	calibro *m*
o	18401	template moulding	moulage *m* au trousseau	Schablonenformerei *f*	formatura *f* a sagoma
o	18402	temporary mould	moule *m* perdu	verlorene Gussform *f*	formatura *f* perduta
o	18403	tenacity	ténacité *f*	Zähigkeit *f*	tenacità *f*
		tender, *s. estimate*			
—	18404	tender loading column	colonne *f* pour le chargement des tenders	Rohrsäule *f* für Ladung der Tender	colonna *f* per riempimento di carri di scorta
—	18405	tengerite	tengérite *f*	Tengerit *m*	tengerite *f*

	English	French	German	Italian
— 18406	tennantite	tennantite _f_	Tennantit _m_	tennantite _f_
— 18407	tenorite	ténorite _f_	Tenorit _m_	tenorite _f_
○ 18408	tensile break	rupture _f_ à traction	Bruch _m_ der Zerreissprobe	rottura _f_ alla trazione
○ 18409	tensile strain	effort _m_ de traction	Zugbeanspruchung _f_	sollecitazione _f_ a trazione
○ 18410	tensile strength	résistance _f_ à la rupture	Bruchfestigkeit _f_	resistenza _f_ alla rottura, forza _f_ tensile
○ 18411	tensile test	essai _m_ de traction	Zugversuch _m_	prova _f_ di trazione, (o tensile)
○ 18412	tensile test bar	éprouvette _f_ de traction	Zerreissstab _m_	provetta _f_ di trazione
○ 18413	tensile testing machine	appareil _m_ pour l'essai de traction	Zerreissmaschine _f_	macchina _f_ per prova di trazione
○ 18414	tension	effort _m_	Spannung _f_	tensione _f_, sforzo _m_
○ 18415	tension cracks	fissures _f pl._ de tension	Spannungsrisse _m pl._	incrinature _f pl._ di tensione
○ 18416	tension brittleness	fragilité _f_ de tension	Spannsprödigkeit _f_	fragilità _f_ di tensione
— 18417	tension fault	faille _f_ d'extension	Dehnungsverwerfung _f_	faglia _f_ di tensione
○ 18417a	tension impact	énergie _f_ du choc	Schlagstärke _f_	energia _f_ dell'urto
— 18418	tension joint	fente _f_ d'extension	Zugspalte _f_	fessura _f_ di tensione
○ 18418a	tension rod	bielle _f_ de traction	Zugstange _f_	biella _f_ di trazione
○ 18419	tension screw	étrier _m_ de serrage	Spannbügel _m_	vite _f_ per registrare i cilindri
○ 18419a	tension test	essai _m_ de tension	Zugprobe _f_	prova _f_ di tensione
○ 18420	tension weight	poids _m_ tendeur	Spanngewicht _n_	peso _m_ tenditore
— 18421	tephrite	téphrite _f_	Tephrit _m_	tefrite _f_
— 18422	tephroite	téphroïte _f_	Tephroit _m_	tefroite _f_
— 18423	terbium	terbium _m_	Terbium _n_	terbio _m_
— 18424	terlinguaite	terlinguaite _f_	Terlinguait _m_	terlinguaite _f_
— 18425	termierite	termiérite _f_	Termierit _m_	termierite _f_
○ 18426	terminal	borne _f_	Drahtklemme _f_	terminale _m_
○ 18427	terminal for cells	serre-fil _m_	Klemme _f_ für Elemente	morsetto _m_ per elementi

		English	French	German	Italian
−	18428	**terminal moraine**	moraine f frontale	Stirnmoräne f	morena f frontale
		terminal nut, _s. union nut_			
		ternary steel, _s. simple alloy steel_			
°	18429	**to terne**	plomber	bleilöten	piombare
°	18430	**terne plate**	tôle f plombée	verbleites Blech n	lamiera f piombata
−	18431	**terrace**	terrasse f	Terrasse f	terrazzo m
°	18432	**terracotta**	terre f cuite	gebrannter Ton m	terra f cotta
−	18433	**terrestrial facies**	faciès m terrestre	Festlandfazies f	«facies» f continentale
−	18434	**terrigenous deposits**	dépôts m $pl.$ terrigènes	terrigene Ablagerungen f $pl.$	depositi m $pl.$ terrigeni
−	18435	**tertiary**	tertiaire m	Tertiär n	terziario m
−	18436	**tertiary era**	ère f tertiaire	Tertiärformation f	era f terziaria
−	18437	**teschemacherite**	teschemachérite f	Teschemacherit m	teschemacherite f
−	18438	**teschenite**	teschénite f	Teschenit m	teschenite f
°	18439	**tesselated plate**	tôle f gauffrée	Waffelblech n	lamiera f a prominenze
		tesseral system, _s. isometric system_			
	18440	**to test**	faire un essai, essayer	erproben	provare
	18441	**test**	essai m	Versuch m	prova f, esame f
°	18442	**test bar**	barreau m d'épreuve	Probebarren n	provetta f, barretta f
°	18442a	**test bloc**	lingot-éprouvette m	Probeblock m	provetta f grezza
−	18443	**test boring**	sondage m de recherche	Aufschlussbohrung f	sondaggio m di prova
		test by bending in opposite directions. _s. alternating bending test_			
	18444	**test certificate**	certificat m d'essai	Prüfbescheinigung f	certificato m di prova
°	18445	**test coupon**	lingot-éprouvette m	Probeblock m	provetta f grezza
		test for weldability, _s. weldability test_			
°	18445a	**test furnace**	four m d'essai	Probierofen m	forno m sperimentale
°	18446	**test glass**	éprouvette f conique	Prüfkelch m	bicchiere m a calice
°	18447	**test load**	charge f d'essai	Prüflast f	carica f di prova
	18448	**test paper**	papier m à réactif	Reagenzpapier n	carta f reagente

		English	French	German	Italian
o	18449	test piece	éprouvette *f*	Probestab *m*	provetta *f*, barretta *f*
o	18450	test piece supported at both ends	distance *f* entre supports	Freilage *f*	posizione *f* libera
o	18451	test plug	fermeture *f* d'essai	Probenverschluss *m*	chiusura *f* dell'organo in prova
o	18452	test pressure	pression *f* d'épreuve	Probedruck *m*	pressione *f* di prova
o	18453	test rod, test piece	baguette *f* de fer d'essai	Probierstange *f*	barra *f* di prova
o	18454	test rod	barreau *m* d'épreuve	Probestab *m*	barretta *f* di prova
o	18455	test strip	barreau *m* plat pour les essais	Probestreifen *m*	nastro *m* o striscia *f* di prova
o	18456	test tube	éprouvette *f*, burette *f*	Prüfglas *n*, Reagenzglas *n*	provino *m*, provetta *f*
o	18457	test tube holder for water baths	support *m* à introduire dans le bain-marie	Einsatz *m* in das Wasserbad für Reagenzröhren	portaprovino *m* per bagno d'acqua
o	18458	test value	valeur *f* expérimentale	Prüfwert *m*	valore *m* di prova
—	18459	test well	sondage *m* d'exploration	Schürfbohrung *f*	sondaggio *m* esplorativo
	18460	tester	aide *m* de laboratoire, piston *m*	Laborant *m*	aiutante *m* di laboratorio
o	18461	testing, examination	prise *f* d'essai	Vornahme *f* der Probe, Prüfung *f*	presa *f* del campione
o	18462	testing conditions	réglement *m* d'essai	Prüfungsvorschrift *f*	prescrizioni *f pl.* di prova
o	18463	testing department	service *m* d'essais	Versuchsabteilung *f*	reparto *m* collaudi
—	18464	testing flange	bride *f* pour essais	Testflansch *m*	flangia *f* per prove
o	18465	testing machine	machine *f* d'essai	Prüfmaschine *f*	macchina *f* di prova
	18466	testing method	méthode *f* d'essai	Prüfungsverfahren *n*	sistema *m* di prova, metodo *m* d'analisi
	18467	testing set	appareil *m* d'essai	Prüfgerät *n*	apparecchio *m* di prova
—	18468	tetradymite	tétradymite *f*	Tetradymit *m*	tetradimite *f*

		English	French	German	Italian
−	18469	tetragonal system	système *m* quater-naire	tetragonales System *n*	sistema *f* tetragonale
−	18470	tetrahedral garnet	helvine *f*	Helvin *m*	helvina *f*
−	18471	tetrahedrite, fahlerz	cuivre *m* gris, panabase *f*	Fahlerz *m*, Tetraedrit *m*	rame *m* grigio, tetraedrite *f*
−	18472	tetrahedron	tétraèdre *m*	Tetraeder *n*	tetraedro *m*
−	18473	texture, structure	structure *f*, texture *f*	Struktur *f*, Gefüge *n*, Textur *f*	struttura *f*, tessitura *f*
−	18474	thalenite	thalénite *f*	Thalenit *m*	thalenite *f*
−	18475	thallium	thallium *m*	Thallium *n*	tallio *m*
−	18476	thaumasite	thaumasite *f*	Thaumasit *m*	thaumasite *f*
°	18477	Theisen's washer	laveur *m* Theisen	Theisenscher Wascher *m*	epuratore *m* Theisen
−	18478	thenardite	thénardite *f*	Thenardit *m*	thenardite *f*
−	18479	theodolite	théodolite *f*	Theodolit *m*	theodolite *f*
	18480	theoretical weight	poids *m* théorique	theoretisches Gewicht *n*	peso *m* teorico
°	18480a	thermal analysis	analise *f* thermique	thermische Analyse *f*	analisi *f* termica
		thermal conduction, *s. heat conduction*			
°	18480b	thermal contraction	retrait *m* thermique	Wärmeschwindung *f*	ritiro *m* termico
°	18481	thermal drive	déplacement *m* par des moyens thermiques	Wärmetrieb *m*	spostamento *m* con mezzi termici
°	18482	thermal efficiency	rendement *m* thermique	thermischer Wirkungsgrad *m*	rendimento *m* termico
°	18483	thermal expansion	dilatation *f* thermique	Wärmeausdehnung *f*	dilatazione *f* termica
°	18484	thermal gradient	degré *m* géothermique	geothermische Tiefenstufe *f*	grado *m* geotermico
°	18485	thermal inertia	inertie *f* thermique	Wärmeleitwiderstand *m*	inerzia *f* termica
°	18485a	thermal insulation	isolation *f* thermique	Wärmeisolierung *f*	isolamento *m* termico
°	18486	thermal metamorphism	métamorphisme *m* de contact	Kontaktmetamorphose *f*	metamorfismo *m* di contatto
°	18487	thermal shock	choc *m* thermique	Wärmeschock *m*	sbalzo *m* termico
°	18487a	thermal spalling	effort *m* thermique	thermische Belastung *f*	sforzo *m* termico
°	18488	thermit crucible	creuset *m* à thermite	Thermittiegel *m*	crogiuolo *m* per termite

	English	French	German	Italian
18489	thermit(e) iron	fer-thermite *f*	Thermiteisen *n*	ferrotermite *f*
18490	thermit mold	moule *m* pour soudure alumino-thermique	Form *f* für aluminothermische Lötung	forma *f* per saldatura alluminotermica
18491	thermit process	aluminothermie *f*	Aluminothermie *f*	alluminotermia *f*
18492	thermit-welding	soudure *f* à la thermite	Thermit-Schweissung *f*	saldatura *f* alla termite, saldatura *f* alluminotermica
18493	thermo-electric pyrometer (Le Chatelier)	électropyromètre *m* Le Chatelier	elektrischer Hitzemesser *m*	pirometro *m* elettrico di Le Chatelier
18494	thermocouple	pyromètre *m* à couple	Thermoelement *n*	pirometro *m* a coppia (termoelettrica)
18494a	thermometal	bimétal *m*	Bimetall *n*	bimetallo *m*
18495	thermonatrite	thermonatrite *f*	Thermonatrit *m*	termonatrite *f*
18496	thermophyllite	thermophyllite *f*	Thermophyllit *m*	termofillite *f*
18497	thermoviscosity test	essai *m* de thermoviscosité à la chaleur	Warmthermoviskositätsprobe *f*	prova *f* della viscosità al calore
18498	thick	gros, épais	dick	grosso (di spessore)
18499	thick plate	tôle ou plaque *f* épaisse	Grobblech *n*	lamierone *m*
18500	thick seam	couche *f* puissante	mächtiges Flöz *n*	strato *m* spesso
18501	thick section	plaque *f* mince	Dünnschliff *m*	piastra *f* sottile
18502	thick sheet iron	grosse tôle *f*	Grobblech *n*	lamiera *f* grossa
18503	thick slab, flat bloom	brame *f*	Bramme *f*	bramma *f*, blumo *m* rettangolare
18504	thick walled tube	tuyau *m* à paroi épaisse	dickwandiges Rohr *n*	tubo *m* a parete spessa
18505	thick wire	gros fil *m* (métallique)	dicker Draht *m*	filo *m* (metallico) grosso
18506	thickener	épaississeur *m*	Eindicker *m*	spessitore, addensatore *m*
18507	thickness, width	épaisseur *m*	Mächtigkeit *f*	potenza *f*
18507a	thickness gauge	calibre *m* d'épaisseur	Dickenmesser *m*	calibro *m* per spessori
18508	thickly liquid iron	fonte *f* froide	mattes Eisen *n*	ghisa *f* fredda
18509	thickness gauge, feeler	calibre *m* d'épaisseur, jauge *m* d'épaisseur	Beilagekaliber *n*	laminette *f pl.* da spessore

		English	French	German	Italian
°	18510	thickness of false mould	largeur *f* de la chemise *f*	Mantelstärke *f*	spessore *m* della camicia
°	18511	thickness of rope	épaisseur *m* de la corde	Seildicke *f*	spessore *m* della corda
—	18512	thickness of wall	épaisseur *m* de la paroi	Wandstärke *f*, Mauerstärke *f*	spessore *m* della parete
°	18513	thickness piece	mouche *f*	Lehmpfropfen *m*	mosca *f*, spia *f*
°	18514	thickness piece	galette *f* d'épaisseur	Wanddickenkern *m*	galletta *f* di spessore
°	18515	thickness strickle	planche *f* secondaire	Fertigschablone *f*	sagoma *f* aggiunta
°	18516	thickening time	temps *m* de prise	Abbindezeit *f*	tempo *m* di presa
^	18517	thief, thief tube	sonde *f*, tube *m* de repêchage	Tiefprober *m*	sonda *f*, bottiglia *f*
^	18518	thief rod, water finder	pipette *f* à échantillons	Pipette *f* für die Probeentnahme	pipetta *f* per prelevare campioni da un serbatoio
^	18519	thief sand	sable *m* absorbant	saugender Sand	sabbia *f* assorbente
^	18520	thief sampling	prise *f* d'échantillons par tarière	Bohrmusterzug *m*	prelevamento *m* di campioni
^	18521	thieving a tank	prise *f* d'échantillons d'un réservoir	Tankmusterzug *m*	prelevamento *m* di campioni da un serbatoio
^	18522	thieving	échantillonnage *m*	Musterzug *m*	campionatura *f*
°	18523	thimble	cuve *f* à laitier	Schlackenpfanne *f*	bacino *m* delle scorie
^	18523a	thimble tube	tube *m* à gobelet	Muffenrohr *n*	tubo *m* a bicchiere
^	18524	thin oil columns	couches *f pl.* minéralisées à huile	Schichten *f pl.* ölgetränkt	strati *m pl.* mineralizzati ad olio
°	18525	thin (drawn) wire	fil *m* (métallique) fin	Feindraht *m*, dünner Draht *m*	filo *m* (metallico) sottile
°	18526	thin plate thin sheet, *s. thin plate*	tôle *f* mince	Sturzblech *n*, dünne Platte *f*	lamiera *f* sottile
°	18527	thin sheet rolling mills	laminoir *m* à tôles minces	Feinblechwalzwerk *n*	treno *m* per lamiere sottili
°	18528	thin sheet-steel, lamina	tôle *f* mince en acier	Folie *f* aus Stahl	lamierino *m* di acciaio

		English	French	German	Italian
o	18529	thin walled casting	pièce f de fonte à parois minces	dünnwandiger Eisenguss m	pezzo m di ghisa sottile
		thin wire, s. thin (drawn) wire			
o	18530	thinly liquid	très fusible	dünnflüssig	fluido
—	18531	thinning	étreinte f	Verdrückung f	compressione f
—	18532	thirl	travers-bancs	Querschlag m, Durchhieb m	galleria f di collegamento, traversobanco m
—	18533	thixotropy	thixotropie f	Thixotropie f	tixotropia f
—	18534	tholeiite	tholéiite f	Tholeiit m	tholeiite f
o	18535	Thomas (or Bessemer) basic plant	aciérie f Thomas	Thomas Stahlwerk n	acciaieria f Thomas
		Thomas-Gilchrist process, s. basic process			
o	18536	Thomas pig	fonte f crue Thomas	Thomasroheisen n	ghisa f Thomas
o	18536a	Thomas process	procédé m Thomas	Thomas-Verfahren n	processo m Thomas
o	18537	Thomas slag	scorie f Thomas	Thomasschlacke f	scoria f Thomas
o	18538	Thomas slag utilization works	installation f pour l'utilisation du laitier Thomas	Thomasschlackenverwertungswerk n	impianto m di utilizzazione della scoria Thomas
o	18539	Thomas steel	acier m Thomas	Thomasstahl m	acciaio m Thomas
o	18540	Thomas steel works	aciérie f Thomas	Thomasstahlwerk n	acciaieria f Thomas
—	18541	thomsenolite	thomsénolite f	Thomsenolith m	thomsenolite f
—	18542	thomsonite	thomsonite f	Thomsonit m	thomsonite f
—	18543	thorianite	thorianite f	Thorianit m	torianite f
—	18544	thorite	thorite f	Thorit m	torite f
—	18545	thoria	oxyde m de thorium	Thoriumoxyd n	ossido m di torio
—	18546	thorium	thorium m	Thorium n	torio m
o	18547	Thornycroft boiler	chaudière f Thornycroft	Thornycroftkessel m	caldaia f Thornycroft
—	18548	thorotungstite	thorotungstite f	Thorotungstit m	thorotungstite f
—	18549	thortveitite	thortveitite f	Thortveitit m	thortveitite f
o	18550	thread	filet m	Gewinde n, Schraubengang m	filetto m, filettatura f
o	18551	thread chasing tool	outil m de filetage extérieur	Gewindedrehstahl m	utensile m per filettare

		English	French	German	Italian
−	18552	thread dope	lubrifiant *m* de filetage	Gewindefett *n*	lubrificante *m* per filettatura
−	18553	thread form	forme *f* de filetage	Gewindeprofil *n*	forma *f* della filettatura
−	18554	thread protector	embout *m* protecteur de filetage	Gewindeschutz- kappe *f*	salvavite *m*
−	18555	threaded and coupled tube	tube *m* taraudé et manchonné	Gewinde - und Muffenrohr *n*	tubo *m* con vite a manicotto
−	18556	threaded casing	tube *m* fileté	Gewinderohr *n*	tubo *m* filettato
		threading, *s. screwing*			
o	18557	three high housing	cage *f* à trio	Dreiwalzenstän- der *m*	gabbia *f* a trio
o	18558	three high mill	trio *m*, train *m* trio	Dreiwalzwerk *n*	treno *m* a trio
o	18559	three high mill stand	cage *f* de laminoir trio	Triogerüst *n*	gabbia *f* di laminatoio a trio
o	18560	three high. plate mill	laminoir *m* trio à tôles	Trioblechwalz- werk *n*	laminatoio *m* a trio per lamiere
o	18561	three high plate mill train	train *m* trio à tôles	Trioblechstrasse *f*	treno *m* per lamiere a trio
o	18562	three high shape	laminoir *m* trio à profilés	Trioprofileisen- walzwerk *n*	laminatoio *m* a trio per profilati
o	18562a	three-high stand	cage *f* trio	Dreiwalzengerüst *n*	gabbia *f* trio
o	18563	three jaw chuck	mandrin *m* à trois mâchoires	Dreibackenfutter *n*	mandrino *m* a tre ganasce
o	18563a	three-part box	châssis *m* en trois parts	dreiteiliger Form- kasten *m*	staffa *f* in tre parti
o	18564	three-phase arc smelting furnace	four *m* à arc électrique à courant triphasé	Drehstromlichtbo- genofen *m*	forno *m* ad arco a corrente trifase
o	18565	three-phase current furnace	four *m* à courant triphasé	Drehstromofen *m*	forno *m* ad arco a corrente trifase
o	18566	three phase current plant	installation *f* triphasée	Drehstromanlage *f*	impianto *m* a corrente trifase
o	18567	three-pole construction	disposition *f* tripolaire	Dreipolanordnung *f*	costruzione *f* tripolare
−	18568	three-stick set	cadre *m*	Türstock *m*	quadro *m*
	18569	three way cock	robinet *m* à trois voies	Dreiweghahn *m*	rubinetto *m* a tre vie
^	18570	three way bit	trépan *m* à trois ailettes	Dreiflügelmeissel *m*	scalpello *m* a tre lame

		English	French	German	Italian
^	18571	three-way valve	soupape *f* à trois sièges	Dreisitzventil *n*	valvola *f* a tre vie
^	18572	thribble	jeu *m* de trois	Dreierzug *m*	lunghezza *f* di tre aste ciascuna
^	18573	thribble-platform	plate-forme *f* intermédiaire pour trois tiges	Zwischenbühne *f* für Dreierzug	piattaforma *f* intermedia per tre aste
°	18574	throat	gueulard	Gicht *f*	bocca *f* d'altoforno
		throat, *s. throat depth*			
		throat, *s. closed top*			
°	18575	throat depth (welding)	distance *f* utile	Nutzabstand *m*	sbraccio *m*, distanza *f* utile
°	18576	throat flame	flamme *f* du gueulard	Gichtflamme *f*	fiamma *f* alla bocca del forno
°	18577	throat of the converter	ouverture *f* de la calotte	Mündung *f* der Birne	becco *m* del convertitore
°	18578	throat opening	ouverture *f* du gueulard	Gichtöffnung *f*	apertura *f* della bocca
°	18579	throat platform	plate-forme *f* du gueulard	Gichtbühne *f*	piattaforma *f* di caricamento
°	18580	throat stopper	fermeture *f* du gueulard	Gichtverschluss *m*	apparecchio *m* di chiusura della bocca del forno
°	18581	throat temperature	température *f* au gueulard	Gichttemperatur *f*	temperatura *f* alla bocca del forno
°	18582	throttling	étouffement *m*	Drosselung *f*	strozzamento *m*
—	18583	through-and-through	tout-venant *m* amélioré	vergütete Förderkohle *f*	carbone *m* di prima estrazione migliorato
°	18583a	through bore	trou *m* traversant	Durchbohrung *f*	foro *m* passante
—	18584	through-coal	charbon *m* tout-venant	Förderkohle *f*	carbone *m* di prima estrazione
—	18585	through fault	fossé *m* d'effondrement	Graben *m*, Versenkung *f*	fosso *m* di cedimento
		through hardening, *s. total hardening*			
	18586	through roller	rouleau *m* pour courber la bande	Muldenrolle *f*	rullo *m* per curvare il nastro
	18587	through shaped iron	fer *m* en forme d'auge	Rinneneisen *n*	ferro *m* a truogolo

		English	French	German	Italian
—	18587a	throw	rejet *m* vertical	Sprunghöhe *f*	rigetto *m* verticale
—	18588	to throw	lancer, jeter	werfen, auswerfen	lanciare, gettare
ˆ	18589	throw	rejet *m* vertical	Sprunghöhe *f*	rigetto *m* verticale
°	18590	throw of pumpe	hauteur *f* de refoulement	Drückhöhe *f* der Pumpe	altezza *f* premente della pompa

to throw out of gear, *s. to disconnect*
to throw out of the clutch, *s. to disconnect*

		English	French	German	Italian
°	18591	through-shaped iron	fer *m* en forme d'auge	Rinneneisen *n*	ferro *m* a truogolo
°	18592	throw-away coil	bobine *f* magnétique à emploi unique	Magnetspule *f* für einmaligen Gebrauch	bobina *f* non recuperabile
	18592a	throwing power	pouvoir *m* couvrant	Streuvermögen *n*	potere *m* ricoprente
—	18593	thrown side	lèvre *f* abaissée	gesenkter Flügel *m*	lembo *m* (o ala *f*) affondato
—	18594	thrust	écroulement *m*, éboulement *m*	Sturz *m*, Bruch *m*, Einsturz *m*	crollo *m*, frana *f*
—	18595	thrust	faille *f* anormale	Aufschiebung *f*	faglia *f* anormale
—	18596	thrust	poussée *f*, pression *f* latérale	Seitendruck *m*, Stoss *m*	spinta *f*, pressione *f* laterale
—	18597	thrust	écrasement *m* des piliers	Pfeilerdruck *m*	pressione *f* dei pilastri
—	18598	thrust-fault	faille *f* de compression	Kompressionsverwerfung *f*	faglia *f* di compressione
ˆ	18599	thrust meter	statimètre *m*	Druckmesser *m*	pressostato *m*, statimetro *m*
—	18600	thrust plane	plan *m* de charriage	Überschiebungsfläche *f*	piano *m* di scorrimento
°	18601	thrust plate	disque *m* de butée	Drucklagerscheibe *f*	disco *m* reggispinta
°	18602	thrust ring	bague *f* de butée	Drucklagerring *m*	anello *m* reggispinta
—	18603	thrusting	charriage *m*, poussée *f*	Überschiebung *f*	dislocamento *m*, spinta *f*
°	18604	thrustor	servo-moteur *m*	Servomotor *m*	servomotore *m*
—	18605	thucholite	thucholite *f*	Thukolit *m*	thucolite *f*

		English	French	German	Italian
o	18606	thulium	thulium *m*	Thulium *n*	tulio *m*
o	18606a	thumb-marked fracture	fracture *f* à rides	Kräuselbruch *m*	frattura *f* a grinze
o	18607	tie	traverse *f*	Querhaupt *n*	traversa *f*, staffa *f*
		tie, *s. inner bar*			
		tie, *s. iron sleeper*			
o	18608	tie-plate	bande *f* de rac-cordement	Längsband *n*	lamiera *f* di raccordo
o	18609	tie rail	rail *m* armé	bewehrte Schie-ne *f*	rotaia *f* armata
o	18610	tie rod	tirant *m*, bielle *f* de traction	Stenanker *m*, Zug-stange *f*	tirante *m*, biella *f* di trazione
o	18611	tie up	armure *f*, empou-tage *m*	Schnürung *f*	strizione *f*
o	18612	tied foundry, attached foundry	fonderie *f* inté-grée	Giesserei *f* für Eigenbedarf	fonderia *f* dipendente
–	18613	tiemannite	tiemannite *f*	Tiemannit *m*	tiemannite *f*
–	18614	tiger-eye	crocidolite *f*	Krokydolith *m*	crocidolite *f*
–	18615	tiger sandstone	grès *m* ferrugi-neux rubané	Tigersandstein *m*	gres *m* ferruginoso stria-to
o	18616	tight coat	revêtement *m* mé-tallique sans dé-fauts	fehlerlose Metall-verkleidung *f*	rivestimento *m* metalli-co senza difetti
–	18617	tight hole	trou *m* rétréci	Engstelle *f*	foro *m* ristretto
^	18618	tight sand	sable *m* peu per-méable	schwer durchläs-siger Sand *m*	sabbia *f* poco impermea-bile
o	18619	tight joint	joint *m* étanche	dichter Abschluss *m*	giunto *m* a tenuta
o	18620	tightness	étainchéité *f*	Dichtheit *f*	tenuta *f*
–	18621	tilaite	tilaïte *f*	Tilait *m*	tilaite *m*
–	18622	tilasite	tilasite *f*	Tilasit *m*	tilasite *m*
–	18623	tillite	tillite *f*	Tillit *m*	tillite *f*
o	18624	to tilt a mould	ramper un moule	eine Form schräglegen	inclinare una forma
o	18625	to tilt the con-verter	relever le conver-tisseur	die Birne auf-richten	raddrizzare il converti-tore

		English	French	German	Italian
		tilt hammer, *s. lift hammer* tilted steel, *s. single-sheat steel*			
o	18626	tilter	culbuteur *m*	Kantvorrichtung *f*	giralingotti *m*
o	18627	tilting converter	convertisseur *m* basculant	kippbarer Konverter *m*	convertitore *m* ribaltabile
o	18628	tilting-furnace, tipping open--hearth furnace	four *m* basculant, four *m* oscillant	Kippofen *m*, kippbarer Ofen *m*	forno *m* a bilico, forno *m* oscillante
o	18629	tilting ladle	poche *f* à bascule	Kipppfanne *f*	siviera *f* (o caldaia *f*) rovesciabile
o	18630	tilting lever	queue *f* de lion	Kipphebel *m*	leva *f* della siviera
o	18631	tilting mixer (blast furnace)	mélangeur *m* basculant	Kippmischer *m*	mescolatore *m* oscillante
o	18632	tilting wagon	culbuteur *m* à wagons	Wagenkipper *m*	rovesciatore *m* di carri
—	18633	timazite	timazite *f*	Timazit *m*	timazite *f*
—	18634	timber drawer	déboiseur *m*	Holzrauber *m*	disarmatore *m*
—	18635	timber man	boiseur *m*	Zimmerbauer *m*	armatore *m*
—	18636	timber set	cadre *m*	Zimmerung *f*, Gerüst *n*	armamento *m*, quadro *m*
—	18637	timbering	boisage *m*	Zimmerung *f*	armatura *f*
	18638	time limit	terme *m*	Termin *m*	termine *m*
^	18639	time on bottom	temps *m* au fond	Bohrzeit auf Sohle	tempo *m* di rotazione
o	18639a	time quenching	trempe *f* interrompue	unterbrochene Abschreckung *f*	tempra *f* interrotta
—	18640	time ring	anneau *m* gradué	Teilring *m*	anello *m* graduato
o	18641	time under load	temps *m* de la limite d'allongement	Zeitstreckgrenze *f*	snervamento *m* di scorrimento viscoso
o	18642	time yield	durée *f* de charge	Belastungsdauer *f*	durata *f* del carico
,o	18643	time-temperature transformation curve	courbe *f* à S	S-Kurve *f*	curva *f* ad S (dell'austenite)
o	18644	to tin	étamer	verzinnen	stagnare
o	18645	tin	étain *m*	Zinn *n*	stagno *m*
o	18646	tin bronze	bronze *m* d'étain	Zinnbronze *f*	bronzo *m* di stagno

	English	French	German	Italian
° 18647	tin containing lead	étain *m* plombifère	bleihaltiges Zinn *n*	stagno *m* piombifero
° 18647a	tin cry	cri *m* de l'étain	Zinngeschrei *n*	grido *m* dello stagno
° 18648	tin foil	feuille *f* d'étain	Zinnfolie *f*	foglia *f* di stagno
– 18649	tin ore, tin spar	cassitérite *f*	Kassiterit *m*	cassiterite *f*
° 18650	tin plate, white latten	fer-blanc *m*, tôle *f* étamée	Weissblech *n*,	lamiera *f* stagnata, latta *f*
° 18651	tin-plate sign	plaque *f* en fer-blanc	(Blech)Schild *n*	insegna *f* di latta
° 18651a	tin plating	étamage *m*	Verzinnen *n*	stagnatura *f*
– 18652	tin pyrites	stannine *f*	Stannin *m*	stannite *f*
– 18653	tin spar, tin ore	cassitérite *f*	Kassiterit *m*	cassiterite *f*
° 18653a	tin sweat	ressuage *m* de l'étain	Zinnausschwitzung *f*	trasudamento *m* dello stagno
° 18654	tin tank	chaudière *f* en étain	Zinnkessel *m*	caldaia *f* di stagno
	tin white cobalt, *s. smaltine*			
° 18655	tin-wood	étain *m* de bois	Holzzinn *n*	stagno *m* di legno
– 18656	tincal	borax *m* brut	Tinkal *m*, roher Borax *m*	borace *m* grezzo
° 18657	tinker	ferblantier *m*	Klempner *m*, Spengler *m*	calderaio *m*, stagnino *m*
° 18658	tinman's shears,	ciseaux *m pl.* à ferblantier	Spenglerschere *f*	forbici *f pl.* da lattoniere
° 18659	tinned copper wire	fil *m* de cuivre étamé	verzinnter Kupferdraht *m*	filo *m* di rame stagnato
⌃ 18660	tinned oil	huile *f* en bidon	Kanisteröl *n*	olio *m* in latte
° 18661	tinned sheet, tinned iron	fer-blanc *m*, tôle *f* étamée	Weissblech *n*, verzinntes Eisenblech	latta *f*, lamiera *f* bianca
° 18662	tinned steel	acier *m* étamé	verzinnter Stahl *m*	acciaio *m* stagnato
° 18663	tinned wire	fil *m* étamé	verzinnter Draht *m*	filo *m* stagnato
° 18664	tinning	étamage *m*	Verzinnung *f*	stagnatura *f*
° 18665	tinning vat	chaudière *f* à étain	Zinnkessel *m*	caldaia *f* per lo stagno
° 18666	tinning vat	bac *m* à fer-blanc	Weissblechkessel *m*	caldaia *f* per latta stagnata
° 18667	tinplate	fer-blanc *m*	Weissblech *n*	latta *f* stagnata

		English	French	German	Italian
o	18668	tinplate works	atelier *m* d'étamage	Verzinnungs-anstalt *f*	stabilimento *m* di stagnatura
—	18669	tinstone, tin ore	cassitérite *f*	Zinnstein *m*, Kassiterit *m*	cassiterite *f*
o	18669a	tinsmithing	étamerie *f*	Klempnerei *f*	bottega *f* del lattoniere
o	18670	to tip	basculer, renverser	kippen	vuotare, inclinare
o	18671	to tip the ladle	verser la poche	die Pfanne kippen	rovesciare la caldaia
	18672	tip	pointe *f*, bout *m*	Spitze *f*, Ende *n*	punta *f*, estremità *f*
o	18673	tip	halde *f*, crassier *m*	Halde *f*	mucchio *m* di scorie
o	18674	tipping bridge	pont *m* basculant	Kippbrücke *f*, Wiege *f*	ponte *m* a bilico

tip skid, *s. electrode tip*

		English	French	German	Italian
o	18675	tipping device	culbuteur *m*	Kippvorrichtung *f*	meccanismo *m* di rovesciamento
o	18676	tipping devices	culbuteurs *m pl.*	Kippvorrichtungen *f pl.*	dispositivi *m pl.* a bilico
o	18677	tipping grate	grille *f* basculante	Kipprost *m*	griglia *f* rovesciabile
o	18678	tipping jetty	estacade *f* de déversement	Sturzgerüst *n*	armatura *f* del palco di gettata

tipping open-hearth furnace, *s. tipping furnace*

		English	French	German	Italian
o	18679	tipping platform	plate-forme *f* à bascule	Plattformkipper *m*	piattaforma *f* a bilico
o	18680	tipping stage	plate-forme *f* de déversement	Sturzbühne *f*	piano *m* di rovesciamento
—	18681	tipping stage	chargeur *m* à bascule	Kippbühne *f*	piano *m* caricatore a bilico

tipping staiths, *s. tipping jetty*

		English	French	German	Italian
o	18682	tipping the box	déchargement *m* de la boîte	Entleerung *f* des Kastens	rovesciamento *m* della cassetta
o	18683	tipping the converter	renversement *m* du convertisseur	Drehen *n* der Birne	rovesciamento *m* del convertitore

tipping wagon, *s. tilting wagon*

		English	French	German	Italian
—	18684	tipple, tippler	recette *f* supérieure	Hängebank *f*	stazione *f* superiore
o	18685	tipple. tippler	culbuteur *m*	Wipper *m*	scaricatore *m* meccanico
o	18686	tire bar	barre *f* à jantes	Stange *f* für Radreifen	barra *f* per cerchioni

	English	French	German	Italian
	tire mill, *s. strip mill*			
− 18687	**titanic acid anhydride**	anhydride *m* titanique	Titandioxyd *n*	anidride *f* titanica
− 18688	**titaniferous iron ore**	minerai *m* de fer titanifère	titanhaltiges Eisenerz *n*	minerale *m* di ferro titanifero
− 18689	**titanite**	titanite *f*	Titanit *m*	titanite *f*
− 18690	**titanium**	titane *m*	Titan *n*	titanio *m*
− 18691	**titanium cyanonitride**	cyanure *m* de potasse et de titane	Cyanstickstoff-titan *n*	cianuro *m* di potassio e di titanio
° 18692	**titanium-iron**	ferro-titane *m*	Titaneisen *n*	ferrotitanio *m*
° 18693	**titanium steel**	acier *m* au titane	Titanstahl *m*	acciaio *m* al titanio
− 18694	**titanomagnetite**	titanomagnétite *f*	Titanomagnetit *m*	titanomagnetite *f*
− 18695	**titanomorphite**	titanomorphite *f*	Titanomorphit *m*	titanomorfite *f*
ˆ 18696	**titer**	titre *m*	Titer *m*	titolo *m*
˄ 18697	**to titrate**	titrer	titrieren	titolare
ˆ 18698	**titration**	titrage *m*	Titrieren *m*	titolazione *f*
− 18699	**toadstone**	crapaudine *f*	Krötenstein *m*	bufonite *f*
− 18700	**toddite**	toddite *f*	Toddit *m*	toddite *f*
⏤ 18701	**toe**	pied *m*, base *f*, sol *m*	Sohle *f*, Basis *f*	piede *m*, suola *f*, base *f*
° 18702	**toe**	joint *m* de soudure	Lötfuge *f*	linea *f* di attacco (saldatura)
° 18703	**toe clip**	cale-pied *m*	Fussverschluss *m*	fermapiedi *m*
− 18704	**toe of a hole**	fond *m* du trou	Bohrlochtiefe *f*	fondo *m* del foro
⏤ 18705	**toellite**	toellite *f*	Toellit *m*	toellite *f*
° 18706	**toggle**	levier *m* coudé	Kniehebel *m*	leva *f* a gomito
° 18707	**toggle lever press**	presse *f* à levier coudé	Kniehebelpresse *f*	pressa *f* a leva articolata
° 18708	**toggle press**	presse *f* à genouillère (à commande par pédale)	Gelenkpresse *f* Kniehebelpresse *f*	pressa *f* chiodatrice (a pedale), pressa *f* a ginocchiera

		English	French	German	Italian
o	18709	tolerance, clearance, fit	tolérance *f*, jeu *m*	Toleranz *f*, Passung *f*, Spiel *n*	tolleranza *f*, gioco *m*
^	18710	toluene	toluène *m*	Toluol *n*	toluene *m*
—	18711	tombolo	tombolo *m*	Tombolo *m*	tombolo *m*
—	18712	tonalite	tonalite *f*	Tonalit *m*	tonalite *f*
		to tone, *s. to shade*			
^	18713	to tong up	serrer par la clé suspendue	mit Schlüssel *m* anziehen	stringere con la chiave sospesa
^	18714	tong-clamp	clé *f* à étau	Klemmschlüssel *m*	chiave *f* per morsetti
^	18715	tong die	peigne *m* à clés suspendues	Kamm *m* für lose Schlüssel	pettine *m* per chiavi sospese
^	18716	tong rope	câble *m* de tenaille	Zangenseil *n*	cavo *m* di tenaglie per blocchi
^	18717	tong torque gauge	enregistreur *m* de couple de clé de serrage	Zangendrehmomentmesser *m*	misuratore *m* di coppia della chiave di serraggio
^	18718	tongs	clés *f pl.* suspendues	lose Schlüssel *m pl.*	chiavi *f pl.* sospese
o	18719	tongs, pair of tongs	tenaille *f*	Zange *f*	tenaglie *f pl.*
		tongs hold, *s. bar hold*			
o	18720	tongue, switch	aiguillage *m*	Weiche *f*	deviatoio *m*
^	18721	ton-mile indicator	enregistreur *m* du rendement des câbles	Leistungsmesser *m* des Förderseils	misuratore *m* del rendimento dei cavi di manovra
	18722	tonnage	tonnage *f*	Tonnage *f*	tonnellaggio *m*
o	18723	tonnage steel	acier *m* courant, acier *m* ordinaire	Massenstahl *m*	acciaio *m* ordinario, acciao *m* semplice ordinario
^	18724	tool car	camion *m* porte--outil	Bohrgerätewagen *m*	autocarro *m* portattrezzi
—	18725	tool dresser	aide-perforateur *m*	Hilfsbohrer *m*	aiuto-perforatore *m*
o	18726	tool for interrupted cut	outil *m* de coupe pour cylindrage sur les surfaces interrompues	Drehstahl *m* fuer unterbrochenen Schnitt	utensile *m* di taglio per cilindratura su superfici discontinue

		English	French	German	Italian
°	18727	tool holder	porte-outil *m*	Stahlhalter *m*	portaferro *m*
—	18728	tool joint	accouplement *m* d'outils de sondage	Bohrgestänge-kupplung *f*	accoppiamento *m* d'u-tensili di sondaggio
—	18729	tool-pusher	contre-maître *m* de forage	Oberbohrmeister *m*	capo-sonda *m*
°	18730	tool-steel	acier *m* à outils	Werkzeugstahl *m*	acciaio *m* da utensili
°	18731	tool steel for the mining industry	acier *m* à outils de mines	Bergbau-Werkzeug-stahl *m*	acciaio *m* per attrezzi da miniera
^	18732	tool-wrench	clés *f pl.* (pour batteries)	Schlüssel *m pl.* (für Batterien)	chiavi *f pl.* (per batte-ria)
°	18733	tooth block	modèle *m* de seg-ment de denture	Zahnlückenmo-dell *n*	modello *m* del dente
°	18734	tooth block holder	fouloir *m* porte-segment	Schablonenhalter *m*	pilastro *m* o colonna *f* della sagoma
		toothed, *s. notched*			
°	18734a	top and bottom process	procédé *m* d'Orford	Orford- Verfahren *n*	processo *m* di Orford
°	18735	top blowing	tuyère *f* supérieure	Oberwinddüse *f*	ugello *m* superiore
°	18735a	top board	plateau *m* de dessus	obere Pressplatte *f*	piastra *f* superiore
°	18736	top box	contre-coussinet *m*	Oberlager *m*	semi-cuscinetto *m*
°	18737	top-brass	contre-coussinet *m*	obere Lagerscha-le *f*	(semi)cuscinetto *m* su-periore
°	18738	to top-cast	couler debout	aufrecht giessen	colare in piedi
		top casting, *s. top pouring*			
°	18739	top charging	chargement *m* par le haut	Beschickung *f* von oben	caricamento *m* dal-l'alto (forno)
°	18739a	top crust	croûte *f*	Salzkruste *f*	crosta *f*
		top ejector plate, *s. upper ejector plate*			
°	18740	top flange plate	semelle *f*, tôle *f* de recouvrement	Kopfplatte *f*, Deckflacheisen *n*	piattabanda *f*, lamiera di ricoprimento
°	18741	top hold down	butée *f* d'ancrage supérieur	Kopfhaltestück *n*	cuscinetto *m* d'ancorag-gio superiore
°	18742	top of hearth or crucible	partie *f* supérieure de l'ouvrage	Obergestell *n*	parte *f* superiore del crogiuolo
°	18743	top of housing	tête *f* de la cage, chapeau *m*	Ständerkopf *m*	testa *f* della gabbia
—	18744	top of the base	sommet *m* ou clé *f* de la sole	Scheitel *m* des Bodens	prominenza *f* del suolo o del terreno

		English	French	German	Italian
o	18745	**top part**	partie f de dessus	Formoberteil n	parte f di sopra
		top plain iron, *s. back iron*			
o	18746	**top plate**	plateau m de dessus	obere Pressplatte f	piastra f superiore
^	18747	**top plug**	deuxième tampon m de cimentation	Oberzementierpfropfen m	secondo tappo m di cementazione
o	18748	**top pouring, top pour**	coulée f en chute directe	fallender Guss m mit einem Metallstrahl	colata f diretta, colata f dall'alto
o	18749	**top print**	portée f de noyau	Kernmarke f	portata f d'anima
o	18750	**top roll**	cylindre m supérieur	Oberwalze f	cilindro m superiore
o	18751	**top surface porosity**	refus m	Luftblase f	rifiuto m, bolla f di aria
—	18752	**top timbering**	boisage m du toit	Dachverzimmerung f	armamento m del cielo
—	18753	**top water**	eau f supérieure	Hangendwasser n	acqua f superiore (o sovrastante)
—	18754	**topaz, topas**	topaze f	Topas m	topazio m
—	18755	**topazolite**	topazolite f	Topazolith m	topazolite f
—	18756	**topped**	rencontré	angetroffen	incontrato
^	18757	**topped crude**	résidu m de première distillation	Rückstand m der ersten Destillation	residuo m di prima distillazione
^	18758	**topped oil**	résidu de première distillation	Rückstand der ersten Destillation	residuo m di prima distillazione
^	18759	**topped petrolium**	pétrole m raffiné	raffiniertes Erdöl n	petrolio m raffinato
o	18759a	**topping**	éboutage m	Schopfen n	spuntatura f
^	18760	**topping**	étêtage m	Toppen n, Toppdestillation f	processo m per ridurre l'olio greggio
o	18761	**topping out of the slag, slagging**	coulée f de la fonte et du laitier	Schlacken- und Eisenabstich m	colata f delle scorie e della ghisa
^	18762	**topping plant**	unité f de première distillation	Benzin- bzw. Kerosenraffinerie f	raffineria f di benzina o cherosene
^	18763	**topping tower**	tour f de première distillation	Fraktionssäule f	colonna f di frazionamento
^	18764	**topping unit**	unité f de première distillation	Fraktionierungsanlage f	impianto m di frazionamento

		English	French	German	Italian
^	18765	**tops**	distillats de premièr raffinage	Destillate *n pl.* der erster Raffination	distillati *m pl.* di prima raffinazione
—	18766	**topslicing stoping**	exploitation *f* par tranches avec foudroyage	Scheibenbruchbau *m*	coltivazione *f* a trance (orizzontali) con framamento del tetto
—	18767	**tobernite** **torch**, *s. blowpipe*	tobernite *f*	Tobernit *m*, Chalkolith *m*	tobernite *f*
°	18768	**torch brazing**	brasage *m* au chalumeau	Lötrohrhartlöten *n*	brasatura *f* ossidrica
		torch burning, *s, flame cutting* **torch cutting**, *s. flame cutting* **torch gouging**, *s. groove cutting*			
°	18769	**torch tip**	pointe *f* du chalumeau	Schweissbrennerspitze *f*	punta *f* del cannello
—	18770	**tordrillite**	tordrillite *f*	Tordrillit *m*	tordrillite *f*
—	18771	**torendrikite**	torendrikite *f*	Torendrikit *m*	torendrichite *f*
—	18772	**tornebohmite**	tornebohmite *f*	Törnebohmit *m*	tornebohmite *f*
—	18773	**to torpedo a well**	torpiller un puits	einen Schacht torpedieren	perforare un pozzo con mine
—	18774	**torpedo sand**	sable *m* à gros grains	grobkörniger Sand	sabbia *f* a grana grossa
—	18775	**torpedoing**	torpillage *m*	Torpedieren *n*	sondaggio *m* di un pozzo con mine
°	18776	**torque**	moment *m* de torsion	Drehmoment *n*	momento *m* torcente
°	18777	**torque converter**	convertisseur *m* de couple	Drehmomentwandler *m*	convertitore *m* di coppia
°	18777a	**torsion impact**	torsion *f* par choc	Stosstorsion *f*	torsione *f* per urto
°	18778	**torsion test**	essai *m* de torsion	Verdrehungsversuch *m*	prova *f* di resistenza alla torsione
°	18779	**torsion, twist**	torsion *f*	Drehung *f*	torsione *f*
°	18780	**torsional elasticity**	élasticité *f* de torsion	Verdrehungselastizität *f*	elasticità *f* di torsione
°	18781	**torsional load**	force *f* de torsion	Drehkraft *f*	forza *f* di torsione
°	18782	**torsional strain**	effort *m* de torsion	Drehbeanspruchung *f*	sollecitazione *f* a torsione
°	18783	**torsional strength**	résistance *f* à la torsion	Drehfestigkeit *f*	resistenza *f* alla torsione

		English	French	German	Italian
—	18784	**toscanite**	toscanite *f*	Toskanit *m*	toscanite *f*
°	18784a	**tossing**	oxydation *f* par cuille-rées	Oxydation *f* durch Löffeln *f*	ossidazione *f* a cucchiaiate
—	18785	**total displacement**	rejet *m* net	wahre Schublänge *f*	rigetto *m* netto
		total aggregate, *s. combined aggregate*			
	18786	**total analysis**	analyse *f* complète	Gesamtanalyse *f*	analisi *f* completa
°	18787	**total carbon**	carbone *m* total	Gesamt-Kohlen-stoff *m*	carbonio *m* totale
°	18787a	**total carburizing**	cémentation *f* totale	vollständige Zementierung *f*	cementazione *f* totale
°	18788	**total grate area**	surface *f* totale de la grille	gesamte Rost-fläche *f*	superficie *f* totale della griglia
	18789	**total magnification**	grossissement *m* total	Gesamtvergrösse-rung *f*	ingrandimento *m* totale
	18790	**total make, total production**	production *f* totale	Gesamterzeugung *f*	produzione *f* totale
		total material loss, *s. total loss of length of both components*			
°	18791	**total melting loss**	pertë *f* au feu glóbale	Gesamt-Abbrand *m*	perdita *f* al fuoco totale
°	18792	**total radiation pyrometer**	pyromètre *m* à ra-diation totale	Gesamtstrahlungs-pyrometer *n*	pirometro *m* a radia-zione totale
°	18793	**total resisting effort**	effort *m* résistant total	Gesamtwiderstand *m*	resistenza *f* totale alla trazione
—	18794	**total throw**	rejet *m* incliné	flache Sprunghöhe *f*	rigetto *m* inclinato
		touch type electrode, *s. contact electrode*			
—	18795	**touchstone**	basanite *f*	Probierstein *m*, Basanit *m*	basanite *f*
°	18796	**tough copper**	cuivre *m* écroui (ou étiré) à froid	zähes Kupfer *n*, Raffinadekupfer *n*	rame *m* indurito, rame *m* raffinato
°	18797	**tough copper wire**	fil *m* de cuivré tenace	zäher Kupferdraht *m*	filo *m* di rame tenace
°	18798	**tough foundry pig iron**	fonte *f* de moulage résistante	zähes Giesserei-eisen *n*	ghisa *f* resistente di fonderia
°	18799	**tough pitch-copper**	cuivre *m* (r)affiné	vergütetes Kupfer, raffiniertes Kupfer *n*	rame *m* raffinato
—	18800	**tough structure**	structure *f* résistante	zähes Gefüge *n*	struttura *f* resistente
°	18800a	**toughener**	renforceur *m* d'alliage	Legierungsverstär-ker *m*	rinforzatore *m* di lega
	18801	**toughness**	ténacité *f*	Zähigkeit *f*	tenacità *f*

		English	French	German	Italian
○	18802	**toughness test**	essai *m* de fragilité	Kerbschlagversuch *m*	prova *f* (o esame) di fragilità
–	18803	**tour report**	rapport *m* de sondage	Bohrbericht *m*	rapporto *m* di sondaggio
–	18804	**tourmaline**	tourmaline *f*	Turmalin *m*	turmalina *f*
○	18804a	**trace**	trace *f*	Spur *f*	traccia *f*
–	18805	**trachyte**	trachite *f*	Trachyt *m*	trachite *f*
–	18806	**trachyandesite**	trachyandésite *f*	Trachyandesit *m*	trachiandesite *f*
–	18807	**trachydolerite**	trachydolérite *f*	Trachydolerit *m*	trachidolerite *f*
–	18808	**trachytic texture**	texture *f* trachytique	trachytische Struktur *f*	struttura *f* trachitica
	18809	**tracing**	calque *m*	Pause *f* (Zeichnung)	còpia *f*, tracciato *m*
		traction load, *s. pull*			
○	18810	**track time**	période *f* de permanence	Verbleibedauer *f*	periodo *m* di permanenza
`	18811	**track-walker**	guarde-pipeline	Streckenwächter *m*	guardalinee *m*
		trade iron, *s. merchant-iron*			
	18812	**trade-mark, brand**	marque *f* de fabrique	Fabrikzeichen *n*	marca *f* di fabbrica
`	18813	**trailermast**	installation *f* auto-transportée à antenne	selbsttragende Anlage *f* mit Antenne	impianto *m* autoportabile ad'antenna
–	18814	**trailerrig**	installation *f* auto-transportée	selbstraggende Anlage *f*	impianto *m* autoportato
–	18815	**trailing cable**	câble *m* traînant	unterlaufendes Seil *n*	cavo *m* portante
○	18816	**training boiler**	chaudière *f* d'instruction	Lehrkessel *m*	caldaia *f* di allenamento
○	18817	**tram lines, parallel laps**	plis *m pl* parallèles	Parallelbiegungen *f pl.*	ripiegature *f pl.* parallele
–	18818	**trammer**	rouleur *m*	Schlepper *m*	trasportatore *m* (operaio)
–	18819	**tramming**	roulage *m*	Streckenförderung *f*	carreggio *m*, trasporto *m*
○	18819a	**tramp iron**	fragments de fer	verteilte Eisenteilchen im Gestein	frammenti *m pl.* di ferro
–	18820	**tramping**	serrage *m* au pied	Verdichten *n* durch Festtreten	pigiatura *f*, costipare con i piedi
○	18821	**tramway rail**	rail *m* de tramway	Strassenbahnschiene *f*	rotaia *f* di tranvai
○	18822	**transcrystalline crack**	fissure *f* transgranulaire	transkristalliner Riss *m*	fessurazione *f* transgranulare

	English	French	German	Italian
° 18823	**transfer die**	moule m à dispositif de transfert	Transferform f	stampo m con dispositivo di trasferimento
— 18824	**transfer elevator**	élévateur m auxiliaire	Hilfselevator m	elevatore m ausiliare
18825	**transformation**	transformation f	Umwandlung f	trasformazione f
° 18826	**transformation range**	intervalle m de transformation	Umwandlungsintervall n	intervallo m (termico) di trasformazione
° 18827	**transformer plate**	tôle f pour transformateurs	Trasformatorenblech n	lamierino m da trasformatori
° 18827a	**transition point**	point m de transition	Übergangspunkt m	punto m di transizione
° 18828	**transformer tube**	tube m pour transformateurs	Umspanner-Rohr n, Transformatorrohr n	tubo m per trasformatori
— 18829	**transition rocks**	roches de transition	Grauwacke f	grovacca f
— 18830	**transition zone**	zone f de transition	Übergangszone f	zona f di transizione
— 18831	**transitional area**	région f actique	aktische Region f	zona f batiale
18831a	**translation**	translation f	Translation f	translazione f
° 18832	**transom plate**	tôle f d'arcasse	Worpplatte f	lamiera f di arcaccia
18833	**transparency**	transparence f	Durchsichtigkeit f	trasparenza f
° 18834	**transparent gas stream**	courant m de gaz transparent	durchsichtiger Gasstrom m	corrente f di gas trasparente
18835	**transport, conveying**	transport m	Verfrachtung f	trasporto m
— 18836	**transport band**	bande f transporteuse	Förderband n	nastro m trasportatore
	transport of charge, $s.$ *conveying of charge*			
18837	**transport of large masses**	transport m en masse	Massenbeförderung f	trasporto m in massa
° 18838	**transportable basket drying stove**	four m à sécher transportable	fahrbarer Trockenofen m	essiccatoio m trasportabile
— 18839	**transporting and depositing action of running water**	action f transportante et déposante de l'eau courante	transportierende und ablagernde Wirkung f des fliessenden Wassers	azione f di trasporto e di accumulazione dell'acqua corrente
— 18840	**transuranic**	transuranique	transuranisch	transuraneo
° 18841	**transverse elasticity**	élasticité f transversale	Schubelastizität f	elasticità f al taglio

		English	French	German	Italian
o	18842	transverse bending test transverse fault, *s. dip fault* transverse flue, *s. cross flue*	essai *m* de pliage en travers	Querbiegeversuch *m*	prova *f* di piegatura trasversale
—	18843	transverse lap transverse moment, *s. bending moment* transverse pitch, *s. back pitch*	pli *m* transversal	Querfalte *f*	piega *f* trasversale
o	18844	transverse seam welding transverse strain, *s. bending strain* transverse stress, *s. bending stress*	soudure *f* transversale continue	kontinuierliche Querschweissung *f*	saldatura *f* continua trasversale
o	18845	transverse test	essai *m* de flexion statique	statischer Biegeversuch *m*	prova *f* di resistenza alla flessione statica, prova *f* sul traverso
—	18846	transverse valley	vallée *f* transversale	Quertal *n*	valle *f* trasversale
—	18847	trap	trapp *m*	Trapp *m*	trappola *f* stratigrafica
o	18848	trap	clapet *m*, trappe *f*	Falltür *f*	botola *f*
—	18849	trap	porte *f* d'aérage	Wettertür *f*	porta *f* di ventilazione
—	18850	trap	dislocation *f*	Verwerfung *f*, Störung *f*	dislocazione *f*
—	18851	trap-bleeder	décharge *f* du séparateur	Abscheider-Ablass *m*	scarico *m* del separatore
—	18852	traprock	roche *f* verte	Grünstein *m*	rocca *f* verde
o	18853	trapeze bars	fers *m pl.* trapéziformes	Trapezeisen *n*	barre *f pl.* per rondelle elastiche
o	18854	trapeze iron	profil *m* en trapèze	Trapezeisen *n*	ferro *m* trapezio
o	18855	trapezoidal thread milling cutter (shank type)	fraise *f* (à queue) pour filetage trapézoïdal	Kurzgewinde-Schaftfräser *m* für Trapezgewinde	fresa *f* a coda per filettaggio trapezoidale
o	18856	travel	course *f*, levée *f*	Gang *m*, Hub *m*	corsa *f*, levata *f*
^	18857	travel of the oil	migration *f* du pétrole	Erdölwanderung *f*	migrazione *f* del petrolio

		English	French	German	Italian
−	18858	travelled	erratique	erratisch	erratico
°	18859	travelling barrel	corps *m* de pompe mobile	beweglicher Pumpenzylinder *m* Pumpenzylinder	cilindro *m* mobile della pompa
−	18860	travelling block	palan *m* mobile	Flaschenzug-block *m*	taglia *f* mobile
°	18861	travelling grate furnace	foyer *m* à grille mobile	Wanderrostfeuerung *f*	focolare *m* a griglia mobile
		travelling ladle, *s. ladle on wheels*			
°	18862	travelling platform	chariot *m* transbordeur	Schiebebühne *f*	piattaforma *f* mobile
−	18862a	travelling plate	transformateur *m* roulant	fahrbahrer Rollgang *m*	camino *m* a rulli mobili
ˆ	18863	travelling valve	soupape *f* à piston	Kolbenventil *n*, Druckventil *n*	valvola *f* a pistone
−	18864	travelling way	passage *m* de circulation	Fahrweg *m*	passaggio *m* di circolazione
−	18865	travertin(e)	travertin *m*	Travertin *m*	travertino *m*
−	18866	tread	gradin *m*	Stufe *f*	gradino *m*
ˆ	18867	treater	installation *f* de traitement	Behandlungsanlage *f*	impianto *m* di trattamento
°	18868	treatment	travail *m* (de préparation), ajustage *m*	Bearbeitung *f*	lavorazione *f*, trattamento *m*
°	18869	treble bolt	triple verrouillage *m*	dreifache Verriegelung *f*	triplice chiusura *f*
ˆ	18870	tree	tête *f* d'éruption	Eruptionskreuz *n*	testa *f* d'eruzione
°	18870a	trees	arborescences *f pl.*	Bäumchen *n*	arborescenze *f pl.*
−	18871	tremolite	trémolite *f*	Tremolit *m*	tremolite *f*
−	18872	to trench	creuser	ausbohren, ausgraben	scavare
−	18873	trench	fosse *f*, tranchée	Einschnitt *m*	fosso *m*, trincea *f*
		trench, *s. gutter*			
−	18874	trenching, trench-work	travaux *m pl.* de creusement	Grabungen *f pl.*	lavori *m pl.* di scavo
−	18875	trend	direction *f*	Streichrichtung *f*	direzione *f*
−	18876	trepan	tarière *f*	Bohrer *m*	trivella *f*

	English	French	German	Italian
° 18877	trepaning	poinçonnage *m* creux, trépanation *f*	Hohlstanzen *n*, Trepanieren *n*	punzonatura *f* cava, trapanazione *f*
° 18878	trestle	chevalet *m*, support *m*	Gestell *n*, Gerüst *n*, Bock *m*	cavalletto *m*, supporto *m*
− 18879	trestle	cadre *m* du puits	Schachtgeviert *n*	quadro *m* del pozzo
− 18880	trial boring	sondage *m* d'essai	Probebohrung *f*	sondaggio *m* d'assaggio
° 18881	trial closing	rappuyage *m*	vorläufiges Zulegen *n* der Form	chiusura *f* di prova (o provvisoria)
− 18882	trial shaft, trial well	puits *m* d'essai	Probeschacht *m*	pozzo *m* d'assaggio o di ricerche
− 18883	trial trip	cordée *f* d'essai	Probetreiben *n*	avanzamento *m* d'assaggio
^ 18884	threshold treatment	traitement *m* limite	Grenzbehandlug *f*	trattamento *m* limite
° 18885	triangular bar	fer *m* triangulaire	Dreikanteisen *n*	ferro *m* triangolare
− 18886	triangular prism	prisme *m* triangulaire	dreiseitiges Prisma *n*	prisma *m* triangolare
° 18887	triangular wire	fil *m* triangulaire	dreikantiger Draht*m*	filo *m* triangolare
− 18888	triassic period	système *m* triassique	Triaszeit *f*	sistema *m* triassico
° 18889	triatomic molecule	molécule *f* triatomique	dreiatomiges Molekül *n*	molecola *f* triatomica
	trickle scale, *s. tail scale*			
° 18890	trickling cooling plant	appareil *m* refroidisseur à irrigation	Rieselkühler *m*	refrigerante *m* a corrente od a irrigazione
− 18891	triclinic system	système *m* triclinique	triklines System *n*	sistema *m* triclino
− 18892	tridymite	tridymite *f*	Tridymit *m*	tridimite *f*
^ 18893	trigger bit	burin *m* à déclic	Auslösemeissel *m*	scalpello *m* con grilletto d'arresto per un «single shot»
− 18894	trigonite	trigonite *f*	Trigonit *m*	trigonite *f*
− 18895	trimer	trimère *m*	Trimer *n*	trimerio *m*
− 18896	trimerite	trimérite *f*	Trimerit *m*	trimerite *f*

		English	French	German	Italian
°	18897	trimmer (forging)	ébarboir *m*	Putzer *m*	sbavatore *m*
°	18898	trimmer (rolling mill)	machine à cisailler, rogneuse *f*	Beschneidmaschine *f*, Besäummaschine *f*	rifilatrice *f*
°	18899	trimming	cisaillage *m*, rognage *m*	Beschneiden *n*, Besäumen *n*	tranciatura *f*, rifilatura *f*
°	18900	trimming (forging)	ébarbage *m*	Abgrat *m*, Entgratung	sbavatura *f*
—	18901	trimming	étançonnement *m*	Unterstützung *f*	puntellatura *f*
°	18901a	trimming	finissage *m*	Zurichtung *f*	rifinitura *f*, sbavatura *f*
°	18902	trimming die	étampe *f* à ébarber	Abgratstempel *m*	sbavatore *m*
		trimming maschine, *s. trimmer*			
°	18903	trimming press	presse *f* d'ébavurage	Abgratpresse *f*	pressa *f* sbavatrice
°	18903a	trimming shear	rogneuse *f*	Saumschere *f*	bordatrice *f*
—	18904	to trip	déclencher, décliqueter	ausschalten	liberare, far scattare
—	18905	trip	cordée *f*	Treiben *n*	avanzamento *m*
—	18906	trip	voyage *m*	Fahrt *f*, Reise *f*	corsa *f*, viaggio *m*
—	18907	trip	train *m* de berlines	Wagenzug *m*	treno *m* di vagoncini
^	18908	trip	manoeuvre *f* de batterie	Batteriemanöver *n*	manovra *f* di batteria
^	18909	trip bob	barre *f* pour actionner un dispositif dans le puits	Betätigungsstange *f*	barra *f* per azionare un congegno in pozzo
^	18910	trip gas	gaz *m* échappé lors d'une manœuvre	Gasaustritt *m* nach einem Roundtrip	fuga *f* di gas durante la manovra
—	18911	triphyline	triphylite *f*	Triphylin *m*	trifilite *m*
°	18912	triple corrugated (sheet) iron	tôle *f* ondulée à onde triple	Dreifachwellblech *n*	lamiera *f* ondulata tripla
°	18913	triple melting-down process	procédé *m* à deux soulèvements	Dreimalschmelzerei *f*	processo *m* con doppia rifusione
°	18914	triplicate plungers	pistons *m pl.* parallèles	nebeneinanderliegende Kolben *m pl.*	stantuffi *m pl.* paralleli
—	18915	triplite	triplite *f*	Triplit *m*	triplite *f*
—	18916	triploidite	triploïdite *f*	Triploidit *m*	triploidite *f*
—	18917	tripod	trépied *m*	Dreifuss *m*	treppiede *m*

		English	French	German	Italian
−	18918	trippkeite	trippkéite *f*	Trippkeit *m*	trippkeite *f*
−	18919	tripuhyte	tripuhyite *f*	Tripuhyit *m*	tripuhyite *f*
ˆ	18920	triptane	triptane *m*	Triptan *n*	triptano *m*
		trisulphide of antimony, *s. antimonite*			
−	18921	tritomite	tritomite *f*	Tritomit *m*	tritomite *f*
−	18922	to triturate	broyer, triturer	zerreiben	macinare, triturare
°	18923	to triturate	désagréger par fusion	aufschliessen	disgregare per fusione
−	18924	triturated clay	argile *f* désagrégée	zerriebener Ton *m*	argilla *f* triturata
−	18925	troctolite	troctolite *f*	Troktolith *m*	troctolite *f*
−	18926	trögerite	troegerit *f*	Trögerit *m*	trogerite *f*
−	18927	trolleite	trolléite *f*	Trolleit *m*	trolleite *f*
−	18928	trolley mine car	wagon *m* de mine, berline *f*	Förderwagen *m*	vagoncino *m* da miniera
°	18929	trolley wire	fil *m* de trolley	Fahrleitungsdraht *m*	filo *m* per trolley
°	18930	trolley wire of figure 8 section	fil *m* de trolley profilé en 8	8-förmiger Fahrleitungsdraht *m*	filo *m* per trolley a sezione di 8
−	18930a	trommel	trieur *m*	Trommelsieb *n*	crivello *m* rotante a tamburo
−	18931	troostite	troostite *f*	Troostit *m*	troostite *f*
°	18932	troostitic steel	acier *m* troostitique	troostitischer Stahl *m*	acciaio *m* troostitico
		tropenas converter, *s. side blown converter*			
−	18933	trouble	dislocation *f*, faille *f*	Störung *f*, Verwerfung *f*	dislocazione *f*, faglia *f*
−	18934	trough	rigole *f* d'écoulement	Abflussrinne *f*, Waschrinne *f*	canale *m* di scolo
−	18935	trough	pli synclinal, auge *m*	Synklinalfalte *f*	piega *f* sinclinale, conca *f*
−	18935a	trough	auge *f* de sédimentation	Ablagerungsmulde *f*	trogolo *m* di sedimentazione
−	18936	trough	élément *m* de couloir oscillant	Schüttelrinne *f*	elemento *m* del trasportatore oscillante
−	18937	trough axis	axe *m* synclinal	Synklinalachse *f*	asse *m* sinclinale
−	18938	trough bend	charnière *f* synclinale	Muldenscharnier *n*	cresta *f* sinclinale
°	18939	trough charging crane	grue *f* d'enfournement des récipients	Muldeneinsetzkran *m*	gru *f* per caricare o per infornare le cassette

		English	French	German	Italian
—	18940	**trough core**	noyau *m* syncli-nal	Muldenkern *m*	nucleo *m* sinclinale
		trough-iron, *s. Zoré-iron*			
—	18941	**trough limb**	flanc *m* syncli-nal	Muldenschenkel *m*	fianco *m* sinclinale
→	18942	**trough line**	arête *f* syncli-nale	Muldenlinie *f*	cerniera *f* della pie-ga sinclinale
°	18943	**troughed core**	boîte *f* en auge	Ausschüttkern-kasten *m*	cassa *f* d'anima a pa-niere conico
°	18944	**trowel**	spatule *f*	Stichel *m*	spatola *f*
°	18945	**truck**	chariot *m*	Karren *m*, Wagen *m*	carrello *m*
°	18946	**truck, telescope carriage**	truck *m* de manœu-vre à télescope	Ausschubwagen *m*	apparecchio *m* di ma-novra a telescopio
—	18947	**truck for yards**	wagonnet *m* pour chantier	Werftwagen *m*	vagonetto *m* per can-tiere
—	18948	**truck-trailer**	remorque *f* de camion	Lastwagenanhänger *m*	rimorchio *m* di camion
°	18949	**truck wheels, bogie wheels**	roues *f pl.* de wagonnet	Drehgestellräder *n pl.*	ruote *f pl.* dei carrel-li
—	18950	**trudellite**	trudellite *f*	Trudellit *m*	trudellite *f*
°	18950a	**true centering spinning**	centrifugation *f* pure	echter Schleuder-guss *m*	centrifugazione *f* pura
°	18951	**true centrifugal**	centrifugation *f* pure	Schleuderguss *m*	centrifugazione *f* pura
		true tensile stress, *s. ultimate tensile stress*			
°	18952	**true rake angle**	angle *m* de coupe	Schnittwinkel *m*	angolo *m* di taglio
°	18953	**trumpet**	entonnoir *m* de coulée	Giesstrichter *m*	imbuto *m* di colata
°	18954	**trumpet**	tube *m* évasé	aufgetriebenes Rohr *n*	tubo *m* svasato
—	18955	**to truncate**	tronquer	abstumpfen	troncare
—	18956	**truncated cone**	cône *m* tronqué	abgestumpfte Ke-gelform *f*	tronco *m* di cono
—	18957	**truncation**	tronquement *m*	Abstumpfung *f*	troncatura *f*
^	18958	**trunk line, main line**	conduite *f* princi-pale	Hauptleitung *f*	condotta *f* principale
°	18959	**trunnion**	tourillon *m*	Schwenkzapfen *m*, Tragzapfen *m*	perno *m* di rotazione (o di articolazione)

		English	French	German	Italian
o	18960	**trunnion ring**	ceinture *f*, anneau *m* à tourillons	Birnenring *m*	anello *m* di cintura del convertitore
o	18961	**trunnion tip waggon**	culbuteur *m* à tourillons	Zapfenkipper *m*	apparecchio *m* di rovesciamento per vagonetto
—	18962	**truscottite**	truscottite *f*	Truskottit *m*	truscottite *f*
o	18963	**truss-girder**	poutre *f* en trellis	Fachwerkbalken *m*	trave *f* reticolare
o	18964	**truss head rivet**	rivet *m* à tête ronde aplatie	Rundniet *n* mit grossem Kopf	chiodo *m* a testa semitonda larga
o	18965	**trussed girder bridge**	pont *m* à poutres en treillis	Fachwerkbalkenbrücke *f*	ponte *m* a travi a traliccio
o	18966	**trussless (supporting) structures**	constructions *f pl.* (portantes) sans fermes	stützenlose Tragwerke *n pl.*	strutture *f pl.* (portanti) senza armatura
—	18967	**tscheffkinite**	tscheffkinite *f*	Tscheffkinit *m*	tscheffkinite *f*
—	18968	**tschermigite**	tschermigite *f*	Tschermigit *m*	tschermigite *f*
—	18969	**tsingtauite**	tsingtauite *f*	Tsingtauit *m*	tsingtauite *f*
—	18970	**tsumebite**	tsumébite *f*	Tsumebit *m*	tsumebite *f*
o	18970a	**TTT curve**	courbe *f* en S	unwandlungs Kurve *f*	curva *f* TTT
—	18971	**tub**	berline *f*, benne *f*	Grubenwagen *m.* Förderwagen *m.*	vagonetto *m*, benna *f*
—	18972	**to tub**	construire un cuvelage	Gussringe *m pl.* einbauen	tubare, rivestire
		tubage, *s. intubation*			
—	18973	**tubber**	pic *m* à deux pointes	Doppelhacke *f*, doppelte Keilhaue *f*	piccone *m* a due punte
—	18974	**tubbing**	tubage *m*, cuvelage *m*	Tübingausbau *m*	tubaggio *m*, rivestimento *m* (di pozzo)
o	18975	**tube and blank for rear axles**	tube *m* et ébauche pour ponts postérieurs	Rohr *n* und Formstück für Hinterrad-Aufhängungen	tubo *m* e sbozzato per ponti posteriori
		tube beader, *s. tube expander*			
—	18976	**tube brush**	brosse *f* à tubes	Rohrwischer *m*	spazzola *f* per tubi
o	18977	**tube casting**	moulage *m* de tuyaux	Rohrguss *m*	formatura *f* di tubi
—	18978	**tube cutter**	coupe-tube *m*	Rohrschneider *m*	tagliatubi *m*
o	18979	**tube drawing**	étirage *m* des tubes	Zieben *n* von Rohren	trafilatura *f* di tubi
—	18980	**tube expander, tube beader**	mandrin *m* à élargir les tubes	Rohraufweitedorn *m*	mandrino *m* per allargare i tubi

		English	French	German	Italian
—	18981	tube extractor	extracteur _m_ de tubes	Röhrenzieher _m_	estrattore _m_ di tubi
o	18982	tube for airplane lever shafts	tube _m_ pour arbres à levier pour avions	Rohr _n_ für Flugzeugsteuer-Knüppel	tubo _m_ per alberi a leva per aeroplani
o	18983	tube for axles of airplanes landing carriage	tube _m_ pour essieux de trains d'atterrissage d'avions	Achsenrohr _n_ für Flugzeuglandungsgestelle	tubo _m_ per assali di carrelli di aeroplano
o	18984	tube for barriers of railway crossings	tube _m_ pour barrières de passage à niveau	Rohr _n_ für Schranken an Bahnübergängen	tubo _m_ per sbarre di passaggi a livello
o	18985	tube for bicycle and motorcycle frames	tube _m_ pour cadre de vélos et motos	Rohr _n_ für den Fahrrad- und Motorradbau	tubo _m_ per telai di cicli e motocicli
o	18986	tube for ball and roller bearing races	tube _m_ pour roulements à billes	Kugellagerrohr _n_	tubo _m_ per cuscinetti a sfere
—	18987	tube for boring wells	tube _m_ pour l'exploitation par forage de gisements	Rohr _n_ zur Ausbeutung von Lagern	tubo _m_ per perforazioni di giacimenti
o	18988	tube for bread bakeries	tube _m_ pour fours de boulangerie	Backofenrohr _n_	tubo _m_ per forni da pane
o	18989	tube for control circuits	tuyau _m_ pour circuits de contrôle	Rohr _n_ für Kontrolleitungen	tubo _m_ per circuiti di controllo
o	18990	tube for control rods	tuyau _m_ pour barres de contrôle	Rohr _n_ für Regulierstangen	tubo _m_ per barre di controllo
o	18991	tube for cracking plants	tube _m_ pour installations de pyroscission (craquage)	Rohr _n_ für Spaltanlagen	tubo _m_ per impianti di cracking
o	18992	tube for disconnectable scaffolding	tube _m_ pour échafaudages démontables	zerlegbares Gerüstbaurohr _n_	tubo _m_ per ponteggi smontabili
o	18993	tube for distillation plants	tube _m_ pour installations de distillation	Rohr _n_ für Destillieranlagen	tubo _m_ per impianti di distillazione
o	18994	tube for electric conduits	tube _m_ pour conduites électriques	Kabelschutzrohr _n_	tubo _m_ per condutture elettriche
o	18995	tube for extinguishing plants	tube _m_ pour installations d'extincteurs	Rohr _n_ für Feuerlöschanlagen	tubo _m_ per impianti antincendio

		English	French	German	Italian
o	18996	**tube for fencings**	tube *m* pour para-pets	Rohr *n* für Brustwehren	tubo *m* per ringhiere
o	18997	**tube for foundry core bars**	tube *m* pour âmes de fonderie	Rohr *n* für Guss-kerne	tubo *m* per anime di fonderia
o	18998	**tube for fuel elements**	tuyau *m* pour élé-ments combusti-bles	Rohr *n* für Spalt-stoffelemente	tubo *m* per elementi combustibili
o	18999	**tube for gates**	tube *m* pour grilles	Rohr *n* für Gitter	tubo *m* per grate
o	19000	**tube for gear rings**	tube *m* pour douil-les	Rohr *n* für Büch-sen	tubo *m* per ghiere
o	19001	**tube for geophysi-cal prospecting work**	tube *m* pour sonda-ges géognostiques	Rohr *n* für Schürf-bohrungen	tubo *m* per sondaggi geognostici
o	19002	**tube for hollow shafting**	tube *m* pour arbres creux de transmis-sion	Rohr *n* für hohle Transmissions-wellen	tubo *m* per alberi di trasmissione cavi
o	19003	**tube for hydraulic and collapsible ladders on motor-cars**	tube *m* pour éléva-teurs hydrauliques d'échelles auto-porteuses	Hubwindrohr *n* für hydraulische Kraftwagenleiter	tubo *m* per elevatori idraulici di scale au-toportate
o	19004	**tube for hydrody-namic plants**	tube *m* pour appa-reillage hydrody-namique	Rohr *n* für hydrody-namische Apparate	tubo *m* per impianti i-drodinamici
o	19005	**tube for irrigation**	tube *m* pour arro-sage	Berieselungsrohr *n*	tubo *m* per irrigazione
o	19006	**tube for mandrels of machine tools**	tube *m* pour man-drins de machines-outils	Rohr *n* für Spann-futter bei Werk-zeugmaschinen	tubo *m* per mandrini di macchine utensili
o	19007	**tube for palisades**	tube *m* pour palis-sades	Palissadenrohr *n*	tubo *m* per palizzate
o	19008	**tube for pneumatic breakers**	tube *m* pour canons de marteaux pneu-matiques	Lufthammerrohr *n*	tubo *m* per canne di martelli pneumatici
o	19009	**tube for pneumatic post**	tube *m* pour instal-lations de poste pneumatique	Luftpostrohr *n*	tubo *m* per postà pneu-matica
o	19010	**tube for pneumatic tools**	tube *m* pour canons de marteaux pneu-matiques	Lufthammerrohr *n*	tubo *m* per canne di martelli pneumatici

		English	French	German	Italian
o	19011	tube for propeller shafts	tube *m* pour arbres porte-hélices	Rohr *n* für Schraubenwellen	tubo *m* per assi porta-elica
o	19012	tube for railings	tube *m* pour balustrades	Rohr *n* für Geländer	tubo *m* per balaustre
o	19013	tube for railways crossing bars	tube *m* pour barres de passage à niveau	Rohr *n* für Schranken an Bahnübergängen	tubo *m* per sbarre di passaggio a livello
o	19014	tube for reforming plants	tube *m* pour installations de reforming	Rohr *n* für Reformieranlagen	tubo *m* per impianti di «reforming»
o	19015	tube for refrigerators	tube *m* pour réfrigérateurs	Rohr *n* für Kühlanlagen	tubo *m* refrigerante
o	19016	tube for rifles	tube *m* pour canons de fusil	Rohr *n* für Gewehrlaüfe	tubo *m* per canne da fucile
o	19017	tube for rolling doors	tube *m* pour devanteurs à rouleaux	Rolladenrohr *n*	tubo *m* per serrande
o	19018	tube for rolling shutters	tube *m* pour volets roulants	Rolladen-Rohr *n*	tubo *m* per serrande
o	19019	tube for scaffolding	tube *m* pour échafaudage	Gerüstrohr *n*	tubo *m* per ponteggi
o	19020	tube for sleeves	tube *m* pour manchons	Rohr *m* für Muffen	tubo *m* per manicotti
o	19021	tube for speaking contrivances	tube *m* pour portevoix et transmission d'ordres	Sprachrohr *n* und Schiffstelegraphen-rohr	tubo *m* per portavoce e trasmissione d'ordini
o	19022	tube for steam generators	tube *m* pour générateurs de vapeur	Dampfkesselrohr *n*	tubo *m* per generatori di vapore
o	19023	tube for submerged mains	tube *m* pour conduites submergées	Rohr *n* für Unterwasserleitungen	tubo *m* per condotte subacque
o	19024	tube for supports	tube *m* pour tiges à tampons	Rohr *n* für Hebebäume	tubo *m* per gambi di forza
o	19025	tube for transmission shafts	tube *m* pour arbres de transmission	Rohr *n* für Kraftübertragungswellen	tubo *m* per alberi di trasmissione
o	19026	tube for wash bottle	pipette *f*	Spritzröhre *f*	cannello *m* della spruzzetta
o	19027	tube for Westinghouse brake conduits	tube *m* pour freins Westinghouse	Bremsrohr *n* für Westinghouse-Bremsleitungen	tubo *m* per freni Westinghouse

		English	French	German	Italian
o	19028	tube for window and door frames	tube *m* pour profilés pour menuiseries métalliques	profiliertes Rohr *n* für Metallfenster und Türen	tubo *m* sagomato per serramenta
o	19029	tube formed by explosion	tube *m* formé par explosion	explosiv- umgeformtes Rohr *n*	tubo *m* formato col processo ad esplosione
o	19029a	tube furnace	four *m* tubulaire	Röhrenofen *m*	forno *m* tubolare
^	19030	tube hook	crochet *m* de tubes de pompage	Pumpenrohrhaken *m*	gancio *m* per tubi di pompaggio
o	19031	tube joint, pipe joint	joint *m* de tube, raccord *m* de tube	Rohrverbindungsstück *n*	raccordo *m* per tubi
o	19032	tube mill	fabrique *f* de tubes	Röhrenfabrik *f*	fabbrica *f* di tubi
o	19033	tube nest	faisceau *m* tubulaire	Rohrbündel *n*	fascio *m* tubiero
o	19034	tube packing	garniture *f* de tube	Rohrpackung *f*	guarnizione *f* per tubi
o	19035	tube plate	plaque *f* de tête, plaque *f* tubulaire	Rohrplatte *f*, Heizrohrwand *f*	lamiera *f* (o piastra *f*) portatubi
o	19036	tube rolling	laminage *m* de tubes	Röhrenwalzen *n*	laminazione *f* dei tubi
o	19037	tube rolling mill	laminoir *m* à tubes	Rohrwalzwerk *n*	laminatoio *m* per tubi
'	19038	tube rolling (Perrins process)	procédé *m* dit «au pas de pélerin»	Pilgerschrittverfahren *n*	processo *m* del «passo di pellegrino»
^	19039	tube scraper	racloir *m* de tubes	Rohrkrätzer *m*	raschiatoio *m* per tubi
o	19040	tube sheet	plaque *f* tubulaire	Heizrohrwand *f*	piastra *f* tubiera
o	19041	tube stand tube staving, *s. staving*	porte-éprouvettes *m*	Probiergläserhalter *m*	portaprovette *m*
o	19042	tube support	support *m* de tube	Rohrträger *m*	portatubi *m*
o	19043	tube weld	soudure *f* de tube	Rohrschweissnaht *f*	saldatura *f* di tubo
o	19044	tube with baffle plates	tuyau *m* à chicanes	Rohr *n* mit Scheidewänden	tubo *m* a pareti distinte o separate
^	19045	tubing	tube *m* de pompage	Pumprohr *n*	tubo *m* di pompaggio
		tubing, *s. timbering*			

		English	French	German	Italian
^	19046	tubing	colonne *f* d'extraction	Steigrohr *n*	colonna *f* d'estrazione
^	19047	tubing block	moufle *f* de tubing	Tubing-Flaschenzugblock *m*	paranco *m* per tubi
^	19048	tubing catcher	mâchoires *f pl.* de suspension pour tubes	Tubing-Fänger *m*	mascelle *f pl.* di sospensione per tubi
^	19049	tubing clamp	collier *m* de serrage	Rohrgreifhaken *m*	cravatta *f* per «tubing»
^	19050	tubing cutter	coupe-tubing *m*	Tubingschneider *m*	taglia-tubi *m*
^	19051	tubing head	tête *f* de tube	Tubing-Kopf *m*	testa *f* del tubaggio
^	19052	tubing head spool	bobine *f* de bridage du tubing	Tubingflanschen-Bobine *f*	rocchetto *m* d'inflangiatura del tubing
—	19053	tubing packer	essayeur *m* de couches	Schichtprüfer *m*	saggiatore *m* di strato
^	19054	tubing pressure	pression *m* de la colonne montante	Steigrohrdruck *m*, Tubingdruck *m*	pressione *f* del tubo montante
^	19055	tubing pump, tubing liner pump	pompe *f* à plongeur	Plungerpumpe *f*	pompa *f* a stantuffo immerso
^	19056	tubing spider	potence *f* pour tubes	Röhrengreifhaken *m*	clampa *f* per tubi
^	19057	tubingless completion	complétion *f* sans colonne de production	Verwendung *f* von Tubing als Casing	uso *m* del tubo senza involucro
°	19058	tubular air caisson	caisse *f* à air tubulaire	Windkessel *m*	cassa *f* d'aria tubolare
		tubular atomiser, *s. tubular sprayer*			
°	19059	tubular axle	essieu *m* tubulaire	Rohrachse *f*	assale *m* tubolare
°	19060	tubular axle with journals	essieu *m* tubulaire avec tourillons	Rohrachse *f* mit Zapfen	assale *m* tubolare completo di fuselli
°	19061	tubular beam	poutre *f* tubulaire	Rohrbalken *m*	trave *f* tubolare
°	19062	tubular boiler	chaudière *f* tubulaire	Röhrenkessel *m*	caldaia *f* tubolare
°	19063	tubular bracket for trolley wires	console *f* tubulaire pour lignes de contact	Rohrausleger *m* für Fahrleitungen	mensola *f* tubolare per linee di contatto

		English	French	German	Italian
°	19064	tubular chandelier	réverbère *m* tubulaire	Rohrkandelaber *m*	candelabro *m* tubolare
°	19065	tubular coils for radiating panels of heating plants	serpentins *m* pl.tubulaires pour installations de chauffage à panneaux à rayonnement	Rohrschlangen *f* pl. fuer Strahlungsheizanlagen	serpentini *m* pl. tubolari per impianti di riscaldamento a pannelli radianti
°	19066	tubular column for station sheds	colonne *f* tubulaire pour les toitures des quais de chemins de fer	Rohrsäule *f* für Bahnsteigüberdachungen	colonna *f* tubolare per pensiline di stazioni ferroviarie
°	19067	tubular core	noyau *m* de tuyau	Rohrkern *m*	anima *f* di tubo
°	19068	tubular cross bar of lateral bracing	traverse *f* tubulaire du contreventement	Rohrriegel *m* des Windverbandes	traversa *f* tubolare di controventatura
°	19069	tubular cylinder lining	tube *m* pour chemises de cylindres	Zylindermantelrohr *m*	tubo *m* per camice di cilindri
—	19070	tubular drill	cloche *f*, cuiller *f*	Schlammbüchse *f*	trapano *m* tubolare
°	19071	tubular earthing rod	poteau *m* de mise à la terre	Erdungs-Rohrpfahl *m*	paletto *m* tubolare per messa a terra
°	19072	tubular expanded and upset at the ends	tube *m* avec les extrémités recoulées et agrandies	aufgeweitetes und beiderseits aufgestauchtes Rohr *n*	tubo *m* allargato e ricalcato alle estremità
°	19073	tubular framework	cadre *m* tubulaire	Rohrgerüst *n*	intelaiatura *f* tubolare
°	19074	tubular guard posts with hotforged bull-heads as curbstones	bornes *f* pl. et bouteroues tubulaires à tête arrondie forgée à chaud	Prallpfosten *m* pl. mit rundgeschmiedetem Kopf	paracarri *m* pl. tubolari a testa arrotondata forgiata a caldo
°	19075	tubular guard ring	anneau *m* de garde tubulaire	Rohrschutzring *m*	anello *m* di guardia tubolare
°	19076	tubular lattice pole for power transmission lines	pylône *m* pour lignes électriques	Rohrgittermast *m* für elektrische Leitungen	palo *m* a traliccio per elettrodotti
°	19077	tubular mill	broyeur *m* tubulaire	Rohrmühle *f*	mulino *m* tubolare
—	19078	tubular pit prop	étançon *m* tubulaire pour galeries de mines	Stahlrohrgrubenstempel *m*	puntello *m* tubolare per gallerie di miniere
°	19079	tubular rivet	rivet *m* tubulaire	Hohlniet *m*	rivetto *m* tubolare

		English	French	German	Italian
°	19080	tubular product	produit *m* tubulaire	Rohrprodukt *n*	prodotto *m* tubolare
°	19081	tubular return boiler, tubular roll for paper mills	*s. return flame boiler* rouleau *m* tubulaire pour fabriques de papier	Hohlzylinder *m* für Papierfabriken	tubo *m* per rulli per cartiere
°	19082	tubular shaped structure	élément *m* structurel tubulaire	rohrförmiger Aufbauteil *m*	elemento *m* strutturale tubolare
°	19083	tubular ship derrick with step tapered sections	mât *m* de charge à troncs rétrécis	Ladebaum *m* in abgesetzten Schüssen	picco *m* di carico a tronchi rastremati
°	19084	tubular single mast	poteau *m* tubulaire	Fahrleitungsmast *m*	palo *m* tubolare a stelo unico
°	19085	tubular small road post as curbstone	bouteroue *f* tubulaire	Prallpfosten *m* mit rundgeschmiedetem Kopf	paracarro *m* tubolare
°	19086	tubular spanner	clef *f* tubulaire	Rohrschraubenschlüssel *m*	chiave *f* a tubo
°	19087	tubular sprayer	pulvérisateur-injecteur *m*	Rohrzerstäuber *m*	polverizzatore *m* a tubo
°	19088	tubular steel derrick crane	derrick *m* tubulaire	röhrenförmiger Bohrturm *m*	derrick *m* tubolare
°	19089	tubular structures	charpentes *f pl.* tubulaires	Stahlrohrkonstruktionen *f pl.*	carpenteria *f* tubolare
°	19090	tubular tank	réservoir *m* tubulaire	röhrenförmiger Tanker *m*	serbatoio *m* tubolare
°	19091	tubular trolley pole	perche *f* tubulaire de trolley	Kontaktstange *f* für Strassenbahnwagen	asta *f* tubolare per trolley
°	19092	tubular turnbuckle	tendeur *m* tubulaire	Rohrspannschloss *m*	tenditore *m* tubolare
°	19093	tubular wall bracket	support *m* mural tubulaire	Rohrausleger *m*	braccio *m* murale tubolare
°	19094	tubular wall brackets for electric wires or lampholders	potences *f pl.* (supports muraux) tubulaires pour fils et lampes	Rohrausleger *m* fuer Leitungen und Lampenhalter	bracci *m pl.* murali tubolari portafili e portalampada
—	19095	tugger hoist	treuil *m* à air comprimé	Presslufthaspel *f*, Säulenhaspel *f*	argano *m* pneumatico, argano *m* a colonna

	English	French	German	Italian
− 19096	tumbler	culbuteur *m*	Wipper *m*	apparecchio *m* di ri-baltamento
− 19097	tumbling	dessablage *m* au tonneau	Trommelverputzen *n*	pulitura *f* al tamburo
− 19098	tumbling barrel, box tumbler	tonneau *m* à des-sabler	Putztrommel *f*	buratto *m* sterratore, barile pulitore
	tumbling down, *s. falling-in*			
^ 19099	tung oil	huile *f* de bois de Chine	Holzöl *n*	olio *m* di legno
° 19099a	tundish	cuve *f* réfractaire	feuerfeste Mulde *f*	serbatoio *m* refrattario
° 19100	tungsten	tungstène *m*	Wolfram *n*	tungsteno *m*, wolfra-mio *m*
− 19101	tungsten carbide bit	trépan *m* au carbu-re de tungstène	Wolfram-Karbid-Bohrer *m*	trapano *m* al carburo di tungsteno
	tungsten inert gas welding, *s. inert gas tungsten arc welding*			
° 19102	tungsten-nickel steel	acier *m* au tungs-tène-nickel	Wolfram-Nickel-Stahl *m*	acciaio *m* al tungsteno nichel
° 19103	tungsten special steel	acier *m* spécial au tungstène	Wolframsonder-stahl *m*	acciao *m* speciale al tungsteno
° 19104	tungsten steel	acier *m* au tungs-tène	Wolframstahl *m*	acciaio *m* al tungsteno
− 19105	tungstenite	tungsténite *f*	Tungstenit *m*	tungstenite *f*
− 19106	to tunnel	creuser un tunnel	Tunnel bohren	scavare una galleria
− 19107	tunnel	tunnel *m*, travers-bancs *m*	Tunnel *m*, Stollen *m*	tunnel *m*, traverso-ban-co *m*
− 19108	tunnel driving	percement *m* de tunnel	Tunnelbau *m*	scavo *m* di una galleria
− 19109	tunnel heading	extrémité *f* de fen-due	Stollenort *m*	estremità *f* di una galle-ria
− 19110	(tunnel) mouth	débouché *m* (de tunnel)	(Tunnel)mündung	sbocco *m*, bocca *f* (di galleria)
− 19111	tunnel ring	anneau *m* de ga-lerie	Tunnelring *m*	anello *m* di galleria
− 19112	tunnel stove	étuve-tunnel *f*	Tunnel-Trockner *m*	stufa *f* a tunnel
° 19113	tunnel type furnace	four *m* tunnel	Röhrenofen *m*	forno *m* a tunnel
° 19114	tup	poire *f* (de casse-fonte)	Fallbirne *f*	pera *f* (per berta spezza-rottami)
− 19115	turanite	turanite *f*	Turanit *m*	turanite *f*

		English	French	German	Italian
○	19116	turbid solution	solution *f* trouble	trübe Lösung *f*	soluzione *f* torbida
○	19116a	turbidimeter	turbidimètre *m*	Turbidimeter *n*	turbidimetro *m*
○	19117	turbine blade	aube *f* de turbines	Turbinenschaufel *f*	pala *f* per turbine
○	19118	turbine blade steel	acier *m* à aubes de turbines	Turbinenschaufelstahl *m*	acciaio *m* per pale di turbina
○	19119	turbine locomotive boiler	chaudière *f* de la locomotive à turbine	Turbinenlokomotivkessel *m*	caldaia *f* della locomotiva a turbina
○	19120	turbine meter	compteur *m* rotatif	Turbinenzähler *m*	contatore *m* rotativo
○	19121	turbine rotor	rotor *m* de turbine	Turbinrotor *m*	rotore *m* di turbina
○	19122	turbine sand blaster	sableuse *f* à turbine	Schleuderradputzmaschine *f*	sabbiatrice *f* a proiezione centrifuga
○	19123	turbine shaft	arbre *m* de turbine	Turbinenwelle *f*	albero *m* di turbina
^	19124	turbining	nettoyage *m* par cure-tubes rotatifs	Reinigung *f* mit rotierenden Rohrputzern	pulizia *f* con nettatubi rotativi
○	19125	turbo dynamo, turbo generator	turbogénératrice *f*, turbodynamo *f*	Turbodynamo *f*	turbo-dinamo *f*
○	19126	turbo blower	turbo-compresseur *m*, soufflerie *f* rotative	Turbogebläse *n*	turbo-soffiante *f*
—	19127	turbo drilling	turbo-rotary	Turbinenbohren *n*	turboperforazione *f* (rotary)
^	19128	turbulent flow	écoulement *m* turbulent	turbulenter Fluss *m*	flusso *m* vorticoso
—	19129	turgite	turgite *f*	Turgit *m*	turgite *f*
○	19130	to turn	tourner	abdrehen	tornire
○	19131	to turn a thread to turn into steel, *s. to steel*	fileter au tour	Gewinde (ein)-drehen	filettare al tornio
○	19132	to turn over the piece	retourner la pièce	das Arbeitsstück wenden	girare il pezzo
○	19133	to turn the box	retourner le châssis	den Formkasten wenden	capovolgere la staffa
○	19134	to turn the ingot	tourner le lingot	den Block wenden	girare il lingotto
○	19135	to turn off the blast	couper le vent	den Wind abstellen	chiudere il vento
○	19136	to turn on the blast	donner le vent	blasen	aprire (o dare) il vento

		English	French	German	Italian
°	19137	**turn**	tour *m*, pas *m*	Windung *f*	giro *m*, avvolgimento *m*
—	19138	**turn (directional drilling)**	déviation *f* du trou	Bohrlochablenkung *f*	deviazione *f* del foro
	19139	**to turn over**	mélanger à la pelle	durchschaufeln	mescolare con la pala
°	19140	**turned**	tourné	gedreht	tornito
°	19141	**turned bars**	barres *f pl.* d'acier écroûtées	geschälter Stabstahl *m*	acciaio *m* pelato
°	19142	**turned edge**	bord *m* tourné	abgedrehter Bord *m*	bordo *m*, od orlo *m* girato
—	19143	**turnerite**	turnérite *f*	Turnerit *m*	turnerite *f*
°	19143a	**turning**	tournage *m*	Drehen *n*	tornitura *f*
°	19144	**turning crane**	grue *f* pivotante	Drehkran *m*	gru *f* radiale
		turning force, *s. torsional load* **turning furnace,** *s. rotary kiln*			
°	19145	**turning-lathe, lathe**	tour *m*	Drehbank *f*	tornio *m*
°	19146	**turning tool (side cutting)**	outil-couteau *m* oblique (à charioter)	Laengsdrehstahl *m*, Seitenstahl *m*	ferro *m* a taglio laterale
°	19147	**turning motion**	mouvement *m* de rotation	Drehbewegung *f*	movimento *m* di rotazione
—	19147a	**turnover board**	plaque *f* à fouler	Stampfplatte *f*	piastra *f* a costipare
°	19148	**turnover top table**	plaque *f* à modèle renversable	Wendeplatte *f*	placca-modello *f* rovesciabile
°	19149	**turnover moulding machine**	machine *f* à démouler avec plaque à modèle renversable	Abhebe(form)-maschine *f* mit Wendeplatte	macchina *f* da formare con piattaforma rovesciabile
°	19150	**turntable**	plaque *f* tournante	Drehscheibe *f*	piattaforma *f* girevole
°	19151	**turntable**	table *f* rotative	Drehtisch *m*	tavola *f* girevole (o rotante)
°	19152	**turntable feeder**	alimentateur *m* à disque rotatif	Tellerspeiser *m*	alimentatore *m* a piatto
°	19153	**turret lathe**	tour *m* (à) revolver	Revolverdrehbank *f*	tornio *m* (a) revolver
—	19154	**turquoise**	turquoise *f*	Türkis *m*	turchese *m*

		English	French	German	Italian
—	19155	turret coal-cutting machine	haveuse *f* à colonne	Säulenschrämmaschine *f*	intagliatrice *f* a colonna
—	19156	turtle stone	septaria *f*	Septarie *f*	septaria *f*
—	19157	tusculite	tusculite *f*	Tuskulit *m*	tusculite *f*
	19158	tutwork	travail *m* à forfait	Gedinge *n*	lavoro *m* a cottimo
°	19159	tuyere	tuyère *f* (à vent)	Windform *f*, Blasform	ugello *m*, tubiera *f*
°	19159a	tuyere cap	couverture *f* de tuyère	Blasformkappe *f*	coperchio *m* di ugello
°	19160	tuyere hole	embouchure *f* de la tuyère	Windöffnung *f*	foro *m* della tubiera
°	19161	tuyere level	niveau *m* des tuyères à vent	Ebene *f* der Windformen	livello *m* degli ugelli
°	19162	tuyere nozzle	nez *m* de la tuyère	Rüssel *m* der Form	muso *m* dell'ugello
°	19163	tuyere opening	chapelle *f*	Formöffnung *f*	strombatura *f* od apertura per l'ugello
°	19164	tuyere plate	taque *f* de varme	Formzacken *m*	placca *f* per l'ugello
°	19165	tuyere saddle	assise *f* de la tuyère	Formsattel *m*	base *f* dell'ugello
°	19166	tuyere stock	tubulure *f* extérieure de la tuyère, coude *f* du porte-vent	Formaussenrohrleitung *f*, Winderhitzerkrümmer *m*	tubatura *f* esterna dell'ugello, gomito *m* del portavento
°	19167	tuyere wall	paroi *f* de la tuyère	Formwand *f*	parete *f* dell'ugello
°	19168	twin angle iron	cornières *f pl.* jumelles	Zwillingswinkel *m*	cantonali *m pl.* gemelli
—	19168a	twin axis	axe *m* de macle	Zwillingsachse *f*	asse *f* dei cristalli geminati
°	19169	twin carbon arc welding	soudure *f* à l'arc à deux électrodes de charbon	Zweikohlenlichtbogenschweissen *n*	saldatura *f* ad arco con due elettrodi di carbone
—	19169a	twin crystal	macle *f*	Zwillingskristall *m*	cristallo *m* geminato
°	19170	twin engine	machine *f* jumelle	Zwillingsmaschine *f*	macchina *f* gemella
—	19171	twin hole	sondages *m pl.* jumeaux	Zwillingsbohrung *f*	perforazioni *f pl.* gemelle
˄	19172	twin-jet charge	charges *f pl.* creuses accouplées	Zwillingshohlladung *f*	cariche *f pl.* cave accoppiate
°	19173	twin rolling mill, two high mill	laminoir *m* duo, train *m* duo	Zweiwalzwerk *n*, Duowalzwerk *n*	treno *m* a duo

	English	French	German	Italian
19174	twin spot welding	soudure *f* à double point	Doppelpunktschweissung *f*	saldatura *f* a doppio punto
19175	twin steam pump	pompe *f* à vapeur jumelle	Zwillingsdampfpumpe *f*	pompa *f* a vapore gemella
19176	twin tuyeres	tuyère *f* double	Doppeldüse *f*	tubiera *f* doppia
	twin-spot welding, *s. making two spot welds in one operation*			
19177	twinned crystal	macle *f* géminée	Zwillingskristall *m*	cristallo *m* geminato
19178	twinning	hémitropie *f*	Zwillingsverwachsung *f*	emitropia *f*
19179	to twist	tordre	verwinden	torcere
	twist, *s. torsion*			
19180	twist-off	cassure *f* de tiges	Gestängebruch *m*, Überdrehung *f*	rottura *f* della batteria in pozzo
19181	twist drill	foret *m* hélicoïdal	Spiralbohrer *m*	punta *f* elicoidale
19182	twisted bar	fer *m* à colonnes	Säuleneisen *n*	ferro *m* storto (o a colonne)
19182a	twisted strip	bande *f* tordue	verdrilltes Band *n*	banda *f* contorta
19183	twisting moment	moment *m* de torsion	Drehmoment *n*	momento *m* di torsione
19184	two cyclic engine	machine *f* à deux temps	Zweitaktmaschine *f*	macchina *f* a due tempi
19185	two-drum boiler	chaudière *f* à deux corps cylindriques	Doppelzylinderkessel *m*	caldaia *f* a due corpi cilindrici
19186	two-grove drill	foret *m* hélicoïdal	Spiralbohrer *m*	punta *f* elicoidale
	two high mill, *s. twin rolling mill*			
19187	two-high rougher	duo dégrossisseur *m*	Duovorwalzwerk *n*	laminatoio *m* sgrossatore a duo
19188	two-high stand	cage *f* duo	Duowalzgerüst *n*	gabbia *f* a duo
19189	two-man ladle	cuiller *f* pour deux porteurs	Giesslöffel *m* für zwei Träger	cucchiaio *m* per due portatori
19190	two-prong grab	harpon *m* de repêchage à deux jambes	Doppelfanghaken *m*	arpione *m* di pescaggio a due gambe
19191	two span moulding hall	halle *f* de moulage à double travée	zweischiffige Formhalle *f*	doppia tettoia *f* per formatura

		English	French	German	Italian
—	19192	two stick set	cadre *m* incomplet	halber Türstock *m*	quadro *m* incompleto
→	19193	two-way bit	trépan *m* à deux ailettes	Zweiflügelmeissel *m*	trapano *m* a due alette
°	19194	two wire system	système *m* à deux fils	Zweileitersystem *n*	sistema *m* a due conduttori
°	19195	twyer	tuyère *f*	Windform *f*	ugello *m*
°	19196	twyer-plate	plaque *f* de varme	Formzacken *m*	piastra *f* di riscaldamento
—	19197	tychite	tychite *f*	Tychit *m*	tychite *f*
°	19198	tymp arch	voûte *f* de la tympe	Tümpelgewölbe *n*	volta *f* del timpano
°	19199	tymp plate, tymp	fer *m* de la tympe	Tümpeleisen *n*	ferrò *m* del timpano
°	19200	tymp sheet iron	tôle *f* de la tympe, gendarme *m*	Tümpelblech *n*	lamiera *f* del timpano
°	19201	tymp stone	tympe *f*	Tümpel *m*, Tümpelstein *m*	timpano *m*
	19202	type approval test	essai *m* d'homologation	Abnahme *f*	prova *f* di omologazione
°	19203	type-foundry	fonderie *f* de caractères	Schriftgiesserei *f*	fonderia *f* di caratteri
°	19204	type metal	alliage *m* sans retrait	schwindungsfreie Legierung *f*	lega *f* senza ritiro (o senza contrazione)
	19205	type specimen	original *m*	Original *m*	originale *m*
—	19206	tyrolite	tyrolite *f*	Tirolit *m*	tirolite *f*
—	19207	tysonite	tysonite *f*	Tysonit *m*	tysonite *f*

		English	French	German	Italian
o	19208	**U-iron, channel bar, channel beam**	fer *m* à U	U-Eisen *n*	ferro *m* a U
		U-pipe, *s. syphon pipe*			
—	19209	**U-shaped valley**	vallée *f* en U	U-förmiges Tal	valle *f* ad U
		U. Steel, *s. channel steel*			
—	19210	**uhligite**	uhligite *f*	Uhligit *m*	uhligite *f*
—	19211	**uintaite**	uintahite *f*	Uintait *m*	uintaite *f*
—	19212	**ulexite**	ulexite *f*	Ulexit *m*	ulexite *f*
^	19213	**ullage**	vidange *f*	unausgenutztes Fassungsvermögen *n*	capacità *f* non utilizzata di serbatoio
—	19214	**ullmannite**	ullmannite *f*	Ullmannit *m*	ullmannite *f*
—	19215	**ulrichite**	ulrichite *f*	Ulrichit *m*	ulrichite *f*
—	19216	**ultimate analysis**	analyse *f* élémentaire	Elementaranalyse *f*	analisi *f* elementare
o	19216a	**ultimate load**	charge *f* limite	Grenzbelastung *f*	carico *m* limite
	19217	**ultimate production**	production *f* finale	Gesamtproduktion *f*	produzione *f* totale
	19218	**ultimate recovery**	production *f* finale	Gesamtproduktion *f*	produzione *f* totale
o	19219	**ultimate tensile strenght**	résistance *f* à la traction	Zugfestigkeit *f*	resistenza *f* alla trazione
—	19220	**ultrabasic rock**	roche *f* ultra-basique	ultrabasisches Gestein *n*	roccia *f* ultrabasica
o	19221	**ultra-light alloy**	alliage *m* ultra-léger	Magnesiumlegierung *f*	lega *f* ultraleggera
o	19222	**ultramicroscopic test or inspection**	examen *m* à l'ultramicroscope	ultramikroskopische Untersuchung *f*	ricerca *f* ultramicroscopica
—	19223	**ultramylonite**	ultramylonite *f*	Ultramylonit *m*	ultramilonite *f*
o	19224	**ultrasonic testing**	contrôle *m* par ultrasons	Ultraschallprüfung *f*	esame *m* all'ultrasuono
^	19225	**ultra-viscoson**	viscosimètre *m* vibratoire	Schwing-Viskosimeter *m*	viscosimetro *m* vibrante
—	19226	**umangite**	umangite *f*	Umangit *m*	umangite *f*
—	19227	**umber**	ombre *f*	Umbra *f*	ombra *f*
—	19228	**umber**	lignite *m* terreux	erdige Braunkohle *f*	lignite *f* terrosa

		English	French	German	Italian
—	19229	unallotted ground	terrain *m* non-concédé	freies Feld *n*	terreno *m* libero da vincolo minerario
o	19230	unalloyed tool steel	acier-outil *m* au carbone	unlegierter Werkzeugstahl *m*	acciaio *m* al. carbonio per utensili
o	19231	un-annealed wire	fil *m* cru, fil *m* clair	blanker Draht *m*	filo *m* non ricotto
o	19232	unblistered steel	acier *m* sans ampoules	blasenloser Stahl *m*	acciaio *m* senza soffiature
—	19233	uncaging	décagement *m*	Wegziehen *n* der Förderwagen	distacco *m* dei vagoncini dalla gabbia
—	19234	uncased hole	trou *m* non tubé	unverrohrtes Bohrloch *n*	foro *m* scoperto
o	19235	to unclamp	déclaveter	die Keile entfernen	schiavettare, togliere le chiavette
o	19236	unclamping	déclavetage *m*	Entfernen *n* der Keile	schiavettatura *f*, rimozione *f* delle chiavette
—	19237	uncompahgrite	uncompahgrite *f*	Uncompahgrit *m*	uncompahgrite *f*
—	19238	unconformable	discordant	diskordant	discordante
—	19239	unconformable bed	couche *f* discordante	diskordante Schicht *f*	strato *m* discordante
—	19240	unconformity	discordance *f*	Diskordanz *f*	discordanza *f*
o	19241	uncovered base, exposed base	creuset *m* libre	freigelegter Boden *m*	fondo *m* libero, base *f* esposta
o	19242	unctuosus clay	argile *f* grasse	fetter Ton *m*	argilla *f* grassa
—	19243	undercutting	sous-cavage *m*, havage *m* au mur	Unterhöhlung *f*	scavo *m* dal disotto, scavo *m* sul muro
	19244	under line bridge	passage *m* sous la voie, passage *m* inférieur	Unterführung *f*	sottovia *f*, sottopassaggio *m*
o	19245	undercooled graphite	graphite *m* de surfusion	Unterkühlungsgraphit *m*	grafite *m* di sovrafusione
		undercooling, *s. supercooling*			
o	19245a	undercut	brèche *f*	Scharte *f*	canalino *m*, incisione *f*
o	19246	undercut	contre-dépouille *f*	Hinterschneidung *f*	controsformo *m*

undercut part, *s grooved part*

		English	French	German	Italian
—	19247	underdigger	burin *m* excentrique pour terrains tendres	Exzenter-Stemmeisen *n* für Weichenboden	scalpello *m* eccentrico per terreni teneri
°	19248	to underface the mould underfill, *s. unfilled section*	saupoudrer les moules	die Formen stäuben	spolverizzare le forme
°	19249	to underfeed	alimenter par le bas	Kohlen *f pl.* von unten zuführen	alimentare dal disotto
°	19250	underfeed furnace	foyer *m* à alimentation par en dessous	Unterschubfeuerung *f*	focolare *m* a caricamento dal disotto
—	19251	underfold	pli *m* secondaire	Hilfsfalte *f*	piega *f* secondaria
—	19252	undergauge hole	trou *m* sous-calibre	verengtes Bohrloch *n*	foro *m* sotto calibro
^	19253	undergraded product	produit *m* de qualité inférieure	minderwertiges Erzeugnis *n*	prodotto *m* di qualità inferiore
°	19254	underground corrosion	corrosion *f* par envasement	Korrosion *f* durch Untergrundeinbau	corrosione *f* per interramento
—	19255	underground dam	cloison *f* souterraine	Grubendamm *m*	paratia *f* sotterranea
*—	19256	underground furnace	foyer *m* d'aérage	Wetterofen *m*	forno *m* di ventilazione
—	19257	underground-glory hole method	exploitation *f* par tranches descendantes	Untergrundabbau *m*	coltivazione *f* a tranche discendenti
^	19258	underground line	canalisation *f* souterraine, ligne *f* souterraine	unterirdische Stromleitung *f*	conduttura *f* sotterranea
—	19259	underground milling	exploitation *f* par tranches descendantes	Untergrundabbau *m*	coltivazione *f* a tranche discendenti
—	19260	underground mining	exploitation *f* en souterain	Untergrundförderung *f*	coltivazione *f* in sotterraneo
—	19261	underground passage	voie *f* de carrière	Tunnelstollen *m*	cunicolo *m*
—	19262	underground pit, winze	puits *m* souterrain, puits *m* intérieur	Gesenk *n*, Blindschacht *m*	pozzo *m* sotterraneo
^	19263	underground storage	stockage *m* souterrain	Untergrund-Speicherung *f*	stoccaggio *m* sotterraneo
_	19264	underground survey	levé *m* souterrain	Vermessung *f* unter Tage	rilevamento *m* sotteraneo

	English	French	German	Italian
— 19265	**underground workings**	exploitation f en souterrain	Untergrundförderung f	coltivazione f in sotterraneo
— 19266	**underhand stope**	gradin m droit	Strossenstoss m	gradino m dritto
— 19267	**underhand stoping**	abattage m par gradins droits	Strossenbau m	abbattimento m a gradini dritti
— 19268	**underlay**	inclination f (de filon)	(Gang) Neigung f	inclinazione f (di filone)
— 19269	**underlier**	mur m	Sohle f	muro m, suola f
— 19270	**underlying lode**	filon m incliné	geneigter Gang m	filone m inclinato
— 19271	**underlying shaft**	puits m incliné au mur	tonnlägiger Schacht m im Liegenden	pozzo m inclinato al muro
o 19272	**undermining pitting**	formation f de piqûres sous la surface	innere Grübchenbildung f	vaiolatura f interna
— 19273	**to underpin**	travailler en sous-œuvre	untermauern, unterstützen	puntellare, incuneare
o 19273a	**underpoling**	perchage m incomplet	unvollständige Polung f	trattamento m insufficiente al legno verde
— 19274	**to underream**	élargir	unterschneiden	allargare (un pozzo)
— 19275	**underreamer**	élargisseur m	Unterschneider m	allargatore m per pozzi
— 19276	**underreamer cutter**	couteau m pour élargisseur	Messer m für Nachnahmebohrer	coltello m per allargatore
— 19277	**underreaming**	élargissement m	Unterschneidung f	allargamento m
o 19278	**underside**, **shoulder**	dos m, partie f convexe	Rücken m, glatter erhabener Teil m	dorso m
o 19279	**undersize**	dimension f inférieure	Untermass n	dimensione f inferiore al normale
— 19280	**undersize**	menu m du crible, passé au crible	Durchfall m, Siebdurchfall m	materiale m di vagliatura, materiale m passante
— 19281	**undertable**	hauteur f de la plaine du terrain	Höhe f der Ebene	altezza f del pianotavola dal terreno
— 19282	**underthrust**	avancée f en profondeur	Unterschiebung f	avanzamento m in profondità
^ 19283	**underwater completion**	achèvement m sous-marin	Unterwasser-Completion f	completamento m sottomarino
19284	**underweight**	manque m de poids	Mindergewicht n	mancanza f di peso

		English	French	German	Italian
^	19285	undissolved re-sidue	résidu *m* insoluble	unlöslicher Rück-stand	residuo *m* insolubile
o	19286	undivided piece for use	pièce *f* utilisable entière	ungeteiltes Ge-brauchsstück *n*	pezzo *m* intero
o	19287	undulating mould joint by banking up	talus *m*	vor- oder zurück-springende Form-teilung *f*	ritrovatura *f*
o	19288	unequal angle	cornière *f* à ailes inégales	ungleichschenkliges Winkeleisen	angolare *m* a lati di-suguali
o	19289	unequal angles with round edges	cornières *f pl.* iné-gales à coins ar-rondis	ungleichschenkliger rundkantiger Winkelstahl *m*	angolari *m pl.* ad L a lati disuguali a spigo-li arrotondati
o	19290	unequal webs	ailes *f pl.* inéga-les	Ungleichschenkli-ge Flansche *f*	lati *m pl.* disuguali
o	19291	uneven fracture	cassure *f* inégale	unebener Bruch *m*	rottura *f* ineguale
o	19292	uneven (soft or hard) ramming	fausse serre *f*	ungleichmässige Verdichtung *f*	stivatura *f* difettosa
o	19293	uneveness	inegalité *f* de surfa-ce	Unebenheit *f*	piano *m* ineguale, su-perficie *f* irregolare
—	19294	unexploded	non explosé	unexplodiert	inesploso
o	19295	unfinished product	produit *m* demi-fini	Halberzeugnis *n*	prodotto *m* semilavo-rato
	19296	unifixed	arbitraire	unfest, unfix	arbitrario, non fisso
o	19297	unfused chaplet	support *m* mal soudé	schlecht ver-schweisste Kernstüt-ze *f*	supporto *m* mal salda-to
o	19298	unfused chaplet	reprise *f* de sup-port	Kaltschweisse *f* an Kernstützen	ripresa *f* da sopporto
—	19299	ungaite	ungaite *f*	Ungait *m*	ungaite *f*
o	19300	ungraded iron	fer *m* de qualité inférieure	minderwertiges Eisen *n*	ferro *m* di qualità in-feriore
^	19301	ungraded steel	acier *m* de quali-té inférieure	minderwertiger Stahl *m*	acciaio *m* di qualità inferiore
		unhardened steel, *s. untempered steel*			
—	19302	uniform blast	courant *m* d'air uniforme	gleichmässige Windströmung *f*	corrente *f* d'aria con-tinua
o	19303	uniform hardening	trempe *f* uniforme	Durchhärtung *f*	tempra *f* al nucleo

		English	French	German	Italian
°	19304	**uniform oxidized pinholes**	piqûres f pl. oxydées homogènes	gleichmässig verteilte oxydierte Poren f pl.	camolatura f ossidata omogenea
		uniform slag, s. slag giving uniform covering			
°	19305	**uniform unoxidized pinholes**	piqûres f pl. homogènes brillantes	gleichmässig verteilte glänzende Poren f pl.	camolatura f lucida omogenea
°	19306	**unilateral force**	force f unilatérale	einseitige Kraft f	forza f unilaterale
°	19307	**uninterrupted spectrum**	spectre m continu	ununterbrochenes Spektrum n	spettro m continuo
		unionmelt welding, s. submerged arc welding			
°	19308	**unistrut space-frame structure**	construction f à ossature spatiale	räumliches «Unistrut» Tragwerk	struttura f spaziale «unistrut»
°	19308a	**unit cell**	cellule f élémentaire	Elementarzelle f	cella f elementare
°	19309	**unit load**	charge f unitaire	spezifische Belastung f	carico m unitario (o specifico)
°	19310	**unit of crucible capacity**	point m (unitaire du creuset)	Tiegelgrössenbezeichnung f nach Schwermetallinhalt	punto m (unitario del crogiuolo)
	19311	**unit of pole**	pôle m ayant une unité d'intensité	Einheitspol m	polo m unitario
°	19312	**unit sand**	sable m unique	Einheitssand m	terra f (o sabbia) unica
		unitemper steel, s. finishing mill			
°	19313	**universal iron**	fers m pl. marchands	Universaleisen n	ferro m universale
°	19314	**universal mill**	laminoir m universel	Universalwalzwerk n	laminatoio m universale
°	19314a	**universal mill plate**	large-plat m	Universalblech n	lamiera f piatta larga
°	19315	**universal mill train**	train m de laminoir universel	Universalstrasse f	treno m del laminatoio universale
		universal plats, s. flats			
°	19316	**universal profile iron**	profilé m courant	übliches Profileisen n	profilato m universale
°	19317	**universal rolling mill**	train m universel ou à larges plats	Universalwalzwerk n	treno m universale od a larghi piatti
°	19317a	**universal rolling**	laminage m universel	Universalwalzen n	laminazione f universale
°	19318	**universale stage**	platine f universelle	Universaldrehtisch m	tavola f rotante universale

	English	French	German	Italian
○ 19319	**unkilled steel, effervescing steel**	acier *m* non calmé acier *m* effervescent	unruhiger Stahl *m*	acciaio *m* non calmato (o effervescente)
— 19320	**unkindly lode**	filon *m* non exploitable	unabbauwürdiger Gang *m*	filone *m* non sfruttabile
— 19321	**unloading, discharging**	déchargement *m*	Ausladen *n*	scarico *m*
○ 19322	**unmelted mass**	masse *f* non fondue	ungeschmolzene Masse *f*	materia *f* non fusa
— 19323	**unopened seam**	filon *m* non exploité	nicht ausgebeuteter Gang *m*	filone *m* o banco *m* non sfruttato
○ 19324	**unoxidized blowholes**	soufflures *f pl.* brillantes	glänzende Blasen *f pl.*	soffiatura *f* lucida (o brillante)
○ 19324a	**unprepared scrap**	mitraille *f* brute	Rohschrott *m*	rottami *m pl.* grezzi
— 19325	**to unram**	débourrer	auskratzen	togliere la ripiena, scalzare
— 19326	**unramming**	débourrage *m*	Auskratzung *f*	rimozione *f* della ripiena
— 19327	**unrefined, coarse**	brut	roh	grezzo
19328	**unreliable building ground**	terrain *m* peu sûr	unzuverlässiger Baugrund *m*	terreno *m* di fondazione poco sicuro
— 19329	**unroasted ore**	minerai *m* non grillé	ungeröstetes Erz *n*	minerale *m* non torrefatto
— 19330	**unscreened coal**	charbon *m* non assorti (ou non trié)	unsortierte Kohle *f*	carbone *m* non assortito
19330a	**unslaked lime**	chaux *f* vive	Ätzkalk *m*	calce *f* viva
— 19331	**unsoiling**	découverture *f*	Aufdeckarbeit *f*	scoprimento *m*
○ 19332	**to unsolder**	dessouder	loslöten	dissaldare
— 19333	**unsorted coal**	charbon *m* tout venant	Förderkohle *f*	carbone *m* di prima estrazione
— 19334	**to unsteel**	adoucir	enthärten	addolcire
ˆ 19335	**unsulfonated residue**	résidu *m* non sulfoné	entschwefelter Rückstand *m*	residuo *m* non sulfonato
— 19336	**unsupported**	sans boisage	unverzimmert	non armato, disarmato
— 19337	**unsymmetrical fold**	pli *m* oblique	schiefe Falte *f*	piega *f* inclinata
○ 19338	**untempered steel**	acier *m* non-trempé	ungehärteter Stahl *m*	acciaio *m* non temperato

	English	French	German	Italian
− 19339	to untimber	déboiser	Holz n rauben	disarmare
− 19340	untimbering	déboisage m	Rauben n der Zimmerung	disarmo m dell'armatura
° 19341	unused sand, virgin sand	sable m frais	ungebrauchter Sand m	sabbia f (o terra f) nuova
° 19342	unwarrantable deflection	flèche f parasite	schmarotzende Durchbiegung f	inflessione f parassita
− 19343	unwashed coal	charbon m non lavé	ungewaschene Kohle f	carbone m non lavato
− 19344	to unwedge	relâcher un coin	einen Keil m auslösen	allentare un cuneo
° 19345	unwrought bar	barre f non travaillée	unbearbeiteter Stab m	barra f non lavorata
^ 19346	up and down working	exploitation f à l'alternat	wechselseitiger Betrieb m	esercizio m in alternata
− 19347	upcast	puits m de retour d'air	Ausziehschacht m	pozzo m di ritorno dell'aria
− 19348	upcast	courant m d'air ascendant	aufsteigender Wetterstrom m	corrente f d'aria ascendente
− 19349	upcast	relèvement m, faille f inverse	Aufschiebung f, abnorme Verwerfung f	rilevamento m, faglia f inversa
− 19350	upcast fault	faille f inverse (ou anormale)	Aufschiebung f, abnorme Verwerfung f	faglia f inversa (o anormale)
− 19351	upcast shaft	puits m de sortie d'air, puits m d'appel	auszichender Schacht m	pozzo m di ventilazione
− 19352	up-dip	amont-pendage m	der Fallrichtung f entgegen	pendenza f a monte
− 19353	up-fold	pli m anticlinal	Antiklinalfalte f	piega f anticlinale
− 19354	up ventilation	aérage m (ou ventilation) montant	aufsteigende Wetterführung f	ventilazione f ascendente
° 19355	upending test	essai m de forgeage	Schmiedeprobe f	prova f di fucinatura
− 19355a	upgraded ore	minerai m affiné	veredeltes Erz n	minerale m concentrato
	uphill casting, *s. bottom casting*			
° 19356	uphill running	attaque f en remonte	Tannenbaumanschnitt m	attacco m in sorgente

		English	French	German	Italian
°	19357	**uphill teeming**	coulée *f* en source	Quellenguss *m*	colata *f* in sorgente
—	19358	**to upkeep**	entretenir	unterhalten	mantenere
—	19359	**uplift**	soulèvement *m*, redressement *m*	Hebung *f*, Aufrichtung *f*	sollevamento *m*, raddrizzamento *m*
—	19360	**uplifted peneplain**	pénéplaine *f* élevée	gehobene Rumpffläche *f*	penepiano *m* elevato
°	19361	**upper box**	châssis *m* supérieur	Oberkasten *m*	coperchio *m*, staffa *f* superiore
°	19362	**upper cylinder**	chaudière *f* supérieure	Oberkessel *m*	caldaia *f* superiore, corpo *m* superiore della caldaia
°	19363	**upper die**	étampe *f* supérieure	Obergesenk *n*	stampo *m* superiore
°	19364	**upper part**	partie *f* supérieure	oberer Teil *m*	parte *f* superiore
	19364a	**upper punch**	poinçon *m* supérieur	Oberstempel *m*	punzone *m* superiore
°	19365	**upper rim**	arête *f* supérieure	Oberkante *f*	spigolo *m* superiore
—	19366	**upraise**	remontage *m*	Überhauen *n*	rimonta *f*, pozzo *m* in rimonta
—	19367	**upraising**	remontage *m*	Schachthochbrechen *n*	rimonta *f* (di pozzo scavato)
°	19367a	**upright, spindle**	arbre *m* de trousseau	Spindel *f*	albero *m* per sagomare
°	19368	**upright, vertical position, raised**	position *f* verticale, droit	senkrechte Stellung *f*, aufrecht	posizione *f* verticale, dritto
—	19369	**upright fold**	pli *m* droit, pli *m* symétrique	aufrechte Falte *f*, stehende Falte *f*	piega *f* diritta
		upright furnace, *s. shaft furnace*			
°	19370	**upright moulding machine**	machine *f* à mouler à chevalet	Bockformmaschine *f*	macchina *f* da formare a cavalletto
°	19371	**to upset, to jump**	refouler, écraser	stauchen, zusammenstauchen	appiattire, schiacciare, ricalcare
^	19372	**to upset**	refouler	stauchen	erogare, rifollare
—	19373	**upset**	ouvrage *m* montant	schwebender Grubenbau *m*	opera *f* di rimonta
°	19374	**upset butt welding**	soudure *f* en bout refoulée	Stauchstumpfschweissung *f*	saldatura *f* di testa per ricalcatura
^	19375	**upset casing**	tube *m* refoulé	Rohr mit angestauchten Enden	tubo *m* rifollato
°	19376	**up-set pass**	cannelure *f* refouleuse ou de champ	Stauchkaliber *n*	profilo *m* per ricalcare

		English	**French**	**German**	**Italian**
^	19377	**upset tubing**	tube *m* de pompage à refoulements extérieurs	Pumprohr mit angestauchten Enden	tubo *m* di pompaggio a rifollatura esterna
°	19377a	**upset welding**	soudure *f* bout à bout	Stauchstumpf-schweissen *n*	saldatura *f* ricalcata
		upsetter, *s. upsetting machine*			
°	19378	**upsetting**	refoulement *m*, refoulage *m*	Stauchen *n*, Stauchung *f*	rifollatura *f*, ricalcatura *f*
°	19379	**upsetting die**	calibre *m* à refouler	Stauchmatrize *f*	calibro *m* per ricalcare
°	19380	**upsetting machine**	machine *f* à refouler	Stauchmaschine *f*	fucinatrice *f* meccanica
		upsetting test. *s. shock crushing test*			
^	19381	**upstroke**	coup *m* montant	Aufwärtshub *m*	colpo *m* (o corsa *f*) ascendente
°	19382	**uptake**	carneau *m* à gaz vertical	senkrechter Gaskanal *m*	canale *m* verticale del gas
		uptake, *s. ascending flue*			
°	19383	**uptake**	carneau *m* montant de gaz chauds	Steigkanal *m*	canale *m* verticale del gas caldo
—	19384	**uptake shaft**	puits *m* de sortie d'air	Ausziehschacht *m*	pozzo *m* di ventilazione
—	19385	**upthrow fault**, **reverse fault**	faille *f* inverse, rejet *m* vers le haut	Aufschiebung *f*, Vertikalverschiebung *f*	faglia *f* inversa, rigetto *m* verticale
—	19386	**uptrusion plate**	intrusion *f* vers le haut	Uptrusion *f*	intrusione *f* verso lo alto
—	19387	**upwards borehole**	forage *m* vers le haut	Firstenbohrloch *n*	perforazione *f* verso l'alto
—	19388	**uralite**	ouralite *f*	Uralit *m*	uralite *f*
—	19389	**uralitization**	ouralitisation *f*	Uralitisierung *f*	uralitizzazione *f*
—	19390	**uran-mica**	mica *f* d'uranium	Uranglimmer *m*	mica *f* d'uranio
—	19391	**uranate**	uranate *m*	Uranat *m*	uranato *m*
—	19392	**uraninite**	uraninite *f*	Uraninit *m*	uraninite *f*
—	19393	**uranocircite**	uranocircite *f*	Uranocircit *m*	uranocircite *f*
—	19394	**uranium**	uranium *m*	Uran *n*	uranio *m*

		English	French	German	Italian
o	19395	**uranium steel**	acier *m* à l'ura- nium	uranlegierter Stahl *m*	acciaio *m* all'uranio
o	19396	**uranium glass**	plaque *f* en verre d'urane	Uranglasplatte *f*	lastra *f* di vetro al- l'uranio
		uranium mica, *s. autunite*			
—	19397	**uranophane**	uranophane *m*	Uranophan *m*	uranofano *m*
—	19398	**uranosphærite**	uranosphérite *f*	Uranosphärit *m*	uranosferite *f*
—	19399	**uranospinite**	uranospinite *f*	Uranospinit *m*	uranospinite *f*
—	19400	**uranothallite**	uranothallite *f*	Uranothallit *m*	uranotallite *f*
—	19401	**uranotil**	uranotile *m*	Uranotil *m*	uranotilo *m*
—	19402	**urao**	urao *m*	Urao *m*	urao *m*, trona *f*
—	19403	**urbainite**	urbainite *f*	Urbainit *m*	urbainite *f*
—	19404	**urbanite**	urbanite *f*	Urbanit *m*	urbanite *f*
—	19405	**Urgonian stage**	étage *m* urgonien	Urgon *n*	urgoniano *m*
—	19406	**urinestone**	anthraconite *f*	Anthrakonit *m*	antraconite *f*
—	19407	**urtite**	urtite *f*	Urtit *m*	urtite *f*
—	19408	**urusite**	urusite *f*	Urusit *m*	urusite *f*
—	19409	**usbekite**	usbékite *f*	Usbekit *m*	usbekite *f*
o	19410	**to use a tail print**	tirer à l'anglaise	Kernmarke *f* aufführen	usare una portata al- la francese (o a stra- scico)
o	19411	**used sand**	sable *m* déjà employé	gebrauchter Sand *m*	sabbia *f* usata
		useful effect, *s. yield*			
o	19412	**useless clay**	argile *f* inutilisable	unbrauchbarer Ton *m*	argilla *f* inservibile
—	19413	**ussingite**	ussingite *f*	Ussingit *m*	ussingite *f*
—	19414	**utahite**	utahite *f*	Utahit *m*	utahite *f*
o	19415	**utilisation of heat**	utilisation *f* de la chaleur	Wärmeausnutzung *f*	utilizzazione *f* del calore
o	19416	**utilisation of slag**	utilisation *f* du laitier	Verwertung *f* der Schlacke	utilizzazione *f* della loppa

	English	French	German	Italian
— 19417	**UTMM shapes**	profils *m pl.* U.T.M.M.	UTMM-Profile *n pl.*	profili *m pl.* UTMM
— 19418	**uvanite**	uvanite *f*	Uvanit *m*	uvanite *f*
— 19419	**uvarovite**	uvarovite *f*	Uwarowit *m*	uvarovite *f*

		English	French	German	Italian
–	19420	**V belt**	courroie *f* en V	Keilriemen *m*	cinghia *f* trapezoidale
^	19421	**V-door side**	porte *f* centrale de la tour	Bohrturmtor *n*	porta *f* centrale della torre
⊃	19422	**V-iron**	fer *m* (en) V	V-Eisen *n*	ferro *m* a V
⊃	19422a	**V-notch**	entaille *m* en V	V-Kerbe *f*	intaglio *m* a V
–	19423	**vaalite**	vaalite *f*	Vaalit *m*	vaalite *f*
	19424	**vacuum**	vide *m*	Luftleere *f*	vuoto *m*
⊙	19425	**vacuum-apparatus**	appareil *m* à faire le vide, machine *f* pneumatique	Verdunstpfanne *f*	apparecchio *m* per fare il vuoto
○	19425a	**vacuum casting**	coulée *f* sous vide	Vakuumguss *m*	colata *f* sotto vuoto
–	19426	**vacuum desiccator**	dessicateur *m* par le vide	Absaugentfeuch-ter *m*	essiccatore *m* a vuo-to
○	19427	**vacuum distillation**	distillation *f* dans le vide	Vakuumdestillation *f*	distillazione *f* nel vuoto
–	19428	**vacuum drier (or dessicator)**	sécheur *m* à vide	Vakuumtrockner *m*	essiccatore *m* a vuo-to
–	19429	**vacuum drying oven**	four *m* à sécher dans le vide	Absaugtrockenofen *m*	fornello *m* essiccato-re a vuoto
^	19430	**vacuum filter**	filtre *m* à vide	Vakuumfilter *n*, Saugfilter *n*	filtro *m* a depressio-ne
○	19430a	**vacuum fusion**	fusion *f* sous vide	vakuum Schmelzen *n*	fusione *f* sotto vuoto
○	19431	**vacuum-hill casting**	coulée *f* en source	steigender Guss *m*	colata *f* in sorgente
–	19432	**vacuum-hill ventilation**	aérage *m* montant	aufsteigende Wetterführung *f*	ventilazione *f* ascen-dente
^	19433	**vacuum jet**	éjecteur *m* par le vide	Vakuuminjektor *m*	eiettore *m* per vuoto
○	19434	**vacuum line of the die**	raccord *m* du creux de la matrice	Vakuumanschluss *m* der Matrize	linea *f* di raccordo a vuoto della matrice
○	19435	**vacuum manome-ter**	manomètre *m* à vi-de	Vakuummeter *n*, Unterdruckmesser *m*	vacuometro *m*
○	19436	**vacuum melting**	fusion *f* sous vide	Vakuumschmelzen *n*	fusione *f* sotto vuoto
○	19436a	**vacuum sintering**	frittage *m* sous vide	Vakuumsintern *n*	sinterizzazione *f* sot-to vuoto
○	19437	**vacuum torque gauge**	torsiomètre *m* par le vide	Vakuumtorsions-messer *m*	torsiometro *m* a vuoto
^	19438	**vacuum ventilation**	ventilation *f* à vide	Vakuumlüftung *f*	ventilazione *f* in de-pressione
–	19439	**valbellite**	valbellite *f*	Valbellit *m*	valbellite *f*

		English	French	German	Italian
−	19440	**vale**	canal *m*	Kanal *m*	canale *m*
−	19441	**valencianite**	valencianite *f*	Valencianit *m*	valencianite *f*
−	19442	**vallevarite**	vallevarite *f*	Vallevarit *m*	vallevarite *f*
−	19443	**valley fen**	tourbière *f* de vallée	Talmoor *n*	torbiera *f* di valle
−	19444	**valley glacier**	glacier *m* de vallée	Talgletscher *m*	ghiacciaio *m* di primo ordine
	19445	**value**	valeur *f*	Wert *m*	valore *m*
°	19446	**valve**	valve *f*, soupape *f*	Ventil *n*	valvola *f*
−	19447	**valve auger**	tarière *f* à soupape	Bohrschappe *f*, Ventilschappe *f*	trivella *f* a valvola
°	19448	**valve box**	boîte *f* de la vanne	Ventilgehäuse *n*	cassa *f* della valvola
°	19449	**valve cage**	carcasse *f* de la soupape	Ventilgehäuse *n*, Ventilkorb *m*	carcassa *f* della valvola
°	19450	**valve cone**	pointeau *m* de soupape	Ventilkegel *m*	tappo *m* della valvola
°	19451	**valve of refractory material**	robinet *m* à l'épreuve du feu	feuerfester Hahn *m*	valvola *f* in materia refrattaria
		valve orifice, *s. reducing valve nozzle*			
°	19452	**valve of the air heater**	fermeture *f* de l'appareil à air chaud	Verschluss *m* des Winderhitzers	valvola *f* di chiusura del ricuperatore
°	19453	**valve regulation**	distribution *f* par soupape	Ventilsteuerung *f*	distribuzione *f* a valvola
°	19454	**valve seat**	siège *f* de soupape	Ventilsitz *m*	sede *f* di una valvola
°	19455	**valve seat puller**	chasse-sièges de soupapes	Ventilsitzauszieher *m*	estrattore *m* per piedi di valvole
°	19456	**valve steel**	acier *m* à soupapes	Ventilstahl *m*	acciaio *m* per valvole
	19457	**van**	voiture *f*, camion *m*	Gepäckwagen *m*	vettura *f*, autocarro *m*
−	19458	**van**	vanneur *m*	Planstossherd *m*	lavatoio *m* a basculla
−	19459	**vanadate**	vanadate *f*	Vanadinsalz *n*	vanadate *f*
−	19460	**vanadinite**	vanadinite *f*	Vanadinit *m*	vanadinite *f*

		English	French	German	Italian
–	19461	**vanadium**	vanadium *m*	Vanadium *n*	vanadio *m*
–	19461a	**vanadium mica**	roscoélite *f*	Vanadiumglimmer *m*	roscoelite *f*
○	19462	**vanadium steel**	acier *m* au vanadium	Vanadiumstahl *m*	acciaio *m* al vanadio
		vane, *s. blade*			
–	19463	**vanner**	crible *m* (oscillant)	Schüttelsieb *n*, Sieb *n*	vaglio *m*, vagliatore *m*, tavola *f* a scosse
–	19464	**vanoxite**	vanoxite *f*	Vanoxit *m*	vanossite *f*
–	19465	**vanthoffite**	vanthoffite *f*	Vanthoffit *m*	vanthoffite *f*
		vapor blasting, *s. liquid honing*			
○	19466	**vaporizing economizer and stay for boilers**	vaporisateur *m* et tirant pour chaudières	Eindampf- und Ankerrohr *n* für Kesselbau	vaporizzatore *m* e tirante per caldaie
○	19467	**vaporizing tube**	tuyau *m* vaporisateur	Verdampferrohr *n*	tubo *m* vaporizzatore
^	19468	**vapour dome**	dôme *m* (ou boîte *f*) à vapeurs	Dampfdom *m*	duomo *m* per vapori
^	19469	**vapour recovery unit**	installation *f* de récupération des vapeurs	Dampfregenerierungsanlage *f*	impianto *m* di recupero vapori
^	19470	**vapour testing apparatus**	installation *f* d'essai des gaz	Gasversuchsapparatur *f*	rivelatore *m* di gas
–	19471	**variegated (copper) ore**	bornite *f*	Bornit *m*	bornite *f*
–	19472	**variegated sandstone**	grès *m* bigarré	Buntsandstein *m*	pietra *f* arenaria screziata
○	19473	**variety of carbon**	variété *f* de carbone	Kohlenstoffart *f*	varietà *f* di carbonio
–	19474	**variolite**	variolite *f*	Variolit *m*	variolite *f*
–	19475	**variolitic structure**	texture *f* variolitique	variolitische Textur *f*	struttura *f* variolitica
–	19476	**variscite**	variscite *f*	Varischit *m*	variscite *f*
○	19477	**to varnish**	vernir	firnissen	verniciare
○	19478	**varnish**	vernis *m*	Firnis *m*	vernice *f*
–	19479	**värnsingite**	värnsingite *f*	Värnsingit *m*	varnsingite *f*
^	19480	**vaseline**	vaseline *f*	Vaselin *n*	vaselina *f*
–	19481	**vaterite**	vaterite *f*	Vaterit *m*	vaterite *f*

		English	French	German	Italian
—	19482	**vaugnerite**	vaugnérite *f*	Vaugnerit *m*	vaugnerite *f*
—	19483	**vauquelinite**	vauquelinite *f*	Vauquelinit *m*	vauquelinite *f*
—	19484	**vauxite**	vauxite *f*	Vauxit *m*	vauxite *f*
—	19485	**vegasite**	végasite *f*	Vegasit *m*	vegasite *f*
°	19485a	**vee weld**	soudure *f* en V	V-Schweissung *f*	saldatura *f* a V
		vein, *s. seam*			
—	19486	**veinfilling**	remplissage *m* filonien	Ausfüllung *f*, Gangmasse *f*	riempimento *m* filoniano
—	19487	**vein of copper**	filon *m* de cuivre	Kupferader *f*	filone *m* di rame
—	19488	**vein quartz**	quartz *m* filonien	Gangquarz *m*	quarzo *m* filoniano
—	19489	**vein rock**	roche *f* filonienne	Ganggestein *n*	roccia *f* filoniana
—	19490	**vein wall**	salbande *f*	Salband *n*	parete *f* laterale di galleria, salbanda *f*
—	19491	**vein with oxidized ore**	filon *m* oxydé	oxydischer Gang *m*	filone *m* di minerale ossidato
—	19492	**vein with sulphide ore**	filon *m* sulphuré	sulfidischer Gang *m*	filone *m* di minerale solforato
°	19492a	**veining**	figures *f pl.* de corrosion	Ätzfläche *f*	figure *f pl.* di corrosione
°	19493	**veining**	gerces *f pl.*	Formriss *m*	escrescenza *f*, bava *f*
—	19494	**veinstone**	gangue *f*	Ganggestein *n*	ganga *f*
°	19495	**velocity of formation of ions**	vitesse *f* de formation des ions	lonenbildungsgeschwindigkeit *f*	velocità *f* di formazione degli ioni
°	19496	**to vent**	tirer l'air	Luft stechen, entlüften	tirare (o dare) l'aria
°	19497	**vent**	trainée *f* d'air	Entlüftungsnut *f*	aria *f*, respiro *m*
°	19498	**vent**	tirage *m* d'air	Luftstechen *n*	tirata *f* d'aria
°	19499	**vent, pop-up**	trou *m* d'air	Luftabführung *f*	foro *m* dell'aria, sfogo *m*
°	19500	**vent board, vent plate**	planche *f* à air	Luftschlagbrett *n*	placca *f* d'aria, sagoma *f* per l'aria
°	19501	**vent connection**	pièce *f* d'échappement	Entlüftungsstück *n*	pezzo *m* di sfiato
°	19502	**vent former**	tirette *f* d'air	Bohrung *f* für Luftspiess	riferimento *m* per tirata d'aria
°	19503	**vent lines**	conduites *f pl.* d'échappement	Entlueftungsleitungen *f pl.*	condutture *f pl.* di sfiato

	English	French	German	Italian
19504	vent pipe	tuyauterie f d'aération	Wetterlutte f, Lutte f	tubazione f di ventilazione
19505	vent pipe	lanterne f	Kernspindel f	lanterna f
19506	vent wire, venting wire	aiguille f à air	Luftspiess m	ago m, spillone m, spillo m
19507	vented	ventilé	belüftet	ventilato
19508	ventilation	ventilation f, aérage m	Ventilation f, Wetterführung f	ventilazione f
19509	ventilating shaft	puits m d'aérage	Wetterschacht	pozzo m di ventilazione
19510	venting	tirage m d'air	Entlüftung f	tiraggio m d'aria
19511	venting channel	canal m de pompage	Pumpensteiger m	canale m di pompa
19512	vents	évents m $pl.$	Entlüftungsventile n $pl.$	valvole f d'aereazione
19513	Venturi apparatus	appareil m de Venturi	Venturi-Rohr n	Venturimetro m, apparecchio m di Venturi
19514	to verify	contrôler, vérifier	überprüfen	verificare, provare
19515	verite	verite f	Verit m	verite f
19516	vermiculite	vermiculite f	Vermikulit m	vermiculite f
19517	vernier caliper	jauge f micrométrique	Mikrometerlehre f	calibro m micrometrico
19518	vertical air heater	appareil m à air chaud vertical	stehender Winderhitzer m	apparecchio m ad aria calda verticale
19519	vertical blower	soufflerie f verticale	stehendes Gebläse n	soffieria f verticale
19520	vertical boiler	chaudière f verticale	stehender Kessel m	caldaia f verticale
19521	vertical casting	coulée f debout (ou verticale)	stehender Guss m	colata f verticale
19522	vertical cross tube boiler	chaudière f verticale à bouilleurs transversaux	stehender Kessel m mit Quersiedern	caldaia f verticale con bollitori trasversali
19523	vertical displacement	rejet m vertical	Vertikalverschiebung f	rigetto m verticale

		English	French	German	Italian
o	19524	vertical drilling machine	perceuse *f* verticale	Vertikalbohrmaschine *f*	trapanatrice *f* verticale
o	19525	vertical drive	commande *f* verticale	stehender Antrieb *m*	comando *m* verticale
		vertical extent, *s. depth*			
—	19526	vertical fault	faille *f* verticale	Vertikalverwerfung *f*	faglia *f* verticale
		vertical kiln, *s. shaft kiln*			
—	19527	vertical lining	boisage *m* vertical	senkrechte Zimmerung *f*	rivestimento *m* con tavole verticali
o	19528	vertical milling machine	fraiseuse *f* verticale	vertikale Fräsmaschine *f*	fresatrice *f* verticale
o	19529	vertical pipe	tuyau *m* vertical	Fallrohr *n*	tubo *m* verticale
o	19530	vertical shaft	arbre *m* de commande principal	Königswelle *f*	albero *m* di comando principale
—	19531	vertical sheet-piling	palplanches *f pl.* verticales	senkrechte Getriebezimmerung *f*	armatura *f* a tavoloni verticali
o	19532	vertical steam boiler	chaudière *f* verticale	stehender Dampfkessel *m*	caldaia *f* verticale
—	19533	vertical stull	étai *m*	Stempel *m*	puntello *m*
		vertical welding, *s. vertical position welding*			
o	19534	very fine drawing	tréfilage *m* très fin	Kratzenzug *m*	stiramento *m* finissimo
o	19535	very mild iron	fer *m* extra-doux	sehr weiches Eisen *n*	ferro *m* extra-dolce
o	19536	very open grained pig iron	fonte *f* à grandes cavernes	grossluckiges Eisen *n*	ghisa *f* a grandi caverne
o	19537	very rapid steel	acier *m* extra-rapide	Extraschnellstahl *m*	acciaio *m* extrarapido
o	19538	very soft steel	acier *m* extra-doux	extraweicher Stahl *m*	acciaio *m* extra dolce
—	19539	vesbite	filon *m* vertical	Saigergang *m*	filone *m* verticale
—	19540	vesicular structure	structure *f* bulleuse	blasige Textur *f*	struttura *f* vescicolare
o	19541	vessel	bouteille *f*	Flasche *f*	bombola *f*, recipiente *m*
	19542	vessel positioning	amarrage *m* de la plate-forme	Stellung *f* des Bohrschiffes auf Ansatzpunkt	sistemazione *f* della piattaforma
—	19543	vesuvianite	vésuvianite *f*	Vesuvian *m*	vesuvianite *f*

	English	French	German	Italian
19544	vestibule	chambre f de pré-combustion	Vorkammer f	precamera f
19545	vetrified bond	agglomérant m céramique	keramisches Bindemittel n	agglomerante m ceramico
19546	vibrating distributor	distributeur m vibrant	Vibrationszuteiler m	distributore m vibrante (o a scosse)
19547	vibrating drain, $s.$ vibratory conveyor vibrating feeder	alimentateur m vibratoire	Aufgabevorrichtung f mittels Vibration	alimentatore m vibrante
19548	vibrating sieve, vibrating-screen	tamis m vibrant	Vibrationssieb n	setaccio m (o vaglio) vibrante, vibrovaglio m
19549	vibration	vibration f	Vibrieren n	vibrazione f, scossa f
19550	vibration ramming	serrage m par vibration	Verdichten n durch Vibrieren	formatura f a vibrazione (o a scosse)
19551	vibrator	vibrateur m	Vibrator m	vibratore m
19552	vibratory	vibratoire	Schüttel	vibratorio
19553	vibratory conveyor	transporteur m par secousses	Schüttelförderer m	trasportatore m a scosse o vibrante
19554	vibro drilling vice (or vise), $s.$ bench vise	vibroforage m	Vibrationsbohren n	sondaggio m a vibrazioni
19555	Vickers hardness test	essai m de dureté Vickers	Vickershärteprobe f, Vickersprobe f	prova f di durezza Vickers
19556	vicoite	vicoite f	Vicoit m	vicoite f
19557	villamaninite	villamaninite f	Villamaninit m	villamaninite f
19558	villiaumite	villiaumite f	Villiaumit m	villiaumite f
19559	Vindobonian stage	étage m vindobonien	Vindobon n	vindoboniano m
19560	vintlite	vintlite f	Vintlit m	vintlite f
19561	violarite	violarite f	Violarit m	violarite f
19562	virgation	virgation f	Virgation f	virgazione f
19563	virgin	vierge	gediegen	di prima fusione
19563a	virgin iron	fer m virginal	Frischeisen n	ferro m vergine
	virgin sand, $s.$ unused sand			
19564	viridine	viridine f	Viridin m	viridina f

	English	French	German	Italian
— 19565	**viridite**	viridite f	Viridit m	viridite f
° 19566	**viscous**	visqueux	zähflüssig	viscoso
° 19567	**visible defect**	défaut m extérieur	äusserer Fehler m	difetto m esterno
° 19567a	**viscomet**	viscosimètre m	Viskosimeter n	viscosimetro m
° 19568	**viscosity**	viscosité f	Viskosität f	viscosità f
— 19569	**visual distance**	champ m de vision	Sehweite f	distanza f visiva, campo m visivo
° 19570	**vitreous**	vitreux	glasig	vetroso, vitreo
° 19570a	**vitreous coating**	revêtement m vitreux	Überglasung f	rivestimento m vetroso
° 19571	**vitreous copper (ore)**	chalcosine f	Chalkosin m	calcosina f
° 19572	**vitreous silica**	verre m quartzeux	Quarzglas n	vetro m quarzoso
° 19573	**vitreous silver**	argentite f	Argentit m	argentite f
° 19574	**vitreous slag**	laitier m vitreux	glasige Schlacke f	scoria f vetrosa
— 19575	**vitreous tuff**	cinérite f	Aschentuff m	cinerite f
° 19576	**vitrification**	vitrification f	Verglasen n	vetrificazione f
° 19577	**vitrification, glaze**	vitrification f	angeschmolzener Sand m	vitrificazione f
° 19578	**vitrification point**	point m de vitrification	Verglasungspunkt m	punto m di vetrificazione
^ 19579	**vitrified bond**	mélange m vitrifié	verglasene Mischung f	impasto m vetrificato
° 19580	**to vitriol**	décaper	dekapieren	decapare
— 19581	**vitrophyre**	vitrophyre m	Vitrophyr m	vitrofiro m
— 19582	**vitrophyric**	vitrophyrique	vitrophyrisch	vitrofirico
— 19583	**vitrophyric texture**	structure f vitrophyrique	vitrophyrische Textur f	struttura f vitrofirica
— 19584	**vivianite, brown ore**	minerai m de fer brun, vivianite f	Braunerz n, Blauerz n	siderite f ossidata alla aria
° 19585	**to a vivid red-heat**	au rouge vif	zur lebhaften Rotglut	al rosso vivo
— 19586	**vogesite**	vogésite f	Vogesit m	vogesite f
— 19587	**voglite**	voglite f	Voglit m	voglite f
° 19587a	**void, blowhole**	cavité f	Höhlung f	cavità f, vuoto m
° 19587b	**void hole**	retassure f interne	Innenlunker m	risucchio m interno

		English	French	German	Italian
o	19588	**to volatilise**	se volatiliser	sich verflüchtigen	volatilizzare
o	19589	**volatility**	volatilité f	Flüchtigkeit f	volatilità f
—	19590	**volborthite**	volborthite f	Volborthit m	volbortite f
—	19591	**volcanic eruption**	explosion f volcanique	Ausbruchserscheinung f	esplosione f vulcanica
—	19591a	**volcanic glass**	obsidiane f	Obsidian m	ossidiana f
—	19592	**volcanic mud**	boue f volcanique	vulkanischer Schlick m	fango m vulcanico
—	19593	**volhynite**	volhynite f	Volhynit m	volhynite f
—	19594	**voltage**	tension f de régime	Verbrauchsspannung f	tensione f al luogo di consumo
	19595	**voltage control**	régulateur m de tension	Spannungsregler m	regolatore m del voltaggio
		voltaic electricity, _s. galvanism_			
o	19596	**voltameter**	voltamètre m	Voltameter n	voltametro m
o	19597	**volumetric flask**	ballon m jaugé	Messkolben m	pallone m volumetrico
—	19598	**voltzite**	voltzite f	Voltzin m	voltzite f
o	19599	**volume energy**	énergie f volumétrique	Volumenenergie f	energia f di volume
o	19599a	**volume(tric) assaying**	essayage m volumétrique	volumetrische Erzprobe f	assaggio m volumetrico
o	19600	**volumetric determination (or analysis)**	analyse f volumétrique	massanalytische oder titrimetrische Bestimmung f	analisi f volumetrica
o	19600a	**volume(tric) fill**	remplissage m volumétrique	Volumenfüllung f	riempimento m volumetrico
o	19601	**volute spring, spiral spring**	ressort m en spirale	Wickelfeder f	molla f a spirale
o	19602	**von Hoff gas exit pipe, von Hoff gastake**	prise f de gaz von Hoff	Von Hoff Gasfang m	presa f di gas Hoff
—	19603	**vonsenite**	vonsénite f	Vonsenit m	vonsenite f
^	19604	**vortex sheet**	couche f tourbillonnaire	Wirbelschicht f	strato m vorticoso
—	19605	**verbaite**	verbaïte f	Verbait m	verbaite f
—	19606	**vredenburgite**	vredenburgite f	Vredenburgit m	vredenburgite f
—	19607	**vug, vugh, vugg**	géode m	Druse f	drusa f, geode m
—	19608	**vulcanised asbestos**	amiante m vulcanisé	vulkanisierter Asbest m, Klingerit m	amianto m vulcanizzato

		English	French	German	Italian
°	19609	**vulcanising pan**	chaudière *f* de vulcanisation	Vulkanisierpfanne *f*	caldaia *f* dà vulcanizzare
—	19610	**vulcanite**	vulcanite *f*	Vulkanit *m*	vulcanite *f*
—	19611	**vulpinite**	vulpinite *f*	Vulpinit *m*	vulpinite *f*
—	19612	**vulsinite**	vulsinite *f*	Vulsinit *m*	vulsinite *f*

	English	French	German	Italian
19613	wabble failure	mise f hors d'usage d'un accouplent d'outils de sondage	Ausserbetrieb-setzung f der Bohrgestängekupplung	messa f fuori uso, per sbattimento in pozzo, d'un tool-joint lasco
19614	wacke	wacke	Wacke f	wacke
19615	wad	wad m	Waderz n	miscela f d'ossidi di manganese
19616	wad **wad punch**, s. *hollow punch* **wadding**, s. *wad*	barbe f intérieure	Innengrat m	cartella f, bava f interna
19617	wafer core	galette f	Kernplatte f	galletta f, anima f per fusioni in conchiglia
19618	waffle ingot	lingot m d'aluminium	Aluminiumblock m	lingotto m sottile di alluminio
19619	wagnerite	wagnérite f	Wagnerit m	wagnerite f
19620	wagon balance	bascule f à wagons	Waggonwaage f	bilancia f per vagoni
19621	wagon (head) boiler	chaudière f à tombeau	Kofferkessel m	caldaia f a cofano
19622	wagon corf	berline f	Förderhund m	vagoncino m, carrello m
19623	wagon loader	chargeur m de berlines	Wagenfüller m	caricatore m di vagoncini
19624	wagon tipping device	basculeur m courbe	Kurvenkipper m	dispositivo m di capovolgimento a curva
19625	wagon tippler workings	culbuteur m de berlines	Wagenkipper m	dispositivo m di ribaltamento dei vagoncini
19626	wailer	trieur m	Scheidearbeiter m	vagliatore m, cernitore m
19627	wailing	triage m à la main	Handklauben n	cernita f a mano
19628	walking beam	balancier m	Bohrschwengel m	bilanciere m
19629	walking-beam furnace	four m à sole oscillante	Ofen mit Schwingsohle	forno m a suola oscillante, forno m a passo di pellegrino
19630	walking beam saddle	support m du balancier	Schwingsattel m	sella f del bilanciere
19631	walkway	passerelle f de sonde	Tanklaufgang m	passerella f di sonda

	English	French	German	Italian
— 19632	wall	mur *m*, paroi *f*	Wand *f*, Mauer *f*	muro *m*, parete *f*
— 19633	wall	salbande *f*	Salbande *f*	parete *f* laterale (di un filone)
— 19634	wall	lèvre *f* (d'une faille)	Flügel *m* (einer Verwerfung)	lembo *m*, ala *f* (di una faglia)
— 19635	wall	front *m* ou fond de taille	Abbaustoss *m*	fronte *m* (o fondo *m*) di taglio
ˆ 19636	wall-building test	mesure *f* du panneau au filtre-presse	Tafelmessung *f* auf der Filterpresse	misura *f* del pannello alla filtropressa
ˆ 19637	wall chase (for tubes)	gorge *f* pour tubes	Rohrhohlkehle *f*	incassatura *f*, gola *f* per tubi
ˆ 19638	wall cleaning guides	grattoir *m* centralizateur	Zentrierungskrätzer *m*	baffi *m pl.* di gatto con funzione anche centralizzante
° 19639	wall crane	grue *f* murale	Wandkran *m*	gru *f* da muro
° 19640	wall creeper type jib crane	grue-vélocipède murale	Wandlaufkran *m*	gru *f* a bicicletta murale
— 19641	wall crib	grand côté *f* du cadre de boisage	Joch *n*	lato *m* maggiore del quadro d'armatura
— 19642	wall face	front *m* de taille	Abbaustoss *m*	fronte *m* di taglio
— 19643	wall hook	caracole *m*	Fanghaken *m*	arpione *m*
° 19644	wall jib crane	potence *f*	Schwenkkran *m*	gru *f* a braccio
° 19645	wall of box	paroi *f* du moule	Formwand *f*	parete *f* della forma
— 19646	wall piece	chapeau *m* sur murs de remblai	Kappe *f* über der Versatzmauer	cappello *m* sul muro della ripiena
— 19647	wall pillar	pilier *m* de sûreté	Sicherheitspfeiler *m*	pilastro *m* di sicurezza
° 19648	wall plate	plaque *f* murale	Wandplatte *f*	lastra *f* murale
° 19649	wall rim	couronne *f* de maçonnerie	Mauerkranz *m*	corona *f* di muratura
— 19650	wall rock	roche *f* encaissante	Nebengestein *n*	roccia *f* incassante
° 19651	wall saddle	selle *m* de mur	Mauersattel *m*	sella *f* di muro
ˆ 19652	wall scraper	grattoir *m* à expansion pour mur	Aufweitkrätzer *m*	raschiatore *m* ad espansione per parete

		English	French	German	Italian
^	19653	**wall-scraper bull nose type**	grattoir *m* pour puits directionnés	Krätzer *m* für gerichtete Schachte	«wall scraper» per pozzi direzionati
°	19654	**wall steam pump**	pompe *f* à vapeur murale	Wanddampfpumpe *f*	pompa *f* da muro a vapore
°	19655	**wall thickness of the casting**	épaisseur *m* de fonte	Eisenstärke *f*	spessore *m* di ghisa
−	19656	**walled shaft**	puits *m* muraillé	gemauerter Schacht *m*	pozzo *m* rivestito di muratura
°	19657	**walling**	muraillement *m*	Mauerung *f*	lavoro *m* di muratura
−	19658	**walling**	revêtement *m* de puits	Schachtausbau *m*	rivestimento *m* del pozzo
−	19659	**walling curb**	trousse *f* conique	Keilkranz *m*	quadro *m* conico di miminiera
°	19660	**Walloon process**	procédé *m* vallon ou à un soulèvement	Wallonenfrischen *n*	processo *m* vallone o ad una sola rifusione
−	19661	**walnut size**	grosseur *f* de noix	Nussgrösse *f*	grossezza *f* di noce
−	19662	**walpurgite**	walpurgite *f*	Walpurgin *m*	walpurgite *f*
°	19662a	**walterization**	waltérisation *f*	Walterisierung *f*	valterizzazione *f*
−	19663	**waluewite**	waluéwite *f*	Waluewit *m*	valuevite *f*
°	1963a	**wandering sequence**	soudure *f* échelonnée	stufenweises Schweissen *n*	saldatura *f* a gradini
−	19664	**wapplerite**	wapplérite *f*	Wapplerit *m*	wapplerite *f*
−	19665	**wardite**	wardite *f*	Wardit *m*	wardite *f*
°	19666	**to warm**	chauffer	anwärmen	scaldare
°	19667	**warm water apparatus, geyser**	appareil *m* à eau chaude	Wasserwärmer *m*	apparecchio *m* per acqua calda
°	19668	**warmed chill**	coquille *f* chauffée	angewärmte Schale *f*	conchiglia *f* scaldata
	19669	**warmed water**	eau *f* réchauffée	erwärmtes Wasser *n*	acqua *f* scaldata
−	19670	**warner**	indicateur *m* de grisou	Schlagwetteranzeiger *m*	indicatore *m* di grisou
°	19671	**warming furnace**	four *m* à réchauffer	Anwärmeherd *m*	forno *m* di riscaldamento
°	19672	**to warp**	s'enrouler	sich aufwickeln	avvolgersi, arrotolarsi
°	19673	**to warp**	se déformer	sich verziehen	deformarsi
		warp, *s. drift*			

		English	French	German	Italian
o	19674	warpage	déformation f, bombement m	Aufwölbung f, Verformung f	distorsione f, deformazione
o	19675	warped, twisted	gauche, oblique	windschief	ritorto
o	19676	warped casting	jet m déformé	verzogener Guss m	getto m deformato, fusione f svergolata
o	19677	warping	bombement m	Verbiegung f, Verzug m	deformazione f
o	19677a	warping	enroulement m	Aufwicklung f	formazione f di corone
		warrant, s. chamotte			
—	19678	warrenite	warrénite f	Warrenit m	warrenite f
—	19679	warthaite	warthaite f	Warthait m	warthaite f
—	19680	warwickite	warwickite f	Warwickit m	warwickite f
—	19681	to wash	laver	schlämmen	lavare
		to wash, s. to dress			
^	19682	to wash in	pomper du pétrole dans le puits démarré	Erdölpumpen n im angelassenen Schacht	pompare petrolio nel pozzo avviato
o	19683	to wash the clay	laver l'argile	den Ton schlämmen	lavare l'argilla
—	19684	wash-boring	perforation f à injection	Spülbohren n	perforazione f a iniezione
o	19685	wash bottle	pissette f	Spritzflasche f	spruzzetta f
^	19686	wash down spear	lance f de repêchage	Einholstange f	lancia f di pescaggio
o	19687	wash-heat	chaleur f dispersée	zerstreute Wärme	calore m disperso
		wash heating, s. swealing			
o	19688	wash metal process	raffinage m au bain de scories	Metallwaschverfahren n	affinaggio m al bagno di scorie
^	19689	wash oil	pétrole m brut	Roherdöl n	petrolio m grezzo
^	19690	wash pipe	tube m de surforage	Überbohrrohr n	tubo m per perforazione ad iniezione
o	19691	wash-plate	tôle f de roulis	Schlingerplatte f	lamiera f di rollio
^	19692	wash tank	réservoir m de lavage	Waschbehälter m	serbatoio m di trattamento
o	19693	washburn core	noyau m de liason	Einschnürkern m	anima f di segmentazione
o	19694	washed argillaceous earth	argile f finement lavée	geschlämmte Tonerde f	argilla f lavata

	English	French	German	Italian
	washed clay, *s. triturated clay*			
19695	washed coal	charbon *m* lavé	gewaschene Kohle *f*	carbone *m* lavato o preparato
	washed graphite, *s. refined graphite*			
19696	washed metal, Bell-Krupp metal	fonte *f* épurée ou de déphosphoration pour tampons de cimentation	entphosphoriertes Roheisen *n* Bell-Krupp-Metall *n*	ghisa *f* depurata o defosforata, metallo *m* Bell-Krupp
19696a	washed out	usé	ausgelaufen	usato
19697	washed out hole	trou *m* cavé	Auskesselung *f*	foro *m* scavato
19698	washer	rondelle *f*	Spurscheibe *f*	rondella *f*
19699	washer	bague *m* en caoutchouc pour bouchons de cimentation	Gummiring *m* für Zementierpfropfen	anello *m* di gomma per tappi di cementazione
19700	washer	laveur *m*	Waschapparat *m*, Wäscher *m*	depuratore *m*
19701	washing	lavage *m*	Verwaschung *f*, Wäsche *f*	lavaggio *m*
19702	washing	raffinage *m* au bain de scories	Vergütung *f* im Schlackenbad	affinaggio *m* al bagno di scorie
19703	washing	revêtement *m* (de métaux)	(Metall)bekleidung *f*	rivestimento *m* (di metalli)
	washing boiler, *s. washing vat*			
19704	washing classifier	laveur-classeur *m*	Wasch- und Klassierapparat *m*	lavatore-classificatore *m*
19705	washing device	installation *f* de lavage	Waschvorrichtung *f*	impianto *m* di lavaggio
19706	washing machine	lessiveuse *f*	Waschmaschine *f*	lavatrice *f*
19707	washing pan	cuve *f* de lavage	Waschbecken *n*	vaschetta *f* di lavaggio
	washing pot, *s. brushing pot*			
19708	washing process	procédé *m* de lavage	Waschverfahren *n*	processo *m* di lavaggio
19709	washing room	chambre *f* de lavage	Spülraum *n*	camera *f* di lavaggio
19710	washing table	table *f* de lavage	Waschherd *m*	tavola *f* di lavaggio
19711	washing trommel	trommel *m* débourbeur	Waschtrommel *f*	tamburo *m* lavatore

		English	French	German	Italian
^	19712	**washout**	sortie *f* de liquide d'une conduite par cassure	Flüssigkeitsaustritt *m* durch Bruch aus einer Rohrleitung	fuoruscita *f* di liquido da una condotta per rottura
^	19713	**washout**	chambre *f* de cimentation	Zementierkammer *f*	camera *f* di cementazione
^	19714	**wash-over shoe**	sabot *m* du tuyau de lavage	Waschrohrschuh *m*	scarpa *f* per tuta di lavaggio
^	19715	**wash-pipe**	tuyau *m* de lavage	Waschrohr *n*, Futterrohr *n*	tubo-guaina, tuta *f* di lavaggio
°	19716	**washmarking**	surface *f* ondulée	wellige Oberfläche *f*	superficie *f* ondulata
°	19717	**waste**	déchets *m pl.*	Hüttenabfälle *m pl.*	rottami *m pl.*
—	19718	**waste**	déchet *m*, résidu *m*	Abfall *m*, Abraum *m*	detrito *m*, residuo *m*, scarto *m*
—	19719	**waste**	remblai *m*, vieux travaux	Versatz *m*, alter Mann *m*	ripiena *f*, miniera *f* abbandonata
°	19720	**waste casting**	pièce *f* défecteuse de fonderie	Fehlgussstück *n*	pezzo *m* difettoso di fonderia
—	19721	**waste chute**	cheminée *f* à remblai	Bergerolle *f*	scivolo *m* per ripiena
°	19722	**waste containing iron**	déchet *m* ferrifère	eisenhaltiger Abfall *m*	detrito *m* di ferro
°	19723	**waste, deads**	perte *f* au feu, déchet *m*	Abbrand *m*	perdita *f*, calo *m* (al fuoco)
°	19724	**waste end, crop end**	chute *f*	Abfallende *n*	ritaglio *m*, rimasuglio *m*
—	19725	**waste fill**	remblayage *m*	Versetzen *n*	ripiena *f*
—	19726	**waste floor**	niveau *m* de remblai	Versatzsohle *f*	livello *m* di ripiena
^	19727	**waste fuel**	combustible *m* de rebut	Abfallbrennstoff *m*	combustibile *m* di scarto
°	19728	**waste gas**	gaz *m* brûlé	Abgas *n*	gas *m* bruciato
°	19729	**waste gas furnace**	foyer *m* à gaz de haut-fourneaux	Feuerung *f* mit Hochofengas	focolare *m* a gas di altoforno
—	19730	**waste gas heat**	chaleur *f* des gaz du gueulard	Gichtgaswärme *f*	calore *m* dei gas alla bocca del forno
°	19731	**waste heap ore**	minerai *m* de halde	Haldenerz *n*	minerale *m* sterile

		English	French	German	Italian
⊃	19732	**waste heat boiler**	chaudière f à chaleur perdue	Abhitzekessel m	caldaia f a recupero (di calore)
⊃	19733	**waste heat flue**	conduit m d'évacuation de gaz chauds	Abhitzekanal m	condotto m dei gas caldi
⊃	19734	**waste iron, scrap iron**	riblon m, mitraille f	Abfalleisen n,	rottami m pl. di ferro
−	19735	**waste ore**	stérile m, débris m de minerai	Berge m pl.	minerale m di scarto
⌃	19736	**waste pipe**	tuyau m de trop-plein	Überlaufrohr m	tubo m di troppo pieno
−	19737	**waste rock**	stérile m, débris de roche	taubes Gestein n, Steinschutt m	sterile m, rifiuti m pl. di roccia
		waste tip, s. waste dump			
○	19738	**waste water containing acid**	eaux-vannes f pl. acides	säurehaltiges Abwasser n	acqua f acida satura
		waster, s. scrap			
○	19738a	**waster plate**	plaque f du paquet	Schutzblech n	placca f protettrice del pacchetto
−	19739	**wasting**	gaspillage m	Raubbau m	sfruttamento m irrazionale
−	19740	**wastrel**	matériaux m pl. de remblayage	Versatzmaterial n	materiali m pl. per ripiena
	19741	**watch glass**	verre m de montre	Uhrglas n	vetro m da orologio
○	19742	**watch spring steel**	acier m à ressorts pour montres	Uhrfederstahl m	acciaio m per molle di orologio
⌃	19743	**water acid**	acide m sulfurique	Schwefelsäure f	acido m solforico
○	19744	**water and steam drum**	corps m d'eau et de vapeur	Wasser- und Dampftrommel f	corpo m d'acqua e di vapore
○	19745	**water balanced lift**	monte-charges m à balance d'eau	Wassertonnenaufzug m	montacarichi m a bilanciere d'acqua
○	19746	**water bath**	bain-marie m	Wasserbad n	bagno m d'acqua, bagnomaria m
○	19747	**water-bath boiler**	chaudière f pour bains-marie	Wasserbadkessel m	caldaia f per bagnomaria
○	19748	**water bath ring**	anneau m de bain-marie	Wasserbadring m	anello-supporto m per il bagno d'acqua
−	19749	**water-bearing**	aquifère	wasserführend	freatico, acquifero

		English	French	German	Italian

water bearing iron ore, *s. iron ore containing water*

		English	French	German	Italian
−	19750	**water bearing layer**	couche *f* aquifère	wasserführende Schicht	falda *f* acquifera
−	19751	**water-bearing stratum**	couche *f* aquifère	wasserführende Schicht *f*	falda *f* acquifera, strato *m* acquifero
−	19752	**water bed**	nappe *f* aquifère	Grundwasserschicht *f*	falda *f* idrica
˄	19753	**water break**	séparation *f* du pétrole par le coagulum des résidus de raffinerie	Erdölabscheidung *f* durch Rückstandskoagulation	separazione *f* del petrolio col coagulo dei residui di raffineria
°	19754	**water column**	colonne *f* d'eau	Wassersäule *f*	colonna *f* d'acqua
˄	19755	**water conditioner**	conditionneur *m* d'eau	Wasseraufbereitungsapparat *m*	depuratore *m* d'acqua
°	19756	**water conduit**	conduite *f* d'eau	Wasserleitung *f*	conduttura *f* d'acqua
−	19757	**water coning**	formation *f* du cône d'eau	Wasserkegelbildung *f*	formazione *f* del cono dell'acqua di strato
°	19758	**water contents per cm³ of air**	teneur *f* en eau par cm³ d'air	Wassergehalt *m* in 1 ccm Luft	tenore *m* in acqua per cm³ d'aria
°	19759	**water cooled**	refroidi par l'eau	wassergekühlt	raffreddato ad acqua
°	19760	**water cooled bottom**	sole *f* à courant d'eau	wassergekühlter Boden *m*	suola *f* raffredata (con acqua)
°	19761	**water cooling**	refroidissement *m* par l'eau	Wasserkühlung *f*	raffreddamento *m* ad acqua
°	19762	**water cooling**	circuit *m* d'eau de refroidissement	Wasserkühlung *f*	circuito *m* d'acqua di raffreddamento
°	19763	**water cooling plant**	installation *f* d'appareils réfrigérants pour les eaux	Wasserkühlanlage *f*	impianto *m* di refrigerazione dell'acqua
˄	19763a	**water core**	noyau *m* refroidi à l'eau	wassergekühlter Kern *m*	anima *f* raffreddata ad acqua
°	19764	**water cut**	rapport *m* huile-eau	Wasser-Ölverhältnis *n*	rapporto *m* acqua-olio
˄	19765	**water disengaging**	séparateur *m* d'eau	Wasserabscheider *m*	separatore *m* d'acqua
˄	19766	**water disposal well**	puits *m* d'injection d'eau	Abwasser-Bohrung *f*	pozzo *m* ad iniezione d'acqua

		English	French	German	Italian
o	19767	water discharge pipe	tuyau *m* de dé-charge	Abflussrohr *n*	tubo *m* di scarico
−	19768	water drill	marteau *m* perfora-teur à injection d'eau	Wasserspülhammer *m*	martello *m* perforatore a iniezione d'acqua
⌃	19769	water drive	poussée *f* des eaux	Wassertrieb *m*	spinta *f* delle acque
⌃	19770	water encroachment	balayage *m* par l'eau	Wasserwäsche *f*	lavaggio *m* mediante acqua
o	19771	water feed piping	tuyauterie *f* d'eau d'alimentation	Speisewasserlei-tung *f*	tubazione *f* dell'acqua di alimentazione
⌃	19772	water finder	pipette *f* de prise des échantillons d'un réservoir	Pipette *f* zur Probeentnahme aus einem Behälter	pipetta *f* per prelevare campioni da un serba-toio
−	19773	water flood intake well	puits *m* à injection d'eau	Abwasserbohrung *f*	pozzo *m* ad iniezione d'acqua
−	19774	water flush	procédé *m* à injec-tion	Spülverfahren *n*	processo *m* a iniezione
−	19775	water flush drill	marteau-perforateur à injection d'eau	Wasserspülhammer *m*, Wasserbohr-hammer *m*	martello-perforatore *m* a iniezione d'acqua
−	19776	water flush drill-ing	sondage *m* à injec-tion	Nassbohren *n*	sondaggio *m* ad iniezio-ne
−	19777	water-gap	percée *f*	Durchbruchstal *n*	valle *f* trasversale
o	19777a	water gas	gaz *m* bleu	Wassergas *n*	gas *m* d'acqua
o	19778	water-gilding	dorure *f* par immer-sion	nasse Vergoldung *f*	doratura *f* a bagno
o	19779	water glass, water gauge	niveau *m* à tube en verre	Glasrohrwasserwaa-ge *f*	livello *m* a tubo di ve-tro

water gauge, *s. water glass*

		English	French	German	Italian
o	19780	to water harden	tremper à l'eau	abschrecken	temprare in acqua
o	19781	water-hardening	trempe *f* à l'eau	Wasserhärtung *f*	tempera *f* in acqua
−	19782	water hole	trou *m* de mine hu-mide	Nassbohrung *f*	foro *m* da mina umido
o	19783	water-hardened steel	acier *m* trempant à l'eau	Wasserhärtungs-stahl *m*	acciaio *m* temprante in acqua
⌃	19784	water in oil emulsion	émulsion *f* d'eau dans l'huile	Wasser-in-Öl-Emulsion *n*	emulsione *f* d'acqua nell'olio

		English	French	German	Italian
o	19785	water inlet pipe	tuyau *m* d'arrivée d'eau	Wasserzuflussrohr *n*	tubo *m* d'entrata nel-l'acqua
−	19786	water intrusion	envahissement *m* d'eau	Wassereindringung *f*	intrusione *f* (o inva-sione *f*) d'acqua
o	19787	water jacketed core	noyau *m* pour chambre à eau	Wassermantelsee-le *f*	anima *f* per camicia d'acqua
o	19788	water jacketed frame	cadre *m* refroidi	gekühlter Rahmen *m*	quadro *m* raffreddato
o	19789	water-jacket(ed) furnace	four *m* à water-jacket	Wassermantelofen *n*	forno *m* con camicia ad acqua
^	19790	water knock out	séparateur *m* d'eau	Wasserabscheider *m*	separatore *m* d'acqua
−	19791	water level	voie *f* d'écoule-ment	Entwässerungs-strecke *f*	galleria *f* di drenaggio
−	19792	water of crystalli-zation	eau *f* de cristal-lisation	Kristallwasser *n*	acqua *f* di cristallizza-zione
o	19793	water outlet pipe	tuyau *m* d'écou-lement	Wasserabflussrohr *n*	tubo *m* d'uscita della acqua
o	19794	water jacketing of the electro-des	refroidissement *m* des électrodes par courant d'eau	Wasserkühlung *f* der Elektroden	raffreddamento *m* ad acqua degli elettrodi
o	19795	water level, spirit level	niveau *m* à bulle d'air	Wasserwaage *f*	livello *m* a bolla d'a-ria
−	19796	water-level	niveau *m* d'eau, bowette, albra-que	Wasserstand, *m* Wasserstrecke,*f* Sumpfstrecke *f*	livello *m* dell'acqua, galleria *f* di scolo dell'acqua
−	19797	water line	niveau *m* de l'eau	Wasserlinie *f*, Wasserspiegel *m*	livello *m* dell'acqua
o	19798	water line	conduite *f* d'eau	Wasserleitung *f*	conduttura *f* dell'ac-qua
o	19799	water meter	compteur *m* d'eau	Wassermesser *m*	contatore *m* d'acqua
−	19800	water of imbebition	eau *f* d'imbébition	Bergfeuchtigkeit *f*	acqua d'imbebizione
−	19801	water opal	hyalite *f*	Hyalit *m*	ialite *f*
−	19802	water pack	remblai *m* hydrau-lique	Wasserversatz *m*	ripiena *f* idraulica
		water parting, *s. water-shed*			
o	19803	water pot	arrosoir *m* de mouleur	Anfeuchter *m*	annaffiatoio *m* del formatore

		English	French	German	Italian
	19804	**water power**	force *f* hydrauli-que	Wasserkraft *f*	forza *f* idraulica
	19805	**water pressure**	pression *f* hydrau-lique	Wasserdruck *m*	pressione *f* idraulica
ˆ	19806	**waterproof grease**	graisse *f* hydro-fuge	wasserdichte Schmiere *f*	grasso *m* idrofugo
	19807	**water purification**	épuration *f* de l'eau	Wasserreinigung *f*	depurazione *f* dell'ac-qua
o	19808	**water quenching**	refroidissement *m* dans l'eau	Wasser-Ab-schreckung *f*	raffreddamento *m* in acqua
—	19809	**water ring**	gargouille *f*	Wasserrinne *f* (am Schachtstoss)	canale *m* dell'acqua (nelle pareti del pozzo)
o	19809a	**water rolling**	nettoyage *m* à l'eau de savonnage	Seifenwasser--Trommelreinigung *f*	pulitura *f* all'acqua di sapone
o	19810	**water-space**	chambre *f* d'eau	Wasserkammer *f*	camera *f* d'acqua
—	19811	**waterborne coal**	charbon *m* transpor-té par mer	auf dem Seeweg Kohle *f*	carbone *m* trasportato per mare
o	19812	**water seal**	fermeture *f* hydrau-lique	Wasserverschluss *m*	chiusura *f* idraulica, giunto *m* idraulico
o	19813	**water seal**	joint *m* hydraulique	wasserdichter Ab-schluss *m*	giunto *m* a tenuta, chiu-sura idraulica
—	19813a	**water separation**	triage *m* à l'eau	nasse Scheidung *f*	cernita *f* all'acqua
—	19814	**water shaft**	puits *m* d'exhaure	Wasserschacht *m*	pozzo *m* di drenaggio
—	19815	**water string**	colonne *f* de ferme-ture d'eau	Wassersperrsäule *f*	colonna *f* d'arresto dell'acqua
	19816	**water supply**	alimentation *f* et distribution d'eau	Wassersperrsäure *f*, Wasservorrat	provvista *f* d'acqua
—	19817	**water swivel**	tête *f* d'injection	Spülkopf *m*	testa *f* d'iniezione
		water-table, *s. water bearing stratum*			
ˆ	19818	**water table opening**	ouverture *f* de la plate-forme du som-met de derrick	Kronenöffnung *f*	apertura *f* della piat-taforma in cima alla torre
o	19819	**water tank**	auge *f* à eau	Wasserkasten *m*	cassetta *f* d'acqua
ˆ	19820	**water tower**	château *m* d'eau	Wasserturm *m*	serbatoio *m* piezo-metrico
ˆ	19821	**water trouble**	embarras *m* d'eau	Wasserschwierig-keiten *f pl.*	difficoltà *f pl.* crea-te dall'acqua

		English	French	German	Italian
o	19822	water trough	rigole f à eau	Wasserrinne f	canale m dell'acqua
o	19823	water tube boiler	chaudière f aqua-tubulaire	Wasserohrkessel m	caldaia f a tubi d'acqua
o	19824	water-tube boiler with curved tubes	chaudière f aqua-tubulaire à tubes courbés	Wasserrohrkessel m	caldaia f a tubi d'acqua
o	19825	water-tube boiler with header	chaudière f aqua-tubulaire à collecteur	Wasserkammer-kessel m	caldaia f a tubi d'acqua con camera d'acqua
o	19826	water-tube boiler with horizontal tubes	chaudière f aqua-tubulaire à tubes horizontaux	Wasserröhrenkessel m mit waagrechten Röhren	caldaia f a tubi d'acqua orizzontali
o	19827	water-tube boiler with inclined tubes	chaudière f aqua-tubulaire à tubes inclinés	Schrägrohrkessel m	caldaia f a tubi d'acqua obliqui
o	19828	water tube boiler with large tubes	chaudière f aquatu-bulaire à larges tu-bes	weitrohriger Wasser-rohrkessel m	caldaia f a tubi d'acqua lunghi
o	19829	water-tube boiler with one header	chaudière f aquatu-bulaire à un seul collecteur	Einkammerkessel m	caldaia f a tubi d'acqua con una camera d'acqua
o	19830	water-tube boiler with simple header	chaudière f aquatu-bulaire à caissons ou à simple collecteur	Ganzkammerkes-sel m	caldaia f a tubi d'acqua con camera d'acqua non divisa
o	19831	water-tube boiler with small tubes	chaudière f aquatu-bulaire à tubes é-troits	engrohriger Wasser-rohrkessel m	caldaia f a piccoli tu-bi d'acqua
o	19832	water-tube boiler with steep tubes	chaudière f aquatu-bulaire à tubes raides	Steilrohrkessel m	caldaia f a tubi d'acqua rapidi
o	19833	water-tube boiler with two headers	chaudière f aquatu-bulaire à deux col-lecteurs	Zweikammerkes-sel m	caldaia f a tubi d'acqua con due camere
o	19834	watercooled valve	valve f à circula-tion d'eau	wassergekühltes Ventil n	valvola f a circola-zione d'acqua
	19835	water vaporization	vaporisation f de l'eau	Wasserverdampfung f	vaporizzazione f del-l'acqua
—	19836	waterglass	orthosilicate m	Orthosilikat n	ortosilicato m

		English	French	German	Italian
^	19837	watermelon	échangeur *m* de chaleur pour puits	Wärmeaustauscher *m* für Schächte	scambiatore *m* di calore (per pozzi)
—	19838	watershed, divide line	ligne *f* de partage	Wasserscheide *f*	linea *f* di displuvio (s)partiacque
—	19839	wavellite	wavellite *f*	Wavellit *m*	wavellite *f*
°	19839a	waviness	surface *f* ondulée	gewellte Oberfläche *f*	superficie *f* ondulata
—	19840	wavy, foliated	feuilleté	blätterig	lamellare
—	19841	wavy vein	filon *m* en chapelet	Linsengang *m*	filone *m* lenticolare
^	19841a	wax	cire *f*	Wachs *n*	cera *f*
^	19842	wax distillate	distillat *m* paraffineux	Paraffindestillat *n*	distillato *m* paraffinoso
		wax pattern, *s. investment pattern*			
^	19843	wax fractionation	fractionnement *m* de la paraffine	Paraffin Fraktionierung *f*	frazionamento *m* della paraffina
		wax insulated wire, *s. wax wire*			
^	19844	wax tailing	résidu *m* de paraffine	Paraffinrückstand *m*	fondame *m* paraffinoso
°	19845	wax vent	rat de cave *m*	Wachsschnur *f*	cerino *m*
°	19846	waxed thread	fil *m* en cire	Wachsfaden *m*	cerino *m*
°	19847	waxed cotton-covered wire	fil *m* sous coton ciré	Wachsdraht *m*	filo *m* rivestito di cotone cerato
°	19848	waxed wire	fil *m* ciré	Wachsdraht *m*	filo *m* incerato (o isolato con cera)
—	19849	way shaft	puits *m* intérieur	Gesenk *n*, Blindschacht *m*	pozzo *m* ausiliario o interno
—	19850	weak roasting	faible grillage *m*	schwaches Rösten *n*	debole calcinazione *f*
°	19851	weak sand	sable *m* maigre	magerer Sand *m*	sabbia *f* magra
°	19852	to weaken the sand	amaigrir un sable argileux	den Sand magern	smagrire la sabbia argillosa (o la terra)
°	19853	wear	usure *f*	Verschleiss *m*	consumo *m*, usura *f*
		wear hardness, *s. passive hardness*			
°	19854	wear of chain	usure *f* de la chaine	Kettenverschleiss *m*	usura *f* della catena
°	19855	wear plate	plaque *f* d'usure	Verschleissplatte *f*	piastra *f* d'usura
°	19856	wear resistance, abrasion resistance	résistance *f* à l'usure	Verschleisshärte *f*, Verschleissfestigkeit *f*	resistenza *f* all'usura

		English	French	German	Italian
o	19857	wear-resisting	résistant à l'usure	verschleissfest	resistente all'usura
o	19858	wear test	essai m de résistance à l'usure	Verschleissfestigkeitsprobe f	prova f di usura
o	19859	wearing depth	limite f d'usure admissible	zulässige Verschleissgrenze f	limite m d'usura ammissibile
o	19860	wearing surface	couche m d'usure	Belag m	strato m di usura
o	19861	weather door	porte f de ventilation	Wettertür f	porta f di ventilazione
o	19862	to weather	décomposer, désagréger	verwittern, verderben	disgregarsi, decomporsi
o	19863	weather-proof. weather-resisting	à l'épreuve des intempéries	wetterfest, wetterbeständig	a prova di intemperie
o	19864	weathered constituent	éléments m $pl.$ décomposés à l'air	Verwitterungsbestandteil m	elementi m $pl.$ decomposti all'aria
^	19865	weathered crude	pétrole m brut vielli	gealtertes Rohöl n	greggio m stagionato
^	19866	weathered distillate	distillat m stabilisé	stabilisiertes Destillat n	distillato m stabilizzato
—	19867	weathered iron ore	minerai m de fer effrité ou désagrégé	verwittertes Eisenerz n	minerale m di ferro disgregato
—	19868	weathered ore	minerai m altéré superficiellement	verwittertes Erz n	minerale m alterato in superficie
—	19869	weathering	effritement m	Verwitterung f	disintegrazione f (di rocce)
^	19870	weathering	vieillissement m	Bewitterung f	perdite $fpl.$ per giacenza
—	19871	weathering	décomposition f par les agents atmosphériques	Verwittern n, Verwitterung f	alterazione f agli agenti atmosferici
o	19872	web	aile f	Schenkel m	lato m, fianco m, ala f
	19873	web	tissu m, toile f	Gewebe n	tessuto m, tela f
o	19874	web of rail	tige f du rail	Schienensteg m	stelo m della rotaia
o	19875	Weber's glass	verre m de Weber	Webersches Glas n	vetro m di Weber

		English	French	German	Italian
−	19876	websterite	webstérite *f*	Websterit *m*	websterite *f*
−	19877	to wedge-split	élargir une fente par un coin	auskesseln	allargare una fessura col cuneo
−	19878	wedge	cale *f*, coin *m*	Keil *m*	zeppa *f*, chiavetta *f*, cuneo *m*
−	19879	wedge cut	entaille *f* en forme de coin	Keileinbruch *m*	intaglio *m* a cuneo
º	19880	wedge gate	attaque *f* à languette	Leistenanschnitt *m*	attacco *m* lamellare (a cuneo o a zeppa)
º	19881	wedge inlet, conical gate	jet *m* de coulée conique	Keileinguss *m*	colata *f* conica
º	19882	wedge piece	voussoir *m*	Keilstück *n*	mattone *m* a sezione trapezoidale
º	19883	wedge pin	goujon *m* de remmoulage à clavette	Führungsstift *m* mit Keilschlitz	pernio *m* (o spina *f*) a chiavetta
−	19884	wedge ring	collier *m* à coins	Rohrkeilklemme *f*	collare *m* a cuneo
−	19884a	wedge roaster	four *m* cylindrique multiple	runder Mehrfachröstofen *m*	arrostitore *m* multiplo cilindrico
º	19885	wedge-shaped iron	fer *m* à biseau	keilförmiges Eisen *n*	ferro *m* a cuneo
º	19886	wedge shaped rabble	fer *m* à biseau	keilförmige Kratze *f*	raschiatoio *m* conico
º	19887	wedge test piece	éprouvette *f* de trempe en coin	Keilprobe *f*	provetta *f* di tempra conica
−	19888	wedge down	abattage *m* au moyen de coins	Hereintreibearbeit *f*	abbattimento *m* con cunei
−	19889	wedge out	amincissement *m* en coin	Auskeilen *n*	restringimento *m* a cuneo
º	19889a	wedge section	profil *m* cunéiforme	keilförmiges Profil *n*	profilo *m* cuneiforme
^	19890	weep hole	trou *m* de ressuage	Treibenloch *n*	foro *m* di trasudamento
−	19890a	weep hole	chantepleure *f*	Tropfloch *m*	foro *m* di drenaggio
−	19891	weeping core	carotte *f* suintante	ausschwitzender Kern *m*	carota *f* trasudante
−	19892	wehrlite	wehrlite *f*	Wehrlit *m*	wehrlite *f*
−	19893	weibullite	weibullite *f*	Weibullit *m*	weibullite *f*
	19894	to weigh	peser	wägen, abwiegen	pesare
	19895	weigh bridge	pont-bascule *m*	Brückenwaage *f*	bilancia *f* o basculla a ponte

		English	French	German	Italian
o	19896	weigh bridge rail	rail *m* du pont (à bascule)	Wägeschiene *f*	binario *m* del ponte
	19897	weighing	pesage *m*	Wiegen *n*	pesata *f*
	19898	weighing appliances	bascules *f pl.*	Brückenwaagen *f pl.*	basculle *f pl.*
^	19899	weighing bottle	pèse-filtre *m*, flacon *m* à tare	Eichglas *n*	pesafiltri *m*
		weighing machine, *s. decimal balance*			
	19900	weighing machine ticket	carton *m* indicateur du poids	Wiegekarte *f*	scontrino *m* o marca *f* della pesata
o	19901	weighing pipette	pipette *f* pour pesées	Wiegestechheber *m*	pipetta *f* per pesare
o	19902	weighing pipette with stopcock	pipette *f* avec robinet à boule	Kugelhahnstechheber *m*	pipetta *f* a robinetto sferico
o	19903	weighing tube	tube *m* de pesée	Wiegeröhrchen *n*	tubetto *m* per pesare
o	19904	weight case	boîte *f* de charge	Belastungsgefäss *n*	cassa *f* o recipiente *m* del contrappeso
	19905	weight deviation	tolérance *f* en poids	Gewichtsabweichung *f*	tolleranza *f* di peso
—	19905a	weight fill	remplissage *m* à poids	Gewichtsfüllung *f*	riempimento *m* a peso
o	19906	weight of charge	poids *m* de la charge	Einsatzgewicht *n*	peso *m* della carica
—	19907	weight on bit	poids *m* sur l'outil	Bohrdruck *m*	peso *m* sull'attrezzo
		weight ring, *s. ring weight*			
	19908	weight table	table *f* des poids	Gewichstabelle *f*	tabella *f* dei pesi
o	19909	weighting a mould	charger un moule	eine Form belasten	caricare una forma
^	19910	weighting material	matières *f pl.* lourdes	Beschwerungsmittel *n*	sostanza *f* per appesantire il fango
	19911	weighting network	réseau *m* filtrant	Bewertungsfilter *n*	struttura *f* filtrante
	19912	weights	poids *m pl.*	Gewichte *n pl.*	pesi *m pl.*
o	19913	weights	plateau *m* de charge	Beschwerplatte *f*	piastra *f* (o placca *f*) per caricare la forma
o	19914	weights	charge *f* du moule	Belastungsgewicht *n*	carica *f* (della forma)

		English	French	German	Italian
°	19915	**weights**	poids *m* de charge	Belastungsge-wicht *n*	peso *m* per caricare le forme
°	19916	**weights case**	caisse *f* à poids	Gewichtskasten *m*	cassetta *f* per pesi
—	19917	**weinschenkite**	weinschenkite *f*	Weinschenkit *m*	weinschenchite *f*
^	19918	**weir**	résidu *m* pétrolifè-re de première ex-traction	Ölreste *f pl.* aus erster Förderung	residuo *m* petrolifero li prima estrazione
—	19919	**weir**	trop-plein *m*, dé-versoir *m*	Überlauf *m*	stramazzo, troppo pie-no *m*
—	19920	**weisbachite**	weisbachite *f*	Weisbachit *m*	weisbachite *f*
—	19921	**weiselbergite**	weiselbergite *f*	Weiselbergit *m*	weiselbergite *f*
—	19922	**weissite**	weissite *f*	Weissit *m*	weissite *f*
°	19923	**to weld**	souder (à chaud)	schweissen	saldare (a caldo)
		to weld through, *s. to penetrate*			
		weld, *s. welding*			
°	19924	**weld bead**	cordon *m* de sou-dure	Schweissnaht *f*	cordone *m* di saldatu-ra
		weld cycle, *s. welding cycle*			
°	19925	**weld decay**	corrosion *f* intergra-nulaire de soudage	interkristalline Korrosion *f* der Schweissstelle	corrosione *f* intercri-stallina della salda-tura
		weld interval, *s: welding time*			
		weld ingot, *s: nugget*			
°	19926	**weld-iron**	fer *m* soudé	Schweisseisen *n*	ferro *m* saldato
		weld machined flush, *s. flush weld*			
°	19926a	**weld nudget**	perle *f* de soudure	Schweissperle *f*	perla *f* di saldatura
°	19927	**weld-steel,**	acier *m* soudant, acier *m* soudable	Schweissstahl *m*, schweissbarer Stahl *m*	acciaio *m* da saldare, acciaio *m* saldabile
		.**weld time**, *s. welding time*			
°	19928	**weldable**	soudable	schweissbar, lötbar	saldabile
°	19929	**weldable homoge-neous iron**	fer *m* homogène	Schweiss·stahl *m*	ferro *m* omogeneo sal-dabile
		weldable steel, *s. weld steel*			

		English	French	German	Italian
o	19930	weldability	soudabilité *f*	Schweissbarkeit *f*	saldabilità *f*
o	19931	welded casing	tube *m* soudé	geschweisstes Rohr *n*	tubo *m* saldato
o	19932	welded gas tube	tube *m* soudé pour gaz	geschweisstes Gasrohr *n*	tubo *m* saldato per gas
		welded iron, *s. weld-iron*			
		welded joint, *s: weld*			
o	19933	welded mesh reinforcement	armature *f* en treillis soudé	geschweisste Baustahlmatte *f*	armatura *f* in rete saldata
		welded seam, *s. weld*			
o	19934	welder	soudeur *m*	Schweisser *m*	saldatore *m*
		welder's goggles, *s: welding goggles*			
		welder's hammer, *s. chipping hammer*			
o	19935	welders handtools	outils *m pl.* à main pour soudure	Schweisser Handwerkzeuge *n pl.*	utensili *m pl.* portatili da saldatore
o	19936	welding	soudure *f*, soudage	Schweissung *f*	saldatura *f*
		welding blowlamp, *s: welding burner*			
o	19937	welding bead	cordon *m* de soudure	Schweissraupe *f*	cordone *m* di saldatura
		welding blowpipe, *s: welding burner*			
	19938	welding by non-transferred or transferred plasma arc	soudage *m* direct ou indirect à plasma	direktes oder indirektes Plasmaschweissen *n*	saldatura *f* diretta o indiretta al plasma
		welding cast steel, *s. mild cast steel*			
		welding converter, *s: welding set*			
		welding current, *s. value of welding current*			
o	19939	welding demand	absorption *f* de soudure	Schweissabsorption *f*	assorbimento *m* di saldatura
o	19940	welding elbow	courbe *f* à souder	Vorschweissbogen *m*	arco *m* per saldatura
o	19941	welding fire	four *m* à souder	Schweissfeuer *n*	fuoco *m* per saldare
o	19942	welding flux	fondant *m* à souder	Schweissflussmittel *n*	fondente *m* per saldatura
		welding from the bottom up, *s. vertical position welding*			
		welding from the top down, *s. vertical position welding*			

		English	French	German	Italian
°	19943	welding furnace	four *m* à réchauffer	Schweissofen *m*	forno *m* di riscaldamento
°	19943a	welding ground	contre-électrode *m*	Gegenelektrode *f*	contro-elettrodo *m*
°	19944	welding gun	pinces *f pl.* à souder	Schweisszange *f*	pinza *f* per saldatura
°	19945	welding heat	chaude *f* suante, chaleur *f* soudante	Schweiss(glüh)-hitze *f*, Weich-glühhitze *f*	calda *f* saldante, caldo *m* sudante
		welding iron, *s. weld-iron*			
		welding joint, *s. weld*			
°	19946	welding machine, electric welder	machine *f* à souder électrique	elektrische Schweissmaschine *f*	saldatrice *f*, saldatrice *f* elettrica
°	19947	welding material	métal *m* d'apport de soudure	Schweisswerkstoff *m*	materiale *m* d'apporto di saldatura
		welding method, *s. welding process*			
°	19948	welding mill	laminoir-soudeur *m*	Schweisswalzwerk *n*	laminatoio-saldatore *m*
		welding motor generator, *s: welding set*			
°	19949	welding neck	col *m* à souder	verjüngtes Vor-schweissrohrstück *n*	bocchetta *f* dal saldatore
		welding operator, *s. man who operates automatic welding machines*			
°	19949a	welding pass	cordon *m* de soudure	Schweissnaht *f*	cordone *m* di saldatura
		welding plant, *s. welding installation*			
		welding pressure head, *s. pressure head*			
		welding rectifier, *s. rectifier welding set*			
		welding rod, *s. filler rod*			
°	19950	welding saddle	collier *m* de renforcement	Verstärkungsring *m*	ghiera *f* di rinforzo
°	19951	welding sand	sable *m* à souder	Schweissand *m*	sabbia *f* per saldare
		welding seam, *s. welding pass*			
°	19952	welding set	soudeuse *f* à l'arc	Lichtbogenschweiss-maschine *f*	saldatrice *f* ad arco
°	19953	welding shop	atelier *m* de soudage	Schweisswerkstatt *f*	reparto *m* saldatura
		welding sleeve, *s. sleeve to protect the arm during welding*			
		welding spats, *s. protective spats for welding*			
		welding steel, *s. weld steel*			

	English	French	German	Italian
°	19954 welding tee	té à souder	Vorschweiss-T-Stück n	pezzo m a T per saldare
°	19955 welding test	essai m de soudabilité	Schweissprobe f	prova f di saldabilità
°	19956 welding torch, welding burner	chalumeau m, soudeur	Schweissbrenner m	cannello m per saldare
°	19957 welding wire	fil m à souder	Schweissdraht m	filo m per saldare
	welding with pressure, s. pressure welding			
°	19958 welding with PVC--sticks	soudure f par baguettes de chlorure de polyvinyle	Schweissen n mit PVC-Stäben	saldatura f mediante bacchetta di cloruro di polivinile
°	19958a weldless tube	tube m sans soudure	nahtlos Rohr n	tubo m senza saldature
	weldment, s. welded assembly			
—	19959 well boring tube	tube m pour sondage	Bohrrohr n	tubo m per trivellazioni
—	19960 well casing	revêtement m de puits	Schachtausbau m	rivestimento m del pozzo
^	19961 well casing starter	sabot m de tubage	Röhrenschuh m	anello m d'acciaio in testa ad una colonna di tubi
—	19962 well chamber	chambre f du puits	Schachtraum m	camera f del pozzo
—	19963 well drilling	sondage m de puits	Schachtbohren n	sondaggio m di pozzi
—	19964 well head	orifice m du trou de sondage	Mündung f der Bohrung	imboccatura f del foro di sondaggio
—	19965 well log	coupe f de sonde	Bohrprofil n	profilo m di sonda
—	19966 well logging	exploration f de puits	Schachtschürfung f	esplorazione f di pozzi
^	19967 well producing oil	sondage m de pétrole	Ölbohrung f	sondaggio m di petrolio
—	19968 well rig	appareil m de sondage	Bohrkran m	castelletto m d'estrazione
—	19969 well sampling	prise f des échantillons de sondage	Bohrprobenahme f	prelevamento m di campione di sondaggio

	English	French	German	Italian
° 19970	well shaft	captage *m* d'une source	Quellfassung *f*	presa *f* d'una sorgente
^ 19971	well spacing	espacement *m* entre puits	Abstand *m* zwischen Schächten	intervallo *m* fra pozzi
° 19972	well tempered steel	acier *m* bien trempé	gut gehärteter Stahl *m*	acciaio *m* ben temprato
° 19973	well tube	tuyau *m* de la prise d'eau	Fassungsrohr *n*	tubo *m* di presa
— 19974	well water	eau *f* de puits	Brunnenwasser *n*	acqua *f* di pozzo
° 19975	wellsite	emplacement *m*	Lage *f*	postazione *f*
^ 19976	welt	pli *m*, coulisse *f*	Falz *m*, einfacher Falz *m*	ripiegatura *f* a contatto, risvolto *m*
— 19977	wennebergite	wennebergite *f*	Wennebergit *m*	wennebergite *f*
— 19978	wentzelite	wentzélite *f*	Wentzelit *m*	wentzelite *f*
— 19979	Werfenian stage	étage *m* werfénien	Werfernenschicht *f*	werfeniano *m*
— 19980	wernerite	wernérite *f*	Wernerit *m*	wernerite *f*
— 19981	weslienite	wesliénite *f*	Weslienit *m*	weslienite *f*
— 19982	Westman's gas fired roasting furnace	four *m* de grillage au gaz de Westman	Westmanscher Gasröstofen *m*	forno *m* di torrefazione a gas di Westman
° 19983	to wet the moulds	asperger les lingotières	die Gussformen besprengen	aspergere o inaffiare le forme
— 19984	wet analysis	analyse *f* par voie humide	Analyse *f* auf nassem Weg	analisi *f* per via umida
° 19985	wet-bottomed boiler	chaudière *f* à lame d'eau sous les cendriers	Kessel *m* mit Wasserraum unter dem Aschenkasten	caldaia *f* con lama d'acqua sotto i cenerari
— 19986	wet cleaning	dépuration par voie humide	Nassaufbereitung *f*	depurazione *f* per via umida
— 19987	wet concentration	préparation *f* par voie humide	Nassaufbereitung *f*	preparazione *f* per via umida
— 19988	wet crushing	broyage *m* à l'eau	Nasszerkleinerung *f*	frantumazione *f* per via umida
° 19989	wet drawing	étirage *m* par voie humide	Nasswalzen *n*	trafilatura *f* a umido

English	French	German	Italian

wet drawn wire, *s. lacquer drawn wire*

— 19990 **wet dressing** — préparation *f* (par voie) humide — nasse Aufbereitung *f* — trattamento *m* per via umida

— 19991 **wet drifter** — perforatrice *f* à injection — Wasserspülhammer *m* — perforatrice *f* ad iniezione

° 19992 **wet enamelling** — émaillage *m* au trempé — Nassemaillierung *f* — smaltatura *f* a immersione

— 19993 **wet iron ore, moist iron ore** — minerai *m* de fer humide — nasses Eisenerz *n*, feuchtes Eisenerz *n* — minerale *m* di ferro bagnato

— 19993a **wet milling** — broyage *m* liquide — Nassmahlen *n* — frantumazione *f* per via umida

— 19994 **wet preparation** — préparation *f* par voie humide — Nassaufbereitung *f* — preparazione *f* per via umida

° 19995 **wet puddling** — puddlage *m* gras — Fettpuddeln *n* — puddellaggio *m* grasso

— 19996 **wet purification, washing** — épuration *f* par voie humide — Nassreinigung *f* — depurazione *f* per via umida

° 19997 **wet separation** — triage *m* par voie humide — nasse Scheidung *f* — separazione *f* umida

^ 19998 **wet seal** — étanchéité *f* hydraulique — Wasserdichtheit *f* — tenuta *f* idraulica

— 19999 **wet stamp mill** — bocard *m* à eau — Nasspochwerk *n* — mulino *m* a pestelli ad acqua

— 20000 **wet stamping** — bocardage *m* à l'eau — Nasspochen *n* — frantumazione *f* (o pestellatura) per via umida

^ 20001 **wettability** — mouillabilité *f* — Benetzbarkeit *f* — soluzionabilità *f*

— 20002 **Wetherill's ore separator** — trieur *m* de minerais de Wetherill — Erzscheider *m* nach Wetherill — separatore *m* di minerali Wetherill

^ 20003 **wetting agent, spreader** — agent *m* mouillant — Netzmittel *n* — soluzionatore *m*

wetting of flux, *s. flowing of flux*

— 20004 **wetting the coal** — arrosage *m* du charbon — Nässen *n* der Kohle — innaffiamento *m* del carbone

20005 **wheat flour** — farine *f* de froment — Weizenmehl *n* — farina *f* di frumento

— 20006 **wheel barrow skip** — benne *f* de chargement, brouette *f* de chargement — Gichtkarren *m*, Erzkarren *m* — vagone *m* da minerale

	English	French	German	Italian
°	20007 wheel hub	moyeu *m* de roue	Radnabe *f*	mozzo *m* della ruota
—	20008 wheel ore	bournonite *f*	Bournonit *m*	bournonite *f*
°	20009 wheel rim	jante *f* de roue	Radkranz *m*	corona *f* di ruota
°	20010 wheel rolling mill	laminoir *m* à roues	Räderwalzwerk *n*	treno *m* per ruote
°	20011 wheel spoke	rayon *m* (de roue)	Radspeiche *f*	raggio *m* di ruota
°	20012 wheel with tyre shrunk-on	roue *f* à bandage serré à chaud	Rad *n* mit aufgeschrumpftem Reifen	ruota *f* con cerchione fissato a caldo
	whetted, *s. ground*			
—	20013 whewellite	whewellite *f*	Whewellit *m*	whewellite *f*
—	20014 whim	manège *m* à chevaux	Pferdegöpel *m*	sollevatore *m* a cavalli
—	20015 whin	grauwacke *f*	Grauwacke *f*	grauwacke *f*
—	20016 whin dike	dyke *m* de basalte	Basaltgang *m*	dicco *m* di basalto
—	20017 whip of winding-rope	coup de fouet	Schleudern *n* des Förderseils	oscillazione *f* della fune d'estrazione
—	20018 whipstock	biseau *m* de déviation	Ablenkkeil *m*	piano *m* inclinato di scorrimento
°	20019 whirlgate dirt trap whirl gate	piège *m* à crasses à canal tangentiel	Schaumtrichter *m*, Kreisel *m*	fermascoria *m* a pozzetto tangenziale
°	20020 whirlgate feeder	masselotte *f* à alimentation tangentielle	Saugkopf *m* mit Tangentialanschnitt	alimentatore *m* ad attacco tangenziale
—	20021 whirlpool	remous *m* d'eau	Wasserwirbel *m*	gorgo *m*, vortice *m*
°	20022 whistler	évent *m*	Luftpfeife *f*	respiro *m*
°	20023 white annealing	recuit *m* blanc	zweite Glühung *f*	ricottura *f* bianca
—	20024 white antimony	valentinite *f*	Valentinit *m*, Antimonblüte *f*	valentinite *f*
—	20025 white bauxite	bauxite *f* blanche	weisser Bauxit *m*	bauxite *f* bianca
°	20026 white cast-iron, white-pig	fonte *f* blanche, fin métal	weisses Roheisen *n*, Weisseisen *n*	ghisa *f* bianca, ferro *m* bianco
—	20027 white cobalt	smaltine *f*	Smaltin *m*	smaltina *f*

		English	French	German	Italian
°	20028	**white cold blast pig iron**	fonte *f* blanche à vent froid	grelles Roheisen *n*, halbweisses Roheisen *n*	ghisa *f* bianca fredda
		white copper, *s. argentan or German silver*			
°	20029	**white crystalline iron**	fonte *f* blanche à facettes	kleinspiegeliges Weisseisen *n*	ghisa *f* bianca sfaccettata
°	20030	**white edge**	bord *m* blanc	weisser Saum *m*	contorno *m* bianco
		white garnet, *s. leucite*			
°	20031	**white-heat**, **white flame heat**	chaude *f* blanche, chaleur *f* blanche	Weissglut *f*, Weissglühen *n*	calda *f* bianca, calore *m* bianco
°	20032	**white hot**	chauffé au blanc, porté à l'incandescence	weissglühend, weisswarm	scaldato al bianco, al color bianco
°	20033	**white iron**	fonte *f* blanche	Weissguss *m*	ghisa *f* bianca
−	20034	**white iron**	marcassite *f*	Markasit *m*	marcassite *f*, pirite *f* bianca
°	20035	**white iron fining**	affinage *m* complet	Garfrischen *n*	affinaggio *m* della ghisa bianca
		white latten, *s. tin plate*			
°	20036	**white lead**	céruse *f*, blanc *m* de plomb	Bleiweiss *n*	biacca *f* di piombo
−	20037	**white lead ore**	cérusite *f*	Weissbleierz *n*	cerussite *f*
°	20038	**white-metal**	métal *m* (ou alliage) blanc	Weissmetall *n*	metallo *m* bianco, lega *f* bianca
−	20039	**white opal**	opale *f* laiteuse	Milchopal *m*	opale *m* latteo
°	20039a	**white pickling**	décapage *m* supplémentaire	zweite Beizung *f*	decapaggio *m* supplementare
°	20040	**white pig iron**	fonte *f* blanche ordinaire	Weisseisen *n*, Matteisen *n*	ghisa *f* bianca calda
^	20041	**white product**	produit *m* blanc	Raffinerie-Produkt *n*	prodotto *m* raffinato
−	20042	**(to a) white red heat**	au rouge blanc	zur Weissglut, in starker Rotglut	al (calor) bianco
°	20042a	**white rust**	couche *f* d'oxyde de zinc	Zinkoxydschicht *f*	strato *m* di ossido di zinco
°	20043	**white spiegel looking pig iron**	fonte *f* blanche à structure rayonnée	Weissstrahl *m*	ghisa *f* bianca a struttura raggiata o radiale
		white vitriol, *s. sulphate of zinc*			
°	20044	**whiteheart cast iron**, **European process iron**	fonte *f* à coeur blanc	Weisskerneisen *n*	ghisa *f* a cuore bianco

		English	French	German	Italian
°	20045	whiteheart malleable cast iron	fonte *f* malléable blanche (ou à coeur blanc)	weisser Temperguss *m*	ghisa *f* malleabile bianca (o a cuore bianco)
°	20046	whiteheart malleable iron casting	pièce *f* moulée en fonte malléable à coeur blanc	Gussteil *m* aus Weisskern--temperguss	getto *m* di ghisa malleabile a cuore bianco
°	20047	whiteheart process	procédé *m* Réaumur	Glühfrischen *n*	processo *m* Réaumur
°	20047a	whitening	couche *f* de métal blanc	Weissmetallschicht *f*	strato *m* di metallo bianco
—	20048	witherite	barolithe *f*, withérite *f*	Witherit *n*, Baryt *m*	barolite *f*, barite *f* carbonata
—	20049	whitneyite	whitneyite *f*	Whitneyit *m*	whitneite *f*
—	20050	whole coal	charbon *m* vierge	unverritzte Kohle *f*	carbone *m* vergine, filone *m* carbonifero non sfruttato
—	20051	whole working	traçage *m*	Vorrichtung *f*	tracciatura *f*, primo sfruttamento (di filoni)
—	20052	whole workings	travaux *m pl.* de traçage	Vorrichtungsbaue *m pl.*	lavori *m pl.* di tracciatura
°	20053	Whitwell stove	récupérateur *m* Whitwell	Whitwellscher Winderhitzer *m*	apparecchio *m* ad aria calda o ricuperatore *m* Whitwell
—	20054	wichtisite	wichtisite *f*	Wichtisit *m*	wichtisite *f*
—	20055	wick	mêche *f*	Docht *m*	lucignolo *m*
°	20056	wicket	fermeture *f* de tuyère	Düsenverschluss *m*	chiusura *f* di ugello
°	20057	wicket door	porte *f* à guichet	Drosseltür *f*	porta *f* a sportello
—	20058	wide meshed sieve	tamis *m* grossier	grobes Sieb *n*, Grobsieb *n*	staccio *m* grossolano od a maglie
^	20059	wide open (slang)	pleine capacité de puits	Schachtleistungs-vermögen *n*	piena capacità di pozzo
	20060	wide spreading	encombrant	sperrig	ingombrante
°	20061	wide strip	bande large	Breitband *n*	banda *f* larga
°	20062	Widmannstatten structure	texture *f* de Widmannstätten	Widmannstättensches Gefüge *n*	struttura *f* di Widmannstätten
°	20063	width of scratch	largeur *f* de la rayure	Strichbreite *f*	lunghezza *f* della scanalatura o della stria

	English	French	German	Italian
°	20064 **width, thickness**	puissance *f*, épaisseur *f*	Mächtigkeit *f*, Stärke *f*	spessore *m*, potenza *f*
°	20065 **widthwise rolling**	laminage *m* dans le sens de la largeur	Breitwalzen *n*	laminazione *f* nel senso della larghezza
	widening, *s. bellying*			
—	20066 **wiikite**	wiikite *f*	Wiikit *m*	wiikite *f*
—	20067 **wild-cast well**	forage *m* de recherche	Aufschlussbohrung *f*	pozzo *m* esplorativo
^	20068 **wild flowing**	éruption *f* d'un sondage	Erdölausbruch *m*	eruzione *f* d'un sondaggio
°	20069 **wild gas**	gaz *m* de haut--fourneau	Hochofengas *n*	gas *m* d'alto-forno
°	20070 **wild heat**	charge *f* effervescente	Brausegicht *f*	carica *f* non calmata
°	20071 **wild steel**	acier *m* sauvage, acier *m* très effervescent	Wilderstahl *m*, wilder Stahl *m*, unberuhigter Stahl *m*	acciaio *m* grezzo, ghisa *f* acciaiosa, acciaio *m* non calmato (o effervescente)
^	20072 **wild well**	sondage *m* éruptif	wild eruptierende Bohrung *f*	pozzo *m* eruttivo
—	20073 **wilkeite**	wilkéite *f*	Wilkeit *m*	wilkeite *f*
—	20074 **willemite**	willémite *f*	Willemit *m*	willemite *f*
—	20075 **williamsite**	williamsite *f*	Williamsit *m*	williamsite *f*
—	20076 **willyamite**	willyamite *f*	Willyamit *m*	willyamite *f*
—	20077 **wiltshireite**	wiltshiréite *f*	Wiltshireit *m*	wiltshireite *f*
—	20078 **wiluite**	wiluite *f*	Wiluit *m*	wiluite *f*
—	20079 **to win, to prepare for mining**	préparer	vorarbeiten	preparare
—	20080 **to win, to mine**	creuser	(aus)bohren	scavare
—	20081 **to win**	séparer	gewinnen, scheiden	separare
—	20082 **winch**	treuil *m*	Winde *f*, Spill *n*	verricello *m*, argano *m*
°	20083 **to wind, to coil**	enrouler	aufwickeln	avvolgere (a spirale)

		English	French	German	Italian
—	20084	to wind up	extraire	fordem	estrarre
o	20085	to wind up	enrouler	aufwickeln, rollen	arrotolare, avvolgere
o	20086	wind	vent *m*	Wind *m*	vento *m*
—	20087	wind	cordée *f*	Treiben *n*	avanzamento *m*
—	20088	wind action, wind agency	action *f* éolienne	Windwirkung *f*	azione *f* eolica
o	20089	wind belt, wind box	boîte *f* à vent	Windkasten *m*	camera *f* del vento
o	20090	wind belt (at tuyere level)	boîte *f* à vent basse	Windkasten *m* (in Höhe der Düsen)	cassa *f* a vento bassa (o inferiore)
o	20091	wind belt (above the tuyeres)	boîte *f* à vent haute	Ringleitung *f*, Windring *m*	cassa *f* a vento alta (o superiore)
o	20092	wind box, blast box	boîte *f* à vent	Windkasten *m*	cassa *f* del vento
o	20093	wind-fall	courant descendant	abfallender Wetterstrom *m*	corrente *f* discendente
		wind furnace, *s. blast furnace*			
o	20094	wind pressure	pression *f* du vent	Winddruck *m*	pressione *f* del vento
—	20095	wind way	voie *f* d'aérage	Wetterstrecke *f*	galleria *f* d'aereazione
—	20096	wind-worn pebble	caillou *m* à facettes	Windkanter *m*, Dreikanter *m*	pietra *f* sfaccettata
		wind work, *s. wind action*			
—	20097	winding	extraction *f*	Förderung *f*	estrazione *f*
o	20098	winding	enroulement *m*	Wicklung *f*	avvolgimento *m*
o	20099	winding	bobinage *m*	Wicklung *f*	bobinaggio *m*
—	20100	winding cable	câble *m* d'extraction	Förderseil *n*	fune *f* d'estrazione
—	20101	winding drum	poulie *m* d'enroulement	Wickeltrommel *f*	tamburo *m* d'avvolgimento
—	20102	winding drum (or rope) pulley	tambour *m* ou molette *f* du câble	Seiltrommel *f*, Seilscheibe *f*	tamburo *m* del cavo
—	20103	winding engine	machine *f* d'extraction	Fördermaschine *f*	macchina *f* d'estrazione
—	20104	winding plant	installation *f* d'extraction	Förderanlage *f*	impianto *m* d'estrazione
—	20105	winding rope	câble *m* d'extraction	Förderseil *n*	fune *f* d'estrazione

	English	French	German	Italian
— 20106	winding shaft	puits *m* d'extraction	Förderschacht *m*	pozzo *m* d'estrazione
— 20107	windway	voie *f* d'aérage	Wetterstrecke *f*	galleria *f* d'aereazione
^ 20108	wing auger	alésoir *m*	Flügelbohrer *m*	alesatore *m*, scalpello *m* ad aletta
^ 20109	wing bit	alésoir *m*	Flügelbohrer *m*	alesatore *m*
° 20109a	wing mixer	mélangeur *m* à ailettes	Paddelmischer *m*	mescolatore *m* ad alette
^ 20110	wing stull	plateforme *f* à aile	Flügelbühne *f*	palchetto *m* ad ala
— 20111	winning	abattage *m*, extraction *f*	Abbau *m*, Gewinnung *f*	estrazione *f*, abbattimento *m*
— 20112	winning level	galerie *f* d'extraction	Förderstrecke *f*	galleria *f* d'estrazione
20113	winnings	produit *m*, profit *m*	Erzeugnis *n*, Gewinn *m*	prodotto *m*, profitto *m*
— 20114	winze	puits *m* borgne, puits *m* intérieur	Blindschacht *m*	pozzo *m* cieco (o ausiliare o interno)
— 20115	winzing	percement *m* de descenderies	Gesenkabteufen *n*	perforazione *f* della galleria discendente (o di ribasso)
° 20116	wiping-cloth	porte-soudure *m*	Lötlappen *m*	stracci *m pl.* per saldatura
° 20117	wipple hammer	martinet *m* à ressort	Wipphammer *m*	maglio *m* a molle
° 20117a	wire	fil *m*	Draht *m*	filo *m*
	wire bar, *s.* wire rod			
° 20118	wire brush with strap	brosse *f* en fil de fer à bride	Drahtbürste *f* mit Gurt	spazzola *f* in filo di ferro a striglia
° 20119	wire cage	cage *f* en fil	Drahtkorb *m*	gabbione *m*
° 20120	wire-clip, wire-cleat, wire clamp	attache *f* pour fils	(Draht)klemme *f*, (Draht)schloss *n*	attacco *m* per fili, serrafili *m*
° 20121	wire cloth	toile *f* métallique	Siebnetz *n*	rete *f* metallica
° 20122	wire drawer's plate	banc *m* à étirer, filière *f*	Drahtzug *m*, Ziehbank *f*	trafila *f*, filiera *f*
° 20123	wire drawing	étirage *m* en fil, tréfilerie *f*	Drahtziehen *n*	trafilatura *f* in fili
° 20124	wire-drawing bench	banc *m* de tréfilerie	Drahtziehbank *f*	banco *m* di trafileria (o di trafila)
° 20125	wire drawing mill	tréfilerie *f*	Drahtzieherei *f*	trafileria *f* per fili

		English	French	German	Italian
o	20126	wire for cables and wire ropes	fil *m* pour câbles	Draht *m* für Seile und Kabel	filo *m* per funi e cavi
o	20127	wire for continuous welding	fil *m* pour soudure continue	Schweissdraht *m* für automatische Schweissmaschinen	filo *m* per saldatura continua
o	20128	wire gauge	jauge *f* à fils	Drahtlehre *f*	calibro *m* per fili metallici
o	20129	wire gauze	tissu *m* ou toile *f* métallique	Drahtgewebe *n*	rete *f* metallica, tessuto *m* metallico
o	20130	wire iron, wire rod	fer *m* à filer, forgis, verges *f pl.* pour tréfilerie	Drahteisen *n*, Reckeisen *n*	ferro *m* da fili, ferro da trafilare, vergelle *f pl.* per trafileria
^	20131	wire line core barrel	carottier *m* retirable	Einsatzkernrohr *n*	carotiere *m* retrattile
^	20132	wire line guide	guide *m* du câble	Seilführung *f*	guida *f* del cavo
^	20133	wire line pumping	pompage *m* au câble	Kabelpumpen *n*	pompaggio *m* alla corda
o	20134	wire mill, looping mill	train *m* à fil, train *m* à verges	Drahtstrecke *f*, Drahtstrasse *f*	treno *m* per fili metallici, treno *m* per verghe
o	20135	wire mill	train *m* à fil, laminoir *m* à fil	Drahtzieherei *f*, Drahtwalzwerk *n*	laminatoio *m* per fili
o	20136	wire netting	toile *f* métallique	Drahtgeflecht *n*	rete *f* metallica
o	20137	wire pliers	pince *f* à tréfiler	Ziehzange *f*	pinza *f* per fili
o	20138	wire rod	fer *m* à étirer	Drahteisen *n*	vergella *f*, bordione *m*
o	20139	wire rod of mild and carbon steel qualities	fil-machine *m* en aciers doux et durs au carbone	Walzdraht *m* aus Fluss-und Kohlens toffstählen	vergella *f* di acciaio dolce e al carbonio
o	20140	wire rod products	produits *m pl.* du fil machine	Walzdrahterzeugnisse *n pl.*	derivati *m pl.* di vergella
o	20141	wire rod rolls	fil *m* machine en rouleaux	Walzdrahtrollen *f pl.*	bordione *m* in rotoli
		wire rods, *s. rod wire*			
o	20142	wire roller	tréfileur *m*	Drahtwalzer *m*	trafilatore *m*
o	20143	wire rolling	tréfilage *m*	Drahtwalzen *n*	laminazione del filo di ferro

	English	French	German	Italian
°	20144 **wire rope, cable**	câble *m* métallique	Drahtseil *n*	cavo *m* metallico
°	20145 **wire rope clip**	serre-câble *m*	Seilklemme *f*	serra-cavo *m*
°	20146 **wire rope plant**	fabrique *f* de câbles	Drahtseilfabrikation *f*	fabbrica *f* di funi
	wire-saddle, *s. wire-clip*			
°	20147 **wire strand**	toron *m* à fils métalliques	Drahtlitze *f*	trefolo *m* (di cavo)
°	20148 **wire triangle**	triangle *m* en fil de fer	Drahtdreieck *n*	triangolo *m* di filo metallico
°	20149 **wire with braided wrapping**	fil *m* sous tresse	Klöppeldraht *m*	filo *m* intrecciato
°	20150 **wire works**	tréfilerie *f*	Drahtzieherei *f*	trafileria *f*
^	20151 **wire wrapped screen**	crépine *f* à fil enroulé	mit Draht umwundenes Filterrohr *n*	succhierola *f* a fili intrecciata
^	20152 **wireline anchor, dead line anchor**	ancrage du brin mort	Totseilanker *m*	ancoraggio *m* della fune morta
°	20152a **wiredrawer's plate**	plaque-filière *f*	Zieheisen *n*	trafila *f*, filiera *f*
°	20153 **with grains of equal size**	à grain homogène	gleichgekörnt	equigranulare
—	20154 **withamite**	withamite *f*	Withamit *m*	Withamite *f*
°	20155 **to withdraw the pattern**	retirer le modèle	das Modell herausheben	estrarre il modello, sformare
°	20156 **to withdraw the plug pin**	retirer les baguettes	die Nadeln zurückziehen	ritirare gli aghi
—	20157 **withdrawal of casing**	extraction *f* des tubes	Entrohrung *f*	estrazione *f* dei tubi
	withdrawing, *s. stripping*			
—	20158 **withdrawing**	déboisage *m*	Holzrauben *n*	disarmo *m*
°	20159 **withdrawing device**	dispositif *m* d'enlèvement	Ausziehvorrichtung *f*	dispositivo *m* per estrarre i lingotti
°	20159a **withdrawing force**	force *f* de retrait	Abziehkraft *f*	forza *f* di ritiro
—	20160 **witherite**	withérite *f*	Witherit *m*	witherite *f*
—	20161 **Witkowitz roasting furnace**	four *m* à griller de Witkowitz	Witkowitzer Röstofen *m*	forno *m* di torrefazione di Witkowitz
—	20162 **wittichenite**	wittichénite *f*	Wittichenit *m*	wittichenite *f*
—	20163 **wittite**	wittite *f*	Wittit *m*	wittite *f*

	English	French	German	Italian
°	20164 **wobbler**	trèfle *m*	Kleeblattform *f*	trefolo *m*
—	20165 **wobbling**	rotation *f* désequi-librée	unbalanzierte Umdrehung *f*	rotazione *f* sbilanciata (di scalpello)
°	20166 **wolfram steel**	acier *m* au tungstène	Wolframstahl *m*	acciaio *m* al wolframio
—	20167 **wolframite**	wolframite *f*	Wolframit *m*	wolframite *f*
—	20168 **wolfsbergite**	wolfsbergite *f*	Wolfsbergit *m*	wolfsbergite *f*
—	20169 **wollastonite**	wollastonite *f*	Wollastonit *m*	wollastonite *f*
	W.O.C. = *waiting on cement*			
	20170 **wood**	bois *m*	Holz *n*	legno *m*
	20171 **wood ash liquor**	eau *f* de cendres de bois	Holzaschenwasser *n*	acqua *f* con cenere di legno
—	20172 **wood bundle**	balai *m*, brindilles	Reisigbündel *n*	fascina *f*
—	20173 **wood construction**	construction *f* en bois	Holzwerk *n*, Holzverband *m*	costruzione *f* in legno
°	20174 **wood fired furnace**	foyer *m* à bois	Holzfeuerung *f*	focolare *m* a legna
°	20175 **wood hurdle**	claie *f* en bois	Holzhorde *f*	graticcio *m* di legno
°	20175a **wood mould**	moule *m* en bois	Holzform *f*	forma *f* di legno
—	20176 **wood-opal**	bois *m* opalisé	Holzopal *m*	legno *m* opalizzato
°	20177 **wood screw**	vis *f* à bois	Holzschraube *f*	vite *f* per legno
—	20178 **wood tar**	goudron *m* de bois	Holzteer *m*	catrame *m* vegetale
—	20179 **wood trough, chute launder**	chicane *f* en bois, chenal *m* en bois	Holzgerinne *n*	labirinto *m* di legno
°	20180 **wood wool rope**	tresse *f* en laine de bois	Holzwollseil *n*	treccia *f* in lana di legno
	wooden box, *s. wooden frame*			
—	20181 **wooden disc**	disque *m* en bois	Holzscheibe *f*	disco *m* di legno
	20182 **wooden frame or box**	châssis *m* en bois	hölzerner Formkasten *m*	staffa *f* di legno
	20183 **wooden handle**	manche *m* en bois	Holzstiel *m*	manico *m* di legno
—	20184 **woodendite**	woodendite *f*	Woodendit *m*	woodendite *f*

	English	French	German	Italian

woodpecker welding, s. *pulsation welding*

		English	French	German	Italian
—	20185	**woodrock**	bois *m* pétrifié	Bergholz *n*	amianto *m*, asbesto *m*
—	20186	**woodwork**	charpente *f*	Holzwerk *n*	armatura *f* (in legno)
°	20187	**Woolff's bottle**	flacon *m* de Woolff	Woolffsche Flasche *f*	bottiglia *f* di Woolff

wooty, s. *Indian steel*

work bench, s. *welding bench*

		English	French	German	Italian
°	20188	**to work harden**	consolider	verfestigen, kalthärten	incrudire
—	20189	**to work in depth**	travailler en profondeur	tiefarbeiten	lavorare in profondità
°	20190	**work-hardening**	écrouissage *m*	Recken *n*, Strecken *n*	incrudimento *m*
°	20190a	**work hardness**	dureté *f* de traitement mécanique	Verfestigung *f*	durezza *f* per trattamento meccanico
°	20191	**work roll**	cylindre *m* de travail	Arbeitswalze *f*	cilindro *m* di lavoro (di laminatoio)

work table, s. *welding bench*

		English	French	German	Italian
^	20192	**work tank**	réservoir *m* de service	Betriebstank *m*	serbatoio *m* di esercizio
°	20193	**workability**	usinabilité *f*	Bearbeitbarkeit *f*	lavorabilità *f*
—	20194	**working, exploration**	exploitation *f*	Betrieb *m*, Ausbeutung *f*	esercizio *m*, lavorazione *f*
°	20195	**working**	allure *f*	Gang *m*	andamento *m*
°	20196	**working (of a furnace)**	conduite *f* (d'un four)	Betrieb *m* (eines Schmelzofens)	condotta *f* (di un forno)
°	20196a	**working**	travail *m*	Bearbeitung *f*	lavorazione *f*
°	20197	**working a bath**	travail *m* du bain	Badbewegung *f*	agitazione *f* del bagno
—	20198	**working area**	chantier *m*	Arbeitsraum *m*	cantiere *m*
—	20199	**working (a rock)**	abattage *m* de la roche	Lösen *n* des Gesteins	estrazione *f* della roccia
^	20200	**working barrel**	cylindre *m* de pompe	Stiefel *m*	cilindro *m* di pompa
°	20201	**working boiler**	chaudière *f* de service	Betriebkessel *m*	caldaia *f* in servizio
°	20202	**working current**	courant *m* de régime	Betriebsstrom *m*	corrente *f* di regime

	English	French	German	Italian
20203	**working down**	traitement *m*	Behandlung *f*, Verfahren *n*	processo *m*, trattamento *m*
20204	**working drawing**	épure *f*	Modelriss *m*	disegno *m* costruttivo
20205	**working expenses**	frais *m pl.* d'exploitation	Betriebsunkosten *n pl.*	spese *f pl.* d'esercizio
20206	**working face**	front *m* d'abattage	Arbeitsseite *f*	fronte *f* d'abbattimento
20207	**working field**	champ *m* d'exploitation	Abbaufeld *n*	campo *m* di coltivazione
20208	**working forwards**	chassage *m*	Feldwärtsbau *m*	galleria *f* in direzione
20209	**working gauge**	calibre *m* de travail	Arbeitskaliber *n*	calibro *m* di lavoro
	working hearth, *s. hearth*			
20210	**working home**	exploitation *f* en rabattant	Rückbau *m*	coltivazione *f* in ritirata
20211	**working in-bye**	exploitation *f* en chassant	Vorbau *m*	coltivazione *f* in direzione
20212	**working in the broken**	abattage *m*	Hereingewinnung *f*	abbattimento *m*
20213	**working inside the blast furnace**	travaux *m pl.* à l'interieur du haut-fourneau	Arbeiten *f pl.* im Ofeninnern	lavori *m pl.* interni nel forno
20214	**working level**	chassage *m*	Vorbau *m*	galleria *f* in direzione
20215	**working of the blast furnace**	marche *f* du haut-fourneau	Gang *m* des Hoch--ofens	andamento *m* dell'alto--forno
20216	**working of the puddling furnace**	marche *f* du travail au four à puddler	Betrieb *m* des Puddelofens	marcia *f* od andamento *m* dell'operazione di puddellaggio
20217	**working out**	exploitation *f* en chassant	Vorbau *m*	coltivazione *f* in direzione
20218	**working-out-bye**	exploitation *f* en rabattant	Rückbau *m*	coltivazione *f* in ritirata
20219	**working pit**	puits *m* d'extraction	Förderschacht *m*	pozzo *m* d'estrazione

	English	French	German	Italian
20220	**working place**	chantier *m*	Förderfeld *n*	cantiere *m* d'estrazione
20220a	**working platform**	plate-forme *f* de manoeuvre	Kanzel *m*	piattaforma *f* di servizio
20221	**working pressure**	pression *f* de marche	Betriebsdruck *m*	pressione *f* d'esercizio
20222	**working room**	salle *f* d'analyse, salle *f* de travail	Arbeitsraum *m*	sala *f* d'analisi, sala *f* di lavoro
20223	**working sill**	bord *m* ou seuil *m* du trou de travail, banc *m*	Arbeitschwelle *f*	banco *m* od appoggio *m* per l'utensile di lavoro
20223a	**working stress**	effort *m* de travail	Beanspruchung *f* bei Nennbetrieb	sforzo *m* di servizio
20224	**working too hot**	allure *f* extra-chaude	heissgarer Gang *m*	andamento *m* o marcia *f* caldissima
20225	**working voltage**	voltage *m* de régime	Betriebsspannung *f*	voltaggio *m* di esercizio o di regime
20226	**working without shocks, smooth working**	marche *f* douce ou sans chocs	stossfreier Gang *m*	funzionamento *m* regolare senza urti
20227	**workmen's dwelling or cottage**	maison *f* ou habitation *f* ouvrière	Arbeiterwohnung *f*	alloggio *m* per operai

works drawing, *s. shop drawing*

	English	French	German	Italian
20228	**works laboratory**	laboratoire *m* de fabrication	Betriebslaboratorium *n*	laboratorio *m* u esercizio
20229	**works railway**	voie *f* ferrée d'atelier	Fabrikbahn *f*	ferrovia *f* d'officina
20229a	**worm**	jet *m* de cuivre fondu	Schmelzkupferstrahl *m*	getto *m* di rame fuso
20230	**worm conveyor**	alimentateur *m* par vis sans fin	Speiseschnecke *f*.	alimentatore *m* a coclea
20231	**worm gear**	transmission *f* par vis sans fin	Schneckengetriebe *n*	ingranaggio *m* a vite perpetua (o senza fine)
20232	**worm gear hob**	fraise-mère *f* hélicoïdale pour roues hélicoïdale	Abwälzfräser *m* für Schneckenräder	fresa *f* madre elicoidale per viti senza fine
20233	**worm rim**	couronne *f* à vis sans fin	Schneckenkranz *m*	corona *f* a vite senza fine

wormhole, *s. pipe*
Worthington pump, *s. duplex pump*

English	French	German	Italian
20234 **wortle**	filière *f* multiple	Mehrfachziehbank *f*	trafila *f* multipla
20284a **wrapping**	revêtement *m*	Umwickeln *n*	rivestimento *m*
20235 **wrench**	clé *f* anglaise	Schraubenschlüssel	chiave *f* inglese
20235a **wrinkle**	pli *m*	Falte *f*	piega *f*
20236 **wrinkle bending**	pliage *m* à rides	Faltenbiegung *f*	piegatura *f* a grinze
20236a **wrinkled**	plissé	gefaltet	rugoso
20237 **wrinkling**	plissement *m*	Faltenbildung *f*	piegatura *f*, arriccia-tura *f*
20238 **writing down the analysis result**	rédaction *f* des résultats de l'ana-lyse	Zusammenstellung *f* der Analyse	verbale *m* sui risul-tati dell'analisi
20239 **wrong contraction allowance**	erreur *f* dans la prévision du retrait	falsches Schwindmass *n*	errore *m* di previsio-ne del ritiro
20239a **wrong shape**	irrégularité *f* de forme	Abweichung *f* der Gestalt	irregolarità *f* di forma
20240 **wrought-iron, malleable iron**	fer *m* doux. fer *m* de forge, fer *m* bat-tu	Schmiedeeisen *n*, gehämmertes Eisen *n*	ferro *m* (fucinato), fer-ro *m* battuto, ferro *m* dolce
20241 **wrought iron frame**	cadre *m* en fer forgé	schmiedeeiserner Rahmen *m*	staffa *f* di ferro for-giato
20242 **wrought iron head**	tête *f* en fer forgé	Hammerkopf *m*	mazza *f* in ferro for-giato
20243 **wrought iron plate**	plaque *f* de fer forgé	Schmiedeeisenblech *n*	piastra *f* di ferro fu-cinato
20244 **wrought iron ring**	cercle *m* en fer forgé	Schmiedeeisenring *m*	cerchio *m* di ferro battuto
20245 **wrought metal**	métal *m* fini	bearbeitetes Metall *n*	lavorato *m*
20246 **wrought steel**	acier *m* forgé, acier *m* battu	Schmiedestahl *m*	acciaio *m* fucinato, acciaio *m* battuto
20247 **wulfenite**	wulfénite *f*	Wulfenit *m*	wulfenite *f*
20248 **wurtzite**	wurtzite *f*	Würtzit *m*	wurtzite *f*
20249 **wye**	raccord *m* à 45°	Y-Abzweigung *f*, Y-Rohr *n*	raccordo *m* a 45°

		English	French	German	Italian
^	20258	**wye connection**	connexion f à étoile	Sternverbindung f	collegamento m a stella
—	20259	**wyomingite**	wyomingite f	Wyomingit m	wyomingite f

	English	French	German	Italian
− 20260	**X-bit**	taillant *m* en cou-ronne	X-Schneide *f*	tagliante *m* a corona
° 20261	**X rays**	rayons *m pl.* X	Röntgenstrahlen *m. pl.*	raggi *m pl.* X
° 20262	**X-ray apparatus for metal inspection**	appareil *m* d'essai radiographique des métaux	Röntgenapparat *m* für Metallprüfung	apparecchio *m* per esame radiografico dei metalli
− 20263	**xantharsenite**	xantharsénite *f*	Xanthoarsenit *m*	xantarsenite *f*
− 20264	**xanthochroite**	xanthochroite *f*	Xanthochroit *m*	xantocroite *f*
− 20265	**xanthophyllite**	xanthophyllite *f*	Xanthophyllit *m*	xantofillite *f*
− 20266	**xanthosiderite**	xanthosidérite *f*	Xanthosiderit *m*	xantosiderite *f*
− 20267	**xenoblast**	xenoblaste *m*	Xenoblast *m*	xenoblasto *m*
− 20268	**xenocryst**	inclusion *f*	Fremdling *m*	inclusione *f*
− 20269	**xenomorphic**	xénomorphe	xenomorph	xenomorfo
° 20270	**xenon**	xénon *m*	Xenon *n*	xeno *m*
− 20271	**xenolith**	enclave *f* énallo-gène	exogener Ein-schluss *m*	inclusione *f* esogena
− 20271a	**xenotime**	xénotime *m*	Xenotim *m*	xenotimo *m*
ˆ 20272	**xilene**	xylène *m*	Xylol *n*	xilolo *m*
− 20272a	**xylogen**	lignin *m*	Lignin *m*	lignina *f*
− 20273	**xyloid lignite**	lignite *m* xyloïde	Xyloidbraunkohle *f*	lignite *f* xiloide
− 20274	**xyloidin**	xyloïdine *f*, ami-don nitré	Xyloidin *m*	xiloidina *f*, amido *m* esplosivo
− 20275	**xylolite**	xylolithe *m*	Xylolith *n*	xilolite *f*
− 20276	**xylopal**	opale *f* xyloïde	Holzopal *m*	opale *m* xiloide
− 20277	**xylotile**	xylotile *m*	Xylotil *m*	xilotilo *m*

		English	French	German	Italian
°	20278	**Yarrow boiler**	chaudière *f* Yar-row	Yarrowkessel *m*	caldaia *f* Yarrow
—	20279	**yatalite**	yatalite *f*	Yatalit *m*	yatalite *f*
—	20280	**yeark-line**	câble *m* à secousses	Stosseil *n*, Zugseil	cavo *m* a strappo, cavo *m* ausiliario
	20281	**yearly make, yearly out-put**	production *f* annuelle	Jahreserzeugung *f*	produzione *f* annuale
—	20282	**yellow arsenic**	orpiment *m*	Auripigment *n*	orpimento *m*
		yellow brass, *s. yellow metal*			
°	20283	**yellow copper**	laiton *m*	Gelbguss *m*, Messing *n*	ottone *m*
—	20284	**yellow copper ore**	chalcopyrite *f*	Chalcopyrit *m*	calcopirite *f*
—	20285	**yellow-earth**	ocre *f* jaune	Gelberde *f*, Goldocker *m*	ocra *f* gialla
—	20286	**yellow lead ore**	wulfénite *f*	Wulfenit *m*	wulfenite *f*
—	20287	**yellow prussiate of potash**	prussiate *m* jaune de potasse	Blutlaugensalz *n*	prussiato *m* giallo di potassa
—	20288	**yellow iron ore**	minerai *m* de fer jaune	Gelbeisenerz *n*	ocra *f* di ferro
°	20289	**yellow metal**	métal *m* jaune	Gelbguss *m*	metallo *m* giallo
°	20290	**yellow-metal-founder**	fondeur *m* de cuivre	Gelbgiesser *m*	fonditore *m* di ottone
—	20291	**yellow ore**	chalcopyrite *f*	Kupferkies *m*	calcopirite *f*
—	20292	**yellow spinel**	rubicelle *f*	Rubicell	rubicella *f*
		yellow untramarine, *s. barium chromate*			
	20293	**yellow variety**	variété *f* jaune	gelbe Abart *f*	varietà *f* gialla
°	20294	**yellowish red field**	champ *m* du spectre rouge jaunâtre	gelbrotes Feld *n*	parte *f* dello spettro giallo-rossastro
—	20295	**yenite**	ilvaïte *f*	Ilvait *m*	ilvaite *f*
—	20296	**yentnite**	yentnite *f*	Yentnit *m*	yentnite *f*
—	20297	**yield**	rendement *m* des minerais	Möllerausbringen *n*	resa *m* dei minerali
°	20298	**yield point**	limite *f* apparente d'étirage	Streckgrenze *f*	limite *m* di snervamento
°	20298a	**yield strenght**	tension *f* de fluage	Fliess-spannung *f*	resistenza *f* allo snervamento
°	20299	**yieldable arch**	cintre *m* déformable	nachgiebiges Streckengestell *n*	arco *m* deformabile

	English	French	German	Italian
— 20300	**yielding prop**	étançon *m* élastique coulissant	federnder Gleitstempel *m*	puntello *m* elastico scorrevole
— 20301	**yogoite**	yogoite *f*	Yogoit *m*	yogoite *f*
° 20302	**yoke**	anse *f*	Tragbügel *m*	gancio *m* ad S
— 20303	**ytterbia**	oxyde *m* d'ytterbium	Ytterbin	ossido *m* d'itterbio
— 20303a	**ytterbite**	gadolinite *f*	Gadolinit *m*	gadolinite *f*
— 20304	**ytterbium**	ytterbium *m*	Ytterbium *n*	itterbio *m*
— 20305	**yttria**	yttria	Yttererde *f*	ossido *m* d'ittrio
— 20306	**yttrialite**	yttrialite *f*	Yttrialit *m*	ittrialite *f*
— 20307	**yttrium**	yttrium *m*	Yttrium *n*	ittrio *m*
— 20308	**yttrocalcite**	yttrocalcite *f*	Yttrokalzit *m*	ittrocalcite *f*
— 20309	**yttrocerite**	ittrocérite *f*	Yttrocerit *m*	ittrocerite *f*
— 20310	**yttrocolumbite**	yttrocolumbite *f*	Yttrocolumbit *m*	ittrocolumbite *f*
— 20311	**yttrofluorite**	yttrofluorite *f*	Yttrofluorit *m*	ittrofluorite *f*
— 20312	**yttrotantalite**	yttrotantalite *f*	Yttrotantalit *m*	ittrotantalite *f*
— 20313	**yttrotitanite**	yttrotitanite *f*	Yttrotitanit *m*	ittrotitanite *f*

	English	French	German	Italian
— 20314	**Z-bit**	taillant *m* en Z	Z-Bohrer *m*	tagliente *m* a Z
° 20315	**Z-bar., Z-iron, zed iron, zed bar**	fer *m* (en) Z, profils *m. pl.* à Z	Z-Eisen *n*	ferro *m* a Z, profilati *m pl.* a Z
— 20315a	zaffre, zaffer	safre *m*	Zaffer *m*	zaffera *f*
— 20316	zaratite	zaratite *f*	Zaratit *m*	zaratite *f*, texasite *f*
— 20317	**Zechstein zeeds, zees,** *s. z. bar*	Zechstein *m*	Zechstein *m*	Zechstein *m*
— 20318	zeolite	zéolite *f*	Zeolith *m*	zeolite *f*
— 20319	zepharovichite	zepharovichite *f*	Zepharovichit *m*	zefarovichite *f*
° 20319a	**zero line**	ligne *f* zéro	Äquator *m*	riga *f* zero
— 20320	zeunerite	zeunérite *f*	Zeunerit *m*	zeunerite *f*
— 20321	**zigger**	infiltration *f* d'eau	Wasserinfiltration *f*	infiltrazione *f* d'acqua
— 20322	**ziment water**	eau *f* cuprifère	kupferhaltiges Wasser *n*	acqua *f* cuprifera
	to zinc, *s. to galvanise*			
° 20323	**zinc**	zinc *m*	Zink *n*	zinco *m*
— 20324	**zinc bloom**	hydrozincite *f*	Hydrozinkit *m*	zinconite *f*
° 20324a	**zinc coated steel**	acier *m* zingué	verzinkter Stahl *m*	acciaio *m* zincato
° 20325	**zinc cuttings**	rognures *f. pl.* de zinc	Zinkspäne *m. pl.*	trucioli *m.pl.* di zinco
° 20326	**zinc cylinder**	cylindre *m* de zinc	Zinkzylinder *m*	cilindro *m* di zinco
° 20327	**zinc deposit**	cadmies *f. pl.*	Gichtschwamm *m*	deposito *m* d'ossido di zinco
° 20328	**zinc dust**	cadmies *f. pl.* fines	Zinkstaub *m*	polvere *f* di zinco
° 20329	**zinc dust primer**	peinture *f* riche en zinc	Anstrich *m* mit hohem Zinkgehalt	vernice *f* a fondo ricco di zinco
° 20330	**zinc gray**	gris *m* de zinc	Zinkgrau *n*	grigio *m* di zinco
— 20331	**zinc-ore**	minerai *m* de zinc	Zinkerz *n*	minerale *m* di zinco
° 20332	**zinc plate for cells**	plaque *f* d'éléments en zinc	Zinkplatte *f* für Elemente	piastra *f* di zinco per elementi
° 20333	**zinc rod**	baguette *f* de zinc	Zinkstab *m*	bastoncino *m* di zinco
— 20334	**zinc silicate**	silicate *m* de zinc	Zinksilikat *n*	silicato *m* di zinco
° 20335	**zinc smeltery**	fonderie *f* de zinc	Zinkhütte *f*	fonderia *f* di zinco
° 20336	**zinc smelting**	fusion *f* du zinc	Zinkschmelzung *f*	fusione *f* di zinco
— 20337	**zinc spar, calamine**	smithsonite *f*	Smithsonit *n*	calamina *f*

		English	French.	German	Italian
−	20338	zinc white	blanc *m* de zinc	Zinkweiss *n*	biacca *f* di zinco
°	20339	zinc wire	fil *m* de zinc	Zinkdraht *m*	filo *m* di zinco
−	20340	zincaluminite	zincaluminite *f*	Zinkaluminit *m*	zincalluminite *f*
°	20340a	zincate treatement	traitement *m* au zincate	Zinkatbehandlung *f*	trattamento *m* allo zincato
−	20341	zincblende	blende *f*, zinc *m* sulfuré	Zinkblende *f*	solfuro *m* di zinco, blenda *f*
−	20342	zinciferous iron ore	minerai *m* de fer zincifère	zinkhaltiges Eisenerz *n*	minerale *m* di ferro con tenore in zinco
		zincification, *s. galvanisati.,n*			
°	20343	to zincify	zinguer	verzinken	zincare, galvanizzare
−	20344	zincite	zincite *f*	Zinkit *m*	zincite *f*
−	20345	zinckenite, zinkenite	zinkénite *f*	Zinkenit *m*	zinchenite *f*
°	20346	zincking	galvanisation *f*, zingage *f*	Verzinken *n*	galvanizzazione *f*, zincatura *f*
−	20347	zincky	zincifère	zinkisch, zinkartig	zinchifero
−	20348	zinkenite	zinkénite *f*	Zinkenit *m*	zinchenite *f*
°	20349	zinking of iron	galvanisation *f* du fer	Verzinkung *f* des Eisens	galvanizzazione *f* del ferro
−	20350	zinkosite	zinkosite *f*	Zinkosit *m*	zincosite *f*
−	20350a	zinn	stannine *f*	Zinnkies *m*	stannite *f*
−	20351	zinnwaldite	zinnwaldite *f*	Zinnwaldit *m*	zinnwaldite *f*
−	20352	zippeite	zippéite *f*	Zippeit *m*	zippeite *f*
−	20353	zircon	zircon *m*	Zirkon *m*	zircone *m*
−	20354	zirconia	zircone *f*	Zirkondioxyd *n*	zirconia *f*
−	20355	zirconium	zirconium *m*	Zirkonium *n*	zirconio *m*
−	20355a	zirconium alloy	alliage *m* de zirconium	Zirkonlegierung *f*	lega *f* di zirconio
−	20356	zirconium steel	acier *m* au zirconium	Zirkoniumstàhl *m*	acciaio *m* allo zirconio
−	20357	zirkelite	zirkélite *f*	Zirkelit *m*	zirchelite *f*
−	20358	zirklerite	zirklerite *f*	Zirklerit *m*	zirklerite *f*
−	20359	zobtenite	zobtenite *f*	Zobtenit *m*	zobtenite *f*
−	20360	zoisite	zoisite *f*	Zoisit *m*	zoisite *f*
−	20361	zonal structure	structure *f* zonale	Zonengefüge *n*	struttura *f* zonale

		English	French	German	Italian
	20362	zone hardened piece	pièce f trempée localement	lokalgehärtetes Stück n	pezzo m temprato localmente
—	20363	zone fossil	fossile m de zone	Gliederungsfossil n	fossile m di zona
°	20364	zone of fusion	zone f de fusion	Schmelzzone f	zona f (o campo)
—	20365	zone of sphere	zone f sphérique	Kugelschicht f	zona f sferica
—	20366	zone of weathering	zone f de l'altération superficielle	Tiefdruckgebiet n	zona f di alterazione superficiale
—	20367	zoogenic rock	roche f zoogène	zoogenes Gestein n	roccia f zoogena
—	20368	zoolite	zoolithe f	Zoolith m	zoolite f
—	20369	zunyite	zunyite f	Zunyit m	zunite f
—	20370	zurlite	zurlite f	Zurlit m	zurlite f
—	20371	zwitter	zwitter m	Zwitter m	zwitter m
—	20372	zygadite	zygadite f	Zygadit m	zygadite f

$27246 = 20372 + 6874$ new terms and synonyms inserted during printing

INDEXES
FRENCH-GERMAN-ITALIAN

French (Francais)   1097

German (Deutscher)   1227

Italian (Italiano)   1378

abaco S. 2513
abaissement de la tempéra-
    ture 11074
abaissement du plan d'exca-
    vation 1342
abaque 2513
— pour enregistrement de
    variables 17845
abattage 17676, 5792, 6906,
    15762, 20212, 15759,
    2449, 2324, 8205
abattage v. attaque
abattage à la lance 16997,
    S. 9527
— à la main 8764, 8786
— à l'eau 13382, 16997
— au feu 7179
— au jour 12607
— au moyen de coins 19888
— au moyen de pinces 1253
— de la roche 20199
— de minerai 12632
— des poussières 6134
— descendant 2189
— du charbon 3828
— du stérile décollé 16496
— en gradins 1490, 1496,
    1078, 12747
— en gradins droits S. 2189
— en montant 2337
— en taille chassante 5866
— en traçage 5276
— hydraulique 9541, 9527
— latéral 16275
— mécanique 11132, 11420
— par explosifs 11770
— par explosif sans havage
    préalable 16165
— par gradins droits 19267
abatteur 2318, 2482, 6745,
    8204
abattre 2300, 8198
— à l'explosif
— du bois 6903
— le minerai 2298, 17665
— par des pinces 1213
abichite 2
ablation 3
— englacial ou interne 6477
abolition de limitation 2138
aboutement 2229
abouter 2634, 27
abrasif 8, 7
abrasion 6
abrasions 15645
abreuvage 11555

abri de sondeur 5596
absarokite 10
absorber l'humidité 11
absorbeur 12
absorption 14
— de chaleur 8973
— de chaleur par vapori-
    sation 19
— de l'hydrogène par
    les métaux 20
— de soudure 19939
— d'oxygène 21
— d'oxygène par la
    houille 22
— des gaz 18
— thermique 8973
acadialite 33
acadien 34
acanthicone 35
acanthite 36
acaustobiolite 336
accélération 38
— de tirage 39
accéléré 831
accéléromètre 40
accès latéral 16262
accessoires à rebord 1369
— d'une fonderie 13762
— en fer 16733
— en laiton 2269
— pour câbles 2659
— pour lampes à arc 748
accident 10245
acclivité 45
accord limite 12466
accouplement 10200
— à friction 7767
— d'outils de sondage
    18728
accouplements 4551
accoupler 4545
accrochage 8811, 10530,
    13532, , 10368, 13399,
    15934, 15949, 9777,
    15574
— (du cubilot) 2390
— des charges 8809, 8805,
    3466
— du fond 2170, 2176
accroche-tube 2940, 13347
accrocher le lingot 8565
accrocheur 17826, 13531,
    12550, 9320, 8378, 8381,
— à pinces 7222
accroissement d'angle 569
— de la réductibilité 9725

accroissement de tempé-
    rature 9723, 18384
accumulateur 12754, 54
— de chaleur 8974
— de compensation 18074
— hydraulique 9511
— hydropneumatique 9512
accumulation 56
— de pétrole 12504
— littorale 16170
accumuler 52
acerdèse 59
acérer 17453
acétate d'ammonium 524
— de baryte 60
— de plomb 10605
— de potasse 61
achevé 7119
achèvement v. parachèvement
    ou finissage
achèvement des pièces
    coulées 7126
achever 4111
achmite 107
achroïte 68
achromatique 69
aciculaire 70, 12210
aciculite 73
acide 74, 13115
— acétique 62
— arsénieux S. 823
— azotique 1032
— brun 2471
— carbonique 2856
— chlorhydrique 9549
— chromique 3539
— concentré 4162
— de récupération 14508
— dilué 5417
— fluorhydrique 9555
— gras 6837
— nitrique 12309
— nitrique fumant 7818
— oléique 12526
— oxalique 12787
— phosphorique 16898
— pour alkylation 365
— régénéré 14785
— sulfonique 17965
— sulfureux 17987
— sulfurique 19743
— sulfurique chimiquement
    pur 3399
— sulfurique du commerce
    4089
— sulfurique libre dans les

résidus 7739
acide tartarique 18331
acidifère 97
acidifiable 98
acidifiant 99
acidité 5139
acier 17454
— à aimants 11184
— à aimants permanents 13107
— à alène 1016
— à aubes de turbines 19118
— à blindages 803
— à boulonnerie 15711
— à burins 3487
— à canons de fusils 8670
— à cémenter 2921
— à chaînes 3248
— à chaudières 1979
— à ciseau 3487
— à coffres-forts 17473
— à coupe rapide 18002
— à décollettage rapide 989
— à double corroyage 5674
— à double raffinage S. 5674
— à faible teneur en carbone 11062, 11046
— à faible teneur en phosphore 11056
— à fleurets 15018
— à fracture rosée S. 15180
— à grain fin 7084
— à haute résistance 9187
— à haute teneur en carbone 9139
— à l'aluminium 462
— à la rose 15180
— à limes
— à locomotives 10952
— à l'oxygène pur 14188
— à l'uranium 19395
— à matrices 5281
— à outils 18730
— à outils au four électrique 6311
— à outils de mines 18731
— à outils pour le façonnage à froid 3981
— à pales 16214
— à pignons 13321
— à plaques 13499
— à plaques de blindages 801
— à poinçons 9220

acier à rails 14364
— à ressort 17200
— à ressort pour montres 19742
— à ressort(s) pour fusil 8675
— à rivets 14974
— à scies 15560
— à scies à ruban 1188
— à soupapes 19456
— à trempe glacée 3449
— à 1,125 de C. 17093
— acide 95
— affiné 16400
— affiné par le vent 317
— allant au feu 8991
— allié 401
— altéré 17143
— anti-magnétique 12357
— argenté 16361
— au bore 2117
— au carbone 2842
— au carbone à haute teneur 9139
— au chrome 3548
— au chrome et nickel 3545
— au chrome-molybdène 3531
— au chrome-silicium 3535
— au chrome-tungstène 3537
— au chrome-vanadium 3538
— au cobalt 3891
— au cobalt-chrome 3886
— au convertisseur 4308
— au creuset 4738
— au four à réverbère 17487
— au manganèse 11277
— au manganèse à fort teneur de carbone 2837
— au molybdène 11883
— au nickel 12281
— au nickel-aluminium 12270
— au nickel-chrome 12273
— au nickel-vanadium 12283
— au seul carbone 17707
— au tungstène 19104, 20166
— au tungstène-nickel 19102

acier au vanadium 19462
— au wolfram S. 19104
— au 0,75% de C. 5382
— au 0,875 de C.
— au zirconium
— austénitique 959
— auto-trempant 284, 15825
— basique S. 18539, 1306
— battu 20246
— Bessemer 95, 76
— Bessemer de petit convertisseur 1041
— bien trempé 19972
— binaire 1592
— bleui 1912
— boursouflé 1784
— brûlé 2615
— bruni 2401, 13629
— calmé 10351, 5039
— calorisé 2762
— cannelé pour ressorts 8595
— carboné 2842
— carré 17248
— cémenté 2870, 2914, 3156
— centrifugé 3214
— -chrome 3548
— chromé 3548
— chrome-nickel 3533
— commercial 4088
— composé 4131
— comprimé 4150
— corroyé S. 16400
— coulé 17463
— courant 18723
— damasquiné 4972
— damassé 4972
— d'affinage au bas-foyer 3306
— d'alliage 17021
— d'alliage complexe 4118
— d'alliage pauvre 11044
— d'alliage riche 9137
— de Brescia 2361
— de cémentation 17469, 3162, 3166
— de cémentation corroyé 16024
— de charrues 13553
— de choix 7090
— de construction 17892
— de construction allié 17883
— de coupe 7731
— de Damas S. 4972

acier de finerie 3306
— de fusion S. 9800
— de haute tension S. 9187
— de moulage 17463, 3069
— de nitruration 12314
— de qualité inférieure 19301
— de qualité supérieure 9 9153
— de remplacement 17933
— demi-doux, 11436, 16844
— demi-dur 2842, 11427
— dénaturé S. 17143, 13102
— deux fois corroyé S. 5674
— deux fois raffiné S. 5674
— diamant 5029, 6703
— double corroyé S. 5674
— doux 11252, 9794, 17498, 5034, 11678
— doux de décolletage 11679
— doux de qualité courante 12625
— du type commercial 4088
— duplex 6114
— dur 2844, 8843
— dur en lingots 8833
— durci S. 8843
— écroui 3994, 3975
— électrique 6304
— en barres 1220
— en billette 1586
— en loupes 1825
— en pains S. 1825
— estampé 13882
— étamé 18660

— étiré 5819
— étiré à froid 3975
— étiré bruni 2395
— eutectoïde 6607
— extra-doux 9794, 5037, 19538, 6705,
— extra-dur 2845
— extra-rapide 19537, 18015
— fabriqué 13982
— fabriqué par le procédé au minerai
— ferreux 8717
— ferritique 3167, 6936
— feuillard 17855
— fin 7090, 9153, 14602
— fin au carbone de construction 9140
— fini 7123

acier fondu 7467, 9800
— fondu au-creuset 16456
— fondu battu 8746
— fondu forgé 8746
— fondu soudable 11676
— forgé 7587, 20246
— graphiteux 8456
— Guillaume S. 9931
— Hadfield 8702, 11277
— harvaysé 8884
— hexagonal 9126
— homogène 9800
— hypereutectoïde 9588
— hypoeutectoïde 9598
— hypoeutectoïde 9600
— inattaquable 17297
— inattaquable aux acides 88
— indéformable 12367
— indien S. 9736
— inoxydable 15394, 15591, 17297
— internissable S. 17297
— Invar 9931
— laminé 15100
— laminé à chaud 9432
— laminé à froid 3994
— lissé 13629
— magnétique 11184
— malléable 7271, 11252
— marchand 6734, 11498
— Martin 8965, 12580
— Martin acide 84
— mi-dur 8714, 11437
— molybdique 11884
— moulé 3018, 17463
— moulé pour dynamo 6156
— nickel-chrome 3533
— nickel-chrome-molybdène 3532
— nitruré 12314
— non allié 12339
— non calmé 14918, 19319
— non-magnétique S. 12357
— non phosphoré 12360
— non trempé 16844, 19338
— non vieillissant 12338
— normal de nitruration 12381
— normalisé 12386
— ordinaire 18723
— -outil S. 18730
— -outil au carbone 19320
— perlitique 13019

acier phosphoreux 13177
— plaqué 3611
— plat 7323
— pour ancrage 559
— pour armes 794, 16725
— pour baleines de corsage
— pour bouterolles et étampes 17471
— pour ciseaux 5908
— pour clavettes 10324, 8214
— pour construction 6476
— pour construction navale 17891
— pour forets 17474
— pour la construction des ponts 17893
— pour obus 16112
— pour forets 9269
— pour perforation de roches 11773
— pour plumes 1179
— pour poinçons 17472
— pour roulements à billes 1152
— pour tours à grande vitesse 9179
— pour travail à froid 4008
— profilé 15785, 15994, 15101
— profilé fort 9039
— profilé laminé à chaud 9433
— profilé pour construction 4236
— puddlé 14100, 14104, 7580
— quaternaire
— raffiné S. 7090, 16400
— raffiné à deux marques 5674
— rainuré 8595
— rapide 14538, 9178
— rapide pour tour-révolver 9180
— recuit 606
— refondu 14698
— réfractaire 7177, 8991
— résistant à haute température 12343
— résistant à la chaleur S. 8991, 8994
— résistant à la corrosion 4492
— résistant aux acides 88

acier résistant aux pro-
   duits chimiques 3392
— revenu 18389
— rond 15292
— sans ampoules 19232,
— sans bulles S.1786
— sans soufflures 1786
— sauvage 20071
— semi-calmé 15845
— semi-doux S. 11436
— semifini 15842
— Siemens-Martin 1300
— soudable 19927
— soudable à haute ré-
   sistance 9188
— soudant 19927
— soudé S. 19927
— spécial S. 7090, 17021
— spécial à alliage 404
— spécial allié 404
— spécial au tungstène
   19103
— spécial pour aéroplanes
   17002
— spécial pour automobi-
   les 17003
— spécial sans alliage
   13446
— supérieur 9153
— sur sole acide 84
— sur sole basique S.1300
— surchauffé 12759
— ternaire 16366
— Thomas 1293, 1549,
   18539
— trempable 8849
— trempant à l'air S. 284
— trempant à l'eau 19783
— trempant à l'huile
— trempé 8856, 8998
— trempé à l'eau 14288
— trempé à l'1,0%K. 18377
— trempé et récuit 8852
— troostitique 18932
— -tungstène S. 19104
— vieilli 217
— Wootz 9736
aciérable 102
aciérage 103, 17523, 17495,
   58,
aciération 103, 58
aciéré 17468
— à la surface 2913
aciérer 17453, 104
aciéreux 17524
aciérie 3025, 17522, 17491

aciérie aux creusets 4747
— Bessemer
— électrique 6308
— Martin 12575, 12577
— Siemens-Martin 12581
— Thomas 1307, 18535,
   18540
aciéries Bessemer et
   Thomas 1557
aclinique 106
acmite S. 107, 182
actinium 109
actinolit(h)e 110
actinote S. 110
action abrasive de la
   glace glaciaire 8548
— de coupe 4914
— d'érosion 10163
— de la gelée 9769
— de la neige 113
— des eaux courantes
   112
— des glaces
— directe 5465
— du vent S. 20088
— éolienne 20088
— extérieure 17730
— intermoléculaire iso-
   trope 10083
— mécanique sur le maté-
   riau 11411
— oxydante de l'air sur le
   charbon 12810
— transportante et dépo-
   sante de l'eau courante
   18839
actions de contract exo-
   morphes 6661
— littorales 16172
activant 118
activer le tirage 14304
activisme 119
adamantin 121
adamine 124
adaptation 46
— du moule
additif 144, 143, 5635
— anti-mousse 5123
addition 5185, 1430, 174
— d'argile 175
— de ferro-manganèse
— de matière argileuse
   10931
— de matière colorante
— de minerai 132
— de minerais 140

addition de nickel 139
— de sable 133, 141
— de scories 3571, 16520
— oxydante 12809
— par gouttes 135
— de chaleur 18027
adelfotype 145
adélite 146
adhérence 17580
— du ciment 3143
adhérer 147
adhésif 150
adipocire 151
adjudication pour gros
   travaux de sondage 1690
adjuvant pour filtre 13826
admission 9853
— d'air 171
— du vent 1730
— par piston S. 13394
— par tiroir S. 16619
adoucir 19334, 18370
— l'acier 16847
adoucissement 16848, 18118
adsorption 177
adulaire 178
adular 178
aegirine S. 107
aegyrine 182
aegyrite 107
aenigmatite 183
aérage S. 188, 19508
aérage v. ventilation
aérage aspirant 6651
— descendant 5702
— diagonal 5311
— montant 19432
aération 188
— des mines 11745
aéréateur aspirateur 17962
aérer v. ventiler
aérer le sable 186
aérification 194
aériphère 195
aérolite 196
aéromagnétomètre 245
aeschynite 197
aétite 198
affaissement 15153, 16417
— du toit 1528, 15146,
   17255, 8248
affilé 8607, 16901, 16006
affiler 16006
— le foret 16007
affinage 14605, 14617,
   14606

affinage v. raffinage ou
  corroyage
— avec du minerai de fer
  14619
— au bain de scorie 16398
— au bas-foyer 14614
— au convertisseur Besse-
  mer 1554
— au four à réverbère
  14609
— complet 20035
— de l'acier 14618
— de l'argent 16958
— de l'or 8349
— des métaux 14615
— du grain 8399
— imparfait 8500
— par soufflage S. 4309
affiné et trempé 14597·
affinement du grain 8400
affiner 7072, 14593
— au moyen de l'électri-
  cité S. 6366
— la fonte 14595
— l'étain 14596
affiner v. raffiner
affinerie 14603
affineur 7100
affinité chimique 3384
affleuré 7480
affleurement 15021, 1403,
  1320
— de faille 6854
affluence 15388
affluer S. 7419
affûtage 16008
aftalose S. 689
aftonite S. 690
afwillite 204
agalite 205
agalmatolite 3467, 206
agaphite 207
agate 208
agaté 213
agate à brunir 2611
— à fortification 7623
— brèche 2355
— jaspée 10137
— moka 11849
— œillée 6728
— rubanée 1181
— sanguine 1817
— tachetée 3787
— agatoïde 212
âge géologique 8172

agent de cémentation S.
  3175
— de fusion 7891
— de précipitation S.
  13705
— de soutènement 14026
— de transports 221
— explosif 1744
— mouillant 20003
— -réceptionnaire 9848
— tensio-actif 18042
agents minéralisateurs
  11762
agglomérant 4392
— céramique 19545
agglomérat 2017, 2018
agglomération de minerais
  12635
aggloméré 2415
— de charbon de bois
  3302
— de liège 13877
— de tourbe 13025
— pour haut-fourneau
  1716
agglomérer 13277, 223, 129
— par frittage 16429
agglutinant 2017
agglutination 2694, 16433
— du coke 2697
aggluttiné 228
s'agglutiner 2690,
  16429
agglutiner 130
agglutinogène 229
agrégat cristallin 4799
agitation 236
— du bain 1953
agitateur 237, 14313,
  17609
agiter 3559
— dans l'eau 17606
agrafe 3637
agrandir le trou 12612
agrandissement du fond
  d'un trou de mine 3274
— par explosion du fond
  d'un trou de mine 17205,
  17267
agrégat quartz-feldspath
  14256
agrégats 234
agricolite 238
aguilarite 239
aide de laboratoire 18460

aide-mineur 15264
— -ouvrier 12302, 15392
— -perforateur 18725
— -sondeur 899, 7412
aigreur du fer 4002
aigue marine 725
aiguillage 18720
— double
aiguille 7900
aiguille S. 10250
— à air 19506
— aimantée 11196
— courbe 4885
— de changement de voie
  18132
— de croisement S. 5233
— de platine 13525
— droite
— infernale 13560
aiguillé 12210
aiguilles noires 1657
aiguilleur 18134
aiguisé 8607
aiguiser 16006
aikinite 12209
aile 19872
— (de cornière) 10666
ailes inégales 19290
ailette de ventilateur 6794
— formant piston 13395
aimant 11183
— d'acier 17483
— de grue 4600
— de repêchage 7220
— en fer à cheval 9383
— fixe 17400
— mobile 12048
— naturel 10923
— permanent 13106
aimantation 11205
air 1698
— aspiré 17950
— comprimé 4134
— de combustion 8986
— de mine(s) 290
— du noyau 291
— entrant 9856
— primaire 13935, 13936
— secondaire 15763
— vicié 1648
aire 18040
— de coulée 3039
ajoutage de pulvérisation
  S. 17184
— pour appareil 5556

ajouter de la fonte brute 13247
ajustage 18868, 164, 163
— au moyen d'intercalcaires 168
ajuster 158
ajusteur de modèles 12991
ajutage à découper 4919
— pour tuyau flexible 7369
akérite 337
akermatite 338
akrochordite 339
alabandine 340
alabandite 340
alabastrite 342
alaïte 343
alambic distillatoire 17592
alamosite 344
alaskaïte 345
albâtre 341
— gypseux S. 342
alberite 346
albien 347
albite 348
albitophyre 349
albraque 5750, 19796, 10961, 11728
album des profils 14001
alcali 355
alcalinisation 363
alcaliser 362
alcool 352
alésage 2076, 2094, 11479
— du cylindre 2086
aléser 14477
aléseur 18281
alésoir 20108, 20109, 2430
— de centrage 3189
— de machine à fût conique Morse 11135
— ébaucheur 16111
— extensible 6670
— flottant 7391
— pour tubes 2954
alexandrite 353
alfénide 8195
algonkien 354
alignement des carbures 2823
alimentateur à disque rotatif 19152
— à tablier 723
— mécanique 13781
— oscillant 15038
— par vis san fin

alimentateur vibratoire 19547
alimentation 9853, 6888, 15378
— à chenal de coulée libre 17172
— à grille 8581
— automatique 981
— forcée 2049
— par godets roulants 6932
alimentation v. chargement
alimenter 15337
— par le bas 19249
allactite 368
allalinite 369
allanite 370
allège 10792
alleghanyte 371
allemontite 372
aller 8341
— aux molettes 12785
alliage 396
— à bas point de fusion 11055
— à base d'aluminium S. 447
— à base de cuivre S. 4351
— à base de nickel 12269
— à faible teneur 400
— à haute teneur 399, 9136, 9142
— binaire 1590
— coulé sous pression 5361
— d'acier 17455
— d'aluminium 447
— d'aluminium hypersilicié 448
— d'apport 8870
— d'argent 16351
— de cuivre 4351
— de deuxième fusion 15764
— de molybdène et nickel 12276
— de plomb 10606
— Delta S. 5158
— fer-carbone 9962
— fusible 7887
— léger 10778
— -mère 11360
— métallique 11538
— pour coussinets S. 1396

alliage pour résistances électriques 14765
— pour rhéostat 14781
— sans retrait 19204
— ultraléger 19221
allié 403
allochroïte 377
allochtone 379, 17742
alloclasite 383
allodelphite 384
allogène 385
allomérisme 386
allomorphe 387
allonge 125
— bombée 1162
allongement 17816, 5412
— à la rupture 6390
— de rupture par fluage 15385
— pour cent après rupture 13074
— visqueux S. 4614
allonger 6388
allothigène S. 385
allotriomorphe 389, 592
allotropie 392
allumage 7188, 10799, 9627
— de convertisseur 7798
— défectueux 11798
— des coups 16203
— du foyer d'une chaudière 7190
— électrique 6259
allumer 7146
— le feu 10777
allumeur du cubilot 4850
allure 20195
— chaude 9455
— de la fusion
— de la soufflerie 114
— du fourneau 4190, 1714
— extra-chaude 20221
— froide 4009
— normale 12384
— variable du haut-fourneau 10039
alluvion 5849
— glaciaire 8251
— stannifère 17773
alluvionnement 230, 410
alluvionner 232
almandin 413
alnique 415
alnöite 416
alpax 417

alquifoux 420
alsbachite 421
alshedite 422
alstonite 424
altaïte 425
alternance de charge 436
— des couches 9865
alternance des couches 435
alumel 442
aluminage 466
aluminate 444
alumine 443
— fuse 7886
alumineux 14873
aluminière 440
aluminium 446
aluminosilicate 470
aluminothermie 18491
alumogel 469
alumnite 445
alun 438
— de plume 6869
alunière S. 439
alunite 471, 473
alunitisation 474
alunitisé 475
amaigrir 5081
— un sable argileux 19852
amalgamable 489
amalgamateur 8560, 492
amalgamation 490, 498
— au tonneau 1240
— aux cuves 501
— aux tambours tournants 500
— sur plaques 13486
amalgame 478
— de mercure 484
— d'or 483
amalgamé 491
amalgamer 477
amarantite 502
amas 56, 13278, 17611
— de minerai 12647
amatol 503
amazonite 8513, 504
ambatoarinite 505
amblygonite 508
ambre 506
ambrite 509
améliorable par trempe et revenu 8997
aménage par rouleaux 15110
aménagement du courant d'air 4556

aménagement du revêtement du cubilot 2889
amenée de gaz 8018
— du charbon 18028, 3832
— du charbon par vis sans fin 18026
américium 513
amésite 514
amétyste 515
amiante 516, 840, 6170
— flexible 12034
— vulcanisé 19608
amidon 17378
— nitré 20274
amincissement 12298, 12300, 19889
— en coin 1595, 18214, 1352
ammoniaque 518
ammonioberite 521
ammoniojarosite 522
ammonite 523
— pyritisée 14215
s'amonceler 25230
amont-pendage 19352
amorçage 13953
amorce 2792
— à étincelle 16982
amorcer une pompe 13946
amortissement par ressort 17194
amortisseur S. 6244
— à air 263
— de pulsation 14145
amosite 532
ampélite 535
ampèremètre 517, 4868
amphibole 536
amphibolisation 538
amphibolite 537
amphigène S. 539, 10698
ampoule à décantation 15880
amygdale 542
anaérobique 545
anagénèse 546
analcime 547
analyse 548, 6675
— chimique 3383, 10471
— complète 18786
— d'arbitrage 734
— de comparaison 17342
— du gaz 7976
— élémentaire 19216
— granulométrique 15687
— gravimétrique 8483

analyse microchimique 11630
— par l'électricité S. 6337
— par voie humide 6632, 19984
— par voie sèche 6633
— préliminaire S. 13845
— qualitative 14245
— quantitative 14250
— quantitative des minerais 12627
— spectrale 17035
— volumétrique 19600
— v. expérience ou essai
analyseur d'Orsat 12679
anamesite 551
anamorphisme 552
anapaïte 553, S. 18226
anatase 554
anatexie S. 555
anatexis 555, 14643
anauxite 556
ancrage à boulon 15714
— de gaz 7978
— du brin mort 20152
— en fers ronds 15286
ancre extensible 6667
andalousite S. 3415
andalousite 561, 9281
andésine 562
andésite 563
andésitique 564
andorite 565
andradite 566
andrewsite 567
anémomètre 568
angle 4478
— axial 1017
— de coupe 4927, 18952
— de dépouille 5726
— de déviation de câble 7364
— de discordance 578
— des étalages 574
— de flexion 1507
— des faces 9880
— d'incidence 576
— d'inclinaison 575
— de stratification 573, 1431
— de torsion 577
anglésite 586, 10623
angulaire 587
anhydrite S. 10285, 593, 4820
— arsénieux 823
— arsénique 814

anhydride carbonique 2832
— phosphotique 13179
— siliceux 16312
— sulfurique 17989
— titanique 18687
anion 595
anisotropique 596
anisotropie 598
ankérite 599, 2477
ankylostomiase 600
annabergite 601
anneau 14920
— à tourillons 1019
— de bain-marie 19748
— de butée 3581
— de charge 14931
— de concassage de coke 3934
— de cuvelage 13273
— denté venu de fonte 3917
— de galerie 19111
— de garde tubulaire 19075
— de porcelaine 13666
— de serrage 1603
— de soutènement 14921
— de support pour creusets 4749
— du piston S. 13392
— en briques 17649
— en fonte 3010
— en tôle de fer 16059
— gradué 18640
— suspendu 18077
anode 626
anodizer 634
anomalie de trempe 3424
anorthite S. 4935, 635, 2710
anorthose 636, 16813
anorthosite 637
anse 1100, 20302
— de l'électrode S. 6327
— de l'élévateur 6380
antédiluvien 638
antenne pour radio 14336
anthophyllite 639
anthosidérite 640
anthracéniques 641
anthracitisation 645
anthracite 642, 8822, 17697
— de qualité inférieure 10495
— de 60 à 100 mm. 2440
— en morceaux 3368

anthracmite 646
anthraconite 649, 18127, 19406
anthraco-silicose 647
anthracose 650
antichambre 653
anticlinal 654, 10054
— asymétrique 911
— caréné 2890
— droit 6537
— en éventail 6803
— en forme de selle 15408
— incliné 14522
— non développé 809
— renversé 12782
— secondaire 11782, 17931
— symétrique 18149
antidétonant 666
antifrictionner S. 13741
anti-incrustant 665
antigorite 664, 10498
antimoine 669, 17575
antimoine gris S. 668
— rouge S. 10312
— sulfureux S. 688
antimonieux 17571
antimonite 668
antimousse 662
antioxidant 12790
antipode 671
antlérite 675
antozonite 676
apachite 679
apatite 680
apex 681
aphanèse 683
aphanite 684
aphanitique 685
aphrite 687
aphrosidérite 688
aphtalose 689
aphthitalite S. 689
aphthonite 690
apjohnite 691
aplanétique 692
aplatir S. 19371, 10246
aplatissement 10251, 7351, 1567
aplatissoire 7355
aplite 693
aplites 694
apochromatique 696
apomagmatique 697
apophyllite 698

apophyse S. 12468, 699
— d'un filon 16450
appareil à air chaud 287
— à air chaud à tuyaux suspendus 288
— à air chaud de Cowper 4575
— à air chaud en fonte 9953
— à air chaud horizontal 9331
— à air chaud vertical 19518
— à air chaud Whitwell S. 20053
— à arroser 17209
— à brome 2451
— à concentrer 6621
— à démouler les lingots 9800
— à dessécher 6054
— à dudgeonner S. 18980
— à enlever le châssis S. 10766
— à essayer le carbone 2830 2830
— à éther d'après Rothe 15236
— à faire le vide 19425
— à jet de sable S. 15522
— à mesurer la pression des gaz S. 11297
— à potasse 13721
— à tronçonner les tuyaux S. 13334
— à ultrasons métalloscopique à poudres magnétiques 18022
— auxiliaire pour coupe circulaire 3580
— classeur 3640
— Cleveland 3722
— d'absorption 15
— d'aération S. 189
— d'alimentation 6890
— d'amalgamation 499
— d'analyse des gaz brûlés 7455
— de chargement 3332
— de chargement automatique 977
— de chargement des minerais 12646
— de chauffage à induction 9752
— de contrôle 14057

appareil de décantation
  15923
— de distillation 5555
— de distillation du di-
  luant 5416
— d'Edison 6214
— d'élévation 10767
— d'essai 18467
— d'essai radiographi-
  que des métaux 20262
— d'extraction 6708
— de forage à la corde
  2663
— de graissage du câble
  15166
— de Kipp 10369
— de mesure électrique
  6287
— de prise de vues descen-
  du dans le puits
— de renversement 15227,
  18136
— de renversement à com-
  mande électrique 6309
— de repêchage 2551
— de sondage S. 4405,
  2104, 19968
— de sublimation 17925
— de tamisage mécanique
  11415
— de Venturi 19513
— diviseur du sable 189
— électromagnétique de
  Siemens 16291
— enregistreur de l'affaissement du toit 4295
— photographique 13186
— pour éteindre les étincelles 16983
— pour l'analyse des gaz
  7977
— pour la détermination du
  point de fusion 706
— pour la fabrication du
  chlore 3501
— pour la production de
  l'acide fluorhydrique
  701
— pour la préparation de
  l'hydrogène sulfuré
  702
— pour la recherche de
  l'arsenic 703
— pour le dosage de l'acide carbonique 705

appareil pour le dosage de
  l'azote 707
— pour le dosage du
  carbone dans le fer 704
— pour l'essai de rupture
  11124
— pour l'essai de traction
  11127, 18413
— pour l'essai du pétrole
  13136
— pour le remplissage des
  bonbonnes 2874
— pour le traitement
  thermique 8999
— pour les essais non
  destructifs 700
— pour serrer et dégager
  les boulons 5281
— réfrigérant 4336
— réfrigérant à ruissellement 18890
— refroidisseur à irrigation
  18890
appareillage du puits 13408
— des briques 17654
— électrique de commande
  automatique 6359
appareiller 14894
appareils auxiliaires 1000
— en porcelaine 13669
— en verre 8286
— physicochimiques 13195
— pour l'essai au chalu-
  meau 1892
appentis 14041
appliquer les attaques de
  coulée 15344
— les évents 14955
appointer v. affiler
apport de matière magmatique 138
appréciation d'après
  l'aspect extérieur 6631
approfondir 5100, 5161
approfondissement 5101
approvisionnement en minerai 11440
aptitude à la trempe 8850
— au serrage 4101
aquifère 19749
arakawaite 730
aramoyoite 731
arandisite 732
araphite 733
araser 17815

arbalétriers d'acier IPN 9947
arbitraire 19296
arbre à calibre 17090
— à noyau 4390, 4447
— à noyauu profilé 15992
— auxiliaire de poulie
  10103
— d'accouplement 4550
— d'attaque 5968
— de commande 10099
— de commande principal
  19530
— d'entraînement 8130
— de renvoi 10840
— de trousse S. 17089
— de turbine 19123
— du pignon 13320
— du tambour 6015
— du ventilateur 6802
— flexible 7368
— moteur 5961
— percé sur toute sa
  longueur 9249
— porte-fraise 4909
— porte-outil 7506
arc-boutant S. 10240
— de circonférence 4872
— de plissement 750
— électrique 6255
archéon 760
ardennite S. 5287, 763
ardoise 8940, 16574
arène granitique S. 8419
aréo-pyknomètre d'Eichorn
  6230
arête 6197
— anticlinale 4625
— de remblai S.12837,
  18038
— supérieure 19365
— synclinale 18942
argent 16350
— allemand 8195
— corné S. 3227
— d'Allemagne S. 8195
— de Chine S. 8195
— de départ 12951
— métallique 11572
— noir S. 2426
— sulfuré S. 774
argental 770, 8195
argentan 771
argenté 16356, 16362
argenter 16349, 16352,
  16355

argentifère 772
argentine 773
argentite 16353, 19573, 774
argentojarosite 775
argentopyrite 776
argenture 16357
argile 777
— (des polders) 11320
— à aveugler 2140
— à blocaux 8259, 2193
— à boue 5919
— à brique(s) 2369
— à mouler 12004
— à silex 7378
— au mur de la veine de charbon 3854
— blanche tendre 13928
— bleue 1902
— colloïdale 4028
— compacte 1317
— cuite S. 18432, 1113
— de frottement 8372
— désagrégée 18924
— ferme 8821
— ferrugineuse 3656
— feuillettée S. 783
— finement lavée 19694
— flint 7378
— gonflante 9025, 18124
— grasse 19242, 16803
— grise 8498
— inutilisable 19412
— maigre 8508, 10639
— marneuse 11337
— métamorphosée 4297
— plastique 16830, 13470
— pour revêtement 1153
— réfractaire 2188, 7182, 7158
— rosée 14553
— rouge 14532
— rubanée 1482
— savonneuse S. 7810
— schisteuse S. 1676, 783, 16577
— schisteuse et ferrugineuse 1864
— sédimentaire 15791
— smectique 7810
— verte 8514
argilisation 784
argillite 783, 15013
argon 787
argyrite S. 774
argyrodite 785
argyropyrite 786

argyrose 774
arite 788
arizonite 789
arkansite 790
arkose 762, 791, 792
arlequin 8877
armangite 795
armature à crochet 9316
— de fer 4417
— de la base de la cheminée 9972
— de renforcement du ciel 17408
— du ciel 17408
— du four 9973
— du noyau 4413, 4412
— en treillis soudé 19933
— longitudinale 10982
armure 18611
— en fer profilé 805
arrache-carotte 4400, 4410
arrache-carottes à coins 16665
— -coulisse 10126
— -étais 5593, 13711, 14010, 14012, 18147
— -tube 1460
arracher 2302
arrangement en couches 807
arrêt 3638
arrêt-barrage 6139, 15019
— -barrage de poussière 17644
— dans le fonctionnement 10040
— de la colonne pendant le tubage 8799
— de la marche du fourneau 17679
— du haut-fourneau 17688
— du soufflage 16246
— momentané 4981
arrière d'une pompe à boue 13784
arrivage des minerais 5153
arrivée d'air 292
arriver à la recette inférieure 10521
arrosage 10042, 17186, 17207, 17207
— du charbon 20004
arroser S. 17179, 17179
arrosseur rotatif 16978
arrossoir de mouleur 19803
arsenic 813
— natif 11567

arsénic pyriteux S. 829
arsénifère 819
arséniopléite 821
arséniosidérite 822
arsénio-sulfure de fer S. 829
arsénite 820
— de soude 16819
arséniobismite 824
arsénoclasite 825
arsénoferrite 826
arsénolamprite 827
arsénolite 828, 820
arsénopyrite 829
arsénosidérite 829
articles en métal 11546
articulation 10200
artinite 837
asbeste 516, 840
— en palladium 12879
asbolane 850
asbolite 850
ascension 14957
— capillaire 2810
ascenseur 10739
ascharite 857
aschister 858
ascoloy 860
asidérite 870
asmanite 871
aspasiolite 872
aspect de la cassure 718
— de la flamme 717
— de la scorie 719
— trouble 3786
asperger les lingotières 19983
aspérités S. 19293
asphalte de qualité inférieure 10520
— de Trinité 1638
— naturel 12181
asphaltique 881
asphaltite 885
aspiration immergée 7397
aspirateur 888
— de poussières 6131
aspirer 5755
— du haut-fourneau 5762
— l'air 17941
assemblage 10200
— à mi-bois 15604
— à tenon et à mortaise 10 10196
— en bout 10197
— par soudure 4222
assembler par vis 15699

assembleuse-démotteuse
  16781
asseoir le modèle 13866
assiette de lampe 10513
— en porcelaine poreuse
  13496
assimilation magmatique
  18167
assise S. 10594, 900
— de briques 4553
— de la chaudière 1975
— de la tuyère 19165
association de minerais
  lourds 894
— symplectique 18151
astate 902
astérisme 905
astien 906
astrakanite 909
astrolite 910
atacamite 915
ataxique 917
atélestite 918
atelier à dolomie 5615
— à noyaux 4425
— de chaudronnerie en fer
  1977
— de cisaillage 17729
— de construction mécani-
  que 11418
— d'ébarbage 3696
— d'étamage 18668
— de forge S. 7575
— de forgeron 7575
— de modelage 12992
— de moulage 12028
— de réparation 14731
— de sondage 19953
— des laminoirs à fils
  15057
— pour la fabrication des
  creusets 4751
atlasite 916
atmosphère 923
— contrôlée 4290
— de mine S. 290
— gazeuse 8069
atome 930
atomiseur 934
atopite 935
attacher 3616
attaque 936
— à fente 16671
— à joints en acier 18142
— à languette 19880
— à talon 16271
— acide profonde 5091
— annulaire 14924
— chimique 6572

attaque de câble à la cage
  d'extraction 2679
— de coulée 8089, 8093
— de coulée en grappe
  3793
— de coulée en évantail
  6804
— de coulée multiple 2257
— de front S. 2350, 5712
— de la corrosion uniforme
  937
— de réchauffage 17562
— de tubage 2941
— des tiges 1216
— dirigée 9778
— dirigée directe 16264
— dirigée latérale 16672
— du manche à la tête 15212
  15212
— du tuyau à la tête d'injection 9387
— en bavure 4227
— en cornichon 9360
— en pluie 4050, 13764,
  13056
— en remonte 19356
— macrographique 11145
— par collier-douche 13057
— par le mur 8374
— par le toit S. 8374
— pivotante 18130
— plate 7335
attaque v. abattage
attaquer à l'acide 6571
atterrissage de la cage 1200
attirail de chauffe 7195
attraction capillaire 2806
aturien 941
aube à turbines 19117
auerlite 942
auge 5711, 12885, 18935
— à eau 19819
— glaciaire 8260
augélite 943
augite 948
— syénite 949
augitique 950
augitophyre 951
augmentation v. accroissement
augmentation de chaleur
  9724
— de vitesse d'avancement
  5917
augmenter la production 9721
  9721
auréole de contact 3445
— de lampe de sûreté 1901
— kélyphitique 2070

aurichalcite 952
aurifère 953
austénite 956
austénitique 957
austénitisation 955
authigène 960
auto-centrant 15813
— -pneumatolyse 997
— -recuit 15814
— -trempant 15824
autocar 3101
autochtone 963
autoclave 965, 17441
— tubulaire 5405
autodécrassant 15829
autogène 966
autogrue 13207
automolite 994
automorphe 995, 6589
autonéomorphique 996
autorefroidissement S. 15816
autunite 998, 10817
auversien 999
auxiliaire 17334
aval-pendage 5698
avaleresse S. 16416
avaleur 15963
avance 6875
— automatique 980
avancée en profondeur
  19282
avancement 5210, 5936,
  6889, 5959
— à air comprimé 276
— d'eau marginale S. 6205
— de travers-bancs 4713
— du forage au mètre 7550
— par cycle de travail 7551
avancer 11230
avant broyage 13843
— -creuset 2054, 7565,
  10000, 14489
— -métré 1580
— -puits 5216, 3134, 7568
— -trou 12038
avec bavures 1221
aventurin 1005
aventurine 1005, 8854
aveugle 1766
avogadrite 1014
awaruite 1015
axe 1021
— à manivelle 4605
— anticlinal 15409
— de rotation 1024
— du cordon de soudure
  1022
— sénaire 9118
— synclinal 18937

axinite 1019
axiolite 1020
azéotrope 1029
azoïque 1031
azote 12319
azotomètre 1034
azurite 1036

B

babingtonite 1039
bac 9484
bac v. chaudière
— à boue 12091
— à cylindres 15086
— à étain S. 18665
— à fer blanc 18666
— à graisse S. 18225
— à piston S. 10177, 8762
— décapage 13230
— d'étalonnage S. 2743
— de lavage 15761
— décanteur 15926
— étalonné 2743
— régulateur 2520
bâche à eau 4345
— de refroidissement 4332
bacnure 17642
bacs autoportants 15832
baddeleyite 1092
bague 2625
— à cames 18295
— en caoutchouc pour bou-
chons de cimentation
— en cuir 10654
— entretoise 16956
— ovale 12723
— ronde 15275
baguette à noyau 4454
— de fer d'essai 18453
— de pompage 13932
— de zinc 20333
— en acier 17496
— en verre 8283
baillement 7969
bain 1338, 8972
bain acide 75
— d'air 240
— d'amalgamation 493
— d'argile S. 15977
— de dérochage 13217
— de fer 9957
— de fonte 13260
— d'huile 12480
— de métal 10595

bain de sable 15470
— de scories 16523
— de sel pour tempéra-
tures élevées 9155
— de trempe 8860. 14291
— de vapeur 17416
— -marie 19746
— métallique S. 10595
bainite 1110
balafré 15244
balai 20172
balance 1122, 8490
— à colonne 4040
— à gaz 7981
— à main 8782
— automatique 973
— automatique pour fines
1587
— d'essai 889
— de laboratoire 550
— de précision 13818
— de Roberval 4091
— hydrostatique 9573
— rapide 14298
balancelle 13060
balancer 12462
balancier 1929, 6918. 10764
14164
— à contrepoids S. 1123
— de pompage 14164
balayage 18116
— par l'eau
baldaufite 1142
ballage 1170
ballast 1169
balle 10192
— de scorie 16522
— en fer S. 1820
ballon 2873
— à fond plat 7327
— à fractionner 7688
— de lavage du brome
2453
— en verre 6544
— gradué 11398
— jaugé 19597
— pour la distillation 5553
— pour la fabrication du
chlore 3502
— rond 15273
banc 16045 , 20218
— à étirer 20122
— à étirer à pince 5799
— à étirer les bandes 7353
— à pousser 14196
— d'étirage 5779,5794
— de gravier 1194
— de manœuvre 20251

banc de moulage 12000
— de mouleur 11992
— de sable 9212
— de schiste 1189
— de tréfilerie 20124
— de tréfilerie à tambours
enrouleurs 5800
— supérieur 2796
bandage du cylindre broyeur
16704
bande 17741, 17844
— abrasive 9
— boueuse S. 5475
— collectrice 3342
— d'acier 17480, 17512
— d'acier des centralisa-
teurs à éléments longi-
tudinaux 17403
— d'acier électrique 6307
— de châssis de moulage
7311
— de magnésium 11182
— de raccordement 18608
— de transport inclinée
9695
— de triage 13214, 16927
— distributrice 5501
— galvanisée 7939
— large 20061
— transporteuse. 4314
— transporteuse (sans fin)
1474
— universelle 9388
bandelette 7340
bandes laminées à froid
3995
bandes noires 1667
banket S. 1198
bannière de trousse S. 17090
banquette 1497
barbe 2618, 14349, 16703
— intérieure 19616
barbotage 2494
barboteur à gaz S. 8052
barbotine 16713
barbure 2618
bardiglio 1224
bardolite 1225
barge de forage mobile S. 11846
11846
barge de stockage S. 5944
baril d'amalgamation S. 492
barkevicite 1235
barolithe 20048
barrage 4964, 10557, 15735
— contre les feux 7164
barranco 1238
barre de fer profilé 15773

barre 1205, 1207, 9782, 13238, 15049
— à ébranler 14421
— à piquer 18301
— à reboucher 12995
— à section ovale 7937
— à souder S. 16862
— cimentée 1782
— d'alimentation 15365
— d'ancrage 2211
— d'attelage 10365
— de battage 945
— de châssis 2223
— de contrôle 8116
— d'ébroulage 14421
— de fixage 9240
— de haveuse 4910
— de piquage 10401
— de pompage 17944
— de rotation 14889
— dégrossiecalibrée 13040
— double 10969
— en rouleaux 3922
— non travaillée 19345
— plate nervurée 14867
— pour actionner un dispositif dans le puits 18909
— pour fers à cheval 9382
— rectifiée 8609
— ronde 15269
barres d'acier écroûtées 19141
— d'acier poli 2402
— étirées 5815
barreau 1205, 9782
— attenant 3011
— coulé à part 15861
— d'épreuve 18442 , 18454
— d'essai S. 18454
— de grille 7147, 8467
— plat de métal 17850
— plat pour les essais 18455
barrière S. 8088, 1247
— de puits 15942
— roulante 16622
bartonien 1255
barylite 1257
barysilite 1258
barysphère 1259
baryte 1260
— carbonatée S. 20048
barytine 1233, 3106, 3127, 9031
barytocalcite 1262
barytocélestite 1263
baryum 1234
bas-foyer 3083, 1827, 18107, 18110

basalte 1267
— à néphéline 12229
— ellipsoïdal 6385
— en nappes 1689
basaltique 1268,
basanite 1271, 18795
bascule 15584
— à bonbonnes 2876
— à wagons 19620
— centésimale 3190
— décimale 5061
basculer 18670
basculeur automatique à charbon 978
basculeur courbe 19624
base S. 2142, 1273, 16336, 18701
— carrée S. 1275
— de pétrole 1282
— du chevalement de sondage 1275
basicité 1308
— proportionnelle 14022
bassanite 1319
basse 7316
— pression 11057
bassin 1309, 10322
— à boue 16718, 17992
— à décantation 15879
— à schlamms 16628
— d'alimentation 5720
— de coulée 1310, 1311, 6877, 11461, 11476, 13747
— de coulée à chicanes 13750
— de coulée à flotteur 13565
— de coulée à quenouille 17686
— de décantation 12085
— de refroidissement 4341 4345
— de surcreusement 15006
— décantateur 15925
— épurateur 3086
— structural 9896
bastite 1323, 15623
bastnaesite 1324
batée 1, 1327, 5513, 8348, 9357, 10586, 12885
batholithe 1339, 12033
bathroclase S. 16065, 2169, 4697, 7341, 9339
bâti 897
bâtiment d'extraction 8014
— de machine d'extraction 8220
— des accumulateurs 55

batiment des chaudières 1969 1969
bâtiment des machines 6468
batrachite 1343
battage de pieux 13285
— du fil 14723
— rapide 14299
batte 1920
battement 7283
batterie 1191, 1346
— de bocard 17309
— de chaudières 1349
— de fours 13726
— de fours à coke 1350
— pour installations de hydrogénation et synthèse 9562
battiture S. 7597, 8742
— de fer 15568
battitures des laminoirs 11692
battre 1402, 1818
— à froid S. 3958
— monnaie 17814
baumhauérite 1355
bauxite 1356
— blanche 20025
bavénite 1358
bavure 7290, 14349, 17109, 2618
bayldonite 1360
bazzite 1362
beaverite 1406
bec 10860
— à gaz 7985
— à gaz incandescent 9684
— amovible 9870
— d'âne 4679
— de canard 6072
— de cornue 4303
— de coulée 13761, 17170
— de décrassage 3575, 15729
— de déversement 7429
— d'étain 1376
— de la cornue S. 18577, 4302
— de passage du laitier S. 16539 16539
— de la poche de coulée 10480
— d'un convertisseur 12204
— d'un convertisseur Bessemer 12390
bécasse 3320
bêche 17105 , 16962
becher 1377
bêcher 16961
beckélite 1407

becquerelite 1411
beegérite 1438
beidellite 1442
bélemnite 1443
bellite 1464
bélonite 1471
bementite 1482
bénitoïte 1525
benjaminite 1526
benne 1359, 2818, 2497, 8219, 9472, 10334
— basculante 6098
— de chargement automatique 3829
— de creusement 16420
— -drague 983
— flottante 11004
— piocheuse 6635
— preneuse 3630
— traînante de pelle 5734
benthos 1529
bentonite 1530, 5180
benzol 1532
béquille 14008
béquilles 2432
beraunite 1533
berceau 15033, 4590
bérésite 1534
berkelium 1536
berline 2206, 2818, 3105, 4508, 9492, 10555, 11020, 18971
— à charbon 3852
— à décharge latérale S. 16260
— en acier 17516
berlinite 1537
berme 1538
berthiérite S. 8707, 1539
bertrandite 1541
berzélianite 1547
berzéliite 1548
beryl 1542
béryllium 1544
béryllonite 1546
besoin d'eau 534
béton 1566
— armé 6943, 14673
— coulé 8945
— damé 17315
béton d'asphalte à gros granulats 9181
beurtiat S. 1779, 17371, 19262, 20114
bézier S. 14395
bicarbonate de soude 16820
bichlorure de mercure 11502

bichromate de potasse 1575
bicône 10942
biebérite 1576
bielle 4220, 13423, 15049
— de suspension 1398
bien serré 18335
bifurcation 7603
bigorne 1375
bigorneau 8753
bigue 8223
bilan calorifique 8980
bilinite 1579
billage 1167, 8874
billette 1581
— carrée 17233
— méplate 14516
— pour forge 7592
billot S. 17614 , 14501
bimétallique 1589
bindheimite 1596
binnite 1607
biolite 1608
biotite 1609, 1656
bioxyde de sodium 13101
bisbeeite 1612
bischofite 1613
biseau de déviation 20018
biseauté 1572
bismite 1614
bismuth 1615
bismuthine 1616
bismuthosphérite 1620
bismuthoplagionite 1619
bismuthotantalite 1621
bisulfure de carbone 2825
bit 1622
bityte 1639
black-band 1643, 1644
blanc (éblouissant) S. 20031
blanc de marge 16273
— de zinc 20338
— soudant S. 19945
blanchir 13624
blastogranitique 1751
bleischweif 1760
blende 1761, 11850, 13031, 15189, 17053, 20341
— concrétionnée 2131
— obscure 1651
bleu de montagne 1036
— minéral S. 1036
— -violacé 4482
bleui 1914
bleuir 1894
bleuissage 1915
blindage 7849, 16087
— du creuset 8958
— du fourneau 7846

blindage en tôle 802
blinder 1765
bloc 1793, 6842, 9958
— à quille 10296
— d'empreinte 9667
— de grès 15531
— de laitier 16525
— mur en béton de laitier 5173
— erratique 6550, 5854
— fixe 7231
— mobile 12047
— octogonale 12452
blocage v. obstruction
— d'une table 18189
— des aiguilles 13609
— du trou de coulée 7745
bloedite S. 909, 1813
blomstrandine 1814
blondin 2667
bloom 1206, 13480, 15253
blooms carrés 1835
blutage 16312
bobéchon S. 17684
bobierrite 1931
bobinage 20099
bobine 3921, 17148
— enrouleuse 17149
— magnétique à emploi unique 18592
— magnétique durable 13105
bocage 15655
bocard 8495, 10756, 12654, 13735, 17312
— à eau 19999
— à pilon simple 16704
bocardage 17313
— à l'eau 20000
— à sec 6047
bocarder 4761, 17257, 17306
bocca 1933
bobenbenderite 1935
boghead 1952
bois 20170
— de garnissage 903, 1085, 10195, 10458, 10490, 17899
— de mine 17541 , 14027
— opalisé 20176
— pétrifié 20185
— sain 16940
boisage 2022,6497, 18637
— à cadres espacés 2228
— armé 14675
— complet 7807
— contrefiché 2231
— de puits en cadres 4634

boisage du niveau de fond
   16341
— du puits 15958, 16040
— du puits à cadres jointfs
   4861
— du toit 1079, 1252,
   10963, 17247, 18752
— en acier 17510
— en acier (pour mines)
   10002
— en porte 7915
— étayé 17907
— horizontal 9344
— jointif 3765
— parallélépipédique 17243
— par cadres jointifs S.
   2228
— vertical 19527
boisé par cadres jointifs
   4632
boiser 1042, 16167
boiseur 10151, 18635
boisseau principal 11362
boîte 2207, 2910
— à carottes 4466, 15455
— à échantillons 15457
— à étincelles S. 3461
— à huile 1027
— à l'épreuve des acides
   87
— à mousse 11945
— à noyaux 4396
— à noyaux à charnière
   9205
— à noyaux à pot de fleur
   9022
— à noyaux-cadre 17130
— à noyaux en douves S.
   16576
— à noyaux multiples 12109
— à ressort pour tampon
   2521
— à slimes 16635
— à souffler 4397
— à tourillon S. 1389
— à vent 242, 1699, 20089,
   20092
— à vent basse 20090
— à vent haute 20091
— -caisson 7712
— de charge 19904
— de distribution 14658, 1742
   17420
— d'essieu 1027
— de la vanne 19448

boîte de pied avec manchon
   1277
— de retrait 16234
— de sluice S. 16709
— en auge 18943
— en verre 8272
bol 2002
— d'Arménie S. 12448
bolivarite 2003
bolivianite 2004
bombe calorimétrique 2756
bombement 2770, 18121,
   19677, 1470
— d'un filon 1853
bomber 5510, 18120
bon mur 8357
— remblai 8359
— toit 8360
bonbonne 2873
bondérisation 2020
bone-bed 2026
bonne soudure 8358
bonsdorffite 2037
boort S. 2047
boothite 2056
boracite 2060
borate de soude 2061
borax 2061, 18656
bord 6198, 16168
— blanc 20030
— de la poche 14916
— de laminage 15095
— du tube de fumée 1368
— ou seuil du trou de travail 20218
— tourné 19142
border 2068
bordure périphérique 3596
borgströmite 2093
borne 18426
— d'élément S. 18427
bornes et bouteroues tubulaires à tête arrondie 19076
— et bouteroues tubulaires
   à tête arrondie forgée à
   chaud 19074
bornite 2115, 6553, 13009,
   14194, 19471
boronatrocalcite 12184
bort 2047, 2118, 2831,
   2847
bossage de centrage d'usinage 3215
bosse 5178
botryogène 2129

bouchage 2135
— au sable S. 15508
bouche de cheminée 3566
— d'incendie à colonne tubulaire 7171
bouché 3751
boucher 3749, 4976, 13557
— le trou de coulée 13558
— les soufflures 7014
bouchon 4467, 1934, 13556
— à haute pression 2553
— de coulée 2133
— de levage 10774
— de vidange 12704
— de remplissage 7024
— du carottier 4433
— en caoutchouc 15314
— ou tampon d'argile ré-
   fractaire 7162
boucle 10995
bouclier 2344
boue 12069, 16627, 16695,
   16715
— à base d'argile 3655
— à diatomées 5344
— à l'émulsion 6429
— à faible teneur en soli-
   des 11061
— active 117
— aérée 187
— anodique 629
— contaminée de ciment
   3147
— de charbon 3856
— de forage 5891
— électrolytique 6349
— gazéfiée 8027
— glaciaire 8253
— schlammeuse 16629
— volcanique 19592
boues acides 94
— aux surfactants S. 18072
— tensio-actives 18072
boueux 16698
bouffoir 1861
bouillie 2067
— bourguignonne 2589
bouillonnement S. 1998, 8600
   8600
— violent 17877
bouillonner 6216
boule de fer 9956
boulet d'anthracite 6220
boulon à chapeau 2804
— à clavette 4522

boulon à ergot 16794
— à goupille 4522
— à oeillet 6729
— à tête 2804
— à tête bombée 4836
— à tête carrée 17236
— à tête conique 4198
— à tête hexagonale 9120
— à tête ronde 15283
— à vis pour fixer les
    éclisses 7211
— avec tête usinée 2013
— d'ancrage 558
— d'assemblage 4221
— d'éclisse 7211
— d'entretoisement 17404
— de fermeture 3783
— de fondation 9314
— de scellement 14350
— écrou 2009
— fileté 15783
— noyé 4539
boulonnage 15718
bouniou S. 17991
bourbe S. 16695
bournonite 2196, 20008
bourrage 2072, 12845,
    17538, 18234
— d'un trou de mine 2568
bourré 14611
bourrelet du tube de fumée S
    1368
bourrer 14389, 18228,
    18230, 17352
— un coup de mine 17535
bourroir 1404, 2569, 14401,
    17357, 18232, 18235
boursoufflé 14154
boursouflement 9019
— de masselotte 14959
— du sol 4622
boussement 17113
boussingaultite 2197
boussole S. 3585
— de minière 5313
— de mineur 11727
bout 6449, 18672
— de tuyau 13658
boute-feu 16163 , 16202
boutefeu 1736, 3329, 5885,
    9252, 11734
bouteille 1172, 4936, 19541
— en guttapercha 8681
— pour gaz comprimés 4937
— pour gaz dissous 4938
— pour gaz liquides 4939

bouterolle 16783
bouterolles 8926
bouteroue tubulaire 19085
boutoir élastique S. 17192
bouton d'essai 890
— de manivelle 4608
— de mise à la masse 17381
    17381
— -démarreur 17381
bowénite 2201
bowette 4666, 4678, 18532,
    19796
bowlingite S. 9615
bowmanite 2204
boyau 2340
branchyanticlinal 2233
brachydôme 2234
brechypinacoïde 2235
bradygénèse 2250
bragite 2251
brai 3851, 13411
braise 16728
braise(tte) S. 3932
brame 1820, 7322, 16494,
    16495, 16499
brancard 2199
branche 16267
branchement en dérivation
    2650
brandsite 2263
brannerite 2264
bras du convoyeur 4321
brasage 2292
— à immersion 5434
— au chalumeau 18768
— au four 7828
brasement 2292
braser 2288
brasquage 14693
brasque 2265, 10850
brassage 3925
— d'un bain 14315
— électromagnétique
    6356
brasse 6828
brasser 14094
— un bain 17605
brasure 2290, 8840
braunite 14085
brazilite 2291
brèche 2353, 3649
— de dislocation S.4766,
    6844, 7766, 16012, 15025
— de faille 6844
— de friction 4766, 6844,
    7766, 15402, 16012

brèche glaciaire 5855
— minéralisée 5735
bréchiforme 2354
breislakite 2359
breithauptite 2360
breunnérite 2363
brevicite 2364
brewstérite 2365
bridage à «boll weevil» 2006
bride 17743 , 8269
— à joint circulaire 14927
— d'ancrage 17150
— de boîte à presse-etoupe
    8269
— de départ 10527
— de fond 2156
— d'orifice 12669
— de serrage 3619
— de serrage (pour mise à
    terre) 8610
— de sûreté 15414
— fausse 1682
— mobile 11003
— pleine 1773
— pour essais 18464
brillance d'une surface 2404
brin collecteur 3342
— distributeur S. 5501
— mort 5032
brindilles 20172
brique 2367
— acide 16313
— alumineuse 467
— -barrage 16463
— basique 1294
— crue 176
— de carbone 2828
— de chamotte 3278
— de cuve 15935
— de dolomie 5609
— de laitier 16528
— de magnésite 11175
— de terre 10925
— Dinas 5428
— du creuset S. 1276
— réfractaire 467, 14627
— séchée à l'air S. 176, 266
    266
— siliceuse S. 16313
— -siphon 18174
— sur champ 2374
briques concassées 2439
— d'étalages 2123
briqueterie 2371, 2415, 6226
briquette v. aggloméré
— désulfurante 5248

briquette de minerai 12634
— de minerais de cuivre
grillés S. 1898
— de pyrite grillée 1898
— frittée 16432
— séchée 5846
brise-manchon 4018
briser 2302
— en pièces 16011
britholite 2419
brochantite 2436
broche 13305, 17088, 17092,
2429
— de remmoulage 12049
— fixe 9253
bromargyrite 2450
brome 2452
bromite 2450
bromyrite S. 2450
bronzage 2461
bronze 2455, 14351, 18646
— à canon 8673
— à cloches 1456
— -acier 17462
— alpha 418
— au manganèse 11268
— au nickel 12271
— au plomb 10610, 12430
— blanc 12272
— d'aluminium 450
— d'art S. 17401
— des monnaies 11543
— manganeux 11268
— phosphoreux 13172
— pour miroirs 17043
— siliceux 16326
— spécial 17006
— statuaire 17401
bronzeur 2460
bronzite 2464
brookite 2466
brosse à main en fils
d'acier 3024
— à tubes 18976
— de nettoyage à main
8756
— en chanvre 9087
— en fil de fer à bride
20118
— pour fontes brutes 3043
broutage d'un outil 10135
brouette à deux roues 4991
— de chargement 16481
broyage 2325, 4775, 4776,
8542, 8546, 11706, 16481
— à l'eau 19988

broyage à sec 6029, 6047
— de minerai 15321
— du charbon 3830
— étagé 17286
— fin 367, 7085, 16637
— grossier 3870, 3875
— primaire 13829
— secondaire 14514
broyer 3645, 8538, 18922
— à la main 16964
— et trier 3883
— finement
broyeur 8556, 8557, 10336,
11685
— à barres 1218
— à barreaux 15055
— à boulets 1104, 1158
— à boulets tubulaires
1168
— à cloche 1450
— à cônes 4197
— à cuve fixe 7237
— à cuve tournante 15230
— à cylindres 3357, 15076,
15122
— à galets 13033
— à mâchoires S. 17641
— à marteaux 8729, 8738
— à meules 4778
— à moules transportable
13694
— à plateau 5523
— à plateau tournant S. 15230
15230
— centrifuge 5520
— de charbon à dispositif
d'échantillonnage 3809
— des fines 7077
— primaire 13828
— secondaire 14513
— tubulaire 19077
— v. concasseur
brûler 2595, 7287
brûleur 2600, 12408
brûleur v. torche
— à benzine 1531
— à embouchure oblongue
10974
— à fente S. 10974
— à gaz S. 7984
— à huile lourde 12492
— à orifice circulaire
3601
— à vent 1887
— Bunsen 2582

brûleur circulaire à jet
en éventail 6806
— de Bunsen à l'acétylène
63
— pour soufflerie 1700
brûlure 2603, 2604
brun 2470
— avec taches 2478
bruni 13626
brünir 2610
brunissage 1915
— au gallet 2462
brushite 2484
brut 1680, 19327
— adouci 18117
— de chaud 9453
— de coulée 15246
— de fonderie 838
— de laminage 839, 15252
— de pétrole commercial
13356
bucklandite 2507
bulle d'air 249
— de gaz 2486
bunsénite 2583
bure 1779, 10094, 10896,
12042, 17371, 17374,
19262, 19849
— d'un haut fourneau 12044
bureaux 12460
burette 2587, 18456
— à gaz 7984
burin 3485, 4918
— à air comprimé 13582
— à quatre ailettes 7683
— de carrier 1927
— excentrique pour terrains
tendres 19247
— pneumatique 253
buriner 3843
buse 2630, 12414
— à jet de sable 15474,
15483
— d'aérage 257
— de l'économiseur 6192
— d'injection 9819
busette de coulée 12407
— de sablage 15474
— de soufflet 12409
bustamite 2629
buszite 2631
but du triage 12431
butane 2632
butée 5592
— d'ancrage inférieur 2161

butlerite 2633
butoir élastique 6244
butane 2632
butte 12030, 14014, 14175,
  17540, 17658, 17906,
  S. 19533
— témoin 2644
buttgenbachite 2646

C

cabestan 2814, 3093, 3094
— de manœuvre 16238
— de triage S. 16238
cabine à manches 15480
— de grenaillage 16197
— de sablage 15481
câble à conducteur unique
  16386
— à secousses 10149
— à section décroissante
  18283
— à torons 7936
— à torons ronds 15293
— aérien 192
— armé 804
— d'alimentation à haute
  tension 9189
— de cabestan 3079, 3098
— de carottage électrique
  10965
— de curage 15501
— d'enroulement 6823
— d'équilibre 1134
— d'extraction 9231, 20100,
  20100, 20105
— de forage 5905
— de mine 11771
— de piston 18092
— de renvoi 18212
— de signalisation 1453
— de sondage 2558
— de tubage 2950
— diminué S. 18283
— et cage d'extraction
  2038
— flottant 12755
— métallique 17505, 20144
— métallique à torons
  méplats 7350
— métallique tordu spi-
  roïdal 14652
— plat 7343

câble pour les tiges de
  pompage 17939
— préformé 13835
— tête 11225
— traînant 18813
câbles et conducteurs isolés
  9849
cabrérite 2668
cacheter 15733
cacoxénite 2669
cadmiage 2675, 2677
cadmié 2674
cadmie 2670
cadmier 2672
cadmies 20327
— fines 20328
cadmifère 2671
cadmium 2673
cadmiumage 2677
cadre S. 2208
cadre 5864, 7709, 15904,
  15912
— à un seul montant
  9716, 13708
— base de cheminée 3567
— complet 7678, 7806
— complexe 759, 14346
— d'acier 17507
— de boisage 16423
— de démoulage 4391
— de galerie 6122
— de presse à centrer les
  châssis 3216
— de presse de précision S.
  3216
— de puits 16107
— de scie 15559
— du puits 4630, 4635,
  15938, 18879
— en fer forgé 20241
— incomplet 7919, 19192
— porteur 1386, 1391, 4629,
  4629, 4860, 18036
— provisoire 6786
— refroidi 19788
— supérieur 7034
— tubulaire 19073
caffut 10636, 15660, 15679
cage 6379, 9466
— à chapeau rapporté 12600
— à cylindres 17331
— à cylindres équilibrés
  1137
— à déchargement automatique 15819
— à deux cylindres 9464

cage à pignons 17091
— à trio 18557
— d'ascenseur 10750
— de blooming 1831
— d'extraction 2680, 5795
— d'extraction à deux étages
  étages 8219
— de filetage 17199
— de laminoir 9465, 15089,
  17335
— de laminoir dégrossisseur
  15262
— de laminoir trio 18559
— de mine 13400
— de noyau à charnière
  2041
— dégrossisseuse 19188
— du noyau S. 4412
— en fil 20119
— fermée ordinaire 12624
— finisseuse des bords
  6211
cahnite 2686
caillebotis galvanisés 7938
cailler 2690
caillou 7377, 8477, 16151
— à facettes 20096
— roulé S. 13034, 15324
caillouteux 7380
cailloutis 4769
caisse 1936, 2208, 2910
— à air tubulaire 19058
— à feu 7152
— à poids 19916
— à poussières 6127
— allemande 17234
— de bocard 17310
— de cémentation 2919,
  3171
— de la balance 1125
— de pilonnage S. 17325
— de recuit 609
— du bocard 13736
— du jig 10174
— en matière réfractaire
  7159
— pointue 17107
caisson allemand 16632
— d'aérage 246
caissons métalliques pour
  hétomages 11552
calage 1807, 7743
calage S. 17582
calaïte 10278
calamination 12803
calamine 2699, 6026, 15583

calamine de four 7853
— de recuit 11700
— résiduelle 14756
calandrage 10507
calandre à cylindres
  rechauffé 15111
calavérite 2700
calcaire 2528, 10819, 18127
— à crinoïdes 4638, 6444,
  6446
— bitumineux 883
— carbonifère 2860
— décomposé 6791
— fétide S. 18127, 17604
— nummulitique 12426
— oolithique S. 6225
— saccharoïde 8434
calcareux 14876
calcédoine 2709, 3253
calcédonite S. 2709
calcimètre 2711
calcination 2604, 15388
calciner 2712
calcite 2702 , 2718
— et fluorine dans la
  salbande 2765
calcium 2721
— -larsénite 2726
calcographie 3256
calcul de l'analyse 2735
— des charges 2733
— du laitier 2734
— du lit de fusion 2736
— du vent 2732
calculer la puissance calorifique d'après l'analyse
  2731
caldeira 2737
cale 8907, 8212, 19878
— à charbon 3834
— de bois 10728, 17909
— de sécurité 15426
calédonite 2739
caler 1792
calibrage 2742
— des cylindres 5231
calibre 7896, 8107, 8111,
  12973, 18400
— à mâchoire 2746
— à mâchoires 16782
— à refouler 19379
— de cylindre de laminoir
  15074
— d'épaisseur 18509
— de laminoir 15084
— de perçage 14183

calibre de référence 14591
— de travail 20209
— entre 10107
— -mâchoire S. 2746
— passe-tube 5851
— pour manchon 9843
— rond 15288
calibrer 17803
caliche 2744
Callovien 2749
calmage 10352
Calomel 2751
calorie 2752
calorifère 14674
calorimètre 2755
calorimétrie 2758
calorisation 2759
calorisé 2761
caloriser 2760
calotte 1468, 2035, 2793
— du convertisseur 4299
calque 18809
cambrage 2769
cambrer 5510
cambrien 2771
cambrure 2770, 5517
came 2764, 18294
camion 11020, 19457
— à explosifs 16943
— citerne 18256
— enregistreur 14507
— porte-outil 18724
campagne de bocard 11698
— de fourneau 7830
— d'un four 10734
camptonite 2772
campylite 2773
camsellite 2774
canal 3284, 16708, 19440
— à ébarbures 8687
— à sluices 8621
— annulaire 3589
— d'aérage S. 19504
— d'alimentation 15363
— d'aspiration 7817
— de coulée 15366
— de coulée directe 5985
— de détente 16480, 16561
— d'écoulement 7433
— de fumée 3459
— de la sole 2158
— de pompage 19511
— de retour 3604
— vertical de coulée 5706
canalisation 3294, 14319
— à pétrole 13355

canalisation aérienne 191
— à parallèle 10999
— souterraine 19258
canard d'aérage 6809
canaux pour recueillir le
  plomb 3293
canbyte 2776
cancrinite 2779
canevas de Wulff 20255
canfieldite 2785
caniveau 2777
caniveau de drainage 3088
canne de sondage 2105
cannel-coal 2782, 14445
canneler 8585
cannelure 8586
— à ébarbures 1059
— à vide 6785
— carrée 17240
— d'étirage 17712
— ébaucheuse S. 15999
— emboîtée S. 3774
— fermée 3774
— finisseuse 7128, 10559
— intermédiaire 11663
— interrompue 18291
— ogive 17115
— ouverte 12587
— ovale 12725
— pour fers carrés 2224
— quadrangulaire 5237
— refouleuse 19376
cannelures à bossages 13096
  13096
— à rails 14361
— à traverses 16587
— de blooming 1822
— pour clous 12162
— pour éclissés 7212
— pour plaques 3250
— pour poutrelles 8242
— profilées 16000
cannizzarite 2788
canon à boucher le trou de
  coulée 6668, 12399
— carottier 15458
— perforateur 8669, 8674
caoutchouc 15304
cap 1374, 4889
capacité 2800, 4822
— d'amortissement 4982
— de charge 10910
— d'emboutissage profond
  5787
— de joint 10209
— de polarisation 13616

capacité de production 13999
13999
— de production par jour
16444
— de résistance de la cuve
14766
— de stockage du derrick
14325
— du fourneau 2801
cape de gaz 7986
capillarity 2805
caporcianite 2811
cappelénite 2812
capsule 1745
— à évaporation 6614
— à filtrer 7063
— d'amiante 842
— de pesée en aluminium
463
— en platine 13515
— en platine pour inciné-
rations 13520
— en plomb 10607
— pour bain de sable 5514
captage de l'eau 13986
— d'eau souterraine 13987
capter 2791
capteur de cendres 3573
capuchon 4607
— de flacon 2136
caracole 4722, S. 7218,
19643
— à trépan 1626
caracolite 2819
caractère du minerai 3297
caractéristiques de pro-
ductivité 9767
— mécaniques 11409
— physiques 13193
Caradocien 2820
carbone 2824
— amorphe 531
— combiné 4064, 7230
— de cémentation 2821
— équivalent 2834
— graphitique 8453
— total 18787
carbonate d'ammoniaque 2848
2848
— de baryum 2849
— de chaux 2851
— de fer 2850
— de magnésie 2852
— de manganèse 11274
— de potasse 2853
— de soude 2854

carbonifère 2858, 2859
carbonisation 2604, 3353
carboniser 2869
carbonite 2865
carbonitruration 2866
carborundum 2872, 16328
carburant à nombre d'octane
élevé 9160
— de réserve 14744
— de synthèse 18169
carburation 2867, 2879,
2883, 2885
— à paquets 12830
— par le carbone solide
2880
carbure de fer 9961
carburer 2884
carcasse 2884, 2930, 7710
cargaison complète 7795
— supplémentaire 18025
carillon S. 17032
carnaline 2895
carnallite 2893
carneau 1962, 2357, 3284,
7449, 13684
— à fumées 16762
— à gaz vertical 19382
— collecteur 4024
— de chauff(ag)e 9012
— de dérivation 10570
— de la cheminée 11221
— de retour 14812
— du four 7836
— latéral 16263
— montant de gaz chauds
19383
— transversal 4687
carnegiéite 2894
carnet 4694
— d'aérage S. 4694
carnotite 2896
carottage 4395, 4464
— à la demande 17156
— à la grenaille 16201
— au diamant 5321
— de courts intervalles S.
17156
— du mur 15462
— électrique 6267, 6319,
9753
— latéral 16282
carotte 4386, 4438, 13555
— de sondage 5890
— exudante 1759
— latérale 16281
— orientée 12672

carotte suintante 19891
carotter 4382
carottier à chemise 15313
— de parois «rotary» 15225
— double 5650
— latéral 16278
— retirable 20131
— rétractile S. 20131
carquaise 615
carreau 18060
carrée d'entrainement 10305
carrés S. 17232
carrière 13397, 14258, 17852
— à ciel ouvert 12589, 18062
18062
— de gravier 8479
— de marbre 13398
carrousel 4264, 12013
carte 4542
carte d'isobathes 4543
carter de moteur-générateur
11952
cartes isopaques 10072
carton d'asbeste 846
— guttapercha 8682
— indicateur du poids
19900
cartouche-amorce 13949
— de bourrage 17539
caryinite 10286
cassage 2321
— des gueuses 4779
cassant 2420, 11995
— à chaud 9439, 14535,
14547
— à froid 3965, 4000
casse-coke S. 3931
— -fonte 3076, 5975, 13254
— -gueuse 11089, 12108, 13253
13253
— -gueuses sur roues 13695
— -pierres S. 17641
casser 2295
— en morceaux 2328
casserole 1312
casseur à gueuses hydraulique 9531
— de gueuses fixe 17273
cassin S. 7559, 8955
cassitérite 18649, 18669
casque 7270
— de soudeur en une pièce
14979
— pour sableur 9069
cassure 7693, 2307, 2333
— à chaud 9408

cassure à coupe 4835
— à froid 3972
— à grain fin 7081
— à gros grain 3873
— au bleu 1900
— céroïde S. 17122
— conchoïdale 7381
— conchoïde 4172
— crochue S. 8700
— de fatigue 6831
— de tiges 19180
— ductile 7699
— écailleuse 17122
— en sifflet 12434
— esquilleuse S. 17122
— fibreuse 6987
— grenue 8432
— hachée 8700
— inégale 19201
— intragranulaire 9882, 9920 9920
— lamellaire 10506
— nette 16772
— raboteuse S. 6623
— terreuse 6172
— unie 6623
cassure v. fracture
castanite 3031
castine 3265, 10814, 10819
castor 3077
cataclastique 3081
catapléite 3085
catégorie 8383
cathétomètre 3096
cathkinite 3097
catoptrique 10292
catoptrite 3104
caustobiolite 3118
cave 3133 , S. 19697
— aux cendres 861
caverne karstique 17175
cavité 3124, 13329, 13605, 16952
— à fond perméable 16795
— de dissolution 16901
— de druse 2525
— de retrait 16227
— miarolitique 11618
cabollite 3129
ceinture 17781, 18960
— de sûreté 15413
— en fer plat 9323
— intermédiaire 11664
— morainique 11929
— porte-vent S. 5515
célestine 3131

cellulaire 3135
cellule de cokéfaction 3952
— de flottaison 7416
celsian 3136
cément 3141
— de cuivre S. 15990
cémentation 2867, 2885, 2917, 3158, 3161, 3169
— au prussiate de potasse 13722
— au prussiate jaune 13722
— de l'acier 17479
— en châssis 2220
— en pots 2209
— gazeuse 7988
— per pression 17259
— par refroidissement dans l'huile 12831
cémenté 3164, 6744
— à la surface 2915
cémenter 2909, 6737, 9832
— à la poudre 13766
— au gaz 7989
cémentite sphéroïdale 17071
cendre volante 7505
cendres de pyrites 2715
cendrier 868, 867
— maçonné S. 2376
cénosite S. 10268, 2687, 3182
cénozoïque 2688
centrage 3188, 11371
— des moules 5370
centrale de distribution 5571
— d'éclairage 10798
— de force motrice 13795
— de malaxage de boue 12084 12084
— de pompage 14168
centralisateur à éléments longitudinaux 17706
— de pression 10564
centrallasite 3194
centré 11370
centre de collecte S. 18246
— en acier fondu 3023
centreur 2934
centreuse 3217
centrifugation 3211
— pure 18951
centrifuger 2966, 3212
céphalopodes 3223
cérargyre S. 9363
cérargyrite 3227, 3493, 9363

cerce 15801
cercle S. 4016, 9321
— en fer forgé 20244
cérésine 3228
cérium 3229
certificat d'analyse 549
— d'essai 1844
céruse 20036
cérusite 3231, 20037
cervantite 3232
césarolite 3233
césium 2678
cesser le chargement 3128
cevelline 9739
ceylanite 3234, S. 10018, S. 13544
chabasie 3235
chaîne 3238
— à clavette 4523
— à godets 2498, 4319, S. 6378, 15640
— à raclettes 15668
— d'arpenteur 11396
— d'entraînement 17210
— de production 13996
— de vissage 17095
— sans fin 4621, 6457
chaînon entraîneur 3090
chaise 3520
— pendante 8802
chaland 14966
chalcanthite 3252, 4367
chalcocite 4366
chalcodite 3255
chalcolamprite 3258
chalcoménite 3259
chalcophanite 3260
chalcophyllite 3257
chalcopyrite 3261, 4363, 20 20284, 20291
chalcosine 3262, 14558, 19571 19571, 3254
chalcostibine 3263
chalcotrichite 3264
chaleur 8971
— accumulée 53
— critique 4644
— de combinaison 8985
— de dissociation 8987
— de fusion 11480
— de la fonte et du laitier 8981
— de réaction 8989
— des gaz du gueulard 19731 19731
— d'incandescence 14540.

chaleur d'ionisation 8988
— dispersée 19687
— incandescente S. 20031
— latente 10567
— soudante 19945
— spécifique 17026
— suante S. 19945
chaleur v. chaud
chalumeau 1863, 1893
— à bouche 12043
— à oxygène comprimé 4139
— coupeur 4915
— électrique 6261
— oxhydrique 12814
— pour découpage à l'oxygène 12819
— soudeur 19956
chambre 1919, 2063, 2342
— à air 250
— à air de la conduite d'aspiration 17951
— à étincelles 16981
— à poussières 6128
— à recuire 611
— de cémentation 6488
— de chauffe 9009, 17633
— de cimentation 19713
— de combustion 4076
— de dessablage 15523
— d'eau 19810
— de filtration 17738
— d'hydrogène sulfuré 17986
— de la pompe à schlamms 251
— de lavage 19709
— de mine 1741
— de précombustion 19544
— de récombustion 14668
— de récupération S. 14648
— de refroidissement 4333
— de régénération 3367, 3372, 3378, 3405
— de séparation 10404
— de vaporisation 7293
— d'injection 9813
— d'une pompe
— du puits 19962
— -écluse 11080
— latérale 16257
— -magasin 16223, 16232
chambrière 1089, 5282, 5592
chamoisite 3276
chamotte 2597, 3277, 15798

champ d'exploitation 20207
— de gaz 8005
— de la lunette 6999
— de pétrole 12489
— de vision 19569
— du spectre rouge jaunâtre 20294
— gazeux S. 8005
— magnétique 11192
champignon 3109, 14358
chandelle S. 17540
— à enlever les modèles 10772
— de démoulage S. 10772
chanfrein 1567
— de rupture 2323
chanfreiné 1572
changement de pendage 1482 14821
— de profil 15720
— normal 17347
— simple 16972
chantier 5147, 20198
— à ciel 12594
— à front normal aux limets 6742
— avec boisage parallélépipédique 17245
— barré 15738
— chassant 5865
— d'abattage 17666
— d'aérage 9854
— d'avancement 8937
— d'avancement frontal 2349
— de coulée 3040
— d'extraction 20216
— de moulage 11999
— du niveau de fond 16340
— en cul-de-sac 5043
— en gradins 17666
— en montant 2065
— montant 2065
— pétrolifère 12518
— suivant clivage 16724
chantiers du fond 2190
chape 9891
chapeau 2031, 2034, 2795, 2799, 4727, 4733, 4735, 5856, 8018, 14709, 17838, 18743 10458
— boulonné 15746
— de châssis 4348
— de fer 4033, 8370, 12807, 14309

chapeau en caoutchouc 15307
— provisoire 6781
— sur murs de remblai 19646
chapelle 19163
chapiteau 9308
— d'entretoisement supérieur 4692
chapmanite 3296
charbon à cendres légères 3843
— à chaudières 1956
— à coke 3953
— à courte flamme 17421
— à électrodes 6326
— à filtrer 7056
— à longue flamme 2786
— à lumière 10794
— à polir 8551
— à souder 16861
— activé 115
— aggloméré 224
— anthraciteux S. 8822
— artificiel 832
— barré 1183, 2028, S. 16777
— bitumineux 1634
— bitumineux dur 17118
— boghead écossais 15649
— brillant 2392
— brut 14452, 15248
— calibré 16445
— Cardiff 2888
— cokéfiable S. 7991
— collant 1119, 2696
— comprimé 13876 ,
— criblé 16590
— cuit 1114
— d'arc 749
— d'arc flambant 7254
— de bois 3298
— de bois de conifères 13314
— de bois en morceaux 3309 3309
— de bois en poudre 3303
— de bois feuillu 8520
— de bois noir 4092
— de bouleau 1611
— de bouleau pulvérisé 13769
— de corne 9359
— de cornue 14796
— de cuir 10649

charbon de forge 7576, 16754
16754
— de générateur 3824
— de hêtre 1437
— de la meilleure qualité
1563
— de la partie inférieure de
la couche 8612
— de lampe à arc 749
— de ménage 9459
— de première qualité
7196
— de retorte S. 14796
— de tourbe 13026
— décolorant 5079
— demi-gras mi lavé 8718
— d'importation 9660
— domestique 5621, 9459
— d'os 2027
— dur 1322
— électrique 6265
— en gaillette(s) S. 3884
— en grélat 3884, 6221
— en morceaux 3747
— en piliers 13291
— en poudre 13770
— en roche 10546
— extrait 11752
— fibreux 1922
— fin 2214, 2590, 16307
— flambant 2781, 7265, 12564
12564
— fossile 7630
— frais 8509
— gras 1634
— gros 4997, 10546
— homogène 16877
— lavé 19695
— luisant 8268, 13008
— maigre 6028, 8818, 10640
— mat 6086, S. 17116
— menu 12288, 16727
— menu de rebut 6006
— minéral 7630
— minéralisé 11760
— mou 1634
— négatif 12213
— non assorti 19330
— non collant 12341
— non lavé 19343
— non scorifère 12345
— normal 17344
— passé à la claie S. 15690
— pauvre 6847, 13653
— pauvre en gaz 12350
— polaire S. 6326

charbon positif 13704
— pour fours métallurgiques
7831
— pour moteur(s) à gaz
8026
— pour projecteurs 15754
— poussiéreux S. 4827,
5838
— préparé 5838
— pulvérisé 14147
— pur 3675
— pyriteux 2281, 3078,
6010, 8578
— qui éclate à cause des
gaz contenus 2577
— riche en cendres 862
— sans fumée 16768
— schisteux 1318, 2025,
2040
— sec 1768, S. 10640
— séché à l'air 267
— subbitumineux 1655
— tamisé S. 15690
— tendre de qualité infé-
rieure 4996
— terreux S. 2028, 2284,
6173, 14430, 16777,
— tout venant 437, 4754,
18584, 19333
— transporté par mer 19811
— très scorifère 3728
— trié 15690
— trituré 16115
— uniforme 3841
— végétal 9298
— vierge 3837, 8509, 20050
charbon v. houille
charbonnage 3839
charbonnaille S.16727
charbonnier 17422
charbonnier S. 3822
charbons d'arc 2871
— imprégnés 9661
— métallisés 11576
charge 1395, 2586, 3315,
6883, 11478, 13706,
13981, 17615
— à la limite convention-
nelle d'élasticité à
0,2% 10907
— alternée 433
— appliquée 720
— chaude 9406
— creuse 10156, 15991
— creuse accouplée 19172
— de coke 428

charge de combustible 3324
— d'eau 8906
— d'essai 18447
— de fonte 3326
— de mine 1747
— de minerai et du fondant
3325
— de pétardement S. 1747
— du couloir 9694
— du creuset 4739
— du moule 19914
— d'un four 7861
— effervescente 20070
— faible S. 3326
— froide 3969
— latérale 5628
— liquide 9406
— maximale 11386
— métallique 4843
— spéciale 17009
— ultime 120
— unitaire 19309
— utile 2904
chargement 3331, 10916,
12065, 17637
— automatique 976
— des minerais 3351
— par câble aérien 193
— par le haut 18739
— serré 5171
chargement v. alimentation
charger 3313, 9832, 10465
— à la main 17631
— automatiquement 17632
— les boîtes S. 3314
— les caisses 3314
— les chaudières 17630
— un moule 19909
— une berline 12057
chargeur 3330, 3350, 3798,
14206
— à alimentation par en-
dessus 12741
— à bascule 18681
— à pelletage automati-
que 16216
— automatique 17635
— de bennes 10335
— de berlines 19623
— de charbon 3822
— de minerai 3321
— descendant 11075
chargeuse à godets 2503
— -convoyeur 10911
— mécanique 12066, 13786,
13787, 15035

chariot 16611, 18945
— à laitier 16563
— à lingots 9784
— contrepoids 1126
— contrepoids d'un plan
  incliné 1236
— de chargement des
  lingots S. 9785
— de coulée 3045, 13765
— d'étuve 6056
— de four à sole mobile
  1949
— de machine à mouler
  11987
— de perforation 5884,
  10242
— de pont 4596
— de pont de coulée 7651
— de pont-roulant 4578
— élévateur 10751
— enfourneur des lingots
  9785
— porte-poche 10473
— -porteur 16681
— transbordeur 18862
charme 9367
charnière 9198, 9199
— anticlinale 754, 655,
  660
— inférieure 11064
— synclinale 18159,
  18938
charpente 20186
— de revêtement S. 18637
— du chevalement 15945
— du monte-charge 9227,
  10747
— en bois S. 20175
— en fer 9960
— métallique de toiture
  17504
charpentes tubulaires 19089
charriage 18603
— de cisaillement 16026
— d'érosion 6547
— tangentiel 18244
chassage 5953, 20208, 20214
chasse-pointes 13244
— -rivet 8926
— -sièges de soupapes
  19455
chasser 11230
châssis 2208, 12002, 16618,
  736, 1208
— à barres 1239

châssis à charnière 16779
— à démotter 9206
— à démoulage intérieur
  18286
— à molettes S. 8911
— à pièces rapportées
  2227
— américain 510
— amovible à démoulage
  intérieur 18287
— coupé 17007
— de cave en acier 17464
— de démoulage 4391
— de dessous 2174, 5731
— de dessus 4349
— de fonderie 7657
— de forme 17007
— de la machine à mouler
  les poulies 12003
— de milieu 3380
— de moulage 2217, 2222,
  7310, S. 7657
— de truck 2898
— du laminoir S. 9465
— en bois 20182
— impostes ouvrants en
  acier 11547
— inférieur 11065
— intermédiaire 11660
— pour colonnes 2218
— supérieur 19361
— universale 2534
château d'eau 19820
Chattien 3359
chaude 8972
— blanche 20031
— rouge 14540
— suante 19945
chaudière 1955
— à boîte à feu surhaussée
  14377
— à bouilleurs 7754
— à caisse feu 7153
— à chambre de vapeur
  unique 1993
— à chauffage 9008
— à chauffage extérieur S.
  6698
— à chaleur perdue 19732
— à circulation 3603
— à circulation forcée 1987
— à circulation rapide 1996
— à clarification 3633
— à contre-courant 4528
— à courant direct 4180

chaudière à deux corps cylindriques 19185
— à deux corps cylindriques
  superposés S. 5655
— à deux foyers intérieurs
  cylindriques S. 10515
— à deux tubes-foyers 10515
  10515
— à deux tubes-foyers
  ondulés 10516
— à double boîte à feu
  5648
— à double chambre de
  vapeur 1984
— à double face 5656
— à eau chaude 9450
— à éléments multiples S.
  12128
— à étages 12120
— à étain 18665
— à faible volume d'eau
  1994
— à flamme directe 5458
— à flamme en retour S.
  14811
— à filtrer 7055
— à foyer 1983
— à foyer amovible 14714
— à foyer extérieur 6698
— à foyer intérieur 7450
— à foyers d'un seul coté
  16389
— à gaz 8006
— à goudron 18320
— à grand débit S. 9163
— à grand volume 10551
— à grand volume d'eau
  1988
— à graisse 18225
— à gros éléments 10551
— à gros tubes d'eau S. 19828
  19828
— à lame d'eau sous les
  cendriers 19985
— à lessive 11109
— à mercure 11504
— à moyenne pression 11431
  11431
— à multibouilleurs 1347
— à naphte 12490
— à plusieurs corps cy-
  lindriques superposés
  12112
— à poix 13416
— à pression 13895

chaudière à puissance élevée 9163
— à réchauffeur 18009
— à réglage automatique
993
— à retour de flamme 14811
. à section ellyptique S.
12722.
— à section ovale 12722
— à siphon 18173
— à tombeau 19621
— à tomberau S. 19621
— à très haute pression
9193
— à tube-foyer avec
bouilleurs transversaux
7451
— à tube-foyer demi-ondulé
1989
— à tube-foyer échelonné
1995
— à tube-foyer excentrique
1985
— à tube-foyer lisse 1990
— à tubes d'acier omega à
haute pression 9167
— à tubes croisés 4714
— à tubes de chauffe S.
16766
— à tubes d'eau étroits et
courbés S. 18547
— à tubes de flammes S. 16766
16766
— à tubes de fumée 7264, S.
S. 16766, 1986
— à tubes de fumée et à
tubes d'eau 4066
— à tubes démontables
1991
— à tubes-foyers ondulés
1983
— à tubes Galloway 7918
— à vapeur 17417, 17426
— à vapeur à basse pres-
sion 11058
— à vapeur à haute pres-
sion 9170
— à vapeur industrielle
11308
— à vapeur à pression
moyenne 11432
— à vaporisation rapide
7291
— à volume moyen 11438

chaudière aquatubulaire
19823
— aquatubulaire à caissons
19830
— aquatubulaire à col-
lecteur 19825
— aquatubulaire à col-
lecteurs non sectionnés
S. 19830
— aquatubulaire à deux
collecteurs 19833
— aquatubulaire à larges
tubes 19828
— aquatubulaire à tubes
courbés 19824
— aquatubulaire à tubes
étroits 19831
— aquatubulaire à tubes
horizontaux 19826
— aquatubulaire à tubes
inclinés 19827
— aquatubulaire à tubes
rapides 19832
— aquatubulaire à un seul
collecteur 19829
— aquatubulaire marine
11325
— alimentaire 6876
— auxiliaire 5626, 1001
— avec boîte à feu en
cuivre S. 1982
— avec grilles mécaniques
17418
— avec foyer en cuivre
1982
— avec tube-foyer à ailettes 1992
— Belleville 1463
— chauffée au bois 1963
— chauffée à paille 1961
— chauffée à tourbe 1960
— chauffée au gaz S. 8006
— chauffée au charbon 1959
1959
— chemisée de vapeur
17437
— combinée 4054
— cylindrique 4945, 16097
— cylindrique à fond ovale
6222
— cylindrique à foyer intérieur 4947
— cylindrique à foyer extérieur 4946
— cylindrique double 5653

chaudière d'évaporation 6617
6617
— d'instruction 18816
— de Cornouailles 4484
— de la locomotive à turbine 19119
— de laiton 2273
— de liquation 10869
— de locomotive 10948
— de marine 11324
— de raffinage 14608
— de réserve 16976
— de ressuage 18102
— de secours S. 1001
— de service 13466
— de vulcanisation 19609
— demi-fixe S. 15847
— double 5645
— électrique 6262
— électrique à vapeur 6303
— en cuivre 4354
— en étain 18654
— fixe 17397
— formée d'un simple corps
cylindrique 16385
— française S. 7754
— horizontale 9352, 9333
— inexplosive 9760
— inférieure 11066
— intérieure mobile 14708
— instantanée S. 7291
— Lancashire 5661, 10515
— lessiveuse à pâte 14144
— locomobile 13691
— mobile 12046
— multitubulaire 12128
— naine 6144
— ordinaire S. 16389
— pour bains-marie 19747
— pour le chauffage central
1965
— pour pompe à incendie 7168
7168
— ronde 17060
— Root 15156
— sans circulation d'eau
1997
— sans fond mouillé 6025
— sans lame d'eau derrière S.
S. 6025
— Schultz 15632
— sectionnelle 15761
— sectionnelle à tubes
d'eau 15667
— semi-fixe 15847

chaudière semi-tubulaire 15850
— simple 16388
— sous pression 1980
— stationnaire S. 17397
— supérieure 19362
— terrestre 10522
— Thornycroft 18547
— timbrée à 12 atmosphères 1964
— tubulaire 19062, 16766
— verticale 19520, 19532
— verticale à bouilleurs transversaux 19522
— Yarrow 20278
chaudron 1955
chaudronnier 1972
— en cuivre 4375
chauffage 7189, 9007, 14667, 17637, 7187
— diélectrique 5386
— direct 5459
— indirect 9744
— mécanique 11414
— à feu nu 1999
— au rouge 2414
— de la tête du lingot 9016
— des chaudières 7192
— du goudron 18315
— par arc électrique 746
— par frottement 3237
— par le fond 2160
— par induction 9751
— par résistance 14768
— préalable 13846
chauffe 7187
chauffé 9004
— au blanc 20032
— au bleu 1903
— au rouge cerise 3409
— au rouge sombre 6087
chauffer 19666
— au rouge 8970
— la fonte 8968
— la poche 8969
chaufferie 7559
chauffeur 17634
chaufour S. 10816
chauler le fil 3266
chaux 10810
— dolomitique 5615
— éteinte 16571
— sodée 16809
— vive 14301
chef d'équipe S. 12770

chef de four 10357
— de poste 16123
— du laboratoire 3417
— fondeur S. 8915
— foreur 11361
— sondeur S. 5915
chemin de fer à crémaillère 14323
cheminé 19507
cheminée 2637 3453, 4847, S. 5347, 14118, 17371, 3563, 14942, 3454
— à charbon 4527
— à minerai 4527, 5780, 7016, 11690, 11694, 11711 11711, 12638, 17670
— à remblai 15012, 19721
— à remblais 15027
— auxiliaire 10189
— de combustion 4083
— de fagotage 4633
— étroite 7105
— indépendante 10063
chemise 2930, 10843, 16139 10100
— de la cuve 15861 , 15961
— de réchauffage 9015
— de revêtement 2931
— d'une pièce 7804
— réfractaire 10855
chemiser v. plaquer ou plomber
chenal 11226
— à barbe 7294
— annullaire 14926
— de coulée 11222, 13753, 15372, 15374, 17171
— de coulée à lingots 13269 13269
— d'écoulement S. 18934
— de fusion 621
— de fusion annulaire 622
— de laitier 16542, 16554
— en bois 20179
chenevixite 3402
chenillé 4612
chercheur d'or 8889
chert S. 3410
chessylite 1036, 3413
chevalement 7921, 8011, 8013, 8021, 8924, 11733, 13405, 13659, 14186, 15960
— de fonçage 16426
— de pompage 14165
— de production 13995

chevalet 9376, 17341, 18878
— avec renvoi inférieur 14166
— de forage 2079
— des rouleaux 2239
— du perforateur 5928
chevauchement S. 12767 16244
— anticlinal 2315
— de distillation 5558
chevaucher (se-) 2530
cheveux de Vénus 8711
cheville 13307
— d'ajustage 6083
chèvre 8231
chevron 14345
chiastolite 3415, 11142
chicane 1094
— en bois 20179
chien 11772
— de mine 4508
chiffre de dureté S. 2408
childrénite 3418
chiléite 3419
chilénite 3420
chillagite 3441
chimie du haut-fournau 3401
chimiste arbitre 735
— assermenté 18143
chiolite 3471
chloanthite 3490
chlorapatite 3492
chlorargyrite 3493
chlorate de potasse 13723
chlore 3500
chlorite 3503, 13005
chloritisation 3506
chloriteux 3504
chloritoïde 3507
chloritoschiste 3505, 13007
chlormanganokalite 3508
chloroaluminite 3491
chlorocalcite 3509
chloromélanite 3510
chloropal 3511
chlorophane 3512
chlorure 17370
— cuivreux 4858
— d'ammoniaque 15433
— d'antimoine 670
— de barium 3494
— de calcium 2722, 3497
— de calcium anhydre 3495
— de fer 3496
— de magnésium 3498
— de mercure 11499

chlorure de platine 13513
— de potassium 3499
— de sodium 4097
chlorures alcalins 357
choc 10395 1848
— thermique 18487
chocs répétés 14733
choix de la force motrice
    15806
— des échantillons 15807
choleur 11412
chromage 3524, 3527,
    3534, 3547
chromate 3525
chromatique 3526
chromatographie 3528
chrome 3544
— magnésie 3530
chromisation 3542
chromiser 3546
— par diffusion 3541
chromite 3529, 3543
— de fer S. 3529
chromologie géologique
    3161
chrysobéril 3550, 4952
chrysocole 4360
chrysolite 3551
chrysoprase 3552
chrysotile 3553
chubutite 3554
churchite 3558
chute 5487, 6002, 19724
— de la cage 6773, 15351
— de sable 5973
— de température 5991
— de tête de lingot 4660
— des roches de la paroi
    16967
— des charges 16656
— libre 7723
chutes 16179
— à malaxer 2628
— de fer S. 19734
ciel 15137
— du foyer 7833
ciment 3140
— calcaire 2704
— de haut-fourneau 1718
— de laitier 16530
— de laitier Portland 9995
— réfractaire 14628
— sursulfaté 18023
cimentant 3180
cimentation 3168
— des fissures 8630

cimentation des fissures
    aquifères 8628
— étagée 12121
— primaire 13937
cimenter 3138
— à haut niveau 3139
cinabre 3578
cinérite 19575
cinglage 10392, 16134
cingler 16130
cingleresse 13699
cingleur 16133
— à levier S. 376
— rotatif S. 16136
cinnamonstone 3579
cintrage à chaud 9417
— de ronds 1211
cintre 2198
— d'acier 17456
— déformable 20299
— en 1 756
cintreuse 1504, 1511
— à rondes 1210
circulation en circuit
    fermé 3766
circuit d'eau de refroidisse-
    ment 19762
— fermé 3767
circuits en tube fer noir
    9451
cire à mouler 3074
— de paraffine 12911,
    13127
— fossile S. 3228; 12821
cirque 3586, 3607
— glaciaire 10284, 10322
cisaillage 18899
cisaille 15022, 16031, 16038
— à balancier 375
— à billettes 1584
— à scraps 15658
— à tôles 16080
— à tronçonner 15866
— d'établi électrique 6258
— -guillotine 8659
— hydraulique pour blooms
    9537
cisaillement 16020
cisailler 16018
cisailles à blooms 1824
— à brames 16502
— circulaires multiples
    16674
ciseau à froid 3970
— de calfat 3111
ciseaux à ferblantier 18658

citerne 18245
citrine 6788
claie 16297
— en bois 20175
clapet 7281, 10727, 18848
— de cheminée 3462
— d'entrée d'air 293
— d'explosion S. 15415
— de fermeture 10947
— de pied 17361
— de retenue 3366
claquer 1445
clarifier 3634, S. 7072
clarite 3635
clarkeite 3636
clarté de la flamme 2405
classement 8384
classer S. 3641
— le charbon 3642
classeur 16925
classificateur à coupe 2203
— à raclettes 5732
— débourbeur 3643
classification 16926
classifier 3641
clastique 3646
clasto-cristallin 3647
clastogène 3648
clastomorphique 3650
claudétite 3651
clausthalite 3652
clavetage 3625
claveter 3618
clavette 4521, 6873, 8212
claviature 8928, 11293
clé v. clef
clé à écrous 16974
clef à chaîne 3281
— à étau 18714
— à tige 8758
— à tubes 13335
— anglaise 202333
— de retenue 10730, 12304
— de serrage 15223
— de serrage électrique
    6284
— de voûte de la sole S.
    18744
— suspendue entrainée mé-
    caniquement 13798
— tubulaire 19086
— universelle 11904
clefs pour batterie 18732
— suspendues 18718
clichage 15964
— pour cages 2682, 6813

cliché-galvano 4356
clicheur S, 17826
cliftonite 3726
clinker 3144
clinochlore 3731
clinoclase 3732, 10388
clinocasite S. 2, 683
clinoenstatite 3733
clinographe 3734
clinohumite 3735
clinomètre 3736, 9709
clinopinacoïde 3737
clinoprisme 3738
clinozoïsite 3739
clintonite 3740
cliquet 5592, 14435
— d'arrêt 12996
clivage 3714, 3716
— de base 1264
— distinct 5564, 6182
— imparfait 9742
— prismatique 13963
— rhomboédrique 2719
cliver 3719
cloche 1073, 1460, 1447, 19070
— à boulet S. 15514, 16697
— à écrou 5379, 1574
— à fraise 11709
— à vis S. 5379
— de barbotage 2488
— de haut fourneau 7858, 1708
— de la pompe à air 310
— de repêchage 1574, 5367, 6914, 15702
— de repêchage à coins 2933
— de treuil 1242
— de toit 12752
— en verre 8271
— Hutter 9489
cloison 908, 2550, 12953, 15867
— d'aérage 247, 327, 1361, 1400, 2285, 5121, 14881, 17687
— de puits 5584
— en planches 13463
— souterraine 19255
cloque 249, 1780
clou à tête cône tronc 4199
— refroidisseur 3435
clous pour chaussures 16155
clou(t)ière S. 12163

Clunien 3791
coaguler 3609
coal-ball 3799
coalescence 3862
coalescer 3861
cobalt 3885
cobaltine 3887
cobaltite 3892
cobaltoménite 3893
coccolite 3896
coefficient d'équivalence 3900
— de mobilité 11848
— de pliage 1508
— de réduction 3901
— de striction 14573
— différé 5112
coenogénèse 3181
coeur en acier au manganèse 11278
— en rails assemblés 2539
coffrage S. 16087, 3902
— latéral 16266
coffrages glissants 16621
coffre S. 2910
coffrer le toit 2378
cohénite 3918
cohésion à sec 6048
— du sable 3920
cohésionmètre 3919
coiffer S. 2791
coin 12055, 7091, 11857, 7900
— à pierre 17653
— à charbon 3857
— actionné directement à pression 13794
— d'ancrage 10528
— spécial pour bridage de colonnes 2005
coincé 9486
coincement 17582
coins de tige de forage 5900
— grinpeurs 16663
coke 3297
— concassé 4768, 6221
— criblé 16304
— d'alambic 17593
— d'allumage 1416, 9011,
— de charbon de forge 7577
— de fonderie 7653, 16746
— de four S. 3940
— de fusion 3319
— de gaz 2648, 7991, 8067

coke de haut-fourneau 1709
— de pétrole 13130
— dense
— des charges S. 3319
— d'usine à gaz S. 8067
— en grains menus S. 16728 16728
— maigre 10641
— métallurgique 3940, 11585 11585
— menu 3935, 16728
— naturel S. 3949
— sans minerai 3323
— tamisé S. 16304
— tout venant 11821
cokéfaction S. 3353, 3950, 3954
cokéfication 3954
cokéfier 3926
cokéite 3949
col 12204
— à souder 19949
— de cygne 8362
— de liaison de la masselotte 6894
— du trépan 1627
colemanite 4011
collage 17581
— de la pièce sur le moule 17583
— de noyau 8666
— de sable 15519
— différentiel 5396
colle 8316
collection minéralogique 4026
collecteur 8925
— à boues 12077
— d'alimentation 6881
— de chaudière 1968
— de gouttes 5949
— de mercure 479
— de poussières 6125
— surchauffeur 18008
coller 8315, (se-) 2690
collet 12204
— du cylindre 4020
collier 3619, 4016
— à coins 17076, 19884
— de renforcement 19950
— de repêchage à lames 10257
colliers de serrage 2935
colline arrondie de moraine 6017
collobriérite 4027

collyrite 4029
colmatage 13566
colmatant 7021, 13567
colmater 12068
colonne 4038, 10970, 13288
— à coke S. 15721
— à avancement pneumatique 13583
— abimée 10256
— coiffée 5988
— d'absorption 13
— d'arrière 14481
— de ciment 3145
— de distillation à reflux 14621
— d'eau 19754
— d'exploitation 12512, 13998
— d'extraction 6707, 19046
— de fermeture d'eau 19815
— de fermeture des eaux 17835
— de laiton 2267
— de liquide 4043
— de minerai 3455, 12639, 13360
— de minerai riche 16161
— de production 10975
— de soutènement 18035
— de tiges S. 5942
— de tubage 2961, 17834
— de tubes de pompage 14167 14167
— des charges 17618
— en fonte 2997
— garnie 12839
— montante 17338
— perdue S. 10842
— pour le chargement des tenders 18404
— support perforatrice 5902
— tubulaire pour les toitures des quais de chemins de fer 19066
colophane 14762, 15188
colophonite 4030
coloradoïte 4032
coloration de la flamme 4036
coloré 378
colorimètre 3549
colorimétrie 4034
columbite 4037
columnaire en éventail 5580
combe 11907
combinaison chimique 3385

combinaison de chaudières S S. 4054
— des métalloïdes avec le fer 4057
comler S. 232
combles à deux versants simples sur fermes 16375 16373
combustible 4069, 7787, 10397
— antidétonant 667
— artificiel 834
— carbonisé 2862
— composé 1764
— de rebut 19727
— de très bonne qualité 9151
— DERV 5222
— Diesel 5388
— en morceaux 11090
— fossile 7631
— gazeux 8010, 8071
— inférieur S. 11051
— liquide 10875
— médiocre S. 11051
— mélangé d'air 7790
— naturel 12191
— nécessaire 5163
— pour jets 10159
— pulvérisé 14148
— pulvérulent 7789, S. 14148
— solide 16882
combustion 4071, 2604
— au charbon 3805
— complète 4113, 13078
— en avance 7625
— in situ 9678
— inverse 14820
— parfaite S. 4113
— rapide 2418
— renversée 9933, 14826
— sous pression constante 4072
— sous volume constant 4073
— souterraine S. 9678
commande électrique du treuil de chargement 6271
— horizontale 9340
— hydraulique 9540
— par manivelle 4606
— verticale 19525
commencer l'exploitation d'un puits 2410

compact 12838
compartiment de l'exhaure 14157
— de ventilation 256
— des skips 16454
compas à ressort 17132
— d'épaisseur 2748, 12714
— d'épaisseur micrométrique 11642
— diviseur 5585
— écarté 4108
compensateur à disque 5481
compensation de la pression 1128
compenser 12462
complétion sousmarine 19283
compliqué 9921
comportement dans le haut-fourneau 1441
composante 4120
composé aliphatique 6838
— oxygéné 12818
— phosphorique 13174
— sulfuré 17982
composition 4125
— chimique 3386
— de la charge 4126
— du gaz 4127
— pour coussinets S. 1396
compound 4133
compressibilité 4151
compression 4153
— des briques 13890
comprimé à l'état fluide 7461
comprimer 13865
compte-coups 17875
compteur 4542
— à gaz 8024
— d'eau 19799
— de débit 12710
— de déplacement 5534
— rotatif 19120
comptonite S. 18543
computation v. calcul
concassage 4775
— de minerai 4757, 12633
concasseur 2317, 4771, 8556
— à calcaire 17641
— à charbon 3808
— à coke 3931
— à cônes 4197
— à cylindres 4777, 15100

concasseur de gros
— giratoire 8237, 8695
— primaire 13942
concasseur v. broyeur
concentration des ions 4167
— en grammes équivalents
d'une solution 6532
— par évaporation 6619
— par gravité 8484
concentré 8933
— de blende 1762
— de minerai 9493
— de triage 13208
concentrés très fins 7096
concession 4171, 10726
— de mine 3613
— minière 388
— pétrolifère 12484
concessionaire 3614
conchoïdale 15601
concordance 4204
— des couches 13447
concrétion 4178
— arrondie 12152
— dure dans le grès 8832
concrétionné S. 4179
condensation 4153, 4181
condenser 4184, 9720
condenseur d'appareil
distillatoire 5560
condition de brume 11809
— de mousse 7510
— générale 1694
conditionner 4188
conditionneur 4191
— d'eau 19755
conditions de livraison 4192
conductance limite de l'é-
lectrolyte 10826
conducteur 4194, 10628,
S. 13955
— de raccordement S.
4224
— extérieur 12698
— neutre 12254
— nu 1228
conductibilité calorique
8977
— thermique 8990
conductivité électrique 6266
conduit v. conduite ou
canal
conduite 13355, 13380,
20196
— à boues 12081
— circulaire de vent 2630

conduite collectrice S.8101
— d'alimentation 6884
— d'admission de l'air comprimé 13916
— d'amenée 8100
— d'aspiration 17954, 17958
17958
— de départ du gaz 8033
— de dérivation S. 10570
— d'eau 19756, 19798
— d'échappement 19503
— d'évacuation de gaz
chauds 19733
— de gaz vers le four 8009
— de méthane 11611
— de refoulement 5151
— de transporteur 15973
— de vent 305
— de vent chaud 9391,
9397
— de vent principale 304
— des flammes 7255
— d'un appareil de fusion
20196
— du laboratoire 10451
— forcée 13913
— oscillant 15043
— pour tuer le puits 10354
— principale 4025, 18958
— principale de gaz 8022
— sous marine 15742
conduite v. canal
cône de cendres 863
— de coulée 13749
— de déjection 407, 18613
— d'éboulis 6807
— de glissement 3337
— décanteur basculant
1272
— des évents 14954
— tronqué 18956
confection. v. construction
confection des briques 13855
13855
conforme aux calculs 49
— aux normes UNI
congé 7027, 9263
— à racler 7028
— au noir 7029
— de cuir 10651
— en cuir 10652
congélation 7742
— étagée 17548
conglomérat 3649, 4206,
8317
— alluvionnaire 6800

conglomérat aurifère 1198
— de base 1278
conglomérer 223
conicité 18282
conique 4208, 18285, 18290
connecter 2016
connecteur rapide 14300
connellite 4226
connexion S. 2021
— à étoile 20258
conservation de gaz 7993
consistance 1937
— sirupeuse 18177
console 2238
— de la plaque antérieure
2241
— de support du tuyau d'eau
d'eau de refroidissement
2245
— en fer 10020
— en fonte 9959
— tubulaire pour lignes de
contact 19063
consoles de la trémie S. 9329
9329
consolidation 3784, 4231
consolider 20188
consommation de carbone
4239
— de chaleur 8978
— de charbon 4240
— de combustible 4244
— de courant 4241
— d'eau 4245
— de force 13774
— de vent 4238
— des limes 4243
— par tonne d'acier en ki-
lowatts-heure 4246
constance de la température
de la solution 4518
constantan 4232
constante d'affinité 3899
— de dissociation 3899
constituant 4120
— de la texture 13700
— d'un alliage 398
— d'une combinaison 4233
constituants du gaz 4234
constitution 4125
— chimique 3387
construction à ossature rigide 14908
— à ossature spatiale
unistrut 19308
— du four 7832

construction du haut-fourneau 1710
— en bois 20173
— en fer 9960
— en ossature de poutres-
creuses rectangulaires
2226
— en pisé réfractaire 3667
— en pisé réfractaire damé
18231
constructions sans fermes
18966
construire 14371
— un cuvelage 18972
contact anormal 4
contenant des scories 4250
conteneur 4249
continent 10518
contour cristallin 4793
— du modèle 12707
— du profil 15987
contract de livraison de
minerais 4283
contracter (se-) 4282, 13310,
16221
contraction 16226
contrainte de flambage 2511
— de rupture 2330
— tangentielle 18242
contraintes admissibles 13114
13114
— alternées 434
— élevées dues à la réson-
nance 9184
contre-balancier 1123
contrebride 4105
contre-coup 1064
— -coussinet 18737
contredépouille 1052, 19246
— -écrou 10119
— -essai 14791
— -fer 1062
— -fiche 10240, 16169,
17225
— fort 29, 17225
— -maître 2126
— -maître de forage 18279
— moulage 4535
— -mouler 4534
— -poids 4536
— poids de la porte 5629
— -poids d'un plan incliné
8614

contre-porte 14042
— -pression 1071
— -rail 8643
— -torsion 1081
— -vapeur 1075
contrôle 3361, 3373, 9846
— de déviation 14752
— d'essuage 17096
— de l'avance 5920
— de la combustion 4077
— de qualité 14248
— des boues 12072
— gammagrophique 7948
— non destructif 12348
— par ultrasons 19224
contrôler 19514
convecteur en plafond 3130
convention de conservation
4228
— de rationnement 14030
conversion 4296
— du fer en acier S. 58
convertir le fer en acier S.
17453
convertisseur 4298
— basculant 18627
— basique 1295
— Bessemer 1550
— de couple 8777
— horizontal 1241
— stationnaire 17398
convexité 5517
convoyer 4317
— à raclettes
convoyeur à secousses
10178, 15969
— -chargeuse 4322
— de coulée 3071
— de taille 6741
convoyeur v. transporteur
cookéite 4325
copeau 3474
copeaux de forage 5947
— métalliques 3482
copiapite 11812
coprolite 4376
coquille 3007, 3423, 3433,
3450, 3615, 3629, 5358, 11551
11551, 16093
— chauffée 13839
— de centrifugation 3204
— de coussinet S. 1387
— de séchage 4398
— d'oeuf 11557
— extérieure 5174

coquille galvanoplastique
4364 , 6371
— inférieure 2148
coquiller 3421
coquilleux 16114
coquimbite S. 1042
corbeille à coke 3928
corde en amiante 841
— en chanvre 9088
— Manilla
cordée 10743, 18905, 20087
— d'essai 18883
cordiérite 4380, 9943
cordite 4379
cordon 1364
— à passe étroite 17833
— à revers 1049
— conique 1568
— de brasage 2293
— d'étanchéité 7031, 10208
— de soudure 19937, 16243,
19924
cordylite 4381
core de pompe fixe 17396
— de pompe mobile 18859
corindon 472, 4507, 5332
— jaune 12665
corkite 4475
cornaline 4476
corne de cerf calcinée 3344
cornéenne 9949, 9372
cornéite 4477
corniche en éléments préfabriqués 4483
cornière 572
— à ailes égales 581, 1381
— à ailes égales et à bords
arrondis 6523
— à ailes inégales 19288
— à arêtes vives 585
— à bourrelet 2542
— à coins arrondis 581,
584
— d'acier 580
— d'angle 6199
cornières jumelles 19168
— inégales à coins arrondis
19289
— à arêtes vives 582
— à boudin 2543
cornubianite 4485
cornue 14795
— à gaz 8048
— cylindrique 3382
— pour distiller 485, 488

cornwallite 4486
coronadite 4487
corps 2930, 4842, 1936
— à vert 8506
— creux 9264
— de la chaudière 1976
— de la coulisse de forage 10132
— d'eau et de vapeur 19741
— de platine 10945
— de rivet 15953
— de soufflante 1856
— du sable 15484
— étranger 7566
— hydraulique 14161
— intrusifs 9925
— supérieur de la chaudière S. 19362
correctifs 3395
corrections 7141
corriger l'acier S. 9670
corroder 15614
corrosion 4491, 6572, 13428
— dispersée 5529
— électrolytique 7882
— fissurante 4627
— intergranulaire 9875
— par envasement 19254
— par érosion 6546
— par piqûres 13429
— sous tension 17786
corroyage v. affinage
corroyer v. raffiner ou affiner
corroyer 13287
corsite 4504
corundellite 4505
corundophyllite 4506
cosalite 4510
coslettisation 4511
cosse de câble 15169
cossyrite 4512
costière 16274
costresse 4526, S. 17919
cote de l'orifice du sondage S. 6376
— du sondage 6376
côte 4824, 16168
— longitudinale 10983
— nominale 12337
côté 16252
— de l'aspiration 17960
— de la sortie 6656
— du refoulement 13918
coton-poudre 8672

cotunnite 4525
couche 1387, 1414, 1686, 3880, 10594, 11393, 15010, 15743, 16084, 17753
— anti-acide 652
— anti-rouille 672
— aquifère 19751
— cémentée 3165, S. 8853
— concentrique 17061
— d'argile 16676
— de base 8611
— de brai 2294
— de calamine 12795
— de cémentation 8853
— de charbon 3844, 3859
— de charbon incandescent 9685
— de coulée 13251, 15471
— de couverture 12769
— de fond 2146, 7198
— de galets 13030
— de gravier 3287
— de houille 15747
— de métal 10595
— de rouille 10597
— de sable étuvé 6042
— de scorie 10598
— d'oxyde 10596
— d'oxyde du laminage 16474
— d'usure 19860
— du toit 18017
— en dressant 9021, 17528
— en plateure S. 7344
— faillée 5535
— filiforme 16157
— filtrante 7043
— guide 10325
— imperméable 9657
— inclinée 13421
— inclinée à 45° 8713
— inférieure de combustible 1417
— marginale 16478
— minéralizée 12997
— nitrurée 12311
— oblique 4671
— ondulée 15411
— plate 7344, 10714
— puissante 18500
— repère S. 10325
— supérieure 2813
— tourbillonaire 19604
eoucher les feux 4559
couches associées 901

couches de transition 1436
— dures 15254
— stériles 1226
— strates 17746
coude 1501, 6254
— de petit rayon 16182
coulabilité 3033
coulable 3032
coulage à noyau 9268
— ou remplissage 7036
coulant porte-matrice S. 5374
coulé 13746, 11878, 11119,
— à la machine 11119
— à mesure 3028
— court 16183
— dans la fosse de coulée 13401
— en acier 17461
— en bloc 2990
— en coquille 2912
— monobloc 2990
coulée 2984, 3037, 7652, 7643, 8972, 17769, 18307 18356
— à attaques étagées S. 16 16272
— à découvert 3057, 12592
— à plat 3064
— à pluie 17183
— de boue 12078
— de fonderie 7670
— de la fonte et du laitier 18761
— de laitier 16558
— debout 19521
— du laitier 16566
— du métal en fusion 18297
— échelonné 16272
— en chassis 7292
— en chute directe 5979, 18748
— en cire perdue 11014
— en coquille par gravité 8486
— en cornichon 9358
— en dépression 3518
— en échelons 16272
— en fosse 13396
— en grappe 3038, 17276
— en plâtre 13467
— en sable 15486, S. 15489
— en siphon 18176
— en source 2151, 14962, 19357, 19431
— étagée 16272
— horizontale 9334

coulée interrompue 9913
— par la force centrifuge 3203
— principale 11223
— rampée 3063
— sous pression 13898
— sous pression centrifuge 3207
— tangentielle 18241
— tranquille 14306
coulée V. fusion
couler 2965, 13737, 18351
— à decouvert 2973
— à froid 2967
— à noyau 2970
— à plat 2971
— de deux côtés 2968
— de la fonte blanche 2982
— debout 13740, 18738
— de métal blanc dans les coussinets 13741
— en coquille 5354
— en moule 2972
— en presse 2974
— en source 2150, 2977, 13739
— la fonte à faible teneur de carbone 2979
— la fonte en gueuses 13246 13246
— le fer en moules 2980
— par la quenouille 2981
— sous pression 5354
— v. mouler
couleur 3035, 7386
— de recuit 8976, 18374
— minérale 11750
couleurs de recuit 612
coulis réfractaire 14634
coulisse 10125, 19975
— de battage 2574
— de forage 10126
— de repêchage 7219
— rotary 15206
coulisseau porte-matrice 5374
couloir 3563, 16162
— à chutes 15677
— d'attaque 5969
— de la tour 13363
— du portail de la tour 1536 15362
— oscillant 2575, 4323, 10178, 15969
— oscillant à billes S. 1159

couloir oscillant à galets 15117
— oscillant suspendu 8812
coup 1849, 10895, 16191
— de bouchon 16792. 17995
— de couronne 15142
— de fond 2162, S. 7541
— de fouet 7284, 20017
— d'eau 9831
— de marteau pilon 1859
— de mine incliné 8569
— de mine vers le toit 2348
— descendant 5715
— montant 19381
— de toit 8927, 15011
coupage des coulées 17215
coupe 4913
— -corde 15165
— courte 3756
— de cristallisation 4809
— de la carotte 16032
— de sonde 19965
— d'un sondage 5894
— -feu 7185, 7253
— -fonte 7778
— géologique 8176
— -jet 8658
— micrographique 11652
— transversale 4677
— -tube 2937, 5898, 18978, 13334
— -tubing 19050
— -verre 8275
coupelle 4838, 4852
— de combustion 4075
coupelot 4844, S. 15939
couper 4891. 4893
— à l'arc 743
— à dimension 5834
— à longueur 16019
— le charbon S. 2297
— le mur 1326, 10737
— le vent 19135
— les barres de fer 2658
coupeur à l'arc 744
couple de blocage 11235
— de forces 4547
— maximum 13010
coupole 2035, 5620
coups de bouchon 10326
courant 12192
— d'air ascendant 19348
— d'air descendant 5696
— d'air montant 14958

courant d'air uniforme 19302
— de convection 4293
— de gaz riche en oxygène 7955
— de gaz transparent 18834
— de régime 20202
— descendant 20093
— électrique 6269
— gazeux 4869, 7994
courbage 1505
courbe S. 1527, 2198, 4875
— à S 18643
— à souder 19940
— à 180° 14810
— de combustion 4080
— de concentration 4877
— de consommation 4237
— de décomposition 4876
— de dilation 10997
— d'injectivité 9811
— de niveau 4281
— de perméabilité 13110
— de refroidissement 4335
— de solubilité 4877
— en ogive 17527
— surbaissée 7331
courbé 1527
courbure S. 1505, 4875
couronne 1681, 2382, 4726, 11300, 14920, 15575
— à dents de scie 15563
— à diamants 5322, 5330
— à grenaille d'acier 122
— à grenailles 3447, 16194
— à vis sans fin 20230
— de cire 9667
— de forme 5796
— de la marâtre 11302
— de maçonnerie 19649
— de paille 17756
— de sondage 4405, 4393
— de support 11302, 12246
— dentée 8129, 14925, 1556(15561
— en fonte 2998, 3009
couronné 2387
couronnement 2388
courroie 7280
— en V 19420
course d'expansion 13796
— du levier 12052
— du piston 13576
coussinet 1387, 13296
— à billes 1150
— de tôle 4887
— de tourillon 3520, 10235

coussinet portant de la table rotary 18192
— -selle 3251
— supérieur S. 18737
coussinets, portées 2279
couteau à liège 4469
— coup-à-droite 14905
— coupe-gauche 10664
— en agate 209
— en platine 13521
— pour élargisseur 19276
— pour trépan élargisseur S 19276
couture 15744
— moulée 3110
— refoulée au matoir S. 31 3110
couvercle 2032, 2793, 4562, 10727
— de la voûte 757
— du presse-étoupe 8266
— en verre 8274
— mobile 14705
— obturateur 3780
couverte 4572
couverture 1687, 4570, 12735 12735
— de laitier 16531
— en feutre 6912
— glaciaire 8257
couvre-jet 4563
— -joint S. 7384
— -manivelle 4607
couvrir 4558, 11299
— d'une toiture 15136
— les feux 4559
covelline 4557
covite 4573
cracher 17230
cracker 4579
craie de Briançon S. 17452
— noire 1646
— phosphatée 13161
— rouge 12448
crain 12298
crampage 3626, 15750
crampe 3622, 4591
— à tubes 2935
cramper 3617
crampon 4591, 14363, 17079, 17372
— à vis 18185
— pour douves 17375
crampons et pattes de fixation 3744
cran 10245

creuset en acier coulé 3019
— en argile 7160
— en graphite 8448
— en platine 13519
— en porcelaine 13662
— en terre réfractaire 4742
— libre 19241
— métallique 13715
— séché S. 7120
— sur roues 13688
creuset v. poche
creux 1850, 8587, 9261
crevasse 4581, 7359, 14893
— dans le coeur 17127
— du cratère 4611
crevassé 4584, 7704
criblage à sec 6046
— du coke 15693
— par dépôt 9457, 10179, 16468
crible 10177, 14883, 16297, 19463
— à deux plateaux 5654
— à secousse 15968, 10185
— -classeur 3644, 8390
— -classeur à air comprimé 295
— -classeur à rouleaux 15116
— .double 5654
— filtrant 10185
— hydraulique à étage fixe 8855 8855
— laveur 4590, 14885, 15033
— laveur à secousses 10226
— rotatif 14842
cribler 14884, 16923
cric 14393
-- à cremaillère 14321
crichtonite 4636
crin S. 12946, 16646
crinanite 4637
crinoïdes 4639
criptogames 4788
crique 7360, 3363
— à la surface 18046
— de décapage 13227
— de fond 1265
— de rétassure 16228
— de retrait 9445, 14786
— de tension 17784
— due à la chaleur 8979
— longitudinale 10979, 17123 17123
— transversale 4676

cran de la règle du cavalier 12402
crandallite 4594
crapaud S. 3619
crapaudine 18699
— de trousseau 3198
craquage 4588
craquelure 3374
— du fond 1265
— du moule 11976
crassé 6007, 15276, 16519
crassier 3572, 6096, 16554, 16560, 18673
cratère adventif 181, 10569
crayon bleu 1910
— d'arc S. 749, 2871
— de gras 1910
— de masselotte 13055
crayons, charbons 10510
crednérite 4613
creédite 4614
crémaillère 14320
— avec pignon moteur 14324 14324
crépelé 1785
crépine 3681, 16788, 17736
— à fil enroulé 20151
— à stries 16689
— d'aspiration 17953
— rainurée S. 16689
crétacé 4626
crête 4724, 14886
— anticlinale 659, 4725
— isoclinale 9222
— de partage S. 19838
creusage des filets 15749
creusage v. taille ou creusement
creuser 2073, 5161, 5447, 11723, 18872, 20080
— en montant 2303
— un filet S. 15698
— un tunnel 19106
creuset 5512, 8950, 11461, 11476, 16455
— à thermite 18488
— couvert 4568
— cuit 7120
— d'attente 7685
— d'essai 891
— de fonderie 11471
— de fusion 4736
— de Gooch 8356
— d'acier coulé 3019
— d'argile 7160
— de graphite 8448

criques transversales 2438
cristal 4791, 14266
— anisotrope 597
— corrodé 2467, 4488
— de première consolidation S. 13149
— de roche 1535, 15014
— du premier stade 13149
— embryonnaire 9643
— en forme de sapin 739
— maclé 8151
— oscillant S. 15228
— taillé 4902
— tournant 15228
— travaillé 4902
cristallin 4798
cristallinité 4805
cristallisation 4810
cristalliser 4812
cristallite 4806, 4811
cristalloblastèse 4813
cristalloblastique 4814
cristalluminescence 4816
cristaux de trempe 3430
— en colonnes 4045
— équiaxiques 6527
— mixtes 11822
cristobalite 4642
croc à feu 14381
— à tourniquet 18141
crochet 7906, 9312, 9999, 10166
— à cercles 43770
— à émerillon 2949
— à ramasser 3684
— à talon 3688
— de mouleur 15650
— de repêchage 7218
— de sauvetage 3089
— de suspension de la grue 4598
— de tubes de pompage 19030
— en S 15403
— de mouleur 9315
crochets de mouleur S. 15511
crocidolite 4651, 8614
crocoïte 4652, 14543
croisement 4718
— de courants d'air 2380
— de cristal 4794
— double 5333
— en·rails assemblés 2539
croisillon de la cloche de sondage 2562
croisillons de la tour 2232

croissance des grains 8398
croix 4664, 13333
cromaltite 4653
Cromérien 4654
cronstedtite 4655
crookésite 4659
crossing 4719
— d'aérage 248, 261, 12737
crossite 4720
croûte 4782 15581, 16094
— calcaire déposée par les eaux de source 128
— de la fonte 16771
— de laminage S. 15580
— de poche de coulée 10485 10485
— de sable 15518
— de scorie 16532
— d'oxyde de fer 12802
— dure à texture blanche rayonnante 8844
— superficielle 18047
— terrestre 10891
cryolite 4784
cryolithionite 4785
cryptoclastique 4786
cryptocristallin 4787
cryptolite 4789
crypton 10438
cryptoperthite 4790
cubane 4817
cube 4822
cubilot 3002, 4841, 4844,
— à air soufflé équilibré 1135
— à aspiration 6797
— à dolomie 5610
— à rigole 14417
— à vent chaud 9394
— avec cuve carrée 4851
— de fonderie 7656
— Ireland 9948
cubilotier 4849
cucalite 4823
cueillir 4825,
cuffat S. 1359, 2202
— à eau 4987
— à fond mobile 5977
— d'épuisement S. 4987
cuiller 947, 983, 1101, 13328, 17151, 19070
— à clapet 12090
— à déchargement automatique 15817
— à éprouvettes 15565
— à mitraille 15661

cuiller de chargement 3335
— de cimentation 6097
— de coulée 8763, 10470
— pour deux porteurs 19189
cuiller v. cuillère
cuillère 17151
— de drague 5827
— en platine 13528
cuillère v. cuiller
cuir embouti 10650
— embouti double 5686
cuirasse ferrugineuse 8838, 8875
cuirasser 798
cuire 1112
— un noyau 4407
cuisson 1116, 2604, 2694,
— à mort 5036
— du coke 2697
cuivrage 4362
cuivre 4350
— à haute conductivité 9141 9141
— affiné 18799
— ampoulé 1769
— anodique 627
— arsénaté prismatique triangulaire S. 2
— silicium 16329
— au 99,75% - 1564
— azuré S. 1036
— brut S. 1647, 1783, 4753
— cémenté 3146
— de cément S. 15990
— de précipitation 13810
— dissous précipité S. 3146
— doux 16832
— dur 8823
— écroui S. 8823
— écroui à froid 18796
— électrolytique 6338
— en lingots 9788
— en saumons 13257
— gris 8499, 18471
— jaune S. 20283
— manganèse 11270
— noir 1647, 1783
— panaché S. 13099, 19471, 9378
— pour jets 3048
— pyriteux 4363
— régénéré 15990
— rosette 15183
— sulfuré gris 3254
— vitreux 3254
cuivré 4374

cuivrer 13478
cul-de-sac 5027
— d'œuf 16546
culbuteur 6100, 18626, 18675
  18675, 18685, 19096
— à tourillons 18961
— à wagons 18632
— automatique 990
— basculant 15222
— de berlines 19625
— de tête 10340
— rotatif 14843
culbuteurs 18676
culée S. 29
culm 4826, 7356
culot 5031
— de mine 2057
culsagééite 4828
cumberlandite 4829
cumbraïte 4830
cumengéite 4831
cummingtonite 4832
cuprifère 4352
cuprite 14533
cupro-aluminium 450
— -béryllium 1545
— -nickel 4857
— -phosphore 13175
— -plomb 4855
euprozincite 4859
curer 1099, 3671, 5764,
  15654
curette 3686, 7471, 15667
— de mineur 14384
curite 4863
curium 4864
curseur 15367
cuspidine 4890
cuve 12885, 15933
— à lessiver 10903
— à mercure 11510
— accessible 43
— avec enveloppe en tôle
  9994
— d'agitation 235
— d'amalgamation 495
— de barbotage 15625
— de décantation 5295
— de décapage 13222
— de four 7854
— de frotteur 12891
— de lavage 18126, 19707
— dégagée 7736, 9733
— d'un haut fourneau 15951
— en porcelaine 13667
— évaporatrice 6616

cuve libre S. 9733
— non isolée S. 7736
— pneumatique 13601
— pour moulage sous pres-
  sion 16592
cuvelage 3903, 16485, 18974
  18974
— descendant 5993
— du puits S. 16040
— en bois circulaire 4631
— en maçonnerie 17652
cuvette 1313, 3221, 5511,
  8561, 9896
— à broyer 11937
— du tamis 17739
cyanite 10444
cyanochroïte 4933
cyanure de potasse et de titane 18691
— de potassium 4931, 13724
  13724
cycle d'exploitation 12614
cyclone 4934
cyclopite 4935
cylindre 15073, 15104
— à air 311
— à froid 3989
— à gorge 8593
— à gradins
— à grande vitesse 9176
— à matricer 5377
— à simple effet 16380
— à tôles 13482, 13494,
  16076
— à vapeur 17425
— applicateur de peinture
  6147
— avec échelle 4943
— bombé 4210
— broyeur 4586, 47714
— cannelé 4497, 8594
— commandé 5457
— de blooming 3914
— de compression 4154
— de dressage 17728
— de flexion 1517
— de laminoir à fils 15058
— de laminoir à pas de pélerin 13282
— de pompe 20200
— de soutien 1082
— de travail 20191
— de zinc 20326
— dégrossisseur 2326
— du frein 2253
— du mouton 8730

cylindre ébaucheur 1823,
  1833, 14099
— éjecteur déclenchement
  10345
— en fonte 2999
— entraîne S. 7770
— étanche 12847
— étireur 5806
— excentrique 6187
— finisseur 7068, 7136
— hydraulique pour le
  renversement 15229
— inférieur 2183
— inférieur fixe 7229
— libre 7770
— médian 11665
— profilé 15988
— supérieur 18750
— supérieur suspendu 1138
cylindré 15094
cylindrer 15069
cylindres à cingler 16153
— à mandrin pour tubes
  soudés 11265
cylindreur S. 15105
cylindrite 4951
cymphane 4952
cyprine 4953
cyprusite 4954

D

dacite 4956
dacitique 4957
dactylite 4958
dahamite 4961
dahllite 4962
dalle 16493
dallot 2219
damage 10851, 14404, 17322
damassé 4971
damasser S. 4973
damasquiner 4973
dame 4964, 4968, 4986,
  18233
— de remblai S. 2534
— -jeanne S. 2873
— pneumatique 316
damer 14387, 17304, 18229
damoir 14402
— à air comprimé 13593
— à main et à air compri-
  mé 8774

damoir en pointe 13049
damourisation 4975
damourite 4974
danaïte 4988
danalite 4989
danburite 4990
dannemorite 4995
darapskite 4999
dartre franche 1674
— volante 1675
datolite 5005
daubréeite 5010
davainite 5013
daviésite 5014
dé de bocard 17311
déballer 5489
débit 9521, 12475
— d'air 14436
— de pipe-line 13374
débimètre 15192
déblalement de terrains recouvrement 1231
déblai 4898, 14638, 12058
déblais 5040, 5577
débloqueur de trépan 1625
déboisage 14011, 14499, 19340, 20158
déboiser 14995, 19339
déboiseur 14010, 17863, 18634
débouché 19110
déboucher le trou de coulée 13242
débourbage 3695
débourber 5764, 7479, 15654
débourbeur 5241
débourrage 5078, 19326
débourrer 5879, 6971, 19325, 5077
débrayer 5504
débris 16695
— de creusets 12521
— de fer 10008, S. 15660
— de forage 4929
— de roche 19731
débutanisation 5047
débutaniseur 5048
débuter 17217
décagement 1201, 5064, 19233
décageteur 1203
décalaminage 3479, 5225
— à la flamme 7256
décalaminé par grenaillage 18196
décalaminer 15579

décalamineur 5224
— hydraulique 9520
décalescence 5049
décantage 5051
décantation du laitier S. 15876
décanter 5050, 15921
décanteur 5293
décapage 3691, 4489, 5452, 13225
— continu 4270
— du fil 13229
— électrochimique 6324
— électrolytique 6346
décapé 13219
décaper 15654, 19580
— à l'acide 13216
décapeur 3687, 13224
décarbonisation au solvant 16909
décarburation 5056, 5057
— complète 4114
décarburé 5055
décarburer 5054, 5058
décharge 12700
déchargement 19321
— automatique 979
— de la boîte 18682
— des deux côtés de la voie 5498
— du convertisseur 5492
déchargeur à bascule S. 18681
— automatique S. 15817
— de charbon S. 3833
— mobile 159
dèche 2444
déchénite 5060
déchet 1598, 16508, 19718, 19723
— de coke 2441
— de fer 10025
— ferrifère 19722
déchets 940, 11035, 14815, 19717
— de criblage 15697
— de forge 7597
déchire-tube 2960
déchirer 18346
déclenchement 14682
déclencher 18904
déclassé S. 19280
déclavetage 19236
déclaveter 19235
déclin 5065
— de pression 13900
décliqueter 18904

déclivité 5066
décochage 10400, 15966
— par barre de piquage 1217
— par secousses 10402
— par vibrations 11408
— pneumatique 13587
décocher 10399, 12560
décocheuse 15967
décoffrage d'un plancher 5527
décollement 16515
— de la roche 16504
décolleter v. fileter
décomposer 19862
décomposition de la castine S. 5069
— des hydrocarbures 5070
— du calcaire 5069
— par les agents atmosphériques 19871
découpage 14182
— à l'arc 743
— en massif d'abattage 1812
découpé S. 7615
découper au ciseau 3484, 4892
— en massifs d'abattage S. 1791
découverte de pétrole 17817 12511
découverture 17867, 19331
découvrir S. 5404
décramper 7719
décrassage 7488, 14385, 16543, 16556
décrasser 14380, 16518
— les scories 5765, 18270
décrasseur 3577
décriquage 3477, 17790
décriquer 721, 3473
décrochage automatique 991
— du minerai 2332
décrocher 2301
— dans le puits 1043
décrocheur 10398
— automatique 992
décroissement v. diminution
décrotter 16692
décroûtage 5238
décuivrage 5074
décuivrer 5073
dédolomitisation 5083
dédoublage 12609
dédoublement 17136
— des ions 17137

dédoubler un moule 2296, 12557
déduction pour excès en silice 5084
défaut 7360
— dans la formation des images 9640
— de cisaillement 6028
— de coulage 6840
— de coulée 7362
— de fonderie 5104
— de laminage 15123
— de soudure 5106
— de surface 18048
— extérieur 19567
— visible S. 19567
défauts de laminage 11693
défect de la fonte 5109
défectuosité v. défect
défecteux 5108
déferrisation 5143
déflagrateur 5116
déflagration 5115
déflagrer 5114
déflation 5117
déflecteur 674
déflection 5120
déflegmateur 5186
défloculation 5122
défoncement 11556
déformabilité 5124
déformation 19674, 5125, 5566
— à col de bouteille 2137
— au retrait 4285
— traitement thermique 5568
— angulaire 426
— de châssis 5569
— par libération des tensions internes 3070, 5567
déformer (se-) 19673
défournement du four 6421
— du minerai 5804
défourneuse S. 20159
— de coke 3943, 14200, 14392
dégagement de chaleur 6627
— de gaz 15707
— de l'air 6563
— de l'oxyde de carbone 7609
— des produits volatils 6567
— d'hydrogène 7612

dégagement d'oxygène 6628
— instantané 9830
— instantané de gaz 7983
dégager 2301
— le modèle 11011
— le trou de coulée à l'arc électrique 12561
dégalvanisation 17866
dégalvaniser 17839
dégarnissage 3713
dégazage 5127
dégazant 5129
dégazation 5127
dégazer 5126
dégorgement 15358
dégorgeoir 7432
dégorger 15348
dégoudronnage 5255
dégoudronner 5254
dégraissage 11541
degré 13412, 17285
— de carburation 5131
— de dissociation 5132
— de dissociation d'une solution 5133
— de dureté 5134
— de pureté 5136
— de qualité 5138
— de serrage 11981
— de trempe 6135
— de trempe de l'acier 8872
— géothermique 18484
dégrossir 1926
dégrossissage 3912, 15258
dégrossisseuse 15257
dehrnite 5140
déhydrogénation 1117, 9559
déioniser 5142
delafossite 5144
délai de déchargement 13094
délaminage 13042
delessite 5146
dellénite 5155
delorenzite 5156
déloupage 16544
deltaïte 5159
delvauxite 5160
démagnétisateur 5162
demande maximum et simultanée 16376
— minimum 11767
demantoïde 5164
démasselottage 14721
démasselotter 14717
déméthanisation 5165

demi-circulaire 8715
— -coussinet intérieur S. 2148
— -coussinet supérieur S. 18737
— -moule inférieur 2174
— -produit 15841
— -rond irrégulier 6871, 7336
— -rond plat 7336
— -ronds pleins S. 76883
demoiselle 5988, 6177, 14400 14400
démolition du noyau 2331
démontable 5166, 5538
démonter 14895, 18347
— une sonde 17280
démoulage 5499, 5802, 10771, 17865
— des modèles 12976
démoulé 17857
démouler 5757, 6235, 17841
— la fonte 12560
— le lingot hors des lingotières 17843
— par renversement 5768
— par retournement 5769
— sur cadre 5766
— sur chandelles 5767
démouleur de noyau 4403, 4432
— par extraction du modèle 12977
démouleuse 10766
dendrite 5168, 6926
dendritique 738, 5169
dennisonite 5170
dénoué 9203
dénoyage 5292
densimètre 9567
densité 5176, 17023
— Baume 1354
— d'un gaz 5177
dent 3908
— à chevron 9062
— brute 3029
dentelé 12401, 15897
déparaffinage par solvant 16910
départ d'usinage 17169
département des fours 7834
dépasser 10261
déphosphoration 5188
déphosphorer S. 5189
déphosphoriser 5189
dépilage 2449

dépilage 5776, 5793, 13293, 13295, 14133, 14140, 14996, 14997, 15759, 17661, 17867
dépilement 17661, 5776
dépiler 14122, 14995, 14715, 17842
dépileur 17660
déplacement 16128
— d'air 328
— de côtes 16123
— de gaz enrichi 6489
— de la tour 14900
— de moule 4696
— des noyaux 4443
— du cavalier 12053
— normal 12376
— suivant la direction 17823
déplétion 5192
déposé par courant 4866
dépôt 5200, 13809
— allochthone 380
— alluvien 5849
— alluvionnaire 231
— chimique 3388
— clastique grossier 6810
— de charbon S. 3845
— de coke 3947
— d'escarbilles 5195
— de graphite 5196, 15872
— de minerais 12659
— de sable alluvionnaire 1691
— de zinc S. 20327
— des acides 92
— des déblais 6105
— des sources 16438
— galvanique 6340
— glaciaire 5857
— hétérotaxique 9109
— hétérotopique 9110
— homotaxique 9300
— isotopique 10082
— provisoire 12860
— superficiel 9603
dépots abyssaux 31
— alluviaux 411
— bathyaux 1340
— contemporains S. 18156
— de la mer profonde 5096
— de poussières atmosphé-riques 6130
— éoliens 185
— glaciaires 5853, 8250
— hétéromésiques 9106

dépôts isomésiques, 10067
— isopiques 10075
— lacustres 10493
— littoraux 10894
— marins 11321
— pélagiques 13050
— sédimentaires 15702
— synchroniques 18156
— terrigènes 18434
dépouille 5274
dépouillement S. 2449
dépoussiérage 6137
dépoussiérer 14716
dépoussiéreur 6132, 6138
dépresseur 5201
dépression de la mine 11951
dépropanation 5202
dépuration 5211
— par voie humide 19986
derbylite 5212
dérivation 17216
— de conduite 10568
dermolithe 5213
dernière cannelure 10559
derrick de production S. 13995
— de sondage 2104
— pour forage multiple 12123
— tubulaire 19088
désaérage 319
désaffleurer 10261
désagrégation 2322
— de la maçonnerie 11012
désagrégation v. effrittemen
désagréger 19862
— par fusion 18923
désaluminage 459
désaréation 5044
désaréateur 5045
désargenter 5239
désarticulé 9203
descenderie 2469, 5436, 5627, 9700, 16680
descendre 5226, S. 15346
— un piston dans le puits 15340
descenseur 8485
descente 15382
— à talons multiple 17563
— braisée de coulée 17563
— de coulée 13742, 17211
— de la cage d'extraction 11013
— de tubage 11076, 11234
— du cône 11073

descente et remontée 5228
déschisteur 15981
descloizite 5229
désémulsionnant 5167
désétamer 5265
déséthanisateur 5102
déshydrateur 5288, 5289
déshydratation 5291
désignation des marques 5234
— du minerai 3639
désilicification 5235
désilicifier 5236
désincrustation 15597
désincruster 15580
désintégrateur 5519
désintégration 5537
— en blocs 1799
desmine 5242
désoxydant 5182, 14564
désoxydation 5179, 5183, 10353, 14571
désoxyder 5184
desquamation 13041
— en écailles S. 6648
dessablage 1742
— au tonneau 14447, 19097
— hydraulique 9545
— par jet de grenaille 16199
dessabler 1696, 7394
dessableur 15476
dessableuse 15478
dessicateur 5232
— par le vide 19426
dessicateur v. séchoir
dessication v. séchage
dessiner 5753
dessouder 19332
dessus du foyer 4730
destinézite 5243
désulfurant 5247
désulfuration 5244
— Doctor 5591
désulfurer 5245
désurchauffeur 5249
détacher 4893
détection de craquelure 4582
— de fissure S. 4582
détendre 14719
détermination calorimétrique 2757
— chimique de la puissance calorique 3389
— de la conductance 5262
— de la densité 5259
— de la grosseur 16446

détermination de la puissance calorifique 5257
— de la solubilité 5261
déterminer la puissance calorifique 5263
— la puissance calorifique par voie calorimétrique 5264
détonateur 1738, 1745, 2792
— électrique 6260
détritus 10254
détroit 16933
détuber 14123
déutéroprisme 13958
devant d'une pompe 10873
devanture de foyer 7843
développement 5275
— de la surface 18049
— de la texture 5277
— en profondeur 2413
— progressif S. 546
développer 5272
devenir argileux 15980
déverser 13738, S. 18354
déversoir 19919
dévêtir le moule S. 12560
déviateurs 5119
déviation 5280
— du trou 19138
dévidoir 17149
dévier 5118
devis 6569
— quantitatif 1580
dévisser 1068
Dévonien 5284
— ancien 12869
— supérieur 12219
devonite 5285
dewalquite 763, 5287
deweylite 5297
dewindtite 5298
dézincage 5299
diabase 5300
diaboléite 5302
diaclase 5303, 11229
— horizontale S. 2169, 7341, 9339
— longitudinale 1045, 17822
— transversale 4908, 5441
diaclases horizontales 16065
diadochite 5304
diaftorèse 5305
diagenèse 5306
diagramme 5312

diagramme d'équilibre 6528
— d'équilibre du fer-carbone 9964
— de niveau 9607
— de procédé 7426
— de solidification 5314
— de traitement thermique 9001
— fer-carbone 9963
— indicateur 10964
diagraphie de magnétisme nucléaire 12418
— de radioactivité S. 12417
— de rayons gamma 7949
— nucléaire 12147
diagraphies de boues 12082
dialogite 5315
diamagnétique 5316
diamant 13169
diamantin S. 121
diamètre du fil S. 5319
— du fourneau 5318
— intérieur 2076
— moyen de filetage 13414
diamétreur 9250, 15774
diamorphisme 5334
diaphorite 5335
diaphragme S. 12671
— de coulée 5484
diaprir 5339
diaschiste 5341
diaspore 5342
diastrophisme 5343
diatomite 11876, 14410, 16309, 16318, 18365
diatrème 5347
dichroïsme 5349
dichroïte 5350
dickinsonite 5351
dickite 5352
didyme 5353
diénerite 5387
diéthanolamine 5023
dietrichite 5390
dietzéite 5391
différence dans les analyses 5393
— d'épaisseur 5394
difficile à usiner 6664
difficilement fusible 9154, 16706
diffuseur 5402, 6217, 17214
diffusion 5403
digital 4959
digitation 7109
digue à déversoir 12739

dihydrite 5409
dilatation thermique 18483
dilatomètre 5413
diluvial 5419
dilivium 5420, 5857
dimension 5421
— inférieure 19279
— intermédiaire 1287
— primitive 7202
dimensions de la pièce de fonte 5424
diminuer la production 14560
diminution de la solubilité 5080
dimorphe 5426
dimorphie S. 5425
dimorphisme 5425
Dinantien 5427
diopside 5429
dioptase 5430, 6408
diorite 5431
— quartzifère 14267
dipyre 5454
dipyrisation 5455
directeur de fonderie 7661
direction 17816, 18875
— axiale 1018
— de faille 6860
— de l'affleurement 4554
— de la déviation 5466
— de pose 9245
— de stratification 10838
— du filon 10836
— du front de taille normale au clivage 2066
— générale 8153
— magnétique 11187
— moyenne 1012
— principale S. 8153
diriger les flammes vers la sole 5456
discordance 5505, 19240
— angulaire 591, 3730, 5582
— mécanique 17885
discordant 12346, 19328
dislocation 5525, 6839, 10645, 18933, 18850
disparition brusque d'une couche 28
dispositif coupe et cône 1448
— d'alimentation des pièces 15379
— d'arrêt 3087
— d'attelage 10190

dispositif d'avance mécanique S. 13781
— de blocage 5359
— de chargement 3346
— de chargement du gueulard 3339
— de contrôle du débit d'un puits 12833
— d'ébranlage 14422
— d'éclairage 9635
— d'enfournement des lingots 9798
— d'enlèvement 20159
— de fermeture du moule 11974
— de levage 10754
— de renversement S. 18675
— de sécurité 15420
— de sûreté 15415
— de tamisage 16306
— doseur 1337
— pour accrocher les lingots S. 9793
— pour enlever le couvercle 10761
— pour la mise hors feu 1872 1872
— pour saisir les lingots 9793
— pour verser à la main 8788
disposition à trois pôles S. 18567
— des convertisseurs 808
— des cordons de soudure 1373
— des leviers 10718
— en couches S. 807
— tripolaire 18567
disque 5479
— de fonte 3000
— de tronçonnage 4928
— en bois 20181
— en flanelle 7278
— polisseur 2523
disséminé 5539
dissociation électrolytique 6341
dissocier 5542
dissolution 16900
dissolvant 5546
distance entre l'épaulement du joint et le calibre 17336
— entre les bras 13501, 9365

distance entre les étages 16958
— entre supports 18450
— horizontale des affleurements 12380, 12463
— focale 7514
— utile 18575
distillat avec paraffine séparée en cristaux 13888
— de goudron 18316
— léger 14462
— paraffineux 19842
— sous pression 13902
— spécial 1705
— stabilisé 19866
distillateur à chaudière 16113
— à vapeur 17448
— de goudron 18321
— discontinu 1335
distillation à la cornue 14801
— à la vapeur d'eau 17427
— atmosphérique 929
— continue 4266
— dans le vide 19427
— extractive 6713
— fractionnée 7687
— intermittante 1331
— lente du charbon 2868
— primaire du pétrole 17868
— sèche 6031
distillé S. 13991
— directement 17714
distiller 5551
— à sec 5552
— par voie sèche S. 5552
distributeur 5576, 8928
— de minerai 12641
— doseur 11600
— vibrant 19546
district minier 11764
distribution à main 8781
— automatique 987
— de la fonte 5573
— de force 13776
— de la presse 4292
— du marteau 8744
— par piston 13394
— par robinet 14659
— par soupape 19453
— par tiroir 16615
ditroïte 5579
diviser le sable 2305
diviseur à broches 17081
— -aérateur 189

diviseur centrifuge 3213
— rotatif 15197
division 12946
— d'Erié 6539
— du courant d'air 327
— en boules 1165
— en oreillers empilés 1329 13297
— en plaques 16503, 16082
dixenite 5588
docimasie 892
dogleg 5597
doigt de démoulage 11986
— en caoutchouc 15309
dolérine 5601
dolérite 5602
dolérophanite 5604
dolomie 13245, 14858
— crue 14453
— cuite 2714, 5607
— stabilisée 17270
dolomite 1633, 5608
— vacuolaire 16767
dolomitisation 5616
dôme 5620
— à vapeurs 19468
— de lave 9930
— de sel 15444
domeykite 5622
domite 5625
donner la trempe à l'acier S. 8848
— le vent 1839, 19136
dopplérite 5636
dorage S. 8125
— à presse 18871
dorer 8224
dorure 8225
— à la main 8760
— à mordant 13272
— à presse 13871
— au feu 9419
— au mercure 8226
— en feuilles 8345
— galvanique 6333
— par immersion 19778
dos 1044, 19278
dosage du carbone 5258
— d'un seul corps 5260
dosse 16492
double décimètre 1571
— -duo 5695
— fermeture 5679
— goujonné 5680
— retrait 5649
— T à ailes ordinaires 5681

double T à larges ailes 8528
doubler 5637
douche 16218
doudgeon 18980
— double 5659, 5682
doughtyte 5692
douglasite 5693
douille à ressort S. 12777
— combinée 4060
— de câble S. 15169
dragage 5823
— à la pelle à vapeur 17446
dragline 5739
drague 1098, 5729, 9045, 12203
— à godet poussant 6754,
— à godets 2501, 15641
— à pelle 16213
— aspirante 7490
— à suction 17952
— chargeuse 10915
drague v. escavateur
draguer 5727
drainage par gravité 8487
drainé 5745
drapeau 17810
draubréelite 5011
dravite 5752
dréelite 5830
dressant 6253, 17528
dresser 158, 17721 6735, 13 13451
— au tour 6759
— une meule 5836
drille à bouchons 4468
droit de tréfonds S. 15300
droits de concession pétro-lifère 15301
— d'exploitation du pétrole 12505
druse 6020
drusiforme S. 6022
drusique 6022
ductile 6073
ductilité 6075
dudgeon s. doudgeon
dufrénite 6079
dufrénoysite 6080
duftite 6081
dumalite 6091
dumontite 6094
dumortiérite 6095
dundasite 6107
dungannonite 6109
dunite 6110
duo dégrossisseur 19187

dur comme le verre 8277
durable 16874
durain 6115, 17116
duralumin 6116
durbachite 6120
durci 8851
durcir 8846
durcissement 8858
— à l'air 252
— par écrouissage 17733
— par précipitation 215
— par revenu 18375
— secondaire 15768
— structural 13815
— superficiel 8826
durdénite 6121
durée critique 4647
— d'arrêt 9247
— de charge 18642
— d'éruption 7443
— de la chauffe 6118
— de la distillation 2864
— de marche 2607
— de passage de la charge 13095
— de poste 1197
— de recuit 616
— de revenu 18399
— de trempe 14294
— d'oscillation 6119
— d'usinage 16988
— du grillage S. 2607
— du réchauffement à coeur 7809
dureté 6117, 8871
— Brinell 2408
— de cémentation 2923
— de tranchant 6201
— Shore 16171
— superficielle 16476
Dyas 6146
dyke 3907, 6148
— de basalte 20016
— différencié 5397
dynagraphe 6149
dynamitage 6153
dynamite 8211
— à base inerte 9759
— -gomme 8664, S. 12318
dynamo à gaz 8000
— à vapeur 17428
dynamomètre S. 6149
dysanalyte 6157
dyscrasite 6158
dysluite 6160

dysprosium 6162
dyssuite 6163

E

eau à souder 16889
— acidulée 101
— alcaline 361
— ammoniacale 520, 10871
— ascendante 854
— boueuse des bocards 14142
— bouillante 2001
— bouillie 1981
— brute 12198
— courante S. 14970
— cuivreuse S. 20322
— cuprifère 20322
— d'amorçage 10914, 13934
— de baryte 1261
— de carrière 14261
— de cendres de bois 13014, 20171
— de cristallisation 19792
— de diaclases 4628
— de galerie 2922
— de graphite 8451
— de puits 19974
— de refroidissement 4346
— de rivière 14970
— d'imbébition 19800
— d'interposition 9710
— épurée 14191
— étrangère 6711
— ferrugineuse 3268
— fluviale S. 14970
— forte pour planches de zinc 6574
— fossile 4214
— gravitationnelle 8496
— hygroscopique 9581
— hypogène 854
— marginale 6204
— martiale 3268
— mécaniquement interpo-sée S. 9710
— mercurielle 14305
— naturelle 12198
— oxygénée 9561
— potassique S. 20171
— réchauffée 19669
— régale 726

eau schlammeuse 16634
— supérieure 18753
— sur-jacente S. 18753
eaux azotées 1033
— dormantes 1091
— vannes acides 19738
ébarbage 3478, 3690, 5843, 6974, 18900
— à la flamme 9222/a
ébarbé 3682
ébarber 2616, 3472, 3672, 3741, 6970
ébarboir 18897
ébarbeur 3702, 6973, S. 17212
ébarbeuse 2620, 3046, 6977, 17212
ébarbure 2339, 2618, 15745, 16703
— inférieure 2157
ébauchage 1808, 1830, 3912
ébauche 1679, 13834
— pour presse à filer 6723
ébauché 15250, 15256
— tubulaire 13373
ébaucher 3904, 15242
— la galette d'argile 13857
ébaucheur 15999
ébavurer 6973
éboulé 3120, 6776
éboulement 2324, 3122, S. 6169, 6766, 6774, 6778, 7639, 10524, 12299, 16607, 16701, 18594
— du toit 6775, 15141
s'ébouler 3119, 15338, 17669
éboulis 15350
éboutage 4660/b
ébranlage 14420
ébranloir 14119
ébullition 1998
écaillage 1787, 13483, 15595, 15582
— sec 6042/a
écaille 15568, 16597
— de laminage 15087, 15129
écailles 15485
— de diamant 5320
écailleux 15601
écart toléré 13113
écartement 16957
— de voie 8109
— des cylindres 5550
échafaud 15576

échafaudage 6789, 15577, 17293
échancrure latérale S. 10321
échange des analyses 6645
échangeur à faisceaux 16095
— de chaleur pour puits 19837
échantillonnage 18522
— en long 10984
échantillon 15453
— choisi 13209
— de carotte 4439
— de fond 2166
— de gisement 14751
— de trépan 1629, 2089
— moyen 366
— obtenu par corrosion 4490
— par prélèvement 4273
— pris au grappin 8382
échantillonner 4023
échauffement 9007
— spontané 17147
s'échauffer 8967
échelle 15586
— de dureté 15590,
echinoderme 6188
éclaboussure 16995
éclair 7289
éclairage 9634
éclat 3474, 7289
— adamantin 123
— bronzé 2456
— de fonte 2996
— de pierre 16963
— gras 16804
— nacré 12153, 13022
— résineux 13415
— schillérisant 15622
éclatement 2261
éclateur 16980
éclimètre S. 3736
éclisse 7210
— plate 7333
éclogite 6189
écluse 16708
écoin S. 2031, 8907
écope S. 1101
écorchure S. 6647
écoulement 12700
— critique 4643
— d'air 279
— laminaire 10501
— par gravité 8489
— turbulent 6195, 19128
s'écouler S. 7419

écran 2368, 5337
écrasement 10251
— de boisage 10096
— de joint 4762
— de moule 4763
— de noyau 4764
— des piliers 16440 18597
écraser 10246, 19371
écrémage 6009, 16465
écrémer 16468, 16469
écrémoir 16461
écrille 7208
écrou 7508, 12427
écrouir 3958, 3988, 5760
écrouissage 3973, 4010, 5797, 5797, 13043, 20190
écroulement 3122, 6778, 18594
s'écrouler 3119, 6771
écrouté 5223
écumoire 16467
écume 15728, 16489
— d'aluminium 452, 7511
— de graphite 10376
— de mer S. 11439
écumer 16459
edingtonite 6213
effectuer une révision 14504 14504
effet calorifique 2753
— calorifique de la réaction 8975
— Custer 12806
— d'entaille 12398
— de la percussion S. 6215
— de masse 11357
— de pelure d'orange 375/a
— de pistonnement 18091
— du coup 6215
— gazéifiant 8077
— Leonard 5774
— thermique v. effet calori-fique
— trempant 3452
effeuillage 6648
s'effeuiller 15578
effilement 2139, 18100, 18202
effiler 18276
effondré S. 3120
effondrement 16414
— circulaire 3107, 6856
— magmatique du toit 11170
effort 17730, 17782, 18414
— appliqué 720/a

effort de compression 4156
— de déformation 7619
— d'extension S. 18409
— de flambage 4640
— de flexion 1518, 1520
— de tension 17798
— de tirage S. 14126
— de torsion 8782
— de traction 14126, 18409,
— de traction au crochet 5777
— de traction au démarrage 17383
— résistant totale 18793
— tranchant 16084
— transversal 1518
effritement 19869
s'effriter 5518
effusiv 6218
égalisateur de pression 373, 6526
eglestonite 6227
égoutteur 5290, 5950
égouttoir 5950
éguisage v. affûtage au meulage
éguisé v. affilé
éguisement v. affûtage ou meulage
eichwaldite 6231
Eifélien 6232
einsteinium 6234
éjecteur 6241
— à déclenchement 10344
— par le vide 19433
— placé dans le puits 5099
— pneumatique 295/a
élargir 7348, 19274
— une fente par un coin 19877
élargissement 1408, 2578, 6487, 19277
— de filon S. 1853
— du fond de trou de mine 2605
élargisseur 19275
élasticité de cisaillement S. 18841
— de compression 6247
— de flexion 6249
— de tension S. 6248
— de torsion 6251
— de traction 6248
— des matériaux 6250
— transversale 18841
élatérite 6252

électricité voltaïque S. 7927
électroaimant 6355
electro-analyse 6337
électrode capsulée 5516
— cylindrique 4950
— de la sole 11067
— de précipitation 13814
— décinormale 5062
— en charbon 2833
— en fer 9971
— enrobée 16119
— normale 17345
— réticulaire 12245
— rétiforme S. 12245
électro-érosion 6331
electroforage 6322
électrolyse 6335, 6354
— de l'eau 9564
— du zinc 6352
électrolyser 6334, 6353
électrolyte 6336
— amphotère 540
électromagnétisme 6357 6358
électrométallurgie 6360
électro-négatif 6363
électron 6362
électropyromètre 18493
électrosténolyse 6369
élément 6374, 10204
— atmophile 922
— broyeur 4772
— combustible 4070
— d'addition 405
— de construction en acier estampé 13883
— de couloir oscillant 18936 18936
— de pile 3132
— structurel tubulaire 19082 19082
éléments chauffants en plaques d'acier 17488
— décomposés à l'air 19864
éléolite 6243, 6372
élévateur 6377
— auxiliaire 18824
— à console 2243
— à godets 2502
— à grille 8580
— à vis 15706
— d'empilage 17279
— de tige 15050, 17945,
— de tiges 5899
— de tubage 2938
— du charbon 3833

élévateur pour sondes 14899
élévation S. 45, 14943, 6375, 10759
— de température S. 18384
— de l'eau 14379
élever 14370
eliasite 6381
élimination de l'eau saline 15446
— des matières sableuses 6383
— d'une fraction gazeuse 16464
— du phosphore 6382
— du sable 15494
éliminer la fraction de kérosène du pétrole 16457
élingue 16641
élinguer 16640
ellsworthite 6387
elpidite 6393
élutriation 6395
éluvial 6396
éluvion 6397, 6398
éluvium S. 6398
elvan 6399
émail 6433
— vitreux 19572
émaillage à chaud 9413
— à froid 3976
— au poudré 6032
— au trempé 19992
— électrique 6272
émailler 6432
emballage 12843
emballer 12824
— un noyau 7008
emballeur 12841
embarras d'eau 19821
— de paraffine 12910
embase 4015, S. 9993
embellissement de la surface 12674
emboîtement S. 10215
embolite 6402
embouchure 10466, 12040
— de la tuyère 19160
— principale du carneau 11218
embouer S. 7479, 12067
embourber 12067
embout à oxygène 12820
— protecteur de filetage 18554
embouti à la presse 5087

embouti de faible profondeur
    5089
emboutir 5509, 7268
— à froid 3960
emboutissage 5417/a
— de reprise 14556
— hydromécanique 9553
— profond 4852/a
emboutissoir 2963
embranchement 14360, 2256
embrayage 3794
— à roue libre 12776
— de voies de manoeuvre
    3795
— mobile 16619
embrayer 4215
émeraude 6407, 16742
émeri 6411, 8553
émerillon 18137
émeriser 6410
emmagasineur 11000
emmancher par frettage
    16224
emmonsite 6418
émoulage v. affûtage ou
    meulage
émoussé 12439
empaquetage de chutes 2659
empaqueter les chutes 2655
empâter (la grille) 2690
empilage 13284
— souple S. 10808
empilement 13284
empiler 1195
emplacement 10943, 19976
— d'exploitation 12708
— de sondage 5907
— de sonde 5893
— du sondage 5940
emplectite 6419
emploi répété des eaux 14736
    14736
empointer v. affiler
empoise S. 9463
empoutage 18611
empreinte 6092, 9666, 9729
    11970, 11973, 16418
empreinte v. estampage
— d'ébauchage 1809
— de finissage 7129
— de matage 7812
— de tenailles 5598
empressité 6420
emprisonné 12442
émulsifiant 6427
émulsification 6425

émulsifier 6130
émulsion 6128
— d'eau dans l'huile 19784
— d'huile dans l'eau 12496
— stable 17272
en argile 1934/a
— asbeste 841
— aval 5714
— bon état 16934
— colonnes 4044
— couches épaisses 9027
— deux parties 4230
— direction de rallonge
    2817
— direction des limets 6452
— état de traitement
    thermique 9679
— forme de cloche 1458
— forme de diabolo 5301
— forme de grille 10582
— forme de loupe 1161
— gradins renversés 12751
— gros morceaux 9676
— marche 9675, 9681
— marche productive 12542
— mauvais état 12690
— mottes 3789
— plusieurs parties 4229
— phase de pompage 12544
— phase de travail 12541
— plaquettes 13534
— rouleau 3923/a
— service 9681, 12554
— talus 45
énargite 6439
encagement 2685, 5064, 12553
    12553
encageur 1465, 2149, 2191,
    2684, 9216, 11722, 15373
— automatique 974
enchevêtré 9884
enchevêtrer 9883
enchevêtrement 9885
enclave S. 6444, 9711
— énallogène 6658,
    20271
— exogénétique 6658
— exogène S. 20271
— homoéogène 3916
enclume 677
— porte-matrice 16949
enclumette 8753
enclusion S. 9711
encoche 10117, 12264,
    12394

encoche de clavette 10328,
    10331
encocher une barre 16684
encombrement 12732
encrassement d'un tuyau
    13330
encrochement d'eau de
    bordure 6205
encroûté 5815
encroûtement 5815/a
endéiolite 8456
endenter 15643
endlichite 6459
endommagement par la
    fumée 4970
endosmose électrique
    6273
endroit de pliage S. 1514
— défectueux 5107, 5110
enduire 3879, 12068
enduit 3880, 5841/a
— contre la rouille 15395
— plastique 13471
endurance 6465
endurcir superficiellement
    6737
énergie du champ 6996
— volumétrique 19599
enfermé 12442
enfler 1467
enfournement du creuset 15919
    15919
enfourner (les matériaux)
    10900
enfourneuse 3340, 3349
— de lingots 9786
enfumer 16758
engin S. 8231
engorgement du creuset 1810
— du four de grillage 3752
— du haut-fourneau 3519
engorger la coulée 3514
engouffrement 7398
engoujonnage 13308
engoujonner 14649
engrenage 3909, 8125
— conique 1569
— cylindrique 17226
engrenages 8124
engrènement des dents 8139
enlèvement de pétrole 12517
— de terrains v. déblaie-
    ment
— des battitures 14722
— des cendres 14710
— des lingots 10771

enlèvement du fond 14712
— du loup 15677
enlever 17842
— à la pelle 15638
— les bavures de joint
    14718
— les creusets 18218
enlevure S. 2340, 10238,
    16596
enregistrement 10964
enregistreur de couple de
    clé de serrage 18717
enrichir 1524
enrichissement 4166
— des minerais 4168,
    12630
— des minerais par flottage
    4161
enrobage secondaire 5718
enroulement 1600, 20098
enrouler 15070, 20085
s'enrouler 19672
— en couronne 20083
enrouleur 17148
ensellement S. 12394
ensemble auxiliaire 1003
— d'élévation 9235
— des opérations pour
    entrer en production
    4117
— souple 10808
enseveli 6192
enstatite 6490
entaillage 12403
entaille 10117, 10373,
    12394, 12403, 16669
entaillé 9254
entaille du couteau 19452
— en forme de coin 19879
entaillement 2777
entailler 4874
entalpie 6491
enterré 2591
enterrer le moule 14390
entonnoir 7820
— à eau chaude 9452
— à filtrer 7047
— à trop-plein 4185
— à tuyau de vapeur 17430
— compte-gouttes 6003
— de coulée 1311, 1313,
    13748, 13756, 18953
— de coulée à tuyau 3591
— de filtre 7044
— de sûreté 14046
— en platine 13518

entonnoir en porcelaine
    13664
— souterrain 8309
entraîné directement 13800
entraîneur en tôle d'acier
    rivetée 14978
— forgé amovible 5251
entrée 9820, 9853,
— d'air 294
— de fendue 152, 155
— de mine 13409
— latérale du laminoir
    9780
entrepôt 17373
entreprise minière 1120
entrer en production 4085
entretenir 19358
entretoisage 8239
entretoise 4668, 4700,
    8245, 9824, 10215,
    16169, 16954
entretoisement 17898
entretoises de la tour de
    sondage 5215
entropie 6494
entuber 2907, 15343
enture 2021
envahissement d'eau 19786
— d'eaux latérales 6447
envasement 12094
enveloppe 2930, 4571,
    10100, 16139
— de gaz 8001
— de la maîtresse-tige
    15571
— de protection 14040
— de tension 16104
— de tuyaux 13352, 13357
— des étalages 16183
— d'une chaudière 1971
— d'une soufflante S. 1856
— d'un haut fourneau 16106
— en tôle 10012
— en tôle de fer 16091
— extérieure de la cuve
    12697
envelopper la tige du noyau
    1593
envoyage S. 13532
Eocène 6698
éolien 921, 6499
éosphorite 6500
épaissement 2535/a
épaisseur 18507, 20064
— de fonte 19655
— de la paroi 18512

épaisseur de sable 19520
— de tôle 13500
— des roues 12092
— des couches rejetées
    S. 17750
— du feuillard 17856
— du fil 5319
— prescrite 17029
épaississeur 5175,
    18506
— des boues 14143
Eparchéen 6504
épaule du trépan 10210
éperon 17224
éphésite 6508
épichlorite 6510
épiclastique 6511
épidiabase 6313
épidesmine 6512
épididymite 6514
épidiorite 6515
épidote 6516
épigène 6517
épigenèse 6518
épigénite 6519
épingle 17191
épingler 6825
épingles des pointes
    15511
épinglette 12205, 16451
épi-roche 6520
épirogénie 6507
épisser un cable dans le
    «rope socket»
épissure à manchon d'un
    câble 16594
épizone 6522
éponge de fer s. 17144
éponte 3379
épontille de cale et
    d'entrepont 5063
époque coloradienne 4031
— glaciaire 5858
— scythienne 16491
épreuve de pression à
    vide 13925
— négative 12212
épreuve positive 13702
— radiale 14329
éprouvette 17030, 18449
    18456
— attenante 3015
— conique 18446
— coulée à part 15862
— de coulabilité 7470
— de métal liquide 11880

éprouvette de métal solidi-
   fié 16893
— de réserve 16977
— de traction 18412
— de trempe 3425, 3437
— de trempe en coin 19887
— en gradins 17543
epsomite 1632
épuiser 5189/a
épurant 14610
épuration à sec du gaz
   6032/a
épuré 20204
épurer 14192, 14593
— par lavage et filtrage
   6394
épuisé 14159
épuisement 5292
— en répétitions 17290
— en un seul jet 16403
épuiser 2141, 5193, 6145,
   13535, 15638
épurateur 15609, 8046
épurateur à gaz 15721
épuration 14607
— à l'air comprimé 323
— à sec des gaz 6038
— de l'eau 19807
— de gaz 8053, 8045
— par voie humide 19996
— pneumatique 323
équarissoir 2430
équation d'état 6525
— d'une combinaison 6524
équerre (de-) 571
— pliante S. 1570
— à lisser 579, 17235
— en fer 572
équilibrage 1139
— hydraulique 9513
— par contrepoids 1140
équilibre calorifique 8984
— de dissociation 6529
équilibrer 1121
équipe 7951
— de foreurs 5921
— de nettoyage 3680
— de sauvetage 9068
— de forage S. 5938
— de forage sous pression
   16793
— électrique dans la tour
   10788
équivalent chimique 3394
— en acier brut 4755
— stœchiométrique 17628

éraillure 7916
erbium 6536
ère 6535
— archéenne 761
— cénozoïque 3184, 10270
— éozoïque 6501
— paléozoïque S. 12872
— psychozoïque 14087
— tertiaire 18436
erikite 6541
erinite 6542
erionite 6543
érosion 6545, 15240
— de sable 15491
— éolienne 184
— par éclatement 13554
— remontante 14805
erratique 6549, 18858
erreur dans la prévision
   du retrait 20238
— de mesure 11397
— de température 18381
errite 6552
érubescite S. 6553, 13154
éruption 1757, 1860, 6558
— d'un sondage 20068
érythrine 6560
érythrosidérite 6561
escarpe 1344
escarpement S. 1916
— de faille 6846
escavateur S. 1098
— à godets S. 15641
escavateur v. drague
escoupe S. 14212
espace annulaire 624
— d'eau S. 19810
espacement 16957, 19971
esprit d'huile 12529
essai 6675, 18441
— à blanc 1685
— à chaud 8996
— à froid 4005
— à la goutte 17158
— à la perle 1366
— à la touche 17159
— à l'étincelle 16985
— à plein 12571
— au chalumeau 1888
— au choc 9647, 16148
— au choc sur éprouvette
   entaillée 16149
— au forgeage 7599
— au refoulement 16144
— aux tiges 5910
— Baumann 1353

essai d'acceptation 41
— de bordage 7276
— de choc sur éprouvette
   entaillée 12397
— de cisaillement 16087
   16025
— de comparaison 4106
— de compression 4157
— de coulabilité 3034
— d'écrasement au choc
   16144
— de décapage 13218
— de dureté Brinell 2409
— de dureté Rockwell 15044
   15044
— de dureté Vickers 19555
— de fatigue 6836
— de fatigue par choc 14732
   14732
— de flambage 2512
— de flexion 1521
— de flexion après trempe
   1522
— de flexion au choc 14734,
   16143
— de flexion statique 18845
— de ductilité 4837/a
— de flottage 7389
— de fluage 4624
— de forage 2107
— de forgeage 19355, 7599
— de fracture par choc sur
   barreaux entaillés 12265
— de fragilité 18802
— d'élargissement 2548
— d'emboutissage 5086,
   6540, 9730
— d'endurance 6836
— d'endurance à la rupture
   au choc 16367
— de macro-attaque 5091
— d'inflammabilité 3721
— de pénétration par striage S. 15682
— de perçage 5911, 5869,
— de pliage 1503, 4689
— de pliage à chaud 9392
— de pliage alterne 430
— de pliage en travers
   18842
— de pression à bille 1155
— de réchauffement par
   acides 80
— de résilience 9648
— de résilience Charpy
   pour l'acier 3352

essai de résistance à l'usure 19858
— de rupture 2309, 2336
— de soudabilité 19955
— de thermoviscosité à la
chaleur 18497
— de torsion 8778
— de tournage en gradins
17545
— de traction 18411
— de traction 18411
— de trempe 8868
— de vieillissement rapide
37
— des minerais 12628
— dynamique 6152
— effectif 7000
— final 7071
— hydraulique 9539
— isolé 16406
— latéral 16277
— mécanique 11416
— par curage 1107
— par pistonnage 18094
— physique 13194
— pneumatique 13600
— préliminaire 13845, 13849
— sclérométrique 15682
— statique 17395
— tangentiel 18243
essayer 6684, 18440
essayeur de couches 19053
— de formations 7614
essence de craquage 4585
— de distillation 17715
— de gaz naturel 12194
— éthylée 10613
— naturelle 2947
— réformée 14622
essieu 1025
— arrière 1047
— portant 1388
— tubulaire 19059
— tubulaire avec tourillons
19060
essonite S. 3579
essorer à l'air 271
essoreuse 3200
estacade de chargement S.
10921
— de déversement 18678
estampage pièce étampée
5983, 5996
estampage v. empreinte
estampe S. 2127
estamper 3924, 5972, 18097
estampillage 16321

estampiller 17305
estimation des réserves
14743
estuaire 7316
étage 17283
— cénomanien 15855
— londinien 10967
— scythien 15757
— sparnacien 16989
— stampien 17320
— stéphanien 17554
— urgonien 19405
— vindobonien 19559
— werfénien 19979
étagère à moules 14322
— à noyaux S. 14322
— à pipettes 13379
étai 14177, 17540, 19533
— métallique 12835
— posé à front 6752
étaiement 14025, 16173
étain 13138, 18645
— à souder 16841, 16864
— d'alluvion 17772
— de Banca 1173
— de bois 18655
— de Malacca 17740
— de roche 11743
— en saumons 1805, 13270
— phosphoreux 13178
— plombifère 18647
— pour soudures 16841
— pur 14189
étais S. 16173
étalage 2118/a
étalages dégagés S. 7737
— libres 7737
étamage 18864
— à chaud 9449
étamer 18644
étampe 8905, 14176, 17329
— à ébarber 18902
— niveler 10031
— de dessous 11377
— inférieure 2187
— supérieure 19363
étamper à chaud 9426
étampes de couverts 4564
— poinçons 4916
étanche 15737
étanchéité à l'air 329
— hydraulique 19998

étancher 12826
étançon 17906
— d'acier 17499
— de cassage 2334

étançon de mines 11738
— élastique coulissant
20300
— extensible 6669
— métallique 11558, 17503
— métallique flexible 160
— télescopique 4014
— tubulaire à télescope
pour ossature de
plancher 18362
— tubulaire pour galeries
de mines 19078
étançonner 1792
étau 1495
— à chaine 3249
— à main 8790
— à pied 9207
— à tubes 13369
— à vis S. 8790
— d'affûtage pour scies
15558
— d'avoyage S. 15558
— de la table 18188
— du Nord S. 9207
— limeur 1494
— ordinaire 9207
étayage 17407
étayer 2230
éteindre 1846
étendue 14412
— de la température 14413
étêtage 18760
éther de pétrole 13133
— sulfurique 6576
étincelle de fer 10017
étincellement 8300
étincelles étoilées 17377
— produites à une fréquence élevée 14418
étiquette 10448
étirabilité 5787
étirage 5791, 17797
— à chaud 9411
— à froid S. 3973
— à froid de tubes coulées
3015/a
— brillante 6031/a
— de tube à mandrin 1213/a
— des tubes 18979
— dû au cylindre supé-
rieur 13911
— du fil 5803
— en fil 20123
— par voie humide 19989
étiré 5814
— de la loupe 16880
étirer 5754, 5763, 6188

étirer à chaud 9410
— à froid 3957
— brillant 2396
— l'acier en barres 5771
— le fer 5761
— les tubes 5772
— sous le marteau 7574
étirer v. tréfiler
étireur 5788
étoile de tailleur de limes 7004
étonner S. 13573
— le quartz 4327
étouffement 1202, 18582
étourpiller une mine 13945
étranglement d'une couche 1352
étrangler 3515, 13312
étrésillon S. 16169
étrésillonnement S. 17898
étrésillonner 16167
étreinte 12298, 12300, 18531
étrier 3724, 7610, 13424, 17743
— d'élévation 10762
— de la poche de coulée 10472, 10478, 10484
— de serrage 18419
— de suspension 18080
— de suspension du tuyau d'arrivée 18029
ettringite 6577
étude chimique 3400
étuvage 17700
étuve 6055, 6061, 17695
— à air pulsé 9398
— à noyaux 4409, 4429, 4448
— à rayonnement infra-rouge 9772
— à recirculation d'air 17699
— à sécher S. 6059
— à sécher et griller 6053
— continue 4275
— de séchage S. 6693
— par parties diélectriques 5384
— tunnel 19112
étuver 17694
étuves de séchage 6063
eucairite 6578
euchroïte 6579
euclase 6580
eucolittitanite 6582

eucrite 6583
eucryptite 6584
eudialyte 6585
eudidymite 6586
eudiomètre 6587
eudnophite 6588
euralite 6591
eurite 6592
euritique 6593
europium 6595
eustatique 6596
eusynchite 6597
eutectique 6598, 6600
eutectique v. eutectoïde
eutectoïde 6606
euxénite 6609
évacuation du ballast liquide 12703
évanouissement 11028
évaporation par m^2 de la surface de chauffe 6620
évaporer 6611
— à siccité 6612
évasement 10860
évent 3454, 8060, 14947, 14952, 20022
évents 19512
évergreenite 6626
évier de séparation 16412
évite-molettes 12786, 8012
exactitude des dimensions convenues 6630
examen à l'ultramicroscope 19222
— dilatométrique 5414
— fluoroscopique 7476
— macrographique 11150
— magnétoscopique 11197
— métallographique 11582
— microscopique 11651, 9936 9936,
— pénétrant 13062
examiner 6634
excavateur 17864, 6636, 12203
— à benne preneuse 3631
— à godets 2499
— à noria 12373
excès 6639
— d'ébranlage 6643
— de réactif de précipitation 6642
— d'oxygène 6641
exclusion d'air 6646
excoriation 6647
exécution des fouilles

de recherche 13427
exécution des tranchées 5578
exempt de cendres 865
— de pailles 7726
— de scorie 7728
exfoliation 6648
exhausteur 6655
— à vapeur 17429
expanseur S. 18980
expansion S. 5412
— de gaz 8002
— de la cape de gaz 7987
expérience v. analyse ou essai
expérimentalement 6677
expert en repêchage 7216
exploitabilité 20193
exploitable 11271, 9671
exploitation 8205, 18766 20194
— à ciel ouvert 12566, 1258 12584, 12588, 12606, 18071, 17291, 17852
— à ciel ouvert à gradin unique 16384
— à échelon remblayée 7017
— à flanc de coteau 153, 5861
— à l'alternat 19346
— à mi-pente 14209
— à puits 15944
— alluviale 8480
— aurifère 8347
— avec boisage parallélé-pipédique et remblayage 17244
— avec foudroyage en tran-ches horizontales 16600
— avec soutènement du toit 18032
— chassante 8332
— de faisceaux de sables 12118
— de placers 13437
— des chambres 7569
— des filons 10956
— des mines pétrolifères 12501
— des niveaux inférieurs 5094
— en aval pendage 5448
— en chassant 7536, 20211, 20219
— en dressant 17530

exploitation en gradins renversés 17564
— en profondeur 5095
— en rabattant 1050, 11779, 14802, 20210, 20220
— en retraite 14802
— en sous étages avec foudrovage 17920
— en souterrain 19260
— filonienne 10956
— hydraulique 9527
— irrationnelle 8367, 2504
— minière 11769
— par chambres et foudroyage des piliers 17300
— par chambres et piliers 1251, 1921, 2064, 3269. 8934, 13290, 15148, 17301
— par chambres magasins 11166, 16233
— par deux tailles jumelles 5685
— par écroulement 3121
— par entonnoirs souterrains 8310, 11713
— par excavateurs 17849, 17869
— par gradin incliné avec remblayage 9692, 9697
— par gradins 1490, 1496
— par grands massifs 15140
— par grand front alligné 10992
— par longue taille 2435
— par longwall 10992, 10994
— par longwall en rabattant 10993
— par panneaux 10972, 12899
— par piliers 3564, 13295, 17253, 17659
— par piliers abandonnés 12595, 13294
— par poche et pilier 2343
— par recoupes transversales 4680, 4717, 16256
— par remblayage 1056
— par tailles chassantes 12716
— par tailles chassantes à front continu 10978
— par tailles en échelon 7318
— par tailles en échelon avec remblayage 7317

exploitation par traçage et dépilage 13709
— par tranches 1484, 16599
— par tranches avec foudroyage 14013
— par tranches descendantes 19257, 19259
— tranches horizontales ascendantes 852
— par tranches horizontales descendantes 5227
— par tranches inclinées descendantes avec foudroyage 9707
— secondaire 15767
— souterraine S. 5095
exploité 17672
exploiter 6679, 11723
— en rabattant 2411
exploration 6680, S. 14036
— de puits 19966
— du filon en direction 3356
— intercalaire 9888
explorer 13968, 14032
exploser 6678
exploseur 1749, 7191
— à poignée 14198
explosibilité 6681
explosif 6685
— à base de nitroglycérine 12323
— au nitrate d'ammonium 527 527
— brisant 6822, 9145
— D 6686
— de sûreté 15417
— gazeux 8070
— liquide 10874
— solide 16881
explosion 6682, 16191
— de gaz 8003
— de grisou 8330
— d'une chaudière 1958
— phréatique 13188
— volcanique 19591
exposer 6690
exposition 6692
expulsion des matières volatiles 6674
— de l'acide carbonique 5965
exudation de graphite 10377
extension en profondeur 5203
— horizontale 10675
extensomètre 6696

extracteur de carottes 10403
— de tubes 18981
extraction 3820, 5873, 9229, 14137, 14378, 20097, 20111
— de minerai 12660
— des cendres S. 14710
— des tubes 20157
— des minerais 12650
— directe du fer de son minerai 5462
— du charbon 3815
— électrique 6282
— équilibrée 1136
— par air comprimé 299
— par cages 2683
— par skip 1103
extraire 26, 5756, 5770. 6706, 8203, 14123, — 14527, 20084
extramagmatique 6714
extrémité de fendue 19109
— de levier 8794
— du four 7835
extrudage 6722
extrudé 6718, 6749

F

fabrication d'acier cémenté 3161
— d'acier au four électrique 6306
— d'éléments spéciaux 17010
— de fonte malléable 7110
— de l'acier sur sole 11307
— des creusets 11306
— du coke 13997
fabrique de câbles 20146
— de tubes 19032
face 6739, 7779
— aciérée de la plaque de blindage 17467
— arrière 18311
— de devant 7780
— portant 1401
— unique 9081
faciès 6755, 8698
— à hippurities 9211
— à rudistes S. 9211
— aciculaire 72

faciès argileux 778
— bathyal 1341
— calcaire 2705
— charbonneux 3863
— coralligène 4378
— côtier S. 11317
— de cristal 4795
— de rivage 10895
— estuarin 6570
— fluviatile 7495
— glacial 8252
— littoral 10895
— marginal 11316
— marin 11323
— néritique 12238
— normal 12379
— nummulitifère 12425
— paléontologique 12876
— pélagique 13051
— pétrographique 13124
— récifal 14587
— sableux 15533
— saumâtre 2248
— terrestre 18433
facilité de cassure par
    tension 18416
façonnage 15998
— à chaud 9454
— à froid 3980
— par enlèvement de
    copeaux 11539
façonné 7615
— à la presse 13886
— par marteau à chute
    5982
façonner 7605
— v. profiler ou modeller
facteur de sévérité 15927
fagot 6762
fahlbande 6765
faible grillage 19850
faille 6839, 14998, 18933
— à rejet horizontal 7361,
    17825
— anormale S. 12740, 14823
    14823, 18595
— anticlinale 656
— béante S. 7968, 12570
— composée 4119, 4129
— conforme 6851, 8704
— conjonctive S. 18598
— contraire 6850, 8703
— courbée 4881
— de compression 18598
— de contraction S. 18598
— d'expansion 6845

faille d'extension 6845, 1841
    18417
— de rejet horizontale
    16124
— diagonale 5308
— disjonctive 6845, 12570
— en escalier S. 17546
— en surplomb S. 14823
— fermée 3759
— horizontale 9355
— imperméable 9655
— inclinée 9698
— inverse 12740, 12765,
    14823, 14948, 19385,
    19349, 19350
— limite 2195
— longitudinale 17818,
    17821
— multiple 12113
— nivelée 13460
— normale 3220, 5446
    5700, 5980, 8488, 8701,
    12377, 16651
— nourricière 11763
— oblique 5308
— orographique 12677
— orthogonale 5437, S.
    19526
— ouverte, 7968, 12570
— principale 5623
— radiale 14327
— ramifiée 2261
— rasée S. 13460
— renversée S. 14823
— réouverte 14725
— rotatoire 15235
— sans relief S. 13460
— simple 16391
— synclinale 18157
— tabulaire 1800
— transversale 4685,
    5437
— verticale 19526
faire apparaitre la texture
    6691
— basculer la poche S.
    18671
— basculer pour couler le
    métal par le bec 2978
— descendre 8202
— éclater 17124
— le plan 13552
— revenir 18371
— revivre 14835
— sauter 1840
— un essai 18440

faire une décompression
    1755
— une prise d'essai de gaz
    18217
fairfieldite 6769
failure 19613
faisceau lumineux 10779
— tubulaire 19033
famatinite 6790
farine 7417
— de fleuret S. 2085
— de froment 20005
— de pieds de boeufs 9310
— de sondage 2085, 2114,
    5577, 16695
faröelite 6816
farrisite 6817
fasibitikite 6818
fasinite 6819
fassaïte 6820, S. 14212
fatigue 6830
— de frottement 7762
fausse charge 1415, 2517,
    3323
— couche 12455
— dame 6783
— équerre 1570
— portée 3711
— serre 19292
— stratification S. 6779
— variation 14394
fausses vis 15678
faute d'ébarbage 6556
— de moulage 6557
— de noyautage 6555
— de remmoulage 6554
faux 15730
— anticlinal 14069
— bedrock 6780
— clivage 16649
— modèle 15510
— toit 5784
— toit schisteux 3612
fayalite 6868
feldspath 6899
feldspathique 6900
feldspathisation 6901
feldspathoïde 6902
feldspathoïdes 7518
felsite 6907
felsitique 6908
felsobanyte 6910
felsophyre 6911
fendage 17135
fendillement S. 4587
fendre 3719, 17124

fendue 5015, 17910
fenêtre 12174
— de ventilation S. 886
— géologique 9823
— métallique 17157
— tectonique 8178
fente 6768, 7359, 7966,
   14727, 16669, 16686
— de compression 4155
— d'extension 18418
— de levage 7107
fer 9952, 1206
— à ajouter 131
— à bandage 9324
— à bande de la cloche de
   sondage 2561
— à barreaux de grilles
   7149
— à biseau 19885, 19886
— à boudin 2544, 2545
— à brancards 3289
— à C 3289
— à cheval 9381
— à clous 12163
— à colonnes S. 14244,
   19182
— à congé 7030
— à côtés 3289
— à crampons 5600
— à crochet 9317
— à dessins 5075
— à étirer S. 20130, 20138
— à face concave 7494
— à faible teneur de sou-
   fre 10028
— à feuille de saule 414
— à filer 20130
— à grain fin 3762, 7082
— à grain serré S. 3762
— à grains 8404
— à grilles 6915
— à gros grain 3874
— à haute teneur de carbone 10027
— à haute teneur en
   phosphore 9162
— à I S. 8697, 9609
— à I à larges ailes 5392
— à L 10447
— à la thermite S. 18489
— à larges semelles S.
   5392
— à l'état pâteux 12963
— à marquer 2262
— à nervures centrales
   14865
— à poutres 8241

fer à raboter 13455
— à rivets 14973
— à segment S. 8716
— à six pans S. 9119
— à souder 16862
— à chauffage automatique
   15826
— à souder à tête carrée
   3488
— à souder droit 13614
— à souder électrique 6302
— à souder à gaz 8014
— à T 18186
— à âme allongée 9192
— à T à large semelle
   2434
— à texture aérée S. 3762
— à U 19208, 3289
— à vitrage 15550
— à Z à aile inclinée
   12441
— aciéré 15848
— aciéreux 17525
— actif 116
— affiné 3308, 7093
— aigre 2423
— alpha 419
— armco 797
— arsénical S. 829
— au bois 1829, 3308
— au bois dit de Suède
   18108
— au coke 3939
— battu à froid S. 5816
— Bessemer 1551
— bêta 1565
— bétonné 14677
— blanc 18650, 18661,
   18667
— blanc électrolytique
   6351
— blanc étamé à chaud 9447
   9447
— brûlé 2613
— brut 12059, S. 14454
— calibré 2741
— carbonaté spathique S.
   16994
— carburé 2878
— carré 17232, 17254
— cassant à chaud 9402,
   9440, 14548
— cassant à chaud mince
   S. 1671
— cassant à froid 4001
— caverneux 13674
— cendreux 7363

fer chimiquement pur 3398
— chromaté 3529
— chromé 3529, 3540
— construction 17887
— contenant de l'oxygène
   15398
— cornière 572, S. 3289
— corroyé S. 20240
— cristallin fin 7094
— cristallisé 4808
— cru 14454
— d'angle 572
— de calfat 3111
— de chaîne 3246
— de construction 4235
— de couleur S. 14548
— de ferraille S. 15660
— de finerie 16835
— de forge 20240
— de fusion 9794
— de masse S. 15660
— de mitraille S. 15660
— de qualité 14601
— de qualité inférieure
   19300
— de ramasse S. 15660
— de riblons S. 15660
— de Suède 18081
— des eaux 16166
— delta 5157
— dégrossi 15255
— demi-rond 16883, 8716
— demi-rond creux 9273
— double corroyé S. 5674
— doux 11675, 16835,
   20240
— doux au bois 16829
— doux au charbon de bois
   S. 16829
— dressé à froid 4004
— du commerce S. 14496
— ductile S. 16835
— dur 3762, 8834
— dur et aigre S. 4001
— ébauché 11691, S. 12059,
   14096, 14103
— écroui 5816
— électrolytique 6344
— émaillé 6435
— en baguettes 15054
— en bandes S. 7340
— en barre 1215
— en barres façonnées
   15772
— en barres pour clous
   12163
— en billette 1582

fer en brames 16500
— en croix 4705
— en forme d'auge 18591
— en forme de gouttière S. 18591
— en forme de quadrant S. 14244
— en feuilles 16058
— en I 9609
— en lame 16058
— en lentilles S. 12551
— en lingot 7464
— en loupe 1105, 10998
— en loupes 9981
— en paquets v. ferraille
— en quart de rond 14244
— en rubans S. 9324
— en T S. 18186
— en U avec âme de grande hauteur 5098
— étamé avec du zinc S. 7932
— étiré 5816
— exempt de scorie 16537
— extra-doux 19535
— façonné S. 15994
— feuillard 9324
— feuillard laminé à chaud 9435
— feuillard laminé à froid S. 3996
— fin 14600
— fondu 7464, S. 9794
— fondu à air froid S. 3963
— fondu en coquille 3443
— forgeable 7578, 7585, S. 20240
— forgé mécaniquement 13782
— fort supérieur S. 5674
— galvanisé 7932, 7941
— gamma 7945
— grenu 8433
— hexagonal 9119, 9121
— hexagone 9119
— homogène 9794, 11678, 19929
— homogène Bessemer 1556
— inoxydable 15397
— L 572
— laminé 15097
— laminé profilé 15098
— liquide 10877
— magnétique 11193, S. 11207
— main-courante 8777

fer malléable 6074, S. 16835
— manganèse siliceux 16324
— marchand 11496
— martelé S. 20240
— méplat S. 7340
— métallique 11568
— météorique 11607
— métis S. 14548
— micacé 11626
— mobile 12054
— mou 16835
— mou et tenace 6826
— nerveux 6988
— obtenu au bas-foyer 1821
— octogonal 12451
— oligiste 11626, 12530
— oligiste concrétionné 6992, 9075
— oligiste rouge fibreux S. 6992
— olive 12721
— oolithique 12551
— ordinaire 8834
— ovale 12724
— oxydé 9969, 15398
— oxydé argillifère 3663
— oxydé brun terreux 2474
— oxydé carbonaté 10016
— oxydulé 11193
— passé à la filière S. 5816
— plat 7340, 9322
— plat à boudin 7329
— plat à bourrelet 2545
— plat à planer à chaud 9415
— plat bombé 7349
— plat rectangulaire S. 17232 17238
— plancher 8238
— poreux 13674, 17144
— pour barreaux 8469
— pour béton armé 4176
— pour cercles de fixation du bandage 17198
— pour clous à ferrer 9380, 12161
— pour clôtures 1370
— pour colonnes S. 19182
— pour fil S. 20130
— pour gardecorps 1190
— pour le mélange 11823
— pour tôles de qualité supérieure 1562
— préparé par voie électrolytique S. 6344

fer profilé 15772, 15775, 15783, 17886, 15993
— profilé à arêtes arrondies 15279, 15777
— profilé à arêtes vives 15776
— profilé à coins arrondis S. 15279
— puddlé 14102
— pur 14187
— rectangulaire 17232
— réduit 14562
— rond 10004, 15046, 15270, 15285
— rond en couronne 15295
— rouge 14542
— rouverin 2598, S. 14548
— sec S. 16181
— sextain 15928
— spathique 16283, 16994
— spathique mûr S. 19584
— spécial 14601
— spéculaire 17040
— spongieux 17144
— sulfuré 10022
— sursaturé 18020
— T S. 18186
— T à larges ailes 2434
— tendre 4001
— thermite 18489
— Thomas 1297
— titané S. 11485
— titanifère S. 18692
— travaillé en onglet 11815
— V 19422
— vernissé S. 6435
— Z 20315
— zingué 7932
ferbérite 6919
ferblantier 18657
ferghanite 6920
fergusite 6921
fergusonite S. 2251, 6922
ferme 6821
— à âme pleine 16887
fermentation 6923
fermer 3616, 3753, 4558,
— les tuyères 3516
fermes du laminoir S. 9465
fermettes en treillis composées de cornières légères 16397
fermeture à clapet 7282
— à genouillière 10415
— à pression directe 5460
— d'épreuve S. 18451

fermeture d'essai 18451
— de l'appareil à air chaud
19452
— de tuyère 20056
— de ventilation 161
— du gueulard 17683,
18580
— étanche 15722
— hermétique 335
— hydraulique 19812
fermium 6924
fermorite 6925
fermandinite 6927
ferraille 10008, 10254,
11824, 15660
— de parc S. 15660
— v. fer en paquets
ferreux 6963
ferriérite 6930
ferrisymplesite 6933
ferrite 6934
ferritization 6937
ferritungstite 6938
ferro 6963
— alliage 6939
— aluminium 454, 6940
— bore 2116, 6941
— chrome 6942
— cobalt 6955
— cyanure de potassium
13725
— cyanide de potasse
13726
ferrolite 6956
ferromagnétique 6957
ferromanganèse 6944, 11279
— siliceux 6949, 6960
— titanifère 6945
ferro-molybdène 6946
ferronatrite 6931
ferro-nickel 6947
ferro-pallidite 6959
— -silicium 6950
ferrotitane 6952, 18692
ferrotungstène 6953
ferrovanadium 6954
ferrozirconium 6967
ferronnerie 10035
ferrures de wagons 2897
fers à arêtes vives 6870
— double T 10216
— en barres 9955
— forgés 7600
— marchands 19313
— marchands et profilés
1254

fers profilés v. profilés
— trapéziformes 18853
— U 3292
feu 7289
— gueulard 6564
— brasqué 3305
— d'affinerie moderne S.
18107
— d'affinerie suédois 18107
18110
— de trempe 18394
feuillard 1175, 1177, 17844
— à chaud 9430
— d'emballage 1144
— de fer 17744
— laminé à chaud 9434
— laminé à froid 3996
— magnétique 3991
feuille 7519, 7526, 13484,
S, 16044 16068
— d'aluminium 461
— d'étain 18648
— de fer 10011
— de laiton S. 2274
— de platine 13526
— de zinc ondulée 4501
— en aluminium S. 457
feuille v. tôle
feuilles de métal sur appui
continu 11560
feuilleté 7529, 19840
feuilleté v. schisteux
fibroferrite 6984
fibrolite 6985
ficelle 17832
fichtélite 6994
fil 14893, 16646, 17832
— à guipage en coton 4524
— à plomb 1930, 13568
— à pointes S. 1222
— à signaux 10410
— à six-pans 9124
— à souder 7025, 19957
— à ronces 1222
— barbelè 1222
— carré 17251
— ciré 19848
— clair 19231
— couvert 4569
— cru 19231
— cuivré 4373
— d'acier 17518
— d'acier à ressort 17201
— d'acier chemisé 4355
— d'acier cuivré 4355
— d'acier double 4355

fil d'acier fondu 11701
— d'aluminium 465
— d'amorce 13955
— de bronze 2459
— de bronze phosphoreux
13173
— de bronze siliceux 16327
— de cuivre 4368
— de cuivre cuit 16846
— de cuivre doux 16833
— de cuivre écroui 8824
— de cuivre étiré à froid S.
8824
— de cuivre galvanisé 7930
— de cuivre tenace 18797
— de départ 10632
— de fer 10026
— de fer clair 1229
— de fer décapé 13223
— de fer malléable 11251
— de fer pour clôture 6917
— de fer pour emballage
1145
— de fer recuit noir 1642
— de fer zingué S. 7933
— de laiton 2277
— de laitier 16559
— de manganine 11285
— de misure 11402
— de platine 13530
— de plomb 10626
— de raccordement 4224
— de renforcement 10558
— de suspension 18082
— de trolley 18929
— de trolley profilé en 8
18930
— de zinc 20339
— écroui 8845
— écroui à froid 8825
— écroui par voie humide
10462
— elliptique 6386
— émaillé 6437
— émaillé sous papier
12905
— en caoutchouc 15315
— en cire 19846
— en fer galvanisé 7933
— en 8
— étamé 18663
— étiré 5821
— étiré à froid S. 8825
— étiré à sec 16800
— étamé au feu 7180
— explosif 9626

fil fin 18525
— fusible 7885
— galvanisé 7940
— guipé coton S. 4524
— guipé et tressé 4565
— hexagonal 9124
— ignifugé 7263
— isolé à l'émail S. 6434
— isolé au parchemin 12931
— isolé sous émail 6434
— laminé 15103
— machine 2012
— machine en aciers doux et durs au carbone 20139
— machine en rouleaux 20141
— méplat 7347
— métallique carré S. 17251
— métallique séparant les cartouches d'un trou de mine chambré 16955
— non recuit S. 19231
— normal 17358
— nu 1228
— plein 16890
— pour câbles 20126
— pour clous 14975
— pour cordes de piano 13196
— pour électrodes 4402, 6329
— pour ressort 17203
— pour résistances électriques 14779
— pour rivets 14975
— pour soudure continue 20127
— pour soudure dans le verre 15741
— profilé 15996 16738
— radisseur 16971
— recuit 607
— sans affleurement 1778
— souple 7370
— sous coton 4524
— sous coton ciré 19847
— sous papier 12904
— sous ramie 14397
— sous ruban en caoutchouc 15316
— sous ruban isolant 18273
— sous soie 16333
— sous tresse 20149
— tréfilé S. 5821
— tressé S. 20149
— triangulaire 18887

fil zingué S. 7940
fil v. cordon
filer à la presse 3977
filet 15748, 17836, 18550
— de minerai 17761
— protecteur 15421
filetage mâle 11244
— sur le tour 15705, 18304
— type long 10977
fileter 4894, 15698
— au tour 19131
filière 5373, 5783, 20122
— à coussinet 17617
— brisée S. 17617
— de repêchage S. 1574, 5365
— fermée 16879
— multiple 20231
— réglable 17199
— ronde 15277
— «sid» 17189
fillowite 7040
film d'oléum 12528
filon 4552, 5147, 7957, 10954, 11756, 15743,
— à échelle 10935
— à incrustation S. 4783
— à pendage fort S. 14383
— aurifère 14584
— bréchiforme 2356
— composé 4124, 4132
— conducteur 2485
— conique 4200
— concrétionné 4783
— conjugué 4213
filon-couche 1422, 9881, 16342,
— horizontal 1686, 1695
filon croiseur 4675, 4699, 470 4709, 14383
— de contact 4247
— de cuivre 19487
— de faille 16660
— de fort pendage 17529
— d'imprégnation 9665
— de quartz 14270
— de remplissage secondaire 14728
— de roche 3286
— en forme de chambres 3273
— épithermal 6521
— éruptif annulaire 14922
— guide 4195
— horizontal 10957
— hypothermal 9604
— incliné 19270

filon irrégulier 8073
— lenticulaire 10680
— mésothermal 11525
— métallifère 10659
— métasomatique 11599
— mince 1174
— oxydé 19491
— pourri 15238
— principal 11365, 11949
— ramifié 2260
— rejecteur 5526
— rocheux 5410, S. 6148
— secondaire 6001
— simple 16408
— sulphuré 19492
— vertical 14383, 19539
— zoné 1184
filonnet 15756
filtrage à percolation 7064
filtration 7062
filtre 7042
— à air 254
— à coke 3944
— à crasses 6008
— à gravier 8481, 13032
— à lumière 10782
— à scories 6008
— à vide 19430
— de dérivation 2651
— de soufflage 15689
— pour amalgame 482
— pour bonbonne 2875
— presse 1838, 7051
— sur le refoulement d'une pompe 5495
filtrer 7041, 13076
— par aspiration 17942
finnemanite 7142
finement divisé 7095
— granulé S. 7080
— rectifié 13823
fines 7103, 16507, 16740
— de charbon 2835. 7074
— de minerai 12649
— lavées 6077
— particules d'or S. 7386
finesse du broyage 7099
finissage 7118
— à la meule 7116
— de la pièce 7132
— de meulage 7116
— des bords 6209
— du noyau 7115
finissage v. achèvement ou parachèvement
finisseur 7128, 7391
— à chaud 18240

finisseuse 3685, 14500
fischérite 7205
fissuration 4587, 10213
— due au traitement thermique 7611
fissure 1045, 3469, 4581, 7399, 14727
— aquifère 2911
— capillaire 8708
— d'angle 4676
— de compression S. 4155
— de dessiccation 17998
— d'exfoliation 6649
— de vieillissement 220
— du bord 6200
— interne 9899
— transgranulaire 18822·
— v. fente
fissuré 2448, 4584
fissures de tension 18415
— en réseau S. 12250
— longitudinales 3377
fissurité S. 7706
fixage 7243
fixation de l'émail au feu S. 7194
fixe 6821
fixé 14589
fixer 3616
fizélyte 7245
flacon à dégagement des gaz 7312
— à densité S. 13231
— à échantillons 15456
— à filtrer dans le vide 7057
— à pipette 13378
— à réactifs 14472
— à tare 19899
— d'absorption 16
— de cobalt 3889
— de Kjeldahl 10383
— de niveau 10715
— de Woolff 20187
— en plomb 10609
— en verre bleu S. 3889
— laveur de gaz 8062
flambage 16473
flamber 7258
— un moule 16470
flamme 7252
— acétylénique 64
— auto-lumineuse 15827
— d'allumage 9628
— de sodium 16821
— du gueulard 18576
— éclairante 11088

flamme pointante 12176
— réductrice 2863
— rouge 14534
flanc (d'un pli) 16254
— anticlinal 658
— d'hydrogène 9560
— d'un anticlinal 10807
— du dôme 5618
— d'un pli 15983
— inférieur 11068
— inférieur d'un pli couché 7405
— médian 4094, 11661, 15855
— médian étiré 5818
— supérieur 758, 15143,
— synclinal 18158, 18941
flandre S. 2795. 4735
flasergneiss 7286
flasque S. 16270
fléau circulaire 3587
flèche 811, 2042, 5120
— de grue 8215
— mobile horizontale 3333
— parasite 19342
fleur 7087
— de zinc S. 9579, 20324
fleurage 2306
fleuret 2077, 2091, 5883, 10250
— à couronne 4728
— à main 8757
— d'amorçage 13211, 16174, 17380
— de mine 5881
— hélicoïdale 3797
fleurs 7430
flexible 13548
flexion 1505
flexure 7372, S. 17547
— anticlinale 657
finkite 7376
flint 7377
— glass 7379
floconneux 7395
floculation 7393
florencite 7413
floss S. 20026
flot S. 12192
flottant 7386
flottation collective 2549
— étagée 17287
— par la mousse 7782
fluage 4615
fluctuation de la tension 7446
fluctuer S. 7429

fluellite 7458
fluide 7459
— boueux 12079
fluidifiant 12093
fluidimètre 10088
fluidité 5528, 7469
fluocérine 7474
fluocérite S. 7474
fluor 7477
fluorescence 1819
— du pétrole 12481
fluorine 1905, 2780, 7475, 10295, 13012
fluorure de calcium S. 7475
flux 7498
— de tête 12750
fluxmètre 7792
flysch 7509
foisonner s. 18120
foliation 7533, 16140
fonçage 15962, 16416, 16965
— à niveau vide 12626
— au poussage 16421
— avec sas à air 13592
— de puits par cimentation 15956
— des puits par cimentation 8628
- des puits par la méthode de la cimentation 8630
— sous stot 16419
— tubulaire 17999
foncer 5971
fonctionnement 15349
— continu 4279
— par cuiller automatique 984
fond 1084
— à coulisse 16617
— amovible 11002, 14703
— arrière S 1053
— avant ou de devant ou antérieur S. 7776
— cylindrique perforé 14706
— de bois gabarié 8113
— de chaudière formé par explosion 6687
— de creuset 8953
— de derrière S. 1053
— de fendue 154
— de poche 15727, 16488
— de synclinal S. 18159
— du creuset 1276, 8959
— du puits 13404
— du sondage 2173, 6747
— du trou 2173, 18704

fond d'un trou de mine 2082
— en scorie 16524
— en terre réfractaire perforé avec des baguettes
13080
— ouvrant 2154
— postérieur 1053
— reposant sur poutrelles
S. 19241
fondage de réduction 14570
fondamental 7819
fondant 7497, 7499 7502
— à souder 16863
— siliceux 16319
fondateur 7638
fondation 7637, 16336
— en briques 2370
— en moellons 2447
— sur pilotis 13280
fonder 7636
fonderie 3066, 7647, 16750
— à fonte grise 8530
— d'acier 17475
— d'aluminium 453
— de bronze 2271
— de caractère 19203
— de cuivre 2278
— de fonte S. 9975
— de fonte malléable 7663
— de zinc 17048
— intégrée 2816, 18612
— sur album 17013
— sur modèles 10188
fondeur 7640, 7879, 10307,
11462, 18355
— au cubilot 4846
— de bronze 2270
— de cuivre 4357, 20290
— de fer 9974
fondoir S. 11476
fondre 7635, 11456
fondu 11460, 11877
— en coquille 3426
fonte 2991, 7643, 9966,
11537
— à air froid 3963
— à coeur blanc 20044
— à coeur noir 1669
— à grain fin 3763
— à grandes cavernes
19536
— à graphite nodulaire
12334
— à graphite sphéroïdal
17067
— à l'anthracite 644

fonte à main 3044
— à matrice hypoeutectoïde
9587, 9599
— petites cavernes S. 3763
— à soufflures 1882,
9304
— aciérée 17484
— aciculaire 71
— aciéreuse 17526
— affinée 14599
— alliée 397
— amagnétique 12355
— anglaise 6481
— au four électrique 6275
— au nickel 13262
— au vent chaud 9399
— austénitique 958
— bainitique 71
— Bessemer 1552, 9076
— blanche 12604, 20026
— blanche à facettes 20029
— blanche à structure
rayonnée 20043
— blanche à texture fran-
chement rayonnée 9194
— blanche à vent froid
20028
— blanche ordinaire 20040
— brillante 9172
— brute 13259
— cassante 16176
— caverneuse 13677
— caverneuse très froide
S. 19556
— chaude 9420
— Cleveland 13180
— contenant des scories
3576
— coulée en sable 15487
— creuse 4458, 9266
— crue électrique 6290
— crue Thomas 18536
— d'acier S. 17463
— d'allure chaude 9442
— de base 1279
— de cubilot 4845
— de deuxième fusion 2993
— de finage 3307
— de Luxemburg 11104
— de moulage 2994, 7665,
8531
— de moulage moyennement
dure 11426
— de moulage résistante
18798
— de moulage pour pièces

résistantes au feu 7667
fonte de moulage pour
pièces résistantes aux
acides 7666
— de première fusion 2992,
13260
— de première qualité 9150
— de puddlage 7579
— de rouleaux 7646
— de Siegen 16288
— de Styrie 17916
— demi-truitée 10800
— douce 11118
— douce de moulage 11249,
16834
— durcie 3443
— dure S. 3443
— écossaise 15652
— électrique 6275, 6320
6299
— en coquille 3442, S. 3443
3451
— en saumons pour fusion
3006
— épurée 19696
— eutectique 6501
— fine 17008
— froide 3986, 18508
— graphiteuse 1660, 8454
— grise 850.2, 8527, 8531
— gris clair 7083, 10783
— gris foncé 5002
— gris noir S. 5002
— ordinaire 8502
— grise riche en silicium
9172, 16363
— hématite 9074
— liquide 11879
— malléable 11249, 11813,
11814
— malléable à coeur noir
1670
— malléable américaine
1670
— malléable blanche 20045
— manganéséée 11269
— martensitique 11348
— Martin 12576
— mazée 3307, 14599
— mécanique 6474, 11138
— métisse S. 3576
— miroitante à texture
grossière 3878
— moirée S. 20026
— moulée 2995
— perlitique 13018

fonte phosphoreuse 13181
— pour meulage en coquille 3432., S. 3443
— provenant des lavoires 9977
— rapide 11060
— refondue 14697
— réfractaire 8993
— résistante 9143
— résistante à la chaleur 8993
— sans retassures 3052
— sans sable 15527
— sans tensions internes 3051
— semiphosphoreuse 11429
— sorbitique 16921
— soufflée 8084
— spéciale 17008
— spéciale pour pièces de machines 1561
— spéculaire 17038
— spiegel à haute teneur en manganèse 9158
— spiegel pour puddlage 17039
— surchauffée 18006
— synthétique 18170
— tendre 8531
— Thomas 1297
— très silicieuse 9172
— trop chaude S. 18006
— truitée 11956, 17879
— truitée blanche 11958
forage S. 2076., 2095, 7583
— à bras 8759
— à carottage 4406
— à chute libre 7724
— à faible diamètre 16626
— à grande profondeur 5090
— à injection 9517
— à l'air 270
— à l'air humide 11810
— à la corde 2661
— avec circulation 7483
— avec circulation renversée 4529
— au gaz 8028
— au large des côtes S. 11322
— de grande profondeur S. 5092
— de limite 12465, 12470
— de recherche 20067
— de secours 14686

forage dévié 16279
— directionnel contrôlé S. 5468
— dirigé 5468, 5469
— en faîte 17675
— en mer 11322
— incliné S. 9708
— intercalaire 9762
— oblique 9708
— par battage 8733
— par percussion S. 8733
— profond 5092
— simultané 16375
— sous pression 13903
— vers le haut 19387
forage v. sondage
foraminifères 7552
forbésite 7553
forçage 18123
force de torsion 18781
— du damage 17776
— du marteau 6215
— hydraulique 19804
— portante 1390
— unilatérale 19306
forcement S. 16226
forcer 18119
forer 2073 , 5874, 13240
— à système rotary 15200
— à travers 5880
— par battage 17216
— par outil creux 4455
— par rodage S. 5918
— par rotation 5918
— un trou de mine 2074
forer v. percer
forer v. perforer
forer v. sonder
foret S. 1622, 5881
— à canon 14890, 17708
— à centre 3195
— à centrer 17168
— à charbon 2827
— à découper 6671
— à langue d'aspic 812, 7332 7332
— à pointe de lancette S. 812
— à téton 3195
— au diamant 5324
— de centrage 3185
— hélicoïdal 19181
— pour trouer le trou de coulée 5927
foreur 5906

foreuse à main électrique d'établi 6278
— d'établi 1486
forge 7575, 16757
— catalane 1827
— fixe à un feu 16302
forgé brut 15349
forgeabilité 7584
forgeable S. 6073
forgeage 7590, 16753
— à chaud 9416
— à induction 9748
— à moule fermé 3770
— creux 9272
— de précision 13822
— de préparation 15496
— de goulot 11666
— libre 12569
— par résistance 6332
— sans barbe 7308
forger 7570, 11257
— à chaud 7573
— à froid 7572
— à la presse 13870
— en matrice S. 18097
— grossièrement 15243
forgeron 7588, 8750,
forgeur 7588
forgis 20130
formage à haute énergie 9144 9144
— à sec 16472
— à très hautes vitesses de déformation 9191
— par explosion 6688
— sans enlèvement de copeaux 3475
formant du laitier 16535
formation 7607
— asphaltique 873
— carbonifère 2858
— de criques 7610
— de dômes 5624
— d'entonnoir 782'
— de métal granulaire 16206
— de Monroe 11917
— de mousse 7784
— de piqûres 13428
— de rainures 15646
— de retassements 13327
— soufflures 9306
— de voûtes 3466, S. 8809
— des cannelures 7881
— des cirques 3608

formation des failles 6863
— des fissures 7706
— d'incrustations 9728
— du cône d'eau 19757
— géologique imprévue 17759
— géologique payante 13000 13000
— houillière 3838
formations métallifères stratiformes 1425
forme 11378
— allotropique 391
— basaltique 1269
— circulaire 3600
— compliquée 9922
— concave 4158, 4160
— concave de la surface 10338
— cristalline 4803
— cubique 4819
— cylindrique 4949
— de brique 2373, 15986
— de filetage 18553
— des grains de sable 4189
— du fond de filet 15152
— finale 7070
— fixe 13108
— ovoïde 6223
— sphérique 1160
former des capuchons 1146
— les loupes 7620
— un cordon S. 19672
fornacite 7621
forstérite 7622
fortement faillé S. 1093
fortunite 7624
fosse tranchée 18873
— à huile 12502
— de coulée 3067, 7668, 13396
— de coulée demi-circulaire 15839
— de coulée pour gueuses 13248
— de moulage S. 3067
fossé 11226
— d'effondrement 5717, 18585
fossile 7629,
— à grande survie S. 13116
— caractéristique 8650, 9734
— de faciès 6756
— de longévité S. 13116

fossile persistant 13116
fossilifère 7632
fossilisation 7633
fossiliser 7634
foudroyage 3121
— en masse du minerai 1797
foudroyé 3120, 17673
fouettement S. 7283
fouler 14388, S. 18229
fouille 4898, 5407
fouloir 14402, S. 18232
— d'établi 16186
— de grand modèle 10973
— porte-segment 18734
— porte-segment mobile horizontalement et verticalement 12980
four 7825, 10356
— à acier cémenté 17465
— à affiner S. 14613
— à air 280
— à arc 745
— à arc électrique à courant triphasé 18564
— à arc et à résistance 742
— à arc indirect 9743
— à atmosphère contrôlée 4291
— à atmosphère gazeuse protectrice 14047
— à avant-creuset 7170
— à bain de sel 15412
— à bascule S. 18628
— à briques, briqueterie 2371
— à bronze 11467
— à brûler les ordures 14639
— à calcinage S^v 2716
— à calciner la blende 1763
— à carbure 2822
— à cémenter 2886, 3160, 3173
— à chariot 1948
— à chaux 10816
— à ciment 3151
— à coke à cycle fermé 3768
— à coke à récupération 3942
— à coke avec récupération des sous-produits 14512
— à combustible 10876

four à combustion 4078
— à contre-courant 4533
— à cornues 14797
— à coupellation 4840
— à courant monophasé 16306
— à courant triphasé 431 18565
— à courant triphasé de Roechling-Rodenhauser 15001
— à creuset 4740, 13719
— à creuset extractible 10749
— à cuire la porcelaine 13661
— à cuire les fonds de convertisseurs 2717
— à cuve 9149, 15939
— à cuve à recuire 15941
— à cuve du Siegerland 16289
— à cuve pour creusets 15937
— à cuve pour minerai de mercure 2624
— à cycle fermé 3769
— à émailler 6438
— à étages 10360
— à extraction de sous-produits 7837
— à gaz 8011
— à griller de Witkowitz 2 20161
— à haute fréquence 9148
— à induction 9749, 11048
— à induction à basse fréquence 11048
— à induction à forger 7394
— à induction à haute fréquence 9147
— à induction pour barres 1256
— à lit facilement fusible 7460
— à loupes 1171, 1828,
— à manche 15939
— à métal blanc 11468
— à minerai de plomb 15551
— à moufle 12097
— à moufle au gaz 8008, 12099
— à moufle électrique 6289

four à pétrole 12491
— à plusieurs creusets 12111
— à pots pour recuire 13718
— à puddler 14109
— à puddler double 5673
— à puddler rotatif 14841
— à puddler système Springer 17204
— à puddler tournant 15214 15234
— à réchauffer 3236, 8308, 9796, 19671, 19943
— à réchauffer à sole mobile 14671
— à réchauffer en sous-sol 14669
— à recuire 9017
— à récupération de chaleur 14524
— à refondre 14700
— à régule 14664
— à résistance 14767
— à résistance de l'arc 751
— à ressuage 10867
— à réverbère à longue sole 14818
— à réverbère à tremper 18393
— à réverbère chauffé au gaz S. 16292
— à réverbère de fonderie 7648
— à ruche 1439
— à sécher S. 6059
— à sécher dans le vide 19429
— à sécher le sable 15492
— à sécher les noyaux 4408
— à sécher transportable 18838
— à sole 8956, 12574
— à sole à secousses 15970
— à sole amovible 7877
— à sole movible 7873
— à sole tournante 14110
— à souder 16888, 19941
— à soufre 17983
— à traitement thermique 9003
— à tremper 8865
— à tremper les limes 7005
— à tubes radiants 14330
— à un seul creuset 16387

four à vent chaud 9395
— à water-jacket 19789
— anglais à cémentation 6479
— annulaire à griller le calcaire 620
— basculant 18628
— basculant à induction 9755
— Borcher 2062
— catalan 3083
— céramique 3226
— chauffé au gaz 18011
— chauffé au pétrole 12491
— circulaire 3593
— Colby 3956
— continu 4267
— cylindrique 4940
— d'affinage 14613
— d'affinerie 7101
— de calcination 2716
— de carbonisation 12727
— de carbonisation de la tourbe 3310
— de cémentation 2926, 3173, 7839
— de céramique 3226
— de chauffage 9013
— de coking intermittent 1330
— de départ 12948
— de fonderie 7658
— de fusion 7644, 11466, 16748
— de fusion à réverbère 14817
— de grillage 7172, 14986, 14990
— de grillage au gaz de Westman 19982
— de grillage de Cleveland 3723
— de grillage de Fillafer 7015
— de grillage maçonnerie 2372
— de grillage styrien 17917
— de liquation 10867
— de maintien 9244
— de puddlage S. 14109
— de réchauffage 3236, 8308
— de réchauffage pour brames 15497
— de recuit 614
— de réduction 14568, 14572

four de ressuage 18104
— de Roessler 15065
— de séchage 6059
— de séchage des moules 11977
— de trempe à cuve 15940
— de trempe au gaz 8007
— de trempe mécanique au gaz 11406
— de verrerie 8276
— diélectrique 5385
— discontinu 429
— dormant 9342
— dormant à tôle 13491
— électrique à affiner 6292
— électrique à arc 6256
— électrique à arc horizontal 6257
— électrique à baguettes rayonnantes 6296
— électrique à creuset 6268
— électrique à cuve 6298
— électrique à induction 3291
— électrique à induction à basse fréquence 11047
— électrique à induction à creuset 4459
— électrique à moyenne fréquence 9890
— électrique à résistance à voûte chauffante 6276
— électrique à résistances 6295
— électrique à sole 6280
— électrique basculant 6310
— électrique d'attente 6283
— électrique de fusion 6288
— en pleine température 7848
— fixe 1143, 7233,
— Frick 7764
— Gérard 8193
— Gin 8232
— Girod 8244
— Hellberger 9067
— Hempel 9089
— Jschewsky 10046
— industriel 9757
— industriel pour le chauffage au gaz 9758
— intermittent 429
— Kjellin 10382
— Martin 12574, 16293
— Martin acide 83

four Martin basique 1299
— mélangeur 11831
— métallurgique 11586
— Nathusius 12180
— oscillant 15039, S. 18628
— Piat 13197
— potager 13406
— pour bauxite 1357
— pour distiller l'amalgame 480
— poussant 14201
— régénérateur à coke 14645
— Röchling-Rodenhauser 15000
— rotatif 14837, 15207, 15210, 15213
— rotatif chauffé au gaz 15208
— rotatoir S. 15213
— sécheur 6059
— sécheur transportable 13693
— Siemens 16292
— Stassano 17387
— statistique sous cloche 17392
— tournant S. 15213
— tubulaire tournant 14844
— tunnel 6313, 19113
— vertical 15948
— vertical à grille tournante 15209
four v. fourneau
fours à tremper 18395
fourche 7602
— à barette 10563
— à cliquet 2055
— à coke 3937
— à poche de coulée S. 10474
— de retenue 7601, S. 10730
fourchette S. 7602
fournaise v. four ou fourneau ou foyer
fourneau 1967, 7825
— à calciner 2703
— à décaper 15599
— à fonte 7442
— à la Wilkinson 4844
— à moufles doubles 5666
— à pétrole 13134
— Chinaglia 10358
— convertisseur 4310

fourneau d'affinage à plomb 10622
— d'affinage de ferraille 6761
— de corroyage de ferraille S. 6761
— de fonderie 2986
— de mine 4576, 8365
— portatif 13686
— système Hoffmann 10359
— volant S. 13686
fourneau v. four
fourniture de chaleur S. 18027 18027
fournée 3316
fourrure de cylindre 4941
— d'un palier 10853
foyer 1967, 7152, 7174, 7516, 7825
— à air comprimé 7866
— à alimentation automatique 15822
— à alimentation par en dessous 19250
— à alimentation par le bas S. 19250
— à autel surplombant 7876
— à bois 20174
— à brûleur 17188
— à charbon 3823, 3825
— à charbon pulvérisé 7842
— à chargement automatique S. 15822
— à circulation d'eau à travers les barreaux de grille 7863
— à cokéification S. 3955
— à flamme renversée 5699
— à gadoues 14641
— à gaz 7838
— à gaz de haut-fourneaux 19729
— à gazéification S. 3955
— à goudron 18318
— à grille 8472
— à grille horizontale 7867
— à grille inclinée 7869
— à grille mobile 18861
— à houille S. 3825
— à huile lourde 7840
— inférieur 7862
— inférieur à grille horizontale 7868
— inférieur à grille inclinée
— intérieur 9909
— intérieur à grille 7371

foyer intérieur tubulaire 7454
— à introduction d'air au-dessus de la grille 7875
— à introduction d'air supérieur S. 7875
— à pétrole 7840
— à poussière de charbon 3819
— à réchauffer 8955
— à récupération intermittente 14646
— à soufflage sous grille 7555, 7865
— à soufflage sous grille avec introduction d'air par barreaux creux 7556
— antérieur 7847
— antérieur à grille horizontale 6695
— automatique 17635
— avec grille à chaîne 3244
— avec grille à étages 7874
— avec grille à gradins 7878
— avec grille à rouleau 7864
— avec grille à secousses 7872
— comtois couvert 4567
— d'aérage 19256
— de chauffage 16749
— de travail 8952
— découvert 12573
— extérieur 6702
— fumifuge 16764
— fumivore 16760
— maçonné 2376
— mécanique 11413
— ondulé 4494
— périphérique 15554
— pneumatique S. 7866
— pour incinération des ordures 14639
— pour résidus de la distillation du pétrole 7841
— sans fumée S. 16764
— simple à grille 16370
fraction 7686
— de coeur 8948
— latérale 16276
fractionnement 7692
— de la paraffine 19843

fractions légères 10781
— lourdes 9030
— résiduelles 14758
fracture 2307, 7693, 9650, 14727
— conchoïdale 7381
— en colonnes 4046
— incomplète 8524
— intercristalline 9876
— par contre-coup 7696
— parallèle à la surface 1418
— simple 16368
— soyeuse 16334
fracture v. cassure
fragile 2420, 20060
— au bleu 1899
fragilité 2427, 7707, 16187
— à chaud 9403, 9441, 14549
— à froid 3966
— à l'entaille 12396
— à l'hydrogène 9558
— au bleu 1900
— caustique 3113
— de corrosion 4489
— de décapage 79
— de revenu 18373, 18392
— de tension 18416
— du fer 2428
— pour grossissement du grain 17410
fragment 1623. 16011
— de minerai 16141
— métallique 18200
fragmentation à masse S. 2566
— étagée S. 17286
— par explosif 2566
fragmenter 2565, 3645
— par explosif 1790
frais d'analyse 4513
— d'exploitation 4516, 20205
— de garnissage 4520
— de transport 2905
fraisage multiple 7952
fraise 4907, 11689, 11708
— à dégrossir 17157
— à lames rapportées 6746
— à profil 14002
— à queue au bout à canne-lures hélicoïdales 17098
— à rainures 17099
— à roder S. 15178

fraise à tailler les engrenages droits 17227
— cylindrique rapide à dé-grossir 9060
— d'entrée 16691
— hélicoïdale 9058
— plate 4537
— plate camuse 4538
— pour filetage trapézoïdal 18855
— profilée 7614, 7618
fraiseuse à modèles 12985
— horizontale 1487
frais-mère hélicoïdale pour roues hélicoïdales 20229
fraisil S. 7356
— de charbon de bois 3299
— de coke 3935
— humide 11861
francium 7713
franckéite 7714
franco à l'usine 7720
francolite 7715
franklinite 7717
frange capillaire 2808
frangibilité 7716
frappe 3925
— en fer S. 20242
frapper 1409, 3924, 10393, 17813
— sur les tuyaux avec le marteau pendant l'épreu-ve hydraulique 8728
freibergite 7750
freieslebénite 7751
frein à sabot 16153
— dynamique 6150
— hydraulique 9515, 9565
freinage 17178
freineur 1196, 17177
freinteur S. 1196
freirinite 7752
frémontite 7753
freyalite 7759
friabilité 4012
friasses 18051
friction hydraulique 8698
friedélite 7772
frieséite 7773
frisure 4865
frittage 7775, 16433
fritter (se-) S. 16429
— ensemble 7774
froissé 4758
fromage 1678, 3381, 17330

froncement 4759, 8339, 14091
front 7779
— à deux ailes 5678
— d'abattage 20206
— d'attaque S. 2342
— d'attaque à 30° avec les limets 10971
— d'attaque à 45° avec la direction 8712
— d'attaque à 60° avec les limets 16180
— d'attaque parallèle aux limets 6751
— d'avancement 5276, 8935
— de charriage 2468, 7777
— de dragage 5826
— d'exploitation 6750
— d'huile 12479
— de taille 2342, 6450, 6749, 7562, 11730, 19642
— de taille d'une houillère 3853
— de taille normal aux li-mets 2635
— d'une galerie 7564
frottage 11707
frotte 4765
frottement 7765, 15319
— de freinage 2254
— du tourillon 10233
— électrolytique des ions 6342
— interne 9901
frotter à l'esprit de vin 15303
— un sable 11699
frotteur 15503
fruit S. 1344
— d'un cône S. 18282
fuchsite 7786
fuel-oil 7791
fuite de gaz 6562, 11029
— de la tuyère 10638
fulgurite 7793
fuligineux 15918
fülloppite 7814
fulminate de mercure 7813
fumée 200, 1767
— brune 2476
fumées de couleur foncée 5001
furfural 7824,
furfurol 7824
fusée 7884

fusée d'essieu 1026
fusibilité 7890
fusible 11459
fusion 7652, 11463, 11464, 14643
— à feu S. 9623
— à gradins 17551
— au creuset 4741
— au cubilot 11469
— au haut-fourneau 1720
— de cloches 1451
— de l'alliage 11474
— de l'émail au fer 7194
— d'oxydation S. 12804
— de précision 13820
— des riblons 16751
— du laitier 11473
— du zinc 20336
— électrique 6299
— électrothermique du fer 6301
— en atmosphère contrôlée 11482
— en fonte 9965
— ignée 9623
— incomplète 9715
— liquéfaction 7893
— mal venue 11807
— oxydante 12804, 12812
— partielle au recuit 12941
— réductrice 14570
— sous vide 19436, 17764
fusulina 7895
fût léger 16509
— productif 12545

G

gabarit 3710, 7896, 18400
— de chargement 10917
— de remmoulage 4442
gabbro 7897
gabbroïde 7899
gabbroïque 7898
gâche 17829
— pour tubes 15497
gadolinite 7902
gadolinium 7903
gagate 7904
gageite 7905
gahnite 7907
gaille 3884

gailleterie 1798, 3470, 3884, S. 15276
gailleteries 12428
gailletin 3895
gailletins 3414
gain 7908
gaîne 4607, 12697
— isolante 10065
— réfractaire S. 16590
galapectite 7910
galaxite 7911
gale fausse 2508
— volante 15567
galène 7912, 10614, 10624
galénobismuthite 7913
galerie 5015
— au jour 11732, 17910
— au mur 7549
— au rocher 15015, 15024, 17642
— costresse 4530
— dans les remblais 8331
— d'aérage S. 281
— d'avancement 180, 5850, 5865, 8931
— d'avancement de fond 2159
— de chassage 14586
— de contournement 2010
— de desserte S. 8095
— de direction 5870
— de drainage 5750
— d'écoulement 5743, S. 575 5750
— d'écoulement de l'eau 16930
— d'exhaure 1777
— d'exploitation 5870, 12645, 12897
— d'exploration 11902
— d'extraction 6709, 20112
— de niveau 11735
— de retour d'air 14809
— de roulage 8893
— de transport 7959
— de ventilateur 6798, 6808
— de ventilation 281, 2338
— du câble 2664
— en cul-de-sac 1771
— en direction 5953
— en pente 16572
— en roche au mur 1502??
— horizontale d'accès 16259
— inclinée S. 16680, 2469
— principale S. 8931, 11220

galerie principale de roulage 2899
— transversale 4684, 8602
— unique 16390
galeries 11725
— jumelles 5658
galet 2192, 13034, 15104, 15324
— conducteur 7546
— de soutien S. 7546
— strié 15683
galets 5267
galette 15375, 19617
— d'épaisseur 18514
galibot 10464
gallium 7917
galvanisation 7926, 20346
— à chaud 9418
— du fer 20349
— électrolitique 7943
galvanisé 7929
— v. zingué
galvaniser 6365, 7928, 7942
galvanisme 7927
galvano S. 6371
galvanoplastic 6330
gammagraphie 7946, 7947
gangue 2465, 7956, 10958, 17905
ganiser 7960
ganoïde 7961
ganomalite 7962
ganophyllite 7963
gant en amiante 844
— en caoutchouc 15310
garantie 11998
garde-coups du gueulard 18199
gare de manœuvre 16239
— d'usine 11742
garewaïte 7971
garganite 7972
gargouille 19809
garnièrite 7974
garnir de planches 10457
garnir v. revêtir
garnissage 8827, 10489, 10849
— acide 82
— de convertisseur 4301
— de la sole 8960
— de scories 149
— du four 6979, S. 1316
— en briques du convertisseur 10856

garnissage monolithe 11912
— réfractaire 14629, 14632
— réfractaire du four 14630
garniture 12845
— à bec 10863
— annulaire 14923
— creuse 9267
— d'étanchéité à coins 16648
— de métal antifriction S. 10853
— de piston en bagues de cuir 10653
— de toit 12902
— d'un palier S. 10853
— en amiante 845
— en cuir embouti 4837
— métallique 11554
— ronde 8078
garnitures en laiton S. 2269
gasoil 8031
gaspillage 19739
— du gisement S. 2504, 4577
gâteau aggloméré 222
— de laitier 16529
— de scories 2692
gauche 19675
gauchissement de l'acier 16230
gaufrage 6404
Gault 8118
gautéite 8119
gay-lussite 8122
gaz à l'eau enrichi 2877
— brulé 14991, 19728
— brûlés 2612
— combustible 7788
— comprimé 4138
— d'acétylène 65
— de circuit 14527
— d'éclairage 9636
— d'explosion 16145, 17603
— de four à coke 3941
— de grillage 14991
— de gueulard 1712
— de pétrole liquéfié 11078
— de raffinerie 17594
— de marais S. 7165
— dégageant 6566
— dégazoliné 17858
— délétères 1767
— détonant 12815
— d'injection 9673

gaz dissous 5548
— du haut-fourneau 20069
— échappé lors d'une manoeuvre 18910
— humide S. 14872
— inclus 12443
— libre 7730
— lift intermittent 9895
— lift par chambre 3271
— liquide de pétrole 10879
— mixte 15851
— naturel 12193
— naturel acide 16944
— naturel liquéfié 10905
— pauvre 282, 10642
— protecteur 14045
— réchauffé 14644
— riche 14872
gazage 8015
gazé 8083
gazéification 8013, 8074
— à la cornue 14795, 14798
— du combustible solide 8075
gazéfier 8076
gazoduct 8036
gazogène 1012, 8042
— avec grille à gradins 17557
— double 5672
— Duff 6078
— Morgan 11932
— Siemens 16295
gazogènes 13988
gazoline naturelle 12194
gazomètre 8079
géanticlinal 8123, 8159
gédanite 8141
Gédinnien 8142
gédrite 8143
gehlénite 8144
geikielite 8145
gel-ciment 8146
gélatine explosive 1748
gélignite 8149
gemme 8150
gendarme 8939, 19200
générateur à grand volume d'eau S. 1988
— de vapeur S. 17417
— v. chaudière
générateurs 13988
génération spontanée 17146
génératrice à vapeur S. 17428 17428
— inférieure d'un tube 2185

geno-holotype 8155
— -paratype 8156
genotype 8157
genouillère 10414
genthite 8158
géochimie 8160
géocronite 8163
géode 8164, 19607
— ferrugineuse S. 188
géodésie 8165
géodésique 8166
géodynamique 8167
géogenèse 8168
géoïde 8170
géologie 8180
— économique
— historique 9608, 17752
— minière 11775
— paléontologique 12877
— régionale 768
— stratigraphique 8169
— structurale 8190
géologique 8171
géologue 8179
géomorphologie 8181
géonomie 8182
géophysique 8183, 8184
georgiadésite 8186
géoscopie 8187
géosynclinal 8188
géotechnique 8189
géothermal 8191
gerbage 13365
gerber les châssis 17275
gerces 19493
gerçure de la lingotière 7605
gerhardtite 8194
gersdorffite 8197
germanium 8196
germe 12419
geyérite 8206
geyser 8207
geysérite 8208
ghizite 8209
gibélite 8217
gibbsite 8216
gieseckite 8218
gigantolite 8221
gigantostraca 8222
gilbertite 8223
gillespite 8229
gilsonite 8230
giobertite 8234
girasol 8236
gisement 1413, 1938, 795 9330

gisement alluvionnaire 406
— de charbon 3821
— de condensat 4183
— de contact 4247/a
— d'hydrocarbures 13650
— de minerai de fer 5197
— de pétrole 12486
— d'imprégnation 9662
— en amas 16884
— épuisé 5194
— filonien 10363
— métasomatique 11598
— minéral 11751
— multiple 6069
— stratifié 17747
— vierge 11216
gisements 5408
— asphaltiques 875
gismodine 8247
gîte S. 1413
— de départ immédiat S.
4247
— de minerai de fer 11729
— de minerai des prés 1944
— disloqué 5524, 6864
— houiller 3800
— justifiant l'exploitation
12999
— métallifère 12640
— minier 11751
— v. gisement
gîtes de remplissage de
fissures 3125
— magmatiques 11169
givétien 8249
glace du fond de la balance
13490
glacier alpin 12031
— de névé 12256
— de second ordre 8264
— de vallée 19444
— norvégien S. 9612
— régénéré 14506
— scandinave 9612
— suspendu S. 8264, 8807
glacis 8265
gladkäite 8267
glaisage 3669
glaise 3653
glaiser 5589
— un châssis 3666
glaubérite 8289
glaucochroïte 8290
glaucodot 8291
glauconie S. 8293, 8511
glauconieux 8294

glauconite 8293
glaucophane 8295
glessite 8298
glissement 710, 16666,
16701
— dans le plan des couches
1432, 16608
— de couches superficiel-
les 15428
— de terrain 6169
glisser 16606, 16644, 16711
glissière 12880, 16610
globulite 8305
gloméophyrique 8307
gluant 18197
glucinium 8314
gmélinite 8318
gneiss 8319
— à biotite 1610
— -granite 8322
— oeillé 944, 6730
— primaire 7815
gobelet en porcelaine 13660
— en verre dur 8830
godet à fusion 4074
— à nettoyer 3699
— de convoyeur 4318
— de coulée 13752
— de pelle mécanique 5449
— rétro 14141
goethite 8338, 12207
goldfieldite 8353
gomme 8663
gonflement 8663, 9019
gonfler (se-) 10095
gonfler 18120
gonnardite 8355
gongarrite 8361
gordonite 8368
gorge 7966, 8586
— pour tubes 19637
goslarite 8369
goudron 18314
— de bois 20178
— de houille 3849
— de préparation 880
gouge S. 3485
— à repêchage 17219
— creuse 5657
goujon 9201, 13306
— à deux pointes 5670
— à embase 4022
— de centrage 3219
— de châssis 7298
— de remmoulage 3782
— tubulaire 9277

goujonner 13304
goulot 11659
— de coulée 17213
— d'écoulement S. 7429
goulotte 3563, 9389
— alimenteuse pour mine-
rais 6880
— d'alimentation 6878
— de décharge 2357
— oscillante à billes 1159
gousset 8679
— d'union 8680
goutte froide 6493
gouttelette séparée par liquation 15802
gouttelettes de fonte 11470
gouttière 8686
— à secousses 4323, 15975
— de transporteur S. 4316
— mobile 14202
— oscillante S. 15043
— transporteuse 4316
— v. conduit ou canal
goyazite 8376
goyot d'aérage S. 6809
gradient de température
18382
— géothermique 8192
gradin 1483, 18866
— de faille 10313
— droit 19266
— droit non remblayé 12601
— incliné 14912
— incliné avec remblayage
7019, 9696
— inférieur 4921
— renversé sans remblaya-
ge 12586
— supérieur 9052
graftonite 8393
grain 8396, 13004, 16646,
— d'acier 8831
— de cassure 7694
— fin S. 7091
— grossier 3871
grains 6840
— de fer 9979
— de fer englobés 6441
— quartzeux 14277
graissage 1336
graisse distillée 17595
— hydrofuge 19806
graisser 12477
— en excès 12771
graisseur 12483
graisseux 8505

graménite 8409
gramion 8412
grammatite 8410, S. 18871
gramme-équivalent 8411
gramme-ion 8412
grammol 8413
grand côté 19641
— front aligné 10991
grande poche de coulée 2552
— production 8603
grandeur de la capacité 2803
— de l'intensité 9863
grandidiérite 8415
granit 8416
— à deux micas 1591
granitisation 8422
granite à biotite 12378
— à tourmaline 8632
— gneiss S. 8322
— -porphyre 8417
granitite 8421
granitoïde 8423
granodiorite 8426
granophyre 8429
granophyrique 8430, 8462
granulation 8440
granuler 8435
granules de charbon S. 8436
granuleux 105, 8443
granulite 8441
granulométrie 8388
graphite 1654, 8447, 13570
— de cornue 14799
— de surfusion 19245
— en rosettes 15184
— interdentritique 9878
— lamellaire 7250
— lavé 14598
— nodulaire 12333
— primaire 13941
— sphéroïdal 17066
graphiter 8458
graphiteux 10380
graphitique 8452
graphitisant 8459
grappe 3792, 17182, 17277
grappin S. 983, 8377, 15817
— à cable 15164
graptolithe 8463
gras des cadavres S. 151
gratte-boësse 15680
gratter 15664, 15673
gratteur de tubage 15684
grattoir 15672, 16962

grattoir à expansion pour mur 19652
— double en fil d'acier 5675
grauwacke 8532, 14448, 2001 20015
graveleux 8577
gravier 8395, 8477
— strié 17801
gravimètre 8482
— statique 17394
greenalite 8521
greenockite 2676, 8522
greenovite 8523
grégarines 8525
grélassons 3895
grélats S. 3884
grenade à gaz 8055
grenaillage 16198
— à chaud 9424
— d'écrouissage 16205
grenaille 16193
— à tarer S. 18324
— d'acier 3448
— de charbon 8436
— de fonte 10014
grenailler 16195
grenailles de criblage 840$
grenat alumino-magnésien 11179
— chromo-calcareux 2725
— de Bohème 7973
grenu 13020
grès 15429, 17640
— à gros grain 8576, 11927
— à·grain fin 12855, 13713
— argileux 779, 5012
— bigarré 19472
— calcaire 2707, 3267
— cristallisé 4641
— ferrugineux 10007
— ferrugineux rubané 18615
— houiller 3831, 11717
— micacé 6770
— pétrolifère S. 12506
— quartzeux 14276, 16314
— rouge 14546, 15529
— schisteux compact 8902
— se débitant en dalles 15496
grésage 16434
grésillé 15526
grésillon 13006
griffe 8572
— à poche de coulée 10474
— automatique 983

griffe d'attaque S. 16619
— de serrage 3624
grillage 14987, 14992
— bien réussi 14020
— de sulfatation 17975
— défectueux 5111
— définitif 7135
— en meules 8944
— en stalles 17303
— magnétisant 11209
— oxydant 12811
— préliminaire 13860
— propre S. 14020
— sulfatant 17977
— superficiel 7300
grille 7844, 8465, 8536, 8579
— à barreau mobile S. 15040 15040
— à chaîne 3243
— à circulation d'eau 8475
— à étages 12126
— à foyer 7844
— à gradins 17549, 17556
— à plusieurs panneaux 15782
— à poissons 7208
— à ruissellement 8474
— à scories 6104
— à secousse 15040
— à un seul panneau 8470
— basculante 18677
— coulissante 16623
— de chauffage 9014
— de décochage 10405
— de foyer 7169
— déplaçable S. 15971
— économique 6191
— en acier fondu 3020
— en fonte 3003
— en rails de fer 8468
— étagée S. 17549
— fixe 17399
— fumivore 16761
— glissante S. 16623
— horizontale 9343
— inclinée 9701
— mobile S. 14938, 15971
— rotative 14838
— tamis 16299
— tournante S. 14838
griller S. 2712, 14983
— à mort 5026
grilleur de minerai 12636
griphite 8570
gripper 10118

grippure 2596
griquaïte 8573
gris d'acier 17477
— de zinc 20330
grisou 200, 4978, 7165,
  7184, 13407,
grisoumètre 7997, 8017
grisouteux 7002
grorudite 8599
gros S. 10546, 15276
— bloc de charbon 10239
— fers 10550
— fil 18505
— gravier 3481
grosse chaudronnerie 1978
— tôle 9037, 18502
grosses cornières 9026
grosseur de noix 19661
grosseur de poing 7225
— d'œuf 6224
— du grain 8401, 16413
grossissement 11212
— réel 14474
— total 18789
— utile 1004
grossulaire 8364, 8605
grothite 8606
groupe 15903, 7607
— d'atomes 11874
— de cimentation 3157
— de machines 15909
— de raies 8626
— de réservoirs 18246
— électrogène 6177, 8154
— Ilgner 9631
— mésozoïque 11528
— moteur 13799
— néozoïque 12227
groupement de failles 8625
— de sources 8627
grue 10167
— à benne 8379
— à câble 2667
— à démouler S. 9803
— à grappin S. 4602
— à lingots pour pits 4597
— à mâchoires ou à griffe
  4602
— à portique 13697
— à potence 13292
— à vapeur 17424
— automotrice 11954
— avec pince à lingots 9790
— avec poinçon et pince
  d'accrochage 4603

grue cantilever 12753
— chevalet de transborde-
  ment 5500
— d'applique S. 19639
— de chargement 3338
— de chargement des lingots
  9786
— de coulée 7654, 13754
— de coulée à bascule
  7655
— d'enfournement des réci-
  pients 18939
— de fonderie 3049
— de fonderie pivotante
  7672
— de fosse de coulée 3065
— démouleuse 17862, 17870
— dragueuse 4602
— fixe à vapeur 7242
— isolée 9732
— mobile 11845
— murale 19639
— pivotante 18128
— pivotante centrale 19144
— pivotante géante 15224
— roulante à vapeur 10950
— roulante à vapeur pour le
  déchargement des bateaux
  10951
— tour 12753
— vélocipède 11915
— vélocipède murale 19640
grues à flèche tournante sur
  rail 10168
grumeaux d'hématite brune
  2475
grunerite 8634
grunligite 8635
grutier 4604
guadalcazarite 8636
guanajuatite 8638
guarinite 8644
gudmundite 8646
guéjarite 8647
gueulard 3341, 3345, 15959
— de chargement 6891
— fermé 3777
— ouvert 12608
— v. gueule
gueule de moule S. 8087
— v, gueulard
gueusat S. 13249
gueuse 13249
— de refonte 13258
— intermédiaire 16948

gueuset 3427, 13249
guidage 15370
— de la poche 10477
— venu de fonte 3013
guide 3649
— du câble 20132
— du porte-segment 12989
— mains 14365
guider 17268
guildite 8657
gummite 8667
gymnite S. 5297
gypse 8235, 8694
— à cristallisation grenue
  S. 341
— cristallisé 4801
— de qualité supérieure
  8613
— ferreux 3562
gyrolite 8697

H

hackmanite 8699
hafnium 3137, 8706
haidingérite 8707
halde 2622, 6096, 6101,
  8941, 18673
halite 8720
halle de coulée 2988, 3054,
  18673
— de fonderie 7659
— de mélange 11835
— de moulage à double tra-
  vée 19191
— des convertisseurs
  4306
— des mélangeurs 11834
hälleflinta 8721
hallérite 8722
halloysite 8723
halogène 8725
haloide 8724
halotrichite S. 6869, 8710,
  8726
hampe porte-drapeau 7248
hancockite 8752
hangar 13072
hanksite 2816
hannayite 8817
happe 10757

hardénite 8869
hardystonite 8876
harmotome 8879
harpion 8460
harpon 3187, 4722, 12996
— à câble 15170
— de repêchage 7796
— de repêchage à deux
    jambes 19190
harrisite 8880
harstigite 8881
hartite 8869, 8882
hastingsite 8886
hatchettite S. 151
hatchettolite 8887
hatherlite 8888
hauban 8690, 12718
hauban-tendeur 16971
haubans de la tour 8691
hauérite 8891
hausmannite 8899
hausse v. accroissement
haut-fourneau 1706, 9149
— à enveloppe en tôle
    1726
— à poitrine fermée 1722
— au charbon de bois 3301
— au coke 3930
— avec massif en maçon-
    nerie 1725
— écossais 15648
— enveloppé 1721
— Héroult 9099
— Stassano 17388
haute pression 9164
— résistance 9182
— tourbière S. 9159
hauteur 6417, 9054
— de chute 9057, 5493
— d'élévation 8906
— de la levée 10676
— de la pièce coulée 5205
— de l'ouvrage 9056
— de plafond S. 8919
— de refoulement 13908,
    18589
— de voûte 9019
— des étalages 9055
— du liquide 16101
— du vide 16108
haüyne 8900
haüynophyre 8901
havage 2128, 3812, 9115,
    10113, 10375
— au mur 19249
havé 9254

havée 4899, 10112, 10321,
    10373
— inférieure 2152
— initiale 17997
haver 3283, 10111, 10320,
    10374, 16685
— le charbon 2297
havrit 1232
havrits 2524
haveuse 3810, 3860, 4681,
    4906, 9982, 10032, 11417
— à barre 793, 1212
— à chaîne 3239
— à colonne 19155
— à disque 5483
— à pic 13204, 14180,
    14184
— chargeuse 4912
— chargeuse Meco-Moore
    11421
— de galerie 8936
— percutante à colonne 1371
    13712
— pour grands fronts 10990
hebronite 9043
hédenbergite 9044
hedrumite 9046
hédyphane 9047
héliodor 9063
héliophyllite 9064
héliotrope 9065
helium 9066
hélvetien 9071
helvine S. 9070, 18470
helvite 9070
hémafibrite 9072
hématite 8705, 9073
— rouge 14541, 15328
— rouge mamellonée S.
    6992
— stratifié 7247
hématolite 9077
hématostibiite 9078
hémiédrique 9082
hémimorphie 9083
hémimorphite 9085
hémitrope 9086
hémitropie 19178
henwoodite 9091
heptorite 9093
hercynite 9095
herdérite 9096
hérédité 9097
heronite 9098
herrengrundite 9100
herschage S. 8789

herschélite 9101
herscheur S. 8896
hessite 9102
hessonite 9103
hétairite 9104
hetairolite S. 9104
hétérogénite 9105
hétéromorphite 9107
hettangien 9111
heulandite 9112
heumite 9113
hewettite 9114
hexahydrite 9127
hexatétraèdre 9129
hexoclaèdre 9128
hiatus 7967, 9131
hiatus stratigraphique 17749
hibbénite 9132
hibschite 9133
hiddénite 9134
higginsite 9135
hillebrandite 9196
hinsdalite 9208
hintzéite 9209
hiordahlite S. 8644
hisser 13201
histrixite 9213
hitchcockite 9215
hodgkinsonite 9221
högbomite 9223
hokutolite 9237
holarctique 9238
holdénite 9241
holmium 9283
holoaxe 9284
holocène 9285
holocristallin 9286
holoédrique 9287
hololeucicrate 9289
holomélanocrate 9290
holomorph S. 9291
holomorphique 9291
holotype 9292
holohyalin 9288
holyokéite 9293
homilite 9295
homoclinal 9296
homoéomorphe 9298
hopéite 9327
horizon 9330
— gazeux 8016
— repère 10327, 11331
hornblende 9369
hornblendite 9371
hornito 1871
hors de service 12473, 12591

horsfordite 9384
horst 9385
hortonolite 9386
hôte 9390
hotte 7817
— de la cheminée 3461
houille 11050, 13403
— à coke S. 3953
— à courte flamme 3757
— agglutinante 2696
— anthraciteuse 15836
— brillante 651
— bitumineuse S. 1634, 16831
— de chaudière 1956
— demi-grasse 15837
— éclatante S. 642
— extraite 11752
— feuilletée 7530, 15978´
— fuligineuse 16919
— grasse 1634, 2782, 16831
— luisante 8268
— maigre 10640, 12341, 12342
— maigre à courte flamme S. 5836
— maigre collante 1118
— maigre sableuse 16487
— matte S. 6115, 17116
— menue 16727
— non collante 12344
— non collante à longue flamme 7721
— poisseuse 13418, 13419
— pyriteuse 2282
— sèche S. 6028
houille v. charbon
houillère 3839, 3858
houilles 5408
houilleur 3840
howlite 9468
hubnérite 9471
hudsonite 9474
hugelite 9475
huile 12478, 11753
— à cordes 1333
— à gaz 8031
— à moules 7606
— anhydre 3679
— brute S. 1283, 4754
— brute asphaltique 874
— combustible 13785
— d'amorçage 10913
— de bois de Chine 19099
— de coupe soluble 16897

huile de créosote 5035
— de goudron de houille 3850
— de lavage 7491
— de paille 17755
— de palmier 12882
— de polissage 15322
— de presse 13869
— de revenu 18397
— de spermaceti 17063
— de stockage 17626
— déparaffinée 5296
— écoulée 5951
— émulsionable 6424
— en place 12495
— épaisse 2581
— épaissie 17337
— fumigène 16776
— graphitée 8455
— grasse 6826
— liquide 16723
— lourde v. naphte ou pétrole
— odoriférante 16712
— pour service sévère 9029
— raffinée par solvant 16911
— récupérée 15608
— redistillée 14741
— réduite 14561
— régénérée 14497
— riche 10898
— sulfurée 17967
— superdense 18014
— trouble 15066
huiler 12477
huiles lourdes dérivées du pétrole 14233
— primaires 17717
hullite 9477
hulsite 9478
humide 4985, 16853
humidité 11863
— de l'iar 9480
humique 9479
humite 9481
humus 11969
huntilite 9487
huronien 9488
hussakite 9491
hyacinthe 9494, 10089
hyalin 9495
hyalite 9497, 19801
hyalocristallin 9498
hyalophane 9499
hyalosidérite 9501

hyalotékite 9502
hydatogenèse 9504
hydatogène 9505
hydrargillite 9507
hydrate de fer 9577
hydroboracite 9546
hydrocarbure asphaltique 882
hydrocarbures 9547
— ramifiés 2259
hydrocérusite 9548
hydrocyanite 9552
hydrocyclone 4934
hydrogène 9557
hydrogène sulfuré 17985
hydrohématite 9563
hydrolyse 9564
hydrométamorphisme 9566
hydromuscovite 9568
hydronéphélite 9569
hydrophane 9570
hydrophilite 9571
hydroséparateur 9543
hydrosilicate de zinc 16317
hydrotalcite 9576
hydrozincite 9579, 20324
hydrure 9542
hygromètre 9580
hypabyssal 9582
hypereutectique 9585
hypérite 9589
hypersthène 9591, 10453
hypersthénite 9592
hypertrempe 2918, 9590
hypidiomorphe 9593
hypochlorure de cuivre 4853
— d'étain 17367
hypocristallin 9080, 9595, 11512
hypoeutectique 9596
— v. hypoeutectoïde
hypoeutectoïde 9597
— v. hypoeutectique
hypogène 9601
hyposulfite de soude 9602

I

icositétraèdre 9614
iddingsite 9615
idioblaste 9616
idiochromatique 9617

idiogène 9619
idiomorphe 9620
idocrase S. 19542
idrialite 9622
ignifuge 12353
ijolite 9629
ijussite 9630
illite 9632
ilménite 9637, 11485
ilmentite 9638
ilvaïte S. 10733, 20295
image virtuelle 9639
immersion en métaux fondus 5453
imperfection interne S. 10566
imprégnation de vapeur 17477
impression 9219
— en taille-douce 3256
imprimer 9668
impureté 4897
impuretés 9672
inaltérable sous l'action des agents atmosphériques S. 19863
inattaquable par les gaz 8043
incandescence 8313, S. 20031
incinérateur 9687
incinération du filtre 2608
incise-tube 2955, S. 2960
inclinable 13789
inclinaison 9688, 14382, 16678
— axiale 7574
— de faille 6848
— de la couche 5444
— de la grille 9689
— primaire 13939
inclinaison v. pendage
incliné 13420
inclus 12442
inclusion 6444, 9712, 16916, 18344, 20268
— carboneuse 2846
— de minerais dans la roche en faible quantité 17208
— de noir 2846
— de pyrite dans la houille 3803
— de sable 15500, 13566
— de scorie 9713

inclusion de scorie congénitale 6462
— de stériles dans une veine 9375
— métallique étrangère 6659
— minérale 11754
— non métallique 12358, 14580
— non métallique étrangère 6660
inclusions de laitier 16540
incombustible 7186
incrustation 9727, 15596
incurvation 5728
index 3882
— Diesel 5389
— d'un atome 932
indicateur à orifice 12670
— de charge 17621
— d'extraction 9738
— de grisou 4984, 19670
— de la descente des charges 17623
— de niveau à flotteur 7387
— de tirage 1728
— des charges 9737
indication de l'année 12423
— de pétrole 12510
indice d'aptitude au serrage 4102
— de basicité 9735
— de finesse 7098
— de grosseur de grain 8402
— d'octane 12454
— de pétrole S. 12510
— de productivité 14000
— naphténique 12170
indigolite 9741
indium 9746
industrie métallurgique 11587
— minière 11769, 11776
— pétrolifère 12497
— sidérurgique 9980
inégalité de surface 19293
inertie thermique 18485
infiltration d'eau 20321
— d'eau 20321
— pétrolifère 12508
inflammable 9765
influence 9768
— atmosphérique 925
— sur la solubilité 9770

infusibilité 9773
infusible 9774
ingénieur de forage 5923
— de l'exploitation 6472
ingression 9806
inhalation 9682
inhibiteur 9807
— de coagulation 13744
injecteur 9818
— à pétrole 13131, S. 17438
— à vapeur d'échappement 6654
injection 9812
— multiple 17274
injectivité 9810
inoculant 9826
inoculation 9827
inondation 7399
inoxydable 12363, 15393, 17296
insensible aux gaz S. 8043
insérer 9832, 15346
insertion 9833
insoluble 9844
inspecter les tuyères 9845
inspection des chaudières 1970
instabilité à l'écoulement 13745
installation 15913
— à antenne 10106
— à basse tension 11063
— à courant alternatif 432
— à courant continu 4265
— d'agglomération 225
— d'amalgamation 496
— d'appareils réfrigérants pour les eaux 19763
— de briquettage 2417
— de broyage 4780
— de chargement à grue pivotante et roulante supérieure 10919
— de chargement et de transport 10920
— de chaudières 1973
— de chaudières découvertes 12590
— de chaudières sous toit 4566
— de classification 16928
— de concentration 4164
— de criblage 15696
— de crochetage 10765
— de déshydratation 12485

installation de distillation
5563
— de distillation sous pression 13920
— d'éclairage 10796
— d'éclairage et de distribution d'énergie 10793
— d'enrichissement 4170
— d'essai des gaz 19470
— d'extraction 20104
— d'extraction du gaz 7975
— de filtrage 7050
— de forage 5938, 14897
— de forage actionnée par
moteurs à combustion
interne 13791
— de foyers 7193
— de granulation 8439
— de grillage 14993
— de hauts fourneaux
1713
— de lavage 19705
— de lessivage 10901
— de lixiviation des mi-
nerais 12644
— de machines électriques
6286
— de nettoyage d'un puits
3701
— de pompage S. 14170
— de pompes 14160
— de préfusion 13864
— de préparation 5844
— de récupération 14509,
19469
— de récupération des gaz
24
— de séchage 6062
— de sondage autotranspor-
tée 10243
— de sondage rotary 15201
— de traitement 18867
— de traitement de minerai
de plomb 1606
— de tréfilage et d'évasement 9412
— de triage 8389, 15694,
15865
— d'une fosse S. 15947
— d'un puits 15947
— métallographique 11580
— monophasée 16395
— pétrolifère 12503
— portative de forage
13692
— pour l'utilisation du laitier Thomas 18538

installation transportable
de sondage S. 10243
— transportable du plan
incliné 8324
— triphasée 18566
installations pour la distillation du goudron 18317
installer 14896
instrument de mesure 11400
— de repêchage des tiges
de sonde 2212
intensité 6997
— de retenue des ions
9860
— lumineuse 2783
— polaire 17777
intercalation 9868, 16045
— d'argile S. 3662 .
— de charbon 3845, 16041
— de charbon pyriteux 2284
— de charbon schisteux
1652
— imperméable 9656
— stérile 5475, 5852
intercalé S. 9864 9887
9915
interchangeable 9869
intercristalline 9874
interdentrique 9877
interrupteur 9894
interrupteur commandé à
distance 14702
intervalle 16957, S. 19971
— carotté 4457
— de fusion 11477
— de solidification 7748,
16892
— de transformation 18826
— entre les barreaux de
grille S. 8473
— entre les coulées 18303
interstratification 9865
interstratifié 9864, 9887,
17762
interstratifier 9917
introduction d'air ample-
ment suffisante 541
introduire 15346
intrusif 9924, 10044
intrusion 9923
— discordante 5507
— rubanée 9816
— vers le haut 19386
intumescence 9929
inverser les circuits 15003
inverseur de polarité 13617

inyoïte 9938
iodobromyrite 9942
iodure de potassium 13729
iodyrite S. 9939
iolite 9943
ion 9944
— acide 81
— basique 1296
— hydroxyle 9578
— multivalent 12129
— neutre 9503
ionite 9945
iridium 9950
iridosmine 9951
irrégularité de forme 20239
irruption 9830
irvingite 10045
isénite 10047
isérite 10048
ishikawaite 10049
isobutane 10052
isobutène 10053
isoclasite 10056
isoclinal 10054
isocline 10057
isoformate 10058
isohydrie des solutions acides 10062
isohydrique 10060
isolant 9850, 12950
isolation phonique en laine
de roche 108
— pour éviter la formation
de ponts thermiques 9852
— thermique 8983
isomerate 10066
isomorphe 10069
isomorphisme 10070
iso-octane 10071
isoparaffine 10073
isopentane 10074
isoprène 10076
isoséiste 10077
isotope radioactif 14335
itabirite 10084, 17041
itacolumite 10085
ittrocérite 20309
ixolite 10087

J

jacobsite 10109
jacupirangite 10110
jade 10114
jadéite 10115
jadéitite 10116

jaillir 7419
— par intermittence 7420
jaillissement 8676, 17231
— de gaz 1885
jais 10152
jale v. poche ou creuset
jambe 10668, 15984, 17228
— de la tour 5220
jamesonite fibreuse 6990
jante de roue 20009
jantes 14919
jargon 10133
jarosite 10134
jaspe-opale 6969
jasperisation 10138
jauge 8107
— à coulisse 2747
— à fils 20128
— à vis 15767
— d'échantillonnage 12513
— d'épaisseur 16070, 18509
— de profondeur 5204
— de remmoulage 8110
— du fil 8115
— micrométrique 11643
— pour les tôles 16055
— pour trous 9251
— pour tuyaux 14310
jefferisite 10144
jeffersonite 10145
jérémejéwite S. 6231, 10148
jeromite 10150
jet 5488, 6886, 10153, 10154
— cassé dans la pièce 2327
— caverneux 13673
— coulé en fosse 13402
— coulé en sable 15490
— d'air 241
— de coulée 15364, 15381
— de coulée annulaire 3592
— de coulée conique 19881
— de coulée coudé 9779
— de coulée rond 16369
— de fer malléable 11813
— de gaz rouge 14534
— de métal 17769
— de remonte 15359
— de sable 15472
— déformé 19676
— en fonte sphéroïdal 17068
— enveloppé 10104
— non venu 15383
— sain 16937
jeter 18586
jets de coulée 8106, 15377
jeu 1065, 13536, 15903,

jeu de coiffage 3709
— de deux 5638
— de la bascule 13537
— de modèles 4056
— de moulage 9776
— de trois 18572
— des pompes étagées 10742
jezekite 10165
jig mobile 11847
joaquinite 10187
joint 2018, 10198, 12850
— à chute libre 7727
— à emboîtement 9834,
— à mâchoires 7209
— de cardan 2887
— de culasse 8908
— de dilatation 6672
— de moulage 11982
— de retrait 10205
— de séparation 12944
— de sûreté 15418
— de tube 19031
— en amiante 845
— étanche 15830, 18619
— gauche 175569
— horizontal 1418
— hydraulique 5925
— isolant 9851
— normal 14653
— rapide 14296
— sphérique 1157
joints obturés 12224
— soudés bout à bout 2639
jonc de freinage 5778
jordanite 10229
josefite 10230
joséite 10231
joséphinite 10232
jour S. 8464, 18041
journal de sondage 5937
julienite 10241
jumillite 10244
jurupaite 10259
juxporite 10263

K

kaersutite 10265
kainite 10266
kainolithe 10267
kainosite S. 2687, 10268
kakoxen 10271
kaliborite 10273
kalinite 10274
kaliophilite 10275
kalium 10276

kalkowskite 10277
kamacite 10279
kamarezite 10280
kammérérite 10281
kampylite 10282
kaolinite 10283
karsténite 10285
kasolite 10287
katagénèse 10288
katamorphique 10289
kata-zone 10291
katophorite 10290
katoptrite 10293
kaustobiolite 10294
kehoenite 10301
keilhauite 10302
kélyphite 10308
kemite 10309
kentrolite 10310
kéramohalite 10311
kermésite 10312
kernite 10314
kérogène 10315
kérosène 10316
— distillé 10317
kerrite 10318
kersantite 10319
khagiarite 10333
kieselguhr 10348
kiesérite 10349
killinite 10355
kilomole 10361
kimberlite 10362
kinetogénèse 10364
kipushite 10370
kir 10371
kirrolite 10372
kjerulfine 10384
klaprothine 10385
klébelsbergite 10386
kleinite 10387
knébélite
kobellite 10418
koechlinite 10420
koppite 10426
kornerupine 10428
kramérite 10431
krantzite 10432
krausite 10434
krochnkite 10437
kyschtymite 10446

L

laboratoire de fabrication 20225
— principal 3416
labourage glaciaire 8254
labradite 10452
labrador 10454
labradorite 10454
l'ac de cirque 18328
laccolithe 7411, 10455
laccolithique 10456
lâchage de la scorie 18308
lacroixite 10463
lacune S. 9131
— d'érosion 6548
— stratigraphique 2313, 11038
lagune 10491
laine d'amiante 849
— de laitier 16465
laisser rebondir le mouton 10695
— se calmer 5033, 14307
lait de chaux 10818
— de ciment 3155
laiter 16519
laitier 3570
— acide 93
— basique 1305
— chaud 14878
— du haut-fourneau 1717
— de haut-fourneau traité à la vapeur 1719
— granulé 8438
— pierreux 17651
— vitreux 19574
laiton 2266, 20283
— à haute résistance 9186
— coulé 2985
— d'aluminium 449
— en feuilles S. 13488
— en lames S. 13488
— en planches 13488
laitonnage 2275, 13504
laitonnerie 2269
lakarpite 10492
lambeau de charriage 6855
lambourde S. 17899
lame 7526, 13479, 15672
— de cisaille 16039
— de rabot S. 13455
— de rasoir 14464
— de ressort 10633, 17195
— de scie 15557
— du trépan 1624
lamellaire 10497, 10500,

lamelle 7249, 10496, 10499
laminable 15092
laminage 15120
— à chaud 9436
— à froid 3997
— à sandwich 15532
— d'acier avec affinage 17045
— dans le sens de la largeur 20065
— dans le sens de la longueur 10677
— de tubes 19036
— des brames 15305
— diagonal 5310
— d'un fil 15056, 15059
— multiple 12836
— transversal 4703
laminé 11703, 15094
— à chaud 9429
— à froid 3610, 3990
— au blanc 2393
laminer 10503, 11682, 15067, 15242
— à froid 3959
— ensemble 15072
— les tôles 16077
— par rotation entre cylindres inclinés 4701
lamineur 11696, 15105
laminoir 10005, 11688, 15125
— à aluminium 460
— à bandes d'acier 7954
— à billettes 1583
— à blindages 800
— à blooms 1826, 1834
— à brames 16501
— à fers moyens 11428
— à feuillards 9325, 17854
— à fil 20135
— à froid pour feuillards 3998
— à largets 16048
— à mouvement alternatif 14495
— à mouvement continu 4272
— à pas de pélerin 13281
— à profilés 15778, 15989
— à quatre cylindres verticaux 7679
— à rails 14362
— à roues 20010
— à scraps 15659
— à tôles 10508, 13497

laminoir à tôles minces 18527
— à tubes 13364, 19037
— belge 1444
— calibreur 16447
— continu à quatre cages en tandem 7681
— d'acier 17502
— duo 19173
— finisseur 7137
— irréversible 12362
— marchand 11497
— oblique 9706
— pour travaux 17019
— réducteur 4569
— réducteur à chaud 9427
— réducteur calibreur 14566
— réversible 14833
— réversible à haute vitesse 9175
— réversible à lingots 14829
— réversible à tôles 14832
— réversible pour laminage à froid 14830
— réversible pour le finissage à chaud 14831
— simple 16394
— souder 19948
— trio à profilés 18562
— trio à tôles 18560
— universel 19314
laminoir v. train
lampadite 10514
lampe à acétylène 66
— à arc 747
— à esprit 17103
— à gaz d'éclairage et à oxygène 8035
— à incandescence 8311
— à mercure 11506
— à pétrole à flamme de sûreté 15422
— au magnésium 11180
— Davy 10097
— de mine 5958
— de sûreté 15419
— électrique à main 6279
— électrique de chapeau
— pour chalumeau 1889
— pour microscope 11650
lamprophyre 10511
lanarkite 10512
lance à jet de sable 12410
— de repêchage 19686

lance de sablage 15475
lancer 18586
langbanite 10532
langbeinite 10532, 10533
langite 10534
languette à sable 15493
lansfordite 10535
lanterne 260, 17077, 17088, 19505
— de cheminée 3456
— de guidage 15053, 17946
— du noyau 4388
lanthane 10537
lanthanite 10536
lapis-lazuli 1035, 10544
laque 10461
laqué 10122
laquer 10460
larderellite 10545
large-plat 7325, 17853
larget 7322, 7340, 16047, 16049
largeur de la chemise 18510
— de la ravure 20063
larnite 10552
larsenite 10556
latéritisation 10574
latérite 10572
latéritique 10573
latite 10580
latte 10575
latter S. 10575
laubanite 10583
laugénite 10584
laumonite 10585
Laurentien 10588
lavage 7481, 14190, 15724, 19701
— à sec 6050
— aux sluices 16710
— contre-courant 1090
— de l'or à la batée 12900
— de minerai 2515
— d'or 7486
— du moule 7439
— par jig 10179
— sur tables oscillantes 15037
lave 10589
— boueuse 11864
— cordée 15172
lavenite 10590
laver 19681
— au crible 10169
— l'argile 19683

laverie 12659
laveur 19700
— à fines 7076,
— Bian 1573
— classeur 19704
— de gaz 8052
— d'or 8352
— du «packer» 10844
— Theisen 18477
lavoir 10586
— à charbon 3855
— à minerais 12659
— à rhéolaveurs 14852
— à schlamms 16633
— à secousses 10170, 10181
— à vis 15715
— rotatif 6016
lawrencite 10591
lawsonite 10592
lazulite 10601
lazurite S. 10544, 10602
leadhillite 10629
lechatelièrite 10655
lecontite 10656
lectotype 10657
ledeburite 10658
ledmorite 10660
leuwfonteinite 10661
lehiite 10669
lehnerite 10670
leidléite 10671
leifite 10672
lengenbachite 10674
lennilite 10678
lent 16707
lentille allongée de minerai 13606
— de Bertrand 1540
— de sable pétrolifère 12499
leonhardite 10681
léonite 10682
léopardite 10683
lépidocrocite 10685
lépidomélane 10687,
leptite 10689
leptochlorite 10690
leptoclase 10691
leptynite 10692
lessingite 10693
lessive de soude 16811
— décuivrée 5082
— zincifère 11108
lestiwarite 10694
lettsomite 10696
leucite S. 539, 10698

leucitite 10699
leucitophyre 10700
leucochalcite 10701
leucocrate 10702
leucophaenicite 10703
leucopyrite 10704
leucosphénite 10705
leucoxène 10706
levage 9229
levé à la planchette 13459
— de plan de mine 10562 10565
— du piston 13577
— préliminaire 13848
— souterrain 19264
leverriérite 10719
levier 4721, 4723, 10717
— basculant 15041
— coudé 18706
— de déviation 9353
— palpeur 6898
lèvre 10807, 16254
— abaissée S. 5716, 11059, 18593
— affaissée S. 5707, 5716, 6000, 11059, 11071
— de faille 6862
— d'un foret S. 10862
— inférieure 5707, 7548, 11072
— soulevée 9171, 10753
— supérieure 8815
lewisite 10720
lewistonite 10721
liant 405, 1597, 1602, 2023, 3142
— aux cendres de lignite 247 2473
liasique 10724
liaison 4224
— d'angle 4479
libethénite 10725
libre de cendres S. 865
liebenérite 10731
liebigite 10732
lier 395
lier (se-) 2690
lieu de chargement 13434
— de déversement 6106
liévrite 10733
ligne aérienne 191
— d'affleurement 10837
— de charnière 9200
— d'ébarbure 7309
— de faille 6852
— de faîte S. 19838

ligne de flexion 1510
— de force 10834
— de fracture 7697
— de glissement 8299
— de joint 10203
— de mouvement 16655
— de partage 9918, 19838
— de pente 16682
— de plongement 10833
— de plus grande pente 7797
— de référence 5009
— élastique de flexion S. 1510
— horizontale 10709
— médiane des·cannelures 1023
— souterraine 19258
lignes de Neumann 12251
lignite 2472, 10802
— fibreux 6991
— terreux 19228
— xyloïde 20273
lignitifère 10804
ligroïne 10805, 11755
lillianite 10806
limaille 7007, 14611
— d'aluminium 451
limburgite 10809
lime à fonte 7003
— d'entrée 14892
limet 6748, 12946, 16646
limets 1063
limeuse 1494
— rotative avec arbre souple 15205
limite apparente d'élasticité 6833
— apparente d'étirage 20298
— conventionnelle d'é-lasticité 14007
— conventionnelle d'endurance 6834
— conventionnelle de fluage 4623
— d'élasticité 6245, 10821
— d'erreurs d'analyse 10822
— de grain 8397
— de proportionnalité 10823, 14024
— de rupture 2329
— d'usure admissible 19859
— eau-pétrole 6206
— élastique conventionnelle 6391
— élastique intérieure 9908

limite élastique vraie 10821
— inférieure d'étirage à chaud 11768
— théorique d'endurance 6833
limnique 10827
limon 12069, 16346, 16695
— en acier 17511
limoneux 18638
limonite 10828
— en cubes 5283
lindoïte 10829
lindströmite 10830
lingot 1206, 3042, 9782
— carré 17237
— cintré 4886
— d'acier 17481, 17489
— d'aluminium 19618
— de départ 14451
— de deuxième fusion 15769 15769
— d'or 2570
— d'or fin 7073
— dégrossi 3910
— éprouvette 18445
— rectangulaire 14518
— rond 15284
— soufflé 1882
lingoter 2975
lingotière 3007, 9795,, 9968
lingots de plomb 10612
— en fonte 9267
liparite 10864
lipopalingénèse 10865
liquation 6384, 10866
liqueur dense 8493
liquide d'arrêt 15739
— sous pression 13907
liquidus 10880
liroconite 10881
liskeardite 10882
lise 5863
lisière d'argile S. 3657, 15835
lissage 16485
lisse 14359, 16601
lisser 10538, 16583
lissoir 16584, 16604
— à cuiller 17153
— à tuyaux 13366
— cintré à grand congé 4882
— d'équerre cintré 16002
— d'équerre cintré à congé 14342

lissoir d'équerre droit à congé 14343
— d'équerre droit vif 16903
— de souder 7641
lit 1274L 10594, 11393, 15743, 17753
— de coke 3929
— de coulée 3041, 13251, 13256, 13751
— de déjection S. 16613
— de fusion 1428, 2586, 11839
— de grillage 14998
— de gueuse S. 16950
litharge 10619
lithium 10885
lithoclase 10886
lithogène 10887
lithologie 10889
lithophyse 10890
lithosphère 10891
livingstonite 10900
livre des charges 3317
— des coulées 3317
livres pour pouce carré 14084
lixiviation 8943
lobe 10936
localisateur·de joint 4019
locomotive à vapeur 17440
— de manoeuvre 5606
log acoustique S. 16915
— sonique 16915
loge de moraine 11930
lollingite 10966
longrine 10985
longueur S. 10204
— de deux tiges 5689
— du coussinet 1394
— du laminoir 15077
— du trou de mine 15353
— en direction 10675
— exacte 6629
— prescrite 13861
longulite 10987
loparite 11015
lopin cinglé 16132
loquet S. 10561
lorandite 11016
loranskite 11017
lorenzénite 11018
lorettoite 11019
loséyite 11021
lotrite 11041
louche S. 3058, 15463
louderbackite 11042

loup 9958, 15434, 16951
— de bec de cornue 16521
loupe 1148, 1382, 1820,
    2531, 9956, 10996, 11043
    11213
— d'acier 17458
— de puddlage 14095
loxoclase 11077
lubrifiant 11079
— de filetage 18552
— pour hautes pressions
    6503
— pour moules 5368
ludlamite 11082
ludwigite 11083
lugarite 11085
luisant S. 13626
lujaurite 11086
lumachelle 11087, 16105
lumière d'admission de l'air
    comprimé S. 13916
— de Drummond 10815
— du jour 5021
— incidente 9659
lumière v. ouverture
luneburgite 11092
lunettes en mica 11625
— protectrices 8340
luscladite 11096
lusitanite 11097
lussatite 11098
lutécite 11100
lutécium 11101
luter les ouvertures 3754
— un moule 11099
Lutétien 11102
lutite 11103
luxullianite 11105
luzonite 11106
lythomorphique 11111

M

macaroni 11112
macédonite 11114
macgovernite 11115
mâchefer 3727
machine à balancier 1378
— à boucher le trou de cou-
    lée 18269
— à brocher 2431
— à bronzer 2463

machine à cingler S. 16133
— à cintrer les tôles 13487
— à cisailler 16030
— à chambre chaude 9404
— à chambre chaude à
    piston 9405
— à chambre chaude à pres-
    sion directe de l'air sur
    le métal 5461
— à chambre froide 3967
— à charger 3340
— à commande par câbles
    15161
— à commande par courroie
    1476
— à compression 17264
— à couler 3059
— à couler les gueuses
    13255, 13267
— à couler par centrifuga-
    tion 3205
— à damer le charbon 3847
— à damer le terrain 3849
— à damer les fonds 13563
— à découper S. 16030
— à découper au chalumeau
    7257
— à découper des lingots
    9799
— à découper les tôles
    16052
— à décriquer 3476
— à démouler 7295
— à démouler à chariot
    élévateur 12017
— à démouler avec plaque
    à modèle renversable
    19149
— à démouler pour pièces
    plates 10776
— à deux temps 19184
— à dresser 17725
— à ébarber 3046, S. 6977
— à élargir les tubes 13361
— à empaqueter les chutes
    2657
— à enfourner S. 3340
— à façonner les moules
    12014
— à faire des tresses de
    paille 17757
— à fondre à air comprimé
    303
— à fondre à piston 13580
— à forer 13595
— à forer v. perceuse

machine à forger à rouleaux
    7596
— à forger automatique 982
— à forger et laminer 7591
— à forger horizontale 9356
— à guillocher 15179
— à honer 9307
— à jet de sable 15473
— à meuler 8544, 8549
— à meuler suspendue
    12756
— à mouler 7313, 12014
— à mouler à chevalet 19370
    19370
— à mouler à compression
    13872
— à mouler à double effet
    12019
— à mouler à la main avec
    plaque à modèle renver-
    sable 8770
— à mouler à main 8767,
    8780
— à mouler avec plateau
    tournant 12018
— à mouler en coquille
    16102
— à mouler hydraulique
    9528
— à mouler les cercles
    de fourneau de cuisine
    8964
— à mouler les engrenages
    à colonne 8135
— à mouler les engrenages
    au moyen d'un fouloir
    porte-segment 11125
— à mouler les engrenages
    avec table 8136
— à mouler les petites
    roues dentées 16730
— à mouler les poulies de
    grand diamètre 11126
— à mouler les roues den-
    tées 8133
— à mouler les roues den-
    tées avec deux plateaux
    8137
— à mouler les tuyaux à ai-
    lettes 12015
— à mouler murale 8134
— à mouler par pression
    12022
— à mouler pour fonderie
    7662
— à noyauter 4422

machine à obturer le trou de
  coulée 18268
— à quatre temps 7677
— à rectifier les engrenages 8128
— à rectifier sans pointes
   3199
— à refendre 16675
— à refouler 19380
— à remblayer 8327, 1058
— à souder 6316, 15748
— à souder en bout 2642
— à souder par points 171
   17165
— à souffler les noyaux
   4394
— à tailler les engrenages
   8127
— à tarauder 18300
— à tirer les noyaux 4444
— à tremper au chalumeau
   7260
— auxiliaire 2050
— compound 4128
— de cimentation 8629
— de démarrage 17385
— d'ébarbage 3704
— d'épuissemnt 5748
— d'essai 18465
— d'extraction 1192, 5798,
   8219, 9232, 20103
— de finissage 7130
— d'induction 9754
— de mine 11777
— de moulage à secousses
   10129
— de moulage à secousses
   avec démoulage par
   renversement 10222
— de moulage à secousses
   et pression 10233
— de moulage par pression
   5363
— de nettoyage S. 3704
— électrique à brazer et
   traiter les pointes
   d'outils 6312
— frigorifique 7744
— hydraulique à mouler
   avec plaque renversable
   à modèle 9529
— jumelle 19170
— motrice 5964
— non polarisée 12361
— outil 11136

machine pneumatique 19425
— pose-tuyaux 13353
— pour couloir 9693
— pour la production de
   cylindres par centrifugation 15075
— pour le moulage à la main
   à tige de soulèvement
   8769
— pour le moulage à la main
   de pièces à forme rebon-
   die 8768
— réversible 14827
— soufflante 1704, 1858,
   1875
— soufflante de Cleveland
   à une bielle 3720
— soufflante horizontale
   9332
— tandem 18238
— télescopique à mouler
   les poulies 18360
— verticale à aléser le
   gabarit 10171
machines à mouler 15507
— dite à coffrages glis-
   sants 16653
machiniste 6471, 11131
— d'extraction 9228
— de monte-charges 6473
mâchoire 8572, 10141, 12041,
   14391
— de serrage 15158
— de tour 10576
— du concasseur 2320
mâchoires de pliage 1509
— de suspension pour tu-
   bes 19048
mackensite 11141
maclage d'acier au four é-
   lectrique S. 6305
macle S. 11142
— de pénétration 13064
— géminée 19177
maclé 11143
macles d'interpénétration
   9911
— juxtaposées 10264
— polysynthétiques 12122,
   13646
maçon de puits 3915
maconite 11144
maçonner 2366
maçonnerie de la cuve 15950
— extérieure de la cuve 12697

macroclastique 11146
macrocristallin 11147
macrodôme
macrographie 11149, 11151
macroprisme 11154
macroségrégation 11156
macrostructure 11157
madeirite 11159
madupite 11160
maenaite 11161
mafite 11163
mafraite 11164
magasin 17691
— à fers 10021
— de modèles 12994
magma 11167
— de second temps 11380
— fractionnel 7690
— primaire 12933
— résiduel 14754
— secondaire 17926
magnalium 455
magnésie 1631, 11181,
— carbonatée S. 2852
magnésiochromite 11171
magnésioferrite 11172
magnésioludwigite 11173
magnésite 11174
magnésium 11178
magnétique 11185
magnétisable 11208
magnétisme 11206
magnétite 10959, 11193,
   11207
— artificielle 835
magnétoplumbite 11211
magnoferrite 11214
maillé 11520
maille 11516
— de tamis 16300
maillechort 12280, 8195
maillet à deux bobines 14425
   14425
— à une bobine 14424
— conique 14423
mailloche 9038
main-courante 14951, 16661
— de cage 16151
mains-courantes 8795, 14128
maintien 9242
maison ouvrière 20224
maître-bocardeur 2815
— des forges 10034
— sondeur 5915
maîtriser 2791

majoration du modèle pour la
  contraction 12993
mal cristallisé 6159
— venu 11806
malachite 8510, 11273
malacolite 11238
malacon 11239
malaxage 11828
— de chuttes 2627
malaxer 11816
malaxeur 11825, 11833
— à argile 3658
— à argile horizontal 9335
— à dolomie 5612
— de ciment 3150
— de sable 15504
malachite 11240
maldonite 11241
malignite 11245
malladrite 11246
mallardite 11247
malléabilisation par décarbo
  nisation 11255
— par graphitisation 11256
malléabilité 11248
malléable 6073
manandonite 11260
manche de manoeuvre S. 2221
— de prise placé sur la tête d'injection 18139
manche de rotary 15211
— du coin 16654
— en bois 20183
— riveté 14977
manchon 13332, 13359,
  16111, 17664
— à soupape 7385
— d'accouplement 4549
— d'arrêt du deuxième
  bouchon 17302
— venu de fente 3012
— de réduction 14563
— de serrage 17128
— de tube 2936
— exothermique 6663
— isolant 8982
— pince 17193
— pour cimentation «Sim-
  plex» 16374
— pour tuyaux 16591
— réducteur à doigts
  d'entraînement 127
mandelstein S. 543
mandrin 15081
— à élargir les tubes
  18980

mandrin à galets S. 18980
— à mors 10142
— à sertir les tubes S.
  18980
— à trois mâchoires 18563
— d'étirage 11264
— expanseur de tubes S.
  18980
— piriforme 13011
— relève-tubes 2958
mandrineur-rabatteur S.
  18980
— -sortisseur S. 18980
manège 9349
— à chevaux 20014
manganèse 11266
— argentin S. 59
manganésé 11282
manganésifère 11280
manganeux 11290
manganite 59, 11286
manganocalcite 11287
mangano-phosphore 13176
manganophyllite 11288
manganosite 11289
mangérite 11292
manifestation de gaz 18219
— d'huile 16217
manipulation de matériel
  11374
manipuler 6896
manivelle 4658
— de serrage 8791
manoeuvre de batterie 18908
— du convertisseur 8797
manomètre 8108, 11297
— à mercure 11507
— à tube élastique S. 17196
— à vide 19435
— de pression 13783
— métallique 17196
— pour les gaz 11296
manque 16184
— de poids 19284
manteau S. 5147
— en tôle 10012
manutention 8796
marais 16624
marâtre 2246
— d'un haut fourneau 11300
maraudage 7628
marauder 7627
marbre S. 8434
— à gros grain 16991
— belge 14409
marbré 17031

marcasite 9092
marcassite 11313, 20034
marche 15349
— de fusion 14005
— de la carbonisation 13975
— de la combustion S.
  13976
— de la trempe 13977
— des opérations de séparation 13979
— douce 20223
— du haut-fourneau 20247
— du lavage S. 19708
— du travail au four à puddler 20248
— régulière du four 14654
marcher à vide 15347
marécageux 1950
marfieldite 11332
margarite S. 4505, 11314
margosanite 11315
marger 2068
marialite 11318
marignacite 11319
mariposite 11326
mariupolite 11327
marloésite 11336
marmatite 11339
marmite 13720
— de Papin 5406
marmolite 11340
marne 10930, 11335
marque 11329
— de fabrique 3521, 18812
marscoïte 11342
marshite 11343
marteau à air comprimé 4136
— à buriner 3480
— à chute 5981
— à dresser 17724
— à ébarber 3480, 6976,
  15600
— à forger 7593
— à friction 7768
— à levier 15943
— à manche S. 15943
— à manivelle 8739
— à planche avec commande
  Müller 5995
— à puits 16424
— à soulèvement 10748
— à transmission 1475
— d'acier 17478
— de forgeron S. 16581
— de mouleur 11993
— de prospecteur 14037

marteau de triage 13210
— guidé 5986
— perforateur 269, 2572, 5881, 8731, 11121, 13390
— perforateur à injection d'eau 19775, 19768
— pilon à simple effet 16383
— pilon à simple jambe S. 17436
— pilon à table 1923
— pilon à vapeur à double effet 5642
— pilon à vapeur avec admission sur le piston 17434
— pilon avec cylindre fixe 17435
— pilon avec montant en col de cygne 17436
— piquer 11404
— pneumatique 269, 13584, 13591
— pour signaux 10409
martelage 8735, 8748
— à froid v. écrouissage
marteler 1818, 8727, 11257
— à froid 3958
marteleur 8750
martensite S. 8869, 11346
martinet à manivelle S. 8739
— à queue 18206
— à ressort 20117
martinite 11350
martite 11351
masanite 11352
mascagnite 11353
maskelynite 11355
masque 6743
— de soudeur 6753
masse 16581
— agglutinée 1115
— charriée 5532, 12780
— de magnésite 11177
— non fondue 19322
— pour boucher 11373
— riche en oxyde de fer S. 11372
— servant à réparer le garnissage 10854
— tige 12356
masselottage 15380
masselotte 3053, 5030, 6886

masselotte à alimentation tangentielle 20020
— à étranglement 6887
— à pression de gaz 13903
— atmosphérique 924
— borgne 1772
— boursouflée 3108
— directe 12598
— ouverte 12598
— ouverte à talon 12599
massette 14932
massicot 11358
massif S. 1339, 4592
— affaissé 5717
— de maçonnerie 2379
— de minerai 4593
— de protection 15952
— de protection du puits 2175
— d'injection 9808
— en maçonnerie 15251
— faillé 6842
— intrusif 2125
— intrusif ayant la forme d'un coin 17056
massifs d'épanchement 6218
mastic 16960
— de fer 9967
— sulfo-asphaltique résistant aux acides 89
mastiquer 7013
mat de charge à troncs rétrécis 19083
matage 7811
matière à bourrer 18234
— à griller 12657
— à polir 8558
— à tremper épaisse 15843
— agglomérante 1602
— agglutinante 3142
— animale 594
— de cémentation 3175
— explosive 6684
matériaux de construction 2535
— d'étayage pour l'étaiement 17011
— de moulage 12020
— de remblayage 7037
— pierreux 233
— pour la confection des routes 14981
matériel absorbant 5634
— de sondage 5913

matériel dragué 17141
matière organique 12663
— plastique 13472
— pour creusets 14633
— pour retarder la cémentation oxydante 5418
— précipitée S. 13809
— première 14456
matières à fondre 3315
— de remplissage 12851
— disséminées dans la masse 5541
— lourdes 19910
— pour l'ébarbage 3705
— premières métalliques 115 11570
— tamisées 16303
mathildite 11375
matlockite 11376
matoir 3112
matras à évaporation 6613
matrice 2127, 2153, 11378, 11379, 11380, 17329
— à estamper 17324
— à étirer 5796
— à recalibrer 14694
— à réduire 14567
— de coulée 3060
— de frappe à froid 3982
— de machine à forger 8567
— de refoulage 8929
— galvanique S. 7925
— pour marteau-pilon 5987
— pour presses 13889
matricer 5972, 18097
matte brute de cuivre 14457
— de cuivre 1908, 4358, 11381, 13302
— de cuivre grillée 2713
— de nickel 12275
— de plomb 10616
— plombeuse 10616
mauchérite 11384
mauvais combustible 11051
— remblai 13655
mazer S. 7072
mazout 7791
mécanisme à brasser 14317
— de commande de la quenouille 17682
— de débrayage de la courroie 1481
— de sondage 14901
mèche S. 1622 S. 2077, 2091, 14581, 17266

mèche à centrer 3195
— à couteaux renversés
  S. 5684
— à deux tranchants 5652
— à pierre 17643
— à trois pointes S. 3195
— cuiller 8373
— de Bickford 1739
— de centrage 3196
— de centrage flûtée 17718
— de centrage sphérique
  15203
— droite à fût conique
  18284
— façon suisse S. 15701
— plate 812, 7332
— rapide 14302
— sensitive 15857
— spirale à fût droit 17719
— styrienne 15701
— torse 5684
méionite 11441
mélaconise 11442, S.
  18407
mélange 11837
— à chaud 9421
— azéotropique 1029
— de dolomie 5611
— de minerais 11838
— eutectique 6603
— gazeux 8025
— physique 13192
mélanger 11817, 11818
— à la pelle 19139
mélangeur 11826, 11829,
  11550, S. 13264
— basculant 18631
— cylindrique de fonte 4948
— de fonte 13264
— de sable 15503
— en discontinu 1329
— Halliburton 9326
— ouvert 12583
— pour solution 16903
mélanite 11443
mélanocérite 11444
mélanocrate 11445
mélanophlogite 11446
mélanotékite 11447
mélanovanadinite 11448
mélantérite 11449
mélaphyre 11450
mélilite 11451
mélinite 11452
mélinophane 11453
mellite 9302, 11454

melonite 11455
mendelyeevite 11489
mendipite 11490
mendozite 11491
meneghinite 11492
menhir 11493
ménilite 11494
ménisque 10338
menu 2214, S. 2590, 4827,
  7356
— de coke 2835
— de la mine 16740
— du crible 19280
menuiserie métallique 16734
  16734
menus de havage S. 2534
— de houille S. 16727
— non classés 11741
mercure 9508, 11503
— métallique 11569
méroxène 11513
merrillite 11514
merwinite 11515
mésocrate 11521
mésolite 11522
mésostasis 11524
mésothorium 11526
mesotype 11527
mésozone 11529
messélite 11530
mesurage 11394
— du réservoir 17745
mesure 11392
— de déviation 5471
— de la dureté 11395
— de porcelaine 13665
— déterminée 7235
— des températures 14231
— du panneau au filtre-
  presse 19636
— du retrait 533
— non destructive 12347
mesurer 6827, 11389
— la température d'un
  corps par son rayonne-
  ment 11390
— les dimensions de l'é-
  prouvette 11391
mesureur S. 8391
  - de la pression de couche
  2015
— de réservoirs 18253
métahewettite 11535
métal 11537
— à canons 8673
— à structure serrée 3764

métal amirauté 170
— antifriction 663, 1038
— après le soufflage 1883
— base 1281
— Bell-Krupp S. 19696
— blanc 20038
— céramique 3230
— chaud 9422
— d'apport 5198, 8870
— d'apport de soudure
  19947
— de base 13938
— de coulée 7645
— de couverture 3610
— de platine 13522
— delta 5158
— déployé 6665
— dur 8828
— entré en fusion 6004
— estampé 17317
— fini 20245
— froid 3985
— fusible 7889
— jaune 20289
— léger 10784
— lourd 9035
— Monel 11894
— mou 16837
— Muntz 12132
— non ferreux 12349
— non précieux 1280
— pour boussoles 2626
— pour coussinets 1396
— précieux 12328
métabrushite 11531
métalcéramique 3224
métacinabre 11532
métaheulandite 11534
métallifère 12629
métallique 11566
métallisation 11574, 11577
— galvanique 7924
métalliser 11575
métallogénétique 11578
métallogénique 11579
métallographie 11583
— spéciale du fer 17015
métalloïde 11584
métallurgie des métaux
  ferreux 11590
— des métaux autres que
  le fer 11591
— des poudres 13788
— par la voie ignée 9624
métamorphique 11592
métamorphisme 18486

métamorphisme de lit par
  lit S. 9814
— d'injection 9814
— dynamique 6151
— par pression 10912
— régional 11595
— régressif 14803
métasilicate 11597
métasomatose 2055, 11600
métasome 8648, 11601
métastibnite 11602
métathénardite 11603
métatype 11604
métavariscite 11605
métavoltite 11606
métaux alcalins 359
méthode à boule et anneau
  1149
— anglaise de percement
  6480
— d'affinage 7111
— d'analyse 11612
— de contrôle 14059
— d'essai 18466
— d'exploitation 11613,
  11778
— d'extraction 18181
— de grandes tailles chassantes 10989
— de l'avancement par ra-
  battage 14913
— de laminage 15126
— de rabattage S. 20210
— de remblayage 16722
— de trempe spéciale 17016
— des massifs courts S.
  13709
— en travers 4711
— française de percement
  7755
— italienne de percement
  d'un tunnel 10086
mètre à ruban 18272
— pliant 11608
mettre à feu le haut fourneau 1845
— à feu les coups de
  mine 17104
— au point 7515
— dans le circuit 9311
— en batterie 4546
— en marche 10337
— en production 2412
— en production par pistonnage 18087
— hors feu 1846

mettre hors feu un haut
  fourneau 3354
— le four hors feu 4977
— sur couche 1412
meulage 8545, 16008
meulé 8607
— brillant 2397
meule 2529, S. 8563, 11716
— à charbon de bois 3304
— à émeri 6413
— d'ébarbage 8562
— supérieure d'un moulin
  15371
meuler 8537, 16770
— à l'émeri S. 6410
meuleur 8543
meuleuse 13690
meurtiat 6049
meymacite 11616
miargyrite 11617
miaskite 11620
mica 5022, 10050, 11621,
  17042
— commun 12139
— comprimé S. 13879
— d'uranium 19390
— magnésien 507
micaceous schist 11623
micanite 11628
micaschite 11623
microclastique 11631
microcline 11632
— perthite 11633
microcrypto-cristallin 11634
microfusion 9937
micrographie 11637
micrographique 11638
microlite 11640
microlitique 11641
microméritique 11644
micropaléontologie 11645
micropegmatite 11646
microperthite 11647
microphyrique 11648
microretassure 11654
microstructure 11655
microtinite 11656
migmatite 4122, 11671
migration des vallées 16129
— du pétrole 18857
miharaïte 11672
mijakite 11673
mijotage 17570
milarite 11674
mille pieds cubes 11403
millérite 11705

millisite 11715
miloschine 11718
mimesite 11719
mimétèse S. 11720
mimétèsite 11720
mince de lamine S. 1674
mine 1120, 11724
— à ciel découvert 5018
— à ciel ouvert 12565,
  17848
— à puits 5860
— de charbon S. 3839
— de dégraissage 6179
— d'empiétage 2335, 2623
— d'étain 17364
— de fer 17364, 9991
— de houille 3858
— de maizières 16265
— de pétrole 12500
— de relevage 2162, 7541,
  10755
— de vernis 10614
mine v. minière
miner 11723
minerai 11749
— à bocarder S. 11710,
  17314
— abattu 1735, 2445
— aciculaire S. 73
— accessoire 11785
— altéré 19868
— associé 47
— bocardé 17318
— briqueté S. 12634
— broyé 5474, 5735
— brut 14458
— carbonaté grillé 16990
— concentré 4163, S. 5839
— d'aluminium 456
— de basse teneur 11052
— de broyage 11710
— de fer 9987
— de fer à stalactites 2481
— de fer argileux 1106, 3663
  3663, 7266, 8645
— de fer argileux non
  compact 11001
— de fer aquifère 9990
— de fer arsénieux 817
— de fer bleu S. 19584
— de fer brun 19584
— de fer brut 14455
— de fer calcareux 2706
— de fer carbonaté 9988
— de fer compact 4100
— de fer cristallin 4802

minerai de fer cuivreux 4854
— de fer dense 5172
— de fer dur 8835
— de fer dur et cassant 2424
— de fer effrité 19867
— de fer en grains 13387
— de fer en rognons 2132
— de fer fibreux 6989
— de fer frais 7756
— de fer friable 7763
— de fer fusible par lui-même 15823
— de fer humide 19993
— de fer jaune 20288
— de fer manganésé 11283
— de fer massif S. 4100
— de fer nickelifère 12285
— de fer phosphoreux 13166
— de fer plombifère 9989
— de fer poreux 13675
— de fer pulvérulent 7086
— de fer sablonneux 15534
— de fer sulfureux 17988
— de fer tendre 16836
— de fer terreux 6175
— de fer titanifère 18688
— de fer veiné d'autres matières 9726
— de fer zincifère 20342
— de filon 10960
— de gangue 7958
— de halde 19730
— de haute teneur S, 9152
— de manganèse propement dit 14019
— de nickel 12277
— de plomb 2059, 2205
— de plomb pulvérulent 1462 1462
— de qualité inférieure 5721
— de remplacement 14060
— de zinc 20331
— de zinc manganésé 11284
— déformé 5817
— des prés 1945
— d'imprégnation 9664
— dichroïque 5348
— difficilement fusible 14631
— difficilement réductible 5400
— disséminé 5540

minerai en cocarde 14928
— en grains 8406
— en menus galets mélangé 14062
— en morceaux 7204, 10411, 10412. 11091
— en prismes raccourcis 16177
— en rognons 12335
— en vue S. 5273
— facilement fusible 6180
— facilement réductible 6181
— ferromagnésien 11162
— finement disséminé 3340
— fondant 7503
— grillé 14985
— gros 10412, 11091
— houiller 1668
— imparfaitement grillé 9717
— lavé 2514, 10175
— non grillé 19329
— normatif 17346
— oolithique 7357
— oxydé 1837
— pauvre 1284, 10643, 11052, 13656
— payant 12998
— préparé 5273, 5839
— riche 2496, 9152, 15692
— riche de plomb 1604
— scheidé 3894
— sec 6033
— sphérique 17058
— trié S. 4163, 15692
— trié au marteau 13215
minéralisable 11757
minéralisation 11758
minéraliser 11759
minerais accessoires 44
— de contact 4248
— essentiels 6568
— formés avec réduction de volume 11786
— lourds 9036
mines d'empiétage 3186
minette 12551, 11765
mineur 11746, 13422, 11549
— à la roche 11549
— de charbonnage 8185
minguétite 11766
minium de fer 9986
minière-v. mine
miocène 11789

mirabilite 11790
mire 13397
— de livellement 9470
miroir de faille S. 6858, 13625
— de glissement 6858, S. 13625, S. 16603
miroitant S. 17037
miroitement de la fonte 18063
miscibilité 11794
— partielle 12942
— totale 4115
miscible 11795
mise à feu 9627
— au mille 12955
— au point 167, 7517
— aux molettes 12762, 14136
— en feu 17382
— en marche du puits 10341 10341
— en place des noyaux 10599 10599
— en place du fond 9838
— en stock S. 52
— en suspension par agitation 17608
— hors feu 1877
— sur couche 1429
misénite 11797
mispickel 829
missourite 11808
mitraille 19734
mixite 11836
mixte 11667
mizzonite 11841
mobile 5531
modderite 11851
mode d'empilage des briques 2538
— d'exploitation S. 18181
— d'extraction S. 18181
— de refroidissement 4339
— de traitement 11615
modelage 12984, 12992
modèle 12972
— à couronne 14917
— au naturel 16109
— comportant le système d'alimentation 12981
— de fonderie 7664
— de jet de coulée 8094
— de segment de denture 18733

modèle déformé 5565
— déformé au serrage 12975
— démontable 11005
— en deux parties 15784, 17131
— en douves 8624
— mal conçu 9718
— non conforme 9719
— pour coulée 15376
modeleur 12982
modeller v. façonner ou profiler
modérer le feu S. 16513
modificateur 11854
module d'élasticité 6246
moellon schisteux 14351
mofette 11856
moissanite 11859
moitié de modèle 12978
molasse 11866
moldavite 11867
molécule 11874
— biatomique 5346
— gramme 11865
— monatomique 11890
— triatomique 18889
molengraffite 11875
molette 3594, 8923, 9234
mollesse 16850
molybdate d'ammonium 526
molybdène 11882
molybdénite 11881, 13731
molybdite 11885
molybdoménite 11886
molybdophyllite 11887
molysite 11888
moment de torsion 8776, 19183
— d'inertie 11889
— fléchissant 1512
monazite 11891
monchiquite 11892
mondhaldéite 11893
monétite 11895
monheimite 11896
monimolite 11897
monite 11898
monitor 11899
monmouthite 11905
monnayer 17814
monocylindrique 11909
monogénique 11911
montage S. 2340, 12037, 14372, 14946, 15913
— auxiliaire 13300

montage d'assemblage 4387
— de circulation 11309, 15900
— de rectification 4418
— des piles de bois 4634
— sur colonne 4042
montanite 11918
montant 45, 10668, 13707, 17897
— aveugle 6093
— de cadre 5862
— de cage 9461
— du marteau 2244
— en semelle 14009
— latéral 9053
monte-charge 9224, 10739
— à balance d'eau 19745
— à câble 10752
— à double effet 5640
— à simple effet 16381
— de haut fourneau 7845
— hydraulique 9526
— incliné 16482, 9702
— pneumatique 13588
monte-jus 77
monté 14589
— sur chariot 12035
— sur patte 16454
montée 45, 856, 14943, 14957
— capillaire 2810
monter 8203, 14370, 14896, 15902
— le moule 2537
monticellite 11920
monticule 12030
montien 11919
montmorillonite 11921
montréalite 11922
montroydite 11923
montures en laiton S. 2269
monzonite 11924
moraine 11928
— de fond 1266, 8618
— de poussée 14199
— déposée 5199
— frontale 18428
— interne 6478
morceau 1623, 3474, 3557, S. 16011, 16700, 17117
— poreux 13676
morcellement par failles 1801
mordançage 3527
morénosite 11931
morganite 11933

moroxite 11935
mortaisage 15296
mortaise 10192, 11938, 16686
mortaiseuse 15297
— combinée 2096
mortier 11936, 11937
— de ciment 10553
— diamant 5317
— en acier 17485
— en agate 210
— réfractaire 14634
morts-terrains 2585
mosandrite 11941
mosesite 11942
mossite 11946
moteur 5962
— à combustion-interne 9898
— à polir 11953
motopompe à combustion interne 13790
motte 3745, 16780
mottramite 11959
mouche 18513
mouchetage 3375
moucheté 17166
moucheter 18219
moudre 8539, 11682
moufle 1796, 12096, 12097, 18196
— à crochet combiné 9313
— au charbon 12098
— de plancher 7403
— en fer 9985
— en fonte S. 9985
— en platine 13524
— en terre réfractaire 7161
— fixe 4729
— mobile 9230
moufles 1804
mouillabilité 20001
mouillé S. 4985, 16853
mouiller 11860
moulable 11989
moulage 3036, 7617, 7643, 11997
— à découvert 7410, 8962
— à la cire perdue 13824
— à la machine 11128, 11133
— à main 8766
— à sec 12007
— à vert 8507, 8518
— au gabarit 12988, 18113

moulage au renversé 16717
— au trousseau 18401
— avec modèles 12986
— centrifuge 3202
— creux compliqué 15896
— d'acier dur 8819
— de construction 17884
— de roues dentées 12021
— de tuyaux 18977
— des engrenages avec modèle à segments traversant la table 12033
— des noyaux 4424
— en acier doux 16828
— en argile 10926
— en chamotte 3279
— en châssis 2215, 3056, 72 7297, 11972, 12008
— en coquille 3428, 3434, 16099
— en fonte grise S. 2995
— en fosse 13410
— en motte 2229
— en plâtre 13469
— en sable 15489, 15506
— en sable au ciment 3152
— en sable sec 6041
— en sable vert 8515, 12009 12009
— en terre 6040, 7733,
— en terre glaise 10929
— mécanique 5362
— par choc contrainte 16146 16146
— par injection 9815
— par introduction et enlèvement du modèle 14131
— par plaque-modèle 11369
— par secousses 10218
— pour pièces de machine 6467, 11120
— soufflé 1880
— sous pression 13901
moule 2983, 3050, 3061, 3067, 5356, 11968, 11980
— à balles 2567
— à découvert 12585
— à élément passant 5998
— à éléments différents 4055
— à éléments interchangeables 11988
— à éléments superposés 17278

moule à empreintes multiples 12114
— à fondre des rouleaux 15114
— à main 8765
— à presser la matière synthétique 836
— à saumons S. 13268
— à vert 8517
— coulissant 16652
— de gueuses 13268
— de moulage sous pression 13899
— de plâtre 13468
— demi-libre 17929
— élémentaire 9871
— en châssis 7296
— en fonte 3007
— en laiton 2272
— en sable 15505
— en terre 10928
— externe 6699
— fermé 3773
— galvanique 7925
— inférieur 5731
— interne 9902
— métallique 5357
— monté 2540
— normal pour aciérie 17353 17353
— perdu 18402
— pour anodes 628
— pour le fond de cornue 4300
— pour moulage en coquille 3055
— pour moulage sous pression 5371
— pour pâtisserie 11979
— pour soudure aluminothermique 18490
— prêt pour la coulée 11985
— semi-permanent 15846
— vide 15383
— vidé 15360
moulé 11878
— de pilonnage 17325
— en coquille 16098
mouler 11960, 11991
— à la machine 11129
— à la table 1491
— à plat 11966
— à vert 2969
— debout 11965
— en motte 11963
— en sable 15468

mouler les creusets 11967
— sur couche 11964
— sur plaque 13495
mouler v. couler
mouleuse d'établi 1492
moulin 8557, 11685
— à amalgamer 494
— à boulets 8301
— à cingler S. 15217, 16136
— à cylindres 15113
— à cylindres annulaires 14929
— à scories 16527
— chilien 3355, 6202, 8559
— de nettoyage transportable 13687
— glaciaire 8255
moulinage 2240
moulineur 2684
mouliste 11991
moulu trop fin 12728
moulure de la face 13476
mourmanite 12136
moussant 7783
mousse 5103, 11943
— d'aluminium 452
mouton 5986, 11900
— à courroie 7366
— à étampage 5984
— en forme de boule 5999
mouvants 5683
mouvement de rotation 19147
— épirogénétique 6506
— hydrocratique 9551
— turbulent 16428
mouvements épirogéniques 6505
moyeu 9469
— de roue 20007
— de trempe 8862
— explosif S. 1744
moyenne des résultats d'essai 1009
mucilagineux 12056
mullite 12102
multiplicateur 12127
— de pression 13922
muniongite 12131
mur 2142, 7346, 7402, 7547, 11070, 11110, 12133, 16338, 19632
— de pierres 14982
— de remblai 12837, 12846
— d'une couche 7409
muraillement 19657

murchisonite 12135
murette 2534
muscovadite 12138
muscovite 4095, 11792
muthmannite 12147
mylonite 12148
mylonitisation 12150
myrmékite 12151

N

nacelle en platine 13157
nacré 13021
nacrite 12154
nadorite 12155
naégite 12156
nagatelite 12157
nagyagite 7532, 12159
nahcolite 12160
nantokite 12167
naphtalène 12168
naphte 6176, 15031
— de précipitation 13816
— léger 10789
— primaire 13947
— solvant 9173
naphte v. pétrole ou huile
    lourde
naphtenate 12169
naphténate de plomb 10618
naphténique 12172
napoléonique 12173
nappe aquifère 727, 19752
— de charriage S. 5532
— d'eau souterraine 8622
— de recouvrement S. 7521
— de ruissellement 10043
— intrusive 9927
— pétrolifère 12498
natroalunite 12183
natroborocalcite S. 19212
natrochalcite 12185
natrojarosite 12186
natrolite 12187
natrophylite 12188
naujaïte 12199
naumannite 12200
nauruite 12201
navette S. 1460
— de plomb S. 13266
navite 12202
nécessitant une réparation
    9680

négatif 12212
nelsonite 12215
némaphyllite 12216
néocomien 12218
néodyme 12220
néogène 12221
néolithique 12222
néon 12223
néotantalite 12225
néovolcanique 3183
néphéline S. 6372, 12228
néphélinite 12230
néphrite 12232
népouite 12233
neptunite 12235
neptunites 12234
neptunium 12336
nerf 6982, 12945, 14882
néritique 12237
nerveux 6986
nervure 14864
— rapportée 9836
nesquehonite 12239
net 3674
netteté de la surface 3698
nettoyage 3673
— des grilles 14711
— du trou de coulée 8098
— par cure-tubes rotatifs
    19124
— supplémentaire 7883
nettoyer les moules 3672
neutraliser 12255
neutre 11423
newberyite 12260
newjanskite 12257
newlandite 12261
nez de la tuyère 19162
nickel 12268
— électrolytique 6345
nickelage 12284
nickeler 12267
nickéline 4359, S. 12263
niccolite 12263
nid à crasses 5476
— de minerais 2036
nids de graphite 10378
nife 12290
nigrine 12295
nigrite 12295
niobate 12296
niobium 12297
nitrate d'argent 16354
— de cobalt 12306
— de mercure basique 1298

nitrate de palladium 14307
— de potasse S. 13730
nitratine 12308, 16812
nitre 13730
nitrobaryte 12316
nitrocalcite 12317
nitrogélatine 12318
nitroglaubérite 12322
nitroglycérine 1740
nitromètre 12324
nitruration 519, 12312, 12321
nitrurer au gaz 8029
— par échange d'ions 9946
niveau 8112
— à bulle 298
— à bulle d'air 19795
— à tube en verre 19779
— d'abattage 11774
— de chargement 3322, 3347
    3347
— de coulée 13760
— d'eau 19796
— de fond 2171, 16539
— de grilles 8582
— de l'eau 19797
— de la fendue 156
— de la nappe souterraine
    10710
— de liquide 7463
— de maçon 13569
— de remblai 19726
— de repère 5007
— des tuyères à vent 19161
— du gueulard 13457
— du sol 8464, 8616
— hydrostatique 9574,
    10711
— inférieur 2142
— intermédiaire 1776, 2649,
    4531
— statique S. 9574
nivelette 2030
nivellement 2029, 8385
— barométrique 1237
nivenite 12326
nobélium 12327
nocérite 12330
nocif 12406
nodulaire 12331
nodule 12336
nodules d'hématite brune S.
    2475
noeud 10413
noir de carbone S. 2826
— d'étuve 17696

noir de fonderie 7649
— de fumée 2826, 16759
— végétal 3311
noircir 1640, 1641
noircissage 1672
noisettes 3414, 12428
noix de charbon coke con-
  cassé 12429
nombre de dureté 2408
non automotrice 12364
— centré 11793
— collant 12340
nonésite 12368
non-étanchéité 10637
— explosé 19264
— graphitique 12351
— homogène 12352
— magnétique 12354
— mouillable 12370
nonne S. 5988, 6177
nontronite 12369
norbergite 12371
nordenskiöldite 12372
noria 6378
norite 12374
normalisation 12388
normalisé 17359
normaliser 12385
normes 17352
northupite 12389
noséane 12392
noséanite 12393
nouméite 12404
nourrice 6886
nourrir 6874
nouveau puits 8504
noyau 4384, 8946, 12405
— à segments 15709
— anticlinal 4426
— anticlinal étranglé
  5253
— borgne 1770
— carapace 16100
— carré 589
— cassé 2442
— central S. 1259
— chambré 3272
— coudé 4878
— de cassure 4428
— d'étranglement 2319
— de grillage 14989
— de la boîte des engrenages 8126
— de liaison 2319
— de tuyau 19067

noyau détachable 14704
— du pli 755
— dur 8820
— emballé 6401
— en sable étuvé 4385
— en sable vert 8516
— en terre 10927
— filtre 17737
— fragile 2421
— galette 12036
— oublié 12537
— passant de centrage S.
  1599
— perdu 11039
— synclinal 4427, 18940
— troussé 18125
— tubulaire cylindrique
  10101
noyautage 4461, 4463, 4465,
  446
noyauter une pièce 4383
noyauteur 4460
noyauteuse 4422, S. 4460
nuée ardente 8312
numéro de la série 12422
— de matière 14592
— du fil 8115

O

objet éclairé 9633
objectif 12432
oblique 16449, 19675
observation 12436
— à l'oeil nu S. 11155
— macroscopique 11155
obsidianite 12438
obsidienne 12437
obstruction v. blocage
obstruer (se-) 3749
obturation au sable 15508
occlusion 12445
ochrolite 12449
ocre 12448
— de fer 12864
— jaune 20285
— rouge 6174, 14554, 15333
octane 12453
oculaire 6731
odinite 12456
odontolite 12457
oeil-de-chat 3080
— de la tuyère 12610

oeil-de-tige S. 18614
offre 6569
offrétite 12461
oisanite 12519
okénite 12520
oléagineux 12525
oléate de plomb 10620
oléfine 12524
oléine 12527
oligiste 9978
oligocène 12531
oligoclase 12532
oligoclasite 12533
olive S. 13011
olivénite 12535
olives S. 12721
olivine 3551, 12536
ombre 19227
omphazite 12538
ondulation secondaire 11783
onégite 12547
onkilonite 12548
onofrite 12549
opale 12555
— à flammes S. 7173
— commune 4096
— de feu 7173
— ferrugineuse 6969
— flamboyante 7173
— incrustante 16320
— laiteuse 20039
— noble 12329
— perlière 13015
— xyloïde S. 20176, 20276
opdalite 12556
opération de tubage 15357
— unique 16401
opérations alternatives 1806
— préparatoires 5845
ophite 12616, 15895
or 8343
— alluvionnaire 8662, 13436
— alluvien 17770
— cémentoire 3148
— en feuilles 16972
— faux 6142
— filonien 10955
— grassulaire 16207
— libre 7732
— pur 7073
orangite 12619
orbite 12621
ordanchite 12622
ordon 14311
ordre de fréquence 12623

oreille 6727, 11084
— régulée 13858
orendite 12662
orientation préférentielle
    13833
orientite 12666
orifice 4017, 12668, 13685
— d'admission 173
— d'admission du vent
    1731
— d'alimentation 6895
— d'amenée S. 9820
— d'amenée d'air S. 292
— d'arrivée d'air S. 292
— de chargement 3341
— de coulée 3047, 7424,
    8140, 9821, 985510482,
    12411, 15906
— de départ 12702
— d'entrée 9822
— d'entrée d'air S. 292
— de nettoyage 3694
— de sortie de gaz 289
— de tréfilage 5781
— du canal de fumée 3460
— du puits S. 12045, 15936
— du trou de sondage 19964
— équivalent 6533
original 19205
ornöite 12675
orogénèse 12676
orpiment 816, 10366, 12678,
    14437, 20282
orthite 370
orthoclase 12680
orthorhombique 12682
orthose S. 12680
orthosilicate 12685, 19836
osmium 12687
osmondite 12688
ouïe d'aspiration 6164
ouralite 19388
ouralitisation 19389
outil à canneler 8596
— à chambrer 14491
— à dégrossir 15263
— à détalonner 12952
— à dresser et à passes
    droites fines 10791
— à ébaucher S. 15263
— à élargir 6486
— à étirer 5812
— à fileter 4926
— à fileter extérieurement
    6700
— à gauche 10664

outil à main 11010
— à matricer 6405
— à rainurer 7493
— à saigner à droite S.
    14905
— à trancher la coulée 8092
— à tronçonner 4904
— couteau oblique 19146
— de coupe 4907, 9032
— de coupe pour cylindrage
    sur les surfaces interrom-
    pues 18726
— d'ébarbage 3706, 6980
— d'emboutissage par re-
    tournement avec découpa-
    ge 4059
— de filetage extérieur 18551
    18551
— de forage 2110, 5883
— de forage à couronne de
    diamant 5223
— de presse à filer 6725
— de repêchage 10130
— gauche à dresser et à
    passes droites fines 1066
    10663
— gauche pour coupes pro-
    fondes 10662
— hydromécanique à embou-
    tissage par retournement
    9554
— ouvert 12597
— pour travail à chaud 9456
— usé 6084
outillage 12699
— de fondeurs 7673
— de forage au câble 2666
— de mines 11780
— de montage 7244
— électrique et pneumati-
    que 13778
— pour le décapage conti-
    nu 13228
outils à main pour soudure
    19935
— de chauffe S. 7196
— de forage 5943
— de fraisage 11714
— de repêchage 7224
— de sondage S. 5943
— de tour 10577
— fraises 15204
— meules 8555
— pour l'usinage des mé-
    taux 11540
ouvarovite 12720, S. 19419

ouverture 7966, 13685
— de défournement 5502
— d'échappement 6653
— d'entrée d'air 292, 6495,
    6893, 9820
— de la calotte 18577
— de la plate-forme du som-
    met de derrick 19818
— de la poitrine 8957
— des puits 2112
— du gueulard 18578
— du trou de mine 9048
— d'un puits 5931
ouvrage en direction 10708
— montant 19373
— souterrain 3779, 5871,
    8631
ouvrages souterrains 5408
ouvrier au gueulard 11259
— aux chutes 15678
— d'about S. 15963
— d'aciérie 17521
— de haut-fourneau 7850
— de transporteur 4324
— noyateur 4421
— sondeur 11122
— spécialisé de raffinerie
    17598
ouvrir 2302, 12602
— au moyen de l'arc voltaï-
    que S. 12561
— une galerie 5952
— une taille 12558
ouwarowite 2725
oxydant 12808
oxydation anodique 632
oxyde acide 96
— basique 1301
— cuivrique 12797
— d'aluminium 443, 472
— de beryllium 1543
— de calcium 10810
— de carbone 2838
— de cuivre en grains 8437
— de fer anhydre 14541
— de fer hydraté 10828
— de fer provenant de la
    fabrication des couleurs
    retirées du goudron 12798
— de magnésium 12800
— de mercure 11500
— d'ytterbium 20303
— de zinc 12801
— ferreux 6965
— ferrique 6928
— manganeux 11291

oxyde manganique 14685
— manganoso-manganique 12796
— mercureux 14545
— plombique 12799
— salin 12796
oxyder 12805
oxygène 12817
— atmosphérique 926
— chimiquement combiné 3396
ozocérite 12821
ozokérite 6178

P

pachnolite 12823
packer composé de deux éléments 17705
padelin 4742
paie suivant le volume extrait 6829
paigéite 12861
paillasse 1428
paille S. 6840, 15746, 17754,
— de fer 17519
— de laminage 17120
— hachée 2784
pailles d'oxyde de fer 15583
paillettes de mica 11622
paillon S. 18648
— d'argent 16360
paisanite 12865
pal étiré 17793
— riveté et soudé 12165
palagonite 12873
palaïte 12874
palan 1795, 3245, 9225, 18196
— à moufle 14133
— électrique 6281
— mobile 18860
— pneumatique 13585
palasome S. 9390
palatinite 12875
paléobotanique 12866
paléocène 12867
paléoclimatologie 12868
paléolithique 12870
paléotypique 12871
paléozoïque 12872
palette 12881
palier S. 7401
— à rouleaux 15106

palier d'appui 1389
— de repos 10467, 10525
— lisse 13441
— pendant 8802
palladium 12878
palmer 11643, S. 15707
palmérite 12883
palmiérite 12884
palonnier 10763
palper 6896
palpeur 6897
palplanche 1066, 10490, 10575, 16075, 17083,
palplanches 17490
— verticales 19531
pan S. 12885
panabase 12892
pandermite 12893
panier de sédimentation 10255
panne 6767
— de marteau 8740, 8734, 12894
panneau 12895
— d'exploitation 16269
— de fermeture de cheminée 3364
— de signalisation routière en acier 17493
pantellérite 12901
papier à amidon 17379
— à l'albumine 350
— à la phénolphtaléine 13152
— à l'émeri 6415
— à l'iodure de potassium 13728
— à ozone 12822
— à réactif 18448
— à sable 15509
— carmin 2891
— Congo 4207
— d'amiante 846
— d'amidon à iodure de potassium 13727
— de curcuma 4862
— de tournesol 10892
— de verre 8280
— filtrant 7049
papillon 2645, 7508
paquet 6762, 12827
— de couches S. 14882
— de fer à souder 13279
— de tôles 11697
paquetage 6763, 13283
— de chutes 15656

paqueter 13276
par couches 9677
— série 2654
parachèvement v. finissage ou achèvement
parachever le moule S. 14730
parachute 2681, 8566, 8568, 9243
— à excentriques 2766
— pour tubes 3091
paraclase 6849
paraffine 12906
— brune 16542
— brute en écailles 15685
— de distillation 17596
— en écailles 15593
— tendre 16838
paragénèse 12912
paragneiss 12913
paragonite 12914
parahopéite 12915
paralaurionite 12916
paralique 12917
paraluminite 12924
paramagnétique 12925
paramètres de forage 5932
— du réseau cristallin 4797
paramorphique 12920
paramorphose 12927
paraurichalcite 12928
paravauxite 12929
parc 17620
— à lingots 9801
— à poutrelles 8243
— à tiges et tuyaux 13362, 13372
— à wagons 15130
— de tanks 18250
parcelle 13552
parcours de l'air 308
— du gaz 8040
pare-étincelles 16979, 16984
— -gouttes S. 4607
parer S. 7112
parfaitement cuit 2599
pargasite 12934
parianite 12935
parisite 12936
parkerisation 12937
paroi 19632
— arrière S. 1053
— avant 7776
— de derrière S. 1053
— de la tuyère 19167
— de latéral 7561
— de séparation fixe 7232

paroi du moule 19645
— latérale 16255, 16280
— postérieure S. 1053
— transversale 4667
parois 3376
— des étages 2119
— latérales de boite à feu
  7156
— réfractaires S. 10855
parpaing de bims 14152
part déterminée S. 14023
— égale S. 14023
particules de fer S. 9979
— en suspension 18078
partie accessoire 9686
— aliquote 14023
— amovible 5252, 9872
— convexe 19278
— creuse de cylindre 8591
— de dessous 2174, 18745
— démontable 11006
— en caoutchouc du «bag
  preventer» 12834
— étroite S. 5148
— inférieure 11069
— interchangeable 9872
— mate 6088
— peu dense 12444, 17389
— rapportée 5252
— saine 16938
— supérieure de l'ouvrage
  18742
— très dure 2594
parties amovibles 14713
— refroidies du haut-
  fourneau 4328
pas 19137
passage 5595, 7959, 12958,
  12959
— au crible 10180
— au-dessus S. 2383
passage d'aérage 1054
— de circulation 18864
— de grisou à travers une
  cloison 1854
— de la flamme 7261
— de l'électrode 8328
— de ventilation 2011
— inférieur 19244
— sous la voie 19244
— supérieur S. 2383
passerelle 3102
— en arc de cercle 15800
— de sonde 19631
passe 12957, 12958
— -courroie 1459

passe de dégrossissage S.
  2326
— sur les bords 6219
passe-diable à paraffine
  12908
passée d'argile 15977
passer par le laminoir S.
  3988
passivation 12960
passoir 5747
pastille 6640
pâte 5633, 8617
— de boue 12075, 12089
— de ciment 3155
— électrolitique Söderberg
  16816
— grasse collante 10932
— très réfractaire 9195
— vitreuse 8279
pâteaux 12962
patentement 12969
patemoite 12970
patin 7537, 7538
— d'ancrage 2177
— du rail 7544
patron d'injection 7400
patronite 12971
patte 16453
— d'usinage 10184
pauvre en graphite 13654
pearcéite 13013
peau 4481, 18101
— de chamois 3275
— de coulée 3068
— de crapaud 9483, 18051
pechblende 13413, S. 19392
peckhamite 13035
pectolite 13036
pegmatisation 13047
pegmatite 13046
pegmatoïde 13048
peigne 17872
— à clés suspendues 18715
— à fileter 15277
— à fileter extérieur 6701
peindre en noir 12862
peinture à base de résine
  acrylique thermodur-
  cissable 17701
— définitive 13104
— légère S. 7197
— riche en zinc 20329
pélicanite 13052
pelle 15639, 16212
— à benne traînante 5739
— à charbon 3846

pelle à vapeur 17445
— automatique S. 983, 3829,
  8377
— de barrage 18310
— de chargement 13039
— de mouleur 11994
— de profondeur 5450
— de retenue 16461
— mécanique 5451, 5828,
  11412, 13792
— niveleuse 16462
pelletage à main 8785
— mécanique 13793
pelleteur 12064
— de chargement S. 3798
pellicule d'oxyde 13054
pendage 14382, S. 16678
— apparent 708
— du charbon 16251
— général 1008
— périclinal 3222
— rayonnant 14254
pendage v. inclinaison
pendagemètre S. 5442
peneplaine 5181, 13061
— élevée 19360
— surélevée S. 19360
pénéplainaison 1289
pénétration de trempe 5207
penfieldite 13066
pennine 13068
penroséite 13070
pente 5066, 5701, 6772,
  9691, 13412, 16253, 16678
  16678
— raide 9034
pente v. inclinaison
pentlandite 13073
penture de charnière S. 9202
pépite 12420, 13933, 15573
pérat(s) S. 10546
percage v. forage
percé 9255
percée S. 2333, 19777
percement 9529
— de descenderies 20115
— de galeries 5873
— de tunnel 19108
percer 2595, 5874,
  5879, 13241
  14172
— dans le sens de la lon-
  gueur 5877
— en montant 14941
— par dessus 5875
— sur le côté 5876

percer un puits 2075
— un tunnel S. 19106
— une galerie S. 5952
— v. forer
perceuse d'établi 1485
— électrique 13780
— pour fer et acier 5926
— radiale 14326
— sensitive 1486
— verticale 19524
— v. machine à forer
perchage 13622
perche tubulaire de trolley
    19091
percoir 10250
percylite 13077
perforateur à balles 8674
— à charge creuse 10158
— à diamants S. 5324
— à percussion 10249
— de tubage 2942, 2951
— mécanique 13777
— pneumatique à colonne
    268
perforation 5916
— à câble des sondages
    peu profonds 17221
— à injection 19684
— mécanique 11130
— v. percage ou forage
perforatrice 5881
— à colonne 4041
— à injection 19991
— à main 7901
— d'avancement 5872
— pour creusement en mon-
    tant S. 277, S. 8732
— rotative 15199
— sur chariot 5903
— télescopique 277
perforé 9255
perforer une roche dure 8199
— v. forer
périclase 13087
péricline 13089
péridot S. 3551, 13090
périmagmatique 13091
périmorphose 13092
période alluvienne 412
— d'affinage S. 16536
— de bouillonnement et
    de projections 1954
— de carbonisation 2864
— de déphosphoration 5187
— d'ébullition 2000

période de formation des
    scories 16536
— de Keewatin 10300
— de la combustion du
    carbone 5059
— géocratique 8162
— glaciaire 9611
— pluviaire S. 9611
périsynclinal 3221
perknite 13097
perle 1365
perlite S. 8839, 13016,
    13098
— globulaire 17072
perlitique 13017
perméabilité 13109
— aux gaz 13111
— magnétique 11198
Permien 6146
permis de recherches 14038
pérovskite 13099, 13099
péroxyde 18076
— de manganèse 11271
— de plomb 13100
perte au feu 5041
— au feu globale 18791,
— au grillage 11025
— au triage 11024, 11026
— de chaleur 11030
— de circulation 11036
— de compression 1855
— de distillation 5557
— de fusion 11027
— de gaz 11029
— de pétrole du réservoir
    18251
— de poids 11033
— de pression 5990, 11032,
    13909
— en eau libre 7048
— en métal 11031
— garantie 8640
— magnétique 11195
— par frottement 11022
— par repliage 11023
pertes des électrodes 4242
perthite 13117
perturbation dans le fraction-
    nement 10040
pesage 19897, 19898
pèse-filtre 19899
pesée 14253
peser 19894
pétalite 13119
petit convertisseur 16726

petit coup de mine 13657
— cubilot 16729
— filon 17831
— flacon capillaire 2807
— métal 12349
— plan incliné 5415
— rail 10787
— train 16735
— tube à fusion 11481
petite berline S. 2526
— bouteille pour appareils
    de respiration 16739
— gueuse 13271
— intrusion 11784
— taille 16189
— tige à enlever les modè-
    les 10769
petites gaillettes S. 3414
— pièces en fer 16733
— pièces en fer de la voie
    16732
petits fers 16731
pétrification 7633, 10884
pétrifier 7634
pétrir 10390, 14116
pétrognèse 13122
pétrographie 13125
pétrographique 13123
pétrolatum 13126
pétrole 6176, 11753, 13129,
    15031, 17646
— à base paraffinique S.
    12907
— avec paraffine et asphal-
    te 11658
— brut 1283, 4754, S. 11753
    11950, 19689
— brut vielli 19865·
— de base mixte 11820
— illégal 9423
— paraffinique 12907
— primaire 13948
— raffiné 18759
— résiduel 7542, S. 14755
— restant 14755
— v. naphte ou huile lourde
pétrolène 13128
pétrosilex S. 6907
petzite 13137
peu sûr 6019
phacelite 13140
phacolite 13142
phanérogène 13143
pharmacolite 13144
pharmacosidérite 4818, 13145

phase 13146
— sigma 16908
phénacite 13147
phengite 13148
phénocristal 9840, 13149
phénol 13150
phénomène de liquation 15803
— exogénétique 6657
phénomène v. action
phénomènes de microsoudure 11657
— qui se produisent dans le haut-fourneau 8152
philadelphite 13153
phillipsite 13154
phlogopite 13155, 14860
phoenicochroïte 13156
pholérite 13157
pholidolite 13158
phonolithe 3729, 13159, 16939
phosgénite 9368, 13160
phosphoration 13168
phosphate de chaux 13163
— de fer 13164
— de soude 13165
— de soude ammoniacal 528
— de soude et d'ammoniaque hydrate 16818
phosphater 13162
phosphoferrite 13170
phosphophyllite 13171
phosphore 13183
phosphore et soufre 5084
phosphorite 13182, 680
phosphosidérite 13184
phosphuranylite 13185
phtanite 13189
phyllite 13190
pic 11383, 11857, 13211, 16673, 18274
— à deux pointes 1440, 5667, 7267, 11262, 18973
— au rocher 17647
— ordinaire 13632
picnomètre 17025
picot de mouleur 14426
picots 2-4 1223
picotite 13232
picrite 13233
picrolite 13234
picromérite 13235
pièce à croix 4663
— à ébarber 13237

pièce à employer 13236
— à laminer 13228
— à lisser ronde 15291
— battue 9841
— brute de fonderie 15247
— d'ancrage 560
— de construction 17888
— d'échappement 19501
— de fonte 2995, 3036, 7643
— de fonte à parois minces 18529
— de fonte massive S. 16818
— de fonte pleine 16878
— de forge 7583, 7589, S. 7590
— de garniture 9463
— de réserve 16977
— d'introduction 9828
— d'usure de boîte 11548
— défectueuse de fonderie 19720
— forgée 7586, 7589, 8736
— manquée 17142
— moulée en fonte malléable à coeur blanc 20046
— noyée 2989
— rapportée 5775
— spéciale de raccord et de branchement 4217
— utilisable S. 13236
— utilisable entière 19286
pièces d'appui 16345
— embouties 13891
— en gattapercha 8633
— forgées brutes 1677
— spéciales 17012
pied 4039
— à coulisse S. 2747
— de biche S. 4723
— de l'arbre à calibre 16805
— de profondeur 5204
— de taille 5152
piège à crasses en dents de scie 15562
— à crasses à canal tangentiel 20019
pierraille S. 4764
pierre S. 2192
— à aiguiser 9301, 14348
— à facettes 5832, 15525
— branlante 15042
— calcaire 3265
— d'aigle 198
— d'arsenic S. 1036

pierre de Lyde S. 18795
— de soleil 18000
— de taille 9116, 15530
— faisant vis à-vis à la dame 1077
— infernale 16354
— lithographique 10888
— meulière 8563
pierres concassées 3481
pierreux 3489
pieu 13707
— de guidage 15424
— en béton armé 4177
piézoclase 4155
pilandite 13275
pile 13278
— de bois 2285, 2362, 3906, 3750, 13273
pilette 7342
pilier 1248, 10367, 13289, 17911
— d'angle 4480
— de bois 4635
— de cabestan 10416
— de charbon 9051, 17360, 17655
— de galerie 6496, 17902, 17912
— de limite 1249
— de protection 17657
— de sûreté 19647
— du puits 10712
— en briques 17648
— en fonte 3001
pilon 10756, 14400
— à main 8778
— de bocard 17307
— de mortier 13118
— en acier 17486
pilonnage S. 17322
pilonneuse électrique 17326
pilot 8213, 14177, 17897
pilotis 17218
pinakiolite 13309
pince 4721, 4723
— à charbon 2836
— à creuset 4748
— à emporte-pièces 9278
— à griffe 13348
— à liège 4470
— à mercure 11509
— à noyau 4411
— à sertir, 2797
— à sodium 16823
— à tréfiler 20137
— d'accrochage 8566, 8571

pince d'élément S. 18427
— de mineur 14932
— de Mohr 3742
— de repêchage 13206
— de support 3623
— pour faire des oeillets 9278
— pour fils S. 20120
pinces 12301. 13550
— à souder 19944
— à tubes 2964
pincette 7558
pinguite 13315
pinnoïte 13323
pintadoïte 13324
piochage S. 13213
pioche 11383, 13202, S. 13211
piotine S. 13325
pipe line 13355
piperno 13376
pipette 13377, 19026
— à échantillons 18518
— à filtrer 7058
— avec robinet à boule 1990 19902
— d'absorption 23
— de prise des échantillons d'un réservoir 19772
— graduée 8392
— jaugée 13444
— jaugée automatique 986
— pour pesées 19901
piquage par la boue 12086
piquée 18264, 18298
piquer 18261
piqueur 4906
— au charbon 3813, 3827
piquet-repère 13701
piqûre de graphite 10379
— due au laminage 15085
piqûres 13316
— de scorie 13318
— de surface 18061
— hétérogènes bleuâtres 10940
— hétérogènes brillantes 10941
— hétérogènes oxydées 10939
— homogènes bleutées 14469
— homogènes brillantes 19305
— oxydées homogènes 19304

piqûres panachées 13317
pisé 11913, 14101,
— siliceux 16321
pisolite 13386
pissette 19685
pistolet de sablage 15482
— -graisseur 8503
— oscillant 18131
piston 13389, 13575, 18088, 18460
— à plaque 16885
— de compression 13875
— de fermeture 11975
— de pompe 14158
— plongeur 9536
— pneumatique 312
pistonner 18086
pistons concentriques 18239
— en tandem 18239
— parallèles 18914
pittinite 13430
pivot 13431, 13432
placage 13481, 13512
— à l'explosif 6689
placé sur anticlinal productif 12543
placer 10517 13435. 15902
— dans le ciment 6400
— de champ 13433
— de terrasse 1489
— le châssis supérieur 14205
placers d'alluvion 6030
plafond de mine 1046
plage 16168
plagioclase 13438
plagionite 13439
plagiophyre 13440
plaine alluvionnaire 408
— de lavage 12719
— élevée S. 18191
plan 13453, 13552
— à chariot-porteur 1124
— automoteur 8660
— d'appui 13452
— de cassure 10206
— de charriage 18600
— de clivage 3717
— de faille 16657
— de haut-fourneau 1711
— de joint 10202
— de la canalisation électrique S. 11311
— de la faille 6857
— de la tour de sondage 14898

plan de macle 4123
— de niveau 5008
— de stratification 1434, 12949, 16090
— de référence S. 5008
— de roulage S. 8895
— de rupture 7701
— directeur 8653
— du réseau électrique 11311
— incliné S. 2469, 2637, 5627, 8491, 8895, 9690, 13454, 14944, 15352
— incliné à voie unique et contrepoids 10173
— incliné automoteur 2255, 15812
— incliné de voie unique 16399
planche 1918
— à air 19500
— à calibrer S. 18114
— à imprimer 12001
— à trousser 17809, 18114
— cylindrique 4883
— de cuivre 4361
— de liège 4474
— léchée par les flammes 13492
— principale 17808
— soudée 2640
plancher 7401, 7920, S. 10554
— de la plate-forme du gueulard 3343
— de manoeuvre 5218
— de sûreté 13071
planchette à lisser 16774
— à polir 8550
planer 7112
— les tôles 17722
planérite 13461
planoferrite 13465
plaque 13479, 13484, 16044, 16493, 18499
— à cadre 7711
— à enlever les modèles 10773
— à filtrer 7045
— à modèle renversable 19148
— à noyaux 4430
— à triturer 4781
— anti-érosion 17110
— butée 2518
— carrée 17241

plaque circulaire 3595
— d'acier au nickel 12282
— d'acier coulé trempé
  8854
— d'amiante 847
— d'ancrage 2177, 9246
— d'appui 678
— d'appui double 5644
— d'argile 5644
— d'assise 1286, 1420
— d'atelier 12166
— d'avant 7560
— de base 1286
— de blindage 799
— de butée 3365
— de calibre 17807
— de chauffage 9425
— de chio S. 7561
— de contrevent 1096
— de contrôle 3362
— de cuivre 4372
— de dame 4967
— d'ébarbage 3743
— d'ébranlage 14427
— d'éjection 6238
— d'élément en zinc 20332
— de fer soudable S. 20243
— de fer soudé 20243
— de fermeture du fond 2178
  2178
— de fond 1286, 1419, 2147,
  6454,
— de fond de la boîte à
  vent 10729
— de garde 4607
— de latéral 7561
— de levage 10773
— de marbre 11312
— de plomb 10611
— de pression à bascule
  13887
— de protection 7306
— de réduction 1811
— de renfort 7381, 14676,
  S. 17590
— de retenue 1097
— de revêtement 2931
— de rustine 1070
— de scheidage 2506
— de séchage 4399
— de serrage 3624, 3628,
  10228, 14406
— de soufflage 1878
— de support 4848
— de tampon 2518
— de tête 19035

plaque de trituration en
  fonte 3005
— de tuyère 12415
— d'usure 19855
— de verme 19196
— de verre 8284
— éclisse 7384
— en acier coulé 3021
— en caoutchouc 15312
— en fer 9993
— en fer blanc 18651
— en forme d'écaille 9641
— en liège 4471
— en losange 5328
— en mica 11624
— en terre réfractaire 3659
— en tronc de pyramide
  14208
— en verre 8281
— en verre d'urane 19396
— en verre poli 4903
— frontale 8939
— harveysée 8883
— horizontale 9348
— intermédiaire d'entretoisement 7404
— laminée S. 15099
— mince 16609, 18501
— modèle 12987
— modèle double 15915
— modèle double face
  5677
— modèle réversible 14828
— modèle simple face
  16492
— murale 19648
— obturatrice 1097
— photographique 13187
— sèche 6035
— signalétique 14440
— striée 12365
— supérieure d'éjection
  6238
— support de moule 12025
— tubulaire 6454, 19035,
  19040
plaque v. tôle
plaquer 13477
— de plomb 10603
plaques baignées par la vapeur 18056
plaquette 7246, S. 16493
— de charnière 9202
— en caoutchouc 15308
plaquiste 12983
plasticité 13474

plastifiant 13473
plastotype 13475
plat 7315
— à arêtes arrondies 15278
— à coupelles 2489
— de barbotage 2490
— de triangulation 10459
— incliné à une voie et
  contrepoids 1048
plateau 18191
— à bordure 14685
— compensateur 1131
— continental 4257
— de balance 1129
— de barbotage 2493
— de charge 19913
— de compresseur 13874
— de dessus 18746
— d'équilibrage S. 1131
— de fond 1285
— de pompe à air 313
— de serrage 17260
— des moules 8561
— fixe 7239
— magnétique 11188
— marécageux 9159
— mobile 12050
— porte-moule 2007
— tournant 13874
plateaux 13502
plate-forme 7316, 7401,
  10554, 13505, 13506,
  17284, 20250
— à bascule 18679
— autonome 15815
— continentale 4258, 16092
— d'abrasion 15007
— d'accrochage 17269
— de coulée 13763, 18302,
  18359
— de déversement 18680
— de forage flottante 5945
— de manoeuvre S. 20251
— de support 1397
— de visite 17294
— des cheminées 3463
— des mélangeurs 11827
— double 5671
— du gueulard 18579
— fixe 7240
— mobile 11846
— supérieure 4732
plates-formes métalliques
  sur poteaux ancrés dans
  la roche 17494
platelage 11382

platinage 13511 13523
platine 13514
— universelle 19318
platinifère 13516
platiniridium 13510
platnérite 13533
plâtre 17969
plats 7340
plazolite 13538
pleine capacité de puits 20059
plein de mottes 3748
pléistocène 13540
pléochroïsme 13543
pléonaste 10018, 13544
plésiosaure 13545
plésiotype 9605, 13546
plessite 13547
pli 7520, 15008, 19975
— allochtone 381
— anticlinal 19353
— composé 4121
— concordant S. 4203
— couché 14523
— de couche 7371
— d'étirement 5733
— de terrain 1502
— déjeté S. 19337
— dénudé 190
— déversé S. 9934
— disharmonique 5506
— dissymétrique 912
— double 5688
— droit 19369
— en éventail 2216, 6799,
— faille 7522
— faillé 2443, 5536
— harmonique 4203
— isoclinal 10055
— longitudinal 13311
— marginal 11317
— monoclinal 17547
— nappe 7521
— normal S. 18150
— oblique 9699
— ouvert 12572
— plongeant 5438
— principal 11228
— renversé 9934, 12783
— resserré 3760
— secondaire 11783, 19251
— synclinal 5711, 10323, 16377, 18935
— symétrique 18150, 19369
— transversal 18843

pliable 13548
pliage à rides 20234
— à 180°
— de bords 7725
— en long 10980
— transversal 4688
plicatulation S. 4759, S. 8339
plié 7523
plier 4873, S. 5637, 1498
— autour d'un mandrin 1499
— en boucle le fer à rivets 1500
pliocène 13539, 13551
plissé 20235
plissement 20236, 7525
— calédonien 2738
— hercynien 9094
plissotement 8339, 11787, 13549, 14091
plomb 10604
— à tarer 18324
— antimonié 8836
— de ressuage 10868
— en feuilles S. 16066
— fusible S. 7885
— laminé 16066
— métal 10617
plombage 10630, 13571
plombagine S. 1654, 8447
plombé 10611
plomber 4561, 10603, 18429
plongée 16678
plongement S. 9688, 14382
plonger 5432, 5433
poche 10469, 13604
— à acier 17482
— à air 302
— à barrage 4969
— à bascule 18620
— à couler 3058, 7660
— à crasse 16541
— à crémaillère 10486
— à dame 4969
— à engrenage 8138
— à fourche 10476, 15985
— à main 8763, 8784
— à mélanger 11832
— à quenouille 2181
— d'air 307
— de coulée 7650, 11472, 13755, 13759, 17681
— de coulée avec dispositif pour verser à la main 8787

poche de dépôt des cendres 869
— de gaz 8038
— de grue 4599
— de minerai 12240, 12966
— de mineur 3585
— en tôle emboutie 17316
— fixe 7234
— mélangeuse 11832
— roulante 10481
— siphon 18342
— théière 18342
— tonneau 6014
poche v. jale ou creuset
pocheur 10487
podolite 13607
poids 19912
— atomique 933
— brut 8604
— de charge 19915
— de la charge 19906
— en grammes molécules 8408
— équivalent chimique S. 3394
— maximum 3336
— moléculaire 11872
— moyen 1013
— mort 16873
— net 12247
— normal 17356
— relatif de combinaison 4068
— spécifique 17024
— sur l'outil 19907
— tendeur 18420
— théorique 18480
poignard 5782
poignée 8793
— pour enlever le modèle 10768
poil de vache 4574
poinçon 13244, 14107, 14176, 14181
— à découper 4922
— à tirer 5809
— d'empreinte 9217
— de réception 17308
— porte-matrice S. 5374
— pour trous d'air 13931
poinçonnage 13085, 13243, S. 14182, 17321,
— creux 17321
— sans détachement de la pièce 16705

poinconner 11939, 14172,
    14173, 17305, 17305
poinçonneuse 12262
point 19310
— chaud 9444
— critique 4645
— d'accrochage 17662
— d'aniline 11819
— de condensation 12730
— de congélation 15920
— de décomposition 13611
— de dessication 6036
— de déviation 10343
— de Fraass 2425
— de fumée 16763
— de fusion 11475
— de grésage 16466
— de pliage 1514
— de ramification d'un fi-
    lon 13612
— de repère 11401
— de rosée 11401
— de soudure 16865
— de vitrification 19578
— dur 8842
— final 6455
— libre 7735
pointe 18672
— à ardoise 16575
— à boucle 14428
— à noyau brevetée
    12968
— à roulements à billes
    1151
— à tête bombée 15282
— à tête-homme pour chaus-
    sures 11037
— à tête plate 7388
— à tête plate fraisée 4540
— à tête plate pour mouleurs
    7334
— à tête très large 12896
— aciérée 17497
— d'aiguille 13613
— du chalumeau 18769
— du coeur 13610
— fraisée pour caisses à
    fruits 11704
— fraisée rayée 3403
— plate rayée 7330
— sans tête 12164
pointeau 12055
— d'éruption 7421
— de soupape 19450
pointer 17176
pointerolle 18274

poire 19114
— en caoutchouc 15306
poisson 7206
poix 13411
— d'asphalte 1636
— de goudron 3851
polarisation de concentra-
    tion 4169
— d'un gaz 8039
— spontanée 15828
polarographie 13618
pôle ayant une unité d'in-
    tensité 19311
poli au sable 15526
— fin 9161
— lustre 13626
polianite 13620
polir 8537, 10538, 13623,
    13624
— à la lime 13450
— à l'émeri 6410
— en relief 14687
— finement 7114
— les moules 16771
— par attaque à l'acide
    6575
polis S. 13625
polissabilité 7134
polissable 13627
polissage 2522, 2403, 15320.
— à l'émeri 6414
— fin 8540
— préparatoire 8541
polissoir rond S. 15291
pollénite 13633
pollucite 13634
pollux S. 13634
polonium 13635
polyadelphite 13636
polyargite 13637
polyargyrite 13638
polyarsénite 13639
polybasite 13640
polychroïlite 13641
polycrase 13642
polyéthylène 13647
polymorphe 13644
polystryrène 15645
pompage 15052
— accouplé 12117
— au câble 20133
— combiné 1051
— jumelé S. 12117
— latéral 1074
— par barre de pompage
    17948

pompage par injection de gaz
    7998
— par pression 17261
— pneumatique 314
pompe à air 309,
— à boue 12088, 16719
— à chambre d'accumula-
    tion S. 7980
— à circulation 3605
— à commande hydraulique
    9532
— à compression 13914
— à double effet 5641
— à étanchéité fluide S.
    7465
— à filtrer 7052
— à garniture liquide 7465
— à long coups 10976
— à main 8776
— à maîtresse-tige 2555
— à membrane 5338
— à piston plongeur 13578
— à plongeur 19055
— à sable 15514
— à schlamms 16630
— à simple effet 16382
— à vapeur 17443
— à vapeur compound 4130
— à vapeur isolée 10064
— à vapeur jumelle 19175
— à vapeur murale 19654
— à vapeur verticale avec
    bâti S. 10064
— actionnée par le groupe
    moteur 18210
— alternative 14494
— aspirante 17959
— auxiliaire 8101,
— centrifuge 3208, 9653
— commandée par courroie
    1477
— d'avaleresse S. 16425
— de circulation 3583
— de compression 13915
— d'épuisement 5748
— de fonçage 16425
— de fond 12516
— de forage 2083
— de puits 15954
— duplex 6113
— mammouth 7980
— pneumatique 7980
— rotative 15215
— Worthington 6113
pomper 15051, 17607
— du pétrole 19682

pompiste 14163
pont 2379, 2383, 2385, 7829, 13508
— à bascule 13509
— à poutres en treillis 18965
— basculant 18674
— bascule 19895
— d'attelage 15423
— de chargement 3318, S. 3338
— de communication 4218
— de coulée 10475
— de faille 12332
— en fer 17460
— grue 2384
— pour fils S. 20120
— pour grues 8240
— roulant 7965, 12758
— roulant à démouler 9803
— roulant de fonderie 7674
— roulant pour le transport des lingots 9789
pequette 1789, 16411
poreux 12146, 14154
porion 11731, 12770
— chef 8010
— d'aérage 7151
porosité 13671
— à pores allongés 6389
— à pores ronds 15289
— de retassure 16231
— globulaire 8303
— superficielle 13426
porpézite 13679
porphyre 14269
— syénitique 18144
porphyrique 13681
porphyrite 13680
porphyroblaste 11533, 14079
porphyroïde 13683
port d'embarquement 16138
portage 2903
porte 8088
— à coulisses 11020
— à guichet 2225, 14662, 20057
— calibre 17089
— centrale de la tour 19421
— contre les feux 7167
— d'aérage 264, 301, 1392, 18849
— d'aérage à guichet 15589
— d'allumage 10795
— de cheminée 3565
— de four à coke 5631

porte de nettoyage 3693
— de préchauffage 2345
— de réglage d'aérage 8114
— de ventilation 15870, 19861
— de vidange 5494
— du foyer 3864
— éprouvettes 19041
— garnitures complet 12832
— glissière 16620
— métallique 17466
— noyaux 4430
— objet 17288
— outil 18727
— rabattante S. 18848
— soudure 20116
— vent 1702
— vis 15710
porté au blanc S. 20032
— au bleu 1903
— au rouge 1661
— au rouge naissant 1662
— au rouge sombre S. 6087
portée 1599, 4431, 16969
— à renflement 1132
— commune 12110
— de modèle 4462, 6484
— de noyau 4423, 1601, 18749
— débordante 12140
— tirée à l'anglaise 3712
portées 2279, 13957
porter 2902
portes glissantes et pliantes 16616
— repliantes 51
pose de tuyaux 13354
poser 15902
— une colonne de tubes 10519
positif 13702
position verticale 19368
possibilité de modification des phases 3282
poste 16122
— de décochage 10406
— de huit heures 6233
— de jour 5019
— de nuit 5599, 12294
— d'incendie 7175
post-tension 13714
pot à recuire 617
— de recuit 610
— de trempage 16797
— en terre réfractaire 4742

pot v. vase
potasse 10272
— caustique 9509
— caustique en bâtonnets 17579 17579
poteau 13707
— de mise à la terre 19071
— oscillant 13059
— tubulaire 19084
potée 5435
potence 19644
potences tubulaires pour fils et lampes 19094
potentiel anodique 630
— de décomposition 13732
poteyage 14629, 14635
— pour creuset 4750
— pour moule 5364
poteyer 5835
poudingue 10422, 12158, 14092
poudre à cémenter 3177
— d'aluminium 458
— d'asphalte 877
— de cémentation 2920
— de charbon de bois 3300
— de dolomie 5613
— d'émeri 6416
— de houille 7075
— de lycopode 11107
— de mine 1750
— de tourbe 13772
— de verre 8282
— impalpable automisée 9651
— v. poussière
poulie à gorge 8588, 8592
— amovible 11009
— automatique du câble de cabestan 975
— de commande en motrice 14132, 5966
— de curage 15517
— d'enroulement 20101
— de forage 4734
— de forage au câble 17222
— de queue 18211
— de retour S. 18211
— de tension S. 9421
— Koepe 5967
— magnétique 11199
— mobile S. 9230
— sur puits 4420

poupée de rabat 14311
poupées du laminoir S. 9465
pour services lourds 9028
pourcentage moyen d'analyses 1007
pourpre 14193
poussage 2046, S. 5959,
  17084
— par palplanches 13286
poussard 2584, 5584, 8213,
  8245
— de pied 2186
poussée 18596, 18603
— des eaux 19769
pousser une galerie 5758,
  15339
pousseuse des lingots 9797
poussier 6077
— de charbon 3936
— de charbon de bois 3303
— de coke S. 2252, 3932
— de graphite 13771
poussière 6124
— d'anthracite 4827
— de charbon 2252, 2358,
  3818
— de coke 16737
— de minerai 12643
— du gueulard 6133
— v. poudre
poussoir 9798
poutrages 1380
poutre de rigidité 17588
— en acier 17457
— en treillis 18963
— transversale 4670, S.
  16586
— tubulaire 19061
poutrelle 8238
— anglaise 6482
— étirée 17791
poutrelles à larges ailes
  2433
— cintrées 3602
pouvoir agglomérant 226
— agglutinant 3178
— calorifique 2754
— cokéfiant 3951
— collant 2695
— d'attraction magnétique
  11186
— dissolvant 16908
— éclairant 2783
— éclairante faible 11054
— scorifiant 7504
powellite 13773

praséodyme 13801
praséolite 13802
prasinite 13803
pré-chauffé 13838
— modèle 11366
— tension 13927
précambrien 13804
préchauffage 13841
préchauffer 13837
préchauffeur 9400
précipitant 13805
précipitation des impuretés
  13817
— structurale 13812
précipité 13809
précipiter en ébullition
  13808
— par l'hydrogène sulfuré
  13807
précision dimensionnelle
  5422
predazzite 13830
preetirage 13831
préfractionneur 13836
préhension automatique 1581
  15811
prehnite 13842
prélèvement d'échantillon
  15460
premier affinage 8500
première cannelure 7200
— couche 7197
prendre un échantillon de
  gaz 18217
préparation 5842, 7203, 1261
  12611
— à air comprimé 13596
— à sec du charbon 6045
— au goudron 879
— de la cartouche-amorce
  13952
— de la pâte 13854
— des éprouvettes 13853
— des minerais S 12642
— des minerais par le froid
  7746
— des paquets 13283
— des pièces d'essai S.
  13853
— des surfaces polies 13859
  13859
— du lit de fusion 11232
— du niveau de base 16314
— humide 19990
— magnétique 11190
— mécanique 11405

préparation par voie humide
  19987, 19994
— physique et chimique
  13191
— v. traçage
préparé 5837, 15250
préparer 5271, 20079
— le lit de fusion 2730
prescription 17027
prescriptions de qualité
  17028
presse 13867
— à amalgame 486
— à bille pour l'essai de
  dureté 1156
— à bouchons 4472
— à briques hydraulique
  9516
— à chanfreiner 1513
— à cingler 374, 376, 1163,
  17263
— à courber S. 1515
— à creusets 4743
— à dorer 8227
— à dorer et à empreindre
  8346
— à dresser 17727
— à estamper S. 17328
— à étirer 5808
— à excentrique 6185, 6186
— à filer 6721
— à filtrer S. 7051
— à forger 7595
— à forger à vapeur 17442
— à forger hydraulique 9523
— à former 374
— à genouillère S. 18707, 1870
  18708
— à laitier 16549
— à levier coudé 18707
— à matricer 10417, 17328
— à mouler 12022
— à mouler à double effet
  12016
— à mouler avec plaque
  renversable 12026
— à plier 1515
— à sodium 16824
— carotte 4410
— de coulée 3621
— d'ébavurage 18903
— de précision à centrer
  les châssis 3218
— étoupe 2058, 12848
— étoupe de cimentation
  3153

presse-étoupe de fond 2163
— -étoupe de Lürmann 11095
  11095
— hydraulique à mouler
  9530
— mécanique inclinable
  13789
— tôle 1683
presser 13865, 17256
pression 13892
— atmosphérique 927
— critique 4646
— de bulle 2491
— de démarrage 17386
— d'épreuve 18452
— d'écoulement 7447
— de fond 2164
— de gisement 3775, 14749
— de l'air S. 927
— de la boue 12087
— de la colonne montante
  19054
— de la terre 14999
— de laminage 13910
— de marche 20217
— de saturation 15556
— de serrage 4103
— de surchage 12736
— de tubage 2952
— des étalages 13912
— d'introduction 9857
— du gaz 8041
— du gisement 13917
— du liquide 7466
— d'utilisation 15899
— du vent 1732, 20094
— effective 13893
— ferro-statique 6962
— finale S. 9164
— hydraulique 19805
— hydrostatique 9575
— intérieure 9903
— latérale 10571, 18596
— maxima 11387
— normale de travail 20252
— osmotique 12689
— par essieu 1028
— préliminaire 11057
— radiale 14328
— souterraine 14746
— statique 3771
— statique de fond 17393
prêt pour l'analyse 14470
pricéite 13930

primer pigmenté 13954
priorite 13959
prise S. 9853
— à l'air 286
— d'eau 9506
— d'échantillons d'un ré-
  servoir 18521
— d'échantillons du sol
  13971
— d'échantillons par tarière
  18520
— d'essai 15454, 15460, 1546
  15461, 18461
— d'essai à la coulée 18309
  18309
— d'essai de métal liquide
  10483
— d'essai séchée 5848
— de gaz 4998, 5000, 8030
  12938
— de gaz annulaire 3590
— de gaz belge 3590
— de gaz Faber du Faure
  8034
— de gaz von Hoff 19602
— de lumière 10786
— de mesures 11394
— des echantillons de sondage 19969
— éclair 7302
— par retrait 16225
— prématurée 13651
prismatine 13966
prismatique 13962
prismatoïde 13967
prisme à section oblique
  13961
— de seconde espèce 13958
— de troisième espèce
  13960
— droit 14906
— oblique 12435
— orthorthombique 12683
— pentagonal 13067
— quadrangulaire 14243
— redresseur 6538
— triangulaire 18886
prisonnier 17904
prix d'achat 4517
— de revient 4515
— de revient de la force
  motrice 4514
— unitaire du fer et du
  manganèse 13920

probertite 13970
procédé à deux soulè-
  vements 18913
— à injection 19774
— à la fonte et au minerai
  13250
— à la presse Ehrhardt
  6269
procédé à une seule fusion
  S. 16398,
— acide 85, S. 1553,
  1559
— allemand S. 18913
— au convertisseur 4304
— basique 1302
— Bessemer 1533
— Brinelle 1166
— d'affinage 18978
— de briquettage 2416
— de congélation 7747
— de craquage 4589
— d'empreinte par pression
  1166
— d'estampage par pression
  S. 1166
— de fonçage par congéla-
  tion 15957
— de fusion 8878
— de galvanisation 7944
— de grillage 11614
— de l'analyse 13972
— de lavage 19708
— de mise en marche
  1874
— de meulage 12029
— de nitruration 12313
— d'oxydation 12791
— de puddlage 14114
— de raffinage 14616
— de recuit 618
— de refonte 14701
— de trempe 8863, 8867
— de trempe au nickel
  12274
— discontinu 1334
— dit «au pas de pélerin»
  19038
— duplex 6112
— électro-chimique 6325
— «en peigne» 4052
— Gayley pour le séchage
  de l'air 8121
— Hydrospark 9572
— Mannesmann 11295

procédé Menne 11495
— métallurgique 11588
— par amalgamation 487
— par fusion de fonte et
  riblons 11465
— Réaumur 20047
— Siemens 16294
— Siemens-Martin 12578
— Thomas 1292
— Thomas-Gilchrist 1302
— vallon 19660
procédé v. méthode
procéder au remblayage
  hydraulique 16714
— au remplissage hydraulique 7478
procédés Bessemer et Martin
  combinés 4063
processus de combustion
  13976
prochlorite 13985
producibilité par heure
  12712
production 8201, 10531
— à cycle ouvert 12568
— annuelle 20281
— consentie 393
— de fer par le procédé
  électrique 6291
— de gaz continue 4268
— de queue 18209
— devenant pire en qualité
  15429
— différée 5113
— éruptive S. 7448, 7485
— finale 19217
— initiale 9809
— intermittente 7441
— latente 3772
— jaillissante 7448
— journalière 4963, 17613
— limite 12469
— moyenne 16902
— par pistonnage 18093
— par puisage 1109
— potentielle 13733
— stabilisée 15922
— totale 18790
produit 20113
— à souder 16858
— blanc 20041
— broyé 8574
— de distillation 13991
— de la décomposition 13990
  13990
— d'oxydation 12793

produit de qualité inférieure
  19253
— de queue 18208
— de tête 8932
— de tête gazeux 2946
— de traitement des boues
  12071
— initiale 9809
— demi-fini 19295
— d'hydroforming 9556
— du grillage 13993
— du triage 13992
— embouti 5088
— filtré 7061
— moussant 7513
— riche en métal 11761
— sans bavures 2619
— stérile 12359
— tubulaire 19080
— utilisable pour la fusion
  13994
produits accessoires du haut
  fourneau 2653
— de boulonnerie 2014
— de l'industrie du fer 1062
  10624
— dispersants 5549
— du fil machine 20140
— gazeux d'explosion 202
— légers 18204
— pour chemins de fer 14367
  14367
— protecteurs 13863
— rectifiés 8619
— sidérurgiques 9954
profil 4704, 16261, 17889
— à gradins en acier extrudé
  à chaud 6720, 17558
— biseauté 7273
— chanfreiné 7273
— de haut-fourneau 1715
— de laminage 15779
— de poteau en I 9610
— en trapèze 18854
— géologique 8174
— moyen 11434, 11435
— spécial 17004
— stratigraphique 4047, S.
  8175
profilage 15998
profilé 7615, 17889
— courant 19316
— d'enjolivage 12673
— demi-rond S. 8716
— léger 10801
— spécial 17018

profiler sur modèle 4896
profiler v. façonner ou modeler
profiles S. 3289
— lourds 9041
— de construction laminés
  en acier 15102
— du commerce 11496
— pour construction S.
  4236
— pour la construction 9041
— pour wagons de chemin
  de fer 10009
profils S. 3289
— à angles vifs 15700
— à coins arrondis 17350
— à Z 20315
— chanfreinés 7274
— creux extrudés 9271
— d'acier spéciaux extrudés
  à chaud 9414
— de fer 17887
— des étalages 15769
— légers 10785
— pour construction de
  wagons 15768
— soudés préfabriqués as-
  semblés sur place par
  rivetage 13832
— spéciaux 17020
— U.T.M.M. 19417
profit 20113
profondeur de l'entaille S.
  1393
— de la saignée 1393
— de la sole du four 5208
— de pénétration 5209
— de pose en puits 15918
— de trempe 3431, 5206,
  8864, 8873
— du sondage 11236
programme de forage 5935
projecteur 16643
projection au pistolet 11562
— d'étincelles 16987
— et fusion 17187
projections du convertisseur
  4305
— vulcaniques 6236
projet de procédé 6475
prométhéum 14006
propène 14015
proportion de gros 8387
— de menu S. 4252
— en poids 14021
propre 3674

propriété liante 2024
propylite 14028
propylitisation 14029
prospecter 2621, 14032
prospection 4519, 14033.
   14036
— d'après les fragments
   troués 16142
— magnétique 11204
prosopite 14031
protactinium 14043
protecteur des tiges 15305
protection 16120
— cathodique 3103
— contre la corrosion 14043
— contre l'éblouissement 661
   661
— de surface S. 18064
— superficielle 18064
protobastite 14049
protogine 14051
protomylonite 14052
protoparaffine 14053
protosulfure de fer S. 10022
protoxyde de baryte 12794
— de baryum 1260
— de cobalt 3890
protusion 14054
proustite 815, 14055, 14550
prussiate jaune de potasse
   20287
psammite 14063
pséphite 14066
pseudoboléite 14070
pseudobrookite 14071
pseudo-clivage 6782, 17735
pseudo-concordance 5503
pseudocristallin 14072
pseudoglaucophane 14073
pseudoleucite 14075
pseudomalachite 14076
pseudomorphe 14077
pseudomorphisme 14078
pseudophite 14080
pseudoschistosité 14074
pseudotalchyte 14082
pseudowavéllite 14083
psilomélane 1649
psittacinite 14086
ptiolite 14088
puchérite 14090
puddlage 14106, 14115,
   14316
puddlage à la main 8775
— au gaz 8044

puddlage brillant 13252
— chaud S. 19995
— de fer 9996
— de fer nerveux 14112
— de l'acier 14113
— de minerai 12648
— du fer 17500
— en fer à grains 14108
— gras S. 13252, 16550,
   19995
— mécanique 11134
— rotatif 14840
— sec 6037
puddler 14093, 94,
puddleur 14105
— mécanique 11410, 11411
puglianite 14119
puisage à l'air comprimé
   270
— au gaz 8020
— électrique 6282
puisard 12074, S. 13397,
   17991, 17993
puisatier 13422
puiser 15638
— par cuiller 1099
puissance S. 18507, 20064
— calorifique brute 8601
— calorifique nette 12241
— de la centrale 2802
puissance v. capacité
puits 8631, 11740, 13397,
   15932
— à bras 6082
— à double production 6068
— à double tube 6067
— à enfoncement sous
   charge 11989
— à gaz 8064
— à grande déviation 9138
— à haute production 1383
— à injection d'eau 19773
— à pétrole 12515
— à remblai 17650, 15027,
— actif 10346
— artésien 830, 2090
— auxiliaire 14689, 15901
— au jour 10786
— borgne 20114
— coffré 10033
— d'aérage 306, 322, S.
   333, 2652, 3987
— d'alimentation 9829,
   10330
— d'appel 19351

puits de bordure 6207
— de combustion 4083
— d'entrée d'air 5696,
   5709, 9858
— d'essai 724, 18882
— d'exhaure 14162
— d'extension 12692
— d'extraction 5813. 6112,
   9233, 14134, 20106,
   20215, 20249
— d'extraction et d'épuisement 6470
— de flanc 7277
— de gaz corrosif 16945
— d'huile corrosive S.
   16945
— d'injection 9817, 13926
— d'injection d'eau 19766
— de la prise d'eau S.
   19962
— de limite 12470
— de recherche 2087,
   14035
— de recherche en zone
   inconnue 14414
— de remblayage 7492
— de repos 17597
— de retour d'air 19347
— de sortie d'air 14814,
   19351, 19384
— de ventilation 306, S.
   322, 333, 5491
— éboulé 6777
— en éruption S. 7494
— en phase de pompage 747
   7473
— en pistonnage 18095
— en pompage 14171
— en puisage 1108
— en quinconce 7228
— fermé 16245
— frigorifique 7749
— hors du gisement 12709
— incliné 5016, 5472, S.
   9690, 9704
— incliné au mur 19271
— incliné au rocher 15029
— injecteur 9674
— intérieur 1779, 10094,
   10896, 15982, 17371,
   19262. 19849, 20114
— intermédiaire 9763
— jaillissant 7444, 8677,
   17174
— maçonné 11356

puits muraillé 19656
— ordinaire 16796
— perdu 16795
— plat 16580
— pompé par balancier 1379
— pour contre-poids 1130
— pourvu de foyer d'aérage 7855
— presque épuisé 17859
— souterrain 19262
— stérile 6076
— tubulaire 7676
— tubulaire de Norton S. 7676
pulaskite 14120
pulsation d'animage 17384
— magnétique 6270
pulsomètre 14146
pulvérisateur 14150
— à fente 16688
— à jet de vapeur 17439
— à tubes concentriques S. 19087
— à tuyère 17185
— centrifuge 3210
— crépine 17206
— d'argile finement lavée 14151
— d'eau 11811
— injecteur 19087
pulvérisation S. 8546, 17186
pulvériser 8539
purger le toit 15598
purifier 7072, S. 14593
purin 7060
purpurite 14195
pustule 1789
puteux S. 200, S. 1648
putréfaction 15239
pylone d'encrage 5617
— de forage 5930
— portephares 1363
— pour lignes électriques 19076
pyramide coiffée 3464, 14369, 6177
pyrargillite 14210
pyrargyrite 5004, 14211 15330, 16359
pyrite 2280, 9970, 10347, 12130, 14214
— arsenicale 818, S. 829
— crêtée 17001
— cuivreuse oxydée 1659
— de fer 9997

pyrite magnétique 11200
pyritoèdre 14216
pyroaurite 14217
pyrobelonite 14218
pyrobitume 14219
— asphaltique 884
pyrochlore 14220
pyrochroïte 14221
pyroclastique 14222
pyrocristallin 14223
pyroélectricité 14224
pyrogénation 14225
pyromètre 14230
— à air 315
— à couple 18494
— à disparition de filament 5478
— à graphite 8449
— à radiation totale 18792
— à résistance 14769
— métallique 11559
— optique monochromatique 11906
— polychromatique 4035
pyrométric 14231
pyromorphite 8512, 14232
pyrope 7973, S. 11179
pyrophanite 14235
pyrophyllite 13058, 14236
pyrophysalite 14237
pyrrhotine 11194
pyroschiste 14238
pyrosmalite 14239
pyrostilpnite 7150, 14241
pyroxène 14242

Q

quadricone S. 4702
quadrillage 8538
quai de chargement 10922
qualité 14247
— de fil de fer 14249
— pour étirage 5810
— d'eau 14252
quantité d'eau par heure de la distribution d'eau 12711
— de lumière 14251
— de vent 1701
quantités chimiquement équivalentes 3397
quartz 14265
— arborisé 741

quartz aurifère 8344
— aventuriné 7251
— enfumé 2556, 2689, 11934 11934, 16769
— en morceaux 14268
— filonien 19488
— finement broyé 14149
— laiteux 11681
— résinite commun S. 4096
quartzeux 14275
quartzite 14271, 14273
quaternaire 14278
quenouille 16593, 17685
queue 1214, 18203
— de lion 18630
— de morue 2479
— de rat pour fontes 3588
— de vache 9090
quille de scellement 15740
quincaillerie 7117
quisquéite 14308

R

rabat 14501
rabattage S. 8205
râble 7176
raboter 13451
racewinite 14318
racine de charriage 15154
raclage 15674
racler 15654
raclette 7374, 15665
racleur à paraffine 12909
— d'huile 12507
racloir 7374, 15666, 16658, 16720, 17805, 17819
raccord 2939, 7125, 7226, 7227, 10252
— à trois pièces 13368
— à vis 12305
— à 45° 20257
— conique 18279
— du creux de la matrice 19434
— de rails 14360
— de tube 19031
— de tuyau 13351, 15318
— pour tiges de sonde 5904
— union 13368
raccordement 4224
raccorder 7113
radiographie 14337
radiolite 14334

radiophyllite 14339
radioscopie 14340
radium 14341
radon 14344
raffinage 14605
— au bain de scories 19688
— par dissolvant 16912
raffinage v. affinage
raffiner 14593
— l'acier 14594
raffineur 7100
rafraîchissement S. 4331
raglanite 14354
raidisseur 17586
raie bleu 1913
— de sodium 16822
— du manganèse 11275
rail armé 18609
— d'applique 17625
— de fer à tête d'acier 9998
— de grande voie 14356
— de tramway 18821
— double tête 5663
— du pont 19896
— pour mines 14355
— pour voie étroite 14357
— Vignole 7328
raimondite 14368
rainage 8597
rainurage 8597
rainure 8586, 17155
— de cylindre 12956
— d'étirage 5369
— de tuyau 4436
— et languette 8598
— longitudinale 10981
— pour la détente de tension 17788
rainuré 3370
rainures 9373
rajeunir 14681
ralentir 16693
— la combustion 16513
rallonge 2795, 2789, 4735, 16378
ralstonite 14386
ramasseur 15676
ramdohrite 14396
ramirite 14398
ramification d'une couche 12468
rammelsbergite 14399
ramollir l'acier S. 16847
ramoneur 8323
rampant ascendant 851

rampe 7373, 8655, S. 9697
— de chargement 10921
ramper un moule 18624
ramsayte 14408
rangée 14412
— de buttes 1351
— de tuyères 15302
— parallèle 12921
ransomite 14415
rappel d'éjection 6240
rapport de basicité 14022
— d'endurance 6466
— d'humidité 17444
— de récirculation 14528
— de sondage 5894, 18803
— gaz-huile dans le gisement 14748
— gaz-pétrole 8004
— huile-eau 19764
rappuyage 14738, 18881
rappuyer 14737
raquette 17266
raréfaction de l'air 14429
raspite 14432
rat de cuve 19845
râteau 14381
râtelier à tiges 7104
— des tiges de pompage 17947
rathite 14438
raumite 14449
rauvite 14450
ravalement 13383
ravin 8297
rayé S. 17800
rayon 20011
— de centrage S. 1516
— de matrice 5376
— de pliage 1516
rayonnant 14331
rayonnement de la chaleur 14332
rayons 20261
— gamma 7950
réactif 14471
réactifs 14473
réaction 14467
— chimique 3391
— des facteurs de milieu 14782
— endothermique 6484
— exothermique 6662
réagir 14466
réalgar 14475
rebancher le mur 16410
reboisage 14692, 14793

reboiser 14792
rebord du cylindre 6203
— du four 14915
rebouilleur 14482
rebuts de diamants 5331
rebuts de coke 14640
rebuts, remblai 940
recarburation 14485
recarburer 14486
recette 8811, 10525, 10530, 13532, 15964
— au niveau du sol 13984
— du fond 9777
— du jour 12713
— inférieure 9839, 15955
— inférieure du puits 2143
— supérieure 682, 18684
— supérieure du plan incliné 1193
receveur S. 1203, 10523, 17826
réchaud à pétrole 13134
réchauffage du modèle 12979 12979
réchauffement par trempe 5440
réchauffer 14665
— à coeur 7808
rechausser la coulée 9722
recherche S. 5407
— métallographique 11581
— par fouilles 14411
recherches au spectroscope 17036
— d'or 12421
récif 14583
— -barrière 1250
récipient 14488
— à chlorure de calcium 1127
— à mercure 11508, 11511
— de chargement 3335
— en verre pour piles 1348
récirculation 14529
récirculer 14526
recoupage du toit 2483
recoupe 2063, 2338, 2340, 2637, 7909, 4682, 4683, 4684, 4710, 4712, 4716, 12464, 16159, 16670, 17542, 17820
— d'aérage 2340, 4694
— de pilier 4674
— de traçage 10147
— de ventilation 324, 11901, 11903

recoupement du méandre
16178
recouper le toit 14937
recoupes de creusets S.
12521
recouvrement 12745, 12767
— horizontal 9020, 9345
— stratigraphique 17751
— stratigraphique apparent
712
recouvrer 15448
recouvrir 6400, 12764
— de drap 4560
recristallisation 14515
recristallisé 5590
rectificateur 14521
rectification 14520
rectifier 14651, 17840
— l'acier 9670
rectifieuse à cylindres de
laminoir 15079
recueillir les étincelles
3095
recuire 602, 7794, 14666
— intermédiairement 17922
— l'acier 603
recuit 604, 608,
— à l'air 12562, 12563
— blanc 2391, 12829,
20023
— bleu 1895, 1897
— complètement 16827
— d'adoucissement 16849
— d'affinage structurale 1
12887
— de dégazage 5128
— de détente 17785
— de l'acier 619
— de malléabilisation 11254
11254
— de précipitation 13813
— de régénération 12387
— d'usinabilité 613
— en boîtes 13716, 13717
— en creuset clos 3755
— excessif 12733
— intermédiaire 13973
— pour l'élimination des
tensions 17789
recul de la dissociation S.
14804
reculer les buses 5759
reculoir S. 1089
— de chariot S. 5280
récupérateur 10128, 14525,
14648

récupérateur de chaleur 8974
— Whitwell 20053
récupération 14510
— de carotte 4435
— primaire 13943
— secondaire 15770
récurage du trou 15610
recuveler 14487
recuvelage 14529
rédaction des résultats de
l'analyse 20237
redescendre dans le puits 14
14740
redevance 15300
— supplémentaire 12775
redistillation 14555, 14742
redressement 19359
réducteur S. 14563, 14565,
14824
réductibilité facile 6183
— difficile 5399
réduction 14571
— d'angle 570
— de fer par la méthode
thermo-électrique S. 6301
— de la durée de la fusion
16188
— de la poussière au fourneau 14575
— de la prise d'essai 14264
— de laminage 14441
— de forgeage 14442
— de section 14574
— de section des cannelu-
res 14576
— du tirage 6812
— indirecte 9745
— mâle 11243
— sans filetage 17918
réduire 14559
— à la fraise 11684
réduisant 14564
réemploi 14735
réémulsionner (se-) 1409
refente S. 17135
reflux 14156
— de circulation 3584
refondre 14695
refonte 14699
— des riblons S. 16751
reforer 5878, 14537
refoulement 5149, 5490,
10251, 19378
— intermittent 8909
refouler 8903, 10246, 13326,
14016, 19371, 19372

refouloir 10250, 11748
réfractaire 2720, 14625,
14626, 16706
— acide 90
— basique 1303
réfractairiété 14624
réfrigérant à cheminée 3457
— intermédiaire 9873
réfrigération 4331, 17936
— du foyer 8471
refroidi à l'eau 14287
— par l'air 158, 6796
— par l'eau 19759
— par vapeur d'eau 17423
refroidir 4326, 4977
refroidissement 4331, 4337,
4347, 14290, 16516
— artificiel 833
— automatique 15816
— dans l'eau 19808
— de four 4340
— des électrodes par cou-
rant d'eau 19794
— entre moules 5375
— lent 18391
— par l'air 259
— par l'eau 19761
refroidisseur d'air à ailettes
278
— de forme 5174
— de surface 18044
— interne 9897
refuge 14490, 14636
refus 12778, 18751
— de récaption 14637
— de tamisage S. 15697
refuser l'échantillon 14680
refusion 14699
regard 9847, 13044
— de réservoirs 18249
— de visite 11258
région abyssale 30
— actique 18831
— aphotique 686
— bathyale S. 16831
— d'ablation 14650
— dysphotique 6161
— épicentrale 6509
— euphotique 6590
— frontale 764
— houillière 3814
— littorale 10897
— plissée 7524
région v. zone
registre 4980, 16614
— à air froid 3964

registre à papillon 2643
— de tirage 7453
— du vent 1727
— tournant 18140
réglage 167, 14657
— de l'air 14660
— de la pression d'eau 14661
— des électrodes 169
— du sable 17828
— du tirage 5751
— par un amplificateur magnétique 11165
règle à dresser 10716
— à modeler 4286
— divisée 15587
— du cavalier 5583
règlement d'essai 5473, 18462
réglettes courbées en laiton 2268
régression 14684
rehausse 13840
— de châssis
— de coulée 14950
régulage 10852
régulateur 162, 8375
— de débit de vent 1703
— de gaz 8047
— de température 938
— de tension 19595
— du niveau du fond 2172
régule 14663
réguler 11536
réichardtite 14672
réinite 14678
réissite 14679
rejet 12383, 16647
— apparent parallèle aux couches 711
— de faille 18588
— en profondeur 5443, 5445
— horizontal 16721, 16211, 17824
— horizontal latéral 9350
— horizontal transversal 9354
— horizontal transversal apparent 709
— incliné 18794
— incliné, glissement 710
— net 12246, 18785
— normal S. 5713
— parallèle aux couches S. 17749

rejet perpendiculaire aux couches S. 17750
— proprement dit S. 710
— stratigraphique 17750
— vers le bas 5716
— vers le haut 19385
— vertical 716, 18587, 19523
relâcher un coin 19344
relais à retardement 5145
relèvement 19349
— géologique 8177
relever 14124
— le convertisseur 18625
relier 4216
remblai 2534, 8325, 8329, 8335, 10707, 12828, 12844, 12854, 19749
— sec 6034
remblayage 8326, 8334, 1057, 12828, 12844, 15022, 17703, 19725
— de galets 15323
— hydraulique 7487, 9538
— partiel 17851
— pneumatique 13589, 98
remblayer 1291, 3905, 8328, 12825, 17702
remblayeur 2533, 3911, 12842, 12842
remblayeuse 1058
— mécanique 8333, 17704
remise en pression 14739
remmoulage 896, 4441, 11971
remmouler 895
remous 18122
— d'eau 20021
remontage 14372, 14375, 14942, 14945, 14946, 14956, 19366, 19367
remonte 856, 10759
remontée 14942
— de la fonte 14960
— de pression 13897
remonter 8203, 14370
remplir 7012
— le moule 7011
remplissage 7033
— de fissures 3126
— filonien 19486
remuer la terre avec un bull-dozer 5719
renard 15569
renardite 14724

rencontré 18756
rencontrer une roche dure 8200
rendant un son métallique 11573
rendement 6143, 8201, 13779
— des minerais 20297
— en coke 3948
— en gaz 8068
— manométrique 11298
— thermique 18482
rendre étanche 12826
— fragile 6406
renflement 2547, S. 2768, 18121, 18278
renforcement 6485
— des parois du tube 17589
renforcer le sable 17780
rensselaerite 14726
rentabilité 14004
renversement 14819, 18135
— d'aérage 14822
— du convertisseur 18683
— du laminage 14834
renverser 18670
réoxyder 14729
réparateur de berlines 4509
réparation du boisage 14476
— d'un guidage 15061
réparer 11487
— le moule 14730
répartition des matières à fondre 5574
— du vent 262
repasser 14808
repêchage 7217
repêcher 7207
repère 1488, 5006, 11330
— à vue 16307
— de départ d'usinage 10183
— de remmoulage 898
répertoire 14590
repos 16209
— d'éjection 6239
reprendre avec de l'eau 5547
— un puits 14846
reprise 3984, 4003
— de support 19298
— des piliers 5793
— du magasin 18220
réseau cristallin 4796, 16953

réseau de canalisation 13385
— de conduites S. 13385
— d'érosion 17645
— de failles 12249
— de veines 12250
— filtrant 19911
réservoir 17692
— à charbon 2580
— à forme de goutte 17062
— à mercure 11505
— à minerais 17693
— à toit fixe 7241
— à toit flottant 7392
— collecteur 8102
— d'air comprimé 4135
— d'air de la conduite de refoulement 5150
— de compensation 18075
— de décantation 57, S. 19790
— de dépôt S. 17690
— d'eau 4098
— d'eau sous pression S. 9156
— d'écoulement 7437
— d'emmagasinage S. 17690
— de filtration 7054
— d'étanchéité 15736
— de lavage 19692
— de service 20192
— de stockage 17690
— intermédiaire 15356
— jaugeur 8117
— pour le transport de gaz 10548
— supplémentaire 142
— surélevé 9156
réservoirs de production 10647
résidu 2144, 7545, 14753, 19718
— aromatique 806
— d'alkylation 364
— de carrière 14260
— de distillation du pétrole brut 4752
— de la combustion 4081
— de la décomposition 14757
— de lessivage 10902
— de paraffine 19844
— de première distillation 18757
— de pyrites grillées 2715

résidu huileux 16677
— insoluble 19285
— insoluble dans l'acide 14759
— non sulfoné 19335
— pétrolifère de première extraction 19918
— primaire 17716
résidus 9049, 11035, 18215
— de pétrole 13135
— de réservoir 18247
résilience 3645, 14760
résine 14761
— phénolique 13151
— polyvinylique 13648
résistance 6117, 17775, 17778
— à chaud 9185
— à la chaleur 14772
— à la corrosion 14771
— à la déformation 5570
— à l'écrasement et au frottement 14774
— à la flexion 1519
— à la pression 14773
— à la rupture 18410
— à la torsion 18783
— à la traction 14776, 1538 15386, 17779, 19219
— à l'usure 14777, 19856
— à noyau 4449
— au choc 9645, 14775
— au cisaillement 16085
— au feu 14624
— au fluage 4617, 4619
— au fluage pour une longue durée 4618
— au striage 15681
— aux efforts alternés 14770
— aux variations de température 16968
— de frottement électrolytique 6343
— de tranchant 6201, 16083
— électrique 6294
— magnétique 11201
résistant 14780
— à la chaleur 8992
— à la rouille 15396
— à l'usure 19857
— au feu 12353
— aux acides 86
— aux intempéries S. 19863
resoufflage 14783

ressort à disque 5485, 13498
— annulaire 625
— conique 4211
— de choc 2519
— de suspension
— de tampon S. 2519
— en spiral 19601
— hélicoïdal 9061
— lame 10634
— spiral (à-) 17101
ressuage 10866, 18103
— eutectique 6602
rester rouge 14696
restriction de concession 14 14787
résultat de l'essai 14789
— quantitatif pour la mise en production d'un puits 4116
retard du procédé 13974
retardateur de prise 14790
retassement 3124, 13329, 13350, 13383
retasser 16220
retassure 307, 13381
— à V 7213
— dispersée 5530
— ouverte 18066
réticulaire 12244
réticule 8709
rétinite 13417, 14794
retirer 1080
— le modèle 20155
— les baguettes 20156
— un pièce tombée au fond 7215
retirure 5773
retorchage 12967
retorcher 12964
retour 14816
retourner la pièce 19132
— le lingot S. 19134
retourneur de moule 15083
retours de fabrication 14813
retrait 4284, 16222, 16226
— contrarié 9197
rétrécir 18275
rétrécissement du creuset 5148
— d'un filon 2039
rétrogradation de la dissociation 14804
retroussement 1506, 5728
retubage 14806
retuber 14807
revenu 5811, 18390

réverbère tubulaire 19064
revêtement 2928, 6757, 7849,
   10489, 13512, 19703,
   20232
— anodique 631
— céramique 3225
— d'antifriction 10853
— de la poche de coulée
   10479
— de magnésite 11176
— de puits 19658, 19960,
— différentiel 5395
— du four 7846, 7856
— du puits 2929
— d'un four 1316
— d'un puits 3902
— métallique sans défauts
   18616
revêtement v. garnissage
revêtir S. 2907, 6735,
   10488, 11299
— la boîte à feu de briques
   réfractaires 10831
— un tuyau 2908
reviser 12749
révision des chaudières S.
   1970
révolution de machine
   d'extraction 2019
rezbanyte 14847
rhabdophane 14848
rhaetizite 14850
rhagite 14851
rhodizite 14853
rhodochrosite 14854
rhodonite 14855
rhodotilite 14856
rhodusite 14857
rhomben-porphyre 14859
rhönite 14861
rhyacolite 14863
riblon 19734
riblons 15805
riche en graphite 14875
— en oxyde de fer 14874
— en silice 14877
richtérite 14879
rickardite 14880
ridage 4871
rideau de fer 7185
rides 18050
riebeckite 14888
riffleur 17133
rifloir 14892
rigole 7472, 10586, S. 16708
— à boue 12076

rigole à chaux 10811
— à eau 19822
— à laitier 7431
— de coulée 10006, 10587,
   15366, 16687, 16950,
   18313
— de décantation 15924
— d'écoulement 16930, 1893
   18934
rigoles à laitier 16533
rim 14914
ringard 13615, 14314, 17636,
   18305
— en fer 18306
— pointu 14107
ringarder 14312
rinkite 14933
rinkolite 14934
rinnéite 14935
ripage et coupe du câble de
   forage 16667
riper une tour de sondage
   16752
ripidolite 14938
risorite 14963
risque de formation des fissures par la trempe 14964
   14964
rittingérite 14965
rivage 16168
rivelaine 9258
riversidéite 14971
rivet à tête cône-tronque
   avec collet 12888
— à tête demi ronde 15290
— à tête demi ronde aplatie
   12142
— à tête fraisée 4541
— à tête perdue 8938
— à tête plate noyée 7337
— à tête ronde noyée 15281
— en fer 10003
— noyé 4541
rizzonite 14980
robinet 3897, 13121
— à boisseau 13564
— à l'épreuve du feu 19451
— à trois voies 18569
— d'arrêt 17663
— d'arrêt sphérique 8302
— de Daniell 4993
— d'équerre 583
— de jonction 4219
— de réglage 14656
— de la tige carrée 10306

robinet en verre 8273
— flotteur 1154
— sphérique de Boëcker
   1942
robinetterie 3898
rochage 11677
roche à radiolaires 14333
— abattue 5477
— alcaline 356
— allochtone 382
— alvéolaire 9305
— amygdaloïde 543, 11261
— argileuse 2790
— aschiste 859
— authigène 961
— avec filonnets de minerai
   5829
— bitumineuse 1637
— broyée 16013
— calcaire 10820
— clastique in situ 920
— clivable 3715
— comagmatique 4049
— composée de pyroxène et
   d'amphibole 14213
— cornéenne 3410
— de base 1290
— d'épanchement 6219
— de fond 11219
— de lit 1435
— de profondeur S. 8405
— des parois 4544
— du toit 15139
— dure 2617
— dure pour construction
   14348
— éolienne 928
— encaissante 2617, 157,
   4544, 6443, 12954, 19650
— endogénétique 6460
— extrusive 6726
— ferme 17339
— filonienne S. 9583, 19489
— gazifère 8049
— grenue 8405
— hydroclastique 9550
— hypabyssale 9583
— intrusive 13065
— magasin 14750
— massive 1321
— mère 12182, 16947
— métamorphisée 14594
— monogénique 11910
— monominèrale 11914
— néovolcanique 10269
— neutre 9892

roche perméable 13112
— plutonienne 8405
— pyrogène 14226
— réservoir S. 14750
— sédimentaire à gros
  grain 15334
— sous-jacente S. 2142
— stérile 2495, 2622, 5028,
  5040, 17671
— stratifiée 1426
— surplombante 15028
— ultra-basiques 19220
— zoogène 20367
rocher 1916
— en forme de champignon
  12143
roches abyssales 32, S.
  5097
— acides 91
— autochtones 964
— basiques 1304
— cristallophylliennes
  11593
— de demi-profondeur S.
  5411
— de profondeur 5097
— de recouvrement 2585
— disjonctives 5521
— endogènes S. 9625
— filoniennes 5411
— hétéromorphiques 9108
— ignées 9625
— imperméables 9658
— intrusives 9926
— métamorphiques 11593
— plutoniennes S. 32
— sédimentaires 15794
— stratifiées S. 15794
— stratifiées coupées par
  filons 2750
rodage à l'émeri 8554
— du train de tige 2312
rodingite 15062
roeblingite 15063
roemérite 15135
roeppérite 15064
rognures de zinc 20325
rolle de blooming S. 3914
roméite 15134
rompre (se-) 10095
rompre 18346
— la circulation 2299
— par traction 18345
ronce artificielle 1222
— artificielle à 2 et 3 fils
  1223

rond 15267, 15271
rondelle 19698
— de support de ballon 1803
  18039
— élastique 17202
ronds 15270
— à béton 15272
— crénelés 4493
ronger S. 8548
— par le feu 2609
rosasite 15174
roschérite 15175
roscoélite 15176
rosélite 15181
rosenbuschite 15182
rosette S. 15710
— de graphite 8450
rosickyite 15186
rosiérésite 15187
rosite 15190
rossite 15191
rotation dans le même sens
  15232
— des cylindres 15233
— en sens inverse 14825
rotogalvanostégie 1243
rotor de turbine 19121
rouage 8125
roue à aubes 9652
— à bandage 20012
— à dents 3909
— à disque laminée en acier
  doux 15096
— coquillée 3444
— de coulée 3075
— de pompe 15368
— dentée 8132
— monobloque 16876
— vis hélicoïdale 9059
roues de wagonnet 18949
— motrices 5970
rouet 1391, 4860
rouge 14536
— à polir 10164
— Bordeaux 3632
— chaude 14540
rougemontite 15241
roulage 7955, 18819
— à bras 8771, 8789
— de charbon par chevaux
  7354
rouleau 15104
— à broyer 4774
— compresseur 13873
— coquillé 3446
— de friction 7769

rouleau en acier 17501
— glisseur 16625
— pour courber la bande 18590
  18590
— tendeur 9621
— tubulaire pour fabriques
  de papier 19081
rouleaux d'alésoir non
  parallèles à l'axe de
  l'outil 1244
— de convoyeur 4320
roulement 15121
— à aiguilles 12206
rouleur 2527, 2573, 5740,
  5789, 7953, 8894, 8896,
  9490, 10172, 15369,
  15373, 18818
rouille 14544, 15391
rouiller S. 10320, 15390
rouilleuse 3811, 16081
rouillure 12287, 16021
roulisse S. 1391, 4629,
  4860
— conique S. 19659
roussier 12335
route en acier amovible
  12051
routivarite 15298
rouverain 16175
rouvillite 15299
ruban à racloirs 15675
— de transport incliné S.
  9695
rubané 1180
rubanement 1185
rubellite 15325
rubicelle 15326, 20232
rubidium 15327
rubis 15329
— balais 1141
— oriental 12664
— spinelle 15331
rudesse de la surface 18065
rugosité 15266
ruisseler 10041
rumpfite 15336
rupture S. 2307, 2333
— à traction 18408
— au bleu 1900
— de boisage 14887
— de chaîne 7698
— de cylindre 7700
— fragile 2422
rustine 1077
ruthénium 15399
rutherfordine 15400

rutile 15401
— aciculaire 11217

S

sablage 3692, 15477
sable 8395, 15469
— à arêtes vives 16005
— à grain moyen 11433
— à grains pointus 590
— à gros grain 8774
— à huile 12506
— à la chamotte 3280
— à noyaux 4440
— à souder 19951
— absorbant 17949, 18519
— argileux 3668
— au ciment 3154
— aurifère 8478
— brûlé 2596, 2614
— ciment 3154
— coulant 9024
— de carrière 14259
— de contact 6758
— de dune 6108
— d'étuve 15497
— de fonderie 7642
— de lac 10494
— de laitier 16553
— de mer 15782,
— de moulage 6758, 6760,
  7178, 7642, 12027
— de moulage à gros grain
  7026
— de moulage adhérent 148
— de nettoyage 15524
— de ponce 14153
— de ravine S. 14967
— de remplissage 1088
— de rivière 14967
— de séparation 12943
— de travail 20253
— déjà employé 19411
— dolomitique 5614
— drainé 5191
— étuvé 6039
— ferrugineux 6968
— fin 7088
— flottant 5863
— fort 17878
— frais 19341
— gazifère 8050
— granitique 8418
— gras 10933, 17878

sable gros 8575
— imbibé S. 9663
— imprégné 9663
— incrusté 2596
— magnétique 11202
— maigre 10644, 19851
— naturel 12196
— net 12243
— neuf 3676, 7757, 12258
— noir 16002
— normal 17348
— payant 13001
— peu perméable 18618
— poreux 12591
— quartzeux 14274
— régénéré 14505
— synthétique 18171
— unique 19312
— vieux 12523
sabler 15466
sablerie 15513
— automatique 988
— continue 4274
sableuse 1737, 15522
— à air comprimé 4137
— à turbine 19122
sableux 8535
sabot 2106, 9993, 16150,
  16152
— à soupape 7388
— de battage 17223
— de bocard 1405, 8017,
  17534
— de cuvelage 2957
— de fonçage 5957
— de fonçage avec denture
  en saillie 15898
— de fraisage 11712
— de guidage 8654
— de la came 2767
— de spudding 17223
— de tubage 19961
— denté de rotary 15218
— du carottier 5882
— du tube porte-carotte
  4453
— du tuyau de lavage 19714
— pour tube de lavage 15226
sac à poudre 6126
— à poussière S. 6128, 6136
— en caoutchouc pour gaz
  7979
sagénite 15427
sagvandite 15430
sahalite S. 15432
Sahélien 15431

saillie 2124, 2647, 10262
saignée 1204, 3285, 4899,
  10321
sain 6866
saisir avec la tenaille 15804
— la barre 8564
saisissement dans l'eau
  13573
salaire au rendement 18332
salbande 907, 3657, 3662,
  15435, 15835, 19490,
  19633
— argileuse 14117
salfemique 15437,
salite 15432, 15438
salle d'analyse 20253
— de combustion 4082
— de pesée 1133
— de préparation des
  échantillons 13856
— des dynamos 6154
— des prises d'échantillon
  15151
— des recherches métallo-
  graphiques 15150
salmiac 15439
salmonsite 15440
Salopien 15441
salpêtre 13730, 15447
— de Chili S. 12308
samarskite 15450
samarium 15449
samirésite 15451
samsonite 15465
sanguine 1816, 12448
sanidine 8287, 14863, 15535
sanidinite 15536
Sannoisien 15537
sans affleuremet S. 1765
— boisage 19336
— criques 7725
— refoulement 12366
— soudure 15751
— tension 7729
santé d'une pièce 16941
santerinite 15538
sanukite 15539
saphir 15541
— astérique 904
saponite 13325, 15540
saprocolle 16639
sapropélite 15542
sarcolite 15543
sarcopside 15544
sardoine 15545, 15546
sardonyx S. 15525

särkinite 15547
särnaïte 15543
sartorite 15549
sas à air 325
— d'aérage 325
sassage 10180
sassolite 15551
saumon 9783, 13249
— de coke 3933
— de fer 9992
— de plomb 13266
saumure 2407
saupoudrer de poussier de
    charbon 6736
saussurite 15552
saussuritisation 15553
sautage 1705
— par chambres 3270, 8366
sauturelle 1570, 11844
savon 16798
Saxonien 15564
scalénoèdre 15594
scandium 15602
scapolite 15603
scawtite 15611
scellement 15704
schafarzikite 15612
schairerite 15613
schalenblende 15614
schallerite 15615
schalstein 15616
schapbachite 15617
scheelite 15618, 16043
scheerérite 15619
schefférite 15620
scheidage 2505, 16966
scheider 10934
scheideur S. 13210
schertelite 15621
schillérisation 1006, 15624
schillerspath 15623
schirmérite 15625
schisolite 15626
schiste 2040
— à disthène 4932
— à hornblende 9370
— alumineux 441
— argileux 780, 6111,
    8461, 12095, 15976
— argileux bleu 1907
— argileux gris 8501
— argileux tendre 1676
— bitumineux 1594, 12509,
    14862
— bitumineux compact
    1325

schiste carton 12903
— charbonneux 1666
— dur 14459
— gazifère 8051
— gonflant 9025
— houiller 1645, 1666,
    2028, 4994, 14444
— primaire 7816
— siliceux 7383
— tacheté 7358, 17167
— talqueux S. 18222
— tendre 2927
schistification 15020, 15979,
schistosité 7534, 3718
— confuse 1775
— de pression 7423
— de stratification 10509
— plan-parallèle 13458,
schlamme de houille 16775
schlich 4163
schlieren 17766
schneebergite 15627
schoepite 15628
schorl 10162
schorlomite 15629
schreibersite 15620
schultenite 15631
schungite 16266
schwartzembergite 15634
schwatzite 15635
scie à charbon 2841
— à chaud 9438
— à froid 3999
— à métaux à grande vites-
    se 9174
— alternative 1178, 7760
— circulaire 3597
scléromètre 15636
scolécite 15637
scorie 6007, 14870, 15726,
    16431, 16347
— basique S. 13167
— Bessemer 1555
— congénitale 6461
— d'affinage 14604
— de bas-foyer S. 3084
— de canal 17173
— de coulée 18312
— de déphosphoration 13167
    13167
— de fer 3727
— de feu d'affinerie 14612
— de forge 7597
— de fourneau 7857
— de puddlage 2564, 7414,
    14097, 18266

scorie de réchauffage 14670
— de ressuage 10870
— douce 14871
— entraînée 16555
— épaisse S. 17585
— finale 7139
— interposée 6442
— pâteuse 17885
— pauvre en fer 16547
— pauvre en phosphore
    16548
— réductrice 14577
— riche 14871
— riche en fer 16551
— riche en phosphore 16552
— Thomas S. 13167, 18537
scorifiant 16535
scorification 16567
— d'enduit 16568
— de phosphore 16570
— de sable 16569
scorifier 16517
scories basiques 1305
scorodite 15647
scraper 5736, S. 15666
scrubber 8063, S. 15721
seau S. 10334
— à pierres 2487
sec 2420
— comme la poudre 13767
séchage 6052
— de l'air 6066
— des moules 6060
séché à l'air 272
— dans le séchoir 5847
sécher 6023
— sur place 6024
sécheur 6051
— à vide 19428
— refroidisseur 4330
séchoir 5232, S. 6059,
    6693
— à moules 11978
Secondaire 15766
secouer 10124
secousse 10225
— consécutive 203
secteur de suspension 9379
section 4704
— carrée 12242
— d'attaque 8091
— de base 16042
— de la buse 12416
— de rupture 7695
— finale 7069
— initiale 7201

section obtenue par cisaillement 16029
— transversale 1941
sédiment 5831
— v. dépôt
sédiments S. 15792
— des mers profondes S. 5096
— terrigènes S. 18434
seebachite 15705
segment du piston 13392
— fouloir S. 18734
ségrégation de fer 10010
— de graphite S. 15873
— majeure 11156
— mineure 11653
sel de Glauber 8288
— gemme S. 8720 15026
— métallique 11571
sélénite 4801, 15809
— fibreuse 15555
sélénium 15810
séligmannite 15833
sellaite 15834
selle 3251, S. 19353
— à crochet 9318
— aérienne 190
— avant de boîte à feu 15410
— de mur 19654
— inverse 9935
sels alcalins 360
semelle 10013, 16335, 16587, 16871, 18740
— avec le dispositif à tourner en cône 7023
— continue en béton avec parties armées 4263
— de base 8620
— de boisage 7540
semences 16156
semi-centrifugation 15838
semicoke 3865
semi-portique 15844
semi-remorque 15849
semséyte 15852
sénaite 15853
senarmontite 15854
sens du laminage 15124
— du mouvement 5467
sensibilité 10248, 15858
— à la température 15859
— à l'entaille 12400
— à l'épaisseur 15760
sensible 15856
séparateur 5508, 15878

séparateur à aimant permanent 15881
— à air comprimé S. 321
— avec agitateur 15863
— calibré 11610
— de boues 16631
— d'eau 17450
— de gaz 8054
— de mesure S. 11610
— de pétrole S. 12514
— de poussières 6132
— magnétique 11203
— pneumatique 321, 13597
séparateur v. trieur
séparation 1758, 12947, 15868
— de carbone 15871
— de graphite 10377
— des éléments de la charge 15876
— des poussières 14720, 15877
— du laitier 15875
— du pétrole par le coagulum des résidus de raffinerie 19753
— électrolitique 6348
— électrostatique 6368
— en feuilles 16064
— par centrifugation 3209
— par gravité 8492
— par liquides denses 9033
— prismatique 13964
— sphéroidale 17069
— structurale 13812
séparation v. triage
séparer 3641, 16923, 20081
sépiolite 11439, 15882
septaria 15883, 19156
septum 15884
Sequanien 15886
sérandite 15888
séricite 15891
séricitique 15892
séricitisation 15893
série 15903
— atlantique 919
— carbonifère 2861
— de pièces de fonte 15907
— de tamis 15911
— de trous de mine 15268
serpentin de chauffage 9010
— pour l'absorption 17
— (à) réchauffeur tournant 6616

serpentin réfrigérant 14483
— refroidisseur 4186
— surchauffeur 18012
serpentine 15895
serpentins tubulaires pour installations de chauffage à panneaux à rayonnement 19065
serrage 14403
— à la main 8779
— au pied 18820
— de couplage à vis 17362
— des cannelures S. 14576
— du moule 14407
— par pression 17262
— par projection 9654
— par secousses 10221
— par vibration 19550
— pneumatique 13594
serre 5137
— câble 20145
— fil 18427
serré à la main 8798
serrement S. 2550, 4966, 11726, 17363
serrer 16241
— par la clé suspendue 18713
serveuses de part et d'autre de la machine 8656
service 939
— d'essais 18463
servo-moteur 18604
sesquioxyde de manganèse 11281
seuil dans le bassin de coulée 4965
— de cirque 15030
— de porte 5632
seybertite 15929
shastaite 16009
shastalite 16010
shattuckite 16016
shérardisation 16117
shonkinite 16158
shoshonite 16190
sial 16247
sialma 16248
sibérite 16249
sicklérite 16250
sidérolite 16284
sidéronatrite 16285
sidérophyllite 16286
sidérose 2850, S. 16994
sidérurgie 16287

siège d'extraction 15905
— de soupape 19454
— du sabot S. 16209
silex 7377, 16910
— corné 9374
silicate d'alumine 16315
— d'alumine hydraté 9510
— de zinc 20334
silice 16311
— combinée 4065
— gélatineuse 8148
siliceux 16316
silicifier 16322
silicium 16323, 16325
silico-calcium 2727
silicose 16331
silicotel 16332
sill 16387
sillimanite S. 6985, 16343
sillons antidérapants 14353
silo 2579
Silurien 16348
silvanyte 18146
simétite 16364
similor 16365
sinopite 16327
sinter 16430
siphon du pétrole 12514
sipylite 16439
sismique à réflexion 14620
— à réfraction 14623
sitaparite 16441
skarn 15606
skip 8671, 16480
— à déversement automati-
   que 15820
— à fond ouvrant 5978
— basculant 12784
sklodowskite 16486
skogbölite 16487
skutterudite 16490
slavikite 16579
slimage 16637
slimage général S. 367
sluice 16708, 16709
smaltine 16741
smaragdite 16743
smectite 16744
smithite 16755
smithsonite 2699, 7922,
   16756, 20337
socle S. 2143, 16868
— continental 4257
sodalite 16814
soddyite 16815
sodium (carbonate de-) 2854

sodium 16817
soggendalite 16852
sol 7547, 11070, 11110,
   18701
— actif 728
— arable 728
— argileux S. 8665
— calcaire 13037
— de la fonderie 7406
— de loessien 10962
— inerte 17932
— limoneux 10962
— marécageux 11344
— qui gonfle 9023
— rocheux 15045
— siliceux 7382
— tourbeux 1951
— vierge 12259
sol v. terrain
sole 2145, 16869, 16870
— à courant d'eau 19760
— à réchauffer 7559
— acide 78
— de four 10449, 7827
— de four de fusion 8951
— de foyer 16872
— de frotteur 12890
— doseuse 15202
— du creuset 8959
— en scories 16538
— oscillante 14493
solide 16934
— de révolution 1939
solidification 7742, 16891
— blanche 3422
— dirigée 5470
solidus 16894
solive 16335
solives-hourdis en tôles
   pliées en U 12375
sollicitation 17782
— aux chocs thermiques
   18380
— de cisaillement 16036
— de fatigue 6835
— de forgeage 7581
sols rayés S. 16895
solubilité 16899
— complète 13079
— limitée 10825
soluble 16896
solution claire 3708
— cristallisée 16886
— de chlorure de calcium
   16904
— d'indigo 9740

solution de potasse caustique 3115
— de résine dans la téré-
   benthine 16905
— de savon 16801
— de soude caustique 3117
— équimoléculaire 6530
— équivalente 6534
— filtrée claire 3707
— normale 17351
— solide 16886
— solidifiée 4205
— trouble 19116
solutions isohydriques
   10061
solvatation 16907
solvsbergite 16913
sommaite 16914
sommet S. 681, 4724
— de la sole 18744
sommier 17199
— de presse 13868
sondage 2076, 2080, 2090,
   2095
— à gaz 8065, 8082
— à grenaille 2763
— à jet 10157
— à injection 19776
— à l'avancement 14044
— à la corde 511, 2665,
   3561, 6801, 15159
— à la grenaille 3436
— à sec 6027
— au câble S. 15159
— au diamant 5325
— d'essai 18880
— d'exploration 17896, 1845
   18459
— d'injection 9829, 9859
— de pétrole 19967
— de plusieurs puits di-
   rectionnés 10051
— de puits 19963
— de recherche 14058,
   18443
— dirigé 2532, 5468
— double 6070
— éruptif 20072
— négatif S. 6140
— non tubé 12582
— par battage rapide 2100,
   10247
— par percussion 8733
— percutant S. 3561
— positif 13651
— rotary 15195

sondage rotatif 2101
— silicieux 16942
— stérile 1246, 6140
— submarine 12471
— tordu 4657
sondage v. forage
sondages jumeaux 19171
sonde 3654, 8608, 13969, 18517
— de mouleur 11996
— de prise d'échantillons 15459, 18254
— éruptive 7444
— submarine 12472
sonde v. tarrière
sonder 2073, 13968, 16932
— au préalable 14439
— le terrain 16935, 16936
— le toit 10394, 14416
— le toit en le frappant 10237 10237
sonder v. forer
sondeur 2091, 5895, 5906
— à câble 15157
sondeuse 6168
— à grenaille 122, 5737
sopement 1320
sorbite 16920
sordawalite 16922
sorte 16924
— de fer 14246
sortie de l'air 274
— de liquide d'une conduite par cassure 19712
— du laminoir 12701
sortir S. 8203, 14124
soubassement 1433, 17934
— cristallin 4792
— en béton 4174
— granitique 8419
souchevé S. 9254
soucoupe en caoutchouc durci 6184
soudabilité 19930,
soudable 19928
soudage 19936
— direct 19938
— en biseau 15605
soudage v. soudure
soude caustique 3116
— à l'arc 7303
soudé à l'autogène 972
— électriquement 6315
— par étincelage S. 7303
— par points 17162
— tendre 16842

souder 16857, 19923
— à froid 4007
— à l'étain 16839
— en biseau 10539
— fort 2288
— la fonte 11488
— par rapprochement S. 2636 2636
soudeur 10211, 16859, 19934
soudeuse à induction à haute fréquence 9146
— par points 17163
soudoir S. 16862
soudure 19935
— à chaud suant 7582
— à cordon 1367
— à double point 19174
— à gaz à droite 14907
— à gaz à gauche 10665
— à gaz en arrière 1060
— à l'aluminium 464
— à l'arc 752
— à l'arc à deux électrodes de charbon 19169
— à l'arc par électrode nue 1227
— à l'argent 16360
— à la thermite 18492
— à l'étain 16843, 16841
— à poussée 14204
— arcatomique 753
— au bismuth 1617
— au chalumeau 16866
— au fer à souder 16867
— au laiton 2276
— autogène par fusion 969
— autogène par pression S. 970
— continue 4278, 15749
— continue à recouvrement 10541
— continue circulaire 3598
— continue en série 15894
— continue parallèle 12922
— continue par points 12119
— de cuivre 8841
— de fils à croix 4708
— de laiton 17047
— de renforcement 1083
— de tube 19043
— électrique 6314
— électrique par pointes 6321
— électrostatique par percussion 6367

soudure en about 2643
— en angle 7032
— en arrière 1076
— en biseau-S. 10542
— en bout 6453
— en T 18353
— en tube avec décapant intérieur 14763
— flashing 7305
— fondante S. 16840
— forte 2289, S. 2290, S. 2292, 8840
— oxyacétylénique 67,968, 12813
— oxydrique 12816
— par baguettes de chlorure de de polyvinyle 19958
— par encollage S. 2643
— par fusion 7894
— par l'hydrogène atomique 931
— par martelage 8745, 9366
— par points 10208, 17161, 17164, 18195
— par pression 970
— par rapprochement S. 2643
— par recouvrement 10542. 12766
— par induction 9756
— par résistance 14778
— par résistance électrique 6297
— parallèle à points 12923
— plastique continue 11354
— progressive par compression 13924
— tendre S. 1843, 16840
soudure v. soudage
souesite 16929
soufflage 244, 1851, 1869, 1870, S. 9019
— à pleine pression 1879
soufflant 13541
soufflante 1864, 1875
— de haut fourneau 1707
— v. soufflerie
soufflard 13375
souffler 1839, 1847
— au vent chaud 1844
— le vent 1842
— un noyau 1841
— une partie de moule S. 1841
soufflerie 243, 1865
— à caisse 2213

soufflerie à cylindres 4944
— à gaz 7982
— à haute pression à co-
  quilles S. 11349
— à pédale 7539
— à piston rotatif S. 15193
— à vapeur 17419
— avec moteur électrique
  1867
— Bibus S. 15193
— de précision 13819
— Encke 6440
— hélicoïdale à haute
  pression 9169
— hydraulique 9514
— Lehmann S. 2925
— Martin 11349
— Root 15155
— rotative 15193
— verticale 19519
— à vapeur 17438
soufflet 8755
— de forge 1466
— en cuir 10648
soufflette 283
soufflure 307, 1754, 1781,
  1852, 1868, 7360, 17138
soufflures 13303
— bleutées 14468
— brillantes 19324
— contenant matières
  charbonneuses 1673
— de scorie 16526
— périphériques 13093
soufre 17981
souillure par des substances
  chimiques 3390
soulèvement 19359
— de moule 10760
— de sable 5974
soulever 2304,
— et baisser alternative-
  ment 14492
— la barre 10738
soumansite 16931
soupape S. 1101, 19446
— à air S. 14688
— à double siège 5676
— à piston 18863
— à trois sièges 18571
— à vent 1734
— d'admission 172
— d'aspiration S. 17361,
  17961
— de contre pression 1072

soupape de décharge 1756,
  1857
— d'échappement 6505
— d'échappement d'air
  318
— de mise en marche 10342
— de refoulement 13923
— de respiration 2351
— de sûreté 12291, 15425,
  1886
— de tirage 5723
soupape v. valve
soupirail S., 10786
— à vent 12145
source de boue bouillonnan-
  te 12863
— d'électricité 16946
— de gravitation 8494
— de lumière extérieure
  6697
— de pétrole S. 12515
sourcière S. 4060, 7221,
  16659
— à clapet 12039
— à tiges 12777
sous-cavage 4913, 4917,
  8205, 10375, 19243
sous-caver 1791, 10111,
  10320, 10374, 16685,
  16790
sous-charriage S. 19282
sous-étage emschérien 6423
sous moteur 6090
sous-oeuvre 8623
soute 3801
— à charbon 3835, 3845
— à minerai 12631
soutènement 18033
— du puits 13398
— d'une galerie 6497
— en acier 17515
— métallique S. 17503
— par piles de bois 13274
spadaïte 16959
spangolite 16973
spath 16975
— calcaire 2718, 2728
— d'Islande 9613
— pesant S. 17968
spatule 8947, 16998, 18944
— de dégagement 17219
— en platine 13527
spécification normale 17352
spectre continu 19307
spectres de déplacement 5533

spectrographie 17033
spectroscope 17034
spéculaire 17037
speiss 17044
spencérite 17049
sperrylite 17050
spessartine 11267, 17051
sphalérite 1761, 17053
sphénoèdre 17055
sphère 17057
sphérique 17059
sphérocobaltite 17052
sphéroïdisation 5587, 17070
sphérolitique 17073
sphérosidérite 17074
sphérule 17064
spilite 17085
spilitique 17086
spinelle 17094
— de chrome 3536
spitz-lutte 9518
spitzlutte 17108
spodiophyllite 17139
spodumène 17140
spongieux 13672
sporogélite 17154
spurrite 17229
squelette 16418
stabilisant 14655
stabilisation 17271
— locale 10937
staffélite 17282
stainiérite 17295
stalactite 5997
stalagmite 5997, 17298
stannate 17365
stannifère 13139, 17368
stannine 18652
stannique 17366
stannite 17369
stassfurthite 17390
statimètre 18599
station centrale de pompage
  3191
— de relais 2053
— primaire 13944
staurolite 17402
steadite 17411
stéatite 16802, 17452
stéphanite 1665, 2426,
  17555
stercorite 17565
stérile 5024, 12103, 12105,
  12359, 17141, 19735,
  19737

stériles S. 940
sternbergite 17567
stewartite 17569
stibiconite 17572
stibine 668, 17577
stiblite 17576
stibnite 668, 8497
stibiopalladinite 17573
stibiotantalite 17574
stichtite 17578
stilbite S. 5242, 17591
stilpnochloran 17599
stilpnomélane 17600
stimulation 17601
stock 17612
stockage 17689,
— du pétrole 18257
— souterrain 19263
stocker 10298
stockwerk 17627
stolpénite 17638
stolzite 17639
stossbau 4900
stot 17911
stratamètre 5442
strate 10594
strates 17746
stratification 1430, 16038
— concordante 15793
— croisée 4672, S. 5867
— de charbon 6748
— diagonale S. 12433
— discordante 10038
— entrecroisée 4698, 4707, 5867, 6779
— lenticulaire 10679
— primaire 12667
— puissante 9040
— torrentielle 4867
stratifié 1423, 10504, 16086
stratigraphe 17748
stratigraphie 17752
strengite 17774
striage 15685
strie 17799
— de laminage 8651
— de la plaquette polie 8547
— de polissage 8210
— d'usinage 8552
— glaciaire 8256
strié 17800
strier 15642
stries 17802
— de polissage 13631
strieux 17763, 17767

stripper 9802
stromeyérite 17876
strontiane 17880
strontianite 17881
strontium 17882
structure 4173, 12974, 18473
— à amygdales 544
— à coeur 4451
— à eozoon 6502
— à grain hétérogène 15890
— à noyaux 544
— à oeil de boeuf 2559
— allotriomorphe 390
— arborescente 740
— bétonnée S. 12134
— botryoïde 2130
— bulleuse 19540
— cataclastique 4767, 13921
— clastique 7708
— crêtée 4051
— cristalline 4804
— de bande 1186
— de coulée 3026
— de la cassure 7703
— de support en acier pour murs-rideaux 17476
— des alliages 402
— des minerais de fer 17893
— des roches écrasées 17765 17765
— diapirique 5340
— divergente 5581
— drusique 6021
— écailleuse 15663
— en acier 17520
— en bandes 1187
— en bilboquet 4834
— en chapelet 1371
— en cocarde 15185
— en colonnes prismatiques juxtaposées S. 4048
— en damier 3411
— dôme 5619
— en étoilement S. 17531
— en éventail 6805
— en gerbes 16017
— en grille S. 10581
— en mortier 12134
— en mosaïque 11940
— en plaquettes 1199
— en tamis 16301
— en tuile 15147
— eutectique 6604
— fenestrée S. 8476
— feuilletée 7531

structure fibreuse 6993
— filamenteuse 13141
— filandreuse S. 13141
— finement lamellaire 16598 16598
— fluidale 13906
— glanduleuse S. 13141
— globulaire 8304
— gloméro-blastique 8306
— gneissique 8320
— granitique 8420
— granitoïde S. 8420
— granophyrique 8428
— granulaire 8403
— granuleuse 4756
— granulitique 8442
— homoéoblastique 9297
— intime 9906
— kélyphitique 12447
— macroméritique 11152
— maillée 11519, 12248
— massive 11359
— métallique 11544
— microgranitique S. 8428, 11636
— micrographique 11639
— micropoecilitique 11649
— mi-idiomorphe 9584
— moléculaire 11873
— mouchetée 11957
— oeillée 6732
— ondulée 15173
— oolithique 12552
— orbiculaire 1164, 12620
— pegmatoïde 8446
— pélithique 13053
— perhyaline 13086
— périclinale 13008, 14255
— pétrosiliceuse 11629, 11635
— plissée 1947
— poreuse 9130, 13678
— prismatique 4048
— profonde 2593
— psammitique 769
— pséphitique 14065
— ptygmatique 14089
— quaquaversale S. 14255
— radiée 14338, 17531
— résistante 18800
— réticulée S. 12248
— rubanée 14869
— saccaroïde 15332
— stratifiée 1427
— strieuse 17768
— stylolitique 17915

structure tachetée 11158
— taxitique 18340
— treillisée 8476
— ultravitreuse 13086
— vitrophyrique 19583
— zonale 20361
— *v. texture
struvérite 17900
struvite 17901
stylolithe 17914
styrienne 15701
sublimation 17924
substance explosive S. 6684
— neutre 12253
— nuisible 5266
— odorante 12458
— riche en oxyde de fer 11372
— secondaire 15765
substitution 11600
substratum 2142, 16868
succinite 17937
suceuse 17955
suite des couches 1421
— normale S. 12382
sulfate d'ammonium 529
— de baryte 17968
— de chaux 17969
— de cuivre 17970
— de fer ammoniacal 6964
— de magnésie 17971
— de potasse 17972
— de soude 17973
— de zinc 17974
— ferreux 6966
— ferrique 6929
sulfite de sodium 16825
sulfoarsénure de fer S. 829
sulfoborite 17978
sulfocyanure d'ammonium 17979
sulfohalite 17980
sulfonate 17964
sulfuration 17966
sulfure d'ammonium 530
— d'antimoine 17976
— de fer 6951, 10022
— de mercure 11501
— de plomb S. 7912, S. 10614
sulfutage 17966
sulvanite 17990
supercarburant 13852
superficie S. 18040
superposé 18016
superposition normale 12382

support 2237, 17332, 18878
— à air comprimé 296
— à anneau 1087
— a introduire dans le bain-marie 18457
— de ballon 7314
— de cornue 14800
— d'électrodes 6327
— de filtre 7053, 7822
— de la plate-forme du gueulard 13507
— de la trémie 9329, 18030
— de la trousse 796
— de levier de battage 15464
— de microscope d'après Martens 11345
— de noyau 3295
— de noyau à double tôle 5664
— de noyau à tige 17536
— de noyau de forme 4280
— de «packer» 10845
— de suspension pour tuyaux 2944
— de tubage à coins 2959
— des paliers du convertisseur 4307
— du balancier 1398
— du massif 11302
— du cadre 17409
— en porcelaine du dessicateur 5233
— mal soudé 19297
— mural tubulaire 19093
— pour panneaux indicateurs 16736
— pour tuyaux 13349
supports de la chaudière 2247
sur chenilles 4612
surcarburé S. 10280
surcharger 11486
surchauffe 18005, 18011
— de la fonte 12760
surchauffeur 18007
— à vapeur 17449
surcreusement 12738
surcroît de chaleur S. 9724
surcuisson 5036
surélévation téléscopique 18361
surépaisseur d'alimentation 12858
— d'usinage 11140
— pour l'usinage 394

surépaisseur prevu sur le modèle 11998
surface 8464, 18040
— anguleuse 6208
— arrondie par frottement 15280
— bombée 4884
— cémentée 2916
— de base 1288
— de charriage 12781, 16608
— de contact 12853
— de contre-pression 765
— de drainage 5744
— de glissement 16603, 16662, 16664
— de grille 8466
— de grille totale S. 18788
— de la cassure 7695
— de la charge 17622
— de la sole 8966
— de refroidissement 4343
— de révolution 15194
— de séparation 5586, 9879
— de solubilité 18058
— dégagée S. 7722
— drainée 5190
— gondolée 4503
— libre 7722
— plane 9347
— polie 13630
— polie propre 3677
— totale de la grille 18788
surfusion 18001
sur le carreau de la mine 914 914
surmoulage 12005
surmoule 11301
surmouler 11961
surperchage 12772
surperché 12773
surpoids 6644
surpresseur 2051
surpression 12774
sursaturation 18021
sursaturer 18018
sursoufflage 199, 12734
surveillance 939, 18024
surveillant 7567
suspendre la marche 4976
— momentanément la marche S. 4976
suspension 8804
— à compensation S. 4109
— compensée 4109
syénite à néphéline 12231

syénite éléolitique 6373
— gneissique 8321
sylvester S. 18147
sylvine 18148
symbole chimique 3393
symplectite 18153
symplesite 18154
synadelphite 18155
synclinorium 18162
synérèse 18163
syngénèse 18164
syngénite 18165
syngonie 18166
syntexis 18167
syphon 18172
système à chutes 15663
— à deux fils 19194
— anglais par deux convertisseurs 6483
— anorthique S. 18891
— anthracolithique 648
— asservi 4416
— binaire 11908
— clinoédrique S. 18891
— conjugué 18178
— crétacé 4626
— cristallin 18179
— cubique 10068
— d'alimentation 8104
— de contrôle 10140
— d'exploitation avec remblayage 7039
— d'exploitation par pan-
neaux 12898
— d'exploitation v. exploitation
— de fermeture du gueulard
américain 512
— de lentilles 18180
— doublement oblique S.
18891
— hexagonal 9122
— oligocène 12531
— orthorhombique 13965
— quadratique S. 18469
— quaternaire 18469
— régulier S. 10068
— rotary 15220
— sénaire S. 9122
— tertiaire 12684
— triassique 18888
— triclynique 18891
— Wetzel 6616
svabite 18084
svanbergite 18085
szaibélyite 18182

szmikite 18183
szomolnokite 18184

T

table 18187
— à secousses 2576, 4165,
15974
— à toile 1693
— d'amalgamation 497
— de coulée 11479
— de dessablage 3697
— d'épuration S. 19710
— d'épuration pneumatique
13599
— de laboratoire 10450
— de lavage 19710
— de poids 19908
— de rotary 15221
— de soufflage 1890
— de triage tournante 14839
— dormante 16589
— du cylindre 1940
— normale 17349
— pour les essais électro-
chimiques 6323
— ronde 15274
— rotative 19151
— tournante à levée 16393
tableau chromologique 8173
— de distribution 18133
— de mise à feu 16986
— des poids atomiques 1819
18190
tables de laminoir 15115
tablier à rouleaux 10775
tabulaire 18194
tache d'argile 3661
taches de diffraction 5401
tacheté 17031, 17166
tachylyte 18198
taillant à vis 5250
— amovible 10092
— de fleuret 10862
— double 5643
— en couronne 16442, 20260
— en croix 4673, 15177, S.
20260
— en Z 20314
— fleuret 1622
taille S. 1919, 2342, 6738
— à mi-pente 14909, 14911
— boisée 18031
— boisée non remblayée 12596

taille chassante 12715
— d'abattage 17677
— de la pierre 12289
— de pierres 1928
— en cul-de-sac 334
— en échelon 7321
— en échelon avec rem-
blayage 9337
— en échelon remblayée
7018
— étayée 17908
— montante 14373
— montante en échelon
7319
— montante en échelon à
boisage parallélépipédi-
que 7320
— remblayée 3776, 7020
— remblayée par matériel du
chantier même 4901
— unique 16405
taille v. creusage
taillé 5837
tailler la pierre 15570, 15572,
16964
— suivant étalon 4896
— un filet 15698
taimyrite 18216
talcage 6141
talcschiste 18222
tallingite 18223
taloche circulaire 3599
talon d'éjection 6237
— de lavage 12744
talquer 6123
talus 1344, 16678, 19287
— continental 4259
— naturel 12197
tamanite 18226
tamaräite 18227
tambour à amalgamer 481
— à câble 2662
— à jet de sable 15521
— à l'extrémité de l'axe
d'un treuil 12292
— à nettoyer la fonte 1345
— cannelé 8590
— d'amalgamation S. 492
— d'enroulement 15162
— d'extraction 9226, 15168
— de forage 2571
— de nettoyage 3703
— de sablage 15479
— de tamisage 15695
— de treuil 9226
— dessableur 14446

tambour du câble 20102
— filtrant 7046
— horizontal 9341
— laveur 14936
— laveur rotatif 14845
— magnétique 11191
— sécheur 6058
tamis 16298, 17736
— à filtrer 7823
— à larges mailles 3876
— à mailles 11518, 11561
— à secousse 15972
— à vibration magnétique 9482
— à vibrations 9646
— d'égouttage 5294, 5749
— fin 7089
— grossier 20058
— hydraulique à étage mobile 8751
— oscillant 12686
— rotatif 15216
— vibrant 19548
— vibreur 9646
tamisage 16905
— à sec 6046
tamiser 16296
tampon 1934, 13559, 17684
— avec les électrodes dans le microlog 15311
— d'avance 2180
— de choc 2516, 9265
— de coulée 2134
— de quenouille 17680
— élastique 17192
— guide du sabot 16154
tamponnage 7035
tamponner 7009, 7010, S. 13557
tan 18236
tangéite 18237
tantale 18260
tantalite 18259
tapalpite 18271
tapure 3363, 4580
— à froid 3971, 3429, 4334
— de trempe 14285
taque à dresser en fonte 17726
— de varme 19164
taquet 2764
— de cage 16242
— pour fils S. 20120
taquets 10299, 10525, 6813
— de calage pour berline dans la cage 3092

tarapacaite 18325
taraud 8783, 15712
— aléseur de repêchage 18288
— de repêchage 5372, 7223
— mâle de repêchage 11242
— pour tiges de pompage 17940
— rattrape-tube 16999
taraudage 18299
tarabuttite 18236
tare 18323
tarer 18322
tarière 946, 8608, 13969, 18876
— à argile 3670
— à boues 12073
— à caisson 2210
— à couronne 588
— à cuiller 16096
— à large spire 6167
— à main 8754
— à rincer 7489
— à sac 15404
— à soupape 15821, 19447
— à tranchant 3486
— à vis cylindrique 17097
— en croix 4661
— en entonnoir 18292
tarif spécial 17022
tarnowitzite 18329
tarrière à glaise S. 946
— v. sonde
tartre 15568
tas 1147, 13278
— à charger 12061
— de charbon 3817
— de minerai 6905
— de minerai à griller 14984, 3620
tassage 17322
tasmanite 18333
tassement 2536, 4104, 5708, S. 15914, 16417
— du remblai 16229
tasser (se-) 2530
tasser 13277
— les feux S. 4559
tater 6896
tatonner 6896
taurite 18334
taux de craquage 4583
— de pompage 14169
tavistockite 18336
tavolatite 18337
tawite 18338

taxite 18339
taylorite 18341
té à souder 19954
teallite 18343
technétium 18349
technique d'exploitation des gisements 14747
— de fonderie 7675
tectonique 18352
teinture de tournesol 10893
— d'iode 9941
téléclinomètre électromagnétique 6370
téléscopique 4152
tellure 18367
tellurifère 18368
tellurite 18366
tellurure d'or 8350
témoin S. 2644, 6814, 12706
— de congé 9889
— d'ébarbure 7309
temiskamite 18369
tempérament 18378
températeur 8971
température 18379
— au gueulard 18581
— critique 4650
— dangereuse 4992
— dans le haut-fourneau 18383 18383
— d'autoallumage 967
— de brillance 714
— de carbonisation 18386
— de cémentation 2922
— de coulée 3027, 13743
— de couleur 713
— de dissociation 5544
— de distension 14691
— de forgeage 7598
— de grillage 14994
— de la réaction 18388
— de radiation 715,
— de réduction 14578
— de trempe 14293
— du recuit 18398
— extérieure 18068
— intérieure 9907
temps au fond 18639
— d'échauffage 9018
— d'étincillage 7307
— de la limite d'allongement 18641
— de prise 18516
— de résistance 2310
— de rotation S. 18639
— de sondage 14902

temps gachè 10407
ténacité 18403, 18801
tenaille 18719
— à déclic 12303
— à lingots 9792, 9804
— d'attelage 8892
tenailles 12301
tenard 14465
tendeur à chaîne 10909
— tubulaire 19092
tendre 9714
teneur 4251
— du minerai 15384
— en carbone 2829
— en carbone fixe 2840
— en cendres 864, 13075
— en eau par cm^3 d'air
— en fer 4254
— en fines 4252
— en gaz 4253
— en oxyde de carbone 2839
— en schiste 4255
— en silice 5139
— garantie 8639
— molaire 11870
tengérite 18405
tennantite 18406
tenon 13307, 13432
— du trépan 1628
— venu de fonte 3014
ténorite S. 11443, 18407
tenseur 17795
tension 17783
— capillaire 2809
— de coulée 3072
— de décomposition 5071
— de pliage 1520
— de régime 19594
— de torsion 9862
— de traction 9861
— électrolytique de la solution 6350
— interne 9905
— magnétomotrice 11210
— superficielle 18003
téphrite 18421
téphroite 18422
terbium 18423
terlinguaite 18424
terme 18638
termièrite 18425
terminer (se-) en coin 6451, 12320, 18277
— en pointe 18275

terrace d'alluvions S. 409
— fluviale 7396
terrain 10518
— boulant 3123
— boueux 11791
— de recouvrement 2796
— ébouleux S. 3123
— faillé 1803, 6865
— houiller 2858, 3838
— non concédé 19229
— peu sûr 19328
— de recouvrement 8814
terrasse 18431
— alluviale 409
— d'accumulation 409, 5868
— de cours d'eau S. 14968
— fluviale 14968
— littorale 14376
— rocheuse 15032
terrassement 8386
terrassier 6637, 8615
terre 10518, 16168
— à cassettes 15798
— à dégraisser S. 7810
— à diatomées 5345, 11876, S. 16309
— à foulon 7810
— à mouler 12012
— à pipe 7158
— à potier 13470
— alumineuse 439
— arable S. 728
— cuite 18432
— de pipe 13331
— de remblayage 1055
— d'infusoires 8661, 9775
— fusible 7888
— glaise S. 3653, 10924, 13470
— meuble 9467
— noire 1663, 3412, 12063
— plastique S. 13470
— réfractaire 7183
— végétale 11969
terrecuite 1113
terres alcalines 358
terreux 3748
terril 1605, 6096, 6101, 14642
terrilleur 8942
tertiaire 18435
— ancien 6166
teschemachérite 18437
teschénite 18438
tessulaire 4821

test au brouillard salin 15445, 15445
tests sur paramètres de forage 5896
tête 8904
— de carottier 4401, 4911
— de cimentation 3174
— de cimentage 3149
— de cuiller 8016
— d'éruption 3522, 7425
— de faille 6859
— de la cage 18743
— de lingotière 3053
— de marteau 8737, 8905
— de rail 14358
— de rivet 14972
— de sondage 2102
— de tubage 2249, 2794, 2943, 5955
— de tubage avec presse-étoupe 2948
— de tube 19051
— d'injection 3582, 18138, 19817
— d'injection de rotary 15219
— de balancier 12100
— du four 6448
— du lingot 9791
— en fer forgé 20242
— flottante 7390
— perdue 5488
têtes de moineau 3414
tétradymite 1618, 18468
tétraèdre 18472
tétraèdrite 6764
texture 6733, 9866, 18473
— à gros grain 3877
— aplitique 12887
— blastoporphyrique 1752
— bréchoïde 7422
— cataclastique 3082
— crystalloblastica 4815
— de Widmannstätten 20062
— fibreuse 10841
— fibroblastique 6983
— fine 7091
— fluidale 7468
— foliacée S. 16140
— globulaire 8304
— glommérophyrique 4833
— graphique 8446
— grainue S. 8403
— granoblastique 8425, 8444

texture granitoïde 8424
— hyalopilitique 9500
— intercalaire 9866
— intersertale 9914
— lamelleuse 10502
— lépidoblastique 10684
— miarolitique 11619
— microporphyrique 11781
— monzonitique 11925
— mylonitique 12149
— nématoblastique 12217
— ophitique 5603, 12617
— orthophyrique 12681
— panidiomorphe 12889
— pegmatique 8446
— pétrosiliceuse 6909
— pilotaxitique 13301
— poecilitique 13608
— porphiroblastique 13682
— protoclastique 14050
— psammitique 14064
— pséphitique 14067
— schisteuse S. 3718
— sphérolitique 17075
— spongieuse 17145
— symplectique 18152
— trachytique 18808
— variolitique 19475
— v. structure
thalénite 18474
thalium 18475
thaumasite 18476
thénardite 18478
théodolite 18479
— à boussole pour mines
  11744
théorie de glaciation 8262
— de la dissociation 5545
thermocouple S. 18493
thermométrie 18385
thermonatrit 18495
thermophyllite 18496
thermostate 14240
thixotropie 18533
tholéiite 18534
thomsénolite 18541
thomsonite 18542
thorianite 18543
thorite 18544
thorium 18546
thorotungstite 18548
thortveitite 18549
thucholite 18605
thulium 18606
tiemannite 18613

tige 15934, 17533, 17903
— à soulever les châssis S.
  8652
— carrée 8534
— carrée d'entraînement
  10303
— de bocard 5605; 15931
— de bouchon S. 16593
— de butée 14502
— de démouleuse 8652
— d'entraînement 945, 14129
  14129
— de forage 5897
— de jaugeage, bécasse 3320
— de la pompe 13393
— de noyau 4417
— de piston 13579
— de pompage 17938
— de pompe 17000
— de repêchage 16807
— de rivet 15953
— de sondage 2557
— de sonde 2088, 2099,
  15048
— de suspension 1454
— du piston 1455
— du rail 19874
— étanche 13628
— masse 5886
— masse à batir sur chan-
  tier 5887
— octogonale 12450
— pour prise de courant
  19090
— pour sondage à la corde 590
  5909
— rallonge 165
— télescopique 2045
tiges à paratonnerre à troncs
  retrécis 10797
— de pompe 16992
tilaite 18621
tiliasite 18622
tillite 18623
timazite 18633
tincal 18656
tir 1743, S. 16191, 17106
— à la limite de portée de
  l'installation 6716
— au charbon 3802
— auxiliaire 17250
— avec chambre d'expan-
  sion 4888
— des mines 16164
— des mines de la surface
  18067

tir électrique 6259
— latéral 16258
— par pétards 1802, 2566
tirage 265, 5722, 18698
— à la main 8773
— d'air 19810, 19498
— de cheminée 3458
— forcé 7554
— naturel 12190
tirant 4669, 5725, 17794,
  18610
— d'extraction 10758
tire-feu 7771
tire-fond 16588
— à modèle 12990
tirer 1697, 5754, 16160,
  17104
— à l'anglaise 19410
— l'air 19496
— un noyau 4445
— une épreuve 13956
tirette 18280
— d'air 19502
tiroir 5786
— à coquille 12144
tissu 19873
— d'asbeste 843
— métallique 20129
titane 18690
titanite 17054, 18689
titanomagnétite 18694
titre 18696
— d'un liquide 17354
— fictif 6531
titrer 18697
— à nouveau S. 1080
tobernite 18767
toc d'entraînement 2900
toddite 18700
toellite 18705
toile 19873
— d'aérage 2286, 4870, 4979
  4979, 5994
— d'amiante 848
— d'émeri 6412
— de refroidissement 4338
— en fil de cuivre 4369
— en fil de cuivre enroulée 1508
  15082
— métallique 8120, 11545,
  20121, 20136
toise 6898
toit 8808, 8806, 8813,
  12768, 15137, 15144
— de galerie 1067

toit éboulé 16118
— protecteur d'une cage
  d'extraction 2033
— solide non boisé 16875
toitures inclinées avec fermes en acier 16683
tôle 7519, 7345, 16014,
  16068, 18499
— à bord rabattu 7272
— à emboutir 5515
— à réservoirs 18252
— à trous forés 5914
— au charbon de bois 3312
— au coke 3945
— avant la boîte à feu S.
  15410
— bombée 2509
— bossée 12107
— brillante 2399
— brute 14460
— circulaire 3595
— cuivrée 4371
— d'acier 16081, 17492
— d'acier au nickel trempé
  8855
— d'acier nervurée galvanisée 14868
— d'aérage 16091
— d'alclad 351
— d'aluminium 457, 16046
— d'arcasse 18832
— de babo 1040
— de blindage 799
— de chaudière 1974
— de construction 17894
— de coque 16110
— de cuivre 16051
— de doublure 5690
— de duralumin 16053
— d'écoulement de la scorie
  16545
— d'enveloppe 10103, 11304
— de fer plombée S. 18430
— de fourrure 17587
— de foyer 7155, 7851
— de la tympe 19200
— de laiton 2274, 16050
— de magnésium 16067
— de navire 16137
— de plomb 16066
— de première qualité
  13950
— de quille 10297
— de rebut 16060, 16079
— de renfort 17590

tôle de roulis 19691
— de zinc 16085
— décapée 13220, 16068
— découpée 5076
— découpée à la presse S.
  17319
— dressée 17723
— du ciel du foyer 4731
— électron 16054
— émaillée 6436
— emboutie 2509, 17319
— en acier bleu 1911
— en acier doux 11680
— en acier embouti 13884,
  13885
— en acier pressé S. 13884
— en fer 1664
— épaisse S. 18499
— étamée S. 18667
— étampée 18650, 18661
— étirée avec mailles en
  forme de losange 5326
— extra fine 6704
— façonnée 17017
— finie 7121
— forte 9037
— galvanisée 7934
— galvanisée à ondes
  trapézoïdales 7935
— gauffrée 18439, 16063
— gouttière 17837
— inclinée 9705
— laminée 15099
— laminée à chaud 9431
— laminée à froid 3992, 3993
  3993
— latérale 8246, 16270
— léchée par l'eau 13493
— lisse 13445, 13448
— lustrée 13462
— martelée 8747
— mate 11367, 13221
— mince 18526
— mince en acier 18528
— moyenne 11430
— nettoyée 7121, 7122
— nickelée 12279
— noire 1661, 1664
— ondulée 4496, 4498
— ondulée à   triple
  18912
— ondulée cintrée 4879,
  4880
— ondulée de duralumin
  4499

tôle ondulée double 5651
— ondulée galvanisée 7931
— ondulée pour poutres 4500
  4500
— ondulée zinguée S. 7931
— perforée 13082
— plombée 18430
— pour couvertures de plan-
  chers 7407
— pour dynamo 6155
— pour emboutissage 13485
— pour emboutissage pro-
  fond 5085
— pour la construction 178
  17890
— pour les induits des dynamos S. 6155
— pour transformateurs
  18827
— profilée 14003, S. 17017
— protectrice 15686
— rainurée 3369, 3404,
  14891
— recuite 605
— striée 673, 3371, 11517,
  14891
— très mince 18201
— unie 16773
— vernissée S. 6436
— zinguée S. 7934
tôle v. feuille
tôle v. plaque
tolérance 13536, 18709
— de laminage 11695
— dimensionnelle 5423
— en poids 19905
tôlerie 16072
tôles 16057
— de ciel de boîte à feu
  7154
— de l'arcasse 17566
— léchées par l'eau 13503
— varangues 7408
toluène 18710
tombac S. 14531
tomber en poussière S. 5068
  5518
tombereau 2906
tombolo 18711
tonalite 18712
tonne 10334
tonneau à dessabler 19098
— de dessablage S. 19098
topaze 18754
topazolite 18755

torbenite S. 4366
torche à souder 2601
— tubulaire 10790
tordre 19179
tordrillite 18770
tordu 1527, 4656
tore 5691
torendrikite 8771
tornebohmite 8772
toron à fils métalliques 20147
tour *m* 19137, 19145
— à chariot S. 16612
— à charioter 16612
— à commande par vis-mère 10578
— à copier 4377
— à cylindres de laminoir 15080
— à décolleter 4920
— à dégager S. 1086
— à dégrossir 15259
— à dépouiller 1086
— à métaux 11564
— à noyaux 4419
— à pédale 7543
— à plateau horizontal 2098
— à pointes 3197
— à potier 13734
— à reproduire S. 4377
— à revolver 19135
— à rosettes S. 15179
— à tubes et à barres 1209
— à vitesse variable 10579
— automatique 962, 985
— de filetage 1493
— mécanique 6469
— parallèle 3197
— revolver 962, 4062
— vertical 2097
tour *f* azéotropique 1030
— de cuvelage S. 5993
— de détente 7301
— de distillation 5522
— d'égouttage 5746
— d'évaporation 6622
— d'exploitation 8930
— d'extinction 14295
— de fractionnement 2492, 7691
— de fractionnement à deux sorties 17134
— de fractionnement secondaire 201
— de percolation 12840

tour de précipitation 13811
— de rectification 17861, 17874
— de réfrigération 4344
— de sondage 2111
— de sondage à pétrole 12487
tourbe 13023
— bitumineuse S. 1635
— comprimée 13880
— draguée 5824
— émergée 6409
— grasse 1635
— moulée 11984
— terreuse 13028
tourbière 1943, 11944, 13024, 13029
— basse 11053
— de plaine 7326
— de vallée 19443
— immergée 9642
tourbillon 6194
touret S. 18137
tourillon 4608, 12204, 18959
— à pignon 13322
— creux 9280
— de cylindre 15093
— de piston 13391
— tranchable 16023
tourmaline 18804
— à grain fin 1909
— noire 10023
— rouge 14551
tournage des cylindres 15090
— en plaques 9443
tourne-à-gauche 2221
— -gauche 17617
— à gauche pour tarauds et alésoirs 18265
tourné 19140
tourner 19130, 14836
— le lingot 19134
tourniquet 946
tournure 2113
— de cuivre 4365
tourte 3381, 17330
tourteau 2691
— de coke 2693
tout-venant 11739, 15248
— amélioré 18583
traçage 5274, 7199, 7569, 11334, 20051
traçage v. préparation
trace de limailles 7038
tracé 5790, 13552

tracé des cannelures S. 5231
tracer 11328
— les cannelures 5230
traces de gaz 8056
trachite 18805
trachyandésite 18806
trachydolérite 18807
trachyte 11840
tracteur porte-tubes 2043
traction 14125
— par câble sans fin 6458
— par câble tête et câble queue 18213
— unitaire 9861
— de gaz 7999
— des rayons 4555
train à bandages 17846
— à blooms 1832
— à feuillards 17847
— à fil 20134, 20135
— à fil continu 4271
— à petits fers S. 16735
— à tôles 16074
— à tôles minces S. 18527
— de berlines 10236, 18907
— de laminoir 11702, 15128, 15128, 15131
— de laminoir universel 19315
— de puddlage 1578, 14098
— de roues motrices 15908
— de sondage 5941
— de sonde 5901
— de tiges 5942, 18289
— duo 19173
— ébaucheur 1578, 3913, 1526, 15260, 15261
— finisseur 7131, 7138
— finisseur des bords 6212
— moyen S. 9893
— normal 17357
— pour locomotives 10953
— préparatoire 12060
— rapide 9177
— réversible 14495
— semi-continu 15840
— trio 18558
— trio à tôles 18561
— universel 19317
train v. laminoir
traineau 9473, 16580
trainée d'air 331, 19497
trainer 5727
traineur S. 9490, 14206

trait 17333, 17741, 17760
traitement 13983, 20203
— à l'acide 100
— à l'hypochlorite 9594
— anodique 623
— austenitique 955
— de surface S. 18070
— d'homogénéisation 9299
— des minerais 16747
— du minerai 12661
— limite 18884
— magnétique des minerais 11189
— mécanique des minerais 12642
— mécaniquement 5833
— métallurgique 11589
— par le froid 17935
— par soufflage au convertisseur 1788
— postérieur 17930
— superficiel 18004, 18070
— thermique 9000
— thermique en atmosphère contrôlée 9002
traiter la fonte par le procédé Bessemer 1560
— les minerais 16745
— ondant 7496
tranchant S. 1622, 2077, 16001
tranche 3485, 10238, 16596
tranchée 8587, 12395
— de recherche S. 14058
— noyée 11843
trancher la coulée 4895
— le jet 4895
tranchet coupe-gauche S. 10664
— v. couteau
transformateur du four 7860
transformation 18825
— en coke S. 3954
— isotherme 10081
— mécanique 8131
— péritectique 13103
transformations endomorphes 6163
transformer en coke S. 3926
transgression concordante 12919
transgressivité concordante 48
— parallèle 12920

transition continue 4277
transmission 5960
— hydraulique 7462
— par câbles 15160
— par chaîne 3242
— par vis sans fin 20228
— rigide 15060
transparence 18833
transport 18835
— au gueulard 4315
— d'énergie 13797
— des lingots 9787
— en masse 18837
— fluvial 14969
— par chemin de fer 14366
— par scrapper 16721
— par terre 12763
transporter 2902
transporteur 4317
— à bande 1473, S. 1474
— à bande articulée 722
— à câble 2660
— à chaîne 5247
— à ébarbe 16778
— à écailles 16573
— à godets 2500
— à palettes 13489
— à raclettes 7375
— à racloirs 14197
— à rouleaux 15108
— à ruban 1176
— à vis 15704
— aérien à câble 12757
— aérien à câble métallique S. 15167
— funiculaire 15167
— par bande 1472
— par inertie S. 19553
— par secousses 19553
— par vibration 19552
— pneumatique 13602
— pour jet de fonderie 13226
— pour sacs 15405
transporteur v. convoyeur
transuranique 18840
trapézoèdre S. 9614
— hexagonal 9123
trapp 18847
trappe 7279, 8088, 18848
— à charnière 9204
travail 17730, 18868
— à ciel ouvert 12565
— à forfait 19158
— à froid 4006

travail à la compression S. 4156
— à la flexion 1518
— à la machine 11137
— à la main 11305
— à la massette 11858
— à la torsion S. 18782
— à la traction S. 18409
— au bas-foyer 7102
— au coin 13649
— au pic et à la pelle 13203 13203
— au rocher 12104
— continu 4261
— d'accès et de traçage 5279
— d'affinage 7092
— d'emboutissage 13878
— de la loupe S. 8500
— des métaux 11565
— du bain 20197
— en fer 10036
— en grand convertisseur 4311
— en petits convertisseurs 4312 4312
— facile 10688
— par plaque-modèle 11368
— préparatoire 5963
— utile S. 6143
travailler à la veine S. 17665
— en profondité 20189
— en sous-oeuvre 19273
— en spudding 17216
travaux à ciel ouvert 12607
— à l'intérieur du haut-fourneau 20213
— de creusement 18874
— de traçage 7203, 20052,
— préparatoires 11736
— sur plate-forme 3556
traver-bancs 1385
travers-banc 4665, 4666, 4678, 4712, 4716, 7909, 8631, 18532, 19107
traverse 4693, 4668, 4706, 16586, 18607
— de grue 4595
— de la grille 7148
— de serrage 3627
— emboutie 13881
— en fer 10015
— métallique S. 10015
— tubulaire du contreventement 19068

travertin 2701, 2708, 7758, 18865
tréfilage 20143
— à sec 16799
— fin 7079
— grossier 13844
— moyen 11424
— très fin 19534
tréfiler 5763
tréfilerie 5801, 20123, 20125, 20150
tréfileur 5779, 5788, 20142
tréfle 20164
treillis S. 8120
— à simple torsion 17252
— à triple torsion 9125
— de poutre 18037
trémie 7820, 9328
— à cendres 866
— à charbon 3801, 3804, S 3836
— à minerai S. 12631
— dans la roche 11694
— d'alimentation 6879
— de broyeur 4773
— de chargement 3334, 3836, 6892, 10918
— de chargement de haut fourneau 7859
— de chargement de skips 16483
— de curage 15502
— de mélange 11830
— pour charbon menu 16510
trémis de chargement S. 6879
trémolite 18871
trempe 3451, 8857, 14283, 14289
— à coeur 7803
— à gradins 17289
— à l'acide 2857
— à l'air 252, 285, 12388
— à la flamme 7259
— à l'eau 14292, 19781
— à l'huile 12494
— au plomb 10608
— bainitique 1111
— brillante 2998, 3678
— de recuit 18396
— de surface S. 2918
— difficile 5398
— douce S. 12494, 16845
— dure 7802
— en bain de cyanure 4930

trempe en bain de sel 15443
— en coquille S. 2918
— en paquet 2918
— et revenu 8859
— étagée bainitique 954
— extra-douce 5038
— finale 7067
— interrompue 9912, 17552
— isothermique 10080
— inverse 9932
— martensitique 11347
— naturelle 12195
— négative 12214
— par filet d'eau S. 7771
— par immersion 9644
— par induction 9750
— par jet d'eau 17771
— par nitruration 8861
— par précipitation 13815
— parfaite 8278
— partielle 15808
— passive 12961
— primaire partielle à transition truitée 11955
— primaire partielle normale 3439
— primaire partielle sans transition 3440
— simple 16371
— spéciale 17014
— superficielle 2606, 16475
— totale 4112
— tenace à coeur 5662
— uniforme 19303
trempé 8851
tremper 8846, 14279
— à l'eau 19780
— dans l'eau 14281
— dans un bain de plomb 10615
— l'acier 8848
— l'acier dans l'eau 14282
— les bords 2069
— superficiellement 18053
— très chaud dans l'eau 14280
— un métal 8847
trépan 1622, 2078
— à carottier continu 13561
— à deux ailettes 19193
— à disques 5480, 5482
— à effacement 4013
— à lames 5730
— à molettes de Reed 14582, 15107
— à oreilles 6165

trépan à quatre ailettes 7682
— à sec S. 3670
— à trois ailettes 18570
— aléseur 14478, 14480
— au carbure de tungstène 19101
— carottier 4393
— chargé S. 19101
— en couronne 17376
— en croix 4702
— en queue de poisson 7214
— excentré 6638
— pilote 13298
— pointu 5329
— pour roches 15009, 15016
— pour sondage au câble 3560
— pour sondage percutant 2092
— rotary 15196
— type normal 11948
trépied 18917
— de sondage 2109
très faillé 1093
— fusible 18530
tresse en laine de bois 20180
tréteau S. 9376
treuil 8897, 20082
— à air comprimé 19095
— à antenne 2044
— à deux tambours 5655
— à main 8792
— à vapeur 17451
— auxiliaire 14139
— de cône 1452
— de curage 15515
— d'extraction 8231, 9236, 15946
— de forage 2560, 5785
— de levage 9236
— de manoeuvre 5822
— de manoeuvre de la cloche 1461
— de traction 10186
— électrique 6318
— léger 17220
— pour corde de sondage 2563 2563
— pour tubage 2740
— rotary 15198
triage 5842, 16305, 16582, 16926
— à la main 15869, 19627

triage à sec 6044
— de minerai 12653
— du fer 15873
— du minerai par tables
    inclinées 18193
— par voie humide 19997
— sec 6044
triangle en fil de fer 20148
Trias moyen 12137
tridymite 18892
trié à la main 8772
trier 3641, 4825, 10934,
    13200, 15860, 16923
— au marteau 13198
trieur 13210, 19626
— de minerais de Wetherill
    20002
— de tourbe 13027
trieur v. séparateur
trigonite 18894
trimère 18895
trimérite 18896
tringlerite 10857
tringles de transmission
    14130
trio 18558
triphane S. 17140
triphyllite 18911
triple 18869
triploïdite 18916
triplite 18915
trippkéite 18918
triptane 18920
tripuhvite 18919
tritomite 18921
tritoprisme S. 13960
triturateur de minerai com-
    mandé mécaniquement
    11419
triturateur en fonte 3004
triturer 18922
troctolite 18925
trogérite 18926
trolléite 18927
trommel 4942, 15216, 16701
— classeur S. 15695
— de nettoyage S.3703
— de préparation 13850
— débourber 19711
— finisseur 7127
trona S. .19402
tronc 17533, 17614
tronçon du tuyau 10204
tronçonner 4891
tronçonneuse 4905
tronquement 18957

tronquer 18955
troostite 8839, 18931
trop-plein 12742, 19919
trou 7966, 9248, 9270
— à crasse 2347, 16542
— à laitier 16539, 16557
— auxiliaire 14690
— borgne 1774
— cavé 19697
— conique 4209
— d'air 19499
— d'avancement 179
— de coulée 8087, 11553,
    13756, 15381, 17213,
    18267
— de décharge 1061
— d'homme S. 3694, 11258
— de la tige carrée 10304
— de laitier 3574, 7415
— de mine 1729, 2081,
    5892, 5939, 16204
— de mine auxiliaire 16498
— de mine horizontal 2778
— de mine humide 19782
— de recherche 14034
— de ressuage 19890
— de sable 15489
— de son de 2076
— de souris 12038
— du noyau 4415
— en semelle 17668
— entubé 2924
— hors calibre 12748
— non tubé 19234
— pilote 13299
— plat 7339
— pour carottage 4414
— rétréci 18617
— sous-calibre 19252
— superficiel 16477
trouer au poinçon S. 14173
trous poinçonnés dans le
    dos du profil 9256
troussage 1424, 17811,
    18115
trousse S. 4860, 6013, 17806
    17819, S. 18734
— à noyau 4450, 4452
— amovible 17812
— conique 19659
— coupante 2182, 16422
trousseau 17804
trousser 17803
— le moule 18112
truck de manoeuvre à té-
    lescope 18946

trudellite 18950
truelle à bout arrondi 15287
— à bout carré 17239
— à coeur 10549
— à lisser 15653
truscottite 18962
trusquin 18052
tscheffkinite 18967
tschermigite 18968
tsingtanite 18969
tsumébite 18970
tubage 2932, 9928, 16089,
    18974
— à emboîtement 9835
— à diamètre constante
    17713
— combiné 4061
— de puits S. 19960
— du puits S. 16040
— libre 7738
— perdu 10842
tube à ailerons 8228
— à boules 2546
— à bouts lisses de
    section cylindrique
    13442
— à chlorure de calcium
    2723
— à combustion 4084
— à dessécher 25
— à deux branches S. 18175
— à éclair S. 7793
— à filtrer 7059
— à fractionner 7689
— à fumée pour locomoti-
    ves 10949
— à genouillère 18129
— à meubles 7880
— à paroi pleine 1684
— à perles 8270
— à potasse S. 13721
— à renflement 9835
— avec assemblages par
    brides mobiles 13371
— avec extrémités chan-
    freinées 13370
— avec les extrémitées
    recoulées 19072
— bimétallique 1588
— bouilleur et réchauffeur
    pour chaudières à tubes
    de fumée 9005
— carottier 4389
— carottier double 5683
— carottier extérieur 12696
— carottier intérieur 9825

tube carottier simple 16407
— collecteur de gaz 7992
— conducteur 4193
— d'absorption S. 17
— d'aérage 18248
— d'ancrage 557
— de condensation 4182
— de connection 6012
— de décharge 5496
— de distillation 5554
— de distribution 5572
— d'égout 18255
— d'épaisseur majorée 904.?
— de fonçage 5956
— de pesée 19903
— de Pitot 13425
— de pompage 19045
— de pompage à refoulements extérieurs 19377
— de pompage normal 13449
— de précision 13825
— de queue 18207
— de repêchage 9364, 18517 18517
— de repêchage à frottement à corps déformé 4495
— de repêchage fondu 3407
— de retour 17087
— de séchage 6057, 6065
— de section carrée 17249
— de section rectangulaire 14519
— de séparation des gaz 8057 8057
— de sûreté 15416
— de surforage 19690
— de trop-plein 12743
— disperseur 16978
— double 5669
— ébauché 9262
— en acier sans soudure 15796
— en bronze 2457
— en fer 9275
— en porcelaine 13668
— en trompette 18175
— en U pour chlorure de calcium 2724
— en verre 8285
— et ébauche pour ponts postérieurs 18975
— et serpentin surchauffeurs 18010
— étiré 5820
— évasé 18954

tube fileté 18556
— fileté à mi-épaisseur 7484
— filtre 15688
— fissuré 16690, 17119
— flexible d'aspiration 1795 17956
— flexible pour sondages 15017
— flexible pour tête d'injection 17506
— formé par explosion 1902 19029
— foyer 7457
— gaz commercial 4087
— gradué 8391
— guide 4196, 10628, 18043
— interstratifié 9916
— lisse de qualité commerciale 13443
— manchonné 4021
— métallique flexible 7367
— noir en fer 1650
— percé 13083
— perforé 10843, 13081
— porte-carotte intérieur 4434
— pour âmes de fonderie 18997
— pour appareillage hydrodynamique 19004
— pour aqueducs 13346
— pour arbre à cames 2775
— pour arbres à levier pour avions 18982
— pour arbres creux de transmission 19002
— pour arbres porte-hélices 19011
— pour arrosage 19005
— pour barres de passage à niveau 18984
— pour barrières de passage à niveau 18984
— pour cadre de vélos et motos 18985
— pour canalisations d'eau industrielle 13338
— pour canalisation de gaz de ville 13345·
— pour canalisations de gaz naturel 13339
— pour canons de marteaux pneumatiques 19008
— pour chemises de cylindres 19069

tube pour conduites électriques 18994
— pour conduites forcées 13341
— pour conduites submergées 19023
— pour devanteurs à rouleaux 19017
— pour douilles 19000
— pour échafaudage 19019.
— pour échangeurs de chaleur 13340
— pour échafaudages démontables 18992
— pour élévateurs hydrauliques d'échelles autoporteuses 19003
— pour essieux de trains d'atterrissage d'avions 18983
— pour exploitation hydraulique des sables 16996
— pour fours de boulangerie 18988
— pour freins Westinghouse 19027
— pour gaz, canalisation de méthane 13342
— pour générateurs 19022
— pour grilles 18999, 19012
— pour installations de distillations 18993
— pour installations d'extincteurs 18995
— pour installations de poste pneumatique 19009
— pour installations de pyroscission 18991
— pour installiations de reforming 19014
— pour installations de sinthèse 18168
— pour installations thermiques 13344
— pour la protection de câbles électriques 6263
— pour l'exploitation par forage de gisements 18987
— pour le réchauffage du mazout 9006
— pour les industries chimiques 13337
— pour manchons 19020
— pour mandrils de machines-outils 19006

tube pour palissades 19007
— pour parapets 18996
— pour porte-voix et transmission d'ordres 19021
— pour profilés pour menui-
series métalliques 19028
— pour raffinerie 13343
— pour réfrigérateurs
19015
— pour roulements à billes
18986
— pour sondage 19959
— pour sondage géognosti-
ques 19001
— pour tiges à tampons
19024
— pour transformateurs
18828
— pour volets roulants
19018
— profilé 15995
— refoulé 19375
— réfractaire 12413
— sans soudure 15752,
15753
— soudé 19931
— soudé en spirale 17102
— soudé par contact 2641
— soudé pour gaz 19932
— soudé par rapprochement
2638
— soudé par recouvrement
10543
— taraudé et manchonné
18555
— taraudé «gaz» 15717
— tirant 17406
— vaporisateur 17431
tuber 2907, 15343
tubes à ailettes 7143
— d'adduction 15355
— de retour 15354
— taraudés type gaz 18293
tubulure 1733, 13336
— à haute pression 9165
— de coulée S. 8087, 12412
— venue de fonte 3012
— extérieure de la tuyère
19166
— fixe 7238
tuer un puits 10350
tuf basaltique 1270
— calcaire 2701, 2729,
6683
tungstène 19100

tungsténite 19166
tunnel 2664, 19107
— sous la voie S. 19244
turanite 19115
turbo-compresseur 19126
turbo-dynamo 19125
turbogénératrice 19125
turborotary 19127
turgite 19129
turnérite 19143
turquoise S. 10278, 19154
tusculite 19157
tuyau à bride 7269
— à chicanes 19044
— à compensation S. 4110
— à emboîtement 16808
— à manchon 13367
— à paroi épaisse 18504
— à pistolet 13388
— bifurqué 1577
— branché 2258
— central 3192
— centrifuge 3206
— cloué 17698
— collecteur général 4093
— compensateur 4110
— condensateur 4187
— coulé en sable 15488
— d'arrivée d'eau 19785
— d'aspiration 17943, 17957
17957
— de décharge 19767
— de déchargeur 5497
— d'écoulement 19793
— de fumée 16765
— de la prise d'eau 19973
— de lavage 19715
— de prise de gaz 12705
— de refoulement 5154,
14949, 14953, S. 17338
— de sablage 15512
— de trop-plein 19736
— descendant 5705
— distributeur 5575
— économiseur 6193
— en caoutchouc 15317
— en fonte 3008
— en plomb 10621
— en tôle 16062
— goudronné 18327
— horizontal 9346
— incliné 9703
— moulé 3030
— pour barres de contrôle
18990

tuyau pour câbles 15163
— pour circuits de contrôle
18990
— pour conduite 10839
— éléments combustibles
18998
— surchauffeur 18013
— suspendu 18079
— vaporisateur 19467
— vertical 19529
tuyauterie 13380
— d'aération 19504
— d'air 300
— d'alimentation 19771
— de gaz 8037
— pour installations de re-
traitement 13384
tuyaux à ailettes de chauffage
7144
— de descente pour eaux
de pluie 8688
tuyauteur 13358
tuyère 7434, 19159, 19195
— à courant d'air descen-
dant 5710
— à laitier 16562
— à laitier Lürmann 11094
— auto-décrassante 15831
— conique 4212
— de pulvérisation 17184
— double 19176
— du trou de laitier S.
16562
— en bronze 2458
— jumelée 4548
— refroidie 4329
— sous pression 6724
— supérieure 18735
tychite 19197
tympe 19201
tymplon S. 19199
type 8383
tyrolite 19206
tysonite 19207

U

uhligite 19210
uintahite 19211
ulexite S. 12184, 19212
ullmannite 19214
ulrichite 19215
ultramylonite 19223

umangite 19226
un filet 15698
uncompahgrite 19237
ungaïte 19299
union 10200
— à marteau 8743
unir 2016
unité de four 7861
— de pompage 14170
— de traitement catalytique 3100
— individuelle 9747
unités idiogènes 9618
uranate 19391
uranite S. 19390
uraninite 13413, 19392
uranium 19394
uranocircite 19393
uranophane 19397
uranosphérite 19398
uranospinite 19399
uranothallite 19400
uranotile 19401
urao 19402
urbainite 19403
urbanite 19404
urtite 19407
urusite 19408
usbékite 19409
usé 6089
usinabilité S. 20193
usinage électronique 6364
usine 11686
— à gaz 8066
— d'acier S. 17522
— d'étirage à froid 3974
— de laminage S. 10005
— sidérurgique 16752
usiné fin 7097
ussingite 19413
ustensile de ménage 2460
ustensiles de chauffe S. 7196
— en platine 13529
— en quartz 14272
usure 19853
— de la chaine 19854
— externe S. 5
— par abrasion sous pression de contact élevée 9183
— rapide du four 14303
utahite 19414
utilisation de la chaleur 19415
— du laitier 19416

uvanite 19418
uvarovite 19419

V

vaalite 19423
vaciller 7285
vacuumètre S. 19435
vagonnette S. 18928
valbellite 19439
valencianite 19441
valentinite 20024
valeur 19445
— comparée 4107
— de décomposition 5072
— de la dispersion 6551
— de refroidissement 3438
— de l'intensité S. 9863
— des chutes 15662
— expérimentale 18458
— limite 10824
vallée d'effondrement 6843
— en U 19929
— glaciaire 8261
— longitudinale 10986
— monoclinale 11907
— sénile 7805
— sous-marine 17927
— submergée 6011
— suspendue 8810
— synclinale 18160
— transversale 18846
— transversale perçante S. 19777
vallevarite 19442
valve 19446
— à air 330
— à circulation d'eau 19834
— à gaz 8058
— à papillon de Siemens 16290
— à vent S. 1736
— d'admission 12615
— rotative de Burger 2588
valve v. soupape
vanadate 19459
vanadinite 19460
vanadium 19461
vanne 16614
— à air chaud 9401
— à air froid 3964
— à coin 8059
— à décharger 6102
— à levier 7365

vanne à opercule S. 8059
— à siège horizontal 5486
— d'éruption 1862
— de sûreté 11363
— d'isolement 3781
— en acier coulé 3022
— pour résidus 18319
vanner 19458
vanoxite 19464
vanthoffite 19465
vapeur admise au dessus du piston 17414, 17415
— d'eau 17413
— de tête 1692
— v. fumée
vaporisateur 17180
— et tirant pour chaudières 19466
vaporisation 6618
— de l'eau 19835
vaporiser 6610
variation 11799
— brusque de température 17963
— de concentration de l'électrolyte 427
— de coquille 11801
— de modèle 11803
— de moule 11802, 16125
— de plaque modèle 11804
— du noyau 16126
variété de carbone 19473
— jaune 20293
variolite 19474
variscite 19476
värmsingite 19479
vase 12069, S. 16695
— à cristallisation 4807
— à décanter 5053
— à égoutter 5747
— d'évaporation 6615
— d'évaporation en porcelaine 13663
— gradué 11399
— poreux 5336
— pour la distillation 5559
vase verte S. 8314
vaseline 13132, 19480
vaterite 19481
vaugnérite 19482
vauquelinite 19483
vauxite 19484
V-Bühne 15412
végasite 19485

véhiculer S. 2902, S. 14016
veine 4552, 6559, 10631, 10954
— aurifère 8351
— irrégulière de charbon 3842
veine v. filon
veinule 7527, 10627, 10631, 17831, 17836
venir de fonte 2976
vent 1698, 20086
— chaud 9393
— de haut fourneau 7826
— froid 3962
vente 15436
ventilateur 275, 1866, 6793, 6811
— à ailettes 7066
— aspirant 6655
— centrifuge 3201, 6795
— de cheminée 3465
— d'extraction 6650
— de Root 15155
— enveloppé 2925
— secondaire 2050, 2052
— soufflant 1873, 13703, 13894
ventilation 188, 19508,
— à vide 19438
— auxiliaire 15771
— descendante 5702
— soufflante 13542
— v. aérage
ventiler 6792
— le sable 186
— un chantier grisouteux 4960
ventouse à air 14688
ventre 1470, 2341, 2768, 15933
— du creuset 1469, 4737
— du haut fourneau 2120
venu à la coulée 3016
— de fonderie à la coulée 3016
venue 9766, 9771, S. 15388
— d'eau 9831
— de gaz 12446
— de gaz dans la boue 7996
ver 14434, 14443
verbaite 19605
vérifier 3361, 19514
vérin 10091
— hydraulique 9525, 9534
— mécanique 15709

vérin métallique 11407
— pneumatique 13586
verite 19515
vermiculite 19516
verni au four 10122
vernir 19477
— au four 10121
vernis S. 13626, 19478
— à l'huile de lin 10859
— anti-rouille 13862
vernissage au four 10123
vernisser v. vernir
verre à clarifier 5052
— de cobalt 3888
— de Jena 10146
— de montre 19741
— de Weber 19875
— dur 8829
— étiré 16056
— pulvérisé S. 8282
verrou 2008, 10561, 15005
— d'arête 7482
— de sûreté 12293
— transversal 4715
verrouillage 10946
vers les chantiers 9683
versant 16253, 16679
verser 18354
— la poche 18671
vert de montagne 12032
— mer 15731
vésuvianite 19542
viaduc supérieur 2383
vibrateur 19551
vibration 19549
— du câble de perforation 10339
vibrer 10124
vibroforage 19554
vice interne 10556
vicoite 19556
vidange 19213
— d'une chaudière 1876
— du four 6422
vide S. 7967, 19424
— d'air 326
vider (se) 10635
— le creuset 18262
— par une pompe 4155
vieilli 216
vieillir 214
vieillissement 218, 19870
— accéléré 219
— dû à refroidissement soudain 14284
— naturel 12189

vieillissement par déformation plastique 17731
— poussé 12731
— soudain 14297
vierge 19563
vieux-fer 15660
— travaux 8235, 8637, 8692, 12522, 19719
vilebrequin 2346, 4609, 4610
villamanite 19557
villiaumite 19558
vintlite 19560
violarite 19561
virgation 19564
viridine 19564
viridite 19565
vis à bois 20177
— de rallonge 18376
— de serrage 166
— fraise 9218
— sans fin 4620
— sans fin d'alimentation 6882
— sans fin d'extraction et transport 14498
viscosimètre vibratoire 19225, 19225
viscosité 1937, 19568
— de rupture 2311
viseur 4690
visiter la mine S. 8202
visqueux 12056, 19566
visser 11231
— les tiges de sonde 11233
vitesse 13063
— ascendante 853
— critique de solidification 4648
vitesse critique de trempe 4649, 4649
vitesse de coulée 3017
— de coupe 4924
— d'extraction 15171
— des formations des ions 19495
— de refroidissement 4342
— de régénération des ions 14647
— de retour des boues de forge 623
— du jet 10161
— spécifique de déionisation 5141
— tangentielle 3606
vitreux 19570
vitrification 19576, 19577

vitrifier (se-) 1410
vitriol 17970
vitrophyre 19581
vitrophyrique 19582
vivianite 1904
vogésite 19586
voglite 19587
voie auxiliaire 16240
— d'aérage 332, 20095, 20107
— de carrière 19261
— de circulation S. 7959
— d'écoulement 19791
— d'exploitation 15149
— de fond 5093, 7959, 8095
— de niveau S. 2637
— de raccordement 10253
— de roulage 8095, 8898, 15119
— de roulement de grue 7964
— de sortie d'air 12717
— de taille 6709
— de ventilation 2652
— électrolytique v. électro-lyse
— en cul-de-sac S. 10147
— étroite 12177
— ferrée d'atelier 20226
— funiculaire de manoeu-vre 16237
— intermédiaire 17919
— jumelle 273
— normale 7801
— portative 13696
— principale 11227
— surélevée pour décharge-ment de charbon 3807
voies d'exploitation 1925
voile 2510
voiture 19457
volant S. 8791
volatiliser (se-) 19588
volatilité 19589
volborthite 19590
volhynite 19593
volée 2042, 4595
voltage de régime 20222
voltamètre 19596
voltzite 19598
volume d'air aspiré 887
— d'air nécessaire S. 4238
— de combinaison 4067
— d'eau S. 19810

volume des pores 13670
— d'un gramme-molécule 8407
— moléculaire 11871
volumètre à gaz 8061
vonsénite 19603
vorscheider 14347
voussoir 19882
voûte 15138
— aérienne rasée S. 190
— anticlinale dénudée 190, 320
— convexe 4313
— de la tympe 19198
— du rampant 7456
— du four 15145
— en briques 2368
— plate 10713
— surbaissée 4159
voyage 18906
vredenburgite 19606
vue isométrique 6916
— tridimensionnelle S. 6916
vulpinite 19611
vulsinite 19612

W

wacke 19614
wad 1946, 19615
wagnérite 19619
wagon à déchargement auto-matique 15818
— basculant 6099
— basculant de côté 16260
— citerne 18256
— de chargement 3328
— de mine 18928
— fermé 3778
— ouvert 12603
— pour la fonte 13265
— trémie rectangulaire 1451 14517
wagonnet 2526, 2818, 9484, 11772
— à lingots 1585
— à minerais 12658
— basculant au bout 7781
— étagé 16116
— pour chantier 18947
walpurgite 19662
waluewite 19663
wapplérite 19664

wardite 19665
warrénite 19678
warthaite 19679
warwickite 19680
wavellite 19839
webstérite 19876
wehrlite 19892
weibullite 19893
weinschenkite 19917
weisbachite 19920
weiselbergite 19921
weissite 19922
wennebergite 19977
wentzélite 19978
wernérite 19980
wesliénite 19981
wet oil 6426
whewellite 20013
wichtsite 20054
wiikite 20066
wilkéite 20073
willémite 20074
williamsite 20075
willyamite 20076
wiltshiréite 20077
wiluite 20078
withamite 20154
withérite 20048, 20160
wittichénite 20162
wittite 20163
wolframite 2698, 20167
wolfsbergite 20168
wollastonite 15592, 20169
woodendite 20184
wulfénite 20254, 20286
würtzite 20256
wyomingite 20259

Z

zaratite 20316
Zechstein 20317
zéolite 20318
— aciculaires 12211
zepharovichite 20319
zeunérite 20320
zinc 17046, 20323
— d'oeuvre 14463
— sulfuré 20341
zincage 7926, 20346
— électrolytique S. 7943
zincaluminite 20340
zincifère 20347
zincite 14552, 20344

zingué v. galvanisé
zinguer 7928, 7942, 20343
zinkénite 20345
zinkosite 20350
zinnwaldite 20351
zippéite 20352
zircon 20353
zircone 20354
zirconium 20355
zirkélite 20357
zobtenite 20359
zoisite 20360
zone S. 900
— d'affaissement 767
— de broyage 4770, 16014
— de carburation 2882
— de cémentation 1478
— de chauffage préalable
— de faille 16027
— de fracture 7702
— de fusion 11484, 20364
— de l'altération superfi-
    cielle 20366
— d'oxydation 12792
— de réduction 14579
— de rupture 15387
— de sédimentation 766
— de transition 18830
— des méandres 11388
— d'exploitation 17678
— envahie 9764
— foudroyée 8329
— fracturée 7705
— limite 12467
— marginale 2071
— morte 5025
— plissée 1479, 2200
— productive 13003
— productive effective
    12242
— sphérique 20365
zone v. région
zoolithe 20368
zunyite 20369
zurlite 20370
zwitter 20371
zygadite 20372

A

Abarten des Verfahrens 11853
Abbau 2449, S. 8205, 17676, 20111
— der Pfeiler 13293, 14140
— durch Richtungsvortrieb 5866
— im steilen Flöz 17530
— mit Rahmenzimmerung und mit Bergeversatz 17244
— mit Unterstützung des Hangenden 18032
Abbauen 2300
abbauen 6679, 11723, 17842, 18347
Abbaufeld 12895, 16269, 20207
Abbauförderband 6741
Abbauhammer 11404
Abbauort 17666, 17667
Abbausohle 11774
Abbaustoss 17666, 19635, 19642
— bei Strebbau mit breitem Blick 10991
— mit Rahmenzimmerung 17245
Abbaustrecke 5870, 6709, 12897, 15149
— aufhauen 12558
Abbauverfahren 11613, 11778
— mit Bergeversatz 7039
Abbauvortrieb 1812, S. 7199
abbauwürdig 11721
abbauwürdige Lagerstätte 12999
— Sandschicht 13002
abbauwürdiges Erz 12998
— Vorkommen 13000
Abbauzone 17678
Abbeizen 5452
Abbeizungsarbeiter 13224
Abbeizungsriss 13227
Abbildungsfehler 9640
Abbindezeit 18516
Abbindung (von Beton) 15914
Abblasen (eines Kernes) 1870
Abblashahn 283

Abblättern 1787, 15578
Abblätterung 15595
Abbohr-Versuch 5896
Abbohrer 10969
Abbrand 5041, 19723,
— der Elektroden 4242
Abbrennen 5115, S. 16473
abbrennen 1753, 5114, 17265
Abbruchwert S. 15662
abdampfen 6611
Abdampfinjektor 6654
Abdampfkasserolle 6615
Abdampfkessel 6617
Abdampfkolben 6613
Abdampfpfanne S. 6617
— mit rotierender Heizspirale 6616
Abdampfschale 6614
abdecken 4558, S. 17842
Abdecker 14763
Abdeckmetall 3610
Abdeckmittel 670a, 4572, S. 7498
Abdeckung 17688a
abdichte Verbindung 15830
abdichten 7010, 12068, 12826
Abdichtring 3111a
Abdichtung S. 12845, 15508
abdrehen 19130
Abdruck 6092, 6699, 11970, 16418
Abdruckbüchse S. 9667
Abdruckstempel 9667
Abfahrtflansch 10527
Abfahrtsmassel 14451
Abfall 1598, 5065, S. 5066, 16508, 19718,
Abfallbrennstoff 19727
Abfälle 10254, 11035, 14815
Abfalleisen 19734
Abfallende 4660, 16179, 19724
abfallende Wetterführung 5702
abfallender Stollen 16572
— Wetterstrom 5696, 20093
Abfallwert 15682
Abfanggabel 7601, 10730, 12304
Abfangplatte 4848
Abflachung 7351

Abflammen 16473
abflammen 7258
Abfliessen 8489
Abfluss 12700
Abflussgraben S. 8621
Abflusskanal 7472
Abflussleitung 7428
Abflussrinne 7433, 18934
Abflussrohr 19767
Abformen S. 11997
Abfuhrrampe 5134a, 6655a
Abfuhrrollgang 15361
Abgaberinne 6878
Abgang S. 11031
Abgas 19728
abgebaut 17672
abgebautes Erz 2445
abgebrochener Kern 2442
abgebrochenes Formteil 2444
abgedrehter Bord 19142
abgeflachtes Rundeisen 7349
abgefallene Sandstücke S. 5973
abgefallener Sand 5973
abgeflammte Form 16471a
abgehobelte Verwerfung S. 13460
abgerissene Form 11556
abgeschlossene Sonde S. 16245
abgeschreckte Charge 14291a
abgeschreckter Stahl 3449
abgeschnürter Sattelkern 5253
abgesetzte Blitzableiterstangen 10797
— Teilfläche 17560
abgesetzter Bau 15738
— loser Führungsstift 5694
abgespülte Sandschülpe 15567
— Schwärzeschülpe 1675
abgestandener Stahl 13102
abgestumpfte Kegelform 16956
abgezogen 17857
Abguss 3036, S. 7643
Abgusstiefe 5205

Abgraten 3478
abgraten 3472, 6972
Abgrathammer 6976
Abgratmaschine 6977, 17212
Abgratpresse 18903
Abgratstempel 18902
Abgratwerkzeug 6980
Abhang 45, 4824, S. 9691,
    16253, 16679
Abhänge und Abdichtungs-
    elemente 16648
abhauen 4893
Abhebeformmaschine 7295,
    12977
Abhebemaschine für flache
    Gegenstände 10776
— mit Hebekarren 12017
— mit Wendeplatte 19149
abheben S. 17841
Abheben auf Stiften 13309/a
Abhebestift 8652, 10772
Abhebevorrichtung 10766
Abhitzekanal 19738
Abhitzekessel 19732
Abichit 2, S. 683
Abkantpresse 1513
Abkantprofil 7273
Abkantprofile 7274
abklären 3634
Abklärflasche S. 5052
Abklärgefäss 5053
Abklingen einer Eigen-
    schaft 11028
Abklopfen der Firste 6018,
    10237
Abklopfvorrichtung 14422
Abkohlen 8205
Abkohler 2318, 8204
abkrammen S. 16459
Abkrammen 16465
abkühlen 4326
Abkühlung 4337
Abkühlungsfläche 4343
Abkühlungsgeschwindgkeit
    4342
Abkühlungskurve 4335
abkuppeln 1043
Ablage für Formen 14322
—, für Kerne S. 14322
ablagern (im Flussbett)
    232
Ablagerung 5200, S. 5849,
    15794/a

Ablagerung von atmosphä-
    rischem Staub 6130
Ablagerungen 15792
Ablagerungsmulde 7384/a,
    18935/a
ablängen auf Mass-
    schneiden 16019
Ablass. schraube 12704
ablassen S. 1775
Ablassen der Schlacke
    18308
— des flüssigen Ballastes
    12703
Ablassrohr S. 12705
Ablassventil 1857
Ablation 3
Ablaufen S. 8489
Ablaufteilung S. 7428
Ablauftrichter 4185
Abläutern der Erze 10182
Ableitung S. 12377
— von Wärme S. 8973
ablenken 5118
Ablenkgerät 5119
Ablenkkeil 20018
Ablenkpunkt 10343
ablöschen 14281
Ablösung S. 12946, 16515
— des Gebirges
— des Gebirges an der
    Firste 16699
Abmesser S. 11609
Abmessung 5421
— des Guss . stückes
Abnahme 5721/a
— der Bohrlochsneigung
    570
— des Kalibers 14576
Abnahmebeamter 9848
Abnahmeprüfung 41
Abnahmestempel 17308
Abnahmezahl 3901
abnehmbarer Deckel 14705
abnormale Verwerfung
    12765
abnormaler Kontakt 4
— Stahl 4a
abnorme Verwerfung 14823
Abnutzungshärte S. 12961
Abpfeilern S. 14138, 14996,
    14997

abpfeilern 14122, 14995
Abplattung S. 7351
Abputzhammer 3480
Abrasion 6
Abrasionen 15645
abrasive 8
Abrauchen 5296/a
Abraum 4898
Abraumdecke 16094
abräumen 17842
Abräumen S. 17867
— von Deckgebirge S. 1231
abreiben 5/a
Abreissen durch Brechstange
    des Stosses 1253
Abrieb 6
abruptes Abbinden 7302
Abrutschkegel 3337
absanden S. 15466
Absanden S. 15477
Absarokit 10
Absatz 1483, 7686, 16209
Absatzbehälter 17996
Absatzgesteine 15794
absatzweise Destillation
    S. 7687
absaugen 5741, 17942
Absaugentfeuchter 11266
Absaugflasche 7057
Absaugöffnung S. 12702
Absaugrohr S. 12705,
    17957
Absaugtrockenofen 19429
Abschälen 3042
abschärfen 18276
abschäumen 16459
Abscheideanlage 15865
Abscheide-und Schüttel-
    vorrichtung 15863
abscheiden S. 5050, 15860
Abscheiden der Schlacke
    15875
— fluoreszenter Stoffe aus
    dem Erdöl 5046
Abscheider 810, 15878
— -Ablass 18851
Abscheidetrichter 15864,
    15880
Abscheidevorrichtung mit
    Dauermagnet 15881
Abscheidung der Bestand-

teile der Mischung 15876
Abscheidung des Erzstaubes
  15877
— von Hand 15869
abscheren S. 16018
Abscherungselastizität S.
  18841
Abscherungsüberschiebung
  16026
Abschiebung 5443, 5716
abschiessen 16506, 17104
Abschiessen der Hilfsspreng-
  schüsse 17250
— von der Oberfläche aus
  18067
Abschlacken 16513
abschlacken 5764, 5765,
  14380, 16458, 16469,
  16518, 16692, 18270
Abschlackmaschine 5241
Abschlackung 16556
Abschlackungshammer S.
  15600
Abschlageisen S. 20240
Abschlagen der Speiser
  14721
Abschlagkasten 9206
Abschlaglänge 5210, 7551
Abschlagrahmen 1598/a,
  S. 9206
Abschlämmen S. 5051
abschlämmen 5237
Abschlämmung 5238
abschleifende Gletscher-
  erosion 8548
Abschleifhärte 9/a
abschlemmen S. 6394
Abschluss des Schachtes
  17683
Abschlusshahn 17663
Abschlussring 7778
Abschmelzdraht S. 7885
Abschmelzen S. 3
abschmelzendes Metall
  6004
Abschmelzung S. 7893
Abschmirgeln S. 6414
Abschrägung 1567
Abschreckalterung 14284,
  14297
Abschreckanomalie 3424
Abschreckbiegeprobe 1522·

Abschreckdauer 14294
Abschrecken 5049, 9590,
  13573, 14283
abschrecken 14279, 19780
Abschreckhärten S. 14283
Abschreckhärtung 14292
Abschreckprobe 3425, 3437
Abschreckkristalle 3430
Abschreckung S. 3451,
  14289, 14290
Abschreckungstemperatur
  14293
Abschreckwert 3438
Abschuppen S. 15595
Absenkung S. 12377
— der Firste 1528, S.
  16440, 18096
— des Hangenden 4760,
  15146, 17255
Absetzapparat 15923
absetzen 10517, 15921
Absetzen einer Schicht
  28
Absetzgrube 15924
Absonderung 12946, 16503
— nach den Schichtflächen
  10509
Absorption 14
— des Wasserstoffes
  durch Metalle 20
Absorptionsanlage 24
Absorptionsapparat 15
Absorptionsflasche 16
Absorptionsgefäss 12
Absorptionsmittel 5634
Absorptionspipette 23
Absorptionsröhre 25
Absorptionsschlange 17
Absorptionsturm 13
Abspaltung S. 4588
Absperrdamm 4966
absperren S. 3753
Absperrhahn für die Spül-
  stänge 10306
Absperrvorrichtung 3781
Abstand zwischen Schächten
  19971
Abstandsring 16956
Abstechbank 4920
abstechen 18261
Abstecher 4904

Abstechstahl S. 4904, S.
  12952
Abstehen 17570
abstehen lassen 5033,
  14307
Abstellen des Gebläses
  16246
Abstelloch S. 14433
Abstich 8972/a, 11458,
  18264, 18297, 18298,
  18307
Abstichkanal S. 18313
Abstichöffnung 11553
Abstichpause 18303
Abstichprobe 18309
Abstichrinne S. 10587,
  17171, 18313
Abstichschaufel 18310
Abstichschlacke 18312
Abstichsohle 13760
Abstrahlen S. 16198
Abstreicheisen 15665
abstreichen 17803, 17815
Abstreichen des Sandes
  17828
Abstreicher 16462, 17819
Abstreichwerkzeug 17805
abstreifen 17843
Abstreifer 9802, S. 17862
Abstreiffestigkeit 10209
Abstreifkamm 17872
Abstreifmeissel 8642
Abstreifplatte S. 17872
abstrippen S. 17843
abstumpfen 18955
Abstumpfung 18957
Absturz 6774
Absturzplatz 6106
Absturzrinne S. 3563
abstützen S. 1792
abteufen 5161
Abteufen 5101, S. 16416
Abteufgerüst 16426
Abteufhammer 16424
Abteufkübel S. 2202, 16420
Abteufung 16416
Abtreiben S. 4839
— des Schachtes 16421
abtreiben s. bohren od
  auffahren
abtrennen S. 5050

Abtropfschale 5747
abwalzen 15067
Abwälzfräser für Stirnräder 17227
— für Schneckenräder 20229
Abwaschung 14190
abwärts 5714
— gleiten 5226
Abwärtsgang 5715
Abwasserbohrung 19773, 19766
abwechselnde Bewegungs-richtung 14834
Abweichgerät S. 5119
Abweichmessung 5471
Abweichung 5280
— der Gestalt 20239
Abweichungsrichtung 5466
Abweisblech 7306
abyssische Ablagerungen 31
— Region 30
Abzichformkasten S. 2227
Abziehkernkasten 7712
Abziehen S. 10400
— von Lager S. 18220
— von Schlacke S. 16465
Abzieher 17826
Abziehkraft 17870/a, 20159/a
Abzug 7817
— für Mehrgehalt an Kiesel-säure 5084
Abzughaube 9309
Abzugskanal 7449, 11221
Abzugsstutzen 2352
Abzweigleitung 10568
Abzweigrohr 3258
Abzweigung S. 2650
Abzweigungspunkt eines Ganges 13612
Acadialith 33
achatähnlich 212
achathaltig 211
achatartig S. 212
Achatmörser 210
Achatschale S. 210
Achatschneide 209
Achroit 68
achromatisch 69
Achsbüchse 1027, 1027/a
Achsdruck 1028

Achse 1021
— der Schweissraupe 1022
— mit durchgehender Bohrung 9249
Achsenrohr für Flugzeuglan-dungsgestelle 18983
Achsgabelbacken S. 8653
achsiale Richtung 1018
Achslager S. 1027
Achsneigung 13574
Achsschenkel 1026
achteckige Mitnehmerstange 12450
achtkantiger Block 12452
Achtkantstahl 12451
achtlitziger Draht 15997
achtstündige Arbeitsschicht 6233
Ackererde 728
Acre 1/160 15087
Actinium 109
Adamin 124
Adapter am Einspritz-kopf angeordnet 18139
additiv 144
Adelfotypus 145
Adelit 146
Ader 10631, 17831, 17836
Aderchen 7527
Adhärenz 17580
Adjustage 164
Adjustagehalle S. 17729
Adjustieren 163
Adlerstein S. 198
Admiralitätsmetall 170
Adsorption 177
Adventivkrater 181. 10569
Aegirit S. 107
Affinieren 14605
— des Silbers S. 16358
Affinitätskonstante S. 3899
Aftonit S. 690
Afwillit 204
Agalit 205
Agalmatolith 206, 3467
Agaphit 207
Agglomerat 221/a, S. 2018
Agglomerationsvermögen 226
Agglomeratkuchen 222

Agglomerieranlage 225
agglomerieren S. 223, 1145/a
agglutinant 227
agglutinieren S. 130
agglutinogen 229
Ägirin 182
Agraffe 3637
Agricolit 238
Aguilarit 239
Ahlenstahl 1016
Aikinit S. 12209
Akadisches 34
Akanthit 36
Akaustobiolith 336
Akerit 337
Akermanit 338
Akkordlohn 18332
Akkumulation S. 56
Akkumulationsterrasse 5868
Akkumulator S. 54, 12754
Akkumulatorenmetall 56
aklinisch 106
Akmit 107
Akrochordit 339
Aktinolith 110
aktische Region 18831
aktivierende Substanz 115/a
aktivierte Kohle 115
Aktivschlamm 117
akustische Prüfung 16916/a
akustisches Log 16915
Alabandin 340
Alabandit S. 340
Alabaster 341, 8431
Alabastergips 342
Alait 343
Alamosit 344
Alaskait 345
Alaun 438
Alaunerde 439
Alaungrube 440, 440/a
Alaunschiefer 441, 470/a
Alaunstein S. 473
Alb 347
Albertit 346
Albit 348
Alexandrit 353
Algonkium 354
Alkali 355
Alkaligestein 356

Alkalimetalle 359
alkalisches Wasser 361
alkalische Erde 358
— Salze 360
alkalisieren 362
Alkalisierung 363
Alkladblech 351
Alkohol 352
Alkylationssäure 365
Alkylatrückstand 364
Allaktit 368
Allanit 370
Alleghanyt 371
Allemontit 372
allgemeine Bedingung 1694
— Vorgänge im Hochofen
    8152
allgemeines Einfallen 1008
allgemeines Streichen 8153
Alligatorquetsche 374, 376
Alligatorschere 375
Allochroit 377
allochromatisch 378
allochton 379, 17742
allochtones Gestein 382
Allodelphit 384
Alloklas 383
Allomerismus 386
allomorph 387
Allophane 387/a
allothigen 385, 385/a
allotriomorph 389, 592
allotriomorphe Struktur 390
Allotropie 392
allotropische Form 391
allseitig beweglicher
    Schablonenhalter 12980
Allunogen S. 10311
Alluvialepoche 412
Alluvialgold S. 13436,
    17770
Alluvialkonglomerat 6800
Alluviallagerstätte 406
Alluvialrevier S. 406
Almandin 413
Almandinspindel 412/a
Alnik 415
Alnoit 416
Alphabronze 418
Alpha-Eisen 419
alpiner Vergletschungstypus

12031
Alquifoux 420
Alsbachit 421
Alshedit 422
Alstonit 424
Altait 425
Alteisenschweissofen S.
    6761
alter Mann S. 8095, S.
    8325, S. 8329, 8692,
    9282, 12522
Alterung 218
alterungsbeständiger Stahl
    S. 12338
alterungsfreier Stahl 12338
Alterungsriss 220
Alterungszähigkeit S. 215
Altsand 12523
Altsandaufbereitung 15516
altvulkanisch S. 12871
Alumel 442
Alumetieren S. 2759
Aluminar 444
Aluminit 445
Aluminium 446, 468/a,
Aluminiumblech 457, 461,
    16046
Aluminiumblock 19618
Aluminiumbronze 450
Aluminiumdraht 465
Aluminiumeisen 454
Aluminiumerz 456
Aluminiumfeilspan 451
Aluminiumgiesserei 453
Aluminiumlegierung 447,
    10778
Aluminiumluppe 452
Aluminiummessing 449
Aluminiumpulver 458
Aluminiumschaum S. 452,
    7511
Aluminiumschweissung 464
Aluminiumseisen 6940
Aluminiumsilikat 470
Aluminiumstahl 462
Aluminiumwalzwerk 460
Aluminothermie 18491
aluminothermische
    Schweissung S. 18492
Alumogel 469
Alundum 472

Alunit 471, 473
Alunitisation 474
alunitisiert 475
Alunogen 476
Amalgam 478, 484
Amalgamation 490, 498
— in Pfannen 501
— in rotierenden Fässern
    S. 500
Amalgamationsanlage 496
Amalgamationstrommel S.
    492
Amalgamationsverfahren
    487
Amalgamator 492 493/a,
    501/a, 8560
Amalgamausbrenntopf 485
Amalgamdestillationsofen
    480
Amalgamfänger 479
Amalgamfilter 482
amalgamieren 477, 489/a
Amalgamierer S. 492
Amalgamierpfanne 495
amalgamiert 491
Amalgamiertisch 497
Amalgamiervorrichtung
    499
Amalgampresse 486
Amalgamretorte 488
Amarantit 502
Amatol 503
Amazonenstein 8513
Amazonit 504
Ambatoarinit 505
Amblygonit 508, S. 9043
Amboss 677
Ambrit 509
Ambroid 509/a
Americium 513
amerikannischer Formkasten
    509/a, 510
— Gichtverschluss 512
Amesit 514
Amethysr 515
Amiant 516
Ammoniak 518
Ammoniakwasser 10871
Ammonioborit 521
Ammoniojarosit 522
Ammonit 523

Ammoniumkarbonat 2848
Ammoniummolybdat 526
Ammonsalpetersprengstoff 527
amorpher Brauneisenstein S. 2474
Amorphie 531/a
Amosit 532
Ampelit 535
Amperemesser 517
Amperemeter 4868
Amphibol 536
Amphibolitbildung 538
Amphibolith 537
Amphibolphonolith 679
amphoterer Elektrolyt 540
amygdaloidische Textur S. 544
an und aus 12539
an und aus Verbindung 12540
Anagenese 546
Analzium 547
Analyse 548
— auf nassem Weg 19984
Analysen-Fehlergrenze 10822
Analysenbefund 14788
Analysenbericht 549
analysenfertig 14470
Analysenkosten 4513
Analysenmethode 11612
Analysenunterschied 5393
Anamesit 551
Anamorphose 552
Anapait 553
anärob 545
Anatas 554
Anatexis 555, 14643
Anauxit 556
anbeizen S. 13837
Anblasen 1872/a, S. 9627, 17382
Anblasetechnik S. 1874
Anblaseverfahren 1874
anbohren 17813
Andalusit 561, 9281, S. 3415, S. 11042
Andesin 562
Andesit 563
andesitisch 564
Andorit 565
Andradit 566, 695

Andrewsit 567
Andruckwerkzeug für Lederhohlkehlen 7030
Anfahrdruck 17386
Anfahren der Erze 5153
— der Kohlen
Anfahrmoment 17383
Anfänger 17380
Anfangskaliber 7200
Anfangsproduktion 9809
Anfangsquerschnitt 7201
anfeuchten 11860
Anfeuchter 19803
anfeuern 7146, 10777
Anfeuern 7188
Anfeuern s. Anheizen
angebrannter Sand 2596
angefeuchtete Kohlenlösche 11861
angefressene Oberfläche 13426
angegossene Führungsleiste 3013
— Leiste S. 3015
— Muffe 3012
— Probeleiste 3011
angegossener Probestab 3015
— Zahnkranz 3917
— Zapfen 3014
angelassener Stahl S. 606, 18389
angelegte Belastung 7209
angelaufen 1914
angelaufener Stahl 1912
angenieteter Stiel 14977
angesäuertes Wasser 101
angeschlossene Giesserei S. 18612
angeschmolzener Sand 19577
angeschwemmt S. 5419
angeschwemmter Boden S. 411
angeschnittener Einguss 9779
angetriebene Walze 5457
angetriebener Rollgang 10899
angewandte Geologie 6190
angewärmte Schale 13839

angiessen 2976
Anglesit 586, 10623
Angriff 937,
Angriffrutsche 5969
Anguss S. 6886, 17211
Angussrest 15375
anhaftender Formstoff 148
Anhaltspunkt 1488, 5008
anhäufen 223
Anhäufung 2536
Anheizbrenner 4850
Anheizen eines Kessels 7190
Anheizkoks 1416
Anhöhe S. 14957
Anhydrit S. 10285, 593, 4820
Änigmatit 183
Anilinpunkt 11819
Anion 595
anisotrop 596
anisotroper Kristall 597
Anisotropie 597/a, 598,
Ankaufspreis 4517
Ankerblech S. 6155
Ankerdraht 8690
Ankerit 599, S. 2477
Ankerkeil 10528
Ankermast 5617
Ankerplatte 2177, S. 19648
Ankerrohrtour 557
Ankerschraube 556/a, 558
Ankerstahl 559
ankolben 18087
Anköpfen 8931/a
Ankunft 1200
Anlage für elektrische Hochfrequenz-Induktionsschweissen 9146
— mit Explosionsmotorenantrieb 13791
— zum Kaltziehen und Warm-Aufweiten 9412
Anlassbad 18390
Anlassdauer 18399
anlassen 14666, 18370, 18370/a, 18371
Anlassen auf Blau S. 1897
Anlasserwasser 13934
Anlassfarbe 18374
Anlasshärte 18396

Anlasshärtung 18375
Anlasskohlenstoff 18373/a
Anlassmaschine 17385
Anlassöl 10913, 18397
Anlass-sprödigkeit 18392
Anlassung S. 5811
Anlasswasser 10914
Anlauf-und Ablaufrollgänge 8656
Anlaufen 1915
Anlauffarbe S. 18374, 612
Anlaufmoment S. 17383
Anlaufscheibe 3365
Anlauftemperatur 18398
Anleg(e)mass-stab 1571
anliegende Antiklinale 14522
Annabergit 601
Annahmeverweigerung 14637
Anode 626
Anodenform 628
Anodenkupfer 627
Anodenoxydation S. 632
Anodenpotential 630
Anodenschlamm 629
anodische Oxydation 632, 634/a
anodischer Oberflächenschutz 631
— Schutz 632/a
Anordnung der Birnen 808
Anorthit 635, 2710, S. 4935
Anorthoklas 636, 16813
Anorthosit 637
Anpassung 46
Anpfahl 8907
Anreger 118
Anreicherung 4166, 6489/a
— der Mineralien 4168
— mit Sauerstoff 12828/a
Anreicherungsanlage 4170
anreissen 11328
Anreissen 11334
ansammeln S. 2530
Ansammlung s. Anhäufung
Ansatz 12857/a, 13230/a
Ansatzpunkt 10943
Ansatzschablone für Unterschneidungen 18280
Ansaugvolumen 887
Anschläger 1203, 1465,

2149, 2684, 9216, 10523, 11722, 12550, 13531, 15373, S. 17826
Anschlagpunkt 17662
— für die Bearbeitung S. 10184
Anschlagring 3581
Anschlagschiene S. 17625
Anschleifen S. 16008
anschliessen 4216
Anschluss für flexiblen Schlauch 7369
Anschlussgleis 10253
Anschlussglied 4219/a, 12902/a
Anschluss-stutzen 1733
Anschnitt 8089, 8093, 8105
— des Ringeingusses S. 13057
Anschwemmung 230, 410, 16170
anschrauben 11231
anspitzen S. 16006
anstählen S. 17453
anstehende Kohle 3837
ansteigender Fuchs S. 851
Ansteigung der Bohrlochsneigung 569
Anstieg 14943
Anstrich mit hohem Zinkgehalt 20329
Antennenanlage 10106
Antennenwinde 2044
Anthophyllit 639
Anthosiderit 640
Antrakonit 18127, 19406
Antrakose 650
Antrakylon S. 651
Anthrazenöl 641
Anthrazit 642, S. 1768, 8822
— von 60 bis 100 mm. 2440
Anthrazitbildung 645
anthrazitische Kohle 15836
Anthrazitkohle S. 642
Anthrazithochofen 643
Anthraziroheisen 644
antiferromagnetisch 661/a
Antigerinnsel 13744

antiklastich 653/a
Antiklinale 654, 657/a
Antiklinalfalte 19353
Antiklinalkamm 659
Antiklinalschenkel S. 10807
Antiklopfbrennstoff 667
Antiklopfmittel 666
Antimagnetstahl S. 12357
Antimon 669, 17571, 17575
Antimonblende S. 10312
Antimonblüte S. 20024
Antimonglanz 668, 17577
Antimonlegierung 667/a
Antimonit S. 668, 8497, S. 17577
Antimonnickel S. 2360
Antimonnickelglanz S. 19214
Antimonocker S. 17576
Antimonsilber S. 6158
Antimonsilberblende S. 14211
Antioxydationsmittel 12790
Antipode 671
Antlerit 675
Antozonit 676
Antriebsmaschine 5962, 5964
Antriebsscheibe 5966
Antriebskette 17210
Antriebswelle 5968
anwärmen 19666
Anwärmeherd 19671
Anzünden 9627, 10799
Anzündöffnung 10795
äolisch 921, 6499
äolische 185
— Seifen 6030
äolisches Gestein 928
Apatit 680
Apex 681
Apfelsinenschaleneffekt 375/a
Aphanit 684
aphanitisch 685
aphotische Region 686
Aphrit 687, S. 773
Aphrosiderit 688
Aphtalos 689
Aphthitalit S. 689
Aphtonit 690
Apjolinit 691
aplanatisch 692

Aplit 693
apochromatisch 696
apomagmatisch 697
Apophyse 699
Apparat für nichtzerstörende
   Untersuchungen 700
— zum Registrieren der
   Firstensenkung 4295
Appreturmaschine S. 7130
Aquamarin 725
Äquator 20319/a
Aquifer 727
äquimolekulare Lösung 653(
Äquivalent 17628
äquivalente Ablagerung S.
   9300
— Grubenöffnung 6533
Äquivalentkonzentration
   einer Lösung 6532
Äquivalenzfaktor 6531
Aragonit 729
Arakawait 730
Aramayoit 731
Arandisit 732
Aräo-Pyknometer nach
   Eichhorn S. 6230
Arapahit 733
Arbeiten im Ofeninnern
   20213
arbeitender Glockenofen
   17392
Arbeiterwohnung 20224
Arbeitsbühne 5218, 20250
Arbeitschwelle 20218
Arbeitsherd 8949, 8252
Arbeitskaliber 20209
Arbeitsort 7562, S. 19642
Arbeitsraum 20198, 20253
Arbeitsseite 20206
Arbeitsstoss 5276, 6750
Arbeitsstück (das) wenden
   19132
Arbeitswalze 20191
Arbeitszacken 7561
archäzoisch 760
archäozoische Ära 761
archatomische Schweissung
   753, 931
Ardennit 763, S.5287
Argental 770
Argentan 8195

Argentit 774, 784/a, 786/a,
   16353, 19573
Argentojarosit 775
Argentopyrit 776
Argillit 783, 15013
Argon 787
Argyrodit 785
Argyropyrit 786
Arit 788
Arizonit 789
Arkanit S. 689
Arkansit 790
Arkose 762, 791
arkosehaltig 792
Armabstand 13501
Armangit 795
Armco Eisen 797
arme Ader 10646
armes Erz 1284, 10643,
   11052, 13656
— Gas S. 10642, 13987/a
Armgas 10642
armiert s. bewährt
Armierung 4413
Armierungseisen 15272
armlegierter Stahl 11044
armschablone 18114
Ärolith 196
Äromagnetometer 245
Aromastoff 12458
aromatischer Rückstand
   806
Arrangement 13652
Arretierung der Säule 8799
Arsen 813
Arsenbestimmungsapparat
   703
Arsenblende 815
Arsenblüte 820
arsenführend 819
arsenhaltiges Eisenerz
   817
arsenige Säure 823
Arseniopleit 821
Arseniosiderit 822
Arsenkies 818, 823/a,
   829
Arsenikkalk S. 820
Arsenobismit 824
Arsenoklasit 825
Arsenolamprit 827

Arsenolith 828
Arsenpyrit S. 829
Arsensäureanhydrid 814
Arsensilberblende S. 14054
artesischer Brunnen 830,
   2090
Artinit 837
Asbest 840, 6170
Asbestschale 842
Asbestdichtung 845
Asbestdrahtnetz 848
Asbestgewebe 843
Asbesthandschuh 844
Asbestpapier 846
Asbestplatte 847
Asbestschnur 841
Asbesttuch S 843
Asbestwelle 849
Ascharit 857
Aschblei S. 6007
Aschenabfuhr 14710
Aschenfänger 3573
aschenfrei 865
Aschengehalt 864
Aschenkasten 867
Aschenkegel 863
Aschenkeller 861
Aschenkohle 862
aschenlochiges Eisen S.
   17144
Aschenrumpf 866
Aschensack 869
Aschenteller 868
Aschentuff 19575
Aschenzacken S. 1070
ascheriges Eisen S. 7363,
   S. 17144
Aschgehalt 13075
aschistisch 858
Aschynit 197
Ascoloy 860
Asiderit 870
Asmanit 871
Asphaltbearbeitung 879
Asphaltbildung 873
asphalthaltig 881
Asphaltgrobbeton 9181
Asphaltbit 885
asphaltischer Kohlenwasser-
   stoff 882
asphaltisches Pyrobitumen

884
Asphaltkalkstein 883
Asphaltlager 875
Asphaltmehl 877
Asphaltofen 876
Asphaltpech 1636
Asphaltrohöl 874
Astatin 902
Asterismus 905
Astian 906
Astrakanit 909
Astrolith 910
ästuarin s. lagunär
asymmetrische Antiklinale
    911
— Falte 912
Atakamit 915
Atelestit 918
Äther S. 6576
Äther-Extraktionsapparat
    nach Rothe 15236
Ätit 198
Atlasit 916
atmoklastisches Gestein
    920
atmophiles Element 922
Atmosphäre 923
atmosphärische Destillation
    929
atmosphärischer Einfluss
    925
— Sauerstoff 926
— Speiser 924
Atmungsventil 2351
Atom 930
Atomgewicht 933
Atomgruppe S. 11874
atomische H-Schweissung
    S. 931
atomisiertes feines Pulver
    9651
Atomzahl 932
Atopit 935
Aturian 941
Ätzen 6572
ätzen 630/a, 6571, 935/b
Ätzfiguren 6573
Ätzfläche 19492/a
Ätzkali 9509
— in Staugen 17579
Ätzkalk 19330/a

Ätzmittel 6571/a
ätzpolieren 6575
Ätzporen 6574/a
Ätzprobe 4490, 6575/a
Auerlith 942
Aufarbeitung 20203
Aufbau S. 1710
— der Ziegel 2538
— des Ofens 7832
aufbauen 9722
Aufbautrichter S. 14954
aufbereiten 1524
aufbereitete Kohle 5838
aufbereitetes Erz 5839,
    11710
Aufbereitungsanlage 4164,
    5844
— für Bleierze 1606
Aufbereitungsgut 13992
Aufbereitungsverlust 11024
Aufblähung 3108
aufblasen 1467
aufbohrbares Material 5913
aufbohren 5878
Aufbohrung 14479
aufbrausen 6216
Aufbrechen 2337, 14945
aufbrechen 2302, 2303,
    2304
Aufbruch S. 14372
Aufdeckarbeit 19331
Auffahren eines Aufhauens
    14375
— von Querschlägen S.
    4713
auffahren s. bohren od
    abtreiben
auffallendes Licht 9659
Auffangen der Funken
    3095
Auffangtank 7437
Auffrischen von verdorbenem
    Stahl 14784
Aufführung S. 3712
Aufgabeschnecke 6882
Aufgabetrichter 6879
Aufgabevorrichtung mittels
    Vibration 19547
Aufgasen S. 13917
aufgebauter Eingusstrichter
    13752

Aufgeben der Erze S. 3351
aufgemufftes Rohr 9835
aufgenieteter Kranz aus
    Winkeleisen 14976
aufgeraucht 14351/a
aufgeschalteter Zündimpuls
    17384
aufgeschraubter Deckel
    15716
aufgeschweisstes Metall
    5198
aufgespeicherte Wärme 53
aufgestriebenes Rohr 18954
aufgeweitetes und beider-
    seits aufgestauchtes
    Rohr 19072
Aufgichten (mit dem) auf-
    hören 3128
Aufgichtvorrichtung 3349,
    3339
aufgraben 5404, 5447
Aufhängebügel 18080
aufhängen S. 10517
Aufhänger 9320
Aufhängung 8804
Aufhängungsdraht 18082
aufhauen 14941
Aufhauen 14372, 14942,
    14946
aufheben 13201
Aufheizzeit 9018
aufklappbarer Formkasten
    S. 9206, S. 16779
aufkochen 1998
aufkohlen 2884
Aufkohlung 2867, 2883,
    2885
Auflage 2237
Auflockerung 2322
Auflösung 16900
aufnehmen 5547
Aufnehmen vom Lager 18220
Aufpressung 9929
aufquellen 18120
aufquellender Ton 18124
aufrecht giessen 18738
aufrechte Antiklinale 6537
— Falte 19369
Aufreiber 2429
aufreissen 3468
Aufriss S. 5790, 6375

Aufrühren 17608
Aufsatzrahmen 7034
Aufsatzstange 165
Aufschichtung 807
Aufschieben der Förder-
  wagen S. 12553
Aufschiebung S. 12740, S.
  12765, 14948, 18595,
  19349, 19350, 19385
aufschliessen 12602
Aufschliessung 936
Aufschluss S. 6692
Aufschlussbohrung 14034,
  14058, 18443, 20067
— zur Ermittlung der
  Grösse des Vorkommens
  6998
Aufschluss. schacht in
  unbekanntem Gebiet
  14414
Aufschluss-strecke 11902
aufschrumpfen 16224
Aufschüttungsmasse 7037
Aufschüttungsterrasse 409
Aufschweisslegierung 8870
Aufschweissmaschine für
  Schneidplättchen 6312
Aufseher 2126
Aufsetzvorrichtung 2682,
  3087, 6813, 10299,
  16242
Aufsicht 18024
Aufspaltung 17135
Aufspannplatten 13502
Aufstapelung 13284
Aufstampfboden 17323
Aufstechen des Abstich-
  loches 13242
aufsteckbarer 5251
Aufsteckreibahle 16111
aufsteigende Geschwindig-
  keit 853
aufsteigende Wetterführung
  19354, 19432
aufsteigender Wetterstrom
  14958, 19348
aufsteigendes Wasser 854
Aufstemmung 11170
Aufstreuen von Sand 15495
Aufsuchen 14033
— der Lagerstätte auf

Grund von Bruchstücken
  derselben 16142
Auftragwalze 6147
Auftriebshöhe S. 9574
Aufwallen S. 1998
Aufwärtshub 19381
Aufweitkrätzer 19652
Aufweitversuch 2548
Aufwerfhammer 10748
aufwickeln 20085
aufwickeln (sich) 19672
aufwinden 20084
aufwölben S. 5510
Aufwölbung 19674, S.
  19677
aufziehen 14370,
  16234/a
Aufzug 9224, 10739
Aufzugkübel 16486
Aufzugmaschine S. 9232
Aufzugvorrichtung 10754
Aufzugwinde S. 9236
Auge der Form 12610
Augenbolzen 6729, 15700
Augelith 943
Augenachat 6728
Augengneis 944
Augenlinse 6731
Augenstruktur 6732
Augit 948
augitartig 950
Augitporphyr 951
Augitsyenit 949
Aureole von Sicherheits-
  lampe S. 1901
Aurichalcit 952
Auripigment S.816, 10366,
  12678, 14437, 20282
Ausbauchen 2347
ausbauchen 5510, S. 10095
Ausbauchung 1470, S.
  2578, 2768, S. 5517,
  18121
ausbauen S. 14124
Ausbeissen S. 1320, 12694
— der Schicht 4662
Aussbessern 2606/a
ausbessern 7113, 11487
Ausbesserung 7125, 12967
ausbesserungsbedürftig
  9680

Ausbesserungsmasse 10854
Ausbesserungswerkstatt
  14731
Ausbeute S. 14511
ausbeuten S. 6679
Ausbeutung S. 20194
Ausbiss 6692, S. 10837,
  15021
Ausblasen 1877
ausblasen 1846
Ausblaseventil 6102
Ausblasevorrichtung 1872
ausbleiben S. 10603
Ausblühungen 17168/a
Ausbohren 2094, S. 5880
ausbohren 18872
ausbreiten 7348
Ausbreit(e)probe 8749
Ausbringen 14511
Ausbruch 1757, 1860, 8558,
  8676
Ausbruchdrosselhahn 7421
Ausbrucherscheinung 19591
Ausbruchkopf 7425
Ausbruchproduktion 7485
Ausbruchschieber S. 1862
Ausbruchventil 1862
ausdehnbare Metallstrebe
  12835
Ausdehnung 1408
Ausdehnungshub 13796
Ausdehnungskurve 10997
Ausdrücker 14200
Auseinandernehmen 12609
ausfahren 8203
Ausfahrt 856, 10759
Ausfallabstich 12460/a
ausfällen S. 13806
Ausfällung der Verunreini-
  gung 13817
Ausflussöffnung 12411,
  18358
Ausflussrohr 7429
Ausfrieren der Erze 7746
Ausfrierungsverfahren S.
  7747
Ausführungsdraht 10632
Ausfüllstoff 12851
Ausfüllung 19486
Ausfüllungsschacht 7492
Ausfunkzeit 16988

Ausfurchung 7881
Ausfütterung S. 8960
Ausgangsblock 2691/a
Ausgangseisen 1279
Ausgangspunkt 10183
ausgebauchte Form 4158
ausgeglichene Produktion S. 15922
ausgeglühter Draht 607, 1896
— Stahl 606
ausgeglühtes Eisenblech 605
ausgehärtet 216
ausgehen (einer Lagerstätte) 12693
Ausgehen 12694
ausgehen lassen S. 1843
Ausgehende 1320, 1403, 5020, 10837, 18059 18069
ausgekehlte Walze 8593
ausgeleert 5745
ausgemauerte Feuergrube 2376
ausgenutztes Bad 10354/a
ausgerichtete Platte 17723
ausgespart S. 7615
ausgesuchtes Muster 13209
ausgewalzt S. 15094
ausgewaschenes Goldteil- chen 7386
ausgezogener Mittelschen- kel 17792
ausgezogenes Glas 16056
Ausgiessen 7036
— eines Lagers S. 10852
ausgiessen 13738, S. 18354
Ausgleichaufhängung 4109
Ausgleichdruck 1136/a
ausgleichen 1121, 18322
Ausgleicher 6526
Ausgleichrohr 4110
Ausgleichschrot 18324
Ausgleichzone 16797/a
ausglühen 602, 7794, S.2712
Ausglühen des Stahls 619
Ausglühverfahren 618
Ausgraben S. 18872
Ausguss 16412
Ausgussanschlüsse

anbringen 15344
Ausgusskopf S. 2943
Aushärten 13813
Aushärtung 13815
Aushärtungsglühung S. 13813
Aushauen 3477/a
aushauen 4892
Aushebeband 7906/a, 10758
Aushebeeisen 5787/a, 13211/a, 14428
Aushebeplatte 10773
Aushebeschraube 12990
Aushebevorrichtung 17871
Aushubtisch 16393
Auskeilen 1352, 12298, 12300, 18214
auskeilen 5355, 6451, 7718
auskesseln 19877
Auskesseln der Bohrlöcher 17205, 17267, 2605
Auskesselung 19697
— des Bohrloches 3274
Auskesselung in der Firste 1073
ausklauben 4825, 13198, 13200
Ausklaubung S. 3213
auskleiden S. 2907, S. 15343
Auskleidung S. 10489, 14629
Auskeilen 1595, 19889
auskeilen 18277
Auskragung S. 10860
auskratzen 5879
Auskratzung 19326
Ausladen 19321
Auslass 10482
Auslasshahn 1756
Auslass-stutzen 12412
Auslassventil S. 1857, 6565
auslaufen 10635
Ausläufer S. 699, 12468, S. 17224
Auslaufplatte 7289/a
Auslauger 6708
Auslaugtrichter 6710
ausleeren 5489, 10399

Ausleeren S. 10400, 15966
— durch Brechstange 1217
— durch Rütteln 10402
— durch Vibration 11408
Ausleerrüttler 15967
Ausleger 12718
Auslegerbohrmaschine S. 14326
Auslegerkran 12753
auslochen 11939
Auslösmeissel 18893
Auslösevorrichtung 12303
Auslösung 14682
Ausmasse 12732
Ausmauern der Birne 10856
Ausmauerung 11355
ausmeisseln 721
Ausmeisselmaschine 3476
Ausnahmesatz 17022
Ausprägen 3925
Auspuffrohr 5496, 6652
Auspumpen durch Pumpen- ständer 17948
— unter Druck 17261
Ausräumen 3713
ausrichten die Blechtafeln 17722
Ausrichtmaschine 3218
Ausrichtrahmen 3216
Ausrichtungs-und Vorrich- tungsarbeiten 5279
ausrückbare Kupplung 16619
Ausrüstung 12699
— des Ofens 9973
ausschalten 18904
Ausschalter 2316
ausschaufeln 15638
Ausscheidung 15868
— von Garschaumgraphit 10377
Ausscheidungshärtung 215
Ausschieben S. 5064
Ausschlacken S. 5240, S. 14385
ausschlacken S. 5765, S. 18270
ausschlagen S. 10399
Ausschlagen 10400, S. 15966
Ausschlagofen 15970
Ausschlagrost 10405

Ausschlagrüttler S. 15967
Ausschlagstelle 10406
ausschleifen S. 8537
ausschmieden 7571, 7574,
    S. 8727
Ausschneiden 1695/a
Ausschneidebohrer 6671
Ausschnitt S. 10117
ausschöpfen S. 15638
Ausschubwagen 18946
Ausschuss 15679
Auschussblech 16060,
    16079
Auschusskohlenklein 6006
Auschuss· stück 10636
Auschüttkankasten 18943
ausschwentbare Gegendruck-
    platte 13887
Ausschwitzen S. 18103
ausschwitzender Kern 19891
Ausschwitzung S. 10866
Aussehen der Schlacke 719
Aussenbedienung S. 15480
Aussenfeuerung 6702
Aussengewinde schneiden
    4894
Aussenkern S. 9841
Aussenkokille 18 /44
Aussenleiter 12698
Aussenrundschleif-
    maschine 15079
ausser Betrieb 12473, 12691
Ausserbetriebsetzung 17688,
    19613
äussere Lichtquelle 6697
äusseres Kernrohr 12696
Aussetzdestillierapparat
    1335
Ausspritzen und Einbrand
    17187
Ausspülung 7481
Ausspülungsöl 7491
Ausstählung S. 103
Ausstampfen 10851, 14404
ausstanzen 14173
Ausstattung S. 12699
Austausch der Analysen
    6145
Austenit 956
austenitisch 957
austenitischer Stahl 959

austenitisches Gusseisen
    958
— Korn 956/a
Austenitisierung 955
Austoss 5499
Austossen 6237/a
austossen S. 6971
austossen s. ausziehen
Austosslochstempel 17858a
Austreiben flüchtiger
    Bestandteile 6674
Austreibung von Wasser
    6694
Ausstreichendes 10837
Ausstrich 4554, S. 10837
Ausströmkanal 6653
Austrittseite 6656
Aus-und Einbau des Bohr-
    gestänges 15294
Auswahl der Proben S.
    15807
auswalzen S. 10503,
    15067, 15120
Auswaschung 6545
auswechselbar 9869
auswechselbare Schnauze
    9870
auswechselbarer Form-
    einsatz 9871
auswechselbares Teil 9872
Auswechseln der Zimmerung
    14692, 14793
Ausweichungsclivage
    6782, 17735
Auswerfauge S. 6237
auswerfen 6235
Auswerfer 6241
Auswerferanschlag 6239
Auswerferdeckplatte 2155
Auswerfformhälfte 12047
Auswerflappen 6237
Auswerferplatte 6238
Auswerferstift S. 6241
Auswirkung der naturge-
    gebenen Kräfte 14782
Auswurfkasten 17197
Auswurflinge 6236
ausziehbarer Formkasten
    Innenherausnehmen
    18287
— Meissel 4013

ausziehen 5757, 6706
ausziehende Wetterstrecke
    12717, 14809
ausziehender Schacht 19351
— Wetterschacht S. 19384
Ausziehschacht 14814,
    19347, 19384
Ausziehvorrichtung 10403,
    20159
Ausziehwinkel 18279/a
Auszugofen 1948
Auszugtiegelofen 10749
auszuschneidende Hohlkohle
    S. 7028
auszuschneidende Kante
    7028
authigen 960, 961/a
authigenes Gestein 961
autochton 963
autochtone Gesteine 964
autogen 966
— geschweisst 972
Autogen-Schweissung
    968
autogene Rillung 8013/a,
    8587/a
autogenes Schweissen 67
Autogenpresschweissung
    S. 970
Autoklav 965
Autoklaventrommel 5405
Automatenkipper S. 990
Automatenstahl 989
Automatenweichstahl 11679
automatische Aufschieb-
    vorrichtung 974
— Beschickungseinrich-
    tung 977
— elektrische Steuerung
    6359
— Futterdrehbank 962
— Sandaufbereitung 988
— Schmiedemaschine 982
— Waage für Kohlenklein
    1587
— Zufuhr 981
automatisches Spill 975
Automolit 994
automorph 995, 6589
autoneomorph 996
Autopneumatolyse 997

Autunit 998, S. 10817
Auversian 999

B

Babingtonit 1039
Babosches Siedeblech 1040
Backe 12041, 14391
backen 1112, 2690
Backen 2694
— des Kokses 2697
— für Nachbohrer S. 19276
Backenbremse 16153
backende Sinterkohle 1118
— Steinkohle S. 2696
Backenfänger 2958
Backenfutter 10142
Backenkupplung 7209
Backenmeissel 11948
Backenschiene 17625
Backkole 1119, 2696
Backfähigkeit 2695
Backofenrohr 18988
Bad 1338, 8972
Badbewegung 1953, 20197
Baddeleyit 1092, S. 2291
Bagger 1098, S. 5729, 6636,
    17864
Baggerbetrieb 5823, 5825
Baggereimer 4318, S. 15639,
    S. 8377
Baggergut 17141
Baggerkette S. 2498
baggern 5727
Baggerschaufel 5729, 5827
Baggertorf 5824
Bainit 1110
Balancier S. 14164
balancieren 12462
Balasrubin 15331
Baldaufit 1142
Balgliese S. 12414
Balkenwerk 1380
Ballen der Walze S. 1940
ballenförmig 1161
ballige Walze 4210
Ballon 2873
Ballonabfüller 2874
Ballonfilter 2875

Ballonkipper 2876
Band 1175, S. 16252, S,
    17781
— (mit) umwickelter
    Draht 18273
Bandachat 1181
Bandage 17781
Bandeisen 1177, 9322,
    9324, S. 17844
Bandeisenstrecke 9325
Bandeisenwalzwerk 7954
Bandertextur S. 14869
Banderton 1182
Bänderung 1185
Bandförderer 1176, 2660
Bandförderung 1472
Bandgesims 13476
Bandjaspis 1183/a
Bandknick 3923
Bandmass 18272
Bandsägestahl 1188
Bandstahl 17855
Bandstärke 17856
Bandstrasse 17847
Bandstreifen-Walzwerk
    17846
Bandwalzwerk 17854
Bandziehmaschine 7353
Bank S. 10594
Bankazinn 1173
bankig S. 13534
bankige Absonderung
    16064, 16082
Bankstampfer 16186
Bär 8730
Bardiglio 1224
Bardolith 1225
Barffschess Verfahren
    1230/a
Barium 1234
Bariumacetat 60
Bariumchlorid 3494
Bariumkarbonat 2849
Bariummonoxyd S. 1260
Bariumoxyd S. 12794
Bariumsulfat S. 17968
Barkevikit 1235
barometrische Höhen-
    messung 1237
barometrisches Rohr 17087
Barranco 1238

Barre S. 9782
Barren 1206, 9783, 13480
Barrenschmelzgrube 13248
Barrenwalzwerk 1219
Barrenzange 8414
Barrieriff 1250
Bart S. 2618
Bartonian 1255
Bartriss 7066
Barylith 1257
Barysilit. 1258
Barysphäre 1259
Baryt 1234/a, 1260, S. 9031
Barytocalcit 1262
Barytocölestin 1263
Barytsulfat 1233
Barytwasser 1261
Baryumfeldspat S. 3136,
    9499
Bärzylinder 8730
Basalkonglomerat 1278
Basalt 1267
basaltartige Form 1269
Basaltgang 20016
Basaltglas S. 18198
basalthaltig 1268
Basalttuff 1270
Basanit 1271, S. 18795
Basis S. 1273, S. 2142,
    16336, S. 18701
basische Gesteine 1304
— Schlacke S. 1305, 13167
basischer Bodenstein
    1293/a
— feuerfester Stoff 1503
— Konverter 1295
— Martinofen 1299
— Siemens-Martinstahl
    1300
— Stahl 1306
— Stein 1294
basisches Oxyd 1301
— Roheisen S. 1297
— Verfahren S. 1302
Basision 1296
Basismetall 12934
Basis-Spaltbarkeit 1264
Basizität 1308
Basizitätsgrad 9735, 14022
Bassanit 1319

Bastit 1323, S. 15623
Bastnäsit 1324
Batholith 1339, 1341/a, 12033
Batrachit 1343
Batroklas 2169, 4697, 9339, S. 16065
bathyale Ablagerungen 1340
— Fazies 1341
Batterie 1346
Batteriekessel 1347
Batteriemanöver 18908
Batterienglas 1348
Baublech 17894
Bauch 2341
Baueisen 4235
baufällig 12690
Baugerüst 15576
Bauguss 17884
Bauhöhe 10741
Baumachat 741
Baumann-Abdruck 1353, 17984
Baume-Dichte 1354
baumförmig 738
Baumhauerit 1355
Baumwolldraht 4524
baumwollumsponnener Draht S. 4524
Bauprofile S. 9041
Baustahl 17892
Baustoff 2535
Bauxit 1356, 1405/a
Bauxitofen 1357
Bauwinde mit Konsole 2243
Bavenit 1358
Bayldonit 1360
Bazzit 1362
Bearbeitbarkeit 11116, 20193
— eines Materials 11117
bearbeiten 7496
bearbeiteter Stahl 13982
bearbeitetes Metall 20245
Bearbeitung 18868, 20196/a
— der Gusstücke 7126
Bearbeitungsasphalt 880
Bearbeitungszugabe 394, 11140
Beanspruchung 17730, 17782, 20220/a
— auf Drehung S. 18782

Beanspruchung auf Knickung S. 4640
— auf Schlagfestigkeit S. 16147
Beaverit 1406
Becherglas 1377
Becherkettenförderer S. 2502
Becherriss 4835
Becherwerk 2500, 2502, 6378
Beckelith 1407
Becken 1309
Becquerelit 1411
bedecken 11299
bedecktes Frischfeuer 4567
Beegerit 1438
beendigt 7119
Befestigungsmuffe für den zweiten Pfropfen 17302
Befestigungsring 17664
Befeuerung der Dampfkessel 7192
Begichter 3330
Begleitelemente 1475/a
Begleitmineral 47
Begleitort 273, 1054
Begleitstrecke S. 273 S. 1054
Behälter 2910
Behälterblech 18252
Behandlung 3673
Behandlungsanlage 18867
Behandlungsmannschaft 3680
Behandlungsweise 11615
behauen 1926
behinderte Schwindung 9197
Beidellit 1442
Beiladung 18025
Beilagekaliber 18509
Beimengung 174
Bein S. 17228, 17911
Beizanlage 13228
Beizbottich 13230
Beizbrüchigkeit 4489
Beizen des Drahtes 13229
Beizer 3687
Beizsprödigkeit 79
Beiztrog 13222

Beizung 3691, 13225
Beizvergoldung 13272
Bekleidung 19703
Bekleidungsblech 18201
beladen S. 10465
Belag 19860
Belagblech für Fussböden S. 7407
Belastung an der Proportionalitätsgrenze 10908
— an der 0,2%-Grenze 10907
Belastungsdauer 18642
Belastungsfähigkeit 10910
Belastungsgefäss 19904
Belastungsgewicht 19914, 19915
Belastungsgrenzen 10921/a
Belastungsmetamorphose 10912
Belastungsplatte S. 19913
Belastungsring 14931
Belemnit 1443
beleuchtetes Objekt 9633
Beleuchtung 9634
Beleuchtungsanlage 10796
Beleuchtungskohle 10794
Beleuchtungsmast 17340
Beleuchtungs-und Kraftübertragungswerk 10793
Beleuchtungsvorrichtung 9635
Beleuchtungswerk 10798
Beleuchtungszentrale S. 10798
belgische Drahtstrasse 1444
belgischer Gasfang S. 3590, 14409
belichten 6690
Bell-Kruppmetall 1452/a
Bellevillekessel 1463
Bellit 1464
belüftet 19507
Belüftungsapparat S. 189
Bementit 1482
Benetzbarkeit 20001
Benetzungszone 17112
Benetzvorrichtung 17209
Benitoit 1525
Benjaminit 1526
Benthos 1529

Bentonit 1530 , 5180
Benutzt 12613
Benzinbrenner 1531
Benzin - bzw. Kerosen-
    raffinerie 18762
Benzin-und Wasserab-
    scheiden aus Erdgas 8080
Benzol 1530, 1532
Beobachtung 12436
bepanzern 798
Beplattung 13512
Beraunit 1533
Berechnung der Analyse
    2735
— der Beschickung 2733
— der Schlacken 2734
— des Möllers 2736
Bereissen der Firste 15598
Bereitung 12642
Beresit 1534
Bergbau S. 1036, 11769,
    11776
— Werkzeugstahl 18731
Berge 14638, S. 19718, 19735
Berghalde 14642
Bergemauer 12837, 12846,
    14982
Bergemittel S. 5475, 5852,
    12945
Bergen versetzen (mit) 3905
Bergerippe S. 12837, 18038
Bergerolle 19721, 15012
Bergeseife 15029/a
Bergezwischenanlage 5475
Bergflachs S. 4651
Bergfeuchtigkeit 19800
Bergglas S. 1535
Berggrün 12032
Bergholz 20185
Bergknappe S. 11746
Bergkristall 1535, 15014
Berglasur 1036
Bergleder 12034
Bergmann 11746; 13422
Bergmilch 207/a
Bergrutsch 16607
Bergschrund S. 2195
Bergsporn 17224
Bergversatz 12828
Bergwachs S. 12821
Bergwerk S. 11724, 13397

Bergwerksanlagen S. 15408
Bergwerksgesellschaft S.
    1120
Bergwerksmaschine S. 11777
Bergzinn 11743
berieseln 10041
Berieselung 10042, 17207,
    S. 17186
Berieselungsfläche S. 10043
Berieselungsrohr 19005
Berkelium 1536
Berlinit 1537
Berme 1537/a
Bernstein 506, S. 17937
Bersten S. 6682
— eines Kessels S. 1958
Berthierit 1539
Bertrandit 1541
Bertrandsche Linse 1540
beruhigter Stahl 10351,
    14886/a
Beruhigung 10352
Beryll 1542
Beryllium 1544
Berylliumbronze 1545
Berylliumoxyd 1543
Beryllonit 1546
Berzelianit 1547
Berzeliit 1548
Besatzeinbringen S. 2568,
    2072, 17538, S. 18234
Besatzpatrone 17539,
Beschaffenheit 14247
beschicken 3313
Beschicken 3331
— der Erze S. 3351
Beschicker S. 3330
Beschickkran 3338
Beschickmaschine S. 3340
Beschickmulde 3335
Beschickung 11478, 17637
Beschickungskran S. 3338
Beschickungsmulde S. 3335,
    S. 7660
Beschickungsoberfläche
    17622
Beschickungsöl 3327
Beschickungssäule 17618
Beschickungstrichter S.
    6879, 6892
Beschickungsvorrichtung S.

S. 3332, S. 3339
Beschickungswagen 1949,
    S. 3328
Beschickwagen 3328
Beschleunigung 38
Beschleunigungsmesser 40
Beschneiden 18899
Beschneidmaschine 18898
beschnittene Kante 16027/a
beschränkte Löslichkeit
    10825
— Mischbarkeit 12942
Beschränkungsaufhebung
    2138
Beschwereisen S. 19915
Beschwerplatte 19913
Beschwerungsmittel 19910
Beseitigen von Ofenbären
    16544
Beseitigung des Glühspans
    14722
Besetzen 8827, 18234
besetzen 14889, 17532,
    18230
besonderes Härtungs-
    verfahren 17016
besponnener Draht S. 4569
bespritzen 17179
Bessemerbirne 1550
Bessemer Eisen 1551
Bessemerfluss·stahl 1556
Bessemerkonverter S. 1550
Bessemern S. 1559
Bessemerroheisen 1552,
    9076
Bessemerschlacke 1555
Bessemerstahl 76
Bessemerstahlwerk 1558
Bessemer-und Thomasanlage
    1557
Bessemerverfahren 1553,
    1554, 1559
beständige Emulsion S.
    17272
Bestandteil einer
    Verbindung 4233
Bestaubung S. 15979
Besteckstanzen 4564
Besteg S. 8372
Bestimmung der Stückgrösse
    durch Absieben 16446

Bestmaschinengusseisen 1561

Beta-Eisen 1565

Betätigungsstange 18909

Beton 1566

Betoneisen 4176, 14677

Betonunterlage 4174

Betrieb 20194, 20196

— des Puddelofens 20248,

— in 9675, 9681

Betriebsdruck 20217, 20252

Betriebsdruckstufe 15899

Betriebsingenieur 6472

Betriebskessel 13466

Betriebskreisprozess 12614

Betriebslaboratorium 20225

Betriebsspannung 15901/a, 20222

Betriebsstoff mit hoher Oktanzahl 9160

Betriebsstörungen 10040

Betriebsstrom 20202

Betriebstänk 20192

Betriebsunkosten 20205

Bettgestein 1435

Bettung S. 1169

Beuge S. 7372

Beule 5178

Beurteilung nach dem Aussehen 6631

bewegliche Aufgabe- vorrichtung 15038

— Aufspannplatte 12050

— Bohrplattform 11846

— Bühne 6787

— Formhälfte S. 12047

— Stahlzapfenlagerung 18142

— Stange 3333

beweglicher Bohrer 11847

— Kessel 13691

— Magnet 12048

— Rost 15971

— Zylinder der Pumpe 18859

Bewegung des Hebels 12052

Bewegungsrichtung 5467

bewehrte Schiene 18609

Bewertungsfilter 19911

bewettern 6792

Bewitterung 19870

Bezahlung mit zu Grunde gelegtem Raummasse 6829

Bezeichnung des Erzes 3639

Bezugsebene 17169

Bezugshorizont S. 11331

Bianscher Wascher 1573

Bichromatbeize 3527

Bieberit 1576

biegbar 13548

Biegebacken 1509

Biegebeanspruchung 1518

Biegebruch 7493/a

Biegehalbmesser 1516

Biegemaschine 1504, 1511

biegen 1498, S. 4873

Biegepfeil 5120

Biegepresse 1515

Biegeprobe 1521

Biegespannung 1520

Biegestelle 1514

Biegeversuch 1503

biegsam S. 13548

biegsame Welle 7368

biegsames Rohr für Einspritzkopf 17506

Biegung 1505

— um 180° 1523

Biegungselastizität 6249

Biegungsfestigkeit 1519

Biegungslinie 1510

Biegungsmoment 1512

Biegungswinkel 1507

Bienenkorbofen 1439

Bildsamkeit S. 13474

Bildstein S. 206

Bildung der Feststehenden 1289

— einer Zwischenphase S. 13103

Bilinit 1579

Bimetall 18494/a

bimetallisch 1589

Bimetallrohr 6114/a

Bimssand 14153

Bimsstein 14152

bimssteinartig 14154

binäre Legierung 1590

Binärstahl 1592

Bindeeigenschaft 2024

Bindekraft 3920

Bindemittel 1597, 1602, 2023, 3142

— zusetzen 130

Bindephase 1599/a

Bindevermögen 3178

Bindefaden 17832

Bindheimit 1596

Bindung von Wärme durch Verdampfung 19

Binnit 1607

Biolith 1608

Biotit 1609, 1656

Biotitgranit 12378

Birkenkohle 1611

Birne aufrichten 18625

— mit Seitenwind 16256/a

Birnenauswurf 4305, 5492

Birnenbodenform 4300

Birneneinguss 17686

birnenförmiger Dorn 13011

Birnenhalle 4306

Birnenring 18960

Birnenständer 4307

Birnenverfahren 4304

Birnenwabenstruktur S. 11940

Bisbeeit 1612

Bischofit 1613

Bismit 1614

Bismutoplagionit 1619

Bismutosphärit 1620

Bismutotantalit 1621

Bittersalz 1632, S. 17971,

Bitterspat 1633, S. 13245

bituminöse Kohle 1634, 16831

bituminöser Tonschiefer 1594

bituminöses Gestein 1637

Bityit 1639

Blackband 1643, 1644

blank gezogener Stahl 2395

— reiben 13624

blanker Draht 19231

blankgeschliffen 2397

blankgezogen 2394

blankgewalzt 2393

Blankglühen 2391

Blankhärtung 2398

Blankschleifen 2403
blankziehen 2396
Blasdüse 12409
Blase 249, 1754, 1780, 1781, 1852, 1868, S. 1955
Blasebalg 1466, 8755
Blasebalgrohr S. 1414
Blasen 1851, 1869
— unter vollem Druck 1879
blasen 1839, 19136
Blasenbildung 17138
blasend 13541
blasende Bewetterung 13542
blasender Ventilator 12703, 13894, 13904
blasenfreier Stahl 1786
Blasenguss 1880, 8084
blasenloser Stahl 19232
Blasenstahl 1784
Blaseofen S. 1706
Bläser 13375
Blasformkappe 19159/a
blasige Textur 19540
blasiger Guss 9304, S. 1880
blasiges Eisen S. 7363
Blaskammer S. 15481
Blaslötrohr 12043
Blaslunker 5774
Blasrohr S. 1861
blastogranitisch 1751
blastoporphyrische Struktur 1752
Blasversatz 13589, 13598
Blatt 7519, 7526, 10499, S. 16044
Blattblei S. 16066
Blättchen S. 7249
blätterig 7529, 10500, 16993, 19840
blätterige Kohle 15978
— Steinkohle S. 7530
Blätterkohle S. 7530
blättern 7528
Blättertellur S. 7534, 12159
Blätterung 13483
Blatterzeolith S. 9112
Blattfeder 10634
Blattgold 8347/a
Blattmessing S. 13488

blättrig S. 10500
blättriger Bruch 10506
blättriges Gefüge 10502
Blattrippe S. 19493
Blattsäge 1178
Blattvergoldung 8345
Blattzinn S. 18648
blau angelassen (auf) S. 1895
— anlaufen lassen 1894
— gefärbte Blasen 14468
Blaubrenner 1902/a
Blaubruch 1900
blaubrüchig 1899
Blaueisenerz S. 1904
blauer Asbest 4651
— Flammensaum 1901
— kupferhaltiger Tonschiefer 1907
— Streifen 1913
— Ton 1902
— Vesuvian S. 4953
blaues Stahlblech 1911
Blauglühen 1897
blauglühend 1903
blaugrüner Saphir 3080/a
Blauofen S. 7442
Blauschimmer 177/a
Blauspat S. 10601
Blausprödigkeit S. 1900
Blaustein S. 1904
Blaustift 1910
Blauwarm S. 1903
Blech 7345, 16044, 16068, 16074/a
— mit gebohrten Löchern 5914
— walzen S. 16077
Blecharbeit 16072
Blechbiegemaschine 13487
Blecheinlage 16129/a
Blechgefäss 17509
Blechglühofen 13491
Blechhalter 1683
Blechlehre 16055, 16070
Blechmantel 2930, 10012
Blechpanzerung 802
Blechplatte 16058
Blechrohr 16062
Blechschere 16080
Blechschild 18651

Blechschneidemaschine 5952
Blechstärke 13500
Blechstrasse S. 16074
Blechstrecke 16074, 16078
Blechtrio S. 18560
Blechwalze 13482, 13494, 16076
blechwalzen 16077
Blechwalzenstreckmaschine 16071
Blechwalzwerk 10508, 13497, 16073
Blei 10604
— anlassen (in) 10615
Bleiacetat 10605
Bleiantimon 8836
Bleibadhärten 10608
bleibender Anstrich 13104
Bleibenzin 10613
Bleiblech 16066
Bleibronze 4357/a, 4855, 10610, 12430
Bleicherde S. 7810
Bleidraht 10626
Bleierz 2205, 2059, 6904
Bleierzofen 15651
Bleiflasche 10609
Bleiglanz 7912, 10614, S. 13266
Bleiglätte S. 10619
bleihaltiges Eisenerz 9989
— Zinn 18647
Bleihornerz S. 9368
Bleiklumpen S. 13266
Bleikönig S. 1365
Bleilegierung 10606
bleilöten 18429
Bleinaphthenat 10618
Bleiofen 10625
Bleioleat 10620
Bleioxyd 10619, 12799
Bleiplatte S. 16066
Bleiröhre 10621
Bleischale 10607
Bleischuss S. 10614
Bleischweif 1760
Bleispiegel 6858
Bleistreifen 7760/a
Bleistege 10612
Bleistein 10616
Bleisuperoxyd 13100

Bleivitriol S. 10623
Bleiweiss 20036
Bleizucker S. 10605
Blende 1761, 5337
Blenden 15931
Blendenkonzentrat 1762
Blenderöstofen 1763
beweglicher Kessel 12046
blind 1766
blinde Strecke S. 10147
blinder Kern 1770
blindes Kaliber S. 6785
— Rohr 1684
Blindflansch 1682, 1773
Blindkaliber 6785
Blindort 334, 1774, 5027,
5043, 10147
Blindpfeiler 6093
Blindschacht 1779, S. 19849,
10094, 10896, 15982,
17374, 20114
Blindspeiser S. 1772
Blindstrecke 1771
Blitz 7289
Blitzkessel 7291
Blitzrohr S. 7793
Blitzröstung 7300
Block 1793, 3042, 9782
— einspannen (den) 8565
— wenden (den) 19134
Block s. Bramme od. Luppe
Blockabstreifkran 9803
Blockausdrücker 9797
Blockblei S. 13266
Blockbruchbau 1797
Blockchargierkran S. 9786
Blockchargierwagen S. 9785
Blockdrücker S. 9797, 9798
Blöcke 1835
Blockeisen 7464
Blockeinsetzkran 9786
Blockeinsetzwagen 9785
Blockeinspannvorrichtung
9793
Blockförderkran S. 9789
Blockform S. 9795
Blockgerüst S. 1831, 15262
blockgiessen 2975, 9781
Blockgreifer 9792
Blockguss 3006, 9805
Blockhalter 2206/a,

13699/a, 17281
Blockkopf 9791
Blockkran 9789
Blockkupfer 9788
Blocklager 9801
Blockschere 1824
Blockstrasse 1832
Blockstrecke S. 1832
Blockteilmaschine 9799
Blocktransport 9787
Blockwagen 1585, 9784
Blockwalze 3914
Blockwalzgerüst 1831
Blockwalzkaliber S. 1833
Blockwalzen 15257/a
Blockwalzwerk 1821/a,
1834
Blockzange S. 9792, 9804
Block-zangenkran 9790
Blockzerfall 1799
Blockziehkran S. 4597
Blockzinn 1805, 13270
Blodit 1813
Blomstrandin 1814
Blumendraht S. 2277
Blumenkohlbildung 11677
Blutstein 6174, 14554
Blutachat 1817
Blutlaugensalz 20287
Blutregen 1815
Bobierrelegierung 1313/a
Bocca 1933
Bock 9376, 11408/b, 17341
S. 18878
Böckerscher Hahnverschluss
1942
Bockformmaschine 19370
Bock'schleifmaschine S.
8544
Bockshorn S. 9202
Boden 1276, S. 2142
— aufbohren (den) 16936
Bodenbenderit 1935
Bodenelektrode 11067
Bodenfalte 1502
Bodenfliessdruck S. 7440
Bodenfluss 16855, 16895
Bodenheizung 2160
Bodenklappe 2154, 5494,
5976
Bodenplatte des Kollergangs

S. 12890
Bodenprobe 2166
Bodensatz 2184, S. 2531,
5831
— im Anschnitt 8090
Bodenschliessdruck 17393
Bodenschrapper für «Bott-
lenecking» 2165
Bodenstampfmaschine 13563
Bodenstein S. 1276, 1678,
3381, 16870, 17656
Bodenvorstosshahn auf dem
Eruptionskreuz 2168
Bogen 2198, S. 4875 ,
Bogenbildung 10746
bogenförmiges Wellblech
4879, 4880
Bogenlampe 747
Bogenlampenkohlen 2871,
10510
Bogenlampenzubehör 748
Bogenreglette S. 4886
Bogenschneidemaschine 744
Bogenschnitt 743
Bogenschweissung mit
nackter Elektrode 1227
Bogensteg 4886
Bogenstruktur 1947
Bogheadkohle 1952
Bohlenbelag 13821,
17615
Bohnerz 1381/a, 13387
Bohranlage 5903, 5938, S.
6168, 14897
Bohrarbeiter 2091, S. 5906,
5895
Bohrautomat 5920
Bohrbarkeit 5912
Bohrbelegschaft S. 5921
Bohrbericht 2103, S. 5894,
18803
Bohrdruck 19907
Bohreinsatz S. 2077, 2091
Bohreisen S. 1622, 10250
bohren 2073, 5874, 13240,
13241, 20080
Bohren S. 2076
— eines Schachtes S. 2112
— im Produktionsgang 4201
— in de. See 11322
Bohrer 5881, 10250, 18876

Bohrer demontieren (einen) 17280
— mit gerader Ausfräsung und konischem Schaft 18284
Bohrerhalter 5882
Bohrerhebezeug 14899
Bohrernachschärfung 17508
Bohrerschneide S. 2077
Bohrerträger 3555
Bohrfaktoren 5932
Bohrfördertrommel 2560
Bohrfortschritt 13063
Bohrgerät S. 5943
Bohrgestänge 2088, 2099, 2557, S. 5897
Bohrgestängekupplung 18728
Bohrgestängezug 5901
Bohrgezähe S. 5883
Bohrgut 4929, 5577
Bohrhaken 2949
Bohrhammer 2572, S. 5881, 8731, 10093, 11121, 13390
Bohrhauer 5906, 11122
Bohringenieur 5923
Bohrinselschuh 5691
Bohrjournal S. 5937
Bohrkern 4386, 4438, 5890
Bohrklappmast 2790
Bohrknarre 14435
Bohrknecht 296
Bohrkopf 2102
Bohrkran 2104, 6168, 19968
Bohrkrone 1681, 4393, 4405, 4726
Bohrkrückel 2221
Bohrlänge 15353
Bohrloch S. 1729, 1741, S. 2080, 5892, 5939, 16204
— besetzen 17535
Bohrloch-Kaliber 9250
Bohrloch klarspülen 15610
— mit grösserem Durchmesser als Meisseldurchmesser 12748
— mit kleinem Durchmesser 16626
— mit starker Neigung 9138
Bohrlochablenkung 19138
Bohrlochanordnung für Fluten 7400

Bohrlochhöhe 6376
Bohrlochkamera 5704
Bohrlochpumpe 2083
Bohrlochreihe 15268
Bohrlochsohle 2173, 6747
Bohrlochsprengen S. 16164
Bohrlochsprengung 16203
Bohrlochtiefe 2082, 11236, 18704
Bohrlochwand 2084
Bohrlöffel 7471, S. 19447
Bohrmaschine für Eisen und Stahl 5926
— mit Bohrsäule 5872
— zum Öffnen des Stichloches 5927
Bohrmaschinengerüst 5928, 5929
Bohrmannschaft 5921
Bohrmast 5930
Bohrmeister 5915, 11361
Bohrmeistergehilfe 899
Bohrmehl 2085, 2114, S. 4929, S. 5577, S. 16695
Bohrmusterzug 18520
Bohrprobe 5911
Bohrprobenahme 19969
Bohrprofil 5894, 19965
Bohrprogramm 5935
Bohrrolle S. 4734
Bohrrohr 19959
Bohrrohrausdehner 6666
Bohrrohrfangkeile 5900
Bohrrohrschelle S. 2935
Bohrrohrschutzring 2953
Bohrrohrstrang 5941
Bohrsäule 5889 , 5902
— mit Pressluftvorschub 13583
Bohrschappe 947, 19447
Bohrschaufelschuh 17223
Bohrschiff 5945
Bohrschlamm 5891, S. 16695, 16695
Bohrschlauch 15017
Bohrschmant S. 4929, 5577
Bohrschneide 2077, 10862
Bohrschuh 2106
Bohrschwengel 19628
Bohrseil 2558, 5905, 5922
Bohrseilrolle 4734

Bohrseiltrommel S. 2560, 2571, S. 2662
Bohrstab 2105
Bohrstahl 14491, 15018
Bohrstange S. 5881
Bohrstangen demontieren 10593
Bohrstelle 5907, 5940
Bohrstrecke 7550
Bohrtagebuch 5937
Bohr-Tender 5944
Bohrton 5919
Bohrtrommelbandbremse 2561, 2561
Bohrtrommelstrebe 2562
Bohrturm S. 2104, 2111, 5214
— walzen 16452
— zum Mehrfachbohren 12123
Bohrturmkeller 5216
Bohrturmplattform 14898
Bohrturmtor 19421
Bohrturmverlegung 14900
Bohrung 2076, 2080, S. 2090, 2095, 5916
— für Luftspiess 19502
— mit Verkehrtspülung 4529, 4529
— niederbringen (eine) 16409
Bohrungsplatz 5893
Bohrversuch 2107
Bohrvorrichtung 14901
Bohrwagen 5884, 10242
Bohrwerkzeug 2110, 5943
Bohrwinde 5785
Bohrzeit 14902
— auf Sohle 18639
Bohrzeug S. 5942
Bolivarit 2003
Bolivian 2004
Bolzen S. 14177, S. 17897
— mit bearbeitetem Kopf 2013
— mit halbrundem Kopf 4836
— mit konischem Kopf 4198
— mit rundem Kopf 15283
— mit Vierkantkopf 17236
Bolzengelenk 13309

Bondern 2020
Bone-bed S. 2026
Bonsdorffit 2037
Boothit 2056
Borax 2061, 18656
Borazit 2060
Borcherscher Ofen 2062
Bordeauxbrühe 2067
Bordeaux-rot 3632
Bordelaise Brühe S. 2067
Bördelblech 13485
Bördelstahlblech 7271
Bördelversuch 7276
Borgströmit 2093
Bornit 2115, 6553, S. 9378
    13009, 14194, 19471
Boronatrocalcit 12184
borsaures Natron S. 2061
Borstahl 2117
Bort 1648/a, 2118, 2047,
    2831, 2847, S. 5331
Böschung 1344, 8265
Böschungsabsatz 1538
Böschungsmauer 15607
Bossenblech 12107
Botryogen 2129
Bouilleurkessel S. 7754
Bournonit 2196, 20008
Boussingaultit 2197
Bowenit 2201
Bowmanit 2204
Brackwasser-Fazies 2248
Brachyantiklinale 2233
Brachydoma 2234
Brachypinakoid 2235
Bradygenese 2250
Bragit 2251
Bramme S. 1206, 16495,
    18503
Bramme s. Luppe od. Block
Brammen 16505
Brammeneisen 16500
Brammenschere 16502
Brammentiefofen 16497
Brammenwalzwerk 16501
Branddamm 7164, 15735
Brandeisen 2262, S. 2613
Brandisit 2263
Brandmauer 7185, 7253
Brandschiefer 1645, 14238
Brandtür S. 7167

Brandungsplatte 15007
Brandwand S. 7185
Brannerit 2264
braun 2470
— mit Purpurflecken 2478
braune Legierung 2475/a
Brauneisenocker S. 2474
Brauneisenstein 10828,
— s. Toneisenstein
Brauneisensteinknollen 2475
bräunen 2610
brauner Rauch 2476
Braunerz 19584
Braunit 2287
Braunkohle 2472
Braunkohlenaschenbinder
    2473
Braunkohlenfeuerung 10803
Braunkohlenteerpech S. 1636
Braunmanganerz 59
Braunsäure 2471
Braunspat 2477
Braunsteinkies S. 340
Brautoneisenstein 2474
Brause 11811, S. 17206
Brausegicht 20070
Brazilit 2291
Brechbacke 10141
Brecheisen 4721, 4723, S.
    14932
brechen 2295, 8538
Brechen 2321
— der Steigerkanten S
    2323
Brecher 2317, S. 4771,
    10336
Brechereintrag 4773
Brechgebirge 12717
Brechkoks 4768, 6221
Brechmaul 2320
Brechprobe 2336
Brechpunkt nach Fraass
    2425
Brechstange 1207, S. 4721,
    10401, S. 14107
— abreissen (mit) 1213
Brechwalze 4586, 4774
Brechwerk 4771
Brechzange S. 14932
Breislakit 2359

Breitband 20061
breite Kammer S. 1919
Breiteisen 7325
breitflanschiger Doppel-T-
    Träger S. 8528
Breitflanschträger 2433, S.
    8528
breitfüssiges T-Eisen 2434
Breithacke 11383
Breithaue S. 11383
Breithauptit 2360
Breitwalzen 20065
Brekzie 2353, 3649
Brekziegang 2356
Bremsberg 2255, S. 2469,
    2637, S. 5627, 8491,
    8895, 9690, 13454,
    14944, 15352, 15812
Bremsen 17178
Bremser 17177
Bremsgestell 16681
Bremsreibung 2254
Bremsrohr für Westinghouse-
    Bremsleitung 19027
Bremsschuh 16152
brennbar 4069
brennbarer Bestandteil 4070
Brenndüse 12408
Brenneisen S. 2262
brennen S. 1112
Brennen 1116, 2604
brennende Steinkohle S. 1634
    1634
Brenner 2600
— für Sauerstoff 4139
Brennerherd 17188
Brennerprobe S. 1888
Brenngas 7788
Brennhärtemaschine 7260
Brennkammer 4076, S. 7152
Brennkaspel 15427/a
Brennkraftmotorpumpe 13790
Brennofen S. 2703, 7825
— für die Birnenböden ?717
Brennpunkt 7516
Brennschmelzofen 11467
Brennschneidemaschine 7257
Brennstoff 7787
— für Düsenflugzeuge 10159
Brennstoffaufwand 4244

Brennstoffbedarf 5163
Brennstoffgicht 3324
Brennstoffluftgemisch 7790
Brennstoffreserve 14744
Brennstoffziegel S. 2415
Brennweite 7514
Brennzeit 2607
Brett 1918
Brettfallhammer 1923
Bretterschalung 13464
Bretterschild 2344
Bretterschloss 3513
Brettscheider am Fusse
    der Stürzrolle zwechs
    Aufhalten der Kohle
    3364
Breunnerit 2363
Brevicit 2364
Brewsterit 2365
Brikett 2415, 6226,
— aus geröstetem Schwefel-
    kies 1898
brikettiertes Erz S.12634
Brikettierungsanlage 2417
Brikettierverfahren 2416
Brille 8269
Brinell-Presse 2255/a
Brinellhärte 2408
Brinellhärteprobe 2409
Brinellprobe S. 2409
brisanter Sprengstoff 6822
Brisanzsprengstoff 9145
Britholit 2419
Brochantit 2436
Brockenfänger 10257
Bröggerit 2437
Brom 2452
Bromargyrit 2450
Bromierungsapparat 2451
Bromit S. 2450
Bromsilber S. 2450
Bromwaschflasche 2455
Bronze 2455
bronzeartiger Glanz 2456
Bronzedraht 2459
Bronzeform 2455
Bronzegiesserei S. 2271
Bronzen – 196/a
Bronzerohr 2457
Bronzierapparat 2463
Bronzierung 2461

Bronzierer 2460
Bronziermaschine S. 2463
Bronzit 2464
Brookit 2466
Bruch 4580, S. 6766, S. 6778
    6778, 7693, 14258, S.
    17125
— der Zerreissprobe 18408
— durch Gegenschlag 7696
— gehen (zu) 15338
Bruchanschnitt 2323
Bruchaussehen 718
Bruchbelastung S. 120
Bruchdehnung 6390, 13074
Brücke 2379, 13508
— einer Verwerfung 12332
Brückenbaustahl 17893
Brückenbildung S. 2382,
    2389
Brückenkran 2384
Brückenwaage 19895
Bruchfalte 2443, 5536, 7522
Bruchfeld S. 7702
Bruchfestigkeit 18410
Bruchfläche 7695, 7701
Bruchgefüge 7694, 7703
Bruchgrenze 2329
brüchiges Eisen S. 16181
Brüchigkeit S. 7707, 7716,
    16199/a
— durch Kornvergrösserung
    17410
Bruchkoks 2441
Bruchlast 120
Bruchlinie S. 6852, 7697,
    10835
Bruchliniestufe S. 6846
Bruchprobe 2309, S. 2336
Bruchriss 6768
Bruchstempel 2334
Bruchstosswiderstands-
    probe 16367
Bruchstufe S. 6841, 10313
Bruchsystem 8625, 18178
Bruchwand 6853
Bruchzone 7702, 7705, 15387
Brünieren 2478/a, S. 1915
— mit Hilfe von Rollen
    2462
Brünierung 2610/a
Brunnenbohren 2112, 5931,

5946
Brunnensystem 8627
Brunnenwasser 19974
Brushit 2484
Brustleier 2346
Brustöffnung 8957
Bruststoss 2349
Brustzacken S. 7561
Bruttogewicht S. 8604
Buchenholzkohle 1437
Büchsensäule 2244, 10234
Buckelplatte 2509
Bucklandit 2507
Buffer S. 2516
Bufferfeder 2519
Bügel S. 2198, 3724, 17610
Bügel-Aufhängungsfeder
    4225
Bühne 7920, 10554, S. 15576,
    17293
Bühnenarbeiten 3556
Bulldogschlacke 2564
Bund 4015
bundled Scrap 1143
Bunker 1589/a, 2580
— für Förderkübelbeschik-
    kung 16483
Bunsenbrenner 2582
Bunsenit 2583
Buntkupfererz S. 6553, 9378,
    S. 130098, S. 14194, S.
    19471
Buntsandstein 19472
Burgersches Drehventil 2588
Burgunderbrühe 2589
Büschel von Verwerfungen
    S. 4129
Büschelkohle S. 7530
Bussit 2631
Bustamenteofen 2624
Bustamit 2629
Butan 2632
Butlerit 2633
Buttgenbachit 2646, S. 4226

C

Cabrerit 2668
Caesium 2678

Cahnit 2686
Calaverit 2700
Calciklas S. 2710
Caldera 2737
caledonische Faltung 2738
Caliche 2744
Californium 2745
Callovien 2749
Camsellit 2774
Camptonit 2772
Canbyit 2776
Cancrinit 2779
Canfieldit 2785
Cannelkohle 2782
Cannizarit 2788
Cappelenit 2812
Caracolit 2819
Caradoc 2820
Cardiffkohle 2888
Carnallit 2893
Carnegieit 2894
Carrollit 2901
Casingdruck S. 2952
Cathkinit 3097
Cebollit 3129
Celsium 3136
cenotyp S. 3183
Centrallasit 3194
Cephalopoden 3223
Cer Epidot S. 370
Cervantit 3232
Cesarolith 3233
Ceylanit 3234, S. 10018
Chabasit 3235
Chalkanthit 3252, 4367
Chalkodit 3255
Chalkolamprit 3258
Chalkomenit 3259
Chalkophanit 3260
Chalkophyllit 3257
Chalkopyrit 20284
Chalkosin S. 3254, 3262, 19571
Chalkostibit 3263
Chalkotrichit 3264, 8707/a
Chamosit 3276
Chapmanit 3296
Charge S. 2586, 6883, 13706. 13981
— s. Gicht od. Beschickung
Chargenofen 1331/a

Chargierkran S. 338
Chargiermaschine S. 3340
Chargiermulde S. 3335, S. 7660
Chargiervorrichtung S. 3332, S. 3340
Charpy-Kerbschlagprobe für Stahl 3352
Chattian 3359
Chemie des Eisens 3400
— des Hochofenganges 3401
Chemikalien S. 14473
chemisch beständiger Stahl 3392
— gebundener Sauerstoff 3396
— gleichwertige Mengen 3397
— reine Schwefelsäure 3399
— reines Eisen 3398
chemische Affinität S. 3384
— Analyse 3383
— Analysenwaage 550
— Bindung 3385
— Einwirkung 3391
— Entplattierung 3392/a
— Gussanalyse 10471
— Heizwertbestimmung 3389
— Reaktion S. 3391
— Verunreinigung 3390
— Verwandtschaft 3384
— Zusammensetzung 3386
chemischer Aufbau 3387
chemisches Äquivalent 3394
— Symbol S. 3393
— Verfahren 3388
— Zeichen 3393
Chenevixit 3402
Chessylit S. 1036, 3413
Chiastolith 3415, 11142
Childrenit 3418
Chileit 3419
chilenische Mühle 3355, 6202
Chilenit 3420
Chilisalpeter S. 12308
Chillagit 3441
Chinaglia-Ofen 10358
Chiolith 3471

Chloanthit 3490
Chlor 3500
Chloralkalien 357
Chloraluminit 3491
Chlorantimon 670
Chlorapatit 3492
Chlorargyrit S. 3227, 3493
Chlorentwicklungsflasche 3501
Chlorentwicklungskolben 3502
Chlorit 3503, 13005
Chloritbildung 3506
chlorithaltig 3504
Chloritisation S. 3506
Chloritoid 3507
Chloritschiefer 3505, 13007
Chlorkalium 3499, S. 18148
Chlorkalk 3497
Chlorkalzium 2722
Chlorkalziumlösung 16904
Chlorkalziumröhre 2724
Chlorkalziumzylinder 2723
Chlorkalzit 3509
Chlorkupfer 4853
Chlormagnesium 3498
Chloromanganokalit 3508
Chloromelanit 3510
Chloropal 3511, S. 8410
Chlorophan 3512
Chlorsilber 9363, 3227, S. 3493
Chrom 3544
Chrom-Magnesit S. 3530
Chromalaun 3528/a
Chromat 3525
chromatisch 3526
Chromatographie 3528
Chromeisen 3529, 3540
Chromeisenerz S. 3529
Chromeisenstein S. 3529, S. 3543
Chromgranat 2725
Chromit S. 3529, 3543
Chrommagnesit 3530
Chrommolybdänstahl 3531
Chromnickel-Molybdänstahl 3532
Chromnickelstahl 3545, 3533
Chromsäureanhydrid 3539

Chromspinell 3536, S. 13232
Chromstahl 3548
Chromvanadium-Stahl 3538
chromwolframlegierter
    Stahl S. 3537
Chromwolframstahl 3537
Chrysokoll 4360
Chrysolith 3551
Chrysopras 3552
Chrysotil 3553
Chubuttit 3554
Churchit 3558
Chusca 3562
Ciminit 3568
Cimolit 3569
Citrin 6788
Clarit 3635
Clarkeit 3636
Claudetit 3651
Clausthalit 3652
Cleveland-Apparat 3722
Clevelander Röstofen 3723
Clevelandsches Gebläse
    mit einer Kurbelstange
    3720
Cliftonit 3726
Clintonit 3740
Clunian 3791
Coenogenese 3181
Cohenit 3918
Colbyscher Ofen 3956
    Colemanit 4011
Cölestin S. 3131
Collobrierit 4027
Coloradian 4031
Coloradoit 4032
Columbit 4037
comagmatisches Gestein
    4049
Comendit 4086
Comptonit S. 18543
Connellit 4226
Constantan 4232
convexes Gewölbe 4313
Cookeit 4325
Copiapit 11812
Cordierit 4380, S. 5350
Corkit 4475
Cornetit 4477
Cornubianit 4485
Cornwallit 4486

Cornwallkessel 4484
Coronadit 4487
Corundellit 4505
Corsit 4504
Cosalit 4510
Coslettisierung 4511
Cossyrit 4512
Cotunnit 4525
Covellin 4557, 9739
Covit 4573
cracken 4579
Crackverfahren 14225
Crandallit 4594
Crednerit 4613
Creedit 4614
Crichtonit 4636
    634/b
Crinanit 4637
Crinoideen 4639
Crinoidenkalk 4638, 6445
Cristobalit 4642
Cromaltit 4653
Cromerian 4654
Cronstedtit 4655
Crossit 4720
Crysoberyll 3550
Cuban 4817
Cucalit 4823
Culsageeit 4828
Cumberlandit 4829
Cumbrait 4830
Cumengeit 4831
Cummingtonit 4832
Cuppe S. 9782
Cuprit 14533
Cuprozinkit 4859
Curcumpapier 4862
Curit 4863
Curium 4864
Cuspidin 4890
Custerit S. 4890
Cyankalium 4931, 13724
Cyanstickstofftitan 18691
Cyclopit 4935
cyklopische Struktur S.
    11940
Cymophan 4952
Cyprin 4953
Cyprusit 4954

D

Dach S. 15137
Dachabdichtung 12902
Dachberge 14395
Dachschicht S. 8815
Dachschiefer 8940
Dachschieferstruktur 15147
Dachsparren 14345
Dachverzimmerung 18752
Dahamit 4961
Dahllit 4962
Daktylit 4958
daktylitisch 4959
damaszener Stahl 4972
damaszieren 4973
damasziert 4971
Damaszierung 4972/a
Damm 10707
Dammbrett 16774
Dammriff S. 1250
Dammerde S. 728
Dammgrube S. 3067, 7668
Dämmleiste 12995
Dammstein 4968, S. 4986,
    16463
Damourit 4974
Damouritbildung 4975
Dampf behandelte Hoch-
    ofenschlacke 1719 (mit) 1719
    1719
Dampfbad 17416
Dampfdestillierapparat 17448
Dampfdom 19468
Dampfdruckschmiedepresse
    17442
Dampfdynamo 17428
dämpfen 4976
Dämpfen 4981
Dampfeinlassventil 172
Dampfeinsaugen 17447
Dampfentwässerer 17450
Dampfentwickler 17426
Dampferzeuger 17432
Dampfgebläse 17419
dampfgekühlt 17423
Dampfhammer 17433
— mit einseitigem oder
    C-förmigem Gestell 17436
— mit feststehendem
    Zylinder 17435

Dampfhammer mit Oberdampf 17434

Dampfkessel für einen betriebsmässigen Überdruck von 12 Atm. 1964

— mit mechanischer Feuerung 17418

Dampkesselkohle S. 1956

Dampfkesselrohr 19022

Dampfkohle S. 1956

Dampfkohlenschiff 17422

Dampfkraftgebläse S. 17419

Dampfkran 17424

Dampflokomotive 17440

Dampfpumpe 17443

Dampfregenierungsanlage 19469

Dampfsauger 17429

Dampfschaufel 17445

Dampfschaufelbetrieb 17446

Dampfstiefel 17425

Dampfstrahlgebläse 17438

Dampfstrahlzerstäuber 17439

Dampftopf 17441

Dampftrichter 17430

Dampfüberhitzer 17449

Dämpfungsvermögen 4982

Dampfwinde 17451

Danait 4988

Danalith 4989

Danburit 4990

Daniellscher Hahn 4993

Dannemorit 4995

Darbys Gasfang 4998

Darrkammer S. 6055

Darstellung S. 12642

Datolith 5005

lauben 17375/a

Daubreeit 5010

Daubreelith 5011

Dauer der Erhitzung 6118

— des natürlichen Ausflusses 7443

Dauerabbeizung 4270

Dauerbeanspruchung 6835

Dauerfestigkeit 6465

Dauerfestigkeitsprobe 6836

Dauerfossil 13116

Dauermagnet 13106

Dauermagnetstahl 13107

Dauerschlagversuch 1473

Dauerschwingbruch 6831

Dauerschwingfestigkeit S. 6466/a, 4617, 4623

Dauerstandfestigkeitsprobe S. 6836

Dauerstandversuch 4624

Daumen S. 2764, 18294

Davainit 5013

Daviesit 5014

Davysche Sicherheitslampe 10097

Dazit 4956

dazitisch 4957

Dechenit 5060

Deckbasalt 1689

Decke 1688, S. 16045,

Deckel 1449, 2032, S. 2793, 4562

— s. Deckplatte

Deckelabhebevorrichtung 10761

Deckelflansch S. 1682

Deckenblech S. 4731

— für die Feuerbüchse S. 7154

Deckenheizkörper 3130

Deckenverankerung 17408

Deckfalte 7521

Deckflacheisen S. 18740

Deckgebirge 2585, 2796, 2798, 8814

Deckgläschen 8274

Decklatte S. 7210, S.7384, 1062

Deckschicht 12769

Deckscholle 6855, 12175

Deckung 4570

— des Erzbedarfes 11440

— nach dem Lot S. 9345

— nach dem Perpendikel S. 17751

Dedolomitisation 5083

Deflagrator 5116

Deflation 5117

dehnbar 6073

— s. schmiedbär od. streckbar

Dehnbarkeit 6075

Dehnung 5412

Dehnungsgrenze 6392

Dehnungsmesser S. 5413 6696

Dehnungsmess. streifen

17732/a

Dehnungstemperatur 14691

Dehnungsverwerfung 6845, 184 18417

Dehrnit 5140

Dehydrierung 1117, 9559

dekantieren 5050

Dekantiergefäss S. 5053

Dekantierklassifikator 3643

dekapieren 19580

Delafossit 5144

Dellenit 5155

Dellesit 5146

Delorenzit 5156

Delta-Eisen 5157

Deltait 5159

Deltametall 5158

Delvauxit 5160

Demantoid 5164

demontieren 14895

Demalgator 5167

Dendrachat S. 741

Dendrit 5168

dendritisch 5169

Dendrit 6926

dendritische Struktur 740

Dennisonit 5170

Densimeter 9567

Dephlegmator 5186

Depilage S. 14997

Depolarisation 5194/a

derbes Eisenerz 4100

Derbyshire-Barit 2748/a

Dermolith 5213

DERV Brennstoff 5222

Descloizit 5229

Desmin 5242

Desoxydation 5179, 5183, 14571

Desoxydieren 10353

desoxydieren 5184

Desquamation S. 6648, 13041

Destillat S. 13991

Destillate der ester Raffination 18765

Destillationsanlage 5563

Destillationsapparat 5555

Destillationsaufsatz 5556

Destillationsbenzin 17715

Destillationskolben 5553

Destillationsrest 5561

Destillationsröhre 5554

Destillationsverlust 5557
Destillationsvorlage 5560
Destillierapparatekoks
    17593
Destillierblase 17592
destillieren 26, 5551
destilliert mit Paraffin in
    Kristallform 13888
destilliertes Paraffin 17596
— Wasser 5562
Destilliertopf 5559
Destinezit 5243
deuterisch 5268
deuteromorph 5270
Deuteroprisma S. 13958
deutliche Spaltbarkeit 5564,
    6182
deutlicher Spaltbarkeit (mit)
    6608
deutsches Frischverfahren
    S. 18913
Devonit 5285
Dewalquit 5287
Deweylith 5297
Dewindtit 5298
Dezimalwaage 5061
Dezinormalelektrode 5062
diabasischkörnige Struktur
    S. 12617
Diaboleit 5302
Diadochit 5304
diagonale Spalte 5309
— Verwerfung 5308
— Wetterführung 5311
Diagonalschichtung S. 4867,
    6779, 12433
Diaklase 5303
Dialogit 5315
Dialogite S. 11274
diamagnetisch S. 5316
Diamantabfälle 5331
Diamantablagerung 1903/a
diamantartig 121
Diamantbohren 5321, 5325
Diamantbohrer 5324
Diamantbohrkrone 5330
Diamantbohrmaschine S. 5324
    5324
Diamantglanz 123
Diamantkernbohren S. 5321
Diamantkrone 5322

Diamantmörser 5317
Diamantschlacke 5320
Diamantschleifscheibe
    5333/a
Diamantstahl 5029, 6703
Diamorphismus 5334
Diaphorit 5335
Diaphragma S. 5336
Diaphtorese 5305
Diapyr 5339
Diapyrstruktur 5340
diaschistisch 5341
Diaspor 5342
Diastrophismus 5343
Diäthanolamin 5023
Diatomeenerde 11876,
    16309, 16318, 18365
Diatrema S. 5347
dichroisches Mineral 5348
Dichroismus 5349
Dichroit 5350
Dichte 5176
dichte Lagerung 5171
Dichteänderung des Elektro-
    lyten 427
Dichtebestimmung 5259
Dichteisen S. 30111
dichter Abschluss 18619
— Ton 1317
dichtes Eisenerz 5172
Dichtheit 18620
Dichtigkeit 1937
Dichtigkeitsmesser 13231
Dichtung 15735/a
Dichtungsfläche 12853
Dichtungsfuge 12850
Dichtungsmittel 8078/a
Dichtungsrand 7031, S.
    10208
Dichtungsrille 10207
Dichtungsring 14923
Dichtungswalze 12847
dick gebänkt 9027
Dicke S. 20064
dicke Oberflächenschicht
    9027/a
dicker Draht 18505
dickflüssiges Härtemittel
    15843
— Öl 2581
Dickinsonit 5351

Dickit 5352
Dicköl 17337
dickwandiges Rohr 9042,
    18504
Didym 5353
dielektrische Absorption
    5383
— Heizung 5386
dielektrischer Ofen 5385
dielen S. 1917
Dieselkessel 12490
Dieselindex 5389
Dieseltreibstoff 5388
Dietrichit 5390
Dietzeit 5391
Differdinger Eisen 5392,
    8528
differenzierter Gesteinsgang
    5397
Diffraktionsflecker 5401
Diffusion 5403
Diffusionsglühen 9299
Diffusor 6217
Dihydrit 5409
Dilatationsfugenleiste 6672
Dilatometer 5413
dilatometrische Prüfung
    5414
diluvial 5419
Diluvium 5420, S. 5857
dimorph S. 5426
Dimorphie 5425
dimorphisch 5426
Dinantien 5427
Dinasziegel 5428
Diopsid 5429
Dioptas 5430, 6408
Diorit 5431
Dipyr 5454
direkt destilliert 17714
— (über einen Motor)
    betätigt 13800
direkte Reduktion 5463
direkter Gusskanal 5985
— Kraftschluss 5460
direktes Ausgiessen 5456/a
— Plasmaschweissen 19938
dirigiertes Bohren S. 5468
Disjunktivbruch S. 6845
diskontinuierlich arbeitender
    Kollergang 1332

diskordant 12346, 19238
diskordante Intrusion 5507
— Parallelstruktur S. 4707
— Schicht 19239
Diskordanz 19240
Diskordanzwinkel 578
Dislokation 5525, 10645
Dislokationsbrekzie S.4766,
S. 6844, S. 16012
Dislokations-Geschwindig-
keits-und Beschleuni-
gungsspektren 5533
Dislokationskontakte S.4
Dislokationslinie S. 6852
Dispersionsmittel 5549
Dissoziationsgrad 5132
Dissoziationsgleichgewicht
6529
Dissoziationsgrad einer
Lösung S. 5133
Dissoziationsgrenze 5543
Dissoziationskonstante
3899
Dissoziationsrückgang
14804
Dissoziationstemperatur
5544
Dissoziationstheorie 5545
Dissoziationswärme S. 8987
dissoziieren S. 5542
Distanzstück 13045
Disthen S. 10444
Disthenschiefer 4932
Distillationsturm 5522
Distillierapparat S. 5416
distillierte Schmiere 17595
distilliertes Kerosen 10317
Ditroit 5579
Divortium S. 9918
Dixenit 5588
Dochkohle S. 4456
Docht 20055
Doctor-Süssung 5591
Dolerine 5601
Dolerit 5601
doleritische Struktur 5603-
12617
Dolerophanit 5604
Dolomit S. 1633, 5608,
13245, 14858,
Dolomitanlage S. 5615

Dolomitbrennofen 5610
Dolomithalle 5615
Dolomitisation 5616
Dolomitkalk 5615
Dolomitmasse 5611
Dolomitmehl 5613
Dolomitmischer 5612
Dolomitsand 5614
Dolomitstein 5609
Dom 5620
Dombildung 5624
Domeykit 5622
Domit 5625
Domstruktur 5619
Doppelbohrung 6070
Doppeldampfraumkessel
1984
Doppelduowalzwerk S. 5695
Doppeldüse 19176
Doppeleisen S. 1062
Doppelfanghaken 19190
Doppelfischschwanzmeissel
4053
Doppelflammrohrkessel S.
10515
Doppelförderungsschacht
6068
Doppelförderungsvorkommen
6069
Doppelformmaschine 12019
Doppelgärbstahl 5674
Doppelgenerator 5672
Doppelhacke 1440, 5667,
18973
Doppelherzstück 5333
Doppelkegel S. 10942
Doppelkeilhaue 7267, 11262
Doppelkernrohr 5650, 5683
Doppelkessel 5645
Doppelkopfhammer 14425
Doppelkopfschiene 5663
Doppelmuffelofen 5666
doppeln 5637
Doppel-Pin 5668
Doppelplanrätter 5654
Doppelpresse 12016
Doppelpuddelofen 5673
Doppelpunktschweissung
19174
Doppelraffinierstahl S. 5674
Doppelrohr 5669

Doppelrohrschacht 6067
Doppelrohrwalze 5659, 5682
Doppelrollmaschine S. 5682
Doppelschneidebohrer S.
5643
Doppelschrägschweissung
5665
doppelseitiger Stehbolzen
5680
Doppelsitzventil 5676
Doppel-T-Eisen S. 10216
doppelt geflanscht 5660
— wirkend 5639
— wirkende Pumpe 5641
— wirkender Aufzug 5640
— wirkender Dampfhammer
5642
doppelte Formpresse S.
12016
— Keilhaue S. 5667, S.
18973
— Liderung 5686
— Modellplatte 15915
doppelter Gichtverschluss
5679
— Schrubber aus Draht 5675
doppeltes Schwindmass 5649
Doppeltragscheibe 5644
Doppelwalzenkessel 5653
doppelwändig 5687
Doppelweiche 14903
Doppelwellblech 5651
Doppelzonenförderungs-
schacht 6071
Doppelzug 5638
Doppelzweiwalzwerk 5695
Doppelzylinderkessel 19185
Doppelzylinderpumpe S.
6113
Döpper 8926
Döpperstahl 17471
Dopplerit 5636
Dorn 735/a
Dornen 5873/a
Dornentfernung 17865/a
Dornwalze für geschweisste
Rohre 11265
Dose 2207
Dosiervorrichtung 1337
Doughtyit 5692
Douglasit 5693

Draht 20117/a
— für Nieten 14975
— für Seile und Kabel 20126
— für Umzäunungen 6917
— (mit) umwundenes Filterrohr 20151
Drahtbügel zum Hohlraumschiessen 16955
Drahtbündel 12930
Drahtbürste mit Gurt 20118
Drahtdreieck 20148
Drahteisen 20130, 20138
Drahtgeflecht 20136
— mit dreifacher Verwindung 9125
— mit einfacher Verwindung 17252
Drahtgewebe 8120, 20129
Drahtkabel 17505
Drahtklemme 18426, 20120
Drahtkorb 20119
Drahtkrampe S. 20120
Drahtkreuzschweissung 4708
Drahtlehre 20128
Drahtlitze 20147
Drahtnummer 8115
Drahtschelle S. 20120
Drahtschloss S. 20120
Drahtseil S. 17505, 20144
Drahtseilbahn 15167
Drahtseilfabrikation 20146
Drahtsorte 14249
Drahtstärke 5319
Drahtstrang S. 17505
Drahtstrasse S. 20134
Drahtstrecke S. 20134, 20135
Drahtwalzen 20143
Drahtwalzer 20142
Drahtwalzwerk S. 20135
Drahtwalzwerkstatt 15057
Drahtwalzung 15056
Drahtziehbank 20124
Drahtziehmaschine S. 5779
·drahtziehen 5763
Drahtziehen 20123
Drahtzieherei 5801, 20125, 20135, 20150
Drahtzug 20122
Dränierung durch

Schwerkraft 8487
Dravit 5752
Drehachse 1024, 15192/a
Drehbank 19145
Drehbank mit veränderbarer Drehzahl 10579
Drehbankbacke 10576
Drehbankgewinde 18304
Drehbankherz 2900
Drehbankspitze 12391
drehbare Haspel 17148
— Modellplatte S. 19148
drehbarer Teiltisch 15197
Drehbeanspruchung 18782
Drehbewegung 19147
drehbohren 5918
Drehbohren 15195
Drehbohrmaschine 15199
Drehbohrstange 14889
Drehbohrung 2101
Dreheisen 12054
Drehen 19143/a
— der Birne 18683
drehende (sich) Waschtrommel 14845
drehendes Bohren S. 5918
Drehfeilmaschine 15205
Drehfestigkeit 18783
Drehgestellräder 18949
Drehherd 14839
Drehherdofen 9706,
Drehofen 15210, 15213
Dreh-Klaubherd S. 14839
Drehkolbenpumpe 15215, 15193
Drehkran 10167 , 18128, 19144, S. 19644
Drehkristall 15228
Drehmoment 18776, 19183
Drehmomentwandler 18777
Drehpuddeln 14840
Drehpuddelofen 14841
Drehrohrofen 14844
Drehrost 14838
Drehschablone S. 17809
Drehschaufelbagger S. 983
Drehscheibe 19150
Drehschieber 18140
Drehspäne 2113, S. 3482·
Drehspannung 9862
Drehstahl für unterbrochenen

Schnitt 18726
Drehstähle 10577
Drehstromanlage 18566
Drehstromlichtbogenofen 18564
Drehstromofen 431, 18565
Drehtisch 9349, 15221, 19151 19151
Drehtischformmaschine 12018 12018
Drehtrichter 15231/a
Drehung 18779
Drehungselastizität S. 6251
Drehungsgleiten 15233/a
Drehungshärtung 17093/a
Drehungswinkel 576/a
Drehverbindung 18130
Drehverwerfung 15235
Drehwinkel 577
Drehzapfen 13431
dreiatomiges Molekül 18889
Dreibackenfutter 18563
dreifache Verriegelung 18869
Dreifachwellblech 18912
Dreiflügelmeissel 18570
Dreifuss 18917
Dreikanteisen 18885
Dreikanter 5832, S. 15525, S. 20096
dreikantiger Draht 18887
Dreimalschmelzerei 18913
Dreipolanordnung 18567
dreiseitiges Prisma 18886
dreiteiliger Formkasten 18563/a
Dreiwalzengerüst 18562/a
Dreiwalzenständer 18557
Dreiweghahn 18569
Dreiwegventil 18571
Dreierzug 18572
Dressierwalzung 13312/a
Drillbohrer S. 5881
Drosselklappe 2645
drosseln 3515, 13312
Drosseltür S. 2225, 20057
Drosselung 18582
Druck 5149, 5490
— ablassen 1755
— (mit) direkt betätigter Keil 13794

Druckabfall 13900
Druckaufbau 13897
Druckausgleich 1128
Druckausgleicher 373
Druckbeanspruchung 4156
Druckbehälter 4249, 8362
Druckbirne 77
Druckbohren 13903
Druckdestillat 13902
Druckdestillationsanlage
13920
Druckelastizität 6247
drücken 17256
drückender Schiefer 9025
Druckfestigkeit 14773
Druckfilter 13905/a
Druckflüssigkeit 13907
Druckgasförderverfahren
8020
Druckgiessverfahren S.
13898
Druckguss 13898
Druckhöhe 8906, 13908
— der Pumpe 18589
Druckkanal 13916
Druckkessel 13895
Drucklager 4887
Drucklagerring 18602
Drucklagerscheibe 18601
druckleeres Gebiet S. 5025
Druckleitung 5151, 14949,
14953
Druckluft-Abscheider 321
Druckluftfeuerung S. 7860
Druckluftgesteinsbohrmaschi-
ne 13595
Druckluftgiessmaschine
5461
Druckluftstrahlanlage 4137
druckluftstrahlen S. 15466
Druckmanometer 13783
Druckmesser 11297, 18599
Druckplatte 2518, 10228
Druckpumpe 13915
Druckreduzierventil 16789
Druckrohr 5154, 14961,
17338
Druckrüttelformmaschine
10223
Druckrüttelformmaschine
mit Stiftenabhebung

10224
Druckschieferung 7423
Druckschraube 166
Druckseite 13918
Druckspalte 4155
Druckspannung S. 4156
Druckübersetzer 13922
Druckventil 13923, S. 18863
Druckverlust 1855, 11032,
13909
Druckversuch 4157
Druckwalze S. 13873
Druckwasserbetrieb 9540
Druckwasserformmaschine
9528
Druckwasserformpresse
9530
Druckwasserschmiedepresse
9523
Druckwasserspeicher 9511
Druckwassersteinpresse
9516
Druckzementierung 17259
Druckzentralisator 10564
Druckzufuhr 2049
Drummel 6017
Druse 6020, 9270, 19607
Drusenförmig 6022
Drusentextur 6021
Dübel 13307
— anbringen S. 13304
Duffscher Generator 6078
Dufrenit 6079
Dufrenoisit 6080
Duftit 6081
Dumalit 6091
Dumontit 6094
Dumortierit 6095
Dundasit 6107
Dungannonit 6109
Dunit 6110
dunkelrotglühend 6087
dunkle (auf) Rotglut 5003
— Zinkblende 1651
dunkles Rotgültigerz S.
14211
dünne Platte S. 18526
dünner Draht S. 18525
dünnes Blatt S. 18526
dünnflüssig 18580

Dünnflüssigkeit 7469
Dünnschliff 16609, 18501,
dünnwandiger Eisenguss
18529
Duowalzgerüst 19188
Duowalzwerk 19187, S.
19173
Duplexmetall 6114
Duplexpumpe 6113
Duplexstahl S. 6114
Duplex-Verfahren 611z
Dural 6116
Duralblech 16053
Duralwellblech 4499
Durbachit 6120
Durchbiegung 7372
durchbohren S. 2073, 5880
Durchbohrung 18583/a
Durchbrennen 2609
durchbrennen 2595
Durchbruch 2333, 2340,
9830
Durchbruchstahl 19777
durcheinander mischen 11818
11818
Durchfall 19280
durchfallender Gang 4213
Durchflussmeter 15192
Durchformen 2769
Durchführkessel 15781
Durchgang S. 7959, 12958,
S. 18864
Durchgangsöffnung 12959
Durchgangsstahl S.19777
durchgegangene Form 15360,
15383
Durchgehen 6002
durchgehendes Betonfunda-
ment mit Verstärkungen
1263
durchgiessen 15348
Durchgiessen einer Form
7439
durchhämmern S. 8727
Durchhärten 7803
Durchhärtung 19303
Durchhieb S. 2063, 4710, S.
4712, 7909, 17542, 17820.
S. 18532
Durchhiebe 4713
durchlässiges Gestein 13112

Durchlässigkeit 13109, 13110
Durchlauf-Trockenofen 4275
Durchlaufofen 4267
durchnässt S. 16853
Durchörtern S. 9259
durchqueren 4683
Durchrühren S. 14094
durchschaufeln 19139
Durchschlag 9259, 13244
Durchschnittsgewicht 1013
durchschnittliche Leistung 1010
— Zuggrösse 1287
durchschnittliches Streichen 1012
Durchschnittsmuster 366
Durschnittsprobe 1011, S. 15454
Durchsetzzeit 13095
durchsichtiger Gasstrom· 18834
Durchsichtigkeit 18833
Durchsieben 10180
Durchspiessungsfalte S. 5339
Durchspülung 2494
Durchstrahlungsprüfung mit Gammastrahlen S. 7948
durchtränkter Sand 9663
durchwachsen S. 9883, 12352
durchwachsenes Eisenerz 9726
Durchwachsung S. 9885
Durchwachsungszwillinge 9911, 13064
durchwärmen 7808
Durchwärmezeit 7809
Durchweichungsgrube S. 16796
Durchziehboden 14706
Durchziehen 14131
Durchziehplatte S. 17872
Durchzugring 3217
Durdenit 6121
Durit 6115, 7116
Düse 7434, 10154, S. 12409 12414, S. 19160
— mit Luftströmung nach unten 5710

Düsen (die) schliessen 3516
— (die) zurückziehen 5759
Düsenbohrung 10157
Düsenflansch 12669
Düsenplatte S. 1878, 12415
Düsenquerschnitt 12416
Düsenreihe 15302
Düsenstick 1702
Düsenstrahlgeschwindigkeit 10161
Düsenverschluss 20056
Dyas 6146
dydrooxygene Schweissung S. 12816
dynamische Festigkeit 6151/a
— Prüfung 6152
dynamischer Metamorphismus 6151
Dynamit 8211
Dynamitsprengung 6153
Dynamometer 6149
Dynamostahlguss 6156
Dysanalyt 6157
Dyskrasit 6158
Dysluit 6160
dysphotische Region 6161
Dysprosium 6162
Dyssnit 6163

E

E-Eisen S. 3289
eben 7480
Ebene S. 13453
— der Windformen 19161
ebene Fläche 9347
— Schieferung 13458
ebener Bruch 6623
— Knoten 3788
Echinoderm 6188
echte Verwefung S. 16651, S. 12377
echter Gang 7224/a
Ecke 4478
Eckpfeiler 4480
Eckventil 583
Eckwinkel 6199

Economizer-Rohr 6193
Edelmetall 12328
Edelopal S. 12329
Edelstahl 14602
Edelstein 8150
Edenit 6196
Edingtonit 6213
edler Feldspat 178
— Opal 12329
Effektkohle 7254
Effusivgestein 6219
Eggsenderkessel 6242
Eglestonit 6227
Ehlit 6228
Eichglas 19899
Eichgerät 14057
Eichofen 2472/a
Eichung 2742
Eichwaldit 6231
Eierbrikett 6220
Eifel-Stufe 6232
Eiform 6223
Eigenart des Erzes 3297
Eigengewicht 16873
Eigenpotential 15828
Eigenspannung 14758/a
eigentliches Manganerz 14019
Eigenvergrösserung 14474
Eigrösse 6224
Eimerbagger 2501
Eimerkette 2498, 15640
Eimerkettenbagger 2499, 15641
Eimerlademaschine 2503
einachsige Strasse 16394
einadriges Kabel 16386
Einäschern des Filters 2608
einatomiges Molekül 11890
Einbau der Verrohrung 11076 11076
einbauen S. 15346
Einbaustück 9463
einbeiniger Türstock 7919
einbetten 6400
Einbettung 12843/a
Einblasen 244, 9682
Einbrechen 2312
Einbrennen des Eisens 11555
— des Emails 7194

Einbrennhärtung 13722
Einbruch S. 16596
Einbruchbohrloch 2335,
2623, 3186
Einbruchschnitt 17997
Einbruchschuss 16792,
17995, 10326
Eindampf-und Ankerrohr
für Kesselbau 19466
Eindampfen 6619
Eindampfer 6621
eindicken 9848/a
Eindicker 18506
Eindickmaschine 5175
eindringen S. 13076
Eindringtiefe 5209
Eindringversuch 13062
Eindrehen der Kaliber 15090
Eindruck 9666
Eindruckleiste S. 12001
Eindruckverfahren 1166
Eindruckvorrichtung S.
9798
Einendekessel 16389
einfach wirkend 16379
— wirkende Pumpe 16382
— wirkender Aufzug 16381
— wirkender Dampfhammer
16383
einfache Härtung 16371
— Keilhaue 13632
— Rostfeuerung 16370
— Sparrendächer 16373
— Strecke 16390
— Verwerfung 16391
— Weiche 16372
einfacher Bruch 16368
— Bruchteil 14023
— Einguss S. 16369
— Gang 16408
— Walzenkessel S. 16385
einfaches Kernrohr 16407
Einfachkessel 16385
Einfach(walzen)-kessel
16388
einfachwirkende Walze 16380
16380
einfahren 8202
— zur tiefsten Sohle 10521
einfallen 3119, 6771
Einfallen 9688, 14382

schlag 18213/a
eingesprengt 5539
eingesprengtem (mit) Achat
210/a, 213
eingesprengtes Erz 5540,
13768, 17208
eingesetzte Rippe 9836
eingestürzt 3120
Eingiessbüchse 9819
Eingiessen 12010
Eingiessloch S. 8087
Eingiessteil 9833
Eingriff der Zähne 8139
Einguss 1311, 7424, 8087
8140, 10153, 15364,
15381
— (den) anschneiden
4895
— mit Vormulde 1313
Eingüsse beseitigen 5130
Eingusskanal 13742, 13758,
S. 15381, S. 17211
Eingusskasten 6877
Eingussmodell 8094
Eingusspfeife 5992
Einguss. schere 8658
Einguss. stock 8096
Eingusstrichter 1310, 13748,
13756
Eingusszeit S. 7231
einhängendes Rohr 18079
Einheitspol 19311
Einheitspreis für Eisen und
Mangan 13929
Einheitssand 19312
Einholstange 19686
Einkammerkessel 19829
Einkerbbruchprobe 12265
einkerben 15643
einklopfen 13866
Einkoks S. 6221
einlagern 9917
Einlagerung S. 9865, 9867,
9868,
Einlassbohrung S. 9829,
9859
Einlassdruck 9857
Einlassonde 9674
Einlauf S. 3047, S. 8140,
S. 9820, 13742, 17211
Einlaufrinne S. 8087, 17213

Einfallen der Verwerfung
6848
— s. Fallen od. Neigung
einfallende Strecke S. 2469
— Schacht S. 5436 , 5439,
5627
Einfallslinie 10833
Einfallstelle 16411
Einführen des Drahtseils
in den Flaschenzug
14588
— des Vapfens in ein
Muffengewinde 17268
Einfüllen der Erze 3351
Einfüllungsbohrung 9762
Einfeuer standschmiede
16392
einflügeliger Abbaustoss
16405
Einfluss 9768
Einflussrinne 8684
einformen S. 11960
einfrieren S. 7740
Eingang 9820
Eingangskonus 18277/a
eingebettet S. 9864, 9887,
17762
eingeformter Kern 6401
eingeführte Kohle 9660
eingegossene Einlage S.
9833
eingegossener Kühlkörper
9897
— Teil 2989
eingeklemmte Scholle 9375,
9377
eingelagerte Schicht S. 9868
eingerollte Barre 3922
eingeschaltet 9915, S. 9887,
eingeschaltete Tuffbank
9916
eingeschlossen 12442
eingeschlossene Eisenkörner
6441
— Produktion 3772
— Schlacke 6442
— Sonde S. 16245
eingeschlossenes Gas
12443
eingeschnittene Stelle 8591
eingesickerter Hammer-

Einlegen der Kerne 10599
Einlegestreifen 10841/a
Einmalschmelzerei 16398
einmauern 2366
Einnehmen S. 9853
einölen 12477
einpacken 12824
Einpacken 12843
Einpacker 12841
Einphasenofen 16396
Einphasenstromanlage 16395
Einpressindex 9810
Einpressprofil 9811
Einpressonde S. 9674, 9817, 9829, S. 9859, 10330, 13926
einpudern S. 1641
Einpudern mit Talkum 6141
Einreissen S. 2312
Einrichten mit Hilfe von Führungsstangen 168
Einrichtung für Krebsbrennen 3580
Einsatz 1327/a, S. 3315, S. 11478
— in das Wasserbad für Reagenzröhren 18457
Einsatzgewicht 19906
einsatzhärten 2909
Einsatzhärten 2917
Einsatzhärtung 2918, S. 3158
Einsatzhärtungsofen 2926
Einsatzofen 2886
Einsatzöffnung 6891
Einsatzpulver 2920
Einsatzpumpe 13057/a
Einsatzschaufel 13039
Einsatzschneide 5250, 10092
Einsatzstahl 2870, 2921, S. 3156, 3162, 17469
Einsatztemperatur 2922
Einsatztopf 2919
einschalten 9311, S. 9917
Einschieben 5064
— der Förderwagen 12553
Einschleifen 8554
Einschluss 6444, 9711, S. 20268

Einschluss von endogener Schlacke 6462
einschmelzen 14695
Einschmelzen 11464
— der Legierung S. 11474
Einschmelzglas 4079
Einschmirgeln S. 8554
Einschnitt 3285, 10312, 12394, S. 12403, 17155, 18873
Einschnürkern 2319, 19693
Einschnürung 14573
Einschränkungsvereinbarung 14030
einseitige Kraft 19306
— Modellplatte 16402
einsenken 5433
einsetzen 9832
Einsetzen S. 2885
— des Tiegels 15919
— gehärtet (durch) 2913
Einsetzer 4074
Einsetzmaschine 3340
Einsetzkran S. 3338
Einsondenpumpanlage S. 9747
Einspannen der Massel 9837
Einsprengling S. 9840, 13149
Einsprengung 5541
einstampfen 17304
Einstampfen 17322
Einstechstahl 12952
Einsteinium 6234
einstellbare Düse 3517
einstellen 7515
Einstellstift 6083
Einstellung 167, 7517, 14657
Einstrahlung 3431
einstufiger Tagebau 16384
Einsturz S. 3122, 6766, 7639
Einsturzbau 3121
Einstürzen S. 6771
eintauchen 5432
Eintauchen 5453
Eintauchplattierung 9644/a
eintiegliger Ofen 16387
Eintrittsöffnung 173, 9822
eintrümmiger Bremsberg 16399

eintrümmiger Bremsberg mit Gegengewicht 1048, 10173, 10173·
Ein - und Ausfahrt 5228
Einwalzen 15069
Einwirkung des Eises 111
— des strömenden Wassers 112
Einwölbung 5708
Einzelaushubtisch S. 16393
Einzelbestimmung 5260
Einzelpumpanlage 9747
Einzelversuch 16406
einzementieren S. 3139
einziehender Schacht 5709, 9858
einziehendes Wetter 9856
Einziehschacht S. 5696
Einziehteil 5782
einzylindrig 11909
eirund s. oval
Eisblumen 7430
Eisen S. 7900, 9952
— mit niedrigem Schwefelgehalt 10028
— strecken (das) 5761
— vergiessen (das) 2980
— vorwärmen 8968
Eisenabbrand 10025
Eisenabflussrinne 10006
Eisenabscheidung 10010
Eisenabtrennung 5143
Eisenalaun S. 6874, S. 8710, S. 8726
eisenarme Schlacke 16547
Eisenausscheidung 15873
Eisenbad 9957
Eisenbahnfracht 14366
Eisenbahnmaterial 14367
Eisenballen 9956
Eisenband S. 9324
Eisenbeton 6943, 14673
Eisenblech S. 1664, 10011, S. 19526
Eisenblechmantel 16061
Eisenblechring 16059
Eisenblock S. 16058
Eisenbor 6941
Eisenbrücke 17460
Eisenchlorid 3496
Eisendraht 10026

Eisenelektrode 9971
Eisenerz 615/a
Eisenfrischerei 10001
Eisenfunken 10017
Eisengehalt 4254
Eisengiesser 9974
Eisengiesserei S. 9975
Eisenglanz 9978, 12530, 17040
Eisenglimmer 11626
Eisenglimmerschiefer S. 17041
Eisengrube 9983
Eisenguss S. 2995, 9965, 9966
eisenhaltiger Abfall 19722
— Sandstein 10007
Eisenhütte 9975
Eisenkarbid 9961
Eisenkarbonat 2850
Eisenkies 7536/a, S. 9997, S. 12130
Eisenklumpen S. 9958
Eisen-Kohlenstoffbestimmer 704
Eisenkohlenstofflegierung 9962
Eisen-Kohlenstoff-Schaubild 9963
Eisenkohlenstoffzustandsschaubild 9964
Eisenkonstruktion S. 9960
Eisenkörnchen 9979
Eisenkranz S. 11302
Eisenkruste 8838, 8875
Eisenlager 10021
Eisenluppen S. 9981
eisenmagnetisch 6957
Eisenmangan S. 6944
Eisenmangantitan 6945
Eisenmassel S. 9992
Eisenmennige 9986
Eisenmetallurgie 6964/a, 11590, 16287
Eisennickellegierung S. 6946
Eisenniet 10003
Eisenocker 12864
Eisenopal S. 6969
Eisenoxyd 6928
— von der Teerfarbenerzeu-

gung 12798
eisenoxydhaltiges Gut 11372
eisenoxydreich 14874
Eisenoxydsulfat S. 6929, 6965, S. 11193
Eisenoxydulammoniumsulfat 6964
Eisenoxydulsulfat 6966
Eisenphosphat 13164
Eisenphosphor 6948
Eisenplatte 9993
Eisenportlandzement 9995
Eisenquerschnitte S. 10009
eisenreiche Schlacke 16551
Eisenreif S. 9324
Eisenrohr 9275
Eisensammelraum 14489
Eisensand 6968
Eisensau 9958
eisenschüssiger Ton 3656
Eisenschwamm S. 17144
Eisenschwarzrohr 1650
Eisensorte 14246
Eisenspat S. 16994
Eisenspiegel S. 17040
Eisenstäbe 15054
Eisenstangen S. 15054
Eisenstärke 19655
Eisensulfid S. 6951, 10022
Eisenteile 7117
Eisentitan S. 18692
Eisenträger 10020
Eisentür 17466
Eisen - und Schlackenwärme 8981
— -und Stahlerzeugnisse 9954
Eisenunterschicht 9991/a
Eisenverband S. 9960
Eisenwalzwerk 10005
Eisenwaren 10035
Eisenwasser 3268
Eisenwerk 9960
Eisenzeug 10024
Eisenzimmerung 10002, 10019
eiserne Richtplatte 17726
— Schwelle 10015
eiserner Hut 4033, 8370, 12807, 14309
— Spiess 18306

eiserner Winderhitzer 9953
eisernes Blech S. 16058
— Tragstück 9959
Eisenerz 9987
Eisenerzgrube 9991
Eisenerzlager 11729
Eisenerzlagerstätte 5197
Eiszeit 5858, 9611
Eläolith 6243, 6372
Eläolithsyenit 6373, S. 12231
elastische Formänderung 6246/a
— Reibahle 6670
elasticher Puffer 6244
Elastizität der Materiale 6250
Elastizitätsgrenze 6245 10821, 14007
Elastizitätsmodul 11855
Elaterit 6252
elektrisch geheizter Dampfkessel S. 6262
— geschweisst 6315
— s. elektro
elektrische Anlage 10788
— Endosmose 6273
— Förderung 6282
— Grubenlampe 6279
— Handbohrmaschine auf Ständer 6278
— Handschleifmaschine 13689
— Kernbohrung 9753
— Kippvorrichtung 6309
— Kopflampe 6264
— Leitfähigkeit 6266
— Lösungstension S. 6350
— Maschinenanlage 6286
— Punktschweissung 6321
— Schweissmaschine 19946
— Schweissmaschine mit Benzinmotorantrieb 6316
— Schweissung 6314
— Stahlerzeugung S. 6306
— Stumpfschweissmaschine 2642
— Tischschere 6258
— Zündmaschine 14198
— Zündung 6259
elektrischer Antrieb 6271

elektrischer Dampfkessel 6303
— Drehmomentschrauben-
    schlüssel 6284
— Entladungsimpuls 6270
— Frischfeuerofen 6292
— Haspel 6318
— Herdofen 6280
— Hitzemesser 18493
— Horizontalofen 6257
— Kippofen 6310
— Lötkolben 6302
— Messapparat 6287
— Muffelofen 6289
— Ofen für Widerstandshei-
    zung mit strahlendem
    Deckelgewölbe 6276
— Röhrenofen 6313
— Schmelzofen S. 6288
— Strom 6269
— Warmhalteofen 6283
— Widerstand 6294
— Widerstandsofen 6295
— Zünder 6260
elektrisches Bohren 6322
— Emaillieren 6272
— Kernen 6267, 6319
— Lötrohr 6261
— Schmelzen S. 6300
Elektrizitätsquelle 16946
Elektroanalyse 6322/a,
    6337
Elektrobeizen 6346
Elektroblech 3991
elektrochemischer Arbeits-
    tisch 6323
elektrochemisches Verfah-
    ren 6325
Elektrodendraht 4402, 6329
Elektrodendurchführung
    6328
Elektrodenhalter 6327
Elektrodenkohle 6326
Elektrodenpotential 16397/a
Elektrodenreglung 169
Elektroflaschenzug S. 6281
Elektrographie 6333/a
Elektrokernbohrungsseil
    10965
Elektro(dampf)kessel 6262
Elektrolyse 6335

Elektrolysenschlamm 6349
elektrolysieren 6334
elektrolysieren 6353
Elektrolysierung 6354
Elektrolyt 6336
Elektrolyteisen 6344
elektrolytisch hergestelltes
    Eisen S. 6344
— raffinieren 6366
— verzinntes Weissblech
    6351
elektrolytische Korrosion
    7882
— Kupferraffination 6339
— Raffination 6347
— Reibung der Ionen 6342
— Spaltung 6341
— Trennung 6348
— Verzinkung S. 7943
elektrolytischer Lösungs-
    druck 6350
— Reibungswiderstand 6343
elektrolytisches Dekapieren
    6324
Elektrolytkupfer 6338
Elektrolytnickel 6345
Elektromagnet 6355
elektromagnetische Bad-
    bewegung S. 6356
elektromagnetischer Apparat
    von Siemens 16291
Elektromagnetismus 6358
Elektrometallurgie 6360
elektrometrische Messung
    6361
Elektron 6362
Elektronblech 16054
elektronegativ 6363
Elektronenoktett 12454/a
elektronisches Verfahren
    6364
Elektroofen 6274
Elektroroheisen 6275, 6290
    6320
Elektroroheisenerzeugung
    6291
Elektrorolle 10898/a
Elektroschachtofen 6298
Elektroschmelzen 6299
Elektroschmelzofen 6288
    6300

Elektroschmieden 6332
Elektroschweissung 6317
Elektrostahl 6304
Elektrostahlband 6307
Elektrostahlerzeugung 6306
Elektrostahlformguss 6305
Elektrostahlwerk 6308
elektrostatische Aufberei-
    tung 6368
Elektrostenolyse 6369
Elektrotiegelofen 6268
Elektrozug 6281
Element 3132, 6374
Elementaranalyse 19216
Elementarzelle 19308/a
Elementkohle S. 14796
Elementstein S. 12329
Elevator-Bügel 6380
Eliasit 6381
ellipsoidaler Basalt 6385
elliptischer Draht 6386
Ellsworthit 6387
eloxieren 634
Eloxieren 466, 633
Elpidit 6393
Elvan 6399
eluvial 6396
eluviale Lagerstätte 6397
Eluvium 6398
Emaildraht S. 6434
Emaillblech 6436
emaillieren 6432
Emaillierofen 6438
emaillierter Draht 6434
emailliertes Blech S. 6437
— Eisen 6435
Embolit 6402
Emmonsit 6418
empfindlich 15856
empfinflicher Bohrer 15857
Empfindlichkeit 10248,
    15858
Emplektit 6419
Empressit 6420
Emscher 6423
Emulgator 6427
emulgieren 6430
emulgiertes Öl 6426
Emulgierung 6425
Emulsion 6428
Emulsionsöl 6424

Emulsionsspülung 6429
Enargit 6439
Enckesches Gebläse 6440
Ende 6449
Endform 7070
endgültiger Versuch 7071
Endkaliber 10559
Endkammer 1968
Endleitfähigkeit 10826
Endlichit 6459
endlose Kette, 6457
endogener Einschluss 3916
endogenes Gestein 6460
endomorphe Kontaktwir-
　kungen 6463
Endplatte S. 6454
Endprodukt 18208
Endproduktion 18209
Endpunkt 6455
Endquerschnitt 7069
enges Rolloch 7105
englische Tunnelbauweise
　6480
englischer Träger 6482
— Zementierofen 6479
englisches Roheisen 6481
engrohriger Wasserrohrkessel
　19831
Engstelle 18617
Enstatit 6490
Entstaubung 6137
entbenziniertes Gas 17858
Entbutanisierung 5047
Entbutanisierungsapparat
　5048
Entdolomitisierung S. 5083
Enteloxieren S. 459, 5042
Entenschnabel 6072
Entethanisierungsapparat
　5102
Entfärbungskohle 5079
Entfernen der Keile 19236
Entfernen der Speiser (od.
　Steiger) S. 14721
Entfernung sandiger
　Bestandteile 6383
Entfernung von Aluminium
　459
Entfettung 11541
Entfeuchter 5232
— getrocknet (im) 5847

entgalvanisieren 17839
Entgalvanisierung 17866
entgasen 5126, 5552
Entgaser 5045
Entgasung 5127, 6031
Entgasungserzeugnis 13991
Entgasungsglühen 5128
Entgasungsmittel 5129
entgegengesetzte Drehung
　14825
Entglasung 5283/a
entgräten 3682, 3741, S.
　6972
Entgratmaschine S. 2620,
　S. 3046
Entgratrille 1059
Entgratungshammer 15600
Enthalpie 6491
enthärten 19334
Enthärtung 7067, 16848
entionisieren 5142
Entionisierungsgeschwindig-
　keit 5141
entkernen 5077, 6971
Entkernen 5078
Entkernung S. 5078
entkohlen 5054, 5058
entkohlt 5055
Entkohlung 5056, 5057
— mit Lösungsmitteln 16909
entkrusten 15580
entkupfern 5073
Entkupfern 5074
entkupferte Lauge 5082
entkuppeln S. 5504
Entladestoss- schweissung
　6367
Entladung nach beiden
　Seiten des Gleises 5498
entlasteter Blaukupolofen
　1135
Entlastungsbohrung 14686
Entlastungsplatte S. 1131
Entlastungsrille 17788
Entleerung des Ofens 6421,
　6422
Entlüftung 319, 5044, S.
　19498, 19499, 19510
Entlüftungsleitungen 19503
Entlüftungsnut S. 331,
　12474, 19497.

Entlüftungsrille 331
Entlüftungssack 12744
Entlütungsstück 19501
Entlüftungsventil 318, 14688
　14688, 19512
Entmagnetisiergerät 5162
Entmethanisierung 5165
entölter Sand S. 5191
Entölungsgebiet 5744
entparaffiniertes Öl 5296
entphosphatieren 5189
Entphosphatierung 5188
Entphosphatierungszeit 5187
entphosphortiertes Roheisen
　19696
Entpropanisierung 5202
entrohren 14123
Entrohrung 20157
Entropie 6494
entsanden 1696, 7394
Entsanden 1696
Entsäuerungsmittel 5182
Entschäumer 5123
Entschieferer 15981
Entschlackung 7488, 14385
entschlämmen 6394
Entschwefeler 5247
entschwefeln 5245
entschwefelter Rückstand
　19335
entschwefeltes Roheisen
　5246
— Rohöl 18117
Entschwefelung 5244,
　18118
entsilbern 5239
entsilizieren 5236
Entsilizierung 5235
entspannen 14719
Entspannungsturm 7301
entstauben 14716
Entstauben 6134
Entstaubungsvorrichtung
　6132, 6138
Entstehen von Ofensätzen
　S. 2388
Entteerung 5255
Entüberhitzer 5249
Entwässerer 5289
entwässern 5288
entwässerter Sand 5191

Entwässerung 5292
Entwässerungsmaschine
    5290
Entwässerungssieb 5294,
    5749
Entwässerungstrecke 19791
Entwässerungsturm 5746
Entweichen der Luft 6563
— flüchtiger Bestandteile
    6567
entweichendes Gas 6566
entwickeln 5272
Entwicklungsfälschung S.
    3181
entwickelte Antiklinale
    (nicht) 809
Entwicklung 5275
— des Gefüges 5277
Entwicklungskaliber 11663
Entziehen S. 26
Entziehung von Wärme S.
    8973
Entziehungsöffnung 12702
Entziehungsrohr 12705
Entzinkung 5299
entzinnen 5265
Entzinnen 5265/a
Entzünden S. 5114
entzundern 15579
Entzunderung 3479, 5225
Entzunderungsapparat 5224
Eosphorit 6500
Eozän 6498
Eozoikum 6501
Eozoon-Struktur 6502
eparchaische Formation 6504,
    6504
Ephesit 6508
Epichlorit 6510
Epidesmin 6512
Epidibas 6513
Epididymit 6514
Epidiorit 6515
Epidot 6516
Epigenese 6518
epigenetisch 6517
Epigenit 6519
Epigestein 6520
epiklastich 6511
Epirogenese 6505, 6507
epirogenetische Bewegung

    6506
epithermaler Gang 6521
Epizentralgebiet 6509
Epizone 6522
Epsomit S. 1632
Erbium 6536
erblasenes Roheisen 1753/a
Erbsenstein S. 13386
Erdarbeit 8386
Erdarbeiter 6637, 8615
Erdballen 3745
Erdbewegung mit Bulldozer
    5719
Erdbohrer S. 8373, 8608,
    13969
Erdböschung S. 16678
Erddruck 15024/a
Erde gleich (mit der) 6625
Erdfliessen S. 16895
Erdfluss S. 16895
Erdgas S. 12193
Erdgasfeld S. 8005
Erdgasrohr 13339
Erdgasruss 2826
erdig 3748
erdige Braunkohle 19228
— Kohle S. 2284, 6173,
    14430, 16777
erdiger Bruch 6172
— Roteisenstein S. 6174
erdiges Eisenerz 6175
Erdkohle 6173
Erdöl 11753, S. 15031, 17646
— mit Paraffin u. Aspalt
    11658
Erdölabscheidung durch
    Rückstandcoagulum
    19753
Erdölanlage 12503
Erdölausbruch 20068
Erdölbasis 1282
Erdölbergwerk 12500
Erdölbohrturm 12487
Erdöleinlagern 18257
Erdölentdeckung 12511
Erdölförderungsrechte 12505
Erdölgrube S. 12500
Erdölindustrie 12497
Erdölkonzession 12484
Erdölkonzessionsrechte
    15301

Erdölpumpen im angelassenen
    Schacht 19862
Erdölwanderung 18857
Erdpech S. 12181
Erdpfeiler S. 3464
Erdpyramide 3464, S. 5988,
    6177, 14369
Erdregenerator 3665
Erdreservoir S. 17993
Erdrutsch 6169, 10524
Erdschlacke S. 3727
Erdschlussklemme 8610
Erdungs-Rohrpfahl 19071
Erdwachs S. 6178
Erdwall S. 12030
Erforschung 6680
Ergussgestein S. 6219
Ergussmassen 6218
Erhärtung 4178
erheben S. 14370
Erhitzen S. 9007, 14667
erhitzt S. 9004
Erhitzung durch Induktion
    9751
Erhöhung der Reduktions-
    fähigkeit 9725
Erian 6539
Erikit 6541
Erinit 6542
Erionit 6543
Erker 10262
Ermüdung 6830
Ermüdungsbruch 6832
Ermüdungszone 6833/a
Erosionsunterbrechung 6548
erproben 18440
erratisch 6549, 18858
erratischer Block 5854,
    6550
errichten 14371
Errit 6552
Erschliessung mit Säure
    S. 100
Erschmelzung des Eisens
    auf elektrothermischem
    Wege 6301
erschöpfen 6145, 13535
erschöpft 14159
erschöpftes (Erdöl) 5194
erschüttern 10124
Erschütterung 16015

Erstarren 3784, 16891
erstarrte Lösung 4205
— Metallprobe 16893
Erstarrung 7742
Erstarrungsbereich 16892,
    S. 7748
Erstarrungsbild 5314
Erstarrungsdiagramm S.
    5314
Erstarrungsebene 15905/a
Erstarrungsintervall 7748
erste Destillation des
    Erdöls 17868
erstes Destillat 8932
Ersticken des Hochofens
    3519
Erstickung 1202
Erstling 13149
ertrunkenes Tal 6011
Eruptionskanal 3454
Eruptionskreuz 3522, 18870
Eruptionskreuzvorrichtung
    3523
Eruptionswolke 8312
eruptiv ausfliessen S. 7419
— fördern S. 7419
Eruptivader 6559
Eruptivsonde 17174
Erwärmen S. 9007
erwärmt 9004
erwärmtes Wasser 19669
Erwärmung 9007
erweitern 14477
— des Schrams S. 16790
Erweiterung 6487
Erweiterungssonde 12692
Erythrin 6560
Erythrosiderit 6561
Erz abbauen 17665
— aufschliessen S. 4761
— brechen 4761
— hereingewinnen 2298
— pochen S. 4761
— quetschen S. 4761
— zermahlen S. 4761
Erzabbau 12632
Erzabfuhr 10557/a
Erzabscheidung mit
    schiefen Ebenen 18193
Erzader 10627, S. 17761
Erzaufbereitung 12630

Erzaufbereitung durch
    Sonderung nach Gleich-
    fälligkeit in Stromappara-
    ten 4161
Erzbehäter S. 12631
Erzbrekzie 5735
Erzbrikett 12634
Erzbrikettierung 12635
Erzbunker 12631
Erzeugnis 20113
Erzeugung von Spezialteilen
    17010
Erzfall 3455, S. 12651,
    13360
Erzflöz 12997
Erzförderung 12650, 12660
Erzförderwagen S. 12658
Erzfragment 16141
erzführend S. 12629
Erzgang 4552, 10659, S.
    10954, S. 11756
Erzgemenge 11838
Erzgicht 12637
Erzgiesser 2270
Erzglühfrischen 14619
Erzhaufen zum Rösten 3620
— zur Aufbereitung 6905
Erzkarren 16481, S. 20006
Erzklassierung 12652/a
Erzklumpen 13933
Erzkonzentrat 9493
Erzkörper 12647
Erzladevorrichtung 12646
Erzlagerplatz 12656
Erzlagerstätte 12640
Erzlaugerei 12644
Erzlieferungsvertrag 4283
Erzlineal 13606
Erzmetallurgie 13974/a
Erznest 2036, 2578, 12240,
    12647/a, 12966
Erzpfeiler 4593
Erzpost S. 3325
Erzpress·stein S. 12634
Erzprobenehmen 12628
Erzpuddeln 12648
Erzquetsche S. 17641
Erzrolle 5780, 7016, S.
    11694, 12638, S. 14118,
    17670
Erzröster 12636

Erzsatz S. 3325
Erzsäule 12639
Erzscheiden 12653
Erzscheider nach Wetherill
    10002
Erzschlauch 12651
Erzschlemme S. 12649,
Erzschnur 17761, S. 17836
Erzsinterung 12652
Erzstahl 5464
Erzstarrungsgesteine 9625
Erzstaub 12643
Erzstock 16161, 16884
Erztasche S. 12240
Erztrübe 12649
Erzverarbeitung 12661
Erzverlader 3321
Erzverteiler 12641
Erzvorrat 12655
Erzwagen 12658
Erzwalzwerk 4777
Erzwaschen S. 2515
Erzzerkleinerung 12633,
    15321
Erzziegel S. 12634
Erzzusatz 132
Essenkanal S. 3459
Essigsäure 62
essigsäures Kali 61
Esskohlenkoks 7577
Etagenkessel 12120
Etagenofen 10360
Etagenrost S. 17549
Etagenwagen 16116
Etagenzementierungsmuffe
    12125
Ettringit 6577
Euchroit 6579
Eudialyt 6585
Eudidymit 6586
Eudiometer 6587
Eudnophit 6588
Eugenglanz S. 13640
eugranitische Struktur S.
    8421
Eukarit 6578
Euklas 6580
Eukolit 6581
— -titanit 6582
Eukrit 6583
Eukryptit 6584

eupelagisch s. pelagisch
euphotische Region 6590
Euralith 6591
Eurit 6592
Europium 6595
eustatisch 6596
Eusynchit 6597
Eutektikum 6598, 6600,
  S. 6603
eutektisch 6599
eutektische Mischung 6603
— Textur 6604
eutektisches Gusseisen
  6601
— Treiben 6602
Eutektoid 6606
eutektoide Umwandlung 6605
eutektoider Stahl 6607
Euxenit 6609
Evergreenit 6626
Exfoliation 6648
Exfoliationsspalte 6649
Exhauster S. 6655
exogener Einschluss 44/a
  6658, 20271
exogenetischer Prozess
  6657
exomorphe Kontaktwirkungen
  6661
exothermer Trichtereinsatz
  6663
Explodierbarkeit 6681
Explosion 16191
— eines Kessels S. 1958
Explosionsschwaden 200,
  202
Explosionschwaden 17603
explosionssicherer Kessel
  9760
Explosionstuff 6683
explosive Abstichloch-
  öffnung 10160
Explosivstoff S. 6684, 6685
explosiv-umgeformtes Rohr
  19029
Explosiv-Verfahren 6688
Exsikkator 6693
extraharter Stahl 2845
Extraktionförderschnecke
  14498

Extraktionsturm 6707
extraktive Destillierung
  6713
extramagmatisch 6714
Extraschnellstahl 18015,
  19537
extraweicher Stahl 5037,
  6705, 19538
extraweiches Tempern 5038
Extrusionslunker 6724/a
Extrusivgestein 6726
Exzentermeissel 6638
Exzenterpresse 6185,
  6186
Exzenterstemmeisen für
  Weichenboden 19247
Exzenterwellenrohr 2775

                F

Fabrik 11686
Fabrikbahn 20226
Fabrikzeichen 18812
Facette 6754/a
Fächerantiklinale 6803
Fächerfalte 6799
Fächergussrinne 6804
Fächerstruktur 6805
Fachwerkausbau 17243
Fachwerkbalken 18963
Fachwerkbalkenbrücke
  18965
Fachwerkbinder aus leichten
  Winkelprofilen 16397
fadenförmige Schicht 16157
Fadenkreuz 8709
Fahlband 6765
Fahlerz 8499, 18471
Fahnenstange 7248
Fahraufhauen 15900
fahrbar 12035
fahrbahre Mühle 13694
— Pfanne 10481
fahbarer Bohrkran 13692
— Dampfkran 10950
— Dampfkran zum Löschen
  der Schiffe 10951
— Kran 11845

fahbarer Masselbrecher
  13695
— Rollgang 18862/a
— Trockenofen 18838
Fahrkorb mit entlasteter
  Oberwalze 1137
Fahrleitungsdraht 3929
Fahrleitungsmast 19084
Fahrseil 6823
— (das) nachnehmen 16667
Fahrt S. 10743, 18906
Fahrtrumm S. 7959
Fahrüberhauen 11309, 11310
Fahrweg 5595, S. 11903,
  18864
Fairfieldit 6769
Fallbirne 19114
fällen 13806
Fällen der Schicht 5444
— s. Neigung od. Einfallen
fallender Guss mit einem
  Metallstrahl 5979, 18748
— Guss mit mehrfachem
  Metallstrahl 4050, 13764
Fallhammer (mit dem)
  geformt 5982
Fallkugel 5999
Fällmittel 13805
Fallprobe 5997/a
Fallrichtung (in der) 5698
— (der) entgegen 19352
Fallrohr 5705, 19529
Fallschutzvorrichtung für
  Förderkörbe 2681
Falltür 18848
Fallwerk 5975, 13254
falsche Formhälfte 6784/a
— Schieferung 14074,
  14081
— Spaltbarkeit 16649
falscher Dammstein 6783
— Firstgebirge 6780
— Sattel 14069
falsches Modell S. 15510
— Schwindmass 20238
Falte 2507/a, 6164/a, 7520,
  15008
— zweiter Ordnung S. 11783
Fältelung S. 4759, 11787
Faltenbiegung 20234/a

Faltenbildung 4871, 20236
Faltenland 7524
Faltengürtel 1479
Faltenstirn S. 4725, 7777
Faltprobe 7525/a
Falttüren 51
Faltung 7525
Faltungsbecken 9896
Faltungszone 2200
Faltversuch S. 1503
Falz 19975
Falzbeitel 7493, 8596
Famatinit 6790
Fangarbeit 7217
Fangdorn S. 7223
— für Pumpengestänge 17940
fangen 7207, 7215
Fanggerät 2551, 7224, 8378, 8381, 10130
Fanggewindebohrer 18288
Fangglocke 1574, 5367, 6914, 15702
Fanggreifer 7222
Fanghaken 1089, 3085, 3187, 4722, 7218, 8460, 16807, 19643
Fangklappe 12039
Fangkorb 10255
Fanglomerat 6810
Fangmagnet 7220
Fangrohr 9294
Fangrutschschere 7219
Fangschere S. 7222
Fangstoff 8204/a
Fangvorrichtung 8566, 8568, 9243
Fangzange 13206
Fangzapfen 11242
Farbstift S. 1910
Farbpyrometer 4035
Farbtemperatur 713
Farbzusatz 136
Farölith 6816
Farrisit 6817
Fase 3274/a
Faseraufbau 6993
Faserbruch 6989/a
faserig s. fibroblastisch
faserige Kohle 1922

faseriger Bruch 6987
— Gips 15555
— Jamesonit 6990
— Lignit 6991
faseriges Eisenerz 6989
Faserkiesel S. 6985
Faserserpentin S. 3553
Faserstruktur 6981, S. 6993
Fasibitikit 6818
Fasinit 6819
Fassait 6820. S. 14212
Fassondraht S. 15996
Fassondrehbank S. 4377
Fassoneisen S. 15772, 1599 15994, 17887
Fassonieren 15998
Fasson-Kernstütze S. 4280, 17192/a
Fassungsraum 2801
Fassungsrohr 19973
Fassungsvermögen 2800
Fastebene S. 13061
faulbrüchiges Eisen 2598
Faustgrösse 7225
Fayalit 6868
Fazies 6755
Faziesfossil 6756
Federblatt 10633, 17195
Federdraht 17203
Federerz 6872, S. 6990
Federgehäuse für Puffer 2521
Federmanometer 17196
Federmessing 17191/b
federnd s. elastisch
federnder Schenkel 17132
Federprellung 17194
Federpuffer 17192
Federring 17202
Federstahl 17200
Federstahldraht 17201
Federstütze 10201
Federung 14760
Federzange 7558
Fehlbohrung 6076, 6140
Fehler S. 7360
— beim Formen 6557
— beim Kernmachen 6555
— beim Putzer 6556

Fehler beim Zusammenbau der Form 6554
— im Material S. 5105
fehlerfrei 6866
Fehlerfreiheit 16941
fehlerlose Metallverkleidung 13616
Fehlstelle 5107, 5110
Fehlguss 17142
Fehlguss · stück 19720
Fehlzündung 11798
Feile 7003
— ebnen (mit der –) 13450
Feilenhärteofen 7005
Feilenhauermeissel 7004
Feilenstahl 7006
Feilenverbrauch 4243
Feilkloben 8790
Feilspan 7007, 7038
Feilstaub S. 7007
fein bearbeitet 7097
fein eingesprengtes Erz 3360
— verteilt 7095
— verteilter Brennstoff S. 7789
Feinarbeit 7092
Feinblech S. 18526
Feinblechwalzwerk 18527
Feindraht 18525
Feineisen 16731
Feineisenstrasse S. 16735
feinen 14593
feinen s. frischen
feiner Draht S. 18525
— Sand 7088
feines Erz 7087/a
— Sieb 7089
Feinergehalt 4252
Feingefüge S. 11655
feingeschliffen 13823
feingeschliffene Oberflächen S. 2406
Feinheitsgrad 7098
Feinkohle 7074, S. 16727
Feinkohlenwäsche 7076
Feinkorneisen 3762, 7082
Feinkorn(guss)eisen 17526
feinkörnig 3761. 7080
feinkörniger Bruch 7081

feinkörniger Sandstein
  12855, 13713
feinkörniges Metall 3764
Feinkornstahl 7084
feinkristallinisches Eisen
  7094
feinlamellare Struktur 16398
Feinlot 7089/a
feinmachen des Silbers S.
  16358
Feinmahlung 16637
Feinmühle 7077
feinnadliger Rutil einge-
  wachsen im Bergkristall
  8711
Feinofen 7100/a
Feinperiode S. 16536
Feinpuddeln 14617
Feinschlacke 14871
Feinschleifen 15527/a
Feinschmelzen 13820
Feinschmieden S. 13822
Feinschmiedung 13822
Feinschraublehre S. 11643
Feinschraubzirkel 11642
Feinsieb S. 7089
Feinstanteil 18004/a
Feinstblech 6704
Feinstellschraube 11643
Feinstrecke 16735
Feinstuhl S. 7130
Feinstahl S. 10801
Feinwaage 13818
Feinwalze 7068
Feinzerkleinerung 7078,
  7085, 12101
Feinzerkleinerungsmühle
  8559
Feinzug 7079
Feldbahn 13696
Feldenergie 6996
Felderbau S. 12898
Feldgestänge 14130
Feldintensität 6997
Feldort S. 7563
Feldortstoss 4921
Feldspat 6899
feldspatartig S. 6900
feldspathaltig 6900
Feldspatisierung 6901
Feldspatvertreter 6902,

  10673
Feldstärke S. 6997
Feldtanks 10647
Feldversuch 7000
Feldwärtsbau 20208
Feldweg 7001
Fels 15004
Felsbecken 15006
Felsen 1916, S. 15504
Felshauer 11549
felsiger Boden 15045
Felsit 6907
felsitisch 6908
felsitische Struktur 6909
Felslöcher 9305
Felsobanyt 6910
Felsophyr 6911
Felssturz 15011
Felsterrasse 15032
Fenster S. 12174
Ferberit 6919
Ferghanit 6920
Fergusit 6921
Fergusonit 6922
Fermentierung 6923
Fermium 6924
Fermorit 6925
Fernandinit 6927
Fernschalter 14702
Ferrierit 6930
Ferrinatrit 6931
Ferriskorbspeisung 6932
Ferrisymplesit 6933
Ferrit 6934
ferritischer Stahl 3167
ferritisches Gusseisen 6935
Ferritizierung 6937
Ferritungstit 6938
Ferro- 6963
Ferrobor 2116
Ferrochrom S. 6942
Ferroferrioxyd S. 11193
Ferrokobalt 6955
Ferrolegierung 6939
Ferrolit 6956
Ferro-Silico-Mangan 6960
Ferromangan S. 6944,
  S. 11279
Ferromangansilizium S. 6949
Ferromangantitan S. 6945
Ferrometer 6958

Ferromolybdän S. 6946
Ferronickel S. 6947
Ferrosilizium 6950. 6961
ferrostatischer Druck 6962
Ferrosulfid S. 10022
Ferrotitan 6952, 18692
Ferrovanadin S. 6954
Ferrowolfram 6953
Ferroxyl 6966/a
Ferrozirkon 6967
fertig walzen 15068
Fertigabdruck 7129
Fertigbearbeitung 7118
— des Werkstückes 7132
fertiges Blech 7121
fertiggeputzt 3683
fertiggestellt S. 7119
Fertigkaliber 7128
fertigmachen 4111
Fertigmachen der Schlag-
  patrone 13952
fertigputzen 6970
Fertigputzen 3690, 5843,
  6974
Fertigschablone 18515
Fertigschleifer 7116
Fertigstahl 7123
fertigstellen S. 4111
Fertigstrasse 7131
Fertigstrecke S. 7131, 7138
Fertigungslinie 13996
Fertigungsstrecke S. 13996
Fertigwalze 7133, 7136
Fertigwalgerüst 7139/a
Fertigwalzwerk 7130/a,
  7137, S. 7138
Fertigwaschtrommel S. 7127
Fertigware
  18650, 18661
fest 6821
— angezogen 18335
Festbau S. 12595
Festdach 7241
feste Aufspannplatte 7239
— Kohle 1322
— Losung 16886
— Rinde A. S. 10891
— Schichten 15254
— unverzimmerte Firste
  16875
fester Brennstoff 16882

fester Rost 17399
— Sand 6826/a
— Schiefer 14459
— schieferiger Sandstein 8902
— Stempelteil 5359/a
festes Gebirge 11219, 17339
— Mass 7235
— Sprengmittel 16881
festgeklemmt 9486
Festigkeit 17775
Festigkeitsschweiss · stahl 9188
Festigkeitsstahl 9187
festklemmen S. 3616
festländische Eisdecke 8257
festliegende Unterwalze 7229
festliegendes Rohr 7238
festmachen S. 1792. 1807
festsitzende Sandschülpe 6673, 1779/a
— Schwärzeschülpe 1674
Festräumer 9253
feststehender Dampfkran 7242
— Dampfkessel 17397
— Konverter 17398
— Magnet 17400
— Ofen 7233
Festungsachat 7623
Festwerden 17582
— durch Differenzdruck 5396
Fett 5633
fetter Formsand 10933
— Sand 17878
— Ton S. 7810, S.11696, 16803, 19242
— Torf 1635
fettes Öl 6826
Fettglanz 16804
Fettkessel 18225
Fettkohle S. 2782
Fettöl S. 6826
Fettpuddeln S. 13252, 19995
Fettsäure 6837
Fettstift S. 1910
Fettverbindung 6838

feucht 4985, 16853
feuchtes Eisenerz S. 19993, 19993/a
— Gas S. 14872
Feuchtigkeit 11863
— (die) aufsaugen 11
Feuchtigkeitsmesser 9580, 11862
Feuchtigkeitsverhältnis 17444
Feuchtluftbohrung 11810
Feuer anzünden 10777
— (das) decken 4559
— zurückschieben S. 4559
feuerbeständig 7186
feuerbeständiger Stahl 7177
Feuerbeständigkeit 14764
Feuerblech 7155, 7851
Feuerbock 7166
Feuerbrücke 2381, 7157, S. 7829
Feuerbüchsendecke 7154, S. 4731 . 7833
Feuerbüchsenseitenwand 7156
Feuerbüchskessel 7153
feuerfest 2720, S. 12353, 14626
feuerfeste Auskleidung 7849, 10849
— Auskleidung des Ofens 14630
— Hülse 16590
— Verkleidung 7163
feurfester Hahn 19451
— Lehm 7183
— Mörtel 14634
— Stein 14627
— Stoff 14625
— Ton 2188, 7158, 7182
— Zement 14628
feuerfestes Futter 14632
Feuerfestigkeit 14624
Feuerflur S. 4730
Feuergeschränk 7843
Feuerhaken 14314
Feuerkistendecke 4730, S. 4731
Feueropal 7173, 8326
Feuerraum 7174, 7152
Feuerrohr 7457

Feuerrohrwand S. 19035
Feuerrost 7169, 7844
Feuerschirm 2368
Feuersetzen 7179
feuersicher 12353
feuersicherer Draht 7263
Feuerspritzenkessel 7168
Feuerstein S. 16310
Feuertür 3864, 7167
Feuerung 7189, 7825, S. 17637
— beschicken 17630
— für rauchfreie Verbrennung S. 16760
— mit Beschickung von oben 12741
— mit Beschickung von unten S. 19250
— mit Hochofengas 19729
— mit Kühlung durch Wasserumlauf in Hohlroststäben 7863
— mit Oberluftzuführung 7875
— mit Petroleumrückständen 7841
— mit selbsttätiger Beschickung S. 15000
— mit umgekehrter Flamme 5699
— mit vorstehender Feuerung 7876
Feuerungsanlage S. 1967, 7193
Feuerungsgerät 7195
Feuervergoldung 7169/.a, 9419
Feuerverzinkung S. 7926, 9418 9418
Feuerverzinnen 9449
Feuerverzinnung S. 9449
feuerverzinnter Draht 7180, 9448
feuerverzinntes Weissblech 9447
fibroblastische Struktur 6983
Fibroferrit 6984
Fibrolith 6985
Fichtelit 6994
Fiedlerit 6995
Filter 7042, S.17736

Filterflasche S. 7057
Filtergestell 7822
Filterhalter 7053
Filterkammer S. 17738
Filterkegel 7044
Filterkohle 7056
filtern 7041
Filterpapier 7049
Filterplatte 7045
Filterpresse 7051
Filterpumpe 7052
Filterrohr 15688
Filterrohrabsetzverbindung 10848
Filterrohrhänger 10845, 15691
Filterrohrgreifer mit Fass- -und Nachfassvorrichtung 10847
Filterrohrwascher 10844
Filterschale 7063
Filterschicht 7043
Filtersieb 7823
Filterstechheber 7058
Filtertank 7054
Filtertrichter 7047
Filtertrommel 7046
Filterung 7062
Filterverlust 7048
Filterzusatz 13826
Filtrat 7061
Filtrationsanlage 7050
filtrieren 13076
Filtrierkessel 7055
Filzstreifen S. 6912
Filzüberzug 6912
Fimmel 7900
Findling S. 5854 , 6550
Fingerbildung 7109
Fingerbühne S. 15423
Fingerkran 4603
Finne 12894
Finnemanit 7142
Fiorit 7145
Firmamentstein S. 12329
Firngletscher 12256
Firnis 19478
firnissen 19477
Firstbrett 903
Firste S. 8808, 15137,

Firste (die) abklopfen 10394
— abklopfen 14416
— einer Strecke 1067
— nachreissen 14937
— (die) verschalen 2378
— verzimmern S. 2378
Firstenbau 1078, S. 1490, 12747, 17564
— mit geneigter Firste 1491 14913
— mit geneigter Firste und mit Bergeversatz 9692, 9697
— mit Selbstversatz 4901
— mit waagrechter Firste 7318
— mit waagrechter Firste und mit Bergeversatz 9336
— mit waagrechter Firste und Versatz 7317
firstenbauartig 12751
Firstenbohrloch 19387
Firstenbruch 15141
Firstenschuss 15142
Firstenschussbohrloch S. 15142
Firstenstempel 6752
Firstenstoss 12746
— mit geneigter Firste 14912
— mit geneigter Firste und mit Bergeversatz 9696
— mit waagrechter Firste 7319, 7321
— mit waagrechter Firste und mit Bergeversatz 9337
— mit waagrechter Firste und Rahmenzimmerung 7320
— ohne Bergeversatz 12586
Firstloch 2348
Fisch 7206
Fischaugenstein 698
Fischerit 7205
Fischrechen 7208
Fisch-schwanzmeissel 7214
Fixieren 7243
Fizelyt 7245

Fjeldgletscher S. 9612
Flachbohrer S. 812
Flachdraht 7347
Fläche S. 7316, 13453, S. 18040
flache Falte 12572
— Kurve 7331
— Schicht 15010
— Sprunghöhe 18794
Fläche (-von Dampf berührt) 18056
Flacheisen 7340, 17744
Flachenwinkel 9880
flacher Bohrer S. 812
— Formstift 7334
— Gang 10957
— gestreifter Stift 7330
— Schacht 5436, 16680
— Stift 7338
flachfallendes Flöz 7344
Flach-Halbrundeisen 7336
Flachkaliber 2224
Flach-Knüppel 14516
Flachlandmoor 7326
Flachlasche 7333
flachlitziges Drahtseil 7350/a
Flachloch 7339
Flachmeissel 3486
Flachmoor S. 11053
Flachpalette 12881
Flachpinsel 2479
Flachsee S. 10897
Flachseil 7343
Flachspitzhammer 14424
Flachstab 7315
Flachstahl 7323
Flachstanze 10031
Flachwulsteisen 2545, 7329
Fladenlava S. 15172
Flämmaschine 9409/a
Flamme 7252
Flämmen 9438/a
— (die) auf den Herd lenken 5456
Flammenentzunderung 7256,
Flammenfärbung 4036, 7262
Flammenhärtung 7259
Flammenloch 7261
Flammenlötung 16866

Flammkohle 2781, 7265, 11760
Flammofen mit gestrecktem Herd 14818
Flammofenfrischen 14609
Flammofenstahl 17487
Flammpunkt 10362/a
Flammpunktprüfung 3721
Flammrohr S. 7457
Flammrohrfeuerung 7454
Flammrohrkessel 7264 , 7450
— mit glatten Flammrohren S. 1990
— mit Quersiederohren S. 7451
— mit Stufenrohr S. 1995
flammsicher s. feuersicher
Flanellscheibe 7278
Flankensonde 7277
Flansch mit Dichtungsring 14927
Flanschenrohr 7269
Flanschwulsteisen S. 2545
Flasche 1172, 4936, 19541
— für Gasentwicklung 7312
Flaschen S. 7310
flaschenhalsartige Verformung 2137
Flaschenkappe 2136
Flaschenschild 10448
Flaschenschraubstock 9207
Flaschenzug 1795, 1796, 1864, 3245, S. 9225, 14133, 18196
Flaschenzugblock 18860
Flasertextur 13141
Flattern S. 7283
Fleckenkorrosion 5529
fleckig 17166
Fleckigwerden 17167/a
Fleckschiefer 7358, 17167
Flecktextur 11158
flexibler Bohrstrang 10808
— Draht 7370
Flexur 657, S. 17547
flicken 12964
fliegende Bahn S. 13696
Fliese S. 16493

Fliess-Sohlendruck 7440
fliessend, s. laufend
fliessende Hitze S. 19945
— Sonde 7444
Fliessfigur 17732
Fliessgrenze S. 4623
Fliesslinie 7429/a
Fliess- spannung 20298/a
Fliessplan 6475
Fliesspressen 3977
Fliesspunkt 13743
Fliess -scheide 12251/a
Fliess - schema 7426
Fliessvermögen S. 3033
Fliessvermögenversuch 3034
Fliessversuch auf freiem Querschnitt S. 12571
Flimmern 8300
Flinkit 7376
Flintglas 7379
Flintstein 2194, 7377
Flint-Ton S. 7378
flockig 7395
Flockung 7393
Florencit 7413
Flossenbett S. 13268
Flossofen 7442
Flotation 7415/a
Flöz 1174, 15743, S. 10594
— von 45° Neigung 8713
— s. Schicht
Flözkanal 3290
Fluchstab 2030
Flugasche 7505
Flügel S. 16254, 18593
Flügelmutter 7508
Fluidalgefüge S. 15173
Fluktuationsstruktur S. 7468
Fluoreszenz 1819
Fluorit 10295, 13012
Fluorkalzium S. 7475·
Flur der Eisengiesserei 7406
Fluss 12192
Flussäurebereitungsapparat S. 701
Flussbett mit Goldgehalt 8685
Flusseisen S. 7464, 9794
flüssig entnommenes Eisen

11880
flüssiger Brennstoff 10875
— Brennstoffofen 10876
— Sprengstoff 10874
flüssiges Eisen 10877
— Gusseisen 11879
flüssigkeitsgekühlt 10872
Flüssigpetroleumgas 10879
Flussmetall S. 7464
Flussmittel 7497, 7498, 7500, 7502
Flussofen S. 7442
Fluss - spat 2780, S. 10295
Fluss - stahl S. 5034, 8714, S. 9794, 9800
Fluss - stahldraht 11701
Fluss- stahlplatte 3021
Flutgold S. 7386
fluviatile Fazies 7495
Flysch 7509
Foraminifera 7552
Forbesit 7553
Förderanlage 20104
— für Gasolin 7975
Förderband S. 1176, 4314, 18836
Förderbandofen 1477/a, 4313/a
Förderbandrolle 4320
Förderdruck 7447
Fördergefäss mit Bodenklappe 5978
Fördergestell 2680, 13400
Fördergerüst 7921, 8911, 8913, 8921, 8924, 9227, 10747, 11733, 13405, 13659, 14186, 15945
Fördergrus 11741
Förderhaken S. 2949
Förderhaspel S. 8231, 9236
Förderhöhe 5493, S. 8906, 10740
Förderhund S. 11772, 19622, S. 20006
Förderkette 4319, 15668
Förderkohle 437, 15248, 18584, 19333
Förderkolonne 12512, 13998
Förderkorb 5795,
— s. Fördergestell
Förderkübel 2202, 9472

Förderkübelabteilung 16484
Förderleistung 9767
förderliche Vergrösserung 1004
Fördermann S. 2527, 2573, 9490
Fördermaschine 8219, 9232, 20103
Fördermaschinengebäude 8220
Fördermaschinist 6473, 9228
fördern 5770
Förderpotential 13733
Förderrinne 4316, 7675/a, 15376/a, S. 17171
Förderrolle S. 3563, 4527
Förderschacht 5813, 6712, 9233, 14134, 20106, 20249
— zur Einführung von Pressgas 8021
Förderschale 6379
Förderschnecke 4620
Förderseil 9157/a, 9231, 20100, 20105
— und Fördergestell 2038
Fördersohle S. 16339
Förderstollen 12645
Förderstrecke 7959, S. 8095, 8893, 8898, 15119, 20112
— im alten Mann 8331
Fördertour S. 12512
Fördertrommel S. 2662, 9226, 15168
Förderturm S. 8911, S. 8913, S. 10747, S. 13659, 13995
Förder-und Pumpenschacht 6470
Förderung 5805, 6707/a, 7955, S. 8201, 10531, 12475, 14378, S. 18819, 20097
— aus der Vorrichtung 5278
— mit endlosem Seil 6458
— mit Seilgewichtsausgleich 1136
— mit Vorder- und Hinterseil 18213
Förderungsstelle 12708
Förderwagen 2206, 3105,

4508, 9484, 9492, 11020, S. 11772, 15118, 18928, S. 18971
Förderwärter 4324
Förderung s. Fördern
Förderzins S. 15300
Forelleneisen S. 11958
Form S. 2208, 2983, 5356, 11968
— abdrehen (die) 18112
— abflammen (eine) 16470
— aufstampfen 7008
— belasten (eine) 19909
— füllen (die) 7011
— für aluminothermische Lötung 18490
— geben S. 7605
— giessen (in) 2972
— giessfertig machen (die) 895
— mit auswechselbaren Einsätzen 11988
— nacharbeiten (die) 14730
— schräglegen (eine) 18624
Formanpassung 5380
Formation S. 7607, S. 7617
Formationsfaktor 7608
Formationsprüfer 7614
Formaussenrohrleitung 19166
Formbank 12000
formbar 11989
Formbett in der Formgrube 2146
Formblech 14003, 17017, 17319
Formbrett 3710, 7896
Formdraht 16738
Formdrehbank 4377
Formeinsatz 5252
Formeisen 15772, 15775, S. 15994, 17887, S. 17889
Formeisenwalzwerk S. 15778
formen S. 7605, 11960
Formen 11869, 11997, S. 15998
— der Zahnräder mit Durchzugringen 12023
— im Boden 7410
— nach dem Guss.stück 12005
— stauben (die) 19248

Formen von Zahnrädern 12021
Formenbauer 11991
Formenbuch S. 14001
Former 11868, S. 11991
Formerbank 11992
Formerschaufel 11994
Formerstifte S. 15511
— stecken 17176
Formerei 1206, 11999, 12028
Formfräser 7618
Formgehung S. 15998
Formgrube 12024
Formguss 11972
Formhalle 12006
Formherd S. 1414
Formhohlraum 11973
förmiger Fahrleitungsdraht 8930
Formierungsspannung 7614/a
Formkaliber 16000
Formkasten 2217, S. 7657, 7310, 12002
— abdichten (einen) 11099
— der Riemenscheibenformmaschine 12003
— für Säulen 2218
— mit auswechselbaren Wänden S. 2541
— mit Innenherausnehmen 18286
— mit Schoren 1239
— stapeln (die) 17275
— verletten (einen) 3666
— wenden (den) 19133
Formkastenband 7311
Formkastenstift 7298
Formkühlung S. 19762
Formlehm 12004
Formmantel 11301
Formmaschine 7313, 12014
— für Doppelpressung S. 12016
— für kleine Zahnräder 1673, 16730
Formmaterialien S. 12020
Formmittelteil 9891
Formoberteil 10745, 18745
Formöffnung 19163
Formplatte 7231
Formpresse 12022

Formpresse mit drehbarer
    Wendeplatte 12026
Formpressverfahren S.2417·
Formpuder 12947/a
Formrahmen 2208, 7710,
    11980
— abnehmen (den) 10736
Formriss 19493
Formsand 1642, 6760, 6758,
    7178, 12012, 12027
— (den) einstampfen 14390
Formsattel 19165
Formschliessmechanismus
    11974
Formschluss mit unmittel-
    bar wirkendem Druck-   ·
    kolben S. 5460
Formschmiermittel S. 5364
Formsenkung 14203
Formstahl 10801, 15994
Formstein 2367
Formstift 9315
Formstoffe 12020
Formstösselführung 12989
Formstück 4217
Formteil blasen (ein) S.
    1841
— löschen (ein –) S. 1841
Formteilfläche S. 11983
Formteilung S. 10202, 11982
Formtrockenplatz 11978
Form-und Giessereimaschi-
    nen 15507
— Verbindungsstücke 17012
    17012
Formunterteil 2174
Formverfahren 12029
Formversatz 11802
Formwagen 11987
Formwand 19167, 19645
Formzacken 19164, 19196
Fornacit 7621
Forsterit 7622
Fortunit 7624
fossiler Brennstoff 7631
fossiles Petroleum 10371
— Wasser 4214
fossilführend 7632
Fossilisation 7633
fossilieren 7634
Fossilwerden S. 7633

Fraktion S. 7686
fraktionierte Destillation
    7687
Fraktionierturm 2492, 7691
— mit zwei Ausgängen 17134
Fraktionierung 7692
Fraktionierungsanlage
    18764
Fraktionssäule 18763
Fraktionskolben 7688
Fraktionsröhre 7689
Francium 7713
Franckeit 7714
Franklinit 7717
Francolith 7715
französische Tunnelbauweise
    7755
französischer Kessel S.
    7754
Fräsbank (auf der) reduzieren
    11684
Fräsdorn 4909
Fräse S. 4907, 11689,
Fräsen S. 4913
fräsen S. 11682
Fräser 11708, S. 4906
— Feilen 15204
Fräserglocke 11709
Fräswerkzeuge 11714
frei Hütte 7720
— Waggon 7734
Freibergit 7750
freie Formerei 7733
— Schwefelsäure in
    Abbränden 7739
— Stelle einer Schachtsaüle
    7741
— Stossfläche 7722
freier Ferrit 7725/a
freies Feld 19229
— Ferritband 8210/a
— Gas 7730
Freieslebenit 7751
Freifall 7723
Freifallbohren 7724
Freifallschere 7725
freigelegter Schacht 7736
Freiheit der Phasen S. 3282
Freilage 18450
Freilegen 17867
— der Deckgebirgsschicht

1231
Freirinit 7752
Freirinnespeisung 17172
freistehende Dampfpumpe 1006·
    10064
— Kesselanlage 12590
— Rast 7737
freistehender Hochofen 9731
— Kran 9732
— Schacht 9733
— Schornstein 10063
Freiteufe 7735
fremder Einschluss 6431, S.
    20271
Fremdkörper 7566 , 14348a
Fremdling S. 9711, 20268
Fremdwasser 6711
Fremontit 7753
fressen 15805/a
Fressen 7916
Freyalith 7759
Frickscher Ofen 7764
Friedelit 7772
friemeln 4701
Frieseit 7773
Friktion 15319
Frischbirne S. 4298
frische Kohle 8509
Frischeisen 365/a, 19563/a
frischen 7072, S. 14593
Frischen 4296
— auf Flusseisen im Flamm-
    ofen 11307
— mit Luft S. 4309
— von Roheisen 13270/a
Frischer 7100
frischer Sand S. 3676
Frischereieisen 3307
Frischereiofen 4991/a
Frischereiroheisen S. 3307
frisches Eisenerz 7756
Frischfeuer S. 7101
Frischfeuerbetrieb 7102
Frischfeuereisen 3303/a, S.
    3308, 7093, 14600
Frischfeuerroheisen S. 3307
Frischfeuerschlacke 14612
Frischherd 7101
Frischmethode S. 7111
Frischofen 14613
Frischsand 7757

Frischverfahren 7111, S.
　14616
Frischvogel S. 149
Fritte 7774/a
Fritten S. 16434
Front der Baggerung 5826
Frontanschnitt 5712
Frontseite eines Kessels
　7776
Frosch 2767
Frosteinwirkung 9769
Frühneolithikum 6166
Fuchs S. 1962
Fuchsbrücke 7452
Fuchsdecke 7456
Fuchsit 7786
Fuchsöffnung S. 13684
Fuge 2018, 10198, 15744
Fugennagel 7755/a, 10214a
Fugenverschluss aus Neo-
　pren 12224
Führung 8649, 15370,
　16610,
— (eines Schmelzofens) S.
　20196
Führungsbüchse 2625
— mit Rundloch 15275
Führungsfläche 1401
Führungsgitter 3938/a
Führungskegel 898, 10942
Führungslappen 11084
— mit ausgegossenem
　Loch 13858
Führungsmeissel 13298
Führungspfahl 13701, 15424,
　17297/a
Führungsrolle für Spillseil
　3099
Führungsschlitten 16661
Führungsschuh 8654, 14951,
　S. 16151
Führungsstange S. 13305
Führungsstift S. 3219,
　11008, 13306
— mit Bund 4022
— mit Keilschlitz 19883
Führungswand S. 8653
Fülldichte 7015
Füllen 7033
Füllererde S. 7810
Füllhöhe 7034/a

Füllkoks 9011
Füllkörpersäule 12839,
　12840
Füllmaterial 7021
Füllmittel S. 5634
Füllöffnung S. 3341
Füllort 2143, 2170, 2176,
　8811, 9777, 9839, 10368,
　13532, 13399, 15934,
　15949, 15955
Füllortarbeiter S. 11722
Füllpfropfen 7024
Füllrahmen 15498
Füllrumpf 3334, 10918
Füllsand 1088
Füllschachtfeuerung S. 15822
　15822
Füllstein S. 15324
Fülltrichter 3836, S. 6879
Füllvorrichtung 3332, 3346
Füllzylinder S. 3334
Fundament auf Pfahlrost
　13280
— aus Bruchsteinen 2447
— aus Ziegelmauerwerk
　2376
fündig werden S. 4085
fünfseitiges Prisma 13067
Funkenerosion 6331
Funkenfänger 16979, 16984
Funkenkammer 16981
Funkenlöschvorrichtung
　16983
Funkenprobe 16985
Funkenschweissung 7305
Funkensprühen 16987
Funkenstrecke 16980·
Funkenzeitpunkt 7307
Furfural 7824
Fusit 7883/a
Fuss 7537, 7538
Fussboden 7401
Fussbodenbelagblech 7407
Fussdrehbank 7543
Fusshaltestück 2161
Fusskasten mit Muffe 1277
Fusspfahl S. 16868
Fussplatte 1097, S. 9993
Fussrolle 7546
Fussventil 17361
Fussverschluss 18703

Fusulina 7895
Futter S. 10849, S. 17587
— eines Brunnens 16040
Futterblech 17587
Futterrohr S. 19715·

G

gabbroid 7899
gabbroide Struktur S. 11940
gabbroisch 7898
Gabeleinguss 5647
gabelförmiges Rohr 1577
Gabelheber 7604
Gabelpfanne 3347, 7660,
　10476, 15985
Gabelschüssel 16974
Gabeltragpfanne S. 10476
Gadolinit 7902, 20303/a
Gadolinium 7903
Gagat 7904, 10152
Gageit 7905
Galapektit 7910
Galaxit 7911
Galenit S. 10614, 10624
Galenobismutit 7913
Galgen 8233
gallertartige Kieselsäure
　8148
Gallium 7917
Gallowaykessel 7918
Galmei S. 2699, S. 6026,
　7922
Galvanisation 7926
galvanisch 7923
galvanische Kohle 6265
— Metallisierung 7924
— Vergoldung 6333
galvanischer Niederschlag
　6340
galvanisieren 6365, 7928
Galvanisierprozess 7944
galvanisiert 7929
— s. verzinkt
galvanisierter Draht 7940
— Kupferdraht 7930
galvanisiertes Eisen 7932,
　7941
Galvanismus 7927

Galvano 6371, 16092/a
Galvanoplastik 6330
Gamma-Eisen 7945
Gamma-Strahlen 7950
Gammastrahlenbild 7947,
. 7949
Gammastrahlenprüfung
7946, 7948
Gang 2165, 5147, 10954,
11756, 15349
— der Analyse 13972
— des Hochofens 20247
— mit Krustenstruktur S.
4783
— mit Lagen 4783
— mit Lagenstruktur 1184
— setzen (in) 10337
Gangabbauvorbereitung
durch das Deckgebirge
8374/a
Gangapophyse 16450, 17181
Gangart S. 7956
gangartige Lagerstätte 7957
Gangausbiss 12695
Gangbergbau 10956
Gängenetz 12250
Gangerz 10960
Gangfüllung S. 9761
Ganggestein 7956, S. 9583 ,
10958, 19489
Ganggesteine 5411
Ganggold 10955
Ganglagerstätte 10363
Ganglette S. 8372
Gangmasse 940, S. 19466
Gangmineral 7958, 17905
Gangspalte S. 6839
Gangquarz 19488
Gangrichtung 10836
Gangstein 11380
Gangstock S. 2578
Gangverdrückung 2039
Ganister 7960
Ganoide 7961
Ganomalith 7962
Ganophyllit 7963
Ganz S. 13249
gänzlich ausbeuten 2141
Ganzrost 8470
garantierte Werkstoffzugabe
11998

garantierter Verlust 8640
gärben 13287
Gärben s. Läutern od. Raffi-
nieren .
Garbenstruktur 16047
Garbstahl 16400
Garewait 7971
Garfrischen 20035
Garfrischentkohlungsperiode
5059
Gargang 9455, 12384
Garnierit 7974
Garnit 7972
Garrösten 7135
Garschaum 14611
Garschaumgraphit 10376,
S. 13941
Garschlacke S. 14604, 14878
Garschlackenboden 16524
garschmelziges Eisen
— Roheisen 11060
Garungsdauer 2864
Garungszeit 5561/a
Gasableitungsrohr 8033
Gasabscheider 8054
Gasabsorption 8082/a
Gasabzugsöffnung 13684
gasanalytischer Apparat
7977
Gasanker 7978
gasarme Kohle 12350
gasartig s. gasförmig
Gasatmosphäre 8069
Gasaufnahme 18
Gasausbeute 8068
Gasausbruch 1885, 7983
Gasausdehnung 8002
Gasaustritt nach einem
Batteriemanöver 18910
Gasbeizung 8035/a
Gasbehandlung S. 8015
Gasbestandteile 4234
Gasblase S. 1781, 2486.
8015
Gasbohrung 8065, 8082
Gasbrenner 7985
gasdicht 8081
Gasdichte 5177
Gasdruckspeiser 13905
Gasdynamo 8000

Gaseinpressen 14739
Gaseinpressung 7998
Gaseinsatzhärtung 7990
Gasentlösungspunkt 2491
Gasentlösungstrieb 5192,
16902
Gasentweichung 6562
Gasentwicklungsapparat
8012
Gasentwicklungsflasche S.
7312
Gaserzeuger 8042
Gaserzeugung 8013
Gasexplosion 8003
Gasfang nach Faber du
Faure 8034
Gasfeld 8005
Gasfeuerung 7838
Gasflammkohle 12564
gasförmiger Brennstoff 8010,
8071
Gasfrischen 8044
gasführendes Gestein 8049
Gasgebläse 7982
Gasgehalt 4253
— im Schlamm 7996
Gasgemenge 8025
Gasgenerator S. 8042
Gasgewinderohre 18293
Gasglühlicht 9684
Gasgranate 8055
gashaltige Spülung 8027
Gashärteofen 8007
Gash-Gang 8073
Gashorizont 8016
Gashülle 8001
Gaskappe 7986
Gaskappenausdehnung 7987
Gaskoks 2648, 7991, 8067
Gasleitung 8036, 8037
— zu dem Herde 8009
Gaslötkolben 8014
Gasmantelrohr 8023
Gasmessröhre 7984
Gasmotorkohle 8026
Gasmuffelofen 8008
gasnitrieren 8029
Gasofen 8011
Gasöl 8031
Gasölkontaktfläche 8032
Gas-Ölverhältnis 8004

Gas-Ölverhältnis im Lager
   14748
Gasometer 8079
Gaspolarisation 8039
Gasprüfer S. 6587
Gaspuddeln S. 8044
Gasregler 8047
gasreiches Öl 10898
Gasreinigung 8045, 8053
Gasretorte 8048
Gassack 7979
Gassammelröhre 7992
Gassand 8050
Gasschmelzschweissung S.
   968
Gasschonung 7993
Gasschutzmaske 8028
Gassonde 8064
Gasspannung 8041
Gassprengstoff 8070
Gasstrom 4869, 7994
Gasteilungsröhre 8057
Gastempern 9002
Gasturbine 8058
Gasuhr 8024
Gasventil 8059
Gasverdrängerpumpe S.7980
Gasverlust 11029
Gasversuchsapparatur 19470
Gasvolumeter 8061
Gasvorkommen 8056, 16219
Gaswaage 7981
Gaswascher 8052, 8063,
   15721
Gaswaschflasche 8062
Gasweg 7999, 8040
Gaswerk 8066
Gaszementation 7988
gaszementieren 7989
Gaszuführung 8018
Gaszuführungskapillar 8019
Gaszusammensetzung 4127
Gatsch S. 16512
gattieren 2730
Gattierung 2586, S. 4843
Gattierungswaage 15584
Gattungsnummer 12422
Gault 8118
Gauteit 8119
Gaylussit 8122

gealterter Stahl 217
gealtertes Rohöl
   19685
gebändert 1180
gebeizt 13219
gebeizter Draht 13223
gebeiztes Blech 13220
Gebilde S. 7607
Gebirgsbildung S. 12676
Gebirgsdruck 12735
Gebirgsprobenentnehmer
   16278
Gebläse 243, S. 1704, 1864
— mit elektrischem Antrieb
   1867
Gebläseanlage 1865
Gebläsebrenner 1700, 1887
Gebläsegehäuse 1856
Gebläseluft 1698
Gebläsemaschine 1704, 1858,
   1875
geblasene Massel 1882
geblasener Kern 1881
Gebläsewinde 241/b
gebogen S. 1527
gebogene Verwerfung 4881
gebrannte Hülse 12413
gebrannter Dolomit 2714,
   5607
— Kalk 14301
— Ton S. 1113, 18432
gebranntes Hirschhorn 3344
Gebrauchsstück 13236
gebrauchter Sand 19411
gebrochenes Härten 17552
gebundene Kieselsäure 4065
— Wärme 10667
gebundener Kohlenstoff
   4064, 7230, 7236
— Sauerstoff 7236
Gedanit 8141
gediegen 19563
gediegenes Eisen S. 14187
Gedinge 19158
Gedinnien 8142
gedreht 19140
Gedrit 8143
gefährliche Temperatur 4992
Gefälle 5701, 6772, 9691,
   13412
gefaltet 20236/a

gefalzt 7523
gefeintes Roheisen S. 14599
geflanschte Platte S. 7272.
gefleckt 17031, S. 17166
geformt 7615
gefräster Stift für Obstkisten
   11704
— und gestreifter Stift 3403
gefrieren S. 7742
Gefrierschacht 7749
Gefrierverfahren 7747, 15957
— beim Schachtabteufen
   15957
Gefüge S. 6733, S. 18473
— bloslegen (das) 6691
— der Legierungen 402
— des Eisenerzes 17895
Gefügeausscheidung 13812
Gefügebestandteil 13700
Gegendampf 1075
Gegendrall 1081
Gegendruck 1071
Gegendruckfläche 765
Gegendruckventil 1072
Gegenelektrode 1085/a,
   19943/a
gegenfallende Verwerfung 6850
   6850, 8703
Gegenflansch 4105
Gegenfüssler S. 671
Gegengewicht 4536
— der Tür 5629
— im Bremsberg 8614
Gegengewichtswagen im
   eintrümmigen Bremsberg
   1236
Gegenmutter 10119
Gegenplatte 1131
Gegensaugzugofen 4533
Gegestromkessel 4528
Gegenstromwaschen 1090
gegenwärtig 12618
geglätteter Stahl S. 13629
gegliedert 9203
gegliederter Telleraufgebe-
   apparat 723
geglüht 604
gegossen 2990, 13746
Gehalt 4251

Gehalt an Schiefer 4255
— einer Flusssigkeit 17354
gehämmerter Guss-stahl 8746
gehämmertes Eisen S. 20240
— Eisenblech 8747
Gehänge 13060
Gehängegletscher 8807
Gehängeschutt 16613
gehärtet 8851, 9756/a
gehärtete Fluss-stahlplatte 8854
gehärteter Stahl 8856, 8998
— Stahl (gut) 19972
— Stahl mit 1,0% C. 18377
Gehäuse S. 2930, 8641
Gehlenit 8144
gehobene Rumpffläche 19360
gehobener Flügel 9171, 10753
Gehrung gearbeitetes Eisen (auf) 11815
Geikielith 8145
gekochtes Wasser 1981
gekohltes Eisen 2878
— Wassergas 2877
gekolbte Sonde 18095
gekörnte Schlacke 8438
gekörntes Eisen 8404
gekrempte Platte S. 7272
gekrümmte Fläche 4884
gekühlter Rahmen 19788
Geländer 14365
— der Gichtbühne 18199
Geländereisen 1370, 1190, 14359
Gelatine-Dynamit 8664
Gelbbleierz S. 20254
gelbe Abart 20293
Gelbeisenerz S. 10134 20288
gelber Ocker S. 20285
Gelberde 20285
gelbes Blutlaugensalz 13725
Gelbgiesser 20290
Gelbgiesserei 2271
Gelbguss 20283, 20289
gelbrotes Feld 20294
Geld prägen S. 17814

Geldschrankstahl 17473
Gelenk 9199
Gelenke 10858
gelenkte Erstarrung 5470
gelenkig S. 9203
gelenkige Platte S. 9202
Gelenkpresse 18708
Gelenksandstein S. 10085
Gelenkverbindung 10857
Gelignit 8149
gelindes Kupfer S. 16832
gelochtes Blech 13082, 14179
— Rohr 13083
gelöschter Kalk 16571
gelöstes Gas 5548
Gelzement 8146
gemahlener Quarz 14149
gemascht 11520
Gemäuer 2377
gemauerter Röstofen 2372
— Schacht 19656
gemeinsam walzen 15072
gemeinsame Kernmarke 12110
gemeinschaftlicher Wasserbehälter 4098
gemeinschaftliches Sammelrohr 4093
gemeiner Opal 4096
Gemenge 4206
Gemisch S. 11837
genaue Länge 6629
Genaugiessverfahren 9937, 11040
Genauigkeit der vereinbarten Abmessungen 6630
geneigt 13420
geneigte Bohrung S. 9708
— Dächer mit Stahlsparren 16683
— Falte S. 9699
— Strecke S. 16680
— Verwerfung 9698, S. 12377
geneigter Gang 19270
— Gesteinsschacht 15029
— Scheibenbruchbau 9707
geneigtes Bohrloch 8569
— Flöz 13421
— Rohr 9703

Generatoren 13988
Generatorkohle 3824
Generatorsatz 6277, 8154
Geno-Holotypus 8155
Geno-Paratypus 8156
genormt 17359
Geoantiklinal S. 8159
Geochemie 8160
Geochronologie 8161
Geodäsie 8165
geodätisch 8166
Geode 8164
Geodynamik 8167
geöffneter Gichtverschluss 12608
Geogenese 8168
Geognosie 8169
Geoid 8170
geokratische Zeiten 8162
Geokronit 8163
Geologe 8179
Geologie 8180
geologisch 8171
geologische Formationskunde S. 17752
— Landesaufnahme 8177
geologisches Alter 8172
— Fenster 9823, 12174
— Profil 8174, S. 8176
Geomorphologie 8181
Geonomie 8182
Geophysik 8184
geophysikalisch 8183
Georgiadesit 8186
Geosynklinal 8188
geothermisch 8191
geothermische Tiefenstufe 8192, 18484
Geotechnik 8189
Gepäckwagen 19457
geprägt 6403
gepresste Kohle 13876
— Schwelle 13881
gepresstes Stahlblech 13885
gepuddelter Stahl S. 14104
gepuddeltes Eisen S. 14102
gepulverte Birkenkohle 13769 13769
geputzt S. 3682
geputztes Blech 7122
gerade Auslöschung 12918

gerade richten 17721
— Zunge 17720
geradefaserig 17710
Geraderichten 11292/a.
    17723/a
Geraderichtung 7907
gerades Prisma 14906
Geradscher Ofen 8193
Geräte für Eisengiesser
    7673
— zur Prüfung von
    Giessereisand 7671
geräuschlose Bohrung 16942
Gerberlohe 18236
gereinigter Graphit 14598
gereinigtes Wasser 14191
Gerhardtit 8194
gerichtete Bohrung 2532
— Erstarrung S. 5470
gerichteter Anschnitt 9776a,
    9778
— Aufprallanschnitt 16264
— seitlicher Anschnitt
    16672
gerichtetes Bohren 5468
geriffelt 3370
geriffeltes Betoneisen 4493
— Blech 11517
geringe Leuchtkraft 11054
geringster Bedarf 11767
geringwertige Kohle 6847
Gerinne 6880, S. 16709
gerinnen 3609
geripptes verzinktes Stahl-
    blech 14868
geritztes Geschiebe 15583
Germanium 8196
Geröll 2192, S. 8387, S.
    8477, 15324, 13034,
    16131
gerolltes Blei S. 16066
gerösteter Kupferstein 2713
geröstetes Erz 14985
Gersdorffit 8197
gerundete Konkretion 12152
Gerüst 6789, S. 15576,
    17264, 17333/a. S.18878
Gerüstständer S. 9465
Gerüstrohr 19010
Gewölbe 15575
Gesamt-Abbrand 18791

Gesamt-Kohlenstoff 18787
Gesamtanalyse 18786
Gesamtarbeiten für den
    Produktionslauf 4117
gesamte Rostfläche 18788
Gesamterzeugung 18790
Gesamtproduktion 19217,
    19218
Gesamtstrahlungspyrometer
    18792
Gesamtvergrösserung 18789
Gesamtwiderstand 18793
geschält 5223
geschälter gedrehter Stahl
    13040
— Stabstahl 19141
Geschiebe 5267
Geschiebebänke 411
Geschiebelehm 2193
Geschiebemergel S. 2193,
    8259
geschichtet 1423, 10504,
    16086
geschichtete Erzlagerstätten
    1425, 17747
— Textur 1427
geschichtetes Gestein 1426
geschlämmte Tonerde 19694
geschliffen S. 8607
geschliffene Glasplatte 4903
— Produkte 8619
geschliffener Krystall S.
    4902
— Stab 8609
geschliffenes Glas 4902
geschlitzte Fangbüchse 3407
geschlitztes Rohr 16690,
    17119
geschlossene Form 3773
— Gicht 3777
— Sonde 16245
— Verwerfung 3759
— Ziehbank 16879
geschlossener Koksofen
    3768
— Kreislauf 3766
— Spreizer 1772
— Steiger S. 1772
— Stempel 3769/a
— Türstock S. 7806
— Wagen 3778

geschlossenes Kaliber 3774
geschmeidiges Eisen 6074,
    S. 16835
Geschmeidigkeit S. 16851
geschmiedet s. gehämmert
geschmiedeter Stahl S. 20246
    20246
geschmiedetes Eisen S. 20240
    20240
geschmolzen 11460, 11877
geschnittener Formkasten
    2227
Geschosskerner 15458
Geschosslocher 8669, S.
    8674
Geschosslochbohrung
    13084
Geschossrohrlocher 8674
geschrämt 9254
geschrammte Geschiebe S.
    17801
geschweisste Baustahlmatte
    19933
geschweisstes Eisen S.
    19926
— Gasrohr 19932
— Rohr 19931
Gesenk S. 1779, 2127,
    S. 10094, 17371, S.20114
Gesenkabschreckung 5875
Gesenkabteufen 20115
Gesenkbau S. 5448
Gesenkhalteramboss 16949
Gesenkoberfläche 12944
Gesenkschmiede 5981
Gesenkschmieden 5983, 5996,
    9426
gesenkschmieden 5972
Gesenkschmiederei S. 5983
Gesenkschmiedestücke S.
    4983
Gesenkschmierstoff 5368
Gesenkstahl 5381, 13882
Gesenkstahlbauteil 13883
gesenkter Flügel 5707, S.
    11059
Gesenkzentrierung 5370
Gesichtsfeld 6999
gesiebte Kohle 15690, 16445
Gesims aus vorgefertigten
    Teilen 4483

Gesimskranz 18099
gesinterter Press·stein
 16432
gespaltet 2448
gespreizter Schenkel 4108
gestaffeltes warmstrangge-
 presstes Stahlprofil 6720,
 17558
Gestalten S. 15998
gestaltloser Kohlenstoff 531
Gestänge 15048
— -Ablegekapazität 14325
— -Abstellfläche 13365
— -Elevator 5899
— -u Rohrlager 13362
Gestängeaufzug 15050
Gestängebruch 19180
Gestängebühne 15423
Gestängeelevator 17945
Gestängefangvorrichtung
 2212
Gestängeführung 15053, 17946
 17946
Gestängekeilfänger S.12777
Gestängepumpe 2555
Gestängerechen 7104
Gestängerohr 5897
Gestängeschlüssel 8758
Gestängeschneider 5898
Gestängestrang 5942
Gestängeverbinder S.18728
Gestängeverbindung 15060
Gestängeversuch 5910
Gestängewechsel 14185,
 17921
Gestängezange 15223
gestanzt s. gepresst
gestanzte Giesspfanne 17316
— Löcher im Steg des
 Profils 9256
Gestehungspreis S. 4515
Gestein S. 2192
— mit Erzadern 5829
Gesteinsarbeit 12104
Gesteinsbohrer 17643
Gesteinsbohrstahl 11773
Gesteinsgang 3286, 3907,
 5410, 6148
Gesteinsschlacke 15644/a
Gesteinsstäubung 15020
Gesteinsstrecke 11542,

15015, 15024, 17642
Gesteinsstaubschrank 17644
Gesteinsstaubsperre S.17644
Gesteinsstruktur 17765
Gestell 7710/a, S. 9376,
 10102, 17332, 18878
Gestellboden 8953
Gestellbremsberg 1124
Gestellförderung 2683
Gestellhöhe 9056
Gestellmantel 8958
gestreckte Struktur 10841
gestreckter Balken 17791
— Pfahl 17793
gestrecktes Eisen 5816
gestreift 17763, 17767,
 17800
gestreifter Sandstein S.
 18615
gestreiftes Schmelzen 17764
Gestübbe 11373
gesunde Stelle 16938
gesundes Holz 16940
gesunken s. gesenkt
gesunkener Flügel S. 5716,
 6000, 11059, 11071,
 11072
geteertes Rohr 18327
geteilter Rost 15782
geteiltes Modell 15784
getrennt gegossener Probebarren 15861
— gegossener Probestab
 15862
Getriebe 8124, 8125
getriebene Aushärtung
 12731
Getriebepfahl 1066, S. 10575,
 17083
Getriebewelle 8130
Getriebezimmerung 13286 ,
 17084
getrocknete Probe 5848
getrockneter Kern 4385
— Press·stein 5846
Geviert S. 4630, S. 4635
Geviertausbau von Schächten
 S. 4634
gewachsener Boden 16854
gewalzt 11703, 15094
— (nur) 839

gewalzte Baustahlprofile
 15102
— Platte S. 15099
gewalzter Stahl S. 15100
gewalztes flusseisernes
 Scheibenrad 15096
Gewäsche 15724
gewaschene Feinkohle S. 6077
 6077
— Kohle 19695
gewaschenes Erz 2514, 10175
 10175
Gewebe 19873
— s. Textur
Gewehrlaufstahl 8670, 8675
gewellte Oberfläche 19839/a
Gewerbekessel 11308
gewetzt S. 8607
Gewichte 19912
Gewichtsabweichung 19905
Gewichtsausgleichung 1139
— durch Gewichte 1140
— durch Wasserdruck 9513
Gewichtskasten 19916
Gewichtstabelle 19908
Gewichtsverhältnis 14021
Gewichtsverlust 11033
Gewinde 15713, 18550
— anschneiden S. 15698
— drehen 19131
— schneiden 15698
— -und Muffenrohr 18555
Gewindebohren 18299
Gewindebohrer 15712, 18263
Gewindebohrstahl 17474
gewindebrechen 1068
Gewindedrehstahl 18551
Gewindefett 18552
Gewindeendform 15152
Gewindeprofil 18553
Gewinderohr 18556
Gewindeschneidbacken 17199
 17199
Gewindeschneideisen 15277
Gewindeschneidmuffe 5365
Gewindeschneiden 4923, 15719
 15719
— auf der Drehbank 4925,
 15705
Gewindeschutzkappe 18554
Gewindestahl 6700

Gewindestrahler 6701
Gewinn 7908, S. 20113
gewinnen S. 5756, 11737,
- S. 17842, 20081
Gewinnen des Gesteins S.
20199
Gewinnung 2324, S. 5805,
S. 5873, S. 6906, S.
20111
— der Pfeiler S. 5793
— durch Presslufteinsatz
299
— mit Trichterschurren
11713
— mittels Bagger 17849,
17869
— von Horizontkomplexen
12118
Gewinnungsart 18181
Gewinnungskopfgestell
8930
Gewinnungskosten 4516
gewöhnlich s. normal
gewöhnlicher Brauneisen-
stein S. 2474
— Fluss · stahl 12625
— Sprung 8701
— Stahl S. 19301
gewöhnliches Abteufverfah-
ren 12626
— graues Roheisen 8502
Gewölbe S. 2770
Gewölbebildung S. 8805, S.
8809
Gewölbedeckel 757
Gewölbelinie 4625
Gewölbemuldenbruch S.
18157
Gewölbeplatte 4731
Gewölbescheitelbruch S.
656
gewonnene Kohle 11752
gewundene Feder 9061
gewundenes Kreuzeisen S.
19182
Geyerit 8206
Geyser 8207
Geyserit 8208
gezängte Luppe 16132
gezahnter Lauf S. 15562
— Rammschuh 15898

gezahnter Rohrschuh 15218
gezimmerter Stoss 18031
gezogen.5814
gezogene Stäbe 5815
gezogener Draht S. 5821
— Stahl 5819
gezogenes Erz 5817
— Rohr 5820
Gibbsit 8216, S. 9507
Gibelit 8217
Gicht S. 2586, S. 3316, S.
6891, 15959, 17615,
— s. Charge od. Beschik-
kung
Gichtanzeiger 9737, 176ì ,
17623
Gichtarbeiter 11259
Gichtaufzug 7845
Gichtbeförderung 4315
Gichtbelag 3343
Gichtbrücke 3318
Gichtbühne 18579
Gichtebene 13475
Gichtflamme 18576
Gichtgas 1712
Gichtgasabzugsrohr
8030
Gichtglocke 1708, 7858,
16727/a
Gichtkarren 20006
Gichtkübel 3351/a
Gichtmann 3350
Gichtöffnung S. 3341, 3345,
12042
— eines Hochofens 12044
Gichtschwamm 20327
Gichtstaub 6133, 7453/a
Gichtstaubverminderung
14575
Gichttemperatur 18581
Gichttrichter 7859
Gichtverschluss 1448, 18580
Gichtwinde 1452
Gichtzacken S. 1096
Gieseckit 8218
Giessabfälle S. 15377
Giessand S. 12027
Giessband 3071
Giessbaum 17277
Giessbett 3039, 3041, 13251,
13256, 15471

Giessbühne 13763, 18302
18359
Giesseinrichtung 13762
giessen 2965, 7635, 13737,
18354
Giessen 3037, 7643
— des Eisens 3062
— in schrägliegende Form
3063
— mit Entspannung 3518
Giesser 3035, 10307, 10487,
11462, 18355
Giesserei 3067, 7647,
— für Eigenbedarf 2816,
935/a, 18612
— für Handels-und Bauguss
17013
Giessereibesitzer 7640
Giessereiflammofen 7648,
7669
Giessereiformmaschine
7662
Giessereikarren S. 13765
Giessereikoks S. 3940,
7653
Giessereikuppelofen 7656
Giessereileiter S. 7640,
7661
Giessereiofen 7658
Giessereiroheisen 2994,
7665
Giessereisand S. 12027
Giessereischachtofen 4841
Giessereiunternehmer S.
7640
Giessereiwesen 7675
giessfertige Form 11985
Giessfertigmachen der Form
11971
Giessform 3050, 3061, S.
7657, S. 9984, S. 11968
Giessformöl 7606
Giessgeschwindigkeit 3017
Giessgrube 3066, 13396,
13762/a
— gegossen (in) 13401
Giessgrubenkran 3065
Giesshalle 2988, S. 3040,
3054, 7659, 13757
Giesshaus S. 7659, S. 13757
Giesskasten S. 2208

Giesskelle S. 10470, S. 11472, 13328, S. 13755
Giesskopf S. 6886
Giesskran 3049, 7654, 13754
— mit selbsttätiger Kipp- vorrichtung 7655
Giesslaufkatze 7651
Giessloch S. 8087, 15906
Giesslochreinigung 8098
Giesslöffel S. 3058, S. 13328 , 13755, S. 15463, 15565
— für zwei Träger 19189
Giessmaschine 3059, S. 13255
Giessofen 2986, 7644, S. 11466
Giesspfanne 2552, 3058, 7650, S. 11472, 13759
— mit Ausguss . schnauze 10861
— mit Getriebe-Kipp- vorrichtung 8138
— mit Handkippvorrichtung 8787, S. 15985
— mit Schlackenstein 4969
— mit Zahnstangengehänge 10486
Giesspfannenausguss 10480
Giesspfannenbügel 10472, 10478
Giesspfannengabel 10484
Giesspfannengehänge S. 104 10472
Giesspfannenkran 10475
Giesspfannenschnauze S. 10480
Giesspfannenwagen 13765
Giessplatz S. 3039, 3040
Giessportalkran 7674
Giessrad 3075
Giessrahmen 11981/a
Giessrinne 10587, S. 15366, 15374
Giess· schnauze 13761, 17170
Giess ·spirale S. 7470
Giess· stelle S. 3040
Giess· strahl 17769
Giess· system 8104, 15379

giesstechnische Verstärkung 12858
Giesstemperatur 3073
Giesstisch 11479
Giesstraube 3792, 17182
Giesstrichter S. 13756, 18953
Giesstrommel 6014
Giesstümpel 13747
— mit Schwimmer 13565
Giesswagen 3045
giftig S. 12406
Gigantolith 8221
Gigantostraken 8222
Gilbertit 8223
Gillespit 8229
Gilsonit 8230
Ginofen 8232
Gipfel 4724
Gips 8235, 8694, S. 17969
Gipsformverfahren 13469
Gipsguss 13467
Gipsmatrize 13468
Gipsspat 4801
Girodofen 8244
Gismondin 8247
Gitter 8536
Gittereinheit 10582
Gittereisen 6915
Gitterflacheisen 10459
Gitterparameter 4797
Gitterprofil 6916
Gitterstruktur 8476, 10581
Givetien 8249
Gladkait 8267
Glanz S. 13626
Glanzdraht S. 6537
Glanzeisenerz S. 17040
glänzende Blasen 19324
Glanzhärtung 3678
Glanzkobalt 3887
Glanzkohle S. 642, 651, 2393, 8268, 13008
Glanzmittel 2402/a
Glanzpunkt 9157/a
Glanzschleifen S. 2522
Glaseinschmelzdraht 15741
Glaserit S. 689
Glasfabrikofen S. 8276
Glasfluss 6433

Glasgerät 8286
Glasglocke 8271
Glashahn 8273
glashart 8277
Glashärte 8278
glasharter Stahl S. 3449
glasieren 8296/a
glasig 19570
— werden 1410
glasige Schlacke 19574
— Zwichenmasse 8279
Glasigwerden S. 19576
Glaskasten 8272
Glasofen 8276
Glaspapier 8280
Glasplatte 8281, S. 8284
Glaspulver 8282
Glasröhre 8285
Glasrohrwasserwaage 19779
Glasscheibe S. 8284
Glasschmelzpfanne S. 4742
Glasschneidemesser 8275
Glastafel 8284
Glastemperofen 615
Glasurbrand 14693
Glasurerz S. 10614
glatt 16601
Glätte S. 13626
glatter Bruch 16772
— erhabener Teil S. 19278
glattes Blech 13445, 13448
Glattwalze S. 13482
Glauberit 8289
Glaubersalz 8288, S. 11790
Glaukochroit 8290
Glaukodot 8291
Glaukokerinit 8292
Glaukonit 8293, 8511
glaukonitisch 8294
Glaukophan 8295
glazial umgeformtes Tal 8261
glaziale Ablagerungen 5853, 8250
— Fazies 8252
Glazialgeschiebe 8251
Glazialtheorie 8262
gleichaltrige Ablagerungen S. 18156
gleichaxische Kristalle 6527
gleichbleibende Richtung 15232

gleichförmige Lagerung S. 4204, S. 13447
gleichgekörnt 20153
Gleichgewichtszustand 17391
gleichmässig körnig 6624
— verteilte blau gefärbte Poren 14469
— verteilte glänzende Poren 19305
— verteilte oxydierte Poren 19304
gleichmässige Kohle 3841
— Windströmung 19302
gleichmässiger Ofengang 14654
gleichschenkliger Winkel- stahl 581, 1381
gleichschenkliges Winkel- eisen 6523
gleichschwer 12459
Gleichstromanlage 4265
Gleichstromkessel 4180
gleichwertige Lösung 6534
Gleichwertigkeitskoeffizient 3900
gleichzeitiger Höchstbedarf 16376
gleichzeitiges Bohren 16375
Gleishammer 5986
Gleitbahn S. 16162
Gleitband 8299
gleiten 16606, 16644
Gleiten S. 16645
gleitende Gussform 16652
Gleitfläche 12880, S. 16603, 16664
Gleitlinie 16655
Gleitplatte 8653
Gleitrolle 16625
Gleitschalungen 16621
Gleitschuh 16151
Gleitschutzbelag 12365
Gleitungsriss 16650
Gleitverschluss 16622
Glessit 8298
Gletscher 8263
Gletscherablagerung 5857
Gletscherabtrag 8254
Gletscherbrekzie 5855
Gletschermühle 8255, S.

13720
Gletscherschlamm 8253
Gletscherschramm 8256, 8258
Gletschertrichter S. 8255
Gliederbandförderer 16573
Gliederkessel 15781
Gliedertransportband 722
Glimmer 5022, 10050, 11621, 17042
Glimmerblättchen S. 11622
Glimmerbrille 11625
Glimmerplatte 11624
Glimmersandstein 6770
Glimmerschiefer 11623
Glimmerschuppen 11622
Globulit 8305
Glocke 12752
— nach Hutter 9489
Glockenboden 2493
glockenförmig 1458
Glockenguss 1451
Glockenmetall 1456
Glockenmühle 1450
glomeroblastische Struktur 8306
glomeroporphyritisch 8307
glomeroporphyritische Struktur 4833
Glückshaken S. 19643
Glühbehandlung S. 9000
Glühdauer 616
Glüheisen 14542
Glühen 608
— (zum) 14537
— für Bearbeitbarkeit 613
glühend bleiben 14696
glühende Kohlenschicht 9685
Glühfadenpyrometer 5478
Glühfarbe 8976
Glühfrischen 11255, 20047
Glühfrischkammer 611
Glühgasatmosphäre 4290
Glühhitze 18387
Glühkohle S. 3757
Glühkurve 9001
Glühlampe 8311
Glühmittel 3175
Glühofen 614, 9017, 15599
Glühprozess S. 618
Glühring 4749

Glührost S. 9014
Glühspan 7597, 15583
Glühspanschicht 12802
Glühtopf 617
Glühzunder 11700
Gmelinit 8318
Gneis 8319
Gneisgranit 8322
Gneisstruktur 8320
Gneissyenit 8321
Goethit 8338, 12207, 14242
Gold 8343
Goldader S. 8351
Goldamalgam 483
Goldbarren 8346/a
Goldblatt S. 16972
Goldfieldit 8353
Goldfolie 16972
goldfreies Gestein 2495
goldführender Sand 8478
goldführendes Konglomerat 1198
Goldgang 8351, 14584
Goldgräber 8889
goldhaltig 953
Goldklumpen S. 12420
Goldocker S. 20285
Goldquarz 8344
Goldschale S. 4852
Goldscheidung 8349
Goldseife 8347, 8480
Goldtellurid 8350
Goldwäscher 8352
Goldwaschen im Waschtrog 12900
Gonnardit 8355
Goochscher Tiegel 8356
Goongarrit 8361
Gordonit 8368
Goslarit 3369
Gosse 11226
Goyazit 8376
graben 16961
Graben 5717, 18585
Grabenscholle S. 5717
Grabental 6843
Grabungen 18874
graduiertes Messrohr 8391
Graftonit 8393
Grahamit 8394
Gramenit 8409

Gramm-Molekülgewicht 8408
— Molekülvolumen 8407
Grammäquivalent 8411
Grammatit 8410
Grammion 8412
Grammol 8413
Grammolekül 11865
Granat 7973
Granatenstahl 16112
Grandidierit 8415
Granit 8416
granitähnlich 8423
granitische Textur 8424
granitischer Untergrund 8419
Granitisierung 8422
Granitit 8421
Granitotrachytische Struktur S. 12617
Granitporphyr 8417
Granitsand 8418
granoblastische Struktur 8425, 8444
Granodiorit 8426
Granolit 8427
Granophyr 8429
granophyrisch 8430, 8462
granophyrisches Gefüge 8428
Granulationsanlage 8439
Granulierung S. 8440
Granulit 8441
Granulitstruktur 8442
Graphit 1654, 8447, 13570,
Graphitablagerung 5196
graphitarm 13654
Graphitausscheidung S. 8457, 15872
graphitisch 8452, 10380
graphitischer Kohlenstoff 8453
— Stahl 8456
graphitisches Gusseisen 8454
graphitisieren 8458
Graphitisierung 8457
Graphitisierungsmittel 8459
graphitiertes Öl 8455
Graphitknötchen S.12336
Graphitkugel mit Ferrithof 2559

Graphitnester 10378
Graphitporen 10379
Graphitpyrometer S. 8449
graphitreich 14875
Graphitrosette 8450
Graphitschwärze 13571
Graphitstabofen 6296
Graphitstaub 13771
Graphittiegel 8448
Graphitwasser 8451
Graptolith 8463
Grat 2339, 7290, 15745,
15746, 16703
Gratanschnitt 4227
grathaltig 1221
Gratlinie 7309
gratloses Erzeugnis 2619
Gratlosschmiedung 7308
Gratrinne 7294, 8687
grauer Ton 8498
graues Gusseisen S. 8531
— Roheisen S. 8502
Graugiesserei 8530
Grauguss S. 2995, 8527,
8529, 8531
Graupe 8406
Graupenbett S. 14532
Grauspiessglanz S. 8497,
17577
Grauwacke 8532, 14448,
18829, 20015,
Gravimeter 8482
gravimetrische Bestimmung 8483
Gravitationsaufbereitung 8492
Gravitationshebezeug 8490
Gravitationskokillenguss 8486
Gravitationsquelle 8494
Gravitationswasser 8496
Greenali 8521
Greenockit 2676, 8522
Greenovit 8523
Gregarine 8525
Greifbagger S. 983, 5451,
8379, 8380
Greifbogen 4246/a
Greifer 983, 3629, 3630,
6635, S. 8377, 8572
Greiferbagger 3631

Greiferbetrieb 984
Greiferkübel 3829, 8377
Greiferkran 4609
Greiwinkel 574/a
Greisen 8526
grelles Roheisen 20028
Grenzbehandlung 18884
Grenzbohrung 12470
Grenzpfeiler 1249
Grenzwert 10824
Greyträger S. 5392, S. 8528
Griffschlitz 7107
Griphit 8570
Griquait 8573
grob bearbeitetes Eisen 15255
Grobblech 9037, 18499,
18502
Grobbrecher 3869
grobe Beimengung des Wassers S. 5267
Grobeisen 10550
grobes Eisenblech S. 18499
— Sieb 20058
Grobgefüge S. 11157
Grobkessel S. 18665
Grobkohle 3747, S. 10546
Grobkorn 3871
Grobkorneisen 3874
grobkörnig 3868, 3872,
17568
grobkörnige Textur 3877
grobkörniger Marmor 16991
— Sand 18774
— Sandstein 8576
grobkristallin S. 11147
grobporphyrisch 11215
Grobsandstein 11927
Grobschleifen 8541
Grobsieb 3876, S. 20058
Grobspiegel 3878
Grobstrecke 1578
Grobzerkleinerung 3870,
3875
Grobzug 13844
Grudit 8599
Grossbessemerei 4311
Grossbohrenakkord 1690
grosse Glocke 11217/a
grosser Kohlenklumpen 10239
Grosskoks 10547

grosskörniger Bruch 3873
— Formsand 7026
grossluckiges Eisen S.
  3874, 19536
Grossraumtank S. 17690
gross- stückig 9676
gross - stückige Kohle S.
  10546,
Grossular 8634, 8605
Grosswasserraumkessel
  1988, 10551
Grothit 8606
Grube 1120, 3858, 11724,
  S. 13397
— mit Schwinghebelvorrich-
  tung ausgepumpt 1379
Grubenanlagen 13408
Grubenaufnahme S. 10565
Grubenbau 5871
Grubenbaue S. 5408
Grubenbezirk 11764
Grubendamm 11726, 19255
Grubeneingang 13409
Grubenexplosion S. 8330
Grubenfeld 388, S. 3613
Grubenformen 13410
Grubengas 7165, S. 13396,
  13402
Grubenhof S. 8464
Grubenholz 14027, 17541
Grubenkabel 11771
Grubenklein 16740
Grubenkompass 5513, 11727
Grubenlampe 5958, 11747
Grubenluft S. 290
Grubenlüftung 11745
Grubenort 11730
— mit Stoss · stellung senkrecht
  zur Schlechtenrichtung
  6742
Grubenpumpe 17994
grubenrichten 14894
Grubenrissenkung 1342
Grubensand 14259
Grubenschiene 14355
Grubenstempel 11738
Grubenwagen S. 9492,
  11772, 18971
Grubenwerkzeugstahl S.
  18731
Grubenwetter 290

Grünbinderkraft 8519
Grünbleierz S. 8512, S.
  11720
Grundbohrer mit
  zylindrischem Schaft
  17718
Grundebene 5008
gründen 7636
Gründer 7638
Grundfläche des Bohrturmes
  1275
Grundflansch 2156
Grundgebirge S. 4792
Grundgerinne 8621
Grundiermittel 8611
Grundierung 7198
Grundkohle 8612
Grundkonglomerat S. 1278
Grundlage 1273
Grundlinie 5009
Grundmasse 8617, 11379
Grundmauer 7637
Grundmetall 1281, 13938
Grundmoräne 1266, 8618
Grundniveauregler 2172
Grundplatte 1285, 1286,
  1420, 2147
— aus Spiegelglas 13490
grundsätzlich 7819
Grundschwelle 7540, 8620, S.
  S. 16335, 16589, 16871
Grundsohle 2171, 8616,
  16339
Grundstock einer Rutsche
  3567
Grundstrecke S. 2171, 5093,
  S. 7959, 8095, S. 11220,
  11224
Grundstück S. 13552
Grundwasser 8622
Grundwassergewinnung 13987
  13987
Grundwasserschicht 19752
grüne Bleischlacke 8531/a
Grüneisenerz S. 6079
grüner Kern 8516
— Sand 8514
— Schlick S. 8514
— Schörl 35
Grünerit 8634
Grünformen 8518

grüngiessen 2969
Grünlandmoor 11053
Grünlingit 8635
Grünsandbinder 2017
Grünsandform 8515
Grünstandfestigkeit 8506
Grünstein 18852
Grünsteinschiefer 5300
Grus S. 2358, S. 4827, 8575
Gruskohle 16507
Gruskohlenbunker 16510
Guadaleazarit 8636
Guanajuatit 8638
Guarinit 8644
Gudmundit 8646
Guejarit 8647
Guildit 8657
Guillaume-Stahl S. 9931
Guillochemaschine 15179
Gumbo 8665
Gummi 15304
Gummiball 15306
Gummiband umwickelter
  Draht (mit) 15316
Gummifaden 15315
Gummifahne 15308
Gummifinger 15309
Gummiform 15310/a
Gummihandschuh 15310
Gummikappe 15307
Gummiplatte 15312
Gummiring für Pfropfen
  19699
Gummischlauch 15317, 15212
Gummistopfen 15314
Gummistöpsel S. 15314
Gummit 8667
Gummittel des «bag preven-
  ter» 12834
günstige Zone 6867
Gürtel S. 9323
Guss 2984, 7652, S. 7643,
  S. 17769, 18356
— für den Maschinenbau
  6474
— mit seitlichem Anschnitt
  16271
— putzen (den) 3672
— über einen Kern S. 9268
Gussatz 15997
Gussbart S. 2618

Gussblase S. 1852, S. 7360,
   S. 249
Gussbrechmaschine 3076
Gussbruch 15655
Gusseisen 2991, S. 7643
— erster Schmelzung 2992
— mit Knotengraphit 12334
— mit Lamellengraphit S.
   8527
— mit Stahlzusatz 17484
— mit Zwischenstufengefüge 71
— schweissen 11488
— zweiter Schmelzung
   2993
Gusseisengitter 3003
Gusseisenkranz 2998, 3009
Gusseisenrohr 3008
Gusseisensäule 2997
Gusseisenscheibe 3000
Gusseisensplitter 2996
gusseiserne Form 3007
— Muffel 9985
— Reibeplatte 3005
— Schale S. 3433
gusseiserner Fuss 3001
— Reiber 3004
— Ring 3010
— Zylinder 2999
Gussfalte 18357
Gussfehler· 5104, 6840,
   7362
Gussförderer 13226
Gussform S. 3061, S.11968
Gussformen besprengen
   (die) 19983
Gussformtrockenofen 11977
Gussgefüge 3026
Gusshaut 3068, 16471, S.
   16479
Gusskran S. 13754
Gusskupfer 3048
Gussloch 1850
— mit Kohlenstoffen 1673
Gussmatrize 3060
Gussmessing 2985
Gussmetall 7645
Gussmodell 7664, 12972,
   15376
Gussnaht entfernen (die)
   14718

Gusspfanne 10470
Gussputzbürste 3043
Gussputzer 5840/a, 6973,
   15476
Gussputzerei 6978
— in Putztrommeln 14447
Gussputzmaschine S. 15478
Gussrinde 16479
Gussringausbau S. 19960
Gussringe einbauen 18972
Gussrinne 3047, 7335, 11222,
   13753 , 15372
Gussrohr 3030
Guss· schaden 5109
Guss·schale S. 3007
Guss·schrot 10014
Guss·spannung 3072
Guss·stahl S. 3018, 3069,
   4738, S. 17463
Guss·stahlblech S.3021
Guss·stahldrahtbürste mit
   Handgriff 3024
Guss·stahlplatte S. 3021
Guss·stahlrost 3020
Guss·stahltiegel 3019
Guss·stahlwerk 3025
Guss·stück S. 3036
— mit Kernen konstruieren
   4383
Gusstrichter 9776, 9821,
   9855
Gusstümpel S. 13747
Gussversatz 4696, 11799
Gusswachs 3074
Gusszapfen S. 17211
gut gelungene Röstung
   14020
guter Versatz 8359
gutes Liegende 8357
Gütestufe 5138
Gütevorschrift 17028
Gutiehre 10107
Guttaperchaflasche 8681
Guttaperchagerät 8683
Guttaperchapapier 8682
Gymnit S. 5297, 8693

H

Haarkies S. 11705
Haarriss 3529/a, 6111/a,
   8708, 16012/a, 3374
— der Form 11976
Haarrisse 7250/a
Haarsalz 6869, S. 8710
Habitus 8698
Hackmannit 8699
Häcksel 2784
Hadfieldstahl 8702
Hafnererz S. 10614
Hafnium 3137, 8706
haften 147
Haftgrundmittel mit
   Pigmentierung 13954
Haftstärke der Ionen 9860
Haftvermittler 150
Hahn. 3897, 13121
Hahnausrüstung 3898
Hahnsteuerung 14659
Haidingerit 8707
Haken S. 2949, 9214, 9312,
   10166, S. 14381
Hakeneisen S. 5600, 9317
Hakengiessform 9316
Hakenplatte 9318
Hakenrolle 16786
Hakenschraube 16794, 18185
Hakenstifte 15511
hakiger Bruch S. 8700
halbberuhigter Stahl 15845
halber Türstock 9716, 13708,
   19192
Halberzeugnis 19295
halbfertiger Stahl 15842
halbfertiges Erzeugnis
   15841
halbfette Kohle 15837
halbflächig S. 9082
halbfreier Stempel 17929
halbgewaschene Halbpech-
   kohle 8718
halbharter Stahl 2843, 11423/a
   11423/a, S. 11427
halbiertes Roheisen 11956,
   11958
Halbkoks 3865
halbkontinuierliche Strasse
   15840
halbkreisförmige Giessgrube
   15839

Halbportalkran 15844
Halbrundeisen S. 8716,
  16883
halbrundes Eisen S. 8716
Halbrundniet S. 15290
Halbrundprofil S. 8716
Halbschleuderguss S.15838
Halbstahl 8717
halbständige Form 15846
halbversenkter Niet 12888
halbweicher Stahl 11436,
  16844
halbweisses Roheisen S.
  20028
Halbwellrohrkessel 1989
Halde 1605, 6101, 8941,
  18673
Haldenarbeiter 8942
Haldenerz ·19730
Halit 8720
Hälleflinta 8721
Hallerit 8722
Halliburtonsmischer 9326
Halloysit 8723
Halogenid 8719
Haloid S. 8719
Halotrichit 8710, 8726
Hals 12204, S. 1468
— einer Bessemerbirne
  12390
haltbar 16874
Haltbarkeit 6117
Haltebügel 2385
Haltepunkte S. 4645
Haltezeit 9247
hältiges Gut 11761
Hämafibrit 9072
Hämatit S. 6992, 8705
— -Roheisen 9074
Hämatolith 9077
Hämatostibiit 9078
Hämere 9079
Hammer prellen (den) 10695
Hammerarbeiter 8750
Hammerbahn 8734, S. 8740
Hammereisen S. 20240
Hämmerer S. 8750
Hammerfinne 8740
Hammergesenk 5987
Hammerkolben 8741
Hammerkopf 8737, 8905

Hammerlötkolben 3488
Hammermühle 8729, 8738
Hämmern 3735
hämmern 8727, 11257
Hammerschlag 1859, S.7597,
  8742, 15568
Hammerschmied S. 7588
Hammerschraube 9314
Hammersteuerung 8744
Hammerschweissen S. 7582
Hammerschweissung 8745,
  9366
Hammerverbindung 8743
Hancockit 8752
Handamboss 8753
Handarbeit 11305
Handbohrer 8754, 8757
Handbohrung 8759
Handbrunnen 6082
Handelseisen 11496
Handelseisenwalzwerk 11497
Handelsstahl 4088, 6734,
  11498
handelsüblicher Stahl S.
  4088
handelsübliches Gasrohr
  4087
— Glattrohr 13443
Handfäustel 14932
Handfeger 8756
Handförderung 8771, 8789
Handformmaschine 8767. 8780
  8780
— für bauchige Gegenstände
  8768
— mit Stiftenabhebung 8769
— mit Wendeplatte 8770
handgeklaubt 8772
Handgewinnung 8764, 8786
Handgiessinstrument 8765
Handgriffe 8795, 14128
Handguss 3044, 8766
Handhabung 8796
Handkelle 8763
Handkippvorrichtung 8788
Handklauben 19627
Handklaubung S. 8773, S.
  19627
Handkloben S. 8790
Handläufereisen S. 1190
Handleiste S. 14359

Handleisteneisen S. 1190
Handlochmaschine 7384/a
Handpfanne 8784
Handpressluftstampfer 8774
Handpuddeln 8775
Handpumpe 8776
Handrad 8791
Handschaufelung 8785
Handschienen-Eisen 8777
Handschraube S. 8790
Handsetzmaschine 8762
Handstampfen 8779
Handstampfer 8778
Handsteuerung 8781
Handvergoldung 8760
Handwaage 8782
Handweiser S. 13708
Handwerkzeuge mit Kraft-
  antrieb 13778
Handwinde 8792
Hanfbürste 9087
Hanfseil 9088
Hanftau 11294
Hängebank 10530, 12713,
  18684
Hängebleiben S. 15574
Hängeeisen 18081
— des Zuflussrohres 18029
Hängegletscher 8264, S.
  8807
Hängekompass 3585
Hängelager 8802
Hängen S. 2382 , 2390, 15774
— der Gicht 3466, 8805,
  8809
hängend 2387
Hangende 8800, 8806, 8808,
  8813, 12768, 15139
hängende Schleifmaschine
  12756
hängender Schenkel 758,
  15143
Hangendewasser 18753
Hangendflöz 18017
Hängerutsche 8812
Hängetal 8810
Hanksit 8816
Hannayit 8817
Hardystonit 8876
Harlequin 8877
Harmetschmelzverfahren 8878

harmoniscne Falte S. 4203
Harmotom 8879
Harnisch S. 13625, S.16603
Harrisit 8880
Harstigit 8881
hart gegossen 2912
hart löten 2288
Hartdraht 8845
Härʲᶻ 8871
harte Kohle S. 10640
— Konkretion im Sandstein
   8832
— Stelle 8842
härten 214, 8846
Härten S. 14283
harter Baustein S. 14348
— Bitumenschiefer 1325,
   1343/a
— Kern 8820
— Stahl S. 8843
— Stahlguss 8819
hartes Eisen 8834
— Eisenerz 8835
— Gestein 1321, 2617,
   8199, 8200
— Weissmetall 8831/a
Härteanlage 8866
Härtebad 8860
Härteflammofen 18393
Härtegrad 5134, 5135,
   18372/a
— des Stahles 8872
Härtemessung 11395
Härtemittel 8862, 14892/a
Härteofen 8865, 18395
Härteprüfung S. 8874
— nach Brinell S. 2409
Härtepulver S. 3177
Härteriss 14285
Härterissgefahr 14964
Härteschicht 8853
Härteschmiedefeuer 18394
Härteskala 15590
Härtetiefe 5206, 8864,
   8873
Härteverfahren 8867
Härtevorgang 8863, 13977
Hartfloss S. 20026
hartgezogener Draht 8825,
   S. 19231
— Kupferdraht S. 8824

Hartglas 8829
Hartglasbecher 8830
Hartguss S. 3433, 3442,
   3443, 3451
Hartgusseffekt 3452
Hartgussform 3055
Hartgussroheisen 3432
Hartgusswalze 3446
Hartit 8869, 8882
Hartkorn 8831
Hartkupfer 8823
Hartkupferdraht 3824
Hartlehm 8821
Hartlot 2290, 2293/a, 8840,
   S. 8841
Hartlöten 2289, 2292
Hartlotnaht 2293
Hartlötung S. 2292
   15636/a
Hartmetall 8828, 8837
Hartmetallbestückung 8839
hartnäckige Emulsion 17272
Hartperlit S. 8839
Hartstahl 8843
Härtung 8857
— durch Altern S. 215
— im Öl S. 12494
Härtungsminderung 1/a
Härtungsprobe 8868
Härtungstiefe 5207
Härtungsverfahren S. 8867
Hartverchromung 8838/a
Hartzinn S. 13188
harveyisierte Platte 8883
harveyisierter Stahl 8884
Harz 8663, 14761
Haspe 12996
Haspelpfosten 10416
Haspeltrommel S. 9226
Hastingsit 8886
Hatchettin S. 151
Hatchettolith 8887
Hatherlit 8888
Haube 1468, S. 2032, S.
   2035
Haubenofen 1451/a
Hauchecornit 8890
hauen 14257
Hauer S. 2318, S. 2482,
   S. 4906, 6745, S. 13422
Hauerarbeit S. 9115

Hauerit 8891
Haufen 1145/a, 1147, 13278,
   17624
Haufenlaugerei 8943
Haufenröstung 8944
haufenweise 1328
Haufwerk 2048, 5477, 12058,
   12061
Hauptbestandteil S. 13938
Hauptdruck S. 9164
Haupteinguss 3053, 14947
Haupteinsatz 11362
Hauptfalte 11228
Hauptförderstrecke 2899,
   S. 11947
Hauptgang 11365, 11949
Hauptgasleitung 8022
Hauptgleis 11227
Hauptguss 11223
Hauptkluft S. 11229
Hauptlaboratorium 3416,
   4025
Hauptleitung 18958
Hauptorientierung 13833
Hauptschablone 17808
Hauptschieber 11363
Hauptschlechte S. 1045
Hauptspalte 11229
Hauptstrecke S. 8931, 11220,
   11947
Hauptstreichrichtung S. 8153
Hauptverwerfung 5623
Hauptwelle S. 10099
Hauptwerk 13944
Hauptwindleitung 304
Hauptwindrohr 13388
Hausbrandkohle 5621, 9459
Haushaltgerät 9460
Hausmannit 8899
Haut 16093/a, S. 16471, S.
   18101
Häutchen 13054
Hauyn 8900
Hauynophyr 8901
Hebebock 10091, S.14393
Hebegruppe 9235
Hebehaken 16642
Hebel 10717
Hebelventil 7365
Hebelwirkung ausheben
   (mit) 14061

Heben S. 9229
— der Blöcke 10771
— der Form 10760
Hebestück 10774
Hebetisch 10775
Hebevorrichtung 10767
Hebewerk S. 5785
Hebezeug 8231, 9225
Hebronit 9043
Hebung 19359
Heckplatten 17566
Hedenbergit 9044
Hedrumit 9046
Hedyphan 9047
heftiges Kochen 17877
Heilguss 16937
heiss ablöschen 14280
— geblasenes Roheisen 9399
— werden 8967, 15345
heissblasen 1844
heissbrüchig s. rotbrüchig
heissbrüchiges Eisen 9402, 9440
Heissbrüchigkeit 9403, 14549 14549
heisse Stelle S. 9444
heisseingeschmolzenes Eisen 9442
Heissen 3326
heisser Schlammsprudel 12863
— Wind 9393
heisses Gusseisen 9420
— Metall 9422
heissgarer Gang 20221
heissgeblasenes Roheisen 9396
heissgewalztes Eisen 9435
heisslaufen S. 15345
Heisswasserkessel 9450
Heisswassertrichter 9452
Heisswasserumlauf in Schwarzblechröhren 9451
Heisswindkupolofen 9394
Heisswindleitung 9391, 9397
Heisswindofen 9395
Heisswindschieber 9401
Heizen S. 17637
— des Blockkopfes 9016
Heizer 17634

Heizfläche 13492
Heizgitter 9014
Heizgrube S. 9796
Heizhaube 12697/a
Heizhülle 9015
Heizkammer 9009
Heizkanal 9012
Heizofen 8308, 9013, 14674
Heizöl 7791, 13785
Heizraum S. 7174, 17633
Heizrohrbord 1368
Heizrohrbördel S. 1368
Heizröhrenkessel 16766
Heizrohrflansch S. 1368
Heizrohrkessel S. 16766
Heizrohrschlange 18012
Heizrohrwand S. 19035, 19040
Heizschlange 9010
Heizstabofen S. 6296
Heizung 7187
— mit offenem Feuer 1999
Heizungskessel 9008
Heizungsofen 3236
Heizwert 2754
— aus der Analyse berechnen (den) 2731
— bestimmen (den) 5263
— durch einen Heizwert-messer ermitteln (den) 5264
Heizwertbestimmung des Kokses 5257
Heizwertmesser 2755
Heizwertuntersuchung 2757
Heizwirkung 2753
Heliodor 9063
Heliophyllit 9064
Heliotrop 1816, 9065
Helium 9066
Hellbergerscher Ofen 9067
helle Rotglut (auf) 2400
hellgraues Gusseisen 10783
Helligkeit der Flamme 2405
Hellrotglühhitze S. 19945
hellstrohgelb 17758
Helvetien 9071
Helvin 9070, 18470
hemiedrisch 9082
hemimorph 9084
Hemimorphie 9083

Hemimorphit 9085
hemitrop 9086
Hemmstange S. 1089, 5282, S. 5592
Hempelofen 9089
Hemwoodit 9091
Heptorit 9093
herausfallen 5971
Herausfallen 16965
herausgesprengtes Erz 1735
herausnehmbarer Einsatz-kessel 14708
Herausnehmen des Modells 10744
— des Modells aus der Form 17865
— der Modelle 5802
hercynische Faltung 9094
Hercynit 9095
Herd 1414, 2145, 8950, 10449, 16869, 16872
— entleeren (den) 18262
— giessen (in) 2973
Herdarbeit auf bewegtem Herde 15037
Herdboden S. 8953
Herdeisen 8963
Herderit 9096
Herdfläche 8966
Herdform 8961
Herdformerei 8962
Herdformschmieden 12569
Herdfrischarbeit 10392
Herdfrischeisen 1821, 1829
Herdfrischen 8954, 14614
Herdfrischroheisen 3307
Herdfrischstahl S. 3306, S. 14104
Herdfutter 8960
Herdgerät 11010
Herdgewölbe 15138
Herdmantel S. 10102
Herdofen 8956, S. 12574
Herdringmaschine 8964
Herdsohle S. 8951, 8959
Herdtiefe 5208
Herdwand 16280
hereingewinnen 2300, 8198
Hereingewinnung 2449, 5792, 6906, S. 8205, 15759, 15762, S. 17676, 20212

Hereingewinnung der Kohle S. 3828
— von der Seite 16275
Hereinreibearbeit 11858, 13649, 19888
Heronit 9098
Heroultscher Hochofen 9099
Herregrundit 9100
Herrichten der Probe 13853
Herschelit 9101
Herstellung der Schliffe 13859
— der Steine 13855
— des Teiges 13854
Herstellungskosten 4515
Herstellungsplatz trocknen (am) 6024
herumlaufender Bord 3596
heruntersickerndes Eisen 11470
hervostehen 10261
Herzblatt-polierschaufel 10549
Herzfraktion 8948
Herstückspitze 13610
Hessit 9102
Hessonit 3579, 9103
Hetairit 9104
Heterogenit 9105
heteromesische Ablagerungen 9106
heteromorphe Gesteine 9108
Heteromorphit 9107
heterotaxe Ablagerung 9109
heterotopische Ablagerung 9110
Hettangien 9111
Heulandit 9112
Heumit 9113
Hewettit 9114
hexagonales System 9122
Hexahydrit 9127
Hexakisoktaeder 9128
Hexakistetraeder 9129
Hiatus 9131, S. 11040
Hibbenit 9132
Hibschit 9133
Hiddenit 9134
Higginsit 9135
Hilfs – 17334
Hilfsarbeiter 12302, 15264, 15392
Hilfsbohrer 7412
Hilfsbohrloch 6179, 14689, 14690, 16498
Hilfselevator 18824
Hilfsfalte 19251
Hilfsgeräte 1000
Hilfsgeviert 6786
Hilfsgruppe 1003
Hilfskessel 1001, 5626
Hilfsmaschine S. 2050
Hilfspumpe 8101
Hilfsrolle für Erze 10189
Hilfsschacht 15901
Hilfsventilator 2050, 2052
Hilfswerkzeug 1002
Hillebrandit 9196
hinabfahren S. 8202
hinauffahren S. 8203
Hingang 8341
Hinsdalit 9208
Hinterachse 1047
Hinterdrehbank 1086
hintere Stirnwand S. 1053
hintereinanderliegende Kolben 18239
hinterfüllen 7009
Hinterfüllen S. 7035
Hintergrund 1084
Hintermauerung des Kern-schachtes 12697
Hintersäule 14481
Hinterschneidung 1052, 14489/a, 19246
Hinterzacken 1070
Hintzeit 9209, S. 10273
Hin-und Herbiegeprobe 14819/a, 430
Hiorthscher Ofen 9210
Hippuritenfazies 9211, 9606
historische Geologie 9608
histrixit 9213
hitchcockite 9215
Hitze S. 8971
hitzebeständig 8992
hitzebeständiger Stahl 8991, 8994, 12343
hitzebeständiges Gusseisen 8993
Hitzebeständigkeit 14772
hitzehärtbarem Akrylharz basierender Anstrich (auf) 17701
Hobeleisen 13455
hobeln S. 13451
Hobelstahl S. 13455
Hobelstichel S. 13455
Hochdruck 9164
Hochdruckadapter 2554
Hochdruckdampfkessel 9170
Hochdruckgebläse 9166
Hochdruckpfropfen 2553
Hochdruckrohr 9165
Hochdruckschraubengebläse 9169
Hochdruckschmiere 6503
Hochebene 18191
hochfestes Gusseisen 9142a, 9143
hochfeuerfeste Masse 9195
Hochfrequenz-Induktions-ofen 9147
Hochfrequenztrockner 5384
hochgekohlter Stahl 9139
Hochgeschwindigkeitsverfor-mung 9191
Hochglanz – 9161
Hochglanzblech 2399
hochglanzpolieren 7114
hochkantig stehender Ziegel 2374
hochkantig stellen 13433
hochkohlenstoffhaltiges Eisen 10027
höckerartige Ausscheidung 9483
hochlegierter Stahl 9137
Hochleistungskessel 9163
Hochleistungs-Längsdreh-stahl 9032
Hochleistungs-Spiralfräser 9060
Hochleistungsumformung 9144
Hochbohrung S. 19387
Hochmoor 9159
Hochofen S. 9149, 1706
— anblasen (den) 1845
— ausblasen 3354
— ausgehen lassen (den) 1843

Hochofen-Gebläse 1707
— mit Blechmantel 1726
— mit eingebautem Gestell 1721
— mit geschlossener Brust 1722
— mit offener Brust 1723
— mit ovalem Gestell 1724
— mit Rauhgemäuer 1725
— -Zement 1718
Hochofenabstich S. 18307
Hochofenanlage 1713
Hochofenarbeiter 7850
Hochofenbau 1710
Hochofenbekleidung 16106
Hochofengas 20069
Hochofenkoks 1709
Hochofenmantel 16139
Hochofenriss 1715
Hochofenschlacke 1717
Hochofenschmelze 1720
Hochofensinter 1716
Hochofenwerk 1713
Hochofenwind 7826
Hochofenzeichnung 1711
hochphosphorhaltiges Eisen 9162
hochprozentige Legierung 399, 9136, 9142
Hochschwemmen von Sandstücken 5974
hochsiliziertes Eisen S. 9172
hochsiliziumhaltiges Eisen 8296
Hochspannungsanlage 9190
Hochspannungsspeisekabel 9189
Höchstdruckkessel 9193
hochstetiges T-Eisen 9192
— U-Eisen 5098
Höchstlast 11386, 14474/a
Höchstpressung 11387
hochstrahliges Roheisen 9194
hochwertiger Brennstoff 9151
— Gips 8613
— Guss 9150
— Stahl 9153
hochwertiges Gusseisen 17008

hochzementieren 3139
Hodgkinsonit 9221
Hoffmann-Ofen 10359
Hoffs Gasfang (von) 19602
Höhe 6417
— der Ebene 19281
Höhenlage 9054
höherer Flügel 8815
hohes Wärmesalzbad 9155
hohl giessen 2970
Hohlbohrer 2210, 8373
Hohlbohrstahl 9269
Hohlcharge 15991
hohle Kammerwalze 9274
— Kernspindel S. 4388
Höhlenfüllung 3126
hohler Gusskern 3272
hohlgebohrte Welle S.9249
Hohlgicht 10156
Hohlgichtbohrer 10158
Hohlguss 9266, 9268
Hohlkanteisen 7494
Hohlkastenrahmenkonstruktion 2226
Hohlkehle 9263, 7027
Hohlkern S. 16100
Hohlkörper 9264
Hohlraum 3124, 16952
Hohlraumschiessen 4888
Hohlschiene S. 3289
Hohlschmieden 9272
Hohlstanzen 18877
Hohlstege 9267
Hohlzylinder für Papierfabriken 19081
Hokutolit 9237
Holdenit 9241
Holhalbrundstahl 9273
Hollandit 9260
Höllenstein 16354
Holm S. 14359
Holmium 9283
holoachsial 9284
Holoarktik 9238
holoedrisch 9287
holohyalin 9288
holokristallin 9286
hololenkokrat 9289
holomelanokrat 9290
holomorphisch 9291
Holotypus 9292

Holozän 9285
Holspat S. 3415
Holz 20170
— rauben 19339
Holzarbeit S. 20186
Holzaschenwasser 13014, 20171
Holzbau S. 20173
hölzerner Formkasten 20182
hölzerne Küvelage 4631
Holzfeuerung 20174
Holzfeuerungskessel 1963
Holzform 20175/a
Holzgerinne 20179
Holzgerüst 10105
Holzhorde 20175
Holzkasten 3906
Holzkeil 8907, 10728
Holzkohle 3298
— in Stücken 3309
Holzkohlenasche 3299
Holzkohlenblech 3312
Holzkohlenbrikett 3302
Holzkohlenhochofen 3301
Holzkohleneisen 3308, S. 7093
Holzkohlenmeiler 3304
Holzkohlenpulver 3300
Holzkohlenstahl S. 3306
Holzkohlenstaub 3303, 3311
Holzkonstruktion S. 20173
Holzlutte 246
Holzöl 19099
Holzopal 20176, 20276
Holzpfeiler S. 2285, 2362, S. 4635, 13273
Holzpfeilerzimmerung S. 4634, 13274
Holzrauben 14011, 14499, 20158
Holzrauber S. 14010, 17863, 18634
Holzscheibe 20181
Holzschrank 3750, S. 4635
Holzschrankzimmerung 4634
Holzschraube 20177
Holzstiel 20183
Holzteer 20178
Holzverband S. 20173
Holzverkleidung S. 18637
Holzwasserscheider 13463

Holzwerk S. 18637, 20173
Holzwollseil 20180
Holzzinn 18655
Homogeneisen S. 9794
— s. Flusseisen
Homogenkohle 224, 16877
Homogenstahl S. 9800
homoklinisch 9296
homöoblastische Struktur 9297
homöomorph 9298
homotaxe Ablagerung 9300
Honen 9306/a
Honigblende 15189
Honigstein S. 9302
Honmaschine 9307
Hopeit 9327
Horizont 9330
horizontale Deckung 9020, 9345
— Schicht 10714
— Schublänge 9338, 16211, 17824
— Sprungweite 9354
— Tischfräsmaschine 1487
— Verschiebung S. 9355
— Verwerfung 9355
horizontaler aufsteigender Scheibenbau 852
— Lagergang S. 1686 , 1695
— Scheibenbau 9351
horizontales Bohrloch 2778
Horizontallinie 10709
Horizontalspalte 1418
Horizontalverschiebung S. 17825
Hornblende 9369
Hornblendeasbest S. 536
Hornblendeschiefer 9370
Hornblendefels 9371
Hornbüchse 9364
Hörneramboss 1375
Hornfels 9372, S. 9374
Hornfelsstruktur S. 11940
Horngiessen 9358
Hornito 1871
Hornkohle 9359
Hornstein 3410, 9374, 9949
Hornzulauf 9360
Horsfordit 9384

Horst 9385
Hortonolith 9386
Hosenrohr 18175
Howlith 9468
Hubbegrenzung 10676
Hubhöhe 9057
Hubkarren 10751
Hübnerit 9471
Hubstange 1455
Hubvergrösserer 12127
Hubwindrohr für hydraulische Kraftwagenleiter 19003
Hubzähler 17875
Hudsonit 9474
Hufeisen 9381
Hufeisenmagnet 9383
Hufeisennagel 9380, 12161
Hufstabeisen 9382
Hügelchen 12030
Hugelit 9475
Hughes-Kegelmeissel 9476
Hülle S. 10100
Hullit 9477
Hulsit 9478
humin 9479
Humit 9481
Hummer-Sieb 9482
Humus 11969
Hund S. 5592, S. 11027, S. 11772
Hunderterwaage 3190
Huntilith 9487
Huron 9488
Hussakit 9491
Hut 2793
Hüttenabfälle 19717
Hüttenbahnhof 11742
Hüttenhartstein 5173
Hüttenindustrie 9980, 11587
Hüttenkoks 11585
hüttenmännische Behandlung 11589
hüttenmännischer Vorgang 11588
Hüttenmeister 10034
Hüttenwerk S. 17522
Hüttenzement S. 1718
Hyazinth 9494
hyalin 9495
Hyalin-Quarz 9496
Hyalit 9497, 19801

hyalokristallin 9498
Hyalophan 9499
hyalopilitische Struktur 9500
Hyalosiderit 9501
Hyalotekit 9502
Hyazinth 10089
hydatogen 9505
Hydatogenese 9504
Hydrant 7175, S. 9506
Hydrargillit 9507
Hydraulik-Sieb mit beweglicher Ebene 8751
— -Sieb mit fester Ebene 8885
hydraulische Blockschere 9537
— Entzunderungsmaschine 9520
— Formmaschine S. 9528
— Formmaschine mit Wendeplatte 9529
— Formpresse S. 9530
— Friktion 8696
— Gewinnung 9527, 9541, 13382, 16997
— Keilpresse 9519
— Prüfung S. 9539
— Pumpe 9535
— Schmiedepresse S. 9523
hydraulischer Abbau S. 9527
— Hebebock 9525
— Masselbrecher 9531
— Pumpenkasten 14161
— Vorschub 9522
hydraulisches Gelenk 5925
— Ziehwerkzeug 9534
Hydrid 9542
Hydrier-und Synthesespeichersäule 9562
Hydrierung 9562/a
hydrobios 9544
Hydroboracit 9546
Hydrocerussit 9548
Hydrocyanit 9552
hydrogeformtes Erzeugnis 9555, 9556
Hydrohämatit 9563
Hydrokarburvorkommen 13650
hydroklastisches Gestein 9550

Hydrolyse 9564
hydromechanisches Ziehen
  9553
— Ziehen mit begrenztem
  Stülpzug 9554
Hydrometallurgie 9565/a
Hydrometamorphismus 9566
Hydromuskovit 9568
Hydronephelit 9569
Hydrophan 9570
Hydrophilit 9571
Hydrosparkverfahren 9572
hydrostatische Waage 9573
hydrostatischer Druck 9575
hydrostatisches Niveau
  9574
— Spiegel 10711
Hydrotalkit 9576
Hydroxylion 9578
Hydrozinkit 9579, 20324
Hydrozyklon S. 4934
Hygrometer S. 9580
hygroskopisches Wasser
  9581
hypabyssisch 9582
hypabyssisches Gestein 9583
  9583
hypautomorphe Struktur 9584
Hyperit 9589
Hypersthen 9591, 10453
Hypersthenit 9592
hypidiomorph 9593
hypidiomorphkörnige Struktur
  8420
Hypochloritbehandlung 9594
hypogen 9601
hypogenes Wasser S. 854
hypokristallin 9080, 9595,
  11512
hypotaxische Lagerstätte
  9603
hypothermaler Gang 9604
Hystereseschleifenschreiber
  6943/a

I

Ichthyophthalm S. 698
Iddingsit 9615

ideales Gas 9614/a
Idioblast 9616
idiochromatisch 9617
idiogen 9619
idiogene Einheiten 9618
idiomorph 8620
Idokras S. 19542
Idrialin 9622
I-Eisen 9609
Ijolith 9629
Ijussit 9630
Ikositetraeder 9614
Ilgnersystem 9631
illegal gefördertes Öl S.
  9423
Illit 9632
Ilmenit S. 11485
Ilmenitit 9638
Ilvait S. 10733, 20295
Impaktionsfraktur 9650
Impfstoff 9826
Impfung 9827
Implikationsstruktur S. 8446
Imprägnationsgang 9665
Imprägnationslagerstätte
  9662
imprägnierte Kohlen 9661
imprägniertes Erz 9664
Inchromieren 3541
Indigolit 1913/a
Indigolith 9741
Indigolösung 9740
Indikatordiagramm 10964
indirekte Reduktion 9745
indirekter Lichtbogenofen
  6746/a, 9743
indischer Stahl S. 9736
Indium 9746
Induktionshärtung 9750
Induktionsheizapparat 9752
Induktionskippofen 9755
Induktionsmaschine 9754
Induktionsofen 6285, 7594,
  9749, S. 9890
— für Bundeisen 1256
Induktionsschmieden 9748
Induktionsschmiedeofen S.
  7594
Induktions-Tiegelofen 4459
induktive Badbewegung 6556
induktives Schweissen 9756

Industrieofen 9757
— für Gasfeuerung 9758
Inertdynamit 9759
infiltrierte Zone 9764
Informationskerne 17156
Infraktion 8524
Infrarot-Trockenofen 9772
Infusorienerde 8661, 9775
Inhibitor 5201, 9807
Injektionsmetamorphose 9814
  9814
Injektor 9818
Inkromieren 3542
Inkrustat S. 9727
Innendruck 9903
Innenfeuerung 9909
Innengrat 19616
Innengussfehler 17086
Innenkernrohr 4434
Innenlunker 9904, 15769/a
Innenmöräne 6478
Innenriss 9899
Innenrohrfänger mit trenn-
  barem Keil 14683
Innentaster S. 9842
Innentemperatur 9907
innere Bekleidung der
  Lagerschalen S. 10853
— Beschaffenheit 9906
— Reibung 567/a, 9901
— Spannung 9905
— Streckgrenze 9908
inneres Abschmelzen 6677
— Kernrohr 9825
Instandhaltung 12963
Instandsetzen S. 12964
Intensitätsgrösse S. 9863
interdendritisch 9877
interdendritische Seigerung
  S. 11653
interdendritischer Graphit
  9878
Interferometer 9880/a
interkristalline Korrosion
  9875, 19925
interkristallinisch 9874
interkristallinischer Bruch
  9876
intermediäres Eruptivgestein
  9892
— Gestein S. 12252

intermittierende Produktion 7441
— Versorgung 8909
intermittierender Gas-Lift S. 9895
Intersertalgefüge 9866
Intersertalstruktur 9914
intersitiell 9915/a
Intervall S. 16957
intrakristalliner Bruch 9920
intratellurischer Kristall S. 13149
Intrusion 9923
intrusiv 9924 , 10044
Intrusivgang S. 6148 13065
Intrusivgesteine 9926
Intrusivkörper S. 9808, 9925
Intrusivlager 9927, S. 16337
Intubation 9928
Inundationsterrasse 7396, 14968
Invarstahl 9931
inverse Verbrennung 14826
— Verwerfung 12740, S. 12765
inverser Sattel 9935
inverses Glühfrischen 9931a
Ion 9944
Ionenbildungsgeschwindigkeit 19495
Ionenspaltung 17137
Ionenverdichtung 4167
Ionisation 9946/a
Ionisationswärme 8988
ionitrieren 9946
I-Pfostenprofil 9610
Irelanscher Ofen 9948
Iridium 9950
Iridosmium 9951
irregulär körniges Gefüge 15890
Irvingit 10045
Ischewskyscher Ofen 10046
Isenit 10047
Iserin 10048
Ishikawait 10049
isländischer Doppelspat 9613

Isobutan 10052
isodimorph 10057/a
Isoformat 10058
Isogone S. 10059
isogonische Linie 10059
Isohydrie der Säurelösungen 10062
isohydrisch 10060
isohydrische Lösungen 10061 10061
Isoklas 10056
Isoklinalantiklinale 10054
Isoklinalfalte 10055
Isoklinalkamm 9222
Isoklinaltal 11907
isoklinisch 10057
Isolation zur Vermeidung von Kaltbrücken 9852
isolierend 9850
isoliermantel 10065
isolierte Kabel und Leiter 9849
Isolierungsstück 9851
Isomerat 10066
isomesische Ablagerungen 10067
isometrische Habitus 12379
isomorph 10069
Isomorphie S. 10070
Isomorphismus 10070
Isooktan 10071
Isoparaffin 10073
Isopentan 10074
isopische Ablagerungen 10075
Isopren 10076
isoseismisch 10077
isostatische Senkung 10078
isotherme Glühung S. 10079
isothermische Härtung 10080 10080
— Umwandlung 10081
isotopische Ablagerung 10082
Isotropen-Molekularwirkung 10083
Itabirit 10084, 17041
Itacolumit 10085
italienische Tunnelbauweise 10086
Ixolith 10087

J

Jacupirangit 10110
Jade 10114, S. 12232
Jadeit 10115
Jadeitit 10116
Jahreszahl 12423
Jahreserzeugung 20281
Jakobsit 10109
Jalousiewellblech 4502
japanieren 10121
Japanieren S. 10123
japaniert 10122
Japanisieren S. 10123
Jargon 10133
Jarosit 10134
Jasperisation 10138
Jaspilit 10139
Jaspisachat 10137
Jaspopal 6969
Jauche 7060
Jefferisit 10144
Jeffersonit 10145
Jenaer Geräteglas 10146
Jeremejewit 10148
Jeromit 10150
Jezekit 10165
Joaquinit 10187
Joch 19641
Jod 9940
Jodargyrit S. 9939
Jodit S. 9939
Jodkalium 13729
Jodkaliumpapier 13728
Jodkaliumstärkepapier 13727
Jodlösung 9941
Jodobromit 9942
Jodsilber 9939
Johannit 10193
Johnstrupit 10194
Jolith 9943
Jonit 9945
Jordanit 10229
Josefit 10230
Joseit 10231
Josephinit 10232
Julienit 10241
Jumillit 10244
jüngeres Kohlenvorkommen 3848

jungfräuliches Gebiet 11216
jungvulkanisch 3183
jungvulkanisches Gestein
    10269
Jurassisch 10260
Jurupait 10259
Juvelierrot S. 10164
Juxporit 10263
Juxpositionszwillinge
    10264

K

Kabeldämpfer 10832
Kabeleisen 2662/a
Kabelgarnitur 2659
Kabelgrube S. 2664
Kabelkran 26 7
Kabelpumpen 20133
Kabelschutzrohr 6263, 18994
Kabeltunnel 2664
Kabelumlenkrolle auf Arbeits-
    bühne 7403
Kabelzubehör S. 2659
kadmieren 2672
kadmiert 2674
Kadmierung 2677
Kadmium 2673
kadmiumhaltig 2671
Kaersutit 10265
Kainit 10266
Kainolith 10267
Kainosit 2687, 3182, 10268
Kakoxen 2669, 10271
Kalabarin 3111
Kalamin S. 2699
Kalander mit geheizten
    Walzen 15111
Kalandrieren 10507
Kalcimeter 2711
Kalcit 2702
Kalciumasrsenit 2726
Kalciumkarbonat 2851
Kalciumoxyd S. 10810
Kalcium s. Kalzium
Kaliber entwerfen (die)
    5230
Kaliberlog 15774
Kalibervertiefung 1295t

Kaiiberwalze 8594
Kaliborit 10273
Kalibrieren S. 5231, 16445a
Kalibriermatritze 14694
kalibriertes Eisen 2741
Kalibrierung der Walzen 5231
    5231
Kalibrierwalzwerk 14869
Kalilauge 3115
Kalinit 10274
Kaliophilit 10275, S. 13140
Kalisalpeter 13730
Kalium 10276
Kaliumbichromat 1575
Kaliumchlorat 13723
Kaliumchlorid S. 3499
Kaliumkarbonat S. 2853
Kalk 10810
Kalkablagerungen von
    Mineralquellen 128
Kalkboden 13037
Kalkchromgranat S. 2725
Kalkeisengranat S. 695
Kalken des Drahtes 3266
Kalkfeldspat 10813
Kalkglimmer S. 11314
kalkige Fazies 2705
kalkiger Sandstein 2707,
    3267
kalkiges Bindemittel 2704
— Eisenerz 2706
Kalkknolle 3799
Kalklicht 10815
Kalkmilch 10818
Kalknatronfeldspat 16810
Kalkofen 10816
Kalkowskit 10277
kalkreich 14876
kalkreiche Fazies S. 2705
Kalsinter S. 7758, 2701,
    2708,
Kalkspat S. 2702, 2718,
    2728
— und Fluss · spat im
    Salband 2765
Kalkstein 2528, 3265,
    10819, 10820
Kalktuff S. 2701, 2729, S.
    7758
Kalkuranglimmer 10817
Kalkwasser S. 10818

Kallait 10278, S. 19154
kalogen 8725
Kalomel 9361, 2751
Kalorie 2752
Kalorimeter S. 2755
Kalorimetrie 2758
kalorimetrische Bombe S.
    2756
kalorisieren 2760
Kalorisieren 2759
kalorisiert 2761
kalorisierter Stahl 2762
kalt ausgearbeitet 3978
— bearbeitet S. 3978
— erblasenes Roheisen
    3963
— gerichtetes Eisen 4004
— giessen 2967
— hämmern 3958
— legen 4977
— stempeln 3960
— walzen 3959
Kaltabschrecken 3987/b
Kaltabspritzen 4003/a
Kaltarbeit 4006
Kaltarbeitsstahl 4008
Kaltauslagern 12189
Kaltbandwalzwerk 3998
Kaltbearbeitung 3980
Kaltbiegeprobe 3961
Kaltbruch 3966, 3972
kaltbrüchig 3965, 4000
kaltbrüchiges Eisen 4001
Kaltbrüchigkeit des Eisens
    4002
Kaltdurchbohrung 3986/a
kalte Verzinkung 7943
kalter Einsatz 3969
— Wind 3962
kaltes Eisen 3986
— Metall 3985
Kalteinsenken 3979
Kaltemaillierung 3976
Kältemaschine 7744
kaltgereckter Stahl 3975
kaltgewalzt 3990
kaltgewalzter Stahl 3994
kaltgewalztes Band 3995
— Blech 3992, 3993
— Eisen 3996
kaltgezogenes Kupfer S. 18796

Kalthammern 13043
Kaltkammer-Druckgiessen 3968
— Druckgiessmaschine 3967
Kaltlegung 4983
Kaltmeissel 3970
Kaltpressen 3987/a
kaltpress· schweissen 4007
Kaltprobe 4005
Kaltpressen 3970/a
Kaltrecken 4010
Kaltreduzier-und Kalibrier-walzwerk 14566
Kaltriss 3429, 3971, 4334
Kaltsägemaschine 3999
Kaltsägen 3999/a
Kaltschlagmatrize 3982
kaltschmieden 7572
Kaltschweisse 3984, 4003, 7360, 19298
Kaltverzinkinkung 3981/a
Kaltwalze 3989
kaltwalzen 3988
Kaltwalzen 3997
Kaltwindschieber 3964
kaltziehen 3957
Kaltziehen von nahtlos gegossenen Röhren 3015/a
Kaltzieherei 3974
Kaltzug 3973
Kalzedon 2709, 3253
kalzinieren 2712
Kalzinierofen 2703, 2716
Kalzium 2721
Kalziumfluorid S. 7475
Kalziumphosphat 13163
Kalziumsilizium 2727
Kamacit 10279
Kamarezit 10280
Kambrium 2771
Kaminbeschlag 9972
Kaminbühne 3463
Kaminhaube 9308
Kaminkühler 3457
Kamm 14886
— für lose Schlüssel 18715
Kammer 2063, S. 2336
Kammerbau 7569, 13294

Kammererit 10281
Kammergang 3273
Kammer-Gasliften 3271
Kammerminenschiessen S. 8366
Kammerpfeilerbau 1251, 1921, 2064, 2343, 3269, 8934, 13290, 15148, 17301
Kammerpfeilerbruchbau 17300
Kammerschiessen 3270, 8366
Kammstruktur 4051
Kammwalze 13319
Kammwalzgerüst 13320/a
Kammwalzenständer 17091
Kampylit 2773, 10282
Kanal 3284, 19440
Kanäle zur Bleigewinnung 3293
Kanalbildung 3294
Kanalisation 14319
Kanister 16509
Kanisteröl 18662
kanneliertes Rohr 7494/a
Kannelkohle S. 2782, 14445
kanoneartiger Bohrer 17708
Kanonenbohrer 14890
Kanonbronze S. 8673
Kanonenmetall 8673
känozoische Formation 3184, 10270
Kante 6197
Kantengeschiebe S. 15525
Kantenriegel 7482
Kantenriss S. 4676, 6200
Kantvorrichtung 18626
Kanzel 12614/a, 20216/a, 20251
Kaolinisierung 10283/a
Kaolinit 10283
Kap 1374, 4889
Kapazitätsgrösse 2803
Kapelle 4838
Kapellenofen 893, 4840
Kapillarfläschchen 2807
Kapillarität 2805
Kapillarkraft 2809
Kapillarsaum 2808
Kapillarsteigung 2810
Kapillarwirkung 2806

Kappe 2031, 2034, 2795, 2799, 4727, 4733, 4735, 5856, 8918, 10458, S. 10727, 14707, S. 17838
— des unteren Trichters S. 2120
— über der Versatzmauer 19646 19646
— · s. Deckplatte
Kappenständer 12600
Kapsel S. 3433
Kapselgebläse à: 15155
Kapselguss S. 3443
Kapselhochdruckgebläse 11349 11349
Kapselmetall 2814/a
Kapselton S. 15798
Kapselwerk 2925
Kar 3586, 3607, 10284, 10322
Karbidanreihung 2823
Karbidkohle 2821
Karbidlampe 66
Karbidofen 2822
Karbildung 3608
Karbon 2859
Karbonformation 2861
Karbonit 2865
Karbonitrierung 2866
Karbonyl 2876/a
Karborundum 2872
Kardangelenk 2887
Karminpapier 2891
Karminit 2892
Karneol 4476
Karneolstein 2895
Karren 18945
Karschwelle 15030
Karsee 18328
Karstenit 10285
Karsthöhle 17175
Karussel 12013
Karusseldrehbank 2098
Karzinit 10286
Käse 4745, 17330
Kasolit 10287
Kasserolle 1312
Kassiterit 18649, S. 18669
Kasten 1208, S. 1936, S. 2208

Kastenfalte 2216
Kastenform 2222, 7296
Kastenformcn 2229
Kastenformen 2229
Kastenformerei 7297, 12008
Kastengebläse 2213
Kastenglühen 3755
Kastenglühofen 13718
kastengeglüht 13716
Kastenglühung 2209, 13717
Kastengriff 8793
Kastenguss 2215, 7292
kastenlos formen 11963
kastenlose Formmaschine
    16781
kastenloser Formblock 16780
Kastenschore S. 2223
Kastenzementation 2220
Kastenzementierung 12830,
Kastenzimmerung 2228
Kastor 3077
Katagenese 10288
Kataklasgefüge 13921
kataklastisch 3081
kataklastisches Gefüge 4767
Kataklasstruktur 3082
katamorph 10289
Kataphorese 3084/a
Katapleit 3085
Katazone 10291
Kathetometer 3096
Katodenzerstaubung 17231/a
    17231/a
kathodischer Schutz 3103
Katophorit 10290
Katoptrit 3104, 10293
katoptritisch 10292
Katzenauge 3080
käufliche rohe Schwefel-
    säure 4089
Kaustobiolith 3118, 10294
Kavitationskorrosion 3123/a
Keewatin 10300
Kegelbohrer 18281
Kegelbrecher 4197, S. 8337
Kegelform S. 18282
kegelförmig 4208
kegelförmige Schraubenfeder
    4211
kegelige Düse 4212
kegeliges Loch 4209

Kegelnaht 1568
Kegelradantrieb 4288
Kegelräder 1569
Kegelrutsche 1159
Kegelschicht 4200
Kegelventil 13564
Kegelverbindung 18279
kehlen 8585
Kehöit 10301
Kehrradantrieb S. 14168
— pumpen (mit) 12117
Kehrwalzwerk S. 14495, S.
    14833.
Keil 4521, 7901, 8212, S.
    10728, S. 11857, S.12055
Keilbolzen S. 4522
Keile entfernen (die) 19235
Keilenbruch 19879
Keileinguss 19881
Keilfänger 7221, 16659
keilförmige Kratze 19886
keilförmiges.Eisen 19885
— Profil 19889/a
Keilhacke S. 16673
Keilhaue 13202, 13211,
    16673
Keilhauen-und Wegfüllarbeit
    13203
Keilhauit 10302
Keilkernzieher 16665
Keilkranz 19659
Keilprobe 19887
Keilriemen 19420
— mit zwei Ringen 8584
Keilring S. 17076
Keilstahl 8214, 10324
Keilstück 19882
Keim 12419
Keller 3133
kelyphitische Textur S.
    12447
Kelyphitrinde 2070
Kempit 10309
Kennzeichen 11329, 16307
Kentrolith 10310
Keps 10526
Keramikerton 1153
keramische Bekleidung 3225

keramischer Brennofen 3226
keramisches Bindemittel
    19545
— Metall 3230
Keramohalit 10311
Kerbe S. 10321, S. 8586,
    10117, S. 10373, 12264,
    S. 12394, 16021
Kerben S. 8585, S. 10320,
    S. 10375, 12287
Kerbmaschine 3811, 16031
Kerbschlagprobe 12397, S.
    16149
Kerbschlagversuch 9648,
    18802
Kerbschlagzähigkeit 9649
Kerbsprödigkeit 12396
Kerbwirkung 12398
Kerbzähigkeit 12400/a
Kermesit 10312/a
Kern 4384, 8946, 12405
— des Bruchquerschnitts
    4428
Kernarbeiter 4421
Kernaufbau 4463
Kernbetätigung S. 4403
Kernbettrahmen 4391
Kernblasmaschine 4394
kernbohren 4382
Kernbohren 4406
Kernbohrer S. 4405
Kernbohrerpfropfen 4433
Kernbohrkopf 4401, 4911
Kernbohrung 4395, 4414
Kernbrecher 4400
Kerndrehlade 4419
Kerne S. 4463
Kerneinlegelehre 4442
Kerneinlegen 4441
Kerneinschnürung 4436
Kerneisen 4388, 4417
kernen aus dem Bohrloch-
    stoss S. 16282
Kernfänger S. 4410
Kernformen 4424
Kernformerei 4425
Kernformkasten 736, 17299
Kernformmäschine 4422
Kernformwanne 4430
Kerngabel 4411

Kerngefüge 4451
Kerngerippe 4412
Kerngewinnung 4435, 4464
Kernguss S. 9268
Kerngussloch 4415
Kernherstellung 4461, 4465
Kernit 10314
Kernkasten 4396, 4466,
 15455
— mit Dauben 16576
Kernkleben 8666
Kernkohle 4456
Kernlagerverstärkung 12036
Kernlehre 4418
Kernluft 291
Kernmacher 4460
Kernmacherei 4446
Kernmagnetismuslog 12418
Kernmarke 4423, 4431,
 4462, 17412, 18749
— aufführen 19410
Kernmarken 19410, 13957
Kernmontagelehre 4387
Kernofen 4429
Kernplatte 19617
Kernprobe 4439
Kernriss 17127
Kernrohr 4389, S. 17077,
 S. 17088, S. 19505
— mit Gummischlauch
 15313
— mit Kernzieher 1315
Kernrohrschuh 4453
Kernrückfeinen 4437
Kernsand 4440
Kernsandbeschaffenheit
 4189
Kernschablone 4450, 4452
Kernschacht 10855
Kernschiessmaschine 4397,
 4444
Kernschnitt 16032
Kernschrott 13858/a
Kernspindel 4390, 4447,
 17077, 17088, 19505
— umwickeln (die) 1593
Kernstrecke 4457
Kernstück 589, S. 9841
Kernstütze 3295, 13329/a
Kerntrockner 4404, 4448
Kerntrockenofen 4408,

4409, S. 4448
Kern-und Formteilzugelement
 5786
Kernversatz S. 11800
Kernschiebung 4443
Kernwiderstand 4449
Kernzähhärtung 5662
Kernzieher 4410
Kernzug 4403, 4432
Kerogen 10315
Kerosen 10316
Kerosenabsonderung vom
 Erdöl 16457
Kerrit 10318
Kersantit 10319
Kessel 1955, S. 6856, S.
 12885, 17417
— mit Aussenfeuerung
 6698
— mit aussen liegender
 Feuerbüchse S. 6698
— mit ausziehbarer
 Feuerung 14714
— mit direkter Flamme 5458
— mit doppeltem Feuer-
 kasten 5648
— mit einem Dampfraum S.
 1993
— mit engen Wasserrohren
 S. 19831
— mit Gasfeuerung 8006
— mit glatten Flammröhren
 1990
— mit grossem Wasserraum
 S. 10551
— mit Kohlenfeuerung S.
 1959
— mit kupferner Feuer-
 büchse 1982
— mit raschem (Wasser)
 Umlauf S. 1996
— mit Siederöhren S. 7754
— mit Strohfeuerung 1961
— mit Torffeuerung S. 1960
— mit Überhitzer 18009
— mit überhöhtem Feur-
 büchsmantel 14377
— mit Wasserraum unter
 dem Aschenkasten 19985
—. mit weiten Wasserrohren
 S. 19828

Kessel mit wiederkehrender
 Flamme 14811
— mit Zwangsumlauf 1987
— mit zwei Dampfräumen
 S. 1984
— ohne Wasserumlauf 1997
Kesselanlage 1973
Kesselauskleidungsmaterial
 1957
Kesselbatterie 1349
Kesselbekleidung 1971
Kesselblech 1974
Kesselbruch 3107, 6856
Kesseldestillierapparat
 16113
Kesselexplosion 1958
Kesselfeuerung 1967
Kesselgruppe S. 1349
Kesselhaus 1969
Kesselkohle 1956
Kesselkörper S. 1976
Kesselisoliermaterial S.
 1957
Kessellagerung 1975
Kesselmantel 1976
Kesselrevision 1970
Kesselschlacke S. 3727
Kesselschmied 1972
Kesselschmiedarbeit S.1978
Kesselschmiede 1977
Kesselstahl 1979
Kesselstein 15581
Kesselsteinbildung S. 9728
Kesselsteinschutz 665
Kesselsteinentfernung
 15597
Kesselstützen S. 2247
Kesselträger 2247
Kesselwand(ung) 16110
Kette 3238
— mit Spannschloss 10909
Kettenantrieb S. 3242
Kettenbahn 3247
Kettenbruch 7698
Ketteneisen 3246
Kettenförderer S. 2500
Kettenrad 3240
Kettenrohrschraubstock
 3249
Kettenrost 3243
Kettenrostfeuerung 3244

Kettenschrämmaschine 3239
Kettenstahl 3248
Kettenverbindung 3241
Kettenverschleiss 19854
Kettenzange 3281
ketzen 3719
Khagiarit 10333
Kielplatte 10297
Kielprobe 10296
Kienruss 3288
Kies S. 4769, 8395, 8477
Kiesabbrand 2715
Kiesel S. 7377, 16310, S. 16311
Kieselboden 7382
Kieselerde 16311
Kieselgur 5345, 10348, S. 11876
kieselig 7380, 16316
kieselige Stampfmasse 16321
Kieselsäure 16312
kieselsäurereich 14877
Kieselschiefer 7383
Kieselsinter 16320
Kieselspat S. 348
Kieselton 7378
Kieselzinkerz 16317
Kieselzuschlag 16319
Kieserit 10349
Kiesfilter 13032
kiesig 8577
Kiesgrube 8479
Kiesmantel 8481
Kiespackung S. 8481
Kiesversatz 13323
Killinit 10355
Kilomal 10361
Kimberlit 10362
Kinctogenese 10364
kippbarer Konverter 18627
— Vorherd S. 18629
Kippbrücke S. 13509
Kippbühne 18681
kippen 18670
Kippen aus der Schnauze giessen (durch) 2978
Kipper S. 6100, 18676
Kippflügeloberlichter aus Stahl 11547
Kipphebel 15041, 18630

Kippkarren 2906
Kippkegeldekantator 1272
Kippkübel 6098, 8671, 12784, 15820
Kippmischer 18631
Kippofen 18628
Kipp ·pfanne 18629
Kipprost 18677
Kippscher Apparat 10369
Kippvorrichtung 18675
Kippwagen 6099, 6103
Kipushit 10370
Kirrolith 10372
kirschrotglühend 3409
Kirschrotglut (auf) 3408
— bringen (auf) S. 2414
kirschrotwarm S. 3409
Kisten laden (die) 3314
Kistenglühung S. 2209
Kjeldahlkolben 10383
Kjellinscher Ofen 10382
Kjerulfin 10384
Klaffen 16957
klaffende Verwerfung 7968, 12570
Klammer 3622, S. 3637, 4591
Klammern lösen (die) 7719
Klampe S. 4591
Klappe 7279
Klappenfänger 12777
Klappenventil 7281
Klapperstein S. 198
Klappkernkasten 9205
Klaprothit 10385
Klärbehälter 57, 5295, 15926
klare Lösung 3708
klares 3707
Klärflasche 5052
Klärpfanne 3633
Klärteich 15925
Klassieranlage 8389, 16928
klassieren S. 3641
Klassieren S. 16446
Klassiersieb 3644, 8390
Klassierung S. 8384
Klassiervorrichtung 3640
klassifizieren 3641
Klassifizierung 8384
klastisch 3646, 5269
klastische Struktur 7708

klasto-kristallin 3647
klastogen 3648
klastomorphisch 3650
Klaubarbeit 8773, 13213
Klaubeband 13214
klauben S. 4825
Klauberz S. 13208, 13215
Klaubplatte 2506
Klauenmehl 9319
Klaviersaitendraht S. 13196
Klebelsbergit 10386
Kleben 17581
— des Guss· stücks in der Form 17583
— des Sandes 15519
klebrig 18197
klebriger Brei 10932
Klebsand S. 7183
Kleeblattform 20164
Kleinbahnschiene 14357
Kleinbessemerbirne 16726
Kleinbessemerei 4312
Kleinbessemerstahl 1041
kleine abgerollte Erzstücke in Ton eingebettet 14062
— Anthrazitart 4827
— Einsatzmenge S. 3326
— Luppe 13271
— Schiene 10787
kleiner Grubenwagen 2526
— Hilfsschacht 10098
kleines Flöz 15727/a
— Schussloch 13657
Kleineisen 16733
Kleineisenzeug 16732, S. 16733
kleinförmiger Intrusivkörper S. 17056
Kleingefüge 7091
Kleinintrusion 11784
Kleinit 10387
Kleinkuppelofen 16729
kleinlückiges Eisen S.3762, 3763
kleinspiegeliges Weisseisen 20029
kleinstückiger Anthrazit 7356
Kleinwasserraumkessel 1994
kleinzackig 12401

Klemme 3619
— für Elemente 18427
klemmen 3616
Klemmschlüssel 18714
Klemmplatte 3624, 3628
Klemmring S. 5954
Klemmschraube 15916
Klemmung 7743
Klemmvorrichtung 3794
— für Verschiebebahnen 3795
Klempner 18657
Klempnerarbeit S. 16072
Kliff 3725
Klinke 5592, 10561
Klinken 11081
— für das Festhalten der Wagen auf dem Gestell 3092
Klinkenfanggabel 2055
Klinochlor 3731
Klinodiskordanz 3730, 5582
Klinograph 3734,
Klinohumit 3735
Klinoklas 683, 3732, 10388
Klinostatit 3733
Klinopinakoid 3737
Klinoprisma 3738
Klinozoisit 3739
Klochmannit 10389
Klopfbrennstoff 10397
klopfen 10393
Klöppeldraht 20149
Klotz 15614
Kluft S. 14727
Kluftlette S. 8372, S. 14117
Kluftton S. 8372
Kluftwasser 4628
Klumpen 3557, 16700, 16700
— bilden 1146
klumpig S. 3748, 3789
Kluppe S. 17617
Knabbelkoks S. 4768, S. 12429
Knallgas 12815
Knallgasgebläse 12814
Knallgold 7813/a
Knallquecksilber 7813
Knappe 10464
Knappersprengung 1802

Knauer 2594
Knebelit 10391
kneten 10390, 11816, 14116
Kneten 11828
Kneter 11825
Knick 5597
Knickbeanspruchung 2511, 4640
Knicklast 2510/a
Knickversuch 2512
Kniehebel 10414, 18706
Kniehebelpresse 18707
Kniehebelverschluss 10415
Kniestück S. 6254
knitterig 4758
Knochenbrekzie 2026
Knochenbruch s. Bruch
Knochenkohle 2027
Knötchen 12336
Knötchengraphit 12333
knötchenförmig 12331
Knoten 10413
Knotenblech 8679
Knotengraphit S. 12333
Knüppel 1581
Knüppeleisen 1582
Knüppelschere 1584
Knüppelstahl 1586
Knüppelwalzwerk 1583
Knutenschiefer S. 17167
Kobalt 3885
Kobaltblüte 3885/a, S. 6560
Kobalt-Chromstahl 3886
Kobaltflasche 3889
Kobaltglanz S. 3887, 3892
Kobaltglas 3888
kobalthaltig 3891/a
Kobaltkies 3890/a
Kobaltmanganerz S. 850
Kobaltnitrat 12306
Kobaltomenit 3893
Kobaltoxydul 3890
Kobaltschwärze 850
Kobaltspat S. 17052
Kobaltstahl 3891
Kobellit 10418
Koch-Eruptionsperiode 1954
kochendes Wasser 2001
Kochit 10419
Kochperiode S. 2000

Kochpuddeln S. 16550
Kochsalz S. 8720
Kochzeit 2000
Koechlinit 10420
Koeffizient der Transformation durch Kracken 4583
Koenenit 10421
Koepe-treibscheibe 5967
Kofferkessel 19621
Kohäsionsmessapparat 3919
Kohle 2040
— bester Qualität 1563
— bester Sorte 7196
— hauen S. 2298
— klassieren (die) 3642
— unterschrämen 2297
— zur Dampferzeugung S. 1956
kohlehaltige Fazies 3863
Kohlen — 3806
— von unten zuführen 19249
Kohlenaufbereitung 3816, 3817
Kohlenförderband 1474
Kohlenbein 9051, 17228
Kohlenbergmann 3840, 8185
Kohlenbergwerk S. 3858
Kohlenbohrer 2827
Kohlenbrechen 3830
Kohlenbrecher 3808
— zur Entnahme von Mustern 3809
Kohlenbunker S. 2580, 3801, 3804
Kohlendioxyd 2832
Kohleneisenstein S. 1643, 1668
Kohlenelektrode 2833
Kohlenfeuerung 3823, 3825
Kohlenfeuerungskessel 1959
Kohlenflöze S. 3838
Kohlenförderung 3815
Kohlenformation S. 2858
Kohlenführende Schicht 3844
Kohlenganggestein 3826
Kohlengebiet 3814
Kohlengebirge 3838
Kohlengestübbe 2265
Kohlengewinnung 3828
Kohlengriess S. 8436

Kohlengrösse 16443
Kohlengrus S. 2835, 4996,
    S. 16507, S. 16727
Kohlenhalter 2836
Kohlenhauer 3813, 3827
Kohlenhaufen 3817
— zur Verkokung S. 3620
Kohlenhund 3852
Kohlenkalk 2860
Kohlenkalkstein S. 2860
Kohlenkeil 3857, 2214,
    2358, 2390, 2835, S.
    4827, 7103, 12288, 16727
Kohlenkörner 8436
Kohlenlader 3798, 3822
Kohlenlager 3800, 3821, S.
    3845
Kohlenmühle S. 3809
Kohlenoxyd 2838
Kohlenoxydentwicklung
    7609
Kohlenoxydgehalt 2839
Kohlenraum 3834, 3835
Kohlensack 4936/a
Kohlensäge 2841
Kohlensandstein 3831, 11717
    11717
Kohlensäure S. 2832, 2856
Kohlensäurebestimmer 705
kohlensäurehaltig S. 4995
kohlensäurehaltiges Eisen-
    erz 9988
Kohlensäurehärtung 2857
kohlensaurer Baryt S. 2849
kohlensaures Ammoniak S.
    2848
— Eisen S. 16994
— Kali 2853
— Magnesium 2852
— Natron 2854
Kohlenschaufel 3846
Kohlenschicht 15747
Kohlenschiefer S. 1645, 1666
    1666, S. 2028, 4994,
    14444
Kohlenschlacke 3727
Kohlenschlamm 3856
Kohlenschlechte 6748
Kohlenschwelung 2868
Kohlenspat 649
Kohlensprengen 3802

Kohlensprengen ohne Unter-
    schrämen 16165
Kohlenstampfmaschine S.
    3808, 3847
Kohlenstaub 2252, 3818,
    7649, S. 13770, 14147
— einpudern (mit) 6736
Kohlenstaubfeuerung 3819,
    7842
Kohlenstaubkessel 1966
Kohlenstifte S. 10510
Kohlenstoff 2824
Kohlenstoffäquivalent 2834
kohlenstoffarmer Stahl 17498
Kohlenstoffart 19473
Kohlenstoffausscheidung
    15871
Kohlenstoffbestimmung
    5258
Kohlenstoffgehalt 2829
Kohlenstoffgehaltverhältnis
    2840
Kohlenstoff-Mangan-Stahl
    2837
Kohlenstoffprüfer 2830
Kohlenstoffstahl 2842,
    17707
Kohlenstoffverbrauch 4239
Kohlenstoffwerkzeugstahl
    S. 19230.
Kohlenstoffziegel 2828
Kohlenstoss 3853
Kohlensturzbahn 3807
Kohlenträger 3833
Kohlenverbrauch 4240
Kohlenverbrennung 3805
Kohlenwäsche 3855
Kohlenwasserstoffe 9547
Kohlenzeche S. 3839
Kohlenzufuhr 3832
Kohlenzufuhr durch Förder-
    schnecke 18026
Kohlenzwischenlage 3845
Kohlung 2879
— durch festen Kohlenstoff
    2880
Kohlungsgrad 5131
Kohlungsstoff 2881, 2886/a
Kohlungszone 2882
Kohlenpfeiler 17360, 17655
Kohlenpulver 3936

Kokardenstruktur 15185
Kokeit 3949
Kokille S. 3007, 3433, 5358,
    9984, 11551
— s. Schreckplatte
Kokillen gegossen (in) 3426
Kokillenbauer S. 11991
Kokilleneinlage 9968
Kokillenform S. 3433
kokillenförmig 16114
Kokillenguss 3056, 3434,
    S. 3443
Kokillenriss 7065
Kokillenversatz S. 11801
Kokingstapelofen 1330
Kokkolith 3896
Koks 3927
— ohne Erz S. 3323
Koksabfall 14640
Koksausbringen 3948
Koksausdrückmaschine
    3943, 14392
Koksblech 3945
Koksbrecher 3931
Koksbrechring 3934
Kokseisen 3939
Kokserzeugung 13997
Koksfilter 3944
Koksfeuerung S. 3955
Koksgabel 3937
Koksgicht 428
Koksgries S. 16728
Koksgrus S. 2835
Kokshochofen 3930
Kokskammer S. 3952
Koksklassierung S. 15693
Koksklein 3935, 16728
Kokskohle 3953
Kokskorb 3928
Kokskuchen 3933
Kokslage S. 3929
Kokslagerplatz 3947
Koksofen 3938
— für Gewinnung der
    Nebenerzeugnisse 3942
Koksofengas 3941
Koksofengruppe 1350
Koksofentür 5631
Koksprobe 3955/a
Kokspulver 16737
Kokssatz 1415

Koksschicht 3929
Koksstaub S. 2252
Kolben 13389, S. 18086, 18088
Kolbenbolzen 13391
Kolbenflügel 13395
Kolbengiessmaschine 9405
Kolbenhub 13577
Kolbenlötung 16867
Kolbenpumpe 14494
Kolbenring 13392
Kolbenspritzgussmaschine 13580
Kolbenstange 13579
Kolbensteuerung 13394
Kolbenträger 7314
Kolbenventil 18863
Kolbenverdichter 18870
Kolbenverdrängung 13576
Kolbenversuch 18093
Kolbenvorlauf 18094
Kolbenwirkung 18091
kollektive Schwimnaufbereitung 2549
Kollergang 4778, 15503
— mit feststehender Schüssel S. 7237
— mit feststehendem Teller 7237
— mit umlaufendem Teller 15230
Kollern 11707
kolloidaler Ton 4028
Kollyrit 4029
Kolonne 7951
Kolonnendruck S. 2952
Kolophonit 4030
Kolophonium 14762, 15188
Kolorimeter 3549
Kolorimetrie 4034
Kombination von Steinmeissel u. Räumer 17602
kombinierte Rohrtour 4061
kombinierter Keilfänger 4060
— Wasser Flammrohr-Kessel 4066
kombiniertes Gestänge 18289
— Modell 4055
kompakter Koks 4099
Kompassmetall 2626

Kompensationsbehälter 18075
Kompensationssammler 18074
kompletter Dichtungsträger 12832
komplettes Modell 1203/a
Komplexstahl 4118
Komponente 4120
Kompressibilität 4151
Kompression 4153
Kompressionsverwerfung 18598
komprimierter Stahl S. 4150
Kondensatfeld 4183
Kondensation S. 4181
Kondensationsröhre 4182
Kondensatorrohr 4187
konditionieren 4188
Konfetti 4202
Konglomerat S. 3649, 8317
Kongopapier 4207
kongruente Schmelzung 4207/a
Kongsbergit 10424
Koninckit 10425
Königsstange 10365
Königswasser 726
Königswelle 19530
konisch 18285, 18290, 1572/a
Konizität 18282
Konjunktivbruch S. 18598
konkordante Falte 4203
— Lagerung 15793
konkretionär 4179
Konsolkran 2242
Konsolträger 2789
Konstruktionsblech 17890
Konstruktionsstahl S. 17892
Konstruktionsteil 17888
Kontakt-Explosion S. 13188
Kontaktgang 4247
Kontakthof 3445
Kontaktlagerstätte 4247
Kontaktmetamorphose 18486
Kontaktmineral 4248
Kontaktplattierung 4248/a
Kontaktstange für Strassenbahnwagen 19091
Kontinentalböschung 4259

kontinentale Fazies 4256
Kontinentalplattform 4258
Kontinentaltafel 4257
kontinuierlich arbeitender Kollergang 4269
kontinuierliche Kaltwalzstrasse 4262/a
— Querschweissung 18844
— Sandaufbereitung 4274
— Stabeisenstrasse 12362
kontinuierlicher Übergang 4277
kontinuierliches Drahtwalzwerk 4271
— Walzwerk 4272
— Walzwerk mit vier Tandem-Walzgerüsten 7681
Kontraktionsspalte 10205
Kontrolle S. 3361, 3373, 9846
Kontrollgerät für die Schachtströmung 12833
Kontrollmarke 3362
Kontrollstab 8116
Kontrollsystem 10140
Konturformkasten 17007
Konvektionsofen 9398
konventionelle Dauerschwingfestigkeit 6834
— Kriechgrenze 4294
Konventionsstrom 4293
Konverter 4298
Konverterauskleidung 4301
Konverterhals 4299
Konverteröffnung 4302
Konverterschnauze 4303
Konverterstahl 4308
Konzentrat S. 7204, 8933
Konzentrations-Herabsetzung 5193
konzentrierte Säure 4162
Konzession 4171, 10726
Konzessionsbeschränkung 14787
Kopf 8904
Kopfabgas 2946
Kopfabschreckung 6453/a
Kopfbolzen S. 2804
Kopfdampf 1692
Kopfende 6448

Kopfhaltestück 18741
kopfloser Niet 8938
— Stift 12164
Kopfplatte 4692, 18740
Kopfrohrverschraubungen
    2945
Kopfschraube 2804
Kopfschussbohrloch 8927
Kopfseite s. Frontseite
Kopfstück 17838
Kopfwipper 10340
Kopierdrehbank S. 4377
kopieren 13956
Koppit 10426
Koprolith 4376
koralligene Fazies 4378
Korb 1314
Korbflasche 8250
Korbmodell 11005
Kordierit S. 9943
Kordit 4379
Kordylit 4381
Koreit S. 206
Kork 4467
Korkbohrer 4468
Korkmesser 4469
Korkplatte 4471, 4474
Korkpresse 4472
Korkzange 4470
Korn 8396, 13004
kornblau 4482
Kornelit 10427
körnen 8435
Körnermetall 16206
Körnerspitze mit Kugellager
    1151
Kornerupin 10428
Kornfraktion 16443/a
Korngrenze 8397
Korngrenzenbruch 9882
Korngrösse 8401, S. 16443
Korngrössenanalyse 15687
Korngrössenverteilung 8388,
    15517/a
Korngrössenzahl 8402
körnig 105, 8443
— kristallinischer Gips
    S. 341
— s. gekörnt
körniger Bruch 8432
— Kalkstein 8434

körniger Perlit 17072
körniges Eisen 8433
— Gestein plutonisches
    8405
— Gold 16207
— Kupferoxyd 8437
Kornpuddeln 14108
Kornseigerung S. 11653
Kornstruktur 8403
Körnung 8440, S. 16443
Kornverfeinerung 8399
Kornvergütung 8400
Kornwachstum 8398
Kornwalze 8400/a
Körper 1936
korrespondierende Lösungen
    S. 10061
korrodieren 15644
korrodierter Kristall 2467,
    4488
Korrosion 4491
— durch Spülung 12086
— durch Untergrundeinbau
    19254
korrosionsbeständig 17296
Korrosionsbeständigkeit
    14771
Korrosionsfortschritt 9760/a
Korrosionsschutz 14043
Korsettfederstahl 17470
Korund 4507
Korundophilit 4506
Korzitivkraft 3901/a
Kosten der Treibkraft 4514
Kostenanschlag 6569
Kottigit 10429
kovalente Bindung 9299/a
Krablit 10430
Krackbenzin 4585
Kracking 4588
Krackprozess 4589
Kräftepaar 4547
Kraftlinie 10834
Kraftöl S. 13785
Kraftstation S. 13795
Kraftstoffzufuhr 13951
Kraftübertragung 13798
Kraftverbrauch 13774
Kraftverteilung 13776
Kraftwagen S. 11020
Kraftwerk 13795

Kragen 4016
Kramerit 10431
Krampe S. 3619, 14363,
    17372
Krampen und Bauklammern
    3744
Kranarm S. 8215
Kranausleger 2042, S. 8215,
Kranbahn 7964,
Kranbalken 4595, 8215
Kranbrücke 8240
Kranhaken 4598
Krankatze S. 4596
Kranlaufkatze 4596
Kranmagnet 4600
Kranmann 4604
Kranpfanne 4599
Kranpressluftstampfer
    4601
Krantzit 10432
Kranwagen 13207
Kranz 14919
— der Diamant-Bohr-
    maschine 5323
Kranz-Pfropfen 2286
Kranzmodell 14917
Kranzrohr S. 13388
Kraterriss 4611
Kratzband S. 15669, 15675
Kratzbandförderer 7375,
    15669
Kratzblech 7374
Krätze 6007, 9999, S. 15728,
    S. 16519
kratzen S. 15642
Kratzerketteförderer S.
    15670
Kratzenklassifikator 5732
Kratzenzug 19534
Krätzer 14384, 15667, 15684,
    S. 16461, S.16962
Kratzerförderer 14197
Kratzerkettenförderer S.
    15669
Kratzerscheibe 15671
Kratzertransporter S.
    14197
Krätzmetall S. 6007
Kraurit S. 6079, 10433
Krauselbruch 18606/a
Krausit 10434

Kräuseln 12738/a
Krauskopf S. 15178
Krebsblech S. 15410
Krebs-Kesselträger S. 15410
Kreide 4626
Kreideformation S. 4626
Kreideprobe 3265/a
Kreisbahn 4264
Kreisbogen 4872
Kreiselbrecher 8237, 8695
Kreiselwipper 14843, 15222
Kreisform 3600
kreisförmiger Balken 3587
Kreislaufgas 14527
Kreislaufmaterial S.- 14813,
    15377
Kreislaufstoffe 14813
Kreismesser 3594
Kreisprozessofen 3769
kreisrunder Laufsteg
    15799/a
Kreissäge 3597
Kremersit 10435
Krennerit 10436
Kreosotöl 5035
Kreuz 4664
Kreuzeisen 4695, 4705
Kreuzgang S. 4675, 4709
kreuzgeschichtet 4866
kreuzgeschlagenes Drahtseil
    S. 14652
Kreuzmeissel 4661, 4679
Kreuzpaket 4700/a
Kreuzschichtung 4672, 4698,
    4707, 4867, 5867
Kreuzschneide 4673, 15177
Kreuzstück 4663, 13333
Kreuztrockenkessel 6025
Kreuzung 4718
Kreuzweiche S. 5333
Kriechen 4615
Kriechfestigkeit 4619
Kriechgalvanometer 7792
Kriechgeschwindigkeit
    4616/a
Kriechgrenze 4616
krispelig 1785
Kristall 4791, 14266
Kristallumineszenz 4816
Kristallbegrenzung 4793

Kristallfläche 6739
Kristallform 4803, 8697
Kristallgitter 4796
Kristallhabitus 4795
Kristallierschale 4809
Kristallierungsgefäss 4807
kristallines Grundgebirge
    4792
kristallinisch 4798
kristallinische Struktur
    4804
kristallinischer Bruch 4800
— Sandstein 4641
kristallinisches Eisen S.
    4808
— Eisenerz 4802
— Gefüge S. 4804
Kristallinität 4805
Kristallisationskeim S.
    12419
Kristallisationswasser S.
    19792
kristallisiertes Eisen 4808
kristallisieren 4812
Kristallisierung 4810
Kristallit 4806, 4811
Kristalloblastese 4813
kristalloblastisch 4814
kristalloblastische Struktur
    4815
Kristallwachstum 4794
Kristallwasser 19792
kritische Erstarrungsge-
    schwindigkeit 4648
— Härtungsgeschwindig-
    keit 4649
— Temperatur 4650
kritischer Druck 4646
— Fluss 4643
Kröhnkit 10437
Krokoit 14543
Krokydolith 18614
Kronenbloch S. 4729
Kronenbohrer 588, 4728
Kronenöffnung 19818
Kronenschneide 16442
Kröpfungsgeviert 1384
Krötenstein 18699
Krücke 7176
Krückelfürer S. 5915

Krümelstruktur 4756
krumm 1527, 4656
krumme Zunge 4885
krümmen 4873
Krümmer 6254
Krümmerkern 4878
krummes Bohrloch 4657
Krümmling 1501
Krümmung S. 2198, S.4875
Kruste 4782
Krustenbildung 9728
Kryolith 4784
Kryolithionit 4785
Kryptogamen 4788
kryptoklastisch 4786
kryptokristallin 4787
Kryptolith 4789
Kryptoperthit 4790
Krypton 10438
Kübel 1359, 2497, 10334,
    S. 18971
— von Schleppschaufel-
    bagger 5734
Kübelfüller 10915
Kuchen 2691
Kügel 16192,
    S. 17057
Kugelbildung 17070
Kügelchen 17064
Kügelchenbildung 18104/a
Kugeldruck 8874
Kugeldruckprobe 1155, S.
    8874
Kugeldruckversuch 1167
Kugelhärteprüfer 1156
Kugelform 1160, 2567
kugelförmig 17065
kugelförmiger Kopf 1162
Kugelgelenk 1157
Kugelgraphit 17066
Kugelhahnstechheber 19902
kugelige Absonderung 1165,
    - 4834, S. 17069
— Struktur 8304
kugeliger Bau S. 8304
Kugellager 1150
Kugellagerrohr 18986
Kugellagerstahl 1152
Kugelmühle 1104, 1158,
    8301. 13033

Kugelpolieren 1152/a
Kugelporosität 8303
Kugelröhre 2546
Kugelschale 17061
Kugel-und Ringverfahren
   1149
Kugelventil 8302
Kugelzone S. 20365
Kuhhaar 4574
Kühlbad 14291
Kühlbett 9391/a
Kühlblech 4338
Kühlfeder S. 4338
Kühlkammer 4333
Kühlnagel 3435
Kühlofen S. 615
Kühlschlange 4186, S.
   14483
Kühlteich 4341
Kühlturm 4344
Kühlung 4331
Kühlvorrichtung 4336
Kühlwasser 4346
Kukkersit 10439
Kulait 10440
Kullait 10441
Kulm 4826
Kümpelblech 7272
Kundengiesserei 10188
Kunstbronze 829/a, 17401
Kunstharzpressform 836
Kunstkohle 832
künstliche Alterung 219,
   831
— Kühlung 833
künstlicher Magnetit 835
— Zug 7554
Kunzit 10442
Kupellenplatte 2489
Kupelofen S. 4844
Kupfer 4350, 4374
— von hoher Leitfähigkeit
   9141
Kupferader 19487
Kupferaluminium S. 450
Kupferberyllium S. 1545
Kupferblau S. 1036
Kupferblech 16051
Kupferchlorid S. 4853, 4858
Kupferdraht 4368, 4373
Kupferdrahtnetz 4369

Kupferdrahtnetzrolle 15082
Kupferdrehspan 4365
kupferführend 4352
Kupfergiesserei 2278
Kupferglanz 3254, S. 19571
Kupferlasur 1036, S. 1906
kupferhaltiges Eisenerz
   4854
— Wasser 20322
Kupferindig S. 9739
Kupferkessel 4354
Kupferkies 3261, 4363,
   14214, 20291
Kupferlasur S. 3413
Kupferläuterung s. Kupfer-
   raffination
kupferlegierter Stahl S. 4353
Kupferlegierung 4351
Kupferlot 8841
Kupfermanganerz 10514
Kupfer-Nickel 4857
Kupferniederschlag 4364
Kupferoxyd 12797
Kupferplatte 4361, 4372
Kupferrafination s. Kupfer-
   läuterung
Kupferrohstein 14457
Kupferstecherei 3256
Kupferschmied 4375
Kupfersmaragd S. 915
Kupferstahl 4353
Kupferstahldraht 4355
Kupferstechkunst S. 3256
Kupferstein 1908, 4358
Kupfersulfat S. 17970
Kupferuranglimmer S. 18767
Kupfervitriol S. 3252, 17970
Kupolofen 3002
Kupolofenbein 10667
Kupolofenguss 4845
Kupolofenkamin 4847
Kupolofensatz 4848
Kupolofenschacht 4842
Kupolofen-Schmelzer 4849
Kupolofenwärter 4846
Kuppe S. 5620
Kuppel 2035
Kuppelflanke 5618
Kuppellation 1146/a
Kuppellieren 4839
kuppeln 4545

Kuppelofen S. 3002, 4844
— mit viereckigem Schacht
   4851
Kuppelofenschmelzen 11469
Kuppelstange 10191
Kuppelvorrichtung 10190
Kupplung ausrücken (die)
   5504
— einrücken (die) 4215
Kupplungen 4551
Kupplungsdraht 7771
Kupplungsmuffe 4549
Kupplungsspindel 4550
Kurbel 4609, 4658
Kurbelhammer 8739
Kurbelschutzhaube 4607
Kurbelstange 4220
Kurbeltrieb 4606
Kurbelwelle 4610
Kurbelzapfen 4608
Kurve 4875, 14810
Kurvenkipper 19624
Kurvenstück 8655
kurzer Abbaustoss 16189
— Bohrer 16174
— Bremsberg 5415
— Einbruch 12464
— Schnitt 3756
kurzflammige Kohle 17421
Kurzgewinde-Schaftfräser
   18855
kurzsäuliges Mineral 16177
Küstengebiet 10897
Künelage 3903
Küvelage überholen 14487
Kylit 10445
Kyschtymit 10446

L

Laborant 18460
Laboratoriumsbetrieb 10451
Laboratoriumstisch 10450
Laboratoriumsvorstand 3417
Labradit 10452
Labrador(it) 10454
Labradorfeldspat S. 10454
Labradorstein S. 10454
Lachter 6828

Lack 10461
Lackbenzin 11755
Lackdraht 6437
lackieren 10460
Lackieren S. 10121, 10125
lackiert S. 10122
Lackmuspapier 10892
Lackmustinktur 10893
Lackpapierdraht 12905
Lacroixit 10463
Lade für die Sandformerei S. 2208
Ladebaum in abgesetzen Schüssen 19083
Lademaschine 12066, 15035
Lademulde S. 3335
Laden S. 7310
laden 10465
Ladeplatz 17273
Ladeprofil S. 10917
Lader 13787, 14206
Ladermulde S. 7660
Laderschablone 10917
Ladestelle 13434
Ladestock 1404, 2569, 14401, 17537, 18232, 18235
Ladung (volle) 7795
Lage S. 4552, S. 10594, S. 12946, S. 17753, 19976
Lagentextur S. 1427, 14869
Lager S. 10594, S. 12133, 13296, S.17620
— mit Weissmetall ausgiessen 11536, 13741
Lagerausguss 10852
Lagerbüchse 1389
Lagerdruck 3775, 13917
Lagerförderungstechnik 14747
Lagerfutter 10853
Lagergang 1422, 9881, S. 9927, 16084, S. 16337, 16342
Lagerkran 17619
Lagerlänge 1394
Lagermetall 663, 1396
lagern 10298
Lagern 17689
Lagerplatz 17620
Lagerschale 1387

Lagerschalen 2279
Lagerschalenausguss S. 10853
Lagersprung 1432
Lagerstätte 1413, S. 1938, S. 5147, 5408
— eines Minerals 11751
Lagerstätten von Hohlraumausfüllung 3125
Lagerstättendruck S. 14749
Lagertank S. 17690
Lagerung S. 1430, 1433, 12133
Lagerungsbruch S. 13909
Lagerungstörung S.5525
Lagerweissmetall 1038
lagunäre Fazies 6570
Lagune 10491
Lahar S. 3983
Lakamit 10492
Lakkolith 7411, 10455
lakkolitisch 10456
lamellar S. 7529, 10497
Lamelle 7249, 10496
Lamellengraphit 7250
lamelliert 7528/a, 10505
laminarer Fluss 10501
Lampenteller 10513
Lamprophyr 10511
Lanarkit 10512
Lancashire-Frischherd 18107, 18110
Lancashirekessel 5661, 10515
Land 10518
Landfracht 12763
Landkessel 10522
langarmig 10968
Langbanit 10532
Langbeinit 10533
Länge von zwei Bohrstangen 5689
Längenriss 15080/a
langer Spitzstampfer 10973
langflammige Kohle 2786
Langfront 10988
Langfrontbau 10978, 10994
langgereckter 9713/a
Langgewinde 10977
Langhubpumpe 10976
Langit 10534

Langkesselplatte S.16110
Langlochbrenner 10974
Langporigeporosität 6389
langsam 16707
langsames Abkühlen S. 18391 18391
langsames Eintauchen 16694
Längsband 18608
Längsbewehrung 10982
Längsdrehstahl 19146
— zum Schruppen S. 9032
Längsfalte 13311
Längsfalz 10980
Längsfurche 10981
Längsprobenahme 10984
Längsrichtung bohren (in der) 5877
Längsrippe 10983
Längsriss 10979, 17123
Längsschwelle 10985
Längsspalte 1045, 17822
Längsspalten 3377
Längstal 10986
langstrahliges Rutil 11217
Längsverwerfung 17821
Längswalzen 10677
Lansfordit 10535
Lanthan 10537
Lanthanit 10536
Lanzette 8947
Lapislazuli 1035, 10544
läppen S. 10538
Larderellit 10545
Larnit 10552
Larsenit 10556
Lasche 7210, 17115/a
Laschenbolzen 7211
Laschenkaliber 7212
Laschenverbindung 10210
Lastdruck 720
Lasteisen S. 19914
Lastwagenanhänger 18948
Lasurit S. 10544, 10602
Lasurstein S. 10544, 10544/a 10544/a
laterale horizontale Trennung 12380, 12463
Laterit 10572
Lateritbildung 10574
lateritisch 10573
Latit 10580

Latte 10575
Laubanit 10583
Laubholzkohle 8520
Lauf S. 15349, 15363, 15365
Laufbühne 17294
laufende Produktion 7448
Läufer 15367
Laufkatze 4578
Laufkran 7672, 7965, 12758
Laufrolle S. 15104
Laufsteg 3102
Laufteufel 8323
Laugeanlage 10901
Laugebottich 10903
Laugenit 10584
Laugensprödigkeit 3113
Laugerückstand 10902
Laumontit 2811, 10585, S. 10681
Laurentium 10588
Läutern S. 4839
— der Metalle 14615
Läuterung 3695
— des Silbers S. 16358
Läuterungskessel 14608
Lava 10589
Lavadom 9930
Lavenit 10590
Lawrencit 10591
Lawsonit 10592
Lasurit 10560
Lazulit 10601
Leadhillit 10629
Leberkies 9092
Lech 11381
Lechatelierit 10655
Lechen der Form 10638
Lecontit 10656
Lectotypus 10657
Ledeburit 10658
Lederhohlkehle 10651, 10652
Lederkohle 10649
lederner Spitzbalg 10648
Lederring 10654
Lederringdichtung 10653
Lederstulp 10650
Ledmorit 10660
leere Koksgicht 3323
leergehen 15347
Leergewicht 18223

leerpumpen 14155
Leerversuch 1685
Leeuwfonteinit 10661
legen S. 15902
legieren 395
legiert 403
legierter Baustahl 17883
— Edelstahl 404
— Stahl 401, S. 17021
legiertes Gusseisen 397
Legierung 396
Legierungselement S. 405
Legierungsguss unter Druck 5361
Legierungsverstärker 18800/a
Lehiit 10669
Lehm 10924, S. 12069, 16627
Lehmannsches Gebläse S. 2925
Lehmform 10928
Lehmguss 10926
Lehmkern 10927
Lehmkuchen herrichten 13857
lehmige Beimengung 10931
Lehmplatte 3664
Lehmpfropfen 18513
Lehmstein 10925
Lehnerit 10670
Lehrboden 8113
Lehre S. 7896, 8107, 8111, 18400
Lehrkessel 18816
Leichenwachs 151
leicht hantierbares Werkzeug 16785
— reduzierbares Erz 6181
— schmelzbares Erz 6180
leichtaschige Kohle 3843
Leichtdestillat 14462
leichte Arbeit 10688
— Fraktionen 10781
— Reduzierbarkeit 6183
— Rohrfackel 10790
Leichter 10792
leichter Abdrehstahl 10663
— Abdreh-und Anflachstahl 10791
leichtes Kübelbohrgerät

17220
leichtflüssig 7459
Leichtlegierung S. 10778
Leichtmetall 10784
Leichtnaphtha 10789
Leichtprodukte 18204
Leidleit 10671
Leierziehbank S. 5800
Leifit 10672
Leim 8316
Leinölfirnis 10859
L-Eis 10447
Leiste S. 10575, S. 15049
Leistenanschnitt 19880
Leistung in offenem Zyklus 12568
— steigern (die) 9721
— vermindern (die) 14560
Leistungsfähigkeit 13999
— des Kraftwerkes 2802
Leistungsmesser 12710
— des Förderseils 18721
Leistungsschild 14440
Leistungsverzeichnis 1580
Leitblech S. 8653
Leiter 4194, 10628
Leitergang 10468, 10935
Leitfähigkeitsbestimmung 5262
Leitfossil 8650, 9734
Leitgang 4195
Leithorizont 5007, 10327, 11331
Leitkolonne S. 4193
Leitrohr S. 10628
Leitrolle 5121/a
Leitschicht 10325
Leitschiene 8643
Leitspindeldrehbank 10578
Leitungslegevorrichtung 13353
Leitungsplan 11311
Leitungsrohr 10839
— für Erdgas 13342
— für Stadtgas 13345
— mit Losflanschverbindungen 13371
Leitwand S. 8653
Lengenbachit 10674
Lennilith 10678
Lentikulargang S. 1372, 19841

Leonhardit 10681
Leonit 10682
Leopardit 10683
lepidoblastische Struktur 10684
Lepidokrolit 10685
Lepidolith 10686, 10833/a
Lepidomelan 10687, S. 16286
Leptit 10689
Leptochlorit 10690
Leptoklase 10691
Leptynit 10692
Leseband S. 13214, 16927
Lessingit 10693
Lestiwarit 10694
Letten 3653
— bekleiden (mit) 5589
Lettenbesteg S. 3657, S. 3662, S. 14117, 15835
Lettenbohrer 3670
Lettenformen 10929
Lettennudel S. 17539
Lettsomit 10696
Leuchtdichte 2404
Leuchtgas 3826/a, 9636
Leuchtgassauerstofflampe 8035
Leucit 10698
Leukaugit 10697
Leukochalcit 10701
leukokrat 10702
Leukophönicit 10703
Leukopyrit 10704
Leukosphenit 10705, 10706
Leukoxen 10706
Leuzitit 10699
Leuzitporphyr 10700
Leverrierit 10719
Lewisit 10720
Lewistonit 10721
Lias S. 1653
liasisch 10724
Libethenit 10725
Lichtbogen 6255
Lichtbogenerhitzung 746
Lichbogenheizung S. 746
Lichtbogen-Kohle 749
Lichtbogenofen 745, 6256
Lichtbogenschweissmaschi-

ne 19952
Lichtbogenschweissung 752
Lichtbogen-und Widerstands-ofen 742
Lichtbogenwiderstandsofen 751
Lichtbündel 10779
lichtes Rotgültig S.815, S. 14055, 14550
Lichtfilter 10782
lichtgraues Roheisen 7083
Lichtmenge 14251
Lichtschacht 10786
Lichtstärke 2783
Liebenerit 10731
Liebigit 10732
Lieferungsbedingungen 4192
liegend formen 11966
— gegossen 2987
— giessen 2971
Liegende 7346, S. 7402, 7547, 11070, 11110, 16338
liegende Falte 14523
— Schmiedemaschine 9356
liegender Antrieb 9340
— Dampfkessel 9333, 9352
— Guss 3064, 9334
— Konverter S. 1241
— Ofen 9342
— Schenkel 11068
— Schenkel einer liegenden Falte 7405
— Winderhitzer 9331
Liegendes 1274
liegendes Gebläse 9332
Liegendgestein 1290
Liegerblech 7408
Lievrit 10733, S. 20295
Lignit 10802
lignitisch 10804
Ligroin 10805
Lillianit 10806
Limburgit 10809
limnisch 10827
Limonit S. 10828
Limonitwürfel 5283
Lindöit 10829
Lindströmit 10830
Liniengruppe 8626
Liniennetz 8533

linker Messerstahl 10664
linkes Seitenmesser S. 10664
Linksautogenschweissung 7563, 10665
Linksmesser S. 10664
Linksschweissung 7626
Linsenerz S. 12551
linsenförmige Lagerung 1067 10679
Linsengang 1372, 10680, 19841
Linsensenkniet 15281
Linsenstruktur 1371
Linsensystem 18180
Liparit 10864
Lipopalingenese 10865
Lippenpackung 10863
Liquiduslinie 10880
Lirokonit 10881
Liskeardit 10882
Litchfieldit 10883
Lithium 10885
lithogen 10887
lithographischer Stein 10888
Lithoklase 10886
Lithologie 10889
Lithophysa 10890
Lithosphäre 10891
litorale Fazies 10895
— Tätigkeit 16172
Litzenseil 7936
Livingstonit 10900
Lizensgebühren 15300
LNG 10905
Lobus 10936
Loch S. 7967, 9248
Locheisen 9278
Locheisenhohlraum 14178/a
lochen S. 14173
Löcher stanzen S. 14173, 14174
lockere Stelle 12444, 17389
lockeres Eisenerz S. 3663
— toniges Eisenerz 11001
löcherig 9303
Lochfeile 14892
Lochfrass 13428, 13429
Lochkaliber S. 14183
Lochlehre 9251
Lochplatte 12671

Lochprobe 5869
Lochstein 12407
Lochstempel 14176
Lochstempelstahl 9220,
    14178, 17472
Lochtaster 9842
Lochung 13085
Lochweite S. 16300
Loch zum Abstellen eines
    Bohrgestänges 12038
Lochzange S. 9278
Lockerung des Steinver-
    bandes 11012
Löffel 5449, 17151
Löffelbagger 5739, 5828,
    13792, 16213
Löffelbohrer 16096
Löffelhaken 10563
löffeln S. 1099
Löffelräumer S. 14384
Löffelseil S. 15501
Löffel-und Rohrgreifhaken
    1102
Lokalschweissbarkeit 10938
Lokomotivkessel 10948
Lokomotivradsatz 10953
Lokomotivrauchrohr 10949
Lokomotivstahl 10952
Löllingit 10966
Londinian 10967
Longulit 10987
Longwall-Schrämmaschine
    10990
Loparit 11015
Lorandit 11016
Loranskit 11017
Lorenzenit 11018
Lorettoit 11019
Losboden 11002, 14703
losbrechen 2301
Losbrechen des Erzes 2332
Lösche 3932
Löschfeuer 3305
Löschfeuerstahl 3306
Löschfrist 13094
Löschturm 14295
Losdrücken der Mündungs-
    bären 15677
lose Rolle 11009/a
— Schlüssel 18718
— Seilscheibe 9230

lose Trümmersedimente
    5521
— Verbindung durch Ein-
    stellung der Pumpen-
    ansaugung 5841
Lösen des Gesteins 20199
loser Führungsstift 12049
— Kern 8920
loses Gebirge 9467, 16496
Loseyit 11021
Losklopfen 14420
Losklopfer 14419
löslich 16896
lösliche Phosphorsäure
    16898
lösliches Schneidöl 16897
Löslichkeit 16899
Löslichkeitsbeeinflussung
    9770
Löslichkeitsbestimmung
    5261
Löslichkeitsfläche 18058
Löslichkeitskurve 4877
Löslichkeitsprodukt 13817a
Löslichkeitsverminderung
    5080
löslöten 19332
Loessboden 10962
Losscheibe 11009
Losschlageisen 14421
Losschlagplatte 14427
Losteil 11006, 14704, 18296
Lösung von Harz in Ter-
    pentin 16905
Lösungsbenzol 9173
Lösungsfähigkeit 16908
Lösungshohlraum 16901
Lösungsmischer 16903
Lösungsmittel 5546, 17189
— raffiniertes Öl (mit)
    16911
Lot S. 10604
Lotaufbringemittel 7499
lötbar S. 19928
Lötbrenner s. Brenner
Löteisen S. 16862
löten 16857, 16932
Löten 16860
Löter 10211
Lötflussmittel S. 7499
Lötfuge 18702

Lötkohle 16861
Lötkolben 16862
— mit Selbstbeheizung
    S. 15826
Lötlappen 20116
Lötmörtel 8711/a, 13571/a
Lötofen S. 16888
Lötpaste 12961/a
Lötrohr 1861, 1863, 1893
— mit Mundstück S. 12043.
Lötrohrfluss 16863
Lötrohrhartlöten 18768
Lötrohrlampe 1889
Lötrohrprobe 1888, 1891
Lötrohrprüfgeräte 1892
Lötstelle 1884, 16865
Lötung S. 16860
— s. Schweissung
Lötwasser 10350/a, 16889
Lötzinn S. 16841, 16864
Louderbackit 11042
Loxoklas 11077
LPG 11078
Lücke 7967
luckiger Guss 13673
luckiges Eisen 13674
— Floss S. 12604, 13677
Ludlamit 11082
Ludwigit 11083
Lujaurit 11086
Luft ansaugen (die) 17941
— stechen 19496
— trocknen (an der) 271
Luftabführung 19499
Luftabsauger 275, 17962
Luftabschluss 6646
Luftakkumulator 9512
Luftauslass 274
Luftbad 240
Luftbild 9639
Luftblase 18751
Luftbohne S. 12744
Luftbohren 271
Luftdämpfer 263
luftdicht 329, 15767
luftdichter winddichter
    Abschluss 335
Luftdichtigkeitsprobe 328a
Luftdruck 927
Luftdruckaufzug 13588
Luftdruckhammer 4136

Luftdruckmeissel 13582
Lufteinflussöffnung S. 292
Lufteinlass S. 292, 294
Lufteinlassöffnung S. 292
Lufteinströmklappe 293
Lufteinströmöffnung 292
Lufterhärtung 286
lufterleichterte Spülung 187
Luftfeuchtigkeit 9480
Luftfilter 254
Luftförderung 328
Luftgas 282
luftgekühlt 258, 6796
Luftgetrocknet 272
luftgetrocknete Kohle 267
Lufthammer 13591
Lufthammerrohr 19008, 19010
Lufthärter S. 284
Lufthärtung 252, 285, 12388
Lufthärtungsstahl 284
Luftherd 13599
Luftkern 4586/a, 13055
Luftkühlung 259
Luftleere 19424
Luftleeremesser 19435
luftleitend 195
Luftofen 280
Luftpfeife 20022
Luftpostrohr 19009
Luftpumpe 309
Luftpumpenglocke 310, 313/a
Luftpumpenkolben 312
Luftpumpenteller 311/a, 313
Luftpumpenzylinder 311
Luftpyrometer 315
Luftraum 326
Luftsack 302, S. 307, S. 12744
Luftsattel 188/a, 190, 320
Luftsauger 888
Luftschacht S. 306
Luftschlagbrett 19500
Luftschlauch 289/a
Luftschleuse 325
Luftschlitz S. 292
Luftsetzmaschine 295
Luftspiess 13931, 19506
Luftspindel 250

Luftstechen 19498
Luftstein 266
Luftstift S. 13055
Luftstrahl 241, 241/a
Lüftungsgerät 12145
Lüftungsverschluss 161
Luftventil 330
Luftverdünnung 14429
Luftverhärtung S. 252
Luftvorbereiter 4191
Luftvorwärmer 9400
Luftweg 308
Luftziegel 176
Luftzieher S. 17962
Luftzufuhr 171
Luftzuführungsöffnung S. 292
Luftzug 265
Lugarit 11085
Lumachell 11087
Lüneburgit 11092
Lunker 307, 7213, 13329, S. 13350, 13605, 16227
Lunkerbildung 13327
lunkerfreier Guss 3052
lunkern 16320
Lunkern 13383, 16224/a
Lunkerstelle 14580/a
Lunkerung 13381
Lunnit 11093
Luppe 1820, 10996, 11043/a, 11213, S. 13249
Luppe s. Bramme od. Block
Luppen S. 1170
— giessen (die) 13246
Luppeneisen 1105, 9981, 10998
Luppenfrischfeuer S. 1827
Luppenkupfer 13257
Luppenmachen 1170, 7620
Luppenmühle 15217
Luppenofen S. 1171
Luppenquetsche 1163, 4651/a, 17263
Luppenschmied 16133
Luppenstahl 1825
Luppenwalzwerk 1826, 15261, 15261
Lürmannsche 11094
— Stopfbüchse 11095
Luscladit 11096

Lusitanit 11097
Lussatit 11098
Lutecin 11100
Lutetian 11102
Lutetium 11101
Lutit 11103
Lutte 6809, 10811
Luxemburger Eisen 11004
Luxemburger Roheisen 11104, 11104
Luxullianit 11105
Lykopodium 11107
lytomorphisch 11111

M

Mäanderstreifen 11388
Mäanderverkürzung 16178
Macedonit 11114
Macgovernit 11115
machtige Ader 18500
mächtige Schichtung 9040
mächtiges Flöz 18500
Mächtigkeit 18507
Mächtigkeitskarten 10072
Mackensit 11141
Maconit 11144
Madeirit 11159
mafisches Mineral 11162
Mafit 11163
Mafrait 11164
Magazinabbau 16232
Magazinbau 11166, 16223, 16233
mager machen 5081
magere Kohle 10640
— Steinkohle 1768, 3757
magerer Sand 10644, 19851
— Ton 8508, 10639
Magerkohle 1677/a, S.1768, 8818, S. 10640, 12341, 12342
Magerkoks 10641
Magma 11167
magmatische Assimilation S. 18167, 11168
— Erzlagerstätten 11169
Magnalium 455

Magnesia 1631, 11170/a, 11181
Magnesiaglimmer S. 13155
Magnesiatongranat 11179
Magnesit S. 1633, 8234, 11174
Magnesitauskleidung 11176
Magnesitmasse 11177
Magnesitstein S. 11175
Magnesitziegel 11175
Magnesium 11178
Magnesiumband 11182
Magnesiumblech 16067
Magnesiumchlorid S. 3498
Magnesiumchromit 11171
Magnesiumferrit 11172
Magnesiumkarbonat S. 2852
Magnesiumlampe 11180
Magnesiumlegierung 19221
Magnesiumludwigit 11173
Magnet 11183
Magnetaufbereitung von Erzen S. 11189
Magneteisensand 11202,
Magneteisenstein 10923, S. 10959
magnetisch 11185
magnetische Anziehungs-kraft 11186
— Aufbereitung 11190
— Aufbereitung von Erzen 11189
— Durchlässigkeit 11198
— Kraftspannung 11210
— Stoffzufuhr 138
magnetischer Stahl S. 11184
— Verlust 11195
— Widerstand 11201
magnetisches Eisenerz S. 11193
— Feld 11192
— Schürfen 11204
— Streichen 11187
magnetisierbar 11208
magnetisierende Röstung 11209
Magnetisierung 11205
Magnetismus 11206
Magnetit 1657/a, 10959, 11207
Magnetkies S. 11194

Magnetnadel 11196
Magnetographie 11209/a
Magnetoplumbit 11211
Magnetopyrit 11194
magnetomotorische Spannung S. 11210
Magnetpulveruntersuchung 11197
Magnetscheider 11203
Magnetspule den Dauerge-brauch 13105
Magnetspule für einmaligen Gebrauch 18592
Magnetstahl 11184
Magnettrommel 11191
Magnoferrit 11214
Mahlbahn 8561
mahlen (fein) 4090, 8539, 11682
Mahlfeinheit 7099
Mahlgut 8574
Mahlkörper 4772
Mahlpulver 4090/a, 5518/a
Makkaronirohr 11112
Makkaronirohrbatterie 11113
Makroaufnahme S. 11149
Makrobild 11149
Makrodom 11148
Makrogefüge 11157
Makrographie 11151
makrographische Ätzung 11145
— Untersuchung 11150
makroklastisch 11146
makrokristallin 11147
makromeritische Struktur 11159
Makropinakoid 11153
Makroseigerung 11156
makroskopische Beobach-tung 11159
— Untersuchung S. 11155
Makroprisma 11154
Makrostruktur S. 11157
Malachit 8510, 11237
Malakkazinn 17740
Malakolith 11238, S. 15438
Malakon 11239
Malchit 11240
Maldonit 11241
Malignit 11245

Malladrit 11246
Mallardit 11247
Mammutpumpe 7980
Manandonit 11260
Mandel 544/a, S. 8164
Mandeleisen 414
Mandelstein 543, 11261
Mandelsteintextur 544
Mangan 11266
Manganbronze 11268
Manganeisen 6944, 11279
manganführend 11280
Manganglanz S. 340
Mangangusseisen 11272
manganhaltig 11282, 11290
manganhaltiges Eisenerz 11283
— Gusseisen 11269
— Zinkerz 11284
Manganhartstahl 11277
Manganindraht 11285
Manganit S. 59, 11286
Mangankupfer 4856, 11270
Manganocalcit 11287
Manganosit 11289
Manganoxyd 11281
Manganoxydul 11291
Manganoxyduloxyd 12796
Manganophyllit 11288
Mangan-Siliziumstahl S. 11274
Manganspat 11274
Manganspektrum 11275
Manganspiegel 11276
Manganstahl S. 11277
Manganstahlherzstück 11278
Mangansuperoxyd 11271
mangelhaft 5108
mangelhafte Röstung 5111
Mangeln 15112
Mangerit 11292
Mannit 11296
Mannloch S. 11258
Mannschaftsunterstand 5596
Manometer 8108, S. 11297
manometrischer Wirkungs-grad 11298
Mantel S. 2930, 10100, 11299/a, S. 16485
Mantelblech 10103, S. 16110
Manteleisen 11304

Mantelguss 10104
Mantelkern 10101
Mantelplatte 11302
Mantelrohr S. 12696
Mantelstärke 18510
Margarit S. 4505, 11314
Margarosanit 11315
Marge 17188/a
Marialith 11318
Marienglas S. 4801, S. 12139
Marignacit 11319
marine Fazies 11323
Mariposit 11326
Mariupolit 11327
Markasit 11313, 20034
Marke 16924
Markenbezeichnung 5234
Markfieldit 11332
Markscheiden 10562, 10565
Marlösit 11336
Marmatit 11339
Marmolith 11340
Marmor S. 8434
Marschenton 11320
Marscoit 11342
Marshit 11343
Martensit S. 8869, 11346
Martensitabschreckung 11341
Martensithärtung 11347
martensitisches Gusseisen 11348
Martin-Gebläse S. 11349
Martinit 11350
Martinroheisen 12576
Martinstahl 8965, 12580
Martinstahlhütte 12581
Martinwerk 12575, 12577
Martit 11351
Masanit 11352
Mascagnin 11353
Masche 11516
Maschensieb 11518, 11561
Maschenstruktur 11519, 12248
Maschine formen (auf der) 11129
— für Riemenbetrieb 1476
— für Seilbetrieb 15161
— mit Abhebewagen S.

12017
Maschine zur Rollenher-stellung durch Zentri-fugierung 15075
maschinelle Aufbereitung 11405
— Fertigbearbeitung 11123
— Gewinnung 11132, 11139, 11420
maschinelles Bohren 11130
Maschinenarbeit 11137
Maschinenbaustahl 6476
Maschinendraht 2012
Maschinendrehbank 6469
Maschinenformerei 11133
maschinengegossen 11119
Maschinenguss 6467, S. 6474, 11120, 11138
Maschinenhaus 6468
Maschinenpuddeln 11134
Maschinenrahmen 897
Maschinenreibahle mit Morsekonus 11135
Maschinensatz 15909
Maschinenschere 16030
Maschinenschliff 11128
Maschinenwärter 6471
Maschinist 11131
Maske 6743
Maskenkern 16100
Mass 11392
Massabweichung 5423, 12460
massanalytische oder titrimetrische Bestimmung 19600
Masse S. 10933
Masseform 6041, 16412
Masseguss 6040
Massel 1148, S. 9782, 13249, S. 14102
— gezogen (aus der) 16880
Masselbett S. 13656
Masselbrecher 11089, 13253
Masselform 13268
Masselgiessmaschine 13255, 13267
Masselgraben 16950
Masselhammer 12108
Masselhartstahl 8833
Massenbeförderung 18837

Masseneffekt 11357
Massenerzeugung 8603
Massenstahl 18723
Massepfropfen 7162
Massenzustellung 3667
Massgenauigkeit 5422
Massicot 11358
massiver Abbau 15140
Massivstruktur 11359
Massmarke für eine Hohl-kehle 9889
Mass · stab 15587
Masut S. 7791
Mattbeizung 11367/a
Materialabbrand 7180/a, 9003/a
Materialbehandlung 11374
Materialbewegung S. 8796
Materialfehler 5105
Materialgüte 8383
Materialstreifen 17850
Matildit 11375
Matlockit 11376
Matrize 1416/a, 11378
— aus Beton 4175
Matrizenhalter 2007
Matrizenstahl S. 5381
Matrizenwalze 5377
Mattblech 13221
Matteisen S. 20026, S. 20040
matte Stelle 6088
Matten 11382
mattes Eisen S. 3986, 18508
— Metall S. 3985
— Wetter 1648
Mattierung 7781/a
Mattkohle 6086
Maucherit 11384
Mauerfuss S. 4860
Mauerkranz 19649
Mauerplatte S. 19648
Mauersattel 19651
Mauersockel 2373
Mauerstärke S. 18512
Mauerung 19657
Mauerwerk S. 19657
Maulweite 6893
Mauzeliit 11385
Mazut 1658
mechanisch betätigter loser Schlüssel 13797

mechanische Bohrmaschine
13777
— Eigenschaften 11409
— Feuerung 11413
— Prüfung 11416
— Schaufelung 13793
— Siebvorrichtung 11415
— Übertragung 8131
— Vorschubvorrichtung
3781
— Werkstätte 11418
— Wirkung auf den Werk-
stoff 11411
mechanischer Gashärteofen
11406
— Hebebock S. 15709
— Puddler 11410
— Schneckenbohrer 11407
mechanisches Schmiedestück
13782
Meco-Moore Schramlade-
maschine 11421
Meerenge 16933
Meeressedimente 11321
meergrün 15731
Meerschaum S. 11439, S.
15882
Mehl 7417
Mehrfachbohrmaschine
(fahrbahr-) 10243
mehrfache Kemmarke S.
12110
mehrfacher Kernkasten
12109
— Walzenkessel 12112
Mehrfachform 12114
mehrfachformen 4534
Mehrfachformerei 4535
Mehrfachfräsung 7952
Mehrfachwalzen 12836
Mehrfachwerkzeug 12122/a
Mehrfachziehbank 20231
Mehrleitersystem 12124
mehrteiliges zerlegbares
Modell S. 11013
— Ion 12129
mehrzylindrig 13643
Meissel 2078
— schärfen (den) 16007
Meisselblatt 1624
Meisselbrecher 1625

Mesothorium 11526
Mesotyp 11527
Mesozoikum 11528, 15766
Mesozone 11529
Messelit 11530
messen 6827, 11389
Messen von Spülungseigen-
schaften 12082
Messer für Nachnahmebohrer
19276
Messerkopf 6746
Messerfehler 11397
Messheber 8392
Messkaliber 14591
Messkelch 11399
Messkette 11396
Messkolben 11398, 19597
Messloch 18363
Messing 2266, 20283
messingartig 2283
Messingblech 2274, 13488,
16050
Messingbogenregletten 2268
Messingdraht 2277
Messingform 2272
Messinglot S. 8840, 17047
Messinglötung 2276
Messingpfanne 2273
Messingplatten S. 13488
Messingsäule 2267
Messingschlaglot S. 17047
Messingteile 2269
Messpipette S. 8392
Messpunkt 11401
Messröhre 2587
Mess-Separator 11610
Messtank 2743
Messtischaufnahme 13459
Mess-und Schreibgerät für
den Schichtdruck 13896
Messung 11394
Messwerkzeug 11400
Metabrushit 11531
Metacinnabarit 11532
Metaheulandit 11534
Metahewettit 11535
Metall 11537
Metall härten 8847
— nach dem Blasen 1883
— gegossen (mit zu wenig)
17183

Meisselfanghaken 1626
Meisselflügel 1630
Meisselhals 1627
meisseln 3473, 3483
Meisseln 3477
Meisselprobe 1629, 2089
Meisselschulter 16210
Meisselstahl 3487, 5908
Meisselzapfen 1628
Mejonit 11441
Melaconit S. 18407
Melanglanz S. 2426, S. 17555
Melanit 11443
Melanocerit 11444
melanokrat 11445
Melanophlogit 11446
Melanotekit 11447
Melanovanadinit 11448
Melanterit 11449
Melaphyr 11450
Melilith 11451
Melinit 11452
Melinophan 11453
Melksonde 17859
Mellit 9302, 11454
Membranpumpe 5338
Menaccanit 11485
Mendelejewit 11489
Mendozit 11491
Meneghinit 11492
Mengenuntersuchung 14250
Mengesteinartig 2354
Menhir 11493
Menilit 11494
Meniskus S. 10338
Menneverfahren 11495
Menschenförderung S. 12065
Mensur S. 11400
Mergel 11335
Mergelboden 11338
Mergelton 11337
Merkantileisen S. 11496
Meroxen 11513
Merrillit 11514
Merwinit 11515
mesocrat 11521
Mesolith 11522
mesosilizisches Gestein
11523
Mesostasis 11524
mesothermaler Gang 11525

Metallbad S. 10595
Metallbearbeitung 11565
Metallbehälter für Minen-
    pulver 10090
Metallblöckchen S. 9783
Metalldachgerüst 17504
Metalldachplatten auf
    Schalung 11560
Metalldichtung 11554
Metalldrehbank 11564
Metallgehalt von Erz 15384
Metallgewebe 11545
Metallegierung 11538
Metallgiessen 15341
Metallgitter 8680, 9976
metallhaltig 12629
Metallhämmern 1404/a
Metallin 13302
metallisch 11566
— klingend 11573
metallische Rohstoffe 11570
metallischer Einschluss
    fremden Ursprungs 6659
metallisches Arsen 12180
— Blei 10617
— Eisen 11568
— Quecksilber 11569
— Silber 11572
— Strahlmittel S. 16193
metallisieren 11575
metallisierte Kohlen 11576
Metallisierung 11574, 11577
metallkeramisch 3224
Metallkorn 890
Metallnebel 11542/a
metallogenisch 11579
metallogenetisch 11578
Metallographie 11583
metallographische Einrich-
    tung 11580
— Untersuchung 11582
Metalloid 11584
metallplattiertes Rohr 1588
Metallpyrometer 11559
Metallsalz 11571
Metallschalen für Betonguss
    11552
Metallschicht 10595
Metallschlauch 7367
Metallschmelztiegel 13715
Metallschmelzwerk S. 14603

Metallspäne 3482
Metallsplitter 18200
Metallspritzen 11562
Metallspritzpistole 11563
Metalltiegelschmelzofen
    13719
Metalltischlerei 16734
Metalluntersuchung 11581
metallurgischer Ofen 11586
Metallverlust 11031
Metallwaren 11546
Metallwaschverfahren 19688
metamorphes Gestein 11593
    11594
Metamorphie 11593/a
metamorphisch 11592
Metarossit 11596
metasomatische Lagerstätte
    11598
metasomatischer Gang 11599
Metasomatose 2855, 11600
Metasome 8648, 11601
Metastibnit 11602
Metathenardit 11603
Metatypus 11604
Metavoltin 11606
Meteoreisen 11607
Metermass · stab 11608
Methanfernleitung 11611
Meymacit 11616
Miargyrit 11617
miarolitische Textur 11619,
miarolitischer Hohlraum
    11618
Miaskit 11620
Miersit 11669
Miesit 11670
Migmatit 4122, 11671
Miharait 11672
Mijakit 11673
Mikanit 11628
Mikrobild 11637
mikrochemische Analyse
    11630
mikrokryptokristallin 11634
mikrofelsitische Struktur
    11629, 11635
Mikrogefüge 11655
mikrogranitische Struktur
    11636
mikrographisch 11638

Mikrohärte 11639/a
mikroklastisch 11631
Mikroklin 11632
Mikroklinperthit 11633
Mikrolith 11640
mikrolitisch 11641
Mikrolunker S. 5530, 11654
mikromeritisch 11644
Mikrometerlehre 19517
Mikrometerschraube S. 11643
Mikrometerzirkel S. 11642
Mikropaleontologie 11645
mikropegmatitische Struktur
    11639
Mikropegmatit 11646
Mikroperthit 11647
mikrophyrisch 11648
mikropoikilitische Struktur
    11649
Mikroporosität 5530
mikroporphyrische Struktur
    11781
Mikroriss 8723/a
Mikroschliff 11652
Mikroschweissphänomene
    11657
Mikroseigerung 11653
Mikroskopgestell nach
    Martens 11345
Mikroskopierlampe 11650
mikroskopische Untersu-
    chung 9936, 11651
Mikrostruktur S. 11655
Mikrotinit 11656
Milarit 11674
Milchopal 20039
Milchquarz 11681
Millerit 8709/a, 11705
Millionen an Kubikfuss 11842
    11842
Millisit 11715
Miloschin 11718
Mimesit 11719
Mimetesit 11720
Mindergewicht 19284
minderwertige Kohle 13653
minderwertiger Asphalt
    10520
— Brennstoff 11051
— Stahl 19301
minderwertiges Eisen 19300

minderwertiges Erzeugnis 19253
Mindest-Warmstreckgrenze 11768
Mine loslassen (eine) 13945
Minenkammer 8365
Minenzünder S. 5116
Mineral 11749
Mineralbildner 11762
Mineralblau S. 1036
Mineraleinschluss 11754
Mineralfarbe 11750
mineralisieren 11759
mineralisierende Verwerfung 11763
Mineralogie 11763/a
Mineralwachs S. 3228, S. 12821
Minette 11765, S. 12551
minieren 11723
Minguetit 11766
Minusmineralien 11786
Minverit 11788
Miozän 11789
Mirabilit S. 8288, 11790
Mischapparat 11829
Mischbarkeit 11794
Mischeisen 11823
mischen 11817
Mischer 11826
Mischerbühne 11827
Mischergebäude S. 11834
Mischerhaus 11834
Mischerpfanne 11832
Mischgas 15851
Mischkristall S. 16886, 11822
Mischmaschine S. 11726, 11833
Mischöl 11820
Mischtrichter 11830
Mischung 11837
Mischungslücke 11795
Mischungsschrott 2628
Misenit 11797
Missourit 11808
mitläufige Teilverbrennung 7625
Mitnehmer 7602, S. 8566, 8571
— für Stirnfräser 737

Mitnehmereinsatz 10305
Mitnehmerglied 3090
Mitnehmerstange 8534, S. 10303
mittelbare Heizung 9744
Mittelblech 10188/a, 11430
Mitteldruckdampfkessel 11432
Mitteldruckkessel 11431
Mittelleiter 12254
Mittelfrequenz-Induktions- ofen 9890
Mittelgut 11667
mittelharter Stahl 11427, 11437
mittelhartes Giessereieisen 11426
Mittelkasten 11660
mittelkörnig 11425
mittelkörniger Sand 11433
mittelporphyrisch 11422
Mittelprodukte 3358
Mittelschenkel 4094, 11661, 15885
Mittelschenkelbruch S. 656
mittelschweres Profil 11434, 11435
mittelst elektrischem Licht- bogen öffnen 12561
Mittelstrecke 11428
Mittelwalze 11665
Mittelwasserraumkessel 11438
Mittelwert der Versuchs- ergebnisse 1009
Mittelzug 11424
mittlere freie Weglänge 11387/a
mittlerer Gewindedurch- messer 13414
Mixit 11836
Mizzonit 11841
Möbelrohr 7880
Mobilitätsverhältnis 11848
Modderit 11851
Modell ausheben 17841
— herausheben (das) 20155
— in den Sand eindrücken (das) 9668
— lockern (das) 11011
— mit doppeltem Schwind-

mass S. 11366
Modell mit Eingüssen und Steigern 12981
— mit Eingusstrichtern 8099
— nochmals eindrücken 14737 14737
Modellabhebung 12976
Modellager 12994
Modellaufbau in Dauben 8624 8624
Modellausschmelze 11014
Modellausschmelzverfah- ren 13824
Modellbauer 12982
Modellegierung 12984/a
Modellform S. 2983
Modellformerei 12986
Modellformung 4281/a
Modellfräsmaschine 12985
Modellhälfte 12978
Modellhammer 11993
Modellheber 10768
Modellhebestift 10769
Modellheizung 12979
Modellherstellung 12984
Modellplatte 12987
— formen (mit der) 13495
Modellplattenarbeit 11368
Modellplattenformen 11369, 12988
Modellpuder S. 12950
Modellriss 20204
Modellsand S. 12027
Modellsatz 4056
Modellschräge S. 5724
Modellträger S. 18734
Modellübermetall zum Aus- gleichen der Schrumpfung 12993
Modellumriss 12707
Modellversatz S. 11803
Modellwerkstatt 12992
modernes Frischfeuer S. 18107
Modifizierungsmittel 11854
Moissanit 11859
Mokkastein 11849
Molasse 11866
Moldavit 11867
Molekül 11874

molekulare Zusammenset-
zung 11873
Molekulargewicht 11872
Molekularvolumen 11871
Molengraaffit 11875
Möller 3325, 11839
Möllerausbringen 20297
Möllerbett 1428
Möllerhaus 11835
Möllerung 11232
Molybdän 11882
Molybdäneisen 6946
Molybdänglanz S. 11881,
13731
Molybdänit 11881
Molybdännickel 12276
Molybdänocker S. 11885
Molybdänsäureanhydrid
11884
Molybdänstahl 11883
Molybdit 11885
Molybdomenit 11886
Molybdophyllit 11887
Molysit 11888
Monazit 11891
Mönch 14405
Mönch(s)kolben 9536
Monchiquit 11892
Mondhaldeit 11893
Mondstein 11926
Monel-Metall 11894
Monetit 11895
Monheimit 11896
Moniereisen S. 4176 , S.
15272
Monimolit 11897
Monit 11898
Monitor 11899
Monmouthit 11905
monogenes Gestein 11910
Monoklinalfalte 17547
monoklines System 11908
monomineralisch 11911
monomineralisches 11914
Monrepit 11916
Montage auf Säule 4042
Montageologie 11775
Montagevorrichtung 7244
Montagezeichnung 10600
Montagemast S. 8233
Montian 1919

Monticellit 1920
montieren 6735, 15902
montiert 14589
Montmorillonit 11921
Montrealit 11922
Montroydit 11923
Monzonit 11924
monzonitische Textur 11925
Moor 1943, 13024
Moos 11943
Moosbüchse 11945
Moräne 11928
Moränenamphytheater 11930
Moränengürtel 11929
Morast 16624
Morenosit 11931
Morganit 11933
Morganscher Generator
11932
Morion 11934
Moroxit 11935
Mörtel 11936
Mörtelstruktur 12134
Mosaikstruktur S. 11940
Mosandrit 11941
Mosesit 11942
Mossit 11946
Motor-Generator-Gehäuse
11952
Motorgruppe 13799
Mottramit 11959
Mrazeks stöchiometrisches
Verfahren 17629
Muffe für mehrstufige Ze-
mentierung 16374
Muffel 12096
— aus Schamotte 7161
Muffelkaliber 9843
Muffelofen S. 4840, 12097
— für Gasheizung 12099
— für Kohlenheizung 12098
Muffenbrecher 4018
Muffenhülse S. 4549
muffenlose Rohrverbindung
S. 9835
Muffenrohr 4021, 13367,
16808, 18523/a
Muffensucher 4019
Muffenventil 16595
Mühlstein 2529, 8563, 11716
Muhrgang S. 12078

Mulde 9992, 10323, 14353
Muldenachse S. 18937
Muldenbiegung 18159, S.
18938
Muldenblei S. 13266
Muldeneinsetzkran 18939
Muldenflügel 18158
Muldenform 4160
Muldenkern S. 4427, 18940
Muldenkopf 8916
Muldenlinie 18942
Muldenrolle 18590
Muldenscharnier 11064,
18938
Muldenschenkel 18941
Muldental 18160
Müllfeuerung 9687, 14641
Mullit 12102
Müllverbrennungsofen 7970,
14639
Mundstück 6895
Mündung 10466, 12040
— der Birne 18577
— der Bohrung 19964
Mündungsbär 16521
Muniongit 12131
Muntzmetall 12132
Münz(en)bronze 11543
Münzstahl 2361
Murchisonit 12135
Murmanit 12136
Muschel 3615, 16093
muschelige Struktur 4173
muscheliger Bruch 4172,
7381
Muschelkalk 12137, 16105
Muschelschieber 12144
Muscovadit 12138
Muskovit 4095, 11792,
12139
Mussfaktor 15927
Muster 15453
Mustermacher S. 12983
Muter 3614
Muthmannit 12147
Mutterblech 17386/a
Mutterblechbad 17858/a
Muttergestein 12182, 16947
Muttermagma 12933
Muttermassel 16948/a
Muttermodell 11366

Mutung 3613
Mylonit 12148
Mylonitgefüge S. 13921
mylonitische Struktur 12149
Mylonitisierung 12150
Myrmekit 12151

N

Nabe 9469
nach abwärts gezogenes
   Gewölbe 4159
— dem Guss · stück formen
   11961
— Massgabe gegossen
   3028
— UNI-Normen 50
Nachbeben 203
Nachbehandlung 17930
Nachblasen 199
Nachfall 16967
Nachfallbank S. 14395
Nachfalldach 3612, 3746,
   5784, 17584
Nachfliessen 200/a
Nachfraktionierturm 201
nachfüllen 7012
Nachgeben des Formkastens
   S. 5569
nachgiebiger Stempel 160,
   S. 2334, 4014, 20300
nachgiebiges Streckengestell
   20299
nachgiessen 6874
Nachglühen 5811
nachlassen S. 18370
Nachlass · spindel 18376
nachlaufen 18372
Nachnahmebohrer 14480
Nachprüfen 3361
Nachreiniger 14500
Nachreinigung 7883
Nachreissen 2483, S. 2777
Nachschlagewerk 14590
nachschleifen 4651
Nachschrumpfen 199/a
Nachsintern 14763/a
nachspeisen S. 6874,
Nachspeisen 6887/a

nachsprengen 1790, 2565
   S. 1802
Nachsprengen 2566
Nachschwaden 1767, S. 16145
nachträglicher Verbund
   13714
Nachtriegel 12293
Nachtschicht 5599, 12294
Nachwalzwerk 18375/a
nackter Draht 1228
nacktes Loch 1230
Nadelboden 13080
Nadeleisenerz S. 12207
Nadelerz 73, 12209
nadelförmig 70, 12210
nadelförmiger Kristallit
   1471
Nadelguss 12208
Nadelgusseisen S. 71, 72/a
Nadelholzkohle 13314
Nadellager 12206
Nadeln zurückziehen (die)
   20156
Nadelstichporen 13316
Nadorit 12155
Nagatelit 12157
Nagel mit versenktem ka-
   riertem Kopf 4540
Nageldraht S. 14975
Nageleisen 5600, 12163
Nageleisenerz S. 8338
Nagelfluh 12158
Nägit 12156
Nagyagit 7534, 12159
Nahcolit 12160
nahtloses Rohr 15752,
   19958/a
— Stahlrohr 15766
Nahtschweissung 4278,
   15749
Nakrit 12154
Nantokit 12167
Naphtha 6176, S. 15031
Naphthalin 12168
Naphthen 12171
Naphthenat 12169
naphtenisch 12172
Naphthenzahl 12170
Napoleonit 12173
narbig 15244
Nasenschraube S. 16794

nass schwärzen 1640
Nassaufbereitung 19986,
   19987, 19994
Nassbohren 19776
Nassbohrung 19782
nasse Aufbereitung 19990,
   S. 19994
— Scheidung 19813/a,
   19997
— Vergoldung 19778
Nassemaillierung 19992
Nässen der Kohle 20004
nasses Eisenerz 19993
Nassgas S. 14872
Nassgussform S. 8517
Nassgussformen 12009
Nassöl S. 6426
Nasspochen 20000
Nasspochwerk 19999
Nasssputzen 9545
Nassreinigung 19996
Nass · streckdraht 10462
Nasswalzen 19989
Nasszerkleinerung 19988
Nathusiusscher Ofen 12179
Natriumammoniumphosphat
   528
Natriumarsenit 16819
Natriumbikarbonat S. 16820
Natriumchlorid 4097
Natriumflamme 16821
Natriumhydroxydbad 3114
Natriumkarbonat S. 2854
Natriumhyposulfit 9602
Natriumlinie 16822
Natriumphosphat S. 13165
Natriumpresse 16824
Natriumsulfat 17973
Natriumsulfit 16825
Natriumsuperoxyd 13101
Natriumzange 16823
Natroalunit 12183
Natrocalcit S. 8122
Natrojarosit 12186
Natrokalzit 12185
Natrolith 12187
Natron 16820
Natronfeldspat S. 348
Natronhydrat 3116
Natronkalk 16809
Natronlauge 3117, S. 16811

Natronmikroklin S. 636
Natronsalpeter 16812
Natrophilit 12188
Naturalasphalt 12181
Naturbenzin 2947
Naturgas 12193
Naturgasolin 12194
Naturgold 15573
Natu .ärte 12195
naturharter Stahl 15825
natürliche Böschung 12197
natürlicher Brennstoff 12191
— Zug 12190
Naturmodell 16109
Natursand 12196
Naturwasser S. 12198
Naujait 12199
Naumannit 12200.
Nauruit 12201
Navit 12202
nebelförmiger Zustand 11809
Nebenbelüftung 15771
Nebenbestandteil 15765
nebeneinanderliegende
    Kolben 18914
Nebenerzeugnisse des Hoch-
    ofens 2653
Nebengang 6001, 6885
Nebengestein 157, 157/a,
    4544, 6443, 12954,
    19650
Nebengleis 16240
Nebenkanäle 16948
Nebenleitung 10999
Nebenproduktkoksofen
    14512
Nebensattel 11782
negative Härtung 12214
— Kohle 12213
Neigung S. 13412, 16678,
    19268
— s. Fallen od. Einfallen
Neigungsanzeiger 5859
Neigungslinie 660, 16682
Neigungsmesser 3736, 9709
Neigungswinkel 575
Nelsonit 12215
Nemaphyllit 12216
nematoblastische Struktur
    12217
Nennmass 12337

Neodevon 12219
Neodym 12220
neogen 12221
Neohexan 12226
Neokom 12218
Neolithikum 12222
Neon 12223
Neotantalit 12225
neozoische Gruppe 12227
Nephelin S. 6242, 12228
Nephelinbasalt 12229
Nephelinit 12230
Nephelinsyenit 12231
Nephrit 12232
Nepouit 12233
Neptunit 12235
neptuinische Gesteine 12234
Neptunium 12236
neritisch 12237
neritische Fazies 12238
Nerv S. 14864.
Nesquehonit 12239
Nettomächtigkeit 12242
— eines Sandsteins 12243
Netzelektrode 12245
netzförmig 12244
Netzfrequenz-Induktionsofen
    11047
Netzmittel 20003
Netzstruktur 10391/a
Neuberyit 12260
Neubildungsgeschwindigkeit
    der Ionen 14647
neubohren 14557
neuer Schacht 8504
Neuland 12259
Neulandit 12261
Neumanlinien 12251
Neusand 12258
Neusilber 771, S. 8195,
    12280
neutral 11423
neutrale Substanz 12253
neutrales Gestein 12252
neutralisieren 12255
Newjanskit 12257
nicht ausgebeuteter Gang
    19323
nichtausgeglühter Draht S.
    19231
nichtbackend 12340

nichtbackende Kohle S.
    12344
nichtgraphitisch 12351
Nichteisenmetall 12349
Nichteisenmetallurgie 11591
nichtmagnetisch 12354
nichtmagnetische Schwer-
    stange 12356
nichtmetallischer Ein-
    schluss 12358, 14580, 16916
— Einschluss fremden
    Ursprungs 6660
nichtverdickt 12366
nichtpassendes Modell 9719
Nichtphosphorstahl 12360
nichtrostend 15393
nichtrostender Stahl 4492,
    15394
nicht selbstfahrend 12364
nichtzementierter Kern
    15539/a
nichtzentrierter Futterrohr-
    bereich 7738
Nickel — 12268
Nickelaluminiumstahl 12270
Nickelbronze 12271,
Nickelchromstahl 12273
Nickeleisen 6947
Nickelerz 12277
Nickelgymnit S. 8158
nickelhaltiges Eisenerz
    12285
— Roheisen 13262
Nickelin 12263
Nickelkupfer 12272
Nickellegierung 12269
Nickeloxydul 12278
Nickelstahl 12281
Nickelstahlplatte 12282
Nickelstein 12275
Nickelvanadiumstahl 12283
Nickelvorkommen 12266
Nickelzusatz 139
niederblasen S. 1846
Niederblasen S. 1877
niederbringen 15346
Niederdruck 11057
Niederdruckdampfkessel
    11058
Niederfrequenz-Induktions-
    ofen 11048

Niedergehen der Gicht 6005
niederhängender Ring 18077
Niedermoor S. 11053
Niederschacht 11058/a
Niederschlag 13809
Niederschlagelektrode 13814
Niederschlagen der Gicht-flamme 5989
Niederschlagkupfer 13810
Niederschlagmittel S. 13805
Niederschlagnaphtha 13816
Niederschlagturm 13811
Niederspannungsanlage 11063
niedersprengen 7288
niedrig prozentiges Erz 5721
niedriggekohlter Stahl 11062
niedriggekohltes Gusseisen S. 17484
niedrigprozentige Legierung 400
niedrigschmelzende Legie-rung 11055
Nierenerz 12335
Niet mit Halbkegelkopf 4199
Nieteisen 14973, S. 14974
— zu einer Schleife biegen (das) 1500
Nietenprüfung 14974/a
Nietkopf 14972
nietlose Schutzmaske S. 14979
nietloser Kopfschutz 14979
Nietschaft 15953
Nietstahl 14974
Nietstempel 16783
Nife-Zone 12290
Nigrin 12295
Niob 12297
Nippel 12305
Nitratin 12318
Nitrieren 12312, 12321
Nitrierhärteverfahren S. 12313
Nitrierhärtung 519, 8861
Nitrierstahl 12314
Nitrierstahllegierung 12310
nitrierte Schicht 12311
Nitrierverfahren 12313

Nitrobarit 12316
Nitrogelatine 12318
Nitrogenstahl S. 12314
Nitroglauberit 12322
Nitroglyzerin 1740
Nitroglyzerinsprengstoff 12323
Nitrokalzit 12317
Nitrometer 12324
Nitronatrit S. 12308
nitrös 12325
Ni-Va-Stahl S. 12283
Niveaudiagramm 9607
Niveauflasche 10715
Niveaukurve 4281
Niveaustrecke 11735
Nivellement 2029
Nivellieren S. 2029
Nivellierlatte 9470
Nivellierung S. 2029, 8385,
Nivenit 12326
Nobelium 12327
Nocerin 12330
Nocken 2764
Nonesit 12368
Norbergit 12371
Norit 12374
Nontronit 12369
Nordenskiöldin 12372
normal ausgebildete weiss-erstarrte Zone 3439
— zur Schlechtenrichtung verlaufender Stoss 2635
Normalangabe 17352
Normaldraht 17358
normale Lagerung 12382
— Verwerfung 3220, 5446, 5700, 5713, 8488, 12377, 16651
Normalelektrode 17345
normaler Nitrierstahl 12381
— Thermit 13448/a
normales Prisma S. 14906
— U-Eisen 17343
Normalgewicht S. 17356
normalglühen 12385
Normalglühen 12387
Normalisieren S. 608
normalisierter Stahl 12386
Normalisierglühung S. 12388
Normalkohle 17344
Normalkrümmer 14262

Normallösung 17351
Normalprobestab 17354/a
Normalprofil 4047, S. 8174, 8175
Normalrohr 17355
Normalsand 17348
Normaltabelle 17349
Normalweiche 17347
Northupit 12389
norwegischer Gletscher 9612
Nosean 12392
Noseanit 12393
Nulleiter S. 12254
Nummulit 12424
Nummulitenfazies 12425
Nummulitenkalk 12426
Nusskohle 3414
Nusskoks 12429
Nussgrösse 19661
Nussgruskohle 6077
Nut S. 16686
Nuten 8597
Nutenfräser 17099
Nutenreisser 15297
Nutenverminderung 6913
Nutsche S. 7057
Nutzabstand 18575
Nutzbohrung 13651
Nutzleistung 6143
Nutzniveau 8112

O

oben bohren (von) 5875
Oberbohrmeister 18729
Oberdampf 17414
Oberdruck der oberen Walze 13911
obere Anschlagbühne 682
— Anschlagbühne eines Bremsberges 1193
— Lagerschale 18737
— Pressplatte 18735/a
— Schicht S. 2796
— Verankerungsschiene 2211, 3627
oberer Etagenschnitt 17548/a, 17562

oberer Heizwert 8601
— Mühlstein 15371
— Stoss 9052
— Teil 19364
Oberfeuer 6564
Oberfläche 2911/a, 18040
oberflächenaktives Mittel
    18042
Oberflächenbeanspruchung
    18003
Oberflächenbehandlung
    18004, 18070
Oberflächenbeschaffenheit
    18045
Oberflächenbiegeprobe der
    Schweiss-stelle 6740
Oberflächenentwicklung
    18049
Oberflächenfehler 18048
Oberflächenglühung 7254/a
Oberflächenhärte 16476
oberflächenhärten 18053
Oberflächenhärtung S. 2918,
    8826, 16475, 18054
Oberflächenkruste 18047
Oberflächenloch 16477
Oberflächenlunker S. 18066
Oberflächenpolierung 4917a
Oberflächenporen 13073/a,
    18061
Oberflächenrauheit 18065,
Oberflächenreinheit 3698
Oberflächenriss 18046
Oberflächenrohrtourloch
    18055
Oberflächenschichten-
    rutsche 15428
Oberflächenschutz 18064
Oberflächenspiel 2306
Oberflächenschönerung
    12674
Obergesenk 19363
Obergestell 18742
oberidische Stromleitung
    191
Oberkante 19365
Oberkasten 4349
— aufsetzen (den) 14205
Oberkessel 19362
Oberlager 18736
Oberschicht 2813

Obersteiger 8910, 11731
Oberstempel 19364/a
Oberwalze 1138, 18750
Oberwinddüse 18735
Oberzementierpfropfen 18747
Objektiv 12432
Objekttisch 17288
Obsidian 12437
Obsidianit 12438
Ocellartextur 12447
Ochrolith 12449
Ocker 12448
ock(e)riger Brauneisenstein
    S. 2474
Odinit 12456
Odontolith 12457
Ofen S. 7825
— für Gewinnung von
    Nebenprodukten 7837
— für kontinuierlichen
    Betrieb 4267
— mit auswechselbarem
    Boden 7877
— mit ausziehbarem Herd
    S. 1948
— mit fahrbarem Herd 7873
— mit kontinuierlichen
    Betrieb 4267
— mit leichtflüssigem Bett
    7460
— mit Schwingsohle 19629
— mit unterbrochenem
    Betrieb 429
Ofenabdeckung 15145
Ofenabkühlung 4340
Ofenbär 1382, 2531, 10155
Ofenbatterie 12726
Ofenblei 13266
Ofenbrand S. 20327
Ofenbrücke 7829
Ofendurchmesser 5318
Ofenende 7835
Ofenform S. 19195
Ofenfuss 4039
Ofengang 4190, 20195
Ofeninneres 9886
Ofenkanal 7836
Ofenkrücke 17636
Ofenmäntel 7846, S. 7849,
    7856
Ofenmuster 17152/a

Ofenpanzer S. 7846
Ofenplatte 9217/a
Ofenrand 14915
Ofenreise 7830, 10734
Ofenrohr 17698
Ofensatz S. 2382
Ofensau S. 2531, 15434
Ofenschacht 7854
Ofenschlacke 7857
Ofensohle 7827, S. 8959
Ofenumformer 7860
Ofenwolf 15434
Ofenzunder 7853
offene Form S. 8961, 12585
— Formteilung 12582/a
— Rolle 12567
offener Bohrlöffel 3654
— Fliessversuch 12571
— Guss 3057
— Herd 12573
— Herdguss 12564/a,
    12592
— Kernkasten mit losen
    Teilen 17130
— Lunker 18066
— Mischer 12583
— Speiser 12598
— Stempel 12568/a
— Wagen 12603
offenes Gerät 12597
— Kaliber 12587
Öffnung S. 7966, 13685
— der Form 10201/a
Öffnungen verstreichen (die)
    3754
Offretit 12461
ohne Motor 6090
— Rücklauf 12546
Ohr 6727
Okenit 12520
Oktan S. 12456
Oktanwert 12454
Öl abgekühlt (in) 14286
— am Ort 12495
Ölabscheider 12514
Ölabstreifer 12507
Ölanreicherung 12504
Ölanzeichen 12510
Ölbohrung 19967
Olefin 12524
Öl-Emulsion in Wasser 12496

Ölentnahme 12517
Ölfeld 12489, 12518
Ölfeuerung 7840
Ölgasbrenner 12492
ölhaltig 12525
Ölhärtung 12494
Ölhärtungsstahl 12493
Ölinfiltration 12508
Öllinse 12499
Ölloch 12502
Ölnebelschmierung 17111
Ölprobenehmer 12513
Ölreste aus erster Förde-
   rung 19918
Olrückstand 16677
Ölsand 12506
Ölsäure 12526
Ölschicht 12498
Ölschiefer 12509
Ölschlamm 12488
Ölsonde 12515
Ölvorkommen 16217
Omega-Stahlrohrkessel in
   Hochdruckausführung
   9167
Omphacit 12538
Onegit 12547
Onkilonit 12548
Onofrit 12549
Oolith 6225
oölithische Struktur 12552
oölithischer Kalkstein S.
   6225
oölithisches Erz 7357
Opal 12555
Opaljaspis S. 6869
Opdalit 12556
Ophit 12616
ophitische Struktur 12617
Orangit 12619, S. 18545
Orbit 12621
Ordanchit 12622
Orendit 12662
Orford-Verfahren 18734/a
organischer Stoff 12663
Orgel 1351
orientalischer Opal S. 12329
— Rubin 12664
— Topas 12665
Orientit 12666
Original 19205

Orizontalverschiebung S.
   16124
Ornöit 12675
Orogenese 12676
orographische Verwerfung
   12677
Orsatscher Apparat S. 7455,
   12679
Ort S. 2336, 6450, 6738
— auf der Grundsohle 16340
Örtebau S. 4680, S. 13294
Orthoklas 12680
orthophyrische Struktur
   12681
orthorhombisch 12682
orthorhombisches Prisma
   12683
Orthosilikat 12685, 19836
örtlicher Kontaktzünder
   10381
ortsfremd S. 379
ortsfremde Ablagerung 380
— Falte 381
Ortsstein S. 8875
Osmium 12687
Osmondit 12688
osmotischer Druck 12689
oval s. eirund or elliptisch
Ovalbüchse 12723
Ovaleisen 12721
Ovalkaliber 12725
Ovalkessel 12722
Ovalstab 7937
Ovalstahl 12724
Oxalsäure 12787
Oxammit 12788
Oxyd 12793/a
Oxydation 12789,
Oxydationsflamme 6641/a,
   12810/a
Oxydationsprodukt 12793
Oxydationszone 12792
oxydfreies Blech 16069
Oxydhäutchen 13054/a
oxydieren 12805
Oxydieren 12808/a
oxydierend 12808
oxydierende Röstung 12811
— Wirkung der Luft über
   Kohle 12810
oxydierender Zusatz 12809

oxydierendes Schmelzen
   12804, 12812
oxydierte Blase 12806
oxydiertes Erz 1837
oxydischer Gang 19491
Oxydschicht 10596
Ozokerit 6178, 12821
Ozonpapier 12822

P

paarweise umzechiger
   Betrieb 6483
Pachnolith 12823
Packband 1144
Packer-Formation 7613
Pa(c)ket 6762
Pa(c)ketierung 6763
Packung 12845
Paddelmischer 12856,
   20169/a
Paisanit 12865
Paket 12827
Paketglühen 12829
paketieren 13276
Paketieren 13283
paketierte Luppeneisenstäbe
   S. 6762
Palagonit 12873
Palait 12874
Paläobotanik 12866
paläolitisch 12870
paläontologische Fazies
   12876
Paläozan 12867
Paläozoikum 12872
Palatinit 12875
paläontologische Geologie
   12877
paläotyp 12871
Palette auf Füssen 13505
Palladium 12878
Palladiumasbest 12879
Palladiumnitrat 12307
Palmerit 12883
Palmfett 12882
panallotriomorphe Struktur
   12887
Pandemit 12893

panidiomorphe Struktur 12889
Pantellerit 12901
Panzerkabel 804
panzern 1765
Panzerplatte 799
Panzerplattenstahl 801
Panzerstahl 803
Panzerstrecke 800
Papierschiefer 12903
papicrisolierter Draht 12904
Papinscher Topf 5406
Pappform 12905/a
Paraffin 12906
Paraffindestillat 19842
Paraffinfraktionierung 19843
Paraffingatsch 16512
Paraffinkratzer 12909
paraffinöses Öl 12907
Paraffinrückstand 19844
Paraffinschabekolben 12908
Paraffinstörung 12910
Paraffinwachs 12911
Paragenese 12912
Paragneis 12913
Paragonit 12914
Parahoepeit 12915
Paralaurionit 12916
paralisch 12917
Parallelbiegungen 18817
Paralleldiskordanz 12920
parallele Rinnen S.16948
Parallelleitung S. 10999
Parallelnahtschweissung 12922
Parallelpunktschweissung 12923
Parallelreihe 12921
Parallelreisser 18052
Parallelreiss · stock S.18052
Paralleltransgression 12919
Paraluminit 12924
paramagnetisch 12925
paramorph 12926
Paramorphose 12927
Paraurikalzit 12928
Paravauxit 12929
Parianit 12935
Parisit 12936
Parkerisieren 12937

Parryscher Gasfang 12938
Parsettensit 12939
Parsonsit 12940
Parzelle S. 13552
Passgenauigkeit 13821
passive Härte 12961
Passivierung 12960
Pass · schiene 14360
Pass· stift S. 17904
Paste für Söderberg-Elektroden 16816
Passung S. 18709
Patentierung 12965
Patentkernnagel 12968
Paternoit 12970
Patrize 9217
Patronit 12971
Pause 18809
Pechblende 13413
Pechglanz 13415
Pechkohle 13418, 13419
Pechkessel 13416
Pechstein 13417
Pechtorf S. 1635
Peckhamit 13035
Pedion 9081
Pegmatisierung 13047
Pegmatit 13046
pegmatitähnlich 13048
pegmatitische Struktur S. 8446
Pektolith 13036
pelagische Ablagerungen 13050
— Fazies 13051
Pelikanit 13052
pelitische Struktur 13053
Pendeldorn 7390/a
Pendelreibahle 7391
Pendelstützbock 13059
Peneplein S. 13061
Penetrationszwillinge S. 9911, S. 13064
Penfieldit 13066
Pennin 13068
Penroseit 13070
Pentagondodekaeder S.14216
Pentlandit 13073
Percylith 13077
pergamentartig 12930
Pergamentdraht 12931

pergamentieren 1935
Pergamentschlauch 19922
perhyalinische Struktur 13086
Peridot 13090
Periklas 13087
Periklin 13089
periklinale Faltenstruktur 14255
— Struktur 13088
periklinales Einfallen 3222
perigmatisch 13091
Perimorphose 13092
periodisches Gas-lift 9895
— Kaliber 13096
peripherischer Herd 15554
peritektische Umwandlung 13103
Perknit 13097
Perkolationsfiltration 7064
perlartig 13021
Perle 1365
Perlit 13016, 13098
perlitischer Stahl 13019
perlitisches Gusseisen 13018, 13018
Perlkoks 13006
Perlmutterglanz 12153, 13022
Perlröhre 8270
Perlspat 13015
Perm S. 6146
Permokarbon 648
Perowskit 13099
persistentes Fossil S.13116
Perthit 13117
Petalit S. 3077, 13119
Petrefact S. 7629
Petrogenese 13122
Petrographie 13125
petrographisch 13123
petrographische Fazies 13124, 13124
Petroläther 13133
Petrolatum 13126
Petrolatumwachs 13127
Petrolen 13128
Petroleum 13129, 15031, S. 17646
Petroleumeinspritzer 13131
Petroleuminjektor S. 13131

Petroleumkocher 13134
Petroleumofen 12491
Petroleumprüfer 13136
Petroleumrückstände 13135
Petrolkoks 13130
Petrologie 13136/a
Petzit 13137
Pfahl S. 13707
Pfahlrammen 13285
Pfanne S. 1955, 10469, S. 12885, 13452
— anwärmen (die) 8969
— kippen (die) 18671
— mit Stopfenausguss 17681
Pfannenamalgamator 12886
Pfannenauskleidung S. 10479
Pfannenbär S. 10485, S. 15727, S. 16488
Pfannenbügel S. 10472
Pfannenführung 10477
Pfannenkruste 10485
Pfannenrand 14916
Pfannenrest 15727, 16488
Pfannenschlacke 10485/a
Pfannenwagen 10473
Pfannenziegel 10473/a
Pfeife 2057, 5031
Pfeifenerde S. 13331
Pfeifenton S. 7158
Pfeil 811
Pfeiler 1248, 4592, 10367, 13289
— abbauen 14715
— abbauen von einem aufgelassenen Bau 7627
Pfeilerabbau S. 13295, 17661
Pfeilerbau 3564, 12898, 12899, 13295, 13709, 17253, 17659
— mit langen Pfeilern 10972
Pfeilerdruck 18597
Pfeilergewinnung von einem aufgelassenen Bau 7628
Pfeilersenkung 16440
Pferdeförderung der Kohle 7354
Pferdegöpel 20014
Pferdekopf 9379
Pflanzenkohle S. 3298

Pflasterstruktur 11940
Pflugstahl 13553
Pfund je. Quadratfuss 14084
Pfropfen 12857
— mit Elektroden im Mikrolog 15311
Pfuhl S. 10323
Phakelit 13140
Phakolith 13142
phanerokristallin 13143
Pharmakolith 13144
Pharmakosiderit 4818, 13145
Phase 13146, S. 17285
Phengit 13148
Phenocryst 9840
Phenol 13150
Phenolharz 13151
Phenolphtaleinpapier 13152
Philadelphit 13153
Phillipsit 13154
Phlogopit 5507, 13155, 14860
Pholerit 13157
Pholidolith 13158
Phönicochroit 13156
Phonolith 3729, 13159, 16939
Phosgenit 9368, 13160
phosphatieren 13162
Phosphatierung 13168
Phosphatkreide 13161
Phosphideutektikum S.17411
Phosphidperle 13169
Phosphoferrit 13170
Phosphophyllit 13171
Phosphor 13183
Phosphorabscheidung 6382, 15874
phosphorartiges Eisenerz 13166
— Roheisen 13180, 13181
phosphorarme Schlacke 16548
Phosphorbronze 13172
Phosphorbronzedraht 13173
Phosphorit 13182
Phosphorkupfer 13175
Phosphormangan 13176
phosphorreiche Schlacke 16552
Phosphorsalz 16818

phosphorsaueres Natron 13165
Phosphorsäureanhydrid 131 13179
Phosphorstahl 13177
Phosphorverbindung 13174
Phosphorzinn 13178
Phosphosiderit 13184
Phosphuranylit 13185
photographische Platte 13187
phreatische Explosion 13188
Phthanit 13189
Phyllit 13190
physikalisch-chemische Geräte 13195
physikalische Eigenschaften 13193
— Metallurgie 13191/a
— Prüfung 13194
— und chemische Vorbereitung 13191
physikalisches Gemisch 13192
Piatofen 13197
Pickelbildung 13302/a
Pickeringit 13212
Pienaarit 13239
Pigmentfarbe 10492/a
Pikotit 13232
Pikrit 13233
Pikrolith 13234
Pikromerit 13235
Pilandit 13275
Pilgerschrittschweissen 16484/a
Pilgerschrittverfahren 19038
Pilgerwalze 13282
Pilgerwalzwerk 13281
pilotaxitische Struktur 13301
Pilzfalte 12141
Pilzfelsen 12143
pilzförmig aufgetriebener Speiser 3109
Pinguit 13315
Pinnoit 13323
Pintadoit 13324
Piotin S. 13325
Pipeline-Öl 13356
Piperno 13376
Pipette 13377

Pipette für die Probe-
entnahme 18518
— zur Probeentnahme
aus einem Behälter
19772
Pipettenflansche 13378
Pipettenständer 13379
Pisolith 13386
pisolinische Struktur S.
12552
pistonieren 18086
Pistonieren 18089
Pistonierkolbengehäuse
18090
Pistonierseil 18092_
Pitot-Rohr 13425
Pittinit 13430
Plagioklas 13438
Plagiophyr 13440
Plan 13552
plandrehen 6759
Pläner 14351
Planerit 13461
Planoferrit 13465
Planparallestruktur 4204,
13447
Planrost 9343
Planrostfeuerung 7867
Planrostinnenfeuerung 7871
Planrostunterfeuerung 7868,
6695
Planstossherd 19458
Plastifiziermittel 13473
Plastik-Überzug 13471
plastische Nahtschweiss-
ung 11354
plastischer Ton 13470,
16830
plastisches Material 13472
Platin 13514
Platinblech 13526
Platinchlorid 13513
Platindraht 13530
Platine 2307/a, 7322, S.
7340, 11852, 15840/a,
16047, 16049, 16415/a,
17853
Platinenwalzwerk 16048
Platingerät 13529
platinhaltig 13516
Platinierung 13523

Platinkegel 13518
Platinlöffel 13528
Platinmesser 13521
Platinmetall 13522
Platinmuffel 13524
Platinnadel 13525
Platinschale 13515
Platinschiffchen 13517
Platinspatel 13527
Platintiegel 13519
Platinveraschungsschale
13520
Platte 7246, 13484
— mit gekremptem Rand S.
7272
platten s. schienen
Plattenamalgamation 13486
Plattendrehen 9443
Platteneisen bester Qualität
1562
Plattenförderband 13489
plattenförmig 13534
plattenförmige Struktur 1199
Plattengelenk 9202
Plattenpaket 11697
Plattenstahl 13499
Plattform 7316
Plattformkipper 18679
plattieren 13477
Plattieren mit Schockwellen
6689
plattierter Stahl 3611
Plattierung 3611/a
plattiger Sandstein 15496
plattiges Erz 7247
Plättmaschine 7355
Plattnerit 13533
Plattstampfer 7342
Plättwerk S. 7355
platzen S. 6678
Plazolith 13538
Pleistozän 13540
Pleochroismus 13543
Pleonast 10018, 13544
Plesiosaurus 13545
Plesiotypus 9605, 13546
Plessit 13547
Pliozän 13539, 13551
plötzlicher Temperatur-
wechsel 17963
— Zufluss im Bohrloch

10346
Plumbaco S. 8447
Plumbokuprit 13572
Plungerpumpe 19055
Plungerventil S. 18863
plutonische Gesteine S.32,
S. 5097
Plutonium 15381
pneumatische Kontrolle
13600
— Transportvorrichtung
13602
— Wanne 13601
pneumatischer Auswerfer
295/a
— Hebebock 13586
— Zug S. 13585
pneumatisches Ausleeren
13587
Pneumatolyse 13603
Pocharbeiter 5840
Pocheisen S. 1405
pochen 17257
Pochen 17313
Pocherz 17314
Pochgestein S. 17314
Pochhammer 13735
Pochkopf S. 8917
Pochmehl 17318
Pochmühle 808/a, 8495
Pochsatz S. 17309
Pochschlage 5605
Pochschuh 1405, 8917,
17534
Pochsohle 17311
Pochsteiger 2815
Pochstempel S. 5605, 10756,
17307
Pochtrog 13736, 17310
Pochtrübe S. 17318 , 14142
Pochwerk 12654, 17309,
17312, 17327
— -Laufzeit 11698
Podolit 13607
poikilitische Struktur 13608
Polarisationskapazität
13616
Polarographie 13618
Polen 13622
Polianit 13620
polierbar 13627

polieren 10538, 13623,
15756/a, 16583
Polieren S. 2403, 2522,
13630/a, 16585
Polierfähigkeit 7134
Polierhaken 7270
Polierknopf 4882, 10970,
13366, 14342, 16002,
16584. 17235, 17711
Polierkratzer S. 8210, 13631
Polierlöffel 17153
Poliermaschine 11953
Polieröl 15322
Polierrot 10164
Polier-S 5657
Polierschaufel 9415, 15653
— mit geradem Blatt 17239
— mit rundem Blatt 15287
Polierscheibe 2523
Polierstange 13628
Polierstein 208/a, 2611
polierte Oberfläche 13630
polierter Stabstahl 2402
— Stahl 13629
Politur 13626
Pollenit 13633
Pollux 13634
Polonium 13635
Polstärke 17777
poltern 14723
Polumschalter 13617
Polyadelphit 13636
Polyargit 13637
Polyargyrit 13638
Polyarsenit 13639
Polyäthylen 13647
Polybasit 13640
Polychroilith 13641
Polygonzimmerung 759,
14346
Polykras 13642
polymorph 13644
polysynthetische Zwillinge
S. 13646
Polystyrol 13645
Polyvinylharz 13648
Porenraum 13670
porig 12146
poriger Sand 12591
poriges Eisenerz 13675
poröse Struktur 9180, S.

13671, 13678
Porosität 13671, S. 13678
Porpezit 13679
porphyrartig 13681
Porphyrit 13680
Porphyroblast 11533, 14079
porphyroblastische Struktur
13682
Porphyroid 13683
Portalkran 8342, S. 13697
portalartiger Fahrleitungs-
mast für elektrische
Bahnen 17734
Porzellanabdampfschale
13663
Porzellanbecher 13660
Porzellanbrennofen 13661
Porzellaneinsatz des
Exsikkators 5223
Porzellangeräte 13669
Porzellanmass 13665
Porzellanring 13666
Porzellanröhre 13668
Porzellantiegel 13662
Porzellantrichter 13664
Porzellanwanne 13667
Positiv 13702
positive Kohle 13704
Posten 13707
Postendestillation 1331
Postenverfahren 1334
Potasche 10272
Potential S. 13733
Powellit 13773
Prägedruck 6404
prägen 3924
Prägestempel 7617/a,
17329
Prägung 9219
Prägwerk 17328
Prallfläche S. 8653
Prallpfosten 19085
— mit rundegeschmiedetem
Kopf 19074
Prallplatte 17110
Praseodym 13801
Praseolith 13802
Prasinit 13803
Präzisionsgebläse 18819
Präzisionsrohr 13825
Predazzit 13830

Prehnit 13842
Prellbolzen 14502
Prellklotz S. 14501
Prellung 14501
Pressdüse 6724
Presse 13867
— giessen (in der) 2974
Pressen 13892
— der Ziegel 13890
— hergestellt (durch) 13886
Presserzeugnis 13891
Pressfilter 1838
Pressflüssigkeit S. 13907
Pressformmaschine S.12022,
13872, 17264
Pressglimmer 13879
Pressgussform 13899
Pressgussmaschine mit
beweglicher Kammer 8363
Presshaut 13891/a
Pressholm 13868
Presskolben 13875
Presskork 13877
Pressling S. 2415
Pressluft 4134
Pressluft-Abscheider 13597
Pressluftbehälter 4135
Pressluftbohren 278/a
Pressluftbohrhammer 269,
283/a
Pressluftbohrmaschine
13590
Pressluftfeuerung 7866
Pressluftflaschenzug 13585
Presslufthammer 13584
— mit Bohrsäule 268
Presslufthaspel 19095
Pressluftmeissel 253
Pressluftstampfer 316
Pressluftstampfmaschine
13593
Pressluftvorschub 276
Pressmatrize 13889
Pressöl 13869
Pressplatte S. 12001, 13874,
13874, 17260
— mit Randwulst 14685,
17258
Presspumpe 13914, 7557
Pressrahmenhammer 5984
Pressrohr 9168

press· schmieden 13870
Press · schweissung 970
Press · stahl 4150
Press · stempel 10417/a
Presstorf 13880
Pressung S. 13892
Pressverfahren nach
  Ehrhardt 6229
Pressvergoldung 13871
Presswalze 13873
Presswasser 13905
Presswasserleitung 13913
Presszylinder 4154
Priceit S. 12893, 13930
Primär-Backenbrecher 13942
primäre Destillationsanlage
  16466
— Förderung 13943
— Schichtenneigung 13939
primäres Mineral 9390,
  12666/a
Primärfraktionierung 17709
Primärgraphit 13941
Primärnaphtha 13947
Primäröle 17717
Primärpetroleum 13948
Primärrückstände 17716
Primärteilchen 16394/a
Primärzementation 13937
Primordialgneis 7815
Primordialschiefer 7816
Prinzmetall 16365
Priorit 13959
Prisma dritter Ordnung S.
  13960
— zweiter Ordnung 13958
Prismatin 13966
prismatisch 13962
prismatische Absonderung S
  13964
— Spaltbarkeit 13963
prismatischsäulige
  Absonderung S. 4048
Prismatoid 13967
Probe S. 15453, 17030
— verwerfen 14680
— für das Fliessvermögen
  7470
Probebarren 18442
Probeblock 4551/a, 18445
Probebohrung 18880

Probedruck 18452
Probeentnahme-Bohrer 18254
Probeglas 15456
Probegut 15461
Probenahme 15460
Probeauswahl 15807
Probelöffel 15463
Probenverschluss 18451
Probertit 13970
Probesonde 15459, 16856
Probeschacht 18882
Probeschachtel 15457
Probestab 18449, 18454
Probestoff S. 15461
Probestreifen 18455
Probetreiben 18883
Probeziehen 4023
Probiergläserhalter 19041
Probiermuffelofen S. 4840
Probierofen S. 4840,
  18445/a
Probierstange 18453
Probierstein S. 7383, 18795
Probiertiegel 891
Produktion 8201
— bringen (zur) 2412
— gehen (in) 4085
— setzen (in) S.2412
Produktionsgang (in) 12542
Produktionskapazität S.
  13733
Produktionssäule 10975
produktive Zone 13003
produktives Ölfass 12545
Produktivitätsindex 14000
Profil 14000/a, S.15779
Profilalbum 14001
Profilbegrenzung 15987
Profilbuch S. 14001
Profildraht 15996
— mit 8-förmigem Quer-
  schnitt S. 15997
Profildrahtbewehrung 805
Profile S. 17887
Profileisen 8241, S. 15101,
  S. 15772, 15783, 15993,
  S. 15994, 17886, 17889
Profileisenschiene 15773
Profilfräser 7610, 14002
profilieren S. 7605
profiliert S. 7615

profilierte Schreckplatte
  5174
— Teilung 17559
profiliertes Rohr 15995
— Rohr für Metallfenster
  und Türen 19028
Profil-Kernstütze 4280,
  10120/a
Profilklotz 12001
Profilkörper 11263
Profilrohr 15780/a
Profilstahl 4236, 15101,
  15785, S. 15994
Profilwalze 15988
Profilwalzwerk 15778,
  15989
progressive Alterung 14005/a
  14005/a
— Druckschweissung 13924
Promethium 14006
Propan 14015
Proportionalitätsgrenze
  10823, 14024
Propylit 14028
Propylitisation 14029
Prosopit 14031
Prospektieren nach gedie-
  genem Gold 12421
Prospektierhammer 14037
Prospektor 14039
Protactinium 14048
Protobastit 14049
Protogin 14051
protoklastische Struktur
  14050
Protomylonit 14052
Protoparaffin 14053
Protrusion 14054
Proustit S. 815, 14055
prozentige Unreinheit 4897
prozentiger Analyse-Mittel-
  wert 1007
Prozentuale-Gewichtszu-
  sammensetzung 11852
Prüfbescheinigung 18444
Prüfdehngrenze 6391
prüfen 6634, 13968
Prüfen der Form durch
  nochmaliges Einlegen
  des Modells 14738
Prüfgerät 18467

Prüfglas 18456
Prüfkelch 18446
Prüflast 18447
Prüfmaschine 18465
Prüfspannung 14007/a
Prüfung S. 18461
— auf nassem Wege 6662
— auf trockenem Wege 6633
Prüfungsverfahren 18466
Prüfungsvorschrift 5473,
18462
Prüfwert 8458
Psammit 14063
psammitische Struktur 769
— Textur 14064
Psephit 14066, 14068
psephitische Struktur 14065,
14067, 15332
Pseudoboleit 14070
Pseudobrookit 14071
Pseudoessigsäure 14080
Pseudoglaukophan 14073
pseudokristallin 14072
Pseudoleucit 14075
Pseudomalachit 14076
pseudomorph 14077
Pseudomorphose 14078
Pseudonitrierung 14078/a
Pseudotachylyt 14082
Pseudowavellit 14083
Pseudozementieren 1681/a
Psilomelan 1649, 14085
Psittacinit 14086
Psychozoische Ära 14087
Ptilolit 14088
ptygmatische Textur 14089
Pucherit 14090
Puddeldrehofen 15234
Puddeleisen 14102
Puddeleisenwalzwerk 14098
Puddelflamme 14105/a
Puddelhütte 14115
Puddelluppe 14095
Puddelmaschine 14111
puddeln 14093
Puddeln 14106, 14316
— auf Korn S.14108
Puddelofen 14109
Puddelpaket 1794
Puddelroheisen 7578/a,
7579

Puddelschlacke S. 2564,
7414, 8742/a, 14097,
18266,
Puddelspiegel 17039
Puddelstahl S. 7580, 14100,
14104
Puddelverfahren 14114
Puddelwalze 14099
Puddelwerk S. 14115
Puddingstein 10422, 14092
Puddler 14105
Puderemaillierung 6032,
9413
Puffer 2516
Pufferbohle S. 2518
Puffertank 2520
Puglianit 14119
Pulaskit 14120
Pulsationsdämpfer 14145
pulsierend fliessen S.7420
Pulsometer 14146
Pultdächer 14041
pulveraufkohlen 13766
Pulverbrennstoff 14148
pulverförmiges Eisenerz
7086
Pulverpressen 13766/a
pulvertrocken 13767
Pumpanlage 14160
Pumpe anlassen (eine)
13946
— von Motoraggregat
angetrieben 18210
pumpen 15051, 17607
Pumpen 15052
Pumpenbock S. 14165
Pumpendruckfilter 5495
Pumpengestänge 16992,
17938
Pumpenkammer 18073
Pumpenkolben 14158
Pumpenlaufrad 15368
Pumpenrohrhaken 19030
Pumpensatz 10742
Pumpensonde 14171
Pumpenständer 17944
Pumpenstange 17080
Pumpensteiger 19511
Pumpenstempel nieder-
bringen 15340
Pumpenstock 13393, 13932

Pumpentrumm 14157
Pumpenvorderteil 10873
Pumpgeschwindigkeit 14169
Pumphauptanlage 3191
Pumprohr 14167, 19045
— mit angestauchten Enden
19377
— ohne Endverstärkung
13449
Pumpturm S. 13995
Pumpwärter 14163
Punktnahtschweissung 12119
punktschweissen 17160
Punktschweissmaschine
17163. 17165
punktschweissen 17162
Punktschweissung 16208,
17161, 17164, 18195
Purpurit 14195
purpurn 14193
Putzbank 3697
Putzbürste 15680
putzen 15654
Putzen S. 2578, 16199
Putzer 2620, 3046, 3702,
18897
Putzerei 3696
Putzerhelm 9069
Putzförderer 16778
Putzhäkchen 15650
Putzhaus S. 15481, S.15523
— mit Schleuderrad 16197
Putzkammer mit Aussen-
bedienung 15480
Putzleder 3275
Putzlöffel 3699
Putzmaschine S. 3046, 3704,
15478
Putzmittel 3705
Putzplatte 3743
Putzsand 15524
Putzscheuertrommel 3703
Putzstück 13237
Putztisch S. 3697
Putztrommel 1345, 14446,
19098
Putzwerkzeug 3706
Pyknometer 14207, 17025
pyramidenförmige Platte
14208
Pyrargillit 14210

Pyrargyrit 5004, 14211, 15330, 16359
Pyrgom 14212
Pyribol 14213
Pyrit 9970, 9997, 10347, 12130, S. 14214
pyrithaltige Kohle 2282, 8578
pyritisierter Ammonit 14215
Pyritöder 14216
Pyroaurit 14217
Pyrobelonit 14218
Pyrobitumen 14219
Pyrochlor 14220
Pyrochroit 14221
Pyroelektrizität 14224
pyrogenes Gestein 14226
pyroklastisch 14222
pyrokristallin 14223
Pyrolyse 14228
Pyrolusit 14227
Pyrometallurgie 9624, 14228/a
Pyrometamorphose 14229
Pyrometer 14230
Pyromorphit 8512, 14232
Pyrop S. 7973, S.11179, 14234
Pyrophanit 14235
Pyrophyllit 13058, 14236
pyrophore Legierung 9627/a, 16987/a
Pyrophysalit 14237
Pyrosmalith 14239
Pyrostilpnit 7150, 14241
Pyroxen 14242

Q

Quaderformation S. 4626
Quadersandstein 15530, 15531
Quaderstein 9116,
Quadranteisen 14244, 17232
quadratische Platte 17241
quadratischer Draht S.17251
Quadratsäuleneisen S. 18854
qualitative Untersuchung 14245

Qualitätseisen 14601
Qualitätsprüfung 14248
Qualitätsstahl S. 9153
Quant 14253/a
quantitative Erzanalyse 12627
— Untersuchung S.14250
Quantumresultat des Produktionsanlaufes 4116
Quartär 14278
Quartieren des Probegutes 14264
Quartzsand aus dem Meer 15732
Quarzdiorit 14267
Quarz-Feldspat Aggregat 14256
Quarzgang 14270
Quarzgerät 14272
Quarzglas 19572
quarzig 14275
quarzige Körner 14277
Quarzit 14271, 14273
Quarzlampe 13280
Quarzporphyr 14269
Quarzsand 6108, 14274
Quarzsandstein 14276, 16314
Quast 9090
Quecksilber 9508, 11503
Quecksilberbüchse 11505
Quecksilberchlorid 11499
Quecksilberchlorür 11502
Quecksilbergefäss 11511
Quecksilberhornerz S. 9361
Quecksilberlampe 11506
Quecksilberoxyd 11500, 14545
Quecksilberoxydulnitrat 1298 1298
Quecksilbersulfid 11501
Quecksilbervergoldung 8226
Quecksilberwanne 11510
Quecksilberzange 11509
Quellen 9019
Quellfassung 19970
Quellenguss 19357
Quellkuppe S. 9930
Querauswalzen S. 4703
Querbalken 4670, S. 10215, S. 16586

Querbau 4680, 4711, 4717, 16256
Querbiegeversuch 18842
Querfalte 18843
Querfaltversuch 4689
Querfalz 4688
Quergang 4532, 4675, 4699, S. 4709, S. 14383
Querhaupt S. 4692, 18607
Querholz S. 4668
Querlauf 15366
querlaufender Rücken 4667
quermagnetisch 5316
Querriegel S. 2008, 4715
Querriss 2438, 4584/a, 4676, 14127
Querschlag 1385, 4665, 4666, 4678, 4693, 4712, 4716, 8602, 18532
Querschnitt 1941, 4677, 4704
Querschnittsabnahme 4624a, 5722/a, 18100/a
Querschnittsempfindlichkeit S. 15780
Querschnittsverminderung 14574
Querschwelle 4706
Quersieder S. 4714
Quersiedekessel 7451
Quersiederohrkessel 4714
Querspalte 4908, 5441
Querstab 4669
Quersteg 4700
Querstollen S. 5850
Querstrecke 2338, S.2340, 4682, 4684, 16159, 16670
Quertal 18846
Querträger S. 4670, 4691, 10215
Querverwerfung 4686, 5437
Querwalzen 4703
Querzug 4687
Querzusammenziehung 12204 12204/a
Quetschhahn 3742
Quetschwerk 3357
Quickmühle 494
Quisqueit 14308

R

Racewinit 14318
Rachenlehre S. 2746, 16782
Rad aus einem Stück 16876
— mit aufgeschrumpftem
  Reifen 20012
Räderformmaschine S.8133
Räderkastenkern 8126
Räderwalzwerk 20010
Radialbohrmaschine 14326
radial-strahlige Struktur
  5581
radiale Struktur 17531
radialer Druck 14328
Radialprobe 14329
Radialsprung 14327
radialstengelig 5580
radialstrahlige Struktur
  14338
radioaktives Isotop 14335
Radioaktivitätslog 12417
Radiographie S. 14337
Radiolariengestein 14333
Radiolith 14334
Radiophyllit 14339
Radium 14341
Radkranz 20009
Radlenker S. 8643
Radnabe 20007
Radon 14344
Radsatz normaler Bauart
  17357
Radschleuder 3213
Radschrämmaschine 5483
Radspeiche 20011
Radstern aus Stahlguss
  3023
Raffinage s. Raffination
Raffination des Eisens auf
  elektrothermischem Wege
  6293
Raffination s. Raffinage
Raffinationsofen S. 14613
Raffinationsverfahren S.
  13978
Raffinationsvorgang S. 13978
Raffinerie-Arbeiter 17598
— -Produkt 20041
raffinieren S. 14593

Raffinieren des Stahls
  14618
raffinieren s. gärben
raffinierter Stahl S. 16400
raffiniertes Erdöl 18759
— Kupfer S. 18799
Raffiniergas 17594
Raffinierofen S. 14613
— für Blei 10622
Raffinierprozess 14616
Raglanit 14354
Rahmen 7709
— abheben (auf) 5766
Rahmenblech S. 7711
Rahmenhammer S. 5986
Rahmenplatte 7711
Raimondit 14368
Ralstonit 14386
Ramdohrit 14396
Ramierdraht 14397
Ramirit 14398
Rammbär 11900, S.14400
Ramme S. 14400
Rammelsbergit 14399
rammen S. 14387
Rammkopf 5955
Rammrohr 5956
Rammschelle 5954
Rammschuh 5957
Rampe S. 16678
Ramsayit 14408
Rand S. 4016, 6198
— des Zylinders 6203
— oder Ring der Walze
  4020
Randbiegung 7275
Randblasen 13093, S.13316
rändeln 2068
Randfalte 11317
Randfazies 11316
randhärten 2069
Randschicht 16478
Randsonde 6207
Randsteg S. 16273
Randverwerfung 2195
Randwasser 6204
Randwasserlinie 6206
Randwulst S. 7031
Randzone 2071
Ransomit 14415

rasche Abnützung des Ofens
  14303
— aufeinanderfolgende
  Funken 14418
Raseneisenerz S. 1945
Rasenhängebank 13984
Rasensohle S. 13984
Rasenerz S. 1945
Rasenerzlagerstätte S.1944
Rasierklinge 14464
Rasorit S. 10314
Raspel 14431
Raspit 14432
Rast 2118/a
— eines Hochofens 2120
Rastdruck 13912
Raster 4690
Rastformen 15789
Rasthöhe 9055
Rastmantel 16103
Rastmauerung 2119
Rastpanzer 2121
Rastplatte 2122
Raststeine 2123
Rastwinkel 574
Rathit 14438
Rattenloch 10304, 14433
Rattenschwanz 14434,
  14443
Rattermarke 3358/a
Raubbau 2504, 4577, 8367,
  19739
rauben S. 14995
Rauben der Zimmerung
  19340
Raubvorrichtung 5593,
  13711, 14012, 18147
Rauch 7816/a
Rauchabzugöffnung 3460
Rauchbeschädigung 4970
rauchende Salpetersäure 7818
  7818
Rauchfang 3461
Rauchgasuntersuchungs-
  apparat 7455
Rauchkanal 3459, 16762
rauchlose Kohle 16768
Rauchöl 16776
Rauchpunkt 16763
Rauchquarz 2689, 16769

Rauchrohr S. 3453, 16765
Rauchrohrkessel 1986
rauchverhütende Feuerung
16764
rauchverzehrender Herd
16760
Rauchverzehrungsrost
16761
Rauchzug S. 16762
Rauheit 15266
rauhes Eisenerz 14455
Rauhgemäuer 15251
Rauhwacke 16767
Rauhwaschtrommel 13850
Raum für die Probenahme
15151
— für metallographische
Untersuchungen 15150
Räumen 2430/a
Räumer 14478
— mit Bodenmeissel 4058
Raumgitter 16953
Raumgruppe 16952/a
Rauminhalt 4822
Raumit 14449
räumliches Tragwerk
«Unistrut» 19308
Räumlöffel S. 15667
Räummaschine 2431
Räumnadel 1408/a, 6668
Räumnadelstütze 15408/a
Raupe 1364
Raupenketten – 4612
Raupenkettenlader 13786
Raupenkettenwagen 3101
Raupenschweissung 1367,
7032
Rauschgelb S. 14437
Rauschgold 6142
Rautenblech 5328
Rauvit 14450
Reagens 14471
Reagentien 14473
Reagentienflasche 14472
Reagenzpapier 18448
reagieren 14466
Reaktion 14467
Reaktionstemperatur 18388
Reaktionswärme 8989
Realgar 14475
Rechen 14381

Rechen für Pumpengestänge
17947
rechnungsmässig 49
rechteckiger Block 14518
rechteckiges Rohr 14519
rechter Messerstahl 14905
rechter Steinmeissel S.
14905
rechtfallende Verwerfung
6851, 8704
rechtsinnige Verwerfung
S. 6851
Reckeisen S. 20130
recken 5760
Recken 20190
— s. Strecken
Redestillation 14555
Redouthit S. 3254
Redruthit 14558
Reduktion S. 14571
— ohne Gewinde 17918
Reduktionsbohrer 18105
Reduktionserdöl 14561
Reduktionsflamme 2863,
6639/a, 14567/a
Reduktionsflansch 126
Reduktionshahn 18106
Reduktionshülse mit Mitneh-
mer 127
Reduktionsmittel 5178/a,
14565
Reduktionsofen 14572
Reduktionsplatte 1811
Reduktionstemperatur 14578
Reduktionszone 14579
reduzieren 14559
reduzierend 14564
reduzierendes Schmelzen
14570
Reduziergesenk 14567
Reduzierstück 14563
reduziertes Eisen 14562
Reduzierwalzwerk 16424/a,
16447
Reed-Rollenmeissel 14582
Reemulgieren 1409
Reflexsismik 14620
Reformbenzin 14622
Refraktionssismik 14623
Regelklappe S. 2645
regelloser Halbrundstahl

6871
Regelschieber 4980
Regelung des Luftstromes 14
14660
Regelweiche S. 17347
Regenerativbrunner 16581
Regenerativfeuerung 14646
Regenerativkoksofen 14645
Regeneratöl 14497
Regenerator 10128
regenerierte Säure 14785
regenerierter Gletscher
14506
Regenerierungskammer 3367,
3372, 3378, 3405
Regenwasserabflussrohre
8689
Regionalgeologie 768
Regionalmetamorphose 11595
Registrierlastwagen 14507
regressive Entwicklung S.
10288
reguläres Krystallsystem
10068
Regulator 162
Regulierhahn 14656
Regulierung 4287
— mit Magnetverstärkern
11165
regulinischer Niederschlag
14662/a
Regulus 14663
Regulusofen 14664
Reibahle 2430, 14917/a,
14863/a
Reibschale 11937
Reibstein 15322/a
Reibstelle 4765
Reibung 7765, S. 15319
Reibungsbreccie 4766, S.
6844, 7766, 15402,
16012
Reibungsermüdung 7762
Reibungshammer 7768
Reibungsheizung 3237
Reibungskorrosion 7761
Reibungskupplung 7767
Reibungsrolle 7769
Reibungsverlust 11022
Reibungsverschleiss 7771/a,
940/a

Reichardtit 14672
reiches Bleierz 1604
— Erz 9152
Reichgas 14872
reichliche Luftzuführung
541
Reifen 9321
reifer Tiegel 7120
Reihennahtschweissung
15894
reine Kohle 3675
— Schleiffläche 3677
reiner 3676
— Stahl 14188, S.16400
reines Eisen 14187
— magnetisches Eisenoxyd
1564/a
— Öl 3679
— Zinn 14189
Reingewicht 12247
Reinheitsgrad 5136
reinigen 3671, 14192, S.
14593, S.15654
Reiniger 3685
Reinigung S. 3673, 5211,
14607
— mit rotierenden Rohr-
putzern 19124
Reinigungsmannschaft S
3680
Reinigungsmittel 14610,
15609
Reinigungsöffnung 3694
Reinugungstür 3693
Reinit 14678
Reise S. 18906
Reisigbündel 20172
Reissblei S. 8447
Reissit 14679
Reitelsäule 14311
Reiterlineal 5583
Reiterverschiebung 12053
Rekristallisation 14515
rekristallisiert 5590
Rektifikation 14520
Rektifikator 14521
Rektifizierungsturm 17861
Rekuperativanlage 14509
Rekuperativofen 14524
Rekuperator 14525
Reliefpolieren 14687

Reliefüberschiebung S. 6547
Renardit 14724
Rennen 5462
Rennenofen 3083
Rennfeuer 1827, S.3083
Rennfeuereisen S. 16835
Rennfeuerschlacke 3084
reoxydieren 14729
Reparatur der Schacht-
führungen 15061
Reparaturwerkstatt S.14731
Reservekessel 16976
Reserveschätzung 14743
Restfraktionen 14758
Restmagma 14754
Restöl 7542, 14755
Retinit 14704
Retortendestillation 14801
Retortenhalter 14800
Retortenkohle 14796
Retortenofen 14797
Retortenvergasung 14798
Retortengraphit S. 14796
Rettungsgürtel 15413
Rettungsmannschaft 9068
Reversierblechwalzwerk
14832
Reversierplatte S. 14828
Reversierwalzwerk 14495,
14833
— für Kaltwalzen 14830
— für Warmfertigwalzen
14831
Revolverdrehbank 19153
Revolverdrehbank mit Leit-
spindel 4062
Rezbanyit 14847
rezyklieren 14526
Rezyklus 14529
Rhabdophan 14848
Rhagit 14851
Rhät S. 14849
Rhätische Stufe 14849
Rhätizit 14850
Rheostat S. 6294
Rheowäsche 14852
rheumatitische Massen S.
6218
Rhipidolith 14938
Rhodanammonium 17979
Rhodizit 14853

Rhodochrosit 14854
Rhodonisieren 14852/a
Rhodonit 14855
Rhodetilith 14856
Rhodusit 14857
Rhombenporphyr 14859
rhombisches System 12684,
13965
rhombödrische Spaltbarkeit
2719
Rhönit 14861
Rhyotaxis S. 7468
Ribelinjektion 9816
richten 158, 17840
Richterit 14879
Richtmaschine 17725
Richtpresse 17727
Richtschiene 10716
Richtstrecke 180, S.5865,
8931, 8937
Richtstreckenstoss 8935
Richtung der Grubenbaue
(in) 9683
— der Kappe (in) 2817
richtungslose Struktur S.
11359
Richtungstunnel 5953,
14586
Richtwalze 17728
Rickardit 14880
Riebeckit 14888
riechendes Öl 16712
Riefenbildung 15646
Riegel 2008, 8245, 15005
Riemen 7280
Riemenpumpe 1477
Riemenschalter 1481
Riemenscheibenformmaschi-
ne 11126
Riemenscheibenmodellsatz
15910
Riemenschieber 1459
Rieselfläche 10043
Rieselkühler 18890
Riesenkessel 13720
Riff 14583
Riffazics 14587
Riffelblech 673, 3369, 3371,
3404, 14891
Riffelprobenteiler 17133
Riffelung S. 8586

Riffelwalze 4497
Rille 8586, 14909
Rillenrad 8588, 8592
Rindertalg 18224
Ring 3921, 14920
— aufwickeln (zu einem)
    20083
— oder Grateinguss 3592
Ringader 14922
Ringanschnitt S. 14924
Ringeinguss 14924
Ringfeder 625
ringförmige Schmelzrinne
    622
ringförmiger Gasfang 3590
— Kanal 3589
ringförmiges Modell 14930
Ringkern 14921/a
Ringleitung 20091
Ringofen 3593
— zum Brennen des Kalk-
    steins 620
Ringraum 624
Ringraumdruck 2952
Ringsiebeinguss 13057
Ringstütze 1087
Ringverleimung S. 15801
Ringwalzenmühle 14929
Rinkit 14933
Rinkolit 14934
Rinne S. 8586, S. 10586,
    S. 16708, S. 17171
Rinneit 14935
Rinneneisen 18591
Rinnen-Induktionsofen 3291
Rinnenschlacke 17173
Rinnentrog 15973
Ripidolith S. 3731
Rippe 1365/a, 7064/a,
    14864
Rippeneisen 14865
Rippenfederstahl 8595
Rippenguss 14866
Rippenrohr 8228
Rippenröhren 7143
Rippenrohrformmaschine
    12015
Rippenrohrheizkörper 7144
Rippenrohrkessel 1992
Rippenschiene 14867
Riss 3363, S. 4580, 7359,

S. 13552, S. 14893
Rissbeseitigung 17790
Rissbildung 7610,
    4587
Risse beseitigen S. 721
Rissfreiheit 7726
Risskorrosion 4627
rissig 4584
Rittingerit 14965
Ritz 15679/a
Ritzhärte 15681
Ritzhärteprüfer 15636
Ritzversuch 15682
Riversideit 14971
Rizzonit 14980
Röblingit 15063
Röchling-Rodenhauserscher
    Dreiphasenofen 15001
Rockwellhärteprobe 15044
Rodingit 15062
Rogenstein 12551
roh 1680, 19327
— gegossen 15246
— geschmiedet 15249
Rohausschneiden 15245
Rohbarren 12059, 14096
Rohblech 14460
Rohbramme 16499
Rohdolomit 14453
Roheisen 12059/a, 13259,
    14454
— frischen 14595
— für feuerbeständigen
    Guss 7667
— für säurebeständigen
    Guss 7666
— zusetzen 13247
Roheisenbad 13261
Roheisengichtsatz 13263
Roheisenguss 2995
Roheisenmassel 3427, S.
    13249
Roheisenmischer 11550,
    11831, 13264
Roheisenwagen 13265
Roherdöl 19689
rohes Erdöl S. 1283
Roherz 14458
Rohfrischen 8500
Rohgang 4009
Rohgas 5476/a

Rohgewalzt 15252
Rohgewicht 8604
Rohguss 838,
    15247
Rohkohle S. 4754, 8526/a,
    14452
Rohkupfer 1769, S. 1783,
    4753
Rohkupferstab 3418/a
Rohling 677, 1679, 9276,
    13834
Rohmasseln 13258
Rohöl 1283, 4754, 11950
Rohölrückstand 4752
Rohr auskleiden (ein-) 2908
— für Backofen 11979
— für Brustwehren 18996
— für Büchsen 19000
— für chemische Anlagen
    13337
— für den Fahrrad- und
    Motorradbau 18985
— für Destillieranlagen
    18993
— für Druckwasserleitungen
    13341
— für Feuerlöschanlagen
    18995
— für Flugzeugsteuer-Knüp-
    pel 18982
— für Geländer 19012
— für Gewehrläufe 13343
— für Gitter 18999
— für Gusskerne 18997
— für Hebebäume 19024
— für hohle Transmissions-
    wellen 19002
— für Hülsen 19020
— für hydrodynamische
    Apparate 19004
— für Industrie-Wasserversor-
    gung 13338
— für Kontrolleitungen
    18989
— für Kraftübertragungswel-
    len 19025
— für Kühlanlagen 19015
— für Pfeiler 19007
— für Puffer 9265
— für Raffinerieanlagen
    13343

Rohr für Reformieranlagen 19014
— für Schranken an Bahnübergängen 19013
— für Schraubenwellen 19011
— für Spaltanlagen 18991
— für Spaltstoffelemente 18998
— für Spannfutter bei Werkzeugmaschinen 19006
— für Syntheseanlagen 18168
— für thermische Anlagen 13344
— für Unterwasserleitungen 19023
— für Wärmeaustauscher 13340
— für Wasserleitungen 13846
— mit abgeschrägten Enden 13370
— mit angestauchten Enden 19375
— mit Gasgewinde 15717
— mit glatter Verbindung 7484
— mit Scheidewänden 19044
— und Formstück für Hinterrad-Aufhängungen 18975
— zur Ausbeutung von Lagern 18987
Rohrachse 19059
— mit Zapfen 19060
Rohransatz 13351
Rohraufhänger 2944
Rohraufweitedorn 18980
Rohrausleger 19093
— für Fahrleitungen 19063
— für Leitungen und Lampenhalter 19094
Rohrbalken 19061
Rohrbatterie 2961
Rohrbirne 2963
Rohrbogen mit engem Radius 16182
Rohrbohrer 2954
Rohrbrunnen 7676
Rohrbündel 19033

Röhre während der Wasserdruckprobe abhämmern (die) 8728
— ziehen 5772
— zusammenschrauben 11233
Röhrenofen 19029/a
röhrenförmiger Bohrturm 19088
Röhrengreifhaken 2935, 19056
Röhrenkessel 19062
Röhrenbiegemaschine 19061
Röhrenschuh 19961
Röhrenstutzplatte 6454
Röhrentour S. 2932
Röhrenwalzapparat S. 18980
Röhrenwalzwerk S. 13364
Rohrfabrik 19032
Rohrfahrt S. 2932, S.17834
Rohrfänger 1460, 2940, 13347, 16999
Rohrfangglocke 2933
Rohrfangtute S. 1460
Rohrfangvorrichtung 3091
rohrförmiger Aufbauteil 19082
Rohrgerüst 19073
Rohrgittermast für elektrische Leitungen 19076
Rohrgreifhaken 19049
Rohrguss 18977
Rohrheber 2938
Rohrhohlkehle 19637
Rohrkabeltragseil 9239
Rohrkaliber 5851, 14310
Rohrkandelaber 19064
Rohrkeilklemme 17076, 19884
Rohrkeilkranz 2959
Rohrkern 19067
Rohrklemmkeile 16663
Rohrkopf 2249, 2794, 2943
Rohrkrätzer 2956, 19039
Rohrkrebs S. 2958
Rohrkrümmer S. 1501
Rohrkugelmühle 11678
Rohrlänge 10204
Rohrlegen 13354
Rohrleger 13358
Rohrleitung 6072/a, 13355,

13380
Rohrleitung für Wiedergewinnungsanlagen 13384
— mit konstantem Durchmesser 17713
Rohrleitungsnetz 13385
Rohrlocher 2942
Rohrlötzinn 14763
Rohrluppe 9262
Rohrmantel 13352, 13357
Rohrmast für Scheinwerfer 1363
Rohrmuffe 2936, 16591
Rohrmühle 19077
Rohrnippel 13359
Rohrpackung 19034
Rohrperforator 2951
Rohrplatte 19035
Rohrprodukt 19080
Rohrprofile 2962
Rohrreibahle 13361
Rohrverstopfung 13330
Rohrriegel des Windverbandes 19068
Rohrsäule für Bahnsteigüberdachungen 19066
— für Feuerlöschhydranten 7171
— für Ladung der Tender 18404
Rohrschelle 13349
Rohrschlangen für Strahlungsheizanlagen 19065
Rohrschleuse 11080
Rohrschlitzer 2955, 2960
Rohrschlüssel 13335, 16784
Rohrschneider 2937, 13334, 18978
Rohrschneidemaschine S. 13334
Rohrschraubenschlüssel 19086
Rohrschuh 2957
Rohrschutzring 19075
Rohrschweissnaht 19043
Rohrschwimmerventil 3172
Rohrspannschloss 19092
Rohrsplitter 13658
Rohrstrang S. 2932
Rohrstreifen 16448/a
Rohrstück 7227

Senkblei 1930
Senkbrunnen 17999
Senkbühne 11075
Senken des Förderkorbes 11013
— des Versatzes 16129
Senklot 13568
Senkniet 7337
senkrechte Getriebezimmerung 19531
— Stellung 19368
— Zimmerung 19527
senkrechter Gaskanal 19382
— und schräger Förderer
senkrechtes Hebewerk 6377
Senkschacht 5993
Senkschuh 16150, 16422
Senkung 15153
— der Firste 8248
— der Tagesoberfläche 5017
— des Kegels 11073
— des Metallspiegels 10338
Senkungsbewegung des Festlandes 9551
Senkwaagedichtigkeitsmesser 6230
Senkzone 767
Senoman 15855
Sense 15780
Separator S. 15878
Sepiolith 11439, 15882
Septarie 15883, 19156
Septum 15884
Sequan 15886
Serandit 15888
Serendibit 15889
Serizitisierung S. 15892
Serizit 15891
Serizitisation 15893
serizitisch 15892
Serpentin 15895
Serpentinmarmor 10904
Servomotor 18604
Setzarbeit 10179, 16468
Setzbett 14352
Setzboden 3322, 3348,
setzen 10169, S. 15902
Setzen auf das Sandbett 1429
Setzhammer 8870/a

Setzmaschine 10170, 10177, 10181, 10226
Setztiefe 15918
Setzwaage 13569
Sextanteisen 15928
Seybertit 15929
S-Haken 15403
Shastait 16009
Shastalith 16010
Shattuckit 16016
Sherardisieren 16117
Shonkinit 16158
Shorehärte 16171
Shoshonit 16190
Sial 16247
Sialma 16248
Siberit 16249
sich anhäufen 2530
— auskeilen 12320
— festfressen 10118
— verjüngen 18275
— zersetzen 5067
— zersplittern 16011
sichere Reserve 14056
Sicherheitsbühne 13071
Sicherheitsgliederklemme 15414
Sicherheitsgurt S. 15413
Sicherheitskabel 10735
Sicherheitslampe 15419
Sicherheitsmuffe 15418
Sicherheitsöllampe 15422
Sicherheitspfeiler 17657, 19647
Sicherheitsröhre 15416
Sicherheitssprengstoff 15417
Sicherheitsstange 1457
Sicherheitsstufenbelag S. 12365
Sicherheitsventil 1886, 12291, 15425
Sicherheitsverbinder S. 15418
Sicherheitsvorrichtung 15415, S. 15420
— am Förderturm gegen Übertreiben 8912
Sichertrog 2513, S. 8348, 9357
sichtbarer Fehler S. 19567
sichten S. 14884, 16923
Sichtungsanlage S. 15865

Sickerloch 16795
Sicklerit 16250
Siderolith 16284
Sideronatrit 16285
Siderophyllit 16286
Sieb 14883, 14885, 16298, S. 17736, S. 19463
Siebanlage 15696
Siebdüse S. 15689
Siebeingussrinne 13056
sieben 16296
Sieberaktion 16298/a
Sieberei S. 15696
Siebkammer 17738
Siebkern S. 6008, 7044/a, 17737
Siebkohle S. 15276
Siebkoks 16304
Siebmasche 16300
Siebnetz 20121
Siebrost 16299
Siebrückstand 15697
Siebsatz 15911
Siebschale 17739
Siebstruktur 16301
Siebtrommel 4942, 15605
Siebung 15693, 16305
Siebvorrichtung 16306
Siede 17431
Siedehitze ausfällen (in der) 13808
Siedekessel 7754
siedendes Wasser S. 2001
Siederohr für Rauchrohrkessel 9005
Siegelerde 2002
Siegerländer Schachtofen 16289
— Roheisen 16288
Siemens-Generator 16295
— -Martin Ofen 12574, 16293
— -Martinofen raffinieren (im) 12579
— -Martinverfahren 12578
— -Ofen 16292
— -Prozess 13250, 16294
Siemenssche Wechselklappe 16290
Signaldraht 10410
Signalhammer 10409
Signalseil 1453

roter Turmalin 14551
rotes Blutlaugensalz 13726
— Pechuran S. 8667
Rotgiesser 4357
Rotglut 14540
— brennen (in) 8970
Rotglühthärte 14539
Rotguss 14331
rotierender Ofen 14837,
    15208
— Puddelofen S.15234
— Trockner 15198/a
Rotierofen S. 15210
rötlicher Ton 14553
Rotnickelkies 4359, S.12263
Rotogalvanostegie 1243
Rotstahleisen S. 17040
rotwarm 14536
Rotwärme bringen (auf)
    2414
rotwarmes Eisen S. 14542
Rotzinkerz S. 20344
Rougemontit 15241
Routivarit 15298
Rouvillit 15299
Rubellit 15325
Rubicell 15326, 20292
Rubidium 15327
Rubin 15329
Rubinbalais 1141
Rückbau 1050, 11779, 14802,
    20210, 20220
— der Pfeiler 5776, 5793,
    14138, 18221
Rückbiegungsverlust 11023
Rückdruckstift 6240
Rücken 19278
Rückenwand 1053
Rückfluss 14156
Rückfüllung 1055
Rückgang S. 5065, 14816
Rückgass·schweissung
    1060, 1089/a, 14907
Rückgewinnungssäure 14508
rückkehrende Rohre 15354
Rückkohlung 14485, 4347
Rücklaufmaterial 8106,
    15377
Rückraupe 1049
Rückschlag 1064
Rückschlagventil 3366

Rückschlagventil in der
    schweren Stange 5934
rückschreitende Erosion
    14805
— Metamorphose 14803
Rückschweissung 1076,
    1084/a
Rückseite 1044, 18311
Rückstand 2144, 7545,
    12778, 9049, 14753,
    18215
— der ersten Destillation
    18758, 18757
Rückstandventil 18319
Rückstein 1077
Rückstosser S. 6240
Rücktitrieren 1080
rückwirkende Elastizität S.
    6247
Rudisten-Fazies S. 9211
Rudit 15334
Ruhebühne 10467, S. 10525
Ruhegrube 17597
ruhiger Stahl 5039
Rühreinrichtung 14317
rühren 3559
Rührhaken S. 9999
Rührstab 8283
Rührstange S. 14381
Rührtank 235
Rührvorrichtung 17609
Rührwerk 237, 14313, S.
    17609
Rumpfit 15336
Rumpffläche 5181, 13061,
    17860
rund 15267
Rundanker 15286
Rundbarre 15284
Rundblech 3595
Runddichtung 8078
runde Gussputzbürste 3588
— Platte S. 3595
Rundeisen 10004, 15046,
    15270, 15285
Rundeisenbiegemaschine
    1210
Rundeisenbiegung 1211
Rundeisenkaliber 15058
Rundeisenwalzung 15059
runder Einguss 1154/a,

    16369
Rundfunkmast 14336
rundgeriebene Oberfläche
    15280
Rundherd 15274
Rundkaliber 15288
Rundkanal 14926
rundkantige Profile 17350
rundkantiger Flachstahl
    15278
— Winkelstahl S. 581, 1381
rundkantiges Formeisen
    15279, 15777
— Winkeleisen 584
Rundkessel 17060
Rundknopf 15291
Rundkolben 15273
Rundkopfstift 15282
Rundkörper 15194
Rundlitzenseil 15293
Rundlochbrenner 3601
Rundnahtschweissung 3598
Rundniet 15290
— mit grossem Kopf 12142,
    18964
Rundplatte 4883
Rundporenporosität 15289
Rundrohling 13373
Rundstab S. 10004, 15269
Rundstahl 15271, 15292
— in Ringen 15295
Rundstrahlbrenner 6806
Russ 16917
Rüssel der Form 19162
russig 16918
Russkohle 16919
Ruthenium 15399
Rutherfordin 15400
Rutil 15401
Rutschausleger 4321
Rutsche 16162, S.17171
Rutschmann 9694
Rutschmaschine 9693
rutschen S. 16644
Rutschen S. 16645, 16666
Rutschfläche 16603, S.
    16664
Rutschrille S. 17799, 17802
Rutschschere 10136, 10125
Rutschscherenfänger 10126,
    10131

Rutschscherenschaft 10132
Rutschstreifen 17799
Rutschung S. 3122, S.4622,
 S. 6778
Rüttelformmaschine 10129,
 10219, 10227
— mit Aushebung 10222
— mit Stiftabhebung 10220
Rüttelformen 10218
Rüttelmaschine 10150/a
Rütteln 10217, 10135,
 10225
Rüttelung S. 10135
Runzel 13549
Runzeln 5984/a, 18050
Runzelung 4759, 8339, S.
 11787, S. 14091

S

Sackbohrer 15404
Sackförderer 15405
Sackloch 1767/a
Sägeblatt 15557
Sägebogen 15559
Sägefeilkluppe 15558
Sägen 15563/a
Sagenit 15427
Sägestahl 15560
Sägezahnkrone 15563
Sägezahnlauf 15562
Sagvandit 15430
Sahelian 15431
saigere Sprunghöhe 716
— Verwerfung S. 19526
saigeres Flöz 9021
Saigergang 19539
Saigersprung S. 19526
Salband 907, 3657, 3662,
 15435, 15835, 19490,
 19633
salfemisch 15437
Salit 15432, 15438
Salmiak 15433, 15439
Salmonsit 15440
Salopian 15441
Salpeter 15447
Salpeterbildung 12315
Salpetersäure 1032, 12309

Salzbadhärten 15443
Salzbadofen 15442
Salzdom 15444
Salzkruste 18739/a
Salzkupfererz S.915
Salzlösung 2407
Salzsäure 9549
Salzsprühversuch 15445
Salzwasserentfernung
 15446
Samarium 15449
Samarskit 15450
Samiresit 15451
Sammler 54
Sammelgebäude 55
Sammelfuchs 4024
Sammelgefäss 14488
Sammelgrube 3086
Sammelherd 10000
Sammelkammer 8925
Sammelkristallisation 15452
Sammelleitung S. 8100
Sammeltank 8103
Sammeltrumm 3342
Samsonit 15465
Sanadin S. 14863
Sand 15469
— auflockern 186
— brechen S. 2305
— magern 19852
— poliert (mit) 15526
— schleudern 2305
— von Guss·stück
 entfernen S. 1696
Sandaufbereitungsanlage
 15513
Sandausscheuerung S. 15491
Sandbad 15470
Sandbadschale 5514
Sandbank 9212
Sandbett S. 13251
— stellen (auf das) 1412
Sandblastraum 15523
Sanddicke 15520
Sandeinschluss 9712, 15509,
 15566
Sandform S. 6041, 15505, S.
 16472
sandformen 15468
Sandformen gegossenes
 Roheisen (in) 15487

Sandformerei 15506
sandfreier Guss 15527
Sandfurche S. 10207
Sandguss 15489, 15490
Sandgussrohr 15488
Sandhaken 3684, 3688, 7906
sandig 8535
sandige Fazies 15533
sandiger Eisenstein 15534
Sandkohle S. 3757, 7721, S.
 10640
Sandkruste 15718
Sandleiste 15493
Sandloch 15499
Sandmischmaschine S.15504
Sandmischer 15504
Sandmodell 15510
Sandnest 15526/a
Sandpapier 15509
Sandpumpe 15514
Sandpyramide 5988
Sandrohr 15512
Sandrückgewinnungsmaschi-
 ne 5293
Sandstrahl 15472
Sandstrahlen S. 15477
Sandschleuder 187/a, 189
Sandschleudern 2337/a,
 15491
Sandstein 7184/a, 15529,
 17640
Sandtrockenofen 15492
Sanduhrstruktur 9458
Sandverdichtung 15508
Sandwichwalzen 15532
Sandwulst 10208
Sandzugabe S. 141
Sandzusammenbacken 15498a
Sandzusatz 133, 141
Sanidin 8287, 15535
Sanidinit 15536
Sannoisian 15537
Santorinit 15538
Sanukit 15539
Saphir 15541
Saponit 13325, 15540
Saprokell 16639
Sapropelit 15542
Sarder 15545
Sardonyx 15546
Sarkinit 15547

Sarkolith 15543
Sarkopsid 15544
Särnait 15548
Sartorit 15549
Sassolin 15551
Sattel 15408
Sattelflügel 658
Sattelkern 4426, 755
Sattelkopf 4725
Sattellinie S. 660, 655, S.
    4625
Sattelplatte 7023
Sattelscharnier 754
Sättigungsdruck 15556
Satz 3316, S. 15903
Satzanzeiger 3320
Satz-Gewindebohrer 8783
Satzkoks 3319, 3946
Satzmischer 1329
satzweise 2654
satzweises Pumpen 17290
Sau 1382/a, S. 9958, 16951
sauber 3674
sauer 13115
Sauerstoff 12817
Sauerstoffabsorption 21
Sauerstoffaufnahme durch
    Kohle 22
sauerstoffaufnehmender
    Zuschlag 5185
Sauerstoff-Azetylen-
    schweissung 12813
Sauerstoffbrennerrohr 12819
Sauerstoffentziehung S.5179
sauerstoffhaltiges Eisen
    9969, 15398
Sauerstofflanze 12819/a
Sauerstoffflasche für
    Atmungsgeräte 16739
Sauerstoffnippel 12820
sauerstoffreicher Gasstrom
    7995
Sauerstoffsprengmittel 10878
Sauerstoffüberschuss 6641
Sauerstoffverbindung 12818
Sauerstoff-Wasserstoff-
    schweissung 12816
Saugbagger 7490
saugen 5755,
Saugen S. 13383
saugende Bewetterung 6651

saugender Sand 18519
— Ventilator 6650
Sauggas 17955/a
Saugkanal 17958
Saugkopf mit Tangential-
    anschnitt 20020
Saugkorb 3681, 16788, 17735
    17735/a, 17953
Saugkuppelofen 6797
Saugleitung 17954
Saugluft 17950
Saugpumpe 17959
Saugschlauch 17943, 17956
Saugventil 17961
Saugvorrichtung 17955
Saugwindkessel 17951
Säule 4038
Säulenbohrmaschine 4041,
    13710
Säulenbohrung 10423
Säuleneisen 14244/a, 19182
säulenförmig 4044
säulenförmige Absonderung
    4048, 13964
— Kristalle 4045
säulenförmiger Bruch 4046
Säulenführungsgestell
    5378/a
Säulenhaspel S. 19095
Säulenschrämmaschine 19155
Säulenverankerungsrolle
    10529
Säulenwaage 4040
Säulenzahnrädformmaschine
    8135
Saum S. 14914
Saumschere 18903/a
Säure 74
saure Bohrung 16945
— Gesteine 91
— Schlacke 93
Säure unlöslicher Rückstand
    (in) 14759
Säurebad 75, 13217
Säurebehandlung 100
säurebeständig 86
säurebeständiger Stahl 88,
    90/a
Säurebildner 99
säurefähig 98
säurefester Anstrich 652

säurefester Kasten 87
säurehaltig 97
säurehaltiges Abwasser
    19738
Säureherd 78
Säureprobe 13218
saurer feurfester Stein 90
— Martinofen 83
— Schlamm 94, 12070
— Siemens-Martinstahl 84,
    92/a
— Stein 16313
Säureerhitzungsprobe 80
Säureraum 92
saures Gas 16944
— Ion 81
— Oxyd 96.
— Verfahren 85, S.1553
Saussurit 15552
Saussuritisation 15553
Saussuritgabbro 369
Saxonian 15564
Schablone 12973, 17806, S.
    18400
Schablonenarm 17810
Schablonendrehbank S. 4377
Schablonenformerei 18113,
    18115, 18401
Schablonenhalter 796, S.
    17810, 18734
Schablonenspindel S.17090
Schablonierbrett 17809,
    18112/a
Schabloniereinrichtung
    17804
Schablonieren 1424, 17811
schablonierter Kern 18125
Schab(e)vorrichtung 15676
Schacht 8631, 11740, 13397,
    15932, 17275/a
— ausserhalb des Lagers
    12709
— in Produktion setzen 2410
— eines Hochofens 15951
— mit Mantel 9994
— mit Stahlausbau 17514
— mit Ziegelmauerung
    11356
Schachtabteufen 15962
— nach dem Zementierver-
    fahren 8628, 8630, 15956

Schachtabteufen unter
 Anwendung von Press-
 luft 13592
Schachtanlage 15905, 15947
Schachtarbeiter S. 13422
Schachtausbau 2929, 3902,
 13398, 15958, 19658,
 19960
— mit Schrotzimmerung
 4861
Schachtausmauerung 15950
Schachtbohren 19963
Schachtbolzen 17897
Schachbrettschacht 7228
Schachbrettstruktur 3411
Schachtbühne S. 10525, S.
 15576, 15577
Schächtchen für Spann-
 vorrichtung 1130
Schachte Kernkabelscheibe
 (auf dem) 4420
Schachtflammofen für Queck-
 silbererze S. 2624
Schachtfördermaschine 1192,
 15946
Schachtförderung 9229
— mit Greiferkübel 1103
Schachtgebäude 8914
Schachtgerüst 15960
Schachtgeviert 4630, 4635,
 15938, 18879
Schachtgewinnung 15944
Schachtgitter 15942
Schachtglühofen 15941
Schachthalle 2240
Schachthängebank 10525
Schachthärteofen 15940
Schachthäuer 15963
Schachthochbrechen 19367
Schachtholz S. 2584
Schachtkranz 16107
Schachtleistungsvermögen
 20059
Schachtmaurer 3915
Schachtmündung 4017
— (an der) 914
Schachtofen S. 3002, 9149,
 15939, 15948
Schachtöffnung 12045,
 15936, 15964
Schachtpfeiler 2175, 10712,

15952
Schachtpumpe 15954
Schachtputzanlage 3701
Schachtraum 19962
Schachträumer 6486
Schachtring 4860, 14921
Schachtscheider S. 5584
Schachtstein 15935
Schachtstoss-Kernbohrung
 15462
Schachtsumpf 17991
Schachtwandung 15961,
 15965
Schadhaftwerden des
 Gestelles 5256
Schaden 6767
schädlich 12406
schädlicher Bestandteil
 5266
Schaffhaken S. 9312
Schaft S. 15931
Schairerit 15613
Schalbrett S. 16492
Schalbretter S. 10489
Schale 4481, 5511, S. 16093,
 18101
Schalen gegossen (in) 16098
Schalenbildung 2606, 11557
Schalenblende 2131
Schalenelektrode 5516
Schaleneisenstein 2132
Schalenform S. 3433
Schalenguss S. 3442, S.3443,
 5360
Schalengussmaschine 16102
Schalenhärtung S. 2918
Schalenkalt S. 729
schalige Absonderung S.
 6648
Schallbrett S. 17899
Schallerit 15615
Schallisolierung aus Stein-
 wolle 108
Schaltbrett 18133
Schaltknopf 17381
Schamotte 97, 3277
Schamotteguss 3279
Schamottesand 3280
Schamottestein 467, 3278
Schapbachit 15617
Schappe S. 16096

scharf 8607, 16001
schärfen 16006
scharfer Sand 16005
scharfkantig 16004
scharfkantiger Stahl 6870
scharfkantiger Winkelstahl
 582
scharfkantiges Formeisen 15776
 15776
— Winkeleisen 585
Schärfmittel 7
Scharfschleifen S. 16008
Scharnier 1501/a, S. 9198
— -Kernkasten 2041
Scharnierplatte S. 9202
Scharte 19245/a
Schaubild 5312
Schaufel S. 15639
Schaufelbolzen S. 9314
Schaufelfeuerung 16216
Schaufellader 11412
Schaufelrad 9652
Schaufelstahl 16214
Schaufelung 16215
Schaufler 12064
schaukeln 15003
Schaukelofen 15039
Schauklappe 8761
Schauloch 18364
Schaum 5103, 16489
Schaumbildung 7784
Schaumdämpfer 662
Schäumer 7513
schaumförmiger Zustand
 7510
schaumig 7783, 13672
schaumige Schlacke 7512
Schaumkalk S. 687, 773
Schaumlöffel 16467
Schaumschwimmaufbereitung
 7782
Schaumstück 13676
Schaumtrichter 20019
Schauöffnung 9847, 13044
Scheelit 15618, 16043
Scheererit 15619
Schefferit 15620
Scheibe 5479, 16596
Scheibenausgleicher 5481
Scheibenbau 16599
Scheibenbruchbau 14013

Scheibenkolben 16885
Scheibenfeder 5485
Scheibenfräser 16268
Scheibenmeissel 5480, 5482
Scheibenwalze 5484/a
Scheibenziehbank 5800
Scheiderarbeiter S. 13210,
    19626
Scheidebecken 15879
scheiden 10934
Scheiden 16582
scheiden von Erzen 3883
Scheideofen 12948
Scheider 2550
— von Edison 6214
Scheiderz 3894, 13208,
    15692
Scheidesilber 12951
Scheidevorrichtung 15694
Scheidewand 15867
Scheidezweck 12431
Scheidung 1758, S. 5842, S.
    12947, S. 16582, 16926,
    16966
— der Erze 2505
scheinbare söhlige Sprung-
    breite 709
— Sprungbreite in der
    Schichtebene 711
— stratigraphische Wechsel-
    breite 712
— Versetzung 14394
scheinbares Einfallen 708
— Gewinde 15708
Scheinwerferkohle 15754
Scheitel S. 4724
— des Bodens 18744
Scheitelbruch 2315
scheitrechter Boden 10713
Schelf 16092
Schelle S. 3619, 15407
Schenkel 10666, 15983,
    15984, 16267, 19872
Schenkelbruch 656
Scherbeanspruchung 16036
Scherbenkobalt 11567
Schere 16022, 16038
scheren 16018
Scherenfehler 16028
Scherenmesser 16039
Scherfestigkeit 16035

Scherspannung 16034
Schertelit 15621
Scherung 16020
Scherversuch 16037
Schicht 1686, S. 3316, S.
    4552, S. 10499, 10594,
    S. 10659, S. 16045,
    16122, 17753
Schichtdauer 1197
Schichtdruckmessgerät 2015
Schichten 17746
— ölgetränkt 18524
Schichtenbildung 7607
Schichtendruck 14749
Schichtenfolge 1421
Schichtenkohle S. 7530
Schichtenpackung 14884
schichtenparallele Verwer-
    fung S. 1432, 16608
Schichtensprung S. 16608
Schichtenstörung S. 10645
Schichtenunterbrechung
    2313
Schichtenwechsel 435
Schichtenfallwinkel 1431
Schichtfalte 7371
Schichtfläche 1434, 12949
Schichtfolge S. 4047
— mit Adern durchsetzt
    2750
Schichtgitter 10594/a
Schichtliegende 7409
Schichtling 782
Schichtprüfer 19053
Schichtsteiger 16123
Schichtung 1430, 16088
Schichtungsdiskordanz 5505
Schichtungswinkel 573
schichtweise 9677
Schiebe-Falttüren 16616
Schiebekassette 16618
Schieberboden 16617
Schieberost 16623
Schiebersteuerung 16615
Schieberteller S. 1131
Schieberventil 16614
Schiebetür 16620
Schiebebühne 18862
Schiebungsmesser 5534
Schiedsanalyse 734

Schiedschemiker 735
schief 16449
— abgeschnittenes Prisma
    13961
schiefe Falte 9699, 19337
schiefer Bruch 12434
Schiefer 15625/a, 16574
schieferig s. blätterig S.
    7530
schieferige Kohle 1318, 2028
    2028
— Textur 7533
schieferiger Ton 16577
Schieferkohle 1183, 2028,
    7530
Schiefernagel 16575
Schieferstein S. 16574
Schieferton S. 783, S. 1676,
    12095
schiefes Prisma 12435
— Winkeleisen 12440
Schieferung 3718, 7531,
    7532, 16140
schiefstreichende Verwerf-
    ung S. 5208
schiefwinkliges Z-Eisen
    12441
Schienenschraube 16588
schienen s. plätten
Schienenfuss S. 7538, 7544
Schienenherzstück 2539
Schienenkaliber 14361
Schienenkopf 14538
Schienennagel S. 14563,
    17079
Schienenrost 8468
Schienensteg 19874
Schienenwalzwerk 14362
Schiessarbeit S. 1743, S.
    16164
Schiessbaumwolle 8672
schiessen S. 16160
Schiesskopfplatte 1878
Schiessloch S. 1741
Schiessmeister S. 1736, S.
    3329, 9252, 11734
Schiessnadel 12205, 16451
Schiessort 14490
Schiess·schalter 16986
Schiffanfertigung 16617/a
Schiffbaustahl 17891

Schiffsblech 16137
Schiffssiederohrkessel 11325
Schiffskessel 11324
Schiffsraum-und Deckstütze
  5063
Schiffstonnage 18722
Schilfglaserz S. 7751
Schiller 15622
Schillerfels 7897
Schillern S. 1006, 3357/a,
  15624
Schillerspat 15623
Schinglengrube 10999/a
Schippe 16212
Schirbel 16494
Schirmerit 15625
Schlacke 3570, 14349, 15728,
  16347, 16431, 16519
Schlacken 16567
Schlackenabfluss 16533
Schlackenabstich S. 16554,
  16558, 16566
Schlackenabstichloch S.7415
Schlackenansatz 149
Schlackenauge 7415
Schlackenbad 16523
schlackenbildend 16535
Schlackenbildung 15596
Schlackenbildungsperiode
  16536
Schlackenblech 16545
Schlackenblock 16525
Schlackendamm 16461/a
Schlackendecke 16531
Schlackeneisenschluss 9713
  16540
Schlackenfaden 16559
Schlackenfang 5476, 6008
Schlackenfänger S.5476
Schlackenfangmulde 16546
Schlackenform 16562
Schlackenformkühler 11901a
schlackenfrei 7728
Schlackenfrischen 13252
Schlackenhalde 3572, 6096,
  S. 6101, 16534, 16560
schlackenhaltig 4250
schlackenhaltiges Eisen S.
  17144
— Roheisen 3576
Schlackenherd 16538

Schlackenkanal 16561
Schlackenkranz 2382
Schlackenkranzbildung 2388
Schlackenkruste 16532
Schlackenkuchen 2962,
  16529
Schlackenkugel 16522
Schlackenloch 2347, 3574,
  6008/a, S. 7415, 13038,
  15729, 16539, 16542,
  16557
Schlackenlöffel 16461, S.
  16467
Schlackenmann 3577
Schlackenmühle 16527
Schlackenöffnung S.16557
Schlackenpfanne 16541,
  18523
Schlackenporen 13318
Schlackenpresse 16549
Schlackenpuddeln 16550
 chlackenreine Kohle 12345
 chlackenreines Eisen 16537
  16537
Schlackenrinne 3576/a
Schlackenrost 6104
Schlackensand 16553
Schlackenschicht 10598
Schlackenschichtaufbrechen
  7282
Schlackensieb 16460/a
Schlackenspur 3575
Schlackenstein 4964, 16528
Schlackentrift 7431
Schlacken-und Eisenabstich
  18761
Schlackenwagen 16563
Schlackenwolle 16565
Schlackenziffer S. 9735
 chlackenzugabe vor dem
  Schmelzen des Metalles
  16514
 chlackenzusatz 3571
Schlackenzuschlag 16520
 chlackiger Brauneisenstein
  S. 2474
 chlag 1848, 1849, 10395
Schlagbeanspruchung 16147
Schlagbiegeprobe 16143
Schlagbiegeversuch 14734
Schlagbohren für geringe

Tiefe 17221
Schlagbohrer 2092
Schlägel 11748
schlagen 1402, 1445, S. 8727
Schlagen 7283
schlagendes Bohren S. 8733
Schlagfestigkeit 9645,
  14775
Schlagformerei 16146
Schlagholz 1920, 15321/a
Schlaglot S. 8840, S.8841
Schlagpatrone 13949
Schlagprobe S.16148
Schlagrohrkrebs 10127
Schlagstärke 17776, 18417a
Schlagstiftmühle S.14929
Schlagversuch 9647, 16148
Schlagwasserplatte S. 19691
Schlagwerkzeug 17724
Schlagwetter 4978, S.7165,
  7184
Schlagwetteranzeiger 4984,
  7997, 8017, 19670
Schlagwetterexplosion 8330
Schlagwettergrube 8072,
  8085
Schlagwirkung 6215
Schlagzähigkeit 9648/a
Schlamm 12069, 16602,
  16695, 16715
schlammartig S. 16638
Schlammauskleidung S.12075
Schlammbecken S. 16718
Schlammbehälter 17993
Schlammbeschlag S. 12075,
  12089
Schlammbohrer 12073
Schlammbüchse S. 1101,
  12090, S. 16697, 19070
schlämmen 7479
Schlämmen 5051
Schlammfang 12077
Schlammgraben 17234
Schlammgrube 12085, 17992
Schlammgrund 11791
Schlammhaspel 15515
  15502
Schlammherd 16632
schlammig 16638, 16698
Schlammischanlage 12084
Schlammkasten 16635

Schlammkohle S. 16775
Schlammkontrolle 12072
Schlammkonzentrator 16636
Schlammkuhle S. 15924,
    16718
Schlammlava 11864, 12078
Schlammleitung 12081
Schlammloch 16696
Schlammlöffel S. 12090
Schlammpressung 12087
Schlammproduktion S. 1109
Schlammpumpe 12088, 16630,
    16697, S. 16719
Schlammpumpenflasche 251
Schlammpumpenrückseite
    13784
Schlammreinigungsöffnung
    3700
Schlammrinne S. 12076
Schlammrolle 15517
Schlammrücklaufige-
    schwindigkeit 623
Schlammscheidemaschine
    16631
Schlammseil 15501
Schlammstrom 3983
Schlammsumpf 16628
Schlammthixotropeffekt
    8147
Schlammtrommel S. 12077
Schlammtrübe 16629
Schlammung der Erze 2515
Schlammverdichter 12092
Schlammwäsche 16633
Schlammwasser 16634
Schlangenbohrer 5684
Schlauchanschluss 9387
schlecht ausgelaufen 11806
— ausgelaufener Guss
    11807
— kristallisiert 6159
— verschweisste Kernstütze
    19297
Schlechte 1063, S. 12946,
    16646
Schlechten zugestellter
    Stoss (auf) 6751, 16724
Schlechtenrichtung (in) 6452
schlechter Versatz 13655
Schlegel 9038
Schleifband 9

Schleifbrett 8550
Schleife 10995
schleifen 8537, 16770
Schleifen 8545, 15320,
    16008
Schleifer 8543
Schleifkohle 8551
Schleifmarke S. 3712
Schleifmaschine 8544, 8557,
Schleifmittel S. 7, 8558
Schleifriss 8210, 8547,
    8552
Schleifscheibe 8562
Schleifscheiben 8555
Schleifschmirgel 8553
Schleifstein S. 8563, 14348
Schleifstuhl 8549
schleimig 12056
schlemmen S. 15654, 19681
schleppen S. 5727
Schlepper 2527, 5740, 5789,
    7953, 8894, 8896, 10172,
    15369, S. 15373, 18818
Schlepperförderung S. 8789
Schlepperhaspel 10186
Schleppfalte 5733
Schlepphalte 8892
Schleppung S. 1506, 5728
Schleppwalze 7770
Schleppzangeziehbank 5799
Schleuder 5519
Schleuderabscheider 3200
Schleuderabscheidung 3209
Schleuderformguss 3207
Schleudergebläse 3201,
    6795
Schleudergiesskokille 3204
Schleudergiessmaschine
    3205
Schleuderguss 3202, S. 3203,
    18951
Schleudergussrohr 3206
schleuderkreiselähnlich
    5301
Schleudermühle 5520
schleudern 2966, 3312
    16640
Schleudern 3211
— des Förderseils 7284,
    20017
Schleuderpumpe 3208, 9653

Schleuderradputzmaschine
    19122
Schleuderstahl 3214
Schleuderstrahlen S. 16195,
    16198, S. 16199
Schleuderstäuber 3210
Schleuse S. 653, 16708
Schleusenschieber 8097
Schlich 4163, 7096
Schlichte 3880, 5841/a,
    14635
schlichten 3879, 5835, 7112
Schlichten 14629
Schlichtmaschine S. 7130
Schlichtstahl 7140
Schlichtung 18089/a
Schlicker S. 16713
Schlickerguss 16648/a
Schieferbank 1189
Schlieg S. 7096
Schlieren 17766, S. 18050,
    18051
Schlierenbildung 7087
schlierige Textur 17768
Schliessblech 17829
Schliessbolzen 4522
schliessen S. 3616, 3753,
    16241
Schliessen des Stichlochs
    2135, 13566
Schliesskolben 11975
Schlimmherstellung 15429
Schlinge 16641
Schlingengrube 11000
Schlingerblech S. 19691
Schlingerplatte 19691
Schlitten 9473, 16580, 16611
Schlitz S. 10321, 10373,
    12403, S. 16686, S. 16687
Schlitzanschnitt 16671
schlitzen S. 10320, S. 10374
Schlitzen S. 8597
Schlitzrohr 16689
Schlitzzerstäuber 16688
Schloss 1599, 1601
Schlossblech 10945
Schlosserschraubstock S.
    9207
Schlossrand 9200
Schlot S. 3454
Schlucht 7966

Schlüssel (für Batterien) 18732
Schlüsselgehäuse 10332
Schlüsselloch 10328, 10331
Schlüsselsonde S.9674
Schlüsskaliber S. 7068, S. 10559
Schlusspfropfen 13556
schmale Bahn S. 12894
Schmalspurbahn 12177
schmarotzende Durchbiegung 19342
Schmelzbad 14094/a
schmelzbar 11459
schmelzbarer Ton 7888
Schmelzbarkeit 7890
Schmelzbereich S. 11477
Schmelzbuch 3317
Schmelzdraht 7885
Schmelze S. 1338
— umrühren (eine) 17605
schmelzen 11456
Schmelzen 7893, 11463, 16747/a
— unter Schutzgas 11482
Schmelzer 7879, S.11462
Schmelzflammofen 14817
schmelzflüssig 11878
Schmelzgang 14005
Schmelzgeschwindigkeit 11477/a
Schmelzgut S. 11478
Schmelzherd 16749
Schmelzhitze 11480
Schmelzhütte 16752
Schmelzintervall 11477, S. 11461
Schmelzkessel S. 11476
Schmelzkoks 16746
Schmelzkupferstahl 20229/a
Schmelzlegierung 7887
Schmelzlöffel 11472
Schmelzmassel 15769
Schmelzmeister 8915
Schmelzmetall 7889
Schmelzmittel 7891
Schmelzofen 11466, 11483, 16748
Schmelzpunkt 11475
Schmelzpunktbestimmungsapparat 706

Schmelzerei 16750
Schmelzrinne 621
Schmelzröhrehen 11481
Schmelzschweissung 969
Schmelzstoff 3315
Schmelztiegel 4736, 4742, 11461, 11471, S.11476,
Schmelztiegelzange 4748
Schmelz- und Giessverlust S. 18791
Schmelzung S. 8972
Schmelzverlauf 13980
Schmelzverlust 11027
Schmelzzone 11484
Schmied 7588
Schmiedearbeit 1978
schmiedbar s. dehnbar od. streckbar
schmiedbarem Guss (Fabrik von-) 7663
schmiedbarer Guss S. 11249
schmiedbares Eisen S.7585, S. 11249
Schmiedbarkeit 7584
Schmiede 7575, 16757
Schmiedeabfälle S.7597
Schmiedearbeit S. 7583
Schmiedebeanspruchung 7581
Schmiedeeisen 7585, 20240
Schmiedeeisenblech 20243
Schmiedeeisenring 20244
schmiedeeiserner Rahmen 20241
Schmiedeeisenpuddeln 9996
Schmiedehammer 7593, S. 16581
Schmiedeknüppel 7592
Schmiedekohle 7576, 16754
Schmiedemaschine mit pneumatischer Kupplung 255
Schmiedemaschinengesenke 8567
Schmiedemessing 7592/a
schmieden 7570, S. 8727
Schmieden 7583, 7590, 16753
— der Einschnürung 11666
— mit geschlossenem

Gesenk 3770
Schmiedepresse 7595
Schmiedeprobe 7599, 19355
Schmiedesinter S. 7597
Schmiedestahl 7580, 7587, 20246
Schmiedestück 7586, 7589, S. 7590, 8736
Schmiedetemperatur 7598
Schmiede- u. Walzmaschine 7591
Schmiede-Verhältnis 14442
Schmiedewerkstatt S.7575
Schmiedezange 13699
Schmiedung S. 7590
Schmiere S. 5633, 11079
Schmirgel 6411
Schmirgelleinen 6412
schmirgeln 6410
Schmirgeln 6414
Schmirgelpapier 6415
Schmirgelpulver 6416
Schmirgelscheibe 6413
schmierig 8505
Schmierpumpe 8503
Schmierung 1336
Schnappauswerfer 10344
Schnappauswerfzylinder 10345
Schnauze 10860
Schneckenbohrer 15701
Schneckenerzwascher 15715
Schneckenfräser 9058
Schneckengetriebe 20228
Schneckenhubförderer 15706
Schneckenkranz 20230
Schneckenrad 9059
Schnecken-Transportrinne 15704
Schneebergit 15627
Schneewirkung 113, 220/a
Schneidbrenner 4915, 4919, 7892
Schneide 1622, 4918
Schneideapparat 4907
Schneideisen 4926
schneiden S. 4891
Schneiden 4913, S.14182
— der Gewinde S.15719
— eines Innengewindes S. 18299

Schneiden von Blechpaketen
    17275/a
schneidend S. 16001
Schneidewirkung 4914
Schneidhaltigkeit 6201,
    16033
Schneidschuh 2182
Schneidvorrichtung
    (Mitlauf –) 7507

schnellaufende Walze 9176
schnellaufendes Reversier-
    walzwerk 9175
Schnellaushärtungsversuch
    37
Schnellbearbeitungsstahl
    7731
Schnelldreh-Revolverstahl
    9180
Schnelldrehstahl 18002
schnelle Metallsäge 9174
Schnellkupplung 14296
schnellauslösbare
    Kabelkupplung 14300
Schnellot S. 16840
Schnellröstung 1732/a
Schnellschlag 14299
Schnellstahl 9178, 14418/a,
    14538
Schnellstossbohrung 2100
Schnellumlaufkessel 1996
Schnellverbrennung 2418
Schnellverdampfungskessel S.
    7291
Schnellwaage 14298
Schnellwalzwerk 9177
Schnellwerkzeugstahl 9179
Schnellzündschnur 14302
Schnitt 4899
Schnittgeschwindigkeit
    4924
Schnittgrat 4915/a
Schnittlinie 4919/a
Schnittstempel 4922
Schnittstülpziehwerkzeug
    4059
Schnittwinkel 4927, 18952
Schnittwirkung S. 4914
Schnürung 18611
Schoepit 15628

Scholle 6842
Schollengebirge 1803
Schollenkante 6859
Schollenland 6865
schöne Politur glänzende
    Oberflächen 2406
Schonung des Ofenfutters
    2889
Schöpfen 4660/,b, 18759/a
Schöpfhaspel S. 15515
Schöpflöffel 1101
— gewinnen (mit dem) 1099
Schöpfprobe 10483
Schöpfproduktion 1109
Schöpfradbagger 12373
Schöpfsonde 1108
Schöpfversuch 1107
Schore 2223, 9824
Schöreisen S. 3111
Schörl 10023, S.10162
Schorlomit 15629
Schornstein 1962, 2357,
    3453
Schornsteinhaube 3456
Schornsteinlüfter 3465
Schornsteinventilator S. 3465
Schornsteinzug 3458
Schotter S. 2446, S. 8477
Schotterbank 1194
Schotterbett 1169, 3287,
    13030
schottische Bogheadkohle
    15619
schottischer Hochofen
    15648
schottisches Roheisen
    15652   ,
schräg stehendes Blech
    9705
Schrägaufzug 9702, 16482
Schrägbau 14209
Schräge 5724, 18278
schräge Bohrung 9708
— Schicht 4671
schräger Winkel 5726
Schrägmass S. 1570
Schrägrohrkessel 19827
Schrägrost 9701
Schrägrostfeuerung 7869,
    7870
Schrägschichtung S. 6779

Schrägstift 11986
Schrägstreb 14910
Schrägwalzen 5310
Schrägwalzverfahren nach
    Mannesmann 11295
Schram 1204, 10112, 10321
Schrämarbeit S. 4913
Schrämeisen 9258
schrämen 3283, 4874, 10320,
    10374
Schrämer 3812, S. 4913,
    10113, 10375
Schrämklein 1232, 2524
Schrämlader 4912
Schrämmaschine 3810, 3860,
    4681, 4906, 9982, 10032,
    11777
Schrämhauer 17660
Schrämstange 4910
Schrämtiefe 1393
Schranke 1247
Schrapper 5736, 15666,
    16658, 16720
Schrapperarbeit 16721
Schrapperförderung 15674,
    S. 16721
Schraubenanker 15714
Schraubenblech 15710
Schraubenbolzen 15703
— mit Mutter 2009
Schraubeneisen 15711
Schraubenerzeugnisse 2014
Schraubengang S. 18550
Schraubenmutter 12427
Schraubenräder 17100
Schraubenschlüssel 20233
Schraubentute 5379
Schraubenweicheisen S. 15711
    15711
Schraubenwinde 15709
Schraublehre 15707
Schraubstock 1495
Schreckplatte s. Kokille
Schreckplatten anlegen
    3421
Schreckschale 3423, 3450
Schreibersit 15630
Schreibfederbandstahl 1179
Schrifterz S. 18146
Schriftgiesserei 19203
Schrifttellur S. 18146

Schrot 8575/a, 16193
Schrotbohren 3436, 16200
Schrotbohrer 122, 5737
Schrotbohrkrone 16194
schrotgezimmert 4632
Schrotkernbohren 16201
Schrotkrone 3447
Schrotmeissel 3485
Schrotstahl S. 15263
Schrott 10008, 11824,
    15655/a, 15660, 15805
— verpacken (den) 2655
Schrottkrone S. 16194
Schrottmann 15678
Schrottmetall 16205/a
Schrottmischung 2627
Schrottmulde 15661
Schrottpaket 2579
Schrottpaketierung 15656
Schrottpresshammer 2657
Schrottrinne 15657
Schrottschere 15658
Schrottverfahren 15663
Schrottverpackung 2656
Schrottwalzwerk 15659
Schrottzimmerung 3758, 3765
Schrumpfbau S. 16233
Schrumpfbüchse 16034
schrumpfen 13310
Schrumpfporosität 16231
Schrumpfring 16235/a
Schrumpfriss 14786, 16228
Schrumpfverbindung 16225
Schruppdrehbank 15259
Schruppstahl 15263
Schubelastizität 18841
Schubfläche 16657
Schubförderrinne S. 14102
Schublange 16647
Schubleistenförderer 15670
Schublehre 2747
Schubmasse 5532
Schubrinne 14202
Schubriss 16022/a
Schubspannung 7435/a
Schuh 10013, 16453
Schuhführung 16154
Schuhnägel 16155
— mit gestauchtem Kopf
    11037
Schultenit 15631

Schulterabstand 17336
Schulterbohrung 4526/a
Schungit 16236
Schuppe 16597
Schuppenblech 9641
Schuppenparaffin 15585,
    15593
Schuppenstruktur 15633
schuppig 15601
Schüreisen S. 14314
schüren 14312
Schurf 2087, S.5407
Schürfbohrung 17896, 18459
schürfen 2621, 14032
Schürfen 4519, 13427,
    14036, 14411
Schürfgraben S. 8587,
    12395
Schürfschacht 14035
Schürfschein 14038
Schürfstange 13615
Schürfung 5407, S. 5408,
    S. 13427
Schuss 1729, S.16191
Schüssel 3221, S. 9357
— des Kollergangs 12891
Schüsselklassierer 2203
Schüssellochreiniger 10329
Schussgerinne S. 6880
Schusskanal S. 5347
Schussverzögerung 9485
Schutt S. 10254, 15350
Schüttbeton 8945
Schüttel — 19552
Schüttelförderer 19553
Schüttelmaschine 14145/a
schütteln S. 3559
Schüttelrinne 15975, 18936,
    S. 19553
Schüttelrost 15040
Schüttelrostfeuerung 7872
Schüttelrutsche 10178, 15969
    15969
Schüttelsieb S. 10186,
    15968, 15972, 19463
Schütteltisch 15974
Schuttfächer 6807
Schuttfeld 12719
Schuttkegel 405/a, 407, S.
    6807
Schüttrinne S. 16162

Schüttrohr 5497
Schüttrost S. 9701
Schüttrostfeuerung 15822
Schutz 16120
Schutzabkommen 12466
Schutzatmosphäre 14045
Schutzblech 19738/a, 15686
Schutzbohrung 12465
Schutzbrett 1095
Schutzbrille 8340
Schutzdach 13072
— der Fördersteige 2033
schützende Zusätze 13863
Schutzgasatmosphäreofen
    4291
Schutzgasofen 14047
Schutzgebiet 12467
Schutzhaube S. 2032, 9825/a
    9825/a, 14040
Schutzmarke 3521
Schutzmaske S. 6743
Schutznetz 15421
Schutzschlacke 4556/a
Schutzsonde S. 12469
Schutztrichter 14046
Schutzvorrichtung 15420
Schutzwand 14042
Schwabbel 13631/a
schwaches Rösten 19850
Schwaden 15797
Schwal 14870
Schwalarbeit 16564
schwammige Textur 17145
schwammiges Eisen 17144
Schwartenbrett 16493
schwarz streichen 12862
Schwarzblech 1661, 1664
schwarzbrüchiges Eisen 1671
    1671
Schwärze 16759, 17696
schwarze Nadeln 1657
Schwärzen 1672
schwarzer Jura 1653
— Lignit 1655
— Temperguss 1670
Schwarzerde 3412
schwarzes Roheisen 1660
Schwarzglühen 609
Schwarzkreide 1646
Schwarzkupfer 1647
schwarzrotglühend 1662

Schwarzsand 1663
Schwarzstreifen 1667
Schwarzit 15635
Schwebebau 14374
schwebende Spalte 7341,
    16065
schwebender Grubenbau
    19373
Schwefelarsen 816
Schwefelbestäubung 6141/a
Schwefeleisen 10022
Schwefelkies 6951
— in Kohle 3803
schwefelkieshaltige Kohle
    3078
Schwefelsäure 19743
schwefelsaurer Strontian
    3131
schwefelsaures Eisenoxyd
    6929
Schwefelung 17966
Schwefelwasserstoffapparat
    702
Schwefelzement 89
Schweissabsorption 19939
Schweissand 19951
schweissbar 19928
schweissbarer Guss ·stahl
    11676
Schweissbarkeit 19930
Schweissbrenner 19956
Schweissbrennerspitze
    18769
Schweiss-oder Losflansch-
    Verbindungen 4222
Schweissdraht 7025, 19957
Schweisseisen 19926
schweissen 19923
Schweissen 7582
— mit PVC-Stäben 19958
Schweisser 19934
— -Schutzschild 6753
Schweissfehler 5106
Schweissfeuer 19941
Schweissflussmittel 19942
Schweissgang 12957
Schweissglühhitze 19945
Schweissknoten 12856
Schweissnaht 16243, 19924,
    19949/a
Schweissnahtvorrichtung

Schweissofen 6761, 16888,
    19943
Schweissofenschlacke 14670
Schweissperle 19926/a
Schweissprobe 19955
Schweissraupe 19937
Schweissrippe 7290/a
Schweiss ·stahl 19927,
    19929
Schweiss· stelle 14939
Schweissung 19936
Schweisswalzwerk 19948
Schweisswerkstatt 19953
Schweisswerkstoff 19947
Schweisszange 19944
Schwelle 16586
Schwellenkaliber 16587
Schwemmebene 408
Schwemmsand 1691
Schwengel 6918, 15034
Schwengelbock 15464
Schwenkkran 19644
Schwenkzapfen 18959
schwer durchlässiger Sand
    18618
— reduzierbares Erz 5400
— schmelzbares Erz 14631
schwere Reduzierbarkeit
    5399
schwerflüssig 9154, 16706
Schweröle 14223
Schwerspat 3106, 3127
Schwerstange 16415
Schwererzverbindung 894
Schwimmdach 7392
Schwimmerhahn 1154
Schwimmerstandanzeiger
    7387
Schwimmkopf 7390
Schwimmprobe 7389
Schwimmschuh 7388
Schwimm- und Sinkverfahren
    16413
Schwimmuffe 7385
Schwimmungszelle 7416
schwinden 16221
Schwinden 16226
Schwindmass 4284
Schwindungshohlraum 5773
schwingen 15002
Schwingrinne 15043

Schwingsattel 19630
Schwingsieb 12686
Schwingung mit dem Fluss
    im Schacht 15036
Schwitzen 18103
Schwitzkugel 16201/a
Schwitzofen 18104
Schwund 16222
schythische Stufe 16491
Searlesit 15756
Sebastianit 15768
Sechskantdraht 9124
Sechskanteisen 9119, 9121
Sechskantschraube 9120
Sechskantstahl 9126
Sechskantstange 9117
Sechsrollenwalzwerk 3793/a
sechsseitiges Trapezoeder
    9123
sechszählige Achse 9118
Sediment 15923/a
sedimentärer Ton 15791
Sedimente S. 15792
Sedimentorium 766
Seeablagerungen 10493
Seebachit 15795
Seelenschweissdraht 4454
Seelenrohr S. 4388
Seesand 10494
Segment 15801, 13120
Segmenteisen 8716
Segmentkern 15799
Sehne 6982
Sehnepuddeln 14112
sehnig 6986
sehniges Eisen 6988
sehr geneigte Verwerfung
    12729
— weiches Eisen 19535
Sehweite 19569
Seidendraht 16333
seideumsponnener Draht S.
    16333
seidiger Bruch 16334
Seife 13435
Seifenblasenmodell 2491/a
Seifenerde S. 7810
Seifengold 8662, 13436.
    17770
Seifenlösung 16801
Seifenwerk 13437

Seifenzinn S. 17772
Seigerblei 10868
seigere Sprunghöhe 6861
seigeres Flöz 6253
Seigerförderer 8485
Seigerherd 10867
Seigerpfanne 10869
Seigerschlacke 10870
Seigerung 6384, 10866
Seigerungserscheinung
    15803
Seil für Pumpengestänge
    17939
Seilablenkungswinkel 7364
Seilaufzug 10752
Seilbahn 192. 12757
Seilbahnbegichtung 193
Seilbohren 511, 2661,
    2665, 3561, 15159
Seilbohrer 15157
Seilbohrgerät 2666
Seilbohrkran 2663
Seilbruch 6773, 15351
Seildicke 18511
Seilfänger 15164
Seilführung 20132
Seilhängeband S. 12757
Seilhülse 15169
Seilklemme 15158, 20145
Seilmesser 15165
Seilöl 1333
Seilrohr 15163
Seilrolle S. 4734
Seilscheibe 8923, 9234, S.
    20102
Seilschlagbohrer 3560
Seilschloss S. 15158
Seilschmierer 15166
Seilspeer 15170
Seiltrommel 2662, 15162,
    S. 15168, 20102
— mit Rillen 8590
Seiltrommelrillen 9373
Seilübertragung 15160
Seilverschlingung der Seil-
    rolle 16787
Seilwinde 2814
Seite bohren (von der) 5876
Seiten giessen (von zwei)
    2968
Seitenansicht 16261

Seitenblech 8246, 16270
Seitendruck 10571, 18596
Seitenfraktion 16277
Seitenführung 16264/a
Seitenkammer 16257
Seitenkipper 16260
Seitenladung 5628
Seitenöffnung 16262
Seitenpfahl 9053
Seitenprobe 16276
Seitenpumpen 1074
Seitenrohrkessel 1985
Seitenschussbohrloch 16265
Seitensteg 16273
Seitenstein 16274
Seitenstreifen 1497
Seitentrumm S. 6001
Seitenverschalung 16266
Seitenverschiebung 7361,
    16121, 16124, 17825
Seitenzug 16258, 16263
seitlich Kerne entnehmen
    16282
— offener Speiser 12599
seitlicher Druck 16279/a
— Kern 16281
Sektionalkessel S. 15781,
    15786
Sektionalwasserrohrkessel
    15787
sekundäre Antiklinale 17931
— Förderung 15770
— Gewinnung S. 15767
sekundäres Magma 17926
Sekundärhärte 15768
Sekundärluft 15763
selbständige Rost-
    beschickungsvorrichtung
    17635
selbstentschlackend 15829
Selbstentlader 15817, 15818
Selbstentleerer S. 15817
Selbstentleerung 979
selbstentschlackende Düse
    15831
Selbstentzündungstempera-
    tur 967·
Selbsterhitzung 17147
selbstfahrender
    Bohrkran
    S. 13692

selbstfahrender Kran 11954,
    13775
selbstgehend 15822/a
selbstgehendes Erz S.15823
Selbstglühen 15814
Selbstkühlung 15816
Selbstlademaschine 4322
Selbstladetransportband
    10911
selbstlaufende Sonde S.7744
selbstleuchterrde Flamme
    11088, 15827
selbstschmelzbares Erz
    15823
selbsttätig laufen S.7419
— öffnen (sich) 12559
selbsttätige Abschlag(e)-
    vorrichtung 992
— Aufgabevorrichtung 976
— Bremsbergvorrichtung
    8660
— Drehbank 985
— Rostbeschickung 11414
— Vollpipette 986
— Waage 973
selbsttätiger Kipper 990
— Kohlenkipper 978
— Vorschub 980
selbsttätiges Abschlagen
    991
— Bruchspill 2314
— Greifen 15811
selbsttragende Pfannen aus
    verzinktem Stahlblech
    15832
— Plattform 15815
selbstwärmender Lötkolben
    15826
selbstzentrierend 15813
selektive Erhitzung 5395/a
selektives Frischglühen
    15807/a
Selen 15810
Selenblei S. 3652
Selenit S. 4801, 15809
Selenkupfer S. 1547
Seligmannit 15833
Sellait 15834
Semseyit 15852
Senait 15853
Senarmontit 15854

Rohrteil ohne Anstrich 9257
Rohrtour 17834
— einbauen 10519
Rohrträger 19042
Rohrträgertraktor 2043
Rohrtrichter 3591
Rohr-und Barrendrehbank
    1209
Rohrverbindung 2941, 13336
Rohrverbindungsstück 7226,
    19031
Rohrverschraubung 13368
Rohrverteiler 11293
Rohrwaagen S. 13509
Rohrwalzwerk 19037
Rohrwischer 18976
Rohrzange 2964, 13348
Rohrzentrierkorb 2934
Rohrzerstäuber 19087
Rohrziehen mit Dorn 1213/a
Rohrzieher 18981
Rohschiene 1560/a, 11691,
    14103
Rohschlacke 14461
Rohstahl 4754/a
Rohstahlgewicht 4755
Rohstein S. 14457
Rohstoff 1297/a, 14456
Rohwasser 12198
Rohzagel S. 12059
Rolladenrohr 19017, 19018
Rolle S. 3563, 15104
— zum Seilbohren 17222
Rollen 15121
Rollenbahn 15108
Rollenblei S. 16066
Rollenblock 2239
Rollenklassiersieb 15116
Rollenlager 15106
Rollenmeissel 4702, 15107
Rollennahtschweissung S.
    4278
Rollenrutsche 15117
Rollenzug S. 1804
Rollfass S. 3703
Rollmaschine S. 18980,
Rolloch 1061
— mit Schrotzimmerung
    4633
Romeit S. 935, 15134
Römerit 15135

Röntgenapparat 20262
Röntgenbild 14337
Röntgen-Durchleuchtung
    14340
Röntgenstrahlen 20261
Rootegebläse 15155
Rootkessel 15156
Röpperit 15064
Rosasit 15174
Rösche 2777
Roscherit 15175
Roscölit 15176
Roselith 15181
Rosenstahl 15180
Rosettengraphit S.8450,
    15184
Rosettenkupfer 15183
Rosickyit 15186
Rosieresit 15187
Rosit 15190
Rossit 15191
Rösslerscher Ofen 15065
Rost 8465, 8579, 14544,
    15391
— mechanisch beschicken
    (den-) 17632
— mit Wasserzirkulation
    8475
Röstanlage 14993
rostbeständig S. 15396
Röstbett 14988
rösten 14983
rosten 15390
Rösten S. 2604, 14987
Röster 14986, S.14990
Rösterzeugnis 13993
Rostfeuerung 8472
Rostfläche 8466
rostfrei 15396
rostfreier Stahl S. 17297
Rostfuge 8473
Röstgas 14991
Röstgut 12657
Rösthaufen 14984
Rosthebewerk 8580
rostiges Gold 15389
Rostkitt 9967
Rostkühlung 8471
Rostlösungsmittel 15396/a
Rostneigung 9689
Röstofen 7172, 7299, 10356

Rostschicht 10597
Rostschlagen 14711
Rostschutz 672
Rostschutzfarbe 13862
Rostschutzmittel 15395
rostsicherer Anstrich S.672
— Stahl S. 17297
Rostsohle 8582
Rostspalt S. 8473
Rostspat 16990
Rostspeisung 8581
Roststab 7147, 8467
Roststabeisen 7149, 8469
Rösttemperatur 14994
Rostträger 7148
Röstverfahren 11614
Röstverlust 11025
rot erleuchteter Gasstrom
    14534
Rotary-Bohranlage 15201
rotarybohren 15200
Rotary Bohrkran S. 15201
Rotary-Bohrverfahren 15220
Rotary-Hebewerk 5822, 15198
    15198
Rotary-Schlagschere 15206
Rotary-Spülkopf 15219
Rotary-Spülschlauch 15211
Rotary-Stosskernbohrer
    15225
Rotary-Tisch S. 15221
Rotarytischlagerung 18192
Rotary-Wascher 15226
Rotationskörper 1939
Rotationspumpe S. 15215
Rotationsverzögerung
    15232/a
Rotbleierz S. 4652
rotbrüchig 14535, 14547.
    16175
rotbrüchiges Eisen S. 9402,
    14548
rote Umränderung 14530
Roteisenerz 15328
Roteisenstein S. 3663, 14541,
    14541,
roter Glaskopf 6992, 9075
— Ocker 15333
— Sandstein 14546
— Tiefseeton 14532
— Toneisenstein S. 3663

Sigmastadium 16308
Signalständer 9738
Silber 16350
Silberantimonglanz S.11617
Silberbarren S. 2570
Silberglanz S. 774, S.19573
silberhaltig 772
Silberhornerz S. 3227, S.
  3493, S. 9363
Silberlot 16360
silbern 16362
Silbernitrat S. 16334
Silbersand S. 6108
Silberscheidung 16358
Silberstahl 16361
siliziumreiches graues Roh-
  eisen 9172
Silikose 16331
Silikospiegel 6949, S.6959,
  16324
Silikotel 16332
Silizierungsgrad 5139
Silizium 16323, 16325
Siliziumbronze 16326
Siliziumbronzedraht 16327
Siliziumeisen S. 6950
Siliziumimpregnierung 9628a
Siliziumkarbid 16328
Siliziumkupfer 16329
Siliziummanganeisen S.16324
Silizium-Manganstahl 11273
siliziumreiches graues Roh-
  eisen 16363
Siliziumstahl 16330
Sill S. 9927, 16337, S.16342
Sillimanit S. 6985, 16343
Silt 16346
Silur 16348
Simetit 16364
Simplektit 18153
Sinerese 18163
Sinklinalfalte 16377
Sinopit 16427
Sinter S. 2018, 16430
Sinterablagerung 16438
Sintereisen 16432/a
Sinterhaut 16438/a
Sinterkohle 3406, 12344,
  16435
sintern 16429
Sintern 16434

sinternde Sandkohle 16437
Sinterofen 16435/a
Sinterpunkt 16436
Sinterung 7775, 16433
Siphoneinguss 18176
Siphonpfanne 18342
Siphonstein S. 16463, 18174
Sipylit 16439
Sirupdichte 18177
Sitaparit 16441
Skafarzikit 15612
Skala 15586
Skalenoeder 15594
Skapolith 15603, S. 19980
Skapolitisation 5455
Skarn 15606
Skelettkristall 9643
Skelettmodell 16418
Skogbolit 16487
Skolezit 13637
Skorodit 15647
Skrubber S. 8052
S-Kurve 18643
Skutterudit 16490
skytische Stufe S. 16491
Slavikit 16579
Slingern S. 9654
Smaltin 16741, 20027
Smaragd 16742
Smaragdit 16743
Smektit 16744
Smithit 16755
Smithsonit S. 2699, 16756,
  20337
Sodalauge 16811
Sodalith 16814
Soddyit 16815
sofortiger Verbund 13927
sogenanntes Kammverfahren
  4052
Soggendalit 16852
Sohle 2142, 7402, 8951,
  13404, 16868, 18701,
  19269
— nachreissen 10737,
  16410
Sohlenauftrieb 4622
Sohlendruck 2164
Sohlenholz S. 7540, 16333
Sohlenkanal 2158
Sohlenloch 17668

Sohlenprobe 14751
Sohlenschussbohrloch 2162,
  7541, 10755
Sohlenspreize 2186
Sohlenstopfbüchse 2163
Sohlenstrecke S. 2637, S.
  7959, S. 8095
Sohlfläche S.2142
Sohlplatte 2179
Sol 16856/a
Soliduslinie 16894
Soll S. 10323
Solvatation 16907
Solvent-Entparaffinierungs-
  verfahren 16910
Solvent-Raffination 16912
Sölvsbergit 16913
Sommait 16914
Sonderbronze 17006
Sonderdestillat 17005
Sonderhärtung 17014
Sondermessing 9186
Sonderprofile 17020
Sonderprofileisen 17004
Sondersatz 17009
Sonderstab S. 7090
Sonderstahl S. 401, 17021
Sonderwalzwerk 17019
Sonnenopal S. 7173
Sonnenstein 18000
Sorbit 16920
sorbitisches Gusseisen
  16921
Sordawalit 16922
Sorption 16922/a
sortieren S. 16923
Sortierer 16925
sortierte Kohle S.15690
Sortierung S. 16926
Somansit 16931
Souesit 16929
Spachtelfarbe 16960
spachteln 7013
Spadait 16959
Spalt 7969, 15965/a, 16669,
  16686, 17125
spaltbares Gestein 3715
Spaltbarkeit 3714, 3716, S
  14893
Spalte S. 1045, 2307, 3469,
  S. 7966, 14727

spalten S. 3719, 16668, 17124,
Spalten S. 3714, S.3716
Spaltfläche 13456
Spaltfunkenzünder S. 16982
Spaltung s. Dissoziation
Spaltungsrichtung 3717
Spaltzünder 16982
Span 3474
spanabhebende Verformung 11539
spanlose Verformung 3475
Spannanalyse 3474/a
Spanndraht 16971
Spanngewicht 18420
Spannkraft 17798
Spannpatrone 17128
Spannplatte 9246
Spannsäule 17796
Spannsprödigkeit 18416
Spannstange 9240
Spannung 17783, 18414
Spannungsbereich 14412/a
spannungsfrei 7729
spannungsfreier Guss 3051
Spannungsfreiglühen 17787, 17271, 10937, 17785, 17789
Spannungsgrösse 9683
Spannungskaltriss S. 3971
Spannungskorrosion 17786
Spannungsregler 19595
Spannungsriss 17784, 18415
Spannungsschwankung 7446
Spannungsverlust 5990
Spannungswarmriss S. 9409
Spannvorrichtung 3621, 17795
Spannwagen 1126
Sparhälfte 12455, S. 15510
Sparnacian 16989
Sparrost 6191
Spat 16975
Spateisenstein 16283
Spatel 16604, 16998
Spaten 16962, 17105
Spatenmeissel 5730
Spatenspeer 17219
Spatenstich S. 17105
Spätschuss 8803
Speckstein S.16802, 17452

Speerkies 17001
Speicherbehälter zur Gasbeförderung 10548
Speichergestein 14750
Speicherstoss S. 16232
Speise S. 17044
Speiseapparat 6890
Speisebecken 5720
Speisefang 6881
Speisekessel 6876
Speiseleitung S. 6884
speisen 15337
Speisen 15378
Speiseschnecke 20227
Speiser 6885/a, 6886, 16702
— abschlagen (die) 14717
— mit Einschnürkern 6887
— s. Steiger
Speisereinschnürung S.6894
Speiserhals 6894
Speisersystem 15380
Speiserwasserleitung 19771
Speiskobalt S. 16741, S. 20027
Speiss 17044
Speisung 6888, S. 9853,
Spektralanalyse 17033, 17035
spektralanalytische Untersuchung 17036
Spektroskop 17034
Spencerit 17049
Spenglerschere 18658
Spermazetöl S. 17063
Sperrflüssigkeit 15739
sperrig 20060
Sperrvorrichtung 5359
Sperrylit 17050
Spessartin 11267, 17051
Spezialfalte 11783
Spezialprofileisen 17018
Spezialstahl 7090, 17003, S. 17021
— für Flugzeugbau S. 17002
spezielle Metallographie des Eisens 17015
— provisorische Deckenstützen 17011
— Schlagschere 2574

spezifische Belastung 19309
— Wärme 17026
Sphalerit S. 1761, S.11850, 17053
Sphäre 17057
sphärisch 17059
Sphäroguss 17068
Sphäroid 17062
sphäroidische Absonderung 1164, 17069
— Textur 12620
Sphärokobaltit 17052
Sphärolith S. 17072
sphärolitisch 17073
sphärolitische Textur 17075
sphärolitisches Gefüge 8304
Sphärosiderit S. 3663, 13069, 17074
Sphärozementit 17071
Sphen S. 17054
Sphenoid 17055
Sphenolith 17056
Spiegel 13625
Spiegelbronze S. 17043
Spiegeleisen 17038, 17078
Spiegelmetall 17043
spiegelnd 17037
Spiel S. 18709
— der Waage 13537
— des Eisens 18063
— des Gebläses 114
Spielraum 394/a, 1065, 13536
— der Kernmarke 3709
Spilit 17085
spilitisch 17086
Spill 12292, S.20082
— zum Brechen 3093
— zum Kontern 3094
— -Kopf S. 12292
— -Trommel S.12292
Spillhilfswelle 10108
Spillkette 17095
Spillseil 3079, 3098
Spilltrommel 1242
Spindel 13705, 17090, 17827, 19367/a
Spindelfuss S.3198, 16805
Spindelstock 17089
Spindelvorgelege 1059/a

Spinell 17094
Spiralbohrer 946, 3797,
  19181, 19186
— mit zylindrischem
  Schaft 17719
Spiralfeder S. 2519, 17101
Spiral-Fingerfräser mit
  zylindrischem Schaft
  17098
spiralgeschweisstes Rohr
  17102
Spiralseil 14652
Spiritus einreiben (mit)
  15303
Spirituslampe 17103
Spitz 14107
— -Antiklinale 2890
Spitzbogenkaliber 17115
Spitzbogenprofil 8371
Spitzbohrer 812, 7332
Spitze 18672, S. 681
Spitzeisen 11857, 12055,
  18274
spitzen S. 16006
Spitzendrehbank 3197
spitzenlose Schleifmaschine
  3199
Spitzfänger 7223
Spitzhammer 14423
spitzig S. 16001
Spitzkasten 17107
Spitzlötkolben 13614
Spitzlutte 9518, 17108
Spitzmeissel 5329
Spitzsand 590
Spitzstampfer 13049
Spitzzirkel S. 5585
Splintkohle S. 17118
Splitter S. 3474, 15568/a,
  17086/a, 17117
splitterfest 17121
splitternde Gletschererosion
  13554
splittersicher S. 17121
splittriger Bruch 17122
Spodiophyllith 17139
Spodium S. 2027
Spodumen 17140
Sprachrohr und Schiffstele-
  graphenrohr 19021
spratzen 17230

Spratzen 17113, 17231
Spreizanker 6667
Spreize 2584, 5584, 8213,
  14465, S. 16169, S. 17225
Sprengarbeit S. 1743, 11770,
  16164
sprengen 1697, 1840, 16160
Sprengen 1705, 1743, S.
  6682
Sprenggelatine 1748, S.
  12318
Sprengkammer 4576
Sprengkaspel 1738, 1745,
  S. 2792
Sprengkaspelzange 1746,
  2797
Sprengladung 1747
Sprengloch 2081, S.5892, S.
  16204
Sprengmeister 1736, 3329,
  5885, 16163, 16202
Sprengmittel 1744, 6684
Sprengpulver 1750
Sprengring-Stahl 17198
Sprengschuss 1748/a, 6682
Sprengstoff S. 1744
Sprengstoffwagen 16943
Sprengung 1698/a
Springer 8677, S.17174
Springerquelle S.8677
Springerscher Puddelofen
  17204
Springquelle S. 8207
Spritze S. 17180
spritzen 5354
Spritzer S. 8677, 8678
Spritzflasche 19685
Spritzgiessen 13901
Spritzguss 5362, 9815,
  S. 13901
Spritzgussbehälter 16592
Spritzgussgesenke 5371
Spritzgussmaschine 303,
  5363
Spritzkugel 6493
Spritzkugelgrube S.16546
Spritzröhre 19026
spröde 11995
spröde machen 6406
sprödes Eisen 2423 , 16181,
— Eisenerz 2424

Sprödglaserz S. 2426
Sprödigkeit 2427, S. 1716,
  16187
— des Eisens 2428
Sprödigkeitsbruch 2422
Sprosseneisen 15550
Sprudelbohrung 8677
Sprung 4581, 10245
— nach unten S. 5716
Sprungbildung 6863
Sprunghöhe 12376, 12383,
  18587
— einer Verwerfung 18588
— senkrecht zur Schichtung
  S. 17750
Sprunglänge S. 16647
Sprungnetz 12249
Sprungsystem S. 8625
Sprungtiefe 5445
Sprungweite parallel zur
  Schichtebene S.17749
Spülbassin S.12074
Spülbohren 7483, 9517,
  19684
Spule 17149
Spüleffekt 10163
spülen S. 7479, S.15654
Spülen 18116
Spülflansch 7435, 17150
Spülgrube 12074
Spülkopf S. 3582, 18137,
  18138, 19817
Spülpumpe S. 2083, S.12088,
  16719
Spülraum 19709
Spülrinne 12076
Spülschappe 7489
Spülschlamm S.12069
Spülung 12079
— mit niedrigem Feststoff
  anteil 11061
Spülungen mit oberflächen-
  entspannenden Zusätzen
  18072
Spülungszusatz 12071
Spülungskuchen 12075
Spülungstank 12091
Spülungsverlust 11036
Spülverfahren 19774
Spülversatz 7487, 9538,
  16722

Spülversatz versetzen (mit) 7478
Spülwirbel 3582
Spundpfahl 16075, 17490
Spundung 8598
Spundwand S. 17490
Spundwandstahl S.17490
Spur 16687
Spurlager 3198
Spurlatte S.15370
Spurofen 14417
Spurrit 17229
Spurscheibe 19698
Spurweite 8109
Stab S. 1205
— mit Schmelzkern 4455/a
— mit zu schmiedendem Ende 13698
Stab-Rohrmühle 15055
— -und Formstahl 1254
Stabeisen 1215, S.9955, S. 15097
— schneiden 2658
Stabilisator 14655
stabilisierter Dolomit 17270
stabilisiertes Destillat 19866
Stabmühle 1218
Stabstahl 1220, 9955
Stabwalzwerk 15055/a
Stacheldraht 2 oder 3-fach 1223
Stadelröstung 17303
Stadium 17285
Staffelbruch 17546
Staffelit 17282
Staffelrost 12126
Staffelrostfeuerung 7874
Stahl 17454
— ausglühen 603
— enthärten (den) 16847/a
— -Fenster 17517
— gärben (den) 14594
— härten 8848
— in Wasser abschrecken 14282
— mit hoher Festigkeit S. 9187
— mit niedrigem Kohlenstoffgehalt 11046
— mit niedrigem Phosphor-

gehalt 11056
Stahl mit 0,75 % C 5382
— mit 0,875 C-Gehalt 15917
— mit 1,125 C-Gehalt 17093
— vergüten (den) 9670
stahlartig 17524
stahlartiges Eisen S. 6705, S. 17526
Stahlausbau S.17503, 17515
Stahlbandeisen 17480, 17512
Stahlbänder der Zentriervorrichtungen mit longitudinal Elementen 17403
Stahlbetonpfeiler 4177
Stahlblech 16081, 17492, 17508/a
— gepresste Platte (aus) 13884
Stahlblock 17481, 17489
Stahlbronze 17462
Stahldraht 17518
Stahleisen S.12576
stählen 17453
stählern 17468
Stahlfassonstücke S.4236
Stahlflasche für flüssige Gase 4939
— für gelöste Gase 4938
— für verdichtete Gase 4937
Stahlformmasse 3280
Stahlgerüst 11544, 17510
Stahlgiesserei 17475
Stahlgiesspfanne S.17482
stahlgrau 17477
Stahlguss 3018, 17463
Stahlgussradstern S.3023
Stahlguss·schieber 3022
Stahlhalter 18727
— -Aufspanndorn 7506
Stahlhammer 17478
Stahlhärtung 17479
Stahlhütte 17522
Stahlkessel 17459
Stahllegierung 17455
Stahlluppe 17458
Stahlmagnet 17483
Stahlmörser 17485
Stahlnadel 17496
Stahlofen 4310

Stahlpfanne 17482
Stahlplatte S. 16081
Stahlplattenheizkörper 17488 17488
Stahlplattformen auf im Felsen verankerten Stützen 17494
Stahlpuddeln 14113, 17500
Stahlpulver 17498/a
Stahlroheisen S. 12576
Stahlrohrkonstruktionen 19089
Stahlrohrgrubenstempel 19078
Stahlschienen (den) 5771
Stahlschrot 3448, 17476/a
Stahlseite der Panzerplatte 17467
Stahlsparren IPN 9947
Stahlstein 10016
Stahlstempel 17499, 17503, 17513
Stahlstössel 17486
Stahlstruktur 17520
Stahlträger 17457
Stahltreppenbaum 17511
Stahltürstock 17507
Stahltute S. 5379
Stählung 17523
Stahlwalze 17501
Stahlwalzen mit Glühen 17045
Stahlwalzwerk 17502
Stahlwerk 17491, S.17522
Stahlwerknormalform 17353
Stahlwerkskokille 9795
Stahlwolle 17519
Stainierit 17295
Stalagmit 17298
stalaktitförmiges Eisenerz 2481
Stamm S. 17533
Stammkernstütze 17536
Stampfbeton 17315
Stampfe 14402
stampfen S. 8727, 14387, 14388, 17306, 18229
Stampfer S. 11748, 14400, 18233
Stampfform 17325
Stampffutter 11912

Stampfmaschine mit elektrischem Antrieb 17326
Stampfmasse 11913
Stampfplatte 1440/a, 15131a, 15131/a, 19147/a
Stampien 17320
Standardmineral 17346
Ständer für Wegweiserschilder 16736
Ständerklemme 3623
Ständerkopf 18743
Ständerschleifmaschine S. 8544
standfester Masselbrecher 17273
Standfestigkeit des Sandes 15484
Standöl S. 17337
Standpfanne 7234
Standrohr 4193, 4196, 18043
Stange 1205, S. 15049, 17533
— für Radreifen 18686
Stangeneisen S. 1215
Stangenreibhammer 5995
Stangenschuss 1216
Stangenschrämmaschine 793, 1212
Stangenschutz 13505
Stangenstahl S. 1220
Stannin 17369, 18652
Stanzboden 2153
Stanze S. 14176, 14181, S. 17324, 4916
Stanzen 13243, 14182, 15296, 17321/a
— ohne Entfernung des Werkstückes 16705
Stanzer S. 14181
Stanzmaschine S. 12262
Stanzmatrize 14183, 17324
Stanzmetall 17317
Stapel S. 13278
Stapelabguss S. 17227
Stapelguss 3038, 17183, 17276
Stapelgussanschnitt 3793
Stapelkran S. 17279
Stapelmatrize 15531/a
Stapelmoräne 5199

stapeln 52
Stapler 17279
stark 16934
— halbiertes Roheisen 17879
— manganhaltiges Spiegeleisen 9158
— schlackende Kohle 3728
— verworfen 1093
Stärke 17378
Stärkepapier 17379
stärkstes Einfallen 7797
starre Form 13108
Startdruck S. 17386
Startventil 10342
Stassanoscher Hochofen 17388
— Ofen 17387
Stassfurtit 17390
stationär s. feststehend
statische Prüfung 17395
statischer Biegeversuch 18845
— Druck 3771
— Sohlendruck S. 17393
statisches Gravimeter 17394
Statuenbronze S. 17401
Staub 6124
Staubabsaugung 6131/a
Staubabscheider S. 6138
Staubbelästigung 6135
Staubbeutel S. 6126
Staubfang 6127, 6128
— mit Sackfilter 1097/a
Staubfänger 6125, S. 6127
staubförmiger Brennstoff 7789, S. 14148
staubförmiges Eisenerz S. 7086
staubiges Bleierz 1462
Staubkammer S. 6128
Staubkohle S. 4827, 6129, 13770
Staubregen S. 1815
Staubsack 6126, 6136
Staubsauger 6131
Staubsperre 6139, 15019
Stauchalterung 17731
stauchen 10246, 19371, 19372
Stauchen 19378

Stauchen mit Schwebestempel 16619/a
Stauchkaliber 19376
Stauchmaschine 19380
Stauchmatrize 19379
Stauchprobe 6101/a, 16144
Stauchung 10251
Stauchverbindung 10247/a
Staumoräne 14199
Staurand S. 12668
Staurandmesser 12670
Staurolith 17402
Stauscheibe 12668
Stauscheibenmesser S. 12670
Stauung 10557
Stauungsbogen 750
Stauungsbruch S. 18598
Stauwasser 1091
Steadit 17411, 16802, S. 17452
Stechheber S. 13377
Stechpipette S. 13377
Stegblech S. 17590
Stehanker 18610
Stehbolzen 17404
stehend formen 11965
— giessen 2977, 13740
stehender Antrieb 19525
— Dampfkessel 19532
— Guss 19521
— Kessel 19520
— Kessel mit Quersiedern 19522
— Winderhitzer 19518
— Zylinder 17396
stehendes Gebläse 18519
Stehkolben 7327
steife Schlacke 17585
steifer Skelettbau 14908
Steigband 9695
Steigleitung S. 14953, S. 19046
Steigen S. 14943
steigend giessen 2150
steigende Bewetterung 855
— Strecke S. 2469
steigender Guss 14962, 19431
— Guss mit Stufenanschnitten 16272
steigendes Giessen 2151

Steiger S. 1203, S. 3053, 8060, 12770
— s. Speiser
Steigereinschnürung S.6894
Steigerhals S. 6894
Steigeröffnung S. 8060
Steigertrichter S. 14947, 14952
Steigkanal 19383
Steigkanalanschnitt S.16671
Steigrohr S. 14961, 19046
Steigrohrdruck 19054
Steigung S. 13412, S.14943, 14957
— des Kegels S.18282
steil gelagerte Schicht 17528 17528
steile Falte 3760
— Kurve 17527
steiler Gang 14383, 17529
steiles Gefälle 9034
Steilrohrkessel 19832
Stein S. 2367
— behauen (einen) 15572
Steinbohrer S.1622, S.17643
Steinbrecher 17641
Steinbruch 12589, S.13397, 17852
Steinebehauen 12289
Steinform 15986
Steingitter 17645
Steingut 1113
Steinhauerlunge S.16331
Steinholz S. 20275
steinig 3489
Steinkeil 17653
Steinkern 9902
Steinklopfen 1928
Steinkohle S. 2858, 7630, 11050, 13403
Steinkohlenflöz 3859
Steinkohlenformation 2858
Steinkohlengrube 3839
Steinkohlenhauer S. 3813
Steinkohlenmehl 7075
Steinkohlenpech 3851
Steinkohlenteer 3849
Steinkohlenteeröl 3850
Steinkohlenzeche S. 3858
Steinmark S. 12154
Steinmehl 15023/a

Steinmeissel 15009,15016
Steinöl S. 15031, 17646
Steinpfeiler 17648
Steinring 17649
Steinsalz 15026
Steinsammlung 4026
Steinschicht 4553
Steinschlag 2446, 3481, 4769
Steinschraube 14350
Steinschutt S. 19737
Steinsockel S. 2375
Steinsplitter 16963
Steinsplittern S. 16967
Steinwolle 15032/a
Steinzustellung 17654
steirischer Röstofen 17917
steirisches Roheisen 17916
Stellschraube 15705/a
stellen S. 15902
Stellring 1603
Stellspindel 9239/a
stellvertretender Gemeng-teil S. 14060
Stellvertreter 14060
Stellwinkel 1570
Stemmnaht 3110
Stemmuffenverbindung 9834
Stempel 10668, S. 10756, S. 13707, 14014, 14175, 14177, 17540, 17658, 17906, .19533
— mit durchgehendem Element 5998
— mit gleitendem Zapfen 7106
— und Grundschwelle 14009
Stempelausbau S. 16173
Stempelbett 16949/a
stempeln 17305
Stempeln 17321
Stempelrauber 14010
Stempelrauberwinde 13619
Stempelschlag 17907
Stempelsetzen 17407
Stempelzimmerung 14025, 16173
stengelig 17082
stengeliger Habitus 72
Stephanien 17554

Stephanit 1665, 2426, 17555
Steppnahtschweissen 17610a
steriles Gut 12359
Sterkorit 17565
sternbildende Funken 17377
Stemmeissel 17376
Sternsaphir 904
Sternverbindung 20258
stetige Destillation 4266
Steuerkasten 17420
Steuern der Presse 4292
Steuerschieber 12615
Steuerungselement S.8655
Stewartit 17569
Stibiconit 17572, 17576
Stibinit S. 668
Stibiopalladinit 17573, 17574
Stich S. 12958
Stichel 18944
Stichflamme 12176
Stichfolge 15129/a
Stichloch 18267/a
— verschliessen (das) 13558
Stichlochpropfen 13555
Stichlochspiess 18301
Stichlochstopfmaschine 12080, 18268,18269
Stichmass S. 8111
Stichtit 17578
stickendes Wetten S.1648
Sticklava 15172
Stickstoff 12319
Stickstoffbestimmungsappa-rat 707
stickstoffhaltige Wässer 1033
Stickstoffhärtung S.12321
Stickwetter S. 1648
Stiefel 20200
Stiefelknechtplatte 15410
Stift 6873, 13305, S.13307, 17903
Stiftbefestigung 17191/a
Stiften befestigen (mit) 6825
Stiftenkorbschleuder 17081
Stiftkern 17092
Stiftschraube 17904

Stilbit 17591
stilles Wasser S. 1091
Stillstand des Hochofen-
   betriebes 17679
Stilpnochloran 17599
Stilpnomelan 17600
Stinkkalk 646, 17604
Stirn S. 4725
Stirnfläche 7780
Stirnmoräne 18428
Stirnplatte S. 6454, 8939
Stirnrad 17226
Stirnseite 7779
Stirnsenker 17157
Stock 2125, 17611
Stockpunkt 15920
Stockpunkterniedriger S.
   13744
Stockwerk 17627
Stollen 5015, S. 8931, 11732,
   11725, 17910
— absenken (einen) 15339
Stollenbergbau S. 5861
Stollenbetrieb 153, 5861
Stollenbrett 6122
Stolleneingang 155
Stollenmundloch S.155
Stollenort 19109
Stollensohle 156
Stollenstoss 154, S.19109
Stollenwasser 8922
Stolpenit 17638
Stolzit 17639
Stopfbüchse 2058, 12848
Stopfbüchsenbrille S. 8269
Stopfbüchsendeckel 8266
Stopfbüchsenstange S. 13628
Stopfen 1934, S.13559,
   17684
— giessen (durch den)
   2981
Stopfengiessforme S. 2181
Stopfenhebevorrichtung
   17682
Stopfenpfanne 2181
Stopfenstange 2134, 17685
Stopfgerät 3112
Stopfmaschine 8668, 12399
Störung S. 18850, 18933
Stoss 2342, S. 6738, S.
   10395, 16255

Stossbalken S. 2518
Stossbau 4900
stossbohren 8733
Stossbohrer S.2663, S.10250
Stossbohrgestängerohr 5909
Stossbohrmaschine 10249, S.
   13390
Stossbohrung 10247
Stosseil 10149, 20280
Stosseisen S. 10401
Stössel S. 18734
stossend wirkende Säulen-
   schrämmaschine 13712
— wirkende Schrämmaschi-
   ne 13204, 14180, 14184
Stösser 13118
stossfreier Gang 20223
Stossherd 2576, 4165
Stosshöhe 8919
Stosslöffelbagger 6754
Stossofen 4270/a, 14201
Stosspfanne S. 2518
Stoss. schweissung 6453,
   14204
Stoss. stellung senkrecht
   zur Schlechtenrichtung
   2066
— von 30° zur Schichten-
   richtung 10971
— von 45° zum Streichen
   8712
— von 60° zur Schlechten-
   richtung 16180
Stossverbindung 10197
stossweise fliessen 7420
Straddle-Packer 17705
Strahldüse für Putzvorrich-
   tung 15474, 15477
strahlen 15466, 16195
Strahlen 3692, 15477
— entzundert (durch) 16196
Strahlengang 4555
Strahlerz S.2, S.683, S.
   3732, S. 10388
Strahlhämmern S. 16205
Strahlhärtung 17771
strahlig 14331
Strahlkammer 15481
Strahlmittellanze 15475
Strahlmittelpistole 15482
Strahlputzen S.3692, S.

15477, 15525/a, S.16199
Strahlputztrommel 15479
Strahlrohr 12410
Strahlrohrofen 14330
Strahlungstemperatur 715
Strahlverfestigung 16205
Strahlzeolith S.5242
Strand S. 16168
Strandablagerungen 10894
Strandterrasse 14376
stranggepresst 6718
stranggepresste Hohlprofile
   9271
Strangguss 4262
Strangpresse 6721, 6722
strangpressen 6717
strangpresserzeugnis 6719
Strangpressrohling 6723
Strangpresswerkzeug 6725
Strapazieröl 9029
Strassenbahnschiene 18821
Strassenbaumaschinen
   16653
Stratameter 5442
Stratigraph 17748
stratigraphische Lücke 11038
   11038
— Sprungbreite in der
   Schichtebene 17749
— Sprunghöhe 17750
— Wechselbreite 17751
Streb 1919
Strebausgang 5152
Strebbau 2350
— mit breitem Blick 2435,
   S. 10978, 10992
— mit breitem Blick nach
   der Baugrenze fortschrei-
   tend 10989
— mit breitem Blick von
   der Baugrenze rückschrei-
   tend 10993
Strebe 29, 4668, S.5584,
   5865, 10240, 12715, S.
   14465, 16169, 16954, S.
   17906, 17225
Streben des Bohrturmes
   5215
Strebestoss S. 6738
Strebförderer 6741
Strebfront S. 6738, 6749

Strebstempel S.6752
streckbar S. 6073
Streckbarkeit S. 6075
Streckdraht 5821
Strecke 5850, S. 7959, S.
    15131
— am Liegenden 7549
— im Liegenden 15023
— mit Begléitort 5658
strecken S. 5754, 6388
Strecken S. 15120, S.20190
— des Drahtes 5803
— des Eisens 5797
— s. Recken
Streckenauffahren 5959,
    5873
Streckengestell 756, 17456
Streckenort 7564
Streckenpfeiler 6496, 17902,
    17912
Streckenschrämmaschine
    8936
Streckenwächter 18811
Streckfestigkeit 17778
Streckgerüste S. 15262
Streckgrenze 20298
Streckkaliber S. 2326,
    5806, 17712
Streckmetall 6665
Streckmetallblech mit
    Rhombusmuster 5326
Streckwalze 2326
Streichen 17816, S.18875
— von Verwerfung 6860
streichende Ausdehnung S.
    10675
— Erstreckung 10675
— Sprungweite 9350
— Verwerfung 17818, S.
    17821
streichender Grubenbau
    10708
Streichlinie 10838
Streichlinienkarte 4543
Streichmass 11333
Streichrichtung 18875
Streichtorf 11984
Streichwinkel 10839
streifen 15642
Streifen 17844
Streikbrecher 15569

Strengit 17774
Streudüse 17184
Streudüsenzerstäuber 17185
Streusand 12943
Streuung S.15020, 15979
Streuvermögen 4572/a
Streuwert 6551
Strich 17741, 17760
Strichbreite 20063
Stringerplatte 17837
strippen S. 17843
Stripper S. 17862
Stripperkran S. 9803,
    17862, 17870
Stripperwerk S. 9802
Stroh 17754
Strohkranz 17756
Strohöl 17755
Strohseilspinnmaschine
    17757
Strom S. 12192
Stromeyerit 17876
Stromschwankung 7445
Stromsteckerstange 19090
Stromverbrauch 4241
Stromverteilungstür 2225,
    14662
Stromzinn 17772
Strontian 17880
Strontianit 17881
Strontium 17882
Strossen S, 1496
Strossenbau 1490, 1496,
    2189, 19267
Strossenstoss 19266
— ohne Bergeversatz 12601
Struktur 12974, 18473
— s. Textur
strukturelle Geologie 8190
Stuverit 17900
Struvit 17901
Stück 1623
— ausgebrochener An-
    schnitt (am) 2327
Stückanthrazit 3368
Stückerz 7204, 10411, 10412,
    11091
Stückgehalt 8387
stückiger Brennstoff 11090
Stückkohle 1798, 3470,
    4997, 10546, 15276

Stückofen 1171, 1828
Stückquarz 14268
stückweise 12965
Stufe 17283, 18866
Stufenbau S. 1496
Stufendrehprobe 17545
Stufeneingusskanal 17563
Stufeneinlauf 16460
Stufenglühung 17555/a
Stufenhärtung 17289, 17550
Stufenmeissel 6165, 17544
Stufenprobe 17543
Stufenrohrkessel 1995
Stufenwalze 17561
stufenweise Flotation 17287
— Zementierung 12121
— Zerkleinerung 17286
stufenweises Schweissen 196
    19663/a
Stulpenliderung 4837
stumpf 12439
— aneinanderfügen 27,
    2634
— schweissen 2636
— verschweisste Stösse
    2639
Stumpf 5487
stumpfe Schweissung S.2643
stumpfgeschweisste Platte
    2640
stumpfgeschweisstes Rohr
    2641
Stumpfkantpolierknopf
    14343
Stumpfschweissen 19377/a
Stumpfschweissmaschine
    7304
Stumpfschweissung 2643,
    10120
stündliche Leistung 12712
— Leistung mit Wasser-
    versorgung 12711
Sturz 6778, 18594
Sturzblech 18526
Sturzbühne 18680
stürzen 16711
Sturzgerüst 18678
Sturzguss 16717
Sturzplatz 6105
Sturzrolle 3563, 4527, S.
    5780, 11690, 11694, 14118

Stürzrollenöffnung 3566
Stürzrollentür 3565
Stützbau S. 12595
Stütze 8801, 14008, S.
 16169
— des Rahmens 17409
Stützen 9389, 17218
— aus doppel-T-profilen
 2432
stützenlose Tragwerke
 18966
Stützit 17913
Stützling S. 13273
Stützplatte S.9246
Stützrohrsäule 18035
Stützung S.18033
Stützwalze 1082
Stützweite 16969
— von 24m 16970
Stützvorrichtung 14026
Stylolith 17914, 18083
stylolithische Textur 17915
Sublimation 17924
Sublimationsapparat 17925
sublimieren 17923
Succinit 17937
Sulfat-Hüttenzement 18023
sulfatisierende Röstung
 17975, 17977
sulfidischer Gang 19492
Sulfoborit 17978
Sulfohalit 17980
Sulfonat 17964
Sulfonsäure 17965
Süllplatten 3867
Sulvanit 17990
Sumpfeisenstein S.1945
Sumpferzlagerstätte 1944
sumpfig 1950
sumpfiger Boden 11344
Sumpfofen 7170
Sumpfstrecke 5750, 10961,
 11728, S. 19796
Sümpfung 5292
Sund S. 16933
Superbrennstoff 13852
Superoxyd 18076
Supportdrehbank 16612
suspendierte Teilchen 18078
Svabit 18084

Svanbergit 18085
Syenitporphyr 18144
Syenoid 18145
Sylvanit 18146
Sylvin 18148
Symmetrie 18166
symmetrische Antiklinale
 18149
— Falte 18150
symplektische Durchwa-
 schung 18151
— Struktur 18152
Symplesit 18154
symptygmatisches Tal S.
 18160
Synadelphit 18155
synchrone Ablagerungen
 18156
synclinale Verwerfung
 18157
Syngenese 18164
Syngenit 18165
Synklinalachse 18937
Synklinale 5711
Synklinalfalte S.5711, S.
 10323, S.18161, 18935
Synklinalkern 4427
Synklinaltal S. 18161
Synkline 18161, S. 18935
Synklinorium 18162
synthetischer Brennstoff
 18169
— Sand 18171
synthetisches Roheisen
 18170
Syntexis S. 11168, 18167
Syphon-Kessel 18173
Szaibelyit 18182
Szmikit 18183
Szomolnokit 18184

T

T-Träger S. 18186
Tabelle der Atomgewichte
 18190
Tablette 6640, S.15375
Tachylyt 18198
Tafel S.13479, S.18191

Tafelblei S.16066
Tafelbruch 1800
Täfelchen S.13484
Tafelflöz 14585
tafelförmig S. 18194
tafelig S. 16993, 18194
Tafelmessing S. 13488
— auf der Filterpresse
 19636
Tafelschere 8659
Tafelspat S. 20169
Tafelwaage 4091
Tage (am) 5
Tagebau 5018, 12565, 12566,
 12584, 12588, 12594,
 12607, 17291, 17848, S.
 17852, 18057
— (im) 12605
Tagebaubetrieb 18071
Tagebaugewinnung 12606
Tagebruch S. 12607
Tagegrube 18062
Tagesanlage 18060
Tageschicht 5019
Tagesförderung 17613
Tagesleitung 4963
Tageslicht 5021
Tagesoberfläche 8464,
 18041
Tagesproduktion 16444
Tagesstollen 152, 16259
Taimyrit 18216
Talgletscher 19444
Talkpseudomorphose S.
 14726
Talkschiefer 18222
Talkum einpudern (mit)
 6123
Tallingit 18223
Talmoor 19443
Talverlegung 16129
Tamanit S. 553, 18226
Tamaräit 18227
Tandemmaschine 18238
Tandemwalzwerk 18039/a
Tangeit 18237
tangentialer Schub 18244
Tangentialguss 18241
Tangentialkraft 18242
Tangentialprobe 18243
Tankauspumpen 15342

Tankbelüftung 18248
Tanker 18245.
Tank-Fassungsvermögen 18258
Tanklager 18246
Tanklaufgang 19631
Tankmesser 18253
Tankmessung 17745
Tankmusterzug 18521
Tanköl 17626
Tankölverlust 18251
Tankpark 18250
Tankrückstände 18247
Tankschauloch 18249
Tankwagen 18256
Tannenbaumanschnitt 19356
Tantal 18260
Tantalit 18259
Tapalpit 16271
tapping Giesstemperatur 3027
Taragewicht S. 18323
Tarapacait 18325
Tarbuttit 18326
Tarierschrot S.18324
Tarnowitzit 18329
Tasmanit 18333
tasten 6896
Taster 6897
Tasterlehre 2746
Tasterzirkel 2748
Tasthebel 6898
taub 5024, 12105
taube Schichten 1226
— Zone 1245
taubes Gestein S.940, 5028, 5040, S.12103, S. 17141, 17671, 19737
tauchende Falte S. 5438
Tauchfalte 5438
Tauchglocke 1447
Tauchhärten 9644
Tauchhartlöten 5434
Tauchheizung 5440
Tauchkolbenpumpe 13578
Taupunkt 5286, 12730
Taurit 18334
Tausend 12955
Tauwerk S. 18196
Tavistockit 18336
Tavolatit 18337

Tawit 18338
Taxit 18339
taxitische Struktur 18340
Taylorit 18341
Technetium 18349
Teclubrenner 18350
Teeblei 18341/a
Teekannenpfanne S.18342
Teer 18314
Teerdestillat 18316
Teerdestillationsanlage 18317
Teerdestillationsapparat 18321
Teerfeuerung 18318
teerhaltiges Gas 18330
Teerkessel 18320
Teerkocherei 18315
Teerkochkessel S. 18320
Teerschicht 2294
teigig gewordenes Eisen 12963
Teilgalvanisierung 12930/a
Teilkammerrohrkessel 1991, S. 15850
Teilmagma 7690
Teilring 18640
Teilsohle S. 1776, 2649
Teilstrahlungspyrometer 11906
Teilstrahlungstemperatur 714
Teilstrecke 4526, 4530, S. 4531, 17919
Teilstrom 17126
Teilung des Reiterlineals 12402
Teilungsebene 10202, S.11983 11983
Teilungsfläche 11983
Teilungslinie 10203
Teilversatz 17851
teilweise zersetzter Kupferpyrit 1659
teilweises Schmelzen beim Glühen 12941
tektomorphisch 18351
tektonisch 18352
tektonische Diskordanz 17885
tektonisches Fenster 8178

Teller aus porigem Porzellan 13496
— des Kollergangs 12890
Teleskopantenne 2045
teleskopartiger Stahlrohrstempel als Dachgeschoss -stütze 18362
Teleskophammer 277, 8732, 17674
Teleskoppumpe 7465
Teleskopriemenscheibenformmaschine 18360
Teleskop-Trichtermodell 4152
Tellerbohrer 6167
Tellerfeder 13498
Tellermühle 5523
Tellerofen 14110
Tellerspeiser 19152
Tellerventil 5486
Tellerwismut S.1618
Tellur 18367
Tellurblei S.425
tellurführend 18368
Tellurit 18366
Tellurnickel S.11455
Tellurrocker S.18366
Tellursilber S.9102
Tellurwismut S.18468
Temiskamit S.11384, 18369
Temper 3462
Temperament 18378
Temperatur S. 8971, 18379
— im Hochofen 18383
Temperaturanstieg S.9723
Temperaturerhöhung S. 9723
Temperaturempfindlichkeit 15859
Temperaturkonstanz der Lösung 4518
Temperaturmessung 14231
Temperaturregler 938
Temperatursenkung 11074
Temperaturspanne 14413
Temperatursteigerung S.9723 9723
Temperaturwechselbeanspruchung 18380
Temperaturwechselbeständigkeit 16968

Temperaturzunahme 9723
Temperglühung S.11254
Temperguss 11249,11250,
  11813, 11814
Tempergusserzeugung
  7110
temperierbarer Stahl 8849
Tempern 11253, 11254,
  18391
— durch Entkohlen S.
  11255
— durch Graphitisieren
  11256
Temperofen S.3160, 7839
Temperprozess S.618
Temperstahlguss S.11249
Tempertopf 610
Tengerit 18405
Tennantit 18406
Tenorit S. 11442, 18407
Tensionsdislokation S.6845,
  S. 18417
Tensionsschale 16104
Tephrit 18421
Tephroit 18422
Terbium 18423
Terlinguait 18424
Termierit 18425
Termin 18638
Ternärstahl 16366
Terrasse 18431
Terrassenseife 1489
terretrische Fazies 18433
terrigene Ablagerungen
  18434
Tertiär 18435
Tertiärformation 18436
Teschemacherit 18437
Teschenit 18438
Tesseralkies S.16490
Testbenzin S. 11755
Testflansch 18464
Tetradymit 1618, 18468
Tetraeder 18472
Tetraedrit 6764, 12892
tetragonales System 18469
Teufelsklaue S. 12303
Texasit S. 20316,
Textur 6733, S.18473
— s. Gewebe
— s. Struktur

Thalenit 18474
Thallium 18475
Thaumasit 18476
Theisenscher Wascher 18477
Thenardit 18478
Theodolit 18479
theoretische Dauerschwing-
  festigkeit 6833
theoretisches Gewicht
  18480
Thermalhärtung 9423/a
thermisch vergütet 7177/a
thermische Analyse 18480/a
— Zersetzung S.14228
thermischer Wirkungsgrad
  18482
Thermiteisen 18489
Thermitschweissung 18492
Thermittiegel 18488
Thermoelement 18494
thermoelektrische Pyrome-
  ter S. 18494
Thermometrie 18385
Thermonatrit 18495
Thermophyllit 18496
Thermostat 14240
Thermoviskositätsprobe
  18497
Thixotropie 18533
Tholeiit 18534
Thomaseisen 1297, 1301/a
Thomas-Gilchrist-Verfahren
  1302
Thomasroheisen 18536
Thomasschlacke 1305,
  18537
Thomasschlacken-
  verwertungswerk 18538
Thomasstahl 1293, 1549,
  18539
Thomasstahlwerk 1307,
  18535, 18540
Thomasverfahren 1292,
  18536/a
Thomsenolith 18541
Thomsonit 18542
Thorianit 18543
Thorit 18544
Thorium 18546
Thoriumoxyd 18545
Thornycroftkessel 18547

Thorotungstit 18548
Thortveitit 18549
Thukolit 18605
Tiefbau 5095, 5095/a,
  5860
Tiefbeizprobe 5091
Tiefbohrung 5090, 5092
Tiefbrunnenelevator 5099
Tiefenanreicherung 5718
Tiefenstreckung 5203
Tiefengesteine S.32, 5097,
  S. 8406
Tiefenlehre 5204
Tiefenmass 11996
tieferer Flügel 7548
Tiefgang 5725
Tiefgewinnung 5094
tiefgezone Teile 5089
tiefgezogen 5087
Tiefkühlung 17936
Tieflöffel 5738, 14141
Tieflöffelbagger 5450
Tiefofen 14669
Tiefofenkran 4597
Tiefprober 18517
Tiefseeablagerungen 5096
Tieftemperaturbehandlung
  17935
Tiefungsprobe 9730
Tiefungsversuch S. 5086,
  6540
Tiefziehhlech 5085
tiefziehen 5509, 7268
Tiefziehen 4852/a
Tiefziehprobe 5086
Tiegel 5512, 11476, 16455
— formen 11967
— herausnehmen 18218
Tiegelaufsatz 13840
Tiegelbauch 1469, 4737
Tiegelbrenner 10357
Tiegelfabrik 4751
Tiegelgiesserei S. 4741
Tiegelglasur 10850
Tiegelguss 4741
Tiegelguss · stahl S.4738,
  16456
Tiegelherstellung 11306
Tiegelinhalt 4739
Tiegelkammerofen 13406
Tiegelmasse 14633

Tiegelpresse 4743
Tiegelraffination 4744
Tiegelschachtofen 15937
Tiegelscherben 12521
Tiegelschlichte 4750
Tiegelschmelzofen 4740
Tiegel-Schutzanstrich S. 4750
Tiegelstahldarstellung 4746
Tiegelstahlhütte 4747
Tiegeluntersatz S.1678, S. 3380, S.17656
Tiegelzange 10757
Tiemannit 18613
tierischer Stoff 594
Tigerauge S. 18614
Tigersandstein 18615
Tilait 18621
Tillit 18623
Timazit 18633
Tisch 18187
— formen (auf dem) 1491
Tischantriebswelle 13320
Tisch-Bandschleifmaschine mit Schmirgelscheibe 7124
Tischbohrer 1485
Tischbohrmaschine 1486
Tischformpresse 1492
Tischgreifhaken 18188
Tischhobelmaschine 1494
Tisch-Leitspindeldrehbank 1493
Tischsperrung 18189
Tischzahnräderformmaschine 8136
Titan 18690
Titandioxyd 18687
Titaneisen S. 9637, 18692
titanhaltiges Eisenerz 18688
Titanit 17054, 18689
Titanomagnetit 18694
Titanomorphit 18695
Titanstahl 18693
Titer 18696
Titration S. 18698
titrieren 18697
Titrieren 18698
Tobernit 18767
Toddit 18700

Toleranz 18709
Töllit 18705
Toluol 18710
Tombolo 18711
Ton 777, S. 3653, 3790
— im Kohlenliegenden 3854
— schlammen (den) 19683
Tonalit 18712
Tonbeimengung 175
Tonbildung 784
Tonboden S. 8665
Toneinlagerung 15977
Toneisenerz 8645
Toneisenstein 3663, 7266, S. 13069
Tonerde 413
tonerdereich 14873
Tonerdezement 468
Tonerdesilikat 16315
Tongalle 3661
tonhaltende Fazies 778
tonhaltiger Formsand 3668
tonhaltiges Eisenerz 1106
— Gestein S. 3790
toniger Sandstein 5012
toniges Eisenerz S. 3663
Tonkiste 7159
tonlägiger Schacht 5016, 9700, 9704, S. 15352
Tonöfchen 3660
Tonplatte 3659
Tonsandstein 779
Tonschiefer 6111, 780, S. 783, 8461, 15976
Tonschlag 14101
Tonschlämme 16713
Tonschneider 3658
Tonspülung 3655
Tontiegel 7160
Tonzelle 5336
Tonzwischenlage S.3662
Topas 18754
Topazolith 18755
Töpfererde S. 13470
Töpfererz S.10614
Töpferscheibe 13734
Töpferton S. 13470
Toppdestillation S.18760
Toppen 16464, 18760
Torbenit 4366
Tordrillit 18770
Torendrikit 18771

Torf 13023
Torfboden 1951
Torfbrikett 13025
Torferde 13028
Torfkessel 1960
Torfkohle 13026
Torfkohlenofen 3310
Torfmehl 13772
Torfmoor 13029
Torfstecher 13027
Torkran 13697
Törnebohmit 18772
Torpedieren 18775
torpedieren Schacht 18773
Torsion S. 18779
Torsionsbeanspruchung S. 18782
Torsionselastizität 6251, S. 18780
Torsionskraft S. 18781
Torsionsmoment S.19183
Torsionsspannung S.9862
Toskanit 18784
Totalfeinmahlung 367
totbrennen 5026
Totbrennen 5036
toter Gang S. 1065
totes Gebiet 5025
— Gewicht S. 18323
totgemahlen 12728
totpumpen 10350
Totpumpleitung 10354
Totseil 5032
Totseilanker 20152
Tourmalin 18804
Trachyandesit 18806
Trachydolerit 18807
Trachyt 11840
trachytische Struktur 18808
Tragachse 1388
Tragbalken 10763, 10764
tragbare Bremsbergvorrichtung 8324
— Putzmühle 13687
tragbarer Ofen 13686
Tragbügel 1100, 20302
tragen 2902
Träger 8238, 10216
— der Vorderplatte 2241
— des Gichtbelages 13507
— des Kühlwasserrohres 2245

Träger des Trichters 9329
Trägergestein S. 14750
Trägerkaliber 8242
Trägerlager 8243
Trägerwellblech 4500
Tragfähigkeit 1390, 2904
Tragfeder 1399
Traggabel 10474
Traggerüst 18037
Traggeviert 1386, 1391,
 1397/a, 1401/a, 16423
Tragheitsmoment 11889
Tragkorb 18036
Tragkraft 3336
Tragkranz S. 1391, 2246,
 4629, S. 4860, 10859/a,
 11300, S. 11302, 11303
Traglappen 2238
Traglast 1395
Tragnocken S. 18959
Tragplatte 1397
Tragpratzen 18034
Tragring S. 11302
Tragschere 2199, 15981/a
Tragseil 16791
Tragstange 1398
Tragwerk aus Stahl für
 Mantelwände 17476
Tragzapfen S. 18959
Tränken 9764/a
Tränkgefäss 16797
Transferform 18823
Transformatorenblech 18827
transkristalliner Riss 18822
Transmission 5960
Transmissionshammer 1475
transportabler Kessel S.
 13691
— Trockner S. 13693
Transportband 1473, S. 4314
Transportfaktor S.221
transportierende und
 ablagernde Wirkung des
 fliessenden Wassers
 18839
Transportkosten 2905
Transportmittel 221, 533/a
Transportvorrichtung 4317
transuranisch 18840
Trapezeisen 18853, 18854
Trapezoeder S. 9614

Trapp 18847
Trapring mit Fingern 7108
Tratschtrommel 7127
traubenartige Bildung 8445
traubige Struktur 2130
Travertin 7758, 18865
Treibachse 5961
Treibbirne S. 2963
Treibeisen S. 20026
treiben S. 8727, 14016,
 18119
Treiben 10743, 18905, 20087
— des Eisens 14960
Treibenkontrolle 17096
Treibfäustel S. 14932, S.
 16581
Treibkeil 13560
Treibladung 14018
Treibmittel 14017
Treibofen S. 10867
Treibräder 5970
Treibradsatz 15908
Treibstelle 18123
Tremolit S. 8411, 18871
Tremolitasbest 10086/a
trennen 4891
Trennfläche 9879
Trennpuder 12950
Trennscheibe 4928
Trennschleifmaschine 4905
Trennschere 15866
Trennung 12947
— mittels schwerer Flüssig-
 keiten 9033
— von Form und Modell
 S. 17865
Trennungsebene 5586
Trennungskammer 10404
Trennungsvorgang 13979
Treppe 7373
treppenartig 17553
Treppenlauf S. 16460
Treppenrost 17549, 17556
Treppenrostfeuerung 7878
Treppenrostgenerator 17557
Treppenschmelzen 17551
Tresorstahl S. 17473
Tretgebläse 7539
Triaszeit 18888
Trichter 7820
Trichterabdeckung 4563

Trichterbau 8310
Trichterbildung 7821
Trichterbohrer 18292
Trichterkopf 13749
Trichterlauf S. 5712
Trichterschurre 8309, S.
 11694, 11711
Trichterverlängerung 14950
Tridymit 18892
Triebsand 5863
Triebradachse 4605
Triebscheibe 14132
Triebstahl 13321
Trigonit 18894
triklines System 18891
Trimer 18895
Trimerit 18896
Trinidadasphalt 1638
Trioblechstrasse 18561
Trioblechwalzwerk 18560
Triogerüst 18559
Trioprofileisenwalzwerk
 18562
Triowalzwerk S.18558
Tripelwellblech S.18912
Triphylin 18911
Triplit 18915
Triploidite 18916
Trippkeit 18918
Triptan 18920
Tripuhyit 18919
Tritomit 18921
Tritoprisma 13960
Tritthammer 12535/a
Trittofen S. 615
trocken schwärzen 1641
— verdampfen S. 5552
Trockenanlage 6062
Trockenapparat 6054
Trockenbinder zusetzen 129
Trockenbohren 6027
Trockenbohrer S.3670
trockene Gasdurchlässig-
 keit 1115/a
— Gasreinigung 6032/a
— Kohle S. 10640
— Sandfestigkeit 6025/a
— Sandschicht 6042
— Scheidung 6044
— Scheidung der Kohle
 6045

trockene Verdampfung S. 6031
— Weichkohle S. 2888
Trockeneinrichtung S.17695
trockener Sand 6039
— Zunder 6042/a
trockenes Erz 6033
Trockengestell 6064
trockengewalzter Draht 16800
Trockenguss· sand 15497
Trockenkammer 6055
Trockenkammerwagen 6056
Trockenkasten S.6061
Trockenkohäsion 6048
Trockenmahlen 6029
Trockenofen 6059, 13693, 17695
— mit Luftumwälzung 17699
Trockenplatte 4399, 6035
Trockenpochen 6047
Trockenpuddeln 6037
Trockenraum 6063
Trockenreinigung der Gase 6038
Trockenriss 17998
Trockenröhre 6065
Trockensandbinder 4392
Trockensandformen 12009
Trockenschale 4398
Trockenschrank 6061, S. 6693
Trockensiebung 6046
Trockentrommel 6058
Trockenturm S. 2723
Trocken- und Röstapparat 6053
Trockenversatz 6034
Trockenvorgang 17700
Trockenwalzen 16799
Trockenwaschen 6050
Trockenzerkleinerung S. 6029
Trockenzylinder 6057
trocknen 6023, 17694
Trocknen S. 17700
— der Formen 6060
Trockner 6051
— mit Kühlstrecke 4330
Trocknung 6052, S. 17700
Trocknungspunkt 6036

Trocknungsriss S.17998
Troktolith 18925
Trog zur Goldwäsche S. 2513
Trogblech S. 2503, S.2509
Trögerit 18926
Trogtal 8260
Trolleit 18927
Trommelamalgamation 500, 1240
Trommelgebläse 15521
Trommelkonverter 1241
Trommelofen 15207
Trommelpfanne S. 6014
Trommelschleuder S. 3213
Trommelsieb 14842, 15216, 16701, 18930/a
Trommelverputzen 19097
Trommelwascher 6016
Trommelwelle 6015
Trona S. 19402
Troostit 18931
troostitischer Stahl 18932
Tropfenfänger 5948, 5949
tropfenweiser Zusatz 135
Tropfloch 18890/a
Tropföl 15608, 5951
Tropfpfanne 5950
Tropfprobe 17158
Tropfstein 5997
Tropftrichter 6003
trübe Lösung 19116
trüber Belag 18328/a
trübes Öl 15066
Trübeverdicker 14143
Trübheit 3786
Trübpunkt 3785
Trudellit 18950
Trümmerachat 2355
Trümmergestein S.8317
Truskottit 18962
Tscheffkinit 18967
Tschermigit 18968
Tschernosem S. 3412
Tsingtauit 18969
Tsumebit 18970
Tubingausbau 18974
Tubing-Fänger 19048
— Flaschenzugblock 19047
— Kopf 19051
Tubingschneider 19050

Tubularplatte S.19035
Tuch überziehen (mit) 4560
Tuchtisch 1693
Tuff S. 16430
Tulle S. 10860
Tümpel 19201
Tümpelblech 19200
Tümpeleisen 19199
Tümpelgewölbe 19198
Tümpelverschlussblech 5484
Tungstenit 19105
Tunnel 19107
Tunnelbau 19108
Tunnelbohren 19106
Tunnelmündung 19110
Tunnelofen 7914
Tunnelring 19111
Tunnelstollen 19261
Tunneltrockner 19112
Tüpfelanalyse 17159
Tüpfelproben S. 17159
Tüpfelung 11958/a
Tür 8088
Turanit 19115
Turbinenbohren 19127
Turbinenlokomotivkessel 19119
Turbinenschaufel 19117
Turbinenschaufelstahl 19118
Turbinenwelle 19123
Turbinenzähler 19120
Turbinenrotor 19121
Turbodynamo 19125
Turbogebläse 19126
turbulenter Fluss 19128
Türgerüst 7915
Turgit 19129
Turkis 19154
Türladung S. 5628
Turmalingranit 8632
Turmankerdrähte 8691
Turmboden S. 5218
Turmdrehkran 15224
Turmkronenbühne 4732
Turmrollenblock 4729
Turmrutscher 13363
Turmspatz S. 5221
Turmständer 5220
Turmsteiger 5221
Turmverstrebung 2232

Turnerit 19143
Türstock 5864, 15904, 15912,
  18568
Türstockbein 5862
Türverschluss 1134/a,
  5630
Tuskulit 19157
Tychit 19197
Tyrolit 19206
Tysonit 19207

U

U-Eisen 3289, 3292
U-Träger aus Falzblech
  12375
über die Modellaussenfläche
  vergrösserte Kernmarke
  12140
— Tage 913
Überbeizung 12771/a
Überblasen 12734
Überbohrrohr 19690
überdachen 15136
überdachte Kesselanlage
  4566
überdichtes Öl 18014
Überdrehung S.19180
Überdruck 12774, 13893
übereutektisch 9585
übereutektische Aluminium-
  -Silizium-Legierung 448
übereutektisches Gusseisen
  9586
übereutektoider Stahl 9588
Überfallrohr S. 8023
Überfaltungsdecke S
  S. 7521
Überfliessen 15358
überfliessendes Giessen
  7432/a, 15358/a
Überflutung 7399
Überführung 2383
Übergabewalzwerk 5735/b
Übergangsrohr 9724/a
Übergangsschichten 1436
Übergangszone 18830
übergares Eisen S. 2613
— Kupfer 6028/a
übergelegte Falte S.9934

übergeneigte Falte S.9934
Überglasung 19570/a
überhängendes Gebirge
  15028
Überhauen S. 13300, S.
  14942, 19366
Überhebevorrichtung 10765
Überhitzen 18011
Überhitzer 18007,
— -Sammelkammer 18008
überhitzter Stahl 12759
Überhitzer und Rohrschlange 18010
Überhitzerrohr 18013
überhitztes Eisen S.2613,
  18006
— Metall S. 9422
Überhitzung 18005
— des Eisens 12760
Überhitzungsempfindlich-
  keit 12761
Überhol-Kupplung 12776
überkippte Antiklinale 12782
— Falte S. 9934, 12783
Überkorn 12778/a
Überlagerung S. 12767
überlappen 12764
überlappt geschweisstes
  Rohr 10543
— schweissen 10539
überlappte Schweissung S.
  10542
Überlapptnahtschweissung
  10541, 12766
Überlappung 10244/a,
  12767; 16244
Überlappungsdestillation
  5558
Überlappungsschweissung
  10542
überlasten 11486
Überlastungsdruck 12736
Überlauf 4965, 12742,
  19919
— an einer Form 7432
Überlaufdeich 12739
Überlaufrohr 12743, 19736
überliegend 18016
überliegende Falte 9934
überpolt 12773
Überpolung 12772
überprüfen 19514
übersättigen 18018

übersättigt 18019
übersättigtes Eisen 18020
Übersättigung 18021
Überschiebung S. 16609,
  18603
Überschiebungsdecke S.
  12780
Überschiebungsfalte 12779
Überschiebungsfläche 12781,
  18600
Überschiebungswurzel
  15154
überschlagene Falte S.9934
überschmieren 12771
überschobene Masse 12780
Überschuss 6639
— des Fällungsmittels
  6642
Überschwemmung 7398
übersetzender Gang 4533/a
Übertiefung 12738
Übertreiben 14135
— der Förderkörbe 12762,
  12785
Überwalzungsfehler 8710/a,
  10539/a, 15742/a
Überwassermoor 6409
Überziehen mit Messing S.
  13504
Überzug 16857, 3881
Überzugsindex 3882
Überzugsmasse 5435
übliches Profileisen 19316
Uchatiusstahl S. 5464
Ufer 16168
Uhligit 19210
Uhrfederstahl 19742
Uhrglas 19741
Uintait 19211
Ulexit S. 12184, 19212
Ullmannit 19214
Ulm 1046
Ulmen 3376, 3379
Ulrichit 19215
ultrabasisches Gestein
  19220
ultramikroskopische Unter-
  suchung 19222
Ultramylonit 19223
Ultraschallprüfung 19224
Umangit 19226
Umber S. 19227

Umbiegung 1506, S.5728, 9198
umbördeltes Zubehör 1369
Umbördelung 1373/a
Umbra 19227
Umdrehung der Fördermaschine 2019
Umfahrungsstrecke 2010
Umfang 14412
Umfangsgeschwindigkeit 3606
umflochtener Draht S. 20149
Umführung 2650
umgebogen S. 7523
Umgebung 6497/a
umgeformte Kesselstirnwand 6687
Umgehungskanal 10570
umgekehrte Verbrennung 9933
umgekehrter Hartguss 9932
umgelegtes Eisenband 9323
umgeschmolzner Stahl 14698
umgeschmolznes Eisen 14697
umgewandelter Ton 4297
umgezogene Platte S. 7272
umgiessen S. 14695
umhüllte Elektrode 16119
Umhüllung 4571
Umhüllungspseudomorphose S. 13092
Umkehr 14819
— der Stromrichtung des Wetterzuges 14822
umkehrbare Maschine 14827
Umkehrblockwalzwerk 14829
Umkehrbock 9353
Umkehrhebel S. 9353
Umkehrprisma 6538
Umkehrscheibe 18211
Umkehrung 18135
Umkleidungsplatte 2931
umklöppelter Draht S.20149
umlaufendes Einfallen 14254
Umlauffilter 2651
Umlaufkessel S. 3603
Umlaufpumpe 3605
Umlaufrückfluss 3584
Umlaufvorrichtung für

«releasing spear» 12852
Umlenkung 1094
ummantelter Draht S.4569
Umrollen ausheben (durch) 5768
Umrollvorrichtung 15083
Umrühren 236
— eines Bades 14315
Umschlagplatte 14828
Umschmelzen 14699
Umschmelzlegierung 15764
Umschmelzofen 14700
Umschmelzverfahren 14701
umsetzbare Stahlstrasse 12051
Umspanner-Rohr 18828
umsponnener Draht 4569
— und umklöppelter Draht 4565
Umsteuervorrichtung 18136
Umströmkanal 3604
Umwälzpumpe S. 3583
Umwandlung 18825
Umwandlungsdauer 4647
Umwandlungsintervall 18826
Umwandlungspunkt 4645
Umwandlungswärme 4644
Umwickeln 20232
Umwicklung 1600
unausgenutztes Fassungsvermögen 19213
unbalanzierte Umdrehung 20165
unbauwürdiger Gang 19320
unbearbeiteter Stab 19345
— Zahn 3029
unbenetzbar 12370
unbrauchbarer Ton 19412
Uncompahgrit 19237
undeutliche Spaltbarkeit 9742
undichte Wettertür 15589
Undichtheit 10637
undurchlässige Schicht S. 9657
— Zwischenlage 9656
undulöse Auslöschung 17032
Unebenheit 10943/a
unebener Bruch 19291
Unebenheit 19293

unedles Metall 1280
unergiebige Bohrung 1246
unexplodiert 19294
unfest 19296
Ungait 19299
unganzes Eisen 7363
ungebrauchter Sand 19341
ungehärteter Stahl S.16844, 19338
ungenauer Ausdruck S. 3015
ungereinigter Baryt 5697/a
ungeröstetes Erz 19329
ungeschichtet 917
ungeschmolzene Masse 19322
ungesinterter Pressling 8509/a
ungespalten S. 858
ungespaltenes Gestein 859
ungeteilter Kernkasten 9022
ungeteiltes Gebrauchsstück 19286
ungewaschene Kohle 19343
ungleichförmig S. 19238
ungleichmässig verteilte blau gefärbte Poren 10940
— verteilte oxydierte Poren 10939
ungleichmässige Verdichtung 19292
ungleichmässiges Kohlenflöz 3842
Ungleichschenklige Flansche 1929
ungleichschenkliger rundkantiger Winkelstahl 19289
ungleichschenkliges Winkeleisen 19288
unharmonische Falte 6506
Universalblech 19314/a
Universaldrehtisch 19318
Universaleisen S. 7340, 19313
Universalschelle 9388
Universalschlüssel 11904
Universalstrasse 19315
Universalwalzwerk 19314, 19317
unkalibriert 10408

unlegierter Baustahl 9140
— Edelstahl 13446
— Stahl 12339
— Werkzeugstahl 19230
unlöslich 9844
unlöslicher Rückstand 19285
unmagnetischer Stahl S. 12357
unmagnetisches Gusseisen 12355
unmagnetisierbarer Stahl 12357
unmittelbare Heizung 5459
— Kraftübertragung 5465
unoxydierbarer Stahl 17297
unregelmässige Schichtung 10038
Unreinheiten 9672
unruhig flackern 7285
unruhiger Stahl 14918, 19319
unrunde Kernspindel 15992
unrundwerden 17114
unschmelzbar 9774
Unschmelzbarkeit 9773
unsicher 6019
unsortierte Kohle 19330
unsortierter Koks aller Korngrössen 11821
unteilbarer Psilomelangraphit S. 850
unten hergiessen (von) 13739
unter Druck stehender Kessel 1980
— Entgasung zersplitterte Kohle 2577
— Kontrolle bringen 2791
— Luftzutritt ausgehärtet 12562
— Wind setzen S.19136
Unterbau S. 7637, 8623, 17934
unterbauen S. 19273
Unterbohrloch 5703
Unterbrecher S. 2316, 9894
Unterbrechung S. 7686
unterbrochene gleichförmige Auflagerung 48, 5503
— Härtung 9912
unterbrochener Guss 9913

unterbrochenes Kaliber 18291
Unterdampf 17415
Unterdevon 12869
untere Abbaugruben 2190
— Lagerschale S.2148
— Rahmenhölzer 16345
— Richstrecke 2159
— Sohle 1288, S.2171, S. 5093
unterer Grat 2157
— Heizwert 12241
— Riss 1265
— Schram
— Teil 11069
untereutektisch 9596
untereutektoidisch 9597
untereutektoidischer Stahl 9598, 9600
untereutektoidisches Gusseisen 9599
Unterfahrung eines Schachtes 16419
Unterfeuerung 7862
Unterflansch S.2156
Unterführung 19244
Untergrundabbau 19257, 19259
Untergrundförderung 19260, 19265
Untergrundpumpe für Erdölgruben 12516
unterirdische Stromleitung 19258
unterirdischer Grubenbau 3779
unterhälten 19358
unterhöhlen 1791
Unterhöhlen S. 2777, S. 4913, 4917, S. 8205, 9115, 19243
Unterhöhlung S. 19243
Unterkasten 5731, 11065
Unterkessel 11066
Unterkorn 16303
Interkühlung 18001
Interkühlungsgraphit 19245
Unterlagplatte 17405
Unterlagplattenkaliber 3250
Unterlagring 18039
unterlaufendes 18815

Unterlegbrett 12025
Untermass 19279
untermauern 19273
Untermodell 11377
Untermoräne S.8618
Untersatz aus Hartgummi 6184
Unterschale 2148
Unterschicht des Brennmaterials 1417
Unterschiebung 19282
unterschneiden 19274
Unterschneider 19275, S. 1052, S.19246, 19277
unterschrämen 10111, 16685, 16790, S.
Unterschrämen S. 9115,
— eines Flözes 2128
Unterschub S. 19282
Unterschubfeuerung 19250
unterseeisches Tal 17927
Unterseil 1134, 18212
Unterseite eines Rohres 2185
Unterstempel 2187, 11069/a
unterstützen 2230, 16167, S. 19273
Unterstützung 18033, 18901,
— des Trichters 18030
untersuchen S. 13968, 16935
Untersuchung auf Anrisse 4582/a
Untersuchungsbohrung 724
Unterwalze 2183
Unterwasserbohrer 12472
Unterwasserbohrung 12471
Unterwasser-Completion 19283
Unterwasserleitung 15742
Unterwassermoor 9642
Unterwerksbau 5448
Unterwind 13935
Unterwindfeuerung 7555, 7865
— mit Luftzuführung durch Hohlroststäbe 7556
Untiefe S. 7316, S.16092
ununterbrochene Gaserzeugung 4268
— Probeentnahme 4273
ununterbrochener Abstich 4276

ununterbrochener Betrieb 4261, 4279
ununterbrochenes Spektrum 19307
ınverliehenes Terrain S. 19229
unverritzte Kohle 20050
unverrohrtes Bohrloch 19234
— Loch 12582
unverrostbarer Stahl S. 17297
unversetzter Stoss mit Stempelzimmerung 12596
unverzimmert 19336
unvollkommen geröstetes Erz 9717
unvollkommene Verschmelzung 9715
unvollständige Polung 19273a
unvollständiger Guss 16184
unvorhergesehene geologische Formation 17759
unzentriert 11793
unzuverlässiger Baugrund 19328
Uptrusion 19386
Uralit 19388
Uralitisierung 19389
Uran 19394
Uranat 19391
Uranglasplatte 19396
Uranglimmer 19390
Uraninit S. 13413, 19392
uranlegierter Stahl 19395
Uranocircit 19393
Uranophan 19397
Uranosphärit 19398
Uranospinit 19399
Uranothallit 19400
Uranotil 19401
Uranpecherz S. 13413
Urao 19402
Urbainit 19403
Urbanit 19404
Urgon 19405
Urkaliber 11364
Urtit 19407
Urusit 19408
Urzeugung 17146
Usbekit 19409
Ussingit 19413

Utahit 19414
Uvanit 19418
Uwarowit S.2725, 12720, 19419

V

V-Eisen 19422
Vaalit 19423
Vakuumanschluss der Matrize 19434
Vakuumapparat S. 19425
Vakuumbüchse 17952
Vakuumdestillation 19427
Vakuumdruckprobe 13925
Vakuumfilter 19430
Vakuuminjektor 19433
Vakuumlüftung 19438
Vakuummeter 19435
Vakuumschmelzen 19436
Vakuumsintern 19436/a
Vakuumtorsionsmesser 19437
Vakuumtrockner 19428
Valbellit 19439
Valencianit 19441
Valentinit 20024
Vallevarit 19442
Vanadin S. 19461
Vanadinbleierz S. 19460
Vanadineisen S. 6954
Vanadinit 19460·
Vanadinsalz 19459
Vanadinstahl 19462
Vanadium 19461
Vanadiumeisen 6954
Vanadiumglimmer 19461/a
Vanoxit 19464
Vanthoffit 19465
Variolit 19474
variolitische Texture 19475
Variscit 19476
Värnsingit 19479
Vaselin 13132, 19480
Vaterit 19481
Vaugnerit 19482
Vauquelinit 19483
Vauxit 19484
Vegasit 19485
Velozipedkran 11915

Ventil 19446
Ventilation 19508
Ventilator 1866, 6793, 6811
Ventilatoreinströmöffnung 6164
Ventilator-Umlaufstrecke 6798 6798
Ventilbohrer 15821, S.19447
Ventilgehäuse 19448, 19449
Ventilkegel 19450
Ventilkorb S. 19449
Ventilsitz 19454
Ventilsitzauszieher 19455
Ventilstahl 19456
Ventilstange 16593
Ventilsteuerung 19453
Venturi-Rohr 19513
Veränderungsmöglichkeit der Phasen 3282
Verankerung gegen Turmwind 5217
— im Gestein gegen Turmwind 5219
Verankerungsdraht S. 8690
Verankerungsstück 560
Verarmung 9660/a
verästelte Verwerfung S. 2261
Verbait 19605
Verbandstift 5670
Verbesserungsmittel 3395
Verbiegung 19677
verbinden 2016
Verbinder mit normalem Durchgang 7800
— mit verengtem Durchgang 14653
— mit vollem Durchgang 9900
Verbindung 10200, 10214, 10252, 16806, 20257
— der Metalloide mit dem Eisen 4057
— für Bohrgestänge 5904
Verbindungsbrücke 4218
Verbindungsgewicht 4068
Verbindungsgleichung 6524
Verbindungshahn 4219
Verbindungskeil 10323/a
Verbindungsplatte 17190
Verbindungsrohr ·6012

Verbindungsschiene S. 18608
Verbindungsschraube 4221
Verbindungsstück 2939
Verbindungsvolumen 4067
Verbindungswärme 8985
Verblasen 1788
Verblattung 15604
Verbleibedauer 18810
verbleien 4561, 10603
verbleit 10611
verbleites Blech 18430
Verbleiung 10630
Verbohrung 2932
Verbohrungsstück 10212
verbolzet 13432
verbrannter Block 2040/a
— Sand 2614
— Stahl 2615
verbranntes Eisen 2613
Verbrauch pro Tonne Stahl
    in Kilowatt-Stunden 4246
Verbrauchskurve 4237
Verbrauchsspannung 19594
Verbrennen 2603, S. 2604
Verbrennung 4071, 9678
— bei gleichbleibendem
    Druck 4072
— bei gleichbleibendem
    Volumen 4073
— verlangsamen 16513
Verbrennungsgase 2612
Verbrennungskontrolle 4077
Verbrennungskurve S. 4080
Verbrennungslinie 4080
Verbrennungsmotor 9898
Verbrennungsofen 4078
Verbrennungsprodukt 13989
Verbrennungsraum S. 4076,
    4082
Verbrennungsröhre 4084
Verbrennungsrückstand 4081
Verbrennungsschacht 4083
Verbrennungsschälchen 4075
Verbrennungsvorgang 13976
Verbrennungswärme 8986
    2454
Verbundbrennstoff 1764
Verbunddampfpumpe 4130
Verbundkessel 4054
Verbundmaschine 4128
Verbundstahl 4131

Verbundstossmaschine 2096
verbürgter Gehalt 8639
verchromen 3546
Verchromung 3524, S. 3527
verdämmen S. 7009, 13557,
    18228
Verdämmen 7035
verdampfen 6610
Verdampferrohr 19467
Verdampfturm 6622
Verdampfung 6618
— per Quadratmeter Heiz-
    fläche 6620
Verdampfungskammer 7293
Verdampfungsprodukt S.
    13991
verdeckte Struktur 2593
verdeckter Gang 1778
— Herd 4568
verderben S. 18348
Verdichtbarkeit 4101
Verdichtbarkeitszahl 4102
verdichten 4184, 9720
Verdichten der Form 14407
— durch Festtreten 18820
— durch Pressen 17262
— durch Rütteln 10221
— durch Schleudern 9654
— durch Vibrieren 19550
— mit Druckluft 13594
verdichtetes Gas 4138
Verdichtung 4104, 4181,
    14403
Verdichtungsgrad 1198, 5137
Verdichtungspolarisation
    4161
Verdoppelungsplatte 5690
verdorbener Stahl 17143
Verdrehungsbeanspruchung
    S. 18782
Verdrehungselastizität
    18780
Verdrehungsversuch 18778
Verdrückung S. 12300, S.
    12298, 18531
verdübeln 14649
verdünnte Säure 5417
verdünnter Mittelschenkel
    5818
Verdünnungsmittel 5418,
    S. 12090

Verdünnungsmitteldestillier-
    apparat 5416
Verdunstpfanne 19425
Verdunstung 194
veredeln S. 14593
veredeltes Erz 19355/a
Veredelungsverfahren 13978
vereidigter Chemiker 18143
Vereinbarung für wirtschaft-
    liche Ausbeutung 4228
vereinigte Flöze 901
vereinigtes Bessemer und
    Martin-Verfahren 4063
verengtes Bohrloch 19252
Verengung 12178
Vererblichkeit 9097
vererzbar 11757
Vererzung 11758
verfeinertes Gusseisen
    14599
verfeinert und gehärtet
    14597
verfestigen 20188
Verfestigung 4231
verflüchtigen (sich) 19588
Verflüchtigung S. 4181
Verflüssiger 12093
Verfolgung eines Ganges
    im Streichen 3356
Verformen S. 5566
Verformung 5125, 5566,
    S. 19674
— des Formkastens 5569
— s. Verzug
Verformungsbruch 7699
Verformungsfestigkeit 5570
Verformungskraft 7619
Verformungsvermögen 5124
Verfrachtung 18835
Verfüllen S. 1057
verfüllen S. 13557
vergasen 8076
Vergasergraphit 14799
vergast 8083
Vergasung 8074
— des festen Brennstoffes
    8075
— mit Wasserdampf 17427
vergiessbar 3032
Vergiessbarkeit 3033,
    7439/a

Verglasen 19576
verglasene Mischung 19579
Verglasungspunkt 19578
Vergleich der Abmessungen
    10600/a
Vergleichsanalyse 17342
Vergleichsversuch 4106
Vergleichswert 4107
vergolden 8224
Vergolden 8225
Vergoldung S. 8225
Vergoldungspresse 8227
Vergoldungs- und Prägepres-
    se 8346
vergraben 2591
Vergrösserung 11212
Verjüngung 18098
vergütbar 8997
vergütete Förderkohle
    18583
vergüteten Zustand (im)
    9679
vergüteter Stahl 8852
vergütetes raffiniertes
    ·Kupfer 18799
Vergütung 8859
— im Schlackenbad 19702
Verhalten im Hochofen 1441
— in der Perle 1366
verhärten 6737
Verhärtung 8858, 17733
verhüttbares Gut 13994
verhütten 16745
Verhüttung 16747
— von Sandzufluss 15494
Verit 19515
verjüngtes Seil 18283
— Vorschweissrohrstück
    19949
Verjüngung 2139, 5148,
    18100, 18202
Verkadmung 2675
Verkauf 15436
verkeilen 1792, 3618
Verkeilen 1807, 3625
verkeilt 16235
verkippen 1195
verklammern 3617
Verklammern 3626, 15750
verkleben S. 12069
verkleideter Schacht

10033
Verkleidung 2928, 6757,
    13511, 16087, 16485,
    17247, S. 18637
verkleistern S.12068
verklemmen 7740
verkohlen 2869
verkohlter Brennstoff 2862
Verkohlung 3359, 3950
verkoken 3926
Verkokung 3954
Verkokungsfähigkeit 3951
Verkokungsfeuerung 3955
Verkokungskammer 3952
Verkokungstemperatur
    18386
Verkrustung 9727
verkupfern 12478
verkupferte Steretypplatte
    4356
verkupferter Stahl S. 4355
verkupfertes Blech 4371
Verkupferung 4362
Verkürzung der Schmelzzeit
    16188
Verladeanlage mit obenlau-
    fendem Drehkran 10919
Verladebockkran 5500
Verladekai 10922
Verladerampe 10921
Verladestation S. 18426
Verlade- und Beförderungs-
    vorrichtung 10920
Verladung 5849, 10916
verlängerte Kernmarke 3711
verlängerter Steigkanal
    15359
Verlängerung der oberen
    Stopfbüchse 12849
verlangsamen 16693
Verlauf des Hochofenganges
    1714
Verletten 3669
verlorene Gussform 18402
verlorener Kern 11805,
    12537
— Kopf 5030, 5488, S.
    12598
— Sandkern 11039
Vermessingen S. 13504
Vermessingung 2275, 13504

Vermessung unter Tage
    19516
vernickeln 12286
vernickeltes Blech 12279
Vernickelung 12284
Verpackungsdraht 1145
Verplatinierung S. 13523
Verpulverung 3266/a
Verreibung 6547
Verriegelung S. 5959, '10946
Verriegelungskeil 15426
verrohren 2907, 14807,
    15343
Verrohren 15357
verrohrtes Loch 2924
Verrohrung 14806, 16089
Verrohrungsbühne 17269
Verrohrungskopf 2948
Verrohrungsseil 2950
Verrohrungssitz ´S. 16209
Verrohrungstrommel 2740
Versatz 2534, 8325, 8329,
    8335, 12844, 12854,
    19749
Versatzabbau 1056
Versatzarbeit 8326, 8336
Versatzarbeiter 2533, 3911,
    12842
Versatzberge S.940, S. 8325,
    S. 8329, S.19740
Versatzmaschine 1058, 8327,
    8333, 8337, 17704
— für unverrohrtes Bohr-
    loch 9319
Versatzmaterial S. 8325,
    19740
Versatzmauer S. 2534
Versatzschacht 15027, 17650
Versatzsohle 19726
verschalen 10457, 10488
Verschalung 1924, S. 10458,
    10489, S. 16087
verschiebbar 5531
Verschiebebahnhof 16269
Verschiebewinde 16238
Verschiebung S. 6839,
    11799/a, 16128, S.18603
— im Streichen 17823
— von angereichertem.Gas
    6489
Verschiebungsbreccie S.6844

Verschiebungsfaktor 5112
Verschiebungskontrolle
  14752
verschiedenartig auf-
  gebrachter Überzug 5395
Verschiffungshafen 16138
verschlacken 16517
Verschlackung des
  Phosphors 16570
— von Sand 16569
— von Schlichte 16568
Verschlackungsfähigkeit
  7504
Verschlag S.1924
verschlämmen 12067
Verschlämmung 12094
Verschleiss 19853
— durch Abrieb unter hohem
  Kontaktdruck 9183
Verschleissanzeiger für
  Meissel 6085
verschleissfest 19857
Verschleissfestigkeit S.
  19856
Verschleissfestigkeitsprobe
  19858
Verschleisshärte 14777
Verschleisseinlage des
  Kernkastens 11548
Verschleissplatte 19855
verschlissen 6088, S.16241
verschlissener Meissel 6084
Verschliessung 15734
Verschluss 3638
— des Winderhitzers 19452
Verschlussdeckel
  3780
Verschlusskegel 1446
Verschlussklappe 9204
  10947
Verschluss · schraube 3783
Verschluss · stopfen 2133
Verschmelzung 11474
Verschmelzungskörper 398
Verschmieren S. 11102
verschobene Produktion
  5113
verschobenes Gebirge S.4544
Verschraubdrehmoment
  11235
Verschraubung 15718,.

  17362
verschüttet 6492
Verschwinden einer Eigen-
  schaft S. 11028
versenkbare Bohrplattform
  17928
Versenkbohrer 15178
Versenker 4537
— (flacher stumpfer Kopf)
  4538
versenkter Bolzen 4539
— Niet 4541
versetze Form S.11082,
  16125
— Kokille 11801
— Modellplatte 11804
versetzen 1291, 8328,
  12825, 17702
Versetzen 1057, S. 8326,
  8334, 15022, 17703,
  19725
versetzter Firstenabbau mit
  waagerechter Firste 701
— Firstenstoss mit
  geneigter Firste 7019
— Firstenstoss mit waage-
  rechter Firste 7018
— Kern 9669, 11800, 16126
— Stoss 3776, 7020
versetztes Modell 11803
Versetzung 2308, S.11799
— des Modells S.11803
versiegeln 15733
versilbern 16349, 16355
versilbert 16356
Versilberung 16357
Versinterung 15388
versplintete Kette 4523
verspritzen 16995
Versprödung 6406/a
verstählbar 102
verstählen 104, S.17453
verstählte Spitze 17497
Verstählung 58, 103, 17495
Verstählungshärte 2923
verstärkte einseitige Kernmarke mit Sicherung 1132
— Kernmarke 6484
— Zimmerung 14675
Verstärkung 2535/a, 6485,
  17587/a

Verstärkungsblech S.17590
Verstärkungslasche 7384
Verstärkungsmittel 9859/a
Verstärkungsplatte S.5690,
  14676, 17590
Verstärkungsring 19950
versteckte Spalte 1775,
  14893
verstecktes Ausgehende 25
  2592
Versteifung der Rohrwände
  17589
Versteifungsblech S.17590
Versteifungselement 17586
Versteifungsträger 17588
versteinern S.7634
Versteinerung S.7629, S.
  7633, 10884
Versteinerungsprozess S.
  7633
verstellbarer Ablader 159
Verstellung 15720
Verstemmen 3110/a, 7811
Verstemmungsdruck 7812
verstopfen, verschlammen
  (sich) 3749
verstopft 3751
Verstopfung des Gestells
  1810
— des Röstofens 3752
— des Stichloches 7745
Verstreben S. 17898
verstrebte Zimmerung 2231
Verstrebung 8239, 17898
Versuch 6675, 18441
Versuchsabteilung 18463
Versuchsergebnis 14789
Versuchskessel 6676
versuchsmässig 6677
Versuchsofen S.4840
Versuchsstab S. 18454
Versuchsverfahren 892
Versuchswaage 889
Verteiler 5576,·S.11293
Verteilerzapfen 5402, 17214
Verteilung der Gruben zum
  Gelände 5933
— der Restspannungen
  17205/a
— des Roheisens 5573
— der Schmelzstoffe 5574

Verteilungsrohr 5575
Verteilungsröhre 5572
Verteilungssystem S.8928
Verteilungstrumm 5501
Verteilungswerk 5571
Verteilungszentrale S.5571
vertiefen 5100
Vertiefung 8587, 9261
Vertikalbohrmaschine 19524
Vertikaldrehbank 2097
vertikale Fräsmaschine 19528
vertikaler Ofen mit Drehrost 15209
Vertikalfuchs 5706
Vertikalkratzer 15237
Vertikalverschiebung 19523
Vertikalverwerfung 19526
Vertonung 15980
verunreinigte Spülung S. 3147
verwachsen 9883, 9884
Verwachsung 3862, 9885, 19701
Verwendung von Tubing als Gasing 19057
Verwerfer 5526
Verwerfung S. 2307, 6839, 12113, 14998, 18850, S. 18933
Verwerfungsbreite S.9354
Verwerfungsbrekzie 6844, 15025
Verwerfungsebene 6857
Verwerfungsfläche 16662
Verwerfungsflügel 10807, 16254
Verwerfungsgang 16660
Verwerfungslinie 6852, 6854
Verwerfungsnetz S. 12249
Verwerfungsspalte 6849
Verwerfungsstufe 6841
Verwerfungston 8372, 14117
Verwerfungswand 6846
Verwertung der Schlacke 19416

verwinden 19179
verwittern 19862
Verwittern 19871
verwitterter Ausbiss 1836
verwittertes Eisenerz 19867
— Erz 19868
Verwitterung 15240, 19869, S S. 19871
Verwitterungsbestandteil 19864
Verwitterungsrückstand 14757
Verwitterungszone 1480
verworfene Lagerstätte 5524
— oder gestörte Lagerstätte 6864
— Schicht 5535
Verwurf S. 6839
Verwurfswinkel 576
verzettelter Hohlraum 15896
verziehen (sich) 19673
Verziehen des Stahls 16230
Verzierung mit erhobener Arbeit 4865
Verzimmerung der Firste 1252
— der Grundsohle 16341
Verzinken 7942, 20346
verzinkt s. galvanisiert
verzinkte Stabroste 7938
verzinkter Eisendraht 7933
— Stahl 20324/a
verzinktes Blech 7934, 7939
— Trapezblech 7935
— Wellblech 7931
Verzinkung S.7926
— des Eisens 20349
verzinnen 18644
Verzinnen 18651/a
verzinnte Bleifolie 348/a
verzinnter Draht 18663
— Kupferdraht 18659
— Stahl 18660
Verzinnung 18664
Verzinnungsanstalt 18668
verzogener Guss 19676
verzogenes Modell 5565
Verzöger er 14790
Verzögerung 13974
verzweigte Kohlenwasser-

stoffe 2259
verzweigte Verwerfung 2261
verzweigter Gang S. 2260
verzwillingt 11143
Verzug 2510, S.5566, 10195, S. 10458, 10490, S.19677
— durch Auslösung innerer Spannungen 3070, 5567
— durch Schwindung 4285
— durch Wärmebehandlung 5568
— s. Verformung
verzugfreier Stahl 12367
Verzugsbrett 16492
Verzugsholz S. 1066
Verzunderung 12803
Vesuvian 19542
Vibration S. 19549
Vibrationsbohren 19554
Vibrationssieb 9646, 19548
Vibrationsspur 10135/a
Vibrationszuteiler 19546
Vibrator 19551
Vibrieren 19549
Vibrosieb S. 9646
Vickershärteprobe 19555
Vicoit 19556
Vielfachanschnitt 2257
Vielfachschweissung 12115
Vielfach-Reliefschweissung 12116
Vielfachschleifmaschine für Formeisen 12011
Vielfachschwarzblech 5654a
Vielfach-Steiganschnitt S. 19356
Vielröhrenkessel 12128
vielröhriger Kessel S.12128
viereckiger Draht S. 17251
viereckiges Rohr 17249
Viererzug 7684
Vierflügelbohrer 7682
Viergespann 7678, 7806
Vierkant-Knüppel 17233
Vierkantblock 17237
Vierkantdraht 17251
Vierkanteisen 17238, S. 17248, 17254
vierkantiger Fasshaken 4370
Vierkantkaliber 5327
Vierkantstahl 17248

Vierkantstange S. 8534, 10303
Vierkantstangenfutter 15571
Vierkantstein S. 17232
Vierschneidmeissel 7683
vierseitiger Wagen 14517
vierseitiges Prisma 14243
Viertaktmaschine 7677
Viertelringeisen S.14244
Vierwalzgerüst 7679/a
Vignoleschiene 7328
Villamaninit 19557
Villiaumit 19558
Vindobon 19559
Vintlit 19560
Violarit 19561
Virgation 19562
Viridin 19564
Viridit 19565
Visiergruppe 13756
Viskosimeter 19567/a
Viskosität S. 1937, 19568
Viskositätsbruch 2311
Vitrier S. 3688
Vitriollösung 16906
Vitrophyr 19581
vitrophyrisch 19582
vitrophyrische Textur 19583
Vivianit 1904
Vogesit 19586
Voglit 19587
Volborthit 19590
Volhynit 19593
Vollandbinder 16887
Vollbahn 7801
Vollbahnschiene 14356
Volldraht 16890
Volldrehen des Kernes 7115
voller Hitze befindlicher Ofen (in) 7848
volles Guss·stück S. 16878
Vollguss 16878
völlige Weisserstarrung 4112
vollkommene Löslichkeit 13079
— Verbrennung 4113, 13078
Vollpipette S. 13444
vollreifes Tal 7805
vollrunder Speer 7796

Vollschrotzimmerung S. 4634
vollständig gar 2599
vollständige Alterung 4642/a
— Entkohlung 4114
— Mischbarkeit 4115
— Verbrennung S.4113
Vollstechheber 13444
Vollzimmerung 7807
Voltameter 19596
Voltzin 19598
Volumenenergie 19599
volumetrische Erzprobe 19559/a
von Hand angezogen 8798
Vonsenit 19603
vorarbeiten 20079
Vorbau 7536, 8332, 12716, S. 20208, 20211, 20214, 20219
vorbearbeitet 15250
vorbereiten zum Abbau S. 1791
vorbereitendes Verfahren 5845
Vorbereitungsraum 13856
Vorblock S. 1835, 9784/a
Vorblockwalze 15260
vorbohren 14439
Vorbohrloch 179, 14044
Vorbrechen 13829, S.13843
Vorbrecher 13828
Vorderplatte 7560
vordere Rohrwand S.19035
Vorderkipper 7781
Vorderseil 11225
vorderseitlicher Rand 8589
Vorderzacken S. 7561
Vordringen von Randwasser S. 6205
Vorfeuerung 7847
Vorform 7202, 11990
Vorformung 13835/a
Vorfraktionator 13836
Vorgang beim Verkoken 13975
vorgebohrtes Loch 13299
vorgefertigte geschweisste Stahlprofile mit an der Baustelle genieteten

Verbindungen 13832
vorgeformtes Drahtseil 13835
vorgekerbter Block 12401/a
Vorgelege 4133
Vorgelegewelle 10840
vorgerichtetes Erz 5273
vorgeschriebene Länge 13861
— Stärke 17029
vorgeschweisst 7303
vorgewalzt 15256
vorgewalzter Block 3910, 15253
vorgewärmt 13838
vorgewärmtes Heizgas 14644
Vorgiessanlage 13864
Vorglühherd 7559
vorhämmern 1818
Vorherd 7565
Vorkaliber 15999
Vorkaliberwalzen S. 15258
Vorkammer 19544
Vorklassierer 10176
Vorkommen 1938
Vorland 764
vorläufige Kappe 6781
vorläufiger Lagerplatz 12860
— Schachtausbaugeviert S. 6786
vorläufiges Zulegen der Form 18881
Vormodellierung 13852/a
Vornahme der Probe 18461
vor- oder zurückspringende Formteilung 19287
Vorofen 2054
Vorprobe 13849
vorputzen S. 7394
Vorratsbehälter 17692, 17693
Vorratsraum 17691
Vorratstank 17690
Vorraum 653
Vorreiniger 15257
vorrichten 5271
Vorrichtung 5274, 7199, 12611, 20051
— für den Krafteinbau des Gestänges in ein unter Druck stehendes Bohrloch 16793

Vorrichtung gegen das
  Übertreiben 12786
— zum Abstossen der
  Abfälle
  auf den Schachtboden
  10258
— zum Lockern und An-
  ziehen der Schrauben
  5281
— zum Reinigen des Bohr-
  loches 5924
Vorrichtungsarbeiten 5963,
  7203
Vorrichtungsbaue 11736,
  20052
Vorrichtungssenkrechtbohr-
  maschine 10171
Vorrösten S. 13860
Vorröstung 13860
Vorrücken von Randwasser
  6205
Vorschacht 3134, S.5216,
  7568
Vorschlaghammer 16587
vorschmieden 15243
Vorschmiedung 15406
Vorschrift 17027
Vorschub 6875, 6881/a,
  6889
Vorschweissbogen 19940
Vorschweiss-T-Stück 19954
Vorspannung 965/a, 2647
Vorsteckgerüst 13648/a
vorstehende Führungsbüchse
  9277
Vorstopfen 2180
Vorstoss 125
Vorstrasse 1830/a
Vorstrecken 3912
Vorstreckung 3912
vorsündflutlich 638
vortreiben 11230
Vortrieb 5936
— der Grundsohle 16344
— mit Getriebezimmerung
  2046
vorübergehender Anstrich
  7197
Vorummantelung des Bandes
  13827
Vorvermessung 13848

Vorwalzabdruck 1809
Vorwalze 1582/a
vorwalzen 3904, 15242
Vorwalzen 1808, 1830,
  12062, 15258
Vorwalzwerk 12060
Vorwärmherd 8955
vorwärmen 13837
Vorwärmerohr für Heizöl
  9006
Vorwärmezone 13847
Vorwärmgrube 9796
Vorwärmöffnung 2345
Vorwärmtür S. 2345, 2602
Vorwärmung 13846, 13841
Vorwaschtrommel S.13850
vorzeitiges Abbinden 13851
Vorzerkleinerung S.13829,
  13843
Vorzug 13831
Vredenburgit 19606
V-Schweissung 19485/a
vulkanischer Schlamm S.
  19592
— Schlick 19592
Vulkanisierkessel S.19609
Vulkanisierpfanne 19609
vulkanisierter Asbest 19608
Vulkanit 19610
Vulpinit 19611
Vulsinit 19612

W

Waage 1122
Waageeinsatz für Chlor-
  calcium 1127
Waagenkasten 1125
waagerechte Kratze 14496
— Platte 9348
— Trommel 9341
— Zimmerung 9344
waagerechter Kratzer 12106
— Tonmischer 9335
waagerechtes Rohr 9346
Waageschale 1129
Wachs 19841/a
Wachsdraht 19847, 19848
Wachsen 8633

Wachsfaden 19846
Wachsschnur 19845
Wacke 19614
Wad 1946
Waderz 19615
Waffelblech 18439
Waffenstahl 794, 16725
wägen 19894
Wagen 2818, 10555, S.18945
Wagenachse 1025
Wagenaufschieben 2685
Wagenbauprofile 15788
Wagenbeschlag 2897
Wagenfüller 19623
Wagenkipper 18632, 19625
Wagenlader S.12064, S.
  14206
Wagenpark 15130
Wagenpfanne S. 13688
Wagenschieber S.14206
Wägeschiffchen aus Alu--
  minium 463
Wagengestell 2898
Wagentiegel S.7660, 13688
Wagenwipper S. 19625
Wagenzug 10236, 18907
Wägeschiene 19896
Wägezimmer 1133
Waggonbauprofile 10009
Waggonwaage 19620
Wagnerit 19649
Wahl der Betriebskraft 15806
wahre Schublänge 12246,
  18784/a
Waldbahn S. 13696
Walkererde 7810
Walkerde S. 16744
Wall S. 12030
Wallonenfrischen 19660
Wallplatte 4967
Wallstein 4986
Walpurgin 19662
Walterisierung 19662/a
walzbar 15092
Walzblech 15099
Walzblei 7341/a, S.16066
Walzdom 15081
Walzdraht 15059/a, 15103
— aus Fluss- und Kohlen-
  stoffstählen 20139
Walzdrahterzeugnisse 20140

Walzdrahtrollen 20141
Walze S. 4774, 15073, S. 15104
Walzeisen 15097
walzen 10503, S.11682
Walzen 15120
Walzenabstand 5550
Walzenbart 7065/a
Walzenbewegung 15233
Walzenbrecher 15076, 15122
Walzenbruch 7700
Walzenbund 1940
Walzendrehbank 15080
Walzendruck 13910
Walzenform 4949
Walzenförmiger Roheisen- mischer 4948
Walzengerüste S. 9465
Walzengestell S. 9465
Walzengiessform 15114
Walzengiesshülse S.15114
Walzenguss 7646,
Walzenkaliber 15074, S. 15084
Walzenkessel 4945
— mit Aussenfeuerung 4946
— Innenfeuerung 4947
— mit Siederöhren S.7754
Walzenmühle 15113
Walzenprofilformmaschine 15078
Walzenquetsche 15109
Walzenring 16704
Walzenrollenvorschub 15110
Walzenrostfeuerung 7864
Walzenschlacke 15087
Walzenschweissung 15091
Walzensinter 11692, 15129
Walzenspindel 13088/a
Walzenständer 9461, 9465
— für stetige Lagerung 12624
— ohne Gewichtsausgleich S. 12624
Walzenstrasse 15131
Walzenstuhl S. 15127
Walzentoleranz 11695
Walzenzapfen 15093
Walzer 11696, 15105
Walzerz S. 11710
Walzfehler 11693, 15123

Walzfertigung 11693/a
Wälzfräser 9218
Walzgerüst 9466, 15089, 17335
Walzhaut 16474
Walzkaliber 15084
Walzkante 15095
Walzkessel 15086
Walzkorb 17331
Walzlinie 1023
Walzmaschine 15125
Walznarbe 15085
Walzprofil 15098
Walratöl 17063
Walzreifeführungsstangen- spur 8651
Walzrichtung 15124
Walzschmiedemaschine 7596
Walzsinter S. 15583
Walzsplitter 17120
Walzspuren 15081/a
Walstahl 15100
Walzstrasse S. 11702, S. 15131
Walzstrecke 11702
Walzstück 13238
— anheben (das) 10738
— erfassen (das) 8564
Walztische 15115
Walzung S. 15120
Walzverfahren 15126
Walz-Verhältnis 14441
Walzwerk 11688, S.15122, 15127
— mit vier stehenden Walzen 7679
Walzwerkausgang 12701
Walzwerkeintrit 9780
Walzwerkprodukt 7120/a
Walzzunder 15114/a, S. 15129
Wand 16252, 19632
Wandbelag S. 12075
Wanddampfpumpe 19654
Wanddickenempfindlichkeit 15780
Wanddickenkern 18514
Wanddickenkontrolle Lehmpfropfen einlegen 8219
Wanudickenlehre 8110

Wanderfeuerung S.18861
wandernder Stempel 6669
Wanderrostfeuerung 18861
Wanderzapfen 13322
Wandformmaschine 8134
Wandkran 19640
Wandplatte 19648
Wandstärke 18512
Wandstärkenkernstütze 5664
Wanze 1780/a, 1789
Wapplerit 19664
Wardit 19665
warm verformt 9453
Warmarbeitwerkzeug 9456
Warmauslagern S.831
Warmbiegen 9417
Warmbiegeprobe 9392
Warmbruch 9408
warmbrüchig 9439
warmbrüchiges Eisen S.9440
Warmbrüchigkeit 9441
Wärme 8971
warme Stelle 9444
Wärmeabsorption S. 8973
wärmeabgebender Trichter- einsatz S. 6663
Wärmeaufnahme 8973
Wärmeausdehnung 18483
Wärmeausgabe 6627
Wärmeausgleichung 8984
Wärmeausnutzung 19415
Wärmeaustauscher S.14525
Wärmeaustauscher für Schächte 19837
Wärmebehälter S. 8995
Wärmebehandlungsapparat 8999
Wärmebehandlungsofen 9003
Wärmebilanz 8980
Wärmeentzug S. 8973
Wärmefestigkeit 9185
wärmegebende Reaktion 6662 6662
Wärmegradient 1836.
Wärmegrube S. 16796
Warmhalteofen 9244
Wärmehaushalt S. 8980
Wärmeisolation 8983
wärmeisolierender Trichter- einsatz 8982
Wärmeisolierung S. 8983'

Wärmeleitung 8977, 8990
Wärmeleitwiderstand 18485
Wärmemessbombe 2756
Wärmemessung S. 2758
Wärmeplatte 9425
Wärmeraum S. 9009
Wärmeschock 18487
Wärmespeicher 8974, 8995,
    14648
Wärmespeicherkessel S.
    8995
Wärmestrahlung 14332
Wärmetönung 8906/a
— der Reaktion 8975
Wärmetrieb 18481
Wärmeverbrauch 8979
Wärmeverlust 11030
wärmeverzehrende Reaktion
    6464
Wärmezufuhr 18027
Wärmezunahme 9724, 18384
Wärmezuwachs S. 9724
Warmgemisch 9421
warmgewalzt 9429
warmgewalzter Formstahl
    9433
— Stahl 9432
warmgewalztes Bandeisen
    9430, 9434
— Blech 9431
Warmhalten 9242
Warmhämmern 9416
Wärmhaube 9449/a, 16413/a
Warmkammer-Druckgiess-
    maschine 9404
Wärmkasten S. 9009
Warmkugelstrahlen 9424
Wärmofen mit beweglichem
    Herd 14671
Warmpressen 9426/a
Warmprobe 8996, 9446
Warmreduzierwalzwerk 9427
Warmriss 8979, S. 9408
Warmrissbildung 7611
warmschmieden 7373
warmstranggepresste
    Sonderprofile aus Stahl
    9414
warmwalzen 9428
Warmwalzen 9436
Warmwalzwerk 9437, 18240

warmerzeugender Verlust
    8990/a
Warmziehen 9411
Warrenit 19678
Wartetiegel 7685
Warthait 19679
Wartung 939
Warwickit 19680
Warzenblech 16063
Wasch- und Klassierapparat
    19704
Waschapparat 19700
Waschbecken 19707,
Wäsche S. 10586, 12659
Wascheisen 9977
Waschen S. 14190
Waschgold S. 13436
Waschbehälter 19692
Waschherd 19710
Waschmaschine 19706
Waschrinne S. 16708, 16709,
    . S. 18934
Wäscherinnearbeit 16710
Waschrohr 19715
Waschrohrschuh 19714
Waschschüssel 1, 1327,
    5513
Waschtrog S. 5513, 8348,
    10586, 12885, 18126
Waschtrommel 14936, 19711
Waschverfahren 19708
Waschvorrichtung 19705
Wasser abgekühlt (in) 1428
— -Abschreckung 19808
— beförderte Kohle (zu)
    19811
— in Berührung stehende
    Platten (mit dem) 13503
— in-Ölemulsion 19784
— überspülte Platte (von)
    13493
— umrühren (im) 17606
Wasserabscheider 19790,
    19765
Wasserabschluss S. 19812
Wasserabflussrohr 19793
Wasserabsperrung 16166
Wasseraufbereitungsapparat
    19755
Wasserbad 19746
Wasserbadkessel 19747

Wasserbadring 19748
Wasserbedarf 534
Wasserbehälter 14745
Wasserbordblech S. 17837
Wasserbrause S. 17206
Wasserbremse 9565
Wasserdamm S. 2550
Wasserdampf 17413
Wasserdampfentwickler S.
    17417
wasserdichte Gesteine 9658
— Schachtmauerung 17652
— Schicht 9655, 9657
— Schmiere 19806
wasserdichter Abschluss
    19813
— Schachtausbau S. 3903
Wasserdichtheit 19998
Wasserdruck S. 9575, 19805
Wasserdruckaufzug 9526
Wasserdruckbremse 9515
Wasserdruckhöhe S. 9574
Wasserdruckprobe 9539
Wasserdruckpumpe 9532
Wasserdruckregelung 14661
Wasserdurchbruch 9831
Wassereinbruch 6447
Wassereindringung 19786
Wasserentzieher S. 5289
Wasserentziehung 5291
Wasserförderung 14379
wasserfreies Chlorkalzium
    3495
— Öl S. 3679
wasserführend 19749
wasserführende Schicht
    19750, 19751
— Spalte 2911
Wassergas 19777/a
Wassergehalt in 1 ccm Luft
    19758
wassergekühlt 19759
wassergekühlte Düse 4329
wassergekülter Boden 19760
— Kern 19758/a
— Ofen S. 19789
wassergekühltes Ventil
    19834
Wassergewinnung 13986
Wassergraben 11843, S.
    16930

Wasserhahnbronze 9516/a
wasserhaltiges Eisenerz 9990
9990
— Eisenoxyd S. 10828
— Tonerdesilikat 9510
Wasserhammer 9524
Wasserhärtung 19781
Wasserhärtungsstahl 19783
Wasserhebung 16403
wässeriges Ammoniak 520
Wasserinfiltration 20321
Wasserkammer S. 8925,
19810
Wasserkammerkessel 19825
Wasserkasten 4345, 19819
Wasserkegelbildung 19757
Wasserkraft 19804
Wasserkraftgebläse 9514
Wasserkühlanlage 19763
Wasserkühlung 19761,
19762
— der Elektroden 19794
Wasserleitung 19756, 19798
Wasserlinie 19797
Wasserlösungsstollen 5743
Wassermantelofen 19789
Wassermantelseele 19787
Wassermenge 9521, 14252
Wassermesser 19799
Wasser-Ölverhältnis 19764
Wasserposten 9506
Wasserpumpe 5748
Wasserraum S. 19810
Wasserreinigung 19807
Wasserrinne 8686, 19809,
19822
Wasserrohrkessel 19823,
19824
— mit einer Kammer S.
19829
— mit geneigten Rohren S.
19827
— mit ungeteilten Wasser-
kammern S. 19830
— mit waagrechten Röhren
19826
— mit Wasserkammer S.
19825
— mit zwei Wasserkammern
S. 19833
Wasserrösche S. 16930

Wassersäule 19754
Wasserschacht 14162, 19814
Wasserscheide 9918, 19838
Wasserscheider 17363
Wasserschlusskolonne 17835
17835
Wasserschwierigkeiten 19821
wassersperrende Rohrtour S.
19815
Wassersperrsäule 19815
Wasserspülhammer 19768,
19775, 19991
Wasserstand 19796
Wasserstoff 9557
Wasserstoffbildung 7612
Wasserstoffflamme 9560
Wasserstoffsuperoxyd 9561
Wasserstollen 16930
Wasserstrecke S. 1777, S.
19796
Wassertonnenaufzug 19745
Wassertrieb 19769
Wasserturm 19820
Wasser-und Dampftrommel
19744
Wasserverbrauch 4245
Wasserverdampfung 19835
Wasserversatz 19802
Wasserverschluss 19812
Wasserversorgung 19816
Wasserwaage 298, 19795
Wasserwärmer 19667
Wasserwäsche 19770
Wasserwirbel 20021
Wasserzuflussrohr 19785
Wasserzuleitung für die
hydraulische Sand-
gewinnung 16996
Wavellit 19839
Weber'sches Glas 19875
Weberschiebung S.14823
Webersprung S. 14823
Websterit 19876
Wechsel im Einfallen 14821
Wechselbeanspruchungen S.
434
Wechseldüsen 4548
Wechselfestigkeit 14770
wechselnde Beanspruchung
436
— Belastung 435

wechselnder Ofengang 10039
wechselseitiger Betrieb
19346
Wechselspannungen 434
Wechselstromanlage 432
wechselweise Arbeiten
1806
— heben und senken 14492
Wegebaustoff 14981
wegmeisseln 3484
Wegschaufel S. 12065
Wegschaufeln 12057
Wegweiser 17493
Wegziehen 1201
— der Förderwagen 19233
Wehrlit 19892
Weibullit 19893
weich 9714
Weichkupferdraht 16846
weich löten 16839
Weiche 18720
weiche schlechte Kohle S.
16919
Weicheisen 11675, 16835
Weichenplatte S. 1420
Weichensicherung 13609
Weichensteller 18134
Weichenzunge 18132
weicher Draht 11251
— Schiefer 2927
— Schiefer mit Kohle 3866
— Stahl 5034, S. 11678
— Stahlguss 16828
— Tonschiefer 1676
— weisser Ton 13928'
weiches Eisenerz 16836
— Giessereieisen 16834
— Gusseisen 11118,
16527/a
— Holzkohleneisen 16829
— Metall S. 16837
— Paraffin 16838
— sehniges Eisen S.16826
— und sprödes Eisen 16826
weichgeglüht 16827
weichgelötet 16842
Weichglühen 5587, 16849
Weichglühhitze S. 19945
Weichguss S. 11249, S.
11250
— giessen 2979

Weichhärtung 16845
Weichkohle S. 1634, S.
  16831
Weichkupfer 16832
Weichkupferdraht 16833
Weichlot 16840, 16841
Weichlöten 16843
Weichlötung S. 16843
Weichmetall 16837
Weichmetallauftrag-
  schweissen 16833/a
Weichstahl S. 9794, 11678
Weinsehenkit 19917
Weisbachit 19920
Weiselbergit 19921
Weissblech 18650, 18661,
  18667
Weissblechkessel 18666
Weissbleierz 20037
Weissbuche 9367
weisse Glut S. 20031
— Hitze S. 20031
Weisseisen S. 20026,
  20040,
— giessen 2982
Weisseinstrahlung S.3431
Weisseln 10817/a
weisser Bauxit 20025
— Bolus S. 7810
— Feldspat S. 348
— Saum 20030
— Temperguss 20045
weisserstarrte Zone mit
  meliertem Übergang 11955
  11955
— Zone ohne Übergang
  3440
Weisserstarrung 3422
Weisserz S. 1668
weisses Gusseisen S.
  20026
— Produkt S. 20041
— Roheisen 20026
Weissglühen S. 20031
weissglühend 20032
Weissglühhitze S. 20031
Weissglühstahl 2401
Weissglut 8313, 20031
Weissguss S. 20026, 20033
Weissit 19922

Weisskerneisen 6594, 20044
Weisskupfer S. 5622, S. 8195
Weisslot S. 16840, 16841
Weissmetall S. 13138, 20038
Weissmetallschicht 20047/a
Weissmetallschmelzofen
  11468
Weissnickelkies S. 3490,
  S. 14399
Weiss·spiessglanz S.20024
Weiss·strahl 20043
weiss.strahlige Hartguss-
  kruste 8844
weisswarm S. 20032
Weite S. 16957
weiteraufkohlen S. 14486
Weiterbohren neben einem
  im Bohrloch steckenge-
  bliebenen Werkzeuge
  16279
weitrohriger Wasserrohr-
  -Kessel 19828
Weizenmehl 20005
Wellblech 4496, 4498
Welle 15933/a
wellenförmiges Flöz 15411
Wellenschlag 18122
Wellherd 4494
wellige Oberfläche 4503,
  19716
Wellrohrkessel 1983
wendbarer Puddelofen S.
  15214
Wendekratzer 15231
Wenden ausheben (durch)
  5769
Wendeofen 15214
Wendeplatte S. 5677, 19148
Wendeplatten-Abhebeform-
  maschine S. 19149
Wendevorrichtung 15227
Wendezylinder 15229
Wennebergit 19977
Wentzelit 19978
werfen 18586
Werfener Schichte 19979
Werftwagen 18947
Werkhalle S. 20189
Werkeisenbahn S. 20226
Werkstoff-Nummer 14592

Werkstoffprüfung S.9846
Werkzeug zum Ausschneiden
  des Laufes 8092
Werkzeuge für Bergwerke
  11780
— für Metallbearbeitung 11540
  11540
Werkzeugmaschine 11136
Werkzeugstahl 11135/a, 1873
  18730
— für Kaltarbeit 3981
Werkzink 14463
Wernerit 19980
Wert 19445
wesentliche Mineralien
  6568
Weslienit S. 935, 19981
Westmanscher Gasröstofen
  19982
wetterbeständig S. 19863
Wetterbrücke 248, 2380,
  12737
Wetterdamm 17687
Wetterdurchhieb 324, S.2010,
  4694, 11901, 11903
wetterfest 6824, 19863
Wetterführung 188, S. 19508
Wetterkanal 6798
Wetterklappe 8114
Wetterkreuz 261, S. 2380,
  4719
Wetterloch 301, 886, 2011,
Wetterlutte 257, 19504
Wetterofen 19256
Wetterrösche S.4694
Wetterschacht 306, 322, 333,
  2652, 3987, 5491, 19509
— mit Feuerung 7855
Wetterscheibe S. 327
Wetterscheider 247, 908,
  1361, 1400, 2285, S.
  4556, 5121, 14881, S.
  17687
Wettersteiger 7151
Wetterstrecke 281, 286/a,
  297, 332, 9854, 20095,
  20107
Wetterstrom 279
Wetterstromverteilung
  mittels Wetterscheider 4556

Wetterteilung 327
Wettertrum 256
Wettertuch 2286, 4870,
   4979 , 5994, 16091
Wettertür 264, 1392, 15870,
   18849, 19860/a
Wetterversorgung S.19508
Wetterwechsel S.188
Whewellit 20013
Whitneyit 20049
Whitwellscherwinderhitzer
   20053
Wickelfeder 19601
Wickelhammer 7366
Wickeltrommel 20101
Wicklung 20098, 20099
Widerlager 678
widersinnige Verwerfung
   S. 12740, S.14823
Widerstandsdraht 14779
Widerstandsdruckhöhe 11951
Widerstandserhitzung 14768
widerstandsfähig 14780
Widerstandsfähigkeit des
   Behälters 14766
— .gegen Druck und Zerrei--
   bung 14774
Widerstandslegierung 14765,
   14781
Widerstandsofen 14767
Widerstandsschweissung
   14778
Widerstandsstumpf-
   schweissung 6297
Widerstandsthermometer
   14769
Widerstandszeit 2310
Widmannstättensches Gefüge
   20062
Wiederanblasen 14783
Wiederauffrischen S. 14681
Wiederaufkocher 14482
wiederaufkohlen 14486
Wiederauflösung 14781/a
wiederbeleben 14835
wiederdestilliertes Öl 14741
wiedereinfahren 14740
wiedereröffneter Gang
   14728
wiedererwärmen 14665
wiedergewinnen 15448

Wiedergewinnung 14510
wiederholte Benutzung des
   Wassers 14736
— Bruchbildung S.12113
— Destillierung 14742
— Injektion 17274
— Schläge 14733
— Wärmebehandlung
   14801/.a
Wiederholungsversuch 14791
Wiederholungszwillinge
   12122, 13646
Wiederverbrennungskammer
   14668
Wiederverwendung 14735
Wiege 4590, 13509, S. 18674
Wiegekarte 19900
Wiegen 14235
Wiegeröhrehen 19903
Wiegestechheber 19901
Wiikit 20066
wild eruptierende Bohrung
   20072
wilder Stahl S. 20071
Wilderstahl 20071
Wilkeit 20073
Willemit 20074
Williamsit 20075
Willyamit 20076
Wilmil S.417
Wiltshireit 20077
Wiluit 20078
Wind S.1698, 1698/a,
   20086
— abstellen (den) 19135
— blasen (den) 1842
Windaufbereitung 13596
Windberechnung 2732
winddichter Abschluss S.
   385
Winddruck 20094
Winde S.2814, S.8231, 8897,
   10770, 14393, 20082
— für die Glocke 1461
Windeisen 18265
Winderhitzer 287, S.20053
— mit hängendem Röhren
   288
— nach Cowper 4575
Winderosion 184
Windform 19159, 19 95

Windfrischen 4309
Windfrischstahl 317, S.4308
Windkammer 250
Windkanal 251/a
Windkanter 15525, 20096
Windkasten 242, 20089,
   20090, 20092
Windkastendeckel 10729
Windkessel 1699, 19058
Windklappe S. 293
Windkranz S. 5575
Windleitung 300, 305, 1469,
   1731/b
Windloch 1731
Windmenge 1701, 14436
Windmesser 568, 1728
Windöffnung 19160
Windpfeife 289
Windpressung 1732
Windring S. 20091
Windschieber 1703, 1727
windschief 19675
Windsichtung 323
Windstock S. 1702, 13388
Windtrocknung 6066
Windtrocknungsverfahren
   8121
Windung 19137
Windventil 1734
Windverbrauch 4238
Windverteilung 262
Windverteilungsrohr 2630
Windwirkung 20088
Windzacken 1096
Windzuführung 1730
Winkeldiskordanz 591
Winkeleisen 568/a, 572,
   589/a
Winkelhebel 14165
— mit Unterzug 14166
winkelig 587
Winkelknopf 579
Winkellasche 571, 579/a
Winkelstahl 580
Winkelstift 17191
Winkelveränderung 426,
   590/a
Winkelverbindung 4479
Winkelwulsteisen 2542
Winkelzahn 9062
winkliges Aushebeeisen 14904

Wipper 18685, 19096
Wipphammer 20117
Wippsägemaschine 7760
Wirbel 6194
Wirbelablenker 674
Wirbelbewegung 16428
wirbelfreies Giessen 14305
Wirbelhaken 18141
Wirbelschicht 19604
Wirbelstrom 6194/a
Wirbelstrombremse 6150
Wirbelströmung 6195
Wirkleitwert 4192/a
wirksames Eisen 116
Wirkung des Walzendurch-
    messers 15088
Wirkungsgrad 13779
wirtschaftlich lohnender
    Sand 13001
Wirtschaftlichkeit 14004
Wismut 1615
Wismutglanz 1616
Wismutlot 1617
Withamit 20154
Witherit 20048, 20160
Witkowitzer Röstofen 20161
Wittichenit 20162
Wittit 20163
Wölbung 2770, 3237/a,
    5517
Wolfram 19100
Wolframeisen S.6953
Wolframit 2698, 20167
Wolfram-Karbid-Bohrer
    19101
wolframlegierter Stahl S.
    19104
Wolfram-Nickel-Stahl 19102
Wolframsonderstahl 19103
Wolframstahl 19104, 20166
Wolfsbergit S. 8647, 20168
Wolfsrachen S. 7222
Wolkenachat 3787
Wollastonit 15592, 20169
wollsackförmige Absonde-
    rung 13297
Woodendit 20184
Woolffsche 20187
Wootzstahl 9736
Worpplatte 18832
Worthingtonpumpe S.6113

Wurfelspat S. 593
Wulfenit 20254, 20286
Wulffsches Netz 20255
Wulst 5778
Wulststahl 2544
Wulstwinkel 2543
Würfelerz. S. 13145
Würfelform 4819
Würfelkohle 3884, 3895
Würfelmischer 4817/a
Wurfschleuder 16643
Wurfsieb 16297
Wurmkrankheit 600
Wurtzit 20256
Wyomingit 20259

X

Xanthoarsenit 20263
Xanthochroit 20264
Xanthophyllit 20265
Xanthosiderit 20266
Xenoblast 20267
xenomorph 20269
Xenon 20270
Xyloidin 20274
Xylol 20272
Xylolith 20275
Xylotil 20277

Y

Yatalit 20279
Yentnit 20296
Yogoit 20301
Ytterbium 20304
Ytthererde 20305
Yttrialit 20306
Yttrium 20307
Yttrocolumbit 20310
Yttrofluorit 20311
Yttrokalzit 20308
Yttrotantalit 20312
Yttrotitanit 20313

Z

Z-Bohrer 20314
Z-Eisen 20315
Zacken 1419
zackig 15897
zackiger Bruch 8700
Zaffer 20315/a
zähe Struktur S.18800
zäher Kupferdraht 18797
zähes Gefüge 18800
— Giessereieisen 18798
— Kupfer 18796
Zähigkeit 18403, 18801
Zählwerk 4542
Zahn 3908
Zahnflankenschleifmaschine
    8128
zähflüssig 19566
Zahnkranz 8129, 14925
Zahnkrone 15561
Zahnkupplung 5594
Zahnlückenmodell 18733
Zahnrad 3909, 8132
Zahnradbahn 14323
Zahnräderdurchzugform-
    maschine 17873
Zahnräderformmaschine
    8133
— mit zwei Planscheiben
    8137
Zahnräderschabloniermaschi-
    ne 11125
Zahnschuh S. 11712
Zahnstange 14320
— mit Getriebe 14324
Zahnstangenwinde 14321
Zange 12301, 13550, 18719
— erfassen (mit der) 15804
zängen 16130
Zängen 16134, 12329/a,
    17264/a
Zangendrehmomentmesser
    18717
Zangeneindruck 5598
Zangenkran S. 9790
Zangenseil 18716
Zängelwalzen 16135
Zapfen 9201
Zapfenband S. 9202

Zapfengewinde 11244
Zapfenkipper 18961
Zapfenlager 3520, 10235
Zapfenloch 10192, 11938
Zapfenreibung 10233
Zapfenverbindung 10196
Zaratit 20316
Zeche S. 13397
Zechenkoks 3940
Zechstein 20317
Zehnerwaage S. 5061
Zehrgebiet 14650
zeichnen 5753
Zeichnung 5790
Zeilengefüge 1187
Zeitdehnbruch 15385
Zeitschalter 5145
Zeitstandfestigkeit 4618
Zeitstreckgrenze 18641
Zeittafel 8173
zeitweilige Löschung 4982a
Zellenbildung 1186
zellig 3135
Zellstoffkocher 14144
Zellstruktur S. 11940
Zement 3140, 3141
— mit Schlackenzusatz
    16530
— verunreinigte Spülung
    (durch) 3147
Zementabbindung 3143
Zementation S. 2918, 3169,
Zementationszone 1478,
    3163
Zementbrennofen 3151
Zementbrühe S. 3155
Zementgold 3148
Zementieraggregate 3157
Zementierbüchse 6097
zementieren 3138
Zementieren 3158
zementierend 3180
Zementierkammer 6488,
    19713
Zementierkiste 3171
Zementierkopf 3149, 3174,
    7535
— mit Pfropfen 13562
Zementiermaschine 8629
Zementierofen S. 2926,
    3160, 3173, S. 7839

Zementierpackung 3153
Zementierpfropfen 3176
Zementierpulver 3177
zementiert 3164, 6744
zementierte Schicht 3165
zementierter Stab 1782
Zementierung 3168, S.8858,
    12831
Zementierungskorb 3170
Zementit 3179
Zementhöhe 3145
Zementkanone 3148/a
Zementklinker 3144
Zementkohle 3159
Zementkupfer 3146, 15990
Zementmischmaschine 3150
Zementmörtel 10553
Zementsand 3154
— -Formverfahren 3152
Zementschlamm 3155
Zementstahl S. 1784, 2914,
    3156, 3166
Zementstahldarstellung
    2915, S.3161
Zemenstahlofen 17465
Zentesimalwaage S.3190
Zentralantrieb S. 14168
Zentralgetriebe 14168
Zentralheizungskessel 1965
Zentrallunker 3186/a
Zentralrohr 3192
Zentrierauge 3215
Zentrierbohrer 3185, 3189
Zentrieren 11371
Zentriermaschine S. 3218
Zentriernabe S. 3215
Zentrierrahmen S.3216
Zentrierstift 3219
zentriert 11370
Zentrierung 3188
Zentriervorrichtung 3193
— mit Längsteilen 17706
Zentrifugalguss 3203
Zentrifugalzerstäuber S.3210
Zentrifuge S. 3200
Zentrifugierung 15075/a
Zentrumbohrer 3195, 3196
Zeolith 20318
Zepharovichit 20319
Zer 3229
zerbrechen S. 16011

zerbrechlicher Kern 2421
Zerbrechlichkeit 4012, 7707
zerbrochenes Erz 5474
Zerbröcklung 16968/a
Zerdrücken S. 12299
— der Form 4763
— des Kernes 4764
— in der Teilung 4762
Zerdrückung S. 17255
Zeresin 3228
Zerfall 5537
zerfallen 5518, 5542
Zerfallen des Erzes 4757
Zerfallgrad einer Lösung
    5133
Zerfallgrenze S. 5543
Zerfallwärme 8987
zerkleinern 3645, S.8538
zerkleinerte Kohle 16145
Zerkleinerung 4775, S.16015
— der Masseln 4779
Zerkleinerungsanlage 4780
Zerkleinerungsmaschine
    8556
Zerkleinerungsplatte 4781
Zerklüftung 7706, 10213
zerlegbar 5166, 5538
zerlegbarer Formkasten 2541
    2541
zerlegbares Gerüstbaurohr
    18992
Zermahlen 8542, 8546
Zermahlung 4776
zerreiben 18922
zerreibener Ton 18824
Zerreibung S. 8546
zerreissen 18345, 18346
Zerreissfestigkeit 5537/a,
    S. 14776, 15386
Zerreissmaschine 11124,
    11127, 18413
Zerreiss-spannung 2330
Zerreiss-stab 18412
Zerrungsbruch S. 6845
zerschlagener Gang 2260
Zerschmelzen im Feuer
    9623
Zerschneiden 4660/a,
    4913/a
zersetzter Gang 15238
— Kalkstein 6791

Zersetzung 5059/a, S.5537
— der Kohlenwasserstoffe
  5070
— des Kalksteins 5069
Zersetzungskurve 4876
Zersetzungspotential 13732
Zersetzungsprodukt 13990
Zersetzungspunkt 13611
Zersetzungsspannung 5071
Zersetzungswert 5072
zerstäuben S. 17179
Zerstäuber S.283, 934,
  14150, 16978, 17180
— für geschlämmte Tonerde
  14151
Zerstäuberluft 13936
Zerstäubung 934/a, 17186
zerstörte Säule 10256
Zerstörung S.15239
zerstörungsfreie Messung
  12347
— Prüfung 12348
zerstreute Wärme 19687
Zerstückelung 2328
zertrümmertes Gestein
  16013
Zertrümmerung S. 7706, S.
  16015
— des Kernes 2331
Zertrümmerungszone 4770,
  16014, 16027
Zerussit 3231
Zeuge S.6814, S.12706
Zeugenberg 2644, 6814,
  S. 12175, 12706
Zeunerit 20320
zickzackförmig angeordnete
  Sonde 17292
Ziegel S. 2367
Ziegelbrennerei S. 2371
Ziegelerde S. 2369
Ziegelform 2373
Ziegelhütte 2371
Ziegelmauerwerk S.2370
Ziegelofen S. 2371
Ziegelsteinbrocken 2439
Ziegelton 2369
Zieharbeit 13878
Ziehbank 5779, 5794,
  14196, S. 20122
Ziehbarkeit 16851

Ziehdorn 11264
Ziehdüse 5373
Zieheisen 5783, 5807,
  13483/a, 20152/a
ziehen 5754
Ziehen 5791, 14137, 17797
— des Erzes 5804
— im Weiterschlag 14556
— von Gräben 5578
— von Rohren 18979
Zieher 5788
Ziehgrenze 7427
Ziehgüte 5810
Ziehkante 5376
Ziehkran 14139
Ziehloch 5781
Ziehmarke 3712
Ziehöffnung 5502
Ziehplatte 17807
Ziehpresse 5808
Ziehriefe 5369
Ziehring 5796
Ziehschablone 17812
Ziehstein 5357
Ziehstempel 5809
Ziehwerkzeug 5812
Ziehzange 20137
Zielbohrung 5469
Zierblech 5076
Ziereisen 5075
Zierleiste 12673
Zimmerhauer 10151, 18635
zimmern 1042
Zimmerung 2022, 18636,
  18637
— auswechseln 14792
— der Firste 10963·
Zimmerungsausbesserung
  14476
Zimmerungsbruch 10096
Zink 17046, 20323
Zinkaluminit 20340
zinkartig S. 20347
Zinkätze 6574
Zinkblech 16085
Zinkblende 11850, 13031,
  20341
Zinkblumen 16973
Zinkblüte S. 9579, S.20324
Zinkdraht 20339
Zinkelektrolyse 6352

Zinkenit 20348
Zinkerz 20331
Zinkgrau 20330
Zinkgries 11946/a
zinkhaltige Lauge 11108
zinkhaltiges Eisenerz 20342
Zinkhütte 17048, 20335
zinkisch 20347
zinkischer Anbruch S.20327
Zinkit 14552, 20344
Zinklot S. 16840
Zinkosit 20350
Zinkoxyd 12801
Zinkplatte für Elemente
  20322
Zinkschmelzung 20336
Zinksilikat 20334
Zinkspäne 20325
Zinkspat 2699, 7922, S.20337
  S. 20337
Zinkstab 20333
Zinkstaub 20328
Zinksulfat S. 17974
Zink-und Kadmiumstab 2670
Zinkweiss 20338
Zinkwellblech 4501
Zinkzylinder 20326
Zinn 13138
Zinn— 13139, 17366
Zinn verfeinern (das) 14596
Zinnbadschlacke 15726
Zinnblech 16083
Zinnbronze 18646
Zinnchlorid 17367
Zinnchlorür 17370
Zinnerz S. 18649
Zinnfolie 18648
Zinngeschrei 18647/a
Zinngrube 17364
zinnhaltig S. 13189, 17368
Zinnkessel 18654, 18665
Zinnkies S. 17369
Zinnlot S. 16841
Zinnober 3578, S.11501
Zinnwaldit 20351
Zippeit 20352
Zirkel 5585
Zirkelit 20357, 20358
Zirkon S. 20355
Zirkondioxyd 20354
Zirkonium 20355

Zirkoniumstahl 20356
Zirkonsilikat 20353
Zirkulation 2299
Zirkulationskessel 3603
Zirkulationspumpe 3583
Zirkulationsverhältniss
  14528
Zirkulationsverlust 12083
Zitrin 3608/a
Zobtenit 20359
Zoisit 20360
Zone 900
— des Abbaues S. 10891
Zonengefüge 20361
Zonenstruktur S. 20361
zu brechende Hohlkehle
  S. 7029
— brechende Kante 7029
— starkes Losklopfen
  6643
— weit getriebener Glüh-
  prozess 12733
Zubereitung S. 12642
zubruchgegangen 6776,
  S. 17673
zubruchgegangener Schacht
  6777
zubruchgegangenes
  Hangende 16118
Zubruchgehen S. 2324
zubruchgehen 17669
Zubruchgehen der Firste
  6775
Zubringerlokomotive 5606
zubruchgeworfen 17673
zufallende Verwerfung S.
  6851
zufälliges Muster 8382
Zufluss S. 9771, 9766,
Zuflussleitung 8100
Zufuhr von Luft S.171
Zufuhrkanal 6884
Zufuhrkrampe 6495/a
Zufuhrrollgang 7776/a,
  15361/a
Zuführung von Luft S.171
Zuführungsöffnung S.9820
Zug 5722, 14125, 17333,
  S. 17797
— beschleunigen (den)
  14304

Zug und Rückzug der
  Schacht 13205
Zugabesperklappe 7453
zugängliche Sohle 42
zugänglicher Schacht 43
Zugangsstück 9828
Zugbalken 17794
Zugbeanspruchung 18409
Zugbeschleunigung 39
Zugbolzen S. 17404, S.
  17794
Zugelastizität 6248
Zugfestigkeit 14776, 17779,
  19219
Zuggestänge S. 14130
Zugkraft 14126
— am Haken 5777
Zugseil S. 10149
Zugspannung 9861
Zugstange 5783/a
Zugstangenbügel 13424
Zugventil 5723
Zugverminderung 6812
Zugversuch 18411
Zugwinde S. 9225
Zulauf S. 9771, 15388
zulässige Abweichung
  13113
zulässige Produktion 393
— Spannungen 13114
— Verschleissgrenze 19859
Zulegemarke S. 898
Zulegestift 3782
Zuleitungsrohr 15355
zum Ring gebogene T-Träger
  3602
Zünddraht 9626, 13955
Zünden eines Konverters
  7798
Zünder 2792, 7884, S.15582
zunderbeständig 12363
zunderbeständiger Stahl
  15591
zunderfrei 7727
Zunderschicht 12795, 15582
Zunderreste 14756
Zündflamme 9628
Zündkaspel S. 1745
Zündmaschine 1749, 7191
Zündschnur 1739, 1747/a,
  14581, 17266

Zündung S.16203, 17106
Zungenspitze 13613
zur festen Rotglut 19585
— Trocknen eindampfen 6612
zurechtschneiden 5834
Zurichterei 7138/a·
Zurichtmaschine 7130
Zurichtungshalle 17729
zurückgehen 14808
zurückkehrender Feuerzug
  14812
zurückwalzen 15071
zusammenbacken S. 2690
Zusammenbacken S.129
zusammenballen 3861
Zusammenbauen der Form
  2537
zusammenbrechen 10095
zusammenbrennen 7774
Zusammenfügung 2021
zusammengebackene Kohle
  1114
— Masse 1115
zusammengegossen 3016
zusammengeklebt 228
zusammengepresste Kohle S. 224
  S. 224
— Falte 4121
— Verwerfung 4119; 4129
zusammengepresster Gang
  4124, 4132
— Kessel mit Heizröhren S.
  15850
zusammengestellte Form
  2540
zusammenlegen 895
Zusammenlegen 896
Zusammenpassen mit Dübeln
  S. 13308
— mit Führungsstiften
  13308
zusammenrollen 15070
Zusammenschmelzverfahren
  11465
zusammenschrauben 15699
Zusammenschweissen 15605,
  S. 19923
Zusammensetzung 4125,
  4126
zusammenstauchen S. 19371
zusammenstellen 4546

Zusammenstellen 15913
Zusammenstellung der Ana-
  lyse 20237
Zusammensturz 3122
zusammenstürzendes Gebirge
  3123
zusammenziehen (sich)
  4282
Zusatz 134, 1397/a
— von Ferromangan 137
Zusatzabgabe 12775
Zusatzbehälter 142
Zusatzberichtigung 7141
Zusatzbunker 2499/a
Zusatzeisen 131
Zusatzelement 405
Zusatzgerät 2051
zusätzliche Abgabe S.12775
— Gemengeteile 44
zusätzliches Erz 11785
Zusatzmaschine S. 2050
Zusatzmetall 7022
Zusatzmittel 143, 5635
Zusatzstoff 234
Zuschlag S.134, 7501
Zuschläge 233
zuschlagen S. 8727
Zuschlagerz 7503
Zuschlaghammer 16581
Zuschleifen 15249/a
Zuschneiden 1627/a
Zusetzen von Erzen 140
zuspitzen S. 16006
Zustandsdiagramm 13146/a
Zustandsgleichung 6525
Zustandsschaubild 6528
Zustellung 6975, S. 10849,
  18901/a
— des Ofens 6979
Zustellungskosten 4520
Zuströmung 9771
Zuteiler 979/a, 11609,
  S. 15202
Zuteilteller 15202
Zutritt 9853
Zwangsschiene 8643
zweiatomiges Molekül 5346
zweibödiges Fördergestell
  S. 8219
zweiflügeliger Abbau 5685
  Stoss 5678

Zweiflügelmeissel 19193
Zweiglimmergranit 1591
Zweigung 7603
Zweikammerkessel 19833
Zweikohlenlichtbogen-
  schweissen 19169
Zweileitersystem 19194
zweirädrige Karre 4991
zweischiffige Formhalle
  19191
Zweischneidebohrer 5643
zweischneidiger Bohrer 5652
zweiseitige Modellplatte
  5677
zweiseitiger Ofen 5656
Zweitaktmaschine 19184
zweite Beizung 20039/a
— Glühung 20023
zweiteilig 4230
zweiteiliger Kohlenkasten S.
  3829
zweiteiliges Modell 4348/a,
  17131
zweiter Ausgang 15760
Zweitgewinnung 15767
Zweitrommelhaspel 5655
Zweiwalzenständer 9464
Zweiwalzwerk 19173
Zweiwellenrohrkessel 10516
Zwergkessel 6144
Zwickstifte 16156
Zwillingsbohrung 19171
Zwillingsdampfmaschine S.
  19170
Zwillingsdampfpumpe 19175
Zwillingsebene 4123
Zwillingshohlladung 19172
Zwillingskristall 19169/a,
  19177
Zwillingsmaschine 19170
Zwillingsverwachsung 19178
Zwillingswinkel 19168
Zwischenbehälter 9328
Zwischenboden 7404
Zwischenbrecher 14513
Zwischenbühne 13506
— für Dreierzug 18573
— für Zweierzug 5671
Zwischengeschirr 2679
zwischenglühen 17922
Zwischenglühen 9910

Zwischenglühung 13973
Zwischengussform 3380
Zwischenkoks 2517
Zwischenkühler 9873
Zwischenlage 16045
— von pyrithaltiger Kohle
  2284
— von schieferiger Kohle
  1652
Zwischenmittel 11662
Zwischenplatte 14406, S.
  17197
Zwischenpumpstation 2053
Zwischenraum S. 7966
Zwischenring 11664
Zwischenschacht 6784
Zwischenschaltung 9865
Zwischenschnitt 11667/a
Zwinschensohle 4531, 1776
Zwischensohlenbruchbau
  17920
Zwischensonde 9763
Zwischenstrasse S.9893
Zwischenstrecke 9893
Zwischenstufenhärtung 1111
Zwischenstufenvergütung
  954
Zwischentank 15356
Zwischenwand 7232, 12953
Zwischenzerkleinern 14514
Zwitterion 9503
Zyanbadhärten 4930
Zyklon 4934
Zylinder mit Teilung 4943
Zylinderausbohrung 2086
Zylinderbüchse 4941
Zylindergebläse 4944
Zylinderkessel S.4945,
  16097
Zylinderkopfpackung 8908
Zylindermantelrohr 19069
Zylinderofen 4940
Zylinderretorte 3382
Zylinderwalzen 5378
Zylindrieren 15112
zylindrische Muntelelektrode
  4950
zylindrischer Schnecken-
  bohrer 17097
Zylindrit 4951

abbassamento del piano di scavo 1342
— del cono 11073
— di temperatura 5991, 11074
abbassare il piano di scavo 1326
— un pistone nel pozzo 15340
abbattere 2300, 6903, 16160
— con esplosivo 7288
— con palanchino 1213
— il minerale 2298, 17665
abbattimento 2324, 2449, 5792, 6906, 8205, 15759, 15762, 18221, 20212
— a camere 3270
— a gradini 12747
— a gradini dritti 19267
— a mano 8764, 8786
— a mezzo palanchini 1253
— col fuoco 7179
— con cunei 19888
— con esplosivi 1705, 11770
— con esplosivi a camere 8366
— con esplosivo senza taglio preventivo 16165
— con tagli in direzione 5866
— della fiamma della bocca 5989
— delle polveri 6134
— dello sterile 16496
— di carbone 3828
— di carbone con esplosivi 3802
— di minerali 12632
— discendente 2189
— idraulico 9541, 9527, 16997
— in rimonta 2337, 14374
— laterale 16275
— magmatico 11170
— meccanico 11139, 11420
— secondo tracciato 5276
abbattimento v. coltivazione
abbellimento della superficie 12674
abbozzo 18498
abichite 2
ablazione 3

ablazione interna 6477
abolizione di limitazione 2138
abrasione 6
abrasioni 15645
abraviso 7, 8
absarochite 10
acadialite 33
acadiano 34
acanticonite 35
acantite 36
acaustobiolite 336
accagliarsi 2690
accampanare 1445
accampanatura 1470
accatastare 1195, 13284
— le staffe 17275
accatastatore 11000, 17279
accavallamento 2536
accavallare 9883
accavallarsi 2530
accecatoio 15177
— a lingua di vipera S. 4537
— piatto 4537
— piatto camoscio 4538
— rigato 15178
accelerazione 38
— del tiraggio 39
accelerometro 40
accendere 7146
— il forno 1842
— il fuoco 10777
— l'altoforno 1845
accenditore del cubilotto 4850
accensione 7188, 9627, 10799, 17382
— del colpo 16203
— di un convertitore 7798
— di una caldaia 7190
— difettosa 11798
— elettrica 6259
accesso v. entrata
accessori a labbro S. 1369
— a risvolta 1369
— di fonderia 13762
— per cavi 2659
— per lampade ad arco 748
acciaiabile 102
acciaiamento S. 58, 103
acciaiare 104, 17453
acciaiato 17468
acciaiatura 58, 103, 17495, 17523

acciaieria 3025, 17491, 17522
— al crogiuolo S. 4747
— Bessemer 1558
— con forni a crogiuolo 4747
— elettrica 6308
— Martin 12581
— Martin-Siemens 12575, 12577
— Thomas 1307, 18535, 18540
acciaierie Bessemer e Thomas 1557
acciaio 17454
— a alto tenore di carbonio 9139
— a grana fine 7084
— a tempra vitrea 3449
— acido 95
— affinato 16400
— affinato al vento 317
— ad altissima velocità 18002
— al basso fuoco 3306
— al boro 2117
— al carbonio 2842
— al carbonio per utensili 19230
— al cobalto 3891
— al cobalto-cromo 3886
— al convertitore 4308
— al crogiolo 4738
— al cromo 3548
— al cromo-cobalto S. 3886
— al cromo-molibdeno 3531
— al cromo-nickel 3533, 3545
— al cromo-silicio 3535
— al cromo-tungsteno 3537
— al cromo-vanadio 3538
— al manganese 11277
— al manganese ad alto contenuto di carbonio 2837
— al molibdeno 11883
— al nichel 12281
— al nichel-alluminio 12270
— al nichel-cromo 12273
— al nichel-cromo-molibdeno 3532
— al nichelio a base di molibdeno S. 3532

acciaio al nichel-tungsteno 19102
— al nichel-vanadio 12283
— al rame 4353
— al silicio 16330
— al silicio-manganese S. 10273
— al solo carbonio 17707
— acciaio al titanio 18693
— al tungsteno 19104
— al vanadio 19462
— al wolframio 20166
— al 0,75% di C 5382
— al 0,875 di C 15917
— all'1,0% di C 18377
— all'1,125 di C 17093
— all'alluminio 462
— all'uranio 19395
— alligato S. 401
— all'ossigeno puro 14188
— allo zirconio 20356
— alterato 17143
— amagnetico 12357
— antinvecchiante 12338
— argentato 16361
— austenitico 959
— automatico 989
— autotemprante 284, 15825
— azzurro 1912
— basico 1306
— battuto 20246
— bene temprato 19972
— Bessemer 76
— Bessemer al piccolo convertitore 1041
— binario 1592
— bonificato 8852
— bruciato 2615
— brunito 13629
— calmato 5038, 10351
— calmo 10351, 16896 a
— calorizzato 2762
— cementato 2914, 2921, 2870, 3156, 3166
— centrifugato 3214
— colato 17463
— colato dolce 16828
— colato duro 8819
— colato per dinamo 6156
— commerciale 6734, 4008, 11498
— complesso 4118
— compresso 4150

acciaio con basso contenuto di carbonio 11062
— con basso tenore di carbonio 11046
— con basso tenore di fosforo
— con frattura rosa 15180
— cromifero 3548
— da aratri 13553
— da armi 16725
— da caldaie 1979
— da catene 3248
— da cementazione 1784, 3162, 17469
— da corazze 803
— da costruzione 6476, 17892
— d'affinazione al basso fuoco S. 3332
— da lime 7006
— da matrici 5381
— da rocchetti 13321
— da rotaie 14364
— da saldare 19927
— da scalpelli 3487
— da seghe 15560
— da taglio 989, 7731
— da utensili 11035 a, 18730
— da utensili per la lavorazione a freddo 3981
— damaschiato 4972
— denaturato 13102, 17143
— di Brescia 2361
— di cementazione affinato 16024
— di forno a riverbero
— di lega 17021
— di lega ricca 9137
— di qualità inferiore 19301
— di qualità superiore 9153
— di sostituzione 17933
— di stiramento a freddo 3975
— di suola acida 84
— diamante 5029, 6703
— dolce 5034, 11046, 11252, 11678, 17498
— dolce ordinario 12625
— dolce per torni automatici 11679

acciaio doppiamente raffinato 5674
— duplex 6114
— duro 2844, 8843
— duro in masselli 8833
— effervescente 14918, 19319
— elettrico 6304
— elettrico per utensili 6311
— eutectoide 6607
— extra dolce 5037, 6705, 19538
— extra duro 2845
— extrarapido 18015, 19537
— acciaio fabbricato col processo Siemens 5464
— ferritico 3167, 6936
— ferroso 8717
— finito 7123
— fino 7090
— fino al carbonio da costruzione 9140
— forgiato 7587
— fosforoso 13177
— fucinato 7580, 7587, 20246
— fuso 3069, 7467, 9800, S. 17463
— fuso al crogiuolo 16456, S. 4738
— fuso battuto 8746
— fuso saldabile 11676
— grafitico 8456
— grezzo 20071
— Hadfield 8702, 11277
— harveyzzato 8884
— in barre 1220, 9955, 15842
— in barre quadrate 17248
— in billette 1586
— in getti 3018, 17463
— in masselli S. 1825
— in moietta 17855
— in pani 1825
— in superficie 2913
— inattaccabile agli acidi 88
— indeformabile 2367
— indiano 9736
— indurito 8843
— inossidabile 17297, 15394

acciaio Invar 9931
— invecchiato 217
— ipoeutettoide 9588, 9598, 9600
— laminato 15100
— laminato a caldo 9432
— laminato a freddo 3994
— laminato piatto 7323
— lavorabile ad alta velo-cità 7731
— lavorato 13982
— legato 401, 4131
— legato da costruzioni 17883
— magnetico 11184
— malleabile 7271, 11252
— manganosilicioso 11273
— Martin 8965, 12580
— Martin acido 84
— nitrurato 12314
— non alligato S. 12339
— non calmato 19319, 20071
— non fosforato 12360
— non legato 12339
— non magnetico 12357
— non temperato 16844, 19338
— normale 4a
— normale da nitrurazione 12381
— normalizzato 12386
— omogeneo 9800
— ordinario 18723
— pelato 19141
— per aereoplani 17002
— per ancore 559
— per armi 794
— per attrezzi da miniera 18731
— per barramine 11773
— per barramine forate 9269
— per bordature 7271
— per bulloni 15711
— per calamite 10184
— per calamite permanenti 13107
— per canne di fucile 8670
— per casseforti 17473
— per chiavette 8214, 10324
— per chiodi 14974
— per costruzione di ponti 17893
— per costruzione navale 17891

acciaio per cuscinetti a sfere 1152
— perfettamente deossida-to 14962a
— per fioretti 15018
— per forzieri 17473
— per granate 16112
— per lavorazione a fred-do 4008
— per lesine 1016
— perlitico 13019
— per locomotive 10952
— per madreviti 17474
— per magneti 11184
— per molle 17200
— per molle da corsetti 17470
— per molle di fucili 8675
— per molle di orologio 19742
— per pale 16214
— per pale di turbina 19118
— per pennini 1179
— per perni o viti 15711
— per piastre 13499
— per piastre di corazza 801
— per punzoni 9220, 14178, 17472
— per scalpelli 5908
— per seghe a nastro 1188
— per stampi 17471
— per torni a grande velo-cità 9179
— per utensileria 18730
— per valvole 19456
— placcato 3611
— povero di carbonio 17498
— pregiato 9153
— pressato 4150
— profilato 15785, 15994
— profilato per costruzio-ni 4236
— acciaio puddellato 14100, 14104
— quaternario 14263
— raffinato 14602, 16400
— raffinato due volte 5674
— rapido 9178, 14418a, 14538
— rapido per tornio-revol-ver 9180

acciaio refrattario 7177, 8994, 8991
— resistente agli acidi 88
— resistente al calore 8994
— resistente alla corrosio-ne 4492, 17297
— resistente alla corrosio-ne chimica 3392
— resistente alle alte temperature 12343
— resistente allo scaglia-mento 15591
— ricotto 606
— ricotto in bianco 2401
— rifuso 14698
— rinvenuto 18389
— sagomato S. 15994
— saldabile 19927
— saldabile ad alta resi-stenza 9188
— saldato 20246
— sbozzato 1912
— sbozzato al laminatoio 15842
— scanalato per molle 8595
— scelto 7090
— semi-calmato 15845
— semidolce 11423a, 11436, 16844
— semiduro 2843, 8714, 11427, 11437
— semi-effervescente 15845
— semplice ordinario 18723
— senza soffiature 1786, 19232
— Siemens-Martin 1300
— speciale 17021
— speciale al tungsteno 19103
— speciale legato 404
— speciale senza lega 13446
— speciale per automobili 17003
— stagnato 18660
— stampato 13882
— stampigliabile 9220
— stirato 5819
— stirato brunito 2395
— surriscaldato 12759
— temperato 8856
— temprabile 8849

acciaio temprante in acqua 19783
— temprante in aria 284
— temprante in olio 12493
— temprato 8998
— temprato in acqua 14288
— ternario 16366
— Thomas 1293, 1549, 18539
— tondo 15292
— trafilato 5819
— trafilato a freddo 3975
— trafilato bianco 2395
— troostitico 18932
— Wootz 9736
— zingato 20324a
acciaioso 17524
acciottolato 1169
accoppiamento 10200
— con perni 13308
— d'utensili di sondaggio 18728
accoppiare 4545, 14649
accoppiatrice-smottatrice 16781
accordo di conservazione 4228
— limite 12466
accumulatore 54, 12754
— di carbone 8974
— di compensazione 18074
— idraulico a carico d'aria compressa 9512
accumulazione litorale 16170
accumulo 56
— di petrolio 12504
acerdese 59
acetato ammonico 524
— di ammonio 524
— di bario 60
— di piombo 10605
— potassico 61
acherite 337
aciculare 70
aciculite 73
acidifero 97
acidificabile 98
acidificante 99
acidificazione dei pozzi 100
acido 74, 13115
— acetico 62
— arsenico 823
— azotico 1032
— carbonico 2856

acido cloridrico 9549
— concentrato 4162
— cromico 3539
— di recúpero 14508
— diluito 5417
— fluoridrico 9555
— fosforico solubile 16898
— grasso 6837
— molibdico 11884
— nitrico 12309
— nitrico fumante 7818
— oleico 12526
— ossalico 12787
— per alchilazione 365
— rigenerato 14785
— scuro 2471
— solfidrico 17985
— solforico 19743
— solforico chimicamente puro 3399
— solforico commerciale 4089
— solforico libero nei residui 7739
— solforoso 17987
— sulfonico 17965
— tartarico 18331
aclinale 106
aclinico 106
acmite 107, 182
acqua acida satura 19738
— acidula 101
— ammoniacale 529, 10871
— ascendente 854
— bollente 2001
— bollita 1981
— con cenere di legno 13014, 20171
— cuprifera 20322
— depurata 14191
— di adescamento 10914, 13934
— di barite 1261
— di calce 10818
— di cava 14261
— di cristallizzazione 197?
— di diaclasi 4628
— di fiume 14970
— di galleria 8922
— di grafite 8451
— d'imbebizione 19800
— di interposizione 9710
— di pozzo 19974
— di raffreddamento 4336

acqua di refrigerazione 4346
— distillata 5562
— estranea 6711
— evaporata al m2 di superficie riscaldata 6620
— fangosa 16634
— fetida 7060
— fossile 4214
— gravitazionale 8496
— igroscopica 9581
— impura 12198
— interstiziale irriducibile 4214
— ipogena 854
— marginale 6204
— marziale 3268
— mercuriale 14305
— naturale 12198
— ossigenata 9561
— scaldata 19669
— sotterranea 8622
— superiore 18753
— regia 726
acque nitrogenate 1033
stagnanti 1091
acquifero 19749
acrocardite 339
acroite 68
acromatico 69
acquaio 16412
acquaforte per lastre di zinco 6574
acquamarina 725
actinoto 110
adamantino 121
adamina 124
adapter a fondo massiccio per alte pressioni 2548
adapters per lavorare al fondo pozzo fissati sul «Cristmass-tree» 2167
adattamento 46
— adattamento dello stampo 5380
addensatore 5175
— dei fanghi 14143
addetto ai carrelli 2527, 2573, 5740, 5789, 7953, 8894
— ai sondaggi 5906
— al decapaggio 13224
— al piano inclinato 9694
— al rottame 15678
— al trasportatore 4324

addetto alla cernita 13210
— alla frantumazione 5840
— alla macchina d'estra-
    zione 9228
— alla ripiena 2533, 12842
— alle cariche 3350, 11259
— alle pompe 14163
— alle scorie 3577, 8942
— alle siviere 10487
additivo 143, 144, 405, 5635
addizione v. aggiunta
— di colore 136
— di ferro manganese 137
— di fondente 7501
— di ghisa fredda 13270 b
— di minerale 132
— di nickel
— di sabbia 133, 141
— riducente 2881
— riduttrice 5185
addolcimento 16848, 18118
— Doctor 5591
addolcire 19334
— l'acciaio 16847
adduzione d'aria 171
adduzione v. entrata
— di calore 18027
adelfotipo 145
adelite 146
aderenza 17580
— del cemento 3143
aderire 147
adescare una pompa 13946
adesivo 150
adipocerite 151
adsorbimento 177
adularescenza 177 a
adularia 178
aenigmatite 183
aerazione delle miniere
    11745
aereare 6792
aereare v. ventilare
aereatore a vento 12145
aereazione 188
aereazione v. ventilazione
aereometro 9567
aerifero 195
aerolito 196
aeromagnetometro 245
aeschynite 197
aetite 198
afanesite 683
afanite 684

afanitico 685
afferrare con la tenaglia
    15804
— la sbarra 8564
affilare 16006, 18276
affilato 8607, 16001
affilatrice 7124, 8544
affilatrice a cinghia da
    banco con disco abrasivo
    7124
— multipla per ferri da
    profilare 12011
— portabile elettrica 13689
affilatura 16008
— dei fioretti 17508
affinaggio 4309, 14605,
    14617
— al bagno di scorie 16398,
    16564, 19688, 19702
— al basso fuoco 14614
— col minerale di ferro
    14619
— del ferro per via elettro-
    termica 6293
— dell'acciaio 14618
— della ghisa 10001
— della ghisa bianca 20035
— della ghisa grigia 8500
— in fossa 8954
— in grandi convertitori
    4311
— in piccoli convertitori
    4312
— su suola 8954
affinamento 14606
— al convertitore Bessemer
    1554
— al forno a riverbero 14609
— dei metalli 14615
— dell'argento 16358
— dell'oro 8349
— elettrolitico del rame
    6339
affinare 7072, 14593
— l'acciaio 14594
— la ghisa 14595
— lo stagno 14596
— per elettrolisi 6366
affinato v. raffinato
— al fuoco 7177 a
— e temprato 14597
affinatore del vuoto 8204 a
affinazione 14606
— al crogiolo 4744

affinazione del grano 8399
— di ghisa grezza 13270 a
— su suola 12579
affinazione v. raffinazione
affineria 14603
affinità 3384
affioramento 1320, 1403,
    5020, 15021, 18059,
    18069
— dello strato 4662
— di faglia 6852, 6854
— di un filone 12695
— mascherato 2592
— ossidato 1836
— superficiale 12694
affiorante 7480
affiorare 12693
afflusso 9766, 9771, 15388
affondare 1412, 5432
affusolamento del cono
    18282
affusto a colonna 17796
— a colonna per perforatri-
    ce 5889
— a colonna pneumatica
    13583
afnio 3137, 3706
afrite 687, 773
afrosiderite 688
aftalose 689
aftitalite 689
aftonite 690
afwillite 204
agafite 207
agalite 205
agalmatolite 206, 3467
agarico minerale 207 a
agata 208
— arborescente S. 741
— arborizzata 741
— -breccia 2355
— da brunire 2611
— -diaspro 10137
— -diaspro argillosa 782
— macchiata 3787
— muscosa 11849
— nastriforme 1181
— nuvolosa S. 3787
— occhiadina 6728
— perigonica 1623
— sanguigna 1817
agatato 213
agatifero 211
agatoide 212

agente antipiombo 15609
— antiruggine 15395
— di fusione 7891
— di sostegno 14026
— di trasporto 221
— esplosivo 1744
— modificante 11854
— per tamponare 13567
— ritardante 14790
— tensio-attivo 18042
agenti disperdenti 5549
— mineralizzanti 11762
agganciare 9311
— il lingotto 8565
aggiungere ghisa grezza 13247
aggiunta 134, 174, 13972a
— a goccie 135
— argillosa 10931
— di argilla 175
— di ferro 131
— di minerali 140
— di scorie 3571, 16520
— ossidante 12809
aggiunta v. addizione
aggiustaggio 163
— per mezzo di barre spaziatrici 168
aggiustatore di modelli 12991
agglomerante ceramico 19545
— per anime 4392
— per anime seccanti all'aria 333a
agglomerare 129, 223, 7774
agglomerarsi 1146
— per compressione a caldo 16429
agglomerato 221a, 1147, 2019, 2415
— di carbone di legna 3302
— di pomice 14152
— di sughero 13877
— di torba 13025
— duro di scorie 5173
— per altoforno 1716
agglomerazione 226a
— di minerali 12635, 12652
agglutinamento 2694, 16433
agglutinante 227, 1602, 2017
agglutinare 130
agglutinato 228
agglutinogeno 229

aggraffatura 3626, 15750
— ribadita 3110
aggregamento 12748a
aggregati 234
aggregativo 144
aggregato 12838
— cristallino 4799
— di quarzo-feldspato 14256
aggiustare 158
aghi neri 1657
aghiforme 12210
agitare 3559
— nell'acqua 17606
— un bagno 17605
agitatore 237, 13615, 14313, 17609, 17636, 18305
— del fango 8669
— discontinuo 1329
agitazione 236, 17608
— del bagno 1953, 17609a, 20197
— elettro-magnetica 6356
ago 19506
— curvo 4885
— d'acciaio 17496
— di scambio 18132
— d'espulsione 12205
— di platino 13525
— diritto
— infernale 13560
— magnetico 11196
— per l'aria 13931
agricolite 238
agucchia 10250
aguglietta 10250
aguilarite 239
aguzzato 8607
aguzzo 16001
aia 8949
aikinite 12209
aiutante di laboratorio 18460
aiuto-perforatore 7412, 18725
— preparatore 899
akermanite 338
ala 10807, 19634, 19872
— abbassata 11059, 11071
— inferiore abbassata 11072
alabandina 340
alabastrite 342
alabastro 341
alaite 343

alamosite 344
alare 7166
alascaite 345
albero 15933a, 17089
— a camme 18295
— a gomito 4610
— ausiliario dell'argano
— d'accoppiamento 4550
— del pignone 13320
— del tamburo 6015
— di comando 5968
— di comando principale 19530
— di comunicazione 8130
— di rinvio 10840
— di turbina 19123
— flessibile 7368
— motore 5968, 10099
— per sagomare 13705, 19367a
— per sagomatura 13705
— porta-fresa 737
— porta-utensile 7506
— primario 5968
alberite 346
albiano 347
albite 348
albitofiro 349
album dei profili 14001
alcale 355
alcaline (terre-) 358
alcalinizzazione 363
alcalizzare 362
alclad 351
alcool 352
alesaggio 2076, 14479
— d'un cilindro 2086
alesare 14477
alesatoio galleggiante 7391
alesatoio per sgrossare 17157
alesatore 2430, 14863a, 14917a
— a lame registrabili 6670
— conico 18281
— di centratura 3189
— elastico 6670
— meccanico con cono morse 11135
alesatrice verticale per maschere 10171
alesatura 14479
alessandrite 353
aletta 7064a

aletta di raffreddamento
    4338
— di saldatura 7290 a
— di stantuffo 13395
alette di avvolgimento 3923
alfenite 8195
algonkiano 354
ali del trapano 1630
alimentare 6874
— dal disotto 19249
— le caldaie 17630
alimentatore 6884, 15363
— a coclea 20227
— a piastre snodate 723
— a piatto 19152
— ad attacco tangenziale
    20020
— di combustibile 17636
— meccanico 11413,
    13781
— oscillante 15038
alimentazione 6888, 9853,
    15378, 17637
— a bocca libera 17172
— ad aria compressa 276
— a griglia 8581
— a rulli 15110
— a tazze rotanti 6932
— automatica 981
— automatica della griglia
    11414
— forzata 2049
— idraulica 9522
alimentazione v. caricamen-
    to
allactite 368
allagamento 2578, 7399
allalinite 369
allanite 370
allargamento 1470, 6487,
    19277
— con esplosivo di un foro
    da mina 17205
— del filone 1853
— del fondo di un foro da
    mina 2605, 3274
— del fondo di un foro da
    mina con esplosioni
    17267
allargare 7348, 14477
— il foro 12612
— una fessura 19877
— (un pozzo) 19274
allargatore 6486

allargatore ad oliva 18105
— fisso 9253
— per pozzi 15667, 19275
— per tubi 2963
allargatubi 13361, 18980
— doppio 5659, 5682
allargatura 1408
alleganite 371
alleggio 10792
allemontite 372
allentamento 16515
allentare un cuneo 19344
allineamento di carburi
    2823
allocroite 377
alloclasite 383
allocromatico 378
alloctono 379, 17742
allodelfite 384
allogeno 385
alloggio per chiavetta 10332
— per operai 20224
allomerismo 386
allomorfo 387
allotriomorfo 389, 592
allotropia 392
allume 438
allumina fusa 7886
alluminato 444
alluminiatura 466
alluminio 446
— piuma 7511
alluminite 445
alluminosilicato 470
alluminoso 14873
alluminotermia 18491
allumogelo 469
allungamento di rottura
    6390
— percentuale dopo rottura
    13074
allungare 6388
— uno scavo 16790
alluvionale 6396
alluvionamento 230, 410
alluvionare 232
alluvione glaciale 8251
— stannifero 17773
almandino 413
alnico 415
alnoite 416
alogeno 8725
alogenuro 8719
aloide 8724

alpacca 12280
alquifoux 420
alsbachite 421
alschedite 422
alstonite 424
alta pressione 9164
altaite 425
altalena col fluido in
    pozzo 15036
altare 2381, 7157, 7166,
    7829
alterazione agli agenti
    atmosferici 19871
— alle intemperie 19869
altezza 6417, 9054
— del crogiuolo 9056
— d'elevazione 10740
— del focolare 5208
— della pressione 13908
— della sacca 9055
— della volta 8919
— del liquido in serbatoio
    16101
— del livello 10741
— del pianotavola dal ter-
    reno 19281
— del pezzo colato 5205
— del vuoto 16108
— d'estrazione 10740-10741
— di caduta 9057
— di riempimento 7034 a
— permanente della pompa
    18589
altipiano 18191
— paludoso 9159
altoforno 1706, 9149
— a carbone di legna 3301
— a coke 3930
— a crogiuolo aperto 1723
— a crogiuolo chiuso 1722
— ad antracite 643
— a petto aperto 1723
— a petto chiuso 1722
— blindato 1726
— con crogiuolo ovale 1724
— con inviluppo 1721
— Héroult 9099
— libero 9731
— in muratura 1725
— rivestito 1721
— scozzese 15648
— Stassano 17388
alumel 442
alundum 472

alunite 471, 473
alunitizzato 475
alunitizzazione 474
alunogeno 476
alzare e abbassare alterna-
    tivamente 14492
— la barra 10738
— la colata 9722
alzata 9057
amalgama 478
— di mercurio 484
— d'oro 483
amalgamabile 489
amalgamare 477
amalgamato 491
amalgamatore 492, 8560
— a bacinella 12886
amalgamazione 490, 498
— al tamburo 1240
— a mezzo tamburi rotanti
    500
— in vasche 501
— su piastre 13486
amarantite 502
amatolo 503
amazonite 504, 8513
ambatoarinite 505
ambiente v. atmosfera
ambligonite 508
ambra 506, 17937
— nera 7904, 10152
ambrite 509
americio 513
amesite 514
ametista 515
amianto 516, 6170
— al palladio 12879
— in lamine flessibili
    12034
— vulcanizzato 19608
amido 17378
— esplosivo 20274
amigdale 542
ammaccatura 5178
ammassi effusivi 6218
ammasso 13278, 17611
— di detriti 15350
— di materiale sterile 1605,
    6101
— di minerali 12966, 12647
— di minerali da arrostire
    14984
— sterile 9377
ammoniaca 518

ammissione 9853
— d'aria 171
ammonioborite 521
ammoniojarosite 522
ammonite 523
— piritica 14215
ammortizzare il colpo del-
    la mazza 10695
ammortizzatore ad aria
    263
— del cavo 10832
— di pulsazioni 14145
ammortizzazione a molla
    17194
ammucchiamento v. accaval-
    lamento
ammucchiare 52, 13284
amorfo 6589
amosite 532
ampelite 535
amperometro 517, 4868
ampiezza di piegatura 1508
anaerobico 545
anagenesi 546
analcite 542
analisi 548, 6675
— al cannello 1891
— allo spettroscopio 17036
— arbitrale 734
— calorimetrica 4034
— chimica 3383
— completa 18786
— di colata 10471
— di confronto 17342
— elementare 19216
— gravimetrica 8483
— media percentuale 1007
— microchimica 11630
— per via secca 6633
— per via umida 6632,
    19984
— polarografica 13618
— qualitativa 14245
— quantitativa 14250
— quantitativa del minera-
    le 12627
— spettrale 17035
— tecnica del gas 7976
— termica 18480a
— volumetrica 19600
— volumetrica ripetuta 1080
analizzatore del gas brucia-
    to 7455
anamesite 551

anamorfismo 552
anapaite 553
anatasio 554
anatessi 555, 14643
anauxite 556
ancherite 599, 2477
anchilostomiasi 600
ancora per roccia per i ven-
    ti della torre 5219
— prolungabile 6667
ancoraggio a bullone 15714
— della fune morta 20152
— in ferri tondi 15286
ancore entroterra per i venti
    della torre 5217
andalusite 561, 9281, 11142
andamento v. marcia
— 20195
— della fusione 13980,
    14005
— della soffieria 114
— della tempera 13977
— dell'altoforno 20247
— generale dell'altoforno
    8152
— (o marcia) caldissimo
    20221
— (o marcia) dell'altoforno
    1714
— (o marcia) freddo 4009
— (o marcia) normale 12384
— regolare del forno 14654
andare in pezzi 16011
andata 8341
andesina 562
andesite 563
andesitico 564
andradite 566, 695
andrewsite 567
anello 10995, 14920
— cava-coke 3934
— continuo di cavo senza
    estremità 8583
— d'acciaio in testa ad
    una colonna di tubi 19961
— del cilindro frantumatore
    16704
— del palo 16150
— dell'involucro 11303
— dello stantuffo 13392
— di arresto di sicurezza
    3581
— di cintura del convertito-
    re 18960

anello di contrappeso 14931
— di cuoio 10654
— di frenaggio 5778
— di galleria 19111
— di ghisa 3010
— di gomma per tappi di
   cementazione 19699
— di guardia tubolare 19075
— di mattoni 17649
— di paglia 17756
— di porcellana 13666
— di pozzo 6013
— di rinforzo 13273
— di ritiro 16225a
— di sostegno del refrattario 4848
— di trafila 5796
— distanziatore 16956
— d'un pozzo 16107
— graduato 18640
— in lamiera di ferro 16059
— intermedio 11664
— portastorte 18039
— reggispinta 18602
— sospeso 18077
— supporto per il bagno
   d'acqua 19748
— tagliente 4860
anemometro 568
anfibolite 537
anfibolizzazione 538
anfibolo 536
anfigeno 539
anfiteatro 11930
anglesite 586, 10623
angolare 587
— a lati disuguali 19288
— ad L a lati uguali 581,
   1381
— d'acciaio 580
angolari 572
— a bulbo 2537
— a spigoli vivi 582
— ad L a lati disuguali a
   spigoli arrotondati 19289
— pesanti 9026
angolo 4478
— assiale 1017
— della sacca 574
— di Bragg 8268a
— di curvatura 1507
— di declinazione
   magnetica 575

angolo di deviazione del cavo 7364
— di discordanza 578
— d'incidenza 576
— d'invito 18279a
— di sformo 18279/a
— di spoglia 5726
— di stratificazione 573,
   1431
— di taglio 4927, 18952
— di torsione 577
— interfacciale 9880
anidride 593, 4820, 10285
— arseniosa 814
— carbonica 2832
— fosforica 13179
— silicea 16312
— solforica 17989
anidrite 4820, 10285
anima 4384, 12405
— a colletto liscio 16209a
— a guscio 16100
— a secco 4385
— a segmentazione 2319
— a sezioni 15799
— a verde 8516
— anulare 14921a
— cava 3272
— cieca 1770
— curva 4878
— del tassello punteria
   18296
— della lista attacco testa
   8920
— della scatola ingranaggi
   8126
— di segmentazione 19693
— di terra 10927
— di tubo 19067
— dimenticata 12537
— filtro 7044a, 17737
— fragile 2421
— imprigionata nella
   sabbia 6401
— mal composta 9669
— mal sistemata 9669
— per camicia d'acqua
   19787
— perduta 11039, 11805
— portafiltro 17737
— percollocata 6401
— quadrata 589
— raffreddata ad acqua
   19758a

anima rotta 2442
— sagomata 18125
— soffiata 1881
— spostata 16126
— tassello 14704
— tubolare cilindrica 10101
— variata 16126
anime 4463
animetta di materozza 13055
animista 4421, 4460
animisteria 4446
anione 595
anisotropia 598
anisotropo 596
annabergite 601
annaffiatoio del formatore
   19803
annata 12423
anodizzare 634
anodizzazione 632
anodo 626
anomalia di tempra 3424
anortite 635, 2710, 4935
anortoclasio 636
anortosi 16813
anortosite 637
antenna per radio 14336
— portabandiera 7248
— telescopica 2045
anticamera 653
anticlinale 654, 10054
— a ventaglio 6803
— asimmetrica 911
— carenata 2890
— coricata 14522
— eretta 6537
— in forma di sella 15408
— non sviluppata 809
— rovesciata 12782, 14522
— secondaria 11782, 17931
— simmetrica 18149
antidetonante 666
antidiluviano 638
antigorite 664, 10498
antimonio 669, 17575
— puro 17375a
— rosso 10312
antimonioso 17571
antimonite 668, 8497
antincrostante 665
antiossidante 12790
antipodo 671
antischiuma 5123
antlerite 675

antofillite 639
antosiderite 640
antozonite 676
antracite 642, 1768 ,
    8822, 13008, 17697
— da 60 a 100 mm 2440
— di qualità inferiore 10495
— in pezzi 3368
antracitizzazione 645
antracmite 646
antraco-silicosi 647
antraconite 649, 17604,
    18127, 19406
antracosi 650
antraxilone 651
apachite 679
apatite 680
apertura 7966, 7969, 13685
— d'entrata 6495, 9820
— d'entrata dell'aria 292
— d'entrata della fiamma
    7261
— d'uscita 12702
— del condotto del fumo
    3460
— del foro di mina 9048
— del petto 8957
— di adduzione dell'aria
    292
— dell'ugello 12610
— della bocca 18578
— della piattaforma in cima
    alla torre 19818
— di bocca 6893
— di colata 7424
— di pozzi 2112
— di stiratura 5781
— di un pozzo 5931
— di una formatura 12609
— di ventilazione 161, 886
— di scappamento 6653
— equivalente 6533
apice 681
apjohnite 691
aplanatico 692
aplite 693
apliti 694
apocromatico 696
apofillite 698
apofisi 699
— d'un filone 16450, 17181
apomagmatico 697
appalto per grandi lavori di
    perforazione 1690

appannatura 18328 a
apparato v. apparecchio
apparecchi ausiliari 1000
— di vetro 8286
— fisico-chimici 13195
— per l'analisi al cannel-
    lo 1892
— per prove terre e sabbia
    di fonderia 7671
apparecchiatura ad ultra-
    suoni metalloscopica a
    polveri magnetiche 18022
— elettrica di comando
    automatico 6359
— per il caricamento auto-
    matico 977
apparecchio a induzione per
    trattamento termico 8999
— ad aria calda 287
— ad aria calda a tubi so-
    spesi 288
— ad aria calda o ricupera-
    tore Whitwell 20053
— ad aria calda orizzontale
    9331
— ad aria calda verticale .
    19518
— automatico di distacco
    992
— Cleveland 3722
— da bronzare 2463
— d'alimentazione 6890
— d'amalgamazione 499
— d'essiccamento e
    calcinazione 6053
— d'estrazione 6708
— d'illuminazione 9635
— d'inversione 18136
— di caricamento 3332,
    3346
— di chiusura della bocca
    18580
— di controllo 14057
— di Edison 6214
— di ghisa ad aria calda
    9953
— di Kipp 10369
— di manovra a telescopio
    18946
— di manovra del tappo
— di Orsat 12679
— di prova 18467
— di prova per formazioni
    7614

apparecchio di ribaltamento
    6100, 19096
— di riscaldamento 7195
— di rovesciamento per
    vagonetto
— di sollevamento 10767
— di sondaggio 2104
— di sondaggio per pulire
    il foro di sonda 5924
— di sublimazione 17925
— di Venturi 19513 ˙
— elettromagnetico di
    Siemens 16291
— fotografico 13186
— generatore di gas 8012
— per acqua calda 19667
— per analisi dei gas 7977,
    12679
— per bromurazione 2451
— per esame radiografico
    dei metalli 20262
— per etere secondo
    Rothe 15236
— per fare il vuoto 19425
— per filettare con maschi
    1830
— per formare a sagoma
    S. 17804
— per i controlli non distrut-
    tivi 700
— per il ribaltamento elet-
    trico 6309
— per inclinare le damigia-
    ne 2876
— per irrigare 17209
— per l'analisi dell'acido
    carbonico 705
— per l'analisi dell'arseni-
    co 703
— per l'analisi dell'azoto
    707
— per l'analisi del carbonio
    2830
— per l'analisi del carbonio
    nel ferro 704
— per l'analisi del punto di
    fusione 706
— per la distillazione 5555
— per la misurazione elettrica
    6287
— per la rotazione 15227
— per l'estrazione di gaso-
    lina 8080

apparecchio per montare i
protettori sulle aste
6666
— per potassa 13721
— per produzione di idrogeno solforato 702
— per raschiettare 15676
— per riempire le damigia-
ne 2874
— per rimuovere benzina e
acqua dal gas naturale
8080
— per riscaldamento a
induzione 9752
— per sagomare 17804
— per spegnere le scintille 16983
— per tagliare bilette e
barre in movimento 7507
— per versare a mano 8788
— separatore ed agitatore
15863
— smagnetizzante 5162
apparecchio v. apparecchiatura o dispositivo
apparizione di globuli
18104 a
appendice di estrazione 6237
appezzamento di terreno
13552
appiattimento 1567, 7351,
7351 a
appiattire 19371
appiccicosità 17581
appiccicoso 18197
applicare i raffreddatori
S. 3421
— il nero 1640
— il tubaggio 15342
— l'argilla 3669
— la creta 3666
— le mosche 18219
— le spie (o le mosche)
S. 18219
applicazione dei montanti
14955
— delle colate 8105
appoggi ricavati da putrelle ad ali larghe 2432
appoggiarsi 27
appoggio per la lavorazione 10184
apporto di materia magmati-
ca 138

approfondimento 5101
— a livello aperto 12626
— del pozzo 16421
— del pozzo ad aria com-
pressa 13592
— del pozzo con cementa-
zione 15956
approfondire 5100, 5161
— una galleria 15339
appuntimento 1595
aprire 2301, 12602
— il vento 19136
— un pozzo S. 2075
— una forma S. 2296
assorbimento di gas 18,
8082 a
— di ossigeno nel carbo-
ne 22
— di saldatura 19939
— dielettrico 5383
assorbire l'umidità 11
assorbitore 12, 15
asta 9294, 17533, 17903
— cava per molle di
paracolpi 2521
— del chiodo 15953
— del mulino a pestelli
5605
— del tampone 13575 a,
17679 a, 17685
— della pompa 16992,
17000
— di controllo 8116
— di perforazione 2105,
— di pescaggio 16807
— di pistone 13579
— di pompaggio 17938,
17944
— di regolazione 165
— di sonda 2088, 2099,
2105, 15048
— di sondaggio 5897
— di trasmissione 14129
— di trivellazione 2557
— liscia 13628
— motrice 8534, 10303
— motrice di sonda 945
— motrice esagonale 9117
— ottagonale 12450
— per perforazione a cavo
5909
— per spillare 18301
— pesante 5886, 16415

asta pesante da fare in
cantiere 5887
— pesante non magnetica
13356
— porta-fresa 8534
— singola 16378
— telescopica 2045
— tubolare per trolley 19091
asta v. barra
astato 902
aste per parafulmini a tronchi
rastremati 10797
— pesanti di trasmissione
14130
asterismo 905
astiano 906
asticella di estrazione 10769
astrakanite 909
astrolito 910
atacamite 915
ataxico 917
atelestite 918
atlasite 916
atmosfera 923
— artificiale 4290
— controllata 4290
— gassosa 8069
— protettiva 14045
atomo 930
atopite 935
attaccare 3616
— con acido 6571
— il lingotto 8565
attacco 936, 3794
— (di fune) 16806
— a bava 4227, 16671
— a coltello 7335
— a corno 9360
— a linguetta S, 19880
— a pioggia 13764
— a pioggia anulare
— acido 6572
— acido macrografico 11145
— acido profondo 5091
— ad aggancio e sgancio
12540
— ad angolo 4479
— anulare 14924
— chimico 6571
— chiodato in lamiera
d'acciaio 14978
— col metodo francese (di
tunnel) 7755

attacco (di tunnel) col metodo inglese 6480
— col metodo italiano 10086
— d'aiuto S. 17562
— dal muro 8374
— dal tetto 8374
— del cavo alla gabbia di
estrazione 2679
— del tubo alla testa
d'iniezione 9387
— del tubo di gomma alla
testa 15212
— della corrosione uniforme 937
— delle aste 1216
— delle cariche 3466, 8805
— di colata 8089, 8093,
9776
— di colata a grappolo 3793
— di colata a piatto 7335
— di colata a pioggia
13056, 13764
— di colata a ventaglio 6804
— di colata con fermascorie
16460
— di colata multipla 2257
— di colata sul piano di
giunzione 17129
— di pulitura 13626a
— di riscaldamento 17458a,
17562
— diretto 5465, 9778
— frontale 5712
— fucinato 5251
— girevole 18130
— guidato 9778
— guidato diretto 16264
— guidato laterale 16672
— in sorgente 19356
— lamellare 19880
— per binari di manovra
3795
— per fili 20120
— per taglio a circolo 3580
— per tubi 2941
— snodato in acciaio 18142
attemperatore 938
attesa 9242
attestarsi 27
attestatura 29
attinio 109
attinolite 110
attitudine alla compressione 4101

attivante 118
attivare il tiraggio 14304
attivazione 17802a
attivismo 119
attizzatoio 13615
attraversare 4683
attrazione capillare 2806
attrezzare 14894
attrezzatura 12699
attrezzatura di miniera 13408
— di montaggio 7244
— per la trivellazione a
pressione 16793
attrezzature di captazione
3523
— d'ottone 2269
attrezzi di perforazione 5943
— per uscire da un casing
11714
attrezzo a forma di barra la-
sciato cadere nel pozzo
8323
— a mano 11010
— a scanalare 8596
— con lame al fondo per
bottlenecking 2165
— da avvitare sul «bottom
hole test adapters 2168
— per brillare una carica
1069
— per formatura a mano
8765
— per raschiare l'interno
di una colonna 2960
— per riportare a calibro
l'interno d'un tubo deformato o irregolare 2954
— per sbavare 3706
— per spingere detriti al
fondo pozzo 10258
— per taglia fresa 4907
attrito 7765
— elettrolitico degli ioni
6342
— di frenatura 2254
— interno 9901
aturiano 941
auerlite 942
augelite 943
augite 948
augite sienite 949
augitico 950
augitofiro 951
aumentare la produzione 9721

aumento eccessivo del diametro 15382a
— d'angolo 569
— della riducibilità 9725
— della sezione trasversale
8102
— della velocità d'avanzamento 5917
— di calore 9724
— di pressione 13897
— di temperatura 18384
aureola della lampada di
sicurezza 1901
— di contatto 3445
— kelyfitica 2070
auricalcite 952
aurifero 953
ausiliario 17334
austenite 956
austenitico 957
austenitizzazione 955
autigeno 960
autobotte 18256
autocarro 19475
— con esplosivi 16943
— -gru 13207
— portatrezzi 18724
— registratore 14507
autocentrante 15813
autoclave 965, 17441
— tubolare 5405
autoctono 963
autofondente 15822
autogeno 966
automezzo cingolato 3101
automolite 994
automorfo 995
autoneòmorfo 996
autopneumatolisi 997
autoricottura 15814
autoscorificante 15829
autotemprante 15824
autunite 998, 10817
auversiano 999
avancrogiolo 2054, 7559,
7565, 14489
avanpozzo 3134, 5216, 7568
avanzamento 180, 2046,
5210, 5276, 5936, 5959,
6875, 6889, 10743, 20087
— a cremagliera 14321a
— a tavolone 2046
— ad aria compressa 276
— automatico 980

avanzamento d'assaggio
   18883
— del sondaggio al metro
   7550
— della perforazione a me-
   tri 7550
— di acqua marginale 6205
— di traverso banco 4713
— in profondità 19282
— per ciclo di lavoro 7551
avanzare 5758
avaria 6767
aventurina 1005, 7251, 8354
aventurismo 1006
avogadrite 1014
avvallamento 1850, 16411
avviare 10337
— (un forno) 10799
— la produzione con pistonaggio 18087
avvitare (tubi) 4546
— (le aste o i tubi) 11231
— le aste di perforazione
   11233
avvitatura 15718
avvolgere 15070
— l'armatura dell'anima
   1593
avvolgimento 1600, 19137,
   20098
awaruite 1015
axinite 1019
axiolite 1020
azionata da motore 15767
azionata direttamente 13800
azione d'erosione 10163
— dei ghiacci 111
— del gelo 9769
— della neve 113
— delle acque correnti 112
— di taglio S. 4914
— di trasporto e di accumulazione dell'acqua corrente 18839
— eolica 20088
— erosiva del ghiaccio
   8548
— intermoleculare isotropa
   10083
— locale 15813a
— meccanica sul materiale
   11411
— ossidante dell'aria so-
   pra il carbone 12810

azioni di contatto endo-
   morfe 6463
— di contatto esogene
   S. 6661
— di contatto esomorfe
   6661
azioni litorali 16172
azoico 1031
azoto 12319
azotometro 1034
azzurrite 1036, 1906, 3413
azzurro-scuro 4482

B

babbit 1038
babingtonite 1039
bacchetta d'apporto 7025
— di vetro per agitare
   8293
bacinella 1327, 5511
— d'evaporazione 6614
— d'evaporazione in
   porcellana 13663
— di colata 13747
— di cristallizzazione 4809
— di piombo 10607
— di sgocciolamento 5747
— di vetro 8272
— per analisi volumetrica
   7063
— per bagno di sabbia 5514
— per lavare l'oro 8348
bacino 1309, 10322, 15933,
   17275a
— a tampone galleggiante
   13565
— carbonifero 3821
— da fanghi 16628
— delle scorie 18523a
— dello staccio 17739
— di alimentazione 5720
— di colata 1311, 6877,
   11476
— di colata a tampone
   S. 17686
— di colata a tappo 17686
— di colata a trappole
   fermascorie 13750
— di colata a vasca 1313
— di decantazione 5295,
   15925, 12085
— di fusione 11461

bacino di raccolta 3086
— di raccolta dei fanghi
   17993
— di refrigerazione 4341
— di roccia 15006
— strutturale 9896
bacino v. vasca
baco di cotone 2005
baddeleite 1092
baffi di gatto 15684
— di gatto orizzontali 12106,
   14496
— di gatto rotativi 3689
— di gatto verticali con la
   punta su un unico filo
   15237
— di gatto verticali con
   punte a spazzola 15231
bagliore 7289
— bronzeo 2456
— grasso 16804
— perlaceo 13022
— resinoso 13415
bagnato 16853
bagno 1338, 8972
— acido 75
— caustico 3114
— d'acqua 19746
— d'aria 240
— d'amalgamazione 493
— d'olio 12480
— di decapaggio 13217
— di ferro 9957
— di fusione 14094a
— di ghisa 13261
— di metallo 10595
— di piombo 10625
— di rinvenimento 18390
— di sabbia 15470
— di sale per alte temperature 9155
— di scorie 16523
— di tempra 8860, 14291,
   14292a
— di vapore 17416
bainite 1110
baldaufite 1142
banchina 1497, 1538
— di caricamento 10922
banco 2147, 15743, 16035
— d'olio 12479
— da formatore 11992
— di carbone 15747
— di formatura 12000

banco di ghiaia 1194
— di manovra 20251
— di sabbia 9212
— di stiramento a pinza 5799
— di stiramento a rulli 5800
— di trafila 5794
— di trafileria 20124
— per l'utensile di lavoro 20218
— per trafilatura 14296
— roccioso incassante S. 4544
— scistoso 1189
— superiore 2796
banda 17760
— contorta 19182a
— della staffa 7311
— di ferrite libera 8210/a
— di fosfuro 13168/a
— di rinforzo 17781
— di selezione 16927
— di tubo 16448a
— larga 20061
— stagnata a caldo 9447
— stagnata elettrolitica 6351
— zincata 7939
bande laminate a freddo 3995
— nere 1667
bandella 17744
— di acciaio 17480
bandiera 17810
baracca di sonda 5596
barcollare 7285
barcone 10792
bardiglio 1224
bardolite 1225
barilite 1257
bario 1234
barisfera 1259
barite 1260
— carbonata 20048
baritina 1233, 3106, 3127, 9031, 17968
baritocalcite 1262
baritocelestite 1263
barkevichite 1235
barolite 20048
barra 1205, 1206, 1207, 13238, 14314, 15049
— a canalino 9273
— a cuneo 7900

barra appesentatrice 16415
— cava gonfiata 14115a
— cementata 1782
— comparatrice 14006a
— con estremo da forgiare 13698
— d'ancoraggio 2211
— d'intragliatrice 4910
— da rilaminare 12059
— di alesatrice 1408a
— di controllo della cementazione 18265a
— di fissaggio 9240
— di manovra 2221
— di metallo prezioso 2570
— di pompaggio 6895a
— di profilato 15773
— di prova 18453
— di rotazione 14889
— di sicurezza 1457
— di sospensione 1454
— di sterratura 10401
— di trazione 10365
— di zincatura 7942
— doppia 10969
— esagona 9121
— greggia 12059
— in rotoli 3922
— mezzo tondo irregolare 7336
— pelata calibrata 13040
— per arpioni 17080
— per azionare un congegno in pozzo 18909
— per cerchielli di fissaggio della ruota al cerchione 17198
— per cerchioni 18686
— per chiodi da ferro di cavallo 9380
— per chiodi del ferro da cavallo 12161
— per distaffare 10401
— per ferri da maniscalco 9382
— per pompare 13932
— per scampanare 14419
— per spillare 18301
— piatta con nervatura 17867
— rettificata 8609
barranco 1238
barre d'acciaio S. 1220
— d'acciaio levigato 2402
— di ferro 9955

barre per rondelle elastiche 18853
— quadre 17254
— trafilate 5815
barretta 18442
— di prova 18454
barriera 1247
— antipolvere 15019
— del pozzo 15942
— di protezione 8643
barsilite 1258
bartoniano 1255
basaltico 1268
basalto 1267
— alla nefelina 12229
— di copertura 1689
— ellissoidale 6385
basamento S. 897
basamento 1273, 1290, 1433, 17934
— cristallino 4792
— in calcestruzzo 4174
basanite 1271, 18795
bascula a ponte 19895
basculle 19898
base 1273, 2142, 3198, 7538, 16336, 16805, 16868, 18701
— del ritto del supporto 10013
— della caldaia 1975
— della rotaia 7544
— della torre di trivellazione 1275
— di petrolio 1282
— per attrezzo di sbavatura 3743
basicità 1308
bassanite 1319
basso fuoco S. 1827, 3305, 8956
bastite 1323, 15623
bastnaesite 1324
bastoncini di ferro S. 15054
bastoncino di vetro per agitare 8283
— di zinco 20333
bastone di colata 8096
batea 1, 9357, 9357, 12885
batholite 1339, 12033
batrachite 1343
batroclasi 2169, 4697, 7341, 9339

battere 1402, 1818, 5760,
  10393, 17304, 17813
— a freddo 3958
— i tubi durante la prova
  idraulica 8728
— in forma 2128 a
— moneta 17814
batteria 54, 1191, 1346
— di aste 5942, 18289
— di caldaie 1349
— di forni 12826
— di forni a coke 1350
— di perforazione 5941
— di piccolo diametro per
  lavori entro le aste 11113
— di puntelli ravvicinati
  1351
— per sondaggi 5941
— presa in pozzo 7785
batti-chiodi 16783
battipalo 11900
— a mano 8778
battisabbia 3688
battitura dei metalli 1404 a
— dei pali 13285
— del filo 14723
— rapida 14299
battola 1920, 14402, 15321
battuta 14403
baumhauerite 1355
bauxite 1356
— bianca 20025
bava 7290, 14349, 15745,
  19493
— di raffreddamento 4338
— di taglio 7717 a
— inferiore 2157
— interna 19616
bavatura 2339, 2618, 7290,
  14349, 16703
bavenite 1358
bayldonite 1360
bazzite 1362
beaverite 1406
becchelite 1407
becco 10860
— a gas 2600, 7985
— a incandescenza 9684
— ad imboccatura oblunga
  10974

becco amovibile 9870
— Bunsen 2582
— Bunsen ad acetilene 63
— circolare 6806
— di colata 13761, 17170
— di combustione 12408
— di scarico 7429
— di stagno 1376
— di Teclu 18350
— del convertitore 4303,
  12204, 18577
— di un convertitore
  Bessemer 12390
— intercambiabile 9870
becco v. bruciatore
beegerite 1438
beidellite 1442
belemnite 1443
bellite 1464
belonite 1471
bementite 1482
ben stretto 18335
benitoite 1525
benjaminite 1526
benna 1359, 2497, 3629,
  3630, 8219, 9472, 10334,
  18971
— automatica 983
— di caricamento 3351 a,
  10335, 16480
— di scavo 16420
— oscillante 11004
— scavatrice 6435
— strisciante di escavatrice
  5734
— trainata 5734
benthos 1529
bentonite 1539, 5180
benzina di cracking 4585
— di distillazione 17715
— etilata 10613
— riformata 14622
benzolo 1532
bequerellite 1411
beraunite 1533
berchelio 1536
beresite 1534
berillio 1544
berillo 1542
berillonite 1546

berlinite 1537
berma 1538
berta 5986, 11900
— a cinghia 7366
— a stampare 5984
— a tavola 1923
— spezzaghisa 5975
— spezza-rottami 13254
berthierite 1539
Bertrandite 1541
berzelianite 1547
berzeliite 1548
betafite 1814
betoniera per cemento 3150
biacca di piombo 20036
— di zinco 20338
bianco (al calore) 20042
— abbagliante S. 20035
— incandescente S. 20031
bicarbonato di soda 16820
bicchiere 1377, 7592, 13373
— a calice 18446
— di porcellana 13660
— di vetro infusibile 8830
bicornia 1375
bicromato potassico 1575
bidone 16047
bieberite 1576
biella 4220, 13423, 15049
— di trazione 5783 a, 18418 a,
  18610
biellismo 10857
biffa di livello 9470
biforcazione 7603
biga 8233
bilancella 13060
bilancia 1122, 8490
— a colonna 4040
— a mano 8782
— a ponte 19895
— automatica 973
— automatica per fini da
  coke 1587
— centesimale 3190
— d'assaggio 889
— da tavolo 4091
— decimale 5061
— di precisione 13818
— idrostatica 9573

bilancia per analisi chimiche 550
— per carri 19620
— per gas 7981
— rapida 14298
bilanciamento 1139
bilanciamento v. equilibratura
bilanciare 12462
bilanciere 4595, 6918, 10763, 15034, 15041, 19628
— di pompa 14164
— di pompa con rinvio inferiore 14166
bilancino 10764
bilancio calorifico 8980
bilico S. 15584
bilinite 1579
billetta 1581
— di ferro crudo 1560a
— quadrata 17233
— rettangolare 14516
bimetallico 1589
binarietto portatile 13696
binario a scartamento normale 7801
— a scartamento ridotto 12177
— del ponte 19896
— di raccordo 10253
— di rovesciamento del carbone 3807
— principale 11227
— secondario 16240
binda 14393
— strappapuntelli 13619
bindheimite 1596
binnite 1607
biolite 1608
biossido di manganese 11271
biossido di piombo 13100
— di sodio 13101
biotite 1609, 1656
bisbeeite 1612
bischofite 1613
bismite 1614
bismutina 1616
bismuto 1615

bismutocra S. 1614
bismutoplagionite 1619
bismutosferrite 1620
bismutotantalite 1621
bisognoso di riparazioni 9680
bisolfuro di ferro 6951
bityite 1639
black-band 1643
blastogranitico 1751
bleischweif 1760
blenda 1761, 11850, 13031, 15189, 17053, 20341
— botrioidale 2131
— cadmifera 2676
— scura 1651
blindare 1765
blindatura 1813
blocca-stampo 5359
bloccaggio 7743, 10946
— della tavola 18189
bloccare 1792
bloccarsi 7740
blocco 1793, 6842, 9958, 16948a
— d'impronta 9667
— da estrudere 6723
— degli scambi 13609
— di loppa 2692, 16525, 16529
— di stampo a guida colonnare 5378a
— dislocato 6842
— erratico 5854
— intrusivo 2125
blomstrandina 1814
blumi quadri 1835
blumo 1820, 13480
bobierrite 1931
bobina 17148
— aperta 12567, 12577
— non recuperabile 18592
— permanente 13105
bobinaggio 20099
bocca 1933, 4017
— d'altoforno 15559, 18574
— d'aspirazione 6164
— del convertitore 4302
del crogiolo 5148

bocca del pozzo 12045, 15936
— dello spezzamasselli 2320
— di altoforno 12044, 15959
— di caricamento 3345, 6891, 12042
— di caricamento aperta 12608
— di caricamento chiusa 3777
— di colata 3047, 9855, 17213
— di scarico 12702
boccame 8106, 15377, 15655
boccetta capillare 2807
bocchetta 17829
bocchettone 1733, 9389
— di sfiato 2352
boccola 2625
— cilindrica 15275
— del supporto 1389
— oblunga 12723
— per pernio a cannone 9277
— tonda 15275
bodenbenderite 1935
boiacca di cemento 3155
bolivarite 2003
bolivianite 2004
bolla 2486
— d'aria 249, 1780
bollicine 13303
bolo 2002
bolo d'America S. 12488
bomba calorimetrica 2756
bombare 18120
bombatura 2770
— del cilindro 15074a
bombola 1172, 4941, 19541
— per gas compressi 4937
— per gas disciolti 4938
— per gas liquefatti 4939
bomboletta per respiratori 16739
bombolone per il trasporto di gas 10548
bonderizzazione 2020
bone-bed 2026
bonifica 8859, 14190
— chimica 5127
— isotermica 954

bonificabile 8997
bonificare l'acciaio 9670
bonsdorffite 2037
boothite 2056
borace 2061
borace grezzo 18656
boracite 2060
borato sodico 2061
borchia 2124
bordatrice 6211, 18903 a, 18980
bordatura 7275, 1373 a
bordino del tubo del fumo 1368
bordione 2012, 15270, 20138
— in rotoli 20141
bordo 3596, 6198, 19142
— del cilindro 6203
— del cratere 14914
— del forno 14915
— della siviera 14916
— di cuoio 10650
— di laminazione 15095
— di una faglia 16254
— inferiore 7548
— rivoltato 5778
— tagliato 16027 a
— (a) vivo 16064
borgstromite 2093
bornite 2115, 6553, 9378, 13009, 14194, 19471
boronatrocalcite 12184
borsa di colata S. 7660
bort 2047
botola 7279, 18848
botola a cerniera 9204
botriogeno 2129
botte d'estrazione 2202
bottiglia 18517
— a pipetta 13378
— d'assorbimento 16
— della pompa per tanghi 251
— di cobalto 3889
— di decantazione 5052
— di guttaperca 8681
— di lavaggio per bromo 2453

bottiglia di lavaggio per gas 8062
— di livello
— di una pompa 18073
— di Woolff 20187
— generatrice di gas 7312
— per acidi corrosivi 2873
— per filtrazione forzata 7057
— per reagenti 14472
bottone d'avviamento 17381
bournonite 2196, 20008
boussingaultite 2197
bowenite 2201
bowmanite 2204
bracci d'erogazione «dell'albero di Natale» 7438
— (a-) lunghi 10968
— murali tubolari portafili e portalampada 19094
braccio 2042, 6828, 16267
— della sagoma 18114
— di gru 8215
— mobile 3333
— murale tubolare 19093
— trasportatore 4321
brace carbonina S. 16728
brachianticlinale 2233
brachidoma 2234
brachipinacoide 2235
bradigenesi 2250
bragite 2251
bramma 1820, 16494, 18503
— grezza 16499
branare v. scampanare o vibrare
branatura 14420
brandisite 2263
brannerite 2264
brasatura 2290, 8840
— ad immersione 5434
— al forno 7828
— all'argento 16351 a
— capillare 2292
— ossidrica 18768
brasilite 2291
braunite 2287, 2477

breccia 2353, 2446, 3649, 7966, 15324,
— di dislocazione 4766, 6844, 7766, 15025
— di faglia 6844
— di frizione 4766, 6844, 7766, 15402, 16012
— glaciale 5855
— mineralizzata 5735
brecciato 2354
breccioso 2354
breislakite 2359
breithauptite 2360
breunnerite 2363
breve galleria di derivazione 12464
brevicite 2364
brewsterite 2365
bricchettatura 2416
bricchetto 2415
— desolforante 5248
brida 14360 a
briglia 5592, 8269, 17079, 17743
— del premistoppa 8269
— di collegamento 4668, 16954
brillamento 1743
brillantatura 2403, 2522
brinellatura 1167, 8874
britholite 2419
broccame 16155
broccia 2429
brochantite 2436
broggerite 2437
bromargirite 2450
bromificazione v. bromurazione
bromirite 2450
bromite 2450
bromo 2452
bronzare 2454
bronzatrice 2463
bronzatura 2461
bronzina 1387
bronzite 2464
bronzo 2455

bronzo acciaio 17462
— al manganese 11268
— al nichelio 12271
— al piombo 10610, 12430
— al silicio 16326
— alfa 418
— bianco 12272
— coniabile S. 11543
— d'arte 17401
— da campane 1456
— da cannone 8673
— da monete 11543
— di stagno 18646
— fosforoso 13172
— manganesifero 11268
— per rubinetteria 9516
— per specchi 17043
— per statue S. 17401
— rosso 14531
— speciale 17006
brookite 2466
bruciare 2712, 7287
bruciatore a benzina 1531
— a gas 12492
— a scanalatura 3601
— a scanalatura circolare 3601
— ad aria 1887
— di cubilotto 4850
— per soffieria 1700
bruciatore v. becco
bruciatura 2603
— di trattamento termico 6602
brucite 2484
brumo rettangolare 18503
brunimetro 13626
brunire 1894, 2610
brunito 1914
brunitoio 1930a
brunitore 2460
brunitura 1915, 2461, 2478, 2610a, 13626
— a rullo 2462
— in palle 1152a
bruno 2470
— a macchie porporine 2478
bucare un forno 14312
bucklandite 2507

bullone 17897
— a cappello 2804
— a chiavetta 4522
— a nasello 16794
— a testa 2804
— a testa accecata 4539
— a testa bombata 4836
— a testa conica 4198
— a testa esagonale 9120
— a testa fresata 4539
— a testa lavorata 2013
— a testa quadrata 17236
— a testa tonda 15283
— con dado 2009
— con testa a T 9314
— con testa ad occhio 6729, 15700
— d'ancoraggio 558, 14350
— della stecca 7211
— di chiusura 3783
— di fondazione 9314
— di giunzione 4221
— filettato 15703
— senza testa 17904
— tirante 17404
bulloneria 2014
bunsenite 2583
buratto sterratore 19098
buretta 2587
— a gas 7984
burrone 8297
bussite 2631
bussola 3585
— combinata 4060
— da miniera 5313, 1727
— di chiusura o di serraggio 17128
— montata a caldo 16234
bustamite 2629
butano 2632
butlerite 2633
butteratura 13428
buttgenbachite 2646

C

cabestano 2814
— automatico 975

cabestano per avvitare 3094
— automatico per svitare 2314, 3093
cabina a maniche 15480
— di granigliatura 16197
— di sabbiatura S. 15481
cabrerite 2668
cacoxenite 2669
cadmia 2670
cadmiare 2672
cadmiato 2674
cadmiatur. 75, 2677
cadmifero 2671
cadmio 2673
caduta 6002, 6772
— di alimentazione 6878, 6880
— della gabbia 6773, 15351
— delle cariche 16656
— dello strato 5444
— di pressione 13900
— di roccie dalla parete 16967
— di temperatura 5991
— di terra 5973
— libera 7723
cahnite 2686
cainite 10266
cainolite 10267
cainosite 2687, 10268
calafatare 12826
calaite 10278
calamina 2699, 6026, 15583, 15917, 20337
calamita di pescaggio 7220
calandra a cilindri iscaldati 15111
calandratura 10507, 15112
calaverite 2700
calcantite 3252
calcare 2528, 3265, 10819
— a crinoidi 4638, 6444, 6446
— bituminoso 883
— carbonifero 2860
— decomposto 6791
— granulare 8434
— nummulitico 12426
— oolitico 6225

calcareo 14876
calcatoio 3-112, 11748
— pneumatico 316
calce 10810
— dolomitica 5615
— sodata 16809
— spenta 16571
— viva 14301, 19330 a
calcedonio 2709, 3253, 4477
calcestruzzo 1566
— asfaltico grosso 9181
— battuto 17315
— colato 8945
calcimetro 2711
calcinare 2712, 7774
calcinatura del filo 3266
calcinazione 2604, 15588
calcio 2721
— fluorato S. 7675
— larsenite 2726
— silicio S. 2727
calcite 2702, 2718, 2728
— e fluorina nella parete
  laterale 2765
calco 2983
calcocite 4366
calcodite 3255
calcofanite 3260
calcofillite 3257
calcografia 3256
calcolamprite 3258
calcolo del letto di fusione
  2736
— dell'analisi 2735.
— dell'aria e del vento
  2732
— della loppa o delle
  scorie 2734
— delle cariche 2733
calcomenite 3259
calcopirite 3261, 4363,
  20291, 20284
calcosina 3254, 3262, 19571
calcostibite 3263
calcotrichite 3264, 8707 a
calda 8972
— bianca 20031
— saldante 19945
caldaia 1955, 17417

caldaia a batterie 1347
— a bollitori sovrapposti
  12120
— a carbone polverizzato
  1966
— a cassa-focolare 7153
— a controcorrente S. 4528
— a cilindri 15086
— a circolazione 3603
— a circolazione forzata
  1987
— a circolazione rapida
  1996
— a cofano 19621
— a corrente diretta 4180
— a corrente invertita 4528
— a doppia camera di vapore 1984
— a doppia cassa-focolare
  5648
— a doppia fronte 5656
— a due corpi cilindrici
  19185
— a due corpi cilindrici
  sovrapposti 5653
— a due focolari ondulati
  10516
— a due tubi di fiamma
  10515
— a estremità ovali S. 6222
— a fiamma di ritorno S.
  14711
— a fiamma diretta 5458
— a focolare asportabile
  14714
— a focolare esterno 6698
— a focolare interno 7450
— a focolare interno con
  bollitori trasversali 7451
— a focolare interno liscio
  1990
— a focolare ondulato 1983
— a gas 8006
— a gran volume d'acqua
  1988
— a grande corpo 10551
— a legna 1963
— a media pressione 11431
— a medio corpo 11438

caldaia a mercurio 11504
— a nafta 12490.
— a piccoli tubi d'acqua
  19831
— a piccolo volume d'acqua
  1994
— a più corpi cilindrici
  12112
— a potenza elevata 9163
— a pressione 13895
— a recupero 19732
— a regolazione automatica
  993
— a ritorno di fiamma 14811
— a sezione elettrica
  S. 12722
— a sezione ovale 12722
— a sezioni 15781
— a sifone 18173
— a torba 1960
— a tubi d'acciaio omega
  ad alta pressione 9167
— a tubi d'acqua 19823
— a tubi d'acqua curvi
  19824
— a tubi d'acqua con ca-
  mera d'acqua 19825
— a tubi d'acqua con camera d'acqua non divisa
  19830
— a tubi d'acqua con due
  camere 19833
— a tubi d'acqua con una
  camera d'acqua 19829
— a tubi d'acqua in sezioni
  15787
— a tubi d'acqua lunghi
  19828
— a tubi d'acqua obliqui
  19827
— a tubi d'acqua orizzon-
  tali
— a tubi d'acqua rapidi
  19832
— a tubi di fiamma 7264
— a tubi di fiamma e d'acqua
  combinati 4066
— a tubi di fumo 1986,
  16766

caldaia a tubi focolari 1983
— a tubi incrociati 4714
— a tubi smontabili 1991
— a tubo di fiamma eccentrico 1985
— a tubo-focolare semiondulato 1989
— a vapore ad alta pressione 9170
— a vapore a bassa pressione 11058
— a vapore a media pressione 11432
— accoppiata 4054
— accumulatrice di calore 8995
— ad acqua calda 9450
— ad altissima pressione 9193
— ad un corpo cilindrico S. 16388
— ad unica camera di vapore 1993
— ausiliare 1001
— Belleville 1463
— cilindrica 4945, 16097
— cilindrica a focolare interno 4947
— cilindrica a focolare esterno 4946
— cilindrica a fondo ovale 5222
— combinata 4054
— con cassa-focolare rialzata 14377
— con camicia di vapore 17437
— con focolare a nervature 1992,
— con focolare interno a nervature S. 1993
— con focolare di rame 1982
— con focolari ad una estremità 16389
— con griglie meccaniche 17418
— con lama d'acqua sotto i cenerari 19985
— con riscaldatore 18009

caldaia con tubo di fiamma a gradini 1995
— Cornovaglia 4484
— d'acciaio 17459
— d'evaporazione 6615
— da vulcanizzare 19609
— della locomotiva a turbina 19119
— di alimentazione 6876
— di allenamento 18816
— di chiarificazione 3633
— di colata 7660
— di colata a tampone S. 2181
— di colata a tino 6014
caldaia di colata v. siviera di colata
— di essudazione 18102
— di evaporazione 6616
— di ferro stampato 17316
— di liquazione 10869
— di locomotiva 10948
— di ottone 2273
— di passaggio per la seconda stagnatura 15761
— di prova 6676
— di raffinazione 14608
— di rame 4354
— di riserva 16976
— di servizio 13466
— di stagno 18654
— divisa ad elementi smontabili 15786
— doppia 5645
— elettrica 6262
— elettrica a vapore 6303
— evaporatrice 6617
— fissa 17397
— francese 7754
— Galloway 7918
— in servizio 20201
— industriale 11308
— inesplodibile 9760
— inferiore 11066
— interiore asportabile 14708
— Lanchashire 5661, 10515
— lisciviatrice da polpa 14144

caldaia locomobile 13691
— marina 11324
— marina a tubi d'acqua 11325
— caldaia mista 4054
— mobile 12046
— nana 6144
— orizzontale 9352
— per bagnomaria 19747
— riscaldata a carbone 1959
— riscaldata a paglia 1961
— per bruciare torba S. 1960
— per catrame 18320
— per filtrare 7055
— per grasso 18225
— per latta stagnata 18666
— per lisciva 11109
— per pece 13416
— per pompa antincendio 7168
— per riscaldamento 9008
— per riscaldamento a termosifone S. 18173
— per riscaldamento centrale 1965
— per stagno 18665
— pluritubolare 12128
— rapida 7291
— registrata a 12 atmosfere 1964
— Root 15156
— rotonda 17060
— rovesciabile 18629
— semifissa 15847
— semi-tubolare 15850
— semplice 16385, 16388
— senza circolazione d'acqua 1997
— senza fondo bagnato 6025
— sotto pressione 1980
— stazionaria S. 17497
— superiore 19362
— supplementare 1001
— terrestre 10522
— Thornycroft 18547
— tubolare S. 16766, 19062
— verticale 19520, 19532
— verticale con bollitori trasversali 19522

caldaia Yarrow 20278
caldaio 1955
caldano 5282 a
caldera 2737
calderaio 1972, 4375
calderone 1955
calderotto S. 1955
calderaio 18657
caldo rosso 14540
caldo sudante 19945
caledonite 2739
calettamento 12416 a
calettare 16224
calettato 16235
calettatura a caldo 16234 a
calibro 6897, 8107, 8111,
    12973, 18400
— a corsoio 2747
— a forcella 16782
— a mascelle 2746
— a sonda 11996
— a vite 15707
— del cilindro di laminatoio
    15074
— del filo 8115
— del laminatoio 15084
— di cilindro 13411 a
— di lavoro 20209
— di profondità 5204
— di riferimento 14591
— di trafila 5373
— intermediario 11663
— micrometrico 19517
— passa 10107
— passa tubi 5851
— per diametri 15774
— per fili metallici 20128
— per lamiere 16055
— per fori 9250
— per fori o per diametri
    9251
— per lamiere 16070
— per manicotto 9843
— per ricalcare 19379
— per soffioni 18507 a
— per tubi 14310
— rotondo 15288
— sagomato 7896
californio 2745

Calloviano 2749
calma 10352
calo della solubilità 5080
— degli elettrodi 4242
calomelano 2751, 9361,
    11502
calore 8971
— bianco 20032
— critico 4644
— della ghisa e della lop-
    pa 8981
— calore dei gas alla boc-
    ca del forno 19731
— di combinazione 8985
— di dissociazione 8987
— d'incandescenza 18387
— d'ionizzazione 8988
— di reazione 8989
— di surriscaldamento 18011
— disperso 19687
— immagazzinato 533
— latente 10567
— rosso 14540
— rosso scuro (al-) 5003
— rovente 14540
— specifico 17026
caloria 2752
calorimetria 2758
calorimetro 2755
calorizzare 2760
calorizzato 2761
calorizzazione 2759
calotta 2793
camma 2764
cambiamento di marcia 14825
— del senso di laminazione
    14834
— improvviso di temperatu-
    ra 17963
cambio del profilo 15720
cambite 2776
cambriano 2771
camera 1919, 2063, 12897
— d'acqua 19810
— d'aria 250
— d'aria aspirante 17951
— d'aria premente 5151
— d'iniezione 9813
— dei forni 17633

camera del pozzo 19962
— del vento 20089
— della polvere 6128
— della tempera S. 615
— di cementazione 6488,
    19713
— di cokefazione 3952
— di combustione 4076
— di decantazione 17738
— di distribuzione 17420
— di essicamento 6055
— di granigliatura 16197
— di lavaggio 19709
— di mina 4576
— di raffreddamento 7559
— di recupero 3367
— di ricombustione
— di ricottura 611
— di rigenerazione 3372,
    3405
— di riscaldamento 9009
— di sabbiatura 15481
— di separazione 10404
— di vaporizzazione 7293
— laterale 16257
— magazzino 16223, 16232
— parascintille 16981
— per l'idrogeno solforato
    17986
— per sabbiatura 15523
— refrigerante 4333
camicia 10100, 10843,
    16129 a, 16139
— d'altoforno 16106
— d'un pezzo 7804
— del tino 15961, 15965
— della soffiante 1856
— del cilindro 4941
— di riscaldo 9015
— esterna in muratura 15251
— refrattaria 10855
camino 3453
— a rulli mobili 18862 a
— del cubilotto 4847
— indipendente 10063
— medio libero 11387 a
camma 18295
camolatura 13316
— da scoria 13318

camolatura eterogenea
   azzurrognola 10940
— eterogenea lucida 10941
— eterogenea ossidata
   10939
— lucida omogenea 19305
— mista 13317
— omogenea azzurrognola
   14469
— ossidata omogenea 19304
— superficiale 13073a,
   18061
campagna del frantoio 11698
— di altoforno 7858
— di un forno 10734
campana 1447, 12752
— a vite 5379
— di altoforno 1708
— di guida per fresa 11709
— di pompa pneumatica 310
— di vetro 8271
— filettante di pescaggio
— Ilutter 9489
campanella 1449
camplite 2773
campionamento 4023
campionatura 10984, 15460,
   15461, 18522
— longitudinale 10983
campione 15453
— d'assaggio 2108
— di carota 4439
— di fondo 2166
— di forno 1338a, 17152a
— di giacimento 14751
— di trapano 1629
— di trivellazione 2089
— essicato 5848
— medio 366, 1011
— ottenuto con attacco
   acido 4490
— per prelevamento continuo
   4273
— prelevato col gancio da
   presa 8382
— scelto 13209
campo 11378
— di colata 3054, 13757
— di coltivazione 20207

campo visivo 6999, 19569,
camptonite 2772
camsellite 2774
canale 3284, 3454, 8586,
   10586, 11226, 19440
— anulare 622
— aperto 12587
— chiuso 3774, 2224
— circolare 14926, 3589
— collettore 4024
— d'alimentazione S. 15363
— d'aria 12474
— d'arrivo del gas 8009
— d'aspirazione 17958
— canale dei fanghi 12076
— del camino 11221
— del fondo 2158
— del vento 251a
— dell'acqua 19822, 19809
— dell'aria 331
— della suola o del fondo
   2158
— delle scorie 3576a, 16533,
   16552a, 16554
— di alimentazione a cascata
   17561a
— di chiusa 16709
— di cilindro 12956
— di circolazione o di
   ritorno 3604
— di colata S. 8087, 8140,
   8684, 9776, 10006, 10153,
   10587, 11222, 13753,
   13758, 15372, 15374,
   16687, 17171, 18313
— di colata a becco 10861
— di colata a caduta di-
   retta 5992
— di colata circolare 3591
— di colata delle scorie
   13038
— di colata diretta 5985
— di colata per lingotti
   13269, 16948, 16950
— di compressione 13916
— di decantazione 15924
— di derivazione 10570
— di fusione 621
— di pompa 19511

canale di riscaldamento
   9012
— di scarico 7433, 7472
— di scolo 7428, 16930
   18934
— di scolo acque 8686
— di sfioro 12742
— di sfogo bavatura 7294
— di trasporto 4316
— distributore 15365, 15366
— fermascorie 16561
— filoniano 3290
— finitore 7128, 10559
— interrotto 18291
— ogivale 17115
— ovale 12725
— per calce 10811
— per ferro piatto 2224
— per le scorie 16539
— profilato 16000
— sbozzatore 15999
— scaricatore 8621
— secondario 16948
— trasportatore a spinta
   14202
— trasportatore oscillante
   15043
— trasversale 4687
— verticale del gas caldo
   19383
— verticale di colata 5706
canaletti 9928
canali per raccogliere il
   piombo 3293
canalino 19245a
canalizzazione 3294, 10283a,
   14319
— parallela 10999
canalizzazione v. conduttura
canalone 4316
cancrinite 2779
candela dei modelli 10772
candelabro tubolare 19064
canfildite 2785
canna di mantice 12414
— di pistola di altoforno
   13388
— fumaria 1962, 2357, 7449
cannello 1863

cannello ad alta pressione
9165
— ad ossigeno 4139
— da taglio 4915, 7892
— della spruzzetta 19026
— elettrico 6261
— ferruminatorio 1861, 2601
12043
— per saldare 19956
cannizzarite 2788
cannone carotiere 15458
cannula di spurgo 5949
cantiere 5147
— petrolifero 12518
— a galleria cieca 5043
— a giorno 12594
— a gradini 17666
— a gradini rovesci 12746
— a gradino rovescio a tagli orizzontali 7321
— a gradino rovescio in
rimonta 7319
— a livello di fondo 16340
— ad avanzamento frontale
2349
— con armatura a
parallelepipedo 17245
— con fronte normale al
piano di stratificazione
6742
— d'abbattimento
17666
— d'avanzamento 8937
— d'estrazione 20216
— in direzione 5865
— in rimonta 2065
— in rimonta a gradino
rovescio con armatura a
parallelepipido 7320
— petrolifero 12489
— riempito 7020
— sbarrato 15788
— secondo il piano di
sfaldatura 16724
cantieri di scavo del fondo
2190
cantina 3133
cantonale 572
— a bordino 2542

cantonale a lati uguali 6523
— ad angolo tondo 584
— ad angolo vivo 585
— d'angolo 6199
— sghembo 12440
cantonali gemelli 19168
caolinite 10283
caolino puro 10283
capacità 2800, 4822,
— del forno 2801
— della centrale 2802
— di carico 3336, 10910
— di giunto 10209
— di polarizzazione 13616
— di portanza 1390
— di resistenza del reci-
piente 14766
— di smorzamento 4982
— di solvente 16908
— non utilizzata di
serbatoio 19213
— produttiva giornaliera
16444
— smorzante 8711
capelli di Venere 8711
capillarità 2805
capo 1374, 2126, 4889
— di estrazione 10773
— di servizio del cabestano 16642
— forgia 10034
— forno 8915, 10357
— frantumatore 2815
— servizio 2126
— servizio della ventila-
zione 7151
— sonda 18729
— squadra 8910, 11731,
12770
— trivellatore 5915, 11361
— turno 16123
capocorda 15169
caporcianite 2811
capovolgere la staffa 19133
cappa 9309
— d'aspirazione 7817
— del camino 3461
— di gas 7986
— di riscaldamento 12697 a

cappelenite 2812
cappelletto di bottiglia 2136
cappello 2031, 2034, 2795,
2799, 4692, 4727, 4733,
4735, 5856, 8918; 10458,
10727, 12694, 14707,
14709
— avvitato 15716
— d'armatura 17838
— d'armatura in legno 2795
— del cubilotto 9308
— di ferro 4033, 8370, 14309
— di guardia 10199
— ossidato 12807
— paraolio S. 4607
— provvisorio 6781
— sul muro della ripiena
19646
cappellotto 1449
— di gorgogliamento 2488
cappuccio di gomma 15307
capra 8231, 9376
capriata ad anima piena
16887
capriatelle a traliccio forma-
te con angolari leggeri
16397
capsula 1738, 2792
— di combustione 4075
— di piombo 10607
— di platino 13515
— di platino per incenera-
zione 13520
— fulminante 1745
captare 2791
caracolite 2819
caradociano 2820
carattere agglutinante 2695
caratteristica del minerale
caratteristiche di produttività 9767
— fisiche 13193
— meccaniche 11409
carbocementazione 2867,
2885
— a gas 7988
carbonado 2847
carbonaia 3304
carbonato ammonico 2848

carbonato basico di rame 1036
— di bario 2849
— di calcio 2851
— di ferro 2850, 10035 a
— di magnesio 2852
— potassico 2853
— sodico 2854
carbone (a-) 3806
— a cubetti 1798
— a corta fiamma 3757, 17421
— a cubi 3895
— a dadi 3884
— a fiamma 11760
— a fiamma corta 1768
— a fiamma lunga 12564, 16435
— a lunga fiamma 2781, 2782, 2786, 7265, 14445
— a miccia 4456
— ad anima S. 4456
— accagliante 2696
— agglomerato 224
— agglutinante 1119, 2696
— agglutinante a fiamma lunga 1118
— amorfo 6086
— antracitico 15886
— artificiale 832
— attivato 115
— bituminoso 1634, 16831,
— bituminoso duro 17118
— boghead 1952
— brillante 8268
— classificato 15690, 16445
— candela S. 1634
— Cardiff 2888
— collante 2696
— compresso 13876
— con alto tenore in cenere 862
— con ceneri leggere 3843
— con molte scorie 3728
— cotto 1114
— crivellato 15690
— d'ardesia 7530
— d'importazione 9660
— da fucina 16657 a

carbone da gassogeno 3824
— da strati di formazione recente 3848
— da vapore S. 1956
— del fondo di miniera 8612
— di betulla 1611
— di betulla in polvere 13769
— di cementazione 2821, 3159
— di coke 3953
— di coke ricco di gas 3796
— di corno 9359
— di cuoio 10649
— di faggio 1437
— di forgia 16754
— di fucina 7576
— di grossa pezzatura 4997
— di legna 3298, 8520, 13314
— di legna in pezzi 3309
— carbone di legna in polvere 3303
— di legna nero o comune 4092
— di ossa 2027
— di pece 13418
— di pezzatura 3414
— di prima estrazione 18584, 19333
— di prima estrazione migliorato 18583
— di prima qualità 7196
— di salice per levigare 8551
— di storta 14796, 14799
— di torba 13026
— dolce S. 3298
— domestico 9456
— duro 1322
— elettrico 6265
— essicato all'aria 267
— estratto 11752
— ferroso 2284
— fibroso 1922
— fino 2214, 2590
— fondente S. 2696
— fossile 2858, 7630, 13403

carbone fresco 8509
— fuligginoso 16919
— grasso 1634
— grasso a fiamma lunga **3406**
— grezzo 4754, 14452
— grezzo di fonderia 15248
— grezzo di miniera 437
— grigliato S. 15690
— in grossi pezzi 10546
— in mattonelle 13876
— in pezzatura media 3884, 3895
— in pezzatura noce 12428
— in pezzetti 16507
— in pezzi 3747, 15276
— in pezzi grossi 1563
— in pilastri 13291
— in polvere 6129, 14147
— lavato 19695
— lucido 2392
— magro 6028, 8818, 12341 12342
— magro a fiamma lunga 16437
— magro secco 10640
— minerale 7630
— mineralizzato 11760
— minuto 3470, 12288, 16727
— minuto a granelli 2835
— minuto di scarto 6006
— negativo 12213
— non assortito 19330
— non crivellato S. 19330
— non collante a lunga fiamma 7721
— non fondente 12344
— non lavato 8526 a, 19343
— normale 17344
— nuovo S. 8509
— omogeneo 16877
— per arco 749
— per arco a fiamma 7254
— per caldaie 1956
— per elettrodi 6326
— per filtri 7056
— per forni metallurgici 7831

carbone per lampade 10794
— per motori a gas 8026
— per proiettori 15754
— per saldare 16861
— piritoso 2281, 2282, 3078, 6010, 8578
— polveroso 4827
— polvcrizzato 14147
— positivo 13704
— povero 6847, 13653
— povero di gas 12350
— preparato 5838
— puro 3675
— scistoso 1183, 1318, 2025, 2040, 7530, 15978
— scolorante 5079
— scoppiettante 2577
— scozzese 15619
— secco 6029, S. 10640
— semigrasso 15837
— semigrasso semilavorato 8718
— senza fumo 16768
— senza scorie 12345
— subbituminoso 1655
— tagliato dal basso e dal lato 10238
— tenero di qualità inferiore 4996
— terroso 2028, 6173, 14430, 16777
— trasportato per mare 19811
— triturato 16115
— uniforme 3841
— vagliato 16445
— vergine 3837, 20050
carbonella 2835
carboni 10510
— imbevuti 9661
— metallizzati 11576
— per lampade ad arco 2871
carboniero 17422
carbonile 2580, 2579, 2876a, 3801, 3835
carbonio 2824
— amorfo 531
— combinato 4064, 7230
— di rinvenimento 18373/1
— equivalente 2834

carbonio grafico 8453
— totale 18787
carbonite 2865
carbonitrurazione 2866
carbonizzare 1869
carbonizzazione 2604, 3353, 4071
carborundum 2872, 16328
carburante 2881
— ad alto numero di otta 9160
— Diesel 5388
— sintetico 18169
carburare 2884
carburazione 2867, 2879, 2883, 2885
— a pacchetto 12830
— col carbonio solido 2880
carburo al silicio 2872
— di ferro 9961
— di silicio 16328
carcassa 2930, 7710
carica 3315, 6883, 11478, 13706, 13981, 17615
— bianca 3323
— calda o liquida per il forno 9406
— cava 10156, 15991
— cava accoppiata 19172
— da minare S. 1747
— dei minerali 3351
— del crogiuolo 4739
— del minerale e del fondente 3325
— della forma 19914
— di coke 428, 3319, 3929, S. 3946
— di combustibile 3324
— di ghisa 3326, 13263
— di lancio 14018
— di minerale 12637
— di prova 18447
— di un cubilotto 4843
— di un forno 7862
— fredda per il forno 3969
— esplosiva 1747

carica metallica 2586
— non calmata 20070
— raffreddata 14291a
— solida 3969
— speciale 17009
caricamento 3331, 10916, 12843
— automatico 976
— compatto 5171
— compresso 5171
— dall'alto 18739
— dei vagoncini nella gabbia 5064
— laterale 5628
— per cavo aereo 193
caricamento v. alimentazione
caricare 3313, 10465, 10906
— a mano 17631
— i fanghi 5764
— il focolare meccanicamente 17632
— le casse 3314
— un vagonetto 12057
— una forma 19909
caricatore 3330, 12841, 14206
— di carbone 3798, 3822
— di vagoncini 19623
— meccanico 13787
— meccanico cingolato 13786
— per minerali 12646
caricatrice 3340
— a cokificazione 3955
— a gru 3338
— a tazze 2503
— a vagone 3328
— ad alimentazione superiore 12741
— ad avanzamento continuo 16216
— meccanica 12066, 15035
— trasportatrice 10911
carico 1395, 2904
— al limite convenzionale di elettricità al 2% 10907

carico al limite di proporzionalità 10908
— alternato 433
— ammissibile 6830/a
— applicato 720
— completo 7795
— d'altoforno 2586
— di flessione 1520
— di rottura 120
— di schiacciamento 2510a
— idrostatico 9574
— limite 19216a
— massimo 11386, 14474a
— sull'asse 1028
— supplementare 18025
— unitario 19309
cariola a due ruote 4991
carminite 2892
carnallite 2893
carnegieite 2894
carnotite 2896
carosello S. 4264
carota 4438, 4386, 8832a, 13555, 13559
— di parete 16281
— di sondaggio 5890
— orientata 12672
— trasudante 1759, 19891
carotaggio 4395, 4464
— a piccoli intervalli 17156
— con corona a diamanti 5321
— con corona a graniglia 16201
— di parete 15462
— di parete laterale 16282
— elettrico 6267, 6319, 9753
carotare 4382
carotiere 4389
— con involucro di gomma 15313
— di parete «rotary» 15225
— retrattile 20131
— doppio 5650
— laterale 16277
carpenteria metallica del tetto 17504
— tubolare 19089

carpino 9367
carreggio 7955, 18819
carrello 2526, 16611, 18945
— a piattaforma solleva-
bile 17279
— argano 4578
— caldaia 10473
— contrappeso 1126
— contrappeso di un piano inclinato 1236
— del forno a suola mobile 1949
— di gru S. 4578
— di gru a ponte 4596
— di perforazione 10242
— di piazzale 5606
— elevatore 10751
— per minerale 12658
— portalingotti 9784
— porta siviera 10473
— portastaffa 11987
carretta a due ruote a scarico posteriore 2906
carro S. 18945
— aperto 12603
— chiuso 3778
— cisterna 18256
— di colata 7651
— da fonderia 7651
— di colata 3045, 10473, 13765
— mescolatore 9422a
— per essiccatoio 6056
— per il caricamento dei lingotti 9785
— per lingotti 1585
— per rimozione scorie 16563
— per sondaggio 5884
carrollite 2901
carroponte 7965
carrucola ad uncino 16786
carta al carminio 2891
— alla curcuma 4862
— alla fenolftaleina 13152
— all'albumina 350
— all'amido 17379
— all'amido e allo ioduro di potassio 13727

carta Congo 4207
— da filtro 7049
— d'amianto 846
— delle isobàte 4543
— del processo di raffineria 10600
— di guttaperca 8682
— di tornasole 10892
— ozonoscopica 12822
— reagente 18448
— smerigliata 6415
— smeriglio 15509
— vetrata 8280
carte isopache 10072
cartella 1598, 19616
carter 8641
cartuccia di costipamento 17539
carynite 10286
cascame di ferro S. 15660
casco per sabbiatore 9069
cassa 1936, 2208, 2910
— a fuoco 7152
— a prova d'acido 87
— a vento alta 20091
— a vento bassa 20090
— a vento inferiore 20090
— a vento superiore 20091
— ad anime multiple 12109
— appuntita 17107
— d'aereazione 246
— d'anima S. 4396
— d'anima a cerniera 9205
— d'anima a contenitore S. 7712
— d'anima a doghe 16576
— d'anima a libro 2041
— d'anima a paniere 7712
— d'anima a paniere conico 18943
— d'anima a telaio 17130
— d'anima multipla 12109
— d'anima per anime soffia-
te 4397
— d'anima tronconica 9022
— d'aria tubolare 19058
— del crivello 10174
— contrappeso 19904
— del motore generatore 11952

cassa del mulino a pestelli 13736
— del vento 1699, 20092
— dell'anima 4412
— della valvola 19448, 19449
— di cementazione 610, 2919, 3171
— di colata 8784
— di distribuzione 14658
— di fondo con manicotto 1277
— di frantoio 17310
— di lavaggio S. 253
— di raccolta della polvere 6127
— di raffreddamento 4332
— in terra 7159
— per anima 4396
— per anima in due parti 17127 a
— per fanghi 16635, 17234
— per la cenere 867
cassa v. staffa o telaio
casserature metalliche per getti in cemento 11552
casseruola 1312
cassetta 16618
— d'acqua 19819
— d'acqua per raffreddamento 4345
— della bilancia 1125
— di ricottura 617
— in materiale refrattario 7159
— per carote 15455
— per la forma 11980
— per pesi 19916
— per rottami piccoli 15661
— refrattaria 15427 a
cassetto di distribuzione 12615
cassina S. 8784
cassiterite 18649, 18653, 18669
cassone per fanghi 16632
castanite 3031
castelletto 8921, 8924, 11733, 15960

castelletto d'estrazione 8911, 8913, 8930, 7921 13405, 13659, 13995, 14186, 19968
— del laminatoio S. 9465
castina 10814, 10819
castorite 3077
cataclastico 3081
cataforesi 3084 a
catagenesi 10288
catalizzatore negativo 9807
catamorfico 10289
catapleite 3085
catasta 3513, 13273
— di legno 3750
catena 3238
— a chiavetta 4523
— a rastrelli 15668
— a tazze 2498, 4319
— d'attacco delle tazze 15640
— d'avvolgimento 17095
— di misurazione 11396
— di produzione 13996
— di trasmissione 17210
— senza fine 4621, 6457
catenaccio S. 2008
— transversale 4715
catetometro 3096
cathkinite 3097
catoptrico 10292
catoptrite 3104, 10293
catrame 18314
— di carbone 3849
— vegetale 20178
cattivo combustibile 11051
caustobiolite 3118, 10294
cava 13397, 14258, 17852
— a cielo aperto 12589, 18062
cavalletto 7964, 9376, 15407 17341, 18878
— di supporto del convertitore 4307
— di sostegno del bilanciere 15464
— per la trave elastica 14311
— posteriore 14481

cavalcavia 2383
cavallino 5626
cavasabbia 3684
cavata 18298
cavedio di luce 10786
caverna carsica 17175
cavernoso 9303
cavi e conduttori isolati 9849
caviglia 13307, 16588
cavità 3124, 9261, 13350, 13605, 16952, 19587 a
— a V 7213
— contenenti materie carboniose 1673
— con terra 15499
— di dissoluzione 16901
— di drusa 2525
— di ritiro 13329, 13381, 16227
— di sfogo bavatura 7294
— marolitica 11618
— punzonata 14178 a
cavo a conduttore unico 16386
— a sezione decrescente 18283
— a strappo 10149, 20280
— aereo senza fine 12755
— armato 804
— a trefoli rotondi 15293
— ausiliario 10149
— d'avvolgimento 6823
— del cabestano 3079, 3098
— del tornello veloce 15501
— d'estrazione 9231
— di alimentazione ad alta tensione 9189
— di ghiaia 8479
cavo di manovra 5922, 9231
— di manovra al parco tubi 9157
— di pistone 18092
— di segnalazione 1453
— di testa 11225
— di tubaggio 2950
— di trivellazione 2558
— metallico 20144
— morto 5032
— per carotaggio elettrico 10965

cavo per le aste di pompag-
    gio 17939
— per miniere 11771
— portante 18813
— preformato 13835
— principale 11225
— protetto 804
catazona 10291
cazzuola a cuore 10549
— a punta arrotondata 15287
— per fonderia 15653
— rettangolare 17239
cebollite 3129
cedimento 4762, 5708, 16414,
    16417
cedimento v. sfondamento
— circolare 3107
— dei pilastri 16440
— del suolo sopra i lavori
    di scavo 5017
— del tetto 1528, 4760,
    8248, 15146, 16440,
    17255, 18096
— della forma 14203
— di roccia 15011
— isostatico 10078
— magmatico del tetto 11170
cefalopodi 3223
ceilanite 3234
celestina 3131
cella 3132
— di flottazione 7416
— di strappamento 17858 b
— elementare 19308 a
cellulare 3135
celsiano 3136
cementante 3180
cementare 2884, 2909, 3138,
    6737, 9832
— ad alto livello 3139
— col gas 7989
— in polvere 13766
— un pozzo 13557
cementato 3164, 6744
cementato in superficie
    2915
cementato per pressione
    17259
cementato superficialmente
    2915

cementazione 3158,
    3168, 3169, 12831

cementazione a gas
    7988
cementazione a stadi
    12121
— al cianuro 13722

— carburante 2883
— carburante a gas 7988
— dell'acciaio 17479
— delle fessure 8630
— delle fessure acquifere
    8628
— gassosa 7990
— in cassetta 2220, 12830
— metallica 2759
— per pressione 17259
— per solidi 16877 a
— primaria 13937
— totale 18787 a
cementite 3179
— sferoidale 17071
cemento 3140
— alluminoso 468
— armato 6943, 14673
— calcare 2704
— d'altoforno 1718
— di guarnizione 8078 a
— di loppa 9995
— di rame S. 15990
— di scorie 1718, 16530
— metallurgico sursolfatato
    18023
— mescolato nella betoniera
    18948
— refrattario 14628
cenerario 868
cenere impalpabile 7505
— umida 11861
— volatile 7453 a, 7505
ceneri di carbone di legna
    3299
— di pirite 2715
cenerino di carbone 3932
cenogenesi 3181
cenosite 3182
cenozoico 2688

centina 15801
centinato 4656
centinatura d'acciaio 17456
centrale di pompaggio 14168
centrale di preparazione dei
    fanghi 12084
— di spinta 2053
— elettrica 13795
— per luce 10798
— per forza motrice 13795
centralizzatore a cerniera
    10564
— a elementi longitudinali
    17706
centrallasite 3194
centrato 11370
centratore 3193
centratore per tubi 2934
centratura 3188, 11371
— stampi 5370
centrifuga 3200
centrifugare 2966, 3212
centrifugazione 3211
— pura 18951
centroclinale 3221
centro di ruota in acciaio
    fuso 3023
— posticcio per tornitura
    3215
ceppo 17911
cera 19841 a
— di distillazione 17596
— di paraffina 12911
— per fusioni 3074
cerargirite 3227, 9363
cercatore d'oro 8889
cerchi di ferro 9324
cerchio 9321, 9323
— di ferro battuto 20244
cerchione 14919
ceresina 3228
cerino 19845, 19846
cerio 3229
cernere 4825, 13200, 14884,
    15860, 16923
cerniera 9198, 9199
— della piega anticlinale
    4625
— della piega sinclinale
    18942

cerniera inferiore 11064

cernita 5842, 16305

cernita a mano 8773, 13213, 16966, 19627

— a mano del minerale 2505

— dell'acqua 19813a

— del minerale 12653

cernitore 19626

certificato d'analisi 549, 14788

— di prova 18444

cerussite 3231, 20037

cervantite 3232

cesarolite 3233

cesellatura 14738a

cesio 2678

cesoia 3594, 16022, 16030

— a ghiliottina 8659

— a rulli per tagli circolari di lamiere 16052

— da banco elettrico 6258

— di lamiere 16080

— da squadrare 16254a

— idraulica per blumi 9537

— per bande 16673a

— per billette 1584

— per rifiuti 15658

cesoie 16038

— ad allegatore 375

— circolari multiple 16674

— per blumi 1824

— per slebi 16502

— trasversali 6455a

— volanti 7507

cessare le cariche 3128

chiave di ritenuta 12304

— di serraggio 15223

— di serraggio elettrica 6284

— per dadi 16974

— per morsetti 18714

— per tubi 13335

— per tubing manovrabile con una sola mano 16784

— chiave per viti 20233

— sospesa azionata meccanicamente 13797

— stringitubi 2964

— universale 11904

chiavetta 4521, 6873, 8212, 19878

— di sicurezza S. 15425

chiavi 18732

— sospese 18718

chiavistello 2008, 10561, 15005

childrenite 3418

chillagite 3441

chimica dell' altoforno 3401

chimico arbitro 735

— giurato 18143

china 45

chinetogenesi 10364

chiodo 4438, 8832a, S. 13555

— a gambo 17536

— a testa cieca 8938

— a testa conica troncata con colletto 12888

— a testa fresata 4541

— a testa semitonda 15290

— a testa semitonda larga 12142

— a testa svasata con calotta 15281

— a testa svasata piana 7337

— a testa tronco conica 4199

— di rinforzo 17191

— di ferro 10003

— raffreddatore 3435

chiolite 3471

chiudere 3753, 16241

— il vento 19135

— la staffa con bulloni 15699

— o tappare le soffiature 7014

chiusa 16708

chiusura 1247

— a tenuta 15722

— a ginocchiera 10415

— a pressione diretta 5460

— a tenuta d'aria 335

— a valvola 7282

— americana 512

— del forno 17683

— dell'organo in prova 18415

chiusura di prova 18881

— di ugello 20056

— doppia 5679

— ermetica 335

— idraulica 19812

chilomole 10361

chubutite 3554

churechite 3558

cianfrinato 1572

cianfrinatura 3110a

cianite 10444

cianocroite 4933

cianosio 4367

cianurazione 4930

cianuro di potassio 4931, 13724

— di potassio e di titanio 18691

cicchetto 13951

ciclo chiuso 3766

— di lavorazione 1261

ciclone 4934

ciclopite 4935

cieco 1766

cielo 8813, 15137

— aperto 18041

— aperto (a-) 5, 12605

— del focolare 7833

— della cassa focolare 4730

— di tunnel 8800, 8806

cileite 3419

cilenite 3420

cilindraia 4777

cilindratore 15105

cilindratura 15069

cilindri fucinatori 16135

— sbozzatori 12062

— sgrossatori 12062

cilindrite 4951

cilindro 15073, 15104

— a canali 8594

— a compressione 4154

— a dischi 5484a

— a gola 8593

— a gradini 17561

— a gran velocità 9176

— a mandrino per tubi saldati 11265

— a matrice 5377

— a passo di pellegrino 13282

cilindro a semplice effetto 16380
— a vapore 17425
— blooming 3914
— bordatore 6203 a
— con scala 4943
— conico 4210
— curvato 4210
— d'acciaio 17501
— della mazza battente 8730
— della pompa d'aria 311
— del freno 2253
— di estrazione a scatto 10345
— di flessione 1517
— di ghisa 2999
— di guarnizione 12847
— di presa 13313
— diagonale 5309 a
— di lamiera per fili 15058
— di lavoro 20191
— di mezzo 11665
— di pompa 20200
— di rinforzo 1082
— di zinco 20326
— direttamente accoppiato 5457
— eccentrico 6187
— essicatore 6057
— finitore 7068., 7133, 7136
— fisso di pompa 17396
— frantumatore 4774
— idraulico ruotante 15229
— inferiore 2183
— inferiore fisso 7229
— lavatore 6016
— libero 7770
— mobile della pompa 18859
— per cloruro di calcio 2723
— per lamiere 13482, 13494, 16076
— per la lavorazione a freddo 3989
— sagomato 15988
— sbozzatore 1823, 1833, 14099
— scanalato 4497
— sgrossatore 2326, 3941, 14099

cilindro sullo scalpello per detriti 10255
— superiore 18750
— superiore sospeso 1138
— trafilatore
cima 681, 4724
cimatura 16464
ciminite 3568
cimolite 3569
cinabro 3578, 11501
cinerite 19575
cinghia 7280, 17743
— di cernita 13214
cinghia di trasporto v. trasportatore a cinghia
— trapezoidale 19420
— trapezoidale con due «grommets» 8584
cingolato 4212
cintura 9323, 17781
— d'aria 242
— di sicurezza 15413
— morenica 11929
ciottoli 5267
ciottolo 2192, 7377, 8395, 13034, 15324, 16131
— scistoso 14351
ciprusite 4954
cipryna 4953
circo 3586, 3607
— glaciale 10284, 10322
circonferenza 4872
circuito chiuso 3767
— d'acqua di raffreddamento 19762
circuiti in tubo di lamiera nera 9451
cisterna 18245
citrina 6788
clampa 3619, 4591
— della tavola 18188
— per tubazioni 19056
— per tubi 2935, 19056
clarite 3635
clarkeite 3636
classificare 3641, 13200, 16923
classificato a mano 8772
classificatore 3640, 16924, 16925

classificatore a coppa 2203
— a raschietti 5732
— idraulico 9518
— slimatore
classificazione 8384, 16926
— dei minerali 3639, 12652 a
— granulometrica 16446
clastico 3646, 5269
clasto-cristallino 3647
clastogeno 3648
clastomorfico 3650
claudetite 3651
claustalite 3652
cliftonite 3726
clinker di cemento 3144
clinoclasi 10388
clinoclasite 683, 3732
clinoenstatite 3733
clinografo 3734
clinohumite 3735
clinometro 3736, 9709
clinopinacoide 3737
clinoprisma 3738
clinozoisite 3739
clintonite 3740
clivaggio 3716
— distinto 5564, 6182
— imperfetto 9742
cloantite 3490
cloraluminite 3491
clorargirite 3493
clorato di potassa 13723
clorite 3503, 3731, 13005
cloritico 3504
cloritizzazione 3506
cloritoide 3507
cloritoscisto 3505, 13007
cloro 3500
clorocalcite 3500°
clorofano 3512
cloromanganocalite 3508
cloromelanite 3510
cloropale 3511
cloropatite 3492
cloruro ammoniaco 15433
— d'antimonio 670
— di bario 3494
— di calcio 3497
— di calcio secco od anidro 3495

cloruro di ferro 3496
— di magnesio 3498
— di mercurio 11499
— di platino 13513
— di rame 4853
— di sodio 4097
— mercuroso 11502
— potassico 3499
— ramoso 4858
— stannico 17367
— stannoso 17370
Cluniano 3791
coadiuvante per filtro 13826
coagulare 3609
coal-ball 3799
coalescenza 3862
cobaltifero 3891 a
cobaltina 3 892
cobaltite 3887
cobalto 3885
cobalto terroso S. 850
cobaltomenite 3893
coccolite 3896
coclea 14498
coda 18203
— di canapa 9090
— di topo 14434, 14443
codolo 1214
— conico 1568
coefficiente d'equivalenza
    3900
— di curvatura 1508
— di mobilità 11848
— di riduzione 3901, 14573
— strizione 14573
— di trasformazione 4583
— di trazione 9861
— differito 5112
coesimetro 3919
coesione a secco 6048
— a verde 8519
— della sabbia 3920, 15484
— della terra 3920
cogliere 4825
cohenite 3918
coke 3927, 3953
— a cubetti 6221
— a pezzi 2441
— come viene 11821

coke compatto 4099
— d'accensione 1416
— d'altoforno 1709, 3940
— d'esercizio 428
— di carbone da fucina 7577
— di fonderia 7653, 16746
— di fusione 3946
— di gas 8067
— di gas illuminante 7991
— di petrolio 13130
— di pezzatura uovo 6221
— di riscaldo 1416, 3929
— di storta 7992, 17593
— frantumato 4768
— grosso 10547
— magro 10641
— metallurgico 3940, 11585
— minuto 3935, 13006,
    16728
— naturale 3949
— non cernito 11821
— per l'accensione 9011
— per uso domestico
— spezzato 4768
— vagliato 16304
cokefazione 3954
cokeite 3949
cokificare 3926
cokizzazione 3950
colabile 3032
colabilità 3033, 7439 a
colame 8103, 8090, 10155
colare 2965, 13737, 15348
— a freddo 2967
— a getto pieno 3514
— allo scoperto 2973
— da due lati 2968
— dal tappo 2981
— il ferro nelle forme 2980
— in forme 2972
— in getti cavi
— in piano 2971
— in piedi 13740, 18738
— in pressa 2974
— in sorgente 2150, 2977,
    13739
— in strettoio 2974
— in torchio S. 2974
— in verde 2969

colare la ghisa in pani 13246
— metallo bianco nei cusci-
    netti 13741
— un metallo 15341
colata 2984, 3037, 7643,
    7652, 8972, 11458, 17769,
    18264, 18307, 18356
— a caduta 5979
— a corno 9358
— a forcella 5647
— a forza centrifuga 3203
— a gradini 17563
— a grappolo 3038, 17276
— allo scoperto 12564 a,
    12592
— anulare 3592
— a pettine 4050
— a piani 16272
— a pioggia 17183
— a sifone 18176
— a sorgente 19357
— centrifugata 3207, 15830
— compressibile 4152
— conica 19881
— continua 4262, 4276
— dall'alto 18748
— della ghisa 3062
— della scoria 18308
— delle scorie e della
    ghisa 18761
— di fianco 9779
— di fonderia 7670
— di metallo in fusione
    18297
— diretta 18748, 5456 a
— diretta a tallone S. 16271
— diretta o a caduta 5979
— di scorie 16558, 16566
— in conchiglia 5360
— a rigetto 16717
— in conghiglia per forza di
    gravità 8486
— in depressione 3518
— in fossa 13396
— in gesso 13467
— in pendenza S. 3063
— in piano 3064
— in sabbia 15489
— in sorgente 2151, 14962,
    19431

colata in sorgente a tallone 16271
— inclinata 3063
— interrotta 9913
— in verde 8507
— orizzontale 3064, 9334
— per gravità 8484
— rotonda 16369
— sotto pressione 13898
— sotto vuoto 17953 a, 19425 a
— tangenziale 18241
— tranquilla 14306
— verticale 19521
colata v. fusione o spillata
colate S. 15377
colato 13746
— alla macchina 11119
— in acciaio 17461
— in conchiglia 2912
— in fossa 13401
— in guscio 16098
— in un sol pezzo 2990
— orizzontalmente 2981
colatoio 7675 a, 15376 a, S. 17171, 17211
colatore 3035
colemanite 4011
colla 8316
collanite 10422
collare 4016
— a cuneo 19884
collarino 6894
collaudatore 9848
collaudo S. 9846
collaudo delle sfere 1167
collaudo finale 7071
collegamento a incastro 8598
collegamento a stella 20258
— di colata 15366
collegare 12204
collettore 8925, 8928, 11293
— del fango 12077
— del surriscaldatore 18008
— del vento 242
— delle polveri 6125
— di alimentazione 6881
— di amalgama 479
— di caldaia 1968

collezione 4023
collegamento dei massetti 9837
collina arrotondata di morena 6017
collo 1468, 12204
— d'oca 8362
— d'un cilindro 15093
— del trapano 1627
— di raccordo della materozza 6894
collobrierite 4027
collocamento 15919
collyrite 4029
colmata 8326, 8335
— idraulica 16722
colofonia 14762, 15188
colofonite 4030
colonna 4038, 4039, 13288, S. 15721
— a riempimento 12839
— d'acqua 19754
— d'arresto dell'acqua 19815
— d'assorbimento 13
— delle cariche 17618
— d'estrazione 13998
— di cemento 3145
— di chiusura delle acque 17835
— di distillazione 7691
— di distillazione a riflusso 14621
— di ferro 10020
— di frazionamento 18762
— di ghisa 2997
— di idrogenazione 9562
— di liquido 4043
— di minerale 3455, 12639, 13360
— di minerale ricco 16161
— di pompaggio 14167
— di produzione 10975, 12512
— di sostegno 18035
— di tubaggio 17834
— di tubi di pozzo 2961
— d'ottone 2267
— fredda 13295 a
— montante 14949, 14953, 14961, 17338

colonna per riempimento di carri di scorta 18404
— perduta 10842
— perduta (lavatore della-) 10844
— perduta filtrante 15691
— premente 13908
— rovinata 10256
— supporto della perforatrice 5902
— tubante 12512
— tubolare per pensiline di stazioni ferroviarie 19066
colonna v. torre
colonnare divergente 5580
colonnetta del tappo 16593
colonnetta di guida cava 9277
colonnina 10667
Coloradiano 4031
coloradoite 4032
colorante al pigmento 10492 a
colorazione della fiamma 4036
— termica 8906 a
colore 7386
— di ricottura 8976, 18374
— minerale 11750
colori d'incandescenza 612
colorimetria 4034
colorimetro 3549
colpire 1402
colpo 1849, 10395, 16191
— ascendente 19381
— d'acqua 9831
— di corona 15142
— di maglio 1859
— di rifinitura 14787 a
— di rottura 17995
— discendente 5715
coltello 13455, 16039
— a destra 14905
— a sinistra 10664
— d'agata 209
— di platino
— elicoidale 9060
— per allargatore 19276
— per sgrossare a gran taglio 9032

coltello per tagliare vetro
8275
— per tappi di sughero 4469
— sbozzatore o da sgrossare S. 15265
coltivabile 11721
coltivare 11723, 11737, 17665,
17842
coltivare v. sfruttare, estrarre, abbattere
— a riporto 2411
coltivazione 8205, 10956,
17676
— a camere 12899
— a camere con franamento
dei pilastri 17300
— a camere e pilastri 1251,
1921, 2064, 3269, 8934,
13290, 15148, 17301
— a camere-magazzino 11166,
16233
— a cielo aperto 12566,
12584, 12588, 12606,
17291, 17852, 18057,
18071
— a cielo aperto a gradino
unico 16384
— a due tagli gemelli 5685
— a giorno 5018
— a gradini 1078, 1490
— a gradini dritti 2350
— a gradini inclinati con
ripiena 9697
— a gradini rovesci 17564
— a gradino inclinato con
ripiena 9692
— a gradino rovescio 7318
— a gradino rovescio con
ripiena 7017, 7317
— a grandi massicci 15140
— a lunghe trance 2435
— a lunghi fronti in direzi-
ne 10978
— a lunghi pilastri 10972
— a lunghi tagli 10994
— a lunghi tagli in ritirata
10993
— a pilastri 3564, 13295,
17253, 17659

coltivazione a pilastri
abbandonati 12595, 13294
— a piramide 14209
— a ripiena 1056
— a sezioni 12899
— a strati intermedi con
franamento 17920
— a tagli a gradino con
ripiena 9336
— a tagli in direzione 12716
— a trance 1484, 16599
— a trance con franamento
del tetto 18766
— a trance discendenti
19257, 19259
— a trance inclinate discen-
ti con franamento 9707
— a trance orizzontali 9351
— a trance orizzontali
ascendenti 852
— a trance orizzontali
discendenti 5227
— a valle dell'inclinazione
5448
— ad avanzamento 8332
— ad imbuti sotterranei
11713
— con accesso a pozzo
153, 5861
— con armatura 17244
— con puntellamento del
tetto 18032
— con (od a) ripiena 4900, 7039
— con scavatrici 17849
— dei filoni 10956
— dei livelli inferiori 5094
— dei pilastri 17661
— delle camere 7569
— delle fasce di sabbia
12118
— di filoni in pendenza
17530
— di giacimenti petroliferi
12501
— di giacimento alluvionale 13437
— di miniere 11769
— di traversobanco 4680
— di traverso banco 4717

coltivazione di una miniera
d'oro 8347
— idraulica 9527
— in direzione 7536, 20211,
20219
— in ritirata 1050, 11779,
14802, 20210, 20220
— in sotterraneo 19260
— irrazionale 2504
— per franamento 3121
— per franamento a blocchi
1797
— per franamento in trance
orizzontali 16600
— per grandi fronti in direzione 10992
— per trance trasversali
16256
— traverso-banco 4711
coltivazione v. abbattimento
columbite 4037
comando a cinghia v. trasmissione a cinghia
— elettrici dell'argano 6271
— verticale 19525
combinarsi 3861
combinazione chimica 3385
— dei metalloidi col ferro
4057
— di rock-bit e reamer 17602
combustibile 4069, 7787
— a pezzi 11090
— antidetonante 667
— artificiale 834
— carbonizzato 2862
— composto 1764
— DERV 5222
— di ottima qualità 9151
— di scarto 19727
— finemente polverizzato
7789
— fossile 7631
— gassoso 8010, 8071
— liquido 10875
— misto ad aria 7790
— naturale 12191
— per reattori 10159
— polverizzato 14148
— pregiato 9151

combustibile solido 16882
combustione 2604, 4071
— a pressione costante 4072
— a volume costante 4073
— completa 4113, 13078
— a carbone 3805
— in avanti 7625
— inversa 14820
— invertita 9933
— perfetta S. 4113
— rapida 2418
— rovesciata 14826
— sotterranea 9678
comendite 4086
comignolo 3456
commissione 10200
commutatore della polarità 13617
comparsa di macchie 17167 a
compasso aperto 4108
— di spessore 2748, 12714
— divisore 5585
— micrometrico 11642
— per fori 9842
compatto non sinterizzato 8509 a
— terminato 12261 a
compensare 12462
compensatore 373
compensazione della pressione 1128
— idraulica 9513
complessi ausiliari 1003
complesso dei preventers 4289
— di sollevamento 9235
completamento 4117
— sottomarino 19283
completare 4111
complicato 9921
componente 4120
— d'una combinazione 4233
— orizzontale dello scorrimento 9020
componenti del gas 4234
componenti litoidi 233
comportamento dell'alto forno 1441
composizione 4125

composizione chimica 3386
— del gas 4127
— della carica 4126
— molecolare 11873
— per cuscinetti S. 1396
— percentuale in peso 11852
— alifatico 6838
— intermetallico 9888 a
— ossigenato 12818
— solforato 17982
compressione 4153, 18531
— a caldo 9426 a
— a freddo 3970 a
— del liquido 7466
— dei mattoni 13890
— della polvere 13766 a
— allo stato fluido 7461
compressore 2051, 4651 a, 17263
— rotativo 15217
compressibilità 4151
comprimere 17256
computo metrico 1580
concentrati sottilissimi 7096
concentrato 7204, 8933
— di blenda 1762
— di minerale 9493
— di minerale scelto 13208
— per fanghi 16636
concentrazione 4104, 4166, S. 4251
— degli ioni 4167
— degli sforzi 17783 a
— equivalente d'una soluzione 6532
— per gravità 8484
concessionario 3614
concessione 4171, 10726
— di una miniera 3613
— mineraria 388
— petrolifera 12484
conchiglia 3007, 3433, 3615, 5357, 5358, 9984, 11551, 16093, S. 18044
— d'essicazione 4398
— esterna S. 5174
— per centrifugazione 3204
— per colata centrifuga S. 3204
— riscaldata 13839

conchiglia scaldata 19668
— scostata 11801
— variata 11801
conchigliare 3421
concio 15530
concoidale 15601
concordanza degli strati 13447
concrescenza 9885
concrescere 9883
concresciuto 9884
concrezionato 4179
concrezione 4178
— dura nel gas 8832
— rotonda 12152
condensare 4184
condensatore 5560, 12754
condensazione 4153, 4181
— per evaporazione 6619
condizionare 4188
condizionatore 4191
condizione di nebbia 11809
— generale 1694
— spumosa 7510
— di consegna 4192
condotta 13355
— collettrice principale 4025
— d'aria 300
— del fango 12081
— del vento caldo 9397
— di scolo 7428
— di un forno 20196
— forzata 13913
— per uccidere il pozzo 10354
— premente 5151
— principale 18958
— sottomarina 15742
condotta v. tubazione
condotto 2777, 6072 a, 7449, 13380, 13684
— aspirante 17954
— d'aereazione 257
— d'aria 6809
— d'aria calda 9391
— d'uscita del gas 8033
— dei fiumi 2357
— dei gas caldi 19733
— del forno 7449, 7836

condotto del fumo 3459.
   16762
— del vento 1469 a
— circolare dell'aria 2630
— delle fiamme 7255
— di ritorno 14812
— di ventilazione 19382
— laterale 16263
— montante od ascendente
   851
— principale del gas 8022
— principale del vento 304
condotto v. conduttura
conduttanza 4192 a
— limite d'elettrolito 10826
— elettrica 6266
— termica 8977
conduttività termica 8990
conduttore 4194. 10628.
   S. 13955
— crudo 8845
— esterno 12698
conduttore v. filo
conduttura 13355, 13380
— aerea 191
— d'acqua 19756
— d'alimentazione 6884,
   8100
— dell'acqua 19798
— sotterranea 19258
conduttura v. condotto
condutture di sfiato 19503
conduzione del calore 8977
confezione dell'impasto
   13854
confini 10562, 10565
conformazione per tagli
   15985 a
conforme ai calcoli 49
confronto delle dimensioni
   10600 a
congegno d'arresto 3087
— di pompaggio idraulico
   14165
— di sicurezza 4416
— di sicurezza del castelletto d'estrazione 8912
— per far circolare il
   «releasing spear» attraverso il pesce 12852

congelazione graduale 17548
congiungere 2016
conglomerare 223
conglomerato 4206, 8317.
   14092
— alluvionale 6800
— aurifero 1198
— di base 1278
conglomerazione 15804 a
congiuntinativo S. 227
conglutinato S. 228
coniare 3924
— moneta S. 17814
coniatura 3925
— a freddo 3979
— di ventilazione 19509
conicità 5724, 18278,
   18282
conico 4208, 18290
con bavatura 1221
connellite 4226
connessione 2021, 10204
cono 14954
— aperto 12608
— decantatore a bilico
   1272
— d'entrata 18277 a
— di chiusura 1446
— di colata 13749
— di deiezione 6807, 16613
— di filtro 7044
— di platino 13518
— risucchio 13329
— di ritiro 13329
— modello per colate 15376
conoide di deiezione 407
conservazione del gas 7993
consistenza 1937
consistenza sciroppposa
   18177
consolidamento 3784, 4231
consumato 6088
consumo 19853
— d'acqua 4245
— d'aria o di vento 4238
— delle lime 4243
— di calore 8978
— di carbone 4240
— di carbonio 4239
— di carburante 4244

consumo di chilowattora per
   tonnellata d'acciaio 4246
— di combustibile 4244
— di corrente 4241
— di forza d'energia 13774
— di vento 4238
— massimo simultaneo
   16376
— minimo 11767
— rapido 14303
conta-colpi 17875
contatore 4542
— d'acqua 19799
— di gas 8024
— di uscita 12710
— rotativo 19120
contatto anormale 4
contenente grisou 7002
— scorie 4250
contenitore 4249
— nella presso-fusione
   16592
— d'acido 77
contenuto 4251
— del crogiuolo 4739
— di carbonio 2829
— di cenere 13075
— di ferro 4254
— di minerale 15384
— d'un serbatoio 18258
contenuto v. tenore
continente 10518
contornato S. 7615
contornitrice 15297
contornitura 15296
contorno bianco 20030
— del modello 12707
— del profilo 15987
— cristallino 4793
— rosso 14530
contraccolpo 1064
contraffisso 16169,
   10240
contrafforte 29, 17225
contropiastrina 15710
contrappeso 1123, 1929,
   4536
— d'un piano inclinato 8614
— della porta 5629
contrarre 16221

contrarsi 13310
contrassegno 11330
contratto di fornitura di
minerali 4283
contrazione 4284, 12298,
16226
— dell'acciaio 16230
controcurvatura 2769
contro-ago 17625
— -dado 10119
— elettrodo 1085 a, 19943 a
controferro S. 1062
controflangia 4105
controlama 1062
controllare 2791
— le tubiere 9845
controllo 3361, 3373, 9846
— del fango 12072
— dell'avanzamento 5920
— della combustione 4077
— di deviazione 14752
— di qualità 14248
— di trasudamento 17906
— gammagrafico 7948
— non distruttivo 12348
contropiastra 9246
— d'iniezione 2155
contro-porta 14042
contropressione 1071
contropunta girevole a
cuscinetto 1151
controrotaia 8643
controsformo 1052, 19246
controspoglia 1052
controtaglia 9235
controtorsione 1081
controvapore 1075
controventare 2230
controventi della torre 8239
controventi v. diagonali
controvento 12718
convenzione di razionamen-
to 14030
conversione 4296
convertire in acciaio 17453
convertitore 4298
— Bessemer 1550
— a soffiaggio laterale
16257 a

convertitore basico 1295
— di coppia 18777
— fisso 17398
— orizzontale 1241
— ribaltabile 18627
convogliatore 4317
— a nastro 1474
— a pendolo 13060
— a piastre 16573
— a scosse 10178, 15969
— continuo 4264
— d'estrazione 6741
— di colata 3071
— di sbarbatura 16778
— di vagoncini 10236
cookeite 4325
copalite 9192 a
coperchio 2032, 2034, 2793,
4349, 4562, 4607, 9891,
10727, 13556, 19361
— del premistoppa 8266
— della volta 757
— di chiusura 3780
— di chiusura del camino
3462
— di staffa 4348
— di ugello 19159 a
— di vetro 8274
— isolante 9449 a, 16413 a
— mobile 14705
coperta del forno 15149
copertura 1687, 2585, 2584,
3881, 4570, 4572, 12058,
12735, 12735, 14040
— con sabbia 15495
— della loppa 16531
— di feltro 6912
— di tubi 13352
— glaciale 8257
copia 18809
copiapite 11812
copiare 13956
coppa 4838
coppella 4838, 4852
coppellazione 4839, 7146 a
coppetta del pistone per
pistonare il pozzo 18090
coppia conica di comando
4288

coppia di bloccaggio 11235
— di forze 4547
— di rulli di rettifica sui
due lati della macchina
8656
— motrice massima 13010
copri-colata 4563
coprigiunto 7384
— piatto 7333
coprire 4558, 11299
— con tela 4560
— con tetto 15136
— il fuoco 4559
— le richieste dei minerali
11440
coprolito 4376
coquinbite 10427
corda d'amianto 841
— di canapa 9088
— di Manilla 11294
— di sicurezza 10735
— spinosa 1222
— spinosa a 2 e 3 fili 1223
cordata 18905
cordierite 4380, 5350, 9943
cordilite 4381
cordite 4379
cordolo della saldatura 16243
— della saldatura a stagno
16865
— di brasatura 2293
cordonato semplice 9273
cordonato doppio 1370
cordone 1364, 5479, 7370,
16280, 17836
— a passata stretta 17833
— a rovescio 1049
— d'angolo 7031
— del cilindro 4020
— di saldatura 19924, 19937,
19949 a
— di sigillatura 10208
— frontale 8589
— rettilineo 17833
coriandoli 4202
corindone 472, 4507, 5332
— giallo 12665
corkite 4475
cornalina 2895, 4476

cornelite 10427
cornice di fascia 13476
corniola 4477, 15545
corno calcinato di cervo
   3344
cornubianite 4485
cornwallite 4486
corona 1046, 1460, 1574,
   1681, 2382, 4393, 4726,
   5367, 11300, 14920
— a cuneo 19659
— a diamanti 5322, 5330
— a graniglia 3447, 16194
— a vite senza fine 20230
— della forma 5796
— del supporto 2246
— dentata 8129, 14925,
   15561, 15563
— di ghisa 2998, 3009
— di muratura 19649
— di ruota 20009
— di sondaggio 4393
— di supporto 11302
— di trivellazione 4405
— di un pozzo 16106
— formata da ferri d'angolo inchiodati 14976
— Kelyfitica 2070
coronadite 4487
coropirometrico 14230a
corpi intrusivi 9925
corpo 1936
— cavo 9264
— d'acqua e di vapore
   19744
— della caldaia 1976
— della piastrina 10945
— della soffiante 1856
— dello scivolone 15973
— di carotiere 12696
— di rotazione 15194
— di uno snodo 10132
— elementare del reticolo
   10582
— idraulico di pompa 14161
— in ferro fuso 1938
— per macinare 4772
— sagomato 11263
— superiore della caldaia
   19362

corazza ferruginosa 8838,
   8875
corazzare 10029
corrente 12192
— d'aria 279, 5722
— d'aria ascendente 14958,
   19348
— d'aria continua 19302
— d'aria discendente 5696
— del parapetto 14359
— di convenzione 4293
— di Faucoult 6194a
— di gas 4896
— di gas ricco d'ossigeno
   7995
— di gas trasparente 18834
— di regime 20202
— discendente 20093
— elettrica 6269
— gassosa 7994
— parziale 17126
correttivi 3395
correttivo 9826
correzione 9827
correzioni 7141
corrimani 8795, 14128
corrimano 14365
corrodere 6571, 15644
corrodizzazione 4490/a
corrosione 4491
— a chiazze 5529
— a fossette 13429
— da fanghi 12086
— elettrolitica 7882
— intercristallina 19925
— intercristallina spontanea
   15757
— intergranulare 9875
— per attrito 7761
— per erosione 6546
— per fessurazione 4627
— per interramento 19254
— sotto tensione 17786
corrosivo 6571a
corrugamento 13549, 14091
— caledoniano 2738
corsa 18906
— ascendente 19381
— del pistone 13576
— d'espansione 13796

corsite 4504
corso 5147
— di mattoni 4553
corundellite 4505
corundofillite 4506
cosalite 4510
coslettizzazione 4511
cossirite 4512
costa 4824
— longitudinale 10983
— mobile 10774a
costantana 4232
costante di dissociazione
   3899
costanza di temperatura
   4518
costi d'estrazione 4516
costiera 16274
costipamento 17322, 18234
— di un foro da mina 2568
costipare 14388, 17304,
   18229
— con i piedi 18820
— un foro da mina 17535
costipatore 2569, 17537
costipatrice elettrica 17326
— pneumatica 13593
costipazione a mano 8779
costituente 4120
costituente della struttura
   13700
— primario 13938
— secondario 9686
costituzione 4125
— chimica 3387
costo della forza motrice
   4514
— di produzione 4515
costruire 14371
— la forma 11960
costruzione ad ossatura
   rigida 14908
— al pestone 18231
— d'altoforno 1710
— del forno 7832
— dei modelli S. 12984
— in ferro 9960
— in legno 20173
— tripolare 18567
cotone fulminante 8672

cotto 1113

cottura 1116, S. 17699

— a morte 5036

cotunnite 4525

covellite 4557, 9739

covite 4573

cracking 4588

crandallite 4594

cratere avventizio 181

— laterale 10569

cravatta di fissaggio 5954

— per aste pesanti 5888

— per cucchiaia e tubing 1102

— per tubing 19049

creatore 9058, 9218

crednerite 4613

creedite 4614

cremagliera 14320, 14324

— a pignone 14323

crematoio S. 16461

crepa 4580, 6111 a, 6768, 7966, 14727, 15965 a

— a caldo 9409

— da compressione 4102 a

— da tempra 14285

— di bavatura 7066 a

— di risucchio 16228

— di ritiro S. 9445

— intergranulare 9882

— interna 3726

— trasversale 8802

crepaccio 7359, 17125

— trasversale S. 4676

crepato 2448, 7704

crepatura della muratura 11012

crescita di cristallo 4794

cresta 4724, 14886

— anticlinale 655, 659, 660, 754, 4725

— di muro 4860

— isoclinale 9222

— sinclinale 18159, 18938

creta fosforosa 13161

— rossa 12448

cretaceo 4626

cricca 7360

— a freddo 3971

cricca al cratere 4611

— da raffreddamento 4334

— di decapaggio 13227

— di fondo 1265

— di ritiro 9445, 14786, 16228

— di scorrimento 16650

— di solidificazione 9408

— di taglio 16022 a

— di tensione 17784

— dovuta al calore 8979

— trasversale 4676, 14127

criccatura 3529 a, 3374

— dello stampo 11976

criccature 7250 a

cricche di laminazione 3429

— intercristalline 3429

cricco 14393, S. 14393

cricco v. martinetto

crichtonite 4636

crinale di displuvio S. 19838

crinanite 4637

crinoidi 4639

criolite 4784

criolitionite 4785

cripto 10438

criptoclastico 4786

criptocristallino 4787

criptogami 4788

criptolito 4789

criptopertite 4790

crisoberillo 3550

— opalescente 4952

crisocolla 4360

crisolite 3551

crisopraso 3552

crisotilo 3553

cristalli colonnari 4045

— di conchigliatura 3430

— equiassici 6527

— geminati da deformazione 11416 a

— misti 11822

cristallinità 4805

cristallino 4798

cristallite 4806, 4811

cristallizzare 4812

cristallizzatore 4807

cristallizzazione 4810

cristallizzazione collettiva 15452

cristallo 4791

— aghiforme 597

cristalloblastesi 4813

cristalloblastico 4814

cristallo corroso 2467, 4488

— di prima generazione 13149

— di quarzo 14266

— di roccia 1535, 15014

— geminato 19177, 19179 a

— immaturo 9643

— luminescenza 4816

— non omogeneo 4456 a

— oscillante S. 15228

— rotante 15228

— tagliato 4902

cristobalite 4642

crivellare 10934

crivellatore 10176

crivellatura 10180, 15693, 16582

— del minerale 10182

crivello 14885, 16297, 16298, 17736

— a maglie fini 7089

— a scosse 9646, 10185, 12686

— idraulico a piano fisso 8885

— idraulico a piano mobile 8751

— meccanico 11415

— oscillante 10170

— oscillante o a scosse 10181

— rotante a tamburo 18930 a

— rotativo 14842

crivello v. vaglio

croce 4664

— d'eruzione 3522, 18870

crocidolite 4651, 18614

crocoite 4652, 14543

crogiuolo 5512, 8950, 11476, 16455

— anteriore 10000, 14489

— bloccato 1810

— chiuso 4568

crogiuolo d'argilla 7160
— d'argilla refrattaria 4742
— di attesa 7685
— di fonderia 11471
— di fusione 4736, 16749
— di piombaggine 8448
— di porcellana 13662
— di prova 891
— essicato 7120
— in acciaio fuso 3019
— metallico 13715
— per termite 18488
— trasportabile 13688
crollare 5971
crollo 6778, 7639, 16607, 18594
cromaltite 4653
cromare 3546
— l'acciaio 3541
cromatazione 3524
cromatico 3526
cromato 3525
cromatografia 3528
cromatura 3534, 3547
— dura 8838 a
— dura porosa 13673
Cromeriano 4654
cromite 3543
cromizzazione 3542
cromo 3544
— magnesite 3530
cronstendtite 4655
crossite 4720
crosta 4782, 15727, 16094, 18739 a
— calcarea depositata dal-le acque sorgive 128
— della secchia di colata 10485
— della ghisa 16479, 16471
— della siviera 10485
— di fusione 3068
— di sabbia 15518
— di scorie 16532
— dura a sezione bianca raggiante 8844
— d'ossido sul pezzo la-minato 16474
— superficiale 18047

crudo ridotto 14561
crumiro 15569
cubano 4817
cubilotto 3002, 4841, 4844, S. 15939
— ad aspirazione 6797
— a vento caldo 9394
— con avancrogiuolo 14417
— con tino quadrato 4851
— equilibrato ad aria sof-fiata 1135
— per ghisa 7656
cucalite 4823
cucchiaia 1101, 3058, 3058, 17151
— di cementazione 6097
— di colata 15463
— di draga 5827
— da pulizia 3699
— pulitrice 12090
cucchiaino piccolo per sag-gi di metallo fuso 15565
cucchiaio 13328, 17151, 17152, 17153
— di platino 13528
— per due portatori 19189
— rovescio 5738, 14141
cucchiaio v. cucchiaia o cucchiarozzo
cucchiaione 10470
cucchiarozzo 13328, 17153
cuffia di guardia 10199
— paraolio 4607
culaccio 1382, 2531, 15727, S. 16488
culm 4826
culsageeite 4828
cumbraite 4830
cumberlandite 4829
cumengeite 4831
cummingtonite 4832
cunei dell'asta di perfora-zione 5900
— della tavola rotary 11362
— di trascinamento della asta motrice 10305
— per aste e tubi 16663
cuneo 1595, 7901, 8212, 11857, 12055

cuneo azionato direttamente a pressione 13794
— da carbone 3857
— da pietra 17653
— di ancoraggio 10528
— di bloccaggio 15426
— di fissaggio 10323 a
— di legno 10728
— di sicurezza 15426
— idraulico 9516
— di legno 8907
— di sostegno 7540
cunicolo 2063, 2340, 5027, 17910, 19261
— cieco 1771
— del ventilatore 6808
— di comunicazione 17374
— di galleria 8931
cuocere al forno 1112
— in stufa 17694
— un'anima 4407
cuore 8946
— cieco 1770
— composto di rotaie 2539
— del tornio 2900
— duro 8820
— in acciaio al mangane-se 11278
cupola 1468, 5620
cupralluminio 450
cuprifero 4352
cuprite 14533
cuproberillio 1545
cuprobiombo 4357 a
cuprofosforo S. 13175
cupromanganese 4856
cupronichelio 4857
— allo zinco S. 12280
cupropiombo 4855
cuprozincite 4859
cura del rivestimento del forno 2889
curio 4864
curite 4863
cursore 15367
curva 2198, 4875, 18970 a
— a 90° 14262
— a 180° 14262
— ad ogiva 17527

curva a raggio stretto 16182
— ad S 18643
— di combustione 4080
— di concentrazione 4877
— di consumo 4237
— di decomposizione 4876
— di dilatazione 10997
— di livello 4281
— d'iniettabilità 9811
— di permeabilità 13110
— di raffreddamento 4335,
5462 a
— ribassata 7331
— di solubilità 4877
curvare 1498, 4873
curvatrice 1504, 1511, 1515
— per tondini 1210
curvatura 1505, 2198, 4872,
4875
— a caldo 9417
— di tondini 1211
curvo 1527
cuscinetto 1387, 2279, 5592,
13296, 15104
— ad aghi 12206
— a sfere 1150
— d'ancoraggio superiore
18741
— di gas 8038
— di spinta 4887
— inferiore 2148
— portante della tavola
Rotary 18192
— superiore S. 18737
cuspidina 4890
custerite 4890

D

dacite 4956
dacitico 4957
dactilico 4959
dactilite 4958
dado 12427
— ad alette 7508
— a farfalla 7508
dama di scorie 16461 a

damascare 4973
damaschinato 4971
damburite 4990
damigiana 2873
damourite 4974
damouritizzazione 4975
danaite 4988
danalite 4989
dannemorite 4995
danno causato dal fumo 4970
dannoso 12406
darapskite 4999
dare il nero di fonderia 1640
— il vento S. 19136
dare la tinta 1640
datolite 5005
daubrecite 5010
daubreelite 5011
davainite 5013
daviesite 5014
deaerazione 319, 5044
debole calcinazione 19850
debutanizzatore 5048
debutanizzazione 5047
decalamanitore idraulico
9520
decalaminatore scrostatore
5224
decalaminazione 5225
alla fiamma 7256
decalescenza 5049
decantare 5050, 15921
decantatore 15923, 15926
decantatrice 5293
decantazione 5051
— delle scorie 15875
decapaggio 3691, 5452,
13225
— continuo 4270
— di gas 8035 a
— elettrochimico 6324
— matto 6086 a, 11367 a
— supplementare 20039 a
decapare 13216, 15654,
19580
decapato 13219
decarbonizzazione 5056,
5057
— con solvente 16909

decarburare 5054, 5057, 5058
decarburazione completa
4114
decarburizzato 5055
decatramare 5254
decatramatura 5255
dechenite 5060
declino 5065
declivio 45, 5066
decomporsi 5067, 5068,
19862
decomposizione 5059 a
— del calcare 5069
— degli idrocarburi 5070
dedolomitizzazione 5083
defalco v, riduzione
defangare 6394, 15654
defangatura 5238
deflagrare 5114
deflagratore 5116
deflagrazione 5115
deflazione 5117
deflemmatore 5186
deflettore 674
deflessione 5120
defloculazione 5122
deformabilità 5124
deformarsi 19673
deformazione 5125, 5566,
19674, 19677
— a collo di bottiglia 2137
— al taglio 16034
— al trattamento termico
5568
— angolare 426
— da contrazione 4285
— da ritiro 4285
— della staffa 5569
— dovuta a tensioni interne
2510, 3070, 5567
— elastica 6246 a
— fluida 7462 a
— plastica 7436
— plastica dei terreni S.
16895
— viscosa 4615
defosforare 5189
defosforazione 5188, 15874
degalvanizzare 17839

degalvanizzazione 17866
— chimica 3392 a, 16906 a
degasante 5129
degasare 5126
degassificazione 5127
dehrnite 5140
deidratatore 5289
deidratazione 5291
deidrogenazione 1117, 9559
deionizzare 5142
delafossite 5144
delessite 5146
dellenite 5155
delorenzite 5156
deltaite 5159
delvauxite 5160
demagnetizzazione 5161 a
demantoide 5164
demetanizzazione 5165
demolire 14122, 17842
— in pilastri 14995
demolizione 15759
— dei pilastri 2449, 5776,
    5793, 13293, 13295,
    14138, 14140, 14996,
    14997
dendrite 5168, 6926
dendritico 738, 5169
dennisoite 5170
denominazione della qualità
    5234
densimetro 9567
densità 5176
— Baumé 1354
— della polvere 18266 a
-- di riempimento 7015
— d'un gas 5177
— relativa 14681 a
dentato 15897
dentatura interna 9274
dente 3908
— d'arresto 5592
— greggio 3029
dentellare 15643
dentellato 12401
deossidante 5182
deossidare 5184
deossidazione 5179
deparaffinazione 5297 a

deparaffinazione con solven-
    ti 16910
deperimento 18346
depolarizzazione 5194/a
depolverare 14716
depolveratore 6138
depositare 15921
depositato dalla corrente
    4866
depositi abissali 31
— batiali 1340
— di mare profondo 5096
— di spiaggia 10894
— eolici 185
— eteromesici 9106
— glaciali 5853, 8250
— isomesici 10067
— isopici 10075
— lacustri 10493
— pelagici 13050
— sedimentari 15792
— sincroni 18156
— terrigeni 18434
deposito 5200, 13809,
    15923 a, 17689
— alloctono 380
— alluvionale 231, 5849
— alluvionale di terrazza
    1489
— calcareo 2708
— calcareo 2708
— clastico grezzo 6810
— compatto 14662 a
— degli acidi 92
— dei rifiuti 14642
— dei tubi 13365
— delle sorgenti 16438
— di cenere 861
— di cenere volante 5195
— di combustibile 2579
— di coke 3947
— di ferrami 10021
— di gas su uno strato
    petrolifero 7986
— di grafite 5196, 15872
— di lingotti 9801
— di loppa 6096
— di minerali 12656
— di pulvis colo atmosferi-
    co 6130

deposito di rame 4364
— di rifiuti 6105
— di sabbia alluvionale
    1691
— di scoria sul becco 16521
— di scorie 16534
— di travature metalliche
— d'ossido di zinco 20327
— elettrolitico S. 6340
— eluviale 6397
— eterotopico 9110
— galvanico 6340
— glaciale 5857
— isotopico 10082
— limitato 12930 a
— omotassico 9300
— per contatto 4248 a
— per immersione 9664/a
— per minerali 17693
— superficiale 9603
deposito v. accumulazione
deposizione chimica 3388
depressione della miniera
    11951
depropanazione 5202
depurante 14610
depurare 14192
depuratore 8046, 15609,
    19700
— a coke 3944
— Bian 1573
— d'acqua 19755
depurazione 5211, 14607
— a secco dei gas 6038
— del gas 8045
— dell'acqua 19807
— di gas 8053
— per via umida 19986,
    19996
— pneumatica 323
deramare 5073
deramatura 5074
derbylite 5212
derivati di vergella 20140
derivazione corrente par-
    ziale 17126
— di condotta 10568
dermolite 5213
derrick tubolare 19088
desalluminatura 5042

descloizite 5229
desetanizzatore 5102
desilicificare 5236
desilicificazione 5235
desolforante 5247
desolforare 5245
desolforazione 5244
desquamazione 6648, 13041
destinezite 5243
desurriscaldatore 5249
detergente 5255 a
deterioramento del crogiuolo 5256
determinare il potere calorifico 5263
— il potere calorifico col
   calorimetro 5264
— il potere calorifico in
   base all'analisi 2731
determinazione calorime-
   trica 2757
determinazione chimica
   del potere calorifico
   3389
— del potere calorifico
   5257
— della conduttanza 5262
— della densità 5259
— della solubilità 5261
— di un solo corpo 5260
detonante 10397
detonatore 1745
— elettrico 6260
detriti 1232, 5891, 11035,
   12065, 12103
— alluvionali 411
— di trivellazione 4929
— e frammenti di diamanti
   5331
detrito 19718
— di ferro 19722
— striato 15683
deuterico 5268
deuterogeno 5269
deuteromorfico 5270
deuteroprisma 13958
devalquite 5287
deviare 5118

deviatoio 18720
deviatori 5119
deviazione 5117, 5280
— del foro 19138
devitrificazione 5283 a
devoniano 5284
— superiore 12219
devonite 5285
dezincare 5265
dezincatura 5266 a, 5299
deweylite 5297
dewindtite 5298
diabase 5300
diaboleite 5302
diaclasi 5303
— longitudinale 1045,
   17822
— orizzontale 2169, 7341,
   16065
— principale 11229
— trasversale 4908, 5441
diadochite 5304
diaforite 5335
diaframma 908, 2550, 2285,
   5337, 5584, 15725, 16463
— antipolvere 17644
— d'aereazione 247, 2362
— di colata 5484
— di terracotta 5336
— di ventilazione 327, 1361,
   1400, 5121, 14881, 17687
diaftoresi 5305
diagenesi 5306
diagonale supporto tamburo
   di manovra 2556
diagonali v. controventi
— della torre 2232, 2236
— della torre di sondaggio
   5215
diagrafia dei raggi gamma
   7949
diagrafia nucleare 12417
— di magnetismo nucleare
   12418
diagrafie dei fanghi 12082
diagramma 5312, 10964
— delle fasi 13046 a
— della soluzione solida
   16894

diagramma delle proporzioni
   di solidificazione 5314
— d'equilibrio 6528
— di livello 9607
— di processo 7426
— di ricottura 9001
— di stato ferro-carbonio
   9964
— di ferro-carbonio 9963
dialogite 5315
diamagnetico 5316
diamante S. 13169
— di trivellazione 2831
— industriale 2118
— industriale per grandi
   mole 1141
— nero industriale 2848
diametro del forno 5318
— interno 2076
— interno d'un tubo 2086
— medio di filettatura 13414
diamorfismo 5334
diapiro 5339
diascistico 5341
diasperizzazione 10138
diastrofismo 5343
diatomite 5345, 11876,
   14410, 16309, 16318,
   18365
diatrema 5347
dicco 3907, 5410, 6148
— di basalto 20016
dicroite 5350
dicroismo 5349
dickinsonite 5351
dickite 5352
didimio 5353
dienerite 5387
dietanolammina 5023
dietrichite 5390
dietzeite 5391
difetto 6767, 7360
— d'anima 6555
— di colata 7362
— di fonderia 5104
— di formatura 6557
— di fusione 6840, 7362
— di ghisa 5109
— di laminazione 11693,
   15085 15123

difetto di materiale 5105

— di piegatura 8710 a, 10539 a

— di ramolaggio 6554

— di sbavatura 6556

— di segatura 15742 a

— di taglio 16028

— esterno 19567

— superficiale 18048

difettoso 5108, 11806

differenza ammessa 13113

differenza d'analisi 5393

— di spessore 5394

difficile lavorazione (di-) 6664

difficilmente fusibile 9154

difficoltà create dall'acqua 19821

diffusione 5403

diffusore 5402, 6217

digrossatura 16134

dihidrite 5409

dilatamento 10860

dilatare 18120

dilatazione 5412

— termica 18483

dilatometro 5413

diluviale 5419

diluvio 5420, 5857

dima S. 8111

dimazzare il minerale 4761

dimensione 5421

— inferiore al normale 19279

— intermedia 1287

— primitiva 7202

— del pezzo di ghisa 5424

— dimensioni di ingombro 12732

diminuire la pressione 1755

— la produzione 14560

diminuzione della sezione 14574

— della solubilità 5080

— di polvere del forno 14575

diminuzione v. calo

dimorfico 5426

dimorfismo 5425

dinamite 1748. 8211

— a base inerte 9759

dinamo a gas 8000

— a vapore 17428

dinamometamorfismo 6151

dinamometro 6149, 6696

dinantiano 5427

diopside 5429

dioptasio 5430, 6408

diorite 5431

— quarzifera 14267

disossidazione 5183

dipirizzazione 5455

dipiro 5454, 11841

diramazione 2256, 2650

direttore di fonderia 7661

direzione 17816, 18875

— assiale 1018

— dei filoni (in-) 6452

— dei raggi 4555

— del cappello (in-) 2817

— del filone 10836

— del fronte di taglio normale al piano di sfaldatura 2066

— del gas

— dell'affioramento 4554

— dell'aria 308

— della pendenza (in-) 5698

— della deviazione 5466

— di faglia 6860

— di laminazione 15124

— di posa 9245

— di stratificazione 10838

— generale 8153

— magnetica 11187

— media 1012

dirigere la fiamma sulla suola 5456

diritti di concessione petrolifera 15301

— di estrazione del petrolio 12505

— di licenza 15300

— supplementari 12775

disalluminatura 459

disareatore 5045

disargentare 5239

disarmare 14715, 14995, 19339

disarmare una sonda 17280

disarmatore 17863, 18634

disarmo 14011, 14499, 14996, 20158

— dell'armatura 19340

— di un solaio 5527

discarica 6096

— delle scorie S. 16560

discendere 5226

— una colonna di tubi 10519

discenderia 2469, 5436

discesa 15382

— della carica 6005

— della gabbia 11013

— del tubaggio 11076. 11234

— è salita 5228

disco compensatore 5481

— d'amianto 842

— da taglio 16675 a

— della molazza 12890

— di controspinta 3365

— di flanella 7278

— di ghisa 3000

— di legno 20181

— di panno 2515 a. 7278

— differenziato 5397

— dosatore 15202

— filtrante 7063

— reggi-spinta 18601

— tranciatore 4928

discordante 12346, 19238

discordanza 5505, 17749, 19240

— angolare 591, 3730, 5582

— concordante 12919

— parallela 12919,, 12920

— tettonica 17885

disegnare 5753

disegno costruttivo 20204

— d'altoforno 1711

disfarsi di scaglie 15578

disgaggio 15598

disgregare per fusione 18923

disgregarsi 19862

disgregazione 15868, 2322

— della muratura 11012

disidratare 5288

disincrostante 665

disincrostare 5765, 15580
disincrostazione 5225, 15597
disinnestare 5504
disinserire 5504
disintegratore centrifugo 3213
disintegratore 5519, 5520
— a birilli 17081
— a perni 17081
— aeratore 189
— della sabbia 15490 a
disintegrazione 5537, S. 11706
— a blocchi 1799
— dei minerali 4757
dislivello 6772
dislocamento 18603
dislocatore 5526
dislocazione 5525, 10645, 18850, 18933
— normale 2376
disluite 6160
disossidante 5182
disossidazione 5179, 10353, 14571
dispositivo a coppa e a cono 1448
— d' arresto 16242
— da presa per lingotti 9793
— d'attacco 10190
— di alimentazione dei pezzi 15379
— di arresto 8566
— di bloccaggio 5359
— di blocco 1089
— di capovolgimento a curva 1924
— di controllo del flusso di un pozzo 12833
— di dosaggio 1337
— di ribaltamento dei vagoncini 19625
— di raffreddamento 4336
— di sicurezza 15415, 15420
— di sollevamento 10754
— di tamponamento di fuga 9462

dispositivo per estrarre i lingotti 20159
— per scampanare 14422
— per estrarre la mezza staffa 10766
— per introdurre od infornare i lingotti 9798
— per prevenire la presa in parete dell'asta pesante 10329
— per spengere l'altoforno 1872
— per vagliare 16306
dispositivo v. apparecchio
disposizione dei convertitori 808
— dei cordoni 1373
— dei mattoni del riempimento 2538
— in strati 807
— parallela 12921
disprosio 6162
dissaldare 19332
disseminato 5539
dissociare 5542
dissociazione elettrolitica 6341
dissolvente della ruggine 15396 a
distaccare 10398
distacco automatico 991
— dei vagoncini dalla gabbia 19233
— della roccia 16504, 16699
— delle gabbie 1201
— del minerale 2332
— di terra 5973
distaffaggio 10400, 15966, 17865
distaffare 10399
distaffatrice a scosse 15967
distaffatura 10400
— a scosse 10402
— mediante vibrazioni 11408
— pneumatica 13587
distanza 16957
— dei cilindri 5550

distanza focale 7514
— fra i bracci 9365, 13501
— fra i piani di scavo 16958
— orizzontale dell'affioramento 12380
— visiva 19569
distendere 14719
distensione locale 10937
disterrare 7394
distillare 26, 5551, 5552
distillati 18765
distillato 13888
— di cracking 13902
— di residuo 18316
— direttamente 17714
— leggero 11755, 14462
— paraffinoso 19842
— stabilizzato 19866
distillatore a caldaia 16113
— a vapore 17448
— del diluente 5416
— discontinuo 1335
— per residui 18321
distillazione alla storta
— atmosferica 929
— continua 4266
— con vapore acqueo 17427
— discontinua 1331
— frazionata 7687
— lenta del carbone 2868
— nel vuoto 19427
— per estrazione 6743
— primaria del petrolio 17868
— secca 6031
distorsione 5566
distretto minerario 11764
distributore 5576, 6208 a
— del minerale 12641
— dosatore 11609
— vibrante 19546
— a cassetto 16615
distribuzione a mano 8781
— a mezzo stantuffo 13394
— a rubinetto 14659
— a valvola 19453
— automatica 987
— del vento 262
— della ghisa 5573

distribuzione dell'inversione
 di marcia della mazza
 battente 8744
— della carica 5574
— della pressa 4292
— di forza 13776
— di pozzi rispetto al terreno 5933
distruggere un tratto di
 casing 11683
dito di gomma 15309
ditroite 5579
divenire argilloso 15980
dividere in piccole palle
 13277
— la sabbia 2305
divisione 12946, 17135
— della terra 15491
— in cuscinetti 13297
— in lastre 16503
— in palle 1165
— lamellare 16082
divisore 17133
dixenite 5588
doccia 16218
doccione alimentatore per
 minerali 6880
— d'alimentazione 6878
dolerina 5601
dolerite 5602
dolerofanite 5604
dolomia 5608
dolomite 5608, 1633, 13245,
 14858
— calcinata 5607
— cotta 2714, 5607
— cruda 14453
— stabilizzata 17270
— vescicolare 16767
dolomitizzazione 5616
domeykite 5622

domite 5625
doppia contrazione 5649
— femmina (a-) 5646
— flangia (a-) 5660
— incavigliatura (a-) 5680
— parete (a-) 5687
— tempra 5662
— tettoia per formatura
 19191
doppio avvolgimento 5688
— decimetro 1571
— -duo 5695
— effetto 5639
— forno per pudellaggio
 5673
— fungo 5663
— maschio (a-) 5668
— ritiro 5649
— T 10216
— tubo per apparecchio di
 distillazione 5556
dopplerite 5636
dorare 8224
doratura 8225
— a bagno 19778
— a fuoco 9419
— a mano 8760
— a mercurio 8226
— a mordente 13272
— ad oro battuto 8345
— al fuoco 7169 a
— a' torchio S. 13871
— alla trancia 13871
— galvanica 6333
dormiente 8620, 16589, 16871
dorso 1044, 19278
dosaggio del carbone 5258
dotazione 12699
dote 1416, 3929
doughtite 5692
douglasite 5693

draga 1098, 6637, 9045,
 10334, 12203
— a benna 3829
— a cucchiaia 16213
— a fondo apribile 5977
— a fondo mobile 5977
— a noria 15641
— a tazze 2501, 15641
— ad azione aspirante 7490
— aspirante 17952
— d'estrazione 2202
— di caricamento 10335,
 10915
— di caricamento 10335,
 10915
— di caricamento ad acqua
 4987
draga v. scavatore o escavatore
dragaggio 5823
dravite 5752
dreelite 5830
drenaggio 5292
— per gravità 8487
dritto 12540 a
drusa 6020, 19607
drusico 6022
dufrenite 6079, 10433
dufrenoisite 6080
duftite 6081
dumalite 6091
dumontite 6094
dumortierite 6095
dundasite 6107
dungannonite 6109
dunite 6110
duomo 5620, 14255
— di lava 9930
— per vapori 19468
— salino 15444
dural 6116

durata 6117
— d'accensione 2607
— d'eruzione 7443
— d'oscillazione 6119
— d'un forno 10734
— del carico 18642
— del forno 7830
— del passaggio della
    carica 13095
— della colata 18303
— della tempera 6118
— del turno 1197
— di distillazione 2864,
    5561 a
— di lavorazione 16988
— di ricottura 616
— di rinvenimento 18399
— di spegnimento 14294
durbachite 6120
durdenite 6121
durevole 16874
durezza 8871,
— al rosso 14539
— Brinell 2408
— dell'acciaio 8872
— di cementazione 2923
— di superficie 16476
— di taglio 6201
— per trattamento termico
    20190 a
— sclerometrica 15681
— Shore 16171
durite 6115, 17116
duro come il vetro 8277
duse regolabile a spillo
    3517
duttile 6073
duttilità 6075, 11248, 1685
Dyas 6146
dynassite 6163
dysanalite 6157
dyscrasite 6158

E

ebollizione 1953, 1998
— violenta 17877
eccedenza d'erosione 6547
eccentricità 18278
eccesso 6639
— d'ossigeno 6641
— di peso 6644
— di precipitante 6642
ecdemite 6242
echinodema 6188
eclogite 6189
edenite 6196
edificio d'estrazione 8914
— della macchina d'estra-
    zione 8220
— delle macchine 6468
— degli accumulatori 55
edingtonite 6213
Efesite 6508
effetto calorifico 2753, 8975
— Custer 12806
— d'intaglio 12398
— del colpo 6215
— del diametro dei cilindri
    15088
— del pistonaggio 18091
— di deformazione 7619
— di massa 11357
— di schermo 15931, 16120 a
— di taglio 4914
— gassificante 8077
— Léonard 5774
— temprante 3452
— termico 2753
— termico della reazione
    8975
— tissotropico del fango
    8147
effluente 12700

egirina 107
eglestonite 6227
eguagliatore di pressione 6526
eguale peso (di-) 12459
ehelite 6228
eichwaldite 6231
eiettore 6239 a
— per vuoto 19433
eiezione 6237 a
Eifeliano 6232
einstenio 6234
elasticità dei materiali 6250
— di compressione 6247
— di flessione 6249
— di tensione S. 6248
— di torsione 6251,, 18780
— di trazione 6248
elaterite 6252
elementi associati 14753 a
— autoportanti in lamiera di
    acciaio zincata 15832
— decomposti 19864
— del gas 4234
— scaldanti a piastre d'ac-
    ciaio 17488
elemento 6374
— atmofilo 922
— ausiliare 15765
— costituente inflangiatura
    per casing 2944
— del trasportatore
    oscillante 18936
— di costruzione in acciaio
    stampato 13883
— di pompe 14152
— nocivo 5266
— strutturale tubolare 19082
eleolite 6243, 6372
elettroanalisi 6322 a, 6337
elettrodeposizione 6330
elettrodo a capsula 5516
— a mantello cilindrico 4950

elettrodo decinormale 5062
— del fondo 11067
— di carbone 2833
— di ferro 9971
— di precipitazione 13814
— normale 17345
— reticolato 12245
— rivestito 16119
elettroerosione 6331
elettrografia 6333 a
elettrolisi 6335, 6354
— dello zinco 6352
elettrolito 6336
— anfotero 540
elettrolizzare 6334, 6353
elettromagnete 6355
elettromagnetismo 6357, 6358
elettrometallurgia 6360
elettrone 6362
elettro-negativo 6363
elettrostenolisi 6369
elettrostrizione 6369/a
elevare 14370
elevatore a benna 16480
— a coclea 15706
— a ganasce 7604
— a griglia 8580
— a mensola 2243
— a paternoster 6378
— a secchi 6378
— a tazze 2502
— a vite 15706
— ausiliare 18824
— di aste 5899, 10730,
  15050, 17945
— di carbone 3833
— per pozzi profondi 5099
— per trivelle 14899
— per tubi 2938
elevazione 6375, 14943
— d'acqua 14379
eliasite 6381
eliminare 23
— la scoria 16130
eliminazione d'elementi
  sabbiosi 6383
— del fosforo 6382
— dell'acqua salina 15446
— dell'alluminio 459, 5042

eliminazione dell'anidride
  carbonica 5965
— della sabbia 15494
— delle scorie 12329 a,
  16544, 17264 a
elio 9066
eliodoro 9063
eliofillite 9064
eliotropio 1816, 9065
ellswortite 6387
elmo protettore senza chiodi
  14979
elpidite 6393
elutriale 6396
eluvio 6398
elvano 6399
elveziano 9071
emanazione 15797
ematostibilite 9078
ematite 8705, 9073, 9978
— a superficie vetrosa 6992,
  9075
— rossa 14541, 15328
— speculare 9878
— stratificata 7247
ematolite 9077
embolite 6402
emiedrico 9082
emimorfia 9083
emimorfo 9084
emimorfite 6263 a, 9085
emitropia 19178
emitropico 9086
emmonsite 6418
emplectite 6419
empressite 6420
emscheriano 6423
emulsionabilità 6425
emulsionare 6430
emulsionatore 6427
emulsione 6428
— d'acqua nell'olio 19784
— d'olio nell'acqua 12496
— naturale di petrolio e
  acqua 15133
— stabile 17272
enantotriopia 6438 a
enargite 6439
endeiolite 6456

endlichite 6469
endosmosi elettrica 6273
energia dell'urto 18417 a
— di campo 6996
— di volume 19599
enomorfo 20269
enstatite 6490
entalpia 6491
entrare in effervescenza 6216
entrata 9820, 9853
— del gas 8018
— del laminatoio 9780
— del pozzo 13409, 15964
— dell'aria 292-293, 1730
— della galleria 155
— laterale 16262
entrata v. accesso
entropia 6494
Eocene 6498
eoliano 921, 6499
eosforite 6500
epiclastico 6511
epiclorite 6510
epidesmina 6512
epidiabase 6513
epididimite 6514
epidiorite 6515
epidoto 6516
epigenesi 6518
epigenite 6519
epigeno 6517
epiroccia 6520
epirogenesi 6505
epirogenia 6507
epizona 6522
epoca carbonifera 2859
— glaciale 5858, 9611
epoca v. periodo
eptorite 9093
epuratore Theisen 18477
epurazione S. 14607
— a secco del gas 6032 a
equazione chimica 6524
equazione di stato 6525
equicoesivo 6527 a
equigranulare 20153
equilibrare 1121
— una mola 5836
equilibratura con contrappeso
  1140

equilibratura v. bilanciamento
equilibrio di dissociazione
6529
— termico 8984
equiripartizione 6530 a
equivalente di acciaio
grezzo 4755
— in carbonio 2834
— stechiometrico 17628
era 6535
— archeozoica 761
— cenozoica 2688, 3184,
10270
— psicozoica 14087
— terziaria 18436
Eriano 6589
erbio 6536
eredità 9097
erichite 6541
erinite 6542
erionite 6543
eritrina 6560, 3885 a
eritrosiderite 6561
erodere 15644
erogare 13326. 19372
erogazione 5149
— intermittente 8909
erosione 6545, 15240
— di sabbia 15491
— eolica 184
— per esplosione 13554
— regressiva 14805
erratico 6549, 18858
errite 6552
errore di misurazione 11397
— di previsione del ritiro
20238
— di temperatura 18381
— nell'immagine 9640
erto 45
erubescite 2115
eruzione 1757, 1760, 6558,
8676, 9830, 17231
— di gas 7983
— d'un sondaggio 20068
— freatica S. 13188
esagoni d'acciaio 9126
— di ferro 9119

esaidrite 9127
esalazione di gas 15797
esalazioni 7816 a
— di grisou 1767
esame 18441
— al microscopio 9936
— all'ultrasuono 19224
— dilatometrico 5414
— macrografico 11150
— magnetoscopico 11197
— metallografico 11582
— microscopico 9936, 11651
— radioscopico 7476
esaminare 6634
esaottaedro 9128
esatetraedro 9129
esattezza della misura 5422
esaurimento 5192
esaurire 5189 a, 6145
esaurirsi 13535
esaurito 14159
esca 7884
esca a scintilla 16982
escavatore 6636, 17864
— a benna strisciante
5739
— a benna trainata 5739
— a cavi 2667
— a cucchiaia livellatrice
16462
— a cucchiaia spingente
6754
— a tazze 2499
— a vapore 17445
— meccanico 13792
escavatore v. draga o scavatore
escavatrice di profondità
5450
— meccanica 5828
escavazione a vapore 17446
esclusione d'aria 6646
escoriazione 6647
escrescenza 19493
eseguire la ripiena idraulica
7478
— una ripiena 1291, 3905,
8328, 17702, 18230
— un'impronta cava 5510

esente da ceneri 865
— da scaglie 7727
— da scorie 7728
esente v. privo
esercizio (in-) 12554
esercizio 20194
— del laboratorio 10451
— in alternata 19346
espansione del «gas cap»
7987
— di gas 8002
esperimento 6675
esplodere 16160
esploditore elettrico 1749,
7191, 14198
esplorare 13968, 14032
esplorazione 5407; 6680
— del filone in direzione
3356
— di pozzi 19966
— intercalata 9888
esplosibilità 6681
esplosione 6682, 16191
— di dinamite 6153
— di gas 8003
— di grisou 8330
— di mine 16164
— di mine partendo dalla
superficie 18067
— di una caldaia 1958
— freatica 13188
— vulcanica 19591
esplosione v. scoppio
esplosivo 6685
— alla nitroglicerina 12323
— all'ossigeno liquido
10878
— al nitrato ammonico 527
— D 6686
— di lancio 14017
— di sicurezza 15417
— dirompente 6822, 9145
— gassoso 8070
— liquido 10874
— solido 16881
esporre alla luce 6690
esposizione 6692
espulsione a candela 1217
— dell'acqua 6694

espulsione di materie volatili 6674
espulsore 6241
essicamento 6052, 6060
essicare 6023, 17694
essicatoio 6054, 6061, 6063
— d'anime 4404
— per forme 11978
— trasportabile 18838
— rotativo 15198 a
essicatoio v. stufa o essicatore
essicatore 4330, 5232, 6051,
   6054, 6693
— a perdite dielettriche
   5384
— a vuoto 19426, 19428
— ad alta frequenza 5384
— di vapore 17450
essicatura delle forme 6060
essicazione 6052
— dell'aria 6066
— in stufa 17700
essonite 3579, 9103
essudazione 6726 a, 18103
estensimetro 17732 a
estensione 14412
— in profondità 5203
— orizzontale 10675
estensiometro 6696
estinzione del coke 4983
— parallela 12918
estrarre 26, 5756, 5770,
   6706, 8203, 17842,
   20084
— con cucchiaia 1099
— da una cava 14257
— il modello 20155
— le forme 5757
— pilastri di una miniera
   abbandonata 7627
— un modello 6235
estrattore 5782
— a scatto 10344
— a trance con franamento
   14013
— a vite per modelli 12990
— d'anima 4403, 4432
— di coke 14200

estrattore di lingotti 9792,
   9797
— di liquido 5948
— di puntelli 13711, 14010,
   14012
— di tubi 18981
   per carote 4410
— per piedi di valvole
   19455
estrattrice 14200
— di carbone 3943
— di coke 14392
estrazione 5792, 5805,
   5873, 6707 a, 9229,
   14137, 14378, 20111,
   20097
— a colonne 13709
— a getto d'acqua 9541
— a mezzo di pozzo 15944
— ad aria compressa 299
— con escavatori 17869
— con gabbie 2683
— con getto di gas com-
   presso 2683
— con immissione di gas
   compresso 8020
— con iniezione di gas
   8020
— con secchie 1103
— dei minerali 12650
— dei modelli 5802
— dei tubi 20157
— del fondo 14712
— del modello su macchina
   a pettine 14131
— della roccia 20199
— di anime 4435
— di carbone 3815, 3820
— di minerale 12660
— elettrica 6282
— equilibrata 1136
— idraulica 13382
— meccanica 11132
estrazione v. coltivazione o
   sfruttamento
estremità 6449, 18672
— del forno 7835
— della bilancia 8794
— dello scarto 16179

estremità di nastro collettore
   3342
— di una galleria 19109
estrudere 6717
estrusione 6722
— a freddo 3977
estruso 6718
estuario 7316
etere solforico 6576
eteromorfite 9107
eterogenite 9105
etichetta 10448
etite 198
ettringite 6577
eucarite 6578
euclasi 6580
eucolite 6581
eucolittitanite 6582
eucriptite 6584
eucrite 6583
eucroite 6579
eudialite 6585
eudidmite 6586
eudiometro 6587
eudnofite 6588
euralite 6591
eurite 6592
euritico 6593
europio 6595
eusinchite 6597
eustatico 6596
eutettico 6598, 6599
eutettoide 6606
euxenite 6609
evacuazione della zavorra
   liquida 12703
evaporare 6611
evaporatore 6621
— a secco 6612
evergreenite 6626
evita-molette 12786
extramagmatico 6714

F

fabbisogno d'acqua 534
— di combustibile 5163
fabbrica 11686

fabbrica di caldaie 1977
— di funi 20146
— di mattoni 2371
— di tubi 19032
fabbricante d'anime 4421
fabbricazione d'acciaio al
    crogiuolo 4746
— di elementi speciali
    17010
— dei mattoni 13855
— dei pacchetti 13283
— dell'acciaio al forno
    elettrico 6306
— dell'acciaio cementato
    3161
— dell'acciaio su suola
    11307
— di ghisa malleabile 7110
— in grande 8603
fabbroferraio 8750
faccetta 6739, 6754 a
faccia 6739, 7779, 7780
— portante 1401
— unica 9081
facelite 13140
facies 6755, 8698
— argillosa 778
— batiale 1341
— calcarea 2705
— carbonifera 3863
— continentale 4256,
    18433
— corallina 4378
— d'acqua salmastra 2248
— di cristallo 4795
— di estuario 6570
— di scogliera 14587
— fluviale 7495
— glaciale 8252
— ippuritica 9211, 9606
— litorale 10895
— marginale 11316
— marina 11323
— neritica 12238
-- normale 12379
— nummulifere 12425
— paleontologica 12876
— pelagica 13051
— petrografica 13124

facies sabbiosa 15533
facolite 13142
faglia 2307, 6839, 10245,
    14998, 18933
— a rigetto orizzontale
    7361, 17825
— anormale 18595
— anticlinale 656
— aperta 7968
— chiusa 3759
— composta 4119, 4129
— conforme 8704
— contraria 8703
— curva 4881
— di compressione 18598
— di contrazione S. 18598
— di estensione 6845
— di rigetto orizzontale
    16124
— di tensione 18417
— diretta 6845
— inclinata 9698
— incrociata 46856
— inversa 6850, 12740,
    12765, 14823, 14948,
    S. 18598, 19349, 19350
    19385
— limite 2195
— longitudinale 17818,
    17821
— mineralizzata 11763
— multipla 12113
— normale 2377, 5446, 5700,
    5713, 5980, 6851, 8488,
    8701, 16651
— obliqua 5308
— orografica 12677
— ortogonale 4686, 5437
— orizzontale 9355
— piatta 13460
— principale 5623
— radiale 14327
— ramificata 2261
— rasata 13460
— riaperta 14725
— rotativa 15235
— semplice 16391
— senza rilievo S. 13460
— sinclinale 18157

faglia tubolare 1800
— trasversale 5437
— verticale 19526
fairfieldite 6769
falce 15730
falda 7521, 10594, 17753
— acquea 19752
— acquifera 19751
— di scorrimento 5532
— idrica 727
— impermeabile 9655
— molto inclinata 12729
falde 17746
falesia 3725
falsa camicia 6784
— carica 2517
— dama 6783
— galena 1761
— placca 12455
— roccia di tetto 6780
— sfaldatura 16649
— sfoglia 2508, 15485
— staffa 1002
— stratificazione 6779
— variazione 14394
falso canale 6785
— modello 15510
— piano 12455
— piano di divisione 17559
— pozzo 2652, 1779
— puntone 14345
— taccone 2508
— tetto 5784, 14395, 17584
— tetto scistoso 3612, 3746
famatinite 6790
fanerogeno 13143
fanghi tensioattivi 18072
fanghiglia 2184, 14101
— di carbone 16775
— di perforazione 5891
fango 12069, 16627, 16695,
    16715
— a basso tenore di solidi
    11061
— a diatomei 5344
— acido 94, 12070
— aerato 187
— anodico 629
— a base d'argilla 3655

fango contaminato dal cemento 3147
— del palmento 14142
— d'emulsione 6429
— di carbone 3856
— di trivellazione 5891
— d'iniezione 12079
— elettrolitico 6349
— gassato 8027
—· glaciale 8253
— in circolazione 117
— vulcanico 19592
fangoso 16698, 16638
farina fossile 10348, 11876
faroelite 6816
far brillare 1697
— colare dal becco rovesciando 2978
— la taglia 17830
— leva 14061
— rinvenire l'acciaio 18372
— rivivere 14835
— saltare 1697, 1840, 16160
— scendere 8202, 15346
fare un cordone 19672
—ͻ un giunto ad ammorsatura 15604
— volta 2390
farina 7417
— di frumento 20005
— di roccia 15023 a
— di sondaggio 2085
— di trivellazione 2114
— d'unghia di bue 9310
— fossile 9775
farfalla 2645
farmacolite 13144
farmacosiderite 3818
farrisite 6817
fascetta 9388
fascia 9891, 11658 a, 11660 3380
— di separazione 9879
fascina 20172
fascio di vene mineralizzate 17627
— luminoso 10779
— tubiero 19033
— fase 13146, 17285

fase di pompaggio (in-) 12544
— signa 16308
fasibitichite 6818
fasinite 6819
fassaite 6820
fatica 6830
— di sfregamento 7762
— per flessione pulsante 6831
fattore di formazione 7608
— di equivalenza 6531
— di severità 15927
fazzoletto d'unione 8680
fayalite 6868
feccia delle scorie 15728
feldspatico 6900
feldspatizzazione 6901
feldspato 6899
— calcare 10813
— sodico-calcico 16810
feldspatoide 6902, 7518 10673
felsite 6907
felsitico 6908
felsöbanyite 6910
felsofiro 6911
fenacite 13147
fenicocroite 13156
fendere 2302
fendersi 3719
fenditura 3714, 15965 a, 17125
— centrale 17127
— di presa 7107
fengite 13148
fenolo 13150
fenocristallo 9840
fenomeni di microsaldatura 11657
fenomeno di separazione 15803
— exogenetico 6657
ferberite, 6919
ferghanite 6920
fergusonite 2251, 6921, 6922
fermaporta 5630
fermascoria a pozzetto tangenziale 20019

fermascorie 5476
fermentazione 6923
fermio 6924
fermo 6821
fermorite 6925
fernandinite 6927
ferraccio 15660
ferramenta 10035
ferri commerciali e profilati 1254
   universali 19313
ferrierite 6930
ferrinatrite 6931
ferrite 6934
ferrite libera 7725 a
ferrisymplesite 6933
ferritizzazione 6937
ferritungstite 6938
ferro 9952
— a bulbo 2544
— a colonne 14244
— a croce 4695, 4705
— a cuneo 19885
— a doccia S. 3289
— a doppio T a larga suola 5392, 8528
— a E o ad U 3289
— a grana fine 3762, 7082
— a grana grossa 3874
— a gronda S. 18591
— a I 9609
— a I a suola ordinaria 5681
— a L 512, 10447
— ad I a lunga base 2434
— a lati concavi 7494
— a mandorla 414
— a nastro 1177, 9324
— a piccolo tenore di zolfo 10028
— a profilo di mandorla S. 414
— a quadrante 14244
— a registro 1062
— a spigoli vivi 6870
— a squadra 572
— a T 18186
— a T ad ali larghe 2434
— a T ad anima alta 9192

ferro a T a bordino 2545
— a truogolo S. 18591
— a U 19208 19208
— a V 19422
— a Z, profilati a Z 20135
— a Z sghembo 12441
— acciaioso 17525
— ad angolo S. 572
— ad alto tenore di carbonio 10027
— al alto tenore di silicio
  8296
— profilato ad angolo vivo
  15776
— ad ogiva S. 12721
— ad oliva 12721
— ad U normale 17343
— addizionale 131
— affinato 3303 a, 7093,
  14600
— agro S. 16181
— al basso fuoco 1829
— al carbone di legna 3308
— al carbone di legno 7093
— al coke 3939
— alfa 419
— angolare 572
— arroventato 14542
— attivo 116
— battuto 20240
— Bessemer 1551
— bianco 20026
— bruciato 2613
— boro 6941
— calibrato 2741
— capovolto S. 9324
— carbonato 1644
— carburato 2878
— chimicamente puro 3398
— cilindrato 15097
— -cobalto 6955
— commerciale 11496
— contenente ossigeno
  9969, 15398
— corrimano 1190, 8777
— cristallino fino 7094
— cristallizzato 4808
— cromato 3529
— -cromo 6942

ferro crudo 14454
— crudo di mescolatore
  11826 a
— d'affinaggio al basso
  fuoco 1829
— da calcestruzzo 4176
— da cavallo 9381
— da costruzione 4235
— da fili 20130
— da ganci 9317
— da grata 6915
— da mescolatore 11823
— da parapetto 1190
— da ridurre in fili S. 20130
— da ringhiera S. 1190
— da scampanare 5787 a,
  13211 a, 14426
— da suggellare 2262
— da uncini S. 9317
— decorativo 5075
— del parapetto 14359
— del profilo Grey 8528
— del timpano 19199
— -delta 5157
— di Differdinger 8528
— di fucina S. 20240
— di pialla 13455
— di qualità 14601
— di qualità inferiore 19300
— di rocca S. 8834
— di secondo affinamento
  S. 14102
— di sospensione 18081
— di Svezia 18109
— di Svezia a carbone di
  legna 18108
— dolce 11675, 16835,
  20240
— duro 8834
— duttile 6074
— elettrolitico 6344
— esagonale 9119
— extra-dolce 19535
— fibroso 6988
— fuso S. 20026
— fosforoso 6948
— fragile 2423, 16181
— fragile a caldo 9402,
  9440, 14548

ferro fragile a caldo ed a
  freddo 2598
— fragile a freddo 4001
— fucinabile 7578, 7585,
  S. 20240
— fucinato 20240
— fuso 2991, S. 7464, 9794
— fuso indurito S. 3443
— galvanizzato 7932
— gamma 7945
— granulare 8404, 8433
— grasso S. 17144
— grezzo 12059, 14103,
  14454
— in barre 1215, 9955
— in billette 1582
— in blumi 1105, 1821, 9981
— in grossi profili 10550
— in lingotti 7464, 10998
— in nastri laminati a caldo
  9435
— in nastri laminati a freddo
  3996
— in piccoli profili 16731
— in verghe S. 1215
— in verghette 15054
— inossidabile 15397
— laminato 15097
— liquido 10877
— magnetico 11193
— malleabile 16835
— manganese al titanio
  6945
— Martin o per acciaio 12576
— mercantile 11496
— metallico 11568
— meteorico 11607
— mezzotondo S. 8716
— mezzotondo irregolare
  7336
— mobile 12054
— molibdeno 6946
— molle a carbone di legna
  16829
— molle e tenace 16826
— ocraceo 2474
— ogivale S. 12721
— oligisto 12530 , 17040
— oligisto micaceo 11626

ferro oligisto rosso
  fibroso 6992
— omogeneo 9794
— omogeneo Bessemer
  1556
— oolitico 12551
— omogeneo S. 7464
— omogeneo saldabile
  19929
— ossidato 9979
— ottagono 12451
— ovale 12724
— pastoso 12963
— per arpioni 5600
— per barrotti 7149
— per catene 3246
— per chiodi 12163, 14964
— per colonne S. 14244
— per corrimano S. 1190
— per lamiere di qualità
  superiore 1562
— per lisciare a caldo 9415
— per pernotti S. 14973
— per ribattini 14973
— per saldare 16962
— per sbarre di griglia 7149
— per scampanare 14419,
  14421
— per slebi 16500
— per spranghe 15550
— per travi 8238, 8241
— piatto 7325, 7340, 9322
— piatto a bordino 7329
— piatto a bulbo 2545
— piatto con nervatura
  centrale 14865
— piatto di traliccio 10459
— piatto rettangolare
  S. 17232, 17238
— poroso 13674, 17144
— privo di scorie 16537
— profilato 15772, 15783,
  15775, 15993, 15994,
  17886
— profilato a spigolo vivo
  15279, 15776
— profilato raccordato
  15279
— profilato speciale 17018

ferro puddellato 14096,
  14102, 14110a
— puro 14187
— quadrato S. 17232
— quadro 17232
— raddrizzato a freddo 4004
— ridotto 14562
— rotondo S. 15270
— rozzo S. 14103
— sagomato 15772, 15994,
  S. 17887
— saldabile S. 19926
— saldato 19926
— sbozzato 11691, 12059,
  14096
— semitondo 8716
— semitondo pieno 16883
— sestante 15928
— sfaldato 7363
— sfoglioso S. 7363
— sgrossato 15255
— silico-manganese 6960,
  16324
— spatico 16283, 16994
— silicio 6961
— silicio manganese 6949
— sintetizzato 16432a
— smaltato 6435
— sodo S. 20240
— soprasaturato 18020
— specolare 17040
— spugnoso 17144
— stirato 5816
— storto o a colonne 19182
— tagliato ad ugnatura
  11815
— Thomas 1297
— titanio 6952
— tondo 10004, 15285,
  15046, 15270
— tondo appiattito 7349
— trafilato 5816
— trapezio 18854
— triangolare 18885
— tungsteno 6953
— universale 7340
— vanadio 6954
— vecchio S. 15660
— vergine 19563a

ferro verniciato S. 6435
— vetrino S. 14548
— vetrino a caldo 1671
— vetrino a freddo S. 4001
— zincato 7932, 7941
ferroboro 2116
ferrocristallo S. 13149
ferrocianuro di potassa
  13725
— potassico 13726
ferrolega 6939
ferrolite 6956
ferromagnetico 6957
ferromanganese 6944, 11279
ferrometro 6958
ferronichelio 6947
ferropallidite 6959
ferrosilicio 6950
ferroso 6963
ferrozirconio 6967
ferrossile 6966a
ferrotitanio 18692
ferrotermite 18489
ferrovia d'officina 20226
— funicolare aerea 15167
fessura 3469, 4581, 6768,
  7370, 14727, 14893, 17125
— a caldo S. 9408
— a freddo 3972
— acquifera 2911
— di scarico 13375
— di sfaldatura 6649
— di tensione 18418
— di un getto 5773
— interna 3726
— longitudinale 10979
— per dissecazione 17998
— superficiale 18046
— trasversale 4676
fessurarsi 3468
fessurato 2448, 7704
fessurazione transgranulare
  18822
fessure longitudinali 3378
fiaccola 1893
fiala per lo sviluppo del gas
  7312
fiamma 7252
— acetilenica 64

fiamma alla bocca del forno
   18576
— autoluminosa 15827
— concentrata 12176
— d'accensione 9628
— del sodio 16821
— di idrogeno 9560
— di pudellaggio 14105 a
— illuminante 11088
— ossidante 12810 a
— ossidrica di gas tonante
— riducente 6639 a , 14567 a
— riduttrice 2863
— rossa 14534
fiammare 7258
— una forma 16470
fiammatura 7259
fianco 10807
— del duomo 5618
— di una pietra 16254
— d'una piega 16983
— inferiore 11068
— inferiore d'una piega
   adagiata 7405
— mediano 4094
— mediano (di faglia) 11661
— mediano stirato 5818,
   17792
— sinclinale 18158, 18941
— superiore 758 , 15143
fibra 6982
— dritta (a-) 17710
fibroferrite 6984
fibrolite 6985
fibroso 6986
fichelite 6994
fiedlerite 6995
filiera per tubi 5367
figulina 1113
figure di attacco 6573
— di corrosione 19492 a
filadelfite 13153
filettaggio S. 15719
filettare 15698
— al tornio 19131
filettatrice da banco 1493
filettatura 15713
filettatura a maschio 11244

filettatura al tornio 4925,
   15705 , 18304
— esterna 11233
— lunga 10977
filetto 18550
filiera 5357 , 5373, 5783,
   13483 a, 20152 a, 17617
— aggiustabile 17199
— chiusa 16879
— rotonda 15277
fillipsite 13154
fillite 13190
fillowite 7040
filo 14893, 17832, 20117 a
— a piombo 1930
— a 8 15997
— aculeato S. 1222
— avvolto e intrecciato 4565
— cadmiato 15059/a
— chiaro S. 19231
— d'acciaio 17518
— d'acciaio fuso 11701
— d'acciaio ovale zincato
   7937
— d'acciaio ramato 4355
— d'alluminio 465
— d'ancoraggio 8690
— da saldare con anim
   4454
— della frizione 7771
— di bronzo 2459
— di bronzo al silicio 16327
— di bronzo fosforoso 13173
— di carbone 6077
— di collegamento 4224
— di ferro 10026
— di ferro decapato 13223
— di ferro lucido 1229
— di ferro per imballaggio
   1145
— di ferro per recinzioni
   6917
— di ferro piatto 7347
— di ferro ricotto 11251
— di ferro galvanizzato
   7933
— di ferro spinato S. 1222
— di ferro zincato 7933

filo di fioraio 2277
— di gomma 15315
— di loppa 16559
— di manganina 11285
— di misura 11402
— di ottone 2277
— di piombo 10626,, 13568
— di platino 13530
— di raccordo 4224
— di rame 4368
— di rame crudo stirato
   8824
— di rame dolce 16833
— di rame galvanizzato
   7930
— di rame ricotto 16846
— di rame stagnato 18659
— di rame tenace 18797
— di resistenza 14779
— di rinforzo 10558
— di sospensione 18082
— di zinco 20339
— duro a freddo 8825
— ellittico 6386
— esagonale 9124
— esplosivo 9626
— flessibile 7370
— fusibile 7885
— galvanizzato 7940
— grosso 18505
— incerato 19848
— incombustibile 7263
— intrecciato 20149
— isolato S. 4569
— isolato allo smalto 643
— isolato con cera 19848
— isolato con pergamena
   12931
— isolato in carta 12904
— isolato in ramié 14397
— laminato 15103
— metallico per separare le
   cariche in un foro da
   mina 16955
— neutro 12254
— non isolato S. 1228
— non ricotto 19231
— normale 17358

filo nudo 1228
— partente 10632
— per chiodi 14975
— per elettrodi 4402, 6329
— per funi e cavi 20126
— per incrostare il vetro
  15741
— per molle 17203
— per saldare 19957
— per saldatura 7025
— per saldatura continua
  20127
— per segnalazioni 10410
— per trolley 18929
— per trolley a sezione di
  8 18930
— pieno 16890
— profilato 15996, 16738
— quadrato 17251
— ramato 4373
— ricoperto 4569
— ricotto 607
— ricotto nero 1642
— rivestito 4569
— rivestito a treccia S.
  20149
— rivestito di cotone 4524
— rivestito di cotone cera-
  to 19847
— rivestito di nastro di
  gomma 15316
— rivestito di seta 16333
— smaltato 6437
— smaltato isolato in carta
  12905
— sottile 18525
— sotto cotone 4524
— sotto nastro isolante
  18273
— spinato 1222
— spinoso 1222
— stagnato 18663
— stagnato al fuoco 718
— tenditore 16971
— trafilato 5821, S. 8825
— trafilato a secco 16800
— trafilato ad umido 10462
— triangolare 18887
— zingato 18658 a

filone 5147, 10954, 11393!
  11756, 15743, 16084,
  17831, 17831
filone v. strato
— a camere 3273
— a coccarda 2356
— a gradini 10468
— a gradini 10935
— a piombo 9021
— alimentatore 6885
— aurifero 14584
— aurifero non sfruttato 14580
— brecciforme 2356
— carbonifero non sfruttato 20050
— complesso 4124
— composto 4124, 4132
— concrezionato 4783
— conduttore 2485
— conico 4200
— coniugato 4213
— d'impregnazione 9665
— di carbone 3844,, 3859,
  15747
— di faglia 16660
— di minerale ossidato
  19491
— di minerale solforato
  19492
— di quarzo 14270
— di rame 19487
— di riempimento seconda-
  rio 14728
— di roccia 3286
— di rottura 7224 a
— di scarso valore 10646
— dislocatore 5626
— epitermale 6521
— eruttivo 5410, 14922
— guida 4195, 10325
— in forte pendenza
  17529
— in pendenza 17528
— inclinato 8713, 13421,
  19270
— incrociato 4675
— ipotermale 9604
— irregolare 8073
— laminato o stratificato
  1184

filone lenticolare 1372,
  19841
— mesotermale 11525
— metallifero 10659
— metasomatico 11599
— non sfruttabile 19320
— orizzontale 10714, 10957
— parallelo al piano di
  stratificazione 1695, 9881
— portante 2903
— principale 11365, 11949
— putrefatto 15238
— ramificato 2260
— roccioso 6148
— senza affioramento 1778
— secondario 6001
— semplice 16408
— sottile 1174
— spaccato 5535
— stratificato 1184
— strato 10680, 16337,
  16342
— tabulare 14584, 14585
— tabulare inclinato 15411
— trasversale 4532,, 4699
  4709
— verticale 6253, 9021,
  14383, 19539
filoni 17766
filtraggio 7062
— a percolazione 7064
filtrare 7041, 13076
— per aspirazione 17942
filtrazione 7062
filtro 7042, 16461, 17736
— a coke 3944
— a ghiaia 8481
— a depressione 19430
— a pressione 13905 a
— d'aria 254
— da damigiana 2875
— di ghiaia 13032
— fermascorie 6008
— in derivazione 2651
— luminoso 10782
— per amalgama 482
— pressa 7051, 1838
— sfiatatoio 15689
— sulla mandata di una
  pompa 5495

fine 6449
finemente diviso 7095
finestra 9823, 12174
— metallica 17517
— tectonica 8178
finezza della frantumazione 7099
— della macinatura 7099
— di carbone 7074
finire 5355
— a cuneo 6451, 6452
— di laminare 15068
finitezza v. finitura
finito 7119
— a freddo 3978
finitore 3685
finitura 5843, 7118, 16479 a
— a macchina 11123
— a spazzola 15554 a
— al laminatoio 693 a
— alla mola 7116
— brillante 2406
finnemanite 7142
fino 7103
fiocco 7249 a
fioccoso 7395
fiore 7087
fior di terra (a-) 6625
fioretti da mina 5943
fioretto 2077, 2091, 10250
— a corona 4728
— a mano 8757
— a punta di diamante 5324
— corto 16174
— da mina 5881
— d'innesco 13211
fiori 7430
— di zinco 16973 a
fiorite 7145
fischerite 7205
fissafili S. 20120
fissaggio 7243
— con punte 17191 a
fissare con punte 6825
fissato 14589
fisso 6821
fissurazione 10213
fizelite 7245
flacone di Kjeldahl 10383

flacone per campioni 15456
flangia 4015
— cieca 1682
— con guarnizione ad anello 14927
— d'ancoraggio 17150
— dell'orifizio 12669
— di fondo 2156
— di partenza 10527
— di riduzione 126
— di scorrimento 7435
— di sicurezza 15414
— mobile 11003
— per prove 18464
— piena 1773
flasergneiss 7286
flessibile 13548
flessione 1505, 7372
flessura 7371, 7372
flinchite 7376
flint 7377
flint-glass 7379
floculazione 7393
flogopite 13155, 14860
florencite 7413
flottazione 7415 a
— a spuma 7782
— collettiva 2549
— granulare 17287
fluellite 7458
fluidificante 12093
fluidimetro 10088
fluidità 7469
fluido 7459, 18530
— fangoso 12079
fluocerina 7474
fluorescenza 1819
— di petrolio 12481
fluorina 1905, 2780, 7475, 10295, 13012
fluorite 7477 a, 13012
fluoro 7477
— di calcio S. 7475
— ammonico 525
flusso 9771, 12192, 12475, 15388
— critico 4646
— d'aria 279, 328
— di testa 12750

flusso vorticoso 19128
flussometro 7792, 15192
fluttuare 7420
flysch 7509
focaccia da rifondere 13258
focolaio 7825
focolaio v. focolare
— da immersione sottogriglia 7865
— con circolazione d'acqua nei barrotti della griglia 7863
— con getto d'aria sotto griglia 7865
— per scrostare 15599
— rotatorio scaldato a gas 15208
focolare 7152, 7174 8949
focolare v focolaio
— a bruciatore 17188
— a carbone 3823, 3825
— a carbone polverizzato 7842
— a caricamento dal disotto 19250
— a caricamento automatico 15822
— a caricamento continuo 15822
— a catrame 18318
— a combustibile liquido 10876
— a fiamma invertita 5699
— a gas 7838,
— a gas di altoforno 19729
— a graticola inclinata 7869
— a graticola inclinata sotto alla caldaia 7870
— a graticola orizzontale 7867
— a graticola orizzontale davanti alla caldaia 6695
— a griglia 8472
— a griglia mobile 18861
— a legna 20174
— a lignite 3819

focolare a polvere di car
   bone 3819, 7842
—— a residui di petrolio
   7841
— a rigenerazione 14616
— a rivestimento di scorie
   16538
— a tubaggio forzato 7555
— a tiraggio inferiore 7555
— ad aria forzata 7866
— ad olio combustibile
   7840
— anteriore 7847
— aperto 12573
— con adduzione 7875
— con altare sporgente
   7876
— con graticola a piani
   7874
— con griglia a catena
   3244
— con griglia a cilindro
   7864
— con griglia a scosse
   7872
— con iniezione d'aria a
   traverso le sbarre cave
   della graticola 7556
— da spezzatura 14641
— esterno 6702
— esterno a graticola orizzontale 7868
— o forno 1967
— fumifugo 16764
— fumivoro S. 16760
— in muratura 2376
— inferiore 7862
— interno 7454, 9909
— interno a graticola
   orizzontale 7871
— meccanico 11413
— ondulato 4494
— per combustione senza
   fumo 16760
— periferico 15554
— pneumatico 7866
— semplice a griglia 16370
— dell'asta quadrata 15571
foggiatura 15998

foglia d'oro 8347 a
— di molla a balestra 10633
— di stagno 18648
fogliazione 7531
foglio 7526
— d'alluminio 457
— d'amianto 84
— di gomma 15308, 15312
— di lamiera 16044
— di lamiera di ferro 10011
folerite 13157
folidolite 13158
fondame 2144
— paraffinoso 19844
fondamenta 7637
fondamentale 7819
fondami 9049
— petroliferi 13135
fondare 7636
fondatore 7638
fondazione 7637, 16336
— in mattoni 2370
— su platea di palafitte
   13280
— in pietrame di cava 2447
fondello 5031
— di mina 2057
fondente 7470 a, 7497, 7498,
   7499, 7502, 10819
— di copertura 4572
— per saldatura 16863, 19942
   19942
— siliceo 16319
fondere 2965, 7635, 11456
— ghisa bianca 2982, 2982
— in conchiglia 5354
— in lingotti 2975
— in pani 9781
— nella qualità bianca 2982
— sotto pressione 5354
fondere v. colare
fonderia 3066, 7647, 1677
   16752
— a mano S. 3044
— d'acciaio 17475
— d'alluminio 453
— di caratteri 19203
— di ferro 9975
— di ghisa malleabile 7663

fonderia di ottone 2271
— di rame 2278
— di zinco 17048, 20335
— dipendente 2816, 18612
— per ghisa grigia 8530
— per lavori su commessa
   10188
—— per terzi 10188
— per uso proprio 2816
— specializzata 17013
— su catalogo 17013
fonditore 7640, 7879, 10307,
   10487, 11462, 18355
— addetto al cubilotto 4846
— di ferro 9974
— di ottone 4357, 20290
— di bronzo 2270
fonditrice per masselli 13255
fonditura 7643
fondo 2142, 5731, 7547, 8616,
   11065, 1084, 12133
— a botola 5976
— apribile 2154, 5976
— buono 8357
— del crogiuolo 1276, 8953
— del foro 2173, 8704
— del serbatoio 2184
— del sondaggio 2173, 6747
— della galleria 154, 156
— di caldaia 15727, 16488
— di colata 16488
— di legno con modello 8113
— di pozzo 13404
— di taglio 19635
— di un foro da mina 2082
— forato 13080
— libero 19241
— mobile 5976, 11002
— perforato 12211 a
— pigmentato 13954
— posteriore 1053
— pozzo 10525
- ricambiabile 14703
— ricambiabile cilindrico
   14706
— scorrevole 16617
fonolite 13159, 16339
fonolitite 3729

fonte di taglio di una miniera di carbone 3853

foraminiferi 7552

forare 2073, 5874, 14172, 13241

— con utensile cavo 4455

— di traverso 5880

— in rimonta 14941

— per rotazione 5918

foratappi 4468

forato 9255

foratoio 9278

foratore a percussione 10249

foratrice elettrica per banco 6278

foratura 13085

forbesite 7553

forbici 16038

— da banco elettriche 6258

— da lattoniere 18658

forca 7602

— per coke 3937

forcella a nottolino 2055

— d'arresto 7601

forchetta 7602

— portante 10474

forgia 16757

forgiare 8727, 11257

— a caldo 5972, 7573

— su stampo 18097

forgiare v. fucinare o stirare

forgiato 7586

forgiato v. fucinato

forgiatura 7583, 16753

— a caldo 9416

forgiatura v. fucinatura

fori punzonati praticati sul dorso del profilo 9256

forma 3050, 3061, 11378, 11968, 11973, 17325

— a elementi intercambiabili 11988

— ad elementi sovrapposti 17278

— a verde 8517

— allo scoperto 12585

— allotropica 391

— basaltica 1269

— cilindrica 4949

— circolare 3600

— complicata 9922

forma concava 4158, 4160

— cristallina 4796, 4803

— cubica 4819

— d'aghi (a-) 12210

— d'ottone 2272

— del fondo filetto 15152

— del mattone 15986

— della filettatura 18553

— di diabolo (a-) 5301

— di campana (a-) 1458

— di colonna (a-) 4044

— di conchiglia (a-) 16114

— di dado 4819

— di gesso 13468

— di gomma 15310 a

— di griglia (a-) 10582

— di guscio (a-) 16101 a

— di legno 20175 a

— di massello 13268

— di mattone 2373

— di palla (a-) 1161

— di pressofusione 13899

— di rete (a-) 12244

— di sondaggio 5577

— fiammata 16471 a

— finale 7070

— fissa 13108

— in fossa 8961

— in sabbia 15505

— in staffa 3773, 7296

— in terra grassa 10928

— intercambiabile 9871

— madre 11363 a

— metallica S. 5357

— montata 2540

— multipla 12114

— normale per acciaieria 17353

— ovoidale 6223

— per anodi 628

— per la fusione dei rulli 15114

— per il fondo del convertitore 4300

— per pallottole 2567

— per saldatura alluminotermica 18490

— primitiva 11990 a

— pronta per colare 11985

forma rotta 2444

— scostata 11802

— semipermanente 15846

— sferica 1160

— dei grani di sabbia 4189

— svuotata 15360

— variata 11802, 16125

forma v. stampo

formabile 11989

formaggella 2124, 3381, 17656

— rullata 1678

formaggio 17330

formare 1926, 11960

— a macchina 11129

— a motta 11963

— a ripetere 4534

— al banco 1491

— con placca 13495

— del pezzo 11961

— in fossa 11962

— in piedi 11965

— le palle 7620

— orizzontalmente 11966

— su falsa placca 11964

— un pacchetto 13276

— verticalmente 11965

formarsi di cavità di ritiro 13327

formato al maglio a caduta 5982

formatore 11991

formatrice 12014

— a compressione 17263, 17264

formatrice a due facce 12016

formatrice a leva 376

— a mano 8767, 8780

— a pressione 13872

— a scosse 10129, 10227

— a scosse con sformatura a ribaltamento 10222

— a scosse e pressione 10223

— a scosse con sformatura a candele 10220

— a scosse e pressione con sformatura a candele 10224

formatrice ad estrazione modello 12977
— con estrazione della forma a carrello 12017
— con piattaforma girevole - 12018
— da banco 1492
— doppia 12019
— e sformatrice ribaltabile 15132
— idraulica 9528
— per anime 4422
—- per fonderia 7662
— per ingranaggi a pettine 17873
— per pezzi piatti 10776
— per staffe 7313
formatrice v. macchina per formare
formatura 7617, 8779., 11997 15998
formatura a bandiera 18115
— a caldo 9454
— a cera persa 13824
— a freddo 3979
— a lancio di terra S. 9654
— a macchina 11133
— a mano 8766
— à motta 2229
— a pettine degli ingranaggi 12023
— a pressione 17262
— a placca modello 12988
— a proiezione 9654
— a proiezione ad aria compressa 13594
— a proiezione pneumatica 13594
— a ripetere 4535
— a sagoma 18113, 18115 18401
— a scosse 10121, 10218
— a secco 6041, 12007, 16472
— a verde 8518, 12009
—- a vibrazione 19550
— ad urto 16146
— allo scoperto 7410, 12592

formatura con modelli 12986
— con piastra modello 11369
— d'anime 4461
— d'ingranaggi 12021
— dal pezzo 12005
— del puntale 18703
— di anime 4424, 4465
— di precisione 13824
— in chamotte 3279
— in fossa 8962, 13410
— in gesso 13469
— in pasta 16649 a
— in sabbia cemento 3152
— in sabbia 15506
— in staffa 2215, 7297, 12008
— in terra grassa 10929
— interna 7733
— meccanica 11133
— per iniezione 9815
— perduta 18402
— senza asportazione di trucioli 3475
— senza modello 7733
formazione 7607
— a grappoli 8445
— asfaltica 873
— carbonifera 2858, 3838
— d'idrogeno 7612
— d'imbuto 7821
— d'incrinature 7610
— d'incrostazioni 9728
— del cono dell'acqua di strato 19757
— del ponte 2390
— dell'ossido di carbonio 7609
— delle incrinature a caldo 7611
— di circhi 3608
— di cordone 19677 a
— di domi 5624
— di faglia 6863
— di fessure 7706
— di groppi 7620
— di masselli 7620
— di metallo granulare 16200
— di risucchi 13383, 16224 a
— di scaglie 15595

formazione di scanalature 7881, 15646
— di schiuma 7784
— di scoria 15596
— di soffiatura 9306
— di volte 8809
— franosa 3123
— geologica imprevista 17759
— geologica produttiva 13000
formazione v. gruppo
formazioni metallifere stratificate 1425
formella 2415
formula d'una combinazione 6524
fornace 7825
— Chinagli 10358
— Hoffmann 10359
— per mattoni 2371
— portatile 13686
— Siemens 16292
fornacite 7621
fornaiolo 4849
fornello 7825, 14372, 14942, 14946, 14956
— a petrolio 13134
— di mina 4576, 8365
— essicatore a vuoto 19429
— in refrattari 3660
— per saldare 16888
— di rinvenimento 18395
fornista 4849
fornitura a sagoma 1424
forno 7825
— a bagno di sale 15442
— a bilico 18628
— a carrello 1948
— a cielo chiuso 3769
— a cilindro per la tempera 15940
— a coke 3938
— a coke a cielo chiuso 3768
— a coke a ricupero 3942
— a coke con recupero dei sottoprodotti 14512
— a coppella 893, 4840
— a corrente alternata 431

forno a corrente monofase 16396
— a crogiolo 4740
— a crogiolo estraibile 10749
— a crogiuolo metallico 13719
— a cupola 4841, 4844
— a funzionamento inter-rotto S. 429
— a gas 8011
— a gas per la tempera 8007
— a induzione 9749
— a induzione a bassa frequenza 11048
— a induzione a crogiuolo 4459
— a induzione a sega canale 4459
— a induzione ad alta frequenza 9147
— a induzione per barre 1256
— a induzione per fucina-tura 7594
— a letto fluido 7460
— a manica 4841, 15939
— a manica od a vento per crogiuoli 15937
— a muffola 12097
— a muffola a gas 8008
— a muffola doppia 5666
— a passo di pellegrino 19629
— a pozzo 13406, 15939, 16796 a
— a recuperatore di calore 14524
— a resistenza 14767
— a resistenza d'arco 751
— a ripiani 10360
— a riverbero 7669, 14817
— a riverbero a suola lunga 14818
— a rivèrbero da fondere 7648
— a riverbero per la tempe-ra 18393

forno a spingitoio 14201
— a spinta 14201
— a storte 14797
— a suola 8956
— a suola girevole 15210
— a suola mobile 7873, 7877
— a suola oscillante 19629
— a tino 9149
— a tino di Siegerland 16289
— a tino per minerale di mercurio 2624
— a tiraggio rovesciato 4533
— a tubi radianti 14330
— a tunnel elettrico 6313, 7914, 19113
— a vento caldo 9395
— ad alta frequenza 9148
— ad alveare 1439
— ad arco 745
— ad arco a corrente trifase 18564, 18565
— ad arco ed a resistenza 742
— ad arco indiretto 9743
— ad aria non soffiata 280
— ad aria pulsata 9398
— ad atmosfera controllata 4291
— anulare per arrostire il calcare 620
— Borcher 2062
— campione 2772 a
— catalano 3083
— ceramico 3226
— cilindrico 4940
— circolare 3593
— Colby 3956
— con atmosfera protetta 14047
— con camicia ad acqua 19789
— con crogiuolo anteriore 7170
— con funzionamento discontinuo 429
— con suola a scosse 15970

forno continuo 4267
— convertitore 4310
— d'affinaggio 7100 a, 14613, 6761
— d'affinaggio del ferro in pacchetti 6761
— d'affinamento per piombo 10622
— d'arrostimento 7172, 10356, 14990
— d'arrostimento della blen-da 1763
— d'arroventamento 614
— da cementazione 2926
— da cemento 3151
— da blumi 1171
— da fonderia 7658
— da puddellaggio girevole 15214
— di arrostimento 2716
— di asfalto 876
— di attesa 9244
— di calcinazione 2703, 2716
— di carbonizzazione 12727
— di carburazione 2886
— di carburo 2822
— di cementazione 2886, 3160 3160, 3173, 7839, 17465
— di coking discontinuo 1330
— di combustione 4078
— di essicazione 6059
— di essicazione della sab-bia 15492
— di essicazione delle anime 4408
— di essicazione delle forme 11977
— di fonderia 2986
— di fusione 2986, 7644, 11466, 16748
— di fusione a piatto girevo-le 14110
— di metallo antifrizione 14664
— di petrolio 12491
— di preriscaldo 9796

forno di primo affinaggio 4991 a
   4991 a, 15381
— di puddellaggio 14109
— di puddellaggio sistema
   Springer 17204
— di ricottura 614, 9017
— di ricottura a cassette
   13718
— di ricottura a tino 15941
— di ricottura continua
   4260
— di ricottura 615
— di riduzione 14568,
   14572
— di rifusione 14700
— di rigenerazione a coke
   14645
— di riscaldamento 9013,
   14669, 14674, 19671
— di riscaldamento per
   slebi 16497
— di riscaldo 3236, 8308,
   8955, 9796
— di riscaldo a suola
   mobile 14671
— di Roessler 15065
— di scarico 3566
— di separazione 12948
— di sinterizzazione 16435 a
— di tempera 8865
— di torrefazione S. 14990
— di torrefazione in muratura 2372
— di torrefazione stiriano
   17917
— di torrefazione a gas di
   Westman 19982
— di torrefazione Cleveland
   3723
— di torrefazione di Fillafer
   7015
— di torrefazione di
   Witkowitz 20161
— di ventilazione 19256
— di zolfo 17983
— dielettrico 5385
— elettrico 6274
— elettrico a crogiuolo
   6268

forno elettrico a frequenza
   intermedia 9890
— elettrico a induzione
   6285
— elettrico a induzione a
   bassa frequenza 11047
— elettrico a induzione a
   canale 3291
— elettrico a induzione con
   nucleo elettrico 3291
— elettrico a muffola 6289
— elettrico a resistenza 6295
— elettrico a resistenza a
   riverbero 6276
— elettrico a resistenza
   irradiante 6296
— elettrico a suola 6280
— elettrico a tino 6298
— elettrico ad arco 6256
— elettrico ad arco orizzontale 6257
— elettrico d'affinazione
   6292
— elettrico di attesa 6283
— elettrico di fusione 6288,
   6300
— elettrico ribaltabile 6310
— fisso 1143, 7233
— Frick 7764
— fusorio 11483
— fusorio per metallo bianco 11468
— fusorio per bronzo 11467
— Gérard 8193
— Gin 8232
— Girod 8244
— Hellberger 9067
— Hempel 9089
— Hiorth 9210
— industriale 9757
— industriale per riscaldamento a gas 9758
— inglese a cementazione
   6479
— in marcia alla temperatura massima 7848
— incineratore 9687
— Ireland 9948

forno Ischewsky 10046
— Kjellin 10382
— Martin 12574
— Martin acido 83
— Martin basico 1299
— Martin Siemens 16293
— meccanico a gas per la
   tempera 11406
— mescolatore 11831
— metallurgico 11586
— Nathusius 12179
— orizzontale 9342
— oscillante 15039, 18628
— oscillante a induzione
   9755
— per anime 4429
— per bauxite 1357
— per blumi 1828
— per calce 10816
— per carbonizzare la
   torba 3310
— per cuocere la porcellana
   13661
— per cuocere i fondi dei
   convertitori 2717
— per distillare l'amalgama
   480
— per dolomite 5610
— per estrazione di sottoprodotti 7837
— per il trattamento termico
   9003
— per la rimozione della
   paraffina in cristalli
   18104
— per minerale di piombo
   15651
— per più crogiuoli 12111
— per riscaldare 19943
— per riscaldamento del-
   le storte 7914
— per cuocere piastre 13491
— per smaltare 6438
— per temperare le lime
   7005
— per un sol crogiuolo 16387
— per vetro 8276
— per vetreria 8276
— Piat 13197

forno Roechling-Rodenhauser 15000
— Roechling-Rodenhauser a corrente trifase 15001
— rotante S. 18628
— rotativo 14837, 15207, 15210
— rotativo per puddellaggio 14841, 15234
— rotatorio 15213
— separatore 10867·
— sperimentale 18445 a
— Stassano 17387
— statico del tipo a campana 17392
— tubolare 19029 a
— tubolare rotativo 14844
— verticale 15948
— verticale a griglia rotatorio 15209
forno v. stufa
foro 7966, 9248
— a piccolo diametro 16626
— accecato 4526 a, 16210 a
— ausiliare 14690
— cieco 1774, 1767 a
— conico 4209
— d'alimentazione 6895
— d'avanzamento 179
— d'ispezione 9847
— d'uomo 11258
— d'uscita 12702
— d'uscita delle scorie fuse 3575
— da mina 1729, 1741, 5892, 16204
— da mina orizzontale 2778
— da mina ausiliario 6179, 16498
— da mina di rilevaggio 7541
— da mina laterale 16265
— da mina umido 19782
— dell'aria 19499
— dell'asta motrice 14433
— dell'asta quadra 10304
— della tubiera 19160
— delle scorie 6008 a, 3574, 7415, 15729, 16542, 16557

foro del vento 1731
— di colata 3074, 5712, 7424, 8087, 8140, 11553, 12411, 13756, 15381, 15906, 18267, 18358
— di frenaggio 19890 a
— di fondo 2162
— di mina inclinato 8569
— di protezione 14044
— di pulizia 16696
— di ricerca 14034
— di scampanatura 14425 a
— di scarico 1061, 8088, 15723
— di scarico stretto 7105
— di scoronamento 1061
— di soglia 5703
— di sonda 2076
— di sondaggio 14034
— di spia 18364, 13044
— di spillatura 18267
— di tiraggio 292
— di trasudamento 19890
— di trivellazione 2081, 5892
— di ventilazione 886
— di visita 3694
— formato dall'anima 4415
— fuori calibro 12748
— in corona 2348
— in soletta 17668
— non tubato 1230
— passante 18583 a
— per carotaggio 4414
— per il «surface string» 18055
— per la scoria 16539
— per lo scarico 5502
— per scaricare le scorie 2347
— piano 7339
— pilota 13299
— profondo 5092
— regolare e di diametro costante 7799
— ridotto 14433
— ristretto 18617
— scavato 19697
— scoperto 12582, 19234
— sotto calibro 19252

foro storto 4657
— sulla pelle 16477
— tubato 2924
fosferite 7622
forti sollecitazioni dovute alla risonanza 9184
fortunite 7624
forza 17775
— a verde 8506
— della battuta 17776
— della terra 15484
— della terra a secco 6025 a
— di ritiro 17870 a, 20159 a
— di torsione 18781
— idraulica 19804
— unilaterale 19306
forzamento 16226
forzare 18119
forzatura 18123
fosfatazione 13168
fosfato sodico ammoniacale 528
— sodico ammonico 16818
fosfoferrite 13170
fosfofillite 13171
fosforite 13182
fosforo 13183
fosfosiderite 13184
fosfuranilite 13185
fosgenite 9368, 13160
fossa a cappi 10999/a
— di colata 3067, 7668, 13256, 13396, 13762 a
— di colata per lingotti 13248
— di colata semicircolare 15839
— per formatura 12024
— per olio 12502
fossato allagato 11843
fossetta di scolo 3088
fossile 7629
— caratteristico 8650, 9734
— di facies 6756
— di zona 20363
— guida 8650, 8734
— longevo 13116
fossilifero 7632
fossilizzare 7634

fossilizzazione 7633
fosso 18873
— di cedimento 18585
fotochimico 13185 a
fotolosi 18321
fragile 2420, 11995
— a caldo 9439, 14535,
    14547, 16175
— a freddo 3965, 4000
fragilità 2427, 7707, 7716,
    16187, 16189 a,
— a bassa temperatura
    3966
— a caldo 9403, 9441,
    14549
— a freddo 3866
— a freddo del ferro 4002
— a soluzioni caustiche
    3113
— al blu 1900
— al colore blu 1899
— all'intaglio 12396
— al rosso 14549
— caustica 3114
— da idrogeno 9558
— del ferro 2428
— di decapaggio 79
— di rinvenimento 18373,
    18392
— di tensione 18416
— intercristallina per cor-
    rosione 3113
— per corrosione 4489
— per ingrossamento del
    grano 17410
frammento 1623, 16011
— di mattoni 2439
— di minerale 16141
frana 5973, 6169, 6766,
    6774, 10524, 12299,
    16607
— circolare 6856
franamento 2324, 3122,
    4622, 6766, 6774, 7639,
    10524, 12299
— del tetto 6775, 15141
— metallico 18200
franare 3119, 5971, 6771,
    15338, 17669

franato 3120, 6776, 17673,
francheite 7714
francio 7713
franco vagone 7734
— stabilimento 7720
francolite 7715
frangia capillare 2808
frangigrumi 11089
franklinite 7717
frantoio 4771, 8557, 10336,
    11685
— a cilindri 3357, 15076,
    15109
— a cilindri anulari 14929
— a cono 4197
— a martelli 8729
— a mascelle primario 13942
—   campionatore per carbone
    3809
— giratore 8237, 8695
— per carbone 3808
— per coke 3931
— per fini 7077
— per pietre 17641
— per triturazione grossa
    3869
— primario 13828
— secondario 14513
frantoio v. molazza
frantumare 2565, 3645,
    8538, 17306
— con esplosivi 1790
— e grigliare 3883
— finemente 4090
— il minerale 4761
frantumato 7708 a
frantumatore 2317, 4771
— per carbone S. 3808
frantumazione 2321, 4775,
    4776, 11706, 16015
— a mezzo esplosivo 2566
— a secco 6029, 6047
— dei minerali 4757, 12633
— fine 15321
— graduale 17286
— per via umida 19988,
    19993 a, 20000
— preliminare 13843
— secondaria 14514

frattura 2307, 7693, 14727
— a coppa 4835
— a grana fine 7081, 16334
— a grana grossa 3873
— a grinze 18607 a
— capillare 8708
— colonnare 4046
— concoidale 7381
— cristallina 4800
— diagonale 5309
— fibrosa 6987, 6989 a
— granulometrica
    16443 a
— infragranulare 9920
— incompleta 8524
— intercristallina 9876
— intergranulare 9882
— lamellare 10506
— netta (a-) 6608
— obliqua 12434
— penetrante 9650
— per contraccolpo
    7696
— scagliosa 17122
— semplice 16368
— su barretta intagliata
    12265
frazionamento 7692
— della paraffina 19843
frazione 7686
— fine 18004 a
— granulometrica 16298 a
— laterale 16278
frazioni finali leggere 10781
— pesanti 9030
— residue 14758
freatico 19749
freccia 811, 5120
freibergite 7750
freieslebenite 7751
freirinite 7752
fremontite 7753
frenatore 1196, 17177
freno idraulico 9565
— di sicurezza per fine
    corsa 12786
— dinamico 6150
— idraulico 9515
frenatura 17178

fresa 11689, 11708
— a coda per filettaggio
   trapezoidale 18855
— a disco 16268
— a ganasce 16153
— a lame riportate 6746
— a profilo 7618, 14002
— a scanalatura 17099
— a vite 9058
— con coda 17098
freieslebenite 7751
freirinite 7752
fremontite 7753
frenatore 1196, 17177
freno idraulico 9565
— di sicurezza per fine
   corsa 12786
— dinamico 6150
— idraulico 9515
frenatura 17178
fresa 11689, 11708
— a coda per filettaggio
   trapezoidale 18855
— a disco 16268
— a ganasce 16153
— a lame riportate 6746
— a profilo 7618, 14002
— a scanalatura 17099
— a vite 9058
— con coda 17098
— da fori 16691
— elicoidale 9058
— madre elicoidale per
   viti senza fine 20229
— per tagliar pignoni
   17227
— sagomata 7616, 7618
fresare 11682
fresatrice orizzontale da
   banco 1487
— per modelli 12985
— verticale 19528
fresatura di pezzi in serie
   7952
freyalite 7759
friabilità 4012
friedelite 7772
frieseite 7773
frizione 15319

frizione interna 9901
fronte 7779
— a doppia ala 5678
— d'abbattimento 20206
— d'attacco a 45° dal piano
   di stratificazione
— d'attacco a 30° rispetto
   al piano di stratificazione
— d'attacco a 60° col piano
   di stratificazione
— d'attacco parallelo al
   piano di stratificazione
   6751
— d'avanzamento 2342,
   5276, 6750, 8935, 11730
— del focolare 7843
— di caldaia sagomata per
   esplosione 6687
— di carriaggio 2468
— di coltivazione 17677
— di dragaggio 5826
— di faglia 7777
— di galleria 7564
— di scavo 2342
— di scavo normale al
   «limets» 2635
— di taglio 6450, 6738,
   6749, 7562, 7564, 11730,
   19635, 19642, 13189
fuchsite 7786
fucile perforatore 8669, 8674,
   17674
fucina 7575
— catalana 1827
— fissa ad un fuoco 16392
— per la produzione di blumi
   sgrossati al laminatoio
   1826
— per la tempera 18394
fucinabile 6073
fucinabilità 6075, 7584
fucinare 7570, 13287
fucinare v. forgiare
— a caldo 7573
— a freddo 7572
— al maglio 7571
— alla pressa 13870
fucinati 7600
fucinato 6719, 7586

fucinato v. forgiato
— grezzo 15249
— ottenuto meccanicamente
   13782
fucinatore 7588
— rotante 16136
fucinatrice 7595, 14500 ,
   16133
— a frizione pneumatica
   255
— a rulli 7596
— automatica 982
— meccanica 19380
— orizzontale 9356
fucinatura 7590, 10392
— a stampo 5983
— a stampo chiuso 3770
— al maglio 8735
— con mandrino 9272
— con riscaldamento a
   induzione 9748
— della strozzatura 11666
— di precisione 13822
— di preparazione 15406
— libera 12569
— per laminazione 15077a
— per resistenza 6332
— senza bava 7308
fucinatura v. forgiatura
fuga 10637
— d'aria 6563
— della tubiera 10638
— di gas 6562
— di gas durante la mano-
   vra 18910
fulgurite 7793
fuligginoso 15918
fulloppite 7814
fulmicotone 8672
fulminante 13949
fulminato d'oro 7813a
— di mercurio 7813
fumo 7816a
— scuro 2476
fungo 8904, 12143, 14963,
   17145a
— della rotaia 14358
'une a trefoli di 7 fili 7936
— d'estrazione 20100, 20105

func di tenuta 16791
— di rinvio 18212
— di ritorno 1134
— di perforazione
— e gabbia d'estrazione
  2038
— metallica 17505
— metallica a trefoli piatti
  7350
— piatta 7343
funzionamento 15349
— a caldo 9455
— a scavo automatico
  984
— ad acqua compressa
  9540
— continuo 4279
— regolare senza urti 20223
funzionamento v. andamento
fuochista 17634
fuoco 7289, 7516
— d'affinaggio 7101
— d'affinaggio chiuso 4567
— d'affinaggio Lancashire
  18107, 18110
— per saldare 19941
fuori servizio 12691
— uscita di liquido da una
  condotta per rottura
  19712
furfurolo 7824
fusibile 11459
fusibilità 7890
fusione 7643, 7893, 11463,
  11464, 14643, 16747 a
— a cera persa industriale
  9937, 11014, 11040
— a guscio 16099
— a mano 3044
— al crogiolo 4741
— al cubilotto 11469
— con forno elettrico 6299
— dei rottami 16751
— della lega 11474
— della loppa 11473
— della scoria 11473
— dello smalto 7194
— di campane 1451
— di precisione 13820

fusione elettrotermica del
  ferro 6301
— ignea 9623
— in atmosfera controllata
  11482
— in conchiglia 3434
— in forma aperta 3057
— in ghisa 9965
— in staffe 3056
— in verde 8507
— in zone 20363 a
— incompleta 9715
— nell'altoforno 1720
— ossidante 12804
— per gradi 17551
  per ossidazione 12812
— per pezzi di macchine
  6467
— riduttiva 14570
— rigata 17764
— scartata alla prova a
  pressione 10636
— sorpassata 5033 a
— sotto pressione 5360,
  5362
— sotto vuoto 19430 a,
  19436
— svergolata 19676
fusione v. colata
fusite 7883 a
fuso 11460, 11877
— a misura 3028
— grezzo 15246
— in conchiglia 3426
— in guscio 16098
— in terra 15486
— in un sol pezzo 2976,
  3016
fusto leggero 16509
— produttivo 12545
fusulina 7895

G

gabbia 6789, 9466, 17331,
  17333 a, 17335
— a due cilindri 9464
— a cilindri equilibrati 1137

gabbia d'estrazione a due
  piani 8219
— a pignoni 13320 a, 17091
— a scarico automatico
  15819
— a trio 18557
— aperta o con cappello
  1 600
— chiusa ordinaria 12624
— da miniera 8671
— del laminatoio 15089,
  15262
— del montacarichi 6379
— d'estrazione 2680, 5795
— di ascensione 10750
— di laminatoio a trio 18559
— di miniera 13400
— (a) duo 9188
— finitrice 7139 a
— protettiva 2344
— quarto 7679 a
— rifinitrice dei bordi 6211
— sgrossatrice 13468 a
— (a) trio 18562
gabbione 20119
gabbro 7897
gabbroico 7898
gabbroide 7899
gadolinio 7903
gadolinite 7902
gageite 7905
gagolimite 20303 a
galapectite 7910
galassite 7911
galena 7912, 10614
galenite 10624
galenobismutite 7913
galleria 5015
— a giorno 11732, 17910
— cieca 334, 1771, 5027,
  10147
— d'aereazione 281, 20095,
  20107
— d'avanzamento 180, 5865,
  8931
— d'avanzamento di fondo
  2159
— d'esplorazione 11902
— d'estrazione 6709, 12645,
  15149, 20112

galleria del cavo 2664
— di carreggio 8893, 809?,
  8898, 15119
— di collegamento 2338,
  4710, 4712, 5595, 7909,
  15159, 17542, 17820,
  18532
— di collegamento di ven-
  tilazione 324
— di coltivazione 5870
— di contorno 2010
— di drenaggio 5743, 5750
— di direzione 5870
— di drenaggio 11728,
  19791
— di fondo 5093, 7959,
  8095, 11224
— di livello 2637, 4530,
  5850, 11735
— di livello a ventilazione
  forzata 6808
— di passaggio 7959
— di ribasso 5436, 5627,
  9700
— di ritorno dell'aria 14809
— di scolo 1777, 10961
— di scolo dell'acqua
  16930, 19796
— di taglio 6709
— di traverso-banco 8631
— di ventilatore 6798
— di ventilazione 281, 297,
  332, 2338, 2340, 9854,
  11901, 11903
— gemella 273
— in direzione 5953, 20208,
  20214
— in direzione entrobanco
  14586
— in roccia 11542, 15024,
  17642, 15015
— in roccia sul fondo
  15023
— intermedia 17919
— in pendenza 16572
— in traversobanco 4678,
  4682, 4684, 4693
— in traversobanco di
  ventilazione 4694

galleria inclinata 2469
— inferiore 2171
— nelle ripiene 8331
— orizzontale d'accesso
  16259
— per l'uscita dell'aria
  12717
— principale 7959, 8931,
  11220, 11224, 11947
— principale di carreggio
  2899
— sul fondo 7549
— trasversale di collega-
  mento 16670
— unica 16390
gallerie 11725
— gemelle 5658
— di sfruttamento 1925
galletta 12036, 19617
— di spessore 18514
galletto 7508
gallio 7917
galvanico 7923
galvanismo 7927
galvanizzare 7928, 20343
galvanizzare v. zincare
galvanizzato 7929
galvanizzazione 7926, 20346
— del ferro 20349
galvano 6371
galvanoplastica 6331 a
gamba 10668, 10807, 17228
— abbassata 11059
— della torre 5220
— inferiore abbassata 11072
gambetto 3724, 15930
gambo 17533
— del pistone 1455
— del supporto per anima
  17132
gambuto 17082
gamma degli sforzi 14412 a
gammagrafia 7946
gammagramma 7947
ganascia 8572, 17115
— del freno 16152
— di serraggio 15158
gancetti da fonderia 15511

gancio 7176, 7906, 10166,
  10756 a, 12303, 16588
— ad S 15403, 20302
— a molinello 18141
— d'arresto 1089
— da fuoco 14314
— da presa 8381
— di salvataggio 3089
— di sospensione 18080
— di sospensione della
  gru 4598
— per perforazioni rotary
  2949
— per rimescolare 14381
— per tubi di pompaggio
  19030
— pescatore 7218
— raddrizzatore 19643
ganga 2465, 7956, 10958,
  17905, 19494
— del carbone 3826
ganistro 7960
ganofillite 7963
ganoide 7961
ganomalite 7962
garewaite 7971
garganite 7972
garnierite 7974
garza 8120
gas acido 16944
— bruciato 19728
— combusti 2612
— combustibile 7788
— compresso 4138
— d'acetilene 65
— d'acqua 19777 a
— d'acqua arricchito 2877
— d'altoforno 1712, 20069
— d'aria 282
— d'arrostimento 14991
— dei forni a coke 3941
— deleteri 1767
— d'esplosione 200, 202,
  16145
— di cartone 3826 a
— d'iniezione 9673
— di petrolio 12491 a,
— di petrolio liquefatto
  11078

gas di raffineria 17594
— di torrefazione 14991
— disciolti 5548
— fulminante 12815
— greggio 5476 a
— ideale 9614 a
— illuminante 9636
— libero 7730
— lift intermittente 9895
— lift per camera 3271
— liquefatto di petrolio 10879
— misto 15851
— naturale 12193
— naturale liquefatto 10905
— occluso 12443
— povero 282.,10642, 13987 a
— purificato 14190 a
— ricco 14872
— ricco di catrame 18330
— rigenerato 14644
— sviluppato 6566
— umido 14872
gasdotto 8036
gasogeno 8012, 8042, 13988
— con griglia a gradini 17557
— doppio 5672
— Duff 6078
— Morgan 11932
— Siemens 16295
gasolina naturale 2947, 12194
gasolio 8031
gasometro 8079
gassaggio 8015
gassato 8083
gassificare 8076
gassificazione 8013, 8074
— alla storta 14798
— del combustibile solido 8075
Gault 8118
gauteite 8119
gavello 15801
gaylussite 8122
gedanite 8141

Gedinniano 8142
gedrite 8143
gehlenite 8144
geichielite 8145
gelatina-dinamite 8664
— esplosiva 1748
gelcemento 8146
gelignite 8149
geminato 8151, 11143
geminazione di penetrazione 13064
geminazioni d'interpene-trazione 9911
— giustapposte 10264
— polisintetiche 12122, 13646
gemma 8150
generatore 8154
— a gas 8000
— cilindrico 4945
— di acido fluoridrico 701
— di cloro 3501
— di vapore 17426, 17432
generatrice inferiore di un tubo 2185
genthite 8158
generazione spontanea 17146
geno-holotipo 8155
genoparatipo 8156
genotipo 8157
geoanticlinale 8123, 8159
geochimica 8160
geocronite 8163
geocronologia 8161
geode 8164, 19607
geodesia 8165
geodetico 8166
geodinamica 8167
geofisica 8184
geofisico 8183
geogenesi 8168
geognosia 8169
geoide 8170
geologia 8180
— cronologica 17752
— stratigrafica 17752
— strutturale 8190
geologico 8171
geologo 8179

geomorfologia 8181
geonomia 8182
geoscopia 8187
geosinclinale 8188
geotecnica 8189
geotermico 8191
gerhardtite 8194
germanio 8196
gersdorffite 8197
germe 12419
gesso 8235, 8694, 17969
— cristallizzato 4801, 15809
— di qualità superiore 8613
— granulare cristallino 8431
— nero 1646
— terroso 3562
gettare 2965, 10261
— in forma di terra 15468
— in terra 15468
gettare v. colare
gettata di ciottoli 15323
gettato 2976, 11878
getto 2984, 10262
— a sifone 18176
— ad anima 9268
— cavo 4458, 9266, 9268
— centrifugato 3202
— con cavità inferiore 9276
— con intercapedine 10104
— con nervatura 14866
— d'acciaio elettrico 6305
— d'aria 241
— deformato 19676
— di acciaio S. 17463
— di colata 8140, 13756, 15364, 15381
— di ferro malleabile 11813
— di ghisa malleabile 11250
— di ghisa malleabile a cuore bianco 20046
— di leva 1871
— di metalli 17769
— di rame fuso 20226 a
— di sabbia 15472
— grezzo 15247
— in conchiglia 3428
— in forma di argilla 10926
— in forma di terra 15490

getto in forma di terra verde
   8515
— in forma di argilla 10926
— in forma di terra 15490
— in forma di terra verde
   8515
— in fossa 13402
— in ghisa 9966
— in ghisa sferoidale 17068
— in staffa 2215, 7292
— incompleto 15360, 15383
— poroso 13673
— principale 11223
— regolato ad ago conico
   12208
— rotto nel pezzo 2327
— sano 16937
— sbarbato 2327
— sdetto 15125
— senza soffiatura 3052
— senza tensioni interne
   3051
— soffiato 1880, 8084, 9304
— spostato 16125
— svuotato 15383
geyerite 8206
geyser 8207
geyserite 8208
ghiacciaio 8263
— alpino 12031
— di primo ordine 19444
— di secondo ordine 8264
— di vallone S. 19444
— norvegese 9612
— riformato 14506
— rigenerato 14506
— sospeso S. 8807
ghiaia 8477
— grossa 3481
— striata 17801
ghiaietto 4769
ghiaioso 8577
ghiera di rinforzo 19950
ghisa 2991, 2995, 11537
— a alta resistenza 9143
— a cuore bianco 6594,,
   20044
— a cuore nero 1669
— a grafite sferoidale
   17067

ghisa a grana fine 7083
— a grandi caverne 19536
— a matrice ipereutettoide
   9587
— a piccole caverne 3763
— a tenore composto 9158
— a vento caldo 9396
— a vento freddo 3963
— acciarosa 9143, 15848,
   17484, 20071
— aciculare 71
— affinata 14599 S. 17008
— al forno elettrico 6275
   6320
— al manganese 11272,
   11269, 11272
— al nickel 13262
— all'antracite 644
— acciaiosa 17526
— alligata 397
— amagnetica 12355
— austenitica 958
— basica S. 1297
— Bessemer 9076, 1552
— bianca 7579 11249
   20026 20033
— bianca a struttura rag-
   giata 20043
— bianca calda 20040
— bianca fredda 20028
— bianca porosa 12604
— bianca sfaccettata
   20029
— brillante 9172
— buona per pezzi di mac-
   chine 1561
— calda 9420
— cavernosa 13677
— Cleveland 13180
— colata in sabbia 15487
— con scorie 3576
— d'altoforno 13260
— da costruzioni 17884
— da fonderia 2994, 7665
— da fonderia semidura
   11426
— da pudellaggio 7579
— da tubi 18977
— del Lussemburgo 11104
— depurata 19696

ghisa desolforata 5246
— di base S. 1279
— di cubilotto 4845
— di partenza 1279
— di prima fusione 2992
— di prima qualità 9150
— di primo affinaggio 3307
— di seconda fusione 2993
— di Siegen 16288
— di Stiria 17916
— di Svezia 18111
— dolce 11118, 16827a
— dolce da fonderia 11249
— dolce per fondere pezzi
   di macchine 16834
— grigia 8527
— grigia da fonderia 2995
— eccessivamente riscaldata 18006
— elettrica 6275, 6299, 6320
— ematite 9074
— eutettica 6601
— fabbricata ad alta temperatura 9399
— ferritica 6935
— fortemente radiale 9194
— fortemente raggiata 9194
— fosforosa 13181
— fragile a caldo 16176
— fredda 3986, 18508
— fusa in conchiglia 3442
— grafitosa 1660, 8454
— grezza 13259, 13260
— grezza elettrica 6290
— grigia 8502, 8529, 8531
— grigia siliciosa 1753a,
   9172, 16363
— grigio chiaro 7083, 10783
— grigio-nera 5002
— grigio-scura 5002
— in conchiglia 3451
— in pani di fusione 3006
— inglese 6481
— indurita 3443
— ipereutettoide 9587
— ipereutettica 9586
— ipoeutettoide 9599
— legata 397
— liquida 11879

ghisa malleabile 11249, 11813, 11814
— malleabile a cuore nero 1670
— malleabile americana 1670
— malleabile bianca 20045
— malleabile nera 1670
— marezzata 11956
— martensitica 11348
— meccanica 6474
— mista 11956
— nera 9172
— nodulare 12334
— nuova 13259
— ottenuta con andamento caldo 9442
— per convertitore Bessemer 1552
— per fondere pezzi resistenti agli acidi 7666
— per fondere pezzi resistenti al fuoco 7667
— per fusione in conchiglia 3432
— per fusioni 7665
— per macchine 11138
— per pezzi di macchine 11120
— per pezzi meccanici S. 6474
— perlitica 13018
— picchiettata 11956
— poliedrica 958
— povera di silicio e manganese 11060
— priva di sabbia 15527
— proveniente dai lavatoi 9977
— raffinata 14599
— refrattaria 8993
— resistente al calore 8993
— resistente di fonderia 18798
— rifusa 14697
— scozzese 15652
— semidura 15838 a
— semifosforosa 11429
— semitrotata 10800
— sferoidale 17067

ghisa sintetica 18170
— soffiata 8084, 9304
— sorbitica·16921
— speciale 17008
— specolare 17038, 17078
— specolare grossolana 3878
— s. colare per pudellaggio 17039
— Thomas 18536
— trotata 11956, 17879
— trotata bianca 11958
ghizite 8209
giacchetta 11981 a, 16654 a
giacenza 17612
giacimenti 5408
— alluvionali 6030
— asfaltici 875
— di riempimento delle cavità e delle fessure 3125
— magmatici 11169
giacimento 1413, 1430, 1938, 5147, 9330, 15747
— a filone 7957
— alluvionale 406, 13435
— d'idrocarburi 13650
— d'impregnazione 9662
— di carbone 3800
— di condensato 4183
— di contatto 4247
— di ferro 9991 a
— di gas 8005
— di limonite 1944
— di minerali di ferro 11729, 5197
— di petrolio 12486
— diamantifero 1903 a
— dislocato 5524, 6864
— esaurito 5194
— filoniano 10363
— massiccio 16884
— metallifero 12640
— metasomatico 11598
— minerario 11751
— multiplo 6069
— produttivo 12999
— stratificato 17747
— vergine 11216
giacinto 9494, 10089

giada 10114, 12232
giadeite 10115, 10116
giallo-paglia 17758
giallomina 2699
gibelite 8217
gibsite 8216
gieseckite 8218
gigantolite 8221
gigantostraca 8222
gilbertite 8223
gillespite 8229
gilsonite 8230
ginocchiera 10414
giobertite 8234
gioco 1065, 13536, 18709
— circolare 3587
— della ghisa 18063
— delle portate 3709
— di colori 2306
— doppio 5638
giorgiadesite 8186
giornale dei sondaggi 5937
giorno (a-) 913, 12605
giostra 4264, 12013
girabecchino 2346
giralingotti 18626
giramaschi 17617
girare a vuoto 15347
— il lingotto 19134
— il pezzo 19132
girasole 7173, 8236
giratoio 17617
giro 19137
gismondite 8247
giudizio secondo i dati esterni 6631
giunti 4551
— di accoppiamento 4551
— per saldatura autogena 971
— saldati di testa 2639
giunto 2018 2021, 10198, 14893
— a bicchiere 9834
— a caduta libera 7725
— a freddo 3984, 4003
— a frizione 7767
— ganasce 7209
— a guarnizioni 12850

giunto a guarnizione 12850
— a passaggio totale 7800
— a tenuta 18619, 19813
— articolato 10411
— cardanico 2887
— del packer 10848
— di dilatazione 5481, 6672
— di dilatazione Lürmann 11095
— di ritiro 10205
— di separazione 12944
— di sicurezza 15418
— diagonale 5309
— idraulico 19812
— isolante 9851
— liscio interno 9900
— normale 14653
— orizzontale 1418
— per draga refluente 4223
— per tubo flessibile 15318
— rapido 14296
— saldato al cannello 1884
— sferico 1157
— a sovrapposizione 10540
— stagno 15830
— virtuale 1775
giunzione 2021, 10200, 10214
— a tenone e a mortista 10196
— ad attestatura 10197
— mediante flange mobili 4222
— mediante saldatura 4222
— ricalcata 10247 a
giurapaite 10259
giurassico 10260
givetiano 8249
glacialismo 8262
gladkaite 8267
glascrite 689
glauberite 8289
glaucocerinite 8292
glaucocroite 8290
glaucodot 8291
glaucofanite 8295
glauconia 8293
glauconifero 8294
glauconite 8511

glessite 8298
globulite 8305
globulo 17064
glomerofirico 8307
glucinio 8314
gmelinite 8318
gneiss 8319
— a biotite 1610
— occhiadino 944, 6730
— primario 7815
gocce 17109
— sparse 16995
goccia fosforosa 13169
— fredda 6493
— segregata 15802
gocciolatoio 5950
godronare 2068
goethite 8338, 12207, 14242 a
goffrato 6403
goffratura 6404
gola 7027, 7966, 8087, 8586
— di caricamento 6891
— di cuoio S. 10651
goldfieldite 8353
gomito 1501
— del portavent. 19166
gomma 8663, 15304
gonfiare 1467, 18120
gonfiarsi 10095
gonnardite 8355
goongarrite 8361
gordonite 8368
gorgia 10192
gorgo 20021
gorgogliamento 2494
goslarite 8369
governare le caldaie 17630
goyazite 8376
gradazione ottanica 12454
gradiente di temperatura 18382
— geotermico 8192
gradinata di faglie 17546
gradinatura 1490, 1496
gradini (a-) 17553
— (a-) a rovescio 12751
gradino 1483, 18866
— di faglia 6841, 10313

gradino dritto 19266
— dritto senza ripiena 12601
— inclinato 14912
— inclinato con ripiena 7019, 9696
— inferiore nella coltivazione a gradini rovesci 4921
— rovescio senza ripiena 12586
— superiore 9052
grado 8383, 13412, 17285
— d'acidità 5139
— di battuta S. 5137
— di carburazione 5131
— di compressione 11981
— di deformazione 5124
— di dissociazione 5132
— di dissociazione d'una soluzione 5133
— di durezza 5134
— di purezza 5136
— di qualità 5138
— di riduzione 14576 a
— di stivaggio 5137
— di tempera 5135
grado di tempera v. durezza
— geotermico 18484
grado v. indice
graffa 3622
graffe e graffette di fissaggio 3744
graffetta 3637
graffiatura 15679 a
graffio 15679 a
grafite 1654, 8447, 8453, 13570
— a noduli 12333
— a rosette 15184
— di segregazione S. 19245
— di sovrafusione 19245
— interdendritica 9878
— lamellare 7250
— lavata 14598
— nodulare 12333
— primaria 13941
— sferoidale 17066
grafitico 8452
— (non-) 12351

grafitizzante 8459
grafitizzare 8458
grafitizzazione 8457
grafitoso 10380
graftonite
grahamite 8394
gramenite 8409
grammatite 8410
grammo-equivalente 8411
— -ione 8412
— -molecola 8413, 11865
grana 8396
— chiusa (a-) 3761
— di ghisa 10014
— fine (a-) 7080
— grossa (a-) 3872, 17568
— regolare (a-) 6624
granaglia 11666
granata chimica 8055
granato 7973
— alumino-magnesico
    11179
— cromo-calcareo 2725
grande campana 11217 a
— fronte 10988
— fronte in direzione 10991
— siviera 2552
grandezza del grano 8401
— dell'intensità 9863
— della capacità 2803
grandi fenocristalli (a-)
grandidierite 8415
granelli di ferro 9979
grani al silicio 16329
— di quarzo 14277
graniglia 8575, 16193
-- d'acciaio 3448, 17477 a
granigliare 16195
granigliatura 8575 a, 16198
granitite 8421
granitizzazione 8422
granito 8416
— a biotite 12378
— a due miche 1591
-- a turmalina 8632
— -gneiss 8322
granitoide 8423
granitura 11707 a
grano 13004, 16646

grano d'acciaio duro 8831
— di frattura 7694
— di prova 890
— elementare 16394 a
grano v. granulo
— grosso 3871
— medio (a-) 11425
— sovradimensionato
    12778 a
granodiorite 8426
granofirico 8430, 8462
granofiro 8429
granolite 8427
granulare 8435
— il quarzo 4327
granulato 13020
granulazione 8440
— superficiale 13202 a
granuli di carbone 8436
— di ferro incorporati 6441
— di zinco 11946 a
granulite 8441
granulo 8396
granulo v. grano
granulometria 8388, 15517 a
granuloso 105, 3789, 8443
grappa 3622
— per fili S. 20120
grappolo 3792, 17277
— di pezzi fusi 17182
graptolite 8463
grasso 5633
— distillato 17595
— idrofugo 19806
grata 8465
— a circolazione d'acqua
    8475
— a sbarre 8468
gratella S. 7170
graticcio di legno 20175
graticola v. griglia
graticola 7844, 17330
— fumivora 17761
grattare 15673
grauwacke 8532, 14448,
    20015
gravimetro 8482
— statico 17394
greenalite 8521

greenockite 8522
greenovite 8523
gregarine 8525
greggio 1680
— asfaltico 874
— non solforoso 18117
— stagionato 19865
greggio v. grezzo
greificazione 16434
greisen 8526
gres 17640
— a grana fine 12855, 13713
— a grana grossa 8576, 11927
    11927
— argilloso 5012
— carbonifero 11717
— ferruginoso 10007
— ferruginoso striato 18615
— in lastre 15496
— micaceo 6770
— petrolifero 12506
— quarzifero 14276, 16314
— scistoso compatto 8902
grezzo 7791, 19327
— commerciale 13356
— di colata 838
— di laminazione 83 9, 15252
griffa 8572
— da tornio 10576
grifite 8570
grigio acciaio 17477
— di zinco 20330
griglia 7844, 8465, 8536,
    8579
griglia v. graticola
— a catena 3243
— a crivello 16299
— a gradini 17549, 17556
— a piani 12126, 15782
— a scorrimento 8474
— a scosse 15040
— a una sola sbarra 8470
— con raffreddamento
    esterno ad acqua 8473 a
— del focolare 7169
— di ghisa 3003
— di riscaldamento 9014
— economica 6191
— fissa 17399

griglia in acciaio fuso 3020
— inclinata 9701
— interna 7169
— isolata 9320
— meccanica 17635
— mobile 14838, 15971
— orizzontale S. 9343
— oscillante 16623
— per distaffare 10405
— per pesci 7208
— per scorie 6104
— piana 9343
— rotante S. 14838
— rovesciabile 18677
grigliati zincati 7938
grigliatura S. 15693
griquaite 8573
grisou 4978, 7165, 13407
gronda in elementi prefab-
    bricati 4483
groppo 2531
grorudite 8599
grossezza d'uovo 6224
— del filo di ferro 5319
— di noce 19661
— di pugno 7225
grosso 3868
— blocco di carbone
grossularia 8364
grossularite 8605
grothite 8606
grovacca 18829
gru a bandiera 10167, 19644
— a benna 8377, 8379
— a bicicletta 1191
— a bicicletta murale 19640
— a braccio 10167, 13292,
    19644
— a braccio girevole su
    rotaia 10168
— a cavalletto 7965, 8342
— a cavalletto zoppo 15844
— a cavi 2667
— a mensola 2242
— a monorotaia 11915
— a ponte 7965, 12758
— a ponte per fonderia 7674
— a portico 13697
— a vapore 17424

gru automotrice 11954, 13775
— con scavatore automatico
    4602
— con tenaglia da presa
    4603
— a tenaglia per lingotti
    9790
— a torre girevole 15224
— da colata 7654
— da deposito 17619
— da fonderia con disposi-
    tivo di scarico automatico
    7655
— da fonderia girevole 7672
— da muro 19639
— della fossa di colata 3065
— di colata 3049, 13754
— di sformatura 17870
— di trasbordo a cavalletto
    5500
— fissa a vapore 7242
— girevole 18128
— indipendente 9732
— mobile a cavalletto 2384
— motorizzata 11954
— per caricare i lingotti
    9786
— per caricare o per inforna-
    re le cassette 18939
— per estrarre lingotti dalle
    lingottiere 9803
— per fonderia o da colata
    7654
— per il trasporto dei lingot-
    ti 9789
— radiale 19144
— scorrevole pei forni di
    riscaldamento 4597
— sopraelevata 12753
— trasportabile 11845
gruista 4604
grunerite 8634
grunlingite 8635
gruppo di atomi 11874
— di faglie 8625
— di linee 8626
— di macchine 15909
— di serbatoi 18246
— di sorgenti 8627

gruppo elettrogeno 6277, 8154
— Ilgner 9631
— motori 13799
— neozoico 12227
gruppo v. formazione
guadagno 7908
guadalcazarite 8636
guaina isolante 10065
guanajuatite 8638
guanto d'amianto 844
— di gomma 15310
guardascambio 18134
guardia 8642, 14040
guardialinee 18811
guarinite 8644
guarnire 12826
guarnissaggio 10489
guarnitura 9463
guarnizione 10849, 12845
— a becco 10863
— a manicotto 4837
— a U 5686
— ad anello 14923
— ad angolo od a manicotto
    4837
— a labbro 10863
— d'amianto 845
— del cuscinetto 10853
— di anelli di cuoio 10653
— metallica 11554
— per testa del cilindro
    8908
— per tetto 12902
— per tubi 19034
— rotonda 8078
— stagna a cubi 16648
guarnizioni 9463
— di neoprene 12224
gudmundite 8646
guejarite 8646
guida 8649, 14951, 15370
— del cavo 20132
— del portasagoma 12989
— dell'asta di pompaggio
    17946
— degli elettrodi 6328
— d'estrazione 6240
— di scorrimento 16610
— fusa in un sol pezzo 3013

guida laterale 16264 a
— per la secchia 10477
— per la siviera 10477
guidare un' asta nel raccordo
   17268
guide del tamburo d'estrazione 9373
guildite 8657
gummite 8667
guscio 16093
gymnite 8693
gyrolite 8697

H

hackmannite 8699
haidingerite 8707
halleflinta 8721
hallerite 8722
halloysite 8723
halotrichite 6869, 8726
hannayite 8817
hanksite 8816
hamlinite 2204
hardystonite 8876
harmotome 8879
harrisite 8880
harstigite 8881
hardenite 8869
hartite 8882
hastingsite 8886
hatchettolite 8887
hatherlite 8888
hauchecornite 8890
hauerite 8891
hauyna 8900
hauynofiro 8901
habronite 9043
hedenbergite 9044
hadrumite 9046
hedyfane 9047
helvite 9070, 18470
hamafibrite 9072
hemera 9079
henwoodite 9091
herderite 9096
heronite 9098
herschelite 9101

hessite 9102
hetairite 9104
hettangiano 9111
heulandite 9112
heumite 9112
heumite 9113
hewettite 9114
hiatus 9131
hibbenite 9132
hibschite 9133
hiddenite 9134
higginsite 9135
hillebrandite 9196
hinsdalite 9208
hintzeite 9209
hiperite 9589
histrixite 9213
hitchcockite 9215
hodgkinsonite 9221
hoghomite 9223
hokutolite 9237
holdenite 9241
hollandite 9260
holoartico 9238
holiokeite 9293
hopeite 9327
horsfordite 9384
horst 9385
howlite 9468
hubnerite 9471
hugelite 9475
hullite 9475 ,
   9477
humite 9481
huntilite 9487
huroniano 9488
hussakite 9491

I

ialite 9497
ialocristallino 9498
ialofano 9499
ialosiderite 9501
ialotekite 9502
icositetraedro 9614
idatogenesi 9504
idatogeno 9505

iddingsite 9615
idioblasto 9616
idiocromatico 9617
idiogeno 9619
idiomorfo 9620
idrante 7175, 9506
— per incendi a colonna tubolare 7171
idrargillite 9507
idrialina 9622
idrobios 9544
idroboracite 9546
idrocarburi 9547
— a catena 2259
idrocarburo asfaltico 882
idrocerusite 9548
idrocianite 9552
idroematite 9563
idrofane 9570
idrofilite 9571
idroformato 9556
idrogeno 9557
— solforato 17603, 17985
idrolisi 9564
idrometallurgia 9565 a
idrometamorfismo 9566
idrometro 9567
idromuscovite 9568
idronefelite 9569
idroseparatore 9543
idrossido di ferro 9577
idrossido di sodio 16810
— ferrico 9577
idrosterratura 9545
idrotalchite 9576
idrozincite 9579
idruro 9542
ignifugo 12353
igrometro 9580
lherzolite 10723
ijolite 9629
illite 9632
ilmentite 9638
ilvaite 10733, 20295
imballatore 12941
imbiancatura 10817 a
imboccatura 152, 12040
— del condotto principale
   del vento 11218

imboccatura del foro di
sondaggio 19964
— della miniera (all'-) 914
— di colata 13742
— di galleria di traverso-
banco 4666
imbragare 16640
imbragatura 16641
imbrigliare 2791
imbutibilità 5787
imbutire 5509, 7268
— a freddo 3960, 3988
imbutito 5088
— alla pressa 5087
— di piccolo spessore
5089
imbutitura 5517a
— a freddo 3973
— di ripresa 14556
— idromeccanica 9553
imbuto 7820
— a tubo per vapore 17430
— contagocce 6003
— d'estrazione 6710
— di alimentazione 18352a
— di carica 3337
— di colata 1313, 13748,
13756, 18953
— di Gooch 8356
— di porcellana 13664
— di scolo 4185
— di sicurezza 14046
— filtrante 7047
— per acqua calda 9452
— separatore 15880
— sotterraneo 8309
— di troppo 4185
immagazzinaggio 17689
immagazzinare 52, 10298
immagine virtuale 9639
immergere 5432, 5433
immersione di metalli fusi
5453
— lenta 16694
— rapida nell'acqua 13573
impacchettare rottami 2655
impacchettatrice per rottami
2657
impacchettatura di rottami
2656, 15656

impalcatura 15576, 15577,
17293
— di sicurezza 13071
impastare 10390, 11816,
14116
— i crogiuoli 11967
impastarsi 1146, 2690
impastatrice 11825
impastatura 11828
impasto 2694, 11828
— d'agglomerati 222
— del coke 2697
— di coke 2693
— di scorie 2692
— siliceo 16321
— vetrificato 19579
impianto 15913
— a bassa tensione 11063
— a corrente alternata 432
— a corrente continua 4265
— a corrente monofasica
16395
— a corrente trifase 18566
— ad alta tensione 9190
— ad antenna 10106
— aspirante 17955
— automatico per lavorare
le terre 988
— autoportato 18814
— azionato da motori a
combustione interna
13791
— autoportabile ad antenna
18815
— continuo per sabbie 4274
— coperto di caldaie 4566
— d'agglomerazione 225
— d'amalgamazione 496
— d'arrostimento 14993
— d'estrazione 20104
— d'estrazione di gasolina
da gas 7975
— d'illuminazione 10796
— di altoforno 1713
— di caldaie 1973
— di caricamento e di
trasporto 10920
— di cernita 8389
— di classificazione 16928

impianto di concentrazione
4164, 4170
— di decapaggio continuo
13228
— di disidratazione del
petrolio 12485
— di distillazione 5563
— di distillazione a pressione 13920
— di distillazione primaria
16466
— di filtraggio 7050
— di frantumazione 4780
— di frazionamento 18764
— di forni 7193
— di granulazione 8439
— di lavaggio 19705
— di lisciviazione 10901
— di macchine elettriche
6286
— di perforazione 14897
— di perforazione marina
12472
— di perforazione mobile
13692
— di pompaggio 14170
— di pompe 14160
— di pozzo 15947
— di prefusione 13864
— di preparazione meccanica 11687
— di recupero 14509
— di recupero dei gas 24
— di recupero vapori 19469
— di refrigerazione
dell'acqua 19763
— di separazione 15865
— di sondaggio sottomarino
12472
— di torrefazione S. 14993
— di trafilatura e di allargamento a caldo 9412
— di trattamento 18867
— di trivellazione 5938
— di trivellazione a rotazione 15201
— di utilizzazione della
scoria Thomas 18538
— di vagliatura 15694,
15696

impianto v. installazione o
  apparecchiatura
— elettrico in torre 10788
— lavorazione e recupero
  terre 15513
— metallografico 11580
— per il trattamento del
  minerale 8544
— per il trattamento del
  minerale del piombo
  1606
— per la fabbricazione dei
  crogiuoli 4751
— per la fabbricazione di
  mattonelle 2417
— per la distillazione del
  catrame 18317
— per l'essiccamento 6062
— per liscivazione dei minerali 12644
— per preparare la dolomite
  5615
— per prepare le sabbie
  15513
— per pulire un pozzo 3701
— per trasbordo a gru gi-
  revole mobile 10919
— petrolifero 12503
— scoperto di caldaie
  12590
— trasportabile d'un pozzo
  inclinato 8324
impilare le staffe 17275
impiombare 10603
— un cavo entro il «rope
  socket» 1037
impiombato 10611
impiombatura a manicotto
  di un cavo 16594
impoverimento 9660 a
impregnazione al silicio
  9628 a
— di vapore 17447
impresa estrattiva 1120
impressione 9729
imprimere il modello 13866
— il modello nella terra
  9668

imprimere un violento moto
  alternativo lungo la
  verticale 17217
impronta 6092, 9666, 11970,
  11973, 16418
— di finitura 7129
— di rifollatura 7811
— di sbozzatura 1809
— di tenaglie 5598
— per bacchettatura 7812
— per rifollatura 7812
improntatura 9219
— cava 5517
impugnatura 8793
— per chiavi a bussola
  11668
— di accensione 17384
— magnetico 6270
impurità 4897, 9672, 14348 a.
  15590 a
— affondata 3520
— chimica 3390
inalazione 9682
inattaccabile dai gas 8043
inattaccabile a v. resistente
  a
imboccatura 10466
incamiciare con piombo S.
  10603
incamiciatura 16485
incamiciato 10611
incandescenza 8313
incassatura 19637
incastellatura 897, 11733,
  15576
— a collo d'oca 13 84
— d'estrazione 8911, 8913,
  8921, 14186, 15945
— del laminatoio 9465
— di perforatrice 5928
— di travi a scatola 2226
— di trivellazione 2079
incastratura di metallo duro
  88 39
incastro a maschio e femmina 8598
— della chiavetta 10331,
  10328
— per il dente di una mortisa 11938

incavatoio s. accecatoio
incavatura S. 12394
incavo dell'anima 4436
inceppamento 17582
incepparsi 17582
inceppato 9486
incenerimento del filtro 2608
inchiavettare 1792, 3618
inchiavettatura 1807
— della forma 3625
inceneratore di rifiuti 14639,
  7970
incisione S. 16418, S. 19245
  19245/a
inclinare una forma 18624
inclinato 13420
inclinazione 9688, 14382,
  16253, 16678, 19268
— apparente 708
— assiale 13574
— del carbone 16251
— della griglia 9689
— di faglia 6848
— divergente 14254
— periclinale 3222
inclusione 6444, S.9711,
  9712, 18344, 20268
— allungata 9713
— di ferro S.15568
— di minerale nella roccia
  in piccola quantità
  17208
— di pirite nel carbone
  3803
— di nero 2846
— di scoria 9713, 16540
— di scoria congenita 6462
— di sterile 9375
— di sterile in una vena S.
  14882
— di terra 15500, 15566
— enallogena 6431, 6658
— endogena 3916
— metallica estranea 6659
— minerale 11754
— non metallica 14580,
  16916
— non metallica estranea
  6660
incollaggio differenziale 539
  5396
incollamento del getto alla
  forma 17583
incollare 8315
incollarsi S. 2690
incollatura d'anime 8666

incombustibile 7186
incominciare lo sfruttamento
    d'un pozzo 2404
incompleto 16185
incontrare una roccia dura
    nello scavo 8200
incontrato 18756
inconveniente causato dalle
    ceneri 6135
incorporamento nella fusione
    12010
incorporato nella fusione
    11990
increspato 1785
incrinato S. 4584
incrinatura S. 3374, 4580,
    4587
— a caldo S. 9409
— a freddo S. 3971
— ai bordi 4584/a
— al bordo 6200
— capillare 8708
— della lingottiera 7065
— di calettamento S.14786
— di invecchiamento 220
— di rettifica 8552
— di ritiro S. 16228
— interna 9899, 17086/b
— longitudinale S. 15049,
    17123
— orizzontale S. 1418
incrinature trasversali 2438
— di tensione 18415
incrocio 4718
— di correnti d'aria 2380
— di pilastri 4674
— di ventilazione 261,
    4719, 12737
— doppio S. 5333
incrostazione 9727, S. 15568
— di caldaie 15581
— di sabbia 2596
incrudimento 4010, 20190
— per invecchiamento 215
incrudire S.5760, 20188
incudine 677
— portastampi 16949
incudinella o incudinetta S.
    8753
incudinuzza 8753
incupolamento 10746
incurvamento 1506
incurvatura S. 5728
indicatore d'estrazione 9738

indicatore d'usura dello
    scalpello 6085
— del livello del galleg-
    giante 7387
— della discesa delle ca-
    riche 17623
— delle cariche 9737
— di carica 17621, 3320
— di grisou 4984
indicazione di raccordo
    7029
indice d'attitudine alla pla-
    sticità 4102
— del filone 2485
— di basicità 9735
— di finezza 7098
— di deposizione 3882
— di produttività 14000
— Diesel 5389
— s. grado
indicolite 1913/a
indigolite 9741
indio 9746
indorare S. 8224
indurimento 8858
— all'aria S. 289
— dovuto all'incrudimento
    17733
— per aereazione 14332/a
— per raffreddamento rapido
    14285/a
— per rotazione 17093/a
— secondario 15768
— strutturale 13815
— superficiale S. 2917,
    8826
— s. tempra
indurire alla fiamma 7258
— superficialmente 6737
indurito 9756/a
industria mineraria S.11769,
    11776
— petrolifera 12497
— siderurgica 9980
inerti 234
inerzia termica 18485
inesploso 19294
infiammabile 9765
non infiammabile 12353
infiltrazione 9764/a
— d'acqua 20321
— metallica 11555
— petrolifera 12508

inflangiatura a boll. weevil
    2006
inflessione parassita 19342
influenza 9768
— atmosferica 925
— sulla solubilità 9770
infornata 3316, 8972
infornatrice 3349
infragilire 6406
infusibile 9774
infusibilità 9773
ingabbiatore 1465, 2191,
    2149, 2684, 9216, 9320,
    12550, 13531, 15373,
    16127, 17826
— automatico 974
ingarbugliarsi del cavo nella
    puleggia 16787
ingegnere addetto alla per-
    forazione 5923
— di servizio 6472
ingolfamento 7398
ingombrante 20060
ingorgo del forno di torre-
    fazione 3752
ingranaggio 8125, 8132
— a spirale 17100
— a vite perpetua 20228
— cilindrico 17226
— conico 1569
— dei denti 8139
— fuso in un sol pezzo
    3917
ingranamento 10244/a
ingranare 10118
ingrandimento 11212
— totale 18789
— utile 1004
ingrassaggio 1336
ingrassare S. 12477
ingrassatore a pompetta
    8503
— per funi 15166
ingressione 9806
ingrippamento 7743
ingrossamento della grana
    8398
ingrossare 9720
inibitore 5201, 9807
— di coagulazione 13744
iniettabilità 9810
iniettore 9818
— a vapore di scarico 6654

iniettore di petrolio 13131
iniezione 9812
— d'aria finale 199
— di gas S.8015
— multipla 17274
iniziare la circolazione 2299
— la produzione 2412, 4085
inizio della produzione spon-
-tanea d'un pozzo 10341
— di condensazione 12730
innaffiamento del carbone
　20004
innaffiare S. 10041
innescare una mina 13945
innesco S. 13949, 13953
innestare S. 9311
— il giunto 4215
innesto a denti 5594
— a ruota libera 12776
innesti S. 4551
inoculante 9826
inoculazione 9827
inossidabile 12363, 15393,
　17296
inquadratura 7709
insabbiare 15467
insaccatura S. 7035
insegna di latta 18651
insellatura 15153
inserire 15346
inserto 9833
— metallico 11548
insieme di canali di colata
　e montanti 8104
insolubile 9844
inspessire 9848/a
instabilità allo scorrimento
　13745
installare 14896
intaccatura 12287
intagliare 16668, 4874, S.
　10111, S. 10374
— v. tagliare
intagliato S. 9254, 15244
intagliatrice 4681, 3810,
　4906
— a colonna 19155
— a disco 5483
— a percussione a colonna
　13712
— a piccone 13204, 14180
— -caricatrice 4912
— per carbone 11417, 11777
intagliatubi 2955

intaglio S. 1204, S. 4899,
　4913, 10117, S. 10321,
　10373, S. 10375, 12264,
　12403, 12394, 16669
— a V 19422/a
— a cuneo 19879
intasamento del foro di cola-
　ta 7745
intasare 18228
intasato 3751
integrità di un pezzo 16941
intelaiatura S. 897
— tubolare 19073
intensità di campo 6997
— di ritenuta degli ioni
　9860
— luminosa S. 2783
— polare 17777
intercalato 9915, 9887, S.
　17762
intercalazione 16045
— da carbone piritico 2284
— di carbone 3845, 16041
— di carbone scistoso
　1652
intercalazione impermeabile
　9656
— sterile 5852, 5475,
　11662, 12945
intercambiabile 9869
intercapedine d'aria 326
intercristallino 9874
interdendritico 9877
interno dell'alto-forno 9886
interramento 12094
interrare S. 12068
interrato 2586, S. 6492
interstratificare 9917
interstratificato S. 9887,
　17762
interstratificazione 9865
interruttore 2316, 9894
— a tempo S. 5145
— telecomandato 14702
interstiziale 9915/a
interstrato 9868
interstratificato 9864
intervallo S. 16957
— carotato 4457
— critico 4647
— di fusione 11477, 11795
— di miscibilità S. 11795
— di solidificazione 7748,
　16892

intervallo di temperatura
　14413
— di trasformazione 18826
— fra pozzi 19971
intonacare 3879
intonaco S. 3880, 584/a
intrapreso e finito 12539
introdurre S. 15346
introduzione d'aria abbon-
　dante 541
intrusione 9923, 9711
— d'acqua 19786
— discordante 5507
— minore S. 11784
— nastriforme 9816
— verso l'alto 19386
intrusivo 9924, 10044
intumescenza 9929
inumidire 11860
invasione 6447
invecchiamento 218
— artificiale 219, 831,
　18375
— completo 4642/a
— con aumento di durezza
　215
— dovuto a rapido raffred-
　damento 14284
— dovuto all'incrudimento
　17731
— martensitico 11311/a
— naturale S. 12189
— progressivo S. 14005/a
— rapido 14297
— spinto 12731
— spontaneo 12189
invecchiare 214
invecchiato 216
inversione 18135
— della ventilazione 14822
— di marcia 14819
invertire i circuiti 15003
inviluppo di gas 8001
invito di rottura 2823
involucro di forno S. 2930
— di protezione 4607
— refrattario 12413
inyoite 9938
iodergirite S. 9939
iodio 9940
iodite 9939
iodobromirite 9942
ioduro di potassio 13729
iolite 9943

ione 9944
— acido 81
— anfoterico 20317/a
— basico 1296
— idrossile 9578
— neutro 9503
— polivalente 12129
ionite 9945
ionitrurare 9946
ionizzazione 9946/a
iperpressione S.12774
ipersaturare S. 18018
ipersaturazione S. 18021
ipersaturo S. 18019
iperstene 10453, 9591
iperstenite 9592
ipertempra 9590
ipidiomorfo 9593
ipoabissale 9582
ipocristallino 9080, 9595, 11512
ipoeutettico 9596
— v. ipoeutettoide
ipoeutettoide 9597
v. ipoeutettico
ipogeno 9601
iposolfito di soda 9602
iridio 9950
iridosmina 9951
irradiato 14331
irradiazione del calore 14332
irregolarità 10943/a
— di forma 20239
irrigare 10041
irrigazione 10042, 17207
irrigidire S. 2230
irrorare S. 17178
irruzione 9830
— d'acqua 9831
irvingite 10045
isenite 10047
iserite 10048
ishikawaite 10049
isobutano 10052
isobutene 10053
isobutilene S. 10053
isoclino 10057
isodimorfo 10057/a
isoformato 10058
isoidria delle soluzioni acide 10062
isoidrico 10060
isolamento acustico in lana

di roccia 108
isolamento per evitare la formazione di ponti termici 9852
— termico 8983, 18485/a
isolante 9850, 12947/a, S. 12950, 16745/a, 17688/a
isomerato 10066
isomorfismo 10070
isomorfo 10069
isoparaffina 10073
isopentano 10074
isoprene 10076
isosismico 10077
isotopo radioattivo 14335
isottano 10071
ispessimento delle estremità di un tubo 17403/a
ispezione delle caldaie 1970
isteresigrafo 6943/a
itabirite 10084, 17041
itacolumite 10085
itterbio 20304
ittrialite 20306
ittrio 20307
ittrocalcite 20308
ittrocerite 20309
ittrocolumbite 20310
ittrofluorite 20311
ittrotantalite 20312
ittrotitanite 20313
iussite 9630
ixolite 10087

J

jacobsite 10109
jacupirangite 10110
jamensonite fibrosa 6990
jaspilite 10139
jeffersite 10144
jeffersonite 10145
jeremejevite 10148
jeromite 10150
jezekite 10165
joaquinite 10187
johannite 10193
johnstrupite 10194
jordanite 10229
josefinite 10232
josefite 10230
joseite 10231

julienite 10241
jumellite 10244
Jura nero 1653
juxporite 10263

K

kaersuite 10265
kakoxen 10271
kaliborite 10273
kalinite 10274
kaliofilite 10275
kalkowskite 10277
kamacite 10279
kamarezite 10280
kammererite 10281
kampylite 10282
karstenite 10285
kasolite 10287
katoforite 10290
keilhauite 10302
kelyfite 10308
kentrolite 10310
keramohalite 10311
kermesite 10312
kernite 10314
kerrite 10318
kersantite 10319
khagiarite 10333
kieserite 10349
killinite 10355
kimberlite 10362
kipushite 10370
kirrolite 10372
kjerulfina 10384
klaprotite 10385
klebelsbergite 10386
kleinite 10387
klockmannite 10389
knebelite 10391
kochite 10419
koechlinite 10420
koenenite 10421
koke in pezzatura noce 12429
kongsbergite 10424
koniackite 10425
koppite 10426
kornerupina 10428
kottingite 10429
krablite 10430
kramerite 10431

krantzite 10432
kraurite 10433
krausite 10434
kremersite 10435
krennerite 10436
krohnkite 10437
kukkersite 10439
kulaite 10440
kullaite 10441
kupferrite 10443
kunzite 10442
kylite 10445
kyschtymite 10446

L

labbro d'una faglia 16254
— della secchia di colata
   10480
— della siviera S. 10480
labirinto a diaframmi 1094
— di legno 20179
laboratorio S. 8949
— d'esercizio 20225
— principale 3416
labradite 10452
labradorite 10454
lacca 10461
laccare 10460
laccato 10122
laccatura 10123
laccolite 7411, 10455
laccolitico 10456
lacroixite 10463
lacuna 7967, S. 9131
— d'erosione 6548
— stratigrafica 2313, 11038,
   17749
— stratigrafica apparente
   S. 711
— stratigrafica verticale
   S. 716
lago di circo 18328
laguna 10491
Lahar S. 3983
lakarpite 10492
lama del trapano 1624
— del ventilatore 6794
— di pialla S. 13455
— di sega 15557
— per raschiare S. 15672
— per rasoio 14464

lamella 7249, 10496, S.10575
lamellare 7529, 10497,
   16993, 19840
lamelle di mica 11622,
   11622
— di polvere 13502/a
lamiera 7345, 7519, S. 16014,
   16068, 17837
— a forma di pacchetti
   16074/a
— a prominenze 16063
— a scaglie 9641
— a sella 15410
— ad orlo rovesciato 7272
— al carbone di legna 3312
— al coke 3945
— bagnata 12107
— brunita S. 13462
— circolare 3595
— con fori trapanati 5914
— d'acciaio 16081, 17492,
   17508/a
— d'acciaio nervata zincata
   14868
— d'alluminio 461, 16046
— di effusione 6817/a,
   7289/a
— d'imbottitura 5690, 17587
— d'irrigidimento 17590
— da caldaie 1974
— da costruzione 17890,
   17894
— da focolare 7155
— da imbutire 5515, 5807
— da rivestimento 10103
— decapata 13220
— del cielo del focolare
   4731
— del focolare 7851
— del nodo 8679
— del timpano 19200
— deossidata 16069
— di acciaio azzurrata 1911
— di acciaio blu S. 1911
— di arcaccia 18832
— di chiglia 10297
— di cintura della cassa focolare S. 15410
— di corazza S. 799
— di corpo 16110
— di duralluminio 16053
— di elektron 16054
— di ferro 10011, 16058
— di ferro omogeneo 11680

lamiera di ferro stagnato S.
   18661
— di ferro striata 673, 11517
   11517
— di fondo 1070
— di laminatoio 1509
— di magnesio 16067
— di ottone 2274, 16050
— di piombo S. 16066
— di platino 13526
— di prima qualità 13950
— di raccordo 18608
— di rame 4361, 16051
— di ricoprimento S.18740
— di rinforzo 17590
— di rivestimento 11304
— di rollio 19691
— di sbarramento delle scorie 16545
— di scarto 16060, 16079
— di testa S. 19035
— di zinco ondulata 4501
— flangiata 13485
— finita 7121, 7122
— forata S. 13082, 14179
— galvanizzata 7934
— grezza 14460
— grossa 9037, 18502
— imbottita S. 17319
— imbutita 2509, S.13884
— in acciaio 13885
— inclinata 9705
— laminata 15099
— laminata a caldo 9431
— a freddo 3992
— larga piatta 19314/a
— laterale d'acciaio 8246
— liscia 13445, 13448,
   16773
— lisciata 13462
— lucida 2399
— martellata 8747
— media 10188/a, 10784/a,
   11430
— nera 1661, 1664
— nera quadrupla 5654/a
— nichelata 12279
— ondulata 4496, 4498
— ondulata curvata 4879,
   4880
— ondulata di duralluminio
   4499
— ondulata doppia 5651
— ondulata galvanizzata 7931

lamiera ondulata per persiane 4502
— ondulata per sostegni 4500
— ondulata tripla 18912
— passata a freddo 3993
— per dinamo 6155
— per navi 16137
— per pavimentazione 7407
— per serbatoi 18252
— per stampaggio profondo 5085
— perforata 13082
— piombata 18430
— polita o brunita S. 13462
— portatubi 19035
— pressata 13884
— protettrice 15686
— raddrizzata 17723
— ramata 4371
— ricoperta di piombo S. 18430
— ricotta 605
— sagomata S. 17017
— sagomata alla presa S. 17319
— smaltata 6436
— sottile 18526
— sottilissima 6704
— stagnata 18650
— stampata S. 2509, 17319, 18439
— stirata 6665
— stirata con maglia a losanga 5326
— striata 3369, 3371, 3404, 14891
— tubolare S. 19035
— zincata ad onde trapezoidali 7935
lamiera v. piastra
lamiere di battente 3867
— di cielo del portafocolare 7154
— di cielo della cassa a fuoco S. 7154
— metalliche su appoggio continuo 11560
— portacerniera 9202
lamierino catodico 17386/a
— da trasformatori 18827
— di acciaio 18528
— perforato da ornamenti 5076

lamierino sottilissimo 18201
lamierone 18499
lamina S. 7526, 7249, 10496, 10499, S. 16597
— di ferro S. 10011
— di rame S. 4361
— di stagno S. 18648
— quarto d'onda S. 14263
laminabile 15092
laminare S. 10497, 10500, 10503, S. 11692, 15067
— a caldo 9428
— a freddo 3959
— all'indietro 15071
— insieme 15072
— le lamiere 16077
laminarsi 7528
laminato 7528/a, 10505, 11703, 15094
— a caldo 9429
— a freddo 3990
— bianco 2393
— di acciaio 15101
laminatoio 7355, 10005, 11688, 15125, 15127
— a barre 15055/a
— a caldo 9437
— a caldo con gabbie in tandem per la finitura 18240
— a cilindri obliqui 15214/a 15214/a
— a freddo per nastri 3998
— a movimento alternato 14495
— a passo di pellegrino 13281
— a quattro cilindri verticali 7679
— a trio per lamiere 18560
— a trio per profilati 18562
— a sei cilindri 3793/a
— belga 1444
— calibratore 16447
— continuo 4272
— continuo a quattro gabbie in tandem 7681
— continuo per fili 4271
— d'acciaio 17502
— di lingotti 15257/a
— di riduzione 16424/a
— duo irreversibile 5735/b, 14128/a
— finitore 7130/a, 7137

laminatoio irreversibile 12362
— lisciatore di tubi 14587/a 14587/a
— medio 11428
— obliquo 9706
— per alluminio 460
— per bandelle 7954
— per barre 1219
— per bidoni 16048
— per billette 1583
— per blumi 1834
— per corazze 800
— per fili 20135, 15057
— per lamiere 13497, 16073
— per lamiere sottili 10508
— per lavori speciali 17019
— per nastri 17854
— per piastrine 17846
— per profilati 15778, 15989
— per profilati commerciali 11497
— per puddellaggio 14098
— per ridurre le lame di metallo fragile in polvere S. 7355
— per rimuovere le scaglie 15587/a
— per rotaie 14362
— per sfrido lamiere 15659
— per slebi 10501
— per tubi 13364, 19037,
— reversibile 14833
— reversibile ad alta velocità 9175
— reversibile per la finitura a caldo 14831
— reversibile per lamiere 14832
— reversibile per la laminazione a freddo 14830
— reversibile per lingotti 14829
— riduttore 14569
— riduttore a caldo 9427
— riduttore e calibratore 14566
— saldatore 19948
— semplice 16394
— sgrossatore 15257
— spianatore 10628/a
— tandem 18039/a
— universale 19314

laminatore 11696
laminatura fra cilindri 5378
laminazione 15120
— a caldo 9436
— a freddo 3997
— a pacco 12836
— a sandwich 15532
— d'acciaio con affinaggio 17045
— d'un filo 15056, 15059
— degli slebi 16505
— del filo di ferro 20143
— di lingotti 15257
— di polvere 15075/a
— di sbozzatura 3912
— di tubi 19036
— diagonale 5310
— nel senso della larghezza 20065
— nel senso della lunghezza 10677
— raddrizzatrice 13312/a
— trasversale 4703
— universale 19317/a
laminette da spessore 18509
lampada a gas illuminante e ad ossigeno 8035
— a mercurio 11506
— a spirito 17103
— ad acetilene 66
— ad arco 747
— al magnesio 11180
— da microscopio 11650
— da minatore 5958
— da miniera 11747
— da saldatore 1889
— Davy 10097
— di sicurezza 15419
— di sicurezza ad olio 15422
— elettrica 6279
— elettrica da elmetto 6264
— incandescenza (ad) 8311
lampadite 10514
lampeggiare 7287
lampo 7289
lampofiro 10511
lana d'acciaio 17519
— d'amianto 849
— di loppa 16565
— minerale 15032/a, 16565
lanarchite 10512
lancia da sabbiare 15475

lancia da sabbiare 15475
— di ossigeno 12819/a
— di pescaggio 19686
lanciare 18586
lanciaterra 15518/a, 15528, 16643
lancio 14018
landsfordite 10535
langbeinite 10533
langite 10534
lantanite 10536
lanterna 4417, S.17077, 19505
— di guida 15053
— per anima S. 4447
— per anime 260, 4388, 17088
— scannellata per anima 15992
lanthanite 10536
lapislazzuli 1035, 10544
lapislazzulite S. 10602
lappare 10538
lappatrice 9307
lappatura 10554
larderellite 10545
largo-piatto 7322, 17853
larnite 10552
larsenite 10556
lasciar calmare 5033
— riposare 14307
lastra S. 13484, 16493,
— a cuscinetto 3251
— cilindrica 4883
— di gomma 15312
— di marmo 11312
— di protezione 7306
— di raddoppiamento 5690
— di rame 4372
— di stereotipia ramata 4356
— di sughero 4471, 4474
— di vetro 8281, 8284
— di vetro all'uranio 19396
— di zinco 16085
— ferma-piede 12365
— fotografica 13187
— grossa S. 18499
— metallica v. lamiera o piastra
— murale 19648
— romboidale 5328
lastrina S. 16609
— di mica 11624

lasurite 10560
laterite 10572
lateritico 10573
lateritizzazione 10574
lati disuguali 19290
latite 10580
lato 10666, 16252, 19872
— anteriore 7780
— aspirante 17960
— del foro di colata 18311
— di uscita 6656
— maggiore del quadro d'armatura 19641
— premente 13918
latta S. 18650, 18661
— imbutita S. 2509
— matta 13221, 11367
— piombata S. 18430
— stagnata 18667
latte di calce 10818
laubanite 10583
lauderbackite 11042
laugenite 10584
laumonite 10585
laumontite 2811, S. 10681
laurenziano 10588
lava 10589
— cordata 15172
— di fango 12078
— fangosa 11864
lavaggio 7481, S.14190, 15724, 16710, 19701
— al crivello S. 10179
— all'aria S. 6050
— controcorrente 1090, 6395
— del minerale 3695, 10182, 2515
— della forma 7439
— dell'oro 7486
— dell'oro alla batea 12900
— gassoso 18116
— mediante acqua 19770
— secco 6050
— su tavole oscillanti 15037
lavagna S. 16574
lavare 19681
— a scosse 10169
— l'argilla 19683
— minerali S. 7479
lavatoio S. 10586
— a reolavatori 14852
— per fanghi 16633

lavatoio per fini 7076
— per minerali 12659
lavatore-classificatore 19704
— d'oro 8352
— per gas 8063
lavatrice 19706
— a coclea 15715
— per fini 7076
lavenite 10590
laveria S.11687
lavorabilità 11116, 20193
— di un materiale 11117
lavorare a specchio S.7114
— in profondità 20189
lavorato 20245
— a caldo 9453
— fine 7097
lavoratore d'acciaieria 17521
lavorazione 13983, 18868, 20196/a
— a freddo 3980, 4006
— a freddo finale S.10352
— a macchina 11139
— con asportazione di trucioli 11539
— d'aggiustaggio 164
— d'imbutitura 13878
— dei metalli 11565
— elettronica 6364
lavori a cielo aperto 12607
— a giorno S.12607
— di accesso e di preparazione 5279
— di ripiena 8326
— di scavo 18874
— di tracciatura 7203, 20052
— di trincee 5578
— in lamiera 16072
— interni nel forno 20213
— preparatori S. 7203
— su piattaforma 3556
lavoro a cielo aperto S. 12565
— a cottimo 19158
— a macchina 11137
— a mano 11305
— al cuneo 13649
— al piccone e alla pala 13203
— alla mazzetta 11858
— alla roccia 12104

lavoro del bagno S.20197
— di calderaio 1978
— di fabbro S. 1978
— di muratura 19657
— di scavo S. 11769
— facile 10688
— in ferro 10036
— in pietra 17654
— in rimonta 14375
— manuale 11305
— mediante placca modello 11368
— preparatorio 5963
— sotterraneo 8623
— utile S.6143
lawrencite 10591
lawsonite 10592
lazulite 10601
lazurite 10602
leadhillite 10629
lechatelierite 10655
lecontite 10656
lectotipo 10657
ledeburite 10658
ledmorite 10660
leeuwfonteinite 10661
lega 396
— a base di alluminio S. 447
— a basso punto di fusione 7887, 11055
— a basso tenore 400
— ad alto tenore 399, 9136, 9142
— antifrizione S. 1038
— bianca S. 20038
— binaria 1590
— colata sotto pressione 5361
— d'acciaio 17455
— d'alluminio S.10778
— d'alluminio ad alto contenuto silicico 448
— d'argento 16351
— di acciaio nitrurato 12310
— di alluminio 447
— di modello 12984/a
— di molibdèno e nickel 12276
— di piombo 10606
— di rame 4351
— di resistenza 14765
— di saldatura 8870

lega di seconda fusione 15764
— di zirconio 20355/a
— eutettica 6600, S. 6598
— ferro-carbonio 9962
— leggera 10778
— -madre 11360
— metallica 11538
— per cuscinetti S.1396
— per reostati 14781
— per saldatura 16858
— pirofórica 9627/a, 16987/a
— rame-manganese S.4856
— rame-piombo S. 4855
— senza ritiro 19204
— ultraleggera 19221
legante S.405, 1597, S.2019, 2023
— covalente 9299/a
— di cenere di lignite 2473
legare 395
legato 403
legname 14027
— per mine 17541
— per rivestimento 1085
legno 20170
— di rivestimento 10195, 17899
— opalizzato 20176
— pietrificato 20185
— sano 16940
lehiite 10669
lehnerite 10670
leidleite 10671
leifite 10672
lembo 10807, 19633
— abbassato (di faglia) 6000, S. 11059
— affondato S. 5715, 5717, 18593
— affossato 5716
— di faglia 6862
— inferiore 5707, S.7405
— sollevato 9171, 10753
— superiore 8815
legenbachite 10674
lennilite 10678
lente 11213
— allungata di minerali 13606
— di Bertrand 1540
— di sabbia petrolifera 12499

lento 16707
leonardite 10681
leonite 10682
leopardite 10683
lepetite 10689
lepidocrocite 10685
lepidolite 10686, 10883/a
lepidomelano 10687
leptoclorite 10690
leptynite 10692
lessingite 10693
lestiwarite 10694
letto 1274, 7547, S.11393, 12133, 16337, S.17753
— del cavo S. 2664
— di colata S. 3039, 3041, 13256, 13751
— di colata per lingotti 13260
— di fiume contente oro 8685
— di formatura 2146
— di fusione 2586, 1428, S. 8951, 11839
— di graniglie 14352
— di stampo 16949/a
— di torrefazione 14988
— falso 12455
lettsomite 10696
leucaugite 10697
leucite S. 539, 10698
leucitite 10699
leucitofiro 10700
leucocalcite 10701
leucocratico 10702
leucofonicite 10703
leucopirite 10704
leucosfenite 10705
leucoxeno 10706
leva S. 4721, 4723, 10717
— a gomito 18706
— della siviera 18630
— di deviazione 9353
leva di tasto 6898
leva puntelli 5593
levare i ganci S. 7719
— i crogiuoli 18218
— il portavento 5759
— le graffe S. 7719
leverrierite 10719
levata del pistone 13577
levigare S. 10538, 13623
— con attacco acido 6575
levigato con sabbia 15526

levigatura 9306/a, 15320
lewisite 10720
lewistonite 10721
lias S. 1653
liassico 10724
libbre per pollice quadrato 14084
liberare 18904
liberazione 14682
— del gas 8019/a
libethenite 10725
liebenerite 10731
liebigite 10732
lievrite 10733
lignitifero 10804
lignite S.1655, 2472, 10802
— fibrosa 6991
— picea 13419
— terrosa 19228
— xiloide 20273
ligroina 10805
lillianite 10806
lima 7003
— da fori 14892
limatrice da banco 1494
— rotativa con albero flessibile 15205
limatura 7007
— d'alluminio 451
limburgite 10809
lime rotanti 15204
limite acqua-petrolio 6206
— apparente di allungamento 6392
— convenzionale di scorrimento 4294
— d'alzata 10676
— d'errore dell'analisi 10822
— d'usura ammissibile 19859
— del bordo 6207
— del grano 8397
— di carico 10921/a
— di dissociazione 5543
— di elasticità 6245, 10821
— di elasticità convenzionale 14007
— di elasticità della prova 6391
— di fatica 6466/a
— di proporzionalità 10823. 14024
— di resistenza alla fatica

6833
limite di rottura 2329
— di scorrimento o di viscosità 4623
— di scorrimento viscoso 4616
— di segregazione 10837/a
— di snervamento S.6833, 20298
— di stiramento 7427
— di viscosità S. 4626
— elastico interno 9908
— minimo di snervamento a caldo 11768
limnico 10827
limo 16346, 16627
limonite 1945, 2474, S.10828
— pisolitica o in grani 13387
— in cubi 5283
— in grani S.13387
lindoite 10829
lindstromite 10830
linea S. 17741
— aerea S.191
— d'affioramento 10837
— d'alimentazione 7776/a
— d'inclinazione 10833
— dei rulli 11701/a
— del manganese 11275
— del sodio 16822
— di attacco 18702
— di bavatura 7309
— di brasatura S. 2293
— di cedimento 6839
— di cerniera 9200
— di combustione S. 4080
— di demarcazione S.10562
— di displuvio 19838
— di divisione 10203, 12946 12946
— di flessione 1510
— di flusso 7429/a
— di forza 10834
— di frattura 7697, 10835
— di giunzione 15744
— di massima pendenza 7797
— di movimento 16655
— di pendenza 16682
— di raccordo a vuoto della matrice 19434
— di riferimento 5009
— di ripartizione 9918

linea di scorrimento 7428
— di slittamento 8299
— di stratificazione 10838
— di taglio 16029
— isogona 10059
— orizzontale 10709
— spartiacque S. 14786
linee di Neumann 12251
lingottare 2975
lingottatura 9805
lingotti d'ottone incurvati 2268
-— vuoti 9267
lingottiera 9795, 9968, 9984
— di caricamento 3335
lingotto 1206, 3042, 9782
— a sezione rettangolare 14518
— con soffiature pronunciate 1882
— curvato 4886
— d'acciaio 17481
— d'oro fino S.7073
— d'oro o d'argento 2570
— di fianco 16273
— di partenza 14451
— di piombo 10612
— di seconda fusione 15769
— incandescente 10996
— incurvato S. 4886
— iniziale 2691/a
— intagliato 12401/a
— pre-laminato 15253
— preliminare 9784/a
— quadrato 17237
— sgrossato al laminatoio 1820
— sottile di alluminio 19618 19618
— tondo 15284
— v. massello
liparite 10864
lipopalingenesi 10865
liquazione 6384, 10866, S. 11474
liquefazione S. 7893
liquido 10880, 7459
— di chiusura 15739
— di decapaggio 13216/a
— per la prova 10483
— per saldare 16889
— premente 13907
lisciare 2610, 16583

lisciatoio 16584, S. 17153
— a S 7270
— a squadra 13366, 14342, 16002
— a squadra per spigoli smussati 14343
— a squadra per spigoli vivi 16003
— a tampone 10970
— concavo 4882
— curvo per raccordi grandi 4882
— d'angolo 579
— doppio 5657
— per raccordi 7030, 17711
— rotondo 15291
lisciatura 15755, 16585
— della superficie di una forma stivata d'argilla 17828
liscio 16601
lisciva deramata 5082
— di soda 16811
— di zinco 11108
lisciviazione a mucchi 8943
liskeardite 10882
lista portacemiera S.9194
listello 10575
litantrace 11050
litargirio 10619
litchfieldite 10883
litio 10885
litoclasi 10886
litofisi 10890
litogeno 10887
litologia 10889
litomorfico 11111
livellamento 2029, 8385
— barometrico 1237
— del piano 1289
livelletta 2030
livello 5015
— a bolla d'aria 298, 19795
— a tubo di vetro 19779
— d'abbattimento 11774
— del liquido 7463
— del suolo 8464, 8616
— dell'acqua 19796, 19797
— della falda sotterranea S. 10710
— della galleria 156
— delle griglie 8582
— degli ugelli 19161
-— di fondo 2171

livello di fondo 2171, 16339
— di riferimento 5007
— di ripiena 19726
— idrostatico 10711, 10710
— inferiore 2142, 5093
— intermedio 1776, 2649, 4526, 4531
— principale S.7959
— produttivo 8112
— stratigrafico 9330
livingstonite 10900
lobo 10936
locale caldaie 1969, 17633
— dei convertitori 4306
— dei mescolatori 11834
— per dosare 11835
— per l'aggiustaggio 17729
— per mescolare o dosare 11835
localizzare 13199
localizzatore di giunti 4019
locomotiva a vapore 17440
log acustico 16915
·lollingite 10966
londiniano 10967
longbanite 10532
longulite 10987
longherina 10985
loparite 11015
loppa 15434, 16519
— acida 93
— calda 14878
— filante 93
— fredda 14461
— granulata 8438
— pietrosa 17651
— v. scoria
lorandite 11016
loranskite 11017
lorenzite 11018
lorettoite 11019
loseyite 11021
lotrite 11041
loxoclasi 11077
lubrificante 5364, 11079
— per alte pressioni 6503
— per filettatura 18552
— per stampi 5368
lubrificare eccessivamente 12771
lubrificatore 11080
lucchetto 10561
— della porta 5630
luce d'entrata e uscita 13685

luce di foro 173
— di scappamento S. 6653
— del giorno 5021
— incidente 9659
— m 24 (di) 16970
lucentezza 13626
— v. splendore
lucidabile 13627
lucidabilità 7134
lucidare 2610, 7114
lucidato a specchio 9161
lucidatura 2522
— in rilievo 14687
— preliminare S. 8297
lucignolo 20055
ludlamite 11082
ludwigite 11083
lugarite 11085
lujaurite 11086
lumachella 11087, 16105
luminosità della fiamma
   2405
luneburgite 11092
lunghezza del cilindro 15077
— del cuscinetto 1394
— del foro 15353
— del tubo S. 10204
— della scanalatura o della
   stria 20063
— di due aste ciascuna
   5689
— di 3 / 4 aste 17333
— esatta 6629
— prescritta 13861
— totale degli stands o di
   tubing contenuta in una
   torre 14325
lunnite 11093
luogo di carico 13434
luscladite 11096
lusitanite 11097
lussatite 11098
lustrare S. 13623
lustrino 14611
lutare una forma 11099
— una staffa S. 3666
lutecite 11100
luteziano 11102
lutezio 11101
lutite 11103
luzonite 11106

M

macchia d'argilla 3661
— locale per contatto 10381
— rossastra 14551/a
macchiato 17166
macchie di essudazione 17
   17168/a
macchina a bilanciere 1378
— a camera calda 9404
— a camera calda a pistone
   9405
— a camera fredda 3967
— a camera fredda per fu-
   sioni sottopressione
   3968
— a colonna per formare ingranaggi 8135
— a comando a funi 15161
— a due piattaforme per
   formare ingranaggi 8137
— a due tempi 19184
— a getto di sabbia 15473
— a quattro tempi 7677
— a sagoma od a sciablona
   per formare ingranaggi
   11125
— a scosse 10159/a
— a tandem 18238
— a tavola per formare ingranaggi 8136
— a telescopio per formare
   puleggie 18360
— ad induzione 9754
— agglomerante 14132/a
— alesatrice 2431
— ausiliare S. 2050
— composta 4128
— compound o composta
   4128
— con camera calda a pressione pneumatica diretta
   sul metallo 5461
— con trasmissione a cin-
   ghia 1476
— d'avviamento 17385
— d'estrazione 1192, 5798,
   8219, 20103
— da affilare 8549
— da formare a cavalletto

19370
macchina da formare a mano
   con piattaforma rovesciabile 8770
— da formare a mano con
   sollevamento a spina
   della staffa 8769
— da formare anelli per
   cucine o per stufe 8964
— da formare con piattaforma rovesciabile 19149
— da parete per formare 8134
   8134
— da spianare sospesa
   12756
— dentatrice per ingranaggi
   8127
— di prova 18465
— elettrica saldapunti per
   utensili 6312
— fotografica per pozzi
   5704
— frigorifera 7744
— gemella 19170
— idraulica per formare a
   mano con piattaforma
   rovesciabile 9529
— motrice 5964
— murale per formare 8134
— non polarizzata 12361
— per alzare il coperchio
   10761
— per cementazione 8629
— per colare o per fondere
   3059
— per colata centrifuga
   3205
— per costipare il fondo
   13563
— per fare il foro di colata
   5927
— per fare la bocchetta
   18269
— per formare 12014
— per formare ingranaggi
   8133
— per formare pentole 8768
— per formare piccoli in-
   granaggi 16730
— per formare puleggie di
   grande diametro 11126

macchina per formare tubi alèttati 12015,
— per formatura a guscio 16102
— per formare v. formatrice
— per fondere masselli 13267
— per fusione sotto pressione 5363
— per impastare S. 11825
— per intrecciare la paglia 17757
— per la fucinatura e la laminazione 7591
— per la prova di trazione 11124, 11127
— per la tempra alla fiamma 7260
— per miniera 11777
— per molare 8557
— per otturare il foro di colata 8668, 18268
— per piano inclinato 9693
— per pigiare il carbone 3847
— per precisare la posizione delle staffe 3218
— per pressofusione a stantuffo 13580
— per pressofusione ad aria compressa 303
— per pressofusione ad aria compressa a camera mobile 8363
— per produzione rulli mediante centrifugazione 15075
— per prova di trazione 18413
— per rettificare gli ingranaggi 8128
— per ripiena 1058, 8327, 3911
— per ripiena meccanica 8333, 17704
— per sbavare 3704
— per sfornare il coke 3943
— per sgretolare il materiale aurifero 17309
— per soffiare le anime S. 4394
— per taglio alla fiamma 7257

macchina per taglio verticale del carbone 3811
— per tamponatura 12080
— per tappare fori di colata 12399
— per tirare le anime 4444
— per triturare 8556
— posa-condotte 13353
— punzonatrice 12262
— reversibile 14827
— rompighisa 12108
— scava-trincea 6671, 6171
— soffiante 1858, 1875
— utensile 11136
macchine dette slip form machines 16653
— di diffrazione 5401
— per formare e per fonderia 15507
macchinista 6471, 11131
— del montacarichi 6473
macedonite 11114
macgovernite 11115
macina 2317
— a campana 1450
— a cilindri 15113
— a disco 5523
— centrifuga 5520
— da mulino 8563
— v. mulino
macina a martelli 8729
macinare 8539, 11682, S. 17257, 18922
— a mano 16964
— finemente 4090
— v. frantumare
macinato troppo fino 12728
macinatoio 4778
— a palmenti 6202
macinatrice 8556
macinatura 8574
macinazione 2325, S. 4775, 4776, 12101, 8542, 8546, 11706
— v. triturazione
— fina S. 7078
— fine 367
maconite 11144
macroclastico 11146
macrocristallino 11147
macrodomo 11148
macrografia 11149, 11151
macropinacoide 11153
macroprisma 11154

macrosegregazione 11156
macrostruttura 11157
mackensite 11141
madeirite 11159
madre di colata 16948
madupite 11160
maenaite 11161
mafraite 11164
mafite 11163
magazzino o deposito di ferrami 10021
maglia d'attacco 3090
— del setaccio 16300
— metallica 11516
maglie (a) 11520
maglio (da forgia) 7593
— a caduta 5981
— a caduta libera 5986
— a cinghia 7366
— a frizione 7768
— a manovella 8739
— a molle 20117
— a tavola 1923
— a vapore 17433
— a vapore a cilindro fisso 17435
— a vapore a doppio effetto 5642
— a vapore ad un sol montante 17436
— a vapore a semplice effetto 16383
— a vapore con immissione superiore del vapore 17434 17434
— ad aria compressa 4136
— con comando sistema Müller 5995
— con trasmissione a cinghia 1475
— per raddrizzare 17724
— spianatore 17724
magma 11167, 7690
— igneo 9625/a
— primario 12933
— residuo 14754
— secondario 17926
magnalio 455
magnetizzazione 11205
magnesia 1631, 11170/a, 11181
magnesiocromite 11171
magnesioferrite 11172
magnesioludwigite 11173

magnesite S. 2852, 11174
magnete 11183
— a ferro di cavallo 9383
— d'acciaio 17483
— da gru 4600
— di pescaggio 7220
— fisso 17400
— mobile 12048
— permanente 13106
magnetico 11185
— (non) 12354
magnetismo 11206
magnetite 10923, 10959, S. 11193, 11207
— artificiale 835
magnetizzabile 11208
magnetoferrite 11214
magnetografia 11209/a
magnetoplumbite 11211
magro 12340
mal cristallizzato 6159
— stivata 19292
malachite 8510, 11237
malacoite 11238
malacon 11239
malchite 11240
maldonite 11241
malignite 11245
mallardite 11247
malladrite 11246
malleabile 6073
malleabilità 11248
malleabilizzazione 11253
— per decarburazione 11255
— per grafitizzazione 11256
malsicuro 6019
malta 11936
— di cemento 10553
— liquida 16713, 16716
— refrattaria 14634
manadonite 11260
mancante S. 11806
mancanza di metallo 16183
— di peso 19284
mandare in pezzi S.16011
mandata 5490
mandriale 14314
mandrinatura 5873/a
mandrino 15081, 17193
— a rulli S. 18980
— autocentrante 10142
— a autocentrante a tre ganasce 18563

mandrino di trafila 11264
— galleggiante 7390/a
— per allargare i tubi 18980
— piriforme 13011
— sollevatubi 2958
manganese 11266
— al ferro 13176
manganifero 11280
manganite S.59, 11286
manganocalcite 11287
manganofillite 11288
manganosite 11289
manganoso 11290
mangerite 11292
manica 16591
manichetta per trivellazioni 15017
manico 8793
— del cuneo 16654
— di legno 20183
— di presa per elevatori posto sulla testa di iniezione 18139
— fuso in un sol pezzo 3014
— ribadito 14977
manicotti a cunei interni e anelli di tenuta 2933
manicotto 4016, 4549, 13332
— d'arresto per il secondo tappo 17302
— di cementazione 17664
— di protezione 2953
— di riduzione 9724/a
— esotermico 6663
— fuso in un sol pezzo 3012
— galleggiante 7385
— isolante 8982
— mobile 16619
— per cementazione a più stadi 12125, 16374
— per tubi 2936
— riduttore per fresatrice 127
manifestazione di gas 12446, 16219
— di olio 16217
— di petrolio 12510
maniglia a vite per estrarre il modello 10768
mannite 11296

manometro 8108, 11297
— a mercurio 11507
— a tubo elastico 17196
— campione 11364
— metallico 17196
— per pressione 13783
manovale 12302, 15264, 15392
manovella 4658
manovra del convertitore 8797
— di batteria 18908
mantello S. 2930, 4571, 4842, 4842, S.10100, 11299/a
— della sacca 16103
— di gas 8023
mantenere 19358
manuale di consultazione 14590
marada 2246
marca 11329
— di fabbrica 18812
marcassite 9092, 11313, 20034
marchio 2262
— di fabbrica 3521
marcia 15349
— a freddo S. 4009
— a vuoto S. 1065
— continua 4261
— d'un forno 4190
— dell'operazione di puddellaggio 20248
— produttiva (in) 12542
— variabile dell'altoforno 10039
— v. andamento
margarite 4505, 11314
margarosanite 11315
margine S. 6198, 17188/a
marialite 11318
marignacite 11319
mariposite 11326
mariupolite 11327
markfieldite 11332
marloesite 11336
marmatite 11339
marmitta 13720
marmo a grana grossa 16991
— belga 14409
— serpentino 10904
marmolite 11340
marna 10930, 11335
marrone S. 2470

marscite 11343
marscoite 11342
martellare S. 1818, 5754,
    8727, 11257
— a freddo 3958
martellatura 8735, 8748
— a penna 13043
martellina 15600
martello 17307
— a leva 15943
— a pedale 12535/a
— ad altalena 18206
— d'acciaio 17478
— del prospettore 14037
— frontale 10748
— idraulico 9524
— per la cernita 13210
— per picchiettare 3480
— per pozzi 16424
— per sbavare 3480
— perforatore 269, 2572,
    5881, 8731, 10093,
    11121, 11404, 13390
— perforatore a iniezione
    d'acqua 19768, 19775
— pneumatico 13584, 13591,
    10099/a
— pneumatico a mano 8774
— sbavatore 6976
— segnalatore 10409
martensite S. 8869, 11346
martinetto 10091, 10770
— a cremagliera 14321
— idraulico 9525, 9534
— libero S. 5986
— meccanico 11407, 19709
— parallelo 5986
— pneumatico 13586
— v. cricco
martinite 11350
martino 5999
martite 11351
masaite 11352
mascagnite 11353
mascella 10141, 14391
mascelle di piegatura 1509
— di sospensione per tubi
    19048
maschera 6743
— antigas S. 8028
— di ramolaggio 8110
maschinatura 18299
maschio 15712
— di pescatore 5372

maschio estrattore 10403
— filettante 18263
— filettante di pescaggio
    18288
— per le aste di pompaggio
    17940
— pescatore 7223
— porta-matrice S.5374
masciatore 8783
massa agglutinata 1115
— d'iniezione 9808
— di carreggiamento 12780
— di magnesite 11177
— di minerali 12647
— di segregazione 10494/a
— inclusiva 9808
— microcristallina 8617
massello 1148, 1820, 9992,
    11043
— d'acciaio 17489
— di ghisa 13249
— ottagonale 12452
— v. pane
— v. salmone
massellotta 5488
massicciata S. 1169
massiccio di protezione
    15952
massicot 11358
masso erratico 2192, 6550
mastice 16960
— di ferro 9967
— solfo-asfaltico 89
masticiare S. 7013
masut 7791
matasse di filo S. 12930
materia agglomerante 3142
— esplosiva 6684
— estranea 7566
— non fusa 19322
— plastica 13472
— prima 14456
materiale alluvionale S.411
— assorbente 5634
— carburante S. 2881
— d'apporto di saldatura
    19947
— da cementazione 3141
— da torrefare 12657
— di riempimento S. 1057,
    12851
— di rivestimento 10850
— di rivestimento per cal-
    daie 1957

materiale di sondaggio 5913
— difficilmente lavorabile
    9919
— dragato 17141
— ferroviario 14367
— legante 1602
— molto refrattario 9195
— non fuso S. 16951
— passante 19280
— per arricchire il rivesti-
    mento 10854
— per levigare 8558
— per ripiena 1055, S.
    2534, 7021, S. 18234
— per sbavare 3705
— refrattario per crogiuoli
    14633
— residuo non fuso 15434
— sterile S. 2584
— vagliato 16303
materiali da costruzione
    2535
— di puntellamento e di
    armamento provvisorio
    dei solai 17011
— per la costruzione delle
    strade 14980
— per la formatura 12020
— per ripiena 7037, 19740
materie prime metalliche
    11570
materozza 3053, 5030, S.
    5488, 6885/a, 6886,
    11034, S. 14947, 15375,
    16702, 17211
— a pressione **di gas** 13905
— aperta 12598
— aperta a tallone 12599
— aperta laterale S.12599
— atmosferica 924
— cieca 1772
— soffiata 3108
— strozzata 6887, 10378/a
materozzatura 15380
matildite 11375
matita bleu 1910
— colorata S. 1910
— grassa S. 1910
— rossa S. 20285
matlockite 11376
matraccio a fondo piatto
    7327
— a fondo rotondo 15273
— d'evaporazione 6613

matraccio conico 6544
— per distillazione frazionata 7688
— tarato S. 11398
matrice 2127, 2153, 2222, S.
   5356, 11378, 11379,
   11380
— a elementi sovrapposti
   15532
— cambiabile 9833/a
— di ricalcatura 8929
— galvanica 7925
— in calcestruzzo 4175
— negativa 12212
   per fusione 3060
— per materie plastiche
   836
— per presse 13889
— per ricalibrare 14694
— per stampare a freddo
   3982
— per stampi 17324
— sezionata 17128/a
— vetrosa 7774/a
— \ stampo
matrici per posaterie 4564
matta di nichel 12275
— di piombo 10616
— di rame 1908, 4358,
   13302
— di rame calcinato 2713
— grezza di rame 14457
mattone 2367
— a coltello 2374
— a sezione trapezoidale
   19882
— a sifone per separare le
   scorie 18174
— acido o siliceo 16313
— basico 1294
— crudo 176, 8506/a, 10925
   10925
— del tino 15935
— di caldaia 10473/a
— di carbone 2828
— di gres fine 5428
— di loppa 16528
— di magnesite 11175
— Dinas 5428
— parascorie 16463
— refrattario 467, 3278,
   14627
— refrattario silico alluminoso S. 467

mattone seccato all'aria S.
   176, 266
mattonella S. 2415, 6226,
   7246
— antierosione 17110
— di minerale 12634
— di pirite arrostita 1898
— secca 5846
— sinterizzata 16432
mattoni della sacca 2123.
maucherite 11384
mauzeleite 11385
mazza 9038, 16581
— a rincalzare 1404, 14401,
   18232
— battente 8737
— d'acciaio 17486
— in ferro forgiato 20242
— rompighisa 12108
mazzeranga 18235, 18233
mazzetta da minatore 14932
mazzuolo conico 14423
— conico a doppia testa S.
   14425
— conico con testa 14424
— da formatore 11993
— doppio 14425
— semplice S. 14424
meccanismo di caricamento
   3339
— di ribaltamento automa-
   tico 990
— di rovesciamento 18675
— di trivellazione 14901
— per rimescolare 14317
meconite 11441
medioporfirico 11422
,melaconite 11442
melafiro 11450
melanite 11443
melanocerite 11444
melanocratico 11445
melanoflogite 11446
melanotec..te 11447
melanovanadinite 11448
melanterite 11449
melilite 11451, 11452
melinofano 11453
mellite 9302, 11454
melonite 11455
menaccanite 11485
mendeleywite 11489
mendozite 11491
meneghinite 11492

menhir 11493
menilite 11494
menisco della ghisa 10338
menoipite 11490
mensola 2238
— di ferro 9959
— di sostegno 18034
— per il tubo dell'acqua
   di refrigerazione 2245
— tubolare per linee di contatto 19063
mercurio 9508, 11503
— metallico 11569
meroxene 11513
merrillite 11514
merwinite 11515
mescolanza gassosa 8025
mescolare 11817, 14094
— con la pala 19139
— insieme 11818
mescolatore 11826, 11829,
   13264
— ad alette 20109/a
— ad ugello e tramoggia
   (Halliburton) 9326
— aperto 12583
— cilindrico per ghisa
   4948
— d'argilla 3658
— d'argilla orizzontale
   9335
— di dolomite 5612
— di ghisa 11550, 11550
— oscillante 18631
mescolatrice 11833
— a doppio cono 4199/a
— ad alette 12859
— per sabbia 15504
mescolo S. 15463, S. 17152
mesocambrico S. 34
mesocrato 11521
mesolito 11522
mesostasi 11524
mesotipo 11527
mesotorio 11526
mesozoico 11528
mesozona 11529
messa a fuoco 7517
— della gabbia alle molette
   12762
— fuori esercizio 1877
— fuori uso 19613
— in marcia 1872/a, S.
   10799, 17382

messa in opera 13354
messelite 11530
mestolo per canali di colata
    S. 8092
metà di modello 12978
metabruscite 11531
metacinabro 11532
metaheulandite 11534
metahewettite 11535
metalceramico 3224
metalli alcalini 359
metallico 11566
metallifero 12629
metallina di rame 4358
— grezza 3875/a, 11381
metallizzare 11575
metallizzazione 11574,
    11577
— a spruzzo 11562
— galvanica 7924
metallo 11537
— a struttura compatta
    3764
— aderente 13230/a
— antifrizione 663, 14663
— base 1281, 13938
— Bell-Krupp 19696
— bianco 20038
— bianco duro 8831/a
— caldo 9422
— ceramico 3230
— comune 1280
— depositato 5198
— delta 5158
— di apporto 7022
— di base 12934
— di colata 7645
— di copertura 3610
— di materozza 8915/a
— di platino 13522
— dolce S. 16837
— dopo il soffiaggio 1883
— duro 8828, 8837
— fondente 6004
— freddo 3985
— fusibile 7889
— fuso S. 7464
— giallo 20289
— in graniglie 16205/a
— leggero 10784
— nobile 12328
— non ferroso 12349
— omogeneo 7464
— per bussole 2626

metallo per cannoni 8673
— per capsule 2814/a
— per cuscinetti 1396
— pesante 9035
— plastico 13472/a
— rosa 10610
— secondario 15765
— solidificato nel canale
    di colata 16951
— stampato 17317
— stirato 6665
— surriscaldato S. 9422
— tenero 16837
— vile S. 1280
metallogenetico 11578
metallogenico 11579
metallografia 11583
— speciale del ferro 17015
metalloide 11584
metallurgia del ferro 6964/a
— delle polveri 13788
— dei metalli ferrosi 1159
— dei metalli non ferrosi
    11591
— dei minerali 13974/a
— fisica 13191/a
metamorfico 11592
metamorfismo 11593/a
— d'iniezione 9814
— per pressione 10912
— regionale 11595
metamorfosi regressiva
    14803
metanodotto 11611
metarossite 11596
metasilicato 11597
metasoma 8648
metasomatosi 2855, 11600
metasome 11601
metastibnite 11602
metatenardite 11603
metatipo 11604
metavariscite 11605
metavoltite 11606
metodo a palla e anello
    1149
— al rottame 15663
— catalano 5462
— d'analisi 11612, 18466
— d'avanzamento a gradini
    inclinati 14913
— d'estrazione 11778,
    18181
— del marcia-avanti 17084

metodo di approfondimento
    per congelamento 15957
— di coltivazione 11613
— di congelamento 7747
— di preparazione per con-
    gelamento 7746
— di separazione con liqui-
    di densi 16413
— d'affinaggio 7111
— speciale di tempera
    17016
— stechiometrico Mrazek
    17629
metro a nastro 18272
mettere 15902
— a fuoco 7515
— a fuoco i colpi da mina
    S. 17104
— a placca 1429
— del mastice 7013
— il forno fuori di marcia
    4977
— il fuoco indietro 4559
— in circuito S. 9311
— le graffe 3617
— le punte 17176
mezza di sotto S. 2174
mezzaforma superiore
    10745, 18745
mezza forma inferiore 2174
mezzo di tempra 8862
— -tondo irregolare
    8862
miagirite 11617
miaschite 11620
mica 11621, 5022, 10050,
    17042
— bianca S. 12139
— compressa S. 13879
— d'ambra 507
— d'uranio 19390
— potassica 12139
— pressata 13879
micanite 11618
micascisto 11623
miccia 14581, 17266
— a rapida combustione
    14302
— di Bickford 1739
microclastico 11631
microcline 11632
microlinperlite 11633
microcriptocristallino
    11634

micro-durezza 11639/a
microfessura 7207/a,
    8723/a
microfirico 11648
microfusione S. 9937
micrografia 11637
micrografico 11638
microlite 11640
microlitico 11641
micromeritico 11644
micrometro 11643
micropaleontologia 11643
micropegmatite 11646
micropertite 11647
microrisucchio S. 11654,
    11654
microritiro 11654
microscopia 11651
microsegregazione 11653,
    4463/a
microfusione 11014
microstruttura 11655
microtinite 11656
miersite 11669
miesite 11670
migliaia di piedi cubi 11403
migmatite 4122, 11671
migrazione del petrolio
    18857
— delle valli 16129
miharaite 11672
mijakite 11673
milarite 11674
milioni di piedi cubi 11842
millepiedi 7324, 11045
millerite 8709/a, 11705
millisite 11715
milonite 12148
milonitizzazione 12150
miloschine 11718
mimesite 11719
mimetesite 11720
mimosite 11719
mina di rilevaggio 10755
— di rottura S. 2162, 2335
— di sondaggio 2623
minaggio di blocchi 1802
minare 11723
minatore 3840, 6745, 8204,
    10464, 13422, 11746,
    15963
— alla roccia 11549
— di carbone 2318, 2482,
    8185
mine di rottura 3186

minerale 11749
— a basso tenore 11052
— a coccarda 14928
— a pezzi S. 11091
— abbattuto 2445
— accessorio 11785
— aciculare S. 73
— alterato in superficie
    19868
— arricchito 4163
— associato 47
— autofusibile 15823
— carbonato torrefatto
    16990
— classificato S. 3894
— concentrato 4163, 19355a
— d'acciaio 10016
— d'alluminio 456
— d'impregnazione 9664
— da macinare 11710
— di ferro 9987, 14457/a
— di ferro a stalattiti 2481
— di ferro a struttura com-
    patta 5172
— di ferro argilloso 1106,
    7266, 8645, S.11001
— di ferro arsenicale 817
— di ferro bagnato 19993
— di ferro cavernoso 11001
— di ferro compatto 4100
— di ferro contenente acido
    carbonico 9988
— di ferro con alto tenore
    di acqua 9990
— di ferro con tenore in
    zinco 20342
— di ferro contenente car-
    bonato di calcio 2706
— di ferro cristallino 4802
— di ferro crudo 14455
— di ferro cuprifero 4854
— di ferro disgregato 19867
— di ferro duro 8835
— di ferro fibroso 6989
— di ferro fosforoso 13166
— di ferro fragile 2424
— di ferro friabile 7763
— di ferro galenico 9989
— di ferro in amioni 2132
— di ferro incrostato 9726
— di ferro manganesifero
    11283
— di ferro nickelifero 12285
— di ferro polverulento
    7086

minerale di ferro poroso
    13675
— di ferro sabbioso 15534
— di ferro scavato di fresco
    7756
— di ferro solforoso 17988
— di ferro tenero 16836
— di ferro terroso 6175
— di ferro titanifero 18688
— di manganese propriamen-
    te detto 14019
— di nichel 12277
— di piombo 2059, 2205,
    6904
— di piombo pulverulento
    1462
— di prima estrazione
    11739
— di qualità inferiore 5721
— di scarto S. 5474, 19735
— di sostituzione 14060
— di zinco 20331
— di zinco manganesifero
    11284
— dicroico 5348
— difficilmente fusibile
    14631
— difficilmente riducibile
    5400
— disseminato 5540,
    13768
— facilmente fusibile 6180
— facilmente riducibile
    6181
— ferromagnesico 11162
— filoniano 10960
— finemente disseminato
    3360
— fino 7087/a
— fondente 7503
— frantumato 5735, 17318
— grezzo 14458
— grosso 11091
— in mattonelle S. 12634
— in pezzatura media 3894
— in pezzatura minuta 1674
    16740
— in pezzi 7204, 10411,
    10412
— in pezzi piccoli 8406
— in piccoli ovuli mescola-
    to con argilla 14062
— in prismi corti 16177
— imperfettamente torrefatto
    9717

minerale lavato 2514, 10175
— macinato con acqua
  12649
— non cernito 11741
— non torrefatto 19329
— normale 17346
— oolitico 7357
— ossidato 1837
— pisiforme 13004/a
— povero 1284, 10643,
  11052, 13656
— polverizzato galleggiante
  7387/a
— preparato 5273
— preparato o trattato
  5839
— primario 9390, 12666/a
— produttivo 12998
— reniforme 12335
— ricco 2496, 9152
— ricco di piombo 1604
— scelto 15692
— secco 6033
— sferico 17058
— sfornato 5817
— spaccato a mano 13215
— spezzato 5474
— sterile 7958, 19730
— torrefatto 14985
minerali accessori 44
— di contatto 4248
— di nichel 12266
— disseminati in una massa
  5541
— essenziali 6568
— formati con riduzione di
  volume 11786
— pesanti 9036
mineralizzabile 11757
mineralizzare 11759
mineralizzazione 11758
mineralogia 11763/a
minetta 11765
minguetite 11766
miniera 1120, S. 5147, S.
  13397, 11724
— a cielo aperto 12565,
  17848
— a giorno 5018
— abbandonata 8637, 8692,
  12522
— con accesso a pozzo
  5860
— con grisou 8072

miniera d'allume 440
— d'oro alluvionale 8480
— di carbone 3858, 3839
— di ferro 9983, 9991
— di stagno 17364
— petrolifera 12500
miniere 5408
minio di ferro 9986
minuterie metalliche 7117,
  16734
minuto 2214, 2418, 7074,
  7356,
— di carbone 8436, S.
  16727
minverite 11788
miocene 11789
mirabilite 11790
mirmechite 12151
miscela 11837
— a caldo 9421
— azeotropica 1029
— d'ossidi di manganese
  19615
— di carica S. 1428
— eutettica 6603
— esclusiva S.7165
— fisica 13192
miscelare 11817
miscelatore S. 11826
— per soluzione 16903
mischiare 11817
miscibile 11796
miscibilità 11794
— completa 4115
— limitata 12942
— parziale 12942
— totale 4115
miscuglio 11837
— di dolomite 5611
— di minerali 11838
misenite 11797
missourite 11808
misura 11392, 11394
— del pannello alla filtro-
  pressa 19636
— del ritiro 533
— della durezza 11395
— di deviazione 5471
— fissa 7235
— nominale 12337
— non distruttiva 12347
misurare 6827, 11389
— la temperatura d'un corpo
  per mezzo della sua ra-

diazione 11390
misurare la dimensione della
  provetta 11391
misuratore 18363
— d'inclinazione del pozzo
  5859
— del rendimento dei cavi
  di manovra 18721
— del tiraggio 1728
— di porcellana 13665
— di pressione di strato 2015
  2015
— di serbatoi 18253
— di spiazzamento 5534
— di umidità 11862
— registratore della pressione di strato 13896
misurazione 11394
— del serbatoio 17745
— elettrometrica 6361
mixite 11836
mizzonite 11841
modderite 11851
modellatura 11869, 12984
modelleria 12992
modellista 11868, 12982
modello 2983, 12972
— a doghe 8624
— a doppio ritiro 11366
— a giorno S.16109
— al naturale 16109
— al vero S. 16109
— anulare 14930
— completo 1803/a
— con colata attaccata
  8099
— con incorporato il sistema di alimentazione 1298
  12981
— d'iniezione 7400
— del dente 18733
— deformato 5565
— deformato nella stivatura
  12975
— di colata 8094
— di fonderia 7664
— di sabbia 15510
— di una corona 14917
— distorto 5565
— esterno 6699
— in due parti 17131
— in due pezzi 15764
— interno 9902
— madre 11376

modello mal progettato 9718
— non conforme 9719
— per colate 15376
— sciolto 11005
— scomponibile 11005
— variato S. 11803
moderare la combustione S.
    16513
modifica della pendenza
    14821
modo di raffreddamento 4339
— di trattamento 11615
modulo d'elasticità 11855,
    6246
— di resistenza 15778/a
— Young 6246
mofetta 11856
moietta S. 1175, 9435
— di ferro S. 9324
moissanite 11859
mola 2529, 8563, 11716
— a diamante 5333/a
— a smeriglio 6413
— per affilare 8562, 14348
— per lucidare 2523
— per sbavare 8562
— superiore d'un mulino
    15371
— trasportabile 13687
molare 8537
molassa 11866
molato S. 8607
molatore 8543
molatrice 8544
— portabile 13690
molatura 8545
— meccanica 11128
molazza a barre 1218
— a disco fisso S.7237
— a disco girevole S.15230
— a vasca girevole 15230
— a vasca fissa 7237
— mescolatrice 12100/a
— miscelatrice intermit-
    tente 1332
— portatile 13694
— v. frantoio
molazzare 8538
— una sabbia 11699
— una terra S. 11699
molazzatura 11707, 12101
moldavite 11867
molecola 11874
— biatomica 5346

molecola monoatomica 11890
— triatomica 18889
molengraaffite 11875
molibdato d'ammonio 526
molibdenite 11881, 13731
molibdeno 11882
molibdite 11885
molibdofillite 11887
molibdomenite 11886
molisite 11888
molla a balestra 10634
— a disco 5485, 13498
— a spirale 17101, 19601
— ad anello 625
— ad elica 9061
— conica 4211
— del respingente 2519
— di sospensione 1399
mollare un tiro 16506
mollettare S. 2068
mollezza 16850
mollone di recupero 14503
moltiplicatore 12127
— di pressione 13922
molto tagliato 1093
momento d'inerzia 11889
— di torsione 19183
— flettente 1512
— torcente 18776
monazite 11891
monchiquite 11892
mondaeldeite 11893
mondatura 18099
monetite 11895
monheimite 11896
monimolite 11897
monite 11898
monitor 11899
monmouthite 11905
monocilindrico 11909
monogenico 11911
monosulfuro di ferro S.
    10022
monotettoide 11915/a
monrepite 11916
montacarichi 6377, 9224,
    10739
— a bilanciere d'acqua
    19745
— a cavo 10752
— a doppio effetto 5640
— a piano inclinato 9702
— a semplice effetto
    16381

montacarichi d'altoforno
    7845
— idraulico 9526
— inclinato 16482
— pneumatico 13588
montaggio 15913
— ausiliare 13300
— dei pali di legno 4634
— del fondo 9838
— di circolazione 11309,
    15900
— di tubi 13354
— su colonna 4042
montagnola 12030
montanite 11918
montante 10668, 13707,
    14947, 15359, 17897
— cieco 6093
— di quadro 5862
— e suola 14009
— laterale 9053
montare 6735, 8203, 14370,
    14896, 15902
— la colata S. 9722
— la forma 2537
montato 14589
— su carro 12035
— su zattero 16454
montiano 11919
monticellite 11920
montmorillonite 11921
montrealite 11922
montroidite 11923
montronite 12369
monzonite 11924
mordente 6572
mordenzatura 3527
mordere 6571
morena 11928
— depositata 5199
— di fondo 1266
— frontale 18428
— interna 6478
— profonda 8618
— viaggiante 14199
moresonite 11931
morganite 11933
moroxite 11935
morsa 1495, 10142
— a bottiglia 9207
— a catena 3249
— a mano 8790
— da tubi 13369
— per affilare le seghe 15558

morsetto 17079, S. 20120
— per elementi 18427
— per terreno 8610
— per treppiede 3623
mortaio d'acciaio 17485
— d'acciaio diamante 5317
— d'agata 210
— da miscela 11937
mortesatrice combinata 2096
mortisa 10192
mosandrite 11941
mosca 18513
mosesite 11942
mossite 11946
mota 12069
moto turbolento 6195, 16428
motore 5962
— a combustione interna 9898
— del verricello 10186
— di trascinamento 5961
— per levigare 11953
motrice 5962
motta 9841, 16780
mottramite 11959
movimento d'avanzamento 6881/a
— dei materiali 8796
— della leva 12052
— di rotazione 19147
— epirogenetico 6506
— idrocratico 9551
mozzo 9469
mucchi (a) 1328
mucchio 1147, 13278
— da caricare 12061
— di carbone 3817
— di minerale 6905
— di minerale pronto per l'arrostimento di carbone da cokificare 3620
— di scorie 3572, 18673
mucillagginoso 12056
muffola 12096, 12097
— a carbone 12098
— a gas 12099
— del tubo 19047
— di ferro 9985
— di platino 13524
— in terra refrattaria 7161
mulinello 6194, S. 2317
mulino 4771, 10756, 11685, 17327
— a barre 15055

mulino a cilindri 15122
— a ganasce 10141/a
— a martelli 8738
— a mascelle 17641
— a palle 1104, 1158, 8301, 13033
— a palle tubolari 1168
— a pestelli 8495, 12654, 13735
— a pestelli ad acqua 19999 19999
— a pestelli primario 13828
— a piloni 15041/a
— a rulli 3355
— ad un pestello 16404
— continuo 4269
— glaciale 8255
— per amalgama 494
— per fini 7077
— per loppa 16527
— per macinazione fine 8559
— per scorie 16527
— tubolare 19077
mullite 12102
muniongite 12131
murare 2366
muratore di pozzi 3915
.muratura 11345
— a secco 6049
— del tino 15950
— di sostegno 12828, 12844
— esterna della camicia 12697
— in mattoni 2377
murchisonite 12135
muretto 7829
murmanite 12136
muro S. 2142, 7402, 7547, 7346, 11070, 11110, 16338, 19269, 19632
— d'uno strato 7409
— di pietre 14982
— di scarpa 15607
— di sostegno 12846
— per ripiena S. 2534, 12837
— tagliafuoco 7185
— v. suola
muschio 11943
muscovadite 12138
muscovite 4095, 11792
muso d'ugello 19162
muthmannite 12147/a

N

nacrite 12154
nadorite 12155
naegite 12156
nafta 6176
— di precipitazione 13816
— leggera 10789
— primaria 13947
— solvente 9173
naftalene 12168
naftalina 12168
naftenato 12169
— di piombo 10618
naftenico 12172
— (indice) 12170
nafteno 12171
nagatelite 12157
nagyagite 7534, 12159
nahcolite 12160
nantochite 12167
napoleonite 12173
nastri d'acciaio dei centralizzatori a elementi longitudinali 17403
nastro 17844
— a rastrelli 15675
— abrasivo 9
— d'acciaio 17512
— d'acciaio al forno elettrico 6307
— di ferro S. 1177, 9322, 17744
— di magnesio 11182
— di materiale 17850
— di piombo 7760/a
— di prova 18455
— inclinato 9434
— laminato a caldo 9434
— magnetico 3991
— trasportatore 4314
natroalunite 12183
natrocalcite 12185
natrofilite 12188
natrojarocite 12186
natrojarosite 12186
natrolite 12187, 12187
natronite 16812
natura 14247
— della superficie 18045
naujalite 12199
naumannite 12200
nauruite 12201
nave carboniera 17422

navicella d'alluminio per
    pesare 463
— di fusione 4074
— di platino 13517
navite 12202
nebbia metallina 11543/a
nebulizzazione 194
nefelina S. 6243, 12228
nefelinite 12230
nefrite 12232
negativa 12212
nelsonite 12215
nemafillite 12216
neocomiano 12218
neodimio 12220
neoesano 12226
neogeno 12221
neolitico 12222
neon 12223
neotantalite 12225
neovulcanico 3183
nepouite 12233
neritico 12237
nero a secco S.17696
— da stufa 17696
— di carbone 2826
— di fonderia 1668/a
— di grafite 13571
— di ossa S. 2027
nerofumo S. 2826, 3288,
    16759
nero per fonderia 7649
— vegetale 3311
nervatura 6982, 14864
— incassata 9836
nervature-riempimento di
    lamiera piegata ad U
    12375
nervo 14882
nervoso 6986
nesquehonite 12239
nettunio 12236
nettunite 12235
neutralizzare 12255
neutro 11423
nevaio 12256
newberite 12260
newjanskite 12257
newlandite 12261
niccolite 12263
nichel elettrolitico 6345
nichelare 12267, 12286
nichelatura 12284
nichelina 4359, 12263
nichelio 12268

nido di grafite 10378
— di minerali 2036,
    12647/a
— di terra 15526/a
nife 12290
nigrina 12295
niobate 12296
niobio 12297
nitradimina S. 20274
nitratina 2744, 16812, 12308
nitrato 15447
— d'argento 16354
— di cobalto 12306
— di mercurio basico 1298
— di palladio 12307
nitride arsenosa S.823
nitrificazione 12315
nitrobarite 12316
nitrocalcite 12317
nitro-carburazione 2866
nitrogelatina 12318
nitrogeno S. 12319
nitroglauberite 12322
nitroglicerina 1740
nitrometro 12324
nitroso 12325, S. 12325
nitrurare col gas 8029
nitrurazione 519, 12312,
    12321
nitruro 12309/a
nivenite 12326
nobelio 12327
nocciolo della frattura 4428
— traversante di fissaggio
    S. 1599
nocerite 12330
nocivo 12406
nodo 9214, 10413, 10995
— piano 3788
nodulare 12331
noduli (a) 12331
— di ematite bruna 2475
nodulo 12336
nolo ferroviario 14366
non allineato 11793
— armato 19336
— auto-motrice 12364
— bagnabile 12370
— bituminoso 12340
— centrato 11793
— compresso 12366
— fisso 19296
nonesite 12368
norbergite 12371
nordenskioldite 12372

noria 6378
— di draga 10466/a
norite 12374
normalizzare 12385
normalizzazione 12388
northupite 12389
noseanite 12393
noseano 12392
noumeite 12404
nube ardente 8312
nucleo della sella anticlina-
    le 755
— di torrefazione 14989
— eroso dell'anticlinale
    5253
— non cementato 15539/a
— sinclinale 18940
numero atomico 932
— d'ordine 12422
— del filo 8115
— indice della dimensione
    del grano 8402
— unificato di materiale
    14592
nummulite 12424

O

obbiettivo 12432
obliquo 16449
occhiali di mica 11625
— di protezione 8340
occhiello 10995
occhio di cavo 15169
— di gatto 3080
occlusione 12445
occluso 12442
ocra 12448
— di ferro 12864, 10134,
    20288
— gialla 20285
— rossa 6174, 14554,
    15333
ocrolite 12449
oculare 6731
odinite 12456
odontolite 12457
odorizzante 12458
officina del gas 8066
— delle riparazioni 14731
— di (ri)finitura 7138/a
— di sbavatura 3696
— meccanica 11418

officina per le anime 4425
ofite 12616, S. 15895
offretite 12461
oggetti metallici 11546
oggetto illuminato 9633
oisanite 12519
okenite 12520
oleaggio 1336
oleato di piombo 10620
oleatore 12483
olefina 12524
oleina 12527
oleodotto 13355
oleoso 12525
oli antracenici 641
— primari 17717
oliare 12477
oligisto 9978
— micaceo 11626
oligocene 12531
oligoclasio 12532
oligoclasite 12533
oligonite 12534
olio combustibile denso
    2575, 7791
— da fonderia 7606
— da taglio solubile 16897
— di recupero 15608
— di lavaggio 7491
— di legno 19099
— di lino cotto 17337
— di pressatura 13869
— di spermaceti 17063
— di stoccaggio 17626
— Diesel 8031
— emulsionabile 6424
— emulsionato 6426
— estraibile 5742
— fumogeno 16776
— grafitato 8455
— grasso 6826
— grezzo 4754, S.11753
— inerte 5035
— in latte 18662
— liquido 16723
— minerale 11753, 15031
— minerale grezzo 1283
— odorizzante 16712
— paglierino 17755
— per casseforme 7606
— per corde 1333
— per lucidare 15322
— per rinvenimento 18397
— per servizi pesanti 9029

olio purissimo 13356
— raffinato con solventi
    16911
— residuo 7542
— residuo di carbone 3850
— ricco di gas 10898
— ridistillato 14741
— rigenerato 14497
— sgocciolato 5951
— solforato 17967
— sul posto 12495
— superdenso 18014
— torbido 15066
oliva 18098, 11263
olivenite 12535
olivina S. 13090, 12536
olmio 9283
oloassiale 9284
olocene 9285
oloedrico 9287
oloialino 9288
ololeucocratico 9289
olomelanocratico 9290
olomorfico 9291
olotipo 9292
ombra 19227
ombrello capovolto 12618
— per cementazioni 1314
— scorrevole per cementa-
    zione 3170, 16605
omeomorfo 9298
omilite 9295
omogeneo (non) 12352
omogeneizzazione 6523/a
omoclinale 9296
onda di laminazione
    13311/a
onegite 12547
onkilonite 12548
onofrite 12549
oolite 6225, 13142
opale 12555
— comune 4096
— di fuoco 7173
— ferruginoso 6969
— incrostante 16320
— latteo 20039,
— nobile 12329
— xiloide 20276
opdalite 12556
opera di rimonta 19373
— in direzione 10708
— sotterranea 3779, 5871
— sotterranea 8631

operaio addetto a caricare
    il minerale 3321
— addetto al cubilotto 4849
— addetto al decapaggio
    3687
— addetto all'affinaggio
    7100
— addetto alle cariche
    11259
— d'alto-forno 7850
— puddellatore 14105
— qualificato di raffineria
    17598
operatore a corda 15157
operazione continua 4261
— di salita e di discesa
    delle aste di sondaggio
    15294
— di tubaggio 15357
— unica 16401
operazioni alternate 1806
opere sotterranee 5408
orangite 12619
orbite 12621
ordanchite 12622
ordine d'ugelli 15302
— di frequenza 12623
orecchio 6727, 11084
— imboccolato 13858
— regolato 13858
orecchione 11084
orendite 12662
organigramma 7422/a
orientamento privilegiato
    13833
orientite 12666
orifizio 12668
— d'adduzione 9822
— d'ammissione 9820,
    9822
— di colata 15906, 9855
— di preriscaldamento
    2345
originale 19205
orizzonte di riferimento S.
    5007, 10327
— gassoso 8016
— guida 11331
— mineralizzato 9330
orlare 2068
orlo 6198
— del crogiuolo 5148
— del tubo di fumo 1368
orneblenda 9369

orneblendite 9371
ornoite 12675
oro 8343
— alluvionale 8662, 13436, 17770
— arruginito 15389
— falso 6142
— filoniano 10955
— granulare 16207
— in foglie 16972
— in lingotti 8346/a
— libero 7732
— olandese 6142
— puro 7073
— raffinato 3148
orogenesi 12676
orpimento 816, 10366, 12678, 20282, 14437
ortite 370
ortoclasio 12680
ortorombico 12682
ortosilicato 12685, 19836
oscillare 15002
oscillazione della basculla o bilancia 13537
— della cinghia 7284
— della fune d'estrazione 20017
osmondite 12688
ossatura 2930
osservazione 12436
— macroscopica 11155
ossidante 12808
ossidare 12805
ossidazione 12808/a, 12789, 12803
— a cucchiaiate 18784/a
— anodica 632, 633
— post-decapaggio 17968/a
ossidiana 12437, 19591/a
ossidianite 12438
ossido 12793/a
— acido 96
— basico 1301
— d'alluminio 443
— d'itterbio 20303
— d'ittrio 20305
— di berillio 1543
— di bario 12794
— di calcio 10810
— di carbonio 2838
— di ferro dalla fabbricazione dei colori di catrame 12798

ossido di magnesio 12800
— di manganese 11291
— di mercurio 11500, 14545
— di nichel 12278
— di rame 12797
— di rame granulato 8437
— di piombo 12799
— di zinco 12801
— ferrico 6928
— ferroso 6965
— magnetico (di ferro) S. 10193
— manganico 11281, 12796
— manganoso 12796
ossigenazione 12820/a
ossigeno 12817
— atmosferico 926
— combinato chimicamente 3396, 7236
osmio 12687
ostruito 2387
ostruzione 15574
— di paraffina 12910
— di un tubo 13330
— periferica 2388
ottagono 12451
ottetto elettronico 12454/a
ottonatura elettrolitica 2275
ottano 12453
ottonatura 13504
ottone 2266, 20283
— (di) 2283
— ad alta resistenza 9186
— commerciale 4091/a
— d'alluminio 449
— da fucinare 7592/a
— facilmente lavorabile 7721/a
— in foglie 2274, S. 13488
— in lamine S. 13488
— in lastre S. 13488
— in lastroni 13488
— per getti 2985
— per molle 17191/b
— per imbutitura 170
— rosso 14877/a
otturare 12068
— con fango 12067
otturarsi 3749
otturazione 15734
— con sabbia 15508
ottuso 12439
ovaletto 7937

ovalizzarsi 17114
ovatta 12859
ovulo d'antracite 6220
oxammite 12788
ozocerite 6178, 12821

P

pacchetto 6762, 12827, 16495
— di ferro 1794
— di ferro da puddellare 13279
— incrociato 4700/a
pacco di lamiere 11697
pachnolite 12823
packer a due elementi 17705
— per colonna perduta con dispositivo di fissaggio 10846
— per colonna perduta con dispositivo di fissaggio e recupero 10847
— per foro scoperto 7613, 9319
packfond 8195
padella d'argilla refrattaria 4742
paga a volume di materiale estratto 6829
paglia 6840, 15746, 17754
— tritata 2784
paglinoli 7408
paigeite 12861
paisanite 12865
pala 15689, 16212
— automatica 8377
— caricatrice 11412, 13039
— caricatrice motorizzata 6072
— d'arresto 18310
— da carbone 3846
— da formatore 11994
— meccanica 5451, 11412
— per caricare 13039
— per livellare 16462
palagonite 12873
palafitta 17083, 17218
palaite 12874
palanchino 1207, 4723
palancola 16075, 17490

palancolata 3903
palatinite 12875
palchetto 17906
— a V 15412
— ad ala 20110
— rinforzato 17907
— volante 6787
paleobotanica 12866
paleocene 12867
paleoclimatologia 12868
paleodevoniano 12869
paleolitico 12870
paleotipico 12871
paleozoico 12872
paletta 7374, 15639
paletti per cartelli indicatori
    16736
paletto incassato 7482
— tubolare per messa a ter-
    ra 19071
palla 1147, 16192
— della berta 5999
— di ferro 1820, 9956,
    11043
— di puddellaggio 14095
— puddellata al maglio
    16132
— di scoria 16522
palladio 12878
pallinare 16195
pallinatura 16205
— a caldo 9424
pallini di piombo per tarare
    18324
pallone di misura 11398
— per fabbricare cloro
    3502
— volumetrico 19597
pallottina di nichelio
    12279/a
palmola 18294
palo 13707, 14177, 14314,
    17897
— a traliccio per elettro-
    dotti 19076
— di calcestruzzo armato
    4177
— di sagoma 17827
— in cemento armato 4177
— oscillante 13059
— per illuminazione 17340
— portafari 1363
— stirato 17793
— tubolare a stelo unico
    19084

palpare 6896
palude 16624
paludoso 1950
pandermite 12893
pane 9783
— di coke 3933
— di ghisa 13249
— di ghisa grezzo 3427
— di piombo 13266
pane v. lingotto o massello
panello 2691
— di fango 12075
paniere da coke 3928
pannello 12895
— di chiusura dello scivolo
    3364
panotto 13271
pantellerite 12901
paracadute 8566, 2681,
    8568, 9243
— a eccentrici 2766
— per tubi 3091
paracarri tubolari a testa
    arrotondata forgiata a
    caldo 19074, 19079
paracarro tubolare 19085
paraclasi 6849
paracolpi del cavo 10832
paraframma 1096
paraffina 12906
— amorfa 13127
— grezza o in scaglie
    15585
— molle 16838
parafuoco 7185
paragenesi 12912
paragneiss 12913
paragonite 12914
parahopeite 12915
paralaurionite 12916
paralico 12917
paralluminite 12924
paramagnetico 12925
parametri del reticolo
    cristallino 4797
— di trivellazione 5932
paramorfismo 12927
paramorfo 12926
paranco 1795, 3245, 8231,
    9225, 18196
— a puleggia doppia 1796,
    1804
— a taglia 14133
— elettrico 6281

parasala 9362
parascintille 16979, 16984
parascorie 3573, 5476
paratia 2550, 5584
— di ventilazione 16091
— sotterranea 19255
paratoia di ventilazione
    325
parauricalcite 12928
paraurti 2516
paravauxite 12929
parco 17620
— dei vagoni 15130
— di stoccaggio 18250
— lingotti 9801, 16503/a
— per aste e tubi 13362
— putrelle 8243
— tubi 13372
parella 7210
parete 3379, 16252, 19632
— del pozzo 2084
— del tino 15975
— dell'ugello 19167
— della forma 19645
— della sacca 2119
— di separazione 12953
— divisoria fissa 7232
— laterale 15835, 16255,
    16280, 19633
— laterale di galleria 907,
    19490
— trasversale 4667
pareti 3376
— laterali della cassa fo-
    colaio 7156
pargasite 12934
parianite 12935
parisite 12936
parkerizzazione 12937
parsonsite 12940
parte amovibile 11006, 11007
— anteriore di una pompa
    10873
— centrale 3379
— combustibile 4070
— dello spettro giallo-ros-
    sastro 20294
— di sopra 18745
— di sotto 2174
— di un tubo rimasta senza
    vernice 9257
— difettosa 5110
— frontale 7779
— in gomma 12834

parte inferiore 11069
— intagliata od intaccata 8591
— intercambiabile 9872
— mobile di sagoma S.18280 18280
— molto dura di un filone 2594
— opaca 6088
— posteriore di una pompa 13784
— proporzionale 14023
— riportata 5252
— sana 16938
— sciolta 1107
— smontabile 5252, 5786
— spugnosa 12444, 17389
— superiore 19364
— superiore del crogiuolo 18742
— superiore d'un filone 682
partenza 10632
parti di ricambio 14713
— raffreddate dell'alto-forno 4328
particelle di ferro 9979
— in sospensione 18078
parzializzare gli ugelli 3516
passaggio 5595, 7959, 12958, 12959
— d'ispezione 11258
— di circolazione 18864
— di grisou attraverso il diaframma 1854
— di ventilazione 1054, 2011
passare nella taglia 14588
— il talco 6123
passerella 3102
passata 12957, 15084/a, 15335
— d'argilla 15977
— sugli spigoli 6210
passerella 3318
— ad arco di cerchio 15800
— di manovra per tubaggi 17269
— di sonda 19631
passivazione 12960
pasta 5633, 8617
— di paraffina 12911, 16512 16512
— elettrodica Söderberg 16816
— grassa 10932

pasta per lucidare 11557/a
— per saldare 12961/a
— vetrosa 8279
pasticca 6440
pastoso 12962
patentamento 12969
paternoite 12970
patina artificiale 12970/a
patronite 12971
pattino 7537, 16453
pavimento 7401
— della piattaforma di caricamento 3343
pearceite 13013
pece 3851, 134011
— d'asfalto o di catrame di lignite 1636
— greca 14742
pechblenda 13413
peckhamite 13035
pectolite 13036
peduccio 8802
pegmatite 13046
pegmatizzazione 13047
pegmatoide 13048
pelicanite 13052
pelle del prodotto sintetizzato 13891/a
— di camoscio 3275
— di coccodrillo S.18051
— di rospo 18051
— di sinterizzazione 16438/a
pellicola 7040/a
— d'ossido 13054
— oleosa 12528
pelo di vacca 4574
peltro 13138/a
pendenza 5701, 9691, S. 13412, 14382
— a monte 19352
— erta 9034
— dello strato S. 5444
— media 1008
pendio 45
penepiano 5181, 13061
— elevato 19360
— fossile 17860
penetrazione di metallo nella forma S. 11556
— di tempra 5207
penfieldite 13066
penna del martello 8740, 12894
— della mazza battente

8734
pennellessa 2479
pennino 13068
penroseite 13070
pentlandite 13073
pentola di Papin 5406
pepita 12420, 13933, 15573
pera di gomma 15306
— per berta spezza-rottami 19114
percentuale molare 11870
perdita 19723
— al fuoco 5041, 7180/a, 9003/a
— al fuoco totale 18791
— alla distillazione 5557
— d'acqua libera 7048
— di calore 11030
— di circolazione 11036, 12083
— di compressione 1855
— di fusione 11027, 11473/a 11473/a
— di gas 11029
— di metallo 11031
— di peso 11033
— di petrolio del serbatoio 18251
— di pressione 5990, 11032
— garantita 8640
— magnetica 11195
— per attrito 11022
— per giacenza 19870
— per ripiegatura 11023
— per torrefazione 11025
— per trattamento 11024
— per trattamento termico 11026
— termogenica 8990/a
perfettamente cotto 2599
perforabilità 5912
perforare 2073, 11230, 13240, 16409
— a percussione 17216
— a fuoco 2609
— ad urto 10124
— di nuovo 5878
— in una roccia dura 8199
— un foro da mina 2074
— un pozzo con mine 18773
— una galleria 5952
perforatore 2091, 5895
— a cannone 8674
— a carica cava 10158

perforatore a pallottola S. 8674
— a punta di diamante 5324
— di tubaggio 2951
— meccanico 13777
— per tubazioni 2942
— pneumatico a colonna 268
perforatrice 5881, 6168, 14180
— a colonna 4041, 13710
— a getto 10157
— ad iniezione 19991
— con corona a graniglia 122
— da cantiere 5872
— da roccia 15016
— montata su carrello 5903
— multipla su carrello 10243
— telescopica 277, 8732
perforazione 2095, 5916, 9259, 13085, 15962, 16416
— a corda 2661
— a gas 8028
— a iniezione 19684
— a mano 8759
— a percussione 511, 2665, 10247
— ad aria compressa 270
— con circolazione inversa 4529
— con corona a graniglia 16200
— con fucile 13084
— con graniglia 3436
— del tetto 17675
— della galleria discendente 20115
— deviata 5468
— di diversi pozzi direzionati dalla stessa posizione 10051
— di pozzi col metodo della cementazione 8630
— direzionata 2532, 5468
— doppia 6070
— in colonna 10423
— in colonna di produzione 4201
— in mare aperto 12471
— iniziale alla corda di giacimenti poco profondi

17221
perforazione meccanica 11130
— pneumatica con iniezione 11810
— silenziosa 16942
— verso l'alto 19387
— v. trivellazione o sondaggio
perforazioni gemelle 19171
periclasi 13087
periclino 13089
peridot 13090
perimagmatico 13091
perimetro 14412
perimorfosi 13092
periodo alluvionale 412
— d'ebollizione 2000
— d'eruzione e d'ebollizione 1954
— di combustione del carbone 5059
— di decarburazione 5059
— di defosforazione 5187
— di formazione delle scorie 16536
— di Keewatin 10300
— di permanenza 18810
— geografico 8162
— glaciale 9611
— v. epoca o sistema
perknite 13097
perla 1365
— di saldatura 19926/a
perlaceo 13021
perlite 6606, 13016, 13098
— globulare 17072
perlitico 13017
permeabilità 10637, 13109
— ai gas 13111
— magnetica 11198
permesso per le ricerche 14038
pernio v. perno
perno a cannone 5694
— a chiavetta 19883
— biconico 10942
— con ingranaggio 13322
— dell'asse 1026
— del vento 9280
— di accompagnamento 3782, 3782
— di biella 4601
— di centratura 3219
— di giunzione 15740

perno di guida 13306
— di pistone 13391
— di ritenuta 9239/a
— di rotazione 18959
— di scalpello 15984
— di testa 13431
— flangiato 4022
— girevole 18137
— inclinato di comando dei maschi 11986
— mobile 11008, 12049, 13305
— per staffa 7298
— tranciabile 16023
— vuoto 9280
perossido 18076
— di manganese 11271
— di piombo 13100
— di sodio 13101
perowskite 13099
pertite 13117
perturbazione di funzionamento 10040
pesa 15584
pesafiltri 19899
pesare 19894
pesata 19897, 14253
pesatura 11706/a
pescaggio 5725
pescare un pezzo caduto in fondo 7215
pesca-snodi 10126, 10131
pescatore 2551, 4722, 6914, 7221, 7796, 9364, 13206, 15702
— a campana 5367, 6914, S. 1460, 1574
— a corona a cunei 16659
— a forchetta con chiavistello a molla 10563
— a frizione a corpo deformato 4495
— a lame 10257
— a maschio 11242
— a pinze 7222
— ad arpione 3187
— delle aste di sonda 2212
— di campioni di petrolio 12513
— di tubi 16999
— interno a cuneo svincolabile 14683
— per trapano 1626
— per tubi 13347, 2940
— Rotary 15206

pescatore svincolabile per aste 12777
pesce 7206
pesi 19912
peso atomico 933
— della carica 19906
— di combinazione 4068
— equivalente chimico 3394
— in grammo-molecole 8408
— lordo 8604
— molecolare 11872
— medio 1013
— morto 16873
— netto 12247
— normale 17356
— per caricare le forme 19915
— sull'attrezzo 19907
— tenditore 18420
— teorico 18480
pestatura 14404
pestellatura per via umida 20000
pestello S. 1920, 7342, 8778, 10756, 10973, 13118, 13309/b, 15321/a
— da banco 16186
— pneumatico 316
petalite 13119
petardo 17266
petrificazione 7629
petrogenesi 13122
petrografia 13125
petrografico 13123
petrolato 13126
petrolene 13128
petrolio 6176, 13129, 15031, 17646
— a base mista 11820
— carburante 13785
— con paraffina e asfalto 11658
— d'adescamento 10913
— di carica 3327
— distillato 10317
— fossile 10371
— grezzo 1283, 4754, 11950, 1658
— illegale 9423
— paraffinico 12907
— primario 13948
— prodotto in più di quello autorizzato 9423

petrolio raffinato 10316, 18759, 19689
— residuo 14755
petrologia 13136/a
pettine 17872
— da filettare 6701
— per chiavi sospese 18715
petzite 13137
pezzare il carbone 3642
pezzatura del grano 16443
pezzi (a) 12965
— (in due) 4230, 4229
— di ricambio 14713
— fucinati grezzi 1677
— grossi (in) 9676
— prodotti con imbutitura 13891
— speciali 17012
pezzo a croce 4663, 4700, 13333
— a T per saldare 19954
— annegato 2989
— colato 7643
— colato a secco 6040
— d'ancoraggio 560
— d'introduzione 9828
— da forgiare 17616
— da laminare 13238
— da sbavare 13237
— da scartare 15679
— di alimentazione 6998
— di anima 5775, 8948
— di connessione 12902/a
— di costruzione 17888
— di ghisa sottile 18529
— di giunzione 12857/a
— di minerale granuloso 3557
— di raccordo 4219/a
— di riempimento dello stampo 17932/a
— di riserva 16977
— di scarto 17142
— di sfiato 19501
— difettoso di fonderia 19720
— formato in staffa 11972
— fucinato 7583, 7589, 7586
— fucinato al maglio 8736
— fuso 3036, 7643
— incorporato S. 2989
— inserito 2989
— intero 19286
— levigato 11652

pezzo massiccio 16878
— pronto all'uso 13236
— speciale di raccordo e derivazione 4217
— stampato 5983, 17322/a
piallare 13451
pialletto 16774
piana alluvionale 408
— di lavaggio 12719
piani 13502
piano 1414, 13453, 13552, 18187
— a carrello trasportatore 1124
— a rulli comandato 10899
— automatico 8660
— caricatore a bilico 18681
— d'acciaio 13452
— dei camini 3463
— dei mescolatori 11827
— della bocca 13457
— della faglia 6857
— della fonderia 7406
— della frattura 14264/a
— della torre di sondaggio 14898
— della torre di trivellazione 5218
— delle condutture 11311
— di caricamento 3322
— di colata 13760, 15471
— di divisione 10202, S. 11981
— di divisione di una forma 11983
— di divisione irregolare 17559
— di faglia 16657
— di fissurazione 3717
— di frattura 3717, 7701, 10206
— di geminazione 4123
— di lavoro 20250
— di levigazione 8550
— di livello 5008
— di macinazione 8561
— di montaggio 10600
— di riferimento 17169
— di rovesciamento 18680
— di rottura 10206
— di scavo 12133
— di scivolo della torre 13363
— di scorrimento 13456
— di separazione 5586

piano di solidificazione
13412/a, 15905/a
— di stratificazione 1063,
1434, 12949, 16090
— di tavole per fondazione
11382
— di uscita 15361
— direttore 8653
— fisso S. 7239
— inclinato 2469, 2637,
5627, 8895, 8491, 9690,
11690, 13454, 14944,
15352, 17371
— inclinato a scosse 15975
— inclinato a via unica
16399
— inclinato a via unica con
contrappeso 1048, 10173
— inclinato automotore 2255
2255, 15812
— inclinato di scorrimento
20018
— inclinato per minerali
11694, 11711
— inclinato v. scivolo
— ineguale 19293
— magnetico 11188
— mobile 12050
— per formare 12001, 12025
— scitiano 16491
pianoro S. 18191
pianura 7316, 13453
piastra 13484, 16493, 17330
— a quadro 7711
— a stipare 19147/a
— anteriore 7560 , 7776
— bordata 14685
— d'ancoraggio 2177
— d'espulsione 2155
— d'essicazione 4399
— d'irrigidimento 17590
— d'usura 19855
— del respingente S. 2518
— della sacca d'altoforno
2122
— di acciaio al nichelio
12282
— di acciaio al nichelio
temperato 8855
— di acciaio fuso 3021
— di acciaio omogeneo S.
3021
— di acciaio omogeneo temperato 8854
— di asbesto S. 847

piastra di base 1285, 9993
— di battuta di un maglio
678
— di chiusura 10947
— di compenso S. 1131
— di compressione 10128
— di controllo 3362
— di corazza 799
— di dama 4986
— di equilibrio 1131
— di estrazione 10773
— di ferro fucinato 20243
— di fondazione 1286
— di fondazione in ferro
9993
— di fondo 1285, 2147, 2177
2177, 6454
— di frantumazione 4781
— di guardia 4964, 4967
— di guida 8653
— di rame 4361
— di riduzione 1811
— di rinforzo 14676
— di riscaldamento 9425,
19196
— di ritegno 9246
— di serraggio 3628, 14406
— di sformatura 17872
— di sostegno 1097
— di terracotta 3659
— di testa S. 19035
— di triturazione di ghisa
3005
— di ugelli 12415
— di unione 17190
— di vetro arrotato 4903
— di zinco per elementi
20332
— direttrice 8653
— filtrante 7045
— frontale 8939
— harveyizzata 8883
— inferiore S. 1285
— intermedia 7404
— lambita dall'acqua 13493
— lambita dalle fiamme
13492
— laterale 16270
— orizzontale 9348
— per caricare la forma
19913
— per la cernita a mano
2506
— per costipare 14404/a
— per pilettare 15131/a

piastra per scampanare o per
branatura 14427
— per soffiare 1878
— per triturazione 4781
— perforata 12671
— piramidale 14208
— porta-espulsori S.6238
— porta estrattori 6238
— portastampi 2007, 2153
— posteriore 1053
— quadrata 17241
— sagomata 1625
— sostegno anime 4430
— sottile 18501
— superiore 18735/a,
18746
— superiore d'espulsione
S. 6238
— tubiera 19040
— tubolare 6454, S.19035
— v. placca o lamiera
piastre a contatto col vapore
18056
— lambite dall'acqua 13503
piastrina 10945, 16609
— a cuscinetto S. 3251
— a rampone 9318
— d'ancoraggio inferiore
2161
— d'appoggio 17405
— d'attacco 9318
— di serraggio 3624
— universale 19318
piastrone 1420, 5644
piattabanda 18740
piattaforma 7316, 7401,
7920, 10554, 12881,
13505, 13506, 17284,
17294
— a bilico 18679
— autonoma 15815
— continentale 4258, 16092
— d'altoforno 7852
— d'attacco 15423
— di caricamento 3348, 1857
18579
— di colata 18763, 18302, 1
18359
— di rifornimento 5944
— di riposo 10467, 10525
— di servizio 12514/a,
20216/a
— di supporto 1397
— doppia 5671
— fissa 7240

piattaforma galleggiante per
   sondaggi 5945
— girevole 9349
— girevole graduata 15197
— mobile 11075, 11846,
   18862
— sommergibile 17928
— spostabile 16393
— superiore 4732
piattaforme 17494
piattello della bilancia 1129
— della lampada 10513
— di bilancia per cloruro
   di calcio 1127
— di ebanite 6184
— reggispinta 3365
piattina 1175
piatto 7315, 7322, 15840/a,
   16047, 16049
— a coppelle 2489
— a costa arrotondata
   15278
— a gorgogliamento 2490
— del respingente 2518
— della pompa pneumatica
   313
— di dispersione 17111
— di gorgogliamento 2493
— di porcellana porosa
   13496
— di ricoprimento S.18740
piattoforma di griglia 8473/a
piazza 20198
— di colata 3040
— v. posto o stazione
piazzale 17620, 18060
piazzare il coperchio 14205
— in piano 13433
— sul letto di terra 1412
picchetto 13701, 17297/a
picchiettato 17031, 17166
picco di carico a tronchi rastremati 19083
piccola campana 16727/a
— intrusione 11784
— vena 7527
— vena di minerale 17761
piccolo convertitore 16726
— cubilotto 16729
— filone 15727/a, 15756
— foro di mina 13657
— materiale di armamento
   16732
— materiale metallico 16733
— pane 13271

piccolo piano inclinato 5415
— pozzo ausiliario 10098
— taglio 16189
— treno 16735
picconatore 4906
— di carbone 3827
picconatura 13213
piccone 11383, 11857,
   13202, 13211, 16673,
   18274
— a due punte 1440 , 5667,
   7267, 11262, 18973
— comune 13632
— per carbone 9258
— per rocce 17647
pickeringite 13212
picnometro 13231, 14207
picotite 13232
picrite 13233
picrolite 13234
picromerite 13235
piede 4039, 7402, 7537,
   16805, 18701
— del martello 1405
— del taglio 5152
— di bue 10730
— di ghisa 3001
piega 7520, 7525, 14090/a,
   15008
— a fungo 12141
— a ventaglio 2216 , 6799
— alloctona 381
— anticlinale 657, 19353
— aperta 12572
— armonica concordante
   4203
— asimmetrica 912
— composta 4121
— concordante 4203
— coricata 14523
— del terreno 1502, 1506
— di carreggiamento 12779
— di colata 18357
— doppia di solidificazione
   14525/a
— di stiramento 5733
— di strato 7371
— diritta 19369
— discordante 5506
— -faglia 7522
— fagliata 2443
— falda 7521
— falsa 10367/a
— in pendenza 5438
— inclinata 14523, 19337

piega isoclinale 10055
— inversa 9934
— longitudinale 10980, S.
   13211
— marginale 11317
— monoclinale 17547
— obliqua 9699
— principale 11228
— ripida 3760
— rovesciata 12783
— secondaria 11783, 19251
— simmetrica 18150
— sinclinale 10323, 16377,
   18161, 18935
— spaccata 5536
— trasversale 4688, 18843
piega v. ruga
piegatrice 1504, 1511
pieghettatura 8339, 11787
pieghevole 13548
piegamento 4759, 7525
— a fondo 1523
— erciniano 9094
piegare 1498
— a nodo 1500
— intorno a un mandrino
   1499
piegato 7523
piegatrice 1513, 1515
— per lamiere 13487
piegatura 7617, 20236
— a grinze 20234
— dei bordi 7275
— dei lembi 7275
piena capacità di pozzo
   20059
pienaarite 13239
pieno 15933
pietra 7377
— aquilina S. 198
— arenaria in blocchi
   15531
— arenaria screziata 19472
— da affilare 9301
— da getto 8694
— da lastrico 7246
— da taglio 15530
— del sole 18000
— della luna 11926
— di dama 4964, 4968
— di paragone S.1271
— infernale 16354
— litografica 10888
— per levigare 15322/a
— per macinare 15322/a

pietra posteriore 1077
— refrattaria 7184/a
— sbozzata 9116
— sfaccettata 20096, 5832, 15525
— sfaldabile 3715
pietrificare 7634
pietrificazione 7633, 10884
pietrisco 2446 , 4769
pietroso 3489, 7380
piezoclasi 4155
pigiare 14387
pigiata 3667, 11913
pigiatoio S. 10973
pigiatura 10851, 14404, 18820
pignone a spina di pesce 13319
— per catena 3240
pignoni 8124
pilandite 13275
pilastro 1248, 4480, 17911, 13273, 13288, 13289, 13707
— della sagoma 18734
— da coltivare 16269
— del pozzo 10712
— dell'argano 10416
— di carbone 9051, 17360, 17655
— di galleria 6496, 17902, 17912
— di legno 2285, 2362
— di limite 1249
— di minerale 4592, 4593
— di protezione del pozzo 2175
— di pietra 17648
— di protezione 17657
— di sicurezza 19647
— montante 10367
— per ripiena 3906
piletta S. 3198, 8778, 10975, 13309/b, 14400, 14402
— a punta 13049
— pneumatica 13593
— pneumatica servita da gru 4601
pilettare S. 14388
pilone d'ancoraggio 5617
— di sondaggio 5930
pinakiolite 13309
pinguite 13315
pinnoite 13323
pintadoite 13324

pinza 4721, 12041
— da crogiuolo 4748
— da minatore 14932
— da presa 8571, 8892
— per fili 20137
— per saldatura 19944
pinze 7558, 12301, 13550
— per capsule 1746, 2797
pinzetta per anima 4411
— per mercurio 11509
— per sodio 16823
pioggia di polvere 1815
piombare 4561, 18429
piombaggine 8447
— polverosa S. 1462
piombatura 10630
piombino 13568
piombo 10604
— all'antimonio 8836
piombocuprite 13572
piombo di liquazione 10868
— in fogli S. 16066
— in lamiere S. 16066
— in lamine 18341/a
— in lastre 16066
— laminato 7341/a, 16066
— metallico 10617
— solforato 10614
piperno 13376
pipetta 13377
— a rubinetto sferico 19902
— d'assorbimento 23
— di misurazione 8392
— filtrante 7058
— gasometrica 23
— per pesare 19901
— per prelevare campioni da un serbatoio 18518, 19772
— tarata 8391, 13444
— tarata automatica 986
pirargirite 16359
piramide di terra 6177, 14369
— di sabbia 5988
— rocciosa 3464
pirargillite 14210
pirargirite 5004, 14211, 15330
pirgome 14212
piribolo 14213
pirite 2230, 9970, 10347, 12130, 14214
— arsenicale 818, 829
— bianca 11313

pirite calcinata 2715
— di ferro 9997
— lanceolata 17001
— magnetica 11194, 11200
— rameosa 4363
— rameosa ossidata 1659
piritoedro ·14216
piroaurite 14217
pirobelonite 14218
pirobitume 14219
— asfaltico 884
piroclastico 14222
pirocloro 14220
pirocristallino 14223
pirocronite 14221
piroelettricità 14224
pirofanite 14235
pirofillite 13058, 14236
pirofisalite 14237
pirolisi 14228
pirolusite 14227
pirometallurgia 9624, 14228a
pirometamorfosi 14229
pirometria 14231
pirometro 14230
— a coppia 18494
— a filamento evanescente 5478
— a grafite 8449
— a radiazione totale 18792
— a resistenza 14769
— ad aria 315
— elettrico di Le Chatelier 18493
— metallico 11559
— ottico monocromatico 11906
— policromatico 4035
piromorfite 8512, 14232
pironafta 14233
pirone a cannone 5694
— a chiavetta S.19883
— mobile 12049
piropo 14234
piroscissione 4588, 14225
piroscisto 14238
pirosmalite 14239
pirossene 14242, 948
pirostilpnite 7150, 14241
pirrotite 14242/b
pisolite 13386
pistonaggio 18089
pistonare 18086
pistone 13389, 13575, 18088

pistone di chiusura 11975
pittinite 13430
placca 13479
— a parella S. 7384
— a stecca 7384
— anteriore 7560
— bordata 14685
— d'argilla 3664
— d'aria 19500
— del focolare 8963
— della suola 2179
— di compressione 10288, 17260
— di controvento 1096
— di fondo 1419, 2147, 2178
— di fondo della cassa del vento 10729
— di forno 9217/a
— di rivestimento 2931
— fissa 7239
— girevole 13874
— in ghisa per raddrizzare 17726
— laterale di lavoro 7561
— mobile 12050
— modello 12455, 12987
— modello a due facce 5677
— modello doppio 15915
— modello reversibile 14828
— modello rovesciabile 19148
— per caricare la forma S. 19913
— per l'ugello 19164
— per sagomare 17807
— porta-modello 7534/a
— protettrice del pacchetto 19738/a
— secca 6035
— variata 11804
— v. piastra
placcare 13477, 1429
— con piombo 10603
placcato 10611
placcatura 3611/a, 13481, 13512
— al palladio 12879/a
— per esplosione 6689
placche S. 13502, 15115
plagioclasio 13438
plagiofiro 13440
plagionite 13439

planerite 13461
planoferrite 13465
plasticità 13474
plastificante 13473
plastotipo 13475
platea 16870
— in calcestruzzo 4174
platina 11852/a, 16415/a, 13511, 13523
platinifero 13516
platino 13514
— iridiato 13510
— spugnoso 13528/a
platorista 12983
plattnerite 13553
plazolite 13538
pleistocene 13540
pleocroismo 13543
pleonasto 13544, 1018
plesiosauro 13545
plesiotipo 13546, 9605
plessite 13547
pliocene 13539, 13551
pliocenico 13571
plumosite 6872
plutonio 13581
pneumatolisi 13603
podolite 13607
poggiastorte 17756
polarizzazione d'un gas 8039
— di cementazione 4169
— spaziale 17032
polarografia 13618
poliadelfite 13636
polianite 13620
poliargirite 13638
poliargite 13637
poliarsenite 13639
polibasite 13640
policraso 13642
policroilite 13641
polietilene 13647
polimorfo 13644
polistirene 13645
politene 13647
pollenite 13633
pollucite 13634
polo unitario 19311
polonio 13635
poltiglia 16629
— bordolese 2067
— borgognona 2589
polvere 6124
— comunicante 4090/a

polvere d'alluminio 458
— d'antracite 4827
— d'oro finissimo 7386
— della gola del forno 6133
— di asfalto 877
— di carbone 2252, 6077, 2358, 13770, 3818
— di carbone fossile 7075
— di cementazione 2920, 3177
— di concia 18236
— di dolomite 5613
— di grafite 13771
— di licopodio 11107
— di minerale 12643
— di smeriglio 6416
— di torba 13772
— di vetro 8282
— di zinco 20328
— esplosiva 1750
— impalpabile atomizzata 9651
— minuta 5518/a
— nera 1750
polverino 2358
— di carbone dolce 3300
— di coke 3936, 16737
polverizzare 4090, 17178
polverizzarsi 5518
polverizzatore 934, 8557, 14150, 17179, 17206
— a fessura 16688
— a getto di vapore 17439
— a tubo 19087
— ad ugelli 17185
— centrifugo 3210
— d'acqua 11811
— per argilla lavata 14151
polverizzazione 3266/a, 8539, 8546, 12101
— catodica 17221/a
— con zolfo 6141/a
— del carbone 3830
pompa a asta 2555
— a comando idraulico 9532
— a compressione 13914
— a doppio effetto 5641
— a guarnizione liquida 7465
— a lunga corsa 10976
— a mano 8776
— a membrana 5338
— a semplice effetto 16382
— a stantuffo immerso 19055

pompa a stantuffo tuffante
13578
— a vapore 17443
— a vapore gemella 19175
— a vapore isolata 10064
— abbassabile nel pozzo
16425
— alternativa 14494
— aspirante 17959
— ausiliaria 8101, 15002,
15057/a
— centrifuga 3208, 9653
— comandata dal gruppo
motore 18210
— «compound» 4133
— «compound» a vapore
4130
— con motore a combu-
stione interna 13790
— con trasmissione a cin-
ghia 1477
— da miniera 17994
— da muro a vapore 19654
— del fango 16719
— di circolazione 3605
— di fondo per pozzi ad
olio 12516
— di trivellazione 2083
— duplex 6113
— filtrante 7052
— idraulica 9532, 9535
— mammut 7980
— per drenaggio 5748
— per fango 12088, 16630,
16697
— per pozzi 15954
— per sabbia 15514
— pneumatica 309, 7980
— premente 7557, 13915
— provvisoria 8101
— rotativa 15215
— Worthington 6113
pompaggio 15052
— a ripetizione 17290
— ad iniezione di gas 7998
— alla corda 20133
— combinato 1051
— con albero di aspirazione
17948
— in un sol stadio 16403
— laterale 1074
— multiplo 12117
— pneumatico 314
— sotto pressione 17261

pompare 15051, 17607
— petrolio nel pozzo avvia-
to 19682
— un serbatoio per svuo-
tarlo 15342
ponte 2379, 2385, 15575
— a bilico 13509, 18674
— a travi a traliccio 18965
— d'aerazione 248
— del canale 7452
— della basculla 13508
— di colata 10475
— di comunicazione 4218
— di faglia 12332
— di lavoro 17906
— metallico 17460
— per gru 8240
ponteggio 6789, 17293
pontista 5221
pontone 14966
porfido granitico 8417
— quarzifero 14269
— sienitico 18144
porfirico 13681
porfirite 13680
porfiroblasto 11533, 14079
porfiroide 13683
pori di attacco all'acido
6574/a
porosità 13671
— a pori allungati 6389
— a pori sferici 15289
— di ritiro 16231
— diffusa 5530
— globulare 8303
— puntiforme 13320
poroso 12146
— (non) 13924/a
porpezite 13679
porporino 14193
porta 8088
— a corsoio 16620
— a sportello 20057
— antincendio 7167
— centrale della torre
19421
— d'accesso o di visita
9822
— del focolare 3864
— del forno a coke
— di preriscaldamento
2345, 2602
— di pulizia 3693
— di scarico 5494

porta di scarico 5494
— di svuotamento S. 5494
— di ventilazione 264, 301,
1392, 15870, 18849
— di ventilazione non ermetica 15589
— dosatrice dell'aria 2225
— metallica 17466
— per regolare l'aria 14662
— per sfornare 5494
portabarrotti 7148
portacarbone 2836
portaferro 18727
portafiltro 7053
portafioretto 3555
porta-guarnizioni completo
12832
portale di ammaraggio di
ferrovie elettriche 17734
portalingotto 13699/a, 17281
portamodello 3217
portante 2199
portantina 8801
portaoggetti 17288
portapezzo 1683
porta-pipette 13379
portare 2902
portasagoma mobile universale 12980
portasbarre 7148
portastampo 11360/a
portata 1599, 9521, 16969,
13957
— a padella 1132
— a strascico 3712
— alla francese 3712,
18207/a
— comune 12110
— d'ascensione 10795
— d'anima 4423, 4431,
4462, 17412, 18749
— del martello 6215
— del modello 4462
— del vento 14436
— dell'anima 1601
— dell'oleodotto 13374
— di modello rinforzata
6484
— falsa 3711
— maggiorata 12140
— massima 2904
— multipla 12110
— oraria dell'impianto
d'acqua 12711

portata .specifica di riduzione 5722/a
portaprovette 19041
portaprovino per bagno
  d'acqua 18457
portato al color rosso scuro
  1662
portatubi 19042
portavento 1702
portavite 15710
porte pieghevoli 51
— scorrevoli e pieghevoli
  16616
portello 8088
— per regolare la ventilazione 8114
— d'ispezione 8761
— d'ispezione per serbatoi
  18249
— di scarico dei cassoni
  per fango 3700
porto d'imbarco 16138
posare 15902
posatore di tubi 13358
positiva 13702
posizione di lavoro (in)
  12541
— libera 18450
— verticale 19368
possibilità di modifica delle
  fasi 3282
postazione 10943, 19976
— di coltivazione 12708
— di perforazione 5907
— di trivellazione 5940
post- tensione 13714
— -riscaldamento della
  zona saldata 13710/a
posto di colata 3040
— di formatura 11999
— per distaffare 10406
posto v. piazza o stazione
potassa 10272
— caustica 9509
— caustica in bacchet-
  te o cannelli 17579
potassio 10276, 15447
potenza 18507, 20064
potenziale di decomposizione 13732
— di elettrodo 16397/a
— spontaneo 15828
potere agglomerante 226,
  3178,
— calorifico 2754

potere calorifico massimo
  8601
— calorifico minimo 12241
— calorifico superiore
  8601
— cokificante 3951
— d'attrazione magnetica
  11186
— illuminante debole 11054
— luminoso 2783
— ricoprente 4572/a, 18592
  18592/a
povero di grafite 13654
— scorificante 7504
powellite 13773
pozzetto d'alloggio dell'a-
  sta di manovra 12038
— dei fanghi 12074
— deviato 14433
— di colata 1310
— di lavaggio 12744
— di scoppio 5939, 16204
— di sfioro 12742
— per contrappeso 1130
— per la cenere 869
— per le scorie 16546
pozzo 8631, 10786, 15932,
  13397
— a doppio completamento
  6067
— a mano 6082
— a «quinconce» 7228
— a ripiena 15027, 17650
— a tubo doppio 6067
— ad eruzione spontanea
  7444, 8677
— ad iniezione d'acqua
  19766, 19773
— artesiano 830, 2090
— attivo 10346
— ausiliare 10094, 10896,
  15901, 15982, 20114,
  17371
— ausiliare interno 19849
— chiuso 16245
— cieco 20114
— con focolare d'aerazione
  7855
— crollato 6777
— d'aerazione 306, 322
— d'alimentazione 10330
— d'allargamento 12692
— d'aspirazione dell'aria
  9858
— d'assaggio 2087, 18882

pozzo d'entrata dell'aria
  5696
— d'estrazione 1413, 5813,
  6712, 20215, 20106,
  20249
— d'estrazione e di sfruttamento 6470
— d'estrazione per immissione di gas compresso 8021
— d'immissione 9674
— d'iniezione 9674, 9817
— d'intervento 14689
— d'uscita dell'aria 14814
— di alta produzione 1383
— di colmata 7492
— di combustione 4083
— di drenaggio 5743, 19814
— di gas 8064
— di gas corrosivo 16945
— di miniera 11740
— di miniera con armatura
  in acciaio 17514
— di prosciugamento 14162
— di prova, 724, 14058
— di ricerca 2087, 14035
— di riposo 17597
— di ritorno dell'aria
  19347
— di scolo 17992
— di sfogo 14689
— di sondaggio 14035
— di ventilazione 322,
  333, 2652, 3987, 5491,
  5696, 19351, 19384
— di ventilazione discen-
  dente 5709
— direzionale 5469
— disposto a quinconce
  17292
— a duplice produzione
  6068
— eruttivo 20072
— esplorativo 20067
— esplorativo in zona scono-
  sciuta 14414
— franato 6777
— frigorifero 7749
— fuori del giacimento
  12709
— improduttivo 6076
— in fase d'estrazione
  1108
— in fase di pompaggio
  7473, 14171
— in muratura 11356

pozzo in pistonaggio 18095
— in rimonta 19366
— inclinato 5016, 5436, 9704, 5472
— inclinato al muro 19271
— inclinato in roccia 15029
— intermediario 9763
— interno (o cieco) 1779
— interno 10094, 10896, 15982
— laterale 7277
— molto deviato 9138
— ordinario 16796
— perdente 16795
— petrolifero 12515, 17174
— petrolifero sotto pressione 9829
— piatto 16680
— poco profondo 6815
— pompato con scarsa produzione 17859
— pompato per mezzo di bilanciere 1379
— producente contemporaneamente da due zone 607 6071
— rivestito 10033
— rivestito di muratura 19656
— sotterraneo 19262
— tubolare 7676, 17999
praseodimio 13801
praseolite 13802
prasinite 13803
praticare gli attacchi di colata 15344
praustite 14550
precambriano 13804
precamera 19544
precaricamento 13927
precipitare 13806
— all'ebollizione 13808
— coll'idrogeno solforato• 13807
precipitato 13809
precipitazione delle impurità 13817
— strutturale 13812
precisione delle dimensioni convenute 6630
— nell'aggiustaggio 13821
predazzite 13830
preformazione 13835/a
prefrazionatore 13836

prefrazionamento 13836
prefucinare 15243
prehnite 13842
prelevamento di campione S. 15460, 18520
— di campioni da un serbatoio 18521
— di campioni dal suolo 13971
— di campioni di sondaggio 19969
— di petrolio 12517
prelevare dal deposito 18220
prelievo 15454
— di ghisa 13410/a
premilamiera 1683
premistoppa 2058, 7535, 12848
— di cementazione 3153
— di fondo 2163
premodellatura 13853/a
premodello 11366
prendere il campione di colata 18309
— la barra 8564
— un campione di gas 18217
preparare 5271, 20079
— il letto di fusione 2730
— la forma per la fusione 895
— le parti di un getto da ottenere con anime 4383
preparato 5837
preparazione 7199, 12611, 5274
— a secco del carbone 6045
— con asfalto 879
— dei pacchetti di ferro 6763
— dei pezzi 16612/a
— del letto di fusione 11232
— dell'innesco 13952
— della prova 13853
— della soletta di base 16344
— delle superfici levigate 13859
— meccanica 11405
— meccanica e chimica 13191
— per via umida 19987,

19994
preparazione pneumatica 13596
— v. trattamento
preriscaldamento 13841
preriscaldare 13837
preriscaldato 13838
preriscaldo S. 13841
prerivestimento del nastro 13827
presa 9853
— all'aria 286
— annegata S. 7397
— ausiliaria 2650
— automatica 15811
— d'acqua 13986
— d'acqua sotterranea 13987
— d'una sorgente 19970
— del campione 18461
— di calcestruzzo 15914
— di gas ausiliare o belga 3590
— di gas Darby 5000, 4998
— di gas di un altoforno 80 8030, 8034
— di gas Hoff 19602
— di gas Parry 12938
— di metallo 10483
— per ritiro 16225
— prematura 13851
— rapida 7302
prescrizione 17027
prescrizioni di prova 5473, 18462
— per la qualità 17028
presellatura 7811
presello da idraulico per calafatare 3112
presenza di gas nel fango 7996
presinterizzazione 13863/a
preso in fonderia 11990
— in fondita 12010
pressa 13867
— a eccentrico 6186
— a ginocchiera 18708
— a leva articolata 18707
— a punzone 13789
— a vapore per forgiare 17422
— chiodatrice 18708
— da dorare 8227
— da estrusione 6721

pressa da filtro 7051
— da formare 12022
— da formare con piattaforma spostabile 12026
— da loppa 16549
— idraulica da formare
  9530
— idraulica da mattoni
  9516
— idraulica per forgiare
  9523
— meccanica 13789
— per amalgama 486
— per bordare le piastre
  16496/a
— per compatti 13287/a
— per coniare 10417,
  17328
— per crogiuoli 4743
— per forgiare 374
— per fucinare 1163, 7595
— per impacchettare i rottami 2657
— per trafilare 5808
— per stampaggio a caldo
  7595
— per tappi di sughero
  4472
— raddrizzatrice 17727
— sbavatrice 18903
pressare 13865, 17256
pressato (non) 12366
pressione 13892
— atmosferica 927
— d'avviamento 17386
— d'esercizio 20217
— d'introduzione 9857
— d'utilizzazione 15899
— dei pilastri 18597
— del gas 8041
— del fango 12087
— del giacimento 3775,
  13917
— del tubo montante 19054
— del vento 20094
— dell'aria 1732
— di compressione 4103
— di fondo 2164
— di giacimento 14749
— di laminazione 13910,
  15128/a
— di lavoro 20252
— di mandata 5493
— di prova 18452
— di saturazione 15556

pressione di scorrimento
  7447, 7440
— di sovraccarico 12736
— di tubaggio 2952
— effettiva 13893
— ferrostatica 6962
— finale 9164
— idraulica 9533, 19805
— idrostatica 9575
— iniziale 11057
— interna 9903
— laterale 10571, 16279/a,
  18596
— massima 11387
— osmotica 12689
— radiale 14328
— sotterranea 14746
— statica 3771, 17393
— sulla sacca 13912
— verticale del cilindro
  13911
pressofusione 5362, 13898,
  13901
pressofuso 13901
prestampaggio 13831
pretella S. 3433
pre-vagliare 14347
prevalenza 8906, 5493
«preventer» a saracinesca
  11363
preventivo 6569
prezzo d'acquisto 4517
— di costo 4515
— unitario del ferro o del
  manganese 13929
priceite 13930
prima carica di metallo 1415
prima fusione (di) 19563
— mano di tinta 7197
— sagoma S. 17808
primo canale 7200
— terziario 6166
priorite 13959
prisma d'inversione 6538
— di secondo ordine 13958
— di terzo ordine 13960
— obliquo 12435
— pentagonale 13067
— quadrangolare 14243
— raddrizzatore S. 6538
— retto 14906
— rombico 12683
prismoide 13967
privo di difetti 6866
— v. esente

probertite 13970
procedere alla ripiena idraulica 16714
procedimento v. processo o
  trattamento
processo 20203
— a iniezione 19774
— a pettine 4052
— acido 85
— Bessemer 1553, 1559
— combinato Bessemer e
  Martin 4063
— con doppia rifusione
  18913
— con forno a riverbero
  12578
— con una sola fusione S.
  16398
— d'affinaggio 7092, 7111,
  7102, 13978, 14606
— d'amalgamazione 487
— d'analisi 13972
— d'essiccazione Gayley
  8121
— d'ossidazione 12791
— del «passo di pellegrino»
  19038
— di combustione 13976
— di conversione 4304
— di cracking 4589
— di formatura 12029
— di formatura rapido 9191
— di formazione del coke
  13975
— di fusione Hamet 8878
— di galvanizzazione 7944
— di laminazione 15126
— di lavaggio 19708
— di nitrurazione 12313
— di Oxford 18734
— di raffinazione 14616
— di ricottura 618
— di rifusione 14701
— di separazione 13979
— di stampo 1166
— di tempra 8863, 8867
— di tempra al nichel 12274
— di torrefazione 11614
— di zingatura 7944
— diretto 5462, 12546
— discontinuo 1334
— duplex 6112
— Ehrhardt col mandrino
  6279
— hydrospark 9572

processo Mannosmann 11295
— Menne 11495
— metallurgico 11588
— per la fabbricazione di
  mattonelle 2416
— per ridurre l'ólio greggio
  18760
— preparatorio 5845
— Réaumur 20047
— Siemens 16294, 13250
— Thomas 1292, 1302,
  18536/a
— vallone 19660
proclorite 13985
prodotto 20113
— d'ossidazione 12793
— dell'industra metallurgica 10024
— della cernita 13992
— della combustione 4081,
  13989
— della decomposizione
  13990
— della distillazione 13991
— di coda 18208
— di laminazione 7120/a
— di qualità inferiore
  19253
— di solubilità 13817/a
— di testa 8932
— di testa gassoso 2946
— di torrefazione 13993
— di trattamento dei
  fanghi 12071
— filtrato 7061
— intermedio 3358
— leggero 18204
— macinato 8574
— pesante 18205
— pronto per altoforno
  13994
— raffinato 20041
— schiumogeno 7513
— semilavorato 19295
— senza sbavatura 2619
— siderurgico 9954
— sinterizzato 4098/a
— sterile 12359
— tubolare 19080
— utile 11761
— v. sostanza
produrre ghisa a basso
  tenore di carbonio 2979
produttività 13999

produttività oraria 12712
produzione 8201, 10531,
  12475
— annuale 20281
— con estrazione a secchie
  1109
— continua di gas 4268
— declinante in qualità
  15429
— di blumi 1170
— di coke 13997
— di coda 18209
— di ghisa elettrica od al
  forno elettrico 6291
— differita 5113
— eruttiva 7485
— giornaliera 4963, 17613
— in ciclo 12568
— iniziale 9809
— intermittente 7441
— latente 3772
— limite 12469
— media 1010
— per espansione di gas
  in soluzione 16902
— per pistonaggio 18093
— potenziale 13733
— spontanea 7448
— stabilizzata 15922
— totale 18790, 19217
profilare 7605
profilati ad U 3292
— cavi estrusi 9271
— cianfrinati 7274
profilato S. 4236, 15772,
  15994, 17889, 20315
— a ali larghe 2433
— a bulbo 2544
— a gradini in acciaio estruso a caldo 6720, 17558
— a I di sostegno 9610
— a lati uguali e spigoli
  arrotondati 6523
— a spigoli arrotondati
  17350
— a spigoli vivi 15790
— a T 18186
— a T con bulbo 2545
— commerciale 11496
— da costruzione 9041
— di acciaio laminato a
  caldo 9433
— di ferro 8241, 17887
— di ferro a spigoli 15777

profilato in acciaio ottenuto
  per estrusione a caldo
  9414
— leggero 10785, 10801
— medio 11434, 11435
— ogivale 8371
— ornamentale 12673
— per costruzioni laminato
  in acciaio 15102
— per vagoni 10009, 15788
— pesante 9041
— pesante di acciaio 9039
— saldato 13832
— semipiatto 8371
— speciale 17020
— tridimensionale 6916
— universale 19316
— v. sagomato
profilite 14028
profilo 4704, 14000/a,
  16261
— con intaccatura a
  intagli 13096
— cuneiforme 19889/a
— d'un altoforno 1715
— di laminazione 15779,
  15098
— di sonda 19965
— di tubaggio 2962
— geologico 8174, 8176
— isometrico 6916
— per ricalcare 19376
— stratigrafico 4047, 8174,
  8175
— smussato 7273
— UTMM 19417
profilatrice 1513
— a rulli 15078
profitto 20113
profondità del sondaggio
  11236
— del taglio 1393
— di penetrazione 5209,
  8873
— di posa in pozzo 15918
— di tempera 3431, 5206,
  8864
progetto di processo 6475
programma dei sondaggi 5935
progresso della corrosione
  9760
proiezione 17113
— del convertitore 4305
— di scintille 16987

proiezione e fusione 17187
— vulcanica 6236
prolunga 125, 1162, 2795, 4735
prolungamento dell'anello superiore di tenuta sopra i cunei 12849
promezio 14006
prominenza 18123
— del suolo o del terreno 18744
promontorio a picco 1916
pronto per l'analisi 14470
propellente 14007
propene 14015
propilene 14005
propilizzazione 14029
proporzione di minerale in pezzi nel giacimento o deposito 8387
— in peso 14021
proprietà legante 2024
prosciugamento 5292
prosciugare 5189/a, 5193, 15635
prosopite 14031
prospettare 14032
prospettore 14039
prospezione 13427, 14033, 14036, 14411
— magnetica 11204
— secondo i frammenti trovati 16142
protettore delle aste 15305
protezione 8641, 16120
— catodica 3103
— con olio 12518/a
— contro la corrosione 14043
— elettrolitica 633
— superficiale 18064
protoattinio 14048
protobastite 14049
protogino 14051
protomylonite 14052
protossido di bario 1260, 3890
protoparaffina 14053
protosulfuro di ferro 10022
protrusione 14054
proustite 815, 14055
prova 6675, 18441
— a caldo 8996
— a freddo 4005
— a pieno flusso 12571

prova a vuoto 1685
— acustica 16915/a
— ad urto S. 9647
— al cannello 1888
— al carico di punta 2512
— al mandrino 2548
— al taglio 16025, 16037
— alla compressione 4157
— alla creta 3265/a
— alla frattura 2336
— alla goccia 17158
— alla perla 1366
— alla tocca 17159
— alla trapanatura 5911
— Baumann 1353, 1798
— Brinell 1155
— con aste 5910
— di durezza Rockwell 15044
— d'estrazione con cucchiaia 1107
— d'imbutitura 5086, 6540, 9730
— d'infiammabilità 3721
— d'invecchiamento rapido 37
— d'urto 9647, 16148
— dei minerali 12628
— dell'attacco acido 6576/a
— della viscosità al calore 18497
— delle scintille alla mola 16985
— con provetta intagliata 12397
— di (a) v. resistente o inattaccabile a
— di appiattimento 16144
— di bordatura 7276
— di chiodi 14974/a
— di colabilità 3034, 7470
— di collaudo 41
— di durezza Brinell 2409
— di durezza Vickers 19555
— di fatica 6836
— di fatica a urti ripetuti 14732
— di flessione 1521
— di flessione agli urti 16143
— di flessione agli urti ripetuti 14734
— di flessione alternata 14819/a

prova di flessione della fronte di saldatura 6740
— di flessione su campione intaccato 16149
— di foratura o di punzonatura 5869
— di fragilità 18802
— di fucinatura 7599, 19355
— di galleggiamento 7389
prova di gas (a) 8043
— di intemperie (a) 19863
— di macro-incisione 5091
— di omologazione 19202
— di penetrazione per striatura 15682
— di perforazione 5911
— di piegamento 1503 7525/a
— di piegatura a caldo 9392
— di piegatura a freddo 3961
— di piegatura alterna 430
— di piegatura dopo la tempra 1522
— di piegatura trasversale 18842, 4689
— di pressione a vuoto 13925
— di punzonatura 6670/a
— di resilienza Charpy per l'acciaio 3352
— di resilienza su provetta intagliata 9648
— di resistenza alla compressione 4157
— di resistenza alla flessione statica 18845
— di resistenza alla rottura all'urto 16367
— di resistenza alla torsione 18778
— di ricalcatura 6101/a
— di riscaldamento con acido 80
— di rottura 2309
— di saldabilità 19955
— di scheggiatura 17121
— di scorrimento viscoso 4624
— di sgretolamento 16968/a
— di sondaggio 2107
— di tempra 8868
— di tensione 18419/a
— di tornitura a scala 17545
— di trazione 18411

prova di usura 19858
— dinamica 6152
— dinamica di caduta 5997/a
— fisica 13194
— idraulica 9539
— in acido 13217/a, 13218
— in nebbia salina 15445
— laterale 16276
— meccanica 11416
— per confronto 4106
— per pistonaggio 18094
— pneumatica 13600
— preliminare 13845, 13849
— radiale 14329
— sclerometrica 15682
— singola 16406
— statica 17395
— su provetta intagliata 9648
— sul posto 7000
— sul traverso 18845
— tangenziale 18243
— tensile 18411
provare 18440
provetta 11399, 17030, 18456
— a chiglia 10296
— a gradini 17543
— campione 17354/a
— colata a parte 15862
— di temperatura 3437
— di tempra 3425
— di tempra conica 19887
— di trazione 18412
— fusa attaccata al pezzo 3015
— fusa col getto 3011
— grezza 4551/a, 18442/a, 18445
— liquida presa per la prova 11880
— solidificata 16893
provino 18456
provvista d'acqua 19816
prussiato giallo di potassa 20287
psammite 14063
psefite 14066, 14068
pseudoanticlinale 14069
pseudobrookite 14071
pseudoboleite 14070
pseudocementazione 1681/a, 14071

pseudofite 14080
pseudoleucite 14075
pseudomalachite 14076
pseudomorfismo 14078
pseudomorfo 14077
pseudonitrurazione 14078/a
pseudoscistosità 14074 14081
pseudoconcordanza 5503
pseudocristallino 14072
pseudoglaucofano 14073
pseudosfaldatura 17735
pseudostratificazione 6782
pseudotachilite 14082
pseudovariazione 14394
pseudowavellite 14083
psilomelano 1649, 14085
ptilolite 14088
pucherite 14090
puddellaggio 14106, 14114, 14316
— a gas 8044
— a grana 14108
— a mano 8775
— a secco 6037
— bollente 13252
— del ferro 9996
— dell'acciaio 14113, 17500
— di ferro fibroso 14112
— di minerale 12648
— grasso 13252, 16550, 19995
— meccanico 11134
— rotativo 14840
puddellare 14093
— al maglio 16130
puddellatore meccanico 11410
puddellatrice 14111
puddellatura v. puddellaggio
puddinga 12158
puglianite 14119
pulaskite 14120
puleggia del tornello veloce 15517
— di comando 14132
— di perforazione al cavo 17222
— di ritorno 18211
— folle 11009
— Koepe 5967
— motrice 5966
— magnetica 11199
— mobile 9230

puleggia per trivellazione 4734
— scanalata 8588, 8592
— sul pozzo per cavo di carotaggio 4420
pulire 3671, 13624, 15654
— a smeriglio S. 6410
— con acido 13216
— il getto 3672
— un'anima 1847
— una forma S. 1847
— le forme 16771
pulito 3674
pulitrice a getto di sabbia 1737
pulitura al tamburo 19097
— all'acqua di sapone 19809/a
— alla sabbia 14447
— dei metalli 2522
— del canale di colata 8098
— del filo 13229
— della sabbia 1742
— elettrolitica 6346
— meccanica 15527/a
— supplementare 7883
pulizia 3673
— con nettatubi rotativi 19124
— del foro 15610
— della superficie 3698
— delle griglie 14711
pulsante 14199/a
pulsometro 14146
punta 1374, 1622, 12205, 18672
— a cannone 14890, 17708
— a colonna 4393
— a due punte 5670
— a gancio 17191
— a gancio per fonderia 9315
— a occhiello per l'estrazione dei metalli 14904
— a squadra 14428
— a testa a grappino 11037
— a testa bombata 15282
— a testa fresata quadrigliata 4540
— a testa piana 7338
— a testa piana larga 12896
— a testa piana per fonderia 7334
— cambretta 17372
— cambretta p. doghe 17375

punta d'acciaio 17497
— da trapano 3195
— da trapano ad elica S.
  19181
— del cannello 18769
— del cuore 13610
— dell'ago 13613
— di girabecchino S.946
— di spilla S. 13316
— di trapano 2077, 7332
— di trapano a due tagli
  5652
— di trapano smontabile
  5250
— elicoidale 19181
— 16575
— fresata per casse da frut-
  ta 11704
— fresata rigata 3403
— per centrare 17168
— per fonderia S.15511,
  17191
— perforatrice a corona
  15250
— piana igata 7330
— se.... testa 12164
puntatura 18196
punte 15708
puntellamento 14025, 16173,
  17407, 17898, 18033
puntellare 1792, 2330,
  16167, 19273
puntellatura 17408, 18901
puntello 29, 2584, 2644,
  5584, 6813, 8213, 8907,
  10240, 10728, 12030,
  13707, 14175, 14014,
  14177, 14465, 17540,
  17906, 16169, 17658,
  19533
— d'acciaio 17499
— del cubilotto 14008
— di base 2186
— di legno 4635
— di miniera 11738
— di rottura 2334
— di sostegno 17909
— di stiva e coperta 5063
— elastico scorrevole
  20300
— metallico 11558, 17503
— metallico allungabile
  12835
— metallico regolabile 160

puntello posato di fronte
  6752
— telescopico 4014
— tubolare a cannocchiale
  per armatura di solaio
  18362
— tubolare per gallerie di
  miniere 19078
punteruolo 12055
punto brillante 9156/a
— caldo 9444
— critico 4645
— d'agganciamento 17662
— d'infiammazione 10362/a
— di anilina 11819
— di decomposizione 13611
— di deviazione 10343
— di essiccazione 6036
— di flessione 1514
— di fumo 16763
— di fusione 11475, 15920
— di gorgogliamento 2491
— di greificazione S. 16436
— di nebbia 3785
— di piegatura 1514
— di ramificazione di un
  filone 13612
— di riferimento 1488,
  5006, 11401
— di rottura 2425
— di rugiada 5286
— di scorrimento 13743
— di sinterizzazione 16436
— di vetrificazione 19578
— difettoso 5107, 5110
— duro 8842
— finale 6455
— focale 7516
— libero 7735
— neutro di una colonna in
  pozzo 7741
— unitario del crogiuolo
  19310
puntoni di acciaio IPN 9947
punzonare 14173, 17305
— i fori 14174
punzonatrice portatile
  1384/a
punzonatura 13243, 14182/a,
  17321
— cava 18877
— senza distacco del pezzo
  16705
punzone 4916, 8233

  13244, 14176, 14181
punzone a vite di tubi 13368
— caccia-cuneo 5850/a
— con espulsore 17858/a
— d'improntatura 9217
— da coniare 17329
— da taglio 4922
— di collaudo 17308
— per imbutitura 5809
— superiore 19364/a
purificare v. affinare
purificazione S.14607
purpurite 14195
putrefazione 5059/a, 15239

Q

quadretto 17232
quadri S. 17232
quadro 5864, 15904, 15912,
  18568
— ad un sol montante
  13708
— base dello scivolo 3567
— complesso 759, 14346
— completo 7678, 7806
— d'acciaio 17507
— del pozzo 4630, 4635,
  15938, 18879
— di base 4629
— di distribuzione 18133
— di sostegno 16423
— di sformatura 4391
— incompleto 7919, 19192
— per armature di gallerie
  6122
— portante 4629, 18036
— provvisorio 6786
— raffreddato 19788
— superiore di riempimento
  7034
— zoppo 9716
qualità 14247
— del filo di ferro 14249
— di ferro 14246
— di trafilatura 5810
quantità chimicamente equi-
  valenti 3397
— d'acqua 14252
— d'aria 328
— d'aria o del vento 1701
— di luce 14251

quanto 14253/a
quartazione 14261/a
quarzifero 14275
quarzite 14271, 14273
quarzo 2556, 14265
— affumicato 2689, 11934, 16769
— aurifero 8344
— filoniano 19488
— finemente macinato 14149
— ialino 9496
— in pezzi 14268
— lattiginoso 11681
— rutilato 11043/a
quaternario 14278
quisqueite 14308
quota del pozzo 6376

R

rabboccare 6874
rabboccatura 6887,'a
raccogliere 4825
raccolta delle scintille 3095
— di minerali 4026
raccordare S. 7113
raccorderia 13336
raccordo 2939, 7125, 7226, 7227, 9263, 10252
— a gomito '6254
— a sospensioni per tubi 13349
— a tre vie 13368
— a vite 12305
— a 45° 20257
— ad ossigeno 12820
— concavo 7027
— conico 18279
— da sagomare 7028
— di binario 14360
— di cuoio 10651
— filettato 12305
— in cuoio 10652
— per aste di perforazione 5904
— per tubi 13351, 19031
racewinite 14318
raddoppiare 5637
radice di una piega 15154
radiofillite 14339

radiofotografia 14337
radiolite 14334
radiometallurgia 14338/a
radioscopia 14340
raddrizzare 158, 17721
— il convertitore 18625
— le lamiere 17722
raddrizzatrice 17725
— a stiramento 17796/a
rad'drizzatura 7907, 11292/a
radio 14341
rado 14344
radon 14344
raffinamento del grano 8400
raffinare 7072, 14593
raffinato v. affinato
raffinatore 7100
raffinazione 14517
— v. affinazione
— con solvente 16912
— duplex 5674/a
— elettrolitica 6347
raffineria 14503
— di benzina 18762
raffreddamento 4331, 4337, 7742
— ad acqua 19761
— ad acqua degli elettrodi 19794
— ad aria 259
— artificiale 833
— automatico 15816
— del forno 4340
— della griglia 8471
— entro stampi 5375
— in acqua 19808
— lento 18391
— per sbalzo termico 16144
— rapido 14283
— rapido di tempera 14290
— rapido a spruzzi 17184/a
— rapido differito 16511/a
— selettivo 5359/a
raffreddare 4326
raffreddato a liquido 10872
— a vapore d'acqua 17423
— ad acqua 19759
— ad aria 258, 6796
— in acqua 14287
— nell'olio 14286
raffreddatore 3423, 3450, 4330, 5174, 9391/a
— a alette 278
— del foro delle scorie

11901/a
raffreddatore inglobato 9897
— interno 9897
— superficiale 18044
raggi gamma 7950
— X 20261
raggiante 14331
raggio della matrice 5376
— di curvatura 1516
— di piegatura 1516
— di ruota 20011
raggrumazione 15727
ragia di petrolio 13133
raglanite 14354
raimondite 14368
rallentare 16693
— la combustione 16513
ralstonite 14386
ramare 13478
ramato 4374
ramatura 4362
ramdohrite 14396
rame 4350
— a grano grosso 6028/a
— ad alta conduttività 9141
— al 99,75 % 1564
— al silicio 16329
— anodico 627
— cementato 15990
— di cementazione 3146
— di concentrazione 13810
— dolce 16832
— duro 8823
— elettrolitico 6338
— fosforoso 13175
— grezzo 1647, 1769
— grigio 8499, 18471
— in fogli 16051
— in lingotti 9788
— in salmoni 13257
— indurito S. 8823, 18796
— manganesifero 11270
— nero 1647, 1783
— per getti 3048
— puro 15183
— raffinato 18796, 18799
— rigenerato 15990
— solforato grigio 3254
— stirato a freddo S. 18796
ramificazione di uno strato 12468
ramirite 14398
rammelsbergite 14399
rammollimento 16847/a
rammollire S. 16847

ramolaggio 896, 4387, 4441, 11971
ramolare 895
rampa 7373
— d'alimentazione 6495/a
— d'uscita 5134/a, 6655/a
— di caricamento 10921
rampino 9312
ramsayite 14408
randa S. 17809, 18112/a
rappezzare 12964
rappezzatura 12967
rappezzo 15567
rappigliarsi S. 2690
rapporto acqua-olio 19764
— di basicità 14022
— di fucinatura 14442
— di perforazione 2103
— di riciclo 14528
— di sondaggio 5894, 18803
— gas-olio nel giacimento 14748
— gas-petrolio 8004
rapprendersi 2690
rarefazione 14429
rasare 17815
rasatura 4287
rasopiano 13061
rasoterra S. 6625
raschia-olio 12507
raschiare 15664
— la torre di perforazione 16152
raschiatoio 9999, 15672, 17805
— conico 19886
raschiatore 15671
— ad espansione per parete 19652
— per paraffina 12908, 12909
— per tubi 19039
raschiatura 15673, 15674
raschietto 3686, 7374, 7471, 16658, 15666, 15671, 16720, S. 17805, 17819
— a cucchiaio 15667
— da minatore 14334
raspa 14431
raspite 14432
rastrelleria per le aste 7104
— per le aste di pompaggio 17947
rastrello 7374, 7471, 14381,

rastremare 18277
rastremato 18285
rastrematura 2139
— d'estremità 18202
rastremazione alle estremità 18100
rathite 14438
raumite 14449
rauvite 14450
ravvivare una mola 5836
reagente collettore 4026/a
— precipitante 13805
reagenti 14473
reagire 14466
realgar 14475
«reamer» con scalpello al fondo 4058
reattivo 6571/a, 14471, 14473
reazione 14467
— chimica 3391
— delle forze ambientali sismiche 14782
— endotermica 6464
— esotermica 6662
recipiente 4249, 19541
— di cristallizzazione 4807
— di decantazione 5053
— di ricottura 617
— metallico 10090
— per mercurio 11508
recuperare 7207, 15448
recuperatore 10128
— Whitwell 20053
recupero 7217
— della terra 15516
— di anime 4435
— primario 13943
— secondario 13770
— v. rigenerazione

redancia 17610
redruite 14558
refrattarietà 14624
refrattario 14625, 2720, 14626, 16706
— acido 90
— basico 1303
refrigerante 5174
— a corrente 18890
— intermedio 9873
— interno S. 9897
refrigeratore a camino 3457
refrigerazione 4331

refrigerazione a circolazione d'acqua 4347
reggetta S. 1177, 9322, 17844
— da imballaggio 1144, 9430
— di ferro 9324
regione abissale 30
— afotica 686
— carbonifera 3814
— corrugata S. 7524
— d'ablazione 14650
— disfotica 5161
— eufotica 6590
— frontale 764
— ripiegata 7524
registratore del cedimento del tetto 4295
registrazione S. 163, 10964
— del tiraggio 5751
registro 4980,
— ad aria fredda 3964
— delle cariche 3317
— delle variabili 17845
— girevole 18140
regolamento di prova 5473
regolatore 162
— di estrazione S. 6240
— del vento 1727
— del voltaggio 19595
— di gas 8047
— di livello di fondo 2172
— di portata 1703
— di pressione 8375
regolazione 163, 167, 4287
— con amplificatori magnetici 11165
— degli elettrodi 169
— del tiraggio 5751
— dell'aria 14660
— della corrente d'aria 4556
— della pressione d'acqua 14661
— di chiusura 166
regolo 15587
— del cavaliere 5583
— di metallo per livellare 10716
regressione 14684
reichardite 14672
relé a tempo 5145
reinite 14678
reintegratore di pressione

reissite 14679
rena v. sabbia
renardite 14274
rendere fragile 6406
— magro 5081
— stagno 12826
rendimento 8201, 13779, 14004
—. in coke 3948
— in gas 8068
— manometrico 11298
— medio 1010
— termico 18482
reniforme 14725/a
rensselaerite 14726
reostato 6294
reparto animisti 4425, S. 4446
— collaudi 18463
— combustione 4082
— degli skips 16484
— formatura 11999, 12006, 12028
— forni 7834
— fusioni 7659
— lavorazione terre 15513
— per il lavaggio del carbone 3855
— pompe 14157
— riempimento e confezionatura prodotti petroliferi 2787
— saldatura 19953
— sbavatura 6978
— tempera 8866
replica 203
resa 6143, 14511, 13779
— dei minerali 20297
— di gas 8068
— elastica 14484
— per mille 12955
residui di cava 14260
— di lavaggio 10902
— di sondaggio 5891
residuo 14753, 19718
— alchilato 364
— aromatico 806
— d'altoforno 2670
— della combustione 4081
— di decompressione 14757
— di distillazione 5561, 13411
— di distillazione di petrolio grezzo 4752

residuo di fondo 7545
— di prima distillazione 18757, 18758
— insolubile 19285
— insolubile nell'acido 14759
— non sulfonato 19335
— oleoso 16677
— petrolifero di prima estrazione 19918
— primario 17716
resilienza 14760
— d'intaglio 12400/a
— su barrette intagliate 9646/a, 9649
resina 14761
— fenolica 13151
— polivinilica 13648
resistente 14780
— a caldo 8992
— all'acido 86
— all'usura 19857, 19860/a
— alla ruggine 15396
— (a) v. inattacabile a resistenza 9182, 17775
— a cuore 4449
— a esigenze alternate 14770
— a snervamento 17778
—. a temperature alternate 16968
— a trazione 17779
— al calore 9185, 14772
— al fuoco 14524, 14764
— al taglio 16024/a, 16033, 16035
— all'urto 9645, 14775
— all'usura 19856
— alla corrosione 14771
— alla deformazione 5570
— alla fatica 6465, 6466
— alla pressione 14773
— alla pressione e alla frant   one 14774
— alla ro   . 15386, 18410
— alla torsione 18783
— alla trazione 19219, 14776
— allo scorrimento 4617
— allo scorrimento a lunga durata 4618
— allo scorrimento viscoso 4619

resistenza allo sfregamento 12961, 14777
— allo snervamento 20298/a 20298/a
— d'attrito elettrolitica 6343
— del sinterizzato 8519
— dinamica 6151/a
— elettrica 6294
— magnetica 11201
— su provetta intagliata 9649
— totale alla trazione 18793 18793
resistività 14780/a
respingente 2516, 9265
— elastico 17192, 6244
respiro 289, 8060, 14947, 14952, 19497, 20022
responsabile del laboratorio 3417
restare rosso 14696
restringere 16221
restringimento 12178, 12300
— a cuneo 1595, 12298, 18214, 19889
restrizione di concessione 14787
rete 20121
— di Babo 1040
— di faglie 12249
— di fili d'amianto 848
— di filoni 12250
— di protezione 15121
— di tubazio   13385
— di Wulf ?   )5
— in filo di rame 4369
— metallica 20129
reticolo 4690, 8533, 8709
— a strati 10594/a
— cristallino 4796
— d'erosione 17645
— spaziale 16953
reticolare 12244
retinite 13417, 14794
retrogradazione della dissociazione 14804
rettifica 14742
rettificare 17840
— ulteriormente 14651
rettificati 8619
rettificato bianco 2397
— di precisione 13823

rettificatore 14521
rettificatrice per rulli 15079
— senza punte 3199
rettificazione 14520
revisionare 14504, 12749
rezbanite 14847
rhabdofanite 14848
rhaetizite 14850
rhagite 14851
rhetiano 14849
rhodizite 14853
rhodonite 14855
rhodotilite 14856
rhodusite 14857
rhonite 14861
rhyacolite 14863
rialzo del crogiuolo 13840
— della staffa 15498
— di colata 13752, 15371a
riarmamento 14793
riarmare 14792
riassorbimento 16922/a
ribaltatore di testa 10340
— girevole 15222
ribaltatrice 15083
ribattere 14737
ribattitura S. 14738
ribollimento 1953, 11677
ribollire l'acciaio S. 14594
ribollitore 14482
ricalcare 8903, 10246,
  19371
ricalcatura 8931/a, 10251,
  19378
— a stampo scorrevole
  16619/a
ricarburare 14486
ricarburazione 14485
ricco d'ossido di ferro
  14874
— di grafite 14875
— in silice 14877
ricerca 5407, 14033, 14036
— a mezzo pozzetti 4519
— di giacimenti 13427,
  14411
— metallografica 11581
— ultramicroscopica
  19222
ricerche d'oro 12421
ricevitore 10523
riciclo 14529
rickardite 14880
ricompressione 14503/a

ricoprimento orizzontale
  9345
— parallelo al piano degli
  strati 17751
— stratigrafico 17751
— tettonico apparente 712
ricoprire con polvere di carbone 6736
— di cemento 6400
ricostituzione della pressione negli strati 14739
ricotto 604
— all'aria 12562
— blu 1895
— completamente 16827
— in cassetta 13716
ricottura 608
— a gradini 17555/a
— al blu 1897
— all'aria 12563
— alla fiamma 7254/a
— azzurra 5001/a
— bianca 20023
— dell'acciaio 619
— di addolcimento 16849
— di affinazione strutturale
  12387
— di coalescenza 5587,
  17070
— di degassificazione 5128
— di distensione 17785,
  17787
— di eliminazione delle
  tensioni 17789
— di grafitizzazione 8457
— di lavorabilità 613
— di malleabilizzazione
  11254
— di rigenerazione 12387
— di precipitazione 13813
— eccessiva 12733
— in bianco 2391, 12829
— in cassetta 2209, 13717
— in pacchetto 12829
— intermedia 9910, 13973
— inversa 9931/a
— isotermica 10079
— nera 609
— selettiva 10936/a,
  15807/a
ricristallizzato 5590
ricristallizzazione 14515
ricuocere 602, 14666,
  18370

ricuocere ad intermittenza
  17923
— alla fiamma 1753
— completamente 7794
— l'acciaio 603
ricuperatore 7221, 14525
— di carbone 8974
ricupero 14510
— di produzione 14813
ridiscendere in pozzo 14740
ridissoluzione 14781/a
ridistillazione 14742, 14555
riducente 5178/a, 14564,
  14565
riducibilità difficile 5399
— facile 6183
ridurre 14559
— alla fresa 11684
— mediante distillazione
  4579
— volontariamente il flusso
  del pozzo 13312
ridursi in polvere 5518
riduttore 14824
riduzione 5721/a, 14571,
  16464
— a cuneo del filo 1352
— a femmina 6913
— a maschio 11243
— con due diversi diametri
  per aste 14185, 17921
— con pali di legno verde
  13622
— d'angolo 570
— d'area 12204/a
— del campione 14264
— del tempo di fusione
  16188
— del tiraggio 6812
— di diametro 16410/a
— di sezione 4624/a,
  18100/a
— di sezione dei canali
  14576
— di spessore 14564/a
— di tempera 1/a
— difficile 5399
— diretta 5463
— indiretta 9745
— locale del diametro
  17949/a
— per tenore eccessivo in
  acido silicico 5084
— senza filettatura 11718

riempimento 7033, 8334, 9761, 13566
— a peso 19905/a
— di cavità 3126
— di metallo bianco 7036
— filoniano 19486
— volumetrico 19600/a
riempire 1291, 3905, 7012, 17702, 8328, 12825
— e battere la forma 7008
— la forma 7011
riemulsionarsi 1409
rifacimento 6975, S. 1267, 18901/a
rifare un rivestimento S. 12964
riferimento 11330, 13308
— a doppio cono 10942
— di ramolaggio 898
— per tirata d'aria 19502
rifilatrice 18898
rifilatura 18899
rifinire 7112
rifinito 3683
rifinitrice 7130
rifinitura 7118
— dei bordi 6209
— dei pezzi colati 7126
— dei pezzi fusi 7126
— del pezzo 7132
— dell'anima 7115
rifiutare la prova 14680
rifiuti 940
— dei crogiuoli 12521
— di cava 14260/a
— di roccia 19737
— di vagliatura 15697
— v. scarti o rottami
rifiuto 10254, 12778, 15679, 18751
— d'accettazione 14637
— di sbollitura 8609
riflusso 14156
— di circolazione 3584
rifollare 8903, 10246, 19372
rifollatura 19378
rifondere 14695
riforare 14557
rifugio 14636
— antimine 14490
rifusione 14699
rifusione parziale di ricottura 12941
riga di laminazione 8651

riga per modellisti 4286
— zero 20319/a
rigare 15642, S.17815
rigato 17763
rigatura 1185, 15646
— della terra S.17828
rigeneratore 14648
— per terre 3665
rigenerazione del nucleo 4437
— dell'acciaio alterato 14784
— v. recupero
rigetto 12883, 16647
— apparente parallelo agli strati 711
— della faglia 6861
— di faglia 18588
— in profondità 5443
— inclinato 710, 18794
— netto 12246, 18785
— normale 5713
— orizzontale 9338, 16121, 16211
— orizzontale laterale 9350
— orizzontale trasversale 9354
— orizzontale trasversale apparente 709
— parallelo agli strati 17749
— perpendicolare 17750
— perpendicolare agli strati S. 17750
— verticale 716, 5445, 18587, 19385, 19523
righe (a) 17767
rigidità di scorrimento 16023/a
rigonfiamento 2541, 3109, 17145/a, 17203/a, 18121, 18123
— del filone 9019
— del suolo 4622
— della ghisa 8633
— della materozza 14959
rilascio della colonna in pozzo 16511
rilevamento 19349
— alla tavoletta 13459
— di crepa 4582
— di fessura 4582
— preliminare 13848
— sotterraneo 19264

rilievo geologico 8177
rimescolamento 17570, 17608
— elettrolitico S. 6356
rimescolare un bagno S. 17605
rimescolatura di un bagno 14315
rimessa in marcia 14783
— in pressione 14739
rimonta 856, 10759, 12037, 14372, 14942, 18101, 14946, 19366
— di pozzo scavato 19367
rimontare 8203, 14370
rimorchiatore leggero 1932
rimorchio a un assale 15849
rimozione 12065
— del mandrino 17865/a
— dell'alluminio 459
— della copertura 17867
— della feccia 6009
— della polvere 6137
— della ripiena 19326
— della scoria 15677
— delle battiture 14722
— delle cricche 17790
— delle scorie di altoforno 7488
— dello strato superficiale 15600/a
— degli imbuti di colata 17215
— di materiale 10557/a
— di sostanze fluorescenti dal petrolio 5046
rimpasto di rottame 2627
rincalzamento 2072, 17538
rincalzare 7009, 14389
rinchite 14933
rincolite 14934
rincrudimento del ferro 5797
rinforzare la terra 17780
rinforzatore 9859/a
— di lega 18800/a
rinforzo 2584, 6485, 17587a
— dei tramezzi 17589
— del cielo S. 17408
— di galleria 6497
rinfrescare lo scalpello 16007
16007
ringhiera 8655
— della gabbia 16151, 16661

ringhiera della piattaforma 18199
ringiovanire 14681
ringrosso di saldatura 12856
rinneite 14935
rinvenimento 5811, 18370/a, 18390
rinvenire 18371
— in olio S. 1753
riossidare 14729
riparare 7113, 11487
— la forma 14730
riparatore di vagoncini 4509
riparazione dell'armatura 14476
— della guida del pozzo 15061
ripartitore 5576
ripartizione degli sforzi residui 17205/a
— del vento S. 262
— della corrente d'aria 327
ripassare 14808
riperforare 5879
ripescaggio 7217
ripescare 7207
ripetizione della prova 14791
ripiazzatura 14738
ripiegatura a contatto 19975
— longitudinale 13311
ripiegature parallele 18817
ripiego 13652
ripiena 1057, 2534, 8325, 8329, 8334, 8335, 12844, 12854, 17703 15022, 19719, 19725
— buona 8359
— cattiva 13655
— con materiale secco 7034
— idraulica 7487, 9538, 19802
— parziale 17851
— pneumatica 13589, 13598
riporto duro 8826
— galvanico 2535/a
— metallico 6371, 16092/a
— secco 6034
riprendere 5547

riprendére un pozzo 14846
ripresa 3984
— da supporto 19298
ripristinare 12964
risalto 2124, 4964, 4965, 11082
— rotondo S. 2647
riscaldamento 7187. 7189, 9007, 14667
— a fuoco scoperto 1999
— a resistenza 14768
— ad arco voltaico 746
— del catrame 18315
— del forno dal basso 2160
— del getto 9016
— del modello 12979
— delle caldaie 7192
— dielettrico 5386
— diretto 5459
— indiretto 9744
— per attrito 3237
— per immersione 5440
— per induzione 9751
— preliminare 13846
— progressivo al rosso dei crogiuoli 12166
— spontaneo 17147
riscaldare 14665
— al color rosso 8970
— al nucleo 7808
— la ghisa 8968
riscaldarsi 8967, 15345
riscaldato al pozzo 14536
rischio d'incrinatura di tempra 14964
riscontro biconico S. 10942
riserva (di) 17334
— di carburante 14744
— di minerale 12655
— liquida di metallo 9050
— sicura 14056
risinterizzazione 14763/a
risucchiare 16220
risucchio 307, 5773, 5790, 13329, 14580/a, 16227
— al centro 3186/a
— aperto 13942/a, 18066
— d'estrazione 6724/a
— inferiore 15769/a
— interno 9904
— inverso 19587/b
— sparso S. 5530
— superficiale S. 18066
risultato della prova 14789
— medio delle prove 1009

risultato quantitativo della messa in produzione di un pozzo 4116
risvolto S. 19975
ritagli di ferro 10025, S. 15660
ritagliare il tetto 14937
ritagliato 7615
ritaglio 19724
— del meandro 16178
— del tetto 2483
ritardo di accensione 8803, 9485
— di rotazione 15232/a
— di scorrimento 16028/a
— operativo 13974
ritirare gli aghi 20156
ritirarsi 4282, 16221
ritiro 4284, 13383, 16222, 16226
— contrastato 9197, 14786a
— d'un filone 2039
— della matrice 17869/a
— dei pilastri 13923
— dei pilastri da una miniera abbandonata 7628
— ritardato 9197
— termico 18480/b
ritorno 14816
— in ciclo 14529
ritorto 19675
ritrovamento del petrolio 12511
ritrovatura 11982, 17560, 19287
— aperta 12582/a
rittingerite 14965
ritto del supporto 2244
ritubaggio 14806
ritubare 14807
rivelare 5272
— la struttura 6691
rivelatore d'incendio 7181
— di gas 7997, 8017, 19470
riversiderite 14971
rivestimento 2928, 3880, 4571, 5841/a, 6757, 7849, 10100, 10489, 13512, 16492, 16857, 18089/a, 20232
— acido 82
— anodico 631
— antiruggine 672
— armato 14675
— ceramico 3225

rivestimento con nero di
   fonderia 1672
— con metallo antifrizione
   10852
— con rinforzi 2231
— con tavole orizzontali
   9344
— con tavole verticali
   19527
— d'acciaio della piastra
   da corazza 17467
— del convertitore 4301
— del cuscinetto 10853
— del forno 1316, 6979,
   7846, 7856
— del pozzo 2929, 3902,
   19658, 19960
— del pozzo a quadri vicini
   4861
— del tetto 1252
— della secchia di colata
   10479
— della siviera 10479
— della suola 8960
— di lamiera 802, 10012,
   17509
— di magnesite 11176
— di mattoni del convertitore 10856
— di metalli 19703
— di scorie 149
— di tensione 16104
— di tubi 13352, 13357
— di una caldaia 1971
— differenziale 5395
— discendente 5993
— dolce 16833/a
— in legno 10458
— isolante 14635, 14763/b
— laterale 16266
— metallico senza difetti
   18616
— monolitico 11912
— per stampi 5364
— plastico 13471
— protettivo S. 14635
— refrattario 5009/a,
   7163, 10849, 10855,
   14629, 14632
— refrattario del forno
   14630, 2265
— vetroso 19570/a
— v. armamento
rivestire 1917, 2907, 3879,
   5835, 6400, 6735, 10488

   11299, 14487
rivestire con metallo bianco
   11536
— con tavole di legno 10457
— di creta 5589
— il focolare con mattoni
   refrattari 10831
— il tetto 2378
— un tubo 2908
riviera 8326
rivoltalamiere 13500/a
rivoluzione di macchina da
   estrazione 2019
rizzonite 14980
rocca verde 18852
rocce abissali 32
— acide 91
— autoctone 964
— basiche 1304
— endogene S. 9625
— eruttive 9625
— eteromorfe 9108
— filoniane 5411
— impermeabili 9658
— intrusive 9926
— iposiliciche S.1304
— metamorfiche 11593
— nettuniche 12234
— plutoniche 32, 5097,
   9926
— sciolte 5521
— sedimentarie 15794
— stratificate 15794
— stratificate tagliate a
   filoni 2750
rocchetti di ancoraggio
   della colonna 10529
— vari d'inflangiatura per
   casing 2945
rocchetto d'inflangiatura del
   tubing 19052
roccia 15004
— a piombo 15028
— a radiolari 14333
— abbattuta 5477
— adiacente S.2610, 12954
— affossata 5717
— alcalina 356
— alloctona 382
— alveolare 9305
— amigdaloide 543, 11261
— ascistica 859
— atmoclastica S.920
— autigena 961
— bituminosa 1637

roccia calcarea 10820
— clastica«in situ» 920
— comagmatica 4049
— con vene di minerale
   5829
— del tetto 15139
— delle pareti 4544
— di base 1290
— di fondo 11219
— di letto 1435, 11219
— di profondità 8405
— dura 1321, 2617
— effusiva 6219
— endogena 6460
— eolica 928
— estrusiva 6726
— ferma 17339
— filoniana 19489
— frantumata 16013
— gassifera 8049
— granulare 8405
— idroclastica 9550
— incassante 4544, 157,
   19650
— interposta 6443
— intrusiva 13065
— ipoabissale 9583
— madre 12182, 16947
— magazzino 14750
— metamorfizzata 11594/a
— monominerale 11914
— neovulcanica 10269
— neutra 9892, 11523,
   12252
— organica 2858
— permeabile 13112
— pirogena 14226
— plutonica 8405
— sedimentaria a grana
   grossa 15334
— silicea 7960
— sterile 2622, 2495,
   5028, 5040, 17671
— stratificata 1426
— traballante 15042
— ultrabasica 19220
— zoogena 20367
«rock-bit» con al centro due
   lame a coda di pesce
   4053
rodaggio del treno dell'asta
   2312
rodaninizzazione 14852/a
rodingite 15062
rodocrosite 5315

roeblingite 15063
roepperite 15064
romben-porfido 14859
romeite 935, 15134
romerite 15135
rompere 2295
rompersi 10095
— per trazione 18345
rompiflange 4018
rompighisa 13253
rondella 19698
— elastica 17202
rosasite 15174
roscherite 15175
roscoelite 15176
roselite 15181
rosenbuschite 15182
rosetta di grafite 8450
rosickvite 15186
rosieresite 15187
rosite 15190
rossite 15191
rosso (al) 14537
— Bordeaux 3632
— ciliegia 3408
— dei crogiuoli 12166
— inglese 15240/a
— per levigare 10164
— vivo (al) 19585
rosticci 3727
rotaia armata 18609
— di carroponte 4606
— di tram 18821
— dolce con fungo duro 9998
— per ferrovia a scartamento ridotto 14357
— per ferrovia normale 14536
— per miniera 14355
— Vignole 7328
rotaietta 10787
rotametro 7792, 15192
rotazione dei cilindri 15233
— sbilanciata 20165
rotella di base 7546
fotogalvanostegia 1243
rotolamento 15121
rotolo 3921
— di filo 12930
— di rete in filo di rame 15082
rotondo 15267
rotore di turbina 19121

rottame da rimpasto 2628
— ferroso 11824
rottami 19717, 15655/a
— assortiti 13358/a
— di ferro 6965/a, 10008, 10025, 15660, 19734
— di produzione propria 9993/a
— greggi 19324/a
— scelti 15805
rottura 2307, 2333, 7693
— a caldo 9408
— a freddo 3972
— alla trazione 18408
— azzurra 1900
— concoide 4172
— del cilindro 7700
— dell'anima 2331, 2442
— dell'armatura 14887
— della batteria in pozzo 19180
— della catena 7698
— di scorrimento viscoso 15385
— fragile 2422
— granulare 8432
— ineguale 19291
— irregolare 8700
— liscia S. 16772
— netta 16772
— per deformazione 7699
— per fatica 6832
— per flessione 7493/a
— piana 6623
— scagliosa 17122
— scheggiata 17122
— terrosa 6172
— uncinata 8700
rougemontite 15241
routivarite 15298
rouvillite 15299
rovesciamento della cassetta 18682
rovesciare il convertitore 18683
— la caldaia 18671
rovesciatore di carr. 8632
rubellite 15235
rubicella 15326, 20292
rubidio 15327
rubinetteria 3898
rubinetto 3897, 13121
— a tre vie 18569
— d'angolo 583
— dell'asta motrice 10306

rubinetto di congiunzione 4219
— di Daniell 4993
— di regolazione 17663
— di riduzione 18106
— di vetro 8273
— regolatore 14656
rubino 15329
— «balais» 1141
— orientale 12664
ruggine 15391, 14544
rughe 18050
rugosità 15266, 18051
rugoso 14351/a, 20235
rullare 4701
rulli d'alesatore non paralleli all'asse dell'attrezzo 1244
— del trasportatore 4320
— per curvare il nastro 18590
rullo 15104, 17148
— automotore 10898/a
— compressore 13873
— conchigliato 3446
— curvatore 1517
— di applicazione della vernice 6147
— di azionamento 13313
— di frizione 7769
— di granitura 8400/a
— di guida 5121/a
— di guida della fune del cabestano 3099
— di scorrimento 16625
— folle 11009/a
— per frantoio 4774
— spianatore 17728
— tenditore 9621
rumpfite 15336
ruota a disco laminato in acciaio dolce 15096
— a palette 9652
— con cerchione fissato a caldo 20012
— conchigliata 3444
— del cavo 8923
— del pentolaio 13734
— dentata 3909
— di pompa 15368
— madre d'una coppia elicoidale 9059
— monoblocco 16876
— per colare 3075
ruote dei carrelli 18949

ruote motrici 5970
rustico 1077
rutenio 15399
rutherfordite 15400
rutilio 15401
— acicolare 11217
ruvidezza 1780/a, 1789

S

sabbia 15469
— assorbente 17949, 18519
— attaccata 2596
— aurifera 8478
— a grana grossa 18774
— a grana media 11433
— a spigoli vivi 590
— al cemento 3154
— bruciata S. 2596
— -cemento S. 3154
— da fonderia 12027
— da formare 12027
— da formare aderente
  148
— di cava 14259
— di duna 6108
— di fiume 14967
— di lago 10494
— di loppa 16553
— di magnetite 11202
— di mare 15732
— di pietra pomice 14153
— di pulitura 15524
— di separazione 12943
— dolomitica 5614
— drenata 5191
— effettivamente produttiva
  12243
— ferruginosa 6968
— fine 7088
— gassifera 8050
— granitica 8418
— grassa 10933
— grossa 8575
— impregnata 9663
— isolante 12943
— lacustre 10494
— magra 10644, 19851
— minuta 7088
— mobile 5863
— nera 16602
— normale 17348
— nuova 7757, 12258,

sabbia per anime 4440
— per forme 7178
— per modellare 6758
— per saldare 19951
— petrolifera 12506
— petrolifera produttiva
  13001
— poco impermeabile 18618
— porosa 12591
— quarzosa 14274
— refrattaria 7178
— rigenerata 14505
— scorrevole 9024
— secca 6039
— silicea 16359/a
— spingente 5863
— a spigoli vivi 16005
— argillosa 3668
— fresca 3676
— usata 19411
— vecchia 12523
— v. terra
sabbiare 15466
sabbiatore 15476
sabbiatrice 1737, 15478,
  15522
— a proiezione centrifuga
  19122
— a tamburo 15479
— ad aria compressa 4137
— pneumatica 4137
sabbiatura 1742, 15477,
  15525/a
— metallica 16198
sabbioso 8535
sacca 15933
— d'aria 302, 307
— dell'altoforno 2120
— di gas 7979
— di minerali 2578, 12240,
  12966
— libera 7737
— per le scorie 16541
sacchetto da spolvero 6126
sacco da polvere 6136, 6126
saettone 16179, 17225
sagenite 15427
saggiatore di strato 19053
saggio 6675, 15454, S. 18445
— colato a parte 15861
— di penetrazione 13062
sagoma 3710, 12973, 17806,
  17809, 17812, 18112/a
— aggiunta 18515
— di carico 10917

sagoma di controllo delle
  anime 4418
— di controllo per anime
  composte 4442
— per anima 4450, 4452
— per l'aria 19500
— principale 17808
sagomare 7605·
— la forma 17803, 18112
— secondo il campione
  4896
— secondo il modello S.
  4896
sagomati 15772, 17887
— di ferro 15772
— v. profilati
sagomato 7615
— alla pressa 13886
— leggero 10801
— v. profilato
sagomatura 17811
sagvandite 15430
Saheliano 15431
sala 1025
— d'analisi 20253
— dei saggi 15151
— delle bilancie 1133
— delle dinamo 6154
— di lavoro 20253
— di ripulitura 6978
— per la preparazione dei
  campioni 13856
— per le analisi metallo-
  grafiche 15150
salamoia 2407
salario a cottimo 18332
salbanda 3657, 3662, 15435
— argillosa 14117
saldabile 19928
saldabilità 19930
saldare 16857, 19923
— a freddo per pressione
  4007
— a ottone 2288
— a punti 17160
— a ricoprimento 10539
— a sovrapposizione
  10539
— a stagno 16839
— la ghisa 11488
— per contatto 2636
saldato a dolce 16842
— all'autogeno 972
— a punti 17162
— all'arco 7303

saldato elettricamente 6315
saldatoio a gas 8014
— a punta 13614
— a testa di martello 3488
— ad autoriscaldamento 15826
— elettrico 6302
saldatore 10211, 11122, 16859, 19934
saldatrice 19946
— a punti 17163, 17165
— ad arco 19952
— ad induzione ad alta frequenza 9146
— elettrica con motore a benzina 6316
— elettrica di testa 2642
— per giunti 15748
— per scintillamento 7304
saldatura 3015/a, 16858/a, 16860, 19936
— a base di stagno 16841
— a cordone 1367
— a doppio punto 19174
— a fuoco sotto pressione 5382/a
— a gas 8063/a
— a gas all'indietro 1060, 14907
— a gas in avanti 10665, 7626
— a gola 7032
— a gradini 18663/a
— a idrogeno atomico 93'
— a martellatura 9366
— a passate multiple 12115
— a passo di pellegrino 164 16484/a
— a percussione 6361/a, 13077/a
— a punti 16208, 17161, 17164, 18195
— a quartabuono 15605
— a raccordo 7032
— a resistenza testa a testa 6297
— a ricoprimento 10542
— a ritroso 1076
— a rulli 15091, 15749
— a sovrapposizione 10542
— a spinta 14204
— a stagno S. 16840, 16843
— a T 18353
— a V 8316/a, 19485/a
— ad arco 752

saldatura ad arco con due eletirodi di carbone 19169
— ad arco con elettrodo metallico nudo 1227
— ad arco schermato 16118/a
— al bismuto 1617
— al saldatoio 16867
— all'alluminio 464
— all'argento 16360
— all'ottone 2276, 17047
— alla fiamma 16866
— alla termite 18492
— alluminotermica 18492
— arcatomica 753
— autogena per fusione 969
— autogena per pressione S. 970
— ben fatta 8358
— con doppio bisello a J 5665
— con perni prigionieri 17904/a
— continua 4278, 15749
— continua a punti 12119, 17610/a
— continua a sovrapposizione 10541
— continua circolare 3598
— continua in serie 15894
— continua parallela 12922
— continua trasversale 18844 18844
— d'angolo 7032
— d'apporto 5836/a
— debole 16840
— del getto alla forma 17583
— di barrette a croce 4708
— di fili a croce 4708
— di rame 8841
— di rinforzo 1083
— di testa 2643, 6453
— di testa per ricalcatura 19374
— di tubo 19043
— diretta o indiretta al plasma 19938
— dolce 16840
— dura 2292, S.8840
— elettrica 6314, 6317
— elettrica a punti 6321
— elettrostatica a percussione 6367

saldatura fine 7089/a
— forte 2289, 8840
— in avanti 7563
— in filo preparata 14763
— leggera S. 16840
— lungo una linea S. 4278
— mediante bacchetta di cloruro di polivinile 19958
— mediante martellatura 8745
— multipla a rilievo 12116
— ondulata 14939
— ossiacetilenica 67, 968, 12813
— ossidrica 12816
— parallela a punti 12923
— per bollitura 7582
— per diffusione 5403/a
— per fucinatura 8745
— per fusione 7894
— per induzione 9756
— per pressione 970
— per resistenza 14778
— per scintillamento 7305
— per sovrapposizione 1276 12766
— plastica continua 11354
— progressiva a pressione 13924
— ricalcata 19377/a
— tenera S. 16840
— testa a testa 2643
saldobrasatura 2289
sale comune o da cucina S. 4097
— di Glauber 8288
— di Mohr 6964
— di Seignette 14999
— metallico 11571
salfemico 15437
salgemma 8720, 15026
sali alcalini 360
salita 14372, 14942, 14943, 14957
salite 15432, 15438
salmiak 15439
salmone 9783
— di piombo 13266
— v. massello
salmonsite 15440
salnitro 13730, 15417
salopiano 15441
salvavite 18554
samario 15449

samarskite 15450
samiresite 15451
samsonite 15465
sanidina 8287, 15535
sanidinite 15536
Sannoisiano 15537
sano 6866, 16934
santorinite 15538
sanukite 15539
sapone 16798
— di montagna 15029/a
saponite 13325, 15540
saprocollo 16639
sapropelite 15542
saracinesca 1662
— a leva 7365
— a paratoia 8097
sarcolite 15543
sarcopside 15544
sarda 15545
sardonio 15546
sarnaite 15548
sartorite 15549
sassolite 15551
sassoniano 15564
sassurite 15552
sassuritizzazione 15553
sbalzo termico 18487
sbarra 14314, 17744
— della griglia 7147, 8467
sbarramento 10557, 11726,
    17363
— antincendio 7164
— delle acque 16166
— di legno 4966
— di ventilazione 2286
sbarre tonde S. 15270
sbattimento 7283
sbavare 1696, 2616, 3472,
    6970, 6972
sbavato 3682
sbavatore 3702, 5840/a,
    6980, 15665, 6973,
    18897, 18902
sbavatrice 2620, 3741,
    6977, 6980
— di colata 17212
— per getti 3046
sbavatura 3478, 3690,
    5843, 6974, 6975
— a freddo 4003/a
— alla fiamma 9222/a
sbocco 19110
— d'acqua 9506
sbozzare 3904

sbozzare al laminatoio 15242
— la torta di argilla 13857
sbozzato 1679, 9276, 15256
— cavo 7592
— tubolare 7592, 13373
sbozzatrice a rulli 7596
sbozzatura 1808, 1830,
    3912
sbozzo 1679, 13834
sbraccio 18575
sbruffino S.283
scabrosità della superficie
    18065
scaffale per forme 14322
scaglia 7249/a, 8742, 15568,
    16597, 17117
— del forno 7853
— di fucinazione 7579/a
— di laminazione 15015/a,
    15087, 15129
— di martellatura 8742
— di paraffina 15593
— di ricottura 11700
— incrostata 5815/a
scagliatura 5225, 15582,
    15595
— secca 6042/a
scaglie 15583
— di diamante 5320
— di laminatoio 11692
scala 15586
— delle durezze 15590
— metrica 11608
scaldare 19666
scaldato 9004
— al bianco 20032
— al color rosso scuro 6087
— al color blu 1903
— al rosso ciliega 3409
— al rosso scuro S. 1662
scalenoedro 16594
scalfittura 15685
scalinata 7373
scalpellare 3483, 3484
scalpellatura 3477
scalpello 8926, 15196
— a croce 4676
— a disco 5480
— a lame 5730
— a quattro lame 5730
— a tre lame 18570
— ad alette 6164/a,
    10160, 20108
— ad aria compressa 13582
— con corona a diamanti

5323
scalpello con grilletto d'ar-
    resto per un «single shot»
    18893
— consumato 6084
— di cavapietre 1927
— di guida 3185
— di un cavaliere 4401
— eccentrico 6638
— per terreni teneri 19247
— per carotieri continui
    13561
— per presellare 3111
— pneumatico 253, 13595
— v. trapano o punta
scalzare 5879, 19325
scambiatore a tubi e mantel-
    lo 16095
— di calore 19837
scambio 5333
— d'analisi 6645
— doppio 14903
— normale 17347
— semplice 16372
scampanare 1445
— il modello 11011
scampanatura 1470, 14420
— eccessiva 6643
scanalare 8585
— una sbarra 16684
scanalatore 7809/a, 7493,
    8596
scanalatura 7811, 8586,
    8597
— al cannello 8013/a,
    8374/a, 8587/a
— di trafilatura 17712
— incanalata 14489/a
— longitudinale 10981
— per eliminare la tensione
    17788
— per sfogo bavatura 1059,
    8687
— provvisoria della trafila-
    tura 5369
— quadrangolare 5327
scanalature per stecche
    7212
scandagliare il terreno
    16935
scandio 15602
scapolato S. 1679
scapolite 15603
scaricatore 10482
— a bilico 978

scaricatore automatico
   15817
— meccanico 18685
— meccanico rotativo
   14843
— mobile 159
scarico 1756, 5499, 6106,
   7432, 19321
— ai due lati del binario
   5498
— automatico 979
— d'aria 274
— dal convertitore 5492
— del forno 6421
— del forno del minerale
   5804
— del separatore 18851
— dei prodotti volatili 6567
— dei vagoncini nella gabbia 5064
— della loppa 7431
— delle scorie 7415, 7431,
   16560
scarn 15606
scarpa 1344, 2106, 16150
— continentale 4259
— del carotiere 5882
— del tubo portacarota
   4453
— dentata per sonda a rotazione 15218
— di guida 8654
— di perforazione 5957
— di perforazione dentata
   15898
— di un carotiere 4401
— per «overshot» 11712
— per tubi 2957
— per tubi con valvola
   7388
— per tuta di lavaggio
   15226, 19714
— tagliente 2182
scarpata 1344, 8265
— costiera 3725
— di faglia 6846
— naturale 12197
scarso 16184
— d'aspirazione 17955/a
scartamento 16957
— dei binari 8109
— dei cilindri 5550
scarti di coke 14640
— di ferro 10025
— v. rifiuti

scarto 12778, 15679, 19718
scatola 2207, S. 2508, 2910
— a prova d'acido 87
— dell'assale 1027
— per campioni 15457
— per carote 4466
— per muschio 11945
— porta espulsori 17197
scatto dopo flessione
   17203/a
scavare 2073, 2300, 5161,
   5404, 5447, 10320, 11723,
   15688, 16961, 18872,
   20080
— al di sotto 16685, 16790
— gallerie traverso-banco
   4683
— in rimonta 2303
— un pozzo 2075
— una galleria 19106
scavatore 6637, 12064
— a noria 12373
— di carbone 3813
— v. draga
scavatrice 8936, 12203,
— a benna a mascella
   3631
— e caricatrice Meco-Moore
   11421
scavezzamento 16134
scavi 5408
— abbondanti 9282
scavo 4898, 5407, 12058,
   16215, 16416, 17676
— a mano 8785
— dal disotto 19243
— di galleria 5873
— di una galleria 19108
— eccessivo 12738
— in profondità 5095
— in rimonta 2337, 14945
— meccanico 13793
— riempito con materiale
   del cantiere 4901
— sotterraneo 5095, 5095/a
— sul muro 19243
scawtite 15611
sceloroscopio 15636/a
scelta dei campioni 15807
— della forza motrice
   15896
scentratura 2510
schafarzikite 15612
schairerite 15613
schalenblenda 15614

schallerite 15615
schalstein 15616
schapbachite 15617
scheelite 15618, 16043
scheererite 15619
schefferite 15620
scheggia 15768/a, 16095/a,
   17086/a, 17117
— di ghisa 2996
— di pietra 16963
scheggiatura 16967
scheletro 16448
schema di processo 7426
schermatura 8958
schermi anabbaglianti 661
schertelite 15621
schiacciamento 10251
— dell'anima 4764
— della forma 4762
schiacciare 19371
schiavettare 19235
schiavettatura 19236
schiller 15622
schillerizzazione 1006,
   15624
schillerspato 15623
schioppo 7249
schisolite 15626
schisto argilloso 12095
— gassifero 8051
— v. scisto
schiuma 5103, 16489
— di alluminio 452, 7511
— di grafite 10376
— di mare 11439
schiumare 5240, 16458
schiumatoio v. schiumatore
schiumatore 16461, 16467
schiumatura 16465
schiumoso 13672
schneebergite 15627
schoepite 15628
schoelomite 15629
schreibersite 15630
schultenite 15631
schungite 16236
schwazite 15635
scintilla di ferro 10017
scintillamento 8300
scintillare 17230
scintille prodotte ad una
   frequenza elevata 14418
scirmerite 15625
scistificazione 15020,
   15979

scisto a orneblenda 9370,
— alluminoso 441
— argilloso 6111, 8461,
  15976
— argilloso blu 1907
— argilloso grigio 8501
— argilloso tenero 1676
— bituminoso 1594, 12509,
  14862, 1645
— bituminoso compatto
  1325
— carbonifero 1645, 1666,
  2028, 4994, 14444
— carbonifero tenero
  3866
— -carbone 12903
— duro 14459
— maculato 7358
— picchiettato 17167
— primario 7816
— silicioso 7383
— talcoso 18222
— tenero 2927
— v. schisto
scistosità 3718, 7532
— confusa 1775
— di pressione 7423
— di stratificazione 10509
— piano-parallela 13458
scivolare 16606, 16644,
  16711
scivolo 2637, 3563, 4316,
  8491, 11690, 16162,
  17371
— a scosse 1159
— con rivestimento in legno
  4633
— d'alimentazione 6878,
  6889
— d'attacco 5969
— del portale di torre 15362
— oscillante a rulli 15117
— per carbone 4527
— per minerali 5780, 7016,
  11694, 12638, 17670
— per ripiena 15012, 19721
— per sfridi 15657
— sospeso 8812
— v. piano inclinato
scivolone ausiliare per minerali 10189
sclerometro 15636
— a sfera 1156
scleroscopio a sfere 1156

scogliera 14583
— di sbarramento 1250
scolatoio 5950
scolatrice 5290
scollamento 16515
scomparsa di una proprietà
  11028
scompartimento di ventilazione 256
scomporre una forma 2296
scontrino della pesata 19900
scoperta di petrolio 17817
scoperto (allo) 12605
scopo della separazione
  12431
scoppiare 6678
scoppio di rocce 8927
— di una caldaia 1958
— v. esplosione
scoprimento 19331
scoprire 17842
scoria 3570, 6007, 14870,
  15728, 16347, 16431,
  16514, 16519, 18489
— acida 93
— basica 1305, 13167
— Bessemer 1555
— congenita 6461
— d'affinazione 14604
— di altoforno 1717
— di altoforno trattata al
  vapore 1719
— d'inclusione 6442
— di bagno di stagnatura
  15726
— di basso fuoco 3084
— di canale 17173
— di forgia 7597
— di forno d'affinazione
  14612
— di liquidazione 10870
— di protezione 4556/a
— di puddellaggio 2564,
  7404, 8742/a, 11692,
  14097, 18266
— di ricottura 14670
— di segregazione 10870
— di siviera 10485/a
— di spillatura 18312
— finale 7139
— fusa galleggiante 7414
— interposta 6442
— locale 10381
— povera di ferro 16547

scoria povera di fosforo
  16548
— ricca di ferro 16551
— ricca di fosforo 16552
— ricca di ossidi 14871
— riduttrice 14577
— secca o pastosa 17585
— spumosa 7512
— Thomas 1305, 18537
— trascinata dalla colata
  16555
— verde di piombo 8531/a
— vetrosa 19574
— vulcanica 15644/a
— v. loppa
scorie del ferro 3727
scorificante 16535
scorificare 5765, 14380, S.
  16458, 16459, 16469,
  16517, 16518, 18270
scorificazione 14385, 16543,
  16544, 16556, 16567
— del fosforo 16570
— di terra 16569
— di tinta 16568, S. 16569
scorodite 15647
scorrere 16606
scorrevolezza 5528
scorrimento 4611
— critico 4643
— iniziale 9808/a
— laminare 10501
— per gravità 8489
scorta 17612
scorticatura 7916
scoscendimento 6778
scosceso 45
scossa 10225
— di replica 203
— dura 10217
scraper 5736
scremare 16458
scrematore 16461
scrematura 6009, S. 16465
screpolarsi 1781/a
screpolato 4584
screpolatura 2308, 3363
— v. criccatura
screziatura 11958/a
scriccare 721, 3473
scriccatore 3476
— alla fiamma 9409
scriccatura 4587, 17790
— al cammello 9428/a

scrostare 16459
scrostato 5223
scrostatore 5224
scudo d'avanzamento 2344
scuotere 10124
scuotimento 10135
sdoppiamento (di strato)
    17136
— degli ioni 17137
searlesite 15756
sebastianite 15758
seccato nell'essiccatore
    5847
secchia di colata 10469
— di colata a tampone S.
    2181
— per le scorie 16541
— v. siviera
secchio per prelevare sassi
    2487
secchione 2552, 13759
— di colata S.7660,
    10469
secco come la polvere
    13767
seconda uscita 15769
Secondario 15766
secondo i calcoli 49
— impiego 14735
— le norme UNI 50
— tappo di cementazione
    18747
sede d'estrazione 15905
— della tubazione 16209
— di colata 12407
— di colata per la secchia
    S. 12407
— di una valvola 19454
sedia 3520
sedimentazione 15794/a
sedimenti di serbatoio
    18247
— marini 11321
sedimento 15923/a, 5831
— zincoso 8845/a
— v. deposito
seebachite 15795
sega a caldo 9438
— a freddo 3999
— alternativa 1178, 14869/a
— circolare 3597
— da traforo alternativa
    7770
— per carbone 2841

sega rapida meccanica da
    metalli 9174
segare 15563/a
— a freddo 3999/a
segmentatore 7778
segmenti di un ombrello di
    cementazione 13120
segno di raccordo 7029
— di riferimento 16307
— di trafila 5369
sego 18224
segregazione S. 10866
    18101, 4481
— di grafite 10377
— infiltrata 11557
— inversa 12214/a
selce 15324
— cornea 3410, 9372,
    9374, 9949
selenite 4801, 15555, 15809
seligmannite 15833
sella 15407
— anticlinale 658
— del bilanciere 19630
— di anticlinale 4426
— di sinclinale 19651
— inversa 9935
— scorrevole 5786
sellaite 15834
sellerine 16156
semicentrifugazione 15838
semicircolare 8715,
semicoke 3865
semicuscinetto inferiore
    2148
— superiore 18737
semiprodotto 15841
semistampo fisso 7231
— mobile 12047
semplice effetto (a) 16379
semseite 15852
senaite 15853
senarmontite 15854
sensibile 15856
sensibilità 15858
— al surriscaldamento
    12761
— all'intaglio 12400
— alla temperatura 15859
— allo spessore 15780
sensività 10248
senso del movimento 5467
senza crepe 7726
— fessure 7726

senza giunzioni 15751
— motore 6090
— tensione 7729
separare 13200, 15860,
    20081, 17124
— il ferro 5143
— mediante fusione 11457
separatore 810, 5508,
    8057, 15878
— ad aria compressa 321
— calibrato 11610
— con magnete permanente
    15881
— d'acqua 19765, 19790
— d'argilla 15981
— di fango 16631
— di gas 8054
— di minerali secondo
    Wetherill 20002
— di polvere 6132, 6139
— di torba 13027
— magnetico 11203
— per gas 8052
— pneumatico 13597
separazione 1758, 12947,
    15868, 17135
— a mano 15869
— a mezzo liquidi densi
    9033
— a secco 6044
— centrifuga 3209
— degli elementi della ca-
    rica 15876
— dei minerali con tavole
    inclinate 18193
— del ferro 15873
— del petrolio col coagulo
    dei residui di raffineria
    19753
— delle polveri 14720,
    15877
— delle scorie 15875
— di carbone 15871
— di ferro 10010
— elettrolitica 6348
— elettrostatica 6368
— in lamine 16064
— per gravità 8492
— prismatica 13964
— sferoidale 17069
— strutturale S.13812
— umida 19997
sepiolite 15882
sepolto 2591, 6492

septaria 15883, 19156
Sequaniano 15886
serandite 15868
serbatoi di produzione
    10647
serbatoio 4249, 14488,
    14745, 17692
— a forma di goccia 17062
— a tetto galleggiante 7392
— collettore 8102
— d'acqua 14745
— dei fanghi 12091
— del fluido di tenuta
    15736
— di compensazione 18075
— di decalcazione 15926
— di decantazione 57
— di esercizio 20192
— di filtraggio 7054
— di lavorazione 15346
— di riserva 142, 17996
— di scolo 7437
— di stoccaggio 17690
— di trattamento 19692
— elevato 9156
— fisso 7241
— generale dell'acqua
    4098
— graduato 8117
— intermedio 15356
— per addizioni 7499/a
— per aria compressa 4135
— per mercurio 11505
— per minerali 17693
— per petrolio 12482
— piezometrico 19820
— refrattario 19099/a
— regolatore 2520
— rifornitore 7437
— supplementare 142
— tarato 2743
serendibite 15889
sericite 15891
sericitico 15892
sericitizzazione 15893
serie 15903
— atlantica 919
— carbonifera 2861
— eparcheana 6504
— di fori da mina 15268
— di funi flessibili per
    perforazione 10808
— di getti 15907
— di modelli per formare

una puleggia 15910
serie di pompe 10742
— di quattro aste 7684
— di stacci 15911
— di stampi per stampaggi
    e tranciatura 4056
— di strati 1421
— (per) 2654
serpentina 15895
— di condensazione 4186
— di raffreddamento 4186
serpentini tubolari per im-
    pianti di riscaldamenti
    a pannelli radianti 19065
serpentino d'assorbimento
    17
— di riscaldamento 14483
— surriscaldatore 18012
serra-cavo 20145
serrafili 1603, 20120
serraggio di un accoppia-
    mento a vite 17362
serramenti in acciaio apribi-
    li 11547
serranda S. 4980
serrare 16241
serrato a mano 8798
serratubi a morsetto 3742
serraviti 5281
servizio 939
— (in) 9675, 9681
servocomando 4416
servomotore 18604
sesquiossido di ferro idrato
    10828
— manganico 11281
setacciare 14884
setacciatura S.15693
setaccio a maglia 11561
— oscillante 12686
— vibrante 19548
— v. vaglio o crivello
setto 15884
— di stoffa 1688
seybertite 15929
sezione d'attacco 8091
— d'un sondaggio 5894
— del tubo 10204
— dell'ugello 12416
— di base 16042
— di colata 7660
— di scavo 12897
— di taglio 16029
— finale 7069

sezione finale 7069
— iniziale 7201
— quadrata 17242
— trasversale 1941, 4704
— verticale 6375
sezioni della sacca 15789
sfaldamento 3479, 16645,
— rotativo 15233/a
sfaldarsi 15578, 1781/a
sfaldatura 6648, 15595
— di base 1264
— distinta 5564, 6182
— netta (a)·6608
— prismatica 13963
— romboedrica 2719
sfalerite S. 1761, 17053
sfangare 5237, 6394
sfangatore 5241
sfangatrice 5241
sfangatura 5238, 16637
sfenoide 17055
sfenolite 17056
sfera 17057
sferetta 17064
sferico 17059
sferocobaltite 17052
sferoidale 17065
sferoide 17062
sferoidite 17072
sferoidizzazione 5587,
    17070
sferolitico 17073
sferosiderite 13069, 17074
— argillosa 3663
— carboniosa 1668
sferula 17064
sfiatatoio 289, S. 7436, S.
    20022
sfioratore 7432
sfoglia aperta 6673, 1779/a
— di tinta aperta 1674
— di tinta libera 1675
— libera 15567
sfogliatura 6648, 13483
sfogo 7432
sfondamento 11556, 6778
— dell'armatura 10096
— della forma 4763
sfondare bruciando 2590
sformare 5757, 6235, 12560,
    17841, 20155
— a candele 5767
— per ribaltamento 5768
— per rotazione 5769

sformare sul telaio 5766
sformatrice 7295, 17871
sformatura 10744, 15966,
    17865
— a candele 13309/a
— dei modelli 12976
sformo 5724, 18278/a
sfornamento 6421
sforzi alternati 434
sforzo 17730, 17782
— di compressione S.4156
— di flessione 1518
— di flusso 7435/a
— di frattura 7701/a
— di fucinatura 7597/a
— di prova 14007/a
— di servizio 20220/a
— di tensione 17798
— di trazione 5777, 14126
— di trazione all'avviamen-
    to 17383
— termico 18487/a
sfregamento 4765, 15319
— del collo 10233
sfridi 14815
— di fucinatura 7597
sfrido 7290
— di lamiera 16508
sfrisetto S. 17837
sfruttabile 9671
sfruttamento 8205
— irrazionale 2504, 8367,
    19739
— irrazionale del giacimen-
    to 4577
— primario 13940
— secondario 15767
— sul giunto 11799
— v. coltivazione o estra-
    zione
sfruttare 11737
— una miniera 11723
sfruttato 12613, 17672
sgocciolamento della ghisa
    11470
sgombero del terreno di co-
    pertura 1231
sgorgare 7419, 15348
— a intermittenza 7420
sgrossare 1926
sgrossato 15250
sgrossatura 5130/a, 15258
— alla mola 15249/a
sgualcito 4758
sguarnitura 3713

shastaite 16009
shastalite 16010
shattuckite 16016
sherardizzazione 16016
shonkinite 16158
shoshonite 16190
sial 16247
sialma 16218
siberite 16249
sicklerite 16250
sidercromo 3540
siderite 16994, 16283
— calcinata 16890
— ossidata all'aria 19584
siderofillite 16286
siderolite 16284
sideronatrite 16285
siderurgia 10037, 16287
sienite a feldspatoidi 18145
— a gneiss 8321
— eleolitica 6373
— nefelinica 12231
sifone 18172
sigillare 7010, 15733
— una forma 11099
sigillatura 10207, 15735/a
sigillo 15734
silicare 16322
silicato d'alluminio 470,
    16315
— di zinco 20334
— di zinco idrossilo 16317
— idrato di allumina 9510
silice 2194, 7377, 16311
— combinata 4065
— cornea 9374
— gelatinosa 8148
siliceo 16316
silicio 16310, 16323, 16325
silicosi 16331
silicotel 16332
sillimanite 16343
siluriano 16348
silvanite 18146
silvina 18148
simbolo chimico 3393
simetite 16364
similoro 16365
simmetria 18166
simplectite 18153
simplesite 18154
sinadelphite 18155
sinclinale 5711, 18161
sinclinorio 18162
sineresi 18163

singenesi 18164
singenite 18165
sinopite 16427
sinterizzazione 7775, 16434
— doppia 5677/a
— sotto vuoto 19446/a
sintesi 18167
sipilite 16439
sismica a riflessione 14620
— a rifrazione 14623
sistema a due conduttori
    19194
— a più conduttori 12124
— antracolitico 648
— cretaceo 4626
— cristallino 18179
— cubico 10068
— delle prove 892
— di accensione 1874
— di alimentazione 15380
— di chiusura v. chiusura
— di coltivazione a camere
    12898
— di coltivazione a camere
    e pilastri 2343
— di coltivazione a sezioni
    12898
— di controllo 10140,
    14059
— di fabbricazione dell'ac-
    ciaio con ghisa e rottami
    11465
— di fratture 18178
— di lenti 18180
— di leve 10718
— di messa in moto 1874
— di prova 18466
— di raffreddamento 4336
— di sondaggio a rotazione
    15220
— lenticolare 18180
— monoclino 11908
— ortorombico 13965
— rombico 12684
— triassico 18888
— triclino 18891
— v. periodo
sistemare 10517
sistemato su anticlinale
    produttivo 12543
sistemazione dei carrelli
    sulla gabbia 12553
— dei massivi 9837
— delle anime 10599
sitaparite 16441

siviera 10469
— a cremagliera 10486
— a forcella 15985
— a ingranaggi 8138
— a mano 8784, 8763
— a portante 10476
— con ferma-scorie 4969
— con piastra di guardia S. 4969
— di colata 3347, 7650, 7660, 11472, 13755, 13759
— di colata a becco 10861
— di colata a botte 6014
— di colata a sifone 18342
— di colata a tampone 2181
— di colata a tino 6014
— di colata con dispositivo di ribaltamento a mano 8787
— fissa 7234
— girevole su carrello 10481
— mescolatrice 11832
— per acciaio 17482
— rovesciabile 18629
— sospesa a gru 4599
— v. secchia
skip 8671
— a botola 5978
— a fondo apribile 5978
— a scarico automatico 15820
— ribaltabile 12784
sklodowskite 16486
skogbolite 16487
skolecite 15637
skutterudite 16490
slavikite 16579
slingottare 17843
slingottatore 17862
slingottatrice 9802
slitta 5786, 9473, 16580, 16611
— porta-matrice 5374
slittamento 4622, 16666
— del piano di stratifica-zione 1432
— di strati superficiali 15428
— sul piano di stratifica-zione 16608
slittoni 15370
smagnetizzatore 5162
smagrire la sabbia argillosa

19852
smaltare 6432
smaltatura 6487
— a caldo 9413
— a freddo 3976
— a immersione 19992
— a secco 6032
— a spolvero 6032
— a vetro 8296/a
— elettrica 6272
smaltina 16741, 20027
smalto 6433
— vetroso 19572
smaragdite 16743
smaterozzare 14717
smaterozzatura 10396, 14721
smectite 16744
smeraldo 6407, 16742
smerigliare 6410, 10538
smerigliatura 6714, 7781/a, 8545, 8554
smeriglio 6411, 8553, 8558
sminuzzare 2328
smithite 16755
smithsonite 7922, 16756
smontabile 5166, 5538
smontare 14895
— le aste 10593
smorzatore di forno doppio 7834
smottamento 4622
— degli strati 16036
— di terreno 6169
smottare 10736
smottarsi 6771
smottato 6776
smottatrice 17871
smuovere la terra con bull-dozer 5719
smussato 1572
smussatura 3274/a, 13614a
snervamento 6835
— di scorrimento viscoso 18641
snervatrice a rulli per lamie-ra 16071
snodato 9203
snodo 10125, 10136
— di pescaggio 7219
— idraulico 5925
società mineraria 1120
soda caustica 3116
sodalite 16814
sodanitro 12308
soddite 16815

sodio 16817
soffiaggio 244, 1869, 1870, 1851
— di una forma S. 1870
soffiante 1704, 1864, 1858, 1867, 1875, 13541
— a gas 7982
— di altoforno 1707
— Martin 11349
— v. soffieria
soffiare 1839
— una forma S. 1841
— con aria calda 1844
— il vento 1842
— un'anima 1841, 1847
soffiatore 283
soffiatrice per anime 4394
soffiatura 1868, S. 1750, 1754, 1781, 1852, 7370, 8015, 13329, 13350, 17138
— a tutta pressione 1879
— azzurrognola 14468
— da scoria 16526
— lucida 19324
— ossidata 12806
— periferica 13093
— spaccata 14982/a
soffice 2153
soffità 16850
soffieria 243, 1865
— a cassa 2213
— a cilindro 4944
— a vapore 17419
— di Cleveland ad una biella 3720
— elettrica S. 1867
— idraulica 9514
— orizzontale 9332
— verticale 19519
— v. soffiante
soffietto 1466
— a cuoio 10648
— a mantice 8755
— a pedale 7539
— a pulsante 283
soffio 1698
soffocamento 1202
soffocare 3515
soggendalite 16852
soglia S. 4964, 4965, 16335, 16345, 16870
— del forno S. 16872
— della porta 5632
— di circo 15030

solchi antislittamento
14353
solco 8587
— principale di colata
11226
soletta di fondazione continua in calcestruzzo 4263
solfato d'ammonio 529
— di- calcio 17969
— di magnesio 1632,
17971
— di rame 17970
— di zinco 17974
— ferrico 6929
— ferroso 6966
— ferroso-ammonico 6964
— potassico 17972
— sodico 17973
solfocianuro ammonico
17979
solfonato 17964
solforazione 17966
solfito di sodio 16825
solfuro ammonico 530
— d'antimonio 17976
— di carbonio 2825
— di zinco 20341
— terroso 10022
solidificazione 7742,
— bianca 3422
— controllata S.5470
— direzionale 5470
solido S. 16894, 16934
— di rotazione 1939
solidus S. 16894
solifluzione 16895
sollecitazione 17782, 17730
— a compressione 4156
— a flessione 1518, 1520
— a temperature alternate
18380
— a torsione 18782
— a trazione 18409
— al carico di punta 2511,
4640
— di forgiatura 7581
— di taglio 16036
— di un corpo all'urto 16147
16147
sollecitazioni alternate 434
436
— ammissibili 13114
sollevamento 9229, 10759,
14378, 19359
— dei lingotti 10771

sollevamento del coperchio
10760
— di terra 5974
sollevare 2304
— in torre 13201
sollevatore a cavalli 20014
solubile 16895
solubilità 16899
— completa 13079
— limitata 10825
soluto 16890/a
soluzionabilità 20001
soluzionatore 17189, 20003
soluzione 16900
— aderente 5733/a
— cristallina 16886
— d'indaco 9740
— di cloruro di calcio
16904
— di ferro 10022
— di potassa caustica
3115
— di resina in trementina
16905
— di sapone 16801
— di soda caustica 3117
— di vetriolo 16906
— equimolecolare 6530
— equivalente 6534
— estratta 5735/a
— filtrata chiara 3707
— gravitazionale 8493
— limpida 3708
— normale 17351
— salina S. 2407
— solida 4205, 16886
— torbida 19116
soluzioni corrispondenti
10061
— isoidriche 10061
solvatazione 16907
solvsbergite 16913
solvente 5546
sommaite 16914
somministrazione di calore
S. 18027
sommità del compressore
13868
sonda S. 2091, 5881, 8608,
13969
— a croce 4661
— a percussione 3560
— a rotazione 15199
— campionatrice 4405,
15459, 16856, 18254

sonda petrolifera 12515
sondaggio 2076, 2080, 2090,
5916
— a circolazione 7483
— a gas 8065, 8082
— a graniglia 2763
— a infezione 19776
— a percussione 2661,
9733
— a percussione rapida
2100
— a rotazione 2101, 15195,
15200
— a vibrazioni 19554
— alla corda 8733
— alla fune 15159
— anticlinale 12465
— d'assaggio 18880
— d'avanzamento 14044
— di delimitazione 12470
— d'iniezione 9829,
9859
— d'intervento 14686
— di petrolio 19967
— di pozzi 19963
— di prova 18443
— di ricerca 14058
— di un pozzo con mine
18775
— elettrico 6322
— esplorativo 17896, 18459
— improduttivo 6140
— in mare 11322
— inclinato 9708
— intercalare 9762
— obliquo 9708
— per carotaggio 4406
— positivo 13651
— profondo 5092
— sterile 1246, 6140
— storto 4657
— v. perforazione o trivellazione
sondare 2621, 14032, 16932
— il terreno 16936
— il tetto 10394, 14416
— il tetto battendolo 6018,
10237
— v. perforare o trivellare
sondatore 5895
sopporto v. supporto
soprafusione 18001
sopralzo di colata 14950
— telescopico 18361
soprasaturazione S. 18021

soprassaturo 18019
sorbite 16920
sordawalite 16922
sorgente d'elettricità 16946
— di fango in ebollizione 12863
— di gravitazione 8494
— di luce esterna 6697
sorvegliante 7567
— della ventilazione 7151
— di miniera 1203
sorveglianza 18024
sospensione 8804
— a molla per staffoni 4225
— compensata 4109
sostanza animale 594
— antischiuma 662
— densa per tempera 15843
— esotermica 6889/a
— esplosiva 1744
— ferrosa 11372
— legante S. 1597
— neutra 12253
— nociva 5266
— organica 12663
— per appesantire il fango 19910
— per cementazione 3175
— per ritardare la cementazione ossidante 5418
— protettiva 13863
sostegni 6813, 10299,
— per gabbie di miniera 2682
sostegno 10240, 14921
— a molla in fondo al «mouse hole» 10201
— ad anello 1087
— della placca frontale 2241
— degli elettrodi 6327
— del filtro 7822
— della caldaia 1975
— della tramoggia 9329, 18030
— di galleria 6497
— Martens da microscopio 11345
— per la storta 14800
— per miniere S. 2764
— telescopico 4014
— v. supporto
sostituire l'armatura 14792

sotterrare la forma 14390
sottopassaggio 19244
sottoporre ad elettrolisi 6353
— all'azione del fumo 16758
sottoposto a forti sollecitazioni 9028
— a sollecitazioni non eccessive 10780
sottoprodotti del gas 2648
— dell'altoforno 2653
sottoraffreddamento S.17936
sottoquadro 1052
sottostruttura 17934
sottosuolo granitico 8419
sottovia 19244
sottrazione di calore S.8973
souesite 16929
soumansite 16931
sovraccaricare 11486
sovradecapaggio 12771/a
sovrametallo 11140
— per ricalcatura 394
sovraossidazione 12734
sovrapporre 12764
sovrapposto 18016
sovrapposizione 12745, 12767, 16244
— anticlinale 2315
— di distillazione 5558
— normale 12382
sovrasaturare 18018
sovrasaturazione 18021
sovraspessore di alimentazione 12858
— di sicurezza 11998
sovrastampo 11301
sovratempra S. 2918
sovratensione 12784/a
spaccare 2302, 17124
— il minerale in pezzi 13198
spaccato verticale 6375
spadaite 16959
spalatura 16215
spalla del trapano 16210
spanatura dei filetti 7916
spanciare S. 1467
spanditoio dell'altoforno 2120
spangolite 16973
spargicolata S. 5402, 17214
sparizione improvvisa d'uno

strato 28
Sparnaciano 16989
spato 6975
— calcare 2718, 2728
— d'Islanda 2718, 9613
— manganico 11274
— perlaceo 13015
— pesante 1233
spatofluoro 7475
spatola 10214/a, 16604, 16998, 18944
— a piatto 8947
— a punta e cucchiaio S. 8947
— da fonditore 7641
— di platino 13527
— per lisciare 16584
spaziatura 16957
spazio anulare 624
— dei pori 13670
— per l'acqua S.19810
spazzola a mano 8756
— a mano in fili d'acciaio 3024
— circolare 8588
— di canapa 9087
— doppia in filo d'acciaio 5675
— in filo di ferro a striglia 20118
— per ghisa grezza 3043
— per sbavare 2480
— per tubi 18976
— raschiatrice 15680
specchio di base della bilancia 13490
— di faglia 6858, 13625
specialista in recuperi 7216
specificazione normale 17352
specie 16924
specolare 17037
specularite 12530
spegnere 14279
— il forno 1843, 3354
— temporaneamente il forno 4976
spegnimento 1877
— del forno 17688
speiss 17044
spellatura 13042
spencerite 17049
sperimentalmente 6677

sperone 1374, 17224
sperrylite 17050
spese d'analisi 4513
— d'esercizio 20205
— di rivestimento 4520
— di trasporto 2905
spessartite 11267, 17051
spessitore 18506
spessore 10843, 13045,
    16129/a, 20064
— degli strati discolati S.
    17750
— dei fanghi 12092
— del filo 8115
— del filo di ferro 5319
— del nastro 17856
- della camicia 18510
— della lamiera 13500
— della parete 18512
— dello strato poroso 15520
— di ghisa 19655
— prescritto 5533
spettri di spostamento 5533
spettro continuo 19307
spettrografia 17033
spettroscopio 17034
spezza-ghisa 3076
spezzamasselli ad eccentri-
    co 6185
— fisso 17273
— idraulico 2531
— portatile 13695
spezzatura dei masselli
    4779
spezzonare barre di ferro
    2658
spezzone 17616
— corto di «casing» 10212
— di tubo 13658
spia 18363, 18513
— a chiavetta S.19883
— del raccordo 9889
spiaggia 16168
spianare alla lima 13450
spianatrice 7352
spianatura alla lima fine
    8540
— alla lima grossa 8541
spianatrice 17725
spiazzo di deposito tempora-
    neo 12860
spigoio 6197
— della ripiena 18038
— superiore 19365

spilite 17085
spilitico 17086
spillare 6825, 18261, 14312
spillata 2984, 8972/a, S.
    18298 , 11458, 18264
— difettosa 12460/a
spillatura 18298
— continua 4276
spillo 19506
— da fonderia 15511
— per l'aria 13931
spillone 19506
spina 6668, 13307
— a cannone 5694
— a chiavetta 19883
— amovibile S. 13305
— d'aggiustaggio 6083
— d'estrazione 8652
— di pesce 9062
— flangiata S.4022
spinatrice 2431
spinatura 12261/b
spinello 7907, 17094
— di cromo 3536
— rosso 15331
spingere 14016
spingitore 9490
spinotto 6668, 9201
— di pistone 13391
spinta 18596, 18603
— dei vagonetti sulla gab-
    bia 2685
— della terra 14999,
    15024/a
— delle acque 19769
— tangenziale 18244
spirito di petrolio 12529
spitzlutte 17108
splendore adamantino 123
— della fiamma 2405
— di una superficie 2404
— perlaceo 12153
spodiofillite 17139
spodumene 17140
spoglia 5724, 15567
— di un modello 18280
spola 17149
spolverare 14716
— con talco 6141
spolverizzare le forme
    19248
spolvero 1294/a, 12950
sporgenza 2647, 10262
sporgere 10261

sporogelite 17154
sportello di fondo 2154
sporto della staffa 15493
spostabile 5531
spostacinghia 1459, 1481
spostamento 11799/a, 16128
— con mezzi termici 18481
— della forma 4696
— delle coste 16129
— dell'impianto di perfora-
    zione 14900
— di anime 4443
— di gas arricchito 6489
— orizzontale degli affio-
    ramenti 12463
— secondo la direzione
    17823
spremere 17257
sprofondamento 16417
spruzzare 17179, 17230
spruzzatore 10154, 17184,
    17206
— a fiato S. 283
spruzzetta 19685
spruzzo metallico 16113
spugnoso 14154
spumeggiante 7783
spuntatura 5487, 18759/a
— di lingotto 4660
spurgare 7479
spurgo 16627
— di una caldaia 1876
spurrite 17229
squadra di ferro 572
— di operai 7951
— di salvataggio 9068
— falsa S. 1570
— per lisciare 579, 17235
— perforatori 5921
— pulitori 3680
— zoppa 1570
squamoso 15601
stabilimento di altoforni 1712
    1712
— di forni per puddellaggio
    14115
— di raffineria catalitica
    3100
— di stagnatura 18668
— siderurgico 10037/a
stabilità 6117
stabilizzante 14655
stabilizzazione 17271,
    17789

staccare (tubi) 2301, 2304
staccarsi 16692
stacchetti da fonderia S.
 15511
stacciare 16296
stacciatura 16302
— per deposito 9457
staccio 16298
— a maglie 11518
— filtrante 7823
— grossolano 20058
— v. vaglio o crivello o
 setaccio
stadio 17283, 17285
— Calloviano 2749
— Cenomiano 15855
staffa 2208, 2217, 2222,
 2238, 7657, 12002,
 17610
— a cerniera 9206
— a due staffe 7680
— a traverse 1239
— americana 510
— apribile S. 9206
— apribile per forme 16780
— con pezzi riportati 2227
— con sformo interno 18286
— da aprirsi lateralmente
 16779
— da colonne 2218
— dell'elevatore 6380
— della puleggia 2239
— della siviera 10472,
 10478, 10484
— di ferro 20241
— di legno 20182
— di sollevamento 10762
— di sospensione 13424
— estraibile con sformo
 interno 18287
— in tre parti 18563/a
— inferiore 2174, 5731
— matta 6784/a
— per gettare in forma 7310
— per getto in conchiglia
 3055
— per smottare 9206
— scomponibile 2541
— scorrevole 16652
— speciale per puleggie
 12003
— superiore 4349, 19361
— v. telaio o cassa
staffata verde 5435
staffatura 2215, 7297

staffelite 17282
staffone 10858
— della testa d'iniezione
 1100
stagnare 18644
stagnatura 18651/a, 18664
— a caldo 9449
stagno 13138, 15737, 18645,
— ai gas 8081
— all'aria 329/a
— alluvionale 17772
— da idraulico 8711/a,
 13571/a
— di Banca 1173
— di legno 18655
— di Malacca 17740
— di roccia 11743
— fosforoso 13178
— in blocchi 1805
— in pani 1805, 13270
— laminato 16083
— per saldare S.16841
— per saldatura 16864
— piombifero 18647
— puro 14189
stainierite 17295
stalagmite 5997, 17298
stalattite 5997
— calcarea 2701
stampaggio 17321/a
— a caldo 5983
— al alta energia 9144
— ad esplosione 6688
— al maglio 5996
— in rilievo 6404
stampare 5972, 13956
— a caldo 9426
— a freddo 3970
stampato 17322/a
— in rilievo 6403
stampiano 17320
stampo 2127, 5356
— a ponte 5998
— aperto 12568/a
— chiuso 3769/a
— con dispositivo di trasfe-
 rimento 18823
— con impronta passante
 5998
— con impronte di partico-
 lari diversi 4055
— con maschi 7106
— con tallone di reazione
 10944
— del frantoio 17311

stampo della pressa 14183
— di fucinatrice 8567
— di ricalcatura 8929
— di riduzione 14567
— inferiore 2187, 11377,
 11069/a
— multiplo 12114
— per imbutitura 5796,
 7617/a
— per maglio 5987
— per pasticcerie 11979
— permanente 5358
— semilibero 17929
— semplice 9871
— smontabile 15799/a
— spianatore 10031
— superiore 19363
— v. forma
stanga a punta 14107
— di ferro 18306
stanghetta di sicurezza
 12293
stannato 17365
stannico 17366
stannifero, 17366, 13139,
 17368
stannite 17369, 18652,
 20350/a
stantuffi paralleli 18914
— sovrapposti a tandem
 18239
stantuffo 13389, 14405
— a piatto 16885
— della mazza 8741
— della pompa 14158
— della pompa d'aria 312
— di compressione 13875
— premente 13875
— tuffante 9536
starato 10408
stassfurtite 17390
statimetro 18599
stato (in buono) 16934
— (in cattivo) 12690
— d'equilibrio 17391
— pastoso 12146/a
staurolite 17402
stazione 10530
— centrale di pompaggio
 3191
— di distribuzione 5571
— di fondo 2170, 2176,
 8811, 9777, 9839, 10368,
 10530, 12713, 13399,
 13532, 13984, 15934,

stazione di manovra 16239
— di pompaggio seconda-
    ria 2053
— inferiore del pozzo 2143
— metallurgica 11742
— per l'erogazione 10793
— primaria 13944
— superiore 18684
— superiore del piano in-
    clinato 1193
steadite ·17411
steatite 16802, 17452
stecca 7210, 10575, 17115
— a squadra 571
— angolare 571
— piatta 7333
stefaniano 17554
stefanite 1665, 2426,
    17555
stelo 17533
— ammortizzatore 14502
— di pompa 13393
— di rotaia 19874
stendere 6388
stercorite 17565
sterile 5024, 5040, 12103,
    12105, 14638, 17141,
    19737
— misto a minerale 2048
sternbergite 17567
sterro 4898, 12058
sterrare 7394
— le anime 5077
sterratura S. 10400
— a getto di graniglia
    16199
— delle anime 5078
stewartite 17569
stibiconite 17572
stibina 668, 8497, 17577
stibiopalladinite 17573
stibiotantalite 17574
stiblite 17576
stibnite 8497
stichite 17578
stilbite 5242, 17591
stilolite 18083
stilpnoclorano 17599
stilpnomelano 17600
stima delle riserve 14743
stimulazione 17601
stiramento 5728
— fine 7079
— finissimo 19534

stiramento iniziale 13844
— medio 11424
— preliminare 13844
— v. raffinatura, fucinatura,
    forgiatura, trafilatura
stirare 5754
— al maglio 7571, 7574
— il ferro 5761
— v. fucinare o forgiare o
    trafilare
stirato 5814
stiratore 5788
stiratura 17797
stiva da carbone 3834
stivaggio di una forma 14407
stivare 12824
stivatura 12843
— a mano S. 8779
— a pressione 17262
— a scossa 10221
stoccaggio del petrolio
    18257
— sotterraneo 19263
stolpenite 17638
stolzite 17639
storta 14795
— cilindrica 3382
— di distillazione 5553
— per gas 8048
— per la distillazione del-
    l'amalgama 485, 488
— verticale 7327
storto 1527
stozzatura 16690/a
stracci per saldatura 20116
stracottura 5036
strada in acciaio amovibile
    12051
stramazzo 19919, 12739
strangolatore 8596
strappa-carote 4400
— a cunei 16665
— a stecche 7108
strappa-puntelli 18147
strappare 18346
strati (a) 1328, 9677
— alternati 435
— associati 901
— di transizione 1436
— duri 15254
— mineralizzati ad olio
    18523
— spessi (a) 9027
— sterili 1226

stratificato 16086, 1423,
    10504
stratificazione 1186, 1430,
    15979, 16045, 16088
— concordante 4204, 15793
— del carbone 6748
— discordante 10038
— incrociata 4672, 4698,
    4707, 5867, 6779
— irregolare 10038
— lenticolare 10679
— obliqua 12433
— pesante 9040
— primaria 12667
— torrenziale 4867
stratigrafia 17752
stratigrafo 17748
strato 1686, 5147, 10594,
    11393, 15743, 16084,
    17753
— acquifero 19751
— anti-acido 652
— antiruggine 672
— cementato 3165, 8853
— concentrico 17061
— contenente sulfuri me-
    tallici 6765
— d'argilla 16676
— d'ossido 10596
— d'ossido di ferro 12802
— del tetto 18017
— di base 8611
— di carbone incandescente
    9685
— di cementazione 8853
— di copertura 12769
— di metallo 10595
— di metallo bianco 20047/a
    20047/a
— di ossido di rame 7179/a
— di ossido di zinco
    20042/a
— di pece 2294
— di ruggine 10597
— di sabbia produttivo
    13002
— di scaglia 12795
— di scorie 10598
— di terra a secco 6042
— di usura 19860
— discordante 19239
— filiforme 16157
— filtrante 7043
— ghiaioso 13030, 3287

strato impermeabile 9657
— inclinato 13421
— inferiore 10325
— inferiore di combustibile 1417
— intrusivo 9927
— marginale 16478
— mineralizzato 12997
— nitrurato 12311
— obbliquo 4671
— orizzontale 10714, 15010
— petrolifero 12498
— piano 10714
— piatto 7344
— residuo di ossido 14756
— sovrastante 2813
— spesso 18500
— superficiale 2916
— trasversale 4671
— vorticoso 19604
— v. filone, banco, vena, letto
stratometro 5442
strengite 17774
stretto 16933
— a mano 8798
stria 17799
— di lucidatura 8210
— glaciale 8256
striato 1180, 3370, 17767, 17800
striatura del pezzo levigato 8547
striature di lucidatura 13631
strie 17802
stringere con la chiave sospesa 18713
stringitubi 13348
strippare 17843
strippato 17857
striscia 17741, 17760
— bleu o turchina 1913
— di riempimento 10841/a
strizione 18611
strofinio 15654/a
strombatura od apertura per l'ugello 19163
stromeyerite 17876
stronziana 17880
stronzianite 17881
stronzio 17882
stropicciare con spirito di vino 15303
strozzamento 18582

strozzamento del passaggio del gas 3519
— di uno strato 1352
strozzatura 11659
strumenti di guttaperca 8683
strumento di misura 11400
struttura 6733, 12974, 18473
— a calcestruzzo S. 3082
— a clessidra 9458
— a coccarda 15185
— a coppa 4834
— a covoni 16017
— a duomo 5619
— a gneiss 8320
— a eozon 6502
— a fibre 10841
— a grana grossa 3877
— a grano eterogeneo 15890 15890
— a griglia 8476
— a maglie 12248, 11519
— a malta 12134
— a occhio di bue 2559
— a pettine 4051
— a scacchiera 3411
— a setaccio 16301
— a tegole 15147
— a ventaglio 6805
— amigdaloide 544
— allotriomorfa 390
— alveolare 11940
— aplitica 12887
— argillosa 781
— blastoporfirica 1752
— botroidale 2130
— brecciata 7422
— brecciata primitiva S. 14050
— cataclastica 3082, 4767, 13921
— clastica 7708
— colonnare 4048, 17915
— compatta 11359
— concoidale 4173
— cristallina 4804
— cristalloblastica 4815
— cumulofirica 4833
— del cuore 4451
— del minerale di ferro 17895
— del nucleo 4451
— delle fibre 6981
— delle leghe 402
— dendritica 740

struttura di colata 3026
— di rocce 17765
— di rottura 7703
— di sostegno in acciaio per per pareti-cortina 17476
— di Widmannstätten 20062
— diapirica 5340
— divergente 5581
— drusica 6021
— eutettica 6604
— felsofirica 11635
— fibroblastica 6983
— fibrosa 6993
— filamentosa 6983, 13141
— fine 7091
— filtrante 19911
— fluidale 7436, 7468, 13906
— fogliacea 16140
— globulare 8304
— glomeroblastica 8306
— granitica 8420, 8424
— granitoide 8424
— granoblastica 8425, 8444
— granofirica 8428
— granolitica 8442
— granulare 8403, 8420
— granulosa 4756
— in acciaio 17520
— ialopilitica 9500
— in forma di strisce 1187
— in legno 4635
— intercalare 9866
— intersertale 9914
— interna 9906
— lamellare 10502, 11627, 16598
— lastriforme 1199
— lenticolare 1371
— lepidoblastica 10684
— macromeritica 11152
— maculata 11158
— marezzata 11957, 17768
— massiccia 11359
— metallica 11544
— miarolitica 11619
— micrografica 11639
— microgranitica 11636
— micropeecilitica 11649
— microporfirica 11781
— milonitica 12149
— molecolare 11873
— monzonitica 11925
— nastriforme 14869
— nematoblastica 12217

struttura nervata S. 14869
— occhiadina 6712
— ocellare 12447
— ofitica 12617
— omeoblastica 9297
— ondulata 15173
— oolitica 12552
— orbiculare 12620
— ortofirica 12681
— panidiomorfa 12889
— pegmatoide 8446
— pelitica 13053
— perialina 13086
— periclinale 13088, 14255
— petrosilicea 6909, 11629, 11635
— pieghettata 1947
— pilotaxitica 13301
— poecilitica 13608
— porfiroblastica 13682
— porosa 9130, 13571, 13678
— prismatica 4048
— profonda 2593
— protoclastica 14050
— psammitica 14064, 769
— psefitica 14065, 14067, 15332
— ptigmatica 14089
— radiale 14338, 17531
— resistente 18800
— reticolare 10391/a, 10581, 12248
— scagliosa 15633
— scistosa 16578, 7533
— semi-idiomorfa 9584
— sferoidale 1164, S. 12620
— sferolitica 17075
— simplettica 18152
— spaziale unistrut 19308
— spugnosa 17145
— stratificata 1427
— taxitica 18340
— trachitica 18808
— variolitica 19475
— vescicolare 19540
— vitrofirica 19583
— zonale 15930/a, 20361
strutture senza armatura 18966
struverite 17900
struvite 17901
studio chimico del ferro 3400
stufa 17695, 6055

stufa a aria calda Cowper 4575
— a galleria S. 19112
— a perdite dielettriche (ad alta frequenza) S. 5384
— a raggi infrarossi 9772
— a tunnel 19112
— con ricircolazione d'aria 17699
— continua 4275
— d'essiccazione 6061, 6693
— per anime 4409, 4448
— per fondere 11466
— portatile 13693
— v. forno
sturare il foro di colata 13242
stutzite 17913
styllite 17914
sublimare 17923
sublimato corrosivo 11499
sublimazione 17924
sub-raffreddamento 17936
substrato 2142, 16868
successione di strati concordanti o paralleli S. 4204
succhiello ad elica 15791
succhierola 3681, 17953, 17206, 17736, 16788
— a fili intrecciata 20151
succinite 17937
suddividere in faglie 1801
suddivisione del regolo del cavaliere 12402
sughero di montagna 12030/a
sulfoborite 17978
sulfohalite 17980
sulfuro di mercurio 11501
sulvanite 17990
suola 2142, 2145, 7402, 8951, 8959, 11110, 16868, 16869, 16870, 16871, 18701
— accessibile 42
— acida 78
— aperta 12573
— che si gonfia 9023
— con congegno da tornire conico 7023
— del crogiuolo 8953
— della rotaia 7544, 7538
— di base 8620

suola di lavoro 8952
— di scorie 16524
— di un filone 7409
— in terra 15484/a
— intermedia 2649
— oscillante 14493
— raffreddata 19760
— v. muro
suolo 11070
— arabile 728
— argilloso 8665
— calcareo 13037
— inerte 17932
— marnoso 11338
— paludoso 1951
— silicioso 7382
— vergine 12259
suono metallico (di) 11573
supercarburante 13852
superficie 2911/a, 18040, 19293
— a vaiolatura 13426
— ad angoli vivi 6208
— appannata 6088
— arrotondata 15280
— bombata 4884
— curva 4884
— d'appoggio 1401
— d'irrigazione 10043
— del focolare 8966
— del suolo 6625
— della carica 17622
— della griglia 8466
— della suola 8976
— di base 1288
— di carreggiamento o di scorrimento 12781
— di contatto 12853
— di contropressione 765
— di divisione 5586
— di drenaggio 5744
— di preparazione 12994
— di raffreddamento 4343
— di rivoluzione 15194
— di rottura 7695
— di scorrimento 12781, 12880, 16662, 16664
— di slittamento 16603, 16608
— di solubilità 18058
— drenata 5190
— irregolare 8101/a
— levigata 13630
— levigata pulita 3677
— libera 7722

superficie lucidata 13630
— ondulata 4503, 14940, 19716, 19839/a
— piana 9347
— ruvida 6208
— scabra 9483
— totale della griglia 18788
supertrattamento al legno fresco 12772, 12773
supporto 7710/a, 17332, 18034, 18878
— ad aria compressa 296
— a rulli 15106
— a scorrimento 13441
— con un gambo a due lamiere 5664
— con due gambe 4108
— dei rulli 2239
— del bilanciere 1398
— del filtro 7822
— del quadro 17409
— del rampino 10765
— della caldaia 2247
— della colonna perduta 10845
— della piattaforma di caricamento 13507
— della sagoma 796
— di alesatrice 15408/a
— di porcellana dell'essiccatore 5233
— di laminatoio 9461
— mal saldato 19297
— mal incorporato S. 19297
— metallico 17513
— pensile 8802
— per anime 3295, 13329/a, 17903/a
— per anime brevettato 12968
— per crogiuolo 17654
— per essiccatoio 6064
— per perni 10235
— per storta 7314
— per tubi 13349
— per tubi a cuneo 2959
— sagomato 4280, 10120/a, 17192/a
— v. mensola o sostegno
surriscaldamento 18005
— della ghisa 12760
surriscaldatore 18007
— di vapore 17449
svabite 18084

svanbergite 18085
sviluppare 5272
sviluppo 5275
— d'idrogeno 7612
— d'ossigeno 6628
— della superficie 18049
— della tessitura 5277
— di calore 6627
— di grosso 15245
— in profondità 2413
— regressivo 10288
svitare (tubi) 2301, 1068
— in pozzo 1043
svitatore 12841
svolgimento 19674
svuotare 5489
— le anime 6971
svuotato 5745
szaibelite 18182
szmikite 18183
szomolnokite 18184

T

tabella 1918
— cronologica 8173
— dei pesi atomici 18190
— di messa a fuoco 16986
— di peso 19908
— normale 17349
tabulare 18194
tacca 1204, 10117, 10321, 12264, 12394, 16021, 16686
tacche 6813, 11081
tacchette della gabbia 3092, 6813, 10526
tachilite 18198
taccone a coda di topo 14443
— falso 15485
tacheometro 11744
taglia fissa 4729
— mobile 9230, 1795, 18860
tagliacavi 15165
tagliacolate 8092
— a disco 4928
tagliafuoco 7253
tagliare 3283, 4891, 4893, 10111, 10374, 16018,
— a misura 5834; 16019
— al di sotto 1791, 10320

tagliare barre di ferro 2658
— il carbone 2297
— il getto 4895
— il muro 10737
— la colata 4895
— la pietra 15570, 15572
— una filettatura 15698
— una filettatura esterna 4894
— una pietra 16964
— via 4892
tagliato 9254
— in sbieco 1572
tagliatore 4906
— di carbone 17660
— di lima 7004
tagliatrice a barra 793
— a picconi 14184
— ad arco 744
— di carbone 3860
— di carbone a barra 1212
— di carbone a catena 3239
— di carbone a disco 5483
— di galleria 8936
— di lingotti 9799
— orizzontale di carbone 9982, 10032
— per grandi fonti 10990
tagliatubi 2937, 5898, 13334, 19050, 18978
tagliente 4918, 16001
— a corona 16442
— a croce 4673
— a vite 5250
— a Z 20314
— di fioretto 10862
— doppio 5643
— regolabile 10092
taglierina 16675
taglio 1204, 1919, 2449, 3285, 4660/a, 4899, 4913, 6738, 10112, 10373, 10375, 16020
— a gradino con ripiena 9337, 7018
— al di sotto 8205
— con arco 743
— con franamento a blocchi 1812
— con ripiena 3776
— corto 3756
— del carbone 3812
— della carota 16032
— della colata 17212/a
— della filettatura 4923

taglio della pietra 12289
— dei bordi 16271/a
— delle lamiere in pacchetto 11275/a
— di pietre 1928
— di soffiatore 10312/a
— di sotto 4917
— filtrante 7823
— in direzione 12715
— in rimonta 14373
— inclinato 14909
— inferiore 2152, 4917, 9115
— iniziale 17997
— intermedio 11667/a
— longitudinale 16672/a
— orizzontale 10113. 10321
— orizzontale del carbone 9115
— orizzontale sotto il filone 2128
— rinforzato 17908, 18031
— rinforzato senza ripiena 12596
— trasversale 4677
— unico 16405
tagliolo 3485
— a freddo, 3970
— con codolo 8870/a
taimyrite 18216
tallingite 18223
tallio 18475
tallone di reazione 5366
tamanite 18226
tamaraite 18227
tamburo 16422
— a cavo 2662
— a corda 2662
— a getto di sabbia 15521
— d'amalgamazione 492
— d'avvolgimento 15162, 20101
— d'essiccazione 6058
— d'estrazione 9226, 15168
— del cavo 20102
— dell'argano 1242, 9226, 12292
— di guarnizione 12847
— di lavaggio finitore 7127
— di manovra 2561, 2740
— di perforazione a corda 2560, 2560
— di trivellazione 2571
— di vagliatura 15695
— filtrante 7046

tamburo lavatore 6016
— magnetico 11191
— orizzontale 9341
— per finire il lavaggio 7127
— per l'amalgama 481
— per lavaggio minerali 14936
— per lavaggio rotativo 14845
— per primo lavaggio 13850
— per togliere la sabbia 3703
— pulitore 14446
— scanalato 8590
tamponatura 1057, 2135, 7035, 13566
tamponare 12068
tampone 1934, 13559, 17680
— con gli elettrodi nel microlog 12857, 15311
— d'avanzamento 2180
— di colata 2134
— fusibile 7889/a
— -guida della scarpa 16154
tangeite 18237
tantalio 18260
tantalite 18259
tapalpite 18271
tappamento localizzato del foro per franamento 2389
tappare il forno 13558
— le aperture 3754
— le soffiature 7014
tappo 13556, 17680, 17684
— ad alta pressione 2553
— d'argilla 2133
— d'argilla refrattaria 7162
— d'estrazione 10774
— del carotiere 4433
— della valvola 19450
— di cementazione 3176
— di colata 2133, 2134
— di gomma 15314
— di riempimento 7024
— di scarico 12704
tara 18323
tarapacaite 18325
tarare 18322
taratura 2742, 16445/a
tarbuttite 18326

tariffa speciale 17022
tarnowitzite 18329
tasca 13604
tasmanite 18333
tassello 11006
— estraibile a mano S.14704 14704
tastare 6896
— il terreno S.16935
tasto 6897
taurite 18334
tavistockite 18336
tavola 1918
— a rulli 10775
— a scosse 4165, 15974, 19463
— con rulli d'entrata 15361a
— con rulli di uscita 15361
— d'amalgamazione 497
— del cilindro 1940
— della sonda a rotazione 15221
— delle passate 12858/a, 15129/a
— di cernita girevole 14839
— di lavaggio 19710
— di protezione 1095
— di rivestimento 10458, 10490
— di sbavatura 3697
— di sostegno 10105
— di tela 1693
— girevole 19151
— per la separazione pneumatica 13599
— per la soletta 16492
— per modelli 17323
— tonda 15274
tavolame 1918
tavolatite 18337
tavolato 1924
— di tubazione del pozzo S. 16040
tavole (in) 13534
tavoletta 12025
tavolo a scosse 2576
— per laboratorio elettrochimico 6323
— da laboratorio 10450
tavolone S.1066, 10575, 16075, 17083
tavolozzo 17323, 12881
— portamodello 8113

tawite 18338
taxite 18339
taylorite 18341
tazza S. 15463, 15639,
  S. 17152
— del trasportatore 4318
— di escavatrice meccanica
  5449
tazzina S. 8784
teallite 18343
tecnezio 18349
tecnica di coltivazione dei
  giacimenti 14747
— di fonderia 7675
— elettrochimica 6325
tectomorfico 18351,
tela a smeriglio 6412
— d'areazione 4870
— di ventilazione 4870,
  5994
— metallica 8120, 20136
telaio 897
— del laminatoio 9465
— del vagone 2898
— della sega 15559
— di cantina in acciaio
  17464
— superiore di riempimento
  7034
— di sformatura 4391
— per centrare le staffe
  3216
— v. staffa, cassa o incastellatura
tefrite 18421
tefroite 18422
teleclinometro elettromagnetico 6370
teleferica 192, S. 2660
telluride d'oro 8350
tellurio 18367
tellurite 18366
tellurifero 18368
telo di ventilazione 4979
tempera v. tempra
temperabilità 8850
temperamento 18378
temperare v. temprare
temperatura 8971, 18379
— alla bocca del forno 6564,
  6564, 18581
— brillante 2398
— critica 4650
— d'affinazione 14613/a
— della reazione 18388

temperatura di autoaccen-
  sione 967
— di brillanza 714
— di cementazione 2922
— di colata 3027
— di colore 713
— di dissociazione 5544
— di distensione 14691
— di forgiatura 7598
— di fusione 11480
— di radiazione 715
— di rammollimento 16849/
  16849/a
— di ricottura 18398
— di riduzione 14578
— di riduzione in coke
  18386
— di spegnimento 14293
— di splendore S.714
— di torrefazione 14994
— esterna 18068
— ideale per fucinare
  7595/a
— interna 9907
— nell'altoforno 18383
— pericolosa 4992
temiskamite 18369
tempo di perforazione 14902
— di permanenza 9247
— di presa 18516
— di resistenza 2310
— di riscaldamento 9018
— di riscaldamento al nu-
  cleo 7809
— di riposo 14782/a
— di rotazione 18639
— di scintillio 7307
— perduto 10407
temporizzatore di sequenza
  15887
tempra 8857, 14283, 14289
— a cartoccio 2918
— ad induzione 9750
— al getto di acqua 17771
— al nucleo 19303, 7803
— al piombo 10608,
  10620/a
— all'acido carbonico 2857
— all'aria 252, 285, 15823/
  15823/a
— all'olio S. 12494
— alla fiamma 7259
— brillante 3678
— calda 9423/a
— col cannello 7259

tempra completa 7803
— delle estremità 6453/a
— di ricottura 18396
— differenziale 17289
— difficile 5398
— dolce 16845
— dura 7802
— extradolce 5038
— finale 7067
— in acqua 19781
— in bagno di piombo 10608
— in bagno di sale 15443
— in crogiuolo chiuso 3755
— in due tempi 11341
— in olio 12494
— interrotta 9912, 17552,
  18639/a
— inversa 9932
— invertita 9932
— isotermica 1111, 10080,
  17552
— martensitica 11347
— naturale 12195
— negativa 12214, 9934/a
— parziale 15808
— per gradi 17550
— per immersione 9644
— per nitrurazione 8861
— per precipitazione
  13815
— perfetta 8278
— primaria parziale a transizione trotata 11955
— primaria parziale normale
  3439
— primaria parziale senza
  transizione 3440
— semplice 16371
— speciale 17014
— superficiale 2606, 18054
— totale 4112
— v. indurimento
temprare 8846
— al color rosso nell'acqua
  14280
— alla superficie 18053
— i bordi 2069
— in acqua 19780
— in un bagno di piombo
  10615
— l'acciaio 8848
— l'acciaio in acqua 14282
— nell'acqua 14281
— un metallo 8847
temprato 8851

tenacità 18403, 18801
tenaglie 12301, 18719
— da fucinatura 7599/a
— occhiellatrici 9278
— per billette 8414
— per fucinare 13699
— per lingotti 9792, 9802
— per tappi di sughero 4470
— per tubi 2964
tenaglione 10757
tenditore 5281, 8690, 17586, 17795
— a catena 10909
— tubolare 19092
tenero 9714
tennantite 18406
tenone 13432
— del trapano 1628
tenore 4251
— garantito 8639
— in acqua 19758
— in carbonio 2829
— in carbonio fisso 2840
— in cenere 864, 13075
— in ferro 4254
— in gas 4253
— in minerale minuto 4252
— in scisto 4255
— v. contenuto
tenorite 18407
tensione v. sforzo
tensione 9861, 17783, 18414
— al luogo di consumo 19594
— capillare 2809
— della vasca 18255/a
— di colata 3072
— di decomposizione 5071
— di formazione 7614/a
— di rottura 2330
— di servizio 15901/a
— di torsione 9862
— elettrolitica della soluzione 6350
— interna 9905
— magnetomotrice 11210
— superficiale 18003
— tangenziale 18242
tenuta 18620
— d'aria (a) 329
— idraulica 19998
teoria della dissociazione 5545
terbio 18423

termierite 18425
terminale 18426
terminare 4111, 5355, 7718
— a punta 18275
termine di scarico 13094
termite normale 13448/a
termoconvettore a soffitto 3130
termodiffusione 16795/a
termofillite 18496
termometria 18385
termonatrite 18495
termostato 14240
terra 10518, S.15469
— a diatomei 5345
— a secco 15497
— alluminosa 439
— argillosa 10924
— bruciata 2614
— cotta 18432
— d'infusori 8661
— da modelli 6758, 6760
— da pipa 13331
— di chamotte 3280
— di fonderia 5435
— di riempimento 1088, 7026
— essiccata 6039
— fine 6758
— forte S. 17878
— gialla S. 20285
— grassa 6826/a, 10933, 17878
— magra 10644
— mista a nero di fonderia 16633
— mobile 9467
— naturale 12196
— nera 12063
— nuova 12258
— per anima 4440
— per formatura 12012
— per formatura a grana grossa 7026
— per tappare 11373
— refrattaria 7183, 15708
— rigenerata 14505
— sintetica 18171
— torbosa 13028
— unica 19312
— vegetale 11969
— v. sabbia
terracotta 1113
terrazza 17294
— d'accumulo 5868

terrazza litorale 14376
terrazzamento 8386
terrazziere 6637, 8615
terrazzo 18431
— alluviale 409
— fluviale 7396, 14968
— roccioso 15032
terlinguaite 18424
terreno 10518
— di copertura 2796, 2798, 12735
— di fondazione poco sicuro 19328
— di ricopertura 8814
— dislocato 6865
— fagliato 1803, 6865
— ghiaioso 8481
— impantanato di fango 11791
— in pendio 4824
— loessiano 10962
— naturale 16854
— paludoso 11344,
— palustre 11344
— roccioso 15007, 15045
— superficiale 8464
terriccio 8941
terroso 3748
terziario 18435
tesa 6828
teschemacherite 18437
teschenite 18438
tessulario 4821
tessuto 19873
— d'amianto 843
— metallico 11545, 20129
testa 4725, 8904
— a croce 4692
— d'attacco 4919
— d'eruzione 7425
— d'iniezione 3582, 19817,
— d'iniezione della sonda a rotazione 15219
— del bilanciere di pompaggio 9379
— del forno 6448
— del lingotto 9791
— del martello 8905
— della cassetta 8916
— della gabbia 18743
— di carotiere 4911
— di cavallo 14244/a
— di cementazione 3174
— di cementazione contenente tappi 13562

testa di chiodo 14972
— di faglia 6859
— di sonda 18138
— di tubaggio 2249, 19051
— di tubaggio con premi-
  stoppa 2948
— di tubazione 2794, 5955
— ermetica dei tubi 2943
— flottante 7390
— nera 3412
— per trivelle 2102
testata frontale 7776
testimonio 6814, 12706
— del raccordo 9889
— di carreggiamento 12175
— di fucinatura 7309
tetradimite 1618, 18468
tetraedrite 6764, 12892
tetraedro 18472
tetrossido di piombo
  12618/a
tetti inclinati con capriate
  in acciaio 16683
tetto 8806, 8808, 8813,
  12768, 15144
— buono 8360
— di galleria 1067
— di miniera 1046
— franato 16118
— galleggiante 7392
— protettore della gabbia
  d'estrazione 2033
tettoia per formatura 12006
tettoie 14041
tettonico 18352
texasite 20316
thalenite 18474
thaumasite 18476
thenardite 18478
theodolite 18479
tholeiite 18354
thomsenolite 18541
thomsonite 18542
thorianite 18543
thorite 18544
thorotungstite 18548
thortveitite 18549
thucolite 18605
tiemannite 18613
tilaite 18621
tilasite 18622
tillite 18623
timazite 18633
timpano 19201

tingere in nero 12862
tino 17275/a
— a camicia libera 9733
— accessibile 43
— basso 11058/a
— blindato 9994
— del forno 7854
— di un altoforno 15951
— libero 9733
— non isolato 7736
tintura di iodio 9941
— definitiva 13104
— di base 7198
— di tornasole 10893
— stabile 13104
tipo 16924
— di casing senza manicotto 6715
— di connessore a stacco
  immediato 14300
— di forno per minerale di
  mercurio 10030
tiraggio 265, 5722
— d'aria 19510
— del camino 3458
— forzato 7554
— naturale 12190
tirante 4669, 4700, 10215,
  17794, 18610
— d'estrazione 7906/a,
  10758
— sospeso del tubo d'en-
  trata 18029
tirare 5727, 5754, 14123,
  17104
— in fili 5763
— l'acciaio in barre 5771
— l'aria 19496
— un'anima 4445
— via 14124
tirata d'aria 13658/a,
  14952, 19498
— forzata 7554
tiro 17106
— al limite di portata del-
  l'impianto 6716
— ausiliare 17250
— con camera d'espansio-
  ne 4888
— della colonna in pozzo
  13205
— di sfondamento 16792
— laterale 16258
tirolite 19206

titanite 17054
titanomorfite 18695
titanio 18690
titanite 18689
titanomagnetite 18694
titolare 18697
titolazione 18698
titolo 4251, 18696
— fittizio 6531
— d'umidità 17444
— d'un liquido 17354
tixotropia 18533
tobernite 18767
toddite 18700
toellite 18705
togliere dal magazzino
  18220
— i ganci 7719
— i tubi 14123
— il colame 5130
— il vento S. 19135
— la ripiena 19325
— la sbavatura 14718
— le graffe 7719
— le incrostazioni 15580
— le scaglie 15579
tolleranza 13536, 18709
— di peso 19905
— dimensionale 5423
toluene 18710
tombino 2219
tombolo 18711
tonalite 18712
tondi in rotoli 15295
— per cemento armato
  15272
— scanalati 4493
tondini di ferro S. 15054
tondino 15270
tondo 15269, 15271
tonnellaggio 18722
topazio 18754
topazolite 18755
torba 11984, 13023
— bituminosa 1635
— compressa 13880
— dragata 5824
— grassa 1635
— terrosa 13028
torbenite 4366
torbida 12649
torbidimetro 19116/a
torbiera 1943, 11944,
  13024, 13029

torbiera bassa 11053
— di pianura 7326
— di valle 19443
— emersa 6409
— sommersa 9642
torcere 19179
torchio di colata 3621
— per sodio 16824
torcia tubolare leggera 10790
    10790
tordrillite 18770
torendrichite 18771
torio 18546
tormalina 18804
— a grana fine 1909
— aerea 10023
tornebohmite 18772
tornello per fune di tornello
    veloce 15502
— veloce 15515
tornio 19145
— a carrello 16612
— a motore 6469
— a pedale 7543
— a punte 3197
— a rabescare 15179
— a revolver 4062, 19153
— a velocità variabile
    10579
— automatico 962, 985
— meccanico a torretta
    4062
— orizzontale 2098
— parallelo per filettare
    10578
— per anime 4419
— per cilindri di laminatoio
    15080
— per copiare 4377
— per metalli 11564
— per spogliare 1086
— per sagomare S.4377
— per troncare 4920
— per tubi e barre 1209
— per sgrossatura 15259
— troncabarré 4920
— verticale 2097
tornire 14836, 19130
— piano 6759
— dei cilindri 15090
tornito 19140
tornitura 19143/a
— di rame 4365
— in lastre 9443
torpedinamento 16164

torre a riempimento 12840
— ad antenna 2790
— azeotropica 1030
— d'attesa 7301
— d'estrazione 6707, 14295
— d'evaporazione 6622
— di distillazione 5522
— di frazionamento 2492,
    7691
— di frazionamento a due
    uscite 17134
— di frazionamento secon-
    daria 201
— di lavaggio 15721
— di perforazione 5214
— di perforazione petrolife-
    ra 12487
— di precipitazione 13811
— di refrigerazione 4344
— di rettifica 17861, 1787
— di rivestimento 5993
— di sgocciolamento 5746
— di trivellazione 2111,
    2104, 5214
— ribaltabile di perforazio-
    ne 5930
— v. colonna
torrente fangoso 3983
torrefazione a morte 5036,
— all'aria 17303
— ben riuscita 14020
— difettosa 5111
— in mucchi 8944
— ossidante 12811
— per eliminazione dello
    zolfo 17975, 17977
torsiometro a vuoto 19437
torsione 18779
— per urto 18777/a
toscanite 18784
trabocco della colata 7432a
    15358/a, 17735/a
tracce a V 4723/a
— di gas 8056
— di mandrino 13562/a
traccia 18805/a
— di bavatura 7309
— di cilindro 15081/a
— di guida 8651
— di limatura 7038
— di vibrazione 3358/a,
    10135/a
tracciamento 5959, 7199
tracciaparallele 18052
tracciare 11328

tracciare i profili 5230
tracciato 5274, 5790, 13552,
    18809, S. 20204
— dei canali 5231
— per chiodi 12162
— per piastre 3250
— per rotaie 14361
— per traverse 16587
— per travi 8242
tracciatore 18052
— a mano 11333
tracciatrice 16030
tracciatura 11334, 20051
trachiandesite 18806
trachidolerite 18807
trachite 18805, 11840
tracimatore S. 7432
trafila 5373, 5794, 5779,
    20122, 20152/a
— a cuscinetti 17617
— multipla 20231
— per nastri 7353
trafilabilità 5787
trafilare 5763
— a caldo 9410
— a freddo 3957, 3988
— bianco 2396
— tubi 5772
trafilato 5814
— bianco 2394
— da massello 16880
trafilatore 20142
trafilatrice 5779
trafilatura 5791
— a caldo 9411
— a freddo 3973
— a secco 16799
— a umido 19989
— brillante 6031/a
— del filo 5803
— di fili 20123
— di tubi 18979
trafileria 5801, 20150
— a freddo 3974
— per fili 20125
traforatrice 7760
traforo di sonda 8602
trainare 5727
traliccio a torsione semplic
    17252
— a torsione tripla 9125
— di travi 18037
— metallico 9976
tramezzo 12953, 15867
— di tavole 13463

tramoggia 9328, 7820
— a carbone 3804
— d'alimentazione 6879
— di caricamento 6892,
  3334, 10918
— di caricamento degli
  skips 16483
— di caricamento per altoforno 7859
— di frantoio 4773
— mescolatrice 11830
— nella roccia 11694
— oscillante 6098
— per carbone 2579, 3836
— per carbone minuto 16510
— per ceneri 866
— per minerali 12631
— rotante 14836/a, 15231a
— separatrice 15864
trancia 4905, 4916, 10238,
  16030, 16031, 16596
— inclinata 14911
— per dorare 8346
tranciare 4891, 16018
tranciatrice 4905
tranciatura 1695/a, 14182,
  18899
transizione continua 4277
transuranco 18840
trapanare 5874
— di fianco 5876
— di sopra 5875
— per lungo 5877
— v. trivellare, perforare,
  sondare
trapanatrice 1486
— portatile elettrica 13780
— radiale 14326
— verticale 19524
trapanazione 18877
trapano 2078, 8373
— a alette 6165
— a coda di carpa 7214
— a colonna 4041, 17796
— a coni di Hughes 9476
— a croce 4702, 17376
— a cricchetto 14435
— a dischi 5482
— a due alette 19193
— a lame 5730
— a petto 2346
— a punta di diamante 5329
— a punta di lancia S. 812
— a quattro taglienti 7682
— a secco 3670

trapano a stadi 17544
— ad archetto 15107
— ad aria compressa 13590
— ad espansione 6671
— al carburo di tungsteno
  19101
— alesatore 14478, 14480
— autocentrante 3196
— da banco 1485
— di Reed 14582
— diritto a gambo rastre-
  mato 18284
— elicoidale a gambo dritto
  17719
— normale 11948
— per sondaggio a percus-
  sione 2092
— piatto 812
— pilota 13298
— retrattile 4013
— scanalato a gambo dritto
  17718
— sensitivo 15857
— sferico a gambo dritto
  15203
— tubolare 19070
— v. scalpello o sonda
trapezoedro 9614
— esagonale 9123
trappola 18847, 18856
trascinamento di liquido
  nel vapore di distilla-
  zione 14121
trasformare in acciaio 104
— in gas 5552
trasformatore della corrente
  per il forno 7860
trasformazione 18825,
— congruente 4201/a
— di transizione 13103
— eutettoide 6605
— in coke S. 3954
— isoterma 10081
— peritettica 13103
trasgressione concordante
  48
traslazione 18831/a
trasmissione 5960
— a catena 3242
— a funi 15160
— di forza 13798
— idraulica 7462
— meccanica 8131
— rigida 15060
trasparenza 18838

trasportatore 4317, 8896,
  15369, 18818
— a catena 3247
— a catena dei detriti
  15169
— a gravità 8485
— a nastro 1473, 2660
— a nastro mobile 11844
— a nastro per carbone
  1474
— a nastro snodato 722
— a piastre 13489, 16573
— a placche 13489
— a raschiatoio 14197
— a rastrelli 7375, 15670
— a rulli 15108
— a scosse 2575, 1323,
  19553
— a tazze 2500
— a vite 15704
— aereo 12757
— di sacchi a nastro 15405
— per getti di fonderia
  13226
— per minerali 5780
— pneumatico 13602
— vibrante 19552
trasportatrice 10911
— a colla 15704
— a nastro 1176
trasporto 18819, 18835
— a mano 8771, 8789
— a nastro 1472
— alla bocca 4315
— con ruspa 16721
— dei lingotti 9787
— dei materiali 8795
— del carbone 18028
— del carbone con cavalli
  7354
— della cenere 14710
— di carbone 3832
— di carbone a coclea
  18026
— fluviale 14969
— in massa 18837
— per terra 12763
trasudamento 4481, 16093/a,
  16202, 17108/a
— della ghisa 14960
— dello stagno 18653/a
trattamento 18868, 20203
— a bassa temperatura S.
  17935
— a mezzo soffiaggio al
  convertitore 1788

trattamento acido dei pozzi
S. 100
— al legno verde 13622
— al tamburo 13217/a
— allo zingato 20340/a
— austenitico 955
— con ipoclorito 9594
— del materiale 11374
— dei minerali 12661, 16747
16747
— di omogenizzazione
9299
— isotermico 954
— limite 18884
— magnetico 11190
— magnetico dei minerali
11189
— meccanico del carbone
3816
— meccanico dei minerali
12642
— metallurgico 11589
— per via umida 19990
— posteriore 17930
— sotto zero 17935
— superficiale 18004, 18070
— termico 9000
— termico in atmosfera
controllata 9002
— termico ripetuto 14801/a
— v. procedimento o processo
trattare al forno 1112
— con fondente 7496
— con galvanostegia 6365
— elettroliticamente 6365
— i minerali 16745
— la ghisa col procedimento
Bessemer 1560
— meccanicamente i mine-
rali 5833
tratto a scintilla 16980
— di nastro distributore
5501
travasare 5050
travate 1380
trave 16335, 16586
— a curvatura circolare
3602
— a mensola 2789
— ad arco 756
— d'acciaio 17457
— del profilo Gray S. 5392
— di collegamento 4700
— di rampa di acciaio 17511

trave di rinforzo 17588
— di sostegno 29
— inglese 6482
— lunga 2042
— portante 1386, 1391
— reticolare 18963
— stirata 17791
— trasversale 4670
— tubolare 19061
traversa 2237, 2584, 4664,
4668, 4691, 4692, 4693,
4706, 9824, 16586,
16954, 18607
— d'ancoraggio 2211
— della griglia portasbarre
7148
— di bloccaggio 3627
— di ferro 10015
— di rinforzo da chiudere
12995
— di staffa 2223
— metallica 10015
— non regolabile 10763
— pressata 13881
— regolabile 10764
— superiore ribaltabile
13887
— tubolare di controventa-
tura 19068
traversobanco 1385, 4665,
4712, 4716
travertino 2701, 2708, 7758,
18865
travetto 10215, 15349,
16586
— inclinato 14346
— orizzontale di sostegno
8245
travicello 10215
trazione 14125, 14136
— a fune senza fine 6458
treccia in lana di legno
20180
trefolo 20147, 20164
tremolite 18871
treno a duo 19173
— a trio 18558
— blooming 1832, 3913
— di laminatoio 11702,
15128, 15131
— di laminatoio universale
19315
— di laminazione 11688
— di perforazione 5901
— di ruote 15998

treno di vagoncini 18907
— finitore 7131, 7138
— per fili metallici 20134
— per lamiere 16074, 16078
— per lamiere a trio 18561
— per lamiere sottili 18527
— per nastri 9325
— per ruote 20010
— preparatore 9893, 12060
— rapido 9177
— rifinitore dei bordi 6212
— sbozzatore 3913, 1578,
15260, 15261
— semicontinuo 15840
— universale 19317
treppiede 17332, 18917
— della sonda 2109
triangolo di filo metallico
20148
— per crogiuoli 4749
Trias medio 12137
tridimite 18892
trifilite 18911
trigonite 18894
trimerio 18895
trimerite 18896
trincarino 17837
trincea 12395, 18873
— a cielo aperto 12588
— allagata 11843
triplice chiusura 18869
triplite 18915
triploidite 18916
tripoli 9775, 10348
tripphyite 18919
trippkeite 18918
triptano 18920
trisolfuro d'arsenico 816
tritomite 18921
tritoprisma S. 13860
triturare S. 17306
— il minerale 4761
trituratore di ghisa 3004
— di minerali a comando
meccanico 11419
triturazione 2325, 4775
— fine 7085, 367
— grossa 3870, 3875
— v. macinazione o frantumazione
trivella 2091, 5881, 5883,
8608, 13569, 18876
— a corona 588
— a corona di graniglia
5737

trivella a croce 4661
— a cucchiaio 947, 8373
— a imbuto 18292
— a mano 8754
— a percussione 2663
— a sacco 15104
— a spirale 5684
— a tranciante 3486
— a tubo 4393, 4405
— a valvola 15821, 19447
— cava 2210, 16096
— d'avanzamento 5872
— d'avviamento 17380
— da suolo a larghe spire 6167
— di pulizia 12073
— elicoidale 3797, 17097
— mobile 11847
— per carbone 2827
— per pietre 17643
— per rocce 15009
— per terreni argillosi 3654
— pneumatica a colonna 13583
trivellare il terreno S. 16936
— il muro 16410
— v. trapanare o sondare
trivellatore 2091, 5895, 5906
trivellatura v. trivellazione o perforazione
trivellazione 2076, 5916, 16416
— a gas 8065
— a iniezione 9517
— a secco 6027
— deviata 16279
— di pozzi 5931
— di pozzi per cementazioni 8628
— per carotaggio 4406
— profonda 5090
— simultanea 16375
— sotto pressione 13903
— v. perforazione o sondaggio
troctolite 18925
trogerite 18926
trogolo 5513
— di lavaggio 2513
— di sedimentazione 7384a, 18985/a
trolleite 18927

trona 19402
troncare 4891, 18955
troncatrice 4905, 15866
troncatura 18957
— delle colate 17215
tronco 17614
— di cono 18956
— di prisma 13961
troostite 8839, 18931
trucioli 2113
— di rame 4365
— di trapanatura 5947
— di zinco 20325
— metallici 3482
truciolo 3474
trudellite 18950
truogolo 18586, 12885, 17741
— glaciale 8260
truscottite 18962
tschęffkinite 18967
tschermigite 18968
tsingtauite 18969
tubaggio 2932, 16089, 18974
— a incastro 9835
— combinato 4061
— discendente 5993
— in muratura 17652
— libero 7738
tubare 15343, 18972
tubatura 13355
— esterna dell'ugello 19166
tubazione 13380
— a diametro costante 17713
— combinata 4061
— del gas 8037
— dell'acqua di alimentazione 19771
— di captazione 8100
— di ventilazione 19504
— v. condotta
tubetto di fusione 11481
— di vetro 8285
tubiera 19159
— conica 4212
— doppia 19176
— raffreddata 4329
— v. ugello
tubierina per la scoria 16562
«tubing» deformato a cava-

turaccioli 4473
tubo a bicchiere 16808
— a alętte 7143
— a bicchiere 18524
— a bulbo 2546
— a due braccia 18175
— a fenditura 16689
— a flangia 7269
— a getto 12410
— a ginocchiera 18129
— a manicotto 4021, 13367
— a parete piena 1684
— a parete spessa 18504
— a pareti distinte 19044
— a raccordo 16808
— a taglio d'ossigeno 12819 12819
— a U per cloruro di caloio 2724
— alettato di riscaldamento 7144
— allargato e ricalcato alle estremità 19072
— biforcato 1577
— bimetallico 1588, 6114/a
— bollitore e scaldatore per caldaie a tubi di fumo 9005
— capillare d'ammissione del gas 8019
— carotiere 4389, 16407
— carotiere con anello strappacarote 1315
— carotiere doppio 5683
— catramato 18327
— centrale 3192
— centrifugato 3206
— chiodato 17698
— colato in sabbia 15488
— collettore generale 4093
— compensatore 4110
— composto 4123/a
— con estremità smussate 13370
— con giunti a flange mobili 13371
— con perle 8270
— con vite a manicotto 18555
— condensatore 4182, 4187
— conduttore 4193
— d'acciaio senza saldatura 15796
— d'ancoraggio 557

tubo d'aspirazione 17943,
    17957
— d'assorbimento 25
— d'entrata nell'acqua
    19785
— d'essiccazione 6065
— d'uscita dell'acqua
    19793
— da fondere rulli S.
    15-114
— da fumo 16765
— da fumo per locomotive
    10949
— del pescatore tagliato
    3407
— dello sfioratore 12743
— di bronzo 2457
— di circolazione 17431
— di coda 18207
— di colata 12412
— di collegamento 6012
— di combustione 4084
— di convogliamento 15355
— di diramazione 2258
— di dispersione 16978
— di respirazione del serba-
    toio 18248
— di distillazione 5554
— di distribuzione 5572
— di ferro 9275
— di freni Westinghouse
    19027
— di gettata 5497
— di gomma 15317
— di gomma alla testa
    15211
— di grosso spessore 9042
— di pergamena 12932
— di pescaggio 9294
— di Pitot 13425
— di piombo 10621
— di pompaggio a rifollatura
    esterna 19377
— di pompaggio normale
    13449
— di porcellana 13668
— di precisione 13825
— di presa 19973
— di presa del gas 12705
— di ritorno 15354, 17087
— di rivestimento 2932
— di scarico 5496, 5705,
    6652, 19767
— di sfiato 18255

tubo di sicurezza 15446
— di sfruttamento 19046
— di troppo pieno 12743,
    19736
— di vetro 8285
— distributore 5575
— divisore per gas 8057
— doppio 5669
— e sbozzato per ponti po-
    steriori 18975
— e serpentino surriscalda-
    tori 18019
— economizzatore 6193
— fenestrato 17119
— fessurato 16690
— fessurato con due punte
    per pescare 9279
— filettato 18556
— filettato del tipo gas
    18293
— -filtro 15688
— fisso 7238
— flessibile di aspirazione
    17956
— flessibile metallico
    7367
— -focolare 7457
— formato col processo ad
    esplosione 19029
— fuso 3030
— gas commerciale 4087
— graduato 8391
— -guida 4196, 18043
— -guaina 19715
— in ghisa 3008
— in lamiera 16062
— inclinato 9703
— liscio cilindrico 13442
— liscio commerciale 13443
— nero in ferro 1650
— normale 17355
— orizzontale 9346
— per acquedotti 13346
— per alberi a camme 2775
— per alberi di trasmissio-
    ne 19025, 19090
— per alberi di trasmissio-
    ne cavi 19092
— per alte pressioni 9168
— per anime di fonderia
    18997
— per assali di carrelli di
    aeroplano
    18983

tubo per assi portaelica
    19011
— per balaustre 19012
— per barre di controllo
    18990
— per camicie di cilindri
    19069
— per cancellate 18999
— per canne da fucile 19016
    19016
— per canne di martelli
    pneumatici 19010
— per cavi 15163
— per cicli e motocicli
    18985
— per circuiti di controllo
    18989
— per condotte 10839
— per condotte di acqua in-
    dustriale 13338
— per condotte forzate
    13341
— per condotte subacque 1902
    19023
— per condutture elettriche
    18994
— per cuscinetti a sfere
    18986
— per distillazione fraziona-
    nata 7689
— per elementi combustibi-
    li 18998
— per elevatori idraulici
    di scale autoportate
    19003
— per filtrare 7059
— per forni da pane 18988
— per gambi di forza 19024
— per gas di città 13345
— per gasdotti 13339
— per generatori di vapore
    19022
— per ghiere 19000
— per impianti antincendio
    18995
— per impianti chimici
    13337
— per impianti di cracking
    18991
— per impianti di distilla-
    zione 18993
— per impianti di «reform-
    ing» 19014
— per rigenerazione 13384

tubo per impianti idrodinamici 19004
— per installazioni termiche 13344
— per irrigazione 19005
— per lo scavo idraulico della sabbia 16996
— per mandrini di macchine utensili 19006
— per manicotti 19020
— per metanodotti 13342
— per mobili 7880
— per palizzate 19007
— per perforazioni 19959
— per pesare 19903
— per ponteggi 19019
— per ponteggi smontabili 18992
— per portavoce e trasmissione d'ordini 19021
— per posta pneumatica 19009
— per protezione di cavi elettrici 6263
— per raffineria 13343
— per ringhiere 18996
— per riscaldamento della nafta 9006
— per rulli per cartiere 19081
— per sbarre di passaggi a livello 18984, 19013
— per scambiatori di calore 13340
— per scarichi pluviali 8688
— per scoria Lürmann 11094
— per serrande 19017, 19018
— per sintesi 18168
— per sondaggi geognostici 19001
— per trasformatori 18828
— per trivellazioni di sfruttamento di giacimenti 18987
— perforato 13081, 13083
— perforatore 5956
— porta-carote 9825
— porta-carote interno 4434
— premente 5154, 14953
— profilato 15780/a,

15995
tubo quadro 17249
— refrattario 16590
— refrigerante 19015
— rettangolare 14519
— rifollato 19375
— sabbiatore 15512
— sagomato per ferramenti 19028
— saldato 19931
— saldato a gas 19932
— saldato a spirale 17102
— saldato ad unghia 10543
— saldato per avvicinamento 2638
— saldato testa a testa 2641
— scanalato 7494/a
— senza saldature 15752, 15753, 19958/a
— snodato per testa d'iniezione
— sospeso 18079
— sottile 11112
— surriscaldatore 18013
— svasato 18954
— tirante 17406
— toroidale 5691
— trafilato 5820
— vaporizzatore 19467, 17431
— verticale 19529
tufo 16430
— basaltico 1270
— calcareo 2729
— d'esplosione 6683
— interstratificato 9916
tungstenite 19105
tungsteno 19100
tunnel 19107
turacciolo 4467
turbina a gas 8058
turbine 6194
turboperforazione 19127
turbo-soffiante 19126
turchese 10278, 19154
turgite 19129
turmalina nera 10162
— rossa 14551
turanite 19115
«turn» molto marcato 5597
turnerite 19143
turno 7951, 16122
— di notte 5599

turno di otto ore 6233
— giornaliero 5019
tusculite 19157
tuta di lavaggio 19715
tychite 19197
tysonite 19207

U

uccidere un pozzo in eruzione 10350
ugello 2630, 7434, 12409, 19159, 19195
— a tubo flessibile 7369
— accoppiato 4548
— autoscorificante 15831
— con correnti (d'aria) verso il basso 5710
— conico 4212
— d'iniezione 9819
— dell'economizzatore 6192
— del getto di sabbia 15474, 15483
— di bronzo 2458
— di pressione 6724
— doppio 4548
— raffreddato 4329
— superiore 18735
uhligite 19210
uintaite 19211
ulexite 19212
ullmannite 19214
ultimato 7119
ultimo canale 10559
umangite 19226
umico 9479
umidificazione della sabbia 15519/a
umidità 11863
— dell'aria 948
umido 4985, 16853
umus 11969
uncinetto da formatore 15650
uncompahgrite 19237
ungaite 19299
unghietta 4679
unificare 7072
unificato 17359
unione 10200
— a martello 8743
unire 2016

unire a tenone 2634
unità di cementazione 3157
— di forno 7861
— idiogene 9618
— singola di pompaggio 9747
untuoso 8505
uralite 19388
uralitizzazione 19389
uranato 19391
uraninite 19392, 13413
uranio 19394
uranocircite 19393
uranofono 19397
uranosferite 19398
uranospinite 19399
uranotallite 19400
uranotilo 19401
urao 19402
urbainite 19403
urbanite 19404
urgoniano 19405
urti ripetuti 14733
urto 1848
urtite 19407
urusite 19408
usare una portata alla francese 19410
usbekite 19409
uscita d'aria 6563
— del laminatoio 12701
uso del tubo senza involucro 19057
— ripetuto dell'acqua 14736
ussingite 19413
usura 19853
— degli elettrodi 4242
— della catena 19854
— per abrasione sotto pressione di contatto 9183
— per attrito 7771/a
— superficiale S. 6
utensile a corda 2666
— aperto 12597
— ausiliario 1002
— da alesare interni 14491
— da perforazioni 2110
— da sgrossare S. 15264
— da taglio 10577, 12952
— da taglio per cilindratura su superfici continue 18726
— da trafilatura 5812

utensile di platino 13529
— di quarzo 14272
— domestico 9460
— idromeccanico 9554
— incorsatoio 4904
— leggero per tornitura e spianatura 10791
— manovrabile facilmente a mano 16785
— per campioni 15459
— per coniare 6405
— per filettare 6700, 18551
— per finitura 7140
— per fonderie 7673
— per il fuoco S. 7195
— per imbutitura a capovolgimento con taglio 4059
— per lavorazione a caldo 9456
— per l'estrusione 6725
— per mine 11780
— per molare 8555
— per pescaggi 7224
— per recuperi 7224
— per sbozzare 15263
— per sfasciare (o per tagliare) a destra S. 14905
— per tagliare 4926
— per tagliare metallo 11540
— portatile da saldatore 19935
— portatile elettrico e pneumatico 13778
— sinistro leggero per tornitura e piallatura 10663
— sinistro per tornitura pesante 10662
— tagliavetri 8275
utahite 19414
utilizzazione del calore 19415
— della loppa 19416
uvanite 19418
uvarovite 2725, 12720, 19419

V

vaalite 19423
vacillare 7285
vacuometro 19435

vagliare 10934, 16296
vagliatore 19626, 19463
vagliatura 15693, 16302, 16305
— a secco 6043, 6046
— per deposito 10179, 16468
vaglio 8579, 10177, 14883, 16297, 16924, 19463
— a due piatti 5654
— a griglia mobile 14145/a
— a maglie larghe 3876
— a mano 8762
— a scosse 9646, 10185, 15968, 15972
— a scosse magnetico 9482
— a tamburo ruotante 15216
— ad aria compressa 295
— cilindrico 4942
— classificatore 3644, 8390
— classificatore a rulli 15116
— di drenaggio 5294
— di sgocciolamento 5749
— fine od a maglie fini 7089 7089
— lavatore 4590, 15033
— lavatore a scosse 10226
— oscillante 10170
— per scorie 16470/a
— rotante 16701
— v. setaccio o crivello
vagoncino 2206, 2526, 3105, 4508, 9492, 9484, 11020, 10555, 15118, 19622
— a più piani 16116
— da miniera 18928
vagone a bilico 6099
— a scarico automatico 15818
— per loppa 16563
— per minerale 12658, 16481, 20006
— per trasportare la ghisa 13265
— ribaltabile 6099
— ribaltabile di lato 16260
— -tramoggia rettangolare 14517
vagonetto 2818, 18971
— a scarico di testa 7781
— in acciaio 17516
— per cantiere 18947

vagonetto per carbone 3852
— per miniera 11772
vaiolatura 13428
— di grafite 10379
— interna 19271/a, 19272
valbellite 19439
valencianite 19441
valentinite 20024
vallata di dislocazione 6843
— senile 7805
valle ad U 19209
— di sinclinale 18160
— glaciale 8261, S. 19209
— longitudinale 10986
— monoclinale 11907
— sommersa 6011
— sospesa 8810
— sottomarina 17927
— trasversale 18846, 19777
vallevarite 19442
valore 19445
— degli scarti 15662
— di confronto 4107
— di decomposizione 5072
— di dispersione 6551
— di prova 18458
— di raffreddamento 3438
— limite 10824
valterizzazione 19662/a
valuevite 19663
valvola 7281, 19446
— a cassetto 8059, 8097, 16414
— a cerniera 7282
— a circolazione d'acqua 19834
— a conchiglia 12144
— a doppia sede 5676
— a farfalla 2645
— a farfalla di Siemens 16280
— a fodero 16595
— a gas 8053
— a maschio 13564
— a pistone 18863
— a sede 5486
— a sfera 8302
— a tre vie 18571
— ad aria 330
— ad aria calda 9401
— aspirante 17961
— d'aereazione 19512
— d'ammissione 172, 12615
— d'aspirazione 17361

valvola d'avvio 10342
— d'eruzione 1862
— del vento 1734, 1735
— di Boecker 1942
— di chiusura 3781
— di chiusura del ricuperatore 19452
— di contropressione 3366
— di emergenza 1886
— di galleggiamento per tubi 3172
— di regolazione 7421
— di regolazione del fumo 7453
— di respirazione 2351
— di riduzione della pressione 16789
— di ritorno 1072
— di scappamento dell'aria 318
— di scarico 1756, 1857, 1862, 6102, 6565
— di sicurezza 12291, 15425
— di tiraggio 5723
— galleggiante 1154
— in acciaio fuso 3022
— in materia refrattaria 19451
— per l'aria 14688
— per l'entrata dell'aria 293
— per residui 18319
— premente 13923
— rotativa Burger 2588
vanadato 19459
vanadinite 19460
vanadio 19461
vanga 16962, 17105
vangare 16961
vano tra sbarre 8473
vanossite 19464
vanthoffite 19465
vapore d'acqua 17413
— di testa 1692
— immesso inferiormente (sotto al pistone) 17415
— immesso sopra al pistone 17414
vapori scuri 5001
vaporizzare 6610
vaporizzatore 17180
— e tirante per caldaie 19466

vaporizzazione 6618
— dell'acqua 19835
varianti di fabbricazione 11853/a
variazione 4696, 11799, 16120
— del modello 11803
— della conchiglia 11801
— della forma 11802
— della placca 11804
— di concentrazione dell'elettrolito 427
— di corrente 7445
— di tensione 7446
— di spessore 5394
varietà di carbonio 19473
— gialla 20293
variolite 19474
variscite 19476
varnsingite 19479
vasca d'agitazione 235
— d'amalgamazione 495
— d'immersione 16797
— del fango 12085, 16718
— della molazza 12890, 12891
— di decapaggio 13222, 13230
— di gorgogliamento 15725
— di lavaggio 18126
— di mercurio 11510
— di porcellana 13667
— di separazione 15879
— pneumatica 13601
— v. bacino
vaschetta 10586, 12885, S. 16411
— di lavaggio 19707
vasellina 13132, 19480
vaso di distillazione 5559
— di vetro per batterie 1348
— per mercurio 11511
vassoio 12025, 12881, 13505
— per anime 4430
vaterite 19481
vaugnerite 19482
vauquelinite 19483
vauxite 19484
vecchi lavori di scavo 8325
vedretta 8807
vegasite 19485
velatura 4871
velocità ascendente 853
— critica di tempera 4649

velocità d'avanzamento
  13063, 14435/a
— d'estrazione 15171
— del fango d'intercapedine
  623
— del jet 10161
— di colata 3017
— di formazione degli ioni
  19495
— di fusione 11477/a
— di pompaggio 14169
— di raffreddamento 4342
— di rigenerazione degli
  ioni 14647
— di scorrimento 4616/a
— di taglio 4924
— tangenziale 3606
vena 4552, 10954, 11393.
  15727/a, 17766
— aurifera 8351
— eruttiva 6559
— irregolare di carbone
  3842
— parallela al piano di
  stratificazione 1422
— secondaria 10627
— trasversale 4533/a
vendita 15436
venti della torre 8691
ventilare 6792
— la sabbia 186
— un cantiere contenente
  grisou 4960
— v. aerare
ventilato 19507
ventilatore 1866, 6811,
  6793
— a getto di vapore 17438
— a palmole 7066
— a spirale ad alta pressione 9169
— ad alta pressione 9166
— aspirante 6650, 6655,
— blindato 2925
— centrifugo 3201, 6795
— del camino 3465
— di precisione 13819
— Encke 6440
— negativo 6655
— Root 15155
— rotativo 15193
— secondario 2050, 2052
— soffiante 1873, 13703,
  13894
ventilazione 19508

ventilazione ascendente
  855, 19354, 19432
— ausiliare 15771
— diagonale 5311
— discendente 5702
— in depressione 19438
— per aspirazione 6651
— soffiante 13542
— v. aereazione
vento 20086
— caldo 9393
— di altoforno 7826
— freddo 3962
ventre 2341, 2768, 15933
— d'altoforno 15951
— del convertitore 4299
— del crogiuolo 1469,
  4737
venturimetro 12670, 19513
venuta di gas nel fango 7996
verbaite 19605
verbale sui risultati dell'a-
  nalisi 20237
verde-mare 15731
verde minerale 12032
verga di ferro S.1206
— profilata in acciaio
  17004
vergella 20138
— d'acciaio per molle
  17201
— di ferro S. 15054
— in acciaio dolce e al
  carbonio 20139
— per trafileria 20130
verifica 3361
— degli spessori 3375
verificare 3361, 19514
verificatore di petrolio
  13136
verite 19515
vermiculite 19516
vernice 10461, 19478
— a base di resina acrilica
  termoindurente 17701
— a fondo ricco di zinco
  20329
— all'olio di lino 10859
— antiruggine 13862
— protettiva per il crogiuolo 4750
verniciare 19477
— al forno 10121
verniciato al forno 10122
verniciatura al forno 10123

verricello 20082
verrina 946
versante 16679
versare 13738, 18354
verso il basso 5714
— il fronte 9683
vescicatura 1787
vesuvianite 19542
veszelite 19543
vetrificarsi 1410
vetrificazione 19576
— superficiale 16434
vetriolo 4367
vetro al cobalto 3888
— da orologio 19741
— di Jéna per apparati
  10146
— di Weber 19875
— duro 8829
— fusibile 4079
— quarzoso 19572/a
— tirato 16056
vetroso 7380, 9495, 9570
vetta 4724
vettura 19457
viaggio 18906
vibrare 10124
vibratore 19551
vibrazione 7283, 14420,
  19549
— della cinghia 7284
— della corda di perfora-
  zione 10339
— d'un attrezzo 10135
vibrovaglio 19548
vicoite 19556
villaminite 19557
villaumite 19558
vindoboniano 19559
vintlite 19560
violarite 19561
virgazione 19562
viridina 19564
viridite 19565
viscosimetro 19567/a
  19225
viscosità 1937, 19568
— di rottura 2311
viscoso 19566
visiera protettrice 6753
visto di lato 16261
vite a occhiello per modelli
  12990
— a pressione 166
— d'alimentazione 6882

vite d'arresto 15916
— di collegamento 4221
— di pressione 1603
— di prolungamento 18376
— di regolazione 15705/a
— di regolazione alla pres-
    sione 13919
— per legno 20177
— per registrare i cilindri
    18419
— senza fine 4620
vitreo 19570
vitrificazione 19577
vitrofirico 19582
vitrofiro 19581
vivianite 1904
vizio di saldatura 5106
— interno 10566
vulcanite 19610
vulsinite 19612
vulpinite 19611
vuotare 15638, 18670
— con una pompa 14155
— il crogiuolo 18262
vuotarsi 10635
vuoto 7966, 19424, 19587/a
— sagomato 15896

W

wacke 19614
wad 1946
wagnerite 19619
«wall scraper» per pozzi di-
    rezionati 19653
walpurgite 19662
wapplerite 19664
wardite 19665
warrenite 19678
warthaite 19679
warwickite 19680
wavellite 19839
websterite 445, 19876
wehrlite 19892
weibullite 19893
weischenchite 19920
weiselbergite 19921
weissite 19922
wennebergite 19977
wentzelite 19978
werfeniano 19979
wernerite 19980

whewellite 20013
wichtisite 20054
wiikite 20066
wilkeite 20073
willemite 20074
willyamite 20076
wiltshireite 20077
wiluite 20078
withamite 20154
witherite 20160
wittichenite 20162
wittite 20163
wolframite 2698
wolfsbergite 20168
wollastonite 20169
woodendite 20184
wulfenite 20254, 20286
wyomingite 20259

X

xantarsenite 20263
xantocroite 20264
xantofillite 20265
xantosiderite 20266
xeno 20270
xenoblasto 20267
xenotimo 20271/a
xiloidina 20274
xilolite 20275
xilolo 20272
xilotilo 20277

Y

yatalite 20279
yetnite 20296
yogoite 20301

Z

zaffiro 15541
— asterico 904
— blu-verdastro 3080/a
zappetta per botti 4370
zaratite 20316
zatteroni della torre 8536
Zechstein 20317

zeolite 20318
— aciculare 12211
zeppa 10728, 16453, 19878
zeunerite 20320
zigrinare 2068
zigrinatura 10417/a
zincalluminite 20340
zincare 7928, 7942, 20343
— v. galvanizzare
zincatura 20346
— a fuoco 9418
— elettrolitica 7943
— per immersione 7263/a
zinchenite 20345, 20348
zincite 14552, 20344
zinco 17046
— grezzo 14463
zinconite 9579, 20325
zincosite 20350
zinwaldite 20351
zippeite 20352
zirchelite 20357, 20358
zircone 20353
zirconia 20354
zirconio 20355, 10133
zobtenite 20359
zoccolo 2142, 16868
— continentale 4257
— del mulino 8917, 17534
— di «spudding» 17223
— della punteria 2767
— in muratura 2375
zoisite 20360
zolfo 17981
zolla 3745, 16700
zona 900, 20364
— batiale 18831
— corrugata 2200
— d'arresto del petrolio
    12514
— d'erosione 1480
— d'estrazione 15905
— d'irrigazione 17112
— dei meandri 11388
— dell'orlo 2071
— della faglia 16027
— di alterazione superficia-
    le 20366
— di carburazione 2882
— di cementazione 1478, 3163
    3163
— di colata S. 3039
— di coltivazione 17678
— di fatica 6833/a

zona di frantumazione 4770
— di frattura 7702
— di fusione 7833/b, 11484
— di ossidazione 12792
— di preparazione 13847
— di riduzione 14579
— di riscaldamento 13847
— di rottura 15387
— di sedimentazione 766
— di subsidenza 767
— di termodiffusione
    16797/a
— di transizione 18830
— dura 8842
— effettivamente produttiva
    12242
— epicentrale 6509
— favorevole 6867
— franata 8329
— fratturata 7705
— infiltrata 9764
— litoranea 10897
— neutra 12251/a
— ripiegata 1479
— sferica 20365
— sterile 1245, 5025
— v. regione
zoolite 20368
zunite 20369
zurlite 20370
zwitter 20371
zygadite 20372